HANDBOOK OF _____

THE MAMMALS OF THE WORLD.

1.
Carnivores

CONSERVATION
INTERNATIONAL

IUCN

AgriLIFE RESEARCH
Texas A&M System

Improving Life Through Science and Technology.

SSC
Species Survival Commission

RED LIST

THE IUCN RED LIST
OF THREATENED SPECIES

HANDBOOK OF

THE MAMMALS OF THE WORLD.

1.
Carnivores

Chief Editors
Don E. Wilson
Russell A. Mittermeier

Associate Editors
Sue Ruff
Albert Martínez-Vilalta

Photographic Editor
Josep del Hoyo

Authors
Paolo Cavallini
Jerry Dragoo
David Garshelis
Philippe Gaubert
Jason Gilchrist
Steven Goodman
Kay Holekamp
Andrew Jennings
Roland Kays
Joseph Kolowski
Serge Larivière
Claudio Sillero-Zubiri
Fiona Sunquist
Mel Sunquist
Geraldine Veron
Fuwen Wei
Zejun Zhang

Color Plates by
Toni Llobet

Recommended citation:
Wilson, D. E. & Mittermeier, R. A. eds. (2009). *Handbook of the Mammals of the World*. Vol. 1. Carnivores. Lynx Edicions, Barcelona.

Citation to individual contributions recommended in the following format:
Gaubert, P. (2009). Family Nandiniidae (African Palm Civet). Pp. 50–53 in: Wilson, D. E. & Mittermeier, R. A. eds. (2009). *Handbook of the Mammals of the World*. Vol. 1. Carnivores. Lynx Edicions, Barcelona.

Printed on Hello Silk paper with FSC and PEFC certification.

Color reproductions by *Edifilm, S.A.* Barcelona
Printed and bound in Barcelona by *Ingoprint, S.A.*
Dipòsit Legal: B-16.135-2009
ISBN: 978-84-96553-49-1

Editors and Authors of Volume 1

Chief Editors

Dr D. E. Wilson
Chairman, Department of Vertebrate Zoology, National Museum of Natural History, Smithsonian Institution, Washington, DC, USA.

Dr R. A. Mittermeier
President, Conservation International; Vice-President, International Union for Conservation of Nature (IUCN); and Chair, IUCN/SSC Primate Specialist Group, USA.

Associate Editors

S. Ruff
A. Martínez-Vilalta

Photographic Editor

Dr J. del Hoyo

Authors

Dr P. Cavallini
Faunalia, Pontedera, Pisa, Italy; also, member of the IUCN/SSC Small Carnivore Specialist Group and Sustainable Use Specialist Group.

Dr J. W. Dragoo
Research Associate, Department of Biology, Museum of Southwestern Biology, University of New Mexico, Albuquerque, New Mexico, USA.

Dr D. L. Garshelis
Bear Project Leader, Minnesota Department of Natural Resources, Grand Rapids, Minnesota, USA; also, Co-chair, IUCN/SSC Bear Specialist Group.

Dr P. Gaubert
Researcher, Département Milieux et Peuplements Aquatiques, Muséum National d'Histoire Naturelle, Paris, France; also, member of the IUCN/SSC Small Carnivore Specialist Group.

Dr J. S. Gilchrist
Lecturer in Animal Biology, School of Life Sciences, Edinburgh Napier University, Edinburgh, Scotland, UK.

Dr S. M. Goodman
Field Biologist, Field Museum of Natural History, Chicago, Illinois, USA; also, Scientific Counselor, Association Vahatra, Antananarivo, Madagascar.

Dr K. E. Holekamp
University Distinguished Professor, Department of Zoology, Michigan State University, East Lansing, Michigan, USA; also, Deputy Director, IUCN/SSC Hyaena Specialist Group.

A. P. Jennings, MSc
Small Carnivore Ecologist and PhD Candidate, Département Systématique et Evolution, Muséum National d'Histoire Naturelle, Paris, France; also, member of the IUCN/SSC Small Carnivore Specialist Group.

Dr R. Kays
Curator of Mammals, New York State Museum, Albany, New York, USA; also, member of the IUCN/SSC Small Carnivore Specialist Group.

Dr J. M. Kolowski
Conservation Biologist, Center for Conservation Education and Sustainability, National Zoological Park, Smithsonian Institution, Washington, DC, USA.

Dr S. Larivière
Affiliate Professor, Department of Biology, Université du Québec à Rimouski, Rimouski, Québec, Canada.

Dr C. Sillero-Zubiri
Bill Travers Fellow for Wildlife Conservation, Wildlife Conservation Research Unit, Zoology Department, University of Oxford, Oxford, UK; also, Chair, IUCN/SSC Canid Specialist Group.

F. C. Sunquist
Science writer, Melrose, Florida, USA.

Dr M. E. Sunquist
Professor, Department of Wildlife Ecology and Conservation, University of Florida, Gainesville, Florida, USA.

Dr G. Veron
Researcher and Curator of Carnivores, Département Systématique et Evolution, Muséum National d'Histoire Naturelle, Paris, France; also, member of the IUCN/SSC Small Carnivore Specialist Group.

Professor F. Wei
Key Lab of Animal Ecology and Conservation Biology, Institute of Zoology, Chinese Academy of Sciences, Beijing, China.

Professor Z. Zhang
Institute of Rare Animals and Plants, China West Normal University, Nanchong, Sichuan, China.

Contents

List of Plates

Out of the White – Snow Leopard
Frontispiece kindly provided by Robert Bateman

FUNDACIÓ
MASCORT
TORROELLA DE MONTGRÍ

Fundació Mascort and Lynx Edicions working together for Nature

Foreword

It gives me great pleasure to introduce this amazing new series on the world's mammals. I had long admired the *Handbook of the Birds of the World*, acquiring each new volume as it appeared, and had asked myself many times, "Wouldn't it be nice if we could do something similar on mammals". So, you can imagine my enthusiasm when Josep del Hoyo contacted me back in 2005 to ask if I might be interested in co-editing and helping to support a new handbook on mammals patterned on the magnificent bird series. I didn't hesitate for an instant, and immediately got to work trying to find resources to help with this historic undertaking. Now, just four short years later, I am delighted to see this first volume on the carnivores appearing in print, the first of at least eight volumes that will constitute this new series. You can see for yourself that the standard of quality set for the *Handbook of the Birds of the World* has again been met, or, dare I say it, even exceeded with this inaugural edition for the mammals.

The Class Mammalia is one of the most important groups of living organisms for many reasons, not the least of which is the fact that it is the Class of which we ourselves are a part. The most recent taxonomic appraisal recognizes some 5339 extant (or presumably extant) species. What is more, as is the case of most groups of organisms, we continue to find new species every year. An average of 223 new species have been described per decade since the birth of modern taxonomic nomenclature in 1758, and this rate is increasing. If the pace of description from recent years continues unabated, it has been estimated that at least 300 new species will be described in the current decade—and we could wind up with 7500 or more mammal species.

This is not just the case for cryptic, nocturnal rodents, insectivores, and bats from the tropical forests or other remote corners of our planet. It is even true for our closest living relatives, the non-human primates. I am a primatologist by training and have worked on these wonderful animals for the past 40 years, and have myself had the privilege of describing ten species of primates new to science (four marmosets and two titi monkeys from Amazonia and four lemurs from Madagascar). But these have been just the tip of the iceberg. Since 2000, primate researchers have described a total of 53 new species, representing more than 13% of the entire Order. Perhaps the most amazing example of all is Madagascar, one of the world's highest priority hotspots with less than 10% of its natural vegetation remaining. In spite of the large scale loss of habitat there and the fact that so little remains, primate researchers since 2000 have more than doubled the total number of taxa to 104, and counting.

Sadly, as is the case with most other life forms on our planet, mammals are on the decline in many areas. The threats are many, and include large-scale conversion of natural habitat for monoculture agriculture (e.g., soy, oil palm), unsustainable logging, poorly regulated mining, flooding of vast areas for hydroelectric projects, and direct harvesting for food, medicine, or other purposes—with perhaps the most striking examples being large-scale bushmeat hunting in Central and West Africa, affecting even our closest living relatives the great apes, and the huge trade in pangolins and lorises in South-east Asia to serve the Chinese medicinal trade. These threats are covered in considerable detail in this series, with a particular focus on what is happening to each individual species.

The results of the Global Mammal Assessment, launched at the IUCN World Conservation Congress in Barcelona in October, 2008, clearly demonstrate what is taking place. The first full-scale, comprehensive assessment of all mammals, this five-year study involving 1700 experts from 130 countries showed that fully 25% of the world's mammal species are known to be threatened in some way. Of these, 188 (3%) are in the Critically Endangered category, 448 (8%) are Endangered, and a further 505 (9%) are considered Vulnerable. Of comparable concern is that fact that the conservation status of 15% of mammals is unknown or Data Deficient. Many of the Critically Endangered mammals, which are all creatures literally on the brink of extinction, are also some of the best known, most charismatic flagship species that are enormously important, not just in ecological terms, but also economically and culturally. Were they to disappear, the world would be a much poorer place in many ways.

Fortunately, there is much that can be done to prevent such loss. We need more attention to targeted species conservation projects seeking to bring those animals at greatest risk back from the brink. We need more focus on protected areas, including much more effective management of existing areas and the creation of new protected areas where species coverage is inadequate. We need to link these protected areas in broader landscapes and seascapes to ensure that they have long-term ecological and evolutionary viability, especially with the threat of climate change so heavily upon us. We need greater involvement of local human communities living in key areas for conservation—to ensure that they also understand and benefit from conservation activities. And we need to further stimulate the interest of the public, to educate, and to create ever greater awareness of the importance of mammals and their role in ensuring our own long term survival. It is in this last dimension that this new *Handbook of the Mammals of the World* is so fundamentally important and can play such an important role. As is the case with the *Handbook of the Birds of the World*, I am certain that this new series, with its sound science, comprehensive coverage, and compelling layout, will go a long way towards furthering global interest in mammals and a greater appreciation of their wonderful diversity and importance to the world at large.

Lastly, I would like to take this opportunity to thank Doris Swanson of Hayden Lake, Idaho, USA, for her long-term support of species conservation, including generous initial support that helped to make this new Handbook a reality.

Russell A. Mittermeier, Ph.D.
President, Conservation International; and
Vice-President, International Union for Conservation of Nature (IUCN)

Introduction

The *Handbook of the Mammals of the World* (HMW) will be an unprecedented reference work for the Class Mammalia. This series of eight volumes will describe every currently recognized mammal species, along with an overview of each mammalian family. It will provide up-to-date information on the systematic relationships, natural history, ecology, and current conservation status for all mammals. Every species will be illustrated and each chapter will also include many color photographs. HMW will provide comprehensive worldwide coverage by involving an international group of expert authors.

This mission began when Josep del Hoyo from *Lynx Edicions* met with Don Wilson to discuss a mammal project to parallel the ongoing, successful *Handbook of the Birds of the World*. Sue Ruff was then recruited to help with the work on this new series. The order Carnivora was chosen as the initial volume and the family Felidae was selected as a pilot project to promote interest for HMW; Mel and Fiona Sunquist were commissioned to produce this chapter. After this successful launch, *Lynx Edicions* enlisted the support of Russell Mittermeier from *Conservation International*, which has been essential to making this project viable. Russ, and also Michael Hoffmann, helped with the selection of outstanding authors for each family.

An important driving force behind HMW is to support the conservation of mammals and their habitats, a task made easier with the involvement of *Conservation International* and IUCN (*International Union for Conservation of Nature*). A major aim of HMW is to illustrate the extraordinary diversity of mammals and to promote poorly known species, especially those in South America, Africa, and Asia, in the hope that this will inspire additional studies. The IUCN Red Data Books play an important role in conservation planning worldwide and highlight how little we know about the status of many mammalian species. A clear goal of HMW is to take an additional step by examining the status of every one of the world's mammal species, describing the threats, and outlining the possible conservation measures.

HMW has followed traditionally accepted classifications, primarily the *Mammal Species of the World* (Wilson & Reeder, 2005). However, we have made several improvements. The views of the authors, all of whom are acknowledged authorities, have been incorporated into this volume. We have taken into account the descriptions of new species and ongoing systematic revisions, which continue to add to our knowledge of the phylogenetic relationships within the Carnivora. The section on Systematics within each family chapter reviews the on-going taxonomic work and recent research using new molecular techniques, which have revolutionized our ability to analyze evolutionary relationships.

Each chapter of this volume is dedicated to a particular family. The **Family Text** gives a general overview of each carnivore family and includes numerous color photographs illustrating members of the family. This is followed by the individual **Species Accounts**, which are concise summaries of the known information from the primary literature. Both sections include an extensive bibliography.

Family Text

In general, each volume will present the taxa in phylogenetic sequence, which reflects the evolutionary relationships as we currently understand them. That sequence for the carnivores is listed in Table 1. For some genera, the phylogenetic relationships of the species are still unknown, and we have listed them alphabetically in those cases. Three additional families of the order Carnivora are not covered in this volume. The walruses, seals, and sea lions will be treated along with cetaceans

SUBORDER	FAMILY	SUBFAMILY	GENUS
Feliformia	Nandiniidae		Nandinia
	Felidae	Pantherinae	Neofelis
			Panthera
		Felinae	Pardofelis
			Catopuma
			Leptailurus
			Profelis
			Caracal
			Leopardus
			Lynx
			Acinonyx
			Puma
			Otocolobus
			Prionailurus
			Felis
	Prionodontidae		Prionodon
	Viverridae	Viverrinae	Viverricula
			Civettictis
			Viverra
		Genettinae	Poiana
			Genetta
		Paradoxurinae	Arctogalidia
			Macrogalidia
			Arctictis
			Paguma
			Paradoxurus
		Hemigalinae	Cynogale
			Chrotogale
			Hemigalus
			Diplogale
	Hyaenidae	Protelinae	Proteles
		Hyaeninae	Crocuta
			Hyaena
			Parahyaena
	Herpestidae	Herpestinae	Atilax
			Xenogale
			Herpestes
			Cynictis
			Galerella
			Ichneumia
			Paracynictis
			Bdeogale
			Rhynchogale
		Mungotinae	Suricata
			Crossarchus
			Helogale
			Dologale
			Liberiictis
			Mungos
	Eupleridae	Euplerinae	Cryptoprocta
			Eupleres
			Fossa
		Galidiinae	Galidia
			Galidictis
			Mungotictis
			Salanoia

SUBORDER	FAMILY	SUBFAMILY	GENUS
Caniformia	Canidae		Canis
			Cuon
			Lycaon
			Chrysocyon
			Speothos
			Cerdocyon
			Atelocynus
			Pseudalopex
			Urocyon
			Nyctereutes
			Otocyon
			Alopex
			Vulpes
	Ursidae	Ailuropodinae	Ailuropoda
		Tremarctinae	Tremarctos
		Ursinae	Helarctos
			Melursus
			Ursus
	Ailuridae		Ailurus
	Procyonidae		Bassaricyon
			Bassariscus
			Nasua
			Nasuella
			Potos
			Procyon
	Mephitidae	Myadinae	Mydaus
		Mephitinae	Conepatus
			Mephitis
			Spilogale
	Mustelidae	Taxidiinae	Taxidea
		Mellivorinae	Mellivora
		Melinae	Arctonyx
			Meles
		Martinae	Eira
			Gulo
			Martes
		Helictidinae	Melogale
		Galictidinae	Galictis
			Vormela
			Ictonyx
			Poecilogale
		Lutrinae	Pteronura
			Lontra
			Enhydra
			Hydrictis
			Lutra
			Aonyx
			Lutrogale
		Mustelinae	Mustela
			Neovison
			Lyncodon

Table 1. *Phylogenetic sequence for families of the order Carnivora*

and sirenians in a later volume dedicated to sea mammals. Such departures from our basic commitment to phylogenetic sequence will be rare in the series, but in this case it makes much more sense to group marine mammals together.

The family texts are also amply illustrated with color **Photographs** that not only depict as many species as possible, but also illustrate particular aspects that are mentioned in the text. Each family chapter includes the following sections:

Summary-box. The summary-box provides a quick reference to the basic details of the family. It includes a brief description of the most distinctive characteristics of its members, the size range, the distribution of the whole family (also illustrated with a world map), the family's habitat characteristics, the number of genera and species, and the number of species listed by various categories in the most recent edition of The IUCN Red List of Threatened Species™. The number for total taxa includes genera, species, and currently recognized subspecies. The number of subspecies changes frequently with new studies, so the numbers given reflect only the number we are recognizing at the time of publication. Numbers of taxa listed as extinct include only those extinctions documented since 1600. Silhouettes of the largest and smallest species and a human figure make comparisons possible. The full-length human figure represents a man 180 cm tall.

Systematics. This section provides an overview of the taxonomy and phylogeny of the species within each family and describes their evolution and origins. The major taxonomic source followed is the *Mammal Species of the World* (Wilson & Reeder, 2005). Any deviations from this reference are based on recent revisions and the opinions of the authors.

Morphological Aspects. This section describes the structure and external appearance of the members of a family and covers topics such as pelage, locomotion, and dentition.

Habitat. This section describes the various types of habitat that are used for feeding, denning, and breeding.

General Habits. This is an additional section in most family chapters, which covers topics that are not included elsewhere, such as activity patterns, and special behaviors like hibernation and defense mechanisms.

Communication. This section describes the different ways in which a carnivore species communicates with conspecifics and other animals, and includes topics such as scent marking, vocalizations, and visual displays.

Food and Feeding. Food requirements, types of food eaten, seasonal variations in diet, and foraging techniques are covered in this section.

Breeding. This section outlines the breeding strategies within each family and includes topics such as delayed implantation, juvenile development, and care of the young.

Movements, Home range and Social organization. This section describes daily, seasonal, and dispersal movement patterns, and discusses the spatial and social organization of the different species within each family.

Relationship with Humans. This section describes the impact that some carnivore species have on humans and the ways they are exploited by people. It also includes the beliefs, legends, and traditions held about them, and the part they play in the everyday life of some cultures.

Status and Conservation. This section summarizes the conservation status of the family members, with regard to their population levels, and details the threats they face. There are discussions of the causes of declines in threatened species and an examination of the conservation measures that can be adopted to secure their survival.

General Bibliography. This section lists the references that were used to compose the text and includes scientific papers, monographs, books, technical publications, and conference proceedings.

Species Accounts

There is a species account for each currently recognized species. Extinct species are usually discussed in the family text, but they are not treated with a species account, while species that are recognized as Extinct in the Wild (see below) are covered by a species account. All of the extant carnivore species are illustrated in the **Plates**, which show the details of the pelage and general morphology. To ensure accuracy, these illustrations are based on photographs of wild and captive animals, museum skins, and detailed descriptions. The form depicted is a male of the nominate subspecies, if not otherwise indicated. Important variations that occur are also illustrated, especially when there are marked differences between the sexes or between different subspecies.

Each species account starts with the English vernacular name, followed by the scientific name. The English names are based on Wilson & Reeder (2005); when alternative versions have been used it has been to increase clarity and to avoid confusion. All vernacular names of mammals are capitalized. Each species name is also given in French, German, and Spanish. French names were reviewed by Normand David, German names were reviewed by Gustav Peters and Rainer Hutterer, and Spanish names were reviewed by the Sociedad Española para la Conservación y Estudio de los Mamíferos (SECEM). Other common names are also listed. Occasionally, the use of a single English name to apply to the entire geographic range of a species might be confusing. An example would be *Ursus arctos*, the Brown Bear. Much of the North American population has long been known as the Grizzly Bear, and it is less confusing to refer to them as Grizzlies, rather than Brown Bears, when documenting facts from the literature.

The **Taxonomy** section lists the name as it was originally described, the author of the original species description, the year of the description, and the type locality. Taxonomic issues are discussed here and the number of recognized subspecies (if none, the species is monotypic). Extinct subspecies are covered here; they are not listed in the section on Subspecies and Distribution.

In the **Subspecies and Distribution** section, the countries and areas in which the species occurs in are given. For each subspecies, the original author is listed, along with the year, always without parentheses. The references for the original species and subspecies descriptions are listed in the References of Scientific Descriptions section at the end of the book. For localities, the following abbreviations are used: N (North), S (South), E (East), W (West), C (Central), I/Is (Island/ Islands), and Mt/Mts (Mountain/Mountains). These abbreviations are sometimes written out in full to avoid confusion. Place names follow the *Times Atlas of the World*, although older country names are occasionally used. For many species, the number of available subspecific names exceeds the currently recognized subspecies. Many species still await comprehensive taxonomic revisions that will establish the correct number of recognizable subspecies. For almost all, the exact limits of subspecies are poorly known, making it difficult to delimit subspecific boundaries in any other than the most general terms.

Each species account is accompanied by a **Distribution map**; since the size and scale of these maps precludes precision they are intended only to give an approximate idea of the range of a species. However, to improve the level of detail, an appropriate scale of each map has been chosen. The range shown on a map should always be taken in conjunction with the section on Distribution, which often gives additional information. We have avoided the indiscriminate shading of large continuous areas that would have represented the original range of the species, and instead attempted to only depict these areas where the species has been recorded recently. Introduced populations are generally not included on the maps. In some cases arrows are used to highlight details of a distribution, such as small islands. In the few cases where a species is thought to be extinct, the last areas in which they were recorded are shaded gray.

The purpose of the **Descriptive notes** section is to complement the detail shown in the color plates. Body measurements are given and a general description of the animal, which includes details of the pelage and other body features. The dental formula is included: I = Incisors, C = Canines, P = Premolars, M = Molars; the numbers refer to the number of teeth on the upper/lower side of half the jaw, e.g. I 3/3, C 1/1, P 4/4, M 2/2, represents three incisors, one canine, four premolars, and two molars, on the upper and lower side of half the jaw, thus the total number of teeth = 20 x 2 = 40.

In the next four sections, **Habitat**, **Food and Feeding**, **Activity patterns**, and **Movements, Home range and Social organization**, the relevant species information is given in a concise form. Although we have attempted consistency, the style and content of the species accounts may vary somewhat from author to author, but is usually uniform within each family. The section on **Breeding** includes a fairly standard series of topics such as breeding season, litter size, gestation period, and the development of the young. The species accounts of poorly known species are sparse because of an almost complete lack of available information.

The **Status and Conservation** section describes the current known status of species/subspecies in terms of populations and range limits, details the threats and factors responsible for declines, and outlines the possible conservation measures that could be implemented. This section also includes *The IUCN Red List* classification (often with the date the species was last assessed—2008 for the most recently updated list for Volume 1 – Carnivores); the categories are as follows:

- **Extinct** – no reasonable doubt that the last individual has died.
- **Extinct in the Wild** – known only to survive in captivity or as a naturalized population(s) outside the past range.
- **Critically Endangered** – an extremely high risk of extinction in the wild.
- **Endangered** – a very high risk of extinction in the wild.
- **Vulnerable** – a high risk of extinction in the wild.
- **Near Threatened** – close to qualifying for a threatened category (Critically Endangered, Endangered, or Vulnerable).
- **Lower Risk/Least Concern** – widespread and abundant.
- **Data Deficient** – inadequate information to make an assessment of the risk of extinction.
- **Not Evaluated/Not Listed** – not yet been evaluated.

The **Bibliography** section lists all the references used to compile the text and includes scientific papers, monographs, books, technical publications, and conference proceedings. References are ordered alphabetically by the surname of the first author; if there are more than two authors, only the first name appears followed by the abbreviation *et al.* There are no citations in the text itself in order to increase the readability of the species accounts for a wide audience, but the references do allow readers to seek further information. Additional references on the species within a family are included in the General Bibliography of the family text. Most species tend to fall into one of two extremes, those that have been well-studied, resulting in a fairly large number of publications, and those that are so poorly known that most of the meager information available can be found only in general works. For the better known species, the authors have tried to at least include the most important original works and recent papers. For poorly known species, references such as field guides and local checklists have also been used.

References

At the end of each volume is a References section, divided into two parts. The first section, **References of Scientific Descriptions**, contains the bibliographical details of the original descriptions of every genus, species, and subspecies accepted in HMW. The only details listed are the name of the author, the year, and the reference of the original publication. The full titles of articles do not appear in order to conserve space.

In the **General List of References** section, we give the full title of each reference. All articles by the author alone are listed first, in chronological order (oldest first), then all the articles with one co-author; and finally all those involving more than two authors. The title of each article is given in its original language. For non-English languages, the title is given in English in square brackets, followed by an indication of the language of the original and a comment if there is a summary in another language. The abbreviations for periodical publications generally follow the format that is used in other scientific literature. The titles of books, monographs, theses, and similar works appear in italics; however, italics are not used for brief reports. If an article appears as part of a conference proceeding or in other collective works, the reference includes only page numbers, the name of the editor(s), and the year of publication.

Index

The index gives the page numbers for all the orders, families, genera, species, and subspecies treated in the volume; the page numbers refer to the relevant species account or, in the case that there is no account, to the first appearance in the family text. Additionally, pages where species appear in photographs are included in the index; these page numbers are given in italics. All scientific names are indexed, including obsolete genera, synonyms, and alternative names mentioned in the text. For species, both the scientific and English names are indexed, as well as synonyms and alternative names. For example, the Red Panda (*Ailurus fulgens*) can be found under all of these entries: *Ailurus*; *fulgens*; *styani* (subspecies); Bear Cat; Fire Fox; Golden Dog; Lesser Panda; and Red Panda. All subspecies names are indexed. Species and subspecies that are extinct and have no species account are only indexed if they appear in the family account.

Acknowledgements

A lot of collaborative hard work has gone into creating HMW Volume 1 and we are very grateful to all of the people who have made important contributions in different ways. We would like to specifically thank Michael Hoffmann and Kristofer Helgen for their assistance in the early stages of the project. Andrew Jennings provided valuable editorial assistance in addition to the sections he authored, and he and Geraldine Veron were on-hand for various types of help throughout the volume's development. Simon Stuart played an essential role in making the contacts to get the project off the ground. Tom Lacher at Texas A&M University has been a generous supporter of Volume 1 and we look forward to his future involvement in the series.

We have been fortunate to receive great assistance in the reviewing of foreign names. The French names for Volume 1 have kindly been reviewed by Normand David. Gustav Peters and Rainer Hutterer (Zoologisches Forschungsmuseum Alexander Koenig, Bonn, Germany) have reviewed the German names. The Spanish names have been reviewed by the Sociedad Española para la Conservación y Estudio de los Mamíferos (SECEM), for which we would like to give special thanks to Miguel Delibes and Luis Javier Palomo.

We are extremely grateful to Robert Bateman for his most generously supplying the wonderful frontispiece to this volume. Our thanks also go to Birgit Freybe Bateman. We would like to thank Xavier Bas and Maider Zulueta of Xavier Bas Disseny for their hard work on the graphic design for the series and for their patience and kindness throughout the process. Jordi Bas has provided the cover photos for most of the volumes of the series, and we greatly appreciate all of his efforts to achieve such wonderful shots.

We are thankful to those who have sent helpful information and material for the volume, including Juan Carlos Chebez, Will Duckworth, Corey Goldman, J. C. Guix, and Chris and Mathilde Stuart. We would also like to express our gratitude to Andy Elliott, Francesc Jutglar, Anna Motis, and Frank Steinheimer for lending assistance in many ways. We are endlessly grateful to all of our families, friends, and colleagues for their important support. Of course, we are also very appreciative of everyone who has shown interest and enthusiasm for the project, as this has been the driving force behind many years of hard work.

The artist, Toni Llobet, wants to thank Jordi Sargatal for his lifelong confidence, support, and enthusiasm for his artistic skills, and also, and especially, Josep del Hoyo, for entrusting him with the overwhelming challenge and privilege of illustrating all of the living carnivores. The staff at Lynx Edicions, notably Albert Martínez-Vilalta and Amy Chernasky, must also be acknowledged for their friendly and limitless help and support. He would also like to thank various natural history museums and their helpful staff for their assistance: Darrin Lunde and Eileen Westwig (American Museum of Natural History, New York), Jacques Cuisin, Geraldine Veron, Julie Villemain, Patrick Boussès, and Anne Préviato (Muséum National d'Histoire Naturelle, Paris), and Jennifer Vladimirsky (Natural History Museum, London). Deli Saavedra and Pablo García served as efficient photographers at the AMNH in New York, while Jordi Palau also supplied valuable photographic material from Brazil. Charlie Rose and Thomas L. Friedman provided endless hours of inspiring and knowledgeable company through the Internet during long nights of work illustrating carnivores, whilst Robert Bateman has been a seminal and inspirational friend and artistic mentor, as distant geographically as close philosophically. David and Josep Giribet have been the technical backbone of the digital illustration process, and Monique François, Grazia and Mauro Pagnucci, and Maurice François have also helped logistically in various ways. Finally, Toni wants to thank Valentina Pagnucci for her patience and companionship, and Laia and Pietro, who patiently waited while their father said, "Quan acabi la feina anirem a la muntanya a veure llops" ("When the work is finished we will go to the mountains to see wolves").

On behalf of the individual authors of HMW Volume 1, we extend our sincere thanks to M. Colyn (University of Rennes, France), Gwen A. Dragoo, RVT, A. Dunham (Rice University, USA), P. Gaubert (Muséum National d'Histoire Naturelle, Paris, France), Matt Gompper, Kris Helgen, M. Hoffmann (Conservation International, USA), J. Kingdon (Cambridge University, UK), K. P. Koepfli (University of California in Los Angeles, USA), M. G. L. Mills, M. L. Patou (Museum National d'Histoire Naturelle, Paris, France), H. Sasaki (Chikushi Jogakuen University Junior College, Japan), L. Smale, C. and T. Stuart (African-Arabian Wildlife Research Centre, Loxton, South Africa), and A. P. Wagner, as well as to the Institut de Recherche pour le Développement, Paris, France, and the US National Science Foundation. Furthermore, Claudio Sillero would like to thank Jed Murdoch and Alan Hesse for their able assistance researching the Canidae chapter. Claudio's position at Oxford, and his role as the Chair of the IUCN/SSC Canid Specialist Group, is generously funded by the Born Free Foundation.

As Mel and Fiona Sunquist prepared the pilot project for the series, they would like to specially thank the following individuals for their significant contributions to the Felidae chapter: Dr Lars Werdelin, Department of Palaeozoology, Museum of Natural History, Stockholm, Sweden, for writing the section on Morphology of felids; Dr Alex Sliwa of the Zoologischer Garten, Wuppertal, Germany, for writing the species accounts for Lion, Cheetah, Black-footed Cat, and Sand Cat; Dr Andrew Kitchener of National Museum of Scotland, Edinburgh, for writing the sections on Systematics and Relationship with Humans, as well as the Wildcat account; Dr Christine Breitenmoser-Würsten and Dr Urs Breitenmoser, KORA, Bern, Switzerland, for writing the Eurasian Lynx and Canadian Lynx accounts; Dr Gustav Peters, Zoologisches Forschungsmuseum Alexander Koenig, Bonn, Germany, for writing about the vocalization of felids; the late Dr David Maehr of the University of Kentucky, USA, for writing the Puma account and co-authoring the Bobcat account with

Dr Jeffrey Larkin of the Indiana University of Pennsylvania, USA; and Kristin Nowell, CAT, Cape Neddic, Maine, for summarizing the Status and Conservation of felids.

They would also like to thank the following individuals for sharing their work and knowledge of felids with them: Ted Bailey, Juan Beltrán, Tim Caro, Arturo Caso, Ravi Chellam, Peter Crawshaw, Eric Dinerstein, Advait Edgaonkar, John Eisenberg, Louise Emmons, Neil Franklin, Helen Freeman, Todd Fuller, Lon Grassman, Luke Hunter, Agustin Iriarte, Peter Jackson, Rodney Jackson, A. J. T. Johnsingh, Warren Johnson, Ullas Karanth, Kae Kawanishi, Linda Kerley, Mohammed Khan, Margaret Kinnaird, Devra Kleiman, Olof Liberg, Tony Lynam, Laurie Marker, Inés Maxit, Jill Mellen, Dale Miquelle, Brian Miller, Hemanta Mishra, Andres Novaro, Steve O'Brien, Tim O'Brien, Gea Olbricht, Tadeu Oliveira, Howard Quigley, Alan Rabinowitz, Rajan and Lynette Rajaratnam, Fateh Singh Rathore, Justina Ray, Jim Sanderson, George Schaller, Krzyzstof Schmidt, Daniel Scognamillo, John Seidensticker, Alan Shoemaker, James L. D. Smith, Michael Tewes, Valmik Thapar, Ron Tilson, Chanthavy Vongkhamheng, Susan Walker, and Per Wegge.

Class MAMMALIA (MAMMALS)

Class MAMMALIA (Mammals)

Mammals include the most dominant life forms on Earth. Humans are mammals, and this fact alone ensures that our interest in the group remains high. Mammals have evolved relatively rapidly over the past 225 million or so years to occupy all continents and oceans. We now recognize more than 5000 species of mammals, and that number will increase as we expand our studies of species limits using the modern molecular toolkit.

The ability to internally regulate their body temperature has allowed mammals to colonize virtually every habitat on earth, from the poles to the equator, including both terrestrial and aquatic niches. Mammals are found from below sea level to very high mountaintops, from stark deserts to lush rainforests, and they occupy niches that range from fossorial forms below the surface to aerial forms capable of flying at great altitudes. Mammals are conspicuous members of our own everyday world, and in addition to the many ways they have benefited humans over our own evolution, they are appreciated for their esthetic appeal. The earliest known cave paintings done by humans depict various species of our fellow mammals. We have domesticated selected species, and used them to further our own ability to thrive on this planet. In a sense, the more we learn about mammals in general, the more we learn about ourselves.

Our ancestors learned about mammals the hard way—they relied on other species of mammals for food, and they also had to avoid being eaten themselves by some other species of mammals. Both as predators and as prey, our fellow mammals provided intense levels of natural selection that helped shape our own development. That early knowledge, passed along from generation to generation as our own faculty for both the assimilation and dissemination of knowledge increased, formed the basis of later, more formalized study of mammals. That more codified study of mammals dates back to early Greek scholars, and thus forms part of our earliest scientific knowledge.

Aristotle's classification of organisms is among the earliest to survive, and his division of life forms into five groups included mammals, which he called viviparous quadrupeds. Knowledge of mammalian anatomy accumulated slowly for the next millennium and a half or so, as early practitioners of medicine plied their trade. In 18th century Europe, amateur naturalists began to document their findings in ever increasing numbers. With the colonization of North America by Europeans, the tradition continued in the New World. Mark Catesby's *The Natural History of Carolina, Florida and the Bahama Islands* is an excellent example, published between 1731 and 1743.

The modern era of mammalian classification began with the 1758 publication of Linnaeus' 10th edition of *Systema Naturae*. This work has served as the foundation for our system of binomial nomenclature. He accepted species as individually created and fixed, and arranged them in the basic taxonomic hierarchy that we continue to use today. Linnaeus recognized 184 species of mammals, and the most recent complete compilation of *Mammal Species of the World* lists 5411.

Mammals evolved from reptilian ancestors in the Triassic Period, with the oldest currently recognized mammal appearing some 225 million years ago. Mammals differ from their

Western Gorilla (*Gorilla gorilla*)
Mary McDonald/naturepl.com

*Defining mammalian features
are the structure of the inner ear,
the presence of hair, and
mammary glands.*

Amadeu Blasco

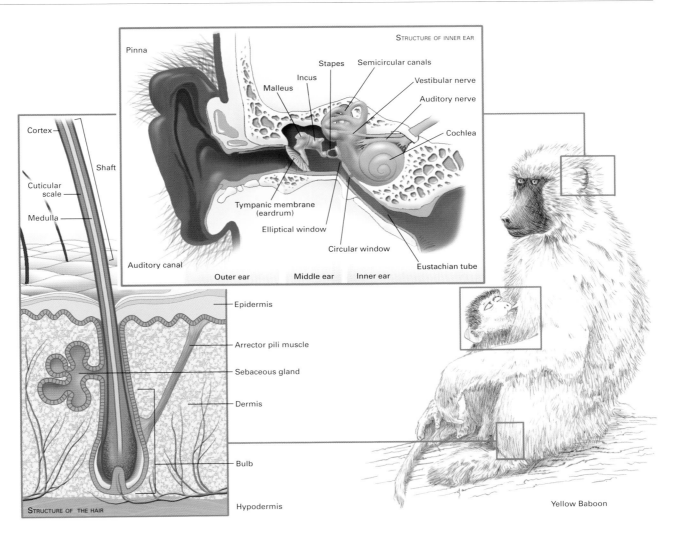

reptilian ancestors in having a lower jaw, or mandible, consisting of only a single bone, the dentary. Two smaller bones that were part of the ancestral reptilian jaw became the inner ear bones that now characterize mammals: the incus and malleus. The third mammalian inner ear bone, the stapes, represents what is left of the entire reptilian stapedial complex.

These inner ear bones (auditory ossicles) are iconic for mammals in that they represent the current state of a long evolutionary history that has allowed for the development of considerable hearing acuity, compared with our reptilian ancestors. In reptiles, sounds are transmitted from the outside to the brain through a stapedial complex, which owes its own evolutionary history to the hyomandibular arch of early, primitive vertebrates. In mammals, that reptilian stapedial complex has evolved into the delicate stapes (stirrup) bone, which rests against the oval window to transmit sounds from the incus (anvil) to the brain. The incus, derived from a homologous structure in the reptilian jaw (the quadrate bone), connects to the malleus (hammer), which has similar evolutionary antecedents (the articular bone). Sound waves first encounter the tympanic membrane (eardrum), and are transmitted to the malleus, which passes them along to the incus, which in turn moves them to the stapes, and from there through the oval window into the appropriate auditory region of the brain. The bones act essentially as mechanical levers to amplify the sounds.

The other defining mammalian characteristics are the presence of hair and mammary glands. Each of these anatomical traits reflects physiological advances that allowed mammals to become so successful. The inner ear bones are related to heightened auditory acuity that allowed mammals to better detect both predators and prey. Hair acts as a thermoregulatory insulating mechanism that allowed mammals to occupy a wider variety of habitats. This, combined with the evolution of homeothermy, the ability of mammals to regulate and maintain their body temperature, freed them from the constraint of using ambient temperature, or sunlight, to remain active. Such freedom included the ability to forage nocturnally, which

lessened predator pressure. Finally, mammary glands allow the production of milk, which allowed for a longer development period for the young of mammals. This, in turn, allowed for increased learning, as the young were able to use that lengthened development period to increase skill sets, and eventually brain size as well.

Although the presence of three (rather than one) inner ear bones, hair, and mammary glands are the most important defining characteristics of mammals, there are several other important differences that mark the distinction of mammals from their reptilian ancestors. Reptiles have dentition that is basically monodont, each tooth a separate peg-like structure. Most mammals, on the other hand, have differentiated dentition, with various distinctive kinds of teeth, some of which have complicated cusps and internal structures. Reptilian teeth have a single root, while those of mammals may have multiple roots.

In addition to having only a single bone, the dentary, in the mandible, that bone articulates with the squamosal bone in the skull in mammals, whereas reptiles have a quadrate-articular jaw joint. Mammals also have a secondary palate, which reptiles lack. This is important, as it keeps the respiratory tract separate from the alimentary tract. This allows young mammals to continue to breathe while they suckle. Reptiles have joined external nares, but those of mammals are separate. The ribs of mammals differ from those of reptiles in at least two important ways: mammals lack lumbar ribs, but reptiles have them; and mammals have fused clavicular ribs while those of reptiles are separate. Internally, this is reflected in mammals having a diaphragm but reptiles lacking one. The scapular of reptiles is flat, and in mammals it bears a spine.

In the pelvic region, the elements are separate in reptiles and fused in mammals. Reptilian limbs project out from the body, but mammalian limbs are underneath the body. The scales of reptiles have been replaced by hair in mammals, and this in turn allows for mammals to be homeothermic in contrast to the heterothermic reptiles.

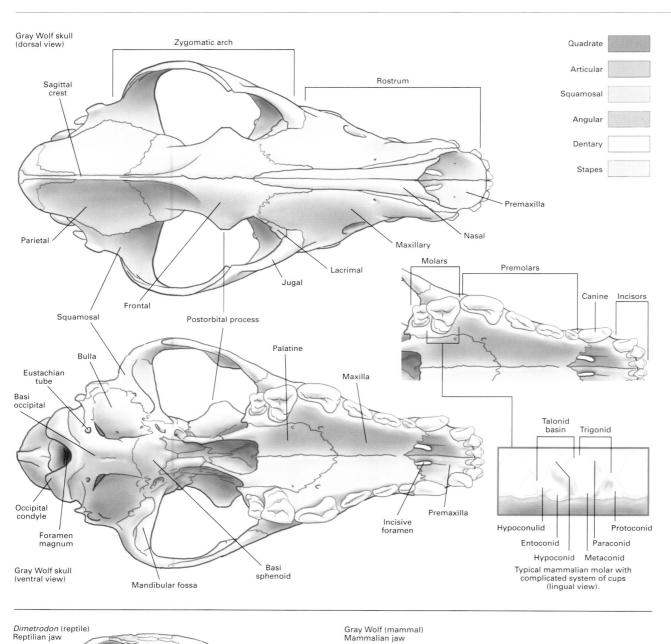

Gray Wolf skull
(dorsal view)

Zygomatic arch

Rostrum

Sagittal
crest

Parietal

Squamosal

Frontal

Postorbital process

Jugal

Lacrimal

Maxillary

Nasal

Premaxilla

The mammalian skull.

Amadeu Blasco

Quadrate
Articular
Squamosal
Angular
Dentary
Stapes

Bulla

Eustachian
tube

Basi
occipital

Occipital
condyle

Foramen
magnum

Gray Wolf skull
(ventral view)

Mandibular fossa

Basi
sphenoid

Palatine

Maxilla

Incisive
foramen

Premaxilla

Molars

Premolars

Canine

Incisors

Talonid
basin

Trigonid

Hypoconulid

Entoconid

Hypoconid

Metaconid

Protoconid

Paraconid

Typical mammalian molar with
complicated system of cups
(lingual view).

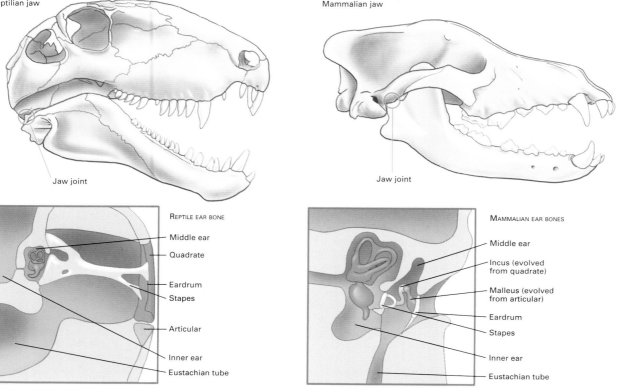

Dimetrodon (reptile)
Reptilian jaw

Gray Wolf (mammal)
Mammalian jaw

Jaw joint

Jaw joint

REPTILE EAR BONE

Middle ear

Quadrate

Eardrum

Stapes

Articular

Inner ear

Eustachian tube

MAMMALIAN EAR BONES

Middle ear

Incus (evolved
from quadrate)

Malleus (evolved
from articular)

Eardrum

Stapes

Inner ear

Eustachian tube

*Differences in reptilian and
mammalian jaws and inner
ear bones.*

Amadeu Blasco

Skeleton

All mammals have an internal bony support structure to which muscles and ligaments are attached. Although an internal skeleton is a characteristic shared with other vertebrate groups, the mammalian skeleton differs in many ways from that of the other vertebrate groups.

The mammalian skull is a complex structure with at least two primary functions. Various parts of the skull serve as attachment sites for jaw muscles that in turn allow the feeding apparatus to function. In addition, the skull provides protection for the brain and other sensory receptors that have allowed mammals to flourish. The general shape of the mammalian skull retains and reflects the evolutionary history of the group. Subsequent radiation of mammals worldwide from early, primitive forms to later, more specialized forms has been accompanied by numerous modifications to the basic mammalian plan. These changes are primarily due to heightened senses of sight, smell, and hearing in particular species of mammals. Perhaps the most important modification has been a tendency towards increased cranial capacity. The variety and complexity of these modifications make the skull one of the most useful anatomi-

cal structures for classification and identification. At the same time, such changes usually provide insight into the animal's lifestyle.

The skull proper is also called the cranium. It is commonly divided into an anterior rostrum and a posterior braincase. The somewhat inflated braincase is the part of the skull that protects the brain. Compared to all of the other vertebrate groups, it is particularly well developed in mammals. The rostrum is the bony portion of the skull inside the snout or muzzle of the animal.

The mammalian skull consists of six major bones, each of which is paired symmetrically on either side. Frontals form the front, parietals the top, and occipitals the back of the head. The sides are formed mainly by the temporals, and the toothrows are held in the maxillae (upper) and mandibles (lower). There are many other small bones in mammalian skulls, with the total number reaching as high as 34. Other important, obvious features are visible on most mammalian skulls. The ventral side includes the auditory bullae, the globular areas that house the inner ear. The dorsal surface frequently has a ridge or saggital crest running the length of the skull, which provides attachment for the jaw muscles, and is more developed in species hav-

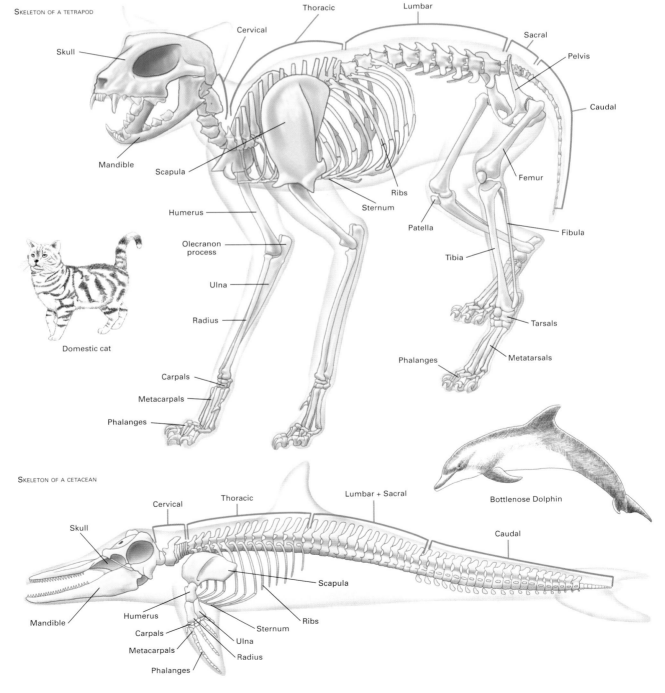

SKELETON OF A TETRAPOD

Thoracic — Lumbar — Cervical — Sacral — Skull — Pelvis — Caudal — Mandible — Scapula — Ribs — Sternum — Femur — Humerus — Patella — Fibula — Olecranon process — Tibia — Ulna — Radius — Tarsals — Phalanges — Metatarsals — Carpals — Metacarpals — Phalanges

Domestic cat

SKELETON OF A CETACEAN

Lumbar + Sacral — Thoracic — Cervical — Skull — Caudal — Scapula — Mandible — Humerus — Ribs — Carpals — Sternum — Metacarpals — Ulna — Phalanges — Radius

Bottlenose Dolphin

The mammalian skeleton.

Amadeu Blasco

ing stronger bite strength. The sides of the skull usually have an obvious zygomatic arch, the bony structure surrounding the separate and flexible jaw articulation area. Muscles from the lower jaw pass through this arch to attach to the skull. There are many additional bones in the mammalian skull, and they vary tremendously from group to group, such that the skull has become a critically important factor in identifying mammals.

Perhaps the most useful area of the skull for identification is the dentition. Mammalian teeth are more complicated than those of other vertebrates, and this complexity allows for considerable variation. Because teeth are so important for feeding, they have evolved into a variety of types, shapes, and sizes. Because mastication works by upper and lower teeth occluding together, strong musculature requiring secure attachments on the skull have also evolved differentially in different groups of mammals. A side benefit of mammal teeth is that they are among the hardest structures in the body, and as such they are more likely to survive as fossils than any other body part. Much of our knowledge of fossil mammals is based on teeth.

Unlike other vertebrates, most mammals are diphyodont, meaning that they have two sets of teeth during their life. The first teeth to erupt in an individual mammal are milk teeth, which are deciduous. Deciduous teeth are restricted to incisors, canines, and premolars, and are replaced by permanent dentition, which also includes 1–4 molars, depending on the group. Teeth are fixed in size, and permanent teeth are relatively large and heavy compared to milk teeth. Replacement of deciduous teeth allows for growth of the jaws, and provides a temporary means of chewing until the jaw bones reach sufficient size to hold the permanent dentition. Similarly, a front-to-back sequence of molar eruption allows for continued growth to accommodate the full complement of cheek teeth by the time the animal reaches full adult size.

There are many variants from this general pattern. Some kangaroos may have sequentially erupting premolars, followed by molars that also erupt sequentially, and move forward in the toothrow as they develop. Although most species have a fixed number of teeth, some may replace them more or less continually as needed. Manatees may have 6–8 teeth in each quadrant at any given time, drawing on a total of up to 20 in each quadrant throughout their lifetime. Elephants usually have only a single tooth active in each quadrant at any given time, with another moving forward to replace it, up to a total of six per quadrant. Some rodents and pinnipeds gain and lose deciduous teeth in utero, leaving only permanent teeth by parturition. Toothed whales lack deciduous teeth altogether, having a single set of permanent dentition.

Mammalian dentition normally includes four different types of teeth: incisors (I), canines (C), premolars (P), and molars (M). Incisors are the most anterior teeth, and the upper incisors are the only teeth carried on the premaxillary bones; the others are on the maxillae. Although marsupial mammals can have up to five upper and four lower incisors, primitive eutherian mammals had three on each side, and that number is frequently reduced in various groups. Incisors tend to be simple in structure, with sharp, wedge-shaped tips that may occasionally be bi- or even tri-lobed in some groups. Most mammals use incisors for initially grasping food items with a pinching action between upper and lower incisors.

Canines lie between the incisors and premolars, and are essentially unicuspid, although there are occasionally small accessory cusps on the cingula of these teeth. They tend to be the longest teeth in the toothrow, and sharply pointed on the end. They are used to grasp and hold prey items, and sometimes aid in killing prey with their stabbing action. There is only a single canine in each quadrant, and they are usually single-rooted teeth. In some mammals they have become elongated into tusks that are used for fighting or digging. Some groups, such as rodents and many ungulates lack canines, probably because they have no need for them owing to their herbivorous food habits. Their absence leaves a gap, called a diastema, between the incisors and premolars.

Premolars lie between the canines and molars, and are attached to the maxillary bones in the upper jaw. Primitively, placental mammals had four premolars and marsupials three, but that number is reduced in many groups. Premolars are quite variable in shape and size, ranging from tiny pegs forced to

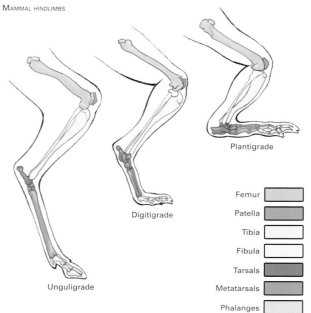

MAMMAL HINDLIMBS

Plantigrade

Digitigrade

Unguligrade

Femur
Patella
Tibia
Fibula
Tarsals
Metatarsals
Phalanges

The variations in forelimbs and hindlimbs of mammals are striking.

Amadeu Blasco

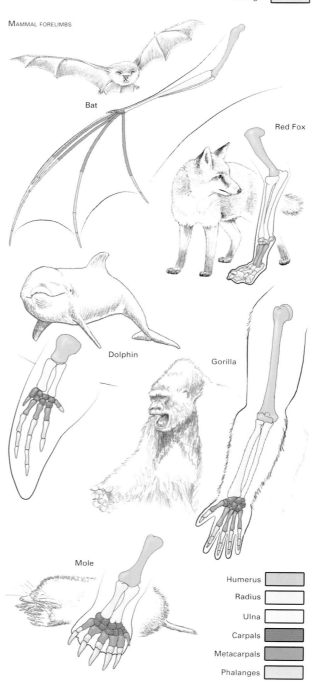

MAMMAL FORELIMBS

Bat

Red Fox

Dolphin

Gorilla

Mole

Humerus
Radius
Ulna
Carpals
Metacarpals
Phalanges

one side of the toothrow, to large and complex teeth used by carnivores to slice meat from prey. In general, they are smaller, slightly less complex versions of molars.

Molars are the large crushing teeth found in the back of the toothrow. They tend to be complex, with various cusps and ridges giving structure to the occlusal surface. Molars have no deciduous antecedents, and frequently their eruption pattern can be used to age young animals. The primitive number for eutherians is three, and for marsupials, four. As adults age, the molar surfaces frequently show signs of wear, depending on the food habits. The degree of wear on the molars can then be used to age animals as well.

Using the initial letter of each tooth type, followed by the number in both upper and lower jaw yields a formula that can then be doubled to yield the total number of teeth. The primitive number for placentals is I 3/3, C 1/1, P 4/4, M 3/3 = 44 total, and for marsupials I 5/4, C 1/1, P 3/3, M 4/4 = 50 total. Humans have I 2/2, C 1/1, P 2/2, M 3/3 = 32. Most deviations from the primitive numbers involve reductions in number of teeth, but in some groups, like toothed whales, the number has increased to as many as 250 in some species.

Between the skull at the anterior end and the tail at the posterior, the mammalian skeleton basically consists of an elongated vertebral column with fore- and hindlimbs as well as ribs attached to it. There is a great deal of variation in the component parts, and in extreme cases, loss of tail or hindlimbs altogether. The skull, spinal column, and ribs are often referred to as the axial skeleton. The vertebral column has evolved primarily to protect the spinal cord, and consists of several different types of vertebrae: cervical, thoracic, lumbar, sacral, and caudal.

The neck region is supported by seven cervical vertebrae in almost all mammals. The articulation with the skull is via the occipital condyles, paired projections at the back of the skull that articulate with the first cervical vertebra, the atlas. The second, the axis, articulates with the atlas via a dorsal projection called the odontoid process.

Thoracic vertebrae form a series of 12–15 vertebrae that support the ribcage. The ribs, in turn, provide protection and support for the lungs, the major respiratory organs of mammals. In a few groups, there are ribs that originate on cervical vertebrae as well. Because the thoracic vertebrae also provide attachment for the muscles that control the head and neck, they frequently feature large dorsal spines. The ribs are connected ventrally by the sternum, or breastbone. The resultant ribcage provides a sturdy, protective shield for the heart and lungs, organs vital to mammalian survival.

The next section of the spine is composed of lumbar vertebrae, usually six or seven, but variable in number with some whales having many more than that. Humans have five, and they form the lower back, a region best known for causing problems owing to stresses generated by our highly derived, upright, bipedal posture. The spinal cord proper ends in the lumbar region, where it divides into a number of smaller roots that travel to the lower body and extremities.

Most mammals have 3–5 sacral vertebrae, frequently fused in various combinations, but some may have as many as 13. Fused into the sacrum, these vertebrae provide support for the pelvic girdle. The sacrum is attached to the pelvic girdle by the sacroiliac joints, another common source of back pain in humans. Although all mammals produce a great deal of stress on the sacroiliac joint through normal locomotion, most do not live long enough for degradation of the joint to have the debilitating effects found in humans.

Caudal vertebrae are highly variable in number, ranging from 5–50 in most mammals. These are the tail vertebrae, and in many tailless mammals, the caudal vertebrae fuse to form a coccyx, as in humans. In those mammals with tails, the caudal vertebrae provide the internal structural support for this appendage, which can be critically important in locomotion for many groups.

The appendicular skeleton consists of those elements that make up the limb bones of mammals. The limb bones are attached to the axial (trunk) skeleton via the pectoral (anterior, or forelimbs), and the pelvic (posterior, or hindlimbs) girdles. The pectoral girdle consists of two bones, the clavicle, or collarbone, and the scapula, or shoulder blade. The clavicle is attached to, and articulates with, the anterior end of the sternum, and extends outward horizontally from the trunk of the body, providing both support and attachment to the scapula. Slender and somewhat rod-like, the clavicle attaches to the acromion, a bony projection of the scapula. The scapula has another bony process, the coracoid, which serves as an attachment for the heavy mass of muscles necessary to control the shoulder area and move the forelimbs. The dorsolateral end of the scapula has a glenoid cavity, into which the humerus (upper arm bone) fits to form a ball-and-socket joint.

At the distal end, the humerus articulates with both forearm bones, the radius through a somewhat shallower ball-and-socket joint; and the ulna, through a simple hinge joint at the elbow. The distal ends of the ulna and radius, in turn, articulate with the carpals, or wrist bones. In some groups, the ulna and radius are fused into a single bone. The carpals, variable in number (e.g. eight in humans) then articulate with metacarpals, and those join distally with a varying number of phalanges. As with most structures, the diversity found within the mammalian forelimb is impressive. Compare the forelimb of a shrew, a bat, a mole, a seal, and an elephant, for example. Although incredibly varied, each of these contains bones that are embryologically homologous.

The hindlimb of most mammals is similar to the forelimb in structure. The pelvic girdle consists of three bones, the ilium, ischium, and pubis, which are commonly fused into a single structure. In most forms, the ilium is the heaviest of the bones, and provides the articulation with the femur, or thigh bone, through a rounded socket called the acetabulum. The two ilia are joined via a wide, flat articulation with the sacrum dorsally. The ischium forms a lower extension of the hip bones, and the paired pubic bones are connected ventrally via a pubic symphysis.

The femur, or upper leg bone, is the longest bone in the body in many forms. It articulates distally with the major lower limb bone, the tibia, at the knee joint. There is frequently a small floating bony element, the patella, that forms the knee-cap. The other lower legbone is called the fibula. These two elements articulate with the tarsal bones at the ankle. Like carpals in the forelimb, the number of tarsals varies (seven in humans), but most forms have a well-developed calcaneum, or heel bone, which provides attachment for muscles and ligaments that allow for walking and running. Tarsals attach to metatarsals forming the arch area of the foot, and these in turn attach to phalanges, or toe bones.

Musculature

The skeleton provides structural support for mammals, but another critical function of many bones is to provide attachment for muscles. The mammalian musculature system provides the infrastructure that allows mammals to move. Movements are highly evolved in mammals, and absolutely vital to virtually all mammalian functions. Muscles are also the major internal heat generators of mammals, clearly an important capability for homeothermic animals. Most of the body weight of mammals is made up of muscles, and in many cases they provide additional protection for vital organs.

Mammalian muscle tissue functions in a simple way—by shortening (contraction), and then lengthening to recover (relaxation). The stimulus for a muscle to flex is a nerve impulse that acts on muscle proteins known as actin and myosin. They react chemically to cause sufficient number of muscle fibers to contract, which results in the muscle becoming shorter and fatter. One function of muscles is to constrict a space, causing air, fluids, and other materials to flow. In most mammalian movements, muscle contraction causes one or more bones to be drawn to another. The subsequent relaxation of that muscle allows the reverse action to occur.

Histologically, muscles are classified as striated, cardiac, and smooth. Skeletal muscles, which make up the bulk of the mammalian body, are striated – tissue consisting of long fibers with transverse bands. The mammalian heart is mainly cardiac muscle, a special type of striated muscle that functions without nervous stimulation. Smooth muscles are those that lack striations, and are found mainly in the walls of blood vessels and surrounding many internal organs.

Terrestrial locomotion.

Vicugna (*Vicugna vicugna*)
Xavier Ferrer & Adolf de Sostoa

The mammalian skeletal musculature system can be divided into axial and appendicular parts, just as is the skeleton. Muscles in the head and neck region associated with feeding and various sensory systems are called branchial and hypobranchial muscles. Large skeletal muscles associated with the trunk and tail form the axial musculature. The axial musculature can be divided into dorsal (epaxial) and ventral (hypaxial) muscles. In most mammals, epaxials consist of four major groups, including iliocostales, intervertebrals, longissimus, and spinales.

Hypaxials also consist of four main groups: rectus abdominis and subvertebrals, as well as oblique and transverse sheets, or parietal muscles. In mammals, part of the oblique group includes the muscles of the diaphragm, a major force in the mammalian respiratory system. The axial bundles continue on into the tail in many mammals, but they are differentially interrupted by the pelvis in various groups.

Appendicular muscles parallel the appendicular skeleton and provide the thrust for mammalian locomotion. In many forms, the appendicular muscles make up the bulk of the muscular system. In general, the major muscles of the limbs can be divided into dorsal and ventral elements. The dorsal muscles act to extend the limbs, and the ventrals do the opposite. Jointly, they provide the propulsive force that causes the trunk to move forward relative to the feet in a moving mammal. They also help to brace the limb bones, supporting the body in an upright position relative to the limbs. Mammals have also evolved a thin muscle under the skin that allows many of them to twitch their skin to shake off insects.

Terrestrial Locomotion

Most species of mammals are terrestrial, and have evolved relatively simple modifications to the terrestrial locomotion systems of their reptilian ancestors. At least partly because they are homeothermic, mammals are capable of considerably longer and more complicated movements than reptiles. Structural modifications that have allowed this greater mobility include the more direct placement of the limbs under the trunk, improving both support and direct forward motion.

Terrestrial locomotion can be classified in various ways, including how the feet strike the ground. The primitive condition for mammals is plantigrade, which means that the heel strikes the ground first, and the entire foot is in contact with the ground. The primitive digit number for mammals is five,

and such pentadactyl mammals are usually plantigrade. In this condition, the wrists, ankles, and digits rest on the ground at each step. Such mammals are not particularly fast, and include generalized forms such as monotremes, marsupials, insectivores, and primates, as well as more specialized groups such as raccoons and bears.

Mammals that run on the ground with structural modifications to enhance both speed and endurance are called cursorial. Cursorial mammals, such as most carnivores and ungulates, have their limbs completely underneath the trunk, and move them in the same parasaggital plane, in a straight forward and backward manner. Most of these cursorial mammals are either predators, which run down their prey, or medium to large herbivores that need to run fast to escape the predators. Mammals that are cursorial can be divided into those that are digitigrade and those that are unguligrade. Carnivores and other digitigrade mammals increase the effective length of their legs by running on the digital arches, or what humans would call the balls of their feet. Ungulates have specialized even further by running on the tips of the digits. The main advantages of cursorial mammals are an increase in speed and endurance.

Mammals that move by jumping are referred to as saltators, or saltatorial mammals. Some saltatorial mammals are arboreal, and leap from branch to branch or tree to tree. Good examples are found among the prosimians, including the tarsiers (*Tarsius*) and galagos. The extreme form of saltation is seen in terrestrial, open-habitat mammals such as kangaroos, kangaroo rats (*Dipodomys*), and springhares (*Pedetes*), which are called ricochetal because they move in a succession of leaps powered by the hind feet in a bipedal fashion. Saltatorial mammals can accelerate very quickly and alter their direction more easily than quadrapedal, cursorial forms.

The evolutionary tendencies in terrestrial mammalian locomotion have mainly involved moving from primitive plantigrade mammals to more advanced cursorial or saltatorial forms. The advantages include speed, endurance, leaping ability, acceleration, and maneuverability.

Aquatic locomotion

Primitive mammals were terrestrial, and their occupation of marine habitats obviously involved a completely different form of locomotion. Almost all mammals can swim, but only a few

groups can be regarded as truly aquatic. Marine mammals in the orders Cetacea and Sirenia are the only completely aquatic forms. Semi-aquatic species, which inhabit fresh water habitats but bear their young on land, are represented in many orders, and occur on all continents. Examples include Monotremata (Platypus), Didelphimorphia (Water Opossum), Afrosoricida (otter shrews), Soricomorpha (desmans), Lagomorpha (Marsh Rabbit), Rodentia (beavers), Carnivora (seals), and Artiodactyla (hippopotamuses).

Water is a much denser medium than air, so aquatic mammals tend to move slower than terrestrial ones, although Cetaceans are capable of speeds of greater than 40 km/h in short bursts. Semi-aquatic mammals tend to swim slowly, but efficiently, using the same basic structure that serves them for terrestrial locomotion. Truly aquatic forms have undergone a variety of structural modifications to allow them to swim much more efficiently. Cetaceans and sirenians have lost their pelvic appendages, and swim via a series of dorso-ventral undulations powered by a horizontal tail, or fluke. Neither they nor earless seals (Phocidae) use their pectoral appendages as thrust mechanisms. Seals swim in a similar fashion, but with lateral undulations driven by sculling motions of the large pectoral flippers. Eared seals (Otariidae) do use their enlarged fore-flippers as propulsive devices. Otariids are also much more adept at terrestrial locomotion, as they can rotate their hind flippers underneath the body to assume a terrestrial, quadrupedal stance.

That marine mammals have truly adapted to a swimming mode of life is attested by their speed and endurance in the water. Some dolphins may reach speeds of up to 40 km/h for short bursts. Blue Whales (*Balaenoptera musculus*) can reach similar speeds for short periods, and are capable of cruising for an hour or two at 25 km/h. Fur seals migrate up to 12,000 km each year, and Gray Whales (*Eschrichtius robustus*) go 19,000 km, at an average speed of 5–6 km/h.

A corollary of swimming for many aquatic mammals is diving, the ability to spend considerable amounts of time under the water, in spite of the necessity of returning to the surface to breathe. Semi-aquatic animals do not reach the depths, or spend as long submerged as do the truly aquatic species. Among pinnipeds, elephant seals (*Mirounga*) are known to dive very deep, perhaps to 2 km or more, and to stay submerged for 1–2 h. Cetaceans, particularly beaked whales and bottlenosed whales (*Hyperoodon*), also may reach such depths, and stay under for equivalent amounts of time.

Aerial locomotion

A number of mammals have evolved gliding mechanisms, but only the bats have true powered flight. Different degrees of aerial locomotion have been defined, and we might think of them as increasingly complicated, from falling through parachuting, gliding, and soaring to flapping flight. Falling is simply allowing gravity to prevail, employing no devices to increase drag or create lift. Some arboreal mammals may use falling as a predator escape mechanism. Parachuting can be defined as falling at greater than 45 degrees from the horizontal, and employing some mechanism to increase drag, and reduce speed. A very rudimentary form of parachuting is seen in cats, which twist their bodies and extend their legs when falling, so that they break their fall, and possibly increase drag. Some primates, notably the Sifakas (*Propithecus*), a species of lemur, are known to behave as though parachuting. Sifakas have thick hair on their forearms that might increase drag, and a small membrane under the forelimbs that might even provide some lift.

Gliding is much more common, and has developed in diverse, unrelated groups such as Diprotodontia (flying phalan-

gers, sugar gliders, Greater Glider, Feather-tailed Glider, etc.), Rodentia (flying squirrels, scaly-tailed squirrels), and Dermoptera (flying lemurs). Gliding can be defined as falling at less than 45 degrees from the horizontal, and animals that glide have clear adaptations for increasing drag and creating limited amounts of lift. All have membranes stretching from fore- to hindlimbs that help to catch the airstream. Glides of over 200 m have been reported for flying squirrels.

Only bats have attained true flight, and only a limited subset of bats use soaring as a method of locomotion. In soaring, practiced by some members of the family Pteropodidae, the flying foxes, the animals ride thermals to stay aloft without flapping the wings. The energy-saving advantage of soaring is obvious.

Bats likely evolved from gliding ancestors, and gradually added flapping motions to add power and agility to their locomotory repertoire. Chiroptera, the name of the order of bats, means hand-wing. The distal half of a bat's wing is contained within the elongated fingers of the hand. This is the part of the wing that provides the majority of the thrust of powered flight. In addition, bats have a uropatagium, or interfemoral membrane that stretches between the hindlimbs, adding lift and maneuverability.

The advantages of flight are many, and include the ability to forage on flying insects, a lifestyle adopted by many bats. In addition, food resources such as terminal flowers and fruits on tall trees that are otherwise difficult to access, become available to flying bats. The increased mobility and maneuverability afforded by flight greatly increases bats' ability to seek food and shelter. Flight provides an excellent escape mechanism from non-volant predators. Long range migration becomes possible with flight; an adaptation that overcomes seasonally available food resources or rigorous climates. Flight has allowed for the worldwide dispersal of bats, as they can easily surmount what might otherwise prove serious barriers to movement.

Feeding and Digestion

Mammals have evolved in such a diversity of forms that they are able to take advantage of a wide range of food items. The largest of mammals, the baleen whales, feed on some of the smallest of organisms, marine plankton. At the other end of this spectrum top carnivores such as Killer Whales (*Orcinus orca*), can feed on very large prey, such as a variety of pinnipeds, and even large cetaceans in some cases. Mammals are frequently classified as carnivores, herbivores, insectivores, frugivores, or omnivores, and each of these can be further subdivided. Furthermore, many mammals take advantage of more than one type of feeding. Although members of the order Carnivora are obviously mainly carnivorous, there are some members that are entirely frugivorous.

The earliest ancestral mammals were probably insectivorous. In addition to evolving into all of the other feeding types, these basal insectivores gave rise to an increasingly specialized variety of forms that continued to feed primarily on insects. Species that feed at least partially on insects or other small invertebrates can be found in most mammalian orders, with the exception of Hyracoidea, Proboscidea, Sirenia, Lagomorpha, Perissodactyla, Artiodactyla, and Cetacea. Insectivores tend to have short, simple digestive tracts.

Bats represent a highly evolved group of insectivores. Although the order Chiroptera contains species that feed on almost every type of food resource, some 705 of the more than 1100 species of bats are insectivorous. There are two main groups of insectivorous bats, divided into foraging guilds. The most common, and probably most highly specialized, are the aerial insectivores. These bats use sophisticated echolocation systems to locate and home in on flying insects. Even though many insect groups have evolved their own defense mechanisms against this type of predation, the success of aerial insectivores is attested to by their appearance on every continent except Antarctica, where bats are lacking entirely.

The second category is that of foliage gleaning bats, those that take their insect prey items directly from the surface of the ground or vegetation. Many of these have a specific set of adaptations including short, broad wings and large ears that allow them to detect their prey, and maneuver to snatch it from the surface while continuing in flight. Foliage gleaning bats have also evolved in several different families, and on several different continents.

Terrestrial insectivores are typically small-bodied forms that forage in the leaf litter, or on the surface of the ground. The order Soricomorpha, the shrews and moles, contains a plethora of species devoted to this food habit. Shrews are the quintessential small terrestrial insectivore. They have very high metabolic rates that force them to forage frequently in order to take in enough food to maintain their energy output. Interestingly, some shrews and a few other kinds of mammals have venom glands that allow them to produce a toxin that helps to immo-

Insectivorous feeding.

Stripe-faced Dunnart
(***Sminthopsis macroura***)
Jiri Lochman/
Lochman Transparencies

Omnivorous feeding.

Common Warthog
(***Phacochoerus africanus***)
Dave Watts/Lochman Transparencies

bilize their prey. Several other orders also contain small forms that forage on terrestrial insects or other invertebrates.

Aquatic insectivores are less common among mammals, but some do forage for invertebrates in freshwater habitats. The Platypus (*Ornithorhynchus anatinus*), a monotreme, forages on benthic invertebrates, which it stores in cheekpouches until it can surface to masticate and swallow them. Star-nosed Moles (Soricomorpha) also forage in freshwater streams for aquatic invertebrates. Several shrews also make use of aquatic habitats to seek out invertebrate prey. Water Opossums (Didelphimorphia) also forage for both invertebrates and fish in streams and ponds in the Neotropics.

Several unrelated kinds of mammals have also specialized in feeding on ants and/or termites. Echidnas (Monotremata), Numbats (Dasyuromorphia), Aardvarks (Tubulidentata), armadillos (Cingulata), anteaters (Pilosa), Aardwolves (Carnivora), and pangolins (Pholidota) all fill this role, and the diversity ensures that anteating forms are found on all of the tropical continents.

Arboreal insectivores are also quite common, as the canopy of tropical forests provides a cornucopia of insect life. Primates have several small insectivores, especially among the prosimians. Many kinds of lemurs are insectivorous, and one form, the Aye-aye, has evolved an elongated third digit with which it probes for insects in tree limbs and dead branches.

Carnivorous mammals are those that feed on other vertebrates. Obviously the order Carnivora contains many examples, but there are carnivorous members of several other orders as well. Dasyuromorphia includes many carnivores, as does Cetacea and Chiroptera. Thus, there are terrestrial, aquatic, and aerial carnivores, just as there are insectivorous forms in each of these categories. One unique form of specialized carnivory is found in the three species of vampire bats, which feed exclusively on the blood of other vertebrates. Carnivore digestive systems tend to be slightly longer than those of insectivores, and often contain a small caecum, or blind pouch off of the intestines that houses bacteria useful in digestion.

Herbivorous mammals are those that feed on plant material. They also occupy several different orders, but many are rodents. Artiodactyls and perissodactyls, as well as proboscideans and hyracoids are herbivores as well. Herbivores have much longer and more complicated digestive systems, because digesting plant parts requires more time than does digesting animal matter. They also have an enlarged caecum, which helps to ferment the plant material and make it more digestible. Many forms also practice coprophagy, or reingesting feces to allow another cycle of digestion on remains that pass through without being absorbed.

Finally, most mammals are actually omnivorous, combining two or more of the other categories. Every order contains examples of omnivores. Humans are a good example of omnivorous mammals. We are both herbivorous and carnivorous. This flexibility in food habits serves many species well in allowing them to forage on one type or the other, depending on seasonal variability and availability of both plant and animal food items.

All of these various food habits are accommodated by an advanced digestive system that has evolved in concert with changes in diet. Improvements in foraging efficiency have been accompanied by similar changes in processing the food to make it available metabolically. Individual food items are initially taken into the oral cavity, assisted by lips, tongue, and teeth, each of which has been affected by natural selection. Ingestion is followed by mastication in most species, although a few kinds of whales and anteaters lack teeth. Chewing reduces the size of food items, and the resultant smaller surface area makes it easier for the initial digestive enzymes, found in the saliva, to begin the chemical process of breaking the food down into metabolically usable components.

Herbaceous material, with highly resistant cell walls, requires considerable mastication to render it digestible. Hence, herbivores have evolved a variety of mechanisms to aid in the initial breakdown of their food material. Some ungulates regurgitate material to masticate it again, known as chewing their cud. Some rodents and lagomorphs reingest soft, partially digested fecal pellets to reprocess them and obtain additional nutrients from them.

For that important first step of mastication, mammals rely on teeth, making mammalian dentition a critically important part of their physical structure. Because of the wide variety of food habits, the teeth have also evolved into an amazingly varied set of structures. Thus, by looking at the teeth of a mammal, inferences can be made about its food habits. For mammalian taxonomists, this evolutionary diversity in dentition allows for a tremendously valuable character set that can be useful to distinguish between species.

Although primitive vertebrates have homodont dentition, mammalian teeth are heterodont, and consist of four basic va-

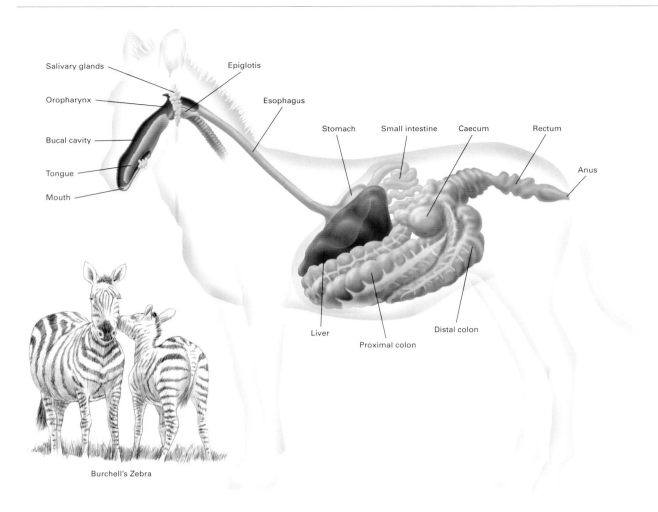

The mammalian digestive system.

Amadeu Blasco

Burchell's Zebra

STRUCTURE OF STOMACH IN RUMINANTS

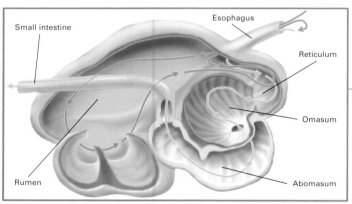

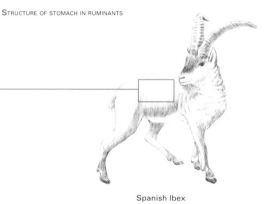

Spanish Ibex

rieties known as incisors, canines, premolars, and molars. The number of each of these types can be used to outline a dental formula for any given species of mammal. The primitive condition for mammals is I 5/4, C 1/1, P 4/4, M 4/4 = 54. Advanced forms almost always have some reduced number from this early maximum. Thus, primitive marsupials had a dental formula of I 5/4, C 1/1, P 3/3, M 4/4 = 50, and primitive placentals I 3/3, C 1/1, P 4/4, M 3/3 = 44. Clearly the maximum reduction is seen in some anteaters and baleen whales, which lack teeth altogether.

Most mammals are diphyodont, meaning they have two sets of teeth during their lifetime. These consist of milk, or deciduous, teeth, and permanent teeth. Again, whales are the exception—baleen whales lack teeth, and toothed whales are monophyodont, or have only a single set, the permanent teeth. Normally, the milk teeth begin to erupt towards the end of the suckling period, and are later replaced by the permanent dentition. Molars have no deciduous precursors, and are permanent only, so that by the time they have completely erupted, the final jaw size has been attained.

Mammalian teeth are arranged in an arc around the roof of the mouth, or palate. Mammals have both a soft and hard pal-

ate, which help to divide the rostrum into oral and nasal parts. Frequently, mammalian palates are rugose, with the ridges helping to hold the food during mastication. The baleen plates of mysticete whales developed from similar ridges. Teeth are arranged on alveolar ridges, or gums, and these are separated from the cheeks by a trench called the oral vestibule. In some mammals, the vestibule contains an opening into an expandible cheek pouch, which can be used to store food for transport to a safer place for lengthy mastication.

Another remarkable aid to mastication is the mammalian tongue. Fleshy lips and cheeks combine with the muscular tongue to adroitly move food items between the occlusal surfaces of the teeth, and the tongue aids in moving the masticated material back into the pharynx. The tongue also bears sensory receptors in the form of taste buds, that aid in determining edibility of food items. Rasping papillae on the tongues of cats and some other carnivores aid in removing flesh from bones. The most remarkable tongue adaptations are seen in anteaters, which may have protrusible tongues that may reach three times the length of the head, and attach all the way back on the sternum, rather than in the throat as is the case with most mammals.

Digestion begins with the injection of enzymes and softening, moisturizing agents into the bolus of masticated food by the salivary glands. A series of these glands pumps the necessary fluids to the mouth, and they are named by their location; e.g., labial, molar, infraorbital, palatal, sublingual, and mandibular. The largest are the parotids, and they provide ptyalin or amylase, the enzyme that begins to digest starch. Variety prevails here as well, with some mammals producing toxins in the saliva, and the highly specialized vampire bats secrete an anticoagulant that helps to keep their blood meal flowing.

The pharynx provides passage from the mouth to the esophagus. The mammalian pharynx is highly specialized to maintain separation of the oral and nasal passages. The back of the oral cavity opens into the pharynx through a narrow slit called the glottis. The upper part of the pharynx also is home to various lymphoidal tissue known as tonsils. These may be palatine, lingual, or pharyngeal (adenoids), and they provide the first line of defense against disease organisms that may invade through the mouth or nose.

The connection between the pharynx and the stomach is called the esophagus. Because this region of the alimentary tract is still subject to some abrasion from rough foods, it is lined with a cornified squamous epithelium. There are mucus and serous secreting glands lining the esophagus, with longitudinal folds allowing for expansion and papillae that help to move the food along the passageway. The accompanying musculature is striated, and the esophagus remains collapsed until swallowed food items distend it.

Food passes from the esophagus into the stomach, where it is mixed with gastric juices that continue the process of digestion. These secretions include hydrochloric acid and enzymes such as pepsin to begin digesting proteins into amino acids, chitinase to hydrolyze insect cuticles, and rennin to curdle milk and make it susceptible to pepsin. Mammals that require long and complex processing of plant material have multi-chambered stomachs. Some artiodactyls have four chambers in sequence: the rumen, reticulum, omasum, and abomasum. The first two chambers contain anaerobic bacteria and ciliated protozoa that help to break down the cellulose. After direct absorption of organic acids formed in the rumen and reticulum, remaining material passes on through the omasum and abomasum for additional protein digestion. The partially liquefied mass then moves on into the duodenum through the pylorus, an opening surrounded by a ring of smooth muscle known as the pyloric sphincter.

From there, material flows into the duodenum, where secretions from the liver and pancreas add to the mix. This helps to reduce the acidity of the mixture, and ready it for the small intestine, where most remaining digestion and absorption takes place. The surface area of the intestine is increased by extensive folding and looping, as well as by an array of villi and microvilli lining the epithelium. From the small intestine, remaining unabsorbed material passes to the large intestine, or colon, where little additional digestion occurs in most mammals. Waste products, in the form of feces from which most of the water has been absorbed in the colon, are excreted through the rectum.

The high level of metabolism of mammals in general is supported by the intake of large amounts of food, which is quickly digested, and passed through the system. The evolution of teeth has allowed for efficient mastication, and a high body temperature and numerous glands combine to accelerate enzyme action. Intestine lengths that may be up to 25 times the body length and adaptations to increase the surface area add to the efficiency of digestion in mammals.

The theory of optimal foraging predicts that animals will maximize energy return relative to the energy needed to secure their food. Mammals have balanced those needs in their foraging activities in myriad ways. Herbivores feed on stationary food items, and have evolved to deal with chemical defenses of plants, while avoiding predators. In many species of ungulates, group foraging adds to their ability to spot and avoid predators. Seasonality of food resources has resulted in relatively sophisticated food storage capabilities in some species. Moving food from one locality to another for comsump-

tion later is known as caching, and many kinds of rodents are particularly adept at it.

Carnivores pursue moving food items, and do so in different ways. Efficiency in killing is common to all, and most mammalian carnivores subdue their prey with bites to vital areas such as the neck or head. Canids, which tend to be solitary hunters, run down their prey with speed or endurance. They are quite adaptable, and capable of learning from experience to increase their hunting efficiency. Felids depend more on surprise and short bursts of speed to catch prey. Some species of herpestids and mustelids have developed unusual behaviors to deal with prey items such as eggs, which they may break against rocks. Similarly, Sea Otters (*Enhydra lutris*) use rocks to break open the shells of molluscs. Carnivores may be solitary hunters, such as many canids and felids, or group foragers such as some mongooses, and specialized canids such as wolves and hunting dogs.

Excretory System

Although the excretion of undigested wastes is clearly a function of the mammalian excretory system, osmoregulation, or water balance, is probably the more important and complex function. For this, the kidneys are the major functional organs. Protein metabolism results in nitrogenous waste products that must be removed, and help to maintain the narrow balance between water and salts that allow mammalian organ systems to function. The high level of metabolism and endothermy of mammals complicates this issue. Water is necessarily lost through the skin and in respiration to help control body temperature. High numbers of renal tubules combine with high systemic blood pressure to allow mammals to filter enormous quantities of body fluid to maintain water balance.

Although most mammals require free water, some desert-adapted species can exist on metabolic water alone. This is augmented by diet when possible, such as ingestion of succulent plant material. The problem is exacerbated by the fact that many desert plant species are halophytic, containing high concentrations of salts. Many rodents have evolved highly efficient kidneys that produce highly concentrated urine. Carnivorous species in arid areas rely on the water content of their prey items to maintain their own internal water balance.

Respiratory water loss associated with maintaining a stable internal body temperature is a major constraint on the distribution of many species of mammals. Loss of pulmonary water is reduced in some heat adapted species through a nasal countercurrent system. Inhaled air below body temperature cools

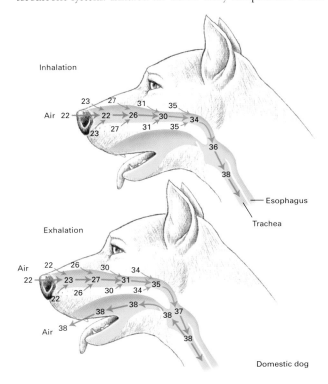

Domestic dog

the nasal mucosa, and then passes into the lungs where it is warmed and becomes saturated with water. Exhaled air passes back across the cool nasal mucosa, resulting in condensation and absorption of water. The exhaled air is thus much warmer than the inhaled air.

A special problem for mammals involves lactation and the maintenance of water balance. Suckling young involves the direct loss of body water, and some mammals have evolved special adaptions to deal with this problem. Several species reingest the feces and urine produced by their young, thus replacing some of the lost fluid. In addition, some species, such as kangaroo rats, produce milk that is very concentrated, allowing the mothers to retain as much water as possible.

Respiratory System

Although the digestive system reduces raw food materials to molecular components, the conversion of those components into usable energy occurs within the cells as oxidation processes. The oxygen necessary for these reactions is provided by the respiratory system. Similarly it helps to rid the mammalian body of an otherwise toxic byproduct of metabolism, carbon dioxide. One of the most important evolutionary adaptations of mammals involves the secondary palate, which allows separation of the digestive and respiratory systems. Mammals have large nostrils above that palate, and their surface area is increased through the action of the turbinal bones, scroll-like bones inside the nasal cavity. Mucous-lined sides of these bones begin the process of warming and moisturizing the air on its way to the lungs.

Air moves from the nasal cavities through the trachea into the lungs. The trachea is supported by a series of cartilagenous rings that help to hold it open even when the neck is twisted. The trachea divides into a pair of primary bronchi from air then enters a network of branching pathways that end in alveoli where oxygen is exchanged for carbon dioxide, which then combines with excess metabolic water, and is exhaled back out the same passages.

Air movement in and out of the lungs is driven primarily by contractions of the muscular diaphragm. Even though lung size is proportional to body size in most mammals, the amount of respiratory surface is more a function of metabolic rate. Primates have large lungs, but relatively small alveolar surface areas. Even so, humans have about 300 million alveoli in their lungs, providing a respiratory surface area equal to about 40 times the surface area of the external body. Rodents have considerably more respiratory surface area, and bats, with their high metabolic rates during flight, have tiny lungs but huge surface areas. Mammalian alveoli secrete a lipoprotein that acts as a surfactant to reduce the surface tension of the oxygenated liquid film that might otherwise cause the lungs to collapse. The alveoli contain an abundance of capillaries to aid in gas exchange.

Although variable between species, on average mammals breathe about once every three heart beats. Many factors can cause an increase in respiratory rate, including temperature and activity levels. Oxygen requirements increase dramatically with increase in activity, and mammals that are running full speed may increase the rate to many times that of the resting rate. Additionally, increased activity may cause internal heat production, requiring increased respiration rate for thermoregulation.

As mentioned briefly above, the respiratory system of mammals is crucial for thermoregulation. As inhaled air passes over the nasal mucosa, it becomes warmer and moister. This results in evaporative cooling of the nasal passages, as heat transfers from them to the air. Conversely returning exhaled air, which is warm and saturated with moisture from the lungs, releases moisture to the cooler, dryer nasal passages, aiding in water conservation. This counter-current exchange system serves both in thermoregulation and water balance, especially in arid zone inhabitants.

Larynx and Vocalization

Within the mammalian pharyngeal passage, the larynx, or voicebox, lies between the glottis and the upper ends of the trachea. The vocal cords are located inside the larynx, and combine with the glottis to produce vocalizations. The expiration phase of the respiratory cycle provides the energy to vibrate the vocal cords, and the resultant passage of sound waves out through the glottis results in mammalian vocalizations. The vocal cords are quite strong, elastic ligaments that stretch between the arytenoid and thyroid cartilages, on either side of the glottis.

When not in use, the vocal cords are relaxed folds that allow expired air to pass between them in silence. However, under tension, the expired air causes these cords to vibrate, producing sounds. The frequency can be varied depending on the amount of tension on the vocal cords. In many mammals, these fundamental frequencies are further modified as they pass through the mouth and lips, allowing considerable variation in vocal repertoires. Some species, such as howler monkeys (*Alouatta*), have modified hyoid bones surrounding

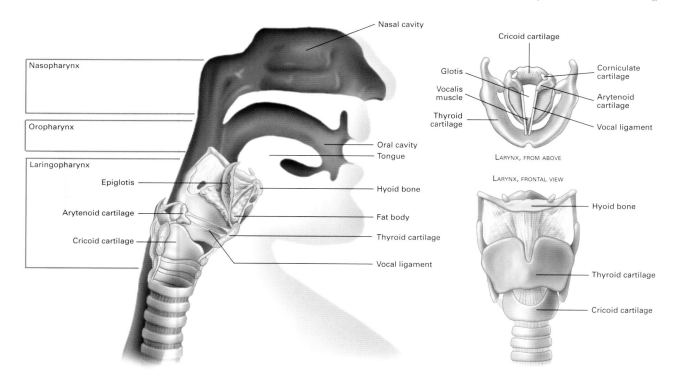

The mammalian pharynx and larynx.

Amadeu Blasco

The mammalian respiratory system.

Amadeu Blasco

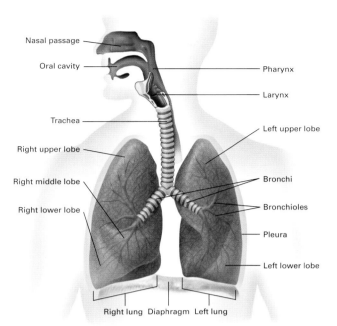

VARIATION OF THE PULMONARY LOBES ON SEVERAL MAMMALS

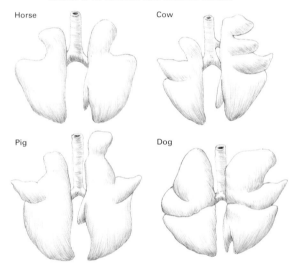

Horse Cow

Pig Dog

an enlarged resonating chamber in the vestibule of the larynx that allows for the production of very loud, penetrating vocalizations. Others have false vocal cords in this same region, allowing the production of other sounds, such as the purring of many species of cats.

During feeding, the larynx is closed off by the glottis as food is swallowed, allowing the food material to pass down the esophagus rather than into the respiratory system. Mammals have developed means of keeping the breathing and feeding passages separate to allow for nursing young to both breathe and eat at the same time. The larynx is situated high in the throat, where it can be pulled upward into the nasopharynx during swallowing, preventing liquid from entering the air passageway. Similarly in marine mammals, the cephalic end of the larynx is beaked so that it can be extended into the nasopharynx, allowing the prolonged passage of air during surfacing, even as the mouth is processing voluminous amounts of seawater.

Mammalian vocal repertoires are immensely variable. Some species have a wide variety of calls, depending on the situation. These include calls for contact, alarm, flight, courtship, food begging, and a variety of other behavioral and ecological specializations. In bats, cetaceans, and a few other groups, the frequencies of calls have been extended to produce echolocation systems. Bats have extended these high frequency calls to provide navigation information allowing them to fly in complete darkness, and to discriminate and pursue feeding targets in an incredibly efficient fashion.

The mammalian circulatory system.

Amadeu Blasco

Circulation

Mammals have the most highly developed circulatory systems among animals, owing to their relatively large size and highly active lifestyles. The mammalian circulatory system centers on the heart, which is a muscular pump that contracts to propel blood out to the body through arteries, and a series of veins that return it to the heart. This system is critical to maintaining homeostasis in mammals by transporting respiratory gases, nutrients, metabolic wastes, hormones, and antibodies throughout the body. There are basically two separate mammalian circulatory systems, a cardiovascular system and a lymphatic system.

Materials enter and leave the blood both by diffusion and by active transport in some cases. As we have seen earlier, blood also acts to conduct heat to and from the skin, playing a vital role in thermoregulation. Thus, the blood is critical in maintaining the internal environment of mammals. Mammalian erythrocytes, or red blood cells, differ from those of other vertebrates in being biconcave disks that lack nuclei (with the remarkable exception of camels), an adaptation to increase oxygen carrying capacity in support of the high metabolic rates of mammals.

Blood itself is generated mainly in the bone marrow of mammals. About half of the volume of mammalian blood is plasma, a rather viscous fluid that is mostly water, with dissolved blood proteins, glucose, fat, amino acids, and salts, as well as internally synthesized enzymes, antibodies, and hormones. In addition, some metabolic waste products are dissolved in the plasma. The other half of the blood is made up of cells of various kinds, including erythrocytes, leukocytes (white blood cells) and thrombocytes (platelets).

The cardiovascular system of mammals is a closed one, and is composed of two separate loops, or a double circuit. The four-chambered heart serves as the pump for both; the right side of the heart receives blood returning from the body through the veins, and pumps it at low pressure to the lungs, where it is re-oxygenated (pulmonary circulation). The left side of the heart then receives this oxygenated blood back

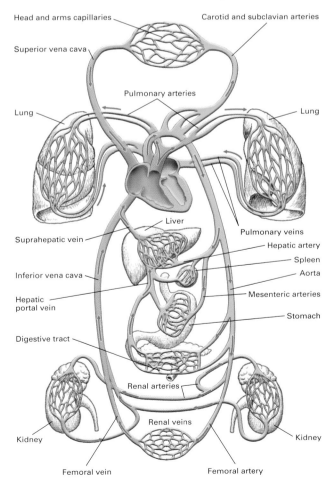

from the lungs, and pumps it at high pressure back out to all parts of the body (systemic circulation).

This high pressure pump is capable of functioning at vastly different rates, and the great variability in size and activity patterns of mammals results in huge differences in pulse rates. Given the size range from the smallest bats and shrews to blue whales, it is hardly surprising that heart rates may vary from 20 to 1300 beats per minute. In general, smaller mammals have much faster heart rates than larger ones. Equally impressive is the ability of many species to increase their individual heart rate enormously through increased activity. Flying bats can almost instantly double their heart rate in taking flight, and reduce it almost as quickly upon landing.

The arteries, veins, and intervening capillaries form a closed system through a continuum of ducts, but fluid manages to escape the system through diffusion, osmosis, hydrostatic pressure, and just plain gravity in some cases. The second component of the circulatory system, the lymphatic system, drains this fluid from the tissues, where it might otherwise accumulate in the form of swelling. The fluid enters lymphatic capillaries which connect with larger lymphatic vessels that eventually dump the fluid back into the venous system. Mammals have a large sinus called the cisterna chyli lying just dorsal to the aorta and behind the diaphragm that receives all of the lymph drainage from caudal to the diaphragm. Forward of there, most of the drainage flows back into the venous system through the subclavian veins.

Lymph nodes are common in mammals, frequently concentrated in the neck, armpits, groin, and mesenteries. These nodes are made up of lymphocytes called lymph follicles, surrounded by reticular fibers and connective tissue. Macrophages in the nodes phagocytize foreign particles in the lymph, and are often the trigger for immune responses to any invading antigens. Other concentrations of lymphatic tissue include the tonsils and thymus glands.

Metabolism and Thermoregulation

In mammals, metabolism and thermoregulation are so closely tied that cause and effect are difficult to disentangle. High rates of metabolism allow mammals to regulate their body temperature internally. The maintenance of a constant body temperature allows mammals to forage temporally and spatially as needed to maintain a high metabolic rate.

Metabolic rates are heavily influenced by body size. The metabolic rate of mammals increases at a rate equal to the 0.75 power of the animal's mass. This universal ratio becomes complicated primarily because the surface to volume ratio of a mammal decreases with increasing body size. Mammals generate metabolic heat in proportion to volume, but lose heat in proportion to surface area. The consequences are potentially far-reaching because small mammals face difficulties in staying warm, and large mammals face similar problems in staying cool. Mammals have evolved a variety of adaptations to meet each of these challenges.

Terrestrial mammals may face temperature extremes from −65°C in the arctic to 55°C in extreme desert regions. For marine mammals, water temperatures can vary from 0°C to 30°C as one moves from the poles to the equator. For a single individual in a given locality, the daily variation in temperature also can be enormous, with nighttime temperatures falling by as much as 50°C from daytime maxima. Even allowing for facultative heterothermy that might allow an individual mammal to withstand a range of body temperatures, the outer limits of body temperature for mammals is in the order of 0°C to 45°C, and activity is possible only at the upper end of that range, between about 30°C and 42°C.

The cost to mammals of maintaining elevated body temperatures is high. At best, mammals expend 5–10 times as much energy to maintain their body temperature as a reptile of the same body size. As the ambient temperature falls, this differential can rise to as much as 100 times more. Small rodents may use up to 90% of their total energy budget on ther-

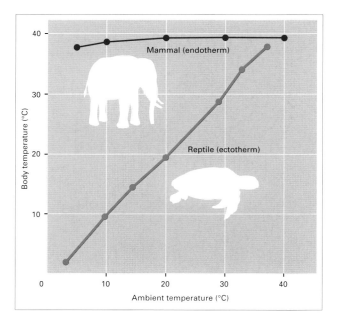

moregulation, with an individual mouse expending 25 times as much energy to forage as a similar-sized lizard.

Clearly, with costs so dear, the advantages of maintaining constant internal body temperature must also be great. High body temperatures aid in chemical reactions and speed up central nervous system functions; information processing times can be reduced and neuromuscular response time shortened; mammals become more efficient at prey capture and also at predator avoidance. In short, mammals have freed themselves from the constraints of ambient temperature fluctuations, both daily and seasonal.

One obvious way of coping with temperature extremes, be they seasonal or daily, is to allow the body temperature to fluctuate as well. Although mammals are basically homeotherms, i.e. they maintain their body temperature by internal physiological means, many are also heterotherms, i.e. they are capable of dormancy. Seasonal dormancy to avoid cold temperature is called hibernation and dormancy to avoid hot temperature is called estivation. In addition, some bats practice a form of daily, temporal heterothermy by maintaining high body temperatures while active, but allowing their body temperature to approach ambient while resting.

The average body temperature for placental mammals is between 36°C and 38°C, and for monotremes and marsupials it is somewhat lower (30°C–33°C), but still maintained quite constantly. Exceptional placentals with lower body temperatures include some members of the orders Pilosa, Cingulata, and Soricomorpha. Mammals generate heat through metabolic processes, and muscular contractions during activity. They lose heat to the environment passively through conduction, convection, and radiation, as well as through evaporative water loss. Ambient factors influencing heat exchange between mammals and their environment include air temperature and movement, solar radiation, thermal radiation, and water vapor pressure of the surrounding air. The area where all of these internal and external factors are roughly in balance is known as the thermoneutral zone for a given species of mammal.

The thermostat that determines the outside temperature in relation to this thermoneutral zone is called the hypothalamus, and is located in the forebrain. As the ambient temperature drops below the animal's thermoneutral zone, metabolic rate increases to generate the necessary internal heat to maintain core temperature. As we have already seen, body size is one ameliorating factor, with larger mammals having higher basal metabolic rates than smaller ones. The other major mitigating factor for mammals is the amount of insulation, or fur, buffering the body from outside temperatures. Thus, maintaining the proper balance between heat production (metabolism) and heat loss (conductance through the insulation) is the key to thermoregulation in mammals.

Nervous System and Senses

The central nervous system (CNS) in mammals consists of the spinal cord and a relatively large, highly evolved brain. Mammals interact with their environment in complicated ways, and these interactions are mediated through the nervous system. Sense organs sample the environment in various ways, and the peripheral nerves relay impulses to the central nervous system, where they are conveyed to the appropriate part of the brain. The brain interprets the incoming signals, and almost immediately sends outgoing signals that are transmitted to muscles and bones to effect the proper action.

In mammals, this simplified view of impulse stimulating action is complicated by an intricately evolved integration system that relies on memory to provide context to the situation. An individual mammal detecting another animal nearby may react quite differently depending on whether it is another individual of the same species, a potential prey item, or a predator. Experience and memory are integrated with the other components of the sense organs and nervous system to provide the appropriate response.

The structural and functional units of the nervous system are specialized nerve cells called neurons. Neurons are somewhat variable, but all contain four basic elements. The trophic segment, or cell body proper, contains the nucleus and metabolic components common to all cells. The neuronal receptors are branching extensions from the cell body called dendrites. Sensory impulses travel from the dendrites through the cell body to long segments called axons, or nerve fibers. Axons are the signal conducting elements of the nervous system, and may carry signals from receptors to the central nervous system, or in the opposite direction from the CNS to effector muscles or organs. Axons terminate in branching arrangements that are the transmissive elements. These terminal branches make contact with others in junctions known as synapses, where nerve signals are carried by neurotransmitters such as acetylcholine, norepinephrine, serotonin, and dopamine.

The interface between a mammal and its environment is mediated by the sense organs. Depending on the group, the senses of vision, olfaction, and hearing are often the most highly developed in mammals. Humans and our primate relatives are visually oriented, so we tend to "view" vision as the most important of our senses. Although many carnivores and ungulates also rely heavily on vision, other groups such as bats, marine mammals, and fossorial forms, may emphasize hearing or olfaction.

Visually orienting mammals tend to have large eyes, but others may have quite small eyes that function basically only to differentiate light from dark. Photoreception, or light detection, is basic to obtaining information about photoperiod, or day length. Many mammalian behavioral and physiological adaptations are tied to photoperiod. Mammals have evolved a variety of improvements to this basic photoreceptor that result in the highly evolved visual systems that provide the explicit picture of their surroundings that allows them to forage, interact with others, and escape predators.

Mammalian photoreceptors are capable of using that part of the spectrum between wavelengths of about 380 nm (violet), and 750 nm (red). Lower wavelengths, known as ultraviolet, is potentially destructive to mammals, as fair-skinned humans subject to sunburn understand all too well. Higher wavelengths, known as infrared, contain insufficient energy to be useful to most mammals, although some mammals may detect these higher wavelengths in the form of heat.

The eyes of mammals function by focusing light on a photoreceptive epithelium, known as the retina, where an image is formed. The retina is highly enervated, and lies at the rear of a liquid-filled vitreous chamber in the eyeball. The retina enjoys a direct connection to the brain via the optic nerve. The neurosensory cells in the mammalian eye are called rods and cones. Rods use a visual pigment called rhodopsin to absorb light across the entire range of the visual spectrum. This results in black and white images that are quite sharp, even at low light levels. Nocturnal mammals have high concentrations of rods in their eyes.

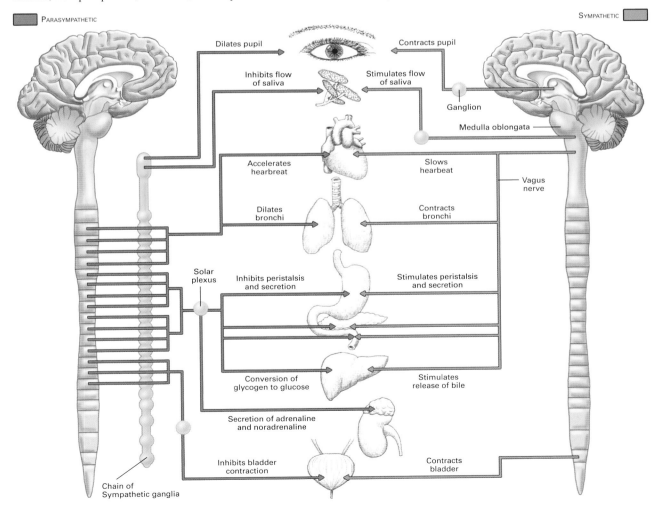

PARASYMPATHETIC

SYMPATHETIC

Dilates pupil

Contracts pupil

Inhibits flow of saliva

Stimulates flow of saliva

Ganglion

Medulla oblongata

Accelerates hearbreat

Slows hearbeat

Vagus nerve

Dilates bronchi

Contracts bronchi

Solar plexus

Inhibits peristalsis and secretion

Stimulates peristalsis and secretion

Conversion of glycogen to glucose

Stimulates release of bile

Secretion of adrenaline and noradrenaline

Inhibits bladder contraction

Contracts bladder

Chain of Sympathetic ganglia

The mammalian nervous system.

Amadeu Blasco

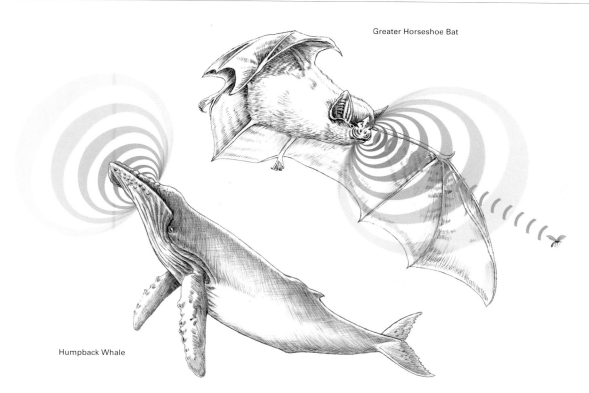

Greater Horseshoe Bat

Humpback Whale

Echolocation is an important navigation and foraging system for many bats and cetaceans.

Amadeu Blasco

Diurnal mammals have higher concentrations of cones, and these cells contain two or three different receptors for detecting light in various parts of the visual spectrum. This differentiation is what allows some mammals to have color vision. Humans and their close primate relatives have three such receptors. The extent of development of color vision in other mammalian groups is not completely understood, but varying degrees of color receptivity are known from at least nine orders containing diurnal species.

Hearing is also quite well-developed in most kinds of mammals. Evidence for this is easily seen in the development of external ears, or pinnae, in most mammals. Hearing is especially acute in those mammals for whom vision is less useful, such as bats, marine mammals, and some others. Basically, mammals use the external pinna to focus incoming sound waves into the ear cavity through an external auditory canal. Once there, they impact a thin membrane, the tympanum, or eardrum. The tympanum vibrates against the first of the three inner ear ossicles, the malleus. The malleus is connected via the incus to the stapes, which fits against the opening into the inner ear, the oval window.

The inner ear consists of a series of coiled tubes called the cochlea, which is lined with extremely sensitive hair cells that eventually transmit sound waves to the brain through the acoustic nerve. This is an oversimplification of a very complicated structural system that functions amazingly well to translate sound waves into audible signals in the mammalian brain. Most mammals are capable of hearing sound over a wide spectrum from about 20–20,000 hertz (Hz). This range is exceeded at the lower end by marine mammals, and some large terrestrial forms such as rhinoceroses and elephants. These mammals may detect frequencies as low as 12 Hz. At the upper end, some carnivores, such as canids, can detect frequencies as high as 40,000 Hz. Those mammals that use echolocation are capable of detecting very high frequencies, with some bats using signals above 200,000 Hz.

Echolocation is a sophisticated system of navigation and foraging important to most species of bats, many cetaceans, and some shrews and their relatives. Although difficult for visually orienting species such as ourselves to understand, these mammals probably receive sufficient information from their echolocation systems to provide a "picture" of the environment in their brain that matches what we obtain by vision. The history of the study of echolocation is a long one, with the first evidence uncovered by the Italian scientist Lazaro Spallanzani in 1793. Donald Griffin and Robert Galambos documented the use of echolocation by bats while undergraduates at Harvard, beginning in 1938. Griffin went on to actually coin the term echolocation, and continued to do seminal studies on bats, as well as other areas of cognitive ethology.

Bat echolocation calls vary in frequency (pitch), intensity (signal strength), and duration (repetition rate). Most echolocation calls are ultrasonic, meaning they are above the range of human hearing, or over 20 kilohertz (kHz; 1 kHz = 1000 Hz). Intensities vary, but many flying bats emit signals between 70 and 100 decibels, as measured about a meter away. Call durations are extremely short, ranging from about 0·25 milliseconds to 100 milliseconds. In addition to these basic components, some bats emit the signals at a constant frequency (with a bandwidth of less than 10 kHz), and others use frequency modulation (FM) to produce calls with bandwidths greater than 10 kHz.

Chemoreception via olfaction is another important sense in mammals. Mammals use smell to detect food and enemies, and in a variety of social situations as well. Olfactory signals are produced by several different kinds of glands in mammals. Many species have a well-developed Jacobsen's organ in the nasal cavity that is used to help detect chemical signals, especially pheromones produced by females that may indicate whether or not they are in heat. Olfaction is less important in cetaceans, and most primates also have limited olfactory capabilities, compared to most species of mammals.

Olfactory neurons are concentrated in the nasal cavity, with their axons bundled together and communicating directly with the brain through the olfactory nerve. Chemical substances known as odorants are dissolved in the mucous coating of the nasal epithelium and detected by receptor molecules that can be extraordinarily sensitive. The nasal passages of mammals contain turbinate bones, whose scroll-like structure greatly increases the surface area of the nasal epithelium. Mammals can detect substances in extremely low concentrations, and in astounding variety. Sensory adaptation is common with olfactory signals, meaning that we detect a new odor immediately, but after continued exposure, we fail to notice it.

Taste is less important to most mammals than the previous senses. The major adaptive feature of taste organs is in the detection of palatable versus unpalatable food items. Taste buds comprise receptor and supportive cells that are innervated by three separate cranial nerves. Interestingly enough, the receptor cells are quite short-lived, and are replaced by the supporting cells on a regular basis. Support cells, in turn, are constantly being replaced by the basal layer of the epithelium. Mammals are able to detect four basic tastes: sour, sweet, salty, and bitter.

A sense of touch is important to many kinds of mammals. Cutaneous receptors consisting of free nerve endings in the

Relative brain size of mammals, birds, reptiles, fish and dinosaurs.

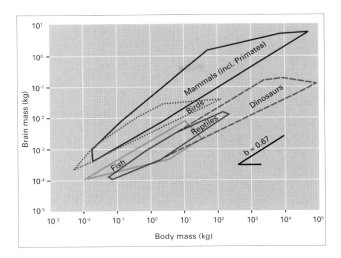

epidermis relay information from external stimuli such as pressure, vibrations, pain, and temperature changes. They are important in relaying information about injuries. Mammals also have neurons at the base of hair follicles, such that stimulation of the hair releases an impulse. This type of specialization is emphasized in vibrissae, common to many mammals. Slight touches or even air movements can be detected by the vibrissae, particularly those of nocturnal species.

Brain

Mammals have the largest relative brain size of all organisms. The bulk of the increase in size compared to other vertebrates lies in the cerebral hemispheres. Although devoted to olfaction and other sensory modalities in lower vertebrates, the mammalian cerebrum is dominated by the neopallium (neocortex), which forms a heavily convoluted and folded mantle over the cerebral hemispheres. This expanded associative area of the brain, combined with the corpus callosum, a band of tissue connecting the two halves of the forebrain, has allowed mammals to combine experience (memory) with associative and cognitive powers not seen in other animals.

The brain serves as the nerve center, receiving input from the sense organs, and providing instruction to the remainder of the body in response. Mammals vary by group in the development of areas of the brain associated with different sensory modalities. Rodents, for instance, have highly developed senses of smell, and corresponding areas of the brain are relatively large in rodents. Similarly, primates are highly visually oriented, with corresponding development of visual receptor centers in the brain. The overwhelming evolutionary development in mammals, however, has to do with the increase in size and surface area of the neopallium.

The neopallium has basically overgrown the entire brain in mammals. In humans, it has been estimated to contain 13 billion neurons. Because it is so large, it is divided into regions, more for convenience and topography than for functional areas. These various lobes are called frontal, parietal, temporal, and occipital. All have become folded into ridges (gyri) and grooves (sulci). This folding is lacking in monotremes, some marsupials, and many rodents, but is extensive in primates. This means that mammals have large brains in an absolute sense, have large brain size to body weight ratios, and have a greatly increased surface area of the major associative areas of the brain.

Reproductive System

Reproduction is the evolutionary purpose of life. The measure of evolutionary fitness is the number of viable offspring produced, and their subsequent reproductive success. To this end, mammals have developed a suite of both structural and functional characteristics that maximize that fitness.

Mammals have internal fertilization and the embryo develops in an enlarged cavity of the oviduct called the uterus. With the exception of the primitive monotremes, all mammals are

viviparous, meaning they bear their young live. The seven orders of marsupial mammals are aplacentally viviparous, meaning that they bear their young at a very early stage of development, and then continue that developmental process in a special external pouch called the marsupium. All remaining mammals have a placenta that is used to provide nourishment to the developing embryo directly from the mother, while allowing it to remain in the uterus until development is much more complete. The evolution of this mobile incubator allows placental mammals to continue their normal activities while the developing embryo is automatically nourished in a secure environment.

The major organs of the male reproductive system are the testes, compact cylinders filled with elongated seminiferous tubules. These tubules are suspended in a loose matrix of tissue containing interstitial cells of Leydig, which produce the main male hormone, testosterone. The sperm-forming cells are called spermatogonia, and these diploid cells divide through mitosis to form spermatocytes, which undergo meiosis to form haploid spermatids. The final step in spermatogenesis involves the loss of cytoplasm and the addition of a flagellate tail. The whole process may take several weeks, depending on the species.

In most mammals, the testes are located outside the body cavity in a special sac called the scrotum. This is most likely an adaptation to avoid the high internal body temperature of most mammals. In monotremes, sloths, armadillos, elephants, manatees, and cetaceans the testes do not descend. Other groups, such as bats, many rodents, lagomorphs, some carnivores, and some ungulates, have testes that descend into the scrotum only during the breeding season, and are withdrawn back into the body cavity at other times.

The major female reproductive organs are the ovaries, where the process of egg maturation, oogenesis, occurs. Although normally paired, one or the other frequently atrophies in some species of mammals. Eggs in the primary oocyte stage are located in primordial follicles around the periphery of the

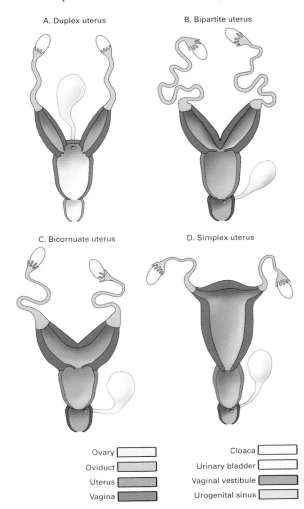

A. Duplex uterus

B. Bipartite uterus

C. Bicornuate uterus

D. Simplex uterus

Ovary		Cloaca	
Oviduct		Urinary bladder	
Uterus		Vaginal vestibule	
Vagina		Urogenital sinus	

Variation of the uterus in mammals.

Amadeu Blasco

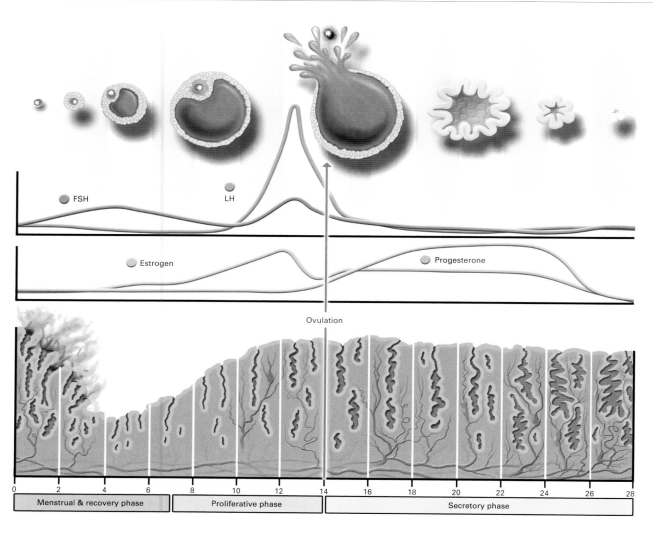

The ovarian cycle.

Amadeu Blasco

FSH

LH

Estrogen

Progesterone

Ovulation

| 0 | 2 | 4 | 6 | 8 | 10 | 12 | 14 | 16 | 18 | 20 | 22 | 24 | 26 | 28 |

Menstrual & recovery phase

Proliferative phase

Secretory phase

ovary. Millions of follicles may exist at birth, but most will atrophy, leaving thousands at puberty, and after further atrophy, a few hundred may eventually ovulate. When mature, they are called Graafian follicles, and may bulge outward from the ovarian surface. The primary oocyte grows and undergoes meiosis to form the mature, haploid ootid. Surrounded by a protective envelope called the zona pellucida, the mature egg ruptures through the surface of the ovary at ovulation, leaving behind a hardened, yellowish body called a corpus luteum. The number of eggs released depends on whether the species normally has a single, or multiple young per litter.

The evolutionary success of mammals owes a great deal to the development of mammary glands, and the subsequent feeding and care that females give to their young. Monotremes represent a very early stage in this evolutionary sequence, and are in some ways intermediate between egg-laying reptiles and live-bearing mammals. The monotreme reproductive tract includes many of the features of viviparous forms, including ovaries that connect to a uterus through fallopian tubes, except that in this case the uteri remain separate on each side. Monotreme eggs have very thin, permeable shells that allow for the accumulation of additional nutrients from the uterus, resulting in intrauterine growth from about 5–15 mm in diameter by the time they are laid. This embryonic development within the egg while it remains in the uterus is intermediate between reptiles and viviparous mammals. The females brood the eggs after they are laid, and although the females lack nipples, the young lap milk produced from the mammary glands as it trickles through the fur.

In the seven orders of metatherian, or marsupial mammals, the shift to viviparity is complete, but development of the young differs in important ways from that of placental mammals. Within the reproductive tract each uterus retains a separate cervix opening into terminal vaginae, and the penis of many male marsupials is bifid, allowing sperm to penetrate into each vagina. The anterior ends of the vaginae are united into a vaginal sinus, and just before birth, a separate pathway called the pseudovaginal canal forms and opens directly into the urogenital sinus.

Gestation is short in marsupials, ranging from about ten days to a month, and during the latter part, a brief yolk sac, or choriovitelline placenta provides a connection to the uterine lining. In some species, such as the Koala (*Phascolarctos cinereus*) and some bandicoots, an actual chorioallantoic placenta develops. This connection terminates quickly with parturition, and the neonates attach to nipples in the marsupium to complete development. Reasons for this early birth and subsequent external development are not known, but thought to be at least partly an immunological rejection stimulated when the mother reabsorbs the shell membrane surrounding the embryo.

Although it is tempting to view marsupials as another intermediate group between the egg-laying monotremes and the placental mammals, this is not the case. Marsupial and placental mammals evolved separately from a common ancestor, and the two types of reproduction are endpoints rather than a transitional series, and each is equally successful. The adaptive significance of the marsupial type of development probably has to do with ephemeral food sources in unpredictable environments. During times of food stress, marsupials can abort either intrauterine or pouch young easily, minimizing energy loss to adult females. Eutherian mammals continue to provide maternal nutrients to developing embryos through the placenta, sometimes to the jeopardy of the mother.

In Eutherians there is a united vagina connected to the uteri in different ways, depending on the group. Duplex uteri are found in elephants, lagomorphs, and many rodents. Most carnivores and many ungulates have a bipartite uterus, with a partition separating the otherwise united uteri into uterine horns. Whales, some carnivores, and some ungulates have a bicornuate uterus, lacking the partition. The most advanced type of uterine fusion is found in the simplex uterus of Cingulata and most primates, where the uterine horns lead to into a completely fused uterus. In all of these, the embryonic trophoblast establishes a firm connection to the uterine lining, or endometrium, through a chorioallantoic placenta. In a few ungulates such as pigs, the epitheliochorial placenta does not actually penetrate the endometrium, and is nondeciduous, meaning it is not shed at birth. Anthropoid primates, as well as many rodents, bats, and soricomorphs have a hemochorial placenta, with the maternal blood bathing the chorion, or covering of the fetus. Other groups, including lagomorphs and some rodents, have a hemoendothelial placenta, where the chorion itself breaks down, allowing the maternal blood to flow directly across the endothelial walls of the fetal capillaries.

Monotremes retain the cloaca of their reptilian ancestors, but it shows the beginnings of division into a dorsal portion for the intestinal exit, and a ventral urogenital sinus, into which feed the ureters and the uterus of females and deferent ducts of males. In all other mammals, the cloaca is completely divided, providing separate passages for the intestine (rectum) and the urogenital tract.

Male and female reproductive tracts develop from undifferentiated embryos, and the resultant external genitalia have common origins. In males, the urethra runs through the prostate gland and pelvic gland out through the penis. A corpus spongiosum develops surrounding the urethra, and the distal end expands into the glans penis. A pair of corpora cavernosa develop, one on either side of the penis. The testes eventually descend into a pair of scrotal swellings that unite at the base of the penis. In females, the distal ends of the oviducts unite into a vagina, and the urogenital sinus also empties into the vaginal vestibule. Only in primates and a few other species are the urethral and vaginal openings separate. The labia minora flanking the vagina are homologous to the part of the male penis surrounding the urethra, and the labia majora are homologs of the scrotal swellings in the male. Females have a glans clitoridis at the junction of the labia minora that is homologous to the male glans penis, and the main body of the clitoris contains erectile tissue comparable to the male corpora cavernosa.

Reproduction in mammals is controlled by hormones, which are in turn secreted under stimulation of follicle stimulating hormone (FSH) and luteinizing hormone (LH). Males produce androgens in the testes, the most important of which are testosterone and cortical androgen. Females produce estrogens in the ovaries, chiefly estradiol and progesterone. Although a few kinds of mammals, including humans, reproduce throughout the year, most are seasonal breeders. The ovarian cycle of females dictates that eggs develop and are released sequentially, in a cycle that may vary from four days in rats to 28 days in humans. Many female mammals come into estrus, or heat, at the time of ovulation, and only then allow the males to copulate with them, thus greatly increasing the chance of fertilization, as males of many species produce sperm continually.

Breeding Behavior

Mammals reproduce sexually, with males and females differentially adapted to maximize their reproductive fitness. Females produce small numbers of energetically costly eggs, and invest their evolutionary capital heavily in each one in an attempt to successfully raise as many offspring as possible. Males produce copious amounts of energetically inexpensive sperm, and try to inseminate as many females as possible. Natural selection acts on both to refine breeding behavior such that fitness is maximized.

Mammals tend to be seasonal breeders, especially those in temperate zones and polar regions, where the rigors of climate dictate a narrow window for reproduction. Females need an abundant food supply to feed the young, both pre- and post-partum. Pregnancy and lactation are both stressful times in terms of energetics for females, and most species are adapted to give birth during those times of year when food is most abundant and easily accessible. In many cases, this means that the cues necessary for initiating reproductive activity must anticipate the time of parturition by some months. Photoperiod is the most likely proximate cue for triggering the endocrine activity necessary to begin breeding, although direct demonstrations of this effect are poorly known for mammals. Temperature and rainfall are the most likely determinants of food supply, and breeding seasons roughly track seasonal changes in both.

Because of the short breeding season in polar and temperate zones, most mammals in those regions have only a single litter or young per year. Some may have a rapid post-partum estrus and complete two or more cycles each year. In tropical regions, the breeding season may be much longer, or even last throughout the year for some species. However, even in tropical regions, seasonal variation in rainfall often dictates fluctuations in food supply that affect the length and timing of breeding seasons.

Territory

The necessity for finding mates provides strong selection for the living habits of most species of mammals. Although many species are solitary, and the sexes come together only during the breeding season, others are gregarious and live in groups, or colonies, throughout their lives.

Because resources are differentially distributed throughout any given habitat, both male and female mammals may form territories in order to maximize their ability to utilize those resources. By defending a resource-rich territory from conspecifics, an individual can essentially hoard the resources and reserve them for their own use. However, in many species only one sex forms territories, and when that is the case the territory is normally defended only against members of the same sex. Individuals of the opposite sex are allowed to enter the territory, maximizing opportunities for breeding.

Territories are frequently marked with scent, either from urination or defecation, or by the use of specialized scent glands. Such marks allow potential intruders to identify occupied territories, and avoid conflict. Some species, such as howler monkeys, use specialized calls to signal their presence and alert other individuals or groups to their whereabouts. Many forms of direct territorial defense rely on visual signals, either through display of structural attributes such as crests or color patterns, or through ritualized behavioral displays.

Colonies

Some species of mammals form large colonies for some or all parts of the year. These colonies are advantageous for a variety of reasons. In some cases, as with many species of bats, roosting sites may be limited, so that colony formation maximizes the number of individuals that can use the habitat. In others, food resources may be concentrated so that high numbers of individuals can be accommodated. Grazing ungulates frequently form herds to increase the potential for spotting predators. Some marine mammals may forage in groups to maximize effectiveness. The same strategy is employed by pack-forming carnivores.

Colony size may vary from small family groups to millions of individuals in the case of some bats using a single cave. Although the main drivers of colony size may have to do with resource distribution or predator avoidance, the breeding system is also obviously affected. Colonial species frequently have highly evolved social systems that influence which of the most common types of breeding system are employed.

Mating Systems

One generalization that emerges for most mammals is that males tend to compete for access to females, resulting in much greater variance in reproductive success in males than in females, almost all of whom breed successfully. However, because of the difference in reproductive strategies, successful males will leave more descendants than successful females. It has been shown that females in good physiological condition produce more successful offspring than do ones in poor condition. Because a successful male offspring will ultimately result in greater fitness for the female, those females in good condition should and do produce more male than female offspring. Because females will likely reproduce at a lower, but steady rate,

Polygyny is the most common mammalian breeding system.

Red Deer (*Cervus elaphus*)
Wim Weenink/Minden Pictures/ASA

regardless of condition, females in poor condition should and do produce more female offspring.

Although this differential sex ratio has been demonstrated in mammals as phylogenetically distinct as opossums and deer, there are counter examples that likely have been adapted to different breeding strategies. In species with female dominance hierarchies, it may be more evolutionarily rewarding for high-ranking females to produce daughters who can inherit that rank than sons who will disperse. In some primates, this is the case, with lower-ranking females producing more sons and higher-ranking ones producing more daughters.

Sexual selection drives adaptations that increase the ability of either sex to attract mates. This may result in things like elaborate courtship rituals and displays directed at the opposite sex, or in functional attributes that allow animals to out-compete other members of the same sex. In some cases both types of selection may be operating, such as when female ungulates choose males with large antlers or horns, and those males in turn use their larger equipment to fight with and dominate less successful males. Male competition may extend beyond pre-copulatory fights when sperm competition occurs. In some species, the first male to copulate leaves behind a copulatory plug that may inhibit later matings. In other species, males may copulate repeatedly with females, producing large amounts of sperm that may simply outnumber those of rivals, enhancing the chances of successful fertilization.

A somewhat draconian example of male competition, infanticide, occurs in some species, including Lions. Males tak-

Monogamous breeding systems are rare, but occur in almost all orders.

Lar Gibbon (*Hylobates lar*)
Dave Watts/Lochman Transparencies

ing over a pride may kill all of the infants, resulting in twofold benefits. Firstly, they will gain a slight advantage in fitness over the males who sired the cubs. Secondly, females losing cubs will come into estrus again quickly, allowing the newcomer to father a new set of cubs within the pride. As mammalian breeding systems become better studied, other examples of this type of behavior are becoming known in groups as widely divergent as rodents and primates.

Mammalian breeding systems run the gamut from monogamy to promiscuity, with polygyny being the most common type. Because females carry the young prior to parturition, and then provide milk for a defined post-partum period, female investment in each young is much greater than that of males. Monogamy, with both sexes contributing to raising of the young, is rare in mammals, although it occurs in a few species in almost all orders. In obligate monogamy, resources are so scarce that both sexes have to share in raising the offspring. Facultative monogamy may occur when population densities are so low that a male may only encounter a single female.

Polygyny, the most common mammalian breeding system, can take various forms. Resource defense polygyny relies on males defending territories from other males, and attracting females based on the quality of the feeding or nesting sites within those territories. Female defense polygyny may occur where males protect harems of females, and prevent other males from breeding with them. Male dominance polygyny is the system where males gather on a common display ground, or lek, to try to attract females with reproductive displays. The result of all of these systems is that a single male breeds with many different females, and some males are left out of the process each year.

Polyandry, where females may breed with more than one male, is much less common among mammals. It occurs in some rodents and some primates, such that occasionally litter mates may have more than one father. In some carnivores, such as African Wild Dogs (*Lycaon pictus*), females may be mated by several males. Males contribute significantly to parental care, and females are the dispersing sex, all of which might be expected to occur in truly polyandrous systems.

Promiscuity, where both sexes breed with several mates, is also fairly common among mammals. Some species may show a great deal of flexibility in breeding system, depending on resource availability and population density. In times of abundant food supply and high population densities, promiscuous mating may be more common.

Nests, Roosts, and Dens

Although mammals produce live young, most species require some amount of post-partum development before the young are ready to be weaned. Many make use of dens or nests of some sort, and bats utilize roosts in which to protect the young. Terrestrial forms frequently dig or burrow into the ground to form a protected den in which to raise the young. Some species utilize burrows dug by other species rather than digging their own. Arboreal forms frequently build tree nests, either in hollows, or using leaves and sticks.

In addition to providing a safe haven from predators, such maternity sites allow the females to nurse their young in a protected environment. Some protection from the elements is also necessary, as young mammals tend to be more susceptible to rain, cold, and wind. In solitary species, nest-building activities are normally undertaken by the female. In colonial species, both sexes may contribute to burrows and den sites. Elaborate constructions are more likely to prevail in colonial species that may occupy the den sites for longer periods of time.

Monotreme Eggs

All mammals have internal fertilization, and only the five members of the order Monotremata lay eggs. In this regard, monotremes greatly resemble their reptilian ancestors. Monotremes have large ovaries that produce large eggs, or oocytes, because they require greater amounts of yolk than do those of placentals. Fertilization occurs in the infundibulum, or upper end of the oviduct, only one of which is functional in monotremes. During passage through the fallopian tubes, a series of coatings surround the egg, forming the shell. Eggs reach about 10 mm in diameter before being laid.

Platypuses are aquatic and lack pouches, so they lay their eggs directly into a nest inside a burrow, and incubate them for about two weeks. Echidnas (Tachyglossidae) on the other hand, lay their eggs directly into the pouch, where the initial stages of development occur. Thus, the pouch serves as an incubator, and allows the mother to be mobile while carrying the egg around. After about ten days, the developing young uses an egg tooth to break out of the shell. The neonate then attaches to a primitive mammary nodule within the pouch, and undergoes another two months or so of development. Once

Monotremes are the most primitive of the mammals.

Platypus (*Ornithorhynchus anatinus*)
Dave Watts/Lochman Transparencies

the spines begin to form on echidnas, the female ejects them from the pouch, understandably enough. However, mothers continue to produce milk, and the young may obtain milk from the mother's fur for another few months.

Monotremes show several other evolutionary advancements over reptiles. Reptile eggs are much larger and contain much more yolk than those of monotremes. Furthermore, there is nourishment from the uterine endometrial gland of monotremes, a stage of development much more like placental mammals than reptiles. Reptile eggs take much longer to hatch, and monotreme young are at a much earlier stage of development when they hatch. Although in laying eggs monotremes are unique among mammals, lactation through the production of milk by mammary glands is a completely mammalian trait.

Marsupial Development

All mammals have internal fertilization, which occurs shortly after ovulation in most species. In placental mammals, the zygote implants in the wall of the uterus through the endometrium, the highly vascularized lining of the uterus. As early cell division occurs, the embryo becomes embedded in the endometrium, and basically invades it, surrounded by a lining called the trophoblast.

In marsupials, the embryo develops rapidly within the uterus, and is born at a very early stage, with subsequent development occurring in the pouch. During the early stages of development in these metatherians, the eggshell membranes are retained, providing a semi-permeable barrier between the embryo and the maternal tissues. Lacking this, there is risk of an immunological rejection of the embryo by the mother. Because the embryo contains paternal tissue, it might provoke an antibody attack by the maternal immune system. This hypothesis has been proposed to explain the early parturition and subsequent pouch development in marsupials. One critical component of the hypothesis is that marsupials were thought to lack a trophoblast, the covering of the embryo that provides such protection to placental mammals.

However, there is evidence that at least some marsupials do have a trophoblast, making the hypothesis less likely. It may be that viviparity evolved before marsupials and placentals diverged, with the resultant evolutionary pathways differing for other reasons. If that hypothetical common ancestor also had the early parturition of embryos seen in marsupials, then the evolution of placentals would simply have been a separate pathway from that of marsupials, which have continued to focus on bearing the young at an embryonic stage, with more emphasis on development during lactation. Such young are called altricial, in contrast to the more developed neonates of most placentals, which are referred to as precocial.

Some kangaroos show a modified reproductive cycle that includes a period of embryonic diapause. An initial pregnancy results in normal sequential development of the young, and when the joey is still in the pouch, at about six months of age, the female mates again, and a new embryo is formed. However, the presence of the joey in the pouch stimulates hormonal production that causes the developing embryo to suspend development for a period of up to eight months, while the joey in the pouch grows and matures. When the joey leaves the pouch at about ten months of age, the developing embryo resumes development, and the next cycle proceeds. This allows the female to focus her resources on a single developing young at a time, but allows for a head start on a subsequent young, should the first be lost.

Placental Gestation and Parturition

Among placental mammals, gestation length varies with body size, litter size, and the degree of development of the young, along the altricial-precocial scale. Some small rodents may have gestation periods as short as twelve days, and at the other end of the scale, African Elephants have a gestation period of 22 months. The exception to the body size rule may be bats, where long gestation lengths of 2–6 months are the norm. Bats are unique in other ways as well, frequently having a single young or twins in some species, with litters of three, four, or five quite rare and found in only a handful of species.

Many other exceptions to the body size rule occur. Blue Whales, the largest of mammals, weighing over 100,000 kg, have a gestation period of only 10–12 months, the same as the Two-toed Sloth (*Choloepus didactylus*), weighing in at less than 10 kg. Primates tend to have long gestation periods for their body size. The young of most primates are precocial but still require long periods of maternal care. Gestation length and litter size in mammals in general are also affected by a host of

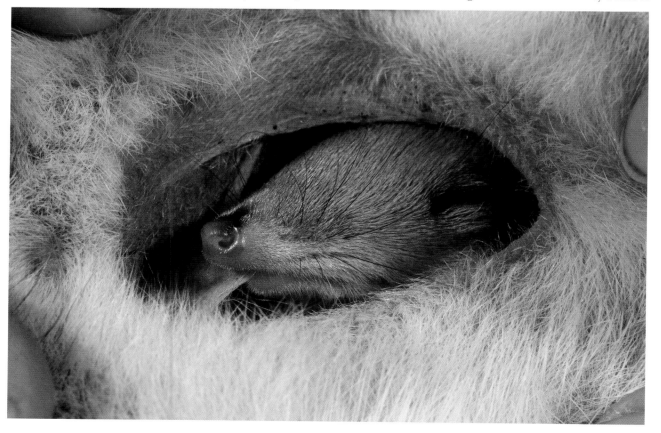

In marsupials, the embryo is born at a very early stage and develops in the pouch.

Western Barred Bandicoot
(*Perameles bougainville*)
Jiri Lochman/
Lochman Transparencies

environmental factors, such as latitude and length of growing season, food availability and other ecosystem related variables.

Because of these variations in environmental conditions, mammals have evolved a series of developmental modifications to adapt their annual cycles. Some species, particularly of bats, undergo delayed fertilization. Mating occurs in the fall, with the females retaining sperm over the winter, and fertilization occurring at the end of hibernation in the spring. This unusual adaptation allows for courtship and copulation to occur before hibernation, allowing development to proceed almost immediately upon awakening, thus greatly increasing the amount of time the young will be able to spend fattening up for their first hibernation.

Other bats have delayed development, such that fertilization and implantation occur normally, but then there is a period of some months of reproductive diapause, with little or no development of the embryo. Then, when environmental conditions are right, development proceeds apace. Such adaptations allow species to synchronize production of young with periods of maximum food availability.

Further along in this continuum of modifications to the basic mammalian reproductive cycle is the phenomenon of delayed implantation. In this case, ovulation and fertilization occur in sequence, and early cleavage of the zygote results in a blastocyst. However, instead of implanting on the uterine wall, the development of the blastocyst suspends, and it floats in the reproductive tract, surrounded by a protective coating called the zona pellucida. After a period ranging from two weeks to eleven months, depending on the species, implantation occurs and development proceeds. Delayed implantation is widespread among mammals, known in the orders Chiroptera, Cingulata, Carnivora, Soricomorpha, Rodentia, and Artiodactyla.

Parturition

Although gestation length varies from two weeks to almost two years among mammals, parturition is similar in almost all species. Birth is initiated by hormonal changes that occur when intrauterine maturation is complete. The fetus itself secretes adrenocortical hormones from the adrenal glands, and the placenta begins to secrete prostaglandins. This in turn causes uterine contractions, and as the fetus presses on the cervix, the hormone oxytocin is produced by the pituitary gland. Oxytocin stimulates the mammary glands to begin milk production and also increases uterine contractions. A hormone called relaxin softens the pelvic ligaments, allowing the birth canal to enlarge as the fetus passes through the vagina. Fetal membranes either rupture during parturition, or the mother tears them away immediately after birth. She then normally consumes them, along with the expelled placenta, or afterbirth.

Newborn mammals (neonates) can be born in a helpless state, with eyes closed and little or no hair (altricial), or better developed, with eyes open and fully haired (precocial). Many rodents, carnivores, and some lagomorphs are born in an altricial state, and are very vulnerable to predation for the first few days or weeks of their lives. Some primates, some rodents, hyraxes, cetaceans and many ungulates are born precocial, able to be up and around and avoid predators in a matter of minutes or hours.

Lactation

Mammary glands are one of the defining characteristics of mammals, and the feeding of young by production of milk is paramount to the success of mammals in general. By providing young with their essential initial nutrition directly from the mother's body, mammals can enjoy a relatively long period of development. This in turn allows for the young to gain knowledge from the mother about foraging and predator avoidance that is essential. Although lactation is almost entirely restricted to females, there is at least one species of bat where males have been reported to produce milk.

As with other aspects of the reproductive cycle, lactation is under endocrine control, and it is the secretion of hormones such as estradiol and progesterone during pregnancy that cause the mammary glands to enlarge. Immediately following parturition, the hormone prolactin replaces estradiol, and stimulates milk production. Initial suckling by the neonate causes the posterior pituitary gland to release oxytocin, facilitating the letdown of milk.

Lactation is the most energetically stressful time for female mammals, even more so than pregnancy. As a result, the reproductive cycles of many species are timed to insure that lactation occurs during times of maximum food resources. The long periods of time spent in the pouch by metatherian young create especially high costs to female marsupials nursing litters. The increase in energy demands caused by lactation varies from 50% to more than 100% in various species.

One mechanism for dealing with these high maternal costs is to speed up the process of lactation. Many marine mammals do this by producing milk of very high energy content. Milk contains fats, proteins, sugars, vitamins, and salts necessary for growth and development of the young. The milk of some marine species may contain from 40% to 50% fat, up to ten times more than domestic cow's milk. This allows for rapid growth of the young, enabling them to disperse successfully under harsh conditions. On the other hand, species with long lactation periods such as the Black Rhinoceros (*Diceros bicornis*), may produce milk with fat content as low as 0·2%.

Length of lactation varies greatly among mammals. One of the shortest is found in the Hooded Seal (*Cystophora cristata*), where females feed the young their energetically very rich milk for only four days. At the other extreme, orangutans (*Pongo*) nurse their young for more than 900 days. Interestingly enough, some marine mammals, such as sea lions and fur seals, not only have milk with relatively high fat content, but also have lactation periods of up to 330 days.

Demographic and Ecological Aspects of Reproduction

The study of population dynamics has yielded a wealth of information about mammal populations worldwide. Left unchecked, any species will rapidly increase in numbers, to the point where the habitat will no longer support the high numbers. In general, populations are limited by food resources, den or roosting sites, and the incidence of disease and parasitism. Density independent factors such as harsh climatic events, can also serve to limit population growth. Large fluctuations in population size are dampened by a variety of density dependent factors, mostly mediated through social interactions such as competition for mates, territoriality, and predator-prey cycles.

Population increase is obviously a function of both birth rate and immigration rate. Birth rates vary with age, such that very young and very old individuals do not breed in most species. Population decrease is driven by mortality and emigration rates. These also vary with age, with very young individuals having the highest mortality rates in most species. Other aspects of reproduction contributing to population size include length of breeding season, litter size, and sex ratio.

Fecundity, the number of offspring produced per unit of time, varies greatly among mammal species. Litter size, number of litters per year, and the age at first breeding all significantly affect fecundity. For most mammals, an individual female's reproductive value increases with age once she begins breeding, reaches a maximum early in life, and then declines rapidly with old age. Most small mammals breed in their first year of age, but larger, longer-lived species may require several years of subadult experience before reaching reproductive maturity.

Natural selection acts on litter size to maximize reproductive fitness, just as it does for other traits. In general, mammals produce the maximum number of young that they can successfully wean. This is obviously affected by energetic constraints on the lactating female, which are considerable. Further selection is provided by the available food supply once the young are weaned, as they have to reach reproductive maturity to contribute to the population size. In species producing more than one litter per year, the average litter size may be lower than in those producing only a single litter per year.

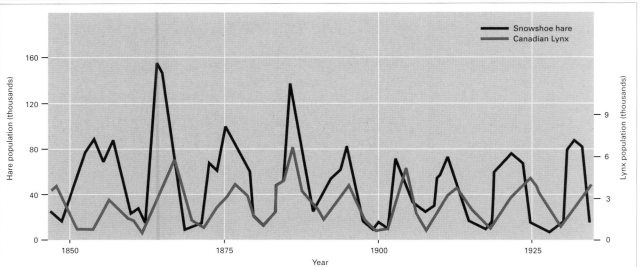

Although some small species of marsupials are known to be semelparous, breeding only once in their lifetime, most mammals are iteroparous, breeding repeatedly during their lifespan. Most mammals also do not live for very long once they are beyond breeding age. Maximum reproductive effort tends to occur early in the breeding life of an individual adult mammal, when physical condition and competitive abilities are maximized.

Migration

Because of climatic fluctuations that greatly affect food supplies, many species of mammals migrate seasonally from one location to another. Although food resources are likely the ultimate driving force behind mammal migrations, they often are triggered by proximal cues such as photoperiod. Migrations are energetically costly, so the rewards have to be considerable in terms of assuring survival. Many mammals take advantage of seasonally rich food resources in temperate or polar regions by feeding heavily there, and laying down fat supplies that allow for migration to more benign climates during the polar or temperate winters. There are species that migrate by walking (ungulates), swimming (marine mammals), and flying (bats).

One simple form of migration is elevational migration, as shown by deer, elk, and various species of wild sheep. In summer, high mountain meadows are lush with plant life, easily available during the long days of an otherwise short growing season. These animals take advantage of the abundant forage by moving into these areas as the snow melts, and access becomes easier. Conversely, in the fall when the weather changes, and snow begins to accumulate, they move downslope to lower valleys that will provide forage during harsh winters.

Other ungulates undergo long-range migrations. One of the best documented is that of the Blue Wildebeest (*Connochaetes taurinus*), in east Africa. There, about 1·5 million wildebeest, somewhat lower numbers of Burchell's Zebra (*Equus quagga burchellii*), Thomson's Gazelle (*Eudorcas thomsonii*), Grant's Gazelle (*Nanger granti*) and assorted other species undergo a circular 2900 km annual migration. Relentlessly tracked by large predators, these animals basically spend their entire lives on the move, in search of grass newly ripened by seasonal rains. Between late January and early March, about 400,000 wildebeest calves are born in the southern part of the Serengeti Plains in Tanzania. Soon after birth, they join the rest of the assembly in a slow clockwise journey northwards to the Masai Mara in Kenya, where they feed on newly ripening grasses fed by summer rains. Then they take a more easterly return route, still following the grass, back to the Serengeti, where the migration continues.

A somewhat different type of migration is seen in the giant rorquals, or baleen whales. Several species move into polar regions during the polar summer, to feed on abundant food resources in the cold, but productive waters of both the arctic and southern oceans. Then, having laid down massive supplies of blubber, they retreat to tropical waters to overwinter, and to produce their calves. In contrast to the constant foraging of the migratory wildebeest, these cetaceans do not feed on the wintering grounds. They undergo the long migration to produce their young in the milder, and in some cases, more protected, tropical seas. The amazingly productive polar oceans provide sufficient advantage to make these long journeys selectively advantageous.

Many species of bats are also migratory. Migration in bats ranges from relatively short seasonal movements of a few dozens or hundreds of kilometers to long distance moves of several thousand. The shorter migrations are usually from summer maternity and feeding roosts to hibernacula, frequently cold caves where the bats overwinter. Longer distance migrations are known for some species that move to north temperate zones in the summer to take advantage of the abundant insect populations there. These species usually also breed in the north during this time of food abundance. Then, to avoid the rigors of the northern winters, they fly to tropical regions to spend the winter. In North America, the long distance movements of the Brazilian Free-tailed Bat (*Tadarida brasiliensis*) from maternity roosts in the south-western USA to wintering grounds in Mexico have been well documented.

Evolution of Mammals

Mammals evolved from a group of reptilian ancestors called Synapsids. A specialized group of Synapsids called Therapsids, or mammal-like reptiles, first occur in the fossil record about 285 million years ago, at the beginning of the Permian Period, before the evolution of dinosaurs. Therapsids flourished for about 40 million years, until the end of the Permian, when a massive extinction event left the evolutionary stage to a relatively few survivors. One such group of survivors led to the Dinosaurs, and another, somewhat later, to the Mammals. These early mammals were tiny compared to most dinosaurs, and perhaps if we had one in hand today, we would think it resembled some of our modern species of shrews. One candidate fossil for the earliest known mammal is *Adelobasileus cromptoni*, from 225 million-year-old Permian beds in Texas.

Our knowledge of almost all of the 225 million years of mammalian evolution is limited to fragmentary remains of the hard, skeletal, parts of mammals that fossilize. Although paleontologists have been able to piece together a remarkably complete record of that evolutionary history, we can only speculate about the accompanying ecological and physiological changes that must have occurred. One singular difference between reptiles and mammals is the development of endothermy, or internal control of body temperature. This fundamental shift essentially freed mammals from relying on external heat sources, and allowed them to forage more or less continually, night or day, and in much harsher climates than their reptilian ancestors.

Dinosaurs and early mammals shared the earth for some 160 million years, but dinosaurs were in general the larger and more dominant life forms. About 65 million years ago, another major extinction event essentially eliminated the dinosaurs, and a subsequent steady radiation of mammalian lineages led to what is known as the Age of Mammals. By that time, mammals had already differentiated into the three major lineages of monotremes, marsupials, and placentals. Recent detailed studies of both fossil evidence and inferences gleaned from modern molecular techniques suggested that additional differentiation had begun to occur even before the extinction event. Furthermore, the real explosive phase of modern mammalian evolution did not begin until about 10 million years after the extinction event.

The earth was undergoing major changes throughout the 225 million year history of mammals. A single super-continent, Pangaea, began to break up, and the continents we know today drifted through tectonic movements to their current locations. Of living mammalian groups, the earliest to evolve were the monotremes. They split from the mammalian mainstream around 130 million years ago, probably in Australia, which was still part of the ancient southern supercontinent of Gondwanaland. These egg-laying mammals were more like their reptilian ancestors than were any other mammalian group. Monotremata, the name of the order, refers to the common cloaca, which bears the openings of both the genital and excretory systems. However, they are clearly mammals because they nurse their young from glands, have fur, possess a four-chambered heart, and are warm blooded. All of these characteristics are in a primitive state compared to other mammals. Milk is secreted through skin glands, and the young suckle by licking the fur. The four-chambered heart is incomplete, and the body temperature averages lower than other mammals. Surviving monotremes include four species of echidna and the Platypus.

The first marsupials appear in the fossil record about 120 million years ago. Fossils are known from Europe and North America, and even a few from Africa, but surviving marsupial orders are limited to Australia and South America. A significant marsupial radiation occurred on Gondwanaland, and these groups were highly successful until a later invasion by placental mammals of various orders.

Four major clades of placental mammals developed in conjunction with the tectonic changes that rearranged the continents. In Africa, a lineage called Afrotheria evolved, which

Gray Whale.
Migratory route in eastern Pacific.

Some species of mammals migrate seasonally long distances.

Amadeu Blasco

Reindeer.
Autumnal migratory routes in Northern Asia.

included elephants, hyraxes, sea cows, elephant shrews, golden moles, tenrecs and the aardvark. In South America, Xenarthra (Cingulata and Pilosa) diversified into sloths, anteaters, and armadillos. North America and Eurasia saw the development of Laurasiatheria, including soricomorphs, carnivores, pangolins, hoofed animals, whales, and bats. A fourth major radiation is called Euarchontoglires: the rodents, lagomorphs, tree shrews, flying lemurs, and primates.

By about 45 million years ago (mid-Eocene), all of the major living groups of mammals were in existence. Many others that also existed then have since gone extinct. In addition to the effects of continental isolation caused by the breakup of the super continents, new connections led to an intermingling of faunas that set the stage for the geographic distribution of major mammalian groups that we see today. Africa came into contact with Europe about 30 million years ago, allowing elephants and some Afrotheria to spread north, while carnivores, ungulates, and primates flowed southward. Later, North and South America were joined, with carnivores and ungulates moving south, and xenarthrans heading north.

Speciation

The most recent complete compilation of living mammal species recognized 5411 species. Each of these arose through a process known as speciation, the evolutionary process that leads to one species being recognized as distinct from another. Although we can easily visualize this on the theoretical level, actually defining the limits of species is a complicated task. For most of the past century, biologists used a biological species concept perhaps best articulated by Ernst Mayr, who held that a species is an actually or potentially interbreeding population that does not interbreed with other such populations when there is opportunity to do so. Systematic mammalogists, or taxonomists, used mainly morphological characters to define the limits of various species, because reproductive isolation was difficult to demonstrate.

Here is a simplified example of how speciation might occur in mammals. Imagine a mainland population of a single species of rodent, living along a major river such as the Amazon. A sizeable chunk of vegetation, containing a pregnant female, or perhaps even a few individuals, washes down the river and out to sea, where it finally comes ashore on an island. The rodents

breed on the island, isolated from the remainder of the species on the mainland. Over the course of many generations in many years, the population on the island accumulates changes in behavior and physiology that lead to structural changes that can be measured morphologically. Because of their reproductive isolation from the mainland populations, which have also continued to change, or evolve, the two groups become more and more different, to the point where a systematist studying the group, affirms that the island population deserves to be recognized as a distinct species.

Modern molecular methods have allowed biologists to delve much more deeply into the process of speciation. By studying the actual DNA of individuals from throughout the range of what might have been formerly thought to be a single species, a molecular systematist might be able to easily differentiate two or more species that otherwise look quite similar morphologically. This augmented biological toolkit will eventually lead to a much better understanding of species limits in virtually all mammals. At this point in time we are in an exciting transition phase where mammalian systematists are trying to reconcile tra-

- Rodentia
- Chiroptera
- Soricomorpha
- Primates
- Carnivora
- Artiodactyla
- Diprotodontia
- Lagomorpha
- Didelphimorphia
- Cetacea
- Dasyuromorphia
- Afrosoricida
- Erinaceomorpha
- Cingulata
- Paramelemorphia
- Scandentia
- Perissodactyla
- Macroscelidea
- Pilosa
- Pholidota
- Paucituberculata
- Monotremata
- Sirenia
- Hyracoidea
- Proboscidea
- Dermoptera
- Notoryctemorphia
- Microbiotheria
- Tubulidentata

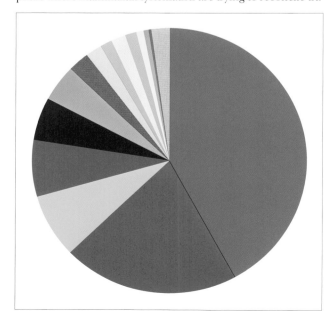

Proportion of extant mammal species in each order.

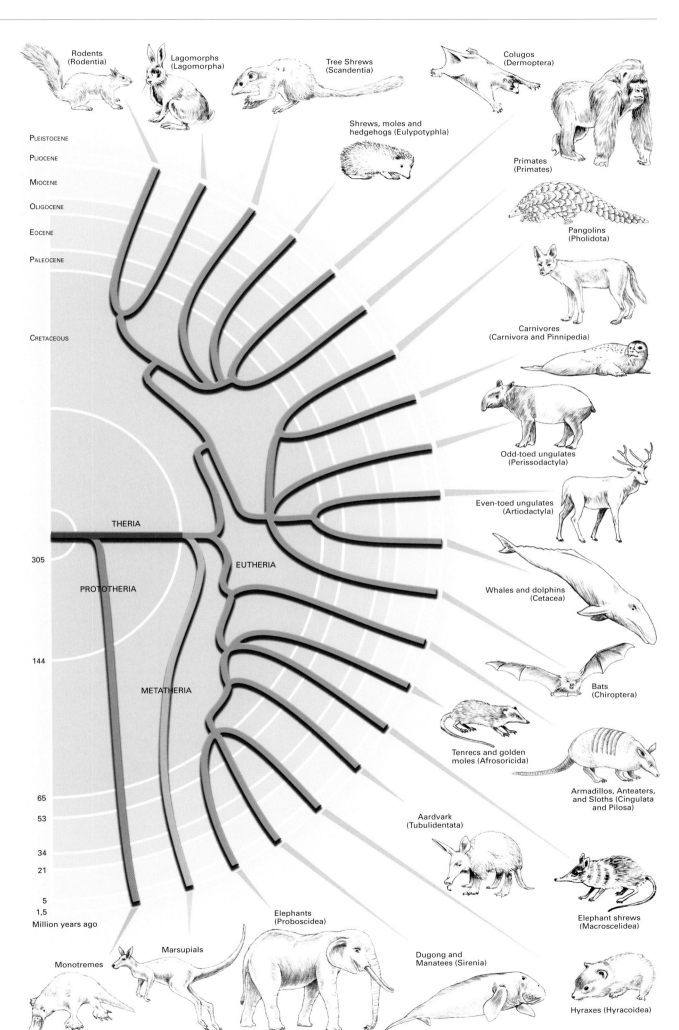

Evolution of extant groups of mammals.

Amadeu Blasco

Rodents (Rodentia)

Lagomorphs (Lagomorpha)

Tree Shrews (Scandentia)

Colugos (Dermoptera)

Shrews, moles and hedgehogs (Eulypotyphla)

Primates (Primates)

Pangolins (Pholidota)

Carnivores (Carnivora and Pinnipedia)

Odd-toed ungulates (Perissodactyla)

Even-toed ungulates (Artiodactyla)

Whales and dolphins (Cetacea)

Bats (Chiroptera)

Tenrecs and golden moles (Afrosoricida)

Armadillos, Anteaters, and Sloths (Cingulata and Pilosa)

Aardvark (Tubulidentata)

Elephant shrews (Macroscelidea)

Elephants (Proboscidea)

Dugong and Manatees (Sirenia)

Hyraxes (Hyracoidea)

Monotremes

Marsupials

PLEISTOCENE

PLIOCENE

MIOCENE

OLIGOCENE

EOCENE

PALEOCENE

CRETACEOUS

THERIA

305

EUTHERIA

PROTOTHERIA

144

METATHERIA

65

53

34

21

5

1,5

Million years ago

45

	Nº of Genera	Nº of Species	Common Name
Class Mammalia	1231	5411	Mammals
Order Monotremata	**3**	**5**	**Monotremes**
Family Tachyglossidae	2	4	Echidnas
Family Ornithorhynchidae	1	1	Platypus
Order Didelphimorphia	**17**	**87**	**American Opossums**
Family Didelphidae	17	87	
Order Paucituberculata	**3**	**6**	**Shrew Opossums**
Family Caenolestidae	3	6	
Order Microbiotheria	**1**	**1**	**Monito del Monte**
Family Microbiotheriidae	1	1	
Order Notoryctemorphia	**1**	**2**	**Marsupial Moles**
Family Notoryctidae	1	2	
Order Dasyuromorphia	**22**	**71**	**Carnivorous Marsupials**
Family Thylacinidae	1	1	Thylacine
Family Myrmecobiidae	1	1	Numbat
Family Dasyuridae	20	69	Dasyurids
Order Paramelemorphia	**8**	**21**	**Bandicoots and Bilbies**
Family Thylacomyidae	1	2	Bilbies
Family Chaeropodidae	1	1	Pig-footed Bandicoot
Family Peramelidae	6	18	Bandicoots
Order Diprotodontia	**39**	**143**	**Kangaroos and relatives**
Suborder Vombatiformes	3	4	Wombats and Koala
Family Phascolarctidae	1	1	Koala
Family Vombatidae	2	3	Wombats
Suborder Phalangeriformes	20	63	Phalangers and relatives
Superfamily Phalangeroidea	8	32	Cuscuses and Pygmy Possums
Family Burramyidae	2	5	Pygmy Possums
Family Phalangeridae	6	27	Cuscuses
Superfamily Petauroidea	12	31	Possums and Gliders
Family Pseudocheiridae	6	17	Ringtail Possums
Family Petauridae	3	11	Gliding and Striped Possums
Family Tarsipedidae	1	1	Honey Possum
Family Acrobatidae	2	2	Feathertail Glider and Possum
Suborder Macropodiformes	16	76	Kangaroos and relatives
Family Hypsiprymnodontidae	1	1	Musky Rat Kangaroo
Family Potoroidae	4	10	Bettongs and Potoroos
Family Macropodidae	11	65	Kangaroos
Order Afrosoricida	**19**	**51**	**Tenrecs and Golden Moles**
Suborder Tenrecomorpha	10	30	Tenrecs
Family Tenrecidae	10	30	
Suborder Chrysochloridea	9	21	Golden Moles
Family Chrysochloridae	9	21	
Order Macroscelidea	**4**	**15**	**Elephant Shrews**
Family Macroscelididae	4	15	
Order Tubulidentata	**1**	**1**	**Aardvark**
Family Orycteropodidae	1	1	
Order Hyracoidea	**3**	**4**	**Hyraxes**
Family Procaviidae	3	4	
Order Proboscidea	**2**	**3**	**Elephants**
Family Elephantidae	2	3	
Order Sirenia	**3**	**5**	**Dugongs and Manatees**
Family Dugongidae	2	2	Dugongs
Family Trichechidae	1	3	Manatees
Order Cingulata	**9**	**21**	**Armadillos**
Family Dasypodidae	9	21	
Order Pilosa	**5**	**10**	**Sloths and Anteaters**
Suborder Folivora	2	6	Sloths
Family Bradypodidae	1	4	Three-toed Sloths
Family Megalonychidae	1	2	Two-toed Sloths
Suborder Vermilingua	3	4	Anteaters
Family Cyclopedidae	1	1	Silky Anteater
Family Myrmecophagidae	2	3	American Anteaters
Order Scandentia	**5**	**20**	**Tree Shrews**
Family Tupaiidae	4	19	Common Tree Shrews
Family Ptilocercidae	1	1	Pen-tailed Tree Shrew
Order Dermoptera	**2**	**2**	**Flying Lemurs**
Family Cynocephalidae	2	2	
Order Primates	**69**	**376**	**Primates**
Suborder Strepsirrhini	23	88	
Infraorder Lemuriformes	14	59	
Superfamily Cheirogaleoidea	5	21	
Family Cheirogaleidae	5	21	Dwarf and Mouse Lemurs
Superfamily Lemuroidea	9	38	

	Nº of Genera	Nº of Species	Common Name
Family Lemuridae	5	19	Large Lemurs
Family Lepilemuridae	1	8	Sportive Lemurs
Family Indridae	3	11	Leaping Lemurs
Infraorder Chiromyiformes	1	1	
Family Daubentoniidae	1	1	Aye-aye
Infraorder Lorisiformes	8	28	
Family Lorisidae	5	9	Lorises
Family Galagidae	3	19	Galagos
Suborder Haplorrhini	46	288	
Infraorder Tarsiiformes	1	7	
Family Tarsiidae	1	7	Tarsiers
Infraorder Simiiformes	45	281	
Parvorder Platyrrhini	16	128	
Family Cebidae	6	56	New World Monkeys
Family Aotidae	1	8	Night Monkeys
Family Pitheciidae	4	40	Sakis and Uakaris
Family Atelidae	5	24	Spider Monkeys
Parvorder Catarrhini	29	153	
Superfamily Cercopithecoidea	21	132	
Family Cercopithecidae	21	132	Old World Monkeys
Superfamily Hominoidea	8	21	
Family Hylobatidae	4	14	Gibbons
Family Hominidae	4	7	Apes and Humans
Order Rodentia	**481**	**2277**	**Rodents**
Suborder Sciuromorpha	61	307	
Family Aplodontiidae	1	1	Mountain Beaver
Family Sciuridae	51	278	Squirrels
Family Gliridae	9	28	Dormice
Suborder Castorimorpha	13	102	
Family Castoridae	1	2	Beavers
Family Heteromyidae	6	60	Pocket Mice and Kangaroo Rats
Family Geomyidae	6	40	Pocket Gophers
Suborder Myomorpha	326	1569	
Superfamily Dipodoidea	16	51	
Family Dipodidae	16	51	Jerboas and Jumping Mice
Superfamily Muroidea	310	1518	
Family Platacanthomyidae	2	2	Tree Mice
Family Spalacidae	6	36	Blind Mole Rats and relatives
Family Calomyscidae	1	8	Calomyscuses
Family Nesomyidae	21	61	Climbing Rats and relatives
Family Cricetidae	130	681	Voles and New World Rats
Family Muridae	150	730	Old World Rats and Mice
Suborder Anomaluromorpha	4	9	
Family Anomaluridae	3	7	Scaly-tailed Squirrels
Family Pedetidae	1	2	Spring Hare
Suborder Hystricomorpha	77	290	
Infraorder Ctenodactylomorphi	4	5	
Family Ctenodactylidae	4	5	Gundis
Infraorder Hystricognathi	73	285	
Family Bathyergidae	5	16	Mole-rats
Family Hystricidae	3	11	Old World Porcupines
Family Petromuridae	1	1	Dassie Rat
Family Thryonomyidae	1	2	Cane Rats
Family Erethizontidae	5	16	New World Porcupines
Family Chinchillidae	3	7	Chinchillas and Viscachas
Family Dinomyidae	1	1	Pacarana
Family Caviidae	6	18	Guinea Pigs
Family Dasyproctidae	2	13	Agoutis
Family Cuniculidae	1	2	Pacas
Family Ctenomyidae	1	60	Tuco-tucos
Family Octodontidae	8	13	Degus and relatives
Family Abrocomidae	2	10	Chinchilla Rats
Family Echimyidae	21	90	Spiny-rats
Family Myocastoridae	1	1	Coypu
Family Capromyidae	8	20	Hutias
Family Heptaxodontidae	4	4	Key Mice
Order Lagomorpha	**13**	**92**	**Rabbits, Hares, and Pikas**
Family Ochotonidae	1	30	Pikas
Family Prolagidae	1	1	Sardinian Pika
Family Leporidae	11	61	Rabbits and Hares
Order Erinaceomorpha	**10**	**24**	**Hedgehogs**
Family Erinaceidae	10	24	
Order Soricomorpha	**45**	**428**	**Shrews and Moles**

	Nº of Genera	Nº of Species	Common Name
Family Nesophontidae	1	9	Nesophontes
Family Solenodontidae	1	4	Soledons
Family Soricidae	26	376	Shrews
Family Talpidae	17	39	Moles
Order Chiroptera	**202**	**1116**	**Bats**
Family Pteropodidae	42	186	Old World Fruit Bats
Family Rhinolophidae	1	77	Horseshoe Bats
Family Hipposideridae	9	81	Old World Leaf-nosed Bats
Family Megadermatidae	4	5	False Vampire Bats
Family Rhinopomatidae	1	4	Mouse-tailed Bats
Family Craseonycteridae	1	1	Hog-nosed Bat
Family Emballonuridae	13	51	Sheath-tailed Bats
Family Nycteridae	1	16	Slit-faced Bats
Family Myzopodidae	1	1	Sucker-footed Bat
Family Mystacinidae	1	2	Short-tailed Bats
Family Phyllostomidae	55	160	American Leaf-nosed Bats
Family Mormoopidae	2	10	Leaf-chinned Bats
Family Noctilionidae	1	2	Bulldog Bats
Family Furipteridae	2	2	Thumbless and Smoky Bats
Family Thyropteridae	1	3	Disk-winged Bats
Family Natalidae	3	8	Funnel-eared Bats
Family Molossidae	16	100	Free-tailed Bats
Family Vespertilionidae	48	407	Vesper Bats
Order Pholidota	**1**	**8**	**Pangolins**
Family Manidae	1	8	
Order Carnivora	**128**	**281**	**Carnivores**
Suborder Feliformia	56	120	
Family Nandiniidae	1	1	African Palm Civet
Family Felidae	14	37	Cats
Family Prionodontidae	1	2	Linsangs
Family Viverridae	14	34	Civets, Genets and Oyans
Family Hyaenidae	4	4	Hyenas
Family Herpestidae	15	34	Mongooses
Family Eupleridae	7	8	Madagascar Carnivores
Suborder Caniformia	72	161	
Family Canidae	13	35	Dogs
Family Ursidae	5	8	Bears
Family Otariidae	7	16	Sea Lions
Family Odobenidae	1	1	Walrus
Family Phocidae	13	19	Earless Seals
Family Ailuridae	1	1	Red Panda
Family Procyonidae	6	12	Raccoons
Family Mephitidae	4	12	Skunks
Family Mustelidae	22	57	Weasels and relatives
Order Perissodactyla	**6**	**17**	**Odd-toed Ungulates**
Family Equidae	1	8	Horses
Family Tapiridae	1	4	Tapirs
Family Rhinocerotidae	4	5	Rhinoceroses
Order Artiodactyla	**89**	**240**	**Even-toed Ungulates**
Family Suidae	5	19	Pigs
Family Tayassuidae	3	3	Peccaries
Family Hippopotamidae	2	2	Hippopotamuses
Family Camelidae	3	4	Camels and relatives
Family Tragulidae	3	8	Chevrotains
Family Moschidae	1	7	Musk Deer
Family Cervidae	19	51	Deer
Family Antilocapridae	1	1	Pronghorn
Family Giraffidae	2	2	Giraffes
Family Bovidae	50	143	Antelopes and relatives
Order Cetacea	**40**	**84**	**Whales and Dolphins**
Suborder Mysticeti	6	13	Baleen Whales
Family Balaenidae	2	4	Right Whales
Family Balaenopteridae	2	7	Rorquals
Family Eschrichtiidae	1	1	Gray Whale
Family Neobalaenidae	1	1	Pygmy Right Whale
Suborder Odontoceti	34	71	Toothed Whales
Family Delphinidae	17	34	Marine Dolphins
Family Monodontidae	2	2	White Whales
Family Phocoenidae	3	6	Porpoises
Family Physeteridae	2	3	Sperm Whales
Family Platanistidae	1	2	Ganges and Indus Dolphins
Family Iniidae	3	3	River Dolphins
Family Ziphiidae	6	21	Beaked Whales

Table 1. *Number of genera and species in each of the currently recognized orders and families of mammals.*

ditional morphological species concepts with modern genetic ones. As a result, we are recognizing more and more species of mammals, as we become better able to differentiate them.

An example of this growth in species can be seen by examining the publication "Mammal Species of the World" through three editions. The first edition, published in 1982 recognized 4170 species. The second edition, published in 1993, recognized 4629. The third edition, published in 2005, recognized 5416. Although some of this increase can be attributed to the discovery and description of new species, most of it is the result of continuing improvements in our ability to detect and understand species limits in mammals. The ultimate number recognized will surely be far higher than the current one.

Phylogeny and Classification

In addition to recognizing species, it is useful to classify mammals into higher categories, and the accompanying table shows the currently recognized orders and the families they contain. In some cases, there is additional hierarchical structure in the classification. The number of genera and species in each family and order is also indicated. Such classifications are constructed by systematists, in order to group related kinds of mammals into a classification that can be used worldwide.

Our current system of biological nomenclature and classification dates from the work of a Swedish botanist named Linnaeus. His 1758 work, the 10th edition of *Systema Naturae* classified all of the organisms known to him at that time, using a system of binomial nomenclature that includes a generic name and the specific epithet that forms the scientific name of each species. The rules for this system of nomenclature have evolved over the years under the guidance of an international group called the International Commission on Zoological Nomenclature.

Although earlier classifications tended to be based mainly on morphology, and in some cases were based more on similarity of form, the current trend is to try to classify mammals phylogenetically. This means to group them according to evolutionary relationship, rather than on the basis of morphological similarity. Unfortunately, there is no sure way to determine evolutionary relationships, but the modern evolutionary biologist has a much better chance of doing so than ever before. Ideally we would need to know the genetic code of every organism to offer a complete phylogenetic classification. Fortunately, modern molecular methods are allowing us to examine the genetics of individual species and populations in much greater detail than in the past.

Bibliography

Adelman (1987), Adolph (1967), Aerts (1990, 1998), Allin (1975), Altman & Dittmer (1971), Altringham (1996), Alvarez (1998), Aristotle (350 B.C.E.), Armstrong & Phelps (1984), Baker (1979), Bentley (1998), Benton (1990), Biewener (1990), Blackburn (1991), Bourne (1972, 1980), Bramble (1978), Bramble & Carrier (1983), Bramble & Jenkins (1993), Brannon (1990), Bubenik & Bubenik (1990), Burnie & Wilson (2001), Butler, P.J. & Jones (1982), Butler, T.H. & Hodos (1996), Carroll (1988, 1997), Catania (1999), Catesby (1731–1743), Chivers & Hladik (1980), Chivers & Langer (1994), Christiansen (1999a), Clutton-Brock & Wilson (2002, 2003) Crompton & Hiiemae (1969), Crompton & Parker (1978), Dantzler (1989), Dawson (1983), Farmer (1997), Feldhamer *et al.* (2007), Fish *et al.* (1988), Franklin & Axelsson (2000), Freeman (1990), Galis (1999), Gambaryan (1974), Gingerich (1994), Goodrich (1986), Gorniak (1985), Gould, E. & Mckay (1998), Gould, S.J. (1977, 1990, 1991), Greaves (1980), Gregory (1991), Griffiths (1978), Hadley (1995), Hanken & Hall (1993), Harrison (1972), Hayssen *et al.* (1993), Hermanson & Macfadden (1996), Hildebrand & Goslow (2001), Hodos & Butler (1997), Holland & Holland (1999), Howell (1930), Jenkins & McClearn (1984), Kays & Wilson (2002), Kemp (1982), Kent & Carr (2001), Kram & Taylor (1990), Krstic (1984), Krubitzer (1995), Kuhn & Zeller (1987), Kurtén (1982) Lauren *et al.* (2000), Liem (1982), Liem & Summers (2000), Liem *et al.* (2001), Lillegraven (1985), Linnaeus (1758), Macdonald (2001), Martin *et al.* (1998), McKenna & Bell (1997), McMahon (1984), Moffat (1975), Mossman & Duke (1973), Nevo (1979), Nieuwenhuys & Donjelaar (1997), Norberg (1990), Norris (1996), Novacek (1992), Nowak (1999), Pabst (2000), Pivorunas (1979), Pough *et al.* (1996), Radinsky (1983), Reynolds & Rommel (1999), Romer & Parsons (1986), Rowe (1996), Rowlatt (1990), Ruff & Wilson (2000), Schwenk (2000), Smith (1992, 1996), Sokolov (1982), Stevens & Hume (1995), Szalay (1982), Tyndale-Biscoe (1973), Tyndale-Biscoe & Renfree (1987), Vaughan *et al.* (2000), Weibel & Taylor (1981), Weibel *et al.* (1998), Weinstein (1999), Werdelin & Nilsonne (1999), Wilson (1997), Wilson & Cole (2000), Wilson & Reeder (2005), Wilson & Ruff (1999), Winston & Wilson (2004), Young & Hobbs (1975).

Order Carnivora

CLASS MAMMALIA

ORDER CARNIVORA

SUBORDER FELIFORMIA

Family NANDINIIDAE (AFRICAN PALM CIVET)

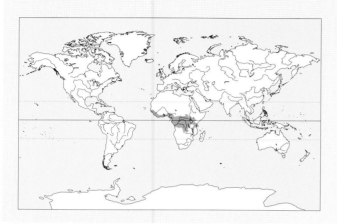

- Small mammals with small ears, heavily-built body, short legs, and tail longer than the head and body; dark brown in color and with a pair of bright scapular spots.
- 71–139 cm.

- Tropical Africa.
- Rain and deciduous forests, from coastal to montane, also savannah woodlands.
- 1 genus, 1 species, 4 taxa.
- No species threatened; none Extinct since 1600.

Systematics

The Nandiniidae is a monogeneric family, represented by a single species the African Palm Civet (*Nandinia binotata*). The taxonomy of the genus *Nandinia* has been debated hotly, notably because of its retention of plesiomorphic traits shared with feliformian fossils, especially on the basicranium, auditory bullae, and carnassials. *Nandinia* differs from all extant carnivorans in the persistence of the cartilaginous condition of the posterior chamber of the auditory bulla (the entotympanic caudal bone). The bulla elements are unfused in adults and the septum usually present in extant Carnivora is absent. The transpomontorial course of the internal carotid artery tends to be small, which may represent the plesiomorphic feliformian condition. Moreover, the shape of the petrosal bone is similar to that of some of the oldest aeluroids, including the stenoplesictines and proailurines from the Oligocene. It was suggested that the different types of feliformian bullae were derived from the bulla conformation found in *Nandinia*, but this hypothesis was not confirmed when tested using a phylogenetic framework. Rather, the viverrid-like conformation seems to be the plesiomorphic state from which extant feliformians—excluding *Nandinia*—evolved.

Fossils are extremely scarce. A first lower molar (M_1) from the Late Miocene (Lukeimo Formation) of Kenya was attributed very recently to *Nandinia*. Nevertheless, some authors have suggested that the genus belongs to a primitive stock of aeluroids that evolved slowly within stable mesic forests of Central Africa. On the other hand, the peculiar traits of the genus, together with the absence or the recent age of fossil records, may suggest that *Nandinia* is a unique, morphologically derived taxon within the Viverridae. Phylogenetic analyses using mostly cranial and dental characters tend to place *Nandinia* as the sister-taxon to the extant Feliformia. Close relationships of the genus with extinct lineages such as Nimravidae or *Paleoprionodon* have been proposed, but still remain open to debate. Molecular phylogenies based on independent portions of the genome have confirmed the sister-group position of *Nandinia* with respect to the rest of the extant feliformians. Molecular clock methods have suggested relatively deep divergence in time estimates for this split, ranging from 36 to 54 million years.

Traditionally, *Nandinia* was considered either as a morphologically peculiar member of the Asiatic subfamily Paradoxurinae (it is commonly called the African Palm Civet) or designated under the monogeneric subfamily Nandiniinae, within the family Viverridae. It was, however, placed in the family Nandiniidae some 70 years ago, because of the unique structure of its perineal scent glands and the conformation of its basicranium. A recent phylogenetic study combining molecular and morphological data concluded that a mosaic of morphological convergences was shared by *Nandinia* and other viverrid-like lineages, including Prinodontidae (Asiatic linsangs) and Eupleridae (Malagasy carnivorans). These convergences can explain the taxonomic confusion that has historically surrounded those carnivorans. *Nandinia* shares most of its convergent traits with other viverrid-like taxa, such as *Cryptoprocta, Fossa, Prionodon,* and *Eupleres*, and to a lesser extent, with the Paradoxurinae (especially as concerns external anatomy). The phylogenetic position of *Nandinia* and the unique mosaic of traits (combining both plesiomorphies and convergences) justify the use of a distinct family for the genus, Nandiniidae, which is followed here.

Morphological Aspects

It resembles a dark brown, heavily-built genet, with a shorter rostrum, large and straight canines, tail longer than the head and body, and a pair of bright scapular spots.

External characteristics make *Nandinia* a very peculiar morphotype, distinct from all the recognized subfamilies of viverrids. For instance, the area between the plantar and digital pads (except digit one) is hairy, and the pads of the third and fourth digits are widely separated. The position of the scent gland (anterior to the genitals), its flatness, and relatively simple structure exhibit no similarity to what is found among viverrids. Besides, additional scent glands are found in the foot sole, the chin, and around the belly when females are lactating.

Habitat

The African Palm Civet is distributed in West and Central African rain and deciduous forests (from Gambia to south–west Sudan), and is also patchily present in montane and subtropical forests in northern Angola and eastern and south–eastern Africa. Common in coastal lowland forests, it also extends upwards into montane forests as high as 2500 m in both West Africa (Cameroon) and East Africa (Tanzania). In addition to rainforest, it is found in riparian forests, deciduous woodlands, and savannah woodlands. It is not restricted to primary, undisturbed forest, and also occurs in secondary forests and degraded woodlands.

Communication

Both males and females emit long, plaintive calls that sound like "hoo", especially during the breeding season or when a female is in estrus. In addition, they may communicate directly with each other through softer, coughing noises. Olfactory communication is equally important. The perineal gland is rubbed on branches, and additional scent glands on the feet may leave odoriferous trails as well.

Food and Feeding

African Palm Civets are primarily frugivorous. Although 80% of their diet is fruit, they take a variety of animal prey as well, if the opportunity arises. They have been known to eat a variety of insects, prey on bird eggs and nestlings, and catch and eat small rodents and even pottos. They may also feed on carrion if available.

They often intersperse fruit-feeding bouts with resting periods of an hour or two. They were documented to feed on at least twelve species of plants in West Africa, and may play a role in seed dispersal. Particularly favored fruit trees may attract several individuals at the same time when fruits are ripe. There is some evidence that females have priority when both genders are feeding at the same source.

Because they occur in such a wide variety of habitats, African Palm Civets often come into contact with agroecosystems where they may prey on crops and poultry. In West Africa, they have been seen drinking palm wine directly from vessels people have hung in trees. They are also reported to drink alcohol in captivity, perhaps a result of prior experience with overripe or fermenting fruit.

They capture animal prey primarily by pouncing, holding the prey item to the substrate with the forefeet, and then using their teeth to bite and kill the prey.

Breeding

The breeding season is likely linked to seasonal rainfall patterns, which in turn affect food supply. They normally give birth during the latter part of the rainy season or beginning of the dry season. The gestation length is about two months. Normally, two young are born per litter, and at least in some areas, there may be two litters per year. The young are altricial, born naked with eyes closed, and weighing an average of 56 g. They reach adult size and weight at around 6–9 months of age, but accompany the mother to fruit sources much earlier than that. Maximum longevity in captivity is 18 years.

Movements, Home range and Social organization

African Palm Civets are nocturnal and somewhat secretive, making detailed study of their movements difficult. Available studies have shown that males tend to have home ranges aver-

aging 85 ha, larger than those of females, which average 45 ha. Presumably, female home ranges are based on availability of food resources. Individual females scent-mark the borders of their territories, and there is very little overlap. Males, on the other hand, seem to have home ranges based on the number of females in the area, rather than on feeding opportunities.

Male home ranges overlap those of females, and dominant males cover much more territory than do smaller, less successful ones. Heavier males tend to be the dominant ones. Less successful males are not only smaller, but have smaller scent glands and testicles. Male home ranges may overlap, and although dominant males meet infrequently, they can fight violently when they do.

Females tend to remain on their mother's home range longer than do males. Young males disperse rapidly once they are weaned, and eventually establish their own territories. Population density varies widely, but 5–8 individuals/ha have been estimated in West Africa. The species is primarily solitary, but males and females are sometimes found resting together.

Relationship with Humans

African Palm Civets regularly forage around and near human settlements. They occasionally prey on domestic animals, particularly fowl. They may also forage on domestic crops and fruiting trees. They are small and secretive, offering no direct threat to humans. They are kept as pets by some native peoples, and they are used as food items in some cultures. They are frequently found for sale in local markets, notably for traditional medicines.

The fur is not particularly valuable, but may be used by local peoples for decorative items. Their populations have surely been lowered by the continuing habitat destruction throughout their range. They may play some minor role in the transmission of trypanosomiasis.

Status and Conservation

The African Palm Civet is not listed on CITES, and is classified as Least Concern on *The IUCN Red List*. Although hard data is scarce, the African Palm Civet is probably one of the most common small carnivorans in forested regions throughout Africa. Population density remains high in undisturbed habitats. Human hunting, both for food and to protect crops and poultry, is probably the biggest threat.

They have the normal assortment of natural predators, such as larger carnivorans, snakes, and large birds of prey. They may also be exposed to falls due to their arboreal lifestyle, but the largest threats are surely anthropogenic. Deforestation continues at an alarming rate throughout Africa, which means that their favorable habitats are probably being reduced.

African Palm Civets may be the most common small carnivores in Africa, but because they are arboreal, secretive, nocturnal, and beautifully camouflaged, they are hard to study. They move with ease through trees and along vines in search of fruit, which comprises about 80% of their diet, using their very long tail for balance. Unfortunately, some of their diet consists of crops and poultry, which brings them into conflict with humans. Females usually have two litters of twins a year. The offspring reach adult size by nine months, at which time males disperse. Scent is crucial in defining territories. The unique structure of the scent gland between the genitals and the anus and the unusual bone structure of the ear justify the inclusion of these mammals in a distinct family, the Nandiniidae, and help distinguish them from the civets, genets, and oyans of the family Viverridae.

Nandinia binotata
Okapi Wildlife Reserve, Epulu, Ituri Rainforest, DR Congo.
Photo: Bruce Davidson/naturepl.com

PLATE 1

inches 6
cm 15

FAMILY NANDINIIDAE
African Palm Civet

Plate 1
Species Accounts

Genus *NANDINIA*
Gray, 1843

African Palm Civet *Nandinia binotata*
French: Nandinie / **German**: Pardelroller / **Spanish**: Nandinia

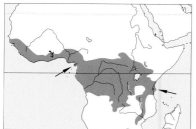

Taxonomy. *Viverra binotata* Gray, 1830, Ashanti region, Ghana.
Four subspecies recognized, but taxonomic boundaries at the subspecific level poorly defined.
Subspecies and Distribution.
N. b. binotata Gray, 1830 – from Gambia to DR Congo, including Bioko I.
N. b. arborea Heller, 1913 – Kenya, S Sudan, N Tanzania, and Uganda.
N. b. gerrardi Thomas, 1893 – Malawi, Mozambique, S&E Tanzania (presumably also Zanzibar I), NE Zambia, and E Zimbabwe.
N. b. intensa Cabrera & Ruxton, 1926 – Angola, S DR Congo, and NW Zambia.
Descriptive notes. Head–body 37–62·5 cm, tail 34–76·2 cm; weight 1·2–3 kg. Two pairs of mammae. Adult males may be slightly larger than females. Head is broad; fairly pointed muzzle; nose pad brown to dark. Ears are short, broad at the base and rounded; there is a single brown-black spot behind ear pinnae. Iris is brownish-orange. Pelage is short, woolly, and dense. Coat color is relatively uniform across the body, and varies from grayish to dark brown; ventral pelage slightly paler. There is a wide range of individual variation in both color and spot markings. Albinism seems extremely rare (one albino individual collected in DR Congo). Back exhibits a characteristic pair of whitish yellow spots on shoulders, and irregularly distributed dark spots that may partly coalesce in the nape (nucchal) region. One to three clearly defined dark lines on neck. Limbs are short, thickset, and poorly spotted. Feet plantigrade; pads extremely well-developed, reaching wrist in forefoot and ankle in hindfoot. Tail is longer than length of head and body (110–120%), densely furred, and has nine to 15 irregularly marked dark rings; rings are generally incomplete on the underside. Both sexes have a glandular abdominal pouch situated anterior to the vulva or penis, about 55 mm long, 20 mm deep, and 20–30 mm wide when open. It shows a simpler structure than the perineal glands usually found in viverrids, and produces a yellowish liquid with a musky odor comparable to the "musk" of civets and genets. Skull differs from other extant carnivorans by the persistence throughout life of the cartilaginous condition of the posterior chamber of the auditory bulla. Rostrum is moderately elongated; zygomatic arches are wide and sagittal crest is generally thin and elevated. Dental formula: I 3/3, C 1/1, P 4/4, M 2/2 = 40. Variation in the presence/absence of M^2 exists. Chromosome number: 2n = 38; FN = 66. Geographic variations in coat pattern have been described. In *gerrardi*, dark stripes on neck are absent, body is sparsely and finely spotted, the pair of bright scapular spots is weakly distinct, and dark tail rings are narrow and sharply defined. In *arborea*, nucchal stripes are present but narrow, lower sides of body are not spotted, and dark tail rings are thin. In *intensa*, coat color is redder and brighter, spots are intense black and the pair of bright scapular spots is more striking to the eye.
Habitat. Occurs from lowland to montane tropical rainforest, up to 2500 m (e.g. Cameroon, Tanzania). Also present in riparian and deciduous forests, savannah woodlands, and disturbed forests after logging or cultivation.
Food and Feeding. Although predominantly frugivorous, they are able to adjust energetic resources with opportunistic foraging on vertebrates (essentially murids, more

rarely pottos), birds' eggs, and arthropods. In Gabon, average stomach content was about 80% fruit and 20% diverse prey items. May frequently raid crops and poultry; can be found eating carrion. Fruits are generally consumed in 5–10 minutes, followed generally by a rest taken on a branch 10–20 m away; such frugivorous meals are taken approximately every two hours. Transit is fast and fruit remains are eliminated 2–3 hours after consumption, which might contribute to seed dispersal across the forest (in Kenya, supposed to spread twelve species of plants). There have been reports of 12–15 individuals feeding at the same time on the fruit of the parasol tree (*Musanga cecropioides*). During encounters between genders, females seem to be given priority access to food. Forefeet used extensively when attacking. Prey is usually pressed and held on the substratum, and then killed by several rapid bites all over the body. They are reported to drink palm wine directly from vessels in palm trees in Sierra Leone and the Niger Delta. Captive individuals showed attraction for alcohol that may result from consumption of fermented fallen fruits and tree exudates in the wild.
Activity patterns. Nocturnal and arboreal. During the day, usually rests on large horizontal branches and lianas, in elevated tree holes, or in crevices formed by vegetation 12–15 m above ground. They use the ground to cross deforested areas or to forage. Plantigrade locomotion and large, deeply carunculated, transversely ridged pads of hindfeet allow agile tree climbing. Able to climb a smooth post and descend head first by "vertical looping", i.e. gripping the trunk, spread-eagled, with claws and hairless pads of forefeet, then bringing both hindfeet forward until they touch the forefeet. Tail may be used as a balancing rod when walking thin branches; although not prehensile, can be wrapped around branches for support. Able to walk on steel wire and jump across gaps up to 1 m wide and as high as 1·8 m. An individual was observed soaring from high branches, with tail extended and legs stretched out, and making a perfect four-point landing.
Movements, Home range and Social organization. Movements of individuals remain poorly understood. In Gabon, males have home ranges between 34 and 153 ha (mean 85 ha), larger than those of females (29–70 ha, mean 45 ha). Home range size in males is dependent on number of available females rather than nutritional resources. Although adult male home ranges often overlap broadly, they consist of distinct sectors. Large males tend to visit all sectors regularly while smaller males stay in their own sectors to avoid dominant males. Home ranges of dominant males may cover home ranges of several females. Adult females have clearly delimited home ranges with narrow overlap zones along borders, where scent marks are deposited. Immature daughters usually remain with their mothers; young males apparently abandon the maternal home range as soon as they are weaned. Dominant males seldom meet, but fights may be extremely violent and fatal to the loser. Sexual competition appears to accentuate weight differences in males, with dominant ones often becoming heavy. Non-dominant males tend to be thinner, with smaller testicles and perineal glands as symptoms of social stress. In Gabon, estimate of minimum mean density was about 5 ind/km², with higher means in inundated forests and river borders (reaching 8 ind/km²). In Bwindi Impenetrable National Park, Uganda, mean density was higher above 2000 m elevation than below 1800 m (3·32 ind/km² and 2·17 ind/km², respectively). Usually, individuals sleep alone, but occasionally a male and female can be found resting close to one another. Scent marking plays a significant role in communication. The perineal gland is rubbed on branches by flexing the hindlimbs; the odor can persist for several months. Other scent glands, such as the one located between the third and fourth toe of each foot, may also be used to scent-mark trails. Individuals produce a typical loud, plaintive cry similar to a lengthy "hoo", which can be heard over a distance of almost 1 km. In Gabon, calls between genders were at their maximum when a female was in estrus, in June.
Breeding. During courtship, a captive pair at close range emitted sounds akin to coughing. In Gabon, births mostly occurred from September to January (wet season and start of short dry season), occasionally in other months, but never during

March–June. Gestation is about 64 days; there are two litters per year, usually of two young each. Birth weight averages about 56 g. Neonates have eyes and ears closed; they accompany mother to visit fruit trees as soon as they are able. They attain adult size and weight at 6–9 months. Captivity records report maximum longevity of 16 to 18 years.

Status and Conservation. CITES: not listed. Classified as Least Concern on *The IUCN Red List*. Probably the most common small carnivore in African forests, although field censuses are rare. In Gabon, biomass estimates neared 11 kg/km^2, which is greater than that of sympatric carnivorans such as genets and civets. Local threats include destruction of individuals caught preying on poultry. They are also hunted for the bushmeat and traditional medicine markets: they are the most common carnivore sold in markets in Equatorial Guinea and Guinea. The skin is used to make ceremonial clothes, wrist-bracelets, and hats. Their association with closed-canopy habitat suggests vulnerability to intense logging, which is occurring at a high rate in western Africa, and to deforestation in eastern and southern Africa. They are preyed upon by larger carnivorans, birds of prey, and pythons. In Cameroon, it is part of the natural reservoir stock for trypanosomiasis. Due to their arboreal mode of life, African Palm Civets are subject to falls and bone fractures.

Bibliography. Allen, G.M. (1939), Allen, J.A. (1924), Andama (2000), Ansell (1960b), Anstey (1991), Basilio (1962), Bates (1905), Bourlière *et al.* (1974), Carpaneto & Germi (1989a), Chapuis (1966), Charles-Dominique (1977, 1978), Coetzee (1977), Colyn, Dudu & Mankoto Ma Mbaelele (1987), Colyn, Dufour *et al.* (2004), Crawford-Cabral (1989), Eisentraut (1973), Engel (2000), Ewer (1973), Flynn (1996), Flynn & Nedbal (1998), Flynn *et al.* (2005), Gaubert (In press a), Gaubert & Veron (2003), Gaubert, Veron & Tranier (2002), Gaubert, Wozencraft *et al.* (2005), Gregory & Hellman (1939), Hamerton (1941, 1945), Happold (1987), Henschel (2001), Herder *et al.* (2002), Hunt (1974, 1987, 1989), IUCN (2008), Jeffrey (1977), Juste *et al.* (1995), Kingdon (1997), Leyhausen (1965), Malbrant & Maclatchy (1949), McKenna & Bell (1997), Meester *et al.* (1986), Mertens (1925), Morales *et al.* (2005), Naughton-Treves (1998), Ngandjui (1998), Ososky (1998), Perkin (2004, 2005), Peters (1984b), Pimley (1999), Pocock (1915f, 1929), Ray & Sunquist (2001), Rettig & Divers (1978), Rosevear (1974), Schouteden (1945), Simpson (1945), Skinner & Chimimba (2005), Smithers & Lobão (1976), Taylor (1970a, 1971, 1974, 1976), Thompson (1858), Thorneycroft (1958), Todd (1967), Van Rompaey (1997), Van Rompaey & Colyn (In press d), Van Rompaey & Powell (1999), Vosseler (1928), Wemmer (1977), Werneck (1948), Wozencraft (1993, 2005), Wurster & Benirschke (1967), Yoder *et al.* (2003).

CLASS MAMMALIA
ORDER CARNIVORA
SUBORDER FELIFORMIA

Family FELIDAE (CATS)

- Small to quite large mammals with rounded head and rather flat face, facial whiskers, and large eyes and ears; sleek and streamlined body with muscular legs.
- 48·6–399 cm.

- Holarctic, Neotropical, Afrotropical, and Oriental regions.
- From desert through forest to mountain areas, from cold temperate zone to tropics.
- 14 genera, 37 species, at least 228 extant taxa.
- 1 species Critically Endangered, 6 species Endangered, 9 species Vulnerable; 5 subspecies Extinct since 1600.

Systematics

Today at least 37 species of cats are recognized throughout the world (excluding only Australasia and the polar regions), although recent morphological and molecular research suggests that there may be several more. In addition to the 37 listed in the species accounts, domestic cats (*Felis catus*) can be considered distinct from Wildcats (*F. silvestris*); Pantanal Cats (*Leopardus braccatus*) and Pampas Cat (*L. pajeros*) distinct from Colocolos (*L. colocolo*); and *Prionailurus iriomotensis* distinct from *P. bengalensis*. Traditionally cats have been classified in two main groups: the big cats, mostly of the genus *Panthera*, and the smaller cats, with the Cheetah (*Acinonyx jubatus*) left as an odd afterthought, representing a very early divergence from the felid line. This basic classification stood the test of time throughout most of the 20th century, until new techniques and analyses became available. The key characteristic that was used to separate the big cats (Pantherinae) from the smaller cats (Felinae) was the presence of an elastic ligament in the hyoid apparatus below the tongue, which apparently allowed big cats to roar, but not purr. Conversely, the bony hyoid of smaller cats allowed them to purr but not roar. The other key characteristic that allowed for the separation of the Cheetah in its own subfamily, the Acinonychinae, was the absence of cutaneous sheaths to protect the retracted claws. However, recent studies comparing the hyoid structure and the vocal abilities of cats have found that this simple correlation does not hold. While it is true that some big cats roar, e.g. Lion (*Panthera leo*) and Leopard (*Panthera pardus*), not all are able or confirmed able to do so, despite having an elastic hyoid. It was found that the fundamental difference between the mostly roaring, non-purring cats and the rest was the structure of the larynx. Long, fleshy, elasticated vocal folds within the larynx of big cats resonate to produce a roar, whereas the smaller cats, including the Cheetah, have simpler vocal folds that only allow purring.

Although the number of species of cats is fairly well known (with a handful of exceptions), the number of genera that have been recognized is very variable. From a proliferation of genera or subgenera during the 19th century, there was a lumping together into a handful during the middle of the 20th century, followed by a final flourish and re-recognition of many of the 19th century names. At one extreme, only two or three genera have been used to classify all felids. Today there is a growing consensus that as many as 14 can be recognized on the basis of several studies of morphology and genetics. This uncertainty is probably due to the high degree of similarity in basic body plan among all felid species, with the exception of the Cheetah, and a lack of congruence between different sets of characters. The rapid accumulation of molecular data provides greater resolution, but results do not always coincide with more traditional arrangements based on morphology. Perhaps the recent radiation of the cat family as we know it today, coupled with the constraints of prey capture and the processing of a highly carnivorous diet, has resulted in a limited range of variation within the felids. G. B. Corbet and J. E. Hill have suggested that there is a case for reducing the number of genera back to only two or three.

Two major developments towards the end of the 20th century have helped change our view of felid systematics. First, the development of molecular techniques, including the polymerase chain reaction, has allowed the sequencing of mitochondrial genes and nuclear microsatellites, so that differences in the sequences of base pairs of DNA can be elucidated.

*Molecular data suggest that the closest relatives to the **Leopard Cat** are the Fishing Cat and the Flat-headed Cat. These cats probably had a common ancestor less than four million years ago. Some scientists think that another Asian species, the tiny Rusty-spotted Cat, is properly included in the genus* Prionailurus, *but other morphological and molecular studies call this classification into question. It may turn out to be more closely related to the Serval.*

Prionailurus bengalensis
East Siberia.
Photo: Terry Whittaker/FLPA

Second, the advent of personal computers and powerful software has allowed vast datasets of morphological and molecular characters to be analyzed in order to produce dendrograms of relationships between species. By correlating known evolutionary events with divergences between species, it has also been possible to construct phylogenies using the so-called molecular clock, for comparison with the fossil record. In broad outline there is a high degree of agreement between the various morphological and molecular phylogenies, but inevitably some species have been difficult to pin down. Even a study of lipids from the anal sacs of 16 cat species showed a high degree of agreement with more typical phylogenies.

The advent of molecular techniques has helped overcome some of the taxonomic conundrums of the past. For example, on the basis of its highly specialized morphology for cursorial hunting, the Cheetah is often placed in its own subfamily and regarded as representing a very early offshoot of the felid line. Another example is the Caracal (*Caracal caracal*), which is often regarded as a close relative of the Bobcat (*Lynx rufus*) and the Eurasian (*Lynx lynx*), Canada (*Lynx canadensis*), and Iberian Lynxes (*Lynx pardinus*) of the Northern Hemisphere, presumably on the basis of its tufted ears and short tail. However, molecular phylogenies based on a variety of techniques demonstrate that the Cheetah is found within the main felid radiation (the non-pantherine lineage) and is closely related to the Puma (*Puma concolor*). The Caracal is also found to have diverged from the pantherine lineage and is unrelated to the other lynxes. Molecular techniques can also be used on fossils, but may be of limited use in elucidating relationships; a recent study showed that the saber-toothed cat, *Smilodon*, is indeed a cat!

The molecular phylogenies show that there was an early divergence between the small South American cats and the rest of the felids, which has been dated to more than five million years ago using the molecular clock. The Panama land bridge formed about 3–5 million years ago to join South and North America. The molecular (and fossil) data suggest that this lineage diverged and radiated at about this time. This is supported by differences in chromosome numbers between the two groups; the small South American cats of this group have two fewer chromosome pairs than the 38 of Old World cats. Within the New World cats there are two main groups, the first one comprising the Andean Mountain Cat (*Leopardus jacobitus*), Colocolo (*Leopardus colocolo*), Geoffroy's Cat (*Leopardus geoffroyi*), Kodkod (*Leopardus guigna*), Margay (*Leopardus wiedii*), Ocelot (*Leopardus pardalis*), and Oncilla (*Leopardus tigrinus*), and the second one, Jaguarundi (*Puma yagouaroundi*) and Puma. Other recent molecular research has confirmed the close relationship between the Ocelot, the Andean Mountain Cat, and Colocolo.

The main Old World lineage of small cats comprised those species that belong to the genus *Felis* proper, including the Wildcat (*Felis silvestris*), Sand Cat (*Felis margarita*), Jungle Cat (*Felis chaus*), the domestic cat (*Felis catus*), and also probably Pallas's Cat (*Otocolobus manul*). The most recent molecular data suggest that *Felis* proper had a common ancestor only six million years ago. From about 4–6 million years ago, the remaining felid genera split off more or less sequentially on a line that leads to the big cats, which emerged only 3·8–1·9 million years ago. This line is known as the pantherine lineage. Within this lineage, there are interesting groupings, which reflect known morphological similarities, but also some surprising convergences—if the molecular data are correct. The most basal of this lineage is the southern Asian genus *Prionailurus*, which includes the generalized Leopard Cat (*Prionailurus bengalensis*) and also the specialized piscivores, the Fishing Cat (*Prionailurus*

Subdivision of the Felidae

Figure: Toni Llobet

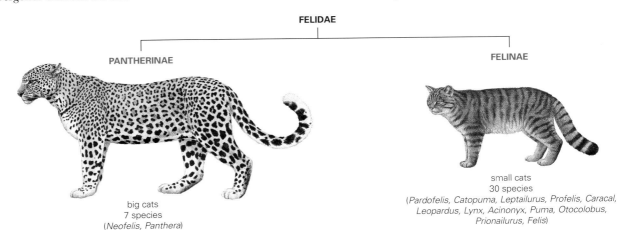

FELIDAE

PANTHERINAE

FELINAE

FAMILY
SUBFAMILY

big cats
7 species
(*Neofelis, Panthera*)

small cats
30 species
(*Pardofelis, Catopuma, Leptailurus, Profelis, Caracal, Leopardus, Lynx, Acinonyx, Puma, Otocolobus, Prionailurus, Felis*)

Body shape does not vary dramatically in cats, which are generally considered to be a morphologically highly uniform family of carnivores. All living cats are remarkably similar in their musculature and bone structure. If the skin is removed, it is a specialist task to distinguish between such externally quite different species as **Lions** and Tigers. An important cause of this uniformity is the relatively young age of the group to which all living cats belong. This subgroup of the family Felidae probably originated no more than seven million years ago. Even at that time, cats were highly adapted and efficient predators, with reduced dentitions and highly specialized skeletons, leaving little room for variation if function was to be maintained in the face of evolutionary pressures. This may be a constraint specific to this group, due to the many compromises that have to be made in such ecologically flexible carnivores as many living cats are. It is not a fundamental constraint in cats, however, as the difference in body shape between living cats and long extinct saber-toothed cats is much greater. Saber-toothed cats also showed a wider range of body shapes than living cats. The skulls of all living cats are very much alike, but small cats have more rounded skulls and more vertical faces than do the big cats in the genus Panthera: the Lion, Tiger, Leopard, and Jaguar. The Lion's massive skull is relatively flat on top.

Panthera leo
Masai Mara National Park, Kenya.
Photo: Gary & Terry Andrewartha/
SAL/www.photolibrary.com

viverrinus) and Flat-headed Cat (*Prionailurus planiceps*). This group is probably one of the most recent felid lineages; molecular data suggest a common ancestor less than four million years ago. The tiny Rusty-spotted Cat (*Prionailurus rubiginosus*) is also included within this lineage by molecular data, although some morphological studies suggest otherwise. The most recent molecular phylogeny suggests that the Rusty-spotted Cat may be closer to the Serval (*Leptailurus serval*) than the prionailurines, but the association is weak.

The Asian Golden Cat (*Catopuma temminckii*) and the Bay Cat (*Catopuma badia*) also form a distinct genus, *Catopuma*, in South-east Asia, but the apparently morphologically similar African Golden Cat (*Profelis aurata*) is closest to the Caracal, which has no close relationship to the lynxes. Also closely associated are the Cheetah, and the Puma and Jaguarundi. Fossil cheetahs (genus *Miracinonyx*) that date back to three million years ago have been found in North America. They are very similar to Pumas and support this relationship, although some palaeontologists regard the similarity between Old World and American cheetahs as an example of convergent evolution. On the basis of the molecular clock, the cheetah/puma group probably diverged from the pantherine lineage more than eight million years ago. As would be expected, the lynxes form a coherent group (genus *Lynx*) that seems to have evolved to exploit the radiation of lagomorphs in the Northern Hemisphere. This is supported by cytological and morphological analyses, there has been some dispute over how many species of lynx there are, but all the most recent studies demonstrate that the Canadian (*Lynx canadensis*), Eurasian (*Lynx lynx*), and Iberian (*Lynx pardinus*) Lynxes are all specifically distinct, as is the Bobcat. The molecular clock suggests a common ancestor dating back some 6·7 million years ago.

The big cats also form a monophyletic group comprising clouded leopards (*Neofelis*), and the remaining big cats (*Panthera*). Molecular data suggest a common ancestor some six million years ago, which at first sight seems discordant with a fossil record that goes back only 2–3 million years. However, clouded leopards represent the earliest divergence from this lineage, and if the common ancestor of this group was also a rainforest inhabitant, it is unlikely that fossils will have survived, owing to poor preservation conditions.

Some cats have been hard to assign using molecular techniques. Pallas's Cat (*Otocolobus manul*) has been included in the *Felis* group on the basis of karyological, albumin genetic distance, and some mitochondrial DNA studies, but the most recent molecular phylogeny does not agree with this. If it is within the *Felis* group, it would make this lineage the most ancient within the Felidae. The Marbled Cat (*Pardofelis marmorata*) has been placed in the *Panthera* group on the basis of karyological, allozyme and albumin genetic distance, morphological (c.f. clouded leopards) and some mitochondrial DNA studies, but again the most recent molecular study shows that it may be closest to the *Prionailurus* group. Clearly more research needs to be done in all fields, not just the molecular side. The recent radiation of the Felidae and their conservative morphology will probably continue to give systematists trouble for some time to come and result in continuing instability in the classification of felid species at the generic level and above.

Recently, an attempt was made to combine carnivore phylogenies from different molecular and morphological studies. In the case of the felids, 38 partial or whole phylogenies were combined. The result is a large data set based on many different characters and approaches. The combined phylogeny for felids still places the Cheetah as a distinct lineage from the other cats, but puts the Marbled Cat back into the Pantherinae, the African Golden Cat into a group with the Asian Golden Cat and Bay Cat, finds the Pallas's Cat and Serval as basal to the *Felis* group, but otherwise places species into the same groups as described above. This exercise demonstrates once more that although there are well-defined groups within the Felidae, their interrelationships are still uncertain.

As mentioned earlier, there may still be some cat species waiting to be recognized. A recent morphological revision of Colocolos proposed that there are three distinct species with eleven subspecies. A recent molecular study suggested that the genetic divergence between these putative subspecies was too small for specific recognition, although this may only indicate recent speciation. The same molecular study suggested that there are two species of Oncilla, one in Central America and the other in south-eastern Brazil. It has been suspected for some time that two or even three species of Oncilla may exist, but samples have been too few to determine this for sure.

The other contentious area concerning felid systematics is subspecies. There is a plethora of subspecies names associated with the cat species, but it must be remembered that in almost all cases, these are not scientific designations, but have been used as handy labels for one or a handful of (often atypical) specimens from a particular geographical location. Putting aside questions of how we define and recognize subspecies, questions that are common to all animals, there is a clear need for taxonomic revisions (based on a variety of studies) of all species to determine whether geographical variation within species is present or not, and if so, whether it is clinal or discrete. Many of the problems of lack of concordance between traditional classifications and molecular studies have arisen because of the misplaced assumption that the traditional classifications have some basis in science. Where revisions have been made, there is a great deal of common ground. For example, there is little support from morphological and molecular studies for the eight subspecies of Tiger (*Panthera tigris*) recognized by most conservationists. Similar agreement has been seen for recent morphological and molecular studies of intraspecific variation in the Jaguar (*Panthera onca*), where again subspecies could not be recognized. However, for other species molecular analyses have been more contentious. The original 24 Leopard (*Panthera pardus*) subspecies were clearly too many, but a combined morphological and molecular study indicated that although there was no support for subspecies in Africa, up to six could be identified in Asia. There were weaknesses in this study: the bulk of samples came from Africa, and almost all the Asian samples were based on captive animals that might be highly inbred and hence not representative of the original variation in populations. A recent molecular study of the Puma (*Puma concolor*) has reduced the 30 subspecies to a more manageable six, but shows that the Florida panther is not a distinctive form. Most of its distinguishing morphological characters (e.g. kinky tail, fur running forward on back) are probably the result of inbreeding.

In recent years there has been a growth in the application of the phylogenetic species concept (PSC) in taxonomic revisions, particularly in ornithology. The PSC defines species on the basis of populations that have at least one diagnosable

A plethora of subspecies names
has been assigned to several cat
species, notably the **Leopard**. In
most cases, these are not scientific
designations, but handy labels
for specimens from a particular
geographical location. There
is a clear need for taxonomic
revisions to determine whether
geographical variation within
species is present. But attempts to
determine subspecies by molecular
analyses have been contentious.
The original 24 Leopard
subspecies were probably too
many. A combined morphological
and molecular study indicated
that while there was no support
for subspecies in Africa, up to
six could be identified in Asia.
However, almost all the Asian
samples were from captive animals
that might have been highly inbred.

Panthera pardus
India.
Photo: Stanley Breeden/
Lochman Transparencies

character. In ornithology this has seen many former subspecies raised to species level. C. P. Groves has recently applied this concept to primates as the only feasible alternative to other species concepts, and this has also resulted in a proliferation of primate species. A recent study on molecular variation in putative Tiger subspecies proposed that the Sumatran Tiger (*Panthera tigris sumatrae*) be recognized as a distinct species from mainland forms, because all specimens had a unique sequence of mitochondrial DNA. However, most if not all the Sumatran Tigers in this study were from captive animals who shared common ancestors, so it is uncertain whether they represent the original genetic variation within the wild population. The fossil record and a biogeographical analysis of Tiger distribution show that Sumatra has been linked to the mainland during glaciations when sea levels fell, so that mainland Tigers have probably colonized Sumatra, perhaps on many occasions, thereby promoting gene flow between populations. Whatever the rights and wrongs of the current situation, it is clear that the PSC could greatly affect our understanding of felid systematics, which could have profound implications for the conservation of felids in future years, especially if the number of species increases significantly.

Morphological Aspects

Cats are generally considered to be a morphologically highly uniform family of carnivores. Indeed, if the skin is removed it is a specialist task to distinguish between such externally quite different species as Lions and Tigers. An important cause of this uniformity is the relatively young age of the group to which all living cats belong. This subgroup of the family Felidae probably originated no more than seven million years ago. In addition, even at that time, cats were highly adapted and efficient predators, with reduced dentitions and highly specialized skeletons, leaving little room for variation if function was to be maintained in the face of evolutionary pressures. In a larger context, however, the Felidae is highly variable in appearance, as one glance at an extinct saber-toothed cat will show. Living cats are simply a subset of this variation.

Cats are probably more variable in size than any other family of mammals. Their size range is more than two orders of magnitude, from about 2–3 kg in the Black-footed Cat (*Felis nigripes*), the Kodkod and the Rusty-spotted Cat to about 300 kg in a large male Tiger. Sexual dimorphism is limited but ubiq-

uitous, with males being about 5–10% larger than females. Cat species with large ranges tend to closely follow Bergman's rule, which states that individuals living near the poles are for physiological reasons on average larger in overall body size than conspecific individuals living near the equator. Thus, species such as the Puma show a distinct size gradient from pole to equator to pole. These gradients can be substantial, with low latitude populations being on average as much as 25% smaller in skull length than high latitude ones, and considerably more so in body weight.

Body shape does not vary dramatically in cats, though some cats are shorter or taller than others. This difference is very noticeable when comparing, e. g. the Cheetah with the lynxes. In general, however, differences between living cats in this respect are slight. This may be a constraint specific to this group, due to the many compromises that have to be made in such ecologically flexible carnivores as many living cats are. It is not a fundamental constraint in cats, however, as the difference in body shape between living cats and saber-toothed cats is much greater. This is true even within the saber-toothed forms, which show a range of body shapes that exceeds that of living cats.

The first thing an observer usually notices about any cat species is the coat pattern. This varies considerably from species to species and also within species. The basic, primitive pattern is one of simple, dark spots on a lighter background. This pattern has been modified in various ways in different lineages. In the domestic cat lineage, it is common to see these spots coalesce into lengthwise stripes in various species. In the South American cat lineage, on the other hand, the spots tend to form swirling patterns, as in the Ocelot. In the lineage leading to the large, pantherine cats, several modifications are in evidence. Some species, such as the Lion (*Panthera leo*), Puma, Caracal, and Jaguarundi (*Puma yagouaroundi*) have lost most of their spots and the adult coat is for the most part a uniform color. However, in juvenile individuals the original spotted pattern can generally be seen in the two former species and rarely in the two latter. In the true large cats, the spots have formed a secondary pattern known as rosettes, in which a number of spots are laid out in a circle that is separated from other such circles. In the Jaguar, there is generally a small spot inside this circle; in the otherwise similar Leopard there is not. The coat patterns of juvenile Lions clearly show that this species also has rosettes. It is possible that the Tiger, which is ostensibly unique in having stripes across rather than along the body, also has rosettes, but that

*In all cats, the hindlimbs are the main propulsors, and cannot be modified for any fundamentally different functions. One feature in which there is some variation in the hindlimb is the degree of "supinatory ability": some cats are more able to roll the ankles of their hindlimbs to the outside than others. This enables the bottoms of the hindpaws to be brought to face inwards for grasping. Some cats are more highly arboreal than others, and in some species, such as the **Margay**, the Indochinese Clouded Leopard, and Diardi's Clouded Leopard, the ankle can be supinated to allow these animals to grasp tree trunks with their hindclaws. The ability to grip a branch equally well with their hind- or forefeet means that Margays can climb down a tree trunk head first, and hang by their hindfeet from a branch. As well as providing an effective gripping surface for climbing, the Margay's broad, soft feet provide a good platform for jumping. Margay and both species of clouded leopard are three of the seven species of cats that are essentially restricted to tropical forest. These tropical forest specialists are among the least known of all felids. For most, even basic information on their biology, distribution, and abundance is lacking. We know that most of them, like the Margay, climb well and are able to exploit the upper levels of the forest. Limited information from the wild supports the notion that Margays do much of their hunting above the ground. Molecular phylogenies show that there was an early divergence between the small South American cats like the Margay and the rest of the felids, which has been dated to more than five million years ago using the molecular clock. The small South American cats have two fewer chromosome pairs than the Old World cats.*

Leopardus wiedii
Tambopata-Candamo Reserved Zone,
Peru.
Photo: Günter Ziesler

The basic function of the coat pattern in cats is clearly that of camouflage, and the differences between species can, in most cases, be explained in terms of habitat differences. **Snow Leopards** inhabit bleak, stony mountains and high deserts in central Asia, where their pale gray or creamy smoke gray upperparts, adorned with darker spots and rosettes, and white underparts, blend into the background. **Lions**, on the other hand, live in open environments, as do the other species that have lost their spots. The coats of adults are generally a uniform sandy or tawny on the upperparts and flanks, and white on the underparts. Differences in coat pattern can make species with essentially similar body shapes, like the Lion and the Tiger, appear very different. Patterns vary considerably not only from species to species, but also within species. The pattern of spots and rosettes on each Snow Leopard, for example, is unique. The basic, primitive felid coat pattern is one of simple, dark spots on a lighter background. This pattern has been modified in various ways in different lineages. Some species, such as the Lion, Puma, Jaguarundi, and Caracal have lost most of their spots, and the adult coat is for the most part a uniform color. However, in juvenile Lions and Pumas the original spotted pattern can generally be seen. Some adult Lions retain the rosettes and spots characteristic of young Lions to a lesser or greater degree, even into their later years. In the true large cats, including both Lions and Snow Leopards, the spots have formed a secondary pattern known as rosettes, in which a number of spots are laid out in a circle, separated from other such circles.

Above: *Panthera uncia*
Altai Mountains, Mongolia.
Photo: Fritz Pölking,/FLPA

Below: *Panthera leo*
Kenya.
Photo: Michael Gore/FLPA

these rosettes are extremely elongated, leading to a striped appearance.

The basic function of the coat pattern is clearly that of camouflage, and the differences between species can in most cases be explained in terms of habitat differences. Cats that live in open environments, for example, tend to have uniform adult coats, and cats that live in closed habitats have stronger coat patterns. This is true also within species. Hence, the Saharan Cheetah has a lighter coat with less distinct spots than its savanna relatives, which live in an environment with more available cover. Some species exist in two color phases, which are especially clear in the Rusty-spotted Cat and the Jaguarundi. These color phases are readily explained by a well known color modifier gene, but their possible ecological or evolutionary basis is not known.

A number of genetic coat color variants are known in low numbers among several cat species. Melanism, in which all coat pigment is darkened, is the most common of these and has been recorded in many species of cats that live in tropical, humid, and densely vegetated habitats. The best known of these melanistic cats are the so-called "black panthers", which are melanistic Leopards (in the Old World) or Jaguars (in the New World). When light shines at a low angle on the coat of a melanistic cat, the underlying coat pattern can be seen clearly. Melanism is due to a recessive gene at the so-called agouti locus for coat color (which controls the development of particolored hairs). The opposite of melanism, leucism, has been observed in a few cats, most conspicuously in Tigers. In such "white" Tigers, the yellow pigment has been modified to white, while the black stripes remain intact, leading to a very striking coat pattern. It is believed that this may be related to true albinism, but there are several genetic pathways by which white coats can be obtained. A famous example of a genetic mutation

for coat color is the so-called "King Cheetah", which was originally described as a separate species, *Acinonyx rex*. The esthetically pleasing, swirling coat pattern of this cat is now known to be due to a single point mutation and both normally-colored and King Cheetahs can occur in the same litter.

The primitive dentition of the order Carnivora consists of three incisors, one canine, four premolars, and three molars in each jaw quadrant. This pattern is highly modified in cats. In the living cats the typical complement is three incisors, one canine, three premolars, and one molar in each quadrant. Lynxes and some other species have only two premolars in each quadrant of the upper jaw. In the most primitive known cat ancestor, the 25 million year old *Proailurus* fossil, the dentition is somewhat more complete, with four premolars and two molars in each quadrant, but the posteriormost molar was lost in evolution before the cat family evolved.

Each subdivision of the dentition has specific functions that have changed very little in cat evolution. The incisors are small and are mainly used for nipping flesh from carcasses. In the extinct saber-toothed cats this function was highly developed and some had powerful, pointed incisors. The incisors of living cats are all blunt and somewhat spatulate in appearance. As in humans, they are generally wider than deep. There is a gradient from the central or first incisor (smallest) to the third incisor, which is closest to the canine. The third incisor is thus the largest of the three, often by a considerable margin. The upper third incisor in some species takes on a slightly canine-like appearance. There is a small gap (diastema) in the tooth row between the third incisor and the canine.

The canine is long, rounded to oval in cross-section, and pointed. Characteristic of the canines of living cats is a lengthwise groove in the enamel, sometimes referred to as the "feline groove", though it is present in some other carnivores as well.

A number of genetic coat color variants are known in low numbers among several cat species. Melanism, in which all coat pigment is darkened, is the most common of these and has been recorded in many species of cats that live in tropical, humid, and densely vegetated habitats. The best known of these melanistic cats are the so-called "black panthers", which are melanistic **Leopards**, in the Old World, or Jaguars, in the New World. When light shines at a low angle on the coat of a melanistic cat, the underlying coat pattern can be seen clearly. Melanistic Leopards are known from several regions of Africa, but there is a much higher frequency of black Leopards from Thailand, Malaysia, and Java.

Panthera pardus
Photo: M. C. Chamberlain/DRK

This groove is present on the labial, or outer surface (closest to the cheek) in all species and also on the lingual, or inner surface (closest to the tongue) in some. It has been suggested that smaller cats kill their prey by searching for and inserting their sensitive canine tips between the neck vertebrae of the prey animal, thereby dislocating the neck and killing the animal. No experimental evidence for this suggestion has as yet been presented, however. Certainly, in many cases the prey is killed simply by using the canines to crush the skull. Larger cats often kill their prey by suffocation, either with a throat bite or a muzzle hold. In either case, the canine is useful for getting a firm grip on the relevant area of the prey. A longer diastema follows between the canine and the first postcanine tooth, which is generally the second premolar.

The premolars of cats are all similar in structure, though the second upper premolar is often a simple, peg-like structure. They have a large, conical central cusp, which is flanked in front and behind by smaller cusps that are also conical in shape. The heights of the cusps relative to the size of the skull and relative to each other varies between species. This variation is presumably related to the specific prey items that each species feeds on, but the details of these differences are not well understood. The overall function of the premolars in cats is also not entirely clear. They probably have some function in holding prey. In species where this has been studied, such as Lions and lynxes, they are often used for crunching up moderately large bones. Unlike hyenas, cats are not specialists in this area, but can nevertheless crack and ingest considerable quantities of bone when the opportunity arises.

The fourth upper premolar has, together with the first lower molar, a specialized function. These are the so-called carnassial teeth, which are the main meat-slicing teeth of the dentition. The two carnassial teeth occlude with each other in a scissor-like fashion, meeting first at the posterior end, with the point of oc-

A famous example of a genetic mutation in coat color is the so-called "King **Cheetah**", which was originally described as a separate species, Acinonyx rex. The esthetically pleasing, swirling coat pattern of this cat is now known to be due to a single point mutation, and both normally-colored and King Cheetahs can occur in the same litter. Distribution of King Cheetahs is restricted to the more densely vegetated areas of southern Africa, centered on Zimbabwe, with an isolated record from West Africa.

Acinonyx jubatus
Photo: Terry Whittaker/FLPA

Tigers are the largest of the living felids, embodying power and grace. Their morphology is specialized for single-handed capture and killing of large prey. The neck is short and thick, and the shoulders and forearms are massive, with long, retractile claws on the broad forepaws. The body is long and lithe and the tail is typically less than half the head-body length. Tigers stand about 1 m high at the shoulder; the hindquarters are slightly lower. There is considerable regional variation in size. On average, adult males from Nepal are 100 kg heavier and females 50 kg heavier than their counterparts in Sumatra.

Panthera tigris
Photo: Gerard Lacz/FLPA

clusion then moving forwards to the front of the lower molar. The upper carnassial retains crushing cusps at its anteriormost end, but the lower carnassial in cats consists almost exclusively of the cutting blade. The lower carnassial is composed of two cusps with a notch (the carnassial notch) between them that keeps the piece of flesh from slipping away while being cut. The upper molar also has a function in this carnassial complex. Occlusion between the upper and lower carnassials must be precise and the upper molar, which is transversely wide but anteroposteriorly short, acts as a mechanism to stop the lower jaw from moving too far back relative to the upper one. A second lower molar is present as an individual anomaly in a number of species of mainly small cats. In the Eurasian Lynx, however, this tooth is more habitually present. In some populations of this species it is present in about 10% of individuals.

The reduced dentition has allowed cats to also reduce the length of the skull (particularly the facial part) and mandibles,

which has the effect of improving the efficiency of the musculature that closes the jaw. Hence, cats have a more powerful bite relative to muscle mass than other carnivores except mustelids, which have a similarly reduced facial part of the skull. In terms of overall skull morphology, cats can be roughly divided into two groups that are correlated with size. The smaller cats have a relatively rounded skull, a more vertical face, and a short muzzle, while the skull of larger cats is more elongated, with a more horizontal face, and a long muzzle. In this respect, the Puma has a skull like that of a small cat, while clouded leopards have a skull like that of a large cat, despite the fact that the former is a larger animal than the latter. Aside from this large cat/small cat split, the skulls of cats are remarkably similar to one another.

The forelimb of cats has a dual function. It is part of the locomotory apparatus, but it also has an important function in prey capture. These two functions are often at odds with each other in the evolutionary process, since a forelimb that

Pumas have proportionally the longest rear legs in the Felidae. The Puma and the Jaguarundi form a separate group from the other small to medium New World cats, and are closely associated with the Cheetah. Fossil Cheetahs very similar to Pumas, dating back three million years, have been found in North America. However, some paleontologists regard the similarity between Old World and American Cheetahs as an example of convergent evolution. On the basis of the molecular clock, the Cheetah/Puma group probably diverged from the pantherine (large cat) lineage more than eight million years ago.

Puma concolor
Photos: Gerard Lacz/FLPA

The lynxes form a coherent group, genus Lynx, which seems to have evolved to exploit the radiation of lagomorphs (rabbits and hares) in the Northern Hemisphere. This is supported by cytological and morphological analyses. There has been some dispute over how many species of lynx there are, but all the most recent studies demonstrate that the **Canadian Lynx**, Eurasian Lynx, and Iberian Lynx are all specifically distinct, as is the Bobcat. The molecular clock suggests a common ancestor dating back to some 6·7 million years ago. The lynx-like Caracal, with its tufted ears and short tail, has been found, using molecular techniques, to be unrelated to the lynxes. The Canadian Lynx is adapted for life in deep snow. Newborns have thick fur, and adults have very large, spreading paws that are furred on the bottom, like those of their primary prey, Snowshoe Hares. The hindlegs are longer than the forelegs, giving the cat a tipped-forward appearance. The lynx's short tail is a result of two morphological modifications: it has fewer vertebrae in its tail than most cats, and each individual vertebra is smaller. Cats such as Leopards and Cheetahs, which have very long tails, use them to counterbalance their body weight when they climb or run. It is not known what the functional basis of very short tails such as the Canadian Lynx's might be. Lynxes have only two premolars in each quadrant of the upper jaw, where most cat species have three.

Lynx canadensis
Photos: Gerard Lacz/FLPA

Lynx pardinus
Doñana National Park, Huelva, Spain.
Photo: Antonio Sabater/Enfoque 10

has optimal running ability cannot also have optimal grasping ability. One key feature that is critical in grasping is supination, the ability to rotate the lower limb outwards along its longitudinal axis so that the bottoms of the paws can be brought together. This requires a considerable degree of mobility at the elbow and wrist. This is, however, at odds with the desire in running animals to maintain a smooth fore-aft motion of the limb, which is best achieved by locking the elbow and wrist joints tightly to avoid any lateral excursions. Since cats are dependent on forelimb grasping they therefore cannot achieve the degree of adaptation to running seen in such carnivores as dogs, which have no forelimb grasping. One feature of cats that in some ways compensates for the grasping problem is the extreme reduction or loss of the clavicle (collar bone). In most mammals, the collar bone forms a brace for the front part of the torso, while in cats the reduction or absence of this bone allows the shoulder blade to swing freely back and forth, forming an extension of the forelimb and thereby increasing stride length. This adaptation is best seen in the Cheetah, while in Leopards the same mechanism differently modified enhances climbing ability.

Differences between cats in the hindlimbs are much less in evidence than in the forelimbs. In all cats, the hindlimbs are the main propulsors and thus cannot be modified for any fundamentally different functions. There are differences in relative limb lengths, with some cats having relatively longer hindlimbs, but when analyzed in detail, these seem mainly to be due to differences in forelimb length. One feature in which there is some variation is the degree of supinatory ability of the hindlimb. Some cats are more able to roll their ankles to the outside than others. As in the case of the forelimb, there is a compromise in the hindlimb between running and grasping. This compromise is less critical than in the case of the forelimb, however, as there is little need for grasping with the hindlimbs. Nevertheless, some cats are more highly arboreal than others, and in some species, such as the Margay and clouded leopards, the ankle can be supinated to allow these animals to grasp tree trunks with their hindclaws while descending head first. This is in complete contrast to the Cheetah, in which the ankle joint is tightly fixed, which is in line with its other running adaptations.

Cats are digitigrade, which means that they stand on their toes and hold their heels and what to us is the sole of the foot off the ground. This stance lengthens the stride by increasing the effective limb length. Cats have five toes on each forefoot but only four on the hindfoot. The first digit of the forefoot (the "thumb") has one joint less that the other digits, just as in humans. In cats it is known as the "dewclaw", and is larger than the other claws, though variably so. In some species, like the Cheetah, the dewclaw is relatively large and has been implicated in prey capture, with the idea that the cat can use it to hook on to the prey, thereby tripping it. In some saber-tooths, the dewclaw was huge, several times as large as the other claws, and may have been used either to secure a firm grip on the prey or for slashing or both. The claws of cats are retractile. In normal situations, e. g. during locomotion, the claw is kept retracted by ligaments. In the retracted position it is protected by a sheath of skin. The second phalanges (the ones articulating with the terminal or claw phalanges) are asymmetric to allow the claw phalanx to pull back to a position beside the second phalanx. When the claws are to be used, the cat spreads its paws and uses special musculature to protract the claws. A cat therefore cannot use its claws without spreading its paw wide. Cheetahs are often said to not have retractile claws. This is only partly true. Claw retraction in Cheetahs is less developed than in other cats, but the claws can, in fact, be retracted to a certain degree. The fleshy sheath protecting the claw is absent in Cheetahs, however, and this creates the appearance that the claw is permanently protracted. Cats have soft footpads to allow for stealthy movement. Again, Cheetahs are an exception. Their pads are hard and ridged, which provides better traction when running across hard terrain.

The spine is supple and flexible in all cats. The articulations between the vertebrae are smooth and rounded and this is one of the factors that allow cats the proverbial ability to always land on their feet. This is accomplished by the cat twisting around its long axis, front end first. The head and upper trunk have already reached landing position while the posterior part of the body is not yet halfway around. If the spine were stiffer or the vertebrae more tightly locked, this twisting motion would not be possible. In Cheetahs the spine is also very flexible in the dorso-ventral direction. This allows the animal to flex its body up and down during running. It has been calculated that the gain in stride length due to this flexibility is more than 10%. This, together with the loss of the clavicle, gives the Cheetah a huge stride length relative to the length of its limbs and is part of the secret to its remarkable running speed.

The tail is of variable length in cats. Some cats, such as Leopards and Cheetahs, have very long tails that serve an important function in counterbalancing the weight of the body when climbing or running. Other cats, such as the lynxes and the Caracal, have short tails (hence the common name "Bobcat" for the North American *Lynx rufus*). The functional basis for this reduction is not known. The shortening of the tail in the latter animals is effectuated by a combination of a reduction in

The forelimb of cats has a dual function: it is part of the locomotory apparatus, and is also used in capturing and grasping prey. A feature critical to grasping is supination, the ability to rotate the lower limb outwards along its longitudinal axis so that the bottoms of the paws can be brought together. This requires considerable mobility at elbow and wrist, which is at odds with the tendency in most running animals to maintain a smooth fore-aft motion of the limb by locking the elbow and wrist joints tightly. In most mammals, the collar bone forms a brace for the front part of the torso. In cats the reduction or absence of this bone allows the shoulder blade to swing freely back and forth, forming an extension of the forelimb and thereby increasing stride length. This is best seen in the **Cheetah**, which is built for speed, with its deep chest, wasp-like waist, and proportionately longer limbs than cats of comparable size. The Cheetah's spine is very flexible in the dorso-ventral direction, which allows the animal to flex its body up and down during running. It has been calculated that the gain in stride length due to this flexibility is more than 10%. This, together with the loss of the clavicle, gives the Cheetah a huge stride length relative to the length of its limbs and is part of the secret to its remarkable running speed. The ankle joint is tightly fixed. Adult Cheetahs have blunt claws that, although retractable, remain exposed, lacking the skin sheaths found in most other felids, providing additional traction like a sprinter's spikes. The digital and metacarpal pads are extremely hard and pointed at the front, an adaptation to sudden braking. Palmar pads with a pair of prominent longitudinal ridges serve as anti-skid devices. The long, laterally flattened tail provides balance as the Cheetah swerves during the chase.

Acinonyx jubatus
Photo: Martin Harvey/DRK

the number of vertebrae in the tail and a decrease in the size of the individual vertebrae. Of these morphological modifications, the latter is the more important by far.

The sense of smell is less important in cats than in other carnivores, as shown by the fact that the areas of the brain concerned with processing smell are smaller in cats than in most other carnivores. Even so, the sense of smell in cats is far more acute than it is in humans. Smell in cats is mainly used for intraspecific communication, rather than for hunting. The muzzle and nose of cats are shorter than in the majority of carnivores. The nose is occupied by two groups of highly folded and wrinkled bones, the maxilloturbinals and the ethmoturbinals. The former lie in an anterior position and are important in cooling and warming of air and the brain, while the latter are covered by the olfactory epithelium, the scent-sensitive tissue. This olfactory epithelium has less surface area in cats than in dogs and hence cats have less tissue with which to detect smell than do dogs.

Another prominent feature of the nose and muzzle of cats is the whiskers or vibrissae. Whiskers in cats occur in three areas: on the sides of the muzzle (mystacial vibrissae), on the cheek (genal vibrissae) and above the eyes (superciliary vibrissae). In most other carnivores whiskers also occur on the chin (interramal vibrissae), but these have been lost in cats. Whiskers are specialized sensory hairs with an important tactile function. This can be clearly seen in walking cats, which extend the mystiacal vibrissae forwards to feel the surroundings. This function is particularly important for cats that hunt at night, and hence the Cheetah, which strictly hunts by day, has less developed whiskers than other cats.

The most prominent feature of the eyes of domestic cats are the pupils, which in strong light can be seen to be vertical and slit-like. The opening and closing of this pupil is carried out by two so-called ciliary muscles, which interlace and draw towards each other. In humans and other animals that have a round pupil, the ciliary muscle is likewise round and constricts to close the pupil. It may be somewhat surprising to learn, however, that not all wild cats have vertical, slit-like pupils. Many species, especially among the larger cats, have round pupils, just like humans do. Exactly why some cats have one or the other is not well understood. Slit-like pupils may confer an advantage to animals that hunt in poor light, as the arrangement of ciliary muscles in them allows for a greater range of pupil size, from extremely large by night to almost entirely closed in bright daylight. A round pupil cannot close completely due to the length of the muscle fibers in the closing musculature. Thus, thanks to the slit-like pupil, cats that hunt in poor light may develop an extremely high sensitivity to light without damaging their eyes should they venture out by day.

Several such adaptations to poor light conditions are known in cats. One way to increase light sensitivity is to increase the size of the pupil itself so as to admit more light. To do this the lens must alter in shape to refract the light more strongly, and the cornea must also be similarly curved to help in this refraction. This causes the part of the eye anterior to the lens to be much larger in cats than in animals that are mostly active by day, such as humans. The light-sensitive area at the back of the eye has two types of receptor cells, called cones and rods. Cones are sensitive to high light levels and are color sensitive, while rods do not detect color and are highly sensitive to low levels of light. Cats, being adapted to low levels of light, primarily have the light sensitive area composed of rods. Some cones are present, but although cats can be trained to see colors, they do not appear to do so in the wild. Another way to increase light sensitivity is to increase the amount of light that reaches the retina. Cats and many other mammals do this with a specialized structure behind the retina called the tapetum lucidum. This structure is strongly reflective and as light is reflected back by the tapetum lucidum it passes the retina a second time, thereby increasing the total amount of light available to the animal. This is the reason cat eyes "glow in the dark". The glow is the light reflected by the tapetum lucidum passing back out of the eye.

Visual acuity varies in cats. Some cats have a relatively broad, rounded area of maximum visual acuity on the retina (the so-called visual streak). Species that hunt by sight, such as the Cheetah, often need to detect prey moving against the horizon, and their visual streak is a narrow line across the retina.

Hearing is an important sense in cats, a fact that manifests itself in both the outer and the inner morphology. They can hear a much wider range of sounds than humans, with the practical range being somewhere between 200 Hz and 65 kHz. The ability to hear very high frequency sounds is especially useful to small cats, as it allows them to detect the ultrasonic (i. e. beyond the hearing range of humans) communication of small rodents, sounds that are of very low intensity. The external ear, or pinna, of cats is large, though generally not as large as in some other carnivores, such as dogs; some cats, however, such as Servals and Sand Cats have very large pinnae. The large pinnae allow cats not only to hear low intensity ultrasounds, but also to detect the sound of small rodents running through the undergrowth. In the skull, the chamber surrounding the ear ossicles, the so-called auditory bulla, is large in cats. This is especially true of desert cats (and, indeed, of other desert animals). It is believed that such a large bulla enhances auditory acuity in the desert situation, where the ambient sound level is much lower than in other biotopes.

Habitat

Felids are found at all altitudes from sea level to 6000 meters, and in all types of habitat from deserts to tropical rainforest. They occur naturally on all continents except Antarctica and Australia. One species, the domestic cat, has been introduced to many remote oceanic islands and Australia. Because cats evolved from a small arboreal forest-living ancestor, it is not surprising that most modern cat species are associated with forest. Closed and open forests and woodlands are home to 89% of cats.

The boreal forest of Canada and the taiga of Eurasia are the least species-rich in cats. At these higher latitudes felid densities are low, both with respect to numbers of species and the density of individual species. Puma and Leopard are found in the southern portions of these zones, but Canadian Lynx and Eurasian Lynx are basically the only felids that have become specialized to exploit northern forest and tundra habitats. Long hindlegs and large, well-furred feet allow them to move across deep snow and pursue prey in conditions where most other cats would flounder. The staple food of the large Eurasian Lynx is small ungulates, but the smaller Canadian Lynx prey almost exclusively on Snowshoe Hares (*Lepus americanus*). Canadian

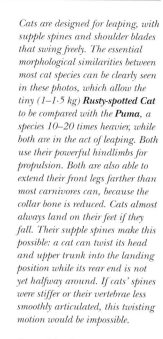

Cats are designed for leaping, with supple spines and shoulder blades that swing freely. The essential morphological similarities between most cat species can be clearly seen in these photos, which allow the tiny (1–1·5 kg) **Rusty-spotted Cat** to be compared with the **Puma**, a species 10–20 times heavier, while both are in the act of leaping. Both use their powerful hindlimbs for propulsion. Both are also able to extend their front legs farther than most carnivores can, because the collar bone is reduced. Cats almost always land on their feet if they fall. Their supple spines make this possible: a cat can twist its head and upper trunk into the landing position while its rear end is not yet halfway around. If cats' spines were stiffer or their vertebrae less smoothly articulated, this twisting motion would be impossible.

Above: *Prionailurus rubiginosus*
Photo: Terry Whittaker/FLPA

Below: *Puma concolor*
Utah, USA.
Photo: Jurgen & Christine Sohns/FLPA

Most cat species are solitary once they reach adulthood. **Lions** *are the only truly social cat species, living in prides, which are groups made up of 4–6 related females and their cubs. Male Lions either live alone, or 2–3 unrelated males (or as many as five who were raised in the same pride) may come together and defend a territory against other males. Males will usually hold a territory, and mating rights within it, for 2–3 years, before losing it to fitter individuals or groups of males. On taking over a pride, a new male will kill any existing cubs.*

Panthera leo
Masai Mara National Park, Kenya.
Photo: Mark Newman/FLPA

Lynx use early successional, fire dependent forest habitats as foraging areas because this is where Snowshoe Hares are most abundant. However, although these habitats have plenty of prey, they do not have the protective cover necessary for the best den sites. When it comes to choosing den sites for kittens Canadian Lynx choose dens facing north to north-east in mature forest, where fallen logs and stumps provide plenty of cover.

Temperate forests are home to a slightly more diverse array of felids. The Bobcat, a more generalized member of the lynx group, occurs throughout much of North America. The Wildcat is found in many of the broad-leafed and mixed woodlands of mainland Europe. In South America, the tiny Kodkod is found only in the southern beech forest and temperate rainforest in Chile and Argentina.

Although as many as seventeen species of felids occur in tropical forest habitats, only seven species of cats are essentially restricted to tropical forest. They include the Marbled Cat, Bay Cat, Asian Golden Cat, Indochinese Clouded Leopard, Diardi's Clouded Leopard, Flat-headed Cat, and Margay. These tropical forest specialists are among the least known of all felids. For most, even basic information on their biology, distribution, and abundance is lacking. We know that most of them climb well and are able to exploit the upper levels of the forest. The little additional information from captive animals and camera-trapping surveys suggests they live at relatively low densities and have small litters; thus they are likely to be more vulnerable to extinction than many other felids.

Deserts and semi-deserts with little vegetation, widely dispersed prey, and no free-standing water would seem to be poor places for felids to live, but several species have adapted to these harsh conditions. The Andean Mountain Cat inhabits the rarified atmosphere between 3000 and 5100 meters on the arid rocky slopes above tree line of the high Andes. Other species, such as the Snow Leopard and Pallas's Cat survive among the bleak stony mountainsides and high deserts of Central Asia. The Sand Cat is found in deserts and semi-deserts throughout the Middle East and arid areas east of the Caspian Sea. These small cats dig their own burrows, where they spend the day resting to avoid the intense heat. The South African Black-footed Cat occurs in deserts and dry grasslands, where it often uses termite mounds and spring hare (*Pedetes* spp.) burrows as daytime rest sites. Sand Cats, Black-footed Cats, Pallas's Cats and several other species that live in deserts can survive without drinking for long periods of time, obtaining all the moisture they need from their prey. Leopards in the Kalahari Gemsbok National Park in South Africa drink when water is available, but are able to survive without it. During one study in which the cats were

followed continuously by tracking their movements in the soft sand, females with cubs did not drink at all in fifteen nights of hunting, during which time they moved 201·4 km.

Savannas and grasslands are inhabited by several felids, among them the Serval, a specialized predator of small mammals. These cats locate their prey primarily by sound, using their large ears. The Cheetahs are found principally in mosaics of grassland and open woodlands where they specialize in stalking and then sprinting after gazelles and other small antelope. Caracal is also strongly associated with savanna and dry open terrain, and their current and former geographic distribution closely mirrors the distribution of the Lion in Africa and Asia.

Habitat in its simplest definition for most carnivores is where the prey are, and for some species this can be almost anywhere. There are several species of cats that seem to be able to survive on almost any type of prey. The Leopard and the Puma are perhaps the best examples of these generalist species, and both have remarkably broad geographic ranges. The Puma's range spans more than 100 degrees of latitude from the Canadian Yukon to the Straits of Magellan and covers just about every biogeographic zone. Puma live in habitats that range from the moist coniferous forest of British Columbia to the deserts of the American south-west, the tropical forests of Central and South America, and south to the cold dry grasslands of Patagonia. Across this broad range of habitats, Puma opportunistically take advantage of the most abundant and vulnerable prey, which can range in size from ground squirrels to Red Deer/Elk (*Cervus elaphus*). Ranging from South Africa to the Russian Far East, Leopards have a similarly broad distribution and occupy a wide range of habitats from desert to tropical forest. While not quite in the same league as the Puma and Leopard, other noted habitat generalists include the Colocolo of South America and the Leopard Cat of Asia.

In areas where two or more felid species live sympatrically, they often manage to coexist by subtle means. In the prey-rich forests of southern India, Leopards prey extensively on medium-size prey and Tigers take the larger prey. Both cats are active at the same time, but Leopards tend to hunt in more open habitats than do Tigers. The dense forests also afford many secure places were Tigers and Leopards can take their kills and avoid encountering each other. In many African parks Leopards are able to avoid confrontations with Lions by taking their kills into trees. Jaguars are the socially dominant cat in Neotropical forests; Pumas tend to use more open areas while Jaguars are closely tied to the interior of forest blocks. Ecological separation among sympatric species is generally favored by

The major period of activity for most cat species is at night. Their movements are related to activities like finding food, and scent marking to indicate to other cats that an area is occupied. **Ocelots** are active for 12–14 hours a day. They typically rest between dawn and late afternoon, choosing sites providing cover, like the tree-fork shown here, or in brush piles or clumps of vines, or under tree roots or fallen trees. They have even been found in concrete culverts. They begin moving an hour or so before sunset, although diurnal activity is not uncommon. In Venezuela, the activity levels of radio-collared Ocelots increased sharply around sunset and remained fairly high throughout the night. Activity levels decreased substantially after sunrise, and the cats usually rested from mid-morning until mid-afternoon. Ocelots were significantly more active during the daytime in the wet season, particularly on cloudy and overcast days. Daytime activity is probably related to the diurnal activity of some prey species such as birds, iguanas, and small primates. Ocelots spend the majority of their active periods walking slowly (0·3–1·4 km/h) about their home ranges. Distances traveled by males during these nightly activities tend to be greater than those of females.

Leopardus pardalis
Central America.
Photo: Alan & Sandy Carey/
www.photolibrary.com

*Unlike most cat species, **Cheetahs** are predominantly diurnal, active during the day when competing nocturnal predators like Lions and Spotted Hyenas are resting. Cheetahs still manage to spend most of the day resting, with hunting peaks between 07:00 h and 10:00 h and 16:00 h and 19:00 h. However, in the absence of larger predators, the Cheetahs of the Saharan mountains often hunt at night when temperatures are cooler. Typically a Cheetah lies on its side to rest, raising its head occasionally. A few clumps of grass can provide enough cover to conceal it almost completely. As can be seen here, the Cheetah's canines are small relative to other felids.*

Acinonyx jubatus
Masai Mara National Park, Kenya.
Photo: Fritz Pölking/FLPA)

structurally complex habitats, which typically support a more abundant and diverse assemblage of prey than do simple environments.

Human modification or degradation of structurally complex forest habitats may have unanticipated consequences for some species of felids. Although direct loss of habitat is a major conservation issue for all felids, it is becoming clear that habitat fragmentation is almost as serious a threat. The effects of habitat fragmentation are generally more subtle, but for interior forest-living species such as clouded leopards, Margay, and Marbled Cat, the effects of habitat fragmentation are severe. Because felids typically occupy large home ranges, travel widely to find food, and disperse long distances, habitat fragmentation can alter home range boundaries, limit social interaction, and modify habitat selection patterns. Fragmentation can also isolate populations by reducing habitat connectivity, lower dispersal success, increase the probability of inbreeding, and ultimately result in local extinction or population declines.

Communication

Generally, mammal sounds are difficult to transcribe in a way that permits another person to get some idea of what the animal actually sounds like. Only rarely can a vocalization be rendered onomatopoetically, because most mammal sounds do not fit into the "sound space" of human speech in any known language, and onomatopoetic renderings for obvious reasons are subjective anyway. No matter what the language, the repertoire of fairly precise colloquial terms for specific mammalian vocalizations is usually small and largely limited to the utterances of domestic species. The domestic cat having been man's close companion for thousands of years, English (like other languages that reflect a long acquaintance with domestic cats) has a relatively well-differentiated vocabulary of specific terms for felid vocalizations, including "purr", "mew", or "meow." Other words, like "roar", "hiss", "spit", "growl", and "snarl", also refer to cat sounds, although less specifically. Like most mammalian vocalizations, felid vocalizations other than these can only be characterized approximately and are often only poorly descriptive.

The use of colloquial terms for specific mammal vocalizations carries a risk: the same term may be applied to different vocalizations, or different terms may be applied to the same

type of vocalization. This practice is equally confusing when dealing with the same or different related or unrelated species.

Felids are among the relatively more vocal mammals and some of their vocalizations, such as the roaring of a Lion, are among the most impressive animal sounds. Nevertheless, under natural conditions in the field chances to hear felids vocalize are relatively low because of the solitary life-style of nearly all species and the secretive habits of most, especially the smaller ones. Knowledge of vocalization in the various species is based to a large extent on observing the behavior of captive animals, because only under these conditions is it possible to register the low intensity calls and sounds that cats use to communicate at close range. For many felid species, knowledge of vocalization

__Tigers__ are found in a great variety of habitat types, including some that are largely wetland, such as the Sundarbans, the mangrove swamps of West Bengal and neighboring Bangladesh. In the outwash areas south of the Himalayas, Tigers inhabit the "terai", a belt of floodplain habitat dominated by marshes, swamps, oxbow lakes, and tall, dense grasslands intermixed with riverine forest. In Russia's Far East, the Amur or Siberian Tiger (Panthera tigris altaica), the subspecies shown here, must cope both with winter temperatures of −34ºC, and with swamps in summer.

Panthera tigris
Photo: Jurgen & Christine Sohns/FLPA

*Feline communication at short range is often "multimodal": signals of more than one kind are applied at the same moment. Vocal signals are usually accompanied by specific visual signals. This is especially true of agonistic encounters. The cats' carriages, postures and expressions, such as the position of the ears and movement of the tail, are likely to be essential components of the communication. This **Snow Leopard** with its ears back, mouth open, teeth showing, and whiskers spread is expressing fury or making a defensive threat. If a fight ensues, the cat will use its forepaws as weapons. If the animal had its ears back and its mouth open, but had not bared its teeth, the emotion would not be as intense, and would probably reflect anger, excitement, or surprise.*

Panthera uncia
Photo: Daniel Cox/
www.photolibrary.com

is very limited, and for a fair number of species absolutely nothing is known. These species can be assumed to share the basic felid vocal repertoire, however. The complete adult repertoire of acoustic signals and their ontogeny is not known for any felid, nor has anyone studied the motivational and functional aspects of vocalizing behavior, sound production mechanisms, or the cause and significance of specific structural characters of the vocalizations.

Like many other mammalian species, felids use auditory signals to communicate at short, medium, and long distance. Communication at short range, and less so at medium range, is often multimodal. That is, signal types of more than one communication channel are applied at the same moment. At short-range, when sender and addressee(s) often can see each other, the acoustic signals are usually accompanied by specific visual signals. This is especially true of agonistic encounters. The cats' postures and expressions—e.g. the position of the ears and carriage or movement of the tail—are highly likely to be an essential component of the communication. In some situations body contact as a tactile signal may be important in addition to an acoustic signal, e.g. in females purring while they suckle their kittens. Chemical signals such as urine, feces, or anal sac secretions function in territorial advertisement, as does the utterance of specific long distance vocalizations, but these are generally not performed simultaneously.

The acoustic signal repertoire of felids comprises vocal (i.e. produced by oscillations of the vocal folds) and non-vocal (i.e. produced in any other way, e.g. by blowing air through the nose) sounds. Most cat sounds belong to the former category. However, studies of sound generation in the larynx and the modification of this sound in the upper respiratory tract (pharynx, oral cavity, nasal cavity) and the adaptive significance of specific structural features of the vocalizations are still in their infancy. The situation is similar for non-vocal sounds. With very few exceptions acoustic signals of the Felidae are produced during exhalation. One of the exceptions is purring, which can be produced continuously during both phases of respiration. Another is a specific call type of the Leopard which is produced during inhalation.

The most likely vocalizations to be heard in free-living individuals of all cat species—apart from hissing and growling or other sounds typical of agonistic behavior—are loud calls that in both sexes are mainly used in territorial advertisement and in attracting a partner for mating. In all species for which

these vocalizations are known, they are specific modifications of the prototypical felid "mew" so well known as the basic vocal utterance of the domestic cat. In some species, such as the Serval, the Caracal, the Marbled Cat, the African Golden Cat, or the clouded leopards the modification of the basic mew/meow pattern is relatively small. Their calls fairly closely resemble mews or meows of a domestic cat, apart from some deviation in pitch, tonality, frequency modulation or other structural character. But in other species, like the Jaguarundi, the Sand Cat, or the Fishing Cat, the relevant calls only distantly remind one of the familiar mew or meow of a domestic cat. The intense calls of Jaguarundi sound like shrill, high-pitched whistles. Sand Cats produce sequences of short calls in rapid succession that rather sound like the barking of a little dog. Fishing Cats also utter sequences of bipartite calls that sound somewhat similar to barking. In many smaller felid species, including medium- to fairly large-sized ones like the clouded leopards, Cheetah, and Puma, sequences of loud calls usually show no regular pattern of intervals between the calls, of duration and relative intensity, or of duration of the sequence. Moreover, other types of vocalizations may be interspersed in these sequences. Some of the smaller cat species, however, like the Sand Cat, Fishing Cat, or the Colocolo and the medium-sized Eurasian Lynx or Asian Golden Cat fairly often produce sequences of intense calls in a relatively regular composition and manner. Of the remaining larger cat species, sequences of intense calls in the Snow Leopard and the Tiger generally follow the usual pattern in smaller and medium-sized cats: they are not usually regular in their composition and structure. Those of the Jaguar, Leopard, and Lion have a species-specific structure with regard to call types and to the average number, temporal pattern of their sequence, and duration of the intervals between them, as well as the average duration of the call sequence and its internal change of intensity. Lions are the only truly social felids, and Lions of the same pride usually join each other when producing the intense calling sequence. Even relatively young cubs may join a "chorus" of their pride with their mews, although with no regular pattern of calling. No other felid species is known in which intense calling of an adult animal is regularly joined by other individuals of the same species. In its typical form the loud calling sequence of Lions starts with a few subdued and temporally fairly spaced calls, followed by calls of longer duration, uttered at an increasingly accelerating pace and steadily increasing volume. Towards the intense climax of the calling

Cats communicate with each other vocally, visually, and especially through scent. This **Caracal** appears to be sharpening its claws, but it is also marking the tree, both visually and with scent from glands between its toes. Most cats go through the ritual of what appears to be claw sharpening on trees, logs, or pieces of furniture. They grip the object with forearms extended and draw the claws backward, either simultaneously or alternately. The action may or may not sharpen the claws, but it probably serves to dislodge loose pieces of claw sheath, deposit scent from the interdigital glands, and leave a conspicuous, permanent mark. Cats have been observed to sniff and rub their cheeks against trees that have been raked in this manner. It is of note that there are also scent glands on the face, around the whiskers, chin, cheek, and lips. The scratching post presumably acts as a visual signal, with added scent marks, but studies of domestic cats suggest there may be a further communication function. Feral domestic cats perform these claw-sharpening routines more often when in the presence of other cats than when they are alone, suggesting it may also be a gesture of visual dominance. Most cats are solitary, and do not meet conspecifics frequently, so leaving a message by depositing scent has advantages. The message is persistent rather than fleeting, and can be read at night or in dense vegetation. Scent serves both to bring cats together, for mating, and to keep them out of each other's territory.

Caracal caracal
Namibia.
Photo: David Hosking/FLPA

Felids are among the more vocal mammals, and some of their vocalizations, such as the roaring of **Lions**, are among the most impressive animal sounds. Under optimal conditions, roaring can be heard up to 5 km away, and may serve to demarcate territory. Lions of the same pride usually join each other in roaring, behavior unknown in any other felid species. Even relatively young cubs may join in with their mews. Lions typically follow a calling sequence that starts with a few relatively soft, spaced calls. The calls steadily increase in frequency, duration, and volume, and then wind down, becoming shorter again, after about 40 seconds. The Lions follow this roaring with a series of grunts. The average sequence consists of 25–30 calls.

Panthera leo
Tanzania.
Photo: Martin Withers/FLPA

sequence, calls become shorter again. After the climax a long series of grunt-like calls follows, with gradually increasing duration of intervals between the calls and slowly decreasing intensity of the grunts towards the end of the sequence. The duration of these grunts remains fairly constant, with the exception of the final grunts, which can be drawn out. An average calling sequence of Lions consists of 25–30 calls and has a duration of about 40 seconds.

This calling sequence of Lions is commonly termed roaring. The comparable sequence of the Leopard has aptly been termed "sawing". It reminds one of the sound of a saw going to

and fro through wood at a relatively high pace because Leopards produce a separate call during each inhalation and exhalation in these call sequences. Leopard sawing is relatively short (usually under 20 seconds), rarely contains more than 15 in- and exhalatory calls each, and for most of its duration has a fairly constant intensity, only decreasing with the last calls of the series. The exhalatory calls usually are more intense than the inhalatory ones. A Jaguar's typical call sequence may also be likened to the sound of sawing wood, but with the saw only moving in one direction, as the call is produced solely during exhalation. Jaguar sawing sequences usually are longer (20–40

In areas where two or more felid species' ranges overlap, they often manage to coexist by subtle means. In Neotropical forests, Pumas tend to use more open areas, while **Jaguars** are closely tied to the interior of forest blocks. Jaguars are found in a variety of forested habitats, from lowland tropical moist forests to humid montane and cloud forests, up to about 2000 m. They avoid open forest and grassland habitats, but commonly found along the edges of forest openings. Jaguars are often found in association with rivers, lakes, and well-watered areas such as the swampy grasslands of the Brazilian Pantanal. They are excellent swimmers and have been seen crossing large rivers. Like Tigers, during the hot season, Jaguars may spend the heat of the day half submerged in a stream.

Panthera onca
Belize.
Photo: Lynn Stone/naturepl.com

The Canadian Lynx and the **Eurasian Lynx** are the only felids specialized to exploit northern forest and tundra habitats. Long hindlegs and large, well-furred feet allow them to move across deep snow, and pursue prey in conditions where most other cats would flounder. In Europe and Siberia, they are found in deciduous, mixed, and coniferous forests, and in tundra. In Central Asia, their habitat includes fairly open and sparsely wooded regions, including semi-deserts, while throughout the northern slopes of the Himalayas, they are found in thick scrub woodland and barren, rocky areas. Range size depends on the productivity of the habitat. In central and western Europe, males roam over 100–450 km², whereas in Scandinavia a male's range may be up to 2200 km².

Lynx lynx
Photo: Rolf Bender/FLPA

seconds) and with a faster repetition rate of the single calls than Leopard sawing and can consist of more than 60 single calls. As in Leopard sawing that of the Jaguar is produced at a fairly steady intensity, which only gradually drops at the end of the series. The single calls in Jaguar sawing last about 0·2–0·25 seconds and are separated from each other by intervals of approximately 0·1 second duration. In Leopard sawing in- and exhalatory calls each are about 0·3–0·4 seconds long, the inhalatory ones usually being shorter. Intervals from one exhalatory call to the next can have a duration of 0·3–0·5 seconds but in this pause the inhalatory sounds are produced.

The loud calls in the intense portion of the Lion roaring sequence are 1–1·5 seconds long. The grunts in its later course last for 0·3–0·5 seconds and are uttered at intervals of 0·5–0·7 seconds. The calls produced during exhalation in the sawing of Leopards and Jaguars are equivalent to the grunts forming the second portion of the Lion's roar. No felid other than these three is known to perform this type of grunt call. Occasionally Leopards and Jaguars utter calls of variable intensity prior to their sawing sequences, which are equivalent to the calls forming the first portion of Lion roaring, but the Leopards and Jaguars never produce calls in a regular temporal and intensity pattern as does the Lion.

All felid species can utter a series of loud calls while they are standing, lying, or walking. Only Jaguars, Leopards, and Lions usually stand still, with their fore- and hindfeet each in line and with a fully extended neck and horizontally held head, when they are intensely sawing or roaing. Leopards and Jaguars, but not Lions, may stand with the head slightly lowered. When Lions roar or Jaguars saw while they are lying down, the neck is also fully straightened and the head is usually lifted slightly. Leopards hardly ever produce their intensive sawing call sequence while they are lying down. In all three species the contraction of the thoracic and abdominal musculature in producing each single call is conspicuous; this is especially striking in Jaguars with a very fast call repetition rate. Most other vocalization types of the Felidae are produced without any apparent respiratory effort.

Mew-like calls of lower intensity in the larger cat species can vary in tonality and pitch over a wide range. Some of them are astonishingly high in pitch compared to the species' size. As a rule of thumb, pitch of vocalizations in vertebrates is negatively correlated with body size, the bigger individuals having lower-pitched calls than the smaller. The same usually holds true when comparing the calls of related species of different size, but in felid vocal communication some obvious exceptions are known. Pumas and Cheetahs have a remarkable variant of the basic mew, a high-pitched whistling call, whereas some of the smaller species, e.g. the Black-footed Cat and Pallas's Cat have mew-like calls that are strikingly low-pitched for their size. The only other cat species known to produce a high-pitched whistling call like the Puma and Cheetah is the Jaguarundi. Its whistle has the highest pitch of any known cat vocalization. Even in felids whose lower intensity mew calls somewhat resemble the equivalent vocalizations of the domestic cat, the character of these calls is very diverse and can vary considerably within the same species. Intraspecific variation of mews is mainly manifest in call characteristics like intensity, duration, pitch, or tonality. Mews of some species have a peculiar quality. For example, Geoffroy's Cat usually produces a somewhat "wavery" bleating sound, and those of the Jungle Cat and Pallas's Cat have a particularly hollow sound.

All felid species have a short, soft, low-intensity, predominantly atonal sound used at close distance for friendly greeting, reassurance, or appeasement. Three of these sound types—the gurgle, prusten, and puffing—are known in the Felidae. Each cat species has just one of them in its repertoire. Puffing, which sounds like a short bout of stifled sneezing, is only known to occur in Leopards and Lions. Five species perform prusten: the Indochinese Clouded Leopard, Diardi's Clouded Leopard, Snow Leopard, Tiger, and Jaguar. Prusten sounds something like the snorting of a horse and differs among the species, e.g. the clouded leopards prusten is much more guttural in character than the prusten of Jaguars, which sounds more like nasally snuffling. Despite the differences in sound the common basic structural pattern of prusten reveals that it is the same vocalization type in the four species. The gurgle is functionally equivalent to puffing and prusten, and likely to be present in all felid species except the six mentioned above. Its character can vary from a form somewhat reminiscent of the sound of bubbling water to forms that have been termed "short purr" because of their similarity in sound to a short stretch of purring. They are less confusingly likened to the staccato element in the cooing of pigeons, because felid purring and gurgling are different types of vocalization. Most cat species seem to perform only one type of gurgle but there are felids whose gurgles sound somewhat intermediate between the cooing and bubbling type. Some species are able to produce gurgles of intermediate character, between the cooing (e.g. African Golden Cat) or the bubbling form (e.g. Flat-headed Cat). The extent of intraspecific variability of the gurgle is not yet known. The gurgle variant a species produces is not correlated with its size, e.g. a Puma gurgle is of the cooing variant like that of a domestic cat and its wild ancestor, the Wildcat, whereas a Cheetah gurgle is of the bubbling type like that of a Geoffroy's Cat. Gurgles of juveniles comply with the form present in adults of the same species. The Cheetah's gurgle has also been aptly termed "stutter" because the rapid sequence of sound pulses in it reminds one of stuttering. Other species with a cooing gurgle are Caracal, Jaguarundi, Serval, Marbled Cat, and Sand Cat; the Colocolo, Asian Golden Cat, Rusty-spotted Cat, and Fishing Cat, among others, have a bubbling gurgle. The Leopard Cat, African Golden Cat, and Flat-headed Cat produce gurgles intermediate in sound between the bubbling and cooing type. African Golden Cats can also produce cooing type gurgles, and Flat-headed Cats can make bubbling gurgles. Because the gurgle is a relatively rarely observable vocalization type, its full range of inter- and intraspecific variability is not yet fully understood. Generally, gurgles can be coupled with mews, forming a coherent vocalization with a short transitional portion of intermediate character. The sequence of the two different sound types in these combined vocalizations is arbitrary. Prusten is sometimes also performed directly coupled to a mew, most often following it; puffing cannot be combined with mewing or any other vocalization type.

The repertoire of agonistic vocalizations in the Felidae is fairly uniform throughout the whole family. All cats hiss, spit, growl, and snarl, although growls and snarls may differ considerably between species, and not only because of differences in size of the animals. In general, vocalizations of felids during agonistic interactions have not yet been studied in sufficient detail to make precise comparative statements as to their structural characteristics. However, some agonistic types of vocalizations seem to be peculiar only to certain species, like domestic cat and other *Felis* males yowling at each other.

A specific felid vocalization that is little known but worth mentioning is the wah-wah sound. The term is onomatopoetic. This sound type is only audible at close distance, its utterance sometimes being accompanied by flicking movements of the ears. It is only present in some cat species; e.g. the Puma, the Jaguarundi, the Caracal, and the African and Asian Golden Cats, and might easily go unnoticed by an untrained observer. In all species it occurs in situations in which two or more individuals approach each other or move past each other. The utterance of this vocalization seems to indicate uneasiness or slight disturbance of the sender. The addressees of the sound signal hardly ever show an observable reaction to the wah-wah, calling into question the communication function of the call. Sounds functionally equivalent to wah-wah are not known in other felid species that do not have this sound type. Another felid vocalization restricted to a few species is the grunt. Grunts are the main components of the sawing call sequences of the Leopard and Jaguar, form the second portion of the Lion's roaring sequence, and are not known in any other felid species.

In all felids copulation is accompanied by vocalizations, usually in both sexes. Some vocalizations uttered by males and females are different, others are shared. Vocalizations such as growling, hissing, and spitting uttered especially by felid females towards the end of copulation—and after it often by males, too—are known from other behavioral contexts. There are a few vocalizations specific to the mating situation. These include a peculiar loud and drawn-out cry known in males of some species, e.g. Tigers and Snow Leopards, which is likely to indicate orgasm. Males of some other felid species have equivalent vocalizations. A specific female vocalization during copulation is produced by Pumas, who start to utter a drawn-out screaming mew at about the moment the male inserts the penis. Similar vocalizations are known in females of other cat species. Such specific vocalizations of each sex during copulation are among the very few vocalization types in which the acoustic signal repertoires of males and females of the Felidae differ; most vocalization types are shared by both sexes. Pumas have other special vocalization types. During estrus the females utter either a series of predominantly loud calls belonging to the mew continuum (a call type shared with Puma males) or a vocalization comprising a nearly continuous utterance of variable intensity and duration. In it mewing and purring are produced alternately and may be mixed at times, with a variable relative contribution of either in the mixed portions. This call combination is not known in Puma males. It is very likely that structural characteristics (e.g. frequency range, pitch, temporal parameters) of some vocalization types that are present in both males and females differ between the sexes, but such differences have not been studied in detail. A specific acoustic alarm and an all-clear signal have been mentioned in the literature about the Black-footed Cat, and other cat species may have equivalent vocalizations. Most vocalizations produced by juvenile and

Ranging from South Africa to the Russian Far East, **Leopards** *occupy a wide range of habitats, from desert to tropical forest. In sub-Saharan Africa, Leopards are found in all habitats that have an annual rainfall above 50 mm, including savannas, acacia grasslands, evergreen and deciduous forests, and scrub woodlands. They are also found in true deserts, but only near river courses, although studies in the Kalahari have shown that Leopards can survive without drinking for as long as ten days. In other hot, dry deserts such as the Namib, Sahara, Sinai, and Arabian, Leopards use caves, burrows, or the shade of dense vegetation to survive daytime temperatures that may reach 70°C.*

Panthera pardus
Masai Mara National Park, Kenya.
Photo: Mark Newman/FLPA

*Deserts and semi-deserts with little vegetation, widely dispersed prey, and no free-standing water, would seem to be poor places for cats to live, but several species have adapted to these harsh conditions. **Snow Leopards** survive among the bleak stony mountainsides and high deserts of Central Asia, where the terrain is broken by steep cliffs, ridges, and ravines. They are also found in alpine meadows, alpine steppe scrub, and high altitude forests. They generally spend the summer above tree line at elevations of 2700–6000 m, but in winter, deep snow often forces prey species like wild sheep and goats to move to lower slopes, and the Snow Leopards follow. The cats have also been found in isolated mountain massifs in Mongolia, which they could only have reached by crossing 20–65 km of flat, open terrain.*

Panthera uncia
Photo: Gerard Lacz/FLPA

adult felids are within the frequency range audible by humans (approx. 20–16·000 Hz), although cats can hear much higher frequencies than are present in their own acoustic signals. With very few exceptions, felid vocalizations are restricted to the frequency range from about 50 Hz to 10,000 Hz, usually only a portion of this range. Ultrasonic and infrasonic components have been reported in acoustic signals of a few species; these still require detailed study.

A rough estimate of the acoustic signal repertoire of the Felidae, that is, the number of different sound types known, would be about twenty, but any given cat species probably has no more than about fifteen different types. As such estimates are based on the classification criteria applied by the human student—and these are likely to differ among different students—they can hardly be an appropriate measure of the communication potential for members of a given cat species. The situation is further complicated by the fact that acoustic signals of felids, like those of many other mammals, can be either discrete or graded. The structural variability of sound types belonging to the same graded system is high and the "pure types" are connected by a continuum of transitional sounds. The variability of discrete sound types is relatively limited and transitional forms with other types are not known for them. Examples of discrete felid vocalization types are spitting and hissing; mews and the gurgle form a graded system. The existence of graded systems makes it particularly difficult for a human student to classify vocalization types the way a conspecific receiver differentiates them, or to pinpoint their communicatory function. There are relatively few "broad" functional contexts in which felids use vocal signals. These include agonistic behavior, mother-young interaction, friendly close contact, and sexual and territorial behaviors. Different vocalization types can occur within the same functional context and the same vocalization type can occur in different functional contexts. There is no doubt, however, that in any given behavioral situation the vocal signal used is highly specific. Even if it is of a general type, subtle structural variations, e.g. in pitch, tonality, frequency modulation, abruptness of onset, and perhaps concomitant other signals, may be decisive for its communicatory function.

As with most mammals, relatively little is known about the juvenile acoustic signal repertoire, as compared with that of

adults, and the specific structural characters of the signals and their function and the changes as the juveniles mature. Limited data are available for the *Panthera* species, the Puma, and a few small cat species. A major portion of the acoustic signal repertoire is already present during the first days of life. Kittens of the smaller and cubs of the larger cat species can already hiss and spit shortly after birth. The spit is impressive for animals of such a small size. Meows used to keep contact at close range, and intense meows uttered as distress calls, are present at a very early age. Purring is also present during the first days of life. Major changes in the structure of vocalizations during ontogeny are a drop in pitch and frequency range, but other structural characters can also be affected. Prusten vocalizations are produced by young juveniles in the four felid species that have this vocalization type, but sound production seems to change to some degree during ontogeny. Purring is exceptional in that it hardly undergoes any change in structure during ontogeny. Some vocalization types like the "sawing" sequences of Leopards and Jaguars and the roaring of Lions, as well as the call types composing these call sequences, are not developed before the animals have become fully adult. The same is true for the specific vocalization types of females and males occurring during copulation. The only vocalization type of juvenile felids that seems to be lost as the cats mature is the intense distress call; older individuals utter other vocalization types in equivalent functional contexts.

The daily routine of a domestic dog urine-marking a car tire or a housecat cheek-rubbing on the leg of a chair are commonly-seen demonstrations of the use of scent in the daily lives of the Carnivora. Olfactory communication play a fundamental role in governing the social lives of carnivores, but while some aspects of scent production are well known and the behaviors associated with scent deposition are frequently observed, relatively little is known about the actual information being transmitted and how the scent marks function. Compared with canids and hyaenids little is known about scent marking among felids, probably because most wild cats are much more difficult to observe.

Cats are believed to have a relatively poor sense of smell compared with other carnivores, but they rely heavily on scent marks to communicate with conspecifics. For solitary-living animals such as felids, which encounter one another infrequently,

The range of the **Puma** spans more than 100 degrees of latitude from the Canadian Yukon to the Straits of Magellan, and covers just about every biogeographic zone. Pumas live in habitats that range from the moist coniferous forest of British Columbia to the deserts of the American south-west, the tropical forests of Central and South America, and the cold, dry grasslands of Patagonia. They can be found from sea level up to more than 4000 m, suggesting a tolerance of environmental conditions that is rare among mammals. Wherever they are found, they require cover for stalking and ambush hunting, secure places to establish natal dens, and at least one species of abundant deer-sized prey. Annual home range size varies from 50 km^2 to more than 1000 km^2 and appears to be related to primary productivity and prey abundance. Habitat use can be highly seasonal, for example where prey species, such as Elk, migrate altitudinally in response to snowfall. In subtropical areas, Pumas' home ranges, like those of their prey, are smaller and more stable. Pumas are increasingly found in landscape patches that have been fragmented by expanding human activity and infrastructure, such as roads, ranches, settlements, and mines. Remnant landscape connections and restored habitat corridors are needed to provide links between individuals and populations.

Puma concolor
N Arizona, USA.
Photo: Daniel Cox/
www.photolibrary.com

*Despite its name, there are few records of the **Jungle Cat** from dense jungle. This adaptable species prefers tall grass, thick bush, riverine swamps, and reed beds, and its association with wetlands has given rise to its alternative and perhaps more appropriate names, Swamp Cat and Reed Cat. However, the Jungle Cat also survives in drier, open forests, and even sandhill desert and steppe habitats, particularly in the vicinity of rivers or oases. It adapts well to irrigated agricultural landscapes, and is sometimes found in association with man-made fishponds and reservoirs. Jungle Cat den sites include holes and burrows made by other species.*

Felis chaus
Photo: David Hosking/FLPA

of avoiding direct contact. In group-living cats, colonies may share a common odor that identifies them as being part of a particular group. Exactly what message is conveyed in a scent mark remains a mystery, but the marks are thought to transmit information on individual identity, sex, status, reproductive state, and the time the mark was made. Individuals probably use urine marks to check on the whereabouts of others. In social interactions, scent marks likely confer an advantage on the animal leaving the mark. There are no specific odors or chemicals that are known to convey status or dominance, but dominant animals typically mark more often or deposit more scent. Among canids, higher rates of scent marking by dominant individuals are well documented. In several species of cats such as Leopards and Black-footed Cats non-breeders or individuals without home ranges rarely scent-mark.

The chemical odors used in scent marks are found in the cat's saliva, urine, and feces, and in secretions produced from a variety of scent glands on the body. On the face, sebaceous glands around the whiskers, cheek, chin, and lips produce and disperse scent. The typical feline greeting involves a chin rub or a bump with the forehead, and cats commonly rub their head, cheeks, neck, and body on objects and sometimes other cats, leaving and collecting traces of scent. For a cat, saliva is a powerful source of information. Laboratory studies have shown that a male domestic cat can tell the difference between the saliva and cheek rubbings of a female in heat and one that is not. Chemical secretions are also produced by the anal glands (a pair of sac-like glands opening into the rectum), the supracaudal gland above the base of the tail, and interdigital glands between the toes.

Very little is known about the chemistry of social odors in carnivores in general or cats in particular. Many compounds have been isolated and identified but individual chemicals have not yet been clearly associated with function. The task of assigning function to a particular chemical is complicated by the fact that many social odors are a complex chemical mixture, which may differ between individuals. An analysis of the anaerobic bacteria in the anal sacs of Red Foxes found that different foxes sometimes harbored identical strains, but the same fox also sometimes yielded different organisms.

Both urine and feces are also used as scent marks. Urination can be performed either in a squatting position or while standing, and spray urination—backward urination against objects—is believed to have evolved specifically as a scent mark-

scent marks have many advantages over vocal and visual communication. Olfactory communication can be used at night, or in dense cover, when other forms of communication are difficult to detect. Scent is also persistent in the environment. Chemical signals have the advantage of being able to convey information for days and even weeks after being deposited.

Most felids are nocturnal, solitary, and live in closed habitats; even when they occur at fairly high densities, individuals rarely see each other. But though they generally travel and hunt alone, cats live within a social system that depends on signals to regulate and order interactions. In some situations, these signals may operate to bring animals together; in others they serve to separate individuals. Scent marks can function to bring the sexes together for mating, they may identify an individual, indicate an area is occupied, or they may be a means

*Lions** have a wide habitat tolerance. Optimal habitat appears to be open woodlands and thick bush, scrub, and grass complexes, providing an ample supply of medium to large prey, some shade for resting in the heat of the day, and the barest of cover to facilitate stalking. They will penetrate deep into the desert, especially along avenues of watercourses, and are common in semi-desert areas. They will drink when water is available, but are not dependent on it, getting their moisture requirements from their prey, and even from plants such as the tsamma melon, which is used as a water source by both humans and wildlife in the Kalahari Desert. Lions survived in the central Saharan desert on the edge of the Air Mountains until about 60 years ago.*

Panthera leo
Kalahari Gemsbok National Park,
South Africa.
Photo: Philip Perry/FLPA

As befits a cat with a very broad geographic range, the **Leopard** *is a generalist, able to survive on almost any kind of prey. Leopards can and do kill large mammals, but much of their diet consists of small prey weighing 2–40 kg. More than 92 species have been recorded in their diets in Africa south of the Sahara. Leopards locate their prey primarily by sight and sound. Having detected an animal, the Leopard will stalk it, preferring to get as close as possible before launching an attack. Alternatively, it will lie in ambush. Leopards drink when water is available, but if necessary, they can sustain themselves for long periods of time on the moisture derived from their food.*

Panthera pardus
Okonjima, Namibia.
Photo: David Hosking/FLPA

ing behavior. During spray urination the urine is spread over a large area, it can be directed at particular objects, and it is deposited at nose level. Chemical signaling with urine and feces usually involves a token deposit, a small amount left at prominent places along travel routes.

A cat's home range is usually too large to be continuously defended by the animal's presence alone, and the most common way of indicating that an area is occupied is by leaving scent marks—usually in the form of urine marks—throughout the range. These marks are continually updated to inform intruders and neighbors that the occupant of the area is still around and was there just yesterday or a few days ago. Scent marks are not distributed at random but strategically placed so that they can be easily found, and usually left at nose level so they can be conveniently investigated. As a cat travels the pathways of its home range, it stops periodically and sprays urine onto bushes, rocks, and tree trunks. Feces are often left on conspicuous or elevated sites. A study of the Iberian Lynx showed that the cats were more likely to leave their feces at trail intersections, a pattern of distribution that maximized the chances of another lynx encountering the mark. Bobcats defecate along trails and on top of elevated objects. Resident male Cheetahs urine mark and deposit feces on prominent landmarks such as solitary trees, rocks, and termite mounds. They frequently revisit and remark the same places. Non-territorial male Cheetahs, on the other hand, urinate and defecate far less frequently than resident males, and do not seek out conspicuous landscape features on which to deposit their marks.

Scent marks were originally thought to create a barrier to intruders, but more recently it has been noted that transients do travel through other animals' home ranges, and residents sometimes make excursions outside their home ranges and trespass on neighbors. There are no direct observations of this sort for felids, but other carnivores such as Brown Hyenas, Coyotes, and Red Foxes often cease to scent-mark during these excursions, suggesting they know they are off their property. The most convincing explanation of the function of scent marking is that territory holders scent-mark to provide intruders with a means of assessment. Territory holders have a great deal at stake, and thus more to lose, which means they will be more likely to fight in an encounter with an intruder. Fights can end with injury or death and should be avoided. When an intruder meets an animal whose scent matches the scent marks deposited around the territory, it knows it has met the territory holder. To avoid a fight, the intruder should withdraw.

It is difficult to quantify scent marking behavior in wild situations and most information comes from cats that occupy open habitats. However, the general impression is that male felids spray urine more often than females. In a study in Nepal, male Tigers sprayed at a slightly higher rate (2·4 per km) than females, who left 1·8 spray marks per km. In Tanzania, a male Serval was seen to spray mark 46 times an hour, compared with a female, who sprayed 20 times an hour. In South Africa a Black-footed Cat scent-marked an estimated 10–12 times per hour. One male was seen to spray mark 580 times in a single night prior to mating—an astonishing feat for an animal that lives in an environment with little or no free standing water. Scent marks convey information on reproductive status, and rates of scent marking may also change depending on the animal's reproductive state. One study of free ranging domestic cats reported that non-breeding males averaged 12·9 urine sprays per hour of travel while breeding males averaged 22 sprays per hour.

After sniffing a urine mark a cat will often give an open-mouthed grimace known as flehmen. When a cat flehms it raises its upper lip, then moves the tongue rhythmically along the roof of the mouth with the head raised. *Panthera* cats open their mouth and wrinkle their upper lip, drawing the lip up in a very obvious grimace. Head shaking sometimes occurs between bouts of sniffing. Cats will flehm after sniffing urine, the anogenital region of another cat, or almost any novel odor. When flehming the cat uses its tongue to draw the scent molecules over the vomeronasal organ, which is located in the roof of the mouth. The organ is visible as two tiny holes on a slightly raised area directly behind the front teeth and can be clearly seen in the domestic cat. The organ detects the presence of sex hormones in the urine. Both sexes flehm, but males do so at a higher rate than females.

Changes in levels of urinary estrogen are an accurate indication of changes in female receptivity, and urine marks and their changing estrogen levels are easily monitored by males. Females scent-mark at an increased rate beginning about two weeks before the onset of estrus. For wide ranging species like Tigers, Snow Leopards, and Black-footed Cats, this probably ensures that a male will locate the female and be present when she is most receptive. In one South African field study, a female Black-footed Cat ceased scent marking after she gave birth and was not seen to mark while her kittens were small. When the kittens became mobile she began scent marking again. Higher rates of scent marking are also associated with territorial behav-

Though most cats are opportunistic hunters, a few are specialists in capturing particular types of prey. The **Serval** is a small mammal specialist, using its large, dish-like ears to locate small prey in tall grass. Over 90% its diet consists of prey weighing less than 200 g, and most weighs less than 2% of the 20 kg cat's body weight. Mice and rats dominate the diet, but Servals also take small birds, snakes, frogs, and insects. They will occasionally kill larger prey such as flamingos, hares, and young antelope. Servals have an almost fox-like hunting style. Their long legs provide the large ears with a raised platform to "hear into" the tall grass. When hunting, the cat walks slowly, stopping periodically to listen. It may sit for 15 minutes at a time, scanning the area for sounds. When it hears something move it locates the exact position of the sound, then pounces like a fox, leaping into the air and striking the prey with a blow from one or both feet. A single pounce may span 3·6 m and may be over 1 m high. If the initial pounce is not successful, it may be followed with a series of stiff-legged bouncing jumps. Servals also use the high bouncing pounce to flush small prey from the vegetation. They gallop through the grass in a zig-zag pattern, leaping high into the air. Anything that runs is caught immediately. Servals have been seen leaping 2–3 m into the air to seize birds and insects in flight. They also probe holes and crevices for nestling birds and rodents, their long mobile toes and strong curved claws serving to hook prey from burrows or beneath vegetation. They can also hook live fish out of water. Strong winds disrupt the Serval's ability to pinpoint the location of prey. Unless they are extremely hungry, these cats rarely bother to hunt in windy weather.

Leptailurus serval
Photos: Martin Harvey/DRK

Solitary, nocturnal, and more strongly associated with forest habitats than any other Neotropical cat, **Margays** exploit the forest canopy for their prey. Their diet consists mainly of nocturnal, arboreal mammals, including opossums, squirrels, and climbing rats. They also take birds, such as tinamous and guans, and amphibians, reptiles, insects, and fruit. Although Margays are supremely adapted to arboreal life, able to dash down tree trunks head first and hang from branches by their hindpaws, they are known to prey on terrestrial mammals such as spiny pocket mice, cane mice, cavy, rabbits, agouti, and paca.

Leopardus wiedii
Photo: Terry Whittaker/FLPA

ior. Tigers mark more often along boundaries with neighbors than in the center of their ranges. They also scent-mark more intensively when establishing a territory.

Scent marks are made up of a complex mixture of chemicals, each of which evaporates at different rates. Scent marks that function in short-term signaling, such as alarm signals, are highly volatile and do not remain at detectable levels for long. On the other hand, compounds that serve a long-term function, such as territorial marking, have low volatility and persist for a long time. It therefore comes as no surprise that cats can distinguish between old and new scent marks. It is not known exactly how long scent remains effective as a communication device; even old marks probably still carry a message. There

are several pieces of behavioral evidence that suggest scent marks are effective for three or four weeks. It has been shown experimentally that for Gray Wolves the stimulus value of scent drops to zero after about 23 days. This also happens to be the interval at which a Wolf pack visits most parts of its territory. Leopards and Tigers showed a similar time interval between revisiting sites to scent mark. New Leopard scrapes appeared at two closely monitored sites at intervals of 25 and 21 days, and in situations where resident Tigers died or disappeared, their vacant ranges were filled within three or four weeks. All the information suggests that resident animals must revisit most parts of their home range every two to three weeks to renew scent marks that likely indicate that the area is occupied.

Hunting **Wildcats** move slowly and quietly along trails and paths, looking and listening. Once prey is detected, the Wildcat creeps forward, using every piece of cover to get as close as possible before making its attack. Prey is seized with the claws and pinned to the ground, or held with the paws until the killing bite is delivered. Wildcats may also wait in ambush outside burrows. The dominant prey species vary throughout the Wildcat's enormous range, but generally consist of small mammals, chiefly rodents (though rabbits and hares in Scotland), followed in importance by birds, including poultry. They also take reptiles, insects, and other small creatures when available. Spiders are a significant food item in the semi-deserts of Botswana.

Felis silvestris
Photo: Michael Callan/FLPA

Caracals generally take prey that weigh less than 5 kg, including hares, hyraxes, small rodents, and birds. They will, however, take larger (over 15 kg) prey like antelope or livestock if the opportunity arises. Like Lions, Caracals are strongly associated with savanna, where clumps of grass provide cover for the stalking phase of their hunt. When close enough, the Caracal sprints and attacks, grabbing the prey with its claws and killing it with a bite to the back of the neck or throat. Larger prey is usually killed by suffocation with a throat bite that crushes the trachea. Their jumping ability is noteworthy: a Caracal can spring 3 m into the air to bat a flying bird.

Caracal caracal
Augrabies Falls National Park,
South Africa.
Photo: Wendy Dennis/FLPA

*Waterbirds, like this common coot, are among the prey of the **Jungle Cat**, which favors habitats close to water such as swamps and reedbeds. Jungle Cats will also take frogs, fish, snakes, and turtle eggs. Mammals, however, are the principal prey, chiefly small species like voles, gerbils, jirds muskrats, jerboas, and ground squirrels, but also larger ones including hares, Coypu, and the occasional Chital fawn. In parts of the range, ground foraging birds like pheasants, partridges, peafowl and jungle fowl, sparrows, and domestic poultry can also be prominent in the diet. Jungle Cats are stalk-and-ambush hunters, and capture most prey on the ground, but can climb and leap well.*

Felis chaus
Jandari Lake, SE Georgia.
Photo: Giorgi Darchiashvili

Chemical information about the time the mark was made may also be useful to individuals sharing overlapping ranges—the information may allow conspecifics to avoid foraging in areas that have just been hunted. It has been argued that scent marks allow domestic cats to make use of a common area on a "timeshare" basis, and that a fresh mark indicates the area is currently in use, while a slightly older mark indicates that the area is free for the next cat to use. Other carnivores, such as European Badgers and Brown Hyenas, which forage alone but in a shared area, scent-mark repeatedly while feeding.

Though urine spraying seems to be the preferred form of scent marking, cats also scrape or scratch the ground with their hindfeet while urinating. While scraping the cat moves each hindfoot backwards alternately, scarring the soil and removing the vegetation. The soil often forms a mound at the end of the two parallel scrape marks. The mound is sometimes marked with feces or urine. Scraping behavior is common among the big cats as well as the cats in the Ocelot lineage. However in the domestic cat lineage, only Pallas's Cat is known to scrape. Most cats also go through the ritual of what appears to be claw sharpening on a tree, log, or piece of furniture. They grip the object with forearms extended and draw the claws backward, either simultaneously or alternately. The action may or may not sharpen the claws, but it probably serves to dislodge loose pieces of claw sheath, deposit scent from the interdigital glands, and leave a conspicuous permanent mark. Cats have been observed to sniff and cheek rub against trees that have been raked in this manner. The scratching posts presumably act as a visual signal with added scent marks, but studies of domestic cats suggest there may be a further communication function. Feral domestic cats perform these claw-sharpening routines more often when in the presence of other cats than when they are alone, suggesting it may also be a gesture of visual dominance.

Feces are also used as scent marks, but much less frequently than urine. The large cats tend to leave their feces exposed, but many of the smaller felids bury them. Females with young often bury their feces, probably to avoid attracting attention to the den site and kittens. Free-ranging domestic cats have been observed to leave their feces and urine exposed while away from the barn, but to bury them when at home near their kittens. Eliminating odors near birth dens may reduce the possibility of a strange male locating and killing kittens. Some species, such as Ocelots, African Wildcats (*Felis silvestris lybica*), and Bobcats leave several feces in a heap at one site, called a latrine. Farm cats living in colonies sometimes have communal latrine sites.

Food and Feeding

Felids are the most carnivorous carnivorans —they are sometimes called hypercarnivores because they require a much higher proportion of protein in their diet than any other mammal. Domestic cats, for example, require a diet containing at least 12% protein, while dogs can thrive on a diet containing only 4% protein. Because of their purely carnivorous diet, felids typically have a short digestive tract with a smaller caecum and a short large intestine.

The world's cats can be divided into three sizes—small, medium, and large—and the diet of cats in each size group is generally different. The large-bodied cats, such as Tigers and

Lions, are predators of very large mammals. They regularly kill ungulates half their own body size or more. Indeed, large felids are the dominant meat-eaters in many modern and fossil mammalian communities. The Tiger dominates in Asia, the Lion in Africa, and the Jaguar in South America. These large cats require a regular supply of large prey to survive and reproduce. Unlike Leopards and other medium-sized cats, Tigers and Lions cannot survive on muntjac-sized (20 kg) prey. Two or three species of deer, pigs, equids, or bovids usually make up the bulk of Lion and Tiger diets within any ecosystem.

The medium-sized cats, such as the Puma, Snow Leopard, and Leopard can kill prey as large as themselves, but much of their diet consists of smaller prey weighing 2–40 kg. Their diets tend to be very broad and typically include an incredible number of different species. Puma, for instance, have been recorded taking more than 60 species of prey ranging in size from a 500 g ground squirrel to a 200 kg Elk. At least 92 species of prey are recorded for Leopards in sub-Saharan Africa.

The small felids such as Ocelot, Bobcat, Black-footed Cat, and Jungle Cat are also predators of mammals, but they frequently include birds, reptiles, amphibians, and insects in their diet. In general the smaller cats concentrate on prey that weigh less than one kilogram. These prey species typically have high potential reproductive rates and can sustain high harvest rates.

Though most cats are opportunistic hunters, a few are specialists in capturing particular types of prey. As the name implies, Fishing Cats hunt for fish (and frogs) by wading in shallow water or waiting on the bank. The cat often plunges its head completely underwater to seize a fish. Completely at home in the water, they have been seen swimming underwater to catch coots and ducks. The 10 kg Serval is a small-mammal specialist. It uses its large, dish-like ears to locate small prey in tall grass. Most of the Serval's prey weighs less than 2% of the cat's body weight. Canadian Lynx feed almost exclusively on Snowshoe Hares. Long powerful hindlimbs and wide, well-furred paws allow them to pursue hares across deep snow. Every aspect of this cat's life history—from density to litter size—is influenced by changes in Snowshoe Hare densities.

Though all cats hunt and kill their own prey, some will scavenge when the opportunity presents itself. Lions take kills from Cheetahs and Leopards, and Pumas are known to appropriate kills from Bobcats. Leopards also scavenge and feed on carrion even when live prey is abundant. Scavenging may help Leopards make it through periods when prey is scarce, and for young Leopards lacking in hunting experience, carrion may play an important role in their survival. Carrion may also be vi-

tal for the winter survival of Bobcats in upstate New York. It has been suggested that to survive the lean winter months, Bobcats in the Adirondack Mountains need to find one or more deer that died of injuries sustained in the fall hunting season.

Because of their cryptic lifestyles, most information on felid diets comes from an analysis of feces and stomach contents. A few species, such as Lions and Cheetahs, can be observed killing and eating their prey, and for these cats the kills are an accurate and detailed representation of their diet. Kill data have also been used to determine the diets of Tigers, Puma, Jaguar, and Leopards, but for many of these species kill data alone do not accurately reflect the cat's diet. Because it takes a Tiger or Puma several days to consume the carcass of a large animal, the kill is more likely to be found. Smaller prey, eaten immediately at the capture site, will remain undetected.

The best and most accurate information about a cat's diet comes from an analysis of its scats. Hair, teeth, bones, and hooves are often found in scats and these allow the researcher to identify what the cat has been eating. However, if the cat is eating a variety of different-sized animals, scats may not give an accurate picture of the proportions of different prey in the diet. Because large prey consists of proportionally more meat and less hide, hair, and bones, it produces fewer collectable feces than small prey. Working with captive Puma, B. Ackerman developed a correction factor to give a more accurate estimate of the relative biomass that prey of different sizes contributes to a cat's diet. Ackerman's correction factor is now used in most studies of felid diets.

One of the problems associated with reconstructing a predator's diet from scats is that it is not always easy to determine which predator left the scat. Many studies assigned identity based on scat size, assuming, reasonably enough, that larger cats leave larger scats. However, the recent development of DNA identification of feces suggests that misidentification was probably common in older studies that did not benefit from DNA analysis. We now know that Ocelot scats can be mistaken for Puma or Jaguar scats, and that size is not necessarily definitive for identification.

Most of the detailed information on diets comes from the larger species of cats. Everywhere Lions live, large to medium-sized ungulates form the mainstay of their diets. In the Serengeti plains, for example, seven species of ungulate accounted for 90% of kills. Blue Wildebeest (*Connochaetes taurinus*) and Burchell's Zebra (*Equus burchellii*) are frequently taken in the wet season, and Thomson's Gazelle (*Eudorcas thomsonii*) and Common Warthog (*Phacochoerus africanus*) are important prey

*In some areas, iguanas and land crabs are important seasonal components of the diet of the **Ocelot**. The occurrence of aquatic and semi-aquatic prey is not unexpected, as Ocelots are reportedly strong swimmers, and in some areas live in seasonally inundated environments. However, Ocelots primarily feed on terrestrial, nocturnal rodents weighing less than 1 kg, and also opossums and small primates, with occasional larger prey like young peccaries and deer. Ocelots usually hunt at night, scanning for prey while walking slowly along trails. They are also sit-and-wait predators, spending up to an hour at one site, then moving to another, where they sit and wait again.*

Leopardus pardalis
Hato el Frío, Llanos de Apure, Venezuela.
Photo: Xavier Ferrer & Adolf de Sostoa

*Although in size and build the **Sand Cat** is like the Wildcat, its ears are larger and broader, and set low on the sides of its head, which may aid the cat in detecting movements of subterranean prey, as well as protecting its inner ears from wind blown sand. Sand Cats are capable of rapid digging to extract prey items. As the picture below shows, Sand Cats will take an occasional snake or lizard, but they feed mostly on small desert rodents such as spiny mice, gerbils, jerboas, and the young of the Cape Hare. They also hunt larks and eat insects. Their claws are blunt, due to lack of sharpening surfaces, and their digging habits. They are nocturnal, sheltering in burrows from the extreme heat of the sun, although during the winter they may be active during the day. Like many desert dwellers, Sand Cats can survive with very little water in addition to what they derive from their food, but they drink readily when water is available. Living in an environment that is relatively poor in prey, Sand Cats need relatively large home ranges, and may need to travel further during the night's hunting than other cat species of similar size.*

Felis margarita
Ténéré, Niger.
Photos: Alain Dragesco-Joffé/
www.photolibrary.com

in the dry season. In the Serengeti woodlands, African Buffalo (*Syncerus caffer*) are the main prey year-round. Of the 12,000 plus Lion kills documented in Kruger National Park, about 60% were Blue Wildebeest, Burchell's Zebra, and Impala (*Aepyceros melampus*), but Lions also killed large bovids, including Sable Antelope (*Hippotragus niger*), Roan Antelope (*H. equinus*), Greater Kudu (*Tragelaphus strepsiceros*), Bushbuck (*T. scriptus*), Waterbuck (*Kobus ellipsiprymnus*), and African Buffalo. Lions in the Kalahari Desert rely heavily on Springbok (*Antidorcas marsupialis*), Gemsbok (*Oryx gazella*), and Blue Wildebeest, but they also take a variety of smaller prey such as Aardvark (*Orycteropus afer*), Cape Porcupine (*Hystrix africaeaustralis*), and ostrich (*Struthio camelus*). Lions in the Gir Forest, India, feed largely on

the abundant Chital (*Axis axis*), but supplement their diet with Sambar (*Rusa unicolor*), Nilgai (*Boselaphus tragocamelus*), and domestic livestock.

The Tiger's distribution is closely linked to the presence of deer and pigs. In the Russian Far East, Red Deer and Wild Boars (*Sus scrofa*) occurred in 84% of 522 kills. Chital, Hog Deer (*Axis porcinus*) and Wild Boar contributed more than 90% of the Tiger's diet in Royal Bardia National Park, Nepal; incidental prey included primates, Nilgai, and Barasingha (*Rucervus duvaucelii*). In Nagarhole National Park, India, Tigers preyed selectively on the two largest preys available, the Gaur (*Bos frontalis*) and Sambar deer, but they also killed Chital, Red Muntjac (*Muntiacus muntjak*), and Wild Boar. These five spe-

cies accounted for 96% of the biomass consumed. The mean weight of prey taken by Tigers in Nagarhole National Park was 91 kg. Little is known of Tiger food habits in Thailand, Peninsular Malaysia, and Sumatra, but large prey are less abundant in this region. In a small number of scats from Huai Kha Khaeng Wildlife Sanctuary, Thailand, the dominant prey was the 20 kg muntjak. Scats also contained the hair of Sambar Deer, Wild Boar, porcupine, Hog Badger, and primates, suggesting that Tigers in this region were probably eking out a fairly precarious existence.

The Leopard's range in Asia overlaps extensively with that of the Tiger, but there is little evidence of competitive interactions. Where both large and medium-sized prey exist, Tigers and Leopards seem to be able to coexist by focusing on different-sized prey. In areas where large prey, such as the 200 kg Sambar, have been eliminated or reduced in number by humans, Tigers may switch to medium-sized prey and reduce Leopard density through competition. Leopards feed on a wider variety of prey than do Tigers, and although they take some of the same prey, many of these are smaller or younger animals of the larger species. In Nagarhole National Park, for example, Chital, Red Muntjak, and young Sambar occurred in 65% of Leopard scats, but Four-horned Antelope (*Tetracerus quadricornis*), chevrotains, primates, hares, and porcupines also contributed to the diet. In China's Wolong Reserve, Tufted Deer (*Elaphodus cephalophus*) were the principal prey (41%) and in the Russian Far East, Siberian Roe Deer (*Capreolus pygargus*) comprised about half of the Leopard's diet. Where Leopards live sympatrically with Lions, they manage to coexist by taking a wider spectrum of prey species, in addition to taking many smaller or younger animals of the larger species that are taken by Lions. In the Serengeti, for example, Leopards kill mainly Thomson's Gazelles, Grant's Gazelles, and a variety of smaller prey. Lions in the same area eat Blue Wildebeest, Burchell's Zebra, Thomson's Gazelles and African Buffalo. Leopards in the Kalahari Desert prey on porcupine, Aardvark, Steenbok (*Raphicerus campestris*), duiker, and Gemsbok calves, whereas Lions in the Kalahari kill mainly adult Gemsbok and Springbok. In contrast, Impala are the dominant prey of both Lions and Leopards in Kruger National Park.

Like Leopards, Puma are generalists with extremely broad diets. Across much of North America White-tailed Deer (*Odocoileus virginianus*) and Mule Deer (*O. hemionus*) make up 60–80% of the Puma's diet, but peccary, porcupine, rabbits, and hares are also taken. The mean weight of prey taken varies

from about 39 to 48 kg, with adult males tending to take larger prey than females. However, in southwestern Florida, where deer habitat is marginal, deer constitute about one-third of the Puma's diet. In this area Puma depend on feral pigs, raccoons, armadillos, and alligators (*Alligator mississipiensis*) for the bulk of their prey. In south Florida, the mean weight of prey taken is about 17 kg. Similarly, smaller prey (1–20 kg) such as armadillo, vizcacha, porcupine, paca, agouti, brocket deer, pudu, hares, and opossums also occur frequently (over 50%) in the diets of Puma in many parts of Central and South America. Puma in the Neotropics also kill larger prey such as Guanaco (*Lama guanicoe*), White-tailed Deer, Marsh Deer (*Blastocerus dichotomus*), Pampas Deer (*Ozotoceros bezoarticus*), Capybara (*Hydrochoeris hydrochaeris*), and peccary. However, in areas where they co-occur with the larger, socially dominant Jaguar, there may be competitive spatial exclusion of Puma by Jaguar. In this situation the Puma's diet may be constrained.

Large mammals are the Jaguar's main prey, but more than 85 different species of wild prey ranging from turtles to tapir have been reported in this adaptable cat's diet. When colonists brought cattle to South America in the 1600s, the versatile Jaguar added livestock to the list. Jaguar hunt anything larger than a rabbit in almost every type of habitat from rainforest to dry Chaco. In the seasonally flooded grasslands of Venezuela and Brazil, these cats feed on Capybara, peccary, deer, and cattle. They also eat caiman and turtles. In the lowland tropical forest of Peru's Manu National Park, the bulk of the Jaguar's diet consists of Collared Peccary (*Pecari tajacu*), agouti, and large turtles. In secondary forest in Belize, armadillo are the single most important prey. In Costa Rica, sloths and iguanas figure prominently in the diet, and in the Paraguayan Chaco brocket deer, rabbits, and marsupials top the list. Jaguars have a predilection for peccaries, often killing them in preference to other, more common prey. Jaguars also have an affinity for water and many items in their diet reflect this association. Capybara, caiman, fish, and turtles form an important part of this cat's diet. Although river turtles seem a rather unlikely food item for a cat, these reptiles can weigh as much as 30 kg and females are quite vulnerable when they come ashore to lay eggs. Jaguars use their powerful jaws to bite through the carapace and gain access to the meat.

The Cheetah is the most specialized of the medium-sized cats and their distribution is closely linked to the presence of gazelles. Wherever the Cheetah is found today there is one or more species of gazelles or gazelle-like antelope. Cheetah feed mainly on medium-sized ungulates; most of their prey weigh less than 40 kg. In the Serengeti and the Kalahari National Park, Thomson's Gazelle are the primary prey, accounting for 91% of kills. In Kruger National Park and the Transvaal, Impala are the dominant prey. In almost all studies to date, fawns and half-grown gazelles make up more than 50% of Cheetah kills, even though young and adolescent ungulates comprise only a small proportion of the prey population.

The majority of small cat species eat rodents, rabbits, and hares. As a food source, rodents and lagomorphs have several major advantages. They have high reproductive potential because they produce several litters per year, young mature quickly, most breed before they are one year old, and litter sizes are often three or more young. With such high rates of reproduction, prey is renewed quickly, and thus they can sustain high rates of cropping by predators. Ocelot, Serval, Leopard Cat, Jungle Cat, Wildcat, Pallas's Cat, and Black-footed Cat are all small-rodent eaters. Bobcat, Iberian Lynx, and Canadian Lynx are basically lagomorph specialists.

Black-footed Cats are opportunistic predators and are known to take a variety of prey. Three-quarters of their prey in Namibia was gerbils, mice, and shrews. However, these small mammals represented only 39% of the prey biomass consumed. The cats also captured small birds such as larks, pipits, chats, and wheatears, and killed adult black bustards (*Afrotis afra*) that weighed about one-half the cat's body weight. Black-footed Cats also eat insects such as lacewings, locusts, grasshoppers, moths, and termite alates. Although mean prey size was 24 g and small birds, rodents, and insects were the staple foods, the occasional large meal was clearly important. Cats scavenged Springbok lambs that weighed twice their body weight—an unusual behavior among small felids that usually sustain themselves on prey weighing one-tenth of their body weight.

Though the Serval is ten times the size of the diminutive Black-footed Cat, this tall, large-eared cat is a specialized small mammal catcher. Serval occasionally kill larger prey such as flamingos, hares, duikers, and young antelope, but over 90% of their diet consists of prey weighing less than 200 g, or about 2% of female body weight. Servals also eat small birds, snakes, frogs, and insects. In Zimbabwe the 20–80 g multimammate mice and the 100–200 g Vlei rats (*Otomys* spp.) make up the bulk of the Serval's diet. In Tanzania the Vlei rat was the dominant prey, particularly in the dry season, followed by the 2–12 g pygmy mouse and the unstriped grass mouse. Indeed, in Tanzania rodents occurred in 98% of all the feces examined and in 90% of all the direct observations of kills. In South Africa's Kamberg Nature Reserve, Natal, an analysis of scats found that 80% of the cat's diet was made up of rodents weighing less than 127 g. The remainder of their diet consisted of shrews, birds, reptiles, and insects.

The disadvantage of relying on prey with a high reproductive potential is that they sometimes go through population crashes, which, in turn, has major repercussions in the predator population. The Canadian Lynx-Snowshoe Hare population cycle is a classic example of the relationship between predator and prey. Canadian Lynx feed heavily on Snowshoe Hares—hares constitute at least 60% of the winter diet and about 40% of the summer diet. Other prey include mice, voles, Red Squirrels (*Tamiasciurus hudsonicus*), flying squirrels, Ruffed grouse (*Bonasa umbellus*), and ptarmigan (*Lagopus*), but only Snowshoe Hares can support high density lynx populations. Lynx occasionally kill deer, Reindeer/Caribou (*Rangifer tarandus*) fawns, and Moose (*Alces*) calves, but most of the scats containing the hair of these ungulates are probably produced after scavenged meals. One exception is Newfoundland Island, where Lynx prey heavily on Reindeer calves.

Because Canadian Lynx depend so much on Snowshoe Hares, the two species have developed a synchronous relationship in which populations of both hare and lynx fluctuate from high to low in a ten year cycle. The basic cause of the cycle is the interaction of the Snowshoe Hare with its food supply. Snowshoe Hares can reach amazing densities of as much as 1700 per square km, and at these levels, lynx densities may reach 1–5 per ten square km. When hares are that numerous they overbrowse their food supply and starve. As hare numbers crash, the lynx decline is not so much due to starvation as lack of recruitment to the population. When hares become scarce, fewer female lynx breed, those that do produce fewer kittens and kitten survival is low. Recruitment to the breeding population virtually ceases, causing the lynx population to decline. The cycle reverses as the hare's food source begin to recover.

Most small cats feed on prey that weighs less than 1 kg, but there are a few exceptions. Eurasian Lynx appear to have evolved as predators of smaller (20–40 kg) ungulates like roe deer (*Capreolus*), chamois (*Rupicapra*), and musk deer (*Moschus*). In this sense Eurasian Lynx behave more like larger felids, routinely killing prey as large as or larger than themselves. Similarly, in South Africa, over half of the Caracal's diet consists of 10–20 kg antelope such as Reedbuck (*Redunca*), Steenbok, Springbok, and duiker.

With few exceptions, all cats hunt in a fairly standard way. They begin by carefully stalking the prey, their body held in a low crouch, ears flattened and eyes riveted on the target. The approach is slow and patient, and they take advantage of every scrap of vegetation or rise and fall in the terrain, to inch closer. A stalk may take half an hour or longer, as the cat typi-

*Only humans can kill adult elephants, but **Lions** can kill elephant calves, and are probably the only important predators of elephants in Africa. Lions rely on very large mammals like zebra, wildebeest, buffalo, and Impala to survive and reproduce. An adult male Lion can eat up to 40 kg of meat at a single meal. But Lions are generalists, taking a large variety of vertebrates, from mice to young rhinos and hippos, Brown Fur Seals on the coast of Namibia, and birds up to the size of an ostrich, as well as reptiles, fish, and even insects. Differences in prey selection and killing techniques in different prides in the same area indicate that learning plays a strong role in the Lion's hunting behavior.*

Panthera leo
Okavango Delta, Botswana.
Photo: Michael Callan/FLPA

The **Cheetah** is the most specialized of the medium-sized cats, and its distribution is closely linked to the presence of gazelles. Most Cheetah prey species weigh less than 40 kg. In the Serengeti and the Kalahari National Park, the Thomson's Gazelle, shown here, is the primary prey species, accounting for 91% of kills. In Kruger National Park and the Transvaal, the Impala is the dominant prey species. In almost all studies to date, fawns and half-grown gazelles make up more than 50% of Cheetah kills, even though young and adolescent ungulates comprise only a small proportion of the prey population. Cheetahs are highly successful hunters: in the Serengeti about 50% of hunts on adult gazelles and 100% on small fawns were successful. In the absence of suitable small to medium antelopes, Cheetahs may entirely subsist on smaller prey like guineafowl and other ground-living birds, and hares. Groups of males can also bring down larger prey like wildebeests. Cheetahs sometimes approach prey at a slow walk before breaking into a sprint from 60–70 m away, and some rushes are launched from as far away as 600 m. All cats employ a final sprint, but the Cheetah can accelerate more rapidly than any other terrestrial animal, attaining a speed of 75 km/h in two seconds. Top speed has been recorded at 102 km/h, strides are up to 9 m, and all four feet are airborne at least twice in each stride. At the end of the chase the Cheetah trips the victim by reaching out with a front paw, or knocks it off balance with a slap to the rump. Like the big cats, the Cheetah usually kills large prey with a bite to the throat or muzzle; suffocation follows in 2–10 minutes. Hares and similar small prey are killed with a bite to the head.

Acinonyx jubatus
Masai Mara National Park, Kenya.
Photos: Fritz Pölking/FLPA

*Like Cheetahs, **Lions** appear to be fairly successful hunters. In Etosha National Park, Lions made a kill every 6·7 hunts, a success rate of 15%. The success rate on zebras was 11%, but on wildebeests it was 30%. The distance covered in the final charge is crucial. Lions in Ngorongoro Crater had a high probability of catching Thomson's Gazelles from 7·6 m, but zero probability at 15·2 m. But at 15·2 m Lions were quite successful at capturing less nimble wildebeests. Lions will often try to cut prey off by running ahead of it. Speeds of 45–60 km/h may be achieved for up to a few hundred meters.*

Panthera leo
Etosha National Park, Namibia.
Photo: Martin Harvey/DRK

cally freezes whenever the prey lifts its head or looks in the cat's direction. When the cat judges it has crept within striking distance it launches the attack, sprinting towards the prey in an all-out charge. Grabbing the victim with its claws, the cat holds on while it delivers a killing bite. Smaller prey is usually bitten on the back of the neck; the canines are driven in between the vertebrae, severing the spinal cord. Larger prey is gripped by the throat, the trachea is crushed, and the victim dies of suffocation. A few cats use more specialized methods of killing prey. In some areas Lions have learned to kill zebra and Gemsbok with a muzzle bite, using their weight to drag the victim down. Jaguar are known to kill Capybara and domestic horses with a bite to the back of the skull, and Serval have been seen killing snakes and other prey with a series of repeated paw blows. The Serval is commonly seen using sound to locate tiny rodents in tall grass. Oddly uncatlike in appearance, the Serval has long legs and elongated feet; it stands 20 cm taller than the similar-sized Ocelot. When hunting, Serval walk slowly through the grass scanning the area for sounds. They use their height in combination with their huge dish like ears to detect small rodents. On hearing something move, the Serval swivels its head to pinpoint the location of the sound, then, after a careful approach, it pounces like a fox, springing high with all four feet off the ground. If the first pounce does not connect, the Serval may follow with a swift series of stiff-legged bouncing jumps. Serval also use the high bouncing pounce to flush small prey from the vegetation. They gallop through the grass in a zig-zag pattern, leaping high into the air. Anything that runs is caught immediately.

Like the Serval, the Cheetah's physique reflects a different hunting style. Cheetah stalk prey in the typical felid manner, but they differ in that the sprint phase of the attack is often started from a distance of 50 m or more. Cheetah sometimes approach prey at a slow walk before breaking into a sprint from 60–70 m away, and some rushes are launched from as far away as 600 m. All cats employ a final sprint, but only the Cheetah attains speeds of 100 km/h. Designed for a short explosive sprint, it can accelerate rapidly, attaining a speed of 75 km/h in two seconds. While following the rapid zig-zag turns of its prey, the Cheetah uses its tail and feet to maintain balance and speed. Longitudinal ridges on the hard pointed pads of the feet function like cleats on a running shoe, providing traction and grip during fast turns. At the end of the chase the Cheetah trips the victim by reaching out with a front paw and hooking it with the large, strongly curved dew-claw. Alternatively, a slap to the prey's rump knocks the prey off balance, and before the victim

can recover the Cheetah grabs it by the throat. Like the big cats, the Cheetah usually kills by strangulation.

Because the majority of felids are difficult to watch, data on hunting success are scarce. Most of the information comes from the "watchable" African cats such as the Lion, Cheetah, Serval, and Black-footed Cat. The hunting behavior of Leopards in the Kalahari Desert has been reconstructed based on interpretations of tracks followed in the sand.

Cheetahs are highly successful hunters. In the Serengeti about 50% of hunts on adult gazelles and 100% on small fawns were successful. Lions also appear to be fairly successful hunters, but not surprisingly the distance covered in the final charge is a crucial variable for success. Lions in Ngorongoro Crater had a high probability of catching a Thomson's Gazelle when the attack was launched from 7·6 m, but the probability fell to zero at 15·2 m. However, at 15·2 m Lions were quite successful at capturing Blue Wildebeest, reflecting differences in prey species' abilities to escape. Similarly, in Etosha National Park, Lions made a kill every 6·7 hunts, a success rate of 15%. The success rate on zebra was 11% but on wildebeest it was 30%. Of 27 hunts of spring hare, Lions were successful 52% of the time.

In the arid, open sands of the south-western Kalahari Desert, Bothma and Le Riche worked with bushman trackers to follow Leopard spoor. This method revealed, in astonishing detail, the hunting attempts, success rates, and kills of leopards surviving in this waterless environment. Leopards stalked and killed everything from hares, genets, and jackals to Gemsbok, Common Eland (*Tragelaphus oryx*), and ostrich. Male Leopards killed 14 prey during 106 stalks for a success rate of 13%. Females with cubs were more successful hunters, making a kill on ten of 44 stalks, or 23% of attempts. However, females with cubs tended to focus on smaller prey such as spring hare, Bat-eared Fox, and jackal. Male Leopards made a kill about every three days compared to every one and a half days for females with young.

Data on hunting success for small felids are almost non-existent, but A. Sliwa's detailed observations of wild Black-footed Cats in South Africa show that this species is an astonishingly able hunter, making one attempt every 30 minutes with a 60% success rate. One male was seen to capture twelve rodents in 3·5 hours. During a typical night's hunting, a cat would kill a bird or mammal every 50 minutes or so, killing between 10–14 rodents or small birds per night. This represents approximately 250–300 g of food or about 20% of the cat's body weight.

Not surprisingly, weather and moon phase have been found to have an impact on felid hunting success. The Serval's specialized sound-hunting technique is so sensitive that a strong wind can interfere with its ability to pinpoint prey. Unless they are extremely hungry, these cats rarely bother to hunt in windy weather. Lions in Etosha National Park were found to be more successful hunting Springbok and Burchell's Zebra when it was windy, and in other areas it has been observed that Lions are more successful when hunting on moonless nights. Ocelots in Peru were observed to avoid hunting in open areas on moonlit nights, instead confining their activity to brushy areas. It is probably difficult for an Ocelot to stalk prey without being detected in bright moonlight unless there is enough cover.

Cooperation also affects hunting success. About 30% of Lion hunts in the Serengeti were successful when several members of the pride were involved, as opposed to 17–19% when only a single Lion was hunting. In Etosha National Park, cooperative hunts by lionesses were also more successful (27%) than hunts by single lionesses (2·3%). Canadian Lynx also have greater success when hunting in groups. One study reported that success rates for groups of one, two, three, and four averaged 14%, 17%, 38%, and 55%, respectively. Success rate also varies with hare density. In the Yukon, with increasing hare densities, a lynx made six kills in eleven attempts (54·5%), but when hare numbers were low the success rate varied from 20–22%.

Cheetah males hunting alone usually pursue Thomson's Gazelles weighing about 20 kg, but groups of males often hunt Blue Wildebeest weighing 80 or more kg. These male groups have no greater hunting success than singleton males, but they kill an animal that is large enough to provide all members of the group with more meat than a single male acquires when it catches a gazelle.

Big cats typically make a large kill every week or so, feed for a few days, then go for several days without eating. It is possible that they kill and consume small prey between the large kills, but that level of detailed information is difficult to acquire. A radio-collared tigress that was located daily for weekly to three week periods killed a large deer or boar every eight or nine days, the equivalent of 40–46 kills per year. She spent an average of three days with each kill. When the same tigress was travelling with her two six- to ten-month-old cubs, she increased her killing rate to once every five or six days, making the equivalent of 61–72 large kills per year. Records for Puma show a similar pattern. Females without cubs and mature males made a large kill every 10·4 days, whereas females with kittens made a kill every 6·8 days. Leopards in Kruger National Park killed one Impala per week, but success rates were higher in the wet season, presumably due to increased stalking cover. Male Leopards in Kruger killed a large prey about once every 7·2 days compared to once every 7·5 days for females without young. In the Serengeti Leopards average one gazelle kill every five or six days.

Large cats can consume a huge amount of meat at a single sitting. They may eat 20% of their body weight in a night when feeding on a large kill, but then go for several days without feeding. In a study of radio-collared Tigers in Nepal, the cats were located with their kills and the carcass was weighed every 24 hours to determine how much the Tigers were eating. Tigresses in Chitwan spent an average of three days with each kill and during this time consumed an average of 46 kg or about 15 kg/day. One large male Tiger ate 35 kg in a single night and there are reports from India of Tigers eating between 18 and 27 kg of meat in a night. There is less information on consumption rates for medium and small cats, but a study in Kruger National Park found that male Leopards consumed 3·1–4·7 kg/day compared to 2·9 kg/day for adult females. The similar-sized Cheetah consumed 2–4 kg/day. Eurasian Lynx, which weigh 15–30 kg, eat 1–2·5 kg/day. Canadian Lynx consume an estimated 0·6–1·2 kg/day—that is, about a hare every day or every second day.

For a 1·5 kg cat, Black-footed Cats seem to eat an enormous amount of food. When feeding on bustards or scavenging on young Springbok, Black-footed Cats consumed about 20% of their body weight in a night. On one occasion a male cat fed on a 3 kg Springbok lamb, consuming 1·1 kg in 2·5 days. One night he returned to the carcass four times, consuming 120 g each time. Amazingly, he continued to hunt and kill small birds and rodents between these scavenged meals.

Not surprisingly, data for many species suggest that carnivore densities are positively correlated with prey density. There are many examples: Snow Leopard density is highest where blue sheep are most abundant, Cheetah and Leopard densities are strongly correlated with lean season prey biomass, and Tigers reach their highest density in areas with the greatest ungulate biomass. Indeed, a knowledge of prey characteristics and biomass allows us to predict many aspects of felid demographics. Felid population size, home range size, and even social organization are all, to a large extent, driven by the distribution and abundance of food.

Radio-tracking studies have illustrated how home range sizes can vary by a factor of ten for the same species. Tigresses

*Members of a **Lion** pride hunt large prey such as buffalo, zebra, or wildebeest cooperatively. Some chase the victim and try to steer it toward others, who ambush and kill it. When stalking herding animals, such as buffalo, Lion prides sometimes bring down more than one individual at a time. Cooperation affects hunting success. About 30% of Lion hunts in the Serengeti were successful when several members of the pride were involved, as opposed to 17–19% when only a single Lion was hunting. In Etosha National Park, cooperative hunts by lionesses were also more successful (27%) than hunts by single lionesses (2·3%).*

Panthera leo
Photo: Fritz Pölking/FLPA

living in the highly productive tall grassland/riverine forest mosaic in southern Nepal, where prey density is about 2000 kg/square km, have home ranges that average 20 square km. In Russia, where prey densities are lower by at least an order of magnitude, tigresses have ranges of 200–400 square km. Other cats show similar variation in home range size with changes in prey density. In East Africa, Lions in areas of low prey availability had larger home ranges than they did in areas with higher prey density, and in Idaho the average size of Bobcat home ranges increased five-fold as lagomorph populations declined.

Prey density and distribution can also affect felid social organization, in that where resources are scarce, widely scattered, and/or migratory, it becomes energetically impossible for an individual to maintain sole rights to an area. Under these circumstances, females and sometimes males end up with large overlapping ranges. On the other hand, small exclusive ranges would be expected where prey is dense and evenly distributed.

Availability of food also influences reproduction and survival of offspring. One of the best examples is the Canadian Lynx, which breed as yearlings when hares are abundant. When hare numbers are low yearling females do not breed and conception rates for adult females are low. Similarly, at high hare densities mean litter sizes are about five, but at lows in the hare cycle the average litter size is about one. Survival rates of young lynx are also lower during the population decline in hares, and the result is little recruitment into the lynx population.

In many parts of the world one of the major obstacles to felid conservation is the fact that many cats prey on domestic animals. Small to medium-sized cats such as Ocelots, Jaguarundi, and even the tiny Kodkod kill chickens, ducks, and geese. Larger cats like Snow Leopard, Puma, Leopard, Jaguar, and Tiger often prey on sheep, goats, cattle, and horses. Almost invariably the cats are regarded as pests and are shot or trapped whenever possible. As people search for new ways to implement conservation programs, livestock predation is one of the conflict areas being examined. Several recent studies of large cats have sought to define some of the factors that predispose felids to kill livestock.

Sixty years ago J. Corbett, the famed Tiger hunter, observed that many of the man-eating and cattle-lifting Tigers that he killed had previous injuries that rendered them unable to hunt their natural prey. Scientists studying Jaguar predation on domestic livestock later quantified this observation. A study in Be-

lize found that ten of 13 cattle-killing Jaguars had prior injuries to the head or body. Five of the ten had missing or broken canine teeth, and five of the ten had old shotgun pellets or wounds in the skull. Ten of 19 skulls of cattle-killing Jaguars examined in Venezuela also showed old bullet wounds.

Felids also kill domestic animals because their natural prey has been depleted and livestock is readily available. In Venezuela, a study of Jaguar predation on cattle found that logging, land clearing, and the conversion of forests to pasture and arable land push both the Jaguar and its prey into areas where they are more easily hunted. Subsistence farmers often follow logging operations, and settlers hunt wild game as a source of food. The resulting scarcity of wild prey means that cattle become the most available prey. Herd management in these areas is often rudimentary, and Jaguar prey on cattle as if they were wild ungulates because the cattle wander freely through the forest. Poaching of natural prey clearly affects Jaguar and Puma predation on cattle, and Jaguar kill more cattle on ranches where Capybara, deer, and peccary are heavily poached.

Injured cats, declining natural prey bases, and poor husbandry practices are also responsible for depredation on livestock by other large felids. In Asia, Snow Leopards kill sheep, goats, and horses, probably because of a combination of lack of natural prey and poor husbandry. Throughout Africa and Asia, Leopards regularly take domestic livestock, usually because it is available and easy to kill. However, ranchers in Africa who keep their livestock in pens at night suffer few losses to Lions and Leopards, and households in Chile who put their ducks and geese in a pen at night reduce predation by small cats. Clearly, proper protection of domestic livestock plays a vital role in reducing felid depredation on livestock, which remains one of the major reasons cats are killed. In addition, it goes without saying that our ability to conserve most of the world's cat species will depend on our ability to protect and conserve their natural prey.

Breeding

Cats typically live in large home ranges where face-to-face encounters with neighbors are rare. Under these circumstances, the two sexes communicate with one another primarily by scent. A female deposits scent marks in the form of urine,

As soon as the prey is down, it is seized by the throat or muzzle to effect strangulation or suffocation. The **Lions** feed at the site of the kill, or drag it to the nearest cover. The belly is ripped open and the stomach and intestines pulled out. A whole pride can feed on a single large kill, the males going first, followed by the females, and then the young. Lions may stay in the vicinity of the carcass for several days, feeding on it and protecting their kill from hyenas and other scavengers. Protection of kills against Spotted Hyenas is greatly enhanced by the presence of a male. Females may lose up to 20% of their kills to Spotted Hyenas, and a further 17% to unrelated Lions. Lions themselves, especially males, frequently scavenge, acquiring up to 53% of food items in the open plains of the Serengeti in this way. They will watch for vultures descending on the kills of other predators. When satiated, the pride will rest in the shade for long periods, usually in compact groups.

Panthera leo
Masai Mara National Park, Kenya.
Photo: Mark Newman/FLPA

*With its large feet, short legs, and long tail, the **Indochinese Clouded Leopard** is well-equipped for moving about in the trees. However, most hunting is probably done on the ground. But little is known about its habitat and other requirements, or even whether, as has been thought, it is primarily nocturnal: an increasing number of camera-trap photographs show it to be active both day and night. A variety of terrestrial and arboreal vertebrates are reported as prey, including porcupines, bearded pigs, small deer species and the young of larger deer, palm civets, and primates, including macaques, langurs, and Proboscis Monkeys. Domestic stock, including goats, pigs, and poultry may also be taken.*

Neofelis nebulosa
Photo: Terry Whittaker/FLPA

before, interactions can be hostile and dangerous. Both sexes have potentially lethal weapons at their disposal and when circumstances are not right an individual can be killed. Thus, it is not surprising that the estrous period in most felids lasts for several days.

The prime example of this are the clouded leopards. In captivity, males frequently kill females during courtship and mating. In zoos across the world, many males have had to be removed from the pool of breeders because of their penchant for killing females. The problem has been partially solved by hand-raising male and female clouded leopard kittens together so they form compatible pairs, but this is not always possible. We know nothing about clouded leopard courtship and mating in the wild, but the act and the behavior surrounding it must involve subtleties that normal captive surroundings do not allow.

Mating pairs often stay together for a few days, and more than one male may attend a female in estrus. There are accounts of female Tigers, Jaguars, Pumas, and Eurasian Lynx being followed by several males. Once the female is truly in estrus and receptive, a courtship sequence begins. Mating patterns are remarkably similar among felids, except for the timing and occurrence of the neck grip. The mating posture is elegantly designed to ensure that the male does not become involved in a fight with the female, and avoids the risk of events escalating to an attack. Usually, the male mounts, and grips the back of the female's neck. After intromission and ejaculation the female may give a low growl and throw the male off her back. There is no copulatory lock. In larger cats the male usually grips the female's neck only at the climax of copulation, a behavior that may be a way of ensuring the female does not injure the male.

Copulations are brief, lasting 3–20 seconds, but many felids copulate repeatedly over one or two days. Lions have been observed copulating 157 times over a 55 hour period, and similar frequencies are reported for Tigers, Leopards, and Puma. Slightly lower rates are reported for the smaller cats.

Most felids are thought to be induced ovulators. This means that ovulation—the rupture of the follicle and the release of the ovum—must be induced by repeated stimulation of the vagina and cervix. The baculum of felids has penile spines, which

around her home range. Males find and "read" these scent marks, then locate the female. Alternatively, females may vocalize to "call in" a male—female Tigers, Black-footed Cats, domestic cats, and several other species vocalize when in estrus. When the male and female find each other the male follows her around—sometimes for several days—making attempts to approach and mate. When individuals are familiar with one another, the preliminaries may be shortened and mating may occur sooner rather than later, but with cats that have not met

*In many areas the diet of the **Leopard** consists largely of small- to medium-sized mammals (5–45 kg), but even ungulates weighing two to three times the cat's body weight are occasionally taken.*

Leopards can also survive on extremely small prey, an ability that allows them to live in areas from which larger prey species have long since been extirpated. Adults of very large prey are rarely pursued, although young, inexperienced animals are sometimes chased for considerable distances. Most hunting is done at night, taking advantage of the cover of darkness, and what little information is available suggests hunting success is higher at night. Leopards go to great lengths to avoid losing their kills to scavengers and larger predators. They will drag dead prey hundreds of meters to areas with dense cover, or carry heavy carcasses into trees.

Panthera pardus
Masai Mara National Park, Kenya.
Photo: Fritz Pölking/FLPA

Radio-tracking studies indicate that **Tigers** *are essentially crepuscular and nocturnal. Activity patterns appear to be driven primarily by the activity patterns of the prey. Tigers studied in Nagarhole National Park, India, took advantage of the cover of darkness; about 27% of kills were made between 06:00 h and 09:00 h, and the remainder were made between 18:00 h and 06:00 h. Cover is important: a Tiger will attempt to get as close as possible to its prey before making a final rush, relying on quickly overtaking prey rather than pursuit for long distances.*

Panthera tigris
Ranthambhore Sanctuary, India.
Photo: Günter Ziesler

suggests a connection between stimulation and ovulation. Thus for most felids, even though the female may come into estrus, ovulation will not occur unless copulation is repeated and prolonged. Induced ovulation is thought to be a way of ensuring that eggs are fertilized. Coupling egg release with mating would seem to make fertilization more likely, although conception rates appear to be low, varying from 20–40% in Lions and Tigers to 50–67% in Leopards, Puma, Snow Leopards, and Ocelots. Low rates of conception are thought to be related to inexperience, incompatibility, or an insufficient number of copulations. Spontaneous ovulation, or ovulation without prior mating, has been reported from zoos for Tigers, Lions, and Leopards, but only in circumstances where the cats were in adjacent cages or were housed together. Spontaneous ovulation is also reported for domestic cats, Bobcats, and Canadian Lynx.

Most cats have repeated estrous cycles during the year and are said to be polyestrous. A few species have a single estrous cycle each year and are monestrous. Most tropical felids are polyestrous and will breed year round. Females continue to cycle and mate until they become pregnant, and if a litter dies the female will usually recycle within a few days or weeks. She can often mate again and bear a new litter within three months. On the other hand, females in areas with severe winters may not recycle after the death of a litter because the optimal time for mating has passed. Snow Leopards, Eurasian and Canadian Lynx, and probably other felids that live in seasonally harsh climates are monoestrous.

Gestation length in felids varies from about 60 days in some of the smaller cats to slightly over 100 days for Tigers, and generally scales with the size of the cat: larger felids have longer gestation periods than smaller felids. The exceptions are the cats in the Ocelot lineage (Ocelot, Margay, Oncilla, Geoffroy's Cat, Colocolo, and Kodkod), which have longer gestation periods than many other cats their size. Compared with other mammals, such as ungulates, felids invest relatively little in gestation. This is probably because females must hunt alone and cannot afford to be handicapped by a large fetus. There is some anecdotal evidence to suggest that Cheetah mothers in the late stages of pregnancy are less able to capture prey.

In the wild, the number of young at birth is rarely known, but information from captivity suggests that for most felids litter size is typically two to three. However, as with gestation length, members of the Ocelot lineage differ. They generally have smaller litters: Margay and Ocelot in particular often give birth to only one kitten per litter. Cats in the domestic cat lin-

eage, Jungle Cat, Sand Cat, and Wild Cat, have larger litters, with three or four young being more typical. Cheetah stand alone in having exceptionally large litters; five and sometimes six young are not uncommon.

Some anecdotal reports suggest that younger females have smaller litters than experienced mothers. Data on litter size are extremely difficult to collect for wild cats, and there are only a few species for which such information exists. However, information from long-term studies of Pumas and Tigers suggests that litter size is similar for first time mothers and experienced mothers. It is possible and even likely that more experienced mothers may be more successful at rearing more cubs to adulthood, which may account for the observed differences in litter sizes.

A brief comparison of the Ocelot and Bobcat illustrates the importance of understanding life history traits when setting harvest limits and writing conservation policy. Ocelots and Bobcats are similar in size but differ in several significant reproductive parameters. Ocelots have a long gestation period, (79–82 days) and small litter size (mode of 1) compared with the Bobcat's short gestation (62 days) and large (2–4) litter size. Ocelot kittens mature slowly and do not attain adult weight until they are 24–30 months old. Adults typically give birth every two years. Bobcats mature quickly and breed every year. Across much of their range these cats are hunted and trapped for their fur or as a game species, and harvest quotas for Bobcats are generally set at about 20% of the population. By comparison, any scheme that involved harvesting Ocelots on a sustained yield basis would have to factor in the cat's specialized requirements and slow rate of reproduction. It seems unlikely that Ocelots would be able to tolerate the annual removal of more than 2–3% of the population.

Just before she gives birth, the female selects a site for the birth den. Usually on the ground, the den can be a depression in tall grass, a cave, the roots of a fallen tree, a hollow inside a dense thicket, or any other secure hiding place. Felid young are altricial. They are born small, blind, and helpless, unable to do much more than crawl to their mother, the source of food and warmth. The mother usually spends the first 24–48 h with the newborn young, grooming them, keeping them warm, and nursing.

Radio-tracking studies of several wild felid species have shown that after birth, and for the first month or so of the kittens' lives, the mother's home range shrinks dramatically. Her movements are focused on the den and her range does not

The **Fishing Cat** is one of the limited number of cat species that are specialists in catching particular kinds of prey, rather than opportunistic generalists. As the name implies, the Fishing Cats hunts for fish, and also frogs, by wading in shallow water or waiting on the bank. The cat often plunges its head completely underwater to seize a fish. It also flicks or scoops fish out of the water with its paws. Completely at home in the water, Fishing Cats have been seen swimming underwater to catch coots and ducks by the legs. Shellfish, crabs, snakes, and water insects all figure in the diet. The Fishing Cat's toes have moderately well developed webs, but its teeth are not specially adapted for holding onto slippery prey. It probably eats any small- to medium-sized vertebrate it can catch, and there are records of Fishing Cats eating rodents, Small Indian Civets, Chital fawns, small pigs, coots, ducks, sandpipers, and a variety of domestic animals such as goats, calves, poultry, and even dogs. Although, as one would expect, Fishing Cats are typically associated with wetlands such as marshes, reed beds, oxbow lakes, mangrove areas, and swamps. In the Nepalese lowlands, three radio-collared individuals spent most of their time in dense grasslands, sometimes well away from water.

Above: **Prionailurus viverrinus**
India.
Photo: Belinda Wright/
www.photolibrary.com

Below: **Prionailurus viverrinus**
Photos: Terry Whittaker/FLPA

begin to expand until the young become mobile. The female leaves the kittens to search for food, and may be away for as long as 24–36 h, but returns to feed them as often as possible. Felid young are very vulnerable to predation in the first month or two of their lives, and almost any predator can kill cubs. The most complete information on early mortality among felids comes from a detailed study of Cheetah cubs on the Serengeti plains, where only 28·8% of an estimated 125 cubs born in 36 litters survived to emerge from the den. Mortality remained high through the first few months. By four months, ten or twelve of the original cubs survived, and by independence (14–18 months of age) only 4·8% or 5–7 of the 125 cubs were still alive. Cubs died in grass fires, were abandoned, or starved to death, but Lions caused most of the mortality. Predation by Lions and Spotted Hyenas accounted for 73·2% of Cheetah cub deaths from known causes. To compensate for this high juvenile mortality, Cheetahs reach sexual maturity at a comparatively early age and have large litters. Similarly detailed information is generally lacking for other cats but among Tigers about 60% of young are thought to die before reaching independence. For Lions, juvenile mortality is exceedingly variable, ranging from 14 to 80%. Food availability also directly affects the number of young in a litter and the survival of these young. Studies of Canadian Lynx have found that during periods of hare scarcity the number of young in utero decreased from a mean of 4·6 to a mean of 3·4. Likewise, when hares are in short supply the growth and development of kittens is retarded and few young survive. In contrast, when hares are abundant, even yearling female Lynx will breed and successfully rear young.

Most female felids are highly aggressive to any adult male who approaches her litter, and with good reason since infanticide is an important cause of juvenile mortality. Some of the best data come from Lions, where infanticide is common: there are many records of new pride males killing cubs soon after a pride takeover. Infanticide is also known to occur in Tigers, Leopards, Puma, and domestic cats. By killing cubs that have been fathered by another male, and impregnating the female himself, a male can achieve two things at once: he reduces the reproductive success of the other male, and increases his own. Female felids quickly come back into estrus after the death of a litter, which allows the new male to mate and father his own cubs without waiting for the cubs of the previous male to grow up. In the Serengeti, lionesses whose cubs are killed in a pride takeover give birth to a new litter about eight months

after losing their cubs. If the incoming males had allowed the females to rear the cubs they had at the time of the takeover, the new males would have had to wait about 18 months for their own cubs to be born. In light of the fact that male Lions in the Serengeti usually only manage to hold a pride of females for two years, infanticide would seem to be an adaptive strategy. During the months after a new male has taken over a pride, females who have lost litters repeatedly come into estrus and mate, but mating success is low. The extended mating period often lasts for several estrous cycles. This protracted period of intense mating probably helps reinforce social bonds between the pride females and the new male.

Lactation places increasing nutritional demands on the female—a month or so after birth the female's energetic needs are 2·5–3 times normal. During this time females increase their hunting efforts, spending more time actively searching for prey. Tigresses without young make a large kill once every eight days; with young to feed the kill rate increases to one every 5–6 days. Cheetah mothers spend more of their time hunting larger prey, hunt more often, and are more successful than females without cubs. In Alberta, Canada, a female Puma killed a deer once every 13 days when she did not have young. A female with small kittens killed a deer every ten days. Her kill rate increased to one deer every seven days when her young were a year old. A radio-collared female Ocelot with young increased her foraging time by 113%, hunting almost continuously for 93% of the day.

Many of the smaller felids are introduced to solid food while they are still at the den. Free-living domestic cats start to bring live prey back to the den when the kittens are about a month old, and this coincides with the beginning of the weaning period. Domestic cat kittens are usually weaned by seven weeks of age, though mothers sometimes allow the kittens to continue suckling for several more months. Among the larger cats, cubs are generally introduced to solid food as soon as they leave the den and begin following the mother, at around two months of age. Just after they have left the den, the mother leaves the cubs in a safe place like a thicket or rocky outcrop and goes off to hunt. If the hunt is successful she will return and lead them to the kill. Cheetah mothers sometimes carry hares and small gazelles to their cubs. Cubs often alternate eating meat and nursing. Even when they are six months old, Tiger cubs will sometimes suckle if their mother allows it. By the time they are three or four months old, most felid young are accompanying their mothers on hunting expeditions. To begin with they

*After eating, prides of **Lions** often move to a river or water hole together, and usually crowd together at the water's edge to drink. Lions drink regularly if water is available, especially in hot weather, and usually take only a few minutes to drink their fill. Cats' tongues are covered with sharp-pointed, recurved, horny papillae, which not only help strip meat from bones, but also make fo efficient drinking.*

Panthera leo
Chobe National Park, Botswana.
Photo: Winfried Wisniewski/FLPA

Panthera pardus
Mala Mala Reserve, South Africa.
Photo: Richard du Toit/naturepl.com

simply follow. As they get older they begin to stalk and rush prey. They spend time stalking and chasing smaller prey such as birds, hares, and small carnivores. As the young grow, the mother gradually provides a series of different types of prey so the young can develop their predatory skills. A domestic cat will first bring dead prey to her kittens, then later carry live prey to the den and release it near the young. She will only intervene if the prey starts to escape. With this behavior, mothers provide opportunities for the young to learn. Examples of wild felids providing their young with similar opportunities are scarce, because most cats are difficult to observe in the wild. Tigresses have been observed bringing their large cubs to bait sites where domestic buffaloes have been tethered to attract Tigers for tourist viewing. The tigress then retreats and watches the cubs try to kill the buffalo. Cheetah mothers carry live prey back to the cubs, then release it. They also sometimes allow their cubs to overtake them in a chase and deliver the knockdown blow. When Cheetah young are between five and seven months old, mothers release almost a third of the prey they catch, and cubs begin to learn how to suffocate prey.

Laboratory experiments with domestic cats have shown that early experience clearly improves predatory skills. Kittens that experience handling prey when young as well as kittens that just watch their mother dealing with prey improve their adult predatory skills significantly. Kittens that have never killed a rat can learn to kill rats simply by watching another cat kill a rat. Studies of domestic cats suggest that a cat's choice of prey and its adult food preferences are strongly influenced by experience with its mother when young. Kittens tend to choose the same food their mother eats, even when it is not what they would normally eat. In one experiment, domestic cat mothers were taught to eat bananas and mashed potato. When their kittens were offered a choice of normal cat food or bananas and mashed potato, most of the kittens followed their mothers and ate the bananas and potato.

Learning which animals are suitable prey is also important. Young felids often stalk and chase totally inappropriate prey. Cheetah and Lion cubs have been seen chasing Giraffe (*Giraffa camelopardalis*), African Buffalo, and rhino, and Tiger cubs sometimes stalk Gaur and rhino. Cubs often ruin their mothers' hunts by playing, moving at the wrong time, or rushing the prey too soon. One study of the effects of cub behavior on maternal hunting success in Cheetah found that cub activity caused 9% of hunts to fail.

As young felids near sexual maturity they begin to disperse, leaving their natal range to establish their own home ranges. Males usually leave, but females often stay, establishing ranges on or near their natal range. Age of dispersal varies with species. Some of the smaller cats like Wildcats and Sand Cats disperse when they are about a year old. Limited information suggests that Ocelots disperse later than other small to medium-sized cats—in Venezuela two young males dispersed at about two years of age.

Larger cats such as Tigers require more time to perfect their hunting skills and often do not leave until they are nearly two years old. Dispersal age also varies within a species and clearly depends on circumstances. Leopards have been recorded dispersing as early as 14 months of age or as late as 36 months of age.

For many species, such as Puma, independence among sub-adult offspring seems to be prompted by the mother's resuming breeding behavior. This would seem to make sense as strange adult males could pose a danger to sub-adult young. Among Tigers, dispersal of young appears to be linked to the mother's beginning to travel with her new litter. Tiger cubs first become mobile and start to travel with their mother when they are about two months old.

Because of the difficulty of keeping track of wide-ranging animals, there have been few studies of dispersal in felids. However, during a long-term study of Puma in New Mexico, twenty-seven dispersing young were followed as they left their natal ranges. The average dispersal distance for males was 116 km, with a maximum of 214·9 km. Many females did not disperse, but those that did traveled an average of 28 km, with a maximum 78·5 km. A study in Nepal found that young Tigers dispersed between 19 and 28 months of age. Males traveled farther than females and settled in poorer habitats; most female young settled next to their mother's range.

In many cases young female felids do not disperse. In a behavior known as philopatry, the young carve out a portion of

*Breeding in **Bobcats** can occur year round, but most occurs from February through May. Like most other cat species, Bobcats are solitary except during the breeding season. However, adult male home ranges often overlap with those of other males and females. Mating pairs often stay together for a few days, and more than one male may attend a female in estrus. Once the female is truly in estrus and receptive, a courtship sequence begins. A male may copulate with a single female multiple times over several days.*

Lynx rufus
Minnesota, USA.
Photo: Gerard Fuehrer/DRK

their mother's range for themselves or squeeze in next to her. Loosely defined as the tendency of an individual to remain in its birthplace as an adult, female philopatry has been documented in several species of felids, including Puma, Tigers, Lions, Leopards, Cheetah, Black-footed Cats, and domestic cats. By allowing her daughter to use her home range a mother provides her offspring with an opportunity to forage in a good area, and protects them from aggressive encounters with others. Remaining in a familiar area is safer than leaving, and familiarity with an area, its hunting sites, and safe den sites can increase a young female's chance of breeding and successfully raising young.

To date, long-term research projects have found that among Leopards, Puma, and Tigers, several generations of daughters often live adjacent to their mothers, creating clusters of related females, in a sort of "exploded" Lion pride. Indeed, neighboring females are often as closely related as lionesses in a pride. These dispersed female kin groups provide insight into how Lion prides evolved.

Female philopatry among solitary felids has been best documented in a population of Puma in the San Andres Mountains of New Mexico. Nearly half the mothers that were monitored in this extensive long-term study formed eight matrilines composed of mothers and adult daughters. The matrilinial females produced more litters and gave birth to more cubs than females that were not matrilineal. Cubs of matrilineal females had a higher survival rate than cubs of non-matrilineal mothers. In this population as in others, reproductive success in females was highly variable, but clearly favored matrilineal mothers. Of course the most familiar example of female philopatry is the Lion pride, in which most female offspring born into the pride stay within the pride for the rest of their lives. Prides are composed of closely related females, usually mothers, sisters and daughters. Territories belong to the females and usually remain stable for decades.

Movements, Home range and Social Organization

The major period of activity for most cat species is at night; consequently they are difficult to follow and many details of

their movements are not well quantified. We do know that their movements are related to four major activities: finding food, scent marking to indicate to other cats that an area is occupied, looking for mates, and finally, dispersal.

Both large and small felids commonly travel less than 1 km/hour as they move slowly about their ranges, listening and looking for prey. Their nightly movements are often punctuated with one or more short periods (30–120 minutes) of inactivity, when the cats appear to be simply sitting and waiting. At other times individuals may move rapidly between distant points within their ranges, sometimes covering 3–5 km in an hour. These movements are often very direct and may represent shifts to alternative hunting sites. Movement paths sometimes criss-cross and zig-zag within a small area, suggesting the cat is searching intensively for prey.

Because the movements of most cats are inferred from radio-tracking data, study methods vary and the results are not always comparable. Many studies record movements as the straight-line distance between consecutive daily locations. However, this does not necessarily provide a good index of distances traveled per day because individuals may move about at night and then return to the same daytime rest site. For example, in New Mexico, the straight-line distance between consecutive daily locations for six adult Puma averaged 4·1 km, but the actual distance traveled was at least 1·5 times farther. Similarly, estimates of actual distances traveled by radio-collared Tigers in Chitwan National Park were actually 2–15 times greater than the corresponding linear distance between consecutive locations. Obviously, the best indication of distances traveled per day comes from obtaining repeated locations over 24 hour periods or during periods of major activity.

A large portion of a cat's daily life revolves around finding and capturing food. Several factors, including prey behavior and abundance, the cat's level of hunting expertise, and interactions with conspecifics and competitors will influence the distance a cat travels and the amount of time it spends moving in its search for food. In general the larger felids tend to travel farther than the smaller felids, but there are some exceptions. Small cats living in desert-like environments, such as Sand Cats in Israel and the Kara Kum Desert area, reportedly travel 7–10 km/night. Similarly, Black-footed Cats in South Africa travel an average of 8 km/night, with a maximum of 16 km. Clearly, food is scarce in desert habitats and these small pred-

*Breeding in **Lions** can take place at any time of year, but with birth peaks in certain regions. Courtship is initiated by either member of the pair, and they remain in close association during the mating period. The male follows the female at all times and rests with her. The female invites copulation by arching the back (lordosis). Other males associated with the pride are tolerated close by, and sometimes there are even multiple male copulations, but strange lions are driven off. The pair may copulate every 15 minutes, with copulation lasting up to one minute. Mating lasts over a period of several hours and also through the night. Between copulations the pair will lie down next to each other, or walk together until the next mating. During copulation the female purrs loudly, and towards the end the male may gently bite the female's neck. Lions have been observed copulating 157 times over a 55 hour period, and similar frequencies are reported for Tigers, Leopards, and Pumas. Slightly lower rates are reported for the smaller cats. The majority of matings do not result in pregnancy. Of 14 Lion mating periods observed, only four resulted in fertilization.*

Panthera leo
Above: Kenya.
Photo: Winfried Wisniewski/ FLPA

Below: Kenya.
Photo: David Hosking/FLPA

*Courtship in **Tigers** is risky, and familiarity appears to be an important prelude to mating. The mating posture is designed to ensure that the male does not become involved in a fight with the female, and avoids the risk of events escalating to an attack. In larger cats like Tigers, the male usually grips the female's neck only at the climax of copulation. After intromission (insertion of the penis) and ejaculation, the female may give a low growl and throw the male off her back. There is no copulatory lock, which would prevent the male withdrawing for a period of time after ejaculation, as happens, for example, in dogs.*

Panthera tigris
India.
Photo: Belinda Wright/
Lochman Transparencies

ators have to cover comparatively long distances to encounter enough prey to sustain themselves. Distances traveled by these small desert-dwelling cats exceed the daily movements reported for most other small felids. Living in habitats where food is more abundant, Wildcats in Europe travel 5–8 km/day, Jungle Cats 3–5 km/night, Jaguarundi 6·6 km/day, and Ocelots 3–7 km/night.

Large cats living in desert habitats also have to move over great distances to find food. Male Leopards living in the interior of the Kalahari Gemsbok National Park traveled an average of 16·1 km/day on days when no kills were made and females with cubs traveled 17·1 km/day. Female Leopards with cubs living in more productive areas along the Nossob River

within Kalahari Gemsbok National Park only traveled a mean of 3·8 km/day, a difference that most likely reflects prey density differences. In the southern Kalahari, Leopards traveled an average of 10·2 km/day on days when they made a kill. However, the distance traveled per day increased with the number of days that elapsed between kills and it was clear that the only way to increase hunting success was to expend more energy and travel farther. By the third day without a kill Leopards in the Kalahari were traveling an average of 21·8 km/day. Lions in the Kalahari travel an estimated 12–13 km/night, compared to only 2–9 km/night for Lions in the prey-rich Serengeti. Tigers living on the floodplain in Chitwan National Park, where prey are abundant, travel about 9–10 km/night, compared to

*Zoo records show that female **Leopards** may come into estrus at any time of the year, and remain in heat for 1–2 weeks. In the wild, mating associations are brief, lasting only 1–2 days. Most felids are thought to be induced ovulators: the rupture of the follicle and the release of the ovum must be induced by repeated stimulation of vagina and cervix. The felid baculum (penis bone) has spines, suggesting a connection between stimulation and ovulation. Coupling egg release with mating may make fertilization more likely, but conception rates seem low, from 20–40% in Lions and Tigers to 50–67% in Leopards, Pumas, Snow Leopards, and Ocelots.*

Panthera pardus
India.
Photo: Stanley Breeden/
Lochman Transparencies

*After a gestation of 68–72 days, **Eurasian Lynx** kittens are usually born in late May to early June. Litter size is from one to four; two is most common. Felid young are altricial: they are born small, blind, and helpless, unable to do much more than crawl to their mother, the source of food and warmth. The mother usually spends the first 24–48 hours with the newborn young, grooming them, keeping them warm, and nursing. She then leaves the kittens to search for food, and may be away for as long as 24–36 hours, but returns to feed them as often as possible. Felid young are very vulnerable to predation in the first month or two of their lives, and almost any predator can kill cubs.*

Lynx lynx
Hardangenvidda, Norway.
Photo: Staffan Widstrand

estimates of 15–20 km/day in the Russian Far East where prey is less abundant and more dispersed.

In any 24 hour period, males almost invariably travel farther than females. Iberian Lynx males travel an average of 8·7 km/day compared to 6·4 km/day for females. In New Mexico, Puma males travel 5·2–7·9 km/day compared to 1·0–3·1 km/day for females with kittens. Not all movement by males is solely for hunting, but it is difficult to distinguish it from travel to scent-mark or to check for receptive females. A notable exception occurred in Chitwan National Park, Nepal, following the death of a resident male Tiger. The neighboring male expanded his territory and thereby increased the number of females within his area from three to seven. To cover this expanded range the male routinely used the east-west park road to move rapidly and easily from one end of his territory to the other. The park's geography was such that the male only had to worry about intruders coming in at the ends of his territory; he visited each end an average of 3·6 to 4·2 times per month, staying an average of 1·4 to 2·1 days each time. His tracks were readily identifiable on the dirt road, and sometimes observers followed them for 9–13 km without seeing any indication that the Tiger stopped or rested en route. On one occasion the Tiger traveled 20·5 km in less than twelve hours; another time he covered 16 km in 7·5 hours.

The greatest distances traveled by felids are often associated with dispersal, which is the movement of an independent or subadult animal from its natal range to a site where it subsequently settles and breeds. The phenomenon is highly variable in terms of age, sex, frequency and duration of exploratory or predispersal movement, and direction and distance moved. Among mammals, young males generally emigrate from their natal ranges, whereas most females tend to be philopatric, staying close to their natal ranges. Felids are no exception.

Information compiled for 148 young Puma (70 females, 78 males) from 13 different studies shows that young usually disperse between the ages of 14 and 21 months, usually prior to reproductive maturity. Young Tigers become independent of their mothers by 17 to 24 months of age but continue to hunt in their natal range. After moving independently within their mother's range for a few months the young typically disperse, which for Tigers occurs at 18 to 28 months of age, prior to sexual maturity. This pattern is common to many mammals and allows the young to hone their hunting skills in a familiar area.

However, not all young disperse. Of 78 male Puma, two remained in their natal range, and at least 21 of 70 females

were philopatric. Some of these females acquired the vacant range of their mother, whereas others settled in vacant ranges adjoining their mothers'. The degree of female philopatry varies among and within areas. The majority of subadult females in the New Mexico, Utah, and Alberta populations stayed on or near their natal ranges, or only dispersed short distances. In other areas only a few females stayed and the majority dispersed. Why some females stay and others leave, even in the same area, is not known. The answer probably lies in a combination of factors, including the availability of vacant ranges, population density on and off the study area, habitat quality, kitten mortality, and hunting pressure.

Dispersal movements of young male Puma may last for several months, during which they commonly travel 85 to 100 km. Indeed, the average dispersal distance for eight males in New Mexico was 101 km. Several males have been found 150 to 275 km from their birthplaces, and one young male marked in Wyoming was later killed in Colorado, about 480 km from his natal area. In contrast, the average dispersal distance for females who left their natal area was about 40 km, although there are a few accounts of females traveling more than 100 km.

Dispersing Leopards in Nepal's Chitwan National Park exhibited a similar pattern. Three young males, two of whom were littermates, dispersed in different directions, but movements were strongly directional. Each spent from two to three days in several small forest patches along the route, taking 2–4 weeks to travel the 8–11 km from their natal ranges to areas where they appeared to settle. The relatively slow rates of travel were probably because Tigers frequented the area and because the young Leopards were exploring unfamiliar terrain. Ocelots in Texas also exhibited a protracted dispersal phase, spending 2–8·5 months or longer in search of a place to settle, although most eventually established themselves on ranges that were less than 9 km from their natal ranges.

Cats are also capable of moving extremely long distances during dispersal. A recent study of Canadian Lynx in the Yukon Territories followed eleven dispersing Lynx that traveled more than 500 km and two others that moved more than 1000 km. Other records are anecdotal but reveal how even the largest cats can travel remarkably long distances. There are historical records of Tigers in the Caspian Sea region appearing in areas hundreds of km from the nearest known Tiger population. In 1996, on two separate occasions, Jaguars were seen and photographed in southern Arizona, an area where the species had not been recorded for ten years. These individuals are thought

For about a month after her cubs are born, the female felid stays close to the den, nursing and caring for her cubs. Thus, she searches for prey within a much smaller home range than before her offspring were born. However, the female's own nutritional needs grow as the kittens grow. By the time the young are a month old, a nursing mother needs up to three times as much food to keep her kittens supplied with milk and to maintain her own strength, so she has to spend more time hunting. A female *Puma* in Canada killed a deer once every 13 days when she did not have young, whereas a female with small kittens made a kill every ten days. As the kittens grew and began to eat solid food, the kill rate increased, reaching one deer every seven days when her young were a year old. Female Leopards in north-east Namibia made a kill about once every five days or so, whereas females with dependent young made a kill every 3·9–4·4 days. Although the kill rate was not much higher for females with young, they did kill larger prey, resulting in a greater per capita food intake. Female *Lions* leave their pride to give birth. Litter size averages 2–3 cubs. The females rejoin the pride with their cubs 4–8 weeks later. Any female member of the pride with milk will allow any cub to suckle. Cubs suckle regularly for 6–7 months, and less after seven months, stopping altogether after twelve months.

Above: *Puma concolor*
Photo: Jurgen & Christine Sohns/FLPA

Below: *Panthera leo*
Kenya.
Photo: David Hosking/FLPA

to have come from a population located 320 to 480 km south in Mexico. Clearly, as long as they are not persecuted and there is even marginally suitable habitat to travel through, felids are capable of dispersing great distances. This bodes well for the long-term persistence and potential for conservation of felids in increasingly fragmented and human-dominated landscapes.

Relationship with Humans

For millennia there has been a complex and varying relationship between cats and people. Since the earliest times, cats have inspired and have been exploited by people, particularly as symbols of power and strength. Our relationship with cats has fluctuated from persecution and exploitation in their worst forms to more benign approaches, including concern for their conservation and caring for them as pets. Wearing their skins, making traditional medicines from them, and domesticating them for our benefit are the main ways that cats have been used by people for thousands of years. However, as natural habitats are increasingly destroyed by human activities, so many cat species are threatened with extinction today.

Our earliest experiences with cats are recorded in the famous cave paintings of south-west France and Spain. Dating from as long as 30,000 years ago, these instantly recognizable images show mainly Lions, although it has been claimed that some show Lynxes or even the extinct scimitar-toothed cats, *Homotherium* sp. Unfortunately, smaller species seem to have been overlooked by our ancestors or at least regarded as unimportant in their art, whatever its purpose.

Since the end of the last Ice Age, the evidence for the influence of cats, especially the larger species, on former civilizations is considerable. Just as Lions and Tigers were and still are regarded as symbols of power and strength in Africa and Asia, so the Jaguar filled a similar cultural niche in the Americas. The Mayan Indians of Central America regarded the Jaguar as the night sun of the underworld that brought fear, night terrors and even death. In areas that were not occupied by Jaguars, the Puma was also deified; the Peruvian city of Cuzco was even built in the shape of a Puma. Jaguars and Pumas were immortalized in paintings, sculptures, and pottery, so important was their role in ancient societies. The influence of cats on religion, art, and culture has continued through the millennia, both in the west and the east. Poetry, paintings, literature, and sculpture had all used cats as their inspiration.

However, it was not just the image of cats that influenced our ancestors and continues to inspire us today. Since the earliest times, it has been believed that wearing the skins, claws, or other body parts of cats endowed the wearer with cats' strength, power, and ability to kill. For example, warriors in Sarawak, Borneo wore Diardi's Clouded Leopard skins decorated with hornbill feathers. Shamans in Africa and Asia were believed to be able to transform themselves into big cats at will, and African chiefs were said to be reincarnated as Lions. The remains of Diardi's Clouded Leopards and Tigers are still used by shamans today in Sumatra in their ritual customs. Masai warriors were once required to hunt a Lion alone in order to prove their

Female **Leopards** use caves, rocky outcrops, abandoned burrows, or dense thickets for birth dens. For the first few days after the cubs are born the mother spends practically all of her time at the den, resting and nursing the young. Similarly, female **Pumas** restrict their movements to the immediate vicinity of natal dens for about two months, after which time the kittens join their mothers at kills. A female cat may move her young from a den that is overloaded with parasites, or because of disturbance or threat. The young are moved one by one, and are carried by the loose skin at the nape of the neck, as this **Lion** is doing, or by the back; or even, as this Leopard seems to be doing, by the head.

Above: *Panthera pardus*
Masai Mara, Kenya.
Photo: Fritz Pölking/FLPA

Below left: *Puma concolor*
Photo: Jurgen & Christine Sohns /FLPA

Below right: *Panthera leo*
Masai Mara National Park, Kenya.
Photo: Winfried Wisniewski/FLPA

*Young **Cheetahs** open their eyes at 4–14 days. At 3–6 weeks, a set of milk teeth erupts, replaced at about eight months by adult teeth. Cheetah cubs can retract their claws up to ten weeks of age, and they are able tree climbers. The cubs accompany their mothers on hunts from eight weeks onward, and are introduced to solid food. Cubs often alternate eating meat with suckling, which terminates at about four months. They are very playful during the first six months, starting to practice hunting afterwards.*

Acinonyx jubatus
Photo: Silvestris Fotoservice/FLPA

manhood. They had to encourage the Lion to attack them so that it could be impaled on a spear, thereby demonstrating the bravery of the hunter, and they were then able to wear their lion-mane cape with manly pride. In Thailand the claws of the Tiger are believed to give the wearer courage. In Indochina floating bones (clavicles or collar bones) of the Tiger are believed to protect the wearer from Tiger attacks and give the wearer physical superiority over his enemies, whereas in China they are worn as talismans of good luck.

In more recent times this tradition was lost in western societies and replaced by the wearing of spotted and striped cat skins as fashion items, although this has now largely fallen out of favor. Although Canadian Lynxes have been exploited commercially for their furs since the 17th century, large-scale trade in spotted and striped cat furs only began in the late 19th century. However, the trade in these skins resulted in a severe decline in the numbers of many tropical cat species during the 1960s and 1970s. In the late 1960s 10,000 Leopards, 15,000 Jaguars, up to 5000 Cheetahs and 200,000 Ocelot (incuding Margay and Oncilla) pelts worth US$ 30 million were imported to the USA each year. In global trade more than half a million cat skins were traded in 1979 and almost 700,000 in the following year, mostly involving Geoffroy's Cat, Bobcat, Jungle Cat, Oncilla, Canadian Lynx, Wildcat, Ocelot, and Margay in order of decreasing numbers. Of course, these figures do not include the pelts that are sold on domestic markets, so this trade has been enormous each year. Just as with the great whales, as one (usually larger) species became over-exploited and commercially extinct, the trappers moved on to other species. There was a five-fold reduction in the number of Leopard skins imported to the USA from 1968 to 1970 as more countries introduced laws to protect their big cats and the International Fur Traders Association imposed a voluntary ban on the use of big cat skins. However, as attention switched to the smaller species, these began to be over-exploited; for example, after the Ocelot became harder to trap, the smaller Geoffroy's Cat succumbed in huge numbers to this trade (more than 145,000 skins in 1980). Remarkably, the Leopard Cat in China still seems to support a considerable trade in furs, despite 100,000 or more being taken annually; a peak of 200,000 was reached in 1987. Indeed, the population of Leopard Cats was said to have increased as larger competitors, such as Asian Golden Cat and clouded leopards, have been eliminated. However, the European Community

banned the import of Leopard Cat skins in 1988 over concern that this level of trade was damaging populations.

The hunting of Bobcats and Canadian Lynxes for fur also still continues in a regulated way in North America today, although some local cat populations still suffer badly from over-exploitation. Quotas are intended to take account of population fluctuations and dynamics caused by prey availability and habitat quality, but even so, the famous Snowshoe Hare-Canadian Lynx population cycles have been disrupted in many areas, including Alaska, and Alberta and Newfoundland in Canada. Highest prices for Canadian Lynx pelts were reached in the mid-1980s (up to US$ 750) when the populations were at their lowest. These high prices seem to have led to over-trapping,

*Female felids take good care of their young, grooming them, like this **Jaguar** mother, and keeping them safe and warm. Jaguar cubs are born after a gestation period of 93–105 days. Litter size varies from one to four, with an average of two. The cubs weigh about 700–900 g at birth and have coarse, woolly, spotted coats. Their eyes open at 13 days of age. They are totally dependent on their mother's milk until they are 10–11 weeks old and may continue to suckle until they are 5–6 months old.*

Panthera onca
Photo: Gerard Lacz/FLPA

resulting in population declines and thus demonstrating the need for governmental regulation and appropriate population monitoring. Overall, trade in cat furs seems to be declining. By 1990 there were only about a quarter of the number of pelts traded in 1980, and modern trade is now dominated by two lynx species from North America, one from Russia, and the Leopard Cat, which is mainly from China.

The problem with using fur for fashion is that it is incredibly wasteful. Only a small part of the pelt can be used, so that many skins of smaller species must be acquired to make a complete coat. For example, although only about 7·5 Canadian Lynx skins are required to make a garment, the pelts of 25 Geoffroy's Cats and 30 Wildcats are needed, because of their smaller size.

The decline in numbers of big and then smaller cats, owing to their demand in the fur trade, was influential in the development and eventual ratification of the Convention on International Trade in Endangered Species (CITES). Today all cat species, except for the ubiquitous domestic cat, are now included on Appendices I and II, which either prevent or limit commercial trade. This change in attitude toward the exploitation of wild species also coincided with the enormous growth of popular concern about the environment and awareness for the need for global conservation. Concern for animal welfare and the cruelty of trapping methods has had a positive result: the wearing of furs has fallen out of favor. However, there is some concern that fur wearing is increasing once more at the beginning of the new millennium as a natural or organic alternative to artificial fabrics. Although this may be acceptable

if the harvest is regulated, and trapping and culling methods are humane, we should be aware that legal exploitation may act as a cover for illicit and cruel practices elsewhere in the world. Certainly there is much less habitat now available for the world's cats than there was forty years ago.

Ever since our hominid ancestors evolved in the savannas of eastern and southern Africa, we have been potential prey for big cats. A cranium of an australopithecine, *Australopithecus africanus*, was found in Swartkrans Cave in Transvaal, South Africa, bearing indentations from the canine teeth of a Leopard from a predation event some 2·5–3 million years ago. More recently, Lions, Leopards, and Tigers have often been recorded as man-eaters. However, Jaguars have largely escaped this title, perhaps because until relatively recently their habitats and prey remained largely intact and human population densities are still relatively low compared with the Old World.

It was once thought that only old or injured cats killed people, because we are easy prey. However, recent studies show that where the natural prey base has been destroyed by human hunting or competition with livestock, healthy cats and their young may also be forced to turn to people for food. This hunting tradition may then be passed down the generations, because a man-eating mother may teach her cubs that we are appropriate prey. Bizarrely, man-eating has inspired art. In the 17th century an Indian ruler, Tipu Sultan, known as the Tiger of Mysore, hated the British so much that he commissioned a model Tiger killing a British soldier. It included a mechanism that simulated the growls of the Tiger and the dying cries of the victim. This remarkable model was eventually captured by the British and can be seen today in the Victoria and Albert Museum in London. There have been some famous victims of potential man-eaters; Dr David Livingstone, the famous missionary who traveled throughout Central Africa, was mauled by a Lion and badly injured. The humerus of his arm never healed completely. Some man-eaters had terrible reputations, although no doubt some of the figures quoted are exaggerations. For example, in 1822, 500 people and 20,000 cattle were said to have been killed by "wild beasts", mostly Tigers, in the Khandesh District of India. Also in India the tigress of Champawat killed 436 people and the Panar Leopard was not far behind with 400 victims and made the hunter who killed them, J. Corbett, famous for doing so. The equally famous man-eating Lions of Tsavo in Kenya were alleged to have killed 28 Indians, dozens of locals, and had injured a European during a nine-week period in 1898 before they were killed by Col. J. H. Patterson. The annual toll from man-eating was once considerable. Before the Second World War 1500 people were killed annually by Tigers in India, although far fewer people (about 60) were killed in Burma during the same period, thus indicating a relationship between high human populations, humans as prey, and Tigers. However, opportunity is everything, and during the retreat of 1942, Tigers fed on the corpses of soldiers who died in the Arakan region of Burma.

In some areas, such as the Sundarbans of Bangladesh and India, lives continue to be lost. A total of 612 people were killed by Tigers during the period 1975-1985. Although prey appear to be abundant here, the supposedly highly dense population of 500–600 Tigers seems to be opportunistically preying on slow-moving people when they are gathering firewood and honey from the forests. The number of people killed by Tigers has fallen in recent years through limiting access to Tiger areas, increasing natural prey such as Wild Boars, providing decoy electrified wood-cutters and honey collectors, and using face masks on the backs of their heads to deter Tigers from attacking.

Today's domestic cats are thought to have originated more than 4000 years ago in Egypt. Their ancestor was the African Wildcat, but it is likely that other Wildcat populations, including Asian Wildcats (*Felis silvestris ornata*), may have also contributed to the domestic cats of today, and domestication may have occurred in more than one place. There is some older evidence for possible earlier attempts at domestication. A tooth found at Jericho and dating from about 8700 years ago is thought by some to represent an early domestic cat, and a jaw bone found at Khirokitia in southern Cyprus and dating from around 8000 years ago is particularly interesting as Wildcats do not occur on this island. However, if this animal was domesticated, its size was still as great as its ancestor, the African Wildcat.

Gestation length in felids varies from about 60 days in some of the smaller cats, to slightly over 100 days for Tigers, and generally scales with the size of the cat: larger felids have longer gestation periods than smaller ones. The exceptions are the cats in the Ocelot lineage: **Margay,** *Ocelot, Oncilla, Geoffroy's Cat, Colocolo, and Kodkod. They have longer gestation periods than many other cats their size. For most felids, litter size is typically 2–3, but again, members of the Ocelot lineage differ. Margays and Ocelots, in particular, often give birth to only one kitten per litter. Most of what is known of Margay reproduction is derived from a small number of captive animals. The gestation is about 76–84 days. Young begin to eat solid food at 7–8 weeks, and by 8–10 months they are nearly adult size. Estrus has been reported in six- to ten-month-old females, but sexual maturity is more commonly attained at about two years of age. Adults typically give birth every two years. This contrasts with species like the Bobcat, which mature faster, breed every year, and have larger litters.*

Leopardus wiedii
Brazil.
Photo: Mike Powles/
www.photolibrary.com

Like in all felids, play in **Leopard** cubs is a useful learning tool. There are usually two or three Leopard cubs in a litter, weighing only 500–600 g each at birth. Compared with other mammals, felids invest relatively little in gestation; the young are born blind and naked, at an early stage of development. This is probably because females must hunt alone and cannot afford to be handicapped by a large fetus. Radio tracking studies of several wild felid species have shown that after birth, and for the first month or so of the kittens' lives, the mother's home range shrinks dramatically. Her movements are focused on the den, and her range does not begin to expand again until the young become mobile. Studies in north-east Namibia found that three-month-old Leopard cubs were left for periods of 1–7 days while their mother hunted. Young generally begin traveling with their mother when they are about three months old and weigh 3–4 kg. There are records of five-month-old cubs killing hares and other small animals, but more commonly this coincides with the appearance of their permanent canines at about 7–8 months of age. By the time Leopards are 12–18 months old, they are usually independent of their mother, but the timing of dispersal varies from 15 to 36 months. Sexual maturity is attained at 2–3 years.

Panthera pardus
Masai Mara National Park, Kenya.
Photos: Fritz Pölking/FLPA

*Play, involving both adults and other cubs, helps young **Lions** develop skills like stalking and pouncing. They learn to hunt by watching the adults in the pride. Female Lions display several kinds of cooperative behavior which are unique among cat species. They tend to give birth at around the same time, particularly after the pride has been taken over by new males. Litters born synchronously have a higher survival rate. The pride, which consists of related females, none of them dominant, raises its cubs communally, even to the extent of suckling other females' cubs. The young grow rapidly during the first three years, remaining with their mothers for 21–30 months. Young males leave the pride at 2–3 years old, but the daughters of the pride remain. Males reach sexual maturity at 26 months, but only get the opportunity to mate when they are about five years old, and usually only during their pride tenure. Females become pregnant for the first time at about 43 months of age and continue to breed until they are about 15 years old, producing a litter every two years. Long term research projects have found that among Leopards, Pumas, and Tigers, several generations of daughters often live adjacent to their mothers, creating clusters of related females, in a sort of "exploded" Lion pride. Indeed, neighboring females are often as closely related as lionesses in a pride. These dispersed female kin groups provide insight into how Lion prides may have evolved.*

Above: ***Panthera leo***
Photos: Albert Visage/FLPA

Below: ***Panthera leo***
Sabi Sabi Private Game Reserve,
South Africa.
Photo: Wendy Dennis/FLPA

*As the young grow, felid mothers gradually provide a series of different types of prey so that they can develop the skills of stalking, pouncing, and killing necessary to be successful hunters as adults. Of course, in the **Fishing Cat**, the training is focused on the essential techniques of fishing. In domestic cats, where such instruction is more easily studied, the female will first bring dead prey to her kittens, then later carry live prey to the den and release it near the young. Laboratory experiments with domestic cats have shown that early experience, even simply watching the mother or other cats killing prey, improves predatory skills. Such studies also suggest that a cat's choice of prey and its adult food preferences are strongly influenced by early experience with its mother.*

Prionailurus viverrinus
Photo: Terry Whittaker/FLPA

Domestication is thought to have occurred when Wildcats were attracted to rubbish tips to scavenge, or to grain stores to prey on mice and rats. Living at high population densities close to people, they probably became predisposed to the final domestication process. It is likely that kittens were taken by people and raised as tame animals. However, it seems that it was the Egyptians who took the domestication of the Wildcat most seriously; there they became common household animals by 3500 years ago. There is in fact a change in the depiction of cats in tomb frescos: before that date, they are shown as hunting animals, and afterwards, as household pets. The male domestic cat became associated with the sun-god, *Re*, because it was believed that *Re* adopted the form of a tomcat during his daily battles with *Apep*, the serpent of darkness. This may have been inspired by observations of cats killing and eating snakes. About 3000 years ago, the female domestic cat became associated with the Egyptian goddess *Bastet*, with one of the eyes of *Re*, and with other goddesses including *Sekhmet, Mut*, and *Hathor*. *Bastet*, one of the most important goddesses, was the "Lady of Life" associated with fertility and maternity, but also with a darker side linked to the spirit world and death. In particular *Bastet* was associated with the moon and the earth's fertility, linking together the 28 day lunar and menstrual cycles. Again there was a change from *Bastet*'s being represented by a Lion to being represented by a cat, as domestic cats spread in popularity. Domestic cats reached the peak of their popularity 2450 years ago, when the Greek writer Herodotus visited Egypt, where he described the magnificent temple at Bubastis and the annual festival to celebrate *Bastet*, which was attended by 100,000 people. By this time, cats were regarded as sacred animals. Intentional killing of a cat could result in the death penalty, whereas unintentional death would result in a fine from a priest. If a cat died, the members of a household would shave off their eyebrows as a mark of respect.

Dead cats were mummified and buried in cat cemeteries at Bubastis (now called Tell Basta) and elsewhere. Most of the cats were domestic cats, but a few Jungle Cats have also been found there. One such cemetery discovered in 1888 was said to have contained more than 80,000 cat mummies. Recent studies of mummified cats have shown that many were young animals of one to four months of age, probably bred in temple catteries and deliberately killed for mummification. Many hundreds of thousands of mummified cats have been excavated, but most were turned into fertilizer during the 19th century. For example, only a single skull survives from a ship-ment of 19 tons brought to Manchester, England. Recently, cat cemeteries have been discovered at Saqqara. Studies of these abundant remains using molecular and morphometric techniques offer a unique opportunity to trace the early domestication of the Wildcat and the possible involvement of other species such as the Jungle Cat.

The domestic cat began to spread around Europe and Asia more than 2000 years ago. The Romans, in particular, transported it throughout their Empire. Before then the Egyptians had been assiduous in preventing the spread of their sacred cats, even sending envoys to retrieve them from overseas. The percentages of different coat colors seen in domestic cat populations in various parts of Europe and the Mediterranean today reflect this early spread of cats and the color mutations that have arisen since Roman times.

Black and sex-linked orange coat color mutations arose in the Middle East and were spread by sea along the Mediterranean and overland by the Romans' main trading routes. They spread via the Rhone and Seine valleys of France to Britain. Non-agouti (black) coloration is heavily influenced by the degree of urbanization of human habitats; the proportion of black cats in a population increases with human population density, suggesting natural selection for dark coats in urban environments.

The ancestral marking of domestic cats was the striped tabby pattern of the African Wildcat. One variant of this tabby form, the blotched tabby, is thought to have first arisen as a mutation in Britain, where today it is most abundant. The percentage of blotched tabby cats in domestic cat populations in different parts of the world reflects the date of colonization of these places by Britain, and as a result the blotched tabby has been dubbed the British Imperial cat. Blotched tabbies are less abundant in North America (colonized in the mid-17th century) than in Australia (mid-19th century), mirroring the proportion of blotched tabbies in the British population at these times. Local climates seem also to have influenced domestic cat morphology, producing thin, short-furred breeds such as the Siamese from South-east Asia and robust, thickly-furred breeds from Britain and Scandinavia. It is likely that hybridization with local Wildcat populations influenced local coat coloration and body morphology.

From being deities in ancient times, cats became associated with the devil and witchcraft during medieval times, owing to their association with the ancient pagan cults of female goddesses. It was believed that witches were able to transform

A greater degree of sociality has been observed among **Cheetahs** than in most felids, with the exception of the Lion. Male and female littermates tend to stay together for about six months after independence, until the female siblings reach sexual maturity and split off. Male littermates remain together in coalitions, and sometimes defend territories. On some occasions, groups of adults with cubs have been reported. Groups of mixed sex have been seen hunting together, probably reflecting mating activity, or a large litter just before independence.

Acinonyx jubatus
Photo: Fritz Pölking/FLPA

themselves into domestic cats and so the cats became surrogate victims. Domestic cats, especially black ones, were treated barbarically and often tortured to death as witches. As recently as the 18th century, dead cats were often built into the walls, floors, or ceilings of new buildings, sometimes with mice or rats, to protect the house against vermin. However, during the 18th century, the Enlightenment brought a change in attitude, and by the late 19th century the cat became revered once more, especially fancy breeds of cat. More than 40 breeds are recognized, including many color varieties and hair lengths. New breeds are being developed by hybridization with wild felids. For example, the Bengal has arisen from matings between male domestic cats and female Leopard Cats; such hybridization has also apparently been recorded from the wild. However, Bengals can only be maintained by crossing them with domestic cats, as the male hybrids are almost invariably sterile.

In some parts of the world, domestic cats have become a major conservation threat. On oceanic islands where animals have evolved in the absence of predators and so show no escape behavior, introduced domestic cats have found it easy to prey on indigenous (native) species. In the worst cases this has led to extinctions. The most famous extinction caused by a single domestic cat was that of the Stephen Island wren (*Xenicus lyalli*), whose total history of discovery and extinction was reported at the same meeting of the Zoological Society of London in the 19th century. This new species of bird was wiped out by the lighthouse keeper's cat in just a few months. Sadly only 16 specimens survive in museums today. Another more recent victim of the domestic cat was the Socorro dove (*Zenaida graysoni*), from the island of Socorro off the coast of California. It fed mainly on the ground and having evolved on an island without predators, it was easy prey for introduced domestic cats. It has since been replaced by the abundant and widespread Mourning Dove. Although the Socorro Dove became extinct in the wild in the 1950s, fortunately some birds were taken into captivity, so the species still survives.

In some parts of Europe, domestic cats are posing a serious threat to the survival of the European Wildcat because of hybridization. Although hybridization has probably always occurred to some extent in the 2000 years or more that domestic cats have been in Europe, the most serious episodes have occurred in some areas only in the last 200 years. For example, in Scotland, sporting estates were developed starting in the middle of the 19th century, after which Wildcats were persecuted nearly to extinction for their alleged predation of gamebirds such as pheasant and red grouse. The First World War

resulted in a relaxation of persecution, and changed economic conditions following the war meant that gamekeepers did not return to Scotland in such great numbers. By 1950 the number of gamekeepers in Britain had fallen to only 5000, less than a quarter of their peak at the beginning of the 20th century. The establishment of the Forestry Commission in 1919 led to much-needed reforestation of Scotland (only 4% woodland cover in 1919) that provided essential habitat for the Wildcat and other woodland species. The Wildcat responded rapidly and began to colonize much of northern central Scotland before the Second World War, from its last stronghold in the northwest Highlands (although there may have been small pockets of Wildcats elsewhere). However, as male Wildcats probably dispersed more widely than females, they would probably have found themselves in areas with no female Wildcats, and they resorted to the local domestic females instead. Since then there have been complex matings between Wildcats, domestic cats, and their hybrids to produce a large hybrid swarm. It is clear that the genetic integrity of Scottish Wildcats may be threatened by introgressive hybridization with domestic cats. This has serious consequences for the conservation and legal protection of Wildcats. In 1990 in a prosecution for the alleged killing of three Wildcats, an expert witness could not say beyond reasonable doubt that the cats were Wildcats. However, recent molecular and morphological research has demonstrated that Wildcats are distinguishable from domestic cats and hybrids. It appears also that not all Wildcat populations are affected in this way. In Italy hybridization is apparently rare and hybrids are few, perhaps because local populations have not been eliminated and then recolonized from elsewhere. Research is urgently needed to determine why hybridization is more prevalent in some populations than others. There is great concern that over time it may be impossible to distinguish between domestic cats and Wildcats in some areas, owing to complete introgression between the two species. In Scotland this process may now be happening.

During the 19th century and first half of the 20th century hunters from western countries traveled the world in search of big game. Their exploits were preserved as trophies to demonstrate to their friends and rivals their prowess as hunters. The aim of these hunters was to kill the biggest animals they could, and big cats were no exception, whether they be measured in total length "between the pegs" or had the longest skulls. These records were immortalized for big cats and other big game in *Rowland Ward's Records of Big Game*. Many of these trophies still survive today as mounted heads, skulls, and rugs. Although collected mainly for

Female **Cheetahs** help their cubs learn to hunt by bringing home live prey such as hares and young gazelles, and releasing them for the cubs to chase and bring down. They also sometimes allow their cubs to overtake them in a chase, and deliver the knockdown blow. When Cheetah young are between five and seven months old, mothers release almost a third of the prey they catch, and cubs begin to learn how to suffocate prey. Cubs often ruin their mothers' hunts by playing, moving at the wrong time, or rushing the prey too soon. One study of the effects of cub behavior on maternal hunting success in Cheetahs found that cub activity caused 9% of hunts to fail. This contrasts with the earlier period, when the young are left behind when the female goes to hunt: at this stage, Cheetah mothers spend more of their time hunting larger prey, hunt more often, and are more successful than females without cubs. Learning which animals are suitable prey is also an important part of the education of young cats. The first independent kills made by young Cheetahs may be the calves of Thomson's or Grant's Gazelles, and calves and half grown gazelles continue to make up more than 50% of Cheetah kills when they reach adulthood. But they also need to learn what not to hunt. Young felids often stalk and chase totally inappropriate prey. Cheetah and Lion cubs have been seen chasing Giraffes, buffaloes and rhinos; and Tiger cubs sometimes stalk rhinos, and also Gaur, the largest species of wild cattle, which has been known to kill adult Tigers.

Acinonyx jubatus
Masai Mara National Park, Kenya.
Photo: Fritz Pölking/FLPA

111

Young **Servals** *acquire their permanent canine teeth at about six months of age and begin to hunt for themselves shortly afterwards. Servals are solitary animals, but newly independent young are sometimes allowed to remain within their natal range for a year or more. One adult female Serval was repeatedly sighted in the same area over a nine-year period, indicating strong site fidelity. In captivity, there are records of females becoming sexually mature when they were just over a year old. Female Servals are polyestrous, that is, they have repeated estrous cycles during the year, and births seem to occur about a month before the peak in murid rodent (rat and mouse) reproduction.*

Leptailurus serval
Ngorongoro Crater, Tanzania.
Photo: Fritz Pölking/FLPA

personal vanity, they are an important record of morphological and genetic variation in populations that may well now be extinct in the wild. Therefore, research on these specimens may provide valuable data for the management of today's critically endangered populations of Tigers and other big cats.

The hunting of big cats still continues and is very controversial. While some argue that killing a few large animals in a regulated way can generate vast amounts of money for conservation, others insist that culling prime animals disrupts the social and breeding systems of local populations. Hunting also requires appropriate regulation and accurate monitoring of populations. There may be a tendency to over-exploit populations as a welcome way to earn much-needed income and not monitor the populations as being too expensive or time-consuming.

In India Cheetahs were traditionally used to hunt deer, gazelles, and Blackbuck. Although coursing with Cheetahs was practiced in India before the arrival of the Mughal emperors, it was they who developed it into the great sport it became. In the 16th century the Mughal emperor Akbar may have had up to 9000 Cheetahs during his lifetime. His successor Jahangir managed to accidentally breed a litter of three cubs in 1613, the only record of captive breeding until 1956 at the Philadelphia Zoo.

The normal practice was to trap adult Cheetahs that were competent hunters and train them for coursing. Prior to the hunt, the Cheetahs' heads were covered in hoods, which were removed just before the Cheetah was released so that it was immediately focussed on the prey animal. By 1900 Cheetahs were very scarce in India, and African animals were imported for hunting. Cheetah coursing died out soon after Indian independence in 1947. The Indian Cheetah was probably last recorded in the 1960s.

Caracals were also used for hunting in a similar way to Cheetahs. They were used to hunt smaller game such as hares and partridge, but it has been claimed that gazelle and even Nilgai were also hunted. Caracals could also be trained to hunt birds such as kites, by throwing food into the air, causing the bird to swoop within striking distance of the Caracal. Braces of Caracals were also pitted against each other to see which pair could bring down the most pigeons from a flock feeding in an arena; the best could manage a dozen birds. This sport has led to the expression of "putting a cat amongst the pigeons".

In the early 20th century the realization was dawning among big game hunters, the so-called penitent butchers, that over-hunting and habitat loss was resulting in the severe decline

of many species. A ban on hunting the Asian Lion (*Panthera leo persica*) in the Gir Forest, its final stronghold, at this time has seen the population increase from a minimum of about 20 to about 250 today. Although game reserves have always been maintained by rulers for their own benefit, many of these have been transformed into national parks for the benefit of wildlife and to encourage tourism, with all its economic benefits. This concept is developing further so that local people are now also benefiting from the presence of large and dangerous wild animals, rather than all monies disappearing to central government. From wholesale illegal poisoning of big cats after the Second World War, as human populations increased dramatically and consumed large areas of wilderness, some communities are now encouraged to live alongside these dangerous predators.

Research has also made a great impact. Pioneering studies on Lions and Tigers since the 1960s, particularly by George Schaller, have led the way into myriad field studies that provide information vital to the future conservation and management of endangered species. In 1973 Project Tiger heralded a new age of conservation efforts for endangered species, which depended on more or less reliable field research. National parks and other protected areas were set aside for the benefit of Tigers and often to the detriment of local people. Project Tiger seems to have been successful and the number of Indian Tigers is thought to have doubled to more than 4000 over the first ten years. However, since the 1990s a huge increase in poaching for Tiger bone and other body parts for traditional oriental medicine and skins for fur has seen most Tiger populations decline or at best remain stable. Most conservation efforts now involve a more holistic approach, which aims to preserve the maximum biodiversity, not just of charismatic megafauna such as Tigers. It also aims to benefit local peoples through tourism or harvesting natural resources. Most protected areas are too small to support viable populations of top predators like Tigers and Lions. Therefore, there will be a need for these species to thrive in the wider human-dominated landscape too, if they are to survive.

Despite some positive signs of greater awareness of and action for the conservation of wild felids, there are still many worrying trends that result from the human-cat relationship, which in large part result from an ever-expanding human population and the growing global economy and mass consumerism. Habitats, particularly tropical forests, continue to be lost at horrific rates. Some species such as the Marbled Cat, Margay, and Flat-headed Cat are probably highly dependent on primary or

At four months, a **Tiger** cub is the size of a setter dog. By six months the cubs are weaned, but lack the ability to kill for themselves. The permanent canines appear between twelve and 18 months of age, and this marks a period of rapid weight gain as the young are now physically equipped to make their own kills. They must, however, still refine their hunting techniques and learn to kill efficiently. Male cubs learn to kill on their own and become independent sooner than their female siblings, and by 15 months of age they may begin spending some time away from their mothers. By 18–20 months young Tigers are typically independent of their mothers, but continue to hunt in their natal range. Dispersal occurs when young are 18–28 months old, and seems to be keyed to the arrival of a new litter, which in Chitwan National Park, Nepal, happens from 20 to 24 months after the birth of the old litter. The average dispersal distance for ten subadult males in Chitwan was 33 km, but for four females was less than 10 km. Only four of the ten males managed to establish breeding territories whereas all four females did. The mean age of first reproduction for females was 3·4 years; for males it was 4·8 years. The average reproductive life span of females was just over 6·1 years, but two females in Chitwan had reproductive life spans of 10·5 and 12·5 years, and during this time reared four and five litters, respectively. These females were exceptional: the mean lifetime reproduction of females was 4·54 young surviving to dispersal age, and 2·0 that survived to breed. Once females had established territories, they spent their entire reproductive lives in them, although some females shifted so that part of their range was acquired by their daughters. The tendency for daughters to settle next to their mothers results in clusters of females that can be as closely related as lionesses in a pride.

Panthera tigris
India.
Photo: Belinda Wright/
Lochman Transparencies

A thick, woolly natal coat helps insulate young **Snow Leopards** from the cold. Snow leopards are unusual among the large cats in that they have a well-defined birth peak. Mating occurs from January through March, and the young are born after a gestation period of 94–103 days. Litter size varies from one to five, with an average of 2·2. The cubs are born in a cave or rock crevice. For the first week after the young are born, females remain at or near the den, grooming, nursing, and resting. Weighing between 320 g and 567 g at birth, the cubs grow rapidly, putting on 300–500 g per week. By two months of age, they weigh about 4 kg, and by ten weeks they are weaned and weigh about 6 kg. They begin following their mother sometime between two and four months of age. During this phase they may be more a hindrance than a help to their mother while she is hunting. Young Snow Leopards disperse as they reach sexual maturity at about two years. They are nutritionally dependent on their mother for a relatively long time, possibly as long as 18 months. Female **Tigers** also have to kill more often or kill larger prey to meet the nutritional demands of their growing offspring, and even large kills may not last long if several Tigers are feeding on the carcass. For example, a tigress and her two large young in Chitwan National Park, Nepal, fed on an adult Sambar for two days, consuming 102 kg of meat, or about 17 kg per Tiger per day, whereas Tigresses in Chitwan without young spent an average of three days with each kill, and during that time consumed 46 kg of meat.

Above: *Panthera uncia*
Photo: Alan & Sandy Carey/
www.photolibrary.com

Below: *Panthera tigris*
Ranthambhore Sanctuary, India.
Photo: David Hosking/FLPA

*Game reserves have changed from exclusive hunting preserves to national parks maintained for the conservation of wildlife, and to encourage tourism, with all its economic benefits. Most conservation now aims to preserve maximum biodiversity, not just charismatic megafauna like **Lions** and Tigers. But most protected areas are too small to support ɒiable populations of top predators. These species need to be enabled to thrive in the wider human-dominated landscape. Despite greater awareness and action, there are many worrying trends, resulting from the clash between wild cats and the needs and demands of an expanding human population.*

Panthera leo
Okavango Delta, Botswana.
Photo: Pete Oxford/naturepl.com

other specialized forest habitat and it is these habitats that are most under threat. Although hunting for fur was damaging to populations in the past, at least with a cessation of trapping, populations could recover. Without habitat, there is no hope. As human populations increase and encroach on protected areas, so the natural prey of cats may decline owing to hunting, disease, or competition from domestic livestock. This may lead to the cats preying on humans and their livestock, resulting in poisoning, trapping, and shooting of the cats.

Illegal trade has also had a significant impact. It falls into three main categories: live animals, furs, and bone and other body parts. Although illegal trade in furs and live animals still occurs, it is probably declining for most species. In the case of many big cat species, there are actually large surpluses available from captive breeding programs in North America and Europe, thus obviating the need for the trade in live animals. Much publicity has occurred in recent years as ever-larger numbers of confiscated skins and bones have been burnt in public in countries such as Kenya, India, and Russia to demonstrate the commitments of governments to the conservation of their big cats. However, it is sad that these items have not been used for research into variation and population genetics, thereby aiding conservation strategies for these species. Perhaps the biggest threat in illegal trade to cats, especially in Asia, is the use of bones and other body parts in traditional oriental medicine. Tiger parts have been used in traditional oriental medicine for 2000 years to treat just about any human ailment. However, it is the relatively recent addition of ground Tiger bone to pills and other packaged medicines for a mass market that has fueled the huge demand and illegal killing of Tigers.

Pollution may also impact negatively on cat populations. PCBs, heavy metals, and other toxic chemicals used in industry and agriculture may become concentrated in top predators from trace amounts in their prey, thereby affecting reproduction and health. Domestic cats have impacted on Wildcats through hybridization (see above) and exposure to domestic cat viral diseases, to which they may be especially susceptible. Other diseases such as rabies and canine distemper virus have decimated carnivore populations. For example, by 1994 up to 30% of the 3000 Lions in the Serengeti National Park in Tanzania died from canine distemper virus, which had spread from the local domestic dog population.

As populations fall to very low levels, there is a real risk that chance disasters can wipe them out completely, or reduce them to such a low level that inbreeding results in severe genetic problems, thereby resulting in their ultimate extinction. In 1961–1962 a population of about 70 Lions in the Ngorongoro Crater in Tanzania fell victim to an infestation of biting flies, after heavy rains. The population fell to only ten animals as a result of infections and starvation. The highly endangered population of 250 Indian Lions in the Gir Forest Reserve is showing signs of the problems caused by inbreeding, such as skull abnormalities and albino animals, which could affect future survival.

Perhaps the most damaging aspect of our relationship with cats is ignorance. It seems incredible that the Iberian Lynx may be the rarest cat in the world today. Only about 250 animals survive, owing to persecution, habitat loss, and, above all, decline of its main prey species, the European Rabbit (*Oryctolagus cuniculus*). Two coat color morphs have been lost forever to extirpation. The Spanish government is working with conservation organizations such as the World Conservation Union to save the Iberian Lynx. As well as protecting cats in the wild, a captive breeding program is being established to act as backup to the wild population and to provide animals for future reintroductions. However, research on this highly endangered species has really only been active in the last ten years or so.

We should reserve our greatest concern of all for those species of which we know virtually nothing. The Iriomote Cat from Japan was only described scientifically in 1968. The Chinese Mountain Cat is known only from a dozen or so skins and a couple of skulls, as is the Andean Mountain Cat, and the Bornean Bay Cat is known from fewer than ten specimens since the announcement of its discovery in 1874.

Status and Conservation

As predators, wild cat populations need relatively large blocks of habitat and sufficient quantities of suitable wild prey. With the increasing pace of human population growth and development over the last century, both habitat and prey for cats have declined widely. The big cats have been heavily persecuted because they are a danger to humans and livestock, and for their skins, and some small cat species have been subject to heavy harvest for the fur trade. All species have declined in range and number, but the situation is illustrated most acutely by the decline of the big cats over the last century.

Big cats once ranged widely across North Africa and southwest Asia, and some countries in the region were home to a spectacular big cat assemblage: Tigers, Lions, Cheetahs, Leop-

ards. But over the last century the Tiger was eliminated from south-west and Central Asia, the Cheetah survives only in a small part of Iran, and the Asian Lion as a single population in the Gir Forest of western India. In North Africa, the Lion was lost, and the Leopard and Cheetah have become very rare. The Tiger disappeared from the Indonesian islands of Java and Bali, and in other countries its range has been reduced to only a fraction of the original distribution. In the Americas, the Jaguar lost an estimated 50% of its range, and by the early 1900s the Puma was already gone from the eastern half of North America (except for the Everglades swamp region of Florida). These extirpations all share common factors: loss of habitat, depletion of the large ungulate prey base, and direct persecution of cats for trade, predator control, and sport.

Today, the Felidae are among the most threatened groups of mammals. *The IUCN Red List* lists 29 species with a population trend of "decreasing". Seven species are included in the categories Critically Endangered and Endangered. In general, the felids categorized as Threatened fall into two groups: those that appear to be naturally rare, with a limited distribution; and those that have become threatened due to human factors. The Critically Endangered Iberian Lynx fits both criteria, and is near to becoming the first cat species to go extinct in modern times.

Between 1960 and 1978, the Iberian Lynx suffered a drastic 80% range loss, and over the 1990s has continued to lose ground. In Spain, Lynx lives currently in only two or three isolated populations—one of which, in the eastern Sierra Morena Mountains, holds over 70% of the total Spanish population. It is possibly already extinct in Portugal. The total population of breeding adult Iberian Lynx is estimated at less than 200. The small, isolated sub-populations of Iberian Lynx are theoretically vulnerable to genetic drift, the situation in which the genetic makeup of a population changes by chance alone. There is preliminary evidence for this happening in Doñana National Park, where the population of approximately 24–33 adults has been isolated from other Lynx populations since the early 1960s. Three pelage patterns were present in the population at that time, but now no animals exhibit the rarer fine-spotted pattern.

The steep decline of the Iberian Lynx has been caused primarily by a decline of their main prey species, the European Rabbit, due to two virulent imported diseases, myxomatosis and rabbit haemorrhagic disease. Rabbit populations have completely disappeared in many areas, and remnant populations still undergo severe periodic mortality. Rabbit populations are now estimated to be at 5–10% of their mid-century abundance. Although some populations are developing immunity, Rabbits are still legally and illegally trapped. They are also preyed upon by competing predators including the Red Fox which, unlike the Lynx, is more tolerant of the agriculture and settlement that have come to dominate much of the peninsula. Traps set for Rabbits and for Red Fox are estimated to result in an annual 25% mortality rate for the main Iberian Lynx population in the Sierra Morena Mountains. Road kills have also become an increasingly significant cause of mortality for Iberian Lynx.

The species is a close relative of the Eurasian Lynx, and only relatively recently has acceptance of its status as a full species been widely recognized. In part for this reason, conservation effort for the Iberian Lynx has lagged behind that of other cat species. Awareness is now growing of the severity of this Lynx's plight. The Large Carnivore Initiative for Europe published a comprehensive action plan detailing the status of Iberian Lynx populations, threats, and recommended conservation action. The World Wide Fund for Nature-UK is leading a campaign for implementation of the action plan, with a major focus on habitat protection under the Europe-wide Natura 2000 conservation initiative. An international workshop to focus on the need for Spain and Portugal to implement habitat protection measures and improved hunting controls was held in 2002 by the IUCN/SSC Cat Specialist Group.

In recent years, the greatest conservation efforts have been directed toward the Tiger, classified as Endangered on *The IUCN Red List*, and of which three subspecies are already extinct (*virgata*, *sondaica*, and *balica*). As previously discussed, the Tiger has suffered steep population declines over the last century, disappearing from much of its historically wide range. However, great advances were made in protecting remaining populations in the 1970s–80s. India led the way with its government-sponsored Project Tiger, which protected a network of key habitats as Tiger Reserves. Most other range states also created important protected areas for Tigers and enacted laws against Tiger hunting. Tigers were banned from international trade through their listing on Appendix I of the Convention on International Trade in Endangered Species (CITES) in 1975. The first behavioral and ecological studies were carried out, and conservationists began actively monitoring the status of many Tiger populations.

In the early 1990s, the Cat Specialist Group sounded the alarm that Tigers were being poached in significant numbers, linking this to the use of Tiger bone in traditional Asian medi-

*Until the end of the twentieth century, it was assumed that the **Jaguar** had some degree of natural protection, because many of its populations were largely inaccessible to people. It then became increasingly apparent that this protection was rapidly disappearing. In the first decade of the twenty-first century, the most important factor affecting Jaguar numbers is habitat loss from timber extraction, and conversion to pasture and agricultural lands. Jaguar habitat is also being lost as forests are modified in association with mining operations, oil drilling, and human settlements. People associated with these settlements and operations often supplement their diet with wild game, and compete directly with Jaguars for prey such as capybara, peccary, and deer. There are no reliable estimates of how much the Jaguar's range has diminished, but one calculation suggests that since European settlement, the cat's range has shrunk by almost half, from 15 million km^2 to 8.7 million km^2. When humans brought cattle to South America in the 1600s, Jaguars added them to more than 85 species of wild prey already figuring in their diets. In the savannas and gallery forest of Colombia, Venezuela, and Brazil, ranchers graze millions of cattle in habitats also used by Jaguar. Some losses are attributable to depredation by Jaguar, but for most ranches the real impact is unknown. In any case, Jaguars are usually targeted by ranchers whenever they are encountered. In some areas, ranchers may be partially responsible for livestock depredation problems when they shoot at and injure Jaguars, because such injuries may force them to subsist on easier to catch livestock. Efforts are being made to build a framework for Jaguar conservation and research throughout its geographic range, much like the model for the Tiger. Priorities include information exchange, standardized research methods, assessment of threats, and cooperation across borders. The Jaguar is classified as Near Threatened on* The IUCN Red List.

Panthera onca
Photo: Gerard Lacz/FLPA

*Widely distributed, with a range that includes Central Asia and the Tibetan highlands, **Pallas's Cat** lives in dry steppe and rocky country up to 3000–4000 m. It preys heavily on pikas, rodent-like relatives of rabbits. It is still relatively common, but populations are more sparse and threatened in the region of the Caspian Sea, and in Pakistan's Baluchistan province. It has the longest, densest fur of any species in the genus* Felis. *Hunting is prohibited in most countries in its range, but some are killed each year for their fur. Habitat destruction and poisoning to control pika populations also threaten it. Pallas's Cat is classified as Near Threatened on* The IUCN Red List.

Otocolobus manul
Photo: Terry Whittaker/FLPA

cines. Tiger medicines had been used to treat rheumatism and other conditions for thousands of years, but increasing Asian economic prosperity gave rise to devastating levels of commercial demand. Reports of intensive poaching in the Tiger's southern Asian strongholds of India and Nepal were underscored in 1993, when Indian officials seized nearly 400 kg of Tiger bone and uncovered a major smuggling route through Nepal into China. Poaching hit even the rare and formerly well protected Amur Tiger population of the Russian Far East, during the time of dissolution of the former Soviet Union. Trade investigations found Tiger bone medicines available in Asian pharmacies around the world.

Shutting down medicinal markets for Tiger bone shot to the top of the global environmental agenda. Under diplomatic pressure and threat of trade sanctions, China, Taiwan, and South Korea took rapid and extraordinary legal and enforcement actions against their domestic traditional medicine markets. In many cases both consumers and practitioners of traditional medicine showed a willingness to stop using Tiger bone in order to help save the species. The conservation community increased its investment in conserving Tiger populations, with major new funding sources developing uniquely for Tigers, such as the Exxon-Mobil Save the Tiger Fund (the Tiger being Exxon's corporate logo). Most Tiger range states drew up

*There is little reliable information on the status of the **African Golden Cat** in the wild. It is thought to be rare in many countries of equatorial Africa, but is also described as locally common in Tai and Azagny National Parks, Ivory Coast, and in secondary forest in Uganda. African Golden Cats are frequently killed while raiding poultry or livestock. The species is believed to thrive in logged forest with dense secondary growth, so it may be in less danger than other small cats. However, loss and degradation of moist forest habitats are threats to its long-term survival, and the African Golden Cat is classified as Near Threatened on* The IUCN Red List.

Profelis aurata
Photo: Roland Seitre

national Tiger Action Plans, and an international body to co-ordinate conservation in the range states has been established, the Global Tiger Forum.

There has been great improvement in reducing trade in traditional Asian Tiger bone medicines, and analyses have shown that many of the Tiger parts and medicines were fake. Still, Tigers continue to be poached throughout their Asian range, and it is likely that black markets have persisted. The Tiger probably numbers no more than 5000–7500. Tigers breed well in captivity, and it is a sad fact that there are now more animals in zoos and other collections than in the wild. But although captive Tigers have served as an illicit source of supply for traditional Asian medicines, with several notorious "Tiger farms" in China and Thailand (which now appear to function only as zoos, and draw large crowds of tourists), the primary source has been wild Tigers.

Tigers are not only killed illegally for trade, but also because they can be a danger to people and an intolerable economic burden when they prey on livestock. Population models suggest that Tiger populations may be able to sustain low levels of mortality, such as would be expected to result from persistent but infrequent conflict with humans. However, moderate to high levels of mortality greatly increase extinction risk, even tens of years after the deaths occur. Also of fundamental importance for Tiger survival are viable populations of their main wild ungulate prey species. An impoverished prey base will support only occasional reproduction. If prey populations continue to decline across the Tiger's range, an increasing number of Tiger populations will exist only at low densities, increasing their vulnerability.

With the development of Geographic Information Systems (GIS) and computer-based habitat mapping and monitoring, progress is being made toward mapping species distributions in detail, evaluating the adequacy of existing habitats for supporting viable cat populations, and identifying priority blocks of habitat for felid conservation. On the species level, Tiger range definition is most advanced. A 1997 mapping exercise by the World Wildlife Fund and the Wildlife Conservation Society delineated habitat for Tigers into blocks of "Tiger Conservation Units" (TCUs). Each TCU was scored for habitat integrity (size and degree of habitat fragmentation within the TCU, and degree of habitat modification and degradation by people), poaching pressure, and Tiger population status, and these scores were used to rank the TCUs in importance for Tiger conservation. A total of 159 separate TCUs were identified, with one-third ranked as highest priority. However, in most cases the Tiger population status was scored as unknown.

While the TCU approach was a breakthrough, it was recently replaced by a framework that relies on the concept of "Tiger Conservation Landscapes" (TCL). This new approach is more data driven and objective, and takes advantage of recent satellite and ground cover data, new knowledge about tiger biology, and an assessment of human influence. A TCL approach provides: a rapid, accurate and easily updateable method to delineate Tiger landscapes; a new spatial database of Tiger status and distribution; standards to evaluate the quality of these landscapes; a systematic measure of human influence on the landscapes; and a way to establish priorities for conservation and recovery of wild Tigers. With this method, 76 Tiger Conservation Landscapes have been identified across the Tiger's range. Each landscape is ranked in terms of global priority, thus ensuring the conservation not only of Tigers, but also of the landscapes to which Tigers are adapted.

Efforts to improve monitoring and protection of Tiger populations are increasing. Track and camera-trap surveys are being carried out in all fourteen range states; prey base abundance is also being measured. There has been increased investment in anti-poaching efforts, protected area infrastructure and capacity building, and conservation education. In a growing number of range states Tiger conservationists are allying with the development community to address the root causes of rural poverty and to develop alternative sources of livelihood for people living close to important Tiger populations, and thus relieve the stress on the natural resource base.

The Snow Leopard is other Endangered big cat of Asia. Dwelling in remote high mountains, the Snow Leopard has not suffered the steep declines of Tiger populations in the crowded tropics, but it still faces similar threats to its survival. There is demand for Snow Leopard bones for use as a substitute for Tiger bone in traditional Asian medicines. Many Central Asian protected areas are too small to support viable populations of Snow Leopards. Large ungulates have been hunted out of many areas, and Snow Leopards prey on domestic livestock more frequently in areas where wild sheep and goat populations have been depleted. Dietary analyses in a number of areas have shown domestic livestock to be a major prey source for Snow Leopards. In such areas, impoverished villagers and herders feel they have no choice but to protect their livelihood by killing Snow Leopards.

Conservation efforts for the Snow Leopard have been improving. Several range states have approved comprehensive action plans. Under the auspices of the International Snow Leopard Trust, a network of Snow Leopard specialists is working to draw up a comprehensive survival strategy for the species. One component is implementation of a standard protocol for recording Snow Leopard sign using transects, to be built into a database for monitoring every major Snow Leopard population. Several conservation programs focus on reducing incidence of livestock predation by helping construct predator-proof corrals and improving other livestock management measures. New mechanisms are being developed to help local people benefit from ecotourism, with emphasis on participatory techniques that fully engage them in the process.

The third Asian felid classified as Endangered is the Bay Cat. It has a very restricted range, being found only on the island of Borneo. It appears to be a naturally rare species, described as such by British naturalist Charles Hose back in the late 1800s, long before the onset of current threats such as commercial logging. In stark contrast to the three previously discussed species, the Borneo Bay Cat has never been studied and little is known about it.

Two other Endangered Asian species, the Flat-headed Cat and the Fishing Cat, are specialized for wetland habitats, and their distribution within forests is strongly localized around water sources. People also tend to concentrate around water sources, and these species are rapidly losing habitat to agriculture and aquaculture, and threatened by pollution and the use of pesticides. Fishing Cats have become very scarce because of these threats in Java and Pakistan.

The Endangered Andean Mountain Cat occurs only in the rocky, arid, sparsely vegetated areas of the high Andes in South America above timberline (approximately 3500–4800 m). There are few museum specimens, none known in captivity, no

*Some species can adapt to or even thrive in human-modified habitats. Others, such as the **Marbled Cat**, Margay, and Flat-headed Cat, are probably highly dependent on primary forest and other specialized forest habitats, the habitats that are most under threat. However, the Marbled Cat has been recorded in secondary forests in Peninsula Malaysia, and in six-year-old logged forest in Sabah. But little or nothing is known of its hunting and breeding needs, its social organization, or its movements and distribution, except that it is rare throughout its range. Without more information, effective conservation is impossible. It is classified as Vulnerable on The IUCN Red List.*

Pardofelis marmorata
N India.
Photo: Terry Whittaker/FLPA

The world's three smallest felid species are all classified as Vulnerable on The IUCN Red List, *and all appear to be naturally rare. The **Rusty-spotted Cat** of India and Sri Lanka, the Kodkod of Chile and Argentina, and the Black-footed Cat of South Africa are similar in being found in just a few habitats with small overall ranges. The first radio telemetry studies of the Kodkod and the Black-footed Cat were carried out in the 1990s, but the Rusty-spotted Cat remains poorly known. Until recently the species was thought to be confined to west-central and southern India, but in 1975 a single record from Jammu and Kashmir extended its range more than 1600 km north from Bombay.*

Prionailurus rubiginosus
Photo: Terry Whittaker/FLPA

skins in the illegal fur trade, and it has only been observed a handful of times in the wild by biologists. Its distribution is similar to the historic range of the Short-tailed Chinchilla (*Chinchilla brevicaudata*), which was hunted nearly to extinction for the fur trade a century ago, and this may be a factor in the present-day rarity of the Andean Mountain Cat. The Andean Mountain Cat is also hunted with dogs, as it is a tradition throughout much of the high Andes to keep dried and stuffed wild cat specimens for harvest festivals, when they are decorated with ribbons and money. The Colocolo (Near Threatened) is very similar in appearance to the Andean Mountain Cat, and may be sympatric with the Andean Mountain Cat at lower elevations.

There has been increased research into the status of the Andean Mountain Cat since publication of the Cat Special-

ist Group's Cat Action Plan in 1996, which drew attention to conservation needs of the smaller, less-studied felids. Status surveys were carried out in Bolivia, Chile, and Argentina. The first video footage of a male Andean Mountain Cat has been made, and the first capture and collaring of an Andean Mountain Cat (adult female) occurred in April, 2004, in south-west Bolivia. Publication of a detailed morphological key is helping field researchers distinguish between Andean Mountain Cats and Colocolos. Interested members of the Cat Specialist Group formed the Committee for Conservation of the Andean Mountain Cat (COCGA). Researchers are sharing information and cooperating to map the species range and define priority areas for conservation. COCGA has published a booklet about the species for distribution to schools and protected areas.

*Around 1900, fewer than 20 of the Asian subspecies of **Lion** remained, in a single population in India's Gir Forest. The population has grown to 300, but remains isolated. People in communities around the forest have been killed by Lions, and there is continual conflict due to Lions preying on livestock. Conservationists have long wanted to establish a second wild population, but there is no suitable habitat unoccupied by people. A previous experiment failed, with reintroduced Lions apparently shot or poisoned. Palpur-Kuno Wildlife Sanctuary in northern Madhya Pradesh has been selected as the best candidate area. Human communities will have to be resettled, but this time great care is being taken to make the process participatory. The Lion is classified as Vulnerable on* The IUCN Red List.

Panthera leo
Gir Forest National Park, India.
Photo: Anup Shah/naturepl.com

As with the Endangered category, the majority of the species categorized as Vulnerable are found in Asia, six out of ten. Of these six, four are most strongly associated with forest habitats. Asian forests, particularly rainforests, have undergone the highest rates of deforestation in the world over the last 20–30 years. Four Vulnerable or Near Threatened felids that often occur together in tropical Asian forests are both clouded leopards, Asian Golden Cat, and Marbled Cat. More information about these cats has become available in the late 1990s with the first radio-telemetry studies in Thailand, and many new records collected from camera traps across South-east Asia. The Marbled Cat appears to be naturally rare and is not frequently seen in trade, but there is concern about substantial illegal trade in skins of clouded leopards and Asian Golden Cat. A survey in 1999 found 95 clouded leopard pelts for sale in Myanmar's notorious Tachilek wildlife market, on the Thai border. Both clouded leopard and Asian Golden Cat bones are also used as substitutes for Tiger bone in traditional Asian medicines.

The world's three smallest felid species are all classified as Vulnerable, and appear to be naturally rare. Although from different parts of the world, the three species, the Kodkod of Chile and Argentina, the Rusty-spotted Cat of India and Sri Lanka, and the Black-footed Cat of South Africa, are similar in being found in just a few habitats with small overall ranges. The first radio-telemetry studies of the Kodkod and the Black-footed Cat were carried out in the 1990s, but the Rusty-spotted Cat remains poorly known, as do the Chinese Mountain Cat and African Golden Cat.

Two Vulnerable big cats, the Lion and the Cheetah, still occur widely in sub-Saharan Africa, but human-predator conflict is rife. Scores of people are killed by Lions every year, particularly in East Africa; the number of Lions killed by people is less easy to know, but is considered a major threat to the Lion's survival. Lions are vulnerable to poisoning of their kills. Cheetahs do not return to their kills, and are therefore not vulnerable to being killed in this way. However, they are considered a major source of livestock depredation, particularly in southern Africa, and in Namibia many Cheetahs are captured each year in box traps set by cattle and game ranchers. Lions are increasingly restricted to protected areas, where they are vulnerable to threats facing isolated populations, including loss of genetic variation, and susceptibility to disease: in the mid-1990s an outbreak of canine distemper virus killed 20–30% of the Lion population of Tanzania's Serengeti National Park. The Cheetah, on the other hand, tends to occur at lower densities in protected areas with large Lion populations, and in some parts of East and southern Africa, is found at higher densities outside parks, in mixed-use bushland where Lions have been eliminated by people.

There has been much more conservation effort directed toward the Lion and the Cheetah than toward the Vulnerable small cats. Both have been studied for decades in key locations in East and southern Africa, providing a solid foundation for understanding species biology. Namibia was the first country to implement a national Cheetah action plan, and has established a unique Large Carnivore Management Forum, which brings together stakeholders for regular meetings to share information and coordinate conservation research and actions. In southern Africa, Lion and Cheetah populations are actively managed, with frequent translocation of problem animals. An African Lion Working Group has been established under the auspices of the Cat Specialist Group, and has highlighted West Africa as the region of greatest conservation concern for the species.

Both the Lion and the Cheetah have small remnant populations outside sub-Saharan Africa. The Asian Lion now exists as a single isolated population numbering approximately 300 in India's Gir Forest complex, in the state of Rajasthan, with a total area of about 1400 km². A considerable number of people live in the area surrounding the Gir and graze their livestock in the buffer area. A number of people have been killed by Gir Lions, and there is continual conflict due to Lions preying on livestock. Conservationists have long been interested in establishing a second wild population to relieve some of the pressure on the Gir population and to decrease the extinction risk, but there is no suitable habitat unoccupied by people. One experiment in the 1960s failed, with reintroduced Lions apparently being shot or poisoned in the Chandraprabha Wildlife Sanctuary. Palpur-Kuno Wildlife Sanctuary in northern Madhya Pradesh has now been selected as the best candidate area. Human communities will have to be resettled to make room for the Lions, but this time great care is being taken to make the process participatory and to attempt to satisfy local needs, and not engender hostility toward Lion conservation.

The Cheetah has disappeared from most of its North African and south-west Asian range primarily due to depletion of its gazelle prey base by illegal hunting. In Asia, the Cheetah

*There is concern about the substantial illegal trade in **Indochinese Clouded Leopard** skins. A survey in 1999 found 95 Indochinese Clouded Leopard pelts for sale in Myanmar's notorious Tachilek wildlife market. Their bones are also used as substitutes for Tiger bone in traditional Asian medicines. Although the species has been classified as Vulnerable on* The IUCN Red List, *there are few observations of the species in the wild, and virtually nothing is known of its status throughout its range. As the Indochinese Clouded Leopard is strongly associated with forested habitats, deforestation and habitat conversion are major threats. Diardi's Clouded Leopard was previously thought to be a subspecies of the Indochinese Clouded Leopard, but recent morphological and molecular evidence has shown it to be a separate species. It is also classified as Vulnerable and suffers from threats of habitat loss and degradation.*

Neofelis nebulosa
Photo: Mike Hill/www.photolibrary.com

is now found only in Iran, where preliminary population estimates suggest a scattered population at low density, probably totaling only 50–100. Neglected for years, the Asiatic Cheetah now stands to benefit from a major World Bank-funded conservation program, which carried out the first status surveys and funded park protection measures. In North Africa, small populations remain in western Egypt and around the Saharan mountain massifs of Algeria, Mali, and Niger. Nomadic Bedouin herders consider Cheetahs to be important predators of small livestock.

The Near Threatened category includes nine species that may in the future qualify as Vulnerable, if declining trends persist. This category includes several New World species, including the largest New World cat, the Jaguar, which occur in the vast lowland rainforest of the Amazon Basin. The more threatened Latin American species are those that occur outside the tropical rainforest. This is in marked contrast to Asia, where most of the threatened species are associated with tropical rainforest and are threatened primarily by deforestation. While the conservation community works to reduce high rates of deforestation in the Amazon, the basin still forms a large refuge for Neotropical felids, approximately 5·5 million km². More heavily settled and degraded are the montane cloud forests, dry deciduous forests, and pampas scrub grasslands, with resulting range loss for the Oncilla, Geoffroy's Cat, and Colocolo.

The Jaguar has been eliminated from much of the drier northern parts of its range and from the pampas scrub grasslands of Argentina and throughout Uruguay. A meeting of Jaguar specialists in 1999 estimated that 50% of the species' range was lost in the last century. The most urgent conservation problem for the Jaguar throughout much of its range is the current level of conflict with livestock ranchers. The vulnerability of the Jaguar to persecution is demonstrated by its disappearance in the mid-1900s from the south-western USA and northern Mexico, areas that remain home to important Puma populations. The Puma is a more adaptable cat, found in every major habitat type of the Americas, but it was nevertheless eliminated from the entire eastern half of North America within 200 years following European colonization. As forests were cut down for timber and fuel, and deer populations were greatly reduced, Pumas were hunted out. The last remaining

known population of the Florida Panther (*Puma concolor coryi*), in eastern North America is found in the Florida Everglades. Its population varies between 80–100, and for two decades the world's most intensive, and expensive, felid conservation program has struggled to maintain the population's viability.

The Pallas's Cat and Sand Cat are still relatively common, but populations of both species are more sparse and threatened in the region of the Caspian Sea, and in Pakistan's Baluchistan province. The first radio-telemetry studies of these species were carried out in the 1990s.

The Eurasian Lynx is also still found across a wide range, and is commercially trapped for the international fur trade, primarily in Russia. There is concern about the effects of uncontrolled trapping for local fur markets in China and the Central Asian republics, where there is little information available about the distribution and status of Lynx populations. Conservation efforts have been most intensive for the Eurasian Lynx in Europe, where the population is estimated at about 7000, most numerous in the north and east of the region. The Eurasian Lynx was completely eradicated from Western Europe over the past 150 years, and was reintroduced clandestinely in several countries in the 1970s. Populations have been well studied and monitored, and a comprehensive pan-European action plan provides the basis for coordinating and prioritizing conservation action. The primary problem for Eurasian Lynx conservationists in Western Europe is to convince local people that large predators are a necessary part of the rural landscape. Compensation is paid for livestock killed by Eurasian Lynx, and problem animals that repeatedly kill livestock are removed. Local people remain largely hostile to large predators, viewing conservation as an urban concept that restricts their opportunities for economic development.

The category Least Concern can be misleading. For example, the Wildcat is probably the most widespread and numerous of the felids. Yet it may be one of the most threatened. Much more research is needed into the extent of hybridization with feral domestic cats, and the resulting loss of unique Wildcat alleles and traits. The domestication process that resulted in our pet cats probably began in North Africa and south-west Asia around the time of the rise of agriculture, when grain stores attracted rodent pests, which attracted Wildcats. Hybridization has been well documented in parts of

The Endangered **Andean Mountain Cat** occurs only in the rocky, arid, sparsely vegetated areas of the high Andes. It is fully protected throughout its range. There are few museum specimens, and none is known in captivity. There has been increased research into the status of the Andean Mountain Cat since publication of the IUCN/SSC Cat Specialist Group's Cat Action Plan in 1996, which drew attention to the conservation needs of the smaller, less studied felids. Status surveys were carried out in Bolivia, Chile, and Argentina. Researchers from the Committee for Conservation of the Andean Mountain Cat (COCGA) are sharing information, and cooperating to map the species' range and define priority areas for conservation.

Leopardus jacobitus
N Chile.
Photo: Günter Ziesler

Europe, particulary Scotland, where feral cat hybrids are estimated to make up approximately 40% of the "wild" population. But the phenomenon is unstudied in Africa, where the process has probably been underway the longest. Habitat loss and fragmentation intensifies the process by bringing people and their cats in closer contact with Wildcats—although feral domestic cats can survive in the wild hundreds of miles from civilization, even in the desert.

Also, the Leopard Cat is probably the most common small cat of Asia, despite the fact that hundreds of thousands per year were trapped for the fur trade in China in the 1980s. But there is debate among cat specialists about whether the Iriomote Cat, found only on the small Japanese island of Iriomote, off the eastern coast of Taiwan, is a unique species (as suggested by morphology) or an isolated subspecies of Leopard Cat (as suggested by genetic analysis). Treated as a species, the Iriomote Cat would qualify as the world's most endangered cat, with a single population of less than 100 animals. As a subspecies or "Evolutionarily Significant Unit", it is one of many that face serious extinction risk.

The Leopard is a good example of an adaptable, widespread species that nonetheless has many Critically Endangered subpopulations. While still numerous and even thriving in marginal habitats from which the other big cats have disappeared in many parts of sub-Saharan Africa, in North Africa Leopards are on the verge of extinction, and only a tiny relict population persists in Morocco and Algeria. Across south-west and Central Asia Leopard populations are small, threatened, and widely separated. Leopards are still relatively abundant in India, China, and South-east Asia, but are Critically Endangered in the north-east of this range. The Amur Leopard, characterized by its large rosettes and lush winter coat, has been reduced to very small populations in Russia, China, and North Korea. The Leopard is also rare on the islands of Java and Sri Lanka.

Three species of the genus *Leopardus*, the Ocelot, Margay, and Oncilla, are very similar in appearance, and were staples of the spotted cat fur trade of the 1960s and 1970s, with nearly a million skins entering international trade during this period. These species are now all protected under the Convention on International Trade in Endangered Species (CITES), and international commercial trade has ceased, although local illegal trade persists. The Jaguarundi still occurs widely in Latin America in a variety of habitats, and is not generally hunted for the fur trade. Ocelot and Jaguarundi populations at the extreme north of their range, in the Mexico–USA border region, are rare and threatened.

In sub-Saharan Africa, the Caracal and Serval are relatively common and widely distributed. In southern Africa, Caracals are trapped in large numbers as livestock predators, and in western Africa, there is concern about the volume of Serval skins in the local fur trade. Servals appear to have become extinct north of the Sahara, with the last confirmed record from Algeria dating back to the 1930s, and the Caracal is threatened in parts of south-west and Central Asia. Jungle Cats are relatively abundant in most of India and parts of south-west and South-east Asia, and are frequently spotted amidst human settlement. The species has been little studied, however, and is reportedly uncommon at the edges of its range: in Egypt, Central Asia, China, and Sri Lanka.

The Canadian Lynx is primarily found in Canada, and its distribution and status are tied closely to its main prey species, the Snowshoe Hare. In the south of its range, in the USA, Snowshoe Hares are less abundant and Canadian Lynx populations are small and listed as threatened. The species was reintroduced unsuccessfully in northern New York state in the late 1980s, and more recently, apparently successfully, in Colorado. Snowshoe Hares go through strong periodic cycles in abundance, and with a 1–2 year lag, so do Canadian Lynx and, in the far north of its range, the Bobcat. Both species are trapped for the international fur trade in Canada, and extensive research has gone into developing management programs to protect against overharvest during cyclic lows, when pelt prices typically rise due to the drop in supply. However, opposition to trapping and hunting of cats as inhumane is growing in North America, as it is around the world. In Mexico, the Bobcat has been designated a priority for conservation research, as little is known about the species from the south of its range.

Reintroduction is a conservation strategy that allows a species to be restored to its former habitat, where it is locally extinct. Reintroductions have rarely been used for cats. There are sporadic cases of individual Lions, Leopards, Cheetahs, and Tigers being returned to the wild, but these are really cases of rehabilitation into existing populations.

*There is no information on the status or abundance of the **Flat-headed Cat**, which has a restricted and patchy distribution around wetlands in lowland forest on the islands of Sumatra and Borneo, and the Malayan peninsula, but it appears to be rare and elusive. It is classified as Endangered on* The IUCN Red List. *Studies suggest that its diet is composed largely of fish. In addition to forest loss, overfishing and pollution of waterways and wetlands by industrial chemicals and pesticides are significant threats. Over 45% of protected wetlands and 94% of globally significant wetlands in South-east Asia are considered threatened.*

Prionailurus planiceps
Malaysia.
Photo: Roland Seitre

Of eight recognized subspecies of
Tiger, *three (Amur or Siberian,*
shown here, South China, and
Sumatran) are classified as
Critically Endangered on The
IUCN Red List, *and the Bali,*
Javan, and Caspian races are
extinct. Otherwise the Tiger is
classified as Endangered. Tiger
populations have declined over
many parts of Asia because of
commercial trade in Tiger bone,
a declining prey base, and loss
and degradation of habitat. The
problem is being attacked on
many fronts. Most Tiger range
states have drawn up national
Tiger Action Plans, and there
is an international body, the
Global Tiger Forum, to coordinate
conservation. Reserves are being
established and habitats restored,
anti-poaching teams are being
trained and deployed, and
economic incentives offered to
local people to participate in Tiger
conservation. There are threats
of sanctions against countries
that do not control trade in Tiger
parts, while other organizations
are working with traditional
Chinese medical practitioners to
find alternatives to Tiger bones. In
a growing number of range states,
Tiger conservationists are allying
with the development community
to address the root causes of rural
poverty, and develop alternative
sources of livelihood for people
living close to important Tiger
populations, and thus relieve
the stress on the natural resource
base. These initiatives have led
to recoveries of Tiger populations
in reserves in India and Nepal,
but with expanding human
populations in the region, pressures
on the natural systems are set to
increase. Fortunately, Tigers are a
resilient species and demographic
modeling suggests that relatively
small Tiger populations, with
fewer than twelve breeding females,
may be viable over a 100 year
timeframe. Even small reserves can
potentially support viable Tiger
populations, if the prey base is
intact. Managing and protecting
these areas will require more
resources, and further research
is needed into the effectiveness of
different management practices.

Panthera tigris
Photo: Jurgen & Christine Sohns/FLPA

The world's most endangered felid, the cat species most likely to slip into extinction in our lifetime, is not hunted for its fur or for traditional medicine; nor does it live in some remote corner of the world. Long regarded as a subspecies of Eurasian Lynx, the conservation needs of the Critically Endangered **Iberian Lynx** *were ignored as it suffered persecution, habitat loss, road traffic casualties, and decline of its main prey species, the European Rabbit. Today an estimated 84–143 adults survive in two or three isolated pockets in south-western Spain; its survival in Portugal is uncertain. Belated conservation initiatives include habitat protection and captive breeding.*

Lynx pardinus
Doñana National Park, Huelva, Spain.
Photo: Antonio Sabater/Enfoque 10

There have been several attempts at reintroducing the Lynx and Wildcat in Europe. Most have not followed the World Conservation Union's reintroduction guidelines and so success has been limited until recent years, when projects have been better planned and implemented. Often too few animals were introduced to prevent the bad effects of inbreeding or to avoid unpredictable losses due to accidents.

Attempts have also been made to reintroduce the Canadian Lynx to Colorado and Montana. Bobcats appear to have been reintroduced successfully to Cumberland Island, Georgia. Elsewhere, Cheetahs, Lions, and Servals have been reintroduced to conservation areas and reserves in South Africa.

This section has focused on species-specific conservation, but it is important to keep in mind that cats are the beneficiaries of a wide range of general conservation actions, with the protection of healthy ecosystems within parks and reserves being of primary importance. Protected areas safeguard important populations, but at present they still comprise only a minority of felid species ranges. Outside protected areas, cats benefit from land use such as sustainable forestry and managed hunting, which prevent habitat loss while providing an economic incentive for conservation. In most range states habitat and species protection laws are gradually being strengthened, with increased public support for and governmental investment in conserving biodiversity. In combination with the dedicated conservation efforts of cat specialists, it is hoped that such positive trends will soon come to reverse the current pattern of decline that threatens many felids with extinction. While captive populations of cats are being increasingly well managed, and great advances have been made in assisted reproduction techniques and gene banking, viable wild habitat with supportive and tolerant neighboring communities and effective species conservation management programs are necessary conditions for long-term survival of wild cat populations.

General Bibliography

Ackerman *et al.* (1984), Adams (1979), Anderson, A.E. (1983), Anderson, A.E. *et al.* (1992), Aranda & Sánchez-Cordero (1996), Asa (1993), Bahn & Vertut (1997), Bailey (1974, 1993), Bauer *et al.* (2001), Beier (1993, 1995), Beier *et al.* (1995), Bininda-Edmonds, Decker-Flum & Gittleman (2001), Bininda-Edmonds, Gittleman & Purvis (1999), Bothma & Le Riche (1986, 1990), Bradshaw & Cameron-Beaumont (2000), Brahmachary & Dutta (1987), Brahmachary *et al.* (1991), Brand & Keith (1979), Breitenmoser *et al.* (2000), Carbone *et al.* (2001), Caro (1994), Caro & Fitzgibbon (1992), Chauvet *et al.* (1996), Clutton-Brock (1988, 1999), Collier & O'Brien (1985), Corbet & Hill (1992), Culver *et al.* (2000), Davis (1987), DeBoer (1977), Delibes *et al.* (2000), Diefenbach *et al.* (2006), Dinerstein *et al.* (2006), Divyabhanusinh (1995), Dunstone *et al.* (1998), Eaton (1970b), Eisenberg & Lockhart (1972), Eizirik *et al.* (2001), Emmons (1987), Estes (1972), Ewer (1973), Foster & Humphrey (1995), Franklin, W.L. *et al.* (1999), Frazer Sissom *et al.* (1991), Fuller & Sievert (2001), Garcia-Perea (1994, 1999), Gettings (1989), Gorman & Trowbridge (1989), Gosling (1982), Grassman (2001), Groves (2001), Hanby *et al.* (1995), Hast (1989), Hayward *et al.* (2007), Hemmer (1966, 1978), Hoage *et al.* (1996), Hoogesteijn & Mondolfi (1992), Hoogesteijn *et al.* (1993), Hunter *et al.* (2007), Husain (2001), Iriarte, A.W. (1998), Iriarte, A.W. & Sanderson (1999), Iriarte, J.A. *et al.* (1990), IUCN (2008), Jackson, P. (1991), Jackson, R.M. *et al.* (1997), Janczewski *et al.* (1992), Jedrzejewska *et al.* (1998), Jhala *et al.* (2008), Johnson, W.E. & Franklin (1991), Johnson, W.E. & O'Brien (1997), Johnson, W.E., Culver *et al.* (1998), Johnson, W.E., Eizirik *et al.* (2006), Johnson, W.E., Pecon-Slattery *et al.* (1999), Karanth & Sunquist (1995), Kitchener (1991, 1999), Kitchener & Dugmore (2000), Kleiman (1966, 1974), Knick (1990), Kurtén & Granqvist (1987), Laing & Lindzey (1993), Larson (1997), Laurenson (1995), Leyhausen (1979), Logan & Sweanor (2001), Lovallo & Anderson (1995), Lucherini *et al.* (1999), Lumpkin (1991), Macdonald (1985), Malek (1993), Masuda *et al.* (1996), Mazak & Groves (2006), McDougal (1991), Mellen (1993), Molteno *et al.* (1998), Movchan & Opahova (1981), Mukherjee (1998a), Nowak (1999), Nowell (2000), Nowell & Jackson (1996), Nuñez *et al.* (2000), Odden *et al.* (2002), Oli (1994), Packer *et al.* (1988), Panaman (1981), Perovic *et al.* (1999), Peters, G. (1978, 1980, 1981, 1983, 1984a, 1984b, 1987, 1991), Peters, G. & Hast (1994), Peters, G. & Tonkin-Leyhausen (1999), Peters, G. & Wozencraft (1989), Peters, R.P. & Mech (1975), Pocock (1917), Poole (1994), Rabinowitz & Nottingham (1986), Ralls (1971), Rasa (1973a), Richardson (1993), Rieger (1979d), Rieger & Peters (1981), Rieger & Walzthony (1979), Ross & Jalkotzy (1996), Ruediger *et al.* (2000), Ruggiero *et al.* (1999), Ruiz-Miranda *et al.* (1998), Ryon & Brown (1990), Saleh *et al.* (2001), Salles (1992), Sanderson (1999), Saunders (1991), Schaller (1967, 1972), Schaller & Crawshaw (1980), Schmidt *et al.* (1997), Seidensticker, Christie & Jackson (1999), Seidensticker, Hornocker *et al.* (1973), Serpell (1991), Seymour (1989), Sliwa (1994a), Smith *et al.* (1989), Stander (1997), Sunde & Kvam (1997), Sunde, Kvam, Moa, Negard & Overskaug (2000), Sunquist (1981), Sunquist & Sanderson (1998), Taber *et al.* (1997), Tabor (1991), Tembrock (1970), Van Orsdol *et al.* (1985), Verberne (1976), Verberne & DeBoer (1976), Villalba & Bernal (1998), Volodina (2000), Walker & Novaro (2001), Wegge *et al.* (2009), Wemmer & Scow (1977), Wentzel *et al.* (1999), Wilson (1984), Yensen & Seymour (2000).

PLATE 2

inches 20

cm 50

ssp *nebulosa*

1

ssp *macrosceloides*

2

cub 3

ssp *sumatrae*

ssp *tigris*

4

cub

ssp *altaica*

Subfamily PANTHERINAE

Genus *NEOFELIS*

Gray, 1867

Lekagul & McNeely (1991), Murphy (1976), Nowell & Jackson (1996), Rabinowitz (1988), Rabinowitz *et al.* (1987), Santiapillai (1989), Sunquist & Sunquist (2002), Werdelin (1983), Wilting *et al.* (2007), Yamada & Durrant (1988).

1. Indochinese Clouded Leopard *Neofelis nebulosa*

French: Panthère longibande / **German**: Nebelparder / **Spanish**: Pantera nebulosa

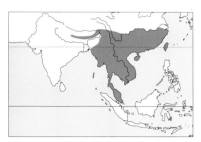

Taxonomy. *Felis nebulosa* Griffith, 1821, Guangdong, China.

Three extant subspecies recognized historically, but recent morphological and molecular evidence suggests reclassification of *diardi*, as a separate species, the Diardi's Clouded Leopard. Two subspecies actually recognized.

Subspecies and Distribution.

N. n. nebulosa Griffith, 1821 – Indochinese region and S China.

N. n. macrosceloides Hodgson, 1853 – Sub-Himalayan zone from Nepal to Myanmar.

Descriptive notes. Head-body 68·6–106·7 cm, tail 61–84·2 cm; weight 11–23 kg, adult males larger than adult females. A large Indochinese Clouded Leopard is nearly the size of small common Leopard. Indochinese Clouded Leopards are short-legged, long-bodied cats with broad feet and long tails. Background coat color varies from buffy-gray or brown to pale yellowish-brown. Coat is marked with distinctive cloud-shaped patches that resemble the markings of Marbled Cats. Posterior borders of the patches are edged in black and the inside of the patches is darker than the background color. The cloud-shaped patches vary in size, with the largest patches occurring on and just behind the shoulders. There are scattered black spots on the legs, feet and underparts. The thickly-furred tail is marked with dark rings. Skull elongated, resembling that of a small Leopard. Canines are exceptionally long, relatively the longest of any felid. The upper canines can measure 4 cm or longer and have been likened to those of saber-toothed cats.

Habitat. Usually associated with primary evergreen tropical rainforest, but little is known of its habitat requirements. Based on a relatively small number of locations visited by two radio-collared Indochinese Clouded Leopards in Thailand, the cats prefer dense primary evergreen forest. In south Nepal a subadult male was captured in dry woodlands, radio-collared and relocated to a nearby national park. During the ten days it was followed it used tall grasslands and hill forest. In other parts of their geographic range there are anecdotal accounts of Indochinese Clouded Leopards using relatively open, dry tropical forest, secondary and logged forest, and mangrove swamps.

Food and Feeding. A variety of terrestrial and arboreal vertebrates are reported as prey, including porcupines, Bearded Pigs (*Sus barbatus*), young Sambars (*Rusa unicolor*), muntjacs (*Muntiacus*), mouse deers (*Tragulus*), and palm civets. Primates include Proboscis Monkeys (*Nasalis larvatus*), Crab-eating Macaques (*Macaca fascicularis*), Southern Pig-tailed Macaques (*Macaca nemestrina*), and langurs. Domestic stock, including goats, pigs, and poultry may also be taken. The Indochinese Clouded Leopard's arboreal abilities are well known and with its large feet, short legs, and long tail, it is well equipped for moving about in the trees. However, most hunting and traveling is probably done on the ground.

Activity patterns. Indochinese Clouded Leopards are thought to be primarily nocturnal but an increasing number of camera-trap photographs show this cat to be active both day and night. The two radio-collared cats in Thailand were active on 35–45% of daytime observations, increasing to 85% at dusk and then declining to 60% at night. Both cats were least active around midday (11:00–14:00 h) and in the predawn hours (02:00–05:00 h).

Movements, Home range and Social organization. The only data on movements and home range sizes comes from the two radio-collared cats in Thailand. In the first two months after capture an adult female's home range measured 33·3 km² and that of an adult male was 36·7 km², but the actual ranges of both cats were thought to be larger, especially that of the male. The two animals used trees primarily for resting; most movements were on the ground.

Breeding. In captivity mating encounters often result in aggressive behavior and males frequently kill females with a neck bite. Thus far the most successful method for breeding these cats in captivity has been to raise a male and female together from the time they are a few weeks old, establishing a pair bond when the cats are young. Estimates of gestation length range from 85–109 days, but 88–95 days is more likely. Litter size is 1–5, but 2–3 is most common. Cubs begin to eat solid food between 7–10 weeks but continue to suckle until 11–14 weeks. Young reach sexual maturity at 20–30 months.

Status and Conservation. CITES Appendix I. Classified as Vulnerable on *The IUCN Red List*. The Indochinese Clouded Leopard has not been recorded in Taiwan in recent times and may be extinct there. There are few observations of Indochinese Clouded Leopards in the wild and virtually nothing is known of the species status throughout its range. Recent camera-trapping surveys have found that this cat is much less common than the Leopard. As the Indochinese Clouded Leopard is strongly associated with forested habitats, deforestation and habitat conversion is a major threat.

Bibliography. Austin & Tewes (1999a), Baudy (1971), Buckley-Beason *et al.* (2006), Dinerstein & Mehta (1989), Eaton (1984), Fellner (1965), Fontaine (1965), Geidel & Gensch (1976), Hemmer (1968), Kitchener *et al.* (2006),

2. Diardi's Clouded Leopard *Neofelis diardi*

French: Panthère de Diard / **German**: Sunda-Nebelparder / **Spanish**: Pantera de la Sonda

Taxonomy. *Neofelis diardi* Cuvier, 1823, Sumatra.

Recent molecular and morphological analyses suggest two subspecies, one on Borneo and the other on Sumatra, but those populations have yet to be properly described.

Distribution. Borneo, Sumatra, and Batu Is.

Descriptive notes. Head-body 70–105 cm, tail 60–85 cm; weight 10–25 kg, adult males larger than adult females. Diardi's Clouded Leopard, and Indochinese Clouded Leopard are similar enough in general appearance and size that the two were considered the same species until 2006. Molecular data indicate Dairdi's Clouded Leopard has been isolated from mainland clouded leopards for 1·4–2·9 million years. The degree of differentiation between the two forms is similar to the differences between the five *Panthera* species. Recent studies of DNA and coat patterns, as well as cranial, mandibular, and dental morphology indicate that Diardi's Clouded Leopards are as distinct from Indochinese Clouded Leopards as are other species of felids from each other. Diardi's Clouded Leopards have longer upper canines, and thicker upper carnassials than Indochinese Clouded Leopards. Compared with the mainland species, Diardi's Clouded Leopard has smaller "cloud" markings with many distinct spots within the clouds. The fur is grayer and generally darker and there is a double dark dorsal stripe.

Habitat. Little is known of its habitat requirements, but long thought to be strongly associated with primary evergreen tropical rainforest up to about 2000 m. However, recent reports suggest its ecological requirements may be more flexible, with observations of clouded leopards in logged forests, degraded secondary forest, scrub habitats, and mangrove swamps.

Food and Feeding. A variety of terrestrial and arboreal vertebrates are reported as prey, but no detailed studies with large sample sizes to date. Prey items known to include young Sambar, muntjac, mouse deer, Bearded Pig, palm civet, Hose's Langur (*Presbytis hosei*), orangutan (*Pongo*), porcupine, birds, and fish. The cat's long, thick tail, large paws, and short legs suggest it is well suited to an arboreal lifestyle, but the majority of sightings on Borneo are of clouded leopards walking on the ground. They are also known to use former or existing logging roads for hunting on Borneo.

Activity patterns. Thought to be primarily nocturnal, but high level of daytime activity reported on Borneo, where other large carnivores are absent. No camera-trap or radio-tracking data are available for Diardi's Clouded Leopards on Borneo or Sumatra.

Movements, Home range and Social organization. Tracks and observations recorded on forest trails and logging roads on Borneo and Sumatra, but otherwise no details available on home range sizes and social organization. Like other felids, these cats are probably solitary, and outside of mating activity the only long-term association is between females and their offspring.

Breeding. Based on captive animals, gestation length varies from 85–109 days, generally 86–93 days. Litter size is 1–5 but 2–3 more common. Cubs begin to eat solid food between 7–10 weeks but continue to suckle until 11–14 weeks. Interbirth interval 10·2 months, range 7–13 months. Young reach sexual maturity at 20–30 months.

Status and Conservation. CITES Appendix I. Classified as Vulnerable on *The IUCN Red List*. No reliable estimates of abundance are available, although a recent study that relied on identifying tracks in Tabin Wildlife Reserve, Sabah, estimated there were nine cats per 100 km². On Sumatra Diardi's Clouded Leopard seems to be present at lower densities than on Borneo. Habitat loss, degradation, and conversion to rubber and oil palm plantations have increased markedly in Sumatra and Borneo, the consequences of which can only negatively impact clouded leopards. It is not known whether clouded leopards are still present on the small Batu Islands near Sumatra.

Bibliography. Buckley-Beason *et al.* (2006), Christiansen (2008), Gordon *et al.* (2007), IUCN (2008), Kitchener *et al.* (2006), Rabinowitz *et al.* (1987), Santiapillai (1989), Santiapillai & Ashby (1988), Sunquist & Sunquist (2002), Wilting, Buckley-Beason *et al.* (2007), Wilting, Fischer *et al.* (2006).

Genus *PANTHERA*

Oken, 1816

3. Snow Leopard *Panthera uncia*

French: Panthère des neiges / **German**: Schneeleopard / **Spanish**: Leopardo de las nieves

Other common names: Ounce

Taxonomy. *Felis uncia* Schreber, 1775, Kopet-Dagh Mountains, near Iran.

Although formerly classified in its own genus *Uncia*, recent genetic analysis suggests

On following pages: 4. Tiger (*Panthera tigris*).

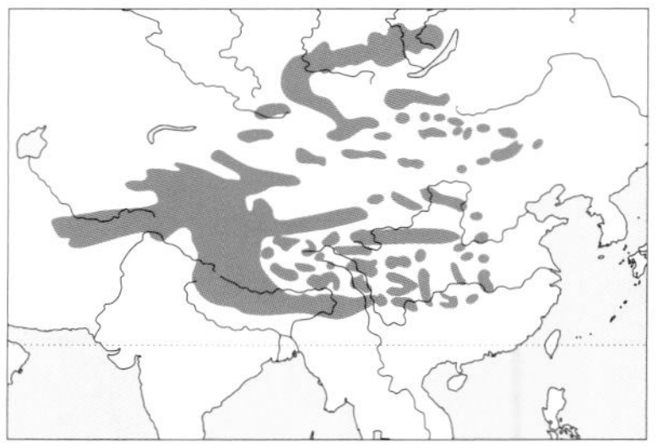

that it was one of the earliest species to diverge within the *Panthera*. Two subspecies recognized.

Subspecies and Distribution.

P. u. uncia Schreber, 1775 – C Asia NE to Mongolia and Russia.

P. u. uncioides Horsfield, 1855 – W China, and the Himalayas.

Descriptive notes. Head-body 86–125 cm, tail 80–105 cm; weight 22–52 kg; adult males are larger than adult females. Fur is long and thick: in winter it may be 5 cm long on the back and sides and almost 12 cm long on the belly. Long fur gives the cat a rather stocky appearance. Background color of the fur varies from smoky-gray to grayish buff and the coat is marked with dark gray and black rosettes and spots. The pattern of spots and rosettes on each cat is unique. Centers of rosettes are usually darker than the background coat color. Chest and underparts are whitish. Adapted for living at high altitudes in mountainous terrain, the Snow Leopard has moderately long, powerful limbs, well-developed chest muscles and large, broad feet. The long, thick tail functions as a balancing aid while the cats are moving about in precipitous terrain. Snow Leopards are also known to be prodigious leapers. The skull has a short muzzle and a high domed forehead to accommodate the expanded nasal cavities. Ears are short, rounded, and set wide apart; the backs of the ears are light-colored and rimmed with black.

Habitat. Snow Leopards inhabit rugged and remote mountainous areas where the terrain is broken by steep cliffs, ridges, and ravines. The cat's habitat is typically high rocky areas, alpine meadows, alpine steppe scrub, and high altitude forests. They generally spend the summer above tree line at elevations of 2700 to 6000 m, but in winter deep snow often forces wild ungulates to move to lower elevations and the Snow Leopards follow. The cats have also been found in isolated mountain massifs in Mongolia, and to reach these sites they would have had to traverse 20 to 65 km of broad, flat, open terrain.

Food and Feeding. Snow Leopards are capable of killing prey as much as three times their own weight. A large percentage of their diet consists of mountain-dwelling sheep and goats. Major prey species include bharal (*Pseudois*), Himalayan Tahr (*Hemitragus jemlahicus*), Markhor (*Capra falconeri*), Siberian Ibex (*Capra sibirica*), Argali (*Ovis ammon*), and Urial sheep (*Ovis orientalis*). In some areas wild asses (*Equus*), musk deer, Wild Boar (*Sus scrofa*), and gazelles are also taken. Smaller prey such as marmots, pikas, hares and rabbits, pheasants, and voles are important food items, especially in summer. One estimate suggests that as much as 45% of the meat in a Snow Leopard's summer diet may come from marmots. The cat also preys on domestic sheep, goats, cows, horses, yaks, and dogs. An unusual amount of vegetation, especially twigs of *Myricaria* and *Tamarix* bushes (Tamaricaceae), have been found in Snow Leopard scats, suggesting that these cats deliberately eat plant matter. Snow Leopards hunt by walking animal trails, ridge lines, river terraces, and the beds of deep gorges. They usually avoid open, unbroken terrain. When hunting, they tend to attack from a vantage point above the prey and have been seen pursuing prey across slopes and down mountainsides in chases of 200–300 m. Prey are killed with a bite to the nape or the throat. Carcasses are often moved to avoid attracting the attention of crows and vultures. The cat will remain with the carcass for 3–5 days, or until only bones remain. Captives require about 1·5 kg of meat per day and in the wild an adult blue sheep will provide the cat with food for a week. Females rearing young require about three times the normal amount of food to rear two to three young. One female and her two cubs consumed an adult Bharal in less than 48 hours; a similarsized kill would sustain a single Snow Leopard for 3–5 days.

Activity patterns. Snow Leopards are most active at dawn and dusk, but may be found hunting at any time of the day or night. In Mongolia, radio-tagged individuals were active 37% of the time, with the lowest level of activity occurring between12:00 and 18:00 h and the highest between 20:00 and 04:00 h. Where it is not subject to human disturbance the cat often hunts during the daytime. In areas where Snow Leopards feed on domestic animals they tend to hunt mainly at night.

Movements, Home range and Social organization. The mean straight-line distance between consecutive daily locations of Snow Leopards in Mongolia was 5 km, but on 18% of these occasions the distance was more than 10 km. The greatest distance traveled was 27·9 km. That Snow Leopards were capable of long-distance movement was also evident when they were located on isolated massifs, which were thought to be used as waypoints when crossing between distant mountain ranges. The cats had to cross 20 to 65 km of flat, open terrain to get to these massifs. The majority of studies on Snow Leopards have been done in areas of good habitat. In these "hotspots," Snow Leopard ranges are surprisingly small (mean 18·6 km^2, range10·7–36·2 km^2), but since there were periods when animals could not be located, they were likely moving over larger ranges. In an area of Mongolia with low prey densities the home ranges were much larger. One female with kittens used an area of only 13·5 km^2, but the range of an old female was conservatively estimated at 585 km^2. Two males roamed areas of 61–141 km^2, but these figures were considered underestimates of their ranges. Snow Leopards communicate mainly by scent marks, which includes feces, urine, and scrapes. Snow Leopards tend to make scrapes along their major travel routes, which include ridgelines, the base of cliffs, and river terraces. Some heavily-used routes are re-marked frequently. In one study area, the heaviest concentration of scrapes occurred around stream confluences. In addition to making scrapes, both sexes also spray urine on rocks and boulders. They appear to spray sites that are protected from the elements, especially the undersides of overhanging rocks and boulders. In captivity, male Snow Leopards urine-spray more frequently than females, but there is no information on sex differences in marking behavior from the wild. Except for females with young and mating pairs, Snow Leopards are solitary. There have been several observations of the cats traveling and hunting in pairs, but radio-tracking studies indicate that these associations are rare. Not surprisingly, only a few density estimates exist. Most suveys show that Snow Leopards typically exist at very low densities but can be locally abundant. In Nepal's Langu Valley the density of adults and subadults was 5–10 animals per 100 km^2. In Nepal's Annapurna Conservation Area, densities reached 5–7 adults per 100 km^2. In the best Snow Leopard habitat in Ladakh, density estimates vary from 2–4 per 100 km^2. Outside these "hotspots," densities are much lower, approximately 0·5–1 adult per 100 km^2.

Breeding. Snow leopards are unusual among the large cats in that they have a well-defined birth peak. Mating occurs from January through March and is marked by a noticeable increase in scent marking and calling. Captive observations indicate that estrus usually lasts from 5–8 days with copulations taking place over 3–6 days. Pairs mate often, 12–36 times per day, and coitus lasts 15–45 seconds. The young are born after a gestation period of 94–103 days. Litter size varies from 1–5, with an average of 2·2. Cubs are born in a cave or rock crevice and weigh 320–567 g. A thick, woolly natal coat helps insulate the young from the cold. For the first week after the young are born, females remain at or near the den, grooming, nursing, and resting. The young gain weight rapidly, putting on 300–500 g per week. By two months of age, they weigh about 4 kg, and by ten weeks they are weaned and weigh about 6 kg. Cubs begin following their mother sometime between 2–4 months of age. During this phase they may be more a hindrance than a help to their mother while she is hunting. Cubs are nutritionally dependent on their mother for a relatively long time—possibly as long as 18 months. In captivity Snow Leopards become sexually mature at 2–3 years of age, but rarely breed before they are four years old.

Status and Conservation. CITES Appendix I. Classified as Endangered on *The IUCN Red List*. Fully protected over most of its geographic range. Status surveys indicate that Snow Leopards live at low densities throughout their geographic range, but in localized areas where prey abundance is high the cats may occur at relatively high densities. The global Snow Leopard population is estimated at 4080–6590 individuals. The major threat to the Snow Leopard is loss of natural prey and conflict with herders over depredation on domestic stock. In areas where Snow Leopards and shepherds live side by side, domestic livestock often form an important part of the Snow Leopards' winter diet. Many Snow Leopards are killed each year in retaliation for stock raiding. The Snow Leopard's prey is subject to fairly intense hunting by humans across the cat's range. Large-scale pika and marmot poisoning programs have depleted populations of these important but smaller prey items. At one time there was a fairly substantial demand for Snow Leopard skins from the fur trade, and in the 1920s approximately 1000 pelts a year were traded in the world fur markets. High quality fur coats made of Snow Leopard skins once fetched US$ 50,000 each. It is no longer legal to export Snow Leopard pelts, but coats and furs are still seen occasionally in shops in Nepal, China, and Taiwan. There is also some demand for Snow Leopard bones for use in the traditional Chinese medicine (TCM) trade. A variety of coordinated efforts are underway to conserve Snow Leopards in the wild. These include compensation schemes for livestock losses and strengthening local conservation institutions through training and support. The International Snow Leopard Trust is currently offering incentives to people to protect local wildlife and helping them find better ways to manage their livestock. In addition, efforts are being made to establish a network of conservation areas across the cat's range.

Bibliography. Ahlborn & Jackson (1988), Blomqvist & Nystrom (1980), Blomqvist & Sten (1982), Chundawat & Rawat (1994), Fox (1994), Fox & Chundawat (1988), Freeman (1980, 1983), Freeman *et al.* (1994), Hemmer (1972), Hillard (1989), Hunter *et al.* (1994), IUCN (2008), Jackson & Ahlborn (1988, 1989, 1990), Koshkarev (1984), Mallon (1988), McCarthy (2000), Miller & Jackson (1994), Nowell & Jackson (1996), Oli (1994), Oli *et al.* (1993), Rieger (1984), Schaller, Ren Junrang & Qiu Mingjiang (1988) Schaller, Tserendeleg & Amarsanaa (1994), Sunquist (1997), Sunquist & Sunquist (2002), Turner (1997).

4. Tiger *Panthera tigris*

French: Tigre / **German**: Tiger / **Spanish**: Tigre

Other common names: Bagh, Sher, Harimau

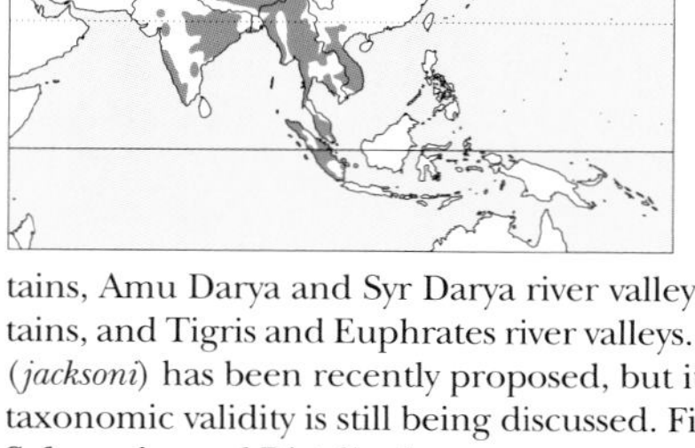

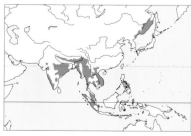

Taxonomy. *Felis tigris* Linnaeus, 1758, Bengal, India.

Recent analyses of morphological and genetic variation in Tigers suggests little evidence for subspecies differentiation. Eight subspecies are recognized historically, but three races are extinct: *balica* (Schwarz, 1912) from Bali, *sondaica* (Temminck, 1844) from Java, and *virgata* (Illiger, 1815) from the river valleys of the Takla Makan, western slopes of the Tian Shan Mountains, Amu Darya and Syr Darya river valleys, shores of the Caspian Sea, Elburz Mountains, and Tigris and Euphrates river valleys. A new subspecies from Peninsular Malaysia (*jacksoni*) has been recently proposed, but it has never been described properly and its taxonomic validity is still being discussed. Five extant subspecies recognized.

Subspecies and Distribution.

P. t. tigris Linnaeus, 1758 – Indian subcontinent.

P. t. altaica Temminck, 1844 – Russian Far East, N Korean Peninsula and NE China.

P. t. amoyensis Hilzheimer, 1905 – SC China (could be extinct in the wild).

P. t. corbetti Mazak, 1968 – S China (Yunnan), S to Indochinese region, and S to the Malay Peninsula.
P. t. sumatrae Pocock, 1929 – Sumatra.

Descriptive notes. Head-body 146–290 cm, tail 72–109 cm; weight 75–325 kg, with considerable regional variation in size. Adult males from Sumatra may weigh 100–140 kg, females 75–110 kg. On average, adult males from Nepal are 100 kg heavier and females 50 kg heavier than their counterparts in Sumatra. Few documented weights exceeding 300 kg, and total length (nose to tip of tail) of three meters or more appear to be exceptional individuals. Background coat color varies from a dark red to a pale yellow and variation also seen in darkness of stripes and stripe pattern. General trend is for Tigers from South-east Asia to have darker ground color and more stripes, while Tigers from northern areas are paler and have fewer stripes. Fur is short in most parts of its range, but winter pelage of Tigers from Russian Far East is thick and long, adding to appearance of great size. Tigers from India are highly variable in coat color and pattern of markings. Markings on head and flanks are individually unique. No melanistic skins or museum specimens exist, but there are three records of black Tigers from the same general area of north-east India and Bangladesh. The last record of white Tigers in India was a male cub captured in the forests of Rewa, Madhya Pradesh, in 1951. All the white Tigers in captivity are descendants of this male; they are not albinos but the result of a mutation that occurred about 100 years ago. Tigers are the largest of the living felids, embodying power and grace. Head is large and foreshortened, increasing the bite force on the large canine teeth. Neck is short, thick, and shoulders and forearms are massive, with long, retractile claws on the broad forepaws. Morphology is specialized for single-handed capture and killing of large prey. Stand about one meter high at the shoulder; hindquarters are slightly lower. Body is long and lithe and the tail is typically less than half the head-body length.

Habitat. Tigers are found in a great variety of habitat types. In Turkmenistan, Uzbekistan, and Tajikistan the Tiger was found in the drainage basins of rivers and lakes, where they hunted in the "tugai," which consists of thickets of low-stature trees (turanga, tamarisk), shrubs, and dense reed beds. In Kazakhstan Tigers sometimes ascended into montane forests in the summer in pursuit of Wild Boar, attaining heights of 2500 m. There are also records of Tigers in the Himalayas at altitudes of almost 4000 m, although in most areas the cats remain well below 2000 m. In China they occupied grass thickets, montane sub-tropical evergreen forests, and mixed forests dominated by oak and poplars. Tigers in the Russian Far East live in low mountainous terrain dominated by nut pine, birch, oaks, fir, and spruce. Winter in this region is harsh, with deep snow and temperatures dropping to −34°C. In Sumatra and Malaysia Tigers are found in lowland humid tropical rainforest, where precipitation exceeds 2000 mm annually. In the outwash areas south of the Himalayas Tigers inhabit the "terai", a belt of floodplain habitat dominated by marshes, swamps, oxbow lakes, and tall, dense grasslands intermixed with riverine forest. Sal forest, a climax form of moist deciduous forest, occurs on the slopes of the adjacent hills. In India Tigers inhabit the tropical, wet evergreen, and semi-evergreen forests of Assam, the mangrove swamps of West Bengal and neighboring Bangladesh, the vast expanses of dry deciduous forest in the central plateau, the tropical moist and dry deciduous forests of the Western Ghats, and the thorn forests of Rajasthan and Gujarat. In Ranthambhore National Park, Rajasthan, Tigers also use the ancient temples and fortresses as places to lie up during the day.

Food and Feeding. The list of prey species found as kills or in Tiger scats (feces) is extensive, but across its vast geographic range the Tiger's diet consists largely of deer and pigs. Over a 54-year period in Sikhote-Alin, Russia, Red Deer (*Cervus elaphus*) and Wild Boar were the dominant prey, representing 437 of 522 kills (84%). Minor prey included Moose (*Alces alces*), Siberian Roe Deer (*Capreolus pygargus*), and Sika Deer (*Cervus nippon*), Siberian Musk Deer (*Moschus moschiferus*), and Long-tailed Goral (*Naemorhedus caudatus*). Surprisingly, the kill records included a small number of adult Brown and Asiatic Black Bears. There is little information available on the food habits of Tigers in South-east Asia, but in a sample (n = 38) of Tiger scats from Huai Kha Khaeng Wildlife Sanctuary, Thailand, muntjac were the dominant prey (42%). Sambar Deer (7%) and Wild Boar (9%) occurred relatively infrequently in scats, whereas smaller prey such as porcupines, Hog Badgers, primates, and lizards collectively occurred in 28% of scats. The diet of Tigers in Royal Bardia National Park, Nepal, was reconstructed from an analysis of 215 scats collected over a 5-year period. Three species, Chital (*Axis axis*), Wild Boar, and Hog Deer (*Axis porcinus*), contributed more than 90% of the biomass consumed. Several other species, including langur monkeys, Nilgai (*Boselaphus tragocamelus*), Barasingha (*Rucervus duvaucelii*), and porcupine occurred infrequently in scats. Larger ungulates such as the Nilgai and Barasingha were not killed preferentially, probably due to their low densities. Wild Boar were taken out of proportion to their availability, although Tiger predation was heaviest on the incredibly abundant (over 200/km²) Chital. Based on an analysis of 472 scats, Tigers in Nagarhole National Park, India, preyed selectively on the largest prey available, the Gaur (*Bos frontalis*) and Sambar, whereas smaller prey such as Chital, Red Muntjac (*Muntiacus muntjak*), and Wild Boar were underrepresented in the diet. These five prey species together provided about 96% of the biomass consumed by Tigers. Among the larger prey species, Tiger predation was biased towards adult male Sambar, Chital, and Wild Boar, and young Gaur. Minor prey identified in scats included Indian Spotted Chevrotain (*Moschiola*), hare, porcupine, Dhole, and primates. Based on the scat data, the average weight of prey taken by Tigers in Nagarhole was 91 kg. In contrast, the average weight based solely on kills was 400 kg; however, because large kills are more likely to be found, this method grossly overestimates the average weight of prey taken. It does indicate, however, that Tigers are capable of taking extremely large prey, including adult male Gaur that may weigh 1000 kg. Tigers are solitary, stalk-and-ambush hunters and they actively search for prey. Habitat features that attract ungulates, such as water holes and the edges of small clearings, are favorite hunting spots. Stalking cover is important: a Tiger will attempt to get as close as possible to its prey before making a final rush, relying on quickly overtaking prey rather than pursuit for long distances. The tiger catches hold of the prey with its claws and holds and kills its prey with a bite from the large canine teeth. Small prey, or those weighing half that of the Tiger, are typically killed with a bite to the nape, with the canines separating the vertebrae and breaking the spinal cord. Large prey are most often killed with a throat bite, leading to strangulation or neck breakage due to twisting on impact. Except for adult Gaur, Tigers in Nagarhole killed their prey where cover density was significantly higher than that of leopard kills. Adult Gaur were killed in areas with significantly less cover, suggesting that attacks on Gaur in dense cover were extremely risky. Tigers in Nagarahole also took advantage of the cover of darkness; about 27% of kills were made between 06:00–09:00 h and the remainder were made between 18:00–06:00 h. Large kills such as Gaur may be too heavy to be moved, but if there is insufficient cover at the kill site the Tiger will drag its kill to an area where it feels secure before beginning to feed. Drag distances may be a few meters or several kilometers, and individual temperament may also influence this behavior. Feeding usually begins on the hindquarters or rump and once the body cavity is opened the stomach is removed and set aside. The carcass is then dragged a short distance before feeding resumes. Tigers use their carnassial or blade-like cheek teeth to slice off large hunks of meat and the rough tongue is used to rasp flesh from bones. The amount of meat consumed can be substantial: one adult male Tiger in Chitwan ate 32 kg in a single night and there are other reports of Tigers consuming 20% of their body weight in a night's feeding. Tigresses in Chitwan spent an average of three days with each kill and during that time consumed 46 kg of meat. However, even large kills may not last long if several Tigers are feeding on the carcass. For example, a tigress in Chitwan and her two large young fed on an adult Sambar for two days, consuming102 kg of meat or about 17 kg per Tiger per day. Tigers often rest near the carcass, feeding intermittently, but if the Tiger leaves it will typically cover the remains, raking leaves, grass, dirt, or even rocks over the carcass. There is little information on kill rates, but tigresses in Chitwan without dependent young killed a large prey animal about every eight or nine days, which translates to 40 to 46 kills per year. Females with dependent young have to kill more often or kill larger prey to meet the nutritional demands of growing offspring.

Activity patterns. Radio-tracking studies indicate that Tigers are essentially crepuscular and nocturnal. Activity patterns appear to be driven primarily by activity patterns of the prey.

Movements, Home range and Social organization. In Nagarhole National Park, India, the rates of movements of radio-collared Tigers were lower during the daytime (mean = 0·07 km/h) than at night (mean = 0·21 km/h). Radio-collared tigresses in Chitwan National Park, Nepal, traveled about 0·7 km/h (range 0·2–1·2 km/h); estimates of the distances traveled in a night by females varied from 3·8 to 9·6 km. These estimates are based on straight-line distances between hourly nighttime locations, so the actual distances traveled would be somewhat greater. On some occasions tigresses crossed their ranges in a single night, while at other times they remained in a portion of it for several days. However, except when they had a kill or young, tigresses in Chitwan normally choose a different rest site each day. Adult females typically occupy relatively small, mutually exclusive territories. The ranges of adult males may also be exclusive, but each male attempts to include as many female ranges as possible within his range, and thus male ranges can vary enormously in size. In Chitwan National Park, Nepal, the average home range size of resident females was 23 km² (range 13–51 km²); overlap of neighboring ranges varied from 3·7–7·1%. These territories function to ensure that females have exclusive access to food, cover, and other resources needed for survival and the successful rearing of young. Females who did not hold territories did not breed. Site fidelity was strong; females spent their entire reproductive lives in these territories, although some females shifted so that part of their range was acquired by their daughters. The tendency for daughters to try to settle next to their mothers resulted in clusters of females that were on average as closely related as lionesses in a pride. Breeding territories of males were established by direct takeovers and sometimes expanded after fights with neighboring males. The average home range size of resident males in Chitwan was 68 km² (range 24 to 151 km²). Males who did not hold territories did not breed. Turnover rates of territorial males were high. The average reproductive life was 2·8 years, but ranged from seven months to 6·3 years. The ranges of resident males overlapped the ranges of two to seven resident females. The home range size of Tigers, especially females, is positively correlated with the abundance of prey, and consequently the density of adult Tigers living in an area is also related to prey biomass density. In the temperate forests of the Russian Far East, Tiger density is estimated at 0·5–1·4/100 km², but prey biomass density is low (400 kg/km² in Sikhote-Alin) and range size of tigresses (200–400 km²) are an order of magnitude larger than those in Chitwan. Prey biomass density in Chitwan is about 2000 kg/km² and Tiger density on the alluvial floodplain is about 8/100 km². The highest Tiger density reported, 16·8/100 km², is from Kaziranga National Park in north-east India. Kaziranga is an alluvial floodplain grassland that supports one of the highest densities of large prey on the subcontinent. Common ungulate prey in Kaziranga include wild Water Buffalo (Bovidae), Barasingha, Hog Deer, Red Muntjac (Cervidae), Wild Boar, and Gaur (Bovidae). High Tiger density (14·7/100 km²) is also reported from the moist deciduous forests of Nagarhole National Park in south India, where prey biomass densities are estimated at 7500 kg/km². The lowest Tiger densities are reported from the lowland tropical rain forests of Peninsular Malaysia, Sumatra, and Laos, where prey densities are typically less than 500 kg/km².

Breeding. In subtropical and tropical areas Tigers mate and give birth at any time of the year, but in temperate areas such as the Russian Far East, young are more likely to be born in the spring. Estrus is preceded by an increase in scent marking, which probably ensures that a male is present when the female is sexually receptive. In captivity, the average length of estrus is five days. In the wild pairs were seldom found together for more than two days, although prolonged associations may be related to inexperience. Courtship in Tigers is risky and familiarity appears to be an important prelude to mating. Once the female is ready to mate copulations occur frequently (e.g.17–52 times/day). Females are thought to be induced ovulators; that is, they require a certain number of copulations within a limited time period to stimulate ovulation. Conception rates are low, about 20 to 40%, and if conception does not occur the female will come into heat again in about a month. Following a gestation of about 103 days the female gives birth to one to seven young. In Nepal, mean litter size for 49 litters was 2·98 (range 2–5); litters were born in all months except February. Birth dens have been found in impenetrable thickets, shallow depressions in dense grass areas, rock crevices, and caves. Kittens are born with eyes closed, helpless, weighing 785 to 1610 g, but they quadruple their birth weight in a month. During the first month of the cubs' lives the tigress spends most of her time at the den and her home range contracts to a small area focused on the den site. Her home range gradually expands as the young become mobile at two to three months of age. At four months of age a Tiger cub is the size of a setter dog. By six months the cubs are weaned, but lack the ability to kill for themselves. The permanent canines appear between twelve and 18 months of age, and this marks a period of rapid weight gain as the young are now physically equipped to make their own kills. They must, however, still refine their hunting techniques and learn to kill efficiently. Male cubs learn to kill on their own and become independent sooner than their female siblings, and by 15 months of age they may begin spending some time away from their mother. By 18–20 months young Tigers are typically independent of their mothers but continue to hunt in their natal range. Dispersal occurs when young are 18–28 months old and it seems to be keyed to the arrival of a new litter. In Chitwan the interbirth interval varied from 20 to 24 months (mean 21·6 months). The average dispersal distance for ten subadult males in Chitwan was 33 km (range 9·5–65 km), but the average for four females was only 9·7 km (range 0·2–33 km). However, only four of the ten males managed to establish breeding territories whereas all four females did. Mean age of first reproduction for females was 3·4 years, and for males it was 4·8 years (range 3·4–6·8 years). Average reproductive life span of females was 6·1 years, but two females in the park had reproductive life spans of 10·5 and 12·5 years, and during this time reared four and five litters, respectively. These females were exceptional: the mean lifetime reproduction of females was 4·54 young surviving to dispersal age and 2·0 that survived to breed. One extraordinary male, who managed to maintain exclusive access to seven females for four years, sired 27 offspring that survived to dispersal age. Most males were far less successful; the mean lifetime reproduction of males was 5·83 young surviving to dispersal age and 1·99 young that survived to breed.

Status and Conservation. CITES Appendix I. Three subspecies (Amur, South China, and Sumatran Tiger) classified as Critically Endangered on *The IUCN Red List*. Otherwise classified as Endangered. Large range reduction (41% over the last decade), and

an estimated global population of 3402–5140 adult Tigers in the wild, with perhaps half of these residing in India. However a recent tiger census carried out in 2007 stated that the wild tiger population in India has come down to approximately 1411. Another 700–1400 Indo-Chinese Tigers live in Myanmar, Thailand, Laos, Cambodia, Vietnam, China, and Peninsular Malaysia. There are about 500 Tigers restricted to some forest tracts on Sumatra. Another 400 or so Siberian Tigers live in the Russian Far East, with a few in neighboring China. The Chinese Tiger has almost been extirpated, and no definite evidence of continued persistence exists. The Bali, Javan, and Caspian races are extinct. Tiger populations have declined over many parts of Asia because of illegal hunting, commercial trade in Tiger bone and derivatives, a declining prey base, and loss and degradation of habitat. Saving the Tiger has become an enormous and complex undertaking, involving efforts by federal, national, and state governments, large corporations, parks and wildlife departments, and non-government organizations. The problem is being attacked on many fronts, including threats of sanctions against countries that do not control trade in Tiger parts, establishing protected reserves, training and deployment of anti-poaching teams, identification of critical conservation units, working with traditional Chinese medical practitioners to find alternatives to Tiger parts, public education campaigns deploring the use Tiger parts, habitat restoration projects, economic incentives to locals, development of suitable survey and monitoring methods, and initiation of baseline ecological research projects. Some of these initiatives have led to recoveries of Tiger populations within a decade in many reserves in India and Nepal, but with expanding human populations in the region the pressures on the natural systems are only going to increase. Fortunately, Tigers are a resilient species and demographic modeling suggests that even relatively small Tiger populations with 6–12 breeding females may be viable over a 100-year timeframe. Even small reserves, 300–3000 km², can potentially support viable Tiger populations if the prey base is intact. However, managing and protecting these areas will require more resources and it will also be important to know which management practices work and which do not.

Bibliography. Bagchi *et al.* (2003), Banks *et al.* (1992), Biswas & Sankar (2002), Brahmachary & Dutta (1987), Brahmachary *et al.* (1991), Dinerstein, Loucks *et al.* (2006), Dinerstein, Wikramanayake *et al.* (1997), Dorji & Santiapillai (1989), Eisenberg & Seidensticker (1976), Franklin, N. *et al.* (1999), Heptner & Sludskii (1992a), Hoogerwerf (1970), IUCN (2008), Jhala *et al.* (2008), Johnson, A. *et al.* (2006), Karanth (1987, 2001), Karanth & Sunquist (1992, 1995, 2000), Karanth *et al.* (2004), Kawanishi & Sunquist (2004) Kitchener (1999), Kitchener & Dugmore (2000), Kleiman (1974), Lanier & Dewsbury (1976), Locke (1954), Luo *et al.* (2004), Maruska (1987), Mazak (2004), Mazak & Groves (2006), Mazák (1981), McDougal (1977, 1981, 1987, 1988, 1991, 1995), McNeely (1979), Miquelle (1998), Miquelle, Merrill *et al.* (1999), Miquelle, Quigley *et al.* (1993), Miquelle, Smirnov *et al.* (1996), Nowell & Jackson (1996), O'Brien *et al.* (2003), Panwar (1987), Perry (1965), Plowden & Bowles (1997), Rabinowitz (1989, 1993), Roychoudhury (1987), Sankhala (1977), Santiapillai & Widodo (1985, 1987), Schaller (1967), Seidensticker (1976a, 1976b, 1987), Seidensticker & Hai (1983), Seidensticker & McDougal (1993), Smith, J.L.D. (1984, 1993), Smith, J.L.D. & McDougal (1991), Smith, J.L.D., McDougal, Ahearn *et al.* (1999), Smith, J.L.D., McDougal & Miquelle (1989), Smith, J.L.D., McDougal & Sunquist (1987), Smith, J.L.D., Tunhikorn *et al.* (1999), Sunquist (1981), Sunquist & Sunquist (2002), Sunquist *et al.* (1999), Thapar (1986, 1989), Thorton (1978), Thorton *et al.* (1967), Tilson *et al.* (1997), Wentzel *et al.* (1999).

Plate 3 ➤

PLATE 3

inches 24

cm 60

ssp *pardus*

melanic morph

ssp *delacouri*

ssp *fusca*

ssp *melanotica*

5

ssp *nimr*

ssp *orientalis*

ssp *saxicolor*

ssp *suahelicus*

5. Leopard *Panthera pardus*

French: Léopard / **German**: Leopard / **Spanish**: Leopardo

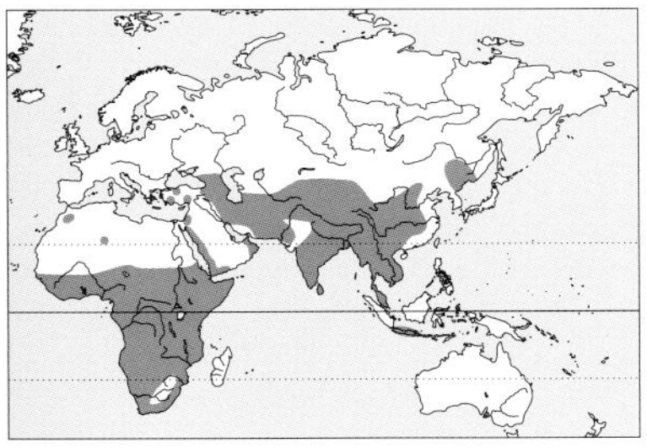

Taxonomy. *Felis pardus* Linnaeus, 1758, Egypt.

Recent morphological and genetic analyses suggests subsuming all African races into *pardus*, all populations on the Indian subcontinent into *fusca*, and all Central Asian races into *saxicolor*. Twenty-four subspecies are currently recognized.

Subspecies and Distribution.

P. p. pardus Linnaeus, 1758 – Sudan and NE Zaire.
P. p. adersi Pocock, 1932 – Zanzibar I (could be extinct).
P. p. adusta Pocock, 1927 – Ethiopian highlands.
P. p. ciscaucasicus Satunin, 1914 – Caucasus mountains.
P. p. dathei Zukowsky, 1959 – S and C Iran (of dubious validity).
P. p. delacouri Pocock, 1930 – S China to Malay Peninsula.
P. p. fusca Meyer, 1794 – Indian subcontinent.
P. p. japonensis Gray, 1862 – NC China.
P. p. jarvisi Pocock, 1932 – Sinai Peninsula.
P. p. kotiya Deraniyagala, 1949 – Sri Lanka.
P. p. leopardus Schreber, 1777 – Rain forests of W and C Africa.
P. p. melanotica Günther, 1775 – S Africa.
P. p. melas Cuvier, 1809 – Java.
P. p. nanopardus Thomas, 1904 – Somali arid zone.
P. p. nimr Hemprich & Ehrenberg, 1833 – S Israel to Arabian peninsula.
P. p. orientalis Schlegel, 1857 – Russian Far East, Korea, and NE China.
P. p. panthera Schreber, 1777 – N Africa.
P. p. pernigra Gray, 1863 – Kashmir through Nepal to SW Xizang and Sichuan.
P. p. reichenowi Cabrera, 1918 – Savannas of Cameroon.
P. p. ruwenzori Camerano, 1906 – Ruwenzori and Virunga mountains of Zaire, Rwanda, and Burundi.
P. p. saxicolor Pocock, 1927 – N Iran and S Turkmenistan E to Afghanistan.
P. p. sindica Pocock, 1930 – SE Afghanistan through W and S Pakistan.
P. p. suahelicus Neumann, 1900 – E Africa, from Kenya S to Mozambique.
P. p. tulliana Valenciennes, 1856 – Turkey.

Descriptive notes. Head-body 92–190 cm, tail 64–99 cm; weight 21–71 kg. Adult males are larger than adult females. There is considerable regional variation in body size and weight. Adult Leopards from Cape Province, South Africa, are among the smallest, with mean weight of males at 30·9 kg and females at 21·2 kg. However, adult males weighing 50 to 60 kg are reported from many regions of the Leopard's range. Background coat color varies from bright golden yellow to a pale yellow to rusty-reddish yellow, depending on region. Underparts are white. Hair is short and coarse in cats from warmer climates, but winter coat of Leopards from Russian Far East is soft, long (3–7 cm), and dense. Black spots are found on head, neck, shoulders, limbs, and hindquarters. Black spots form broken circles or rosettes on sides and back. The rosettes typically lack a black spot in center, as seen on the Jaguar. Melanistic Leopards are known from several regions of Africa, but there is a much higher frequency of black Leopards from Thailand, Malaysia, and Java. Tail is relatively long, more than half the head-body length, and covered with dark spots, bands, and blobs; tip is black above and white below. Backs of ears are white on upper half and dark below. Pattern of markings on coat, head, and muzzle are individually unique.

Habitat. As might be predicted from its broad geographic distribution, Leopards are able to live in almost every type of habitat. In sub-Saharan Africa the cats are found in all habitats that have an annual rainfall above 50 mm. They are also found in true deserts, but only where river courses extend into this otherwise inhospitable habitat. In the Kalahari Gemsbok National Park, South Africa, Leopards inhabit arid, open-dune sandveld with scattered shrubs and trees. They escape the intense midday heat by sheltering in porcupine or aardvark burrows. Tracking studies in the Kalahari have shown that Leopards can survive without drinking for as long as ten days. In other hot, dry deserts such as the Namib, Sahara, Sinai, and Arabian, Leopards also use caves, burrows, or the shade of dense vegetation to survive daytime temperatures that may reach 70°C. In other parts of Africa Leopards occur in the wetter habitats, including savannas, acacia grasslands, evergreen and deciduous forests, and scrub woodlands. They also occur in the rain forest habitats of Central and West Africa, where annual rainfall typically exceeds 1500 mm. Leopards are common throughout the Indian subcontinent, from the moist deciduous, teak, and shola forests of the Western Ghats to the dry, deciduous, bamboo, and mixed forests of the rugged tableland in central India. In the north they live in sal forest and the tall grasslands on the outwash plains of the Himalaya as well as in the mountainous terrain of Pakistan and Kashmir to 5200 m. In Myanmar, Thailand, Peninsular Malaysia, and Java the cats are found in dense, primary rain forest and a variety of other forest types. In the Russian Far East Leopards inhabit mountainous forested regions. They prefer broken topography with Korean pine and second growth oak forest. In this area, a key limiting factor is snow depth. The cats prefer habitats where the average long-term snow cover does not exceed 15 cm. Whatever type of habitat they live in, Leopards are often able to persist in close proximity to people, as long as they are not persecuted and have access to secure den sites. Remarkably, three Leopards were discovered living in an abandoned engine at the railroad station in Kampala, Uganda. In India it is not uncommon to read newspaper accounts of villagers finding leopards hiding in sheds and outbuildings.

Food and Feeding. Leopards are adaptable generalists, able to survive on an extraordinary variety of large or small prey. In many areas the cat's diet consists largely of small to medium-sized mammals (5–45 kg), but even ungulates weighing two to three times the cat's body weight are occasionally taken. Leopards can also survive on extremely small prey, an ability that allows them to live in areas from which larger prey has long since been extirpated. The cat has a truly catholic diet, taking an incredible variety of different prey sizes and types. At least 92 prey species are known from the Leopard's diet in sub-Saharan Africa. Where Leopards live near villages their diet often includes dogs, cats, sheep, goats, calves, and pigs. A large number of sheep or goats can be killed in a single incident when a Leopard finds itself in a pen with a frightened flock. The Leopard's fondness for dogs is well known and there are many accounts of family pets or village dogs disappearing in the night. Food habit studies from different parts of the Leopard's geographic distribution illustrates the cat's adaptability. In the Serengeti, Impala (*Aepyceros melampus*) and Thompson's Gazelles (*Eudorcas thomsonii*) are the principal prey, but other bovids (Bushbuck *Tragelaphus scriptus*, Common Reedbuck *Redunca redunca*, Blue Wildebeest *Connochaetes taurinus*, Grant's Gazelle *Nanger granti*, Topi *Damaliscus korrigum*, Hartebeest *Alcelaphus buselaphus*) are also taken. Less frequently taken prey incude Common Warthog (*Phacochoerus africanus*), Burchell's Zebra (*Equus burchellii*), hyrax, spring hare, baboons, birds, and small carnivores. Impala are also the dominant prey (78% of kills) in Kruger National Park, although the cats occasionally prey on other bovids (Bushbuck, Reedbuck, Blue Wildebeest, Waterbuck *Kobus ellipsiprymnus*, Kudu *Tragelaphus strepisceros*, Nyala *T. angasii*, Common Tsessebe *Damaliscus lunatus*, Common Eland *Taurotragus oryx*, Sable Antelope *Hippotragus niger*, and African Buffalo *Syncerus caffer*). In the Kalahari, Springbok (*Antidorcas marsupialis*) is the most important prey (65% of kills), but duikers, Steenbok (*Raphicerus campestris*), Blue Wildebeest, Hartebeest, and Gemsbok (*Oryx gazella*) are also taken. Incidental prey included small carnivores, birds, rodents, Cheetahs, Aardwolves, and Aardvarks. Duikers were the most important prey in north-east Namibia; Steenbok ranked second. A variety of other carnivorous animals were also killed, including Aardwolf, Cheetah, Genet, Bat-eared Fox, Wildcat, and python. A major difference in the diets of African Leopards is that cats from tropical rain forests take signifi cantly more primates. In the Ituri Forest, Zaire, primates comprised 25% of prey items in Leopard scats. Of 13 species of diurnal anthropoid primates in the area, remains of at least eleven species were identified in scats. Arboreal guenons, mangabeys, and colobines (Cercopithecidae) were taken in proportion to their abundance, but predation on L'Hoest's Monkey (*Cercopithecus lhoesti*), a terrestrial species, was much greater than expected based on their availability. Despite the increased percentage of primates in the diets of Ituri Forest Leopards, their principal prey was medium-sized ungulates. In the Taï National Park, Ivory Coast, primate remains were found in 25% of scats; Leopards killed at least eight species of primate (Ceropithecidae, Lorisidae). Duikers were the dominant prey in the park, but bushpigs (*Potamochoerus*), Forest Hogs (*Hylochoerus meinertzhageni*), porcupines, pangolins, hyrax, Water Chevrotain (*Hyemoschus aquaticus*), and rodents were also taken. Leopards in Asia prey largely on small to medium-sized ungulates. In Nagarhole National Park, India, Chital, muntjac, and Sambar (Cervidae) were found in 65% of scats; the remains of Gaur and Four-horned Antelope (*Tetracerus quadricornis*), Wild Boar, and chevrotain were found in 19% of scats. Incidental prey included primates, hares, porcupines, and Dhole. The small (15–20 kg) muntjac was the dominant prey (43%) in Huai Kha Khaeng Wildlife Sanctuary, Thailand. Primates ranked second (11%) in scats, followed by porcupines (10%). Less frequently occurring prey included Sambar, Wild Boars, Hog Badgers, pangolins, rodents, birds, lizards, and crabs. In Wolong Reserve, China, Tufted Deer (*Elaphodus cephalophus*) are the principal prey (41%). Musk deer, Sambar, Wild Boar, and several species of bovids (Serow *Capricornis*, Takin *Budorcas taxicolor*, Goral *Naemorhedus*) were taken occasionally. Surprisingly, rodents were the second most frequently occurring prey (17%) in scats. The remains of a Red Panda and a Giant Panda were each found in a scat. In the Russian Far East more than half of the Leopard's diet consists of Siberian Roe Deer. Secondary prey include Siberian Musk Deer, Sika Deer, Wild Boar, hare, badger, Raccoon Dog, and pheasants. Leopards locate their prey primarily by sight and sound, and they spend considerable time looking and listening for prey as they walk slowly about their home ranges. Having detected an animal, the Leopard will stalk it, preferring to get as close as possible before launching an attack. Alternatively, it will lie in ambush, waiting for the prey to come close enough to attack. Adult prey are rarely pursued, although young, inexperienced animals are sometimes chased for considerable distances. Most hunting is done at night, taking advantage of the cover of darkness, and what little information is available suggests hunting success is higher at night. Leopards occasionally hunt during the daytime, but typically only in areas with dense cover. Few people have actually observed Leopards trying to capture an animal. In Kruger National Park, Leopards were unsuccessful on thirteen daytime attempts, but two attempts at night were both successful. In the Serengeti National Park, only one of nine and three of sixty-four daytime attempts to capture prey were successful. Like other large felids, Leopards commonly kill large prey with a bite to the throat. Small prey are usually dispatched with a bite to the nape or back of the head. Leopards go to great lengths to avoid losing their kills to scavengers and larger predators. They will drag carcasses hundreds of meters to get to areas with dense cover or to cache kills in trees. Hauling a carcass into a tree involves a great feat of strength. One Leopard managed to haul a 125 kg giraffe calf up into a tree to a height of 5·7 m. The habit of caching kills in trees appears to be more common in Africa, where large carnivores such as Lions and hyenas will quickly steal kills from the smaller and less powerful leopard. In the Serengeti, Leopard kills stored in trees lasted about four times longer than similar-sized kills stored on the ground. How often a Leopard kills depends on variables such as size of prey, seasonal changes in cover, individual differences in levels of experience, and reproductive constraints. Leopards in Kruger National Park killed on average about one Impala per week. The longest interval between kills of large prey was 19 days. In the Serengeti, where Thompson's Gazelles were the principal prey, Leopards made a kill about every five to six days. A female Leopard in South Africa's Londolozi Game Reserve was seen with 28 kills weighing more than 10 kg in 330 days, or about one kill every 11·8 days. The kill rates in Kruger were slightly higher in the wet season than in the dry season, which was thought to be related to the increased density of stalking cover following the onset of the rains. Males in Kruger killed a large prey animal about once every 7·2 days compared to once every 7·5 days for females without young. In the Kalahari Desert, male Leopards made a kill about every three days, compared to once every 1·5 days for females with cubs. As the interval between kills got longer, Leopards in the Kalahari increased the distances they traveled each day to increase contact rates with prey. Females in north-east Namibia without young made a kill about once every 5–5·6 days, whereas females with dependent young made a kill every 3·9–4·4 days. Although the kill rate was not much higher for females with young, they did kill larger prey, resulting in a greater per capita food intake. The amount of meat consumed varies, depending on the size of the prey, how much meat is lost to scavengers, and the percentage of carcass that is inedible. Estimates of consumption vary from 4·7–3·1 kg/day for adult male Leopards in Kruger to 2·9 kg/day for adult females in the same area. Leopards in captivity are maintained on about 1·2 to 2·6 kg/day, but they surely have less caloric demands than animals in the wild.

Activity patterns. In most areas where Leopards have been studied the cats are largely nocturnal. In Sri Lanka, where they are the only large carnivore, they are commonly sighted in open habitats during the daytime, suggesting that their activity patterns are influenced by the presence of other large carnivores.

Movements, Home range and Social organization. Few studies have actually monitored the movements of Leopards, but in the interior dune areas of the Kalahari Desert, males traveled an average of 14·3 km/day. Females with cubs averaged 13·4 km/day. The maximum distances traveled by males were 27·3 km per day (non-mating period) and 33 km/day (mating period). The maximum distance traveled by a female with cubs was 24·6 km/day. In more productive habitats the distances traveled per day are considerably less. Leopards in Tsavo National Park averaged 2·6 km/day (range 0·9–4·2 km/day) and in the South-west Cape Province the distances traveled by three males were usually less than 3 km/day. There is great variation in home range sizes of Leopards. In high-quality habitats females can meet their needs within relatively small areas. The home range of an adult female living on the prey-rich floodplain of Nepal's Chitwan National Park measured only 8 km², while the ranges of two females living along the edge of the park were 6–13 km². In Kruger National Park, females living in riparian habitats had similarly small ranges, averaging about 14·8 km². The ranges of resident females on a livestock ranch in Kenya were about 14 km². Male ranges in these areas were two to three times larger than female ranges. The year-round home ranges of two female Leopards in the Russian Far East were 33 and 62 km²; a male's range was at least 280 km². In areas of extremely low prey density, female ranges of 128 to 487 km² have been reported. The home range of a male in the interior dune area of the Kalahari Desert was estimated at 800 km². Leopards are solitary, and outside of mating the only long-term association is a female and her young. Each male's range usually overlaps the range of one or more adult females. The larger male ranges will often include areas of less productive habitats; females compete for the best areas, because habitats with abundant resources enhance their reproductive success. In some parts of Africa, long-term sightings of individually-recognizable Leopards suggest that females are philopatric, in that daughters tend to establish ranges next to their mothers'. Density estimates of leopards vary from a low of 0·6/100 km² in the interior dune area of the Kalahari Desert to 30·3/100 km² in the riparian forest areas of Kruger National Park. Estimates of 3·5 to 12·5/100 km² appear to be more common.

Breeding. Zoo records show that females may come into estrus at any time of the year and they remain in heat for one to two weeks. In the wild mating associations are brief, lasting only one or two days. Young are born after a gestation period of about 96 days. Litter size varies from 1–3, but there are records of females having as many as six cubs. Most litters consist of two young. Females use caves, rocky outcrops, abandoned burrows, or dense thickets for birth dens. For the first few days after the cubs are born the mother spends practically all her time at the den, resting and nursing the young. Later, when she leaves to hunt, she may be away from the den site for 24–36 hours. Leopard cubs are very vulnerable to predation during this time. Most cub mortality occurs during the first few months of life. Older cubs are also left unattended for long periods of time. Studies in north-east Namibia found that three-month-old cubs were left for periods of one to seven days while their mother hunted. Young generally begin traveling with their mother when they are about three months old and weigh 3–4 kg. There are records of five-month old cubs killing hares and other small animals, but more commonly this coincides with the appearance of their permanent canines at about 7–8 months of age. By the time Leopards are 12–18 months of age, the young are usually independent of their mother, but the timing of dispersal varies from 15 to 36 months. Sexual maturity is attained by two to three years of age.

Status and Conservation. CITES Appendix I. Four subspecies (Arabian, Amur, North African, and Anatolian Leopard) classified as Critically Endangered on *The IUCN Red List*. Four subspecies (Caucasus, Sri Lankan, North Chinese, and Javan Leopard) listed as Endangered. Otherwise classified as Near Threatened on *The IUCN Red List*. The Leopard is in the odd position of being endangered in some parts of its range and a pest in others. Leopards clearly have the ability to survive near humans. They feed on almost any type of prey and do not have highly specific habitat requirements. However, they are vulnerable to persecution. The greatest threat to the Leopard's continued survival is the loss of habitat and wild prey as livestock activities expand.

Bibliography. Arivazhagan *et al.* (2007), Bailey (1993), Bertram (1982), Bothma & LeRiche (1984, 1986, 1989, 1990), Cat News (2006), Desai (1975), Eaton (1977), Eisenberg & Lockhart (1972), Grassman (1998b), Grobler & Wilson (1972), Hamilton (1976), Hart *et al.* (1996), Hayward *et al.* (2006), Heptner & Sludskii (1992b), Hes (1991), Hoppe-Dominik (1984), Ilany (1981, 1990), Jenny (1996), Johnson *et al.* (1993), Karanth & Sunquist (1995, 2000), Khorozkyan & Malkhasyan (2002), Le Roux & Skinner (1989), Martin & Meulenar (1988), McDougal (1988), Mendelssohn (1989), Mills (1984b), Miquelle *et al.* (1996), Miththapala, Seidensticker & O'Brien. (1996), Miththapala, Seidensticker, Phillips *et al.* (1989), Mizutani & Jewell (1998), Muckenhirn & Eisenberg (1973), Norton & Henley (1987), Norton & Lawson (1985), Nowell & Jackson (1996), Odden & Wegge (2005, In press), Pienaar (1969), Pocock (1932a), Rabinowitz (1989), Sadleir (1966), Schaller (1967), Scott (1985), Seidensticker (1976a, 1977), Seidensticker *et al.* (1990), de Silva & Jayaratne (1994), Smith (1977), Stander *et al.* (1997), Stuart & Stuart (1991), Sunquist (1983), Sunquist & Sunquist (2002), Turnbull-Kemp (1967), Wilson (1977).

Plate 4 ➤

inches   35
cm   90

♂
ssp *leo*

cub

6

♀
ssp *nubica*

♂

♂
ssp *persica*

ssp *onca*

7

ssp *arizonensis*

melanic morph

ssp *centralis*

6. Lion *Panthera leo*

French: Lion / **German:** Löwe / **Spanish:** León

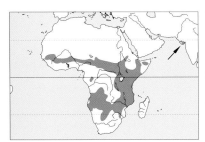

Taxonomy. *Felis leo* Linnaeus, 1758, Morocco, North Africa.
Proposed races *massaica*, *somaliensis* and *roosevelti* are included in *nubica*. Nominal race *leo* (Linnaeus, 1758) from north-west Africa and race *melanochaita* (C. E. H. Smith, 1858) from Cape region, South Africa, are extinct. Six extant subspecies currently recognized.

Subspecies and Distribution.
P. l. azandica J. A. Allen, 1924 – NE Zaire.
P. l. bleyenberghi Lönnberg, 1914 – S Zaire, Zambia, and Angola.
P. l. krugeri Roberts, 1929 – NW (Kalahari), N, and SE South Africa.
P. l. nubica de Blainville, 1843 – NE and E Africa.
P. l. persica Meyer, 1826 – from Iraq to C India in the 19th century; now restricted to the Gir Forest, India.
P. l. senegalensis Meyer, 1826 – West Africa E to the Central African Republic.

Descriptive notes. Head-body 172–250 cm (males), 158–192 cm (females), tail 61–100 cm. Shoulder height 107–123 cm; weight 190 (150–225 kg; record 272 kg) for males, and 126 (122–192 kg) for females. The Lions of the Asian subspecies *persica* are in general smaller. Brown amber to clear cream-colored iris. Eyes edged with white underneath. Coat of adults is generally a uniform sandy or tawny on the upperparts and flanks and white on the underparts. Some adults retain the rosettes and spots characteristic of young lions to a lesser or greater degree, even into their later years. Backs of rounded ears are black, tail is just over half the length of head and body, with well-developed tuft of long tawny to black hairs on the tip concealing a horny spur. Melanistic forms are extremely rare, very pale individuals known from Kaokoland, Namibia, and south-west Botswana. Some nearly white individuals, not albinos, from Timbavati, north-east South Africa. Hair on face, upper body parts, flanks and tail is short, on underparts softer and longer. Adult males have a mane of long hair (up to 16 cm) on the sides of the face and on top of the head, extending onto the shoulder, around the neck, and for a short distance along the spine. In sub-adults mane color is sandy, yellowish, or tawny, but may change to black with advancing age. Adult Lions lacking manes occur in the Tsavo region, Tanzania, and elsewhere uncommonly. The mane serves as a sexual signal to females and distinguishes the male at great distances. It is also an indicator of individual fitness: mane development is strongly influenced by testosterone. Some adult males have tufts of long hair on the elbows and a long band of hair extending from the mane over the chest to the anterior part of the abdomen. In the extinct North African nominate subspecies this covered the whole belly. Long whitish whiskers are arranged in parallel rows on the sides of the upper lip, each arising from a black spot, but with the top row of spots without whiskers. Recognition of individuals from this pattern of spots is possible. The massive skull is relatively flat on top. The distinguishing morphological character of the remaining Asian Lions, rarely seen in African Lions, is a longitudinal fold of skin along their bellies. Male Asiatic Lions have only moderate mane growth on top of the head, so that their ears are always visible.

Habitat. Lions have a wide habitat tolerance. They are not found in dense lowland forests of West Africa and the Congo Basin, but will penetrate deep into desert, especially along avenues of watercourses. They are common in semi-desert areas. They will drink when water is available, but are not dependent on it, getting their moisture requirements from their prey and even plants (tsamma melon in the Kalahari Desert). Optimal habitat appears to be open woodlands and thick bush, scrub, and grass complexes, providing ample supply of food in the form of medium to large-sized ungulates, some shade for resting in the heat of the day, and the barest of cover to facilitate stalking of prey. Range up to 4000 m in Ethiopia. The Lion formerly ranged from North Africa through south-west Asia, where it disappeared from most countries within the last 150 years, west into Europe, where it became extinct almost 2000 years ago, and east into India. Lions survived in the central Saharan Desert on the edge of the Air Mountains until about 60 years ago.

Food and Feeding. Medium- to large-sized ungulates make up the bulk of their diet, but Lions are generalists, taking a large variety of vertebrates from mice to young rhinos, Hippos (*Hippopotamus amphibius*), and African Elephants (*Loxodonta africana*), birds up to the size of an ostrich (*Struthio camelus*), as well as reptiles, fish, and even insects. Major large ungulate species include a large variety of bovids like African Buffalo, Blue Wildebeest, Hartebeest, Waterbuck, Kob (*Kobus kob*), Sable Antelope, Gemsbok, eland, Impala, Springbok, as well as Giraffe (*Giraffa camelopardalis*), warthog, and zebra in Africa, and deer as well as a high percentage of livestock in Asia. Individual differences in prey selection and killing techniques are discernible in different prides in the same area, indicating that learning plays a strong role in the Lion's hunting behavior; i.e. hunting of Brown Fur Seals (*Arctocephalus pusillus*) on the Namibian coast. In the Serengeti 30% of stalks were successful when members of the pride took part, against 17–19% when only a single individual was involved. Lions do not take account of wind direction when stalking prey; however, they will often try to cut prey off by running ahead of it. Speeds of 45–60 km/h may be achieved in a rush for up to a few hundred meters (usually not more than 100–200 m). The attack is delivered to the rump or shoulders, with the weight of the Lions often bringing the prey to the ground. Sometimes the prey's neck is broken in falling. As soon as the prey is down it is seized by the throat or muzzle to effect strangulation. The Lions feed at the site of the kill or drag it to the nearest cover. The belly is ripped open and the stomach and intestines pulled out. Lions, especially males, frequently scavenge, acquiring up to 53% of food items in the open plains of the Serengeti this way. This figure decreases to 5% in more arid environments, where prey occurs at lower density. However, in the woodlands of Kruger National Park, male Lions acquire most of their food by hunting rather than scavenging. In Kruger the main prey of male Lions was African Buffalo; females fed on the most abundant medium-sized ungulates, such as Blue Wildebeest and Burchell's Zebra. Lions will watch vultures descending on kills of other predators. Protection of kills against Spotted Hyenas, is greatly enhanced by the presence of a male. Females may lose up to 20% of their kills to Spotted Hyenas and a further 17% to unrelated Lions. In the absence of their normal prey, Lions can cause grave losses to cattle and small stock, or may even become "man-eaters". The individuals involved are not always old and decrepit.

Activity patterns. Lions usually hunt at night, but there are exceptions. Major hunting peaks usually occur between 02:00 h and 04:00 h, but in Etosha, most hunts occurred from 21:30–22:30 h. In Botswana's Chobe National Park, Lions seem to be most successful on moonless nights. Hunting levels may be increased during storms, when noise, wind, and waving vegetation make it difficult for prey to detect Lions. They will sleep and rest, usually in compact groups, for long periods when satiated. They avoid exerting themselves during the heat of the day. Although a terrestrial species, they are good climbers and will sometimes drape themselves along branches of trees to take advantage of cool breezes and avoid flies or dangerous animals. Resting periods are interrupted by short periods of intense activity when hunting or exhibiting aggression. Their roar can, under optimal conditions, be heard from as far as 5 km away, appears to serve to demarcate territory, and may be individually distinctive. Prides often indulge in communal roaring. They also use scats, urine spraying, and scrapes for demarcation.

Movements, Home range and Social organization. Mostly sedentary but some populations follow migratory prey seasonally. Some individuals nomadic, especially males and subadults. In the arid savanna of Etosha National Park Lions move a mean 13·2 km in 24 hours; in the S Kalahari an average 15·2 km (range 11–34 km). In contrast, Serengeti Lions averaged 4·5–6·5 km in 24 hours. Pride home range size varies from 25–226 km², but can be considerably larger in low prey density areas, e.g., Etosha National Park, with up to 2075 km². In some areas there is an overlap of home ranges but in others ranges are largely exclusive, and actively defended, meriting the term territories. Whether ranges are defended appears to be dependent on the local movement of prey species. Average emigration/mortality of pride Lions in Etosha National Park was 17%. Core unit of the Lions' matriarchial society is the pride, which consists of a group of related females, none dominant, and their cubs. Pride size, measured by the number of adult females, varies from a minimum average of 2·2 in very arid environments to an average of 4–6, up to eight in year-round high prey-density areas like the Ngorongoro Crater, Tanzania. Maximum pride size was 39. Subspecies *persica* has on average smaller prides of 2–5 females. Prides are "fission-fusion" social units. Membership is stable, but pride members are often scattered in small subgroups throughout the pride's range, and each member spends considerable time alone. Female pride members display several cooperative behaviors unique among felids, giving birth in synchrony, raising cubs communally, with allosuckling of cubs and cooperative hunting. Males, for the short time they are living together with females, concentrate their energy on defending their tenure over the pride(s). In Etosha males only participated in 4% of 461 hunting opportunities, in the Serengeti in only 3%, but more recent studies show that males elsewhere are efficient hunters, tackling especially large and dangerous prey like Buffalo. Prides often divide into smaller sub-groups when foraging. In some regions there is a complex division of labor among lionesses. Some, often larger and heavier individuals, repeatedly play the role of "center", and others the role of "wing", chasing the prey towards the "center". A single male or coalition of up to seven males holds tenure over one or more prides, and effectively excludes strange males from siring cubs with pride females. The average tenure is only 2–3 years. Only in exceptional cases do male Lions breed with related pride females. Coalition males in pre- and post-tenure periods hunt and scavenge cooperatively. Larger coalitions of 4–6 males can maintain tenure more than twice as long as 1–2 males. Coalitions of more than four males are always related, but pairs frequently consist of unrelated males. Despite maternal defense, infanticide is common when males take over a new pride. Most females with dependent cubs lose their cubs within a month of takeover, and pregnant females lose the cubs shortly after giving birth. In this way, males assure paternity during their short reproductive lifetime. Females show a burst of heightened sexual activity for about three months following a takeover, attracting other males and encouraging competition. This ensures that the fittest coalition is able to gain tenure. Females remain infertile during this "testing" phase, and afterwards, when tenure has stabilized, tend to breed in synchrony. Litters born synchronously have a higher survival rate and tend to show a sex ratio biased towards males. Sociality in Lions may have evolved to increase hunting success on very large prey, defense of young and kills, maintenance of long term territories, and insurance against individual injury or incapacity.

Breeding. Largely aseasonal, but with birth peaks in certain regions. Courtship initiated by either member of pair; pair remain in close association during the mating period. The male follows the female at all times and rests with her. Female invites copulation by

On following pages: 7. Jaguar (*Panthera onca*).

lordosis. Other males of the coalition are tolerated close by, and sometimes there are even multiple-mate copulations, but strange lions are driven off. At least one member of male coalitions larger than two fails to breed successfully, but through kin selection, related non-breeding helpers still benefit. Pair may copulate every 15 minutes, with copulation lasting up to one minute. Mating lasts over a period of several hours and also through the night. Between copulations the pair will lie down next to each other or walk together until the next mating. During copulation the female purrs loudly and towards the end the male may gently neckbite the female. The majority of matings do not result in pregnancy; of 14 observed mating periods only four resulted in fertilization. Lions are polyestrous, estrus lasting 4–16 days, interestrus interval varying from a few days to over a year, on average 16 days, gestation mean of 110 days (range 100–114). Litter size averages 2·5–3, range 1–6, but 89% is 1–4. The mean interbirth interval is 20 months (range 11–25) if previous litter survives to maturity, or 4–6 months if previous litter was lost. For parturition females leave their pride for 4–8 weeks. Mass at birth is about 1·5 kg. Females rejoin the pride with their 4–8 week-old cubs; any female with milk will allow suckling. Cubs will suckle regularly for 6–7 months, suckling less after seven months and discontining by twelve months. They remain with their mothers for 21–30 months and grow rapidly for the first three years. Cub mortality is high, with a 40–50% survival rate, depending on food supply and pride takeover. Young Lions learn to hunt by watching the adults in the pride, and leave their natal pride at the age of 24–42 months. Males reach sexual maturity at 26 months, but only get the opportunity to mate when they are about five years old, and usually only during their pride tenure. Female become pregnant for the first time at about 43 months of age and continue to breed until they are about 15 years old, producing a litter every two years.

Status and Conservation. CITES Appendix II. Classified as Vulnerable on *The IUCN Red List*. There are no sound estimates of the total number of Lions in Africa. Most recent data range from 16,500 to 30,000. They occur throughout most of Africa, but are increasingly restricted to protected areas. They are of great social-economic value for trophy hunting, game viewing, and negatively as stock-raiders. Man eating Lions are also a problem, especially in Tanzania. Recent increase in reintroduction of Lions into smaller fenced reserves. Hunting restricted to "problem" animals in most places, in some countries prohibited but in others no legal protection. Generally considered problem animals, whose existence is at odds with human settlement and cattle cultures. Scavenging makes them vulnerable to poisoned carcasses. Some populations already isolated, Namibia–Etosha National Park c. 300, Zimbabwe Hwange National Park complex 500. Subspecies *persica* up from less than 20 in Gir forest around 1900 to about 300 in 1995. Lions are sparsely distributed in West and Central Africa. Densities vary from 0·17 adults/subadults/100 km² in Savuti, Chobe National Park, Botswana, to 1·5–2/100 km² in Ngalagadi-Transfrontier Park (Botswana/South Africa) and Etosha National Park, Namibia; to 3–10 and up to 18/100 km² in East and South African protected areas; and 14/100 km² in Gir National Park, India. Highest known density is in Maasai Mara National Reserve, Kenya with 30/100 km². Translocation of Asian lions to a second protected area outside of Gir National Park, which is at carrying capacity, is planned. Recent canine distemper outbreak in Serengeti-Mara ecosystem killed 33% of an estimated population of 3000 lions. Other threatening diseases include bovine tuberculosis, and FIV. Lions are heavily parasitized by all manner of external and internal parasites.

Bibliography. Barnett *et al.* (2006), Bauer & Van der Merwe (2004), Berry (1981), Bertram (1975a, 1975b), Bosman & Hall-Martin (1997), Bothma (1998), Bothma & Walker (1999), Bridgeford (1985), Bryden (1978), Caraco & Wolf (1975), Chellam (1987, 1993), Chellam & Jonsingh (1993), Cooper, J. (1942), Cooper, S.M. (1991), Cowie (1966), Eloff (1964, 1973a, 1973b), Fagotto (1985), Funston & Mills (1997), Funston *et al.* (2001), Grant *et al.* (2005), Grinnell & McComb (2001), Guggisberg (1975), Hanby *et al.* (1995), Hunter (1999), Hunter *et al.* (2007), Jackson (1995), Jonsingh & Chellam (1991), Joslin (1973), Kingdon (1971-1982), Kruuk & Turner (1967), Makacha & Schaller (1969), McBride (1990), Mills (1990), Mills & Shenk (1992), Mills *et al.* (1989), Mitchell *et al.* (1965), Moser (2008), Munson *et al.* (1995), Nowell & Jackson (1996), Ogutu & Dublin (2002, 2004), Orford *et al.* (1988), Owens & Owens (1984), Packer & Kock (1995), Packer & Pusey (1983, 1987, 1997), Packer, Ikanda *et al.* (2006), Packer, Scheel & Pusey (1990), Patterson, B.D., Kasiki *et al.* (2004), Patterson, B.D., Kays *et al.* (2006), Patterson, G. (1988), Pienaar (1969), Pusey & Packer (1987), Rashid (1991), Rodgers (1974), Rosevear (1974), Rudnai (1973a, 1973b, 1974), Ruggiero (1991), Schaller (1972), Scheel & Packer (1991), Schenkel (1966), Skinner & Smithers (1990), Smuts (1979, 1982), Smuts, Hanks & Whyte (1978), Smuts, Robinson & Whyte (1980), Spong (2002), Stander (1991, 1992a, 1992b, 1997), Van Orsdol (1982, 1984), Verberne & Leyhausen (1976), Walker (1994), West & Packer (2002), Woodroffe & Frank (2005).

7. Jaguar *Panthera onca*

French: Jaguar / **German**: Jaguar / **Spanish**: Yaguar

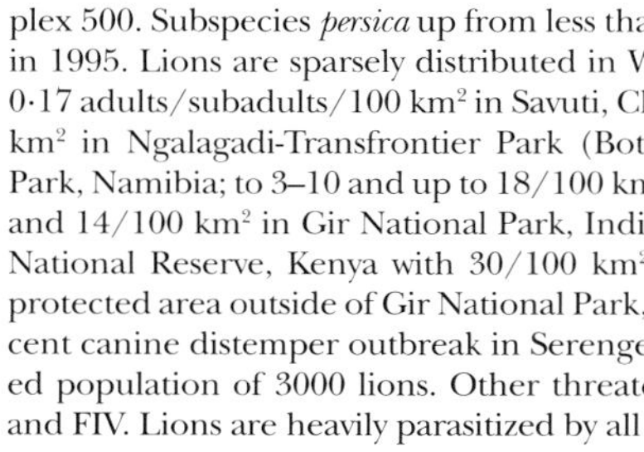

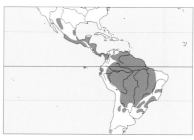

Taxonomy. *Felis onca* Linnaeus, 1758, Pernambuco, Brazil.

Based on the patterns of mtDNA and microsatellite variation, two phylogenetic groups were identified. One consists of individuals from Mexico, Central America, and South America N of the Amazon River; the other encompasses animals from Peru and Brazil S of the Amazon River. These analyses do not support the major geographic partitioning among traditional Jaguar subspecies, suggesting a taxonomic revision is needed. Nine subspecies recognized.

Subspecies and Distribution.

P. o. onca Linnaeus, 1758 – Amazon and Orinoco basin rainforests.

P. o. arizonensis Goldman, 1932 – SW USA (Arizona) to NW Mexico (Sonora).

P. o. centralis Mearns, 1901 – Nicaragua to Colombia.

P. o. goldmani Mearns, 1901 – Yucatan Peninsula of Mexico S to Belize and N Honduras.

P. o. hernandesi Gray, 1857 – W Mexico (S Sonora to Oaxaca).

P. o. palustris Ameghino, 1888 – S Brazil S through Uruguay to N Argentina (the Río Negro in Chaco province).

P. o. paraguensis Hollister, 1914 – Paraguay.

P. o. peruviana de Blainville, 1843 – coastal regions of Ecuador and Peru.

P. o. veraecrucis Nelson & Goldman, 1933 – S USA (C Texas, now extinct) to SE Mexico (Chiapas).

Descriptive notes. Head-body 116–170 cm, tail 44–80 cm. Adult males heavier (37–121 kg) than adult females (31–100 kg), and there is considerable regional variation in size. Jaguars from Central America are about half the size of cats from the Pantanal of Brazil and the Venezuelan Llanos. Background coat color varies from pale gold to a rich rusty red, and is patterned with a series of circular dark markings or rosettes that enclose one or more smaller black spots. In the similar-looking Leopard, there are no spots inside the black rosettes. A row of black spots along the middle of the Jaguar's back sometimes merges into a solid line. The underparts are whitish and marked with dark spots. The tail is marked with black spots and there are several black rings or bands on the terminal half. The ears are short and rounded, black on the back with a faint buff central spot. Melanistic individuals are common, and in bright light the spots on these black cats are often visible through the darker background of the fur. The Jaguar is a powerful, deep-chested, stocky cat with an unusually large, rounded head and short, sturdy limbs. The skull is heavy-boned, short, and broad, with a well-developed sagittal crest for muscle attachments, and the bite force on the robust canines is greater than that of all other big cats.

Habitat. Jaguars are found in a variety of forested habitats, including lowland tropical moist forest, gallery forests along rivers and streams, seasonally flooded wooded savannas, mangrove swamps, premontane moist forest, semi-deciduous forest, and humid montane and cloud forests to about 2000 m. Jaguars are often found in association with rivers, lakes and well-watered areas such as the swampy grasslands of the Brazilian Pantanal. They are excellent swimmers and have been seen crossing large rivers. Like Tigers, during the hot season Jaguars may spend the heat of the day half-submerged in a stream. They may occasionally be found in arid areas, but typically only where watercourses penetrate this drier habitat. Jaguars avoid open forest and grassland habitat but are commonly found along the edges of forest openings.

Food and Feeding. Jaguars are opportunistic predators, capable of killing almost any prey they encounter. The cat's powerful jaws and robust canine teeth enable it to kill livestock weighing three to four times its own weight, often with a bite to the back of the skull, rather than the more common neck or throat bite employed by other large cats. The canines are also strong enough to penetrate the hard shells of large river turtles and the thick hides of crocodilians. More than 85 prey species are listed in the cat's diet. In the seasonally flooded savannas of Venezuela, Jaguars preferred Capybara (*Hydrochoerus hydrochaeris*) and Collared Peccary (*Pecari tajacu*), but they also preyed on White-tailed Deer (*Odocoileus virginianus*), caiman, freshwater turtles and turtle eggs (Chelidae, Pelomedusidae), tortoises, iguanas, and cattle. Collared Peccary, agouti, and large turtles also formed the bulk of the Jaguar's diet in the lowland tropical forest of Manu National Park, Peru. Jaguars in Iguaçu National Park, Brazil, fed mainly on Collared Peccary, White-lipped Peccary (*Tayassu peccari*), Brocket (*Mazama*) and White-tailed Deer; minor prey included coati, agouti, marsupials, armadillos, rabbits, Paca (*Cuniculus paca*), squirrels, birds, reptiles and primates. In the Cockscomb Basis of Belize armadillos were the single most important prey, occurring in half of all Jaguar feces. Three-toed sloths (*Bradypus*) and iguanas were the prominent prey items in the Jaguar's diet in La Selva, Costa Rica. In the Paraguayan Chaco, small and medium-size mammals, principally Brocket Deer, rabbits, armadillos, and marsupials were important prey. Although Jaguars are especially fond of peccaries, the cat's basic diet tends to reflect the relative abundance of the various prey species in an area. In areas where native ungulates have been depleted and forest habitats converted to pastures for domestic stock, Jaguars subsist to a large extent on cattle. The Jaguar can climb trees if it has to, but it is essentially a terrestrial hunter. Like many other felids, Jaguars hunt by walking slowly along game trails and roads, listening and looking for prey. They will wait in ambush at waterholes or wallows for peccaries or patrol river banks in search of basking crocodilians or turtles. Having spotted an animal they will stalk it, using every bit of cover to get as close as possible, before launching an attack. After one or two bounds the prey is seized with the claws and killed with a bite. Jaguars have been seen jumping into the water after Capybara and managing to catch them before they can dive to safety. Prey may be eaten on the spot or carried for several hundred meters or more to a site where the cat presumably feels comfortable.

Activity patterns. Radio-telemetry studies show that Jaguars have variable activity patterns. In Mexico, Belize, and Venezuela the cat is primarily nocturnal, spending the daytime resting in tangled thickets, caves, or in dense cover before becoming active around sunset. In Peru and Brazil Jaguars were just as active during the daytime as they were at night. Variation in activity patterns is common and probably reflects differences in the daily and seasonal activity patterns of the prey, changes in prey availability, and possibly human disturbance. Cattle are often taken during the daytime, as are crocodilians and turtles; deer and peccary are more likely to be active at night or around sunrise and sunset. Cats that are frequently harassed by people during the daytime typically become nocturnal.

Movements, Home range and Social organization. There are few precise estimates of distances traveled by Jaguars during their nightly movements, but based on following tracks, experienced hunters guessed that females moved 3–4 km per night and males about 10 km. In W Mexico, radio-collared Jaguars travelled up to 20 km in a night of hunting. Home range sizes show considerable variation between sites and by season. At one ranch in the southern Pantanal, the dry season home ranges of four females varied from 97 to 168 km² and overlapped extensively. To what extent this overlap was influenced by relatedness is unknown, but two of the females were mother and daughter. An adult male's range in the same area was 152 km². During the wet season their ranges were four to five times smaller than in the dry season, because large areas were inundated to depths of eight to nine feet, and prey were concentrated on the high ground. At a ranch in the western Pantanal, where wet season flooding was not as severe, the home ranges of a presumed mother and daughter overlapped completely and measured 38 km². Their ranges overlapped slightly with another female's whose range was 25 km². An adult male's range overlapped the ranges of all these females. The average home range size of three adult male Jaguars in Iguaçu National Park, Brazil, was 110 km² (range 86–139 km²); an adult female's range was 70 km². In the dry tropical forest of W Mexico, female Jaguar ranges are about 25 km² in the dry season and 65 km² in the wet season. In this habitat, prey that was concentrated around water sources during the dry season disperses throughout the forest with the onset of the rains. Jaguar densities are remarkably similar across the cat's range. At sites in Brazil, Peru, Colombia, Venezuela, and Mexico, densities range from 1–3·5 adults per 100 km². Jaguar density in Belize was estimated at 8·8 adults/100 km², while the highest densities recorded (10-11 Jaguars/100 km²) are in the Brazilian Pantanal, a vast natural floodplain.

Breeding. Both male and female Jaguars roar, and roaring may serve to bring the sexes together for mating. There are anecdotal reports that females in heat travel widely, calling for a mate. Estrus lasts 6–17 days and copulation is rapid and frequent: a pair may mate 100 times per day. The young are born after a gestation period of 93–105 days. Litter size varies from 1–4, with an average of two. Births occur throughout the year in tropical areas but in the more temperate portions of the Jaguar's range there is some evidence suggesting a summer birth peak. Kittens weigh about 700–900 g at birth and have coarse, woolly, spotted coats. Their eyes open at 13 days of age. The young are totally dependent on their mother's milk until they are 10–11 weeks old and may continue to suckle until they are 5–6 months old. Males grow faster than females and at two years of age young males may be 50% heavier than their female siblings. At 15–18 months young Jaguar are usually traveling independently within their mother's range, making their own kills. Dispersal occurs at 16–24 months of age. Females attain sexual maturity at 24–30 months and males at 3–4 years.

Status and Conservation. CITES Appendix I. Classified as Near Threatened on *The IUCN Red List*. All countries within the range of the Jaguar are members of CITES, and all countries with Jaguar populations have laws that forbid killing them. However, these laws are not always well enforced and most allow a rancher to kill Jaguars to protect domestic stock. Jaguar numbers are declining across most of South and Central America. The greatest losses have occurred in the drier northern parts of the cat's range in the USA, where there is some recent evidence of a resident population. Mexico, and at the southern end, in the scrub grasslands of Argentina. There are no reliable estimates of how much the Jaguar's range has been diminished, but one calculation suggests that since European settlement the cat's range has shrunk from 15 million km² to 8·7 million km². Currently, the species' stronghold is the six million km² Amazon Basin rainforest, but even there efforts are underway to open the area to development. Today, the most important factor affecting Jaguar numbers is habitat loss from timber extraction and conversion to pasture and agricultural lands. Jaguar habitat is also being lost as forests are modified in association with mining operations, oil drilling, and human settlements. People associated with these settlements and operations often supplement their diet with wild game and thus compete directly with Jaguars for prey such as Capybara, peccary and deer. When Spanish and Portuguese settlers introduced cattle to the New World they provided the Jaguar with large, easy-to-kill prey. Today, in the savannas and gallery forest of Colombia, Venezuela, and Brazil, ranchers graze millions of cattle in habitats also used by Jaguar. Herd management is rudimentary and pre- and post-natal mortality of calves is high. Some losses are attributable to depredation by Jaguar, but for most ranches the real impact is unknown. The impacts can also vary from site to site. On the Miranda Ranch in the southern Pantanal, cattle comprised 46% of Jaguar kills and 35% of Puma kills. One ranch in the Venezuelan Llanos reported that cattle depredation by felines accounted for 6% of all calf losses. At another ranch in the same area, depredation caused 30% of calf losses. For small cattle operations, the value of calf loss can be high. The result is that Jaguars are usually targeted whenever they are encountered. A few attempts have been made to modify cattle management practices, but with no analysis of effectiveness or cost-benefit. Some efforts have been made to control "problem or nuisance" animals by removal or translocation to other areas, but since relocated Jaguars are seldom followed the effectiveness of this practice remains unknown. The few studies that have been conducted show that not all Jaguars kill cattle. During a 2-year study on a large cattle ranch in the Venezuelan Llanos, researchers found that only 13% of all calf mortality was due to large cats, and that Puma were responsible for 86% of the cat mortality. At a site in Belize, most confirmed cattle-killing Jaguar showed signs of previous shotgun wounds. In some areas ranchers may be partially responsible for livestock depredation problems when they shoot at and injure Jaguars, because such injuries may force these cats to subsist on the easier to catch livestock. Until recently it has been assumed that the Jaguar had some degree of natural protection because many of its populations were largely inaccessible to people. Over the last decade there has been a growing realization that this protection is rapidly disappearing. Recently, efforts have been made to build a framework for Jaguar conservation and research throughout its geographic range, much like the model for the Tiger. Priorities include information exchange, standardized research methods, assessment of threats, and cooperation across borders.

Bibliography. de Almeida (1976), Aranda & Sánchez-Cordero (1996), Azevedo (2008), Bisbal (1989), Crawshaw & Quigley (1991), Eizirik *et al.* (2001), Emmons (1987, 1989), Hoogesteijn & Mondolfi (1992, 1996), Hoogesteijn *et al.* (1993), IUCN (2008), Jorgenson & Redford (1993), Leopold (1959), Maffei *et al.* (2004), McCain & Childs (2008), Medellín *et al.* (2001), Mondolfi & Hoogesteijn (1986), Nowell & Jackson (1996), Perry (1970), Quigley & Crawshaw (1992), Rabinowitz (1986a, 1986b), Rabinowitz & Nottingham (1986), Sanderson, E.W. *et al.* (2002), Schaller & Crawshaw (1980), Schaller & Vasconcelos (1978), Scognamillo *et al.* (2003), Seymour (1989), Silver *et al.* (2004), Soisalo & Cavalcanati (2006), Sunquist & Sunquist (2002), Swank & Teer (1989), Taber *et al.* (1997), Zimmermann *et al.* (2005).

PLATE 5

inches 16

cm 40

8

9

ssp *temminckii*

10

ssp *tristis*

11

ssp *aurata*

12

ssp *celidogaster*

ssp *caracal*

13

ssp *schmitzi*

Subfamily FELINAE
Genus *PARDOFELIS*
Severtzov, 1858

8. Marbled Cat *Pardofelis marmorata*
French: Chat marbré / **German**: Marmorkatze / **Spanish**: Gato jaspeado

Taxonomy. *Felis marmorata* Martin, 1837, Sumatra.
Two subspecies recognized.
Subspecies and Distribution.
P. m. marmorata Martin, 1837 – Continental SE Asia, from SW China to Malaysia, and islands of Sumatra and Borneo.
P. m. charltoni Gray, 1846 – Sub-Himalayan region, from Nepal to Mynamar.
Descriptive notes. Head-body 45–62 cm, tail 35·6–55 cm. Few weights available, but 2–5 kg is likely range. About the size of a domestic cat, with an extremely long, bushy tail, which may be almost as long as head-body. When standing or resting, this cat assumes a characteristic position with its back arched. Fur is thick, color variable from gray-brown to yellowish gray and reddish brown. The sides and back are marbled with large, dark-edged blotches that vary in size and spacing. Tail is spotted throughout and legs are spotted. Face is short and broad, and the short, rounded ears have a central white spot on back.
Habitat. A forest dwelling species, primarily in moist evergreen forests. Also reported from hill-evergreen-bamboo mixed forest in Thailand, mixed deciduous forest in Thailand, lowland primary rain forest and secondary forests in Peninsula Malaysia, in clearings in dipterocarp forests in Sarawak, and in six-year-old logged forest in Sabah.
Food and Feeding. Anecdotal evidence suggests that birds form a major part of this cat's diet. Probably preys on squirrels, rats, and frogs. In captivity, this cat is an adept climber and on two occasions when it was seen in the wild, it was in a tree. The long tail and broad feet suggest the cat is adapted for an arboreal lifestyle, but nothing known of its hunting behavior in the wild.
Activity patterns. Apparently nocturnal. No more information available.
Movements, Home range and Social organization. Nothing known.
Breeding. Very limited information, only from captivity. Two litters of two kittens each. Gestation estimated at 66–82 days.
Status and Conservation. CITES Appendix I. Classified as Vulnerable on *The IUCN Red List*. Rare throughout its range. Little known of the species biology, distribution, and status.
Bibliography. Barnes (1976), Grassman & Tewes (2000, 2002), Lekagul & McNeely (1991), Nowell & Jackson (1996), Payne *et al.* (1985), Pocock (1932b), Sunquist & Sunquist (2002).

Genus *CATOPUMA*
Severtzov, 1858

9. Bay Cat *Catopuma badia*
French: Chat de Bornéo / **German**: Borneo-Goldkatze / **Spanish**: Gato badia
Other common names: Bornean Bay Cat

Taxonomy. *Felis badia* Gray, 1874, Sarawak, Borneo [Malaysia].
Has been sometimes considered conspecific with *C. temminckii*, but genetic analysis shows that the two are better considered separate species. Monotypic.
Distribution. Borneo.
Descriptive notes. Resembles a small *C. temminckii*. Head-body of a female 53·3 cm, tail measured 39·1 cm; weight 1·95 kg but animal in emaciated condition. Coat color is dimorphic, mahogany red, faintly speckled with black markings, or blackish gray. Of twelve known specimens, ten were red phase. Belly fur is pale golden brown and speckled with black. Ears are short and rounded, set low on side of head. Backs of ears are dark. Underside of chin is white and there are two faint brown stripes on cheeks. A yellowish-white stripe runs down the underside of the terminal half of the tail.
Habitat. Most early specimens were collected in dense forest, along rivers. In 2003, two individuals were snared in Sabah, in traps set in a five-year-old pulp-wood plantation that was formerly lowland dipterocarp forest. A compilation of 15 recent observations show that Bay Cats occur in a variety of forested habitats, including low and hill dipterocarp forests, mangrove, riverine, and montane forests.
Food and Feeding. Nothing known.
Activity patterns. Nothing known.

Movements, Home range and Social organization. Nothing known.
Breeding. Nothing known.
Status and Conservation. CITES Appendix II. Classified as Endangered on the *The IUCN Red List*. Fully protected over most of its range. Hunting and trade prohibited. Extremely rare, probably fewer than eight individuals have been trapped since 1928. Local trappers and animal dealers are aware of the species value and demands for live specimens have increased illegal trapping pressure, which may jeopardize this rare species.
Bibliography. Azlan & Sanderson (2007), Gray (1874), Guggisberg (1975), Hose (1893), Johnson, Shinyashiki *et al.* (1999), Nowell & Jackson (1996), Sunquist & Sunquist (2002), Sunquist *et al.* (1994).

10. Asian Golden Cat *Catopuma temminckii*
French: Chat de Temminck / **German**: Asiatische Goldkatze / **Spanish**: Gato dorado asiático
Other common names: Temminck's Cat

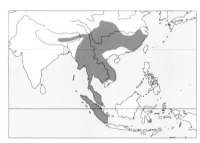

Taxonomy. *Felis temminckii* Vigors & Horsfield, 1827, Sumatra, Indonesia.
Has been sometimes considered to include *C. badia* as a subspecies, but genetic analysis shows that the two are better considered separate species.
Three subspecies recognized.
Subspecies and Distribution.
C. t. temminckii Vigors & Horsfield, 1827 – Sub-Himalayan region from Nepal, India and Bhutan S to Malaysia and Sumatra.
C. t. dominicanorum Sclater, 1898 – S China.
C. t. tristis Milne-Edwards, 1872 – highlands of SW China.
Descriptive notes. Head-body 66·2–105 cm, tail 42·5–57·5 cm. Adult males are heavier (12–15·7 kg) than adult females (8·5 kg). Coat polymorphic, varying from a uniform golden brown to dark brown, black, pale cinnamon, bright red, or gray. Golden cats from some parts of China show another variation: the pelt may be marked with dark spots and stripes. The backs of the short, rounded ears are black with a faint central gray area. The underside of the terminal one-third to one-half of the tail has a whitish stripe. The face is marked with a white line extending downward for a short distance from the corner of each eye and the white lines extending outward from the nose look like a moustache.
Habitat. Found in tropical lowland rainforest and sub-tropical moist evergreen and dry deciduous forests to elevations of 3000 m in the Himalayas. Occasionally reported from more open, rocky areas and grasslands.
Food and Feeding. In Peninsular Malaysia, diet included Dusky Leaf Monkey (*Trachypithecus obscurus*), mouse deer, murids, birds, and lizards. Has also been recorded killing sheep, goats, and a buffalo calf. Anecdotal information suggests hunts primarily on the ground. However, can also climb well.
Activity patterns. Largely nocturnal (69% of photos taken at night), but daytime activity not uncommon.
Movements, Home range and Social organization. Nothing known.
Breeding. Limited information, only from captive animals. One estrous cycle lasted 39 days, with estrus lasting six days. Gestation period 78–80 days. Litter size typically one, range from 1–3. Sexual maturity about two years of age.
Status and Conservation. CITES Appendix I. Classified as Near Threatened on *The IUCN Red List*. Fully protected over most of its range, hunting and trade prohibited in most range states. Uncommon and threatened by deforestation across its range. The species is also illegally hunted for its pelt and bones. The largest skin harvest has come from China.
Bibliography. Acharjyo & Mishra (1980), Guggisberg (1975), Kawanishi & Sunquist (2008), Lekagul & McNeely (1991), Louwman & Van Oyen (1968), Mellen (1993), Nowell & Jackson (1996), Pocock (1939), Sunquist & Sunquist (2002).

Genus *LEPTAILURUS*
Severtzov, 1858

11. Serval *Leptailurus serval*
French: Serval / **German**: Serval / **Spanish**: Serval

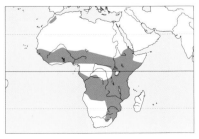

Taxonomy. *Felis serval* Schreber, 1776, Cape region of South Africa.
Subspecific taxonomy in need of revision.
Seven subspecies recognized.
Subspecies and Distribution.
L. s. serval Schreber, 1776 – S Zaire and Tanzania, S to Eastern Cape, South Africa.
L. s. brachyurus Wagner, 1841 – Sierra Leone.
L. s. constantinus Forster, 1780 – N Morocco and Algeria.

On following pages: 12. African Golden Cat (*Profelis aurata*); 13. Caracal (*Caracal caracal*).

L. s. hindei Wroughton, 1910 – Kenya E of the Rift Valley.
L. s. liptostictus Pocock, 1907 – Uganda, Zaire, and N Angola.
L. s. phillipsi G. M. Allen, 1914 – Lake Chad E to Ethiopian highlands.
L. s. tanae Pocock, 1944 – dry zone of Ethiopia, Eritrea, and N Somalia.

Descriptive notes. Head-body 59–92 cm, tail 20–38 cm; weight 7–13·5 kg, with adult males slightly larger than adult females. Tall, lightly-built cats with a short tail. Background coat color is tawny, marked with fine, freckle-sized black dots or larger black spots along the back and sides. The spots may form bars on the neck, shoulders, and limbs. The spot pattern is similar to that of the Cheetah and the skins of the two species are sometimes confused. Melanistic individuals are common in the highlands of Kenya and Ethiopia. For its size, has the longest legs of any member of the cat family. Elongated metatarsal bones add considerably to the cat's height. An adult stands 60 cm at the shoulder– more than 20 cm taller than the similar-sized Ocelot. The face is small and delicate and the skull is lightly built. Ears are extremely large and oval shaped; backs of ears are black and marked with a white spot or line. Auditory bullae are large and well-developed.

Habitat. Found in almost all types of grasslands and savannas in Africa. Their distribution is closely tied to water and associated vegetation, reed beds and marshes. Sometimes found along watercourses that penetrate semi-desert and desert and in forest areas interspersed with grassy glades and edges. Also found in subalpine habitats and high moorlands to 3000 m, and in farmlands with high rodent densities. They are absent from the dense rain forests of Central Africa. Use medium and tall grasslands and reed beds as rest sites, although in areas with greater disturbance from people and livestock frequently retreat to patches of woody vegetation during the day.

Food and Feeding. Specialized small mammal predators, well equipped to capture rodents in tall grass. Over 90% of the diet consists of prey weighing less than 200 g. Murid rodents dominate the diet. The multimammate mouse, Vlei rat, pygmy mouse, and various grass mice make up the bulk of the diet. Other murid prey include water rats, mole rats, gerbils, climbing mice, pouched mice, veld rats, groove-toothed rats, and black rats. Also eat shrews (Soricidae), golden moles (Chrysochloridae), cane rats (Thryonomyidae), and Scrub Hare (*Lepus saxatilis*). They occasionally take larger prey such as young Thomson's Gazelle and duikers, flamingos, black-bellied bustards (*Lissotis melanogaster*), and rails. They also prey on smaller birds such as waxbills and quail-finches, larks, pipits, weavers, cisticolas, and swallows. Other prey includes grass and sand snakes (Colubridae), lizards (Agamidae), frogs, crabs, grasshoppers, crickets, and locusts. They have a specialized, almost foxlike, hunting style. Their long legs provide the large ears with a raised platform to "hear into" the tall grass. Long mobile toes and strong curved claws serve to hook prey from burrows or beneath vegetation. They locate their prey primarily by hearing and when hunting the cat walks slowly, stopping periodically to listen. It may stop and sit for 15 minutes at a time, scanning the area for sounds. When it hears something move it locates the exact position of the sound, then pounces like a fox, leaping into the air and striking the prey with a blow from one or both feet. A single pounce may span 3·6 m and may be over one meter high. If the initial pounce is not successful it may be followed with a series of stiff-legged bouncing jumps. Have been seen leaping 2–3 m into the air to seize birds and insects in flight. They also probe holes and crevices for nestling birds and rodents and can hook live fish out of water. Strong winds disrupt its ability to hear and pinpoint the location of prey and hunting is often curtailed on windy days.

Activity patterns. In Ngorongoro Crater, Tanzania, were largely crepuscular. Typically rested during midday and occasionally at night. One female reduced her daytime activity significantly when she had kittens, spending more time traveling in search of food. In the Kamberg Biosphere Reserve, Natal, were predominantly nocturnal, possibly because of human disturbance.

Movements, Home range and Social organization. In the Ngorongoro Crater an adult male and an female traveled an estimated at 2–4 km per night. Home range sizes of an adult male and an adult female in the Crater were at least 11·6 and 9·5 km², respectively. The full extent of their ranges could not be ascertained because they were not radio-tagged and there were times when they disappeared for several months from their normal haunts. However, one adult female was repeatedly sighted in the same area over a nine-year period, indicating strong site fidelity. Two radio-collared females in the farmland that is part of the Kamberg Biosphere Reserve, Natal, had home ranges of 19·8 and 15·8 km²; a tagged male's range was 31·5 km². The adult male's range in the Crater overlapped the smaller ranges of at least two adult females, but the home ranges of three adult females showed little overlap. In Kamberg, the adult male's range overlapped extensively with that of an adult female. Two adult females utilized common areas, but they did so at different times. Adults of both sexes regularly scent mark as they move about their home ranges, although males mark at a much higher frequency. Urine spraying on trees, bushes, and other conspicuous objects is the most frequent type of marking, but also make scrape marks on the ground with their fore- and hindfeet and leave their feces in prominent locations. They are solitary animals: sighting of groups or pairs consist of a mother with her young or a mating pair. Density estimates vary from eight per 100 km² in Natal's Kamberg Biosphere Reserve to 41 per 100 km² in Ngorongoro Crater.

Breeding. Females are polyestrous and in general births seem to occur about a month before the peak in murid rodent reproduction. Estrus lasts from 1–4 days, and after a gestation period of about 74 days females typically give birth to two kittens (range 1–4 young). Young weigh about 250 g at birth. Birth dens are usually in dense vegetation or disused Aardvark or porcupine burrows. The mother begins to bring food back to the den when young are about a month old. Young acquire their permanent canine teeth at about six months of age and begin to hunt for themselves shortly thereafter. Newly independent young are sometimes allowed to remain within their natal range for a

year or more. In captivity, there are records of females becoming sexually mature when they were just over a year old, and a male was first seen mating at 17 months of age.

Status and Conservation. CITES Appendix II. Listed as species of Least Concern on *The IUCN Red List*. Not protected by national legislation over most of its geographic range. Widely distributed in grasslands south of the Sahara but are declining in number in the west and extreme south of Africa. Their continued existence in Morocco and Algeria is doubtful. As specialized rodent hunters, present species is highly tolerant of agricultural activities and can play an important role in keeping rodent numbers down. They readily adapt to abandoned cultivation and second growth areas and as long as they are not persecuted may be able to live alongside humans in rural agricultural areas. Occasionally prey on poultry and young sheep and goats, but the problem is not considered serious. Attain their highest densities in wetland areas and wetland conservation is thought to be the key to their conservation.

Bibliography. Boland (1990), Boland & Perrin (1993), Geertsema (1976, 1981, 1985), Kingdon (1971-1982), Mellen (1993), Nowell & Jackson (1996), Rosevear (1974), Smithers (1978), Stuart (1985), Sunquist & Sunquist (2002), Wackernagel (1968).

Genus *PROFELIS*
Severtzov, 1858

12. African Golden Cat *Profelis aurata*

French: Chat doré / **German**: Afrikanische Goldkatze / **Spanish**: Gato dorado africano

Taxonomy. *Felis aurata* Temminck, 1827, West Africa. Probably from the coastal region of Lower Guinea.
Two subspecies recognized.
Subspecies and Distribution.
P. a. aurata Temminck, 1827 – C Africa E to Kenya.
P. a. celidogaster Temminck, 1827 – W Africa.

Descriptive notes. Head-body 61·6–101 cm, tail 16·3–34·9 cm; adult males heavier (11–16 kg) than adult females (6–8 kg). Coat color and pattern highly variable, with a reddish-brown and a grayish phase; coat can be spotted or plain. Melanistic and partially melanistic individuals also known. Throat, chest, and undersides whitish with large dark spots or blotches. Face round with heavy muzzle. Ears small, blunt and almost completely black on back. Short tail with distinct bands, unbanded, or intermediate banding. Fur between shoulders and crown of head points forward, with whorls and low ridge marking junction where hair changes direction. Thought to have an extensive vocal repertoire, including hiss, meow, growl, purr, and gurgle.

Habitat. Primary habitat is moist forest, often along rivers. Also found in secondary undergrowth, logged forest with dense understory, montane forest, alpine moorlands, and bamboo forest. Recorded from riverine forest where watercourses penetrate open savannas.

Food and Feeding. Variety of different-sized prey, including dwarf-antelope and duikers, primates (Cercopithecidae), brush-tailed porcupine, shrews, elephant shrews (Macroscelididae), rats, pangolins, squirrels, hyraxes, unidentified birds, and small mammals. Stalk and ambush hunter, catching most of its prey on the ground.

Activity patterns. Primarily crepuscular and nocturnal but some diurnal activity reported.

Movements, Home range and Social organization. Nothing known.

Breeding. One observation of a female with single nursing young in Ituri Forest, Zaire. Only two captive births recorded; both were of two kittens, following 75-day gestation. A captive male first bred successfully at 18 months of age.

Status and Conservation. CITES Appendix II. Classified as Near Threatened on *The IUCN Red List*. Little reliable information on status in the wild. Thought to be rare in many countries of equatorial Africa but also described as locally common in Tai and Azagny National Parks, Ivory Coast, and in secondary forest in Uganda. The species is believed to thrive in logged forest with dense secondary growth, so it may be in less danger than other small cats. However, the species is frequently killed while raiding poultry or livestock. Loss or degradation of moist forest habitats are threats to long-term survival.

Bibliography. Hart *et al.* (1996), Kingdon (1971-1982), van Mensch & van Bree (1969), Nowell & Jackson (1996), Peters (1984b), Peters & Hast (1994), Ray & Sunquist (2001), Rosevear (1974), Sunquist & Sunquist (2002), Tonkin & Kohler (1978), Wilson (1987), Wozencraft (1993).

Genus *CARACAL*
Gray, 1843

13. Caracal *Caracal caracal*

French: Caracal / **German**: Karakal / **Spanish**: Caracal
Other common names: Red Lynx, Caracal Lynx

Taxonomy. *Felis caracal* Schreber, 1776, Table Mountain, near Cape Town, South Africa.

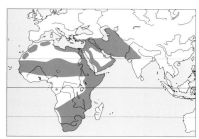

Caracal were originally thought to be allied with *Lynx lynx*, *L. canadensis*, *L. pardinus*, and *L. rufus*. However, recent genetic analyses show that the caracal is not part of the lynx group but rather is more closely allied with *Profelis aurata*. The two species are thought to have shared a common ancestor 4·85 million years ago. Nine subspecies recognized.

Subspecies and Distribution.
C. c. caracal Schreber, 1776 – E & S Africa.
C. c. algira Wagner, 1841 – N Africa.
C. c. damarensis Roberts, 1926 – Namibia.
C. c. limpopoensis Roberts, 1926 – N Transvaal.
C. c. lucani Rochebrune, 1885 – grasslands of SE Gabon.
C. c. michaelis Heptner, 1945 – deserts of Caspian Sea region, E to Amu Darya River.
C. c. nubica Fischer, 1829 – Cameroon E and N to Nubian Desert.
C. c. poecilotis Thomas & Hinton, 1921 – W Africa.
C. c. schmitzi Matschie, 1912 – Turkey, Palestine E to India.

Descriptive notes. Head-body 61–105·7 cm, tail 19·5–34 cm. Adult males heavier (8–20 kg) than adult females (6·2–15·9 kg). Caracals are slender, long-legged, medium-sized cats. Hindlegs are powerfully built and longer than the front legs, giving the cat the appearance of being taller at the rump than at the shoulder. The short tail extends only to the animal's hocks. Fur is short and unspotted. Coat color on back and sides varies from a uniform tawny gray to brick red. Belly, chin, and throat are whitish and marked with pale spots or blotches. Melanistic individuals have been recorded. The large, conspicuous ears are black on the back and adorned with black tufts that may be 4·5 cm long. The skull is high and rounded and the jaw is short and heavily built, with large powerful teeth. Facial markings include a dark line running from the center of the forehead to near the nose and white patches above and below the eyes and on either side of the nose.

Habitat. Caracal are found in dry woodlands, savanna, acacia scrub, hilly steppe, and arid mountain areas to 2500 m. They do not live in true desert or dense tropical rainforest. They are often associated with edge habitats where forest and grassland meet, and though they use open grasslands at night, they require access to bushes and rocks for daytime rest sites.

Food and Feeding. Caracal generally take prey that weigh less than 5 kg, including hares, hyrax, small rodents, and birds. They will, however, take larger (over 15 kg) prey if the opportunity arises. In two studies in South Africa's Mountain Zebra National Park, hyrax were found in 53 and 60% of scats, and Mountain Reedbuck were found in eleven and 20% of scats, respectively. Due to their greater size, reedbuck contributed 62 and 72% of meat consumed. Caracal also killed a variety of other bovids in and outside the park, including Springbok, duiker, and Steenbok. Bovids, including Reedbuck, Common Duiker (*Silvicapra grimmia*) and Blue Duiker (*Philatomba monticola*), Steenbok, Bushbuck, Common Rhebok (*Pelea capreolus*), and Klipspringers (*Oreotragus oreotragus*) were the most frequently occurring (43·6%) prey items in the stomach contents of Caracal from the Eastern Cape Province, South Africa. Hyrax and Scrub Hare combined ranked second at almost 20%. In Botswana, Caracal fed mainly on small mammals but they also ate hares, spring hares, quail, partridge, and lizards. Mammals were also the dominant prey of caracal in Israel, and hares were the principal prey. Birds, mainly partridges, made up 24% of the cat's diet in this area. Incidental prey included mole rats, hedgehogs, the Egyptian Mongoose, and reptiles and insects. In Turkmenistan, small prey such as hare, sand rats, jerboas, and ground squirrels dominate the Caracal's diet. Caracal stalk as close as possible to their prey before making a final sprint; they also use their powerful hindlegs to make prodigious leaps into the air to capture birds. Hare-sized prey is killed with a bite to the nape. Larger prey is usually killed with suffocation with a throat bite.

Activity patterns. The Caracal is predominantly nocturnal. One study in Israel found the cats were most active from dusk to dawn, although they sometimes extended their activity into the early morning. Differences in the duration of daytime activity were largely dependent on daytime temperatures and the activity patterns of their prey, which are also affected by ambient temperatures. Caracals in the Sahara are crepuscular and nocturnal, but only in the hot season. At cooler times of the year or on overcast days during the rainy season the cat may be active until mid-morning or become active by mid- to late afternoon. In more hilly terrain, where there is abundant escape cover, Caracals have a tendency to become bold and move around in the daytime.

Movements, Home range and Social organization. In Israel, radio-collared males traveled an average of 10·4 km per day; females traveled an average of 6·6 km. Home ranges of five adult males in Israel were large, averaging 220 km^2, compared to an average of 57 km^2 for four adult females. Female home ranges were greatly reduced when they had small young but gradually expanded as the young became mobile. Each male's range overlapped the smaller ranges of one or more females and there was considerable overlap (50%) between adjacent male ranges. Female ranges showed much less overlap (25%). In the western sector of Cape Province, South Africa, the home range size of four adult females averaged 18·2 km^2 while an adult male's home range measured 65 km^2. In Mountain Zebra National Park the home ranges of males and females residing inside the park averaged 15·2 and 5·5 km^2, respectively. The home ranges of males living in the farmlands outside the park averaged 19·1 km^2. Caracals are solitary and most sightings are of single adults. Observations of two to four animals together most likely represent mating pairs or females with their large young.

Breeding. Caracal are polyestrous and in South Africa births have been recorded in every month of the year, with a peak from October to February. Anecdotal observations from the wild suggest estrus lasts from 3–6 days and mating pairs moved together for about four days. In Israel, Caracals were found to have a rather unusual mating system in which a female copulated with several different males in succession. The mating order appeared to be determined by age and weight of the male. After a gestation period of 68–81 days the female typically gives birth to two kittens. Litter size ranges from 1–6. Young are born in caves, tree cavities, or burrows and weigh 198–250 g at birth. Permanent canine teeth erupt at 4–5 months and by ten months the young have a complete set of permanent teeth, which coincides with the timing of dispersal. Subadults leave their natal ranges when they are 9–10 months old. Males and females are sexually mature by 12–15 months of age.

Status and Conservation. CITES Appendix I (Asian population); otherwise CITES Appendix II. Classified as Least Concern on *The IUCN Red List*. Not protected by national legislation over most of its geographic range. The Caracal is rare in North Africa, Turkmenistan, Pakistan, and Arabia, and on the verge of extinction in India. It is common in Israel and over much of the southern African portion of its range. Caracal is in the unique position of being classified as endangered in the Asian portion of their range and hunted as a problem animal in southern Africa. In parts of Namibia and South Africa, domestic livestock make up a significant portion (17–55%) of the Caracal's diet and large numbers of Caracal are destroyed annually by farmers. However, Caracal typically recolonizes these heavily hunted areas. Habitat loss is one of the main threats to the species in the eastern portion of its range and the Caracal has suffered heavy losses from fur trappers in India. However, Caracal pelts have a low value on the international market and the world fur trade does not pose a threat to the species.

Bibliography. Bernard & Stuart (1987), Dragesco-Joffé (1993), Grobler (1981, 1982), Johnson & O'Brien (1997), Mendelssohn (1989), Mukherjee *et al.* (2004), Norton & Lawson (1985), Nowell & Jackson (1996), Pringle & Pringle (1979), Rosevear (1974), Smithers (1983), Stuart (1981, 1984, 1986), Stuart & Hickman (1991), Stuart & Stuart (1985), Sunquist & Sunquist (2002), Visser (1976a), Weisbein & Mendelssohn (1990), Werdelin (1981).

ssp *pardalis*

14

15

ssp *mitis*

16

ssp *colocolo*

ssp *braccatus*

ssp *pajeros*

17

ssp *guigna*

19

ssp *tigrillo*

ssp *tigrinus*

18

melanic morph

ssp *oncilla*

20

PLATE 6

inches 14

cm 35

ssp *paraguae*

ssp *geoffroyi*

Genus *LEOPARDUS*
Gray, 1842

14. Ocelot *Leopardus pardalis*
French: Ocelot / **German**: Ozelot / **Spanish**: Ocelote

Taxonomy. *Felis pardalis* Linnaeus, 1758, State of Veracruz, Mexico.
Recent phylogenetic analyses of mtDNA show present species partitioned into four major geographic groups. The Central American and southern South American populations form monophyletic groups, but populations in northern South America are divided into two distinct, ancestral clusters. One geographic cluster is in NNE South America (French Guyana and N Brazil) and the other cluster is in NNW South America (Panama, Trinidad, Venezuela, and N Brazil). Ten subspecies are recognized.

Subspecies and Distribution.
L. p. pardalis Linnaeus, 1758 – S Mexico through Central America.
L. p. aequatorialis Mearns, 1902 – N Andes.
L. p. albescens Pucheran, 1855 – S USA (SW Texas) to NE Mexico.
L. p. melanurus Ball, 1844 – Venezuela E to the Guianas highlands, also Trinidad I.
L. p. mitis Cuvier, 1820 – S Brazil through Paraguay to N Argentina.
L. p. nelsoni Goldman, 1925 – W Mexico (from Sinaloa to Oaxaca).
L. p. pseudopardalis Boitard, 1842 – N Colombia and W Venezuela.
L. p. pusaeus Thomas, 1914 – coastal Ecuador to Peru.
L. p. sonoriensis Goldman, 1925 – NW Mexico, and formerly USA (Arizona).
L. p. steinbachi Pocock, 1941 – Bolivian highlands.

Descriptive notes. Head-body 72·6–100 cm, tail 25·5–41 cm. Adult males are slightly larger (7–15·5 kg) than adult females (6·6–11·3 kg). Medium-sized cat with a relatively short tail. Background coat color highly variable, from cream to tawny-yellow, reddish-gray, or gray. Fur is short and sleek. Coat is marked with solid or open-centered dark spots that sometimes form elongated transverse lines across the body. The black spots coalesce into streaks on the neck. Underparts are whiteish with occasional dark spots. The tail is marked with dark bars on the upper surface. Backs of the rounded ears are black with a central white spot. The front paws are much larger than the hind paws.

Habitat. Occurs in a broad range of subtropical and tropical habitats, including dense thorny chaparral in S Texas, subtropical moist forest in Belize, lowland riverine rain forest in Peru, gallery forest and shrub woodlands in Venezuela, semi-deciduous forest and seasonally flooded marshes in the Brazilian Pantanal, and subtropical forest in southern Brazil. This diversity of habitats might suggest that they are habitat generalists, but close monitoring of radio-collared animals indicates they are highly dependent on dense ground or forest cover. Indeed, they occupy a much narrower range of microhabitats than would have been predicted by their wide geographic distribution. Ocelots often rest during the daytime in brush piles, clumps of vines in trees, among the roots of large trees, under tree falls, and even in concrete culverts. Recorded from sea level to about 1200 m

Food and Feeding. Primarily on terrestrial, nocturnal rodents weighing less than 1 kg. The small rodents include rice rats, cotton rats, marsh rats, Black Rats, cane mice, pocket mice, and spiny rats. They also prey on opossums, squirrels, cavies, rabbits, and small primates (Callictrichidae, Cebidae). Larger prey are taken relatively infrequently and include tamanduas, armadillos, sloths, pacas, agoutis and acouchis, porcupines, young Collared Peccaries, and young White-tailed Deer and brocket deer. In some areas young iguanas and land crabs (Trichodactylidae) are important seasonal components of the diet. There are also records of ocelots taking guans, doves, tinamous, frogs, fish, and insects. The occurrence of aquatic and semi-aquatic prey in the diet is not unexpected, as Ocelots are reportedly strong swimmers and in some areas they live in seasonally inundated environments. Ocelots usually hunt at night, scanning for prey while walking slowly along trails. They are also sit-and-wait predators. On occasion they spend 30–60 minutes sitting motionless at a site, then move rapidly to another hunting site where they sit and wait again. Though they hunt mostly in dense cover they sometimes forage in open areas at night.

Activity patterns. Commonly active twelve to14 hours a day. They typically rest between dawn and late afternoon, then begin moving an hour or so before sunset. Diurnal activity is not uncommon. In Venezuela, activity levels of radio-collared Ocelots increased sharply around sunset and remained fairly high throughout the night. Activity levels decreased substantially after sunrise and the cats usually rested from mid-morning until mid-afternoon. Ocelots were significantly more active during the daytime in the wet season, particularly on cloudy and overcast days. Daytime activity is probably related to the diurnal activity of some prey species such as birds, iguanas, and small primates. Activity levels may also change in response to other circumstances. In Peru, one female increased her hunting efforts to 17 hours a day to try to feed her single young. For reasons unknown, a male in the same area walked for 31 out of 34 consecutive hours.

Movements, Home range and Social organization. Ocelots spend the majority of their active periods walking slowly (0·3 to 1·4 km/h) about their home ranges. Distances traveled by males during these nightly activities tend to be greater than those of females. Detailed radio-tracking studies in Venezuela showed that in the dry season, adult males traveled about 7·6 km per night compared to 3·8 km per night for adult females. Their movements were sometimes nearly continuous and at other times their travels were punctuated by short periods (30–60 minutes) of no detectable movement, when the cats were probably sitting and waiting for prey to pass by. Distances traveled by both sexes in the wet season were reduced by 18 to 24%. Information on home range sizes of adult females indicates remarkably small variation across the species' geographic distribution, varying only from 0·8 to 15·6 km². For adult males, home range size varies from 3·5 to 17·7 km². Ocelots are solitary, and the larger ranges of adult males typically overlap the smaller home ranges of two to three adult females. Density estimates of Ocelots vary from 13·7/100 km² in southern Brazil to 40/100 km² in the Venezuelan llanos and 80/100 km² in the lowland rain forest of the Peruvian Amazon. High Ocelot density reduces the density of smaller sympatric felids.

Breeding. Ocelots have a long gestation period (79–82 days). Litter size is small, with one young per litter being the mode. Young weigh about 250 g at birth and grow and mature slowly; they begin following their mother at about three months of age and remain dependent on her for food for several more months. Young do not attain adult weight until they are 24–30 months of age. In the wild the interbirth interval is every two years. Young disperse from their natal ranges when they are 2–3 years old. Dispersal distances for 13 radio-tagged young varied from 2·5 to 30 km. The lifetime reproductive potential for an eight-year old female is about 4–6 young. In captivity, Ocelots are known to live for 20 years, but longevity in the wild is likely to be half that.

Status and Conservation. CITES Appendix I. Classified as Least Concern on *The IUCN Red List*. In the 1960s, as populations of large spotted cats began to dwindle, the fur trade shifted to the smaller spotted cats, particularly the Ocelot. From the early 1960s to the mid-1970s an estimated 200,000 ocelot were killed annually for the skin trade. A variety of wildlife protection laws were enacted during the same time interval and many countries outlawed the commercial export of wildlife. Other consumer countries began to prohibit the import of spotted cat skins and the number of ocelot skins in trade dropped significantly. The species was upgraded to Appendix I in 1989 and international trade ceased, but illegal hunting continues in some areas. Compared with the similar-sized Bobcat, present species has a low reproductive potential, and thus would appear to be vulnerable to even low levels of exploitation.

Bibliography. Aliag-Rossel *et al.* (2006), Bianchi & Mendes (2007), Broad (1987), Caldwell (1984), Crawshaw & Quigley (1989), Emmons (1987, 1988), Harveson *et al.* (2004), Konecny (1989), Laack *et al.* (2005), Ludlow & Sunquist (1987), Maffei & Noss (2008) Maffei *et al.* (2005), McMahan (1986), Meza *et al.* (2002), Mondolfi (1986), Moreno *et al.* (2006), Nowell & Jackson (1996), Oliveira *et al.* (In press), Sunquist (1992), Sunquist & Sunquist (2002), Sunquist *et al.* (1989), Tewes & Schmidly (1987), Trolle & Kery (2003).

15. Margay *Leopardus wiedii*
French: Margay / **German**: Baumozelot / **Spanish**: Margay

Taxonomy. *Felis wiedii* Schinz, 1821, Morro de Arará, rio Mucurí, Bahia, Brasil. Sometimes considered conspecific with *L. tigrinus*. Eight subspecies recognized.

Subspecies and Distribution.
L. w. wiedii Schinz, 1821 – SE Brazil to NE Argentina.
L. w. amazonicus Cabrera, 1917 – upper Amazonas, Brazil.
L. w. boliviae Pocock, 1941 – Andean slopes.
L. w. cooperi Goldman, 1943 – SE Texas to N Mexico border (could be extinct).
L. w. glauculus Thomas, 1903 – dry country of Mexico.
L. w. nicaraguae J. A. Allen, 1919 – Central America.
L. w. vigens Thomas, 1904 – NE Brazil to the Guianas.
L. w. yucatanicus Nelson & Goldman, 1931 – rainforest regions of Mexico.

Descriptive notes. Head-body 42·5–79·2 cm, tail 30–51·8 cm; weight 2·3–4·9 kg. Adult males and females are about the same size. A small, lightly built cat with a long tail. Resembles a small Ocelot. Fur is thick and soft and background color varies from grayish to cinnamon. Coat is marked with dark brown or black open and solid spots and longitudinal streaks. The belly is white. Tail is long and bushy, about 70% of head-body length, and marked with about twelve dark rings and a black tip. Compared with the Ocelot, present species has shorter, more rounded head, with strikingly large, almost bulging, eyes. Backs of the ears are black with a central white spot. Paws are relatively large and flexible, with mobile digits.

Habitat. Forest dwellers, more strongly associated with forest habitats than any other neotropical cat. In Mexico, found in coastal lowland, tropical deciduous, and evergreen gallery forests; in Belize, radio-collared cats preferred late second-growth forests to mature forests. In Venezuela, it is reported from humid lowland tropical forests, premontane moist forests, cloud forest, and shaded coffee or cocoa plantations. There are also reports in Bolivia using xerophytic thickets and the Bolivian Chaco. In the Linhares Forest Reserve, Brazil, seen in human-modified areas containing stands of bamboo and palm plantations. Rarely found at elevations above 1200 m.

On following pages: 16. Colocolo (*Leopardus colocolo*); 17. Andean Mountain Cat (*Leopardus jacobitus*); 18. Oncilla (*Leopardus tigrinus*); 19. Kodkod (*Leopardus guigna*); 20. Geoffroy's Cat (*Leopardus geoffroyi*).

Food and Feeding. Diet consists mainly of arboreal mammals, including opossums, squirrels, and climbing rats (Muridae); they also prey on terrestrial mammals such as spiny pocket mice, cane mice, cavy, rabbits, agouti, and paca. Birds such as tinamous and guans are also taken, as are amphibians, reptiles, insects and fruit. Most prey is nocturnal and arboreal, but also hunts on the ground. Agile climbers and leapers and can climb down a tree trunk head first and hang by their hindfeet from a branch. Several anatomical adaptations allow them to perform these acrobatics: they can pronate and supinate the hindfeet, allowing them to grip a branch equally well with their hind- or forefeet; and their broad, soft feet provide a good platform for jumping and an effective gripping surface for climbing. Limited information from the wild supports the notion that they do much of their hunting above the ground.

Activity patterns. In captivity, two peaks of activity: one between 01:00–02:00 h and another between 04:00–05:00 h. A young male radio-tracked in Belize was strictly nocturnal, but a radio-collared male in S Brazil was active at anytime of the daytime or night. Daytime rest sites are usually in trees, and cats have been located in tangles of vines or in the bole of palm trees.

Movements, Home range and Social organization. They are solitary animals and appear to live at much lower densities than the Ocelot. A young adult male in Belize traveled about six km per day and over the six months he was tracked, used an area of 11 km². The home range of an adult male in S Brazil measured 15·9 km².

Breeding. Most of what is known of reproduction is derived from a small number of captive animals. The estrous cycle is 32–36 days and estrus lasts 4–10 days; the gestation period is about 76–84 days, which is longer than that recorded for other small cats. Litter size is commonly one, and at birth the young weigh about 85–125 g, although two young weighed 163 and 170 g at birth. Young begin to eat solid food at 7–8 weeks of age and by 8–10 months they are nearly adult size. Estrus has been reported in 6–10-month old females, but sexual maturity is more commonly attained at about two years of age.

Status and Conservation. CITES Appendix I. Classified as Near Threatened on *The IUCN Red List*. Despite their small size, heavily hunted for their skins in the past. In 1977, ranked first among the Neotropical cats in terms of number of skins in trade. In 1989, when the species was moved to CITES Appendix I, international trade ceased, but illegal hunting continues in some areas. As the species is closely tied to forested habitats, deforestation and habitat loss is a major threat.

Bibliography. Armstrong et al. (1972), Azevedo (1996), Bisbal (1989), Crawshaw (1995), Eizirik, et al. (1998), Fagen & Wiley (1978), Konecny (1989), Mellen (1993), Mondolfi (1986), Nowell & Jackson (1996), Oliveira (1998), Paintiff & Anderson (1980), Petersen (1977, 1979), Petersen & Peterson (1978), Pocock (1941b), Sunquist (1992), Sunquist & Sunquist (2002), Tello (1986), Wiley (1978), Ximénez (1982).

16. Colocolo *Leopardus colocolo*

French: Colocolo / **German**: Pampaskatze / **Spanish**: Gato de las pampas
Other common names: Pampas Cat, Grass Cat

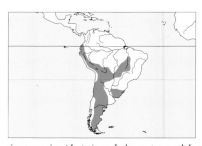

Taxonomy. *Felis colocolo* Molina, 1782, Province of Valparaiso, Chile.
The validity of the name *colocolo* was questioned, with the next available name that of *pajeros*. Sometimes placed in monotypic genus *Lynchailurus*, also in genus *Oncifelis*. Taxonomy in need of review. A recent biogeographic study of pelage characteristics and cranial metrics suggest that present species should be classified into eleven distinct species (*L. pajeros*, *L. braccatus*, and *L. colocolo*). Phylogenetic analysis show mtDNA lineages in western Argentina or central Chile are distinct from lineages in Uruguay and Brazil, which supports the more commonly accepted subspecies partitions (see below) but not the species-level divisions. Phylogenetic analysis also shows evidence of natural hybridization between *L. tigrinus* and present species in areas of range overlap. Eight subspecies currently recognized, although *braccatus* and *pajeros* likely represent distinct species.

Subspecies and Distribution.
L. c. colocolo Molina, 1782 – C Chile.
L. c. braccatus Cope, 1899 – C Brazil (Mato Grosso) to N Argentina.
L. c. budini Pocock, 1941 – Salta highlands in NW Argentina.
L. c. crespoi Cabrera, 1957 – Salta lowlands in NW Argentina
L. c. garleppi Matschie, 1912 – Andes in Ecuador, Peru and Bolivia.
L. c. munoai Ximénez, 1961 – extreme S Brazil and Uruguay.
L. c. pajeros Desmarest, 1816 – Pampas grasslands from Buenos Aires Province to S Argentina and Chile.
L. c. thomasi Lönnberg, 1913 – Ecuador.
Descriptive notes. Head-body 42·3–79 cm, tail 23–33 cm. Few weights available (1·7–3·7 kg). Tail is relatively short, full, and well-furred, sometimes with distinct black bands. Ears are large and more pointed than other South American felids. Backs of ears are black. Appearance and coloration varies greatly across geographic range. Fur may be short and soft or long and coarse, spotted, striped or almost unmarked. Subspecies *braccatus* tends to be rusty-red, with black bands on limbs and underparts. In Argentina the fur is long, yellowish-brown, gray-brown, gray or tan, sometimes with faint brown rosettes and black lines. The only constant is often the dark stripes on the limbs. In Chile the back and flanks are mottled reddish brown and gray with faint banding. Underparts white and forelimbs marked with bold black stripes.

Habitat. Found in the greatest variety of habitats of any South American felid. Mainly associated with open habitats. In Brazil it is found in savanna-like woodlands, open grasslands, seasonally flooded grasslands and forest. In other areas it is reported from scrub thickets, semi-arid deserts, mangroves, marshes, swamps, and even cloud forest. It is not reported from lowland tropical and temperate rainforest. From sea-level to 4800 m.

Food and Feeding. No detailed information from the wild. Thought to feed on small mammals, guinea pigs, mountain viscachas, and ground dwelling birds (Tinamidae). Has been seen taking penguin eggs and chicks from nests in Patagonia.

Activity patterns. Thought to be mainly terrestrial and nocturnal, but have also been observed during the day.

Movements, Home range and Social organization. Nothing known.

Breeding. Little information. Litter size 1–3. One female in captivity gave birth at twenty-four months of age.

Status and Conservation. CITES Appendix II. Classified as Near Threatened on *The IUCN Red List*. Formerly hunted. At one time it was one of the most important species in the South American fur trade; over 78,000 skins were exported from Argentina between 1976 and 1979. Today the species is widely distributed and common in many areas, but scarce in museum collections and zoos. Little is known of its ecology and behavior.

Bibliography. Daciuk (1974), Eaton (1984), Garcia-Perea (1994), Johnson, Pecon-Slattery et al. (1999), Mellen (1993), Miller (1930), Napolitano et al. (2008), Nowell & Jackson (1996), Osgood (1943), Pearson (1951), Redford & Eisenberg (1992), Silveira (1995), Sunquist & Sunquist (2002), Texera (1973).

17. Andean Mountain Cat *Leopardus jacobitus*

French: Chat des Andes / **German**: Andenkatze / **Spanish**: Gato andino
Other common names: Andean Cat, Mountain Cat, Andean Highland Cat

Taxonomy. *Felis jacobita* Cornalia, 1865, Bolivia.
Monotypic.
Distribution. C & S Peru, SW Bolivia, NW Argentina and NE Chile.
Descriptive notes. Head-body 57·7–64 cm, tail 41·3–48 cm. One male weighed 4 kg. About the size of a large house cat. The thick, long fur is pale, silvery gray, spotted, and striped with dark markings. Underparts are white and marked with dark spots. Chest and forelegs marked with black bars. The long, uniformly bushy tail is marked with about seven dark bands.

Habitat. High (3000-4500 m), rocky treeless zone in the Andes mountains to below 1000 m in Patagonian steppe of Neuquen Province, Argentina. Probably less than a dozen confirmed sightings of live cats in the wild, all in arid and semi-arid areas above tree line. Vegetation is sparse, consisting of scattered dwarf shrubs, clumps of grass, and cold-hardy cushion plants. One specimen collected at 5100 m in Peru.

Food and Feeding. Little information available. Probably also preys on ground-dwelling birds, small rodents, and lizards.

Activity patterns. Little information available, but in three of the four observations the cat was hunting in Mountain Viscachas colonies during the daytime.

Movements, Home range and Social organization. Nothing known.

Breeding. Nothing known.

Status and Conservation. CITES Appendix I. Classified as Endangered on *The IUCN Red List*. Fully protected throughout range; hunting and trade prohibited. Restricted distribution, rare throughout range. There have been few observations of this cat in the wild and its biology and status are almost completely unknown. Recent survey work in Bolivia, Argentina, and Chile found few signs of the species.

Bibliography. Delgado et al. (2004), Garcia-Perea (2002), Lucherini et al. (1998), Martino et al. (2008), Napolitano et al. (2008), Nowell & Jackson (1996), Sanderson (1999), Scrocchi & Halloy (1986), Sorli et al. (2006), Yensen & Seymour (2000).

18. Oncilla *Leopardus tigrinus*

French: Oncille / **German**: Ozelotkatze / **Spanish**: Tigrillo
Other common names: Little Tiger Cat, Little Spotted Cat, Ocelot Cat

Taxonomy. *Felis tigrinus* Schreber, 1775, Cayenne, French Guiana.
Recent genetic analysis of present species show at least two phylogeographic clusters. When mtDNA from specimens in Costa Rica and Brazil were examined, the genetic distances between these forms were as great as those separating other species in the *L. pardalis* lineage. When specimens from other geographic areas are also examined genetically, present species may be split into two, three or possibly four species. Four subspecies are currently recognized.

Subspecies and Distribution.
L. t. tigrinus Schreber, 1775 – Venezuela, the Guianas, N Brazil.
L. t. guttulus Hensel, 1872 – E and S Brazil, Paraguay, N Argentina.
L. t. oncilla Thomas, 1903 – Costa Rica.

L. t. pardinoides Gray, 1867 – N Andes from Colombia to Bolivia.

Descriptive notes. Head-body 38–55·6 cm, tail 22·5–42 cm; weight 1·5–3·5 kg; adult males slightly heavier than females. Smallest of the South American spotted cats. Resembles a Margay, but smaller and slimmer, with relatively larger ears and a shorter tail. Fur thick and soft; ground color of upperparts varies from pale to rich ocher, becoming paler on flanks. Belly whitish and heavily marked with dark spots. Upperparts and sides of body marked with longitudinal rows of black-bordered blotches or rosettes, usually enclosing a patch of the ground color. Pattern of black spots and stripes similar to that of Margay. Melanistic individuals not uncommon. Tail with 7–13 irregular dark bands. Ears black on back, with a conspicuous white spot.

Habitat. Found in a variety of forest types, including semi-arid thorny scrub in northeast Brazil, subtropical forest in E Brazil, cloud forest in Costa Rica, and from semi-dry deciduous forest at 350 m to montane cloud forest at 3000 m in Venezuela. There are also records in early secondary forest, abandoned eucalyptus plantations and areas close to human settlements.

Food and Feeding. Limited information suggests diet consists mainly of rodents (Muridae, Heteromyidae, Cricetidae), shrews (Soricidae), opossums (Marmosidae), lizards (Teiidae, Tropiduridae), birds (Emberizidae), and insects. Hunts on the ground, but can climb well.

Activity patterns. Primarily nocturnal and usually seen alone.

Movements, Home range and Social organization. Nothing known.

Breeding. Nothing known of reproduction in the wild. Limited information from captivity suggests estrus lasts from 3–9 days, the gestation period is 62 to 76 days, and litter size is 1–2, mode is 1. Kittens develop slowly.

Status and Conservation. CITES Appendix I. Classified as Vulnerable on *The IUCN Red List*. Rarely observed and as yet unstudied in the wild. In the 1970s and 1980s the species was trapped in large numbers for the fur trade, but international trade in pelts was largely terminated after 1985. The species was transferred to Appendix I in 1989 and thus there is no legal market for skins.

Bibliography. Bisbal (1989), Cabrera (1961b), Emmons & Feer (1997), Gardner (1971), Johnson, Pecon-Slattery *et al.* (1999), Leyhausen & Falkena (1966), Mondolfi (1986), Nowell & Jackson (1996), Oliveira (1994), Olmos (1993), Quillen (1981), Sunquist & Sunquist (2002), Tortato & Oliveira (2005), Widholzer *et al.* (1981), Ximénez (1982).

19. Kodkod *Leopardus guigna*

French: Kodkod / **German**: Chilenische Waldkatze / **Spanish**: Huiña

Other common names: Guigna

Taxonomy. *Felis guigna* Molina, 1782, Valdivia, Chile.

Sometimes placed in genus *Oncifelis*. Molecular and morphological data show that present species and *L. geoffroyi* are closed related sister taxa. Analyses of mtDNA lineages show that these two species last shared a common ancestor about 2·3 million years ago. Two subspecies recognized.

Subspecies and Distribution.

L. g. guigna Molina, 1782 – S Chile and Argentina.

L. g. tigrillo Schinz, 1844 – C Chile.

Descriptive notes. Head-body 39–51 cm, tail 19·5–25 cm. Adult males heavier (1·7–3 kg) than adult females (1·3–2·1 kg). Gray-brown coat marked with small, round, black spots and flecks. Forehead and neck with dark spots and streaks. Tail thick, bushy, marked with series of narrow black bands. White central spot on backs of ears. Melanism common.

Habitat. Southern beech forest and temperate rain forest. A study population on the north-west coast of Isla Grande de Chiloé, in Chile, used fragmented remnants of natural forest interspersed with ravines and steep coastal forest strips. They avoided agricultural fields, pastures, and cleared areas. They moved between forest tracts by travelling along vegetated corridors. Below about 2000 m.

Food and Feeding. Diet includes birds, primarily ground-dwelling thrushes (Turdidae), lapwings (Charadiidae), tapaculos (Rhinocryptidae), domestic geese, and chickens. Other prey include small rodents (*Rattus* spp.) and lizards (Iguanidae).

Activity patterns. Adept climbers, often use tree branches as travel paths, escape cover, rest sites, and for hunting. Rest during the day along streams in thick vegetation. Active at all times of the day and night, but generally more active at night.

Movements, Home range and Social organization. Males on Isla Grande de Chiloé sometimes crossed home ranges in a single day. Movement rates for males averaged 62 m per hour, females 36 m per hour. In the fragmented forest, home range size of males was 357 ha; females in same area had home ranges of 126 ha. Home range size of males in unfragmented habitat was 179 ha. Little overlap among home ranges of same sex animals on Isla Grande de Chiloé; male ranges ovelapped those of females. In Laguna San Rafael National Park in south Chile, mean home range size was 150 ha, with no significant differences between sexes.

Breeding. The gestation period is 72–78 days, litter size varies from 1–4. Longevity is up to eleven years.

Status and Conservation. CITES Appendix II. Classified as Vulnerable on *The IUCN Red List*. Has one of the smallest geographic ranges of any felid species and the species is restricted to dense forest areas. Logging and forest clearance are increasingly fragmenting its habitat.

Bibliography. Dunstone, Durbin, Wyllie, Freer *et al.* (2002), Dunstone, Durbin, Wyllie, Rose & Acosta (1998), Greer (1965), Johnson, Pecon-Slattery *et al.* (1999), Nowell & Jackson (1996), Osgood (1943), Sanderson, J.G. al. (2002), Scosta-Jamett & Simonetti (2004), Sunquist & Sunquist (2002).

20. Geoffroy's Cat *Leopardus geoffroyi*

French: Chat de Geoffroy / **German**: Kleinfleckkatze / **Spanish**: Gato de Geoffroy

Other common names: Mountain Cat

Taxonomy. *Felis geoffroyi* d'Orbigny & Gervais, 1844, banks of the Rio Negro, Patagonia.

Recent microsatellite data and mtDNA show a monophyletic lineage, suggesting that present species has maintained a large panmictic population since diverging from the *L. pardalis* line. Phylogenetic analyses failed to confirm the four currently recognized subspecies.

Subspecies and Distribution.

L. g. geoffroyi d'Orbigny & Gervais, 1844 – Argentina (Pampas grasslands from Buenos Aires Province S to Patagonia).

L. g. euxanthus Pocock, 1940 – Bolivian highlands.

L. g. paraguae Pocock, 1940 – S Paraguay, S Brazil, Uruguay, and N Argentina.

L. g. salinarum Thomas, 1903 – Chaco region (Paraguay–Bolivia border).

Descriptive notes. Head-body 43–88 cm, tail 23–40 cm; weight 1·8 – 7·8 kg. Adult males heavier than adult females. Animals from southern end of the range are larger than those from northern areas. About the size of a domestic cat but with a shorter tail and a longer, more flattened head. Background color of fur varies considerably across the geographic range, from bright tawny yellow in the north to silvery gray in the south, with intermediate forms in between. Melanistic individuals are common. The body is covered with small black spots, which coalesce into transverse bands on sides and limbs. The tail is marked with narrow dark bands. The backs of the ears are black with a central white spot.

Habitat. Found in a variety of temperate and subtropical habitats. Not well studied, but there are records in mesquite brush in the Paraguayan Chaco; in xeric shrublands and mixed steppe of grass and shrubs in foothills of Andes in Argentinean Patagonia; in coastal lagoons, marshes and grasslands in Buenos Aires Province, Argentina; and in open woodlands, brushy areas, and savanna marshes in Uruguay. In Chile the cats preferred dense cover in areas dominated by trees and shrubs. From sea-level to 3300 m in Andes.

Food and Feeding. Diet is known to include small rodents (Muridae), cavies (Caviidae), tuco-tucos (Ctenomyidae), Coypu (Myocastoridae), birds (Psittacidae, Anatidae, Tinamidae, Cariamidae, Furnariidae), fish (Cichlidae, Characidae), and frogs (Leptodactylidae). Porcupine quills (Erethizontidae) were found around the mouth of a specimen collected in Uruguay. In south Chile, the introduced European Hare occurred in more than 50% of all feces examined. Forages mainly on the ground, but they also hunt in water and are known to be good swimmers. In a study in southern Chilean Patagonia, one radio-collared female swam across a 30 m wide, fast-flowing river at least 20 times and two males crossed the river while dispersing. Cats in this area were also seen carrying hare carcasses into trees.

Activity patterns. Radio-collared cats in southern Chile were primarily nocturnal, with peaks of activity around sunset and sunrise. They used hollows and cavities in trees as well as dense ground vegetation as daytime rest sites.

Movements, Home range and Social organization. Three adult females in southern Chile occupied nonexclusive home ranges measuring about 3·5–6·5 km². Site fidelity appeared strong: two females maintained their home ranges for 2–3 years. The home ranges of five adult males in the same area tended to be larger (3·9–12·4 km²) and showed little overlap. Of 20 observations of free-ranging cats, 15 were of solitary individuals and five were of females with kittens, suggesting a solitary lifestyle typical of most felids. Scent marking appears to play an important role in maintaining the cat's social system as marking sites in three different areas were known to be used repeatedly and many feces were deposited in the crooks of trees, 3–5 m above the ground. At one site in southern Chile, 302 of 325 feces were found in arboreal middens. At another site in an almost treeless area in Argentina, 34 of 190 feces were found in arboreal middens.

Breeding. In captivity, estrus lasts 1–12 days and gestation length varies from 62–76 days, with 70–74 days being most common. Litter size varies from 1–3 and kittens weigh 65–90 g at birth. Young develop slowly compared to domestic cat kittens. Weaning begins about seven weeks of age and by the time they are six months old the young are nearly as large as their mother. In captivity, both males and females become sexually mature at about 18 months of age, although there are a few observations of sexual activity as early as 9–12 months.

Status and Conservation. CITES Appendix I. Classified as Near Threatened on *The IUCN Red List*. Occurs in a wide variety of habitat types and has been described as the most common of small South America felids. Despite this, little is known of the ecology of the species. Heavily exploited for its pelt; more than 250,000 skins in international markets in 1979–1980. The species was moved to Appendix I in 1992 and international trade has declined.

Bibliography. Anderson (1977), Cabrera (1961b), Canepuccia *et al.* (2007), Foreman (1988), Johnson & Franklin (1991), Johnson, Pecon-Slattery *et al.* (1999), Kachuba (1977), Law & Boyle (1984), Lucherini, Manfredi *et al.* (2006), Lucherini, Soler *et al.* (2000), Novaro, Funes & Walker (2000), Nowell & Jackson (1996), Pereira *et al.* (2006), Scheffel & Hemmer (1975), Sunquist & Sunquist (2002), Texera (1974), Ximénez (1975, 1982), Yanosky & Mercolli (1994).

PLATE 7

inches 24

cm 60

ssp *rufus*

ssp *fasciatus*

21

ssp *texensis*

ssp *floridanus*

winter

22

summer

ssp *lynx*

summer

winter

23

ssp *dinniki*

ssp *carpathicus*

ssp *wrangeli*

24

color variants

Genus *LYNX*
Kerr, 1792

21. Bobcat *Lynx rufus*

French: Lynx roux / **German**: Rotluchs / **Spanish**: Lince rojo
Other common names: Red Lynx, Bay Lynx, Cat Lynx

Taxonomy. *Felis rufus* Schreber 1777, "Provinz New York in Amerika".
Taxonomists currently recognize twelve subspecies. Some studies, however, suggest that the actual number of subspecies may be less, and that modern taxonomy should be reassessed.

Subspecies and Distribution.
L. r. rufus Schreber, 1777 – C Canada (Saskatchewan, Manitoba & W Ontario) and C & NE USA (North Dakota, South Dakota, Nebraska, Kansas, Oklahoma, Arkansas, Iowa, Illinois, Indiana, Ohio, Pennsylvania, New York, New Jersey, Delaware, Maryland, Virginia, West Virginia, Kentucky & Tennessee).
L. r. baileyi Merriam, 1890 – SW USA and NW Mexico.
L. r. californicus Mearns, 1897 – SE USA (California).
L. r. escuinapae J. A. Allen, 1903 – Pacific coast and C Mexico.
L. r. fasciatus Rafinesque, 1817 – NW coast of USA.
L. r. floridanus Rafinesque, 1817 – SE USA.
L. r. gigas Bangs, 1897 – E Canada (Maritime Provinces), and NE USA (New England).
L. r. oaxacensis Goodwin, 1963 – S Mexico (Oaxaca).
L. r. pallescens Merriam, 1899 – SW Canada (British Columbia & Alberta), and W USA (Montana, Wyoming, Colorado, Utah, Nevada & Idaho).
L. r. peninsularis Thomas, 1898 – NW Mexico (Baja California).
L. r. superiorensis Peterson & Downing, 1952 – S Canada (Ontario), and N USA (Michigan, Wisconsin & Minnesota).
L. r. texensis J. A. Allen, 1895 – S USA (Texas), and NE Mexico (Tamaulipas, Nuevo Leon & Coahuila).

Descriptive notes. Medium-sized, short-tailed cat. Head-body length is 65–105 cm, and tail length is 9–11 cm. Adult males average 8·9–13·3 kg. Adult females average 5·8–9·2 kg. Cranial measurements and adult weights indicate a size gradient that decreases with latitude. Kittens weigh 0·3–0·4 kg at birth. The pelage contains various shades of buff-brown, and is mottled with dark spots and streaks. Some may have a rufous tint to the pelage. Cranial fur is streaked with black, and the back of the ears is heavily marked with black. Forest subspecies are darker in color compared to subspecies inhabiting more open habitats. Melanism has been documented ten times in Florida and once in New Brunswick, both peripheral and peninsular portions of the species' range. Adults have 28 teeth. Where range overlap occurs, can be confused with Canadian Lynx, another medium-sized, short-tailed felid. In comparison to it however, present species is generally smaller, and has shorter, more slender legs, smaller feet, ear tufts that are smaller than 3 cm or completely missing, and a longer tail. Additionally, the ventral tail tip is white, whereas the tail tip is completely black in Canadian Lynx. Usually silent, but they can make loud vocalizations that may be associated with mating behavior.

Habitat. Throughout its range, uses a wide variety of natural habitats. These range from coniferous and deciduous forest in Maine to brushlands in Oklahoma, bottomland hardwoods in Louisiana, semi-deserts in Arizona and New Mexico, humid tropical forests in Florida, dry scrubland and forests of pine and oak in Mexico, mountainous terrain in Oregon, mixed mesophytic forests of the Cumberland Plateau, and prairies in eastern Montana. They can also inhabit human-altered landscapes such as agricultural lands, if sufficient cover exists nearby. Generally prefer rugged, rocky landscapes with dense cover. Prey density is the most important factor influencing habitat selection. However, other factors affecting habitat selection include protection from severe weather, availability of den sites, adequate cover for hunting and escape, and low human disturbance. Females will establish natal dens in small caves, rock crevices, thickets, hollow trees, brush piles, stumps, and root-masses from fallen trees.

Food and Feeding. Like most felids, use dense cover to stalk prey or to conceal themselves to ambush their prey. Although they feed on a diverse array of species, lagomorphs are commonly utilized throughout the species' range. Cottontails and Snowshoe Hares are the two lagomorphs most commonly eaten. Generally select small to medium-sized prey (0·7–5·5 kg), but they will kill prey as large as White-tailed Deer, especially in northern climates during winter. Usually kill deer by stalking a resting animal, pouncing on the back and head, and repeatedly biting the victim's throat. However, most use of White-tailed Deer results from the opportunistic discovery of carrion. Ultimately, the kind of prey utilized is dependent upon geographic location. In Florida, Eastern Cottontail (*Sylvilagus floridanus*), Marsh Rabbit (*S. palustris*), and Hispid Cotton Rat (*Sigmodon hispidus*) account for 66–78% of the diet. Florida subspecies prey on birds more frequently and ungulates less frequently than do more northern populations. Snowshoe Hare (*Lepus americanus*), Mule Deer (*Odocoileus hemionus*), and Mountain Beaver (*Aplodontia rufa*) are primary prey in the Cascade Mountains of Oregon. In New England and New York, cottontail, Snowshoe Hare, and White-tailed

Deer are the most important prey species. Snowshoe Hare, White-tailed Deer, and North American Porcupine (*Erethizon dorsata*) compose over 90% of the winter diet in northern Minnesota. In eastern Nevada and Utah, 69% of the diet is cottontail and Black-tailed Jackrabbit. Cottontail, squirrels, cotton rat, Eastern Woodrat (*Neotoma floridana*), and mice (*Peromyscus* spp.) are important components of diets in Arkansas. Females appear to prefer smaller prey than do males. Where ranges overlap, interference competition between Coyote, Red Fox, Puma, and present species may occur. Likely suffer most severely from this competition, because they show the greatest dependence on a single food source, lagomorphs. In Idaho, Pumas killed them during the winter while defending or stealing food.

Activity patterns. Crepuscular and nocturnal activity mostly coincides with peak activity of lagomorphs, their dominant prey. In general, the daily activity pattern is bimodal, with the first period of activity from one hour before sunrise to three hours after sunrise, and the second from three hours before sunset to midnight. In Florida, are most active between 18:00–24:00 h and least active between 12:00–15:00 h. Several studies have reported increases in daylight activity during winter. Adult females with kittens exhibit reduced activity during the first month following birth. However, after kittens are weaned, adult females increase diurnal activity. Usually inactive during periods of extreme heat or severe weather.

Movements, Home range and Social organization. Solitary except during the breeding season. A variety of methods are utilized by this species to mark its territory including urine and feces deposition, soil scraping, tree scratching, and scent marking via anal gland secretions. Home range sizes vary with geographic location, sex, prey availability, and in some regions, season. Home ranges at higher latitudes are larger than those from more southern regions. Mean annual home range size for adult males varies from 2·6 km² in Alabama to 163 km² in Idaho. Adult male home ranges often overlap with those of other males and females. Several studies reported that adult male home ranges expand during winter. This is apparently a response to maximizing breeding opportunities and seasonal shifts in prey availability. Adult female home ranges are usually 2–3 times smaller than those of adult males, and range from 1·2 km² in Alabama to 69·7 km² in Idaho. Overlap between adult female home ranges rarely occurs. However, a high level of intra-sex home range overlap was observed in Illinois. Adult females constrict home ranges during the summer due to parturition and kitten rearing. Annual home range sizes can fluctuate over time in response to changing prey densities. For example, adult male and female annual home ranges in south-east Idaho increased from 20·4 km² to 123 km² and 11·6 km² to 69·7 km², respectively, over a three-year period. These increases were attributed to declining Black-tailed Jackrabbit and Cottontail populations. Nightly movements range between two and 20 km. Young disperse when they are approximately one year old. Dispersal involves a series of nomadic movements punctuated with temporary occupancy of activity areas that can last 60 days. Dispersal distances range from less than 1 km to nearly 200 km. In Florida, two females dispersed at least 12 km and 30 km respectively.

Breeding. Breeding can occur year-round, but most occurs from February through May. Most females do not breed until two years of age, but breeding by yearlings has been documented. The estrous cycle is approximately 44 days, and females are usually in heat 5–10 days. Males do not breed until they are two years of age. A male may copulate with a single female multiple times over several days. Gestation takes approximately 62 days. One litter is produced per year, but there is evidence that a second litter may be produced by females that lose their first litter soon after parturition. Litters average three, but range from one to six kittens. Offspring open their eyes 9–10 days after birth, are weaned after two months, and begin traveling with their mother at about 3–5 months of age.

Status and Conservation. CITES Appendix II. Classified as Least Concern on *The IUCN Red List*. Historically, population trends have been driven by economic factors such as value of pelts, poultry depredation, and competition with humans for wildlife resources. Bounties were offered in the early 1700s as a means of controlling bobcat depredation on livestock and poultry. Prior to the 1970s, little concern was given to the conservation of predatory furbearers, including this species. Then public concern over the exploitation of wildlife led to the Convention on International Trade of Endangered Species of Wild Fauna and Flora (CITES), which made it illegal to trade any species listed in Appendix I. This species was not placed in Appendix I of CITES, however, which allowed for the continued trade of its pelts. Demand for pelts increased dramatically throughout the 1970s as the trade in other spotted cats declined. Annual harvests in the United States averaged 10,000 in the early 1970s (pre-CITES) at US$ 10 per pelt. By the end of the 1979–80 trapping season, more then 86,000 bobcats had been harvested at up to US$ 150 per pelt. In 1975, concern over decreasing populations led to its placement in Appendix II of CITES, which allowed the export of pelts only if harvest was shown not to be detrimental to the population. Currently, remains on Appendix II and it is the only spotted felid in the world that can be trapped legally. Today, inhabits 47 of the 48 contiguous states (absent only from Delaware). Of the 47 states in which it occurs, 37 allowed the species to be harvested through 1996. Indiana, Ohio, New Jersey, and Iowa list it as "Endangered," and Illinois classifies the species as "Threatened." A recent study in Illinois concluded that it was widely distributed and no longer warranted classification as "Threatened" in the state. Populations in Mexico and Canada are also faring well. However, still persecuted by Mexican ranchers due to its alleged depredation of sheep. Because of conservation laws and its tolerance of moderate amounts of habitat change, the species appears to be secure throughout much of its range. In fact, the species is recolonizing many parts of its historic range from which it had been extirpated.

On following pages: 22. Canadian Lynx (*Lynx canadensis*); 23. Eurasian Lynx (*Lynx lynx*); 24. Iberian Lynx (*Lynx pardinus*).

Bibliography. Anderson (1987), Bailey (1974), Banfield (1974), Buie *et al.* (1979), Buttrey (1974), Cochrane *et al.* (2006), Crowe (1975), Delibes *et al.* (1997), Dibello *et al.* (1990), Diefenbach *et al.* (2006), Fickett (1971), Fritts & Sealander (1978a, 1978b), Gashwiler *et al.* (1960), Hall, E.R. (1981), Hall, H.T. & Newsom (1976), Hamilton & Hunter (1939), Harrison (1998), Hutchinson & Hutchinson (1998), Jackson & Jacobson (1987), Kamler & Gipson (2000), Knick (1990), Knick *et al.* (1984), Koehler & Hornocker (1991), Kolowski & Woolf (2002), Labisky & Boulay (1998), Landholt & Genoways (2000), Larivière & Walton (1997), Litvaitis & Harrison (1989), Litvaitis *et al.* (1986), López-González *et al.* (1998), Lovallo & Anderson (1996), Lovell *et al.* (1998), Maehr (1997), Maehr & Brady (1986), Major & Sherburne (1987), Marston (1942), McCord (1974), Miller & Speake (1978, 1979), Nielsen & Woolf (2002), Nielsen-Clayton & Woolf (2001), Nowak (1999), Pollack (1951a, 1951b), Progulske (1955), Read (1981), Regan & Maehr (1990), Rolle & Ward (1985), Rollings (1945), Rucker *et al.* (1989), Samson (1979), Smith, D.S. (1984), Story *et al.* (1982), Sunquist & Sunquist (2002), Thornton *et al.* (2004), Tischendorf & McAlpine (1995), Towell & Anthony (1988), Wassmer *et al.* (1988), Whitaker & Hamilton (1998), Wiggington & Dobson (1999), Wilson & Reeder (2005), Winegarner & Winegarner (1982), Woolf & Hubert (1998), Woolf *et al.* (2000).

22. Canadian Lynx *Lynx canadensis*

French: Lynx du Canada / **German**: Kanadischer Luchs / **Spanish**: Lince canadiense

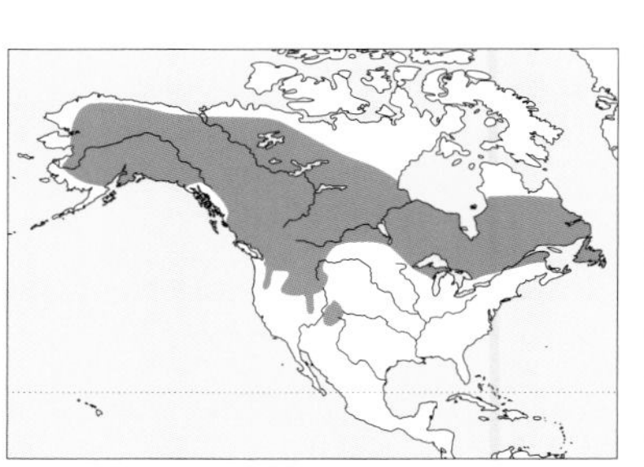

Taxonomy. *Lynx canadensis* Kerr, 1792, Canada.

Present species and *L. lynx* sometimes considered conspecific. Two subspecies recognized.

Subspecies and Distribution.

L. c. canadensis Kerr, 1792 – mainland Canada and N USA.

L. c. subsolanus Bangs, 1897 – NE Canada (Newfoundland I).

Descriptive notes. Head-body 76·2–106·7 cm, tail 5–12·7 cm; weight 5·0–17·3 kg. Little geographic variation in size but males larger and heavier than females. In Newfoundland the mean weight of adult males was 10·7 kg (range 6·3–17·3 kg) versus 8·6 kg (range 5·0–11·8 kg) for adult females. The fur, except for the undersides, is unspotted and the background color is buff-gray. Undersides are white and mottled with black spots. The long, pale-colored belly fur is valued by the garment industry. The winter fur of cats in Newfoundland is thick and silvered over with hoary tips, giving the cat a uniform gray color. In other areas winter pelts are more grayish-brown mixed with buff or pale brown. There are no records of melanistic cats but there are a few records of "blue lynx". The cat's cheeks are fringed with a ruff of long hair. Backs of the ears are black at the base and the tips are adorned with an elongated tuft of black hair. Tail tip is completely black, which distinguishes it from the Bobcat, in which the tip is dark only on the dorsal half. Paws are covered with long, dense fur and feet are large and snowshoe-like, which provides additional support in soft snow. Cat is muscular, leggy, and stands about 48–56 cm high at the shoulder. Hindlimbs are longer than front, giving the cat a tipped-forward appearance.

Habitat. A variety of forest types within the broad belt of boreal forest that stretches from Alaska to Newfoundland. They are also found in the coniferous forests of the northern Cascade Mountains of Washington and the Rocky Mountains of north-east Utah and central Colorado at elevations above 2700 m. Prey almost exclusively on the Snowshoe Hare and thus the habitats used by the cat coincide with habitats where hares are abundant, especially early successional fire-dependent forests. Mature forests containing tangles of blown-down trees and stumps are often used for denning sites. In areas where coexists with Bobcats and Coyotes, appears to avoid possible conflicts by using areas at higher elevations and areas with greater snow depth.

Food and Feeding. Prey extensively on Snowshoe Hares, but their abundance is cyclic and densities can vary enormously during the 8–11 year cycle. Snowshoe Hare numbers may reach 2300 per km^2 one year and then plummet to as few as 12 per km^2 a few years later. Regardless, Snowshoe Hares contribute 60 to 97% of the Lynx's diet and in some areas the cat hunts little else. On Cape Breton Island, Nova Scotia, for example, 198 of 200 attempts to capture prey involved Snowshoe Hares. Squirrels and grouse appear as incidental prey in the winter. The appearance of Moose and Deer in scats is probably related to feeding on carrion, since ungulates do not figure prominently in the cat's diet. Summer diets are more diverse and typically include a greater number of small birds and rodents, but even then Snowshoe Hares contribute more than half of all meat consumed. Different methods are employed to capture prey depending on environmental conditions. In Newfoundland, when Snowshoe Hares were abundant, about 60% of kills were made from ambush, but this method was not effective in Alberta, Canada, when Snowshoe Hare density was low. Neither active searching nor ambushing Snowshoe Hares was more effective during a low in their numbers in the Yukon, but hunted more often from ambush, presumably because this method is more energy efficient when prey are scarce. In an area in southern Yukon with relatively high Snowshoe Hare densities and dense vegetation, Canadian Lynx had little success ambushing Snowshoe Hares. These findings suggest that hunting success is more dependent on stalking conditions than on Snowshoe Hare densities or habitat type. Indeed, even in areas with abundant Snowshoe Hares but where the vegetation is particularly dense, Canadian Lynx may be more successful hunting in open areas where Snowshoe Hare densities are lower. Based on tracking animals in snow, Canadian Lynx kill one Snowshoe Hare per day or one every other day, but capture success is variable. In the Yukon, when Snowshoe Hare numbers were increasing, a Canadian Lynx made six kills in eleven attempts (54·5%). However, when Snowshoe Hare numbers were low the success rates varied from 20–22%. The highest hunting success rates are achieved by groups. One study reported that the success rates for groups of one, two, three and four averaged 14%, 17%, 38% and 55%, respectively. In the Yukon, female-kitten groups killed Snowshoe Hares more frequently than did single cats, but the return per individual was lower. However, in groups comprising accomplished hunters, the return per individual was higher than that of single animals. Hunting success is also related to the distance between the Canadian Lynx and Snowshoe Hare when it begins to run. Results from several studies show Canadian Lynx leaping 1·5 to 2·5 m per jump, and Canadian Lynx were generally more successful the fewer jumps they had to make. In contrast, a study on Cape Breton Island showed that Canadian Lynx made an average of 11·1 jumps (covering 24 m) per successful capture compared to 8·4 jumps (covering 16·3 m) for unsuccessful captures. Snowshoe Hares are sometimes eaten where killed and sometimes taken to another site, which may be close by or some distance away. Canadian Lynx on Cape Breton Island initially opened the thoracic cavity of Hares and then fed on the organs, followed by the shoulders and neck. The stomach and intestines were not eaten, nor were the paws. Canadian Lynx consume an estimated 600 g to 1200 g per day, which is equivalent to from one Snowshoe Hare every other day to one per day. Uneaten parts of kills may be cached, covered with leaves or snow, or left uncovered at the site. Caching behavior was related to hunting success; few kills were cached when Snowshoe Hares were difficult to catch. The impact of predation on Snowshoe Hare populations depends on where their populations are in the cycle. Studies in Alberta, Canada, estimate that Canadian Lynx account for 20% of winter losses during a low in the Snowshoe Hare cycle, but during a peak the impact was negligible.

Activity patterns. Snowshoe Hares are basically nocturnal and thus Canadian Lynx are primarily nocturnal, although when Snowshoe Hare densities are low, some daytime hunting is not unusual to try to meet their energy requirements.

Movements, Home range and Social organization. Lynx may move rapidly between distant parts of their ranges without stopping, but when hunting, the cats zig-zag, cross, and recross areas and inspect patches of cover searching for prey. Travel rates range from 0·75 to 1·45 km/hour and it is not uncommon to cover 8–9 km per day. The distances traveled per day may increase as Snowshoe Hare densities decline. Home range sizes vary from three to 783 km^2, but most are relatively small, about 15 to 50 km^2. The home ranges of resident males are commonly larger than those of resident females. Surprisingly, studies in Alberta and the Yukon found no significant correlation between home range size and Snowshoe Hare densities or Canadian Lynx densities. However, studies in other areas suggest that home range sizes are tied to Snowshoe Hare densities and that the home ranges are typically larger in areas where there are few Snowshoe Hares. Home ranges in Washington, Montana, Minnesota, and Manitoba, which represent the southern periphery of the Canadian Lynx's geographic distribution, tend to be larger (39–243 km^2) than elsewhere and densities in these areas are typically low (2–3/100 km^2). Furthermore, densities in these marginal areas show little fluctuation, presumably because Snowshoe Hare populations in these areas do not cycle; Snowshoe Hare densities remain low, probably due to predation. Within areas of favorable habitat densities may reach 45/100 km^2, which includes adults, yearlings, and kittens. Despite all the field studies on the species, remarkably little is known about the social system of the animal. Canadian Lynx are, like most other felids, solitary and the only prolonged association is between a female and her young. Spatial arrangements are highly variable, and run the gamut from complete home range overlap between Canadian Lynx of the same sex to exclusive ranges for both males and females. In the Northwest Territories most social interactions between Canadian Lynx were classified as neutral, even between individuals whose ranges overlapped extensively. The cyclical nature of the prey base does, however, have a great influence on the Canadian Lynx's land tenure system. It has been shown that at extremely low Snowshoe Hare densities the system may collapse and Canadian Lynx will abandon their home ranges and wander widely in search of food. During these times, adults suddenly appear in places like North Dakota or Iowa, far from their normal haunts. It is not known if any remain on their ranges during such lows, but it is suggested that a "core population" maintain their territories throughout the cycle. To what extent fur trapping represents another disruptive influence is not well known, but the removal of residents may alter established relationships among neighbors as well as modify the age and sex structure of the population.

Breeding. The breeding season is short, lasting about one month. Estrus lasts for 3–5 days, and females probably only have a single annual estrous cycle. They are thought to be induced ovulators, but this may depend on their densities: they may be induced ovulators when mates are scarce and spontaneous ovulators when mates are abundant. Gestation length is about 63–64 days. Litter size ranges from 1–8 and, unlike most other felids, shows considerable flexibility. When Snowshoe Hares are scarce, ovulation rates, pregnancy rates, and litter size decrease; when Snowshoe Hares are abundant these same rates increase. During a peak in Snowshoe Hare density (74/km^2) in the Yukon, mean litter size for adult females was 5·3 and for yearling females it was 4·2. When Snowshoe Hare densities declined the following year, adult litter size decreased to 4·9 and no yearlings reproduced. In the third year, when Snowshoe Hare densities were even lower (13/km^2), no adult or yearling produced a litter. During a low in Snowshoe Hare densities in central Alberta, litter size averaged 1·3, but increased to 3·5 as Snowshoe Hare densities increased. At the low in Snowshoe Hare density, only 33% of adult females conceived, compared to 73% when Snowshoe Hares were abundant. Even if females do produce kittens during times of low Snowshoe Hare abundance, infant mortality rates are likely to be high (60–95%), as kittens die of starvation or other nutritional stresses. Mating occurs in most areas from March–April, and young are born in May–June. Birth dens have been found in dense tangles of blown-down trees or under tree roots. The arrival of young is marked by a contraction in the home range of a female, and her movements become focused on the den site.

Young weigh about 175–235 g at birth, eyes are closed, and their grayish buffy-fur is marked with dark streaks. When Snowshoe Hares are abundant, growth and development are rapid and kittens are weaned by twelve weeks of age. By mid-winter young will weigh 4·5 kg. When Snowshoe Hares are scarce, growth is slowed and few young survive. Young begin following their mother at five weeks and by seven weeks may be actively participating in hunts. Young remain with their mother until they are about ten months old, but they do not reach adult size until they are two years old. When Snowshoe Hares are abundant, females may breed at ten months of age. Otherwise breeding occurs at 22–23 months of age. Males probably do not attain sexual maturity until they are two or three years old. Dispersal from the natal range occurs as early as 10–11 months of age, but most are 16–17 months old when they leave. In one study the mean dispersal distance was 163 km (range 17–930 km) and distances traveled did not differ by sex or age. In another study, eleven dispersers traveled more than 500 km and two others moved more than 1000 km.

Status and Conservation. CITES Appendix II. Listed as species of Least Concern on *The IUCN Red List*. Canadian Lynx have been extirpated from Prince Edward Island and mainland Nova Scotia; the species is considered endangered in New Brunswick. Formerly widespread in the southern provinces of Canada, but their distribution has retreated northward, apparently in response to timber harvest and habitat changes. Fur trapping in Canada is regulated through closed seasons, quotas, limited entry, and long-term concessions. There are concerns that the species may be overharvested during lows in the Snowshoe Hare cycle. Canadian Lynx in the continental USA were listed as Threatened under the Endangered Species Act in 2000. Fewer than 200 are estimated to live in the USA. Efforts to reestablish the species in upstate New York have not been very successful; 83 were released over three winters, but mortality has been high and there has been no sign of successful reproduction.

Bibliography. Bailey *et al.* (1986), Banfield (1974), Barash (1971), Bergerud (1983), Berrie (1973), Bittner & Rongstad (1982), Brand & Keith (1979), Brand *et al.* (1976), Breitenmoser, Slough & Breitenmoser-Würsten (1993), Brocke, Gustafson & Fox (1991), Brocke, Gustafson & Major (1990), Carbyn & Patriquin (1983), De Vos & Matel (1952), Dolbeer & Clark (1975), Elton & Nicholson (1942), Gunderson (1978), Haglund (1966), Keith (1963, 1990), Koehler (1990), Koehler *et al.* (1979), Krebs, C.J., Boonstra *et al.* (2001), Krebs, C.J., Boutin *et al.* (1995), McCord & Cardoza (1982), Mech (1973, 1980), Merriam (1886), Mowat *et al.* (1996), Murray & Boutin (1991), Murray *et al.* (1994), Nellis & Keith (1968), Nellis *et al.* (1972), Nowell & Jackson (1996), O'Connor (1986), O'Donoghue, Boutin, Krebs, Murrary & Hofer (1998), O'Donoghue, Boutin, Krebs, Zuleta *et al.* (1998), Parker (1981), Parker *et al.* (1983), Poole (1994, 1995, 1997), Quinn & Parker (1987), Quinn & Thompson (1985, 1987), Saunders (1963, 1964), Schwarz (1938), Slough & Mowat (1996), Sunquist & Sunquist (2002), Tumlinson (1987), Ward & Krebs (1985).

23. Eurasian Lynx *Lynx lynx*

French: Lynx d'Europe / **German**: Eurasischer Luchs / **Spanish**: Lince boreal

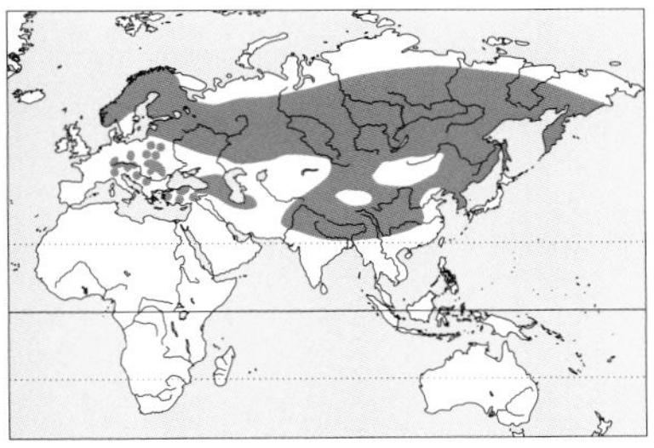

Taxonomy. *Felis lynx* Linnaeus, 1758, Wennersborg, S Sweden.

Seven subspecies recognized.

Subspecies and Distribution.

L. l. lynx Linnaeus, 1758 – N and W Europe E to the Yenisei River in Russia.

L. l. carpathicus Kratochvíl & Stollman, 1963 – Carpathian Mts S to Bulgaria and Greece.

L. l. dinniki Satunin, 1915 – Caucasus Mts S to Turkey and N Iran.

L. l. isabellinus Blyth, 1847 – Pamir and Kunlun Mts, Kashmir, C & W China.

L. l. kozlovi Fetisov, 1950 – C Siberia, from the R Yenisei to Lake Baikal.

L. l. neglectus Stroganov, 1962 – Russian Far East, Korea, and NE China (Manchuria).

L. l. wrangeli Ognev, 1928 – E Siberia, S to the Stanovoy Mts.

Descriptive notes. Largest of the four lynx species. Head-body 80–110 cm, tail 16–23 cm; weight 15–29 kg (unconfirmed over 30 kg) for adults; males 25% heavier than females. The species is largest in the eastern portion of its range. Characteristic of the genus, it has a short, black-tipped tail, black ear tufts up to 6 cm long, and relatively long legs. The hindlegs are longer than the front legs. The round face is framed by pronounced sideburns. Reduced number of molars and 28 teeth in total: I 3/3, C 1/1, P 2/2 and M1/1. About 30% of the animals have a second reduced molar in the lower jaw. There are four different coat patterns on a ground color that varies (grayish, rusty, yellowish, or reddish): large black spots, small black spots, no spots, and spots in form of brownish rosettes. The proportion of these types varies greatly between populations.

Habitat. Deciduous, mixed, and coniferous forests in Europe and Siberia; fairly open and sparsely wooded regions, including semi-deserts in Central Asia. Thick scrub woodland and barren, rocky areas throughout the northern slopes of the Himalayas. In northern latitudes, also roam in the tundra.

Food and Feeding. In contrast to the three other lynx species, the Eurasian Lynx is not a hunter of lagomorphs, but of smaller ungulates. Although the diet often contains a long list of species, the staple prey is roe deer, chamois (*Rupicara*), or musk deer. In northern Scandinavia, the most frequent prey is semi-domestic Reindeer. In many areas also prey on livestock, mainly sheep, goats, and farmed Fallow Deer (*Dama dama*). Larger prey such as Red Deer, Wild Boar, or ibex is only sporadically taken. In areas where small ungulates are lacking, feed on smaller prey such as hares or grouse. Eat 1–2·5 kg of meat/day, and return to a kill until all edible parts are consumed. Kill 50–70 ungulates/year.

Activity patterns. Mainly active during dawn and dusk, but there is no hour during the day with less than 25% activity. In the Bialowieza Primeval Forest, Poland, radio-tagged Eurasian Lynx had a peak in activity between 15:00 and 07:00 h and on average they were active and moving for 6·5 h/day. The majority (73%) of movement by males occurred at night, whereas females were as active during the daytime as they were at night. While the general pattern of activity of females with and without kittens was similar, females with young were active twice as long per day than non-reproducing females. Males were active significantly longer in the mating season (January–March). The length of time of activity on a daily basis varied greatly and depended largely on whether the cat had a kill. On the first day after killing a deer, only active 1·6 h/day, but the time spent moving increased steadily with each day afterwards, reaching 6·8 h/day by the fourth day post-kill and thereafter increasing to as much as 12·5 h/day on days when searched for prey but made no kill. Activity was not greatly affected by temperatures and rainfall, except that they moved little on days with heavy rains or when ambient temperatures exceeded 30°C.

Movements, Home range and Social organization. Daily movements vary between a few hundred meters and 40 km, but the average from several areas is about 10 km/day. Especially during the mating season, males are roaming far. Eurasian Lynx are solitary animals, except for females with young of the year. Both sexes occupy exclusive territories, with one male usually covering the range of 1–3 females. Home range size varies greatly with the region. In central and western Europe, males roam over 100–450 km² and females over 45–250 km², whereas in Scandinavia males roam over 400–2200 km² and females over 200–1850 km². The range size depends on the productivity of the habitat.

Breeding. Mating occurs from March to mid-April and is frequently marked by calling by both sexes. Gestation length ranges from 68–72 days. Kittens are usually born in late May to early June. Females will recycle if they lose their litter soon after birth, but otherwise they are not polyestrous. Litter size is 1–4; two is most common. Cubs stay with the mother for 9–11 months. Young females reach sexual maturity at 22 months, males at 34 months. Females reproduce the first time at the age of two, but often not until three years.

Status and Conservation. CITES Appendix II. Classified as Least Concern on *The IUCN Red List*. Vulnerable to the destruction of their ungulate prey base and the habitat. In certain areas, clear-cutting can have at least a short-term negative effect on abundance. Other examples show that they can adapt to more open habitat over time. There is no information on the impact of commercial trapping on the population status. In Russia, 2800–5800 pelts were harvested annually until the late 1980s. Since 1993, Russia and China have set export quotas of 2800 and 1000 per year, respectively. However, fewer than 1000 total have been exported lately, which could indicate a decrease in the population. Predation on livestock and wild ungulates can lead to severe conflicts with sheepbreeders and hunters, and poaching can threaten a local population. Dispersing subadult Eurasian Lynx showed little ability to cross highways, which has consequences that need to be considered in recovery strategies of the species in fragmented landscapes.

Bibliography. Andersen *et al.* (1998), Andrén *et al.* (1998), Breitenmoser & Haller (1993), Breitenmoser, Kaczensky *et al.* (1993), Breitenmoser-Würsten *et al.* (2001), Goszczynski (1986), Haller (1992), Heptner & Sludskii (1992a), Herfindal *et al.* (2005), Jedrzejewski, Jedrzejewska *et al.* (1996), Jedrzejewski, Schmidt *et al.* (1993), Jobin *et al.* (2000), Kvam (1991), Linnell *et al.* (1996), Matjuschkin (1978), Nowell & Jackson (1996), Okarma *et al.* (1997), Pulliainen *et al.* (1995), Schmidt (1999), Schmidt *et al.* (1997), Sunde & Kvam (1997), Sunde, Kvam, Moa, Negard & Overskaug (2000), Sunde, Kvam, Moa & Overskaug (2000), Sunquist & Sunquist (2002), Tumlinson (1987), Zimmermann *et al.* (2007).

24. Iberian Lynx *Lynx pardinus*

French: Lynx ibérique / **German**: Pardelluchs / **Spanish**: Lince ibérico

Other common names: Pardel Lynx, Spanish Lynx

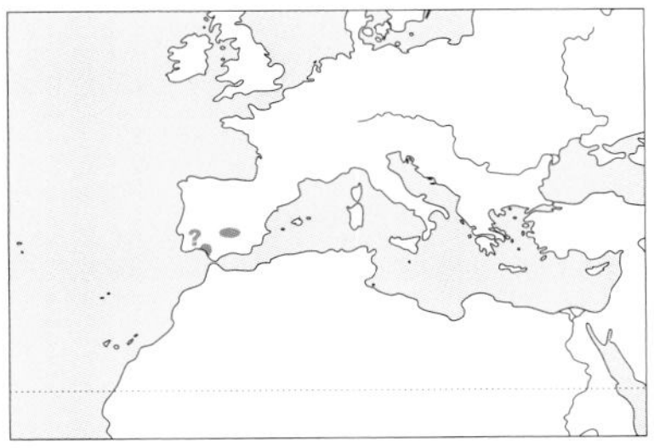

Taxonomy. *Felis pardinus* Temminck, 1827, Portugal.

Formerly considered a subspecies of *L. lynx*, but a recent molecular phylogenetic assessment suggests specific status. Monotypic.

Distribution. SW Spain and Portugal.

Descriptive notes. Head-body 68·2–82 cm, tail 12·5–16 cm; weight 7–14 kg. About half the size of Eurasian Lynx, and are closer in size to the Bobcat and Canadian Lynx. Males are about 25% larger than females. A long-legged cat, with a short tail, short body, and relatively small head. Both sexes have a prominent facial ruff and the ears are tipped with a long tuft of black hair. Easily recognizable as the most heavily spotted member of the genus. The basic coat color is bright yellowish red or tawny with dark spots and white underparts. The coat is sparse, short and coarse.

Habitat. Generally, most abundant in areas of high habitat diversity, particularly in a mosaic of open forest mixed with extensive dense brush or shrub. In Doñana National Park in south-west Spain, consistently prefer Mediterranean scrubland habitat over all other habitat types. They also use ash stands but avoid pine and eucalyptus plantations. Not unexpectedly, the two preferred habitats contained the highest densities of rabbits, the cat's main prey. More than 90% of daytime rest sites are in thick heather scrub. The presence of permanent water sites and relatively low disturbance by humans are also important components of high quality habitat.

Food and Feeding. Feed almost exclusively on European Rabbits (*Oryctolagus cuniculus*); unlike Eurasian Lynx, which is principally a predator of small ungulates. In Doñana National Park, rabbits contribute 75 to 93% of the diet, but in other areas their diet includes a few other taxa. Fawns and juvenile Fallow Deer and Red Deer form a minor part of the diet in fall and winter, and a variety of small murid rodents, snakes, and lizards are also occasionally taken. Also prey on birds, principally ducks and geese, and red-legged partridge (*Alectoris rufa*). In Doñana hunt mainly in the open pastures and scrub forest edge between the scrublands and marshes. Kill rabbits with a bite to the base of the skull. Deer are killed by suffocation, with one or more throat bites. Deer kills are dragged into dense cover where they provide food for a single Lynx for several days. Like many other cats, they attempt to conceal kills by raking leaves, soil, and other debris over what remains of the carcass. In captive feeding trials the maintenance diet for a male is estimated at 912 Kcal/day compared to 673 Kcal/day for a female. Feeding solely on rabbits could satisfy these energy requirements with 379 rabbits/year for males and 277 rabbits/year for a non-reproducing female.

Activity patterns. Radio-telemetry studies show that are primarily nocturnal, but there is a good deal of individual and seasonal variation. Radio-telemetry studies in Doñana found that in summer are primarily nocturnal and activity is high around sunrise and sunset. In winter, were commonly found moving around during the daytime. In general the activity patterns are closely synchronized with its major prey, the rabbit.

Movements, Home range and Social organization. Travel extensively and probably visit most parts of their home range every few days. One adult male traveled an average of 9·3 km per day over four 24-hour periods; the distances traveled varied from 5·9 km to 13·6 km per night. Males traveled an average of 8·7 km per day compared to 6·4 for females. Based on radio-tracking data, the average home range size of resident males was 10·3 km² and for resident females it was 8·7 km². The social organization is similar to that of other felids. There is little range overlap for resident animals of the same sex, but male ranges overlap female ranges. Occupancy of ranges is indicated primarily by scent marking, principally with urine and feces. They leave their feces at non-random locations within their ranges, preferring to deposit their scats at intersections of trails and roads. Apart from females with young and mating pairs, are essentially solitary.

Breeding. There are surprisingly few details available on the mating behavior. Mating is thought to begin in January and February, and following a 63–73 day gestation period, kittens are born in March or April. Litter size varies from 1–4, but the most common number is two. Females with young kittens restrict their movements to a small area around the den site: one female used an area of only 1·7 km² until her kittens were two months old. Young remain in their natal ranges until they disperse at about 20 months of age.

Status and Conservation. Possibly the most endangered of the world's felids. Listed on CITES Appendix I and classified as Critically Endangered on the *The IUCN Red List*. Legally protected throughout its range. Between 1960 and 1978 the habitat shrank by some 80%. Agriculture programs and large scale conversion of native forest to pine and eucalyptus plantations in Spain and Portugal, coupled with myxomatosis epidemics among the rabbit population, reduced the population to an estimated 880–1050 animals in Spain, with perhaps another 50 in Portugal. Since then there has been a further reduction in population size and today an estimated 84–143 adults survive in two or three isolated pockets in south-western Spain. Its survival in Portugal is uncertain at present. There are only two known breeding populations in Spain: in the Coto Doñana (24–33 adults) and Andújar-Cardeña in the eastern Sierra Morena (60–110 adults). These populations are isolated from one another making them even more vulnerable. Estimates of density in Doñana varies from 10–18/100 km². The current population exists in small, isolated, and highly fragmented patches of habitat. Few die of natural causes, some 75% of mortality being due to human related activities, such as shooting, poisoning, or trapping. Many are killed while trying to cross roads. After several years of unsuccessful attempts, new efforts are being made to breed them in captivity for possible reintroduction to the wild.

Bibliography. Aldama & Delibes (1991), Aldama *et al.* (1991), Aymerich (1982b, 1992), Beltrán (1991), Beltrán & Delibes (1993, 1994), Beltrán, Aldama & Delibes (1992), Beltrán, Rice & Honeycutt (1996), Beltrán, San José *et al.* (1985), Delibes (1980), Delibes *et al.* (1975), Ferreras, Aldama *et al.* (1992), Ferreras, Beltrán *et al.* (1997), García-Perea *et al.* (1985), IUCN (2008), Moreno & Villafuerte (1995), Nowell & Jackson (1996), Palomares, Delibes *et al.* (2001), Palomares, Rodríguez *et al.* (1991), Rau *et al.* (1985), Robinson & Delibes (1988), Rodríguez & Delibes (1992), Rogers (1978), Serra & Sarmento (2006), Sunquist & Sunquist (2002), Vargas *et al.* (2005), Werdelin (1981, 1990), Zapata *et al.* (1997).

Plate 8 ➤

PLATE 8

inches 20

cm 50

typical morph

"rex" morph

ssp *jubatus*

25

cub

ssp *soemmeringii*

ssp *venaticus*

iron gray morph

26

red-brown morph

ssp *coryi*
spotted morph

27

ssp *concolor*

ssp *missoulensis*

cub

Genus *ACINONYX*

Brookes, 1828

25. Cheetah *Acinonyx jubatus*

French: Guépard / **German**: Gepard / **Spanish**: Guepardo

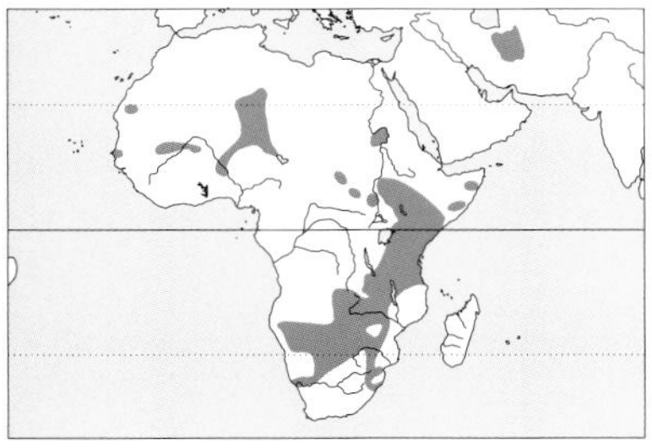

Taxonomy. *Felis jubata* Schreber, 1775, Western Cape Province, South Africa.

A single-locus genetic mutation produces the blotched tabby pattern of the so-called King Cheetah, once classified as a separate species, *A. rex*, its distribution restricted to the more densely vegetated areas of southern Africa, centered on Zimbabwe, with an isolated record from West Africa. Described race *raddei* merged with *venaticus*. Races *ngorongoroensis*, *obergi*, *raineyi*, and *velox* included in *fearonii*. Five subspecies recognized.

Subspecies and Distribution.

A. j. jubatus Schreber, 1775 – S Africa.

A. j. fearonii A. Smith, 1834 – E Africa.

A. j. hecki Hilzheimer, 1913 – NW Africa.

A. j. soemmeringii Fitzinger, 1855 – Somalia to Lake Tchad.

A. j. venaticus Griffith, 1821 – Iran.

Descriptive notes. Head-body 121–145 cm, tail length 63–76 cm. Mean weight 54 kg (39–59 kg) for males and 43 kg (36–48 kg) for females in Namibia. Shoulder height 79–94 cm. Males average larger than females. Cheetahs of the Sahara are smaller: two adult males had a shoulder height of only 65 cm. Tail about half the head-body length, height at the shoulder accentuated by an erectile crest of hair. Profile of back slightly concave; the hindquarters are lower than the shoulders. Eyes edged with white underneath, iris orange-yellow, pupils round. Ears small and widely set, with black and white markings behind. Head and face are rounded, with characteristic "tear lines", heavy black lines that extend from the inner corner of each eye to the outer corner of the mouth. Coat of adults is slightly harsh with short hair. Color pale fawn to yellow, darker along the mid-back, covered all over with evenly spaced, small round black spots. Chin, throat and posterior parts of the belly are white. Distal part of the tail is spotted; the spots tend to coalesce into two to three black tail rings; tail tip is white. Front limbs spotted inside and outside, the hindfeet from the ankles to the toes devoid of spots. Top of the head and cheeks finely spotted; pattern of spots individually unique. Both melanistic and albino Cheetah specimens recorded. Remarkably pale animals with short hair, ocher spots, and muted "tear lines" and tail rings are reported from the Sahara. The "*rex*" form has longer, silkier hair with the erectile crest of neck and shoulders up to 7 cm long. Very young Cheetah have extraordinary coloring for camouflage, a mantle of smoky white long hair above, near black below. Their underparts lighten and spots emerge before two months of age, but the pale mantle disappears more slowly and traces of it are still present in animals one year old. The Cheetah is built for speed, with a deep chest, wasp-like waist, and proportionately longer limbs than cats of comparable size. Flexion of elongated spine increases stride length. Canines are small relative to other felids. The reduced roots of the upper canines allow for a larger nasal aperture for increased air intake, critical for allowing the Cheetah to recover from its sprint by "panting" while suffocating its prey for up to 20 minutes. The diastema behind the canines is very small or missing, unique in cats. Adult Cheetah have blunt claws that although retractable, remain exposed, lacking the skin sheaths found in most other felids, providing additional traction like a sprinter's spikes. Claw marks visible in the spoor. Prominent sharp dew claws, set well up on the front foot, used as hooks to trip up fast-running prey. The digital and metacarpal pads are extremely hard and pointed at the front, an adaptation to sudden braking. Palmar pads with a pair of prominent longitudinal ridges serve as anti-skid devices. Long laterally- flattened tail provides balance as Cheetah swerves during the chase. Enlarged bronchi, lungs, liver, heart, and adrenals. The top of the skull is raised as are the large eyes.

Habitat. Distributed primarily throughout the drier parts of sub-Saharan Africa, avoiding forest and only thinly distributed in more humid woodland. Most frequently observed on open grassy plains, but may prefer a mosaic of woodland and grassland using bush, scrub, and open woodlands. May expend less energy for hunting with more cover present. Range up to 1500 m in Ethiopia and 2000 m in the mountains of southeast Algeria. Well adapted to arid conditions, surviving in small populations around central Saharan mountain ranges.

Food and Feeding. Specialized on gazelles and small to medium-sized antelopes as prey. Major prey is Thomson's and Grant's Gazelle, Gerenuk (*Litocranius walleri*), Impala, Lesser Kudu (*Tragelaphus imberbis*), and dik-dik (*Madoqua*) in East Africa; Springbok, Impala, calves of Greater Kudu, Giraffe and even African Buffalo, Southern Reedbuck, Puku (*Kobus vardonii*), and Common Warthog in southern Africa; Hartebeest, Oribi (*Ourebia ourebi*), and Kob in Central Africa. Saharan Cheetahs occasionally take Barbary Sheep and ostrich. In the absence of ungulate prey, Cheetahs may entirely subsist on smaller prey like guineafowl and other ground-living birds and hares, the latter especially in Iran, but male coalitions also bring down large prey like Blue Wildebeest. In all studies, young prey animals are taken in preference to adults. One case of male cannibalism reported. Cheetahs often lose their kills to Lions, Leopards and hyenas. They rarely scavenge or return to a previously abandoned kill; however, may remain near large kills in the absence of more powerful predators on ranchland. The Cheetah starts eating at the hindquarters first. An individual can consume 14 kg at one sitting and a group of four finished an impala carcass in just 15 minutes. This fast swallowing helps to counter loss to competitors. Average meat consumption is 2–4 kg/day. Cheetahs hunt by sight. Prey is often detected from a vantage point. They prefer to stalk toward vigilant adult prey, walking semi-crouched, freezing in mid-stride or crouching if the quarry looks up, to within less than 50 m, before racing out at about 60 km/h. They also wait crouched if they see an unsuspecting prey moving toward them, or walk slowly toward a herd of gazelles in full view, then break into a sprint from 60–70 m away if the herd has not run off. Some rushes are started from as far as 600 m away if prey is grazing or is oblivious to Cheetah's presence, particularly toward a standing or nursing neonate gazelle. Sprints rarely last longer than 200–300 m, maximum of 600 m. Top speed has been recorded at 102 km/h, strides are up to 9 m, and all four feet are airborne at least twice in each stride. The respiratory rate climbs from 60 to 150 breaths per minute in a high-speed chase. When drawing level with its prey, a Cheetahs knocks an antelope off balance by slapping it with a front paw on the shoulder, rump, or thigh. The dew claws help to secure the prey. The Cheetah then reaches for the throat and clamps the muzzle or windpipe shut with its jaws. Larger prey is suffocated within 2–10 minutes, then the kill is dragged into the nearest shade or cover. Hares are killed with a bite through the head. Hunting success was slightly over 50% on adult gazelles and was 100% on small fawns in the Serengeti. Single Cheetahs killed prey every 25–60 hours in Nairobi National Park. In Kalahari Desert they travel an average of 82 km between drinks of water, mainly satisfying their moisture requirements by drinking blood or urine of their prey or eating tsamma melons.

Activity patterns. Predominantly diurnal, when competing predators like Lions and Spotted Hyenas are less active. Cheetahs spend most of the day resting, with hunting peaks between 07:00 and 10:00 h and between 16:00 and 19:00 h. Cheetahs of the Saharan mountains, in the absence of larger predators, often hunt at night when temperatures are cooler. Territories and preferred routes are marked with sprays of urine, feces, and occasionally by claw raking. Markings are frequently made near regularly used observation points like termitaries, rocks, or leaning trees, so-called "play trees", or at path junctions. Cheetahs purr when greeting known individuals; the striking contact call is an explosive yelp that can carry for 2 km. Juveniles make a "whirr", or fast growl, which may rise to a squeal or subside to a rasp during fights over a kill. Bird-like chirps, hums, purrs, and yelps are unique to this species, which can be very vocal in its rare social encounters.

Movements, Home range and Social organization. A greater degree of sociality has been observed among Cheetahs than for most felids, with the exception of the Lion. Male and female littermates tend to stay together for about six months after independence, when female young split off upon reaching sexual maturity. Male littermates remain together in coalitions and sometimes defend territories. Male coalitions in the Serengeti, in particular trios, may include unrelated males. Males in coalitions are more likely than solitary males to gain and maintain territories; they are in better condition and have better access to females during periods of gazelle concentration. Non-territorial males, representing 40% of the Serengeti male population, live a nomadic existence and wander widely. Groups of up to 14–19 animals occasionally reported where other large predators have been eradicated. On some occasions groups of adults with cubs have been reported. Groups of mixed sex have been seen hunting together, probably reflecting mating activity and a large litter just before independence. Solitary Serengeti males and female adults are semi-nomadic, with large, overlapping home ranges 800–1500 km²; male coalitions defend territories of 12–36 km², but up to 150 km². Mortality of adult male Cheetah is as high as 50% as a result of competition for territories. Territories are centered around areas with periodically high Thomson's Gazelle numbers, attracting females to their favorite prey. In Kruger National Park, South Africa, where prey species are non-migratory, both males and females occupy small home ranges of similar size, on average 175 km².

Breeding. Largely aseasonal with birth peaks during the rainy season (November–May) in Serengeti. Cheetahs have a long, drawn out, and complex courtship. Females are polyestrous, cycling approximately every twelve days (range 3–27). Length of estrus varies from 1–3 days, being shorter when mating occurs; there are some reports of females being receptive for 10–14 days. Cheetahs are induced ovulators. Mating lasts a minute or more and can be followed by gaps of eight hours before the next episode. Gestation lasts 92 days (range 90–98). Litter size averages four (range 1–8), larger than in most other felids, with larger litters in Namibian rangeland in absence of larger predators. Interbirth interval 15–19 months, but females readily go into estrus and conceive after losing a litter. Large litter size may be a strategy to offset high juvenile mortality caused by predators. Birth weight is 250–300 g. Sex ratio is 1 male: 0·95 female. The blind, helpless cubs are born in a lair of long grass, thickets, or in a temporary "borrowed" burrow and remain hidden for approximately eight weeks. They open their eyes at 4–14 days and are frequently carried to a fresh hiding place by the mother. At 3–6 weeks a set of milk teeth erupts, replaced by adult teeth at about eight months. Cheetah cubs can retract their claws for up to ten weeks of age, and they are able tree climbers. Nursing terminates at about four months. The cubs accompany their mothers on hunts from eight weeks onward and are introduced to solid food. They are very

On following pages: 26. Jaguarundi (*Puma yagouaroundi*); 27. Puma (*Puma concolor*).

playful during the first six months, starting to practice hunting afterwards, but are still not adept when leaving their mothers. Mothers sometimes bring back live prey for the cubs to practice their skills. Cub mortality up to the age of three months is very high. Cubs are killed by other large carnivores and even baboons (*Papio* sp.). In Nairobi National Park, cub mortality is as low as 43%. In the Serengeti, with high Lion density, 95% of 125 cubs failed to survive to independence; 73% of the cub deaths were due to predation. Cubs become independent at 18 months (range 13–20 months), while females leave their sibling groups with 17–27 months. Sex ratio of subadults and adults changes to 1 male: 1·9 females, suggesting differential male dispersal and mortality. Wild female Cheetah reproduce at 2–3 years for the first time, and males reproduce at 2·5–3 years. In captivity males are normally fertile at 1–2 years, females at 2–3 years. Females remain fertile up to ten years, males up to 14 years. Longevity in the wild is up to 14 years; however, the female average in the Serengeti is seven years. Territorial males may live longer than single males. Captive Cheetahs live on average 10·5 and up to 21 years. Difficult to breed in captivity, with females conceiving infrequently, but social setting may not be adequate. High levels of sperm abnormalities (71–76%) in both wild and captive Cheetahs, but no evidence that reproduction is compromised in the wild. Cheetahs were kept by nobility and trained to hunt dating back 5000 years to the Sumerians. 3000 Cheetahs were kept during the lifetime of one Moghul emperor. By the early 1900s Indian Cheetahs were so scarce that African animals were imported to sustain the stables, as there was no success breeding them.

Status and Conservation. CITES Appendix I, quota system for live animals and trophies in some southern African countries. Classified as Vulnerable on *The IUCN Red List*, with subspecies *venaticus* and *hecki* classified as Critically Endangered. Population estimate for sub-Saharan Africa was 15,000 in the 1970s, 9000–12,000 in the 1990s. Two largest meta-populations occur in East Africa (Kenya, Tanzania, Ethiopia) and southern Africa (Namibia, Botswana, Zimbabwe, Zambia). Cheetahs are very rare in Sahel and semi-arid zone of West Africa, much of it having been degraded by humans through hunting of prey animals and livestock overgrazing. Extinct from 20 countries. Possibly present in low numbers in isolated Qattara Depression in N Egypt. Subspecies *venaticus* has largely been exterminated from Near East and Asia, with possibly fewer than 50 individuals surviving in north-central Iran. About 95% of present Namibian population of 2000–3000 occurs on privately owned land; number of Cheetah believed to have declined by half in Namibia since 1980. Cheetah densities may range from a high density of one adult per 6 km^2 following concentrations of migratory gazelle, to low density areas of one adult per 191 km^2. Cheetahs exist in higher densities in pastoral areas outside of protected areas than inside them. On Namibian ranchland, the species' stronghold, average is one adult per 50 km^2. Genetic research demonstrated a very high level of homogeneity in coding DNA, suggesting a series of population bottlenecks in its history, the first and most significant occurring 10,000 years ago. Lack of genetic diversity may render the Cheetah exceptionally vulnerable to changing environmental conditions and disease. In captivity, epidemics of infectious disease have occurred, with high mortality. No epidemics reported from the wild, although high incidence of mange in some parks. Strategy of relying solely upon the limited system of protected areas within the Cheetah's range may not be sufficient to ensure conservation, due to the impact of other predators, which kill offspring and drive Cheetahs off their kills. Outside protected areas in Namibia, there are conflicts with people over predation on livestock: annual losses of 10–15% for sheep and goats and 3–5% for cattle calves are reported. Stock losses are especially severe where natural prey base has been eliminated or reduced. Cheetahs are not especially susceptible to taking poisoned bait, but their numbers in Namibia have been reduced through shooting and trapping at "play trees". Permitting trophy hunting in southern Africa has the goal of encouraging landowners to accept and profit from Cheetahs on their lands. Non-governmental organizations (NGOs) work to educate farmers about appropriate management steps to minimize stock losses, such as using fencing, guard dogs, and donkeys, to aid in the conservation of the wild prey base and to protect its habitat.

Bibliography. Bertram (1979), Bosman & Hall-Martin (1997), Bothma (1998), Bottriel (1987), Broomhall *et al.* (2003), Caro (1982, 1994), Caro & Collins (1986, 1987a, 1987b), Caro & Laurenson (1994), Caro, Fitzgibbon & Holt (1989), Caro, Holt *et al.* (1987), Divyabhanusinh (1995), Dragesco-Joffé (1993), Durant (1998), Eaton (1970a, 1970b, 1974), Ewer (1973), Fitzgibbon & Fanshawe (1989), Floria & Spinelli (1967), Frame (1975-1976, 1980, 1992), Frame & Frame (1981), Gros (1990, 2002), Hills & Smithers (1980), Hunter & Skinner (1995), Kingdon (1971-1982), Kruuk & Turner (1967), Labuschagne (1979, 1981), Laurenson (1995), Laurenson *et al.* (1992), Lindburg (1989), Marker-Kraus (1992), Marker-Kraus & Grisham (1993), Marker-Kraus & Kraus (1991), McKeown (1992), Mills (1990), Mills & Biggs (1993), Mitchell *et al.* (1965), Morsbach (1987), Nowell & Jackson (1996), O'Brien (1994), O'Brien *et al.* (1983), Philips (1993), Pienaar (1969), Pocock (1916e, 1927), Ruggiero (1991), Schaller (1968, 1972), Sharp (1997), Skinner & Smithers (1990), Smithers (1971), Stander (1990), Stuart & Stuart (1996), Sunquist & Sunquist (2002), Van Aarde & Van Dyk (1986), Van Dyk (1991), Van Valkenburgh (1996), Wildt *et al.* (1987), Yalden *et al.* (1980).

Genus *PUMA*

Jardine, 1834

26. Jaguarundi *Puma yagouaroundi*

French: Jaguarondi / **German**: Jaguarundi / **Spanish**: Yaguarundi

Taxonomy. *Felis yagouaroundi* Geoffroy Saint-Hilaire, 1803, Cayenne, French Guiana. Genus sometimes merged into *Herpailurus*. Mitochondrial DNA sequences show present species and *P. concolor* in a monophyletic group with an ancestral association with *Acinonyx jubatus*. Eight subspecies recognized.

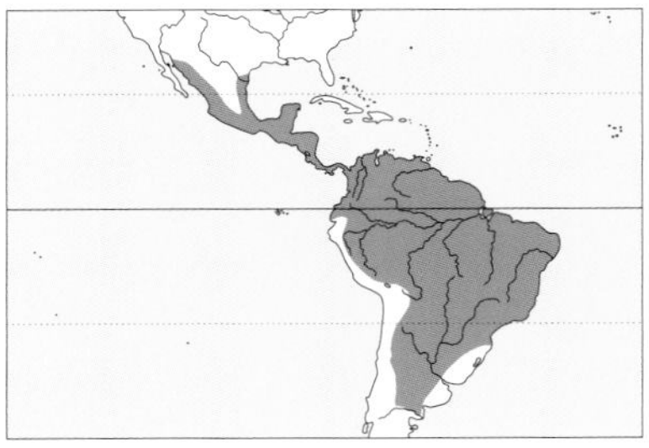

Subspecies and Distribution.

P. y. yagouaroundi Geoffroy Saint-Hilaire, 1803 – the Guianas highlands S to Amazon Basin of Brazil.

P. y. ameghinoi Holmberg, 1898 – W Argentina (from Jujuy S to N Patagonia).

P. y. cacomitli Berlandier, 1859 – NE Mexico, possibly extinct in S USA (Texas).

P. y. eyra Fischer, 1814 – S Brazil through Paraguay to N Argentina.

P. y. fossata Mearns, 1901 – S Mexico to Honduras.

P. y. melantho Thomas, 1914 – Andean valleys of Peru and W Brazil (upper Amazonia).

P. y. panamensis J. A. Allen, 1904 – Nicaragua, Costa Rica, Panama, W Colombia to Ecuador.

P. y. tolteca Thomas, 1898 – NW Mexico (Sinaloa), extinct in SW USA (Arizona).

Descriptive notes. Head-body 48·8–83·2 cm, tail 27·5–59 cm; weight 3–7·6 kg. Adult males are larger and heavier than adult females. Except for a few faint markings on the face and belly, the Jaguarundi's fur is uniform in color. There are two main color phases: iron gray and red-brown. Kittens of both color phases can be born in the same litter. Jaguarundi can be distinguished from other small and medium-sized Neotropical felids by its unspotted pelage, short legs, elongate body, and relatively long tail. The small, slim head has short rounded ears and the backs of the ears lack the characteristic white spot found in many other felids. The Jaguarundi has an almost weasel or mustelid-like appearance and is occasionally mistaken for the Tayra.

Habitat. Found in a wide variety of habitats, including semi-arid thorn forest, pastures, brushland, scrub, chaparrel, swampy grasslands, tropical thorn forest, tropical deciduous forest, semi-deciduous forest, and humid premontane forest. They are most often seen in areas of dense cover mixed with openings and edges. In Belize, radio-collared Jaguarundi were most frequently associated with riparian and old field habitats. In Paraguay, it is found in thickets, along forest edges, and in hedge-like strips of scrub intermingled with spiny bromeliads. Radio-tagged Jaguarundi in Mexico spent 53% of their time in forested habitats and 47% in grasslands.

Food and Feeding. Dietary information is largely anectodal. Jaguarundi are thought to feed primarily on animals weighing less than one kg, but they occasionally take larger prey. In Belize, an examination of 46 Jaguarundi scats revealed that small mammals, principally rats and mice (Muridae, Heteromyidae), were the dominant prey. Birds ranked second in frequency of occurrence, followed by opossums and fruit. Arthropod remains were found in 72% of scats. In Venezuela, cotton rats, rice rats, cane mice, and rabbits occurred in about half the stomachs of 23 road-killed Jaguarundi; reptiles (Teiidae, Iguanidae) and birds occurred in about half the stomachs. The stomachs of two Jaguarundi in Brazil contained the remains of a cavy, a teiid lizard, and several birds (Tinamidae, Columbidae). Jaguarundi has also been observed feeding on characid fish that were trapped in small pools. Most prey is taken on the ground, and many of the birds identified in scats are species that spend considerable time foraging on the ground.

Activity patterns. Based on radio-tracking data from Belize and Mexico, Jaguarundi is mainly diurnal. In Belize, Jaguarundi began moving just before dawn and remained active throughout the day until sunset. In Mexico, 85% of the cat's activity occurred during the daytime and 15% occurred at night.

Movements, Home range and Social organization. In Belize radio-collared cats traveled about 6·6 km per day and there was little backtracking or criss-crossing during these daytime movements. Home ranges of females vary from 8·3 km^2 in Mexico to 20 km^2 in Belize. The home ranges of two males in Belize were much larger (88 and 99 km^2) than the female's range, but male ranges in Mexico were roughly the same size (8·9 km^2) as female ranges. Most observations of Jaguarundi in the wild are of solitary individuals; however, in captivity family members are quite gregarious.

Breeding. Most of the information on breeding is from captive animals. Estrus is short, about 3–5 days, and the estrous cycle lasts for about 53 days. Females in estrus vocalize while urine-marking about their enclosures. After a gestation period of 70–75 days the female gives birth to 1–4 kittens. Average litter size for twelve litters was 1·83. In the wild, birth dens have been located in thickets, hollow trees, and thick clumps of grass. Kittens have plain coats and spotted bellies. In captivity, young reach sexual maturity from 1·4 years to 2·2 years.

Status and Conservation. Central and North American subspecies are listed on CITES Appendix I. Considered relatively common in South America, listed on CITES Appendix II. Classified as Least Concern on *The IUCN Red List*. Jaguarundi is not subject to the same levels of hunting pressure as the small spotted cats. The species is not tied to primary forest and can live in human-modified habitats. As long as it is not persecuted, this cat will likely survive alongside humans.

Bibliography. Armstrong *et al.* (1972), Bisbal (1986), Davis & Schmidly (1994), Hall & Dalquest (1963), Hulley (1976), Johnson & O'Brien (1997), Konecny (1989), Leopold (1959), Manzani & Monteiro (1989), McCarthy (1992), Mellen (1993), Mondolfi (1986), Nowell & Jackson (1996), Sunquist & Sunquist (2002), Tewes & Schmidly (1987), Ximénez (1982).

27. Puma *Puma concolor*

French: Couguar / **German**: Puma / **Spanish**: Puma

Other common names: Cougar, Mountain Lion, Catamount, Panther; Florida Panther (*coryi*)

Taxonomy. *Felis concolor* Linnaeus, 1771, Cayenne region, French Guiana.

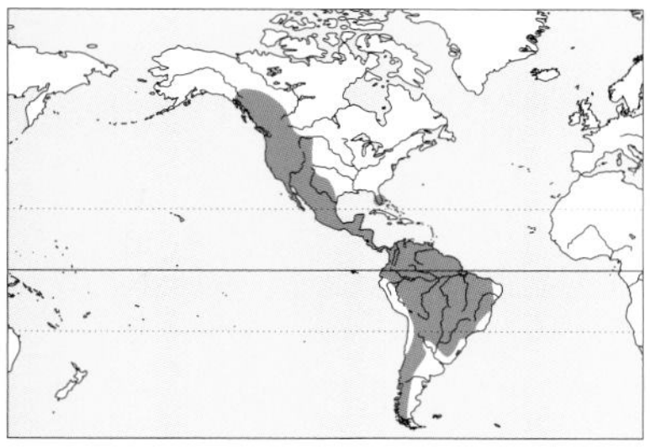

In the Western Hemisphere the Puma ranges from Patagonia to northern British Columbia, a span of about 100 degrees of latitude. Recent analyses based upon mitochondrial gene sequences suggest the North American Puma derived from a small number of founders about 10,000 years ago and that sufficient genomic differentiation exists to support the recognition of two subspecies in the Western Hemisphere. Regardless, a taxonomic revision is needed for this species and its many recognized races. Earlier taxonomic work based upon phenotypic characters formed the basis for the recognition and classification of at least thirty subspecies.

Subspecies and Distribution.

P. c. concolor Linnaeus, 1771 – E Venezuela through the Guianas to lower Amazonian Brazil.
P. c. acrocodia Goldman, 1943 – C Brazil (Matto Grosso), SE Bolivia, and the Chaco of Paraguay and Argentina.
P. c. anthonyi Nelson & Goldman, 1931 – S Venezuela and adjacent N Brazil.
P. c. araucanus Osgood, 1943 – S Chile and S Argentina.
P. c. azteca Merriam, 1901 – SW USA (Arizona and New Mexico); NW Mexico.
P. c. bangsi Merriam, 1901 – Andean Colombia.
P. c. borbensis Nelson & Goldman, 1933 – Amazonian Brazil, Colombia, Ecuador, and Peru.
P. c. browni Merriam, 1903 – NW Mexico (N Baja California).
P. c. cabrerae Pocock, 1940 – NW Argentina.
P. c. californica May, 1896 – SW USA (California).
P. c. capricornensis Goldman, 1946 – SE Brazil and NE Argentina.
P. c. coryi Bangs, 1899 – SE USA (Florida).
P. c. costaricensis Merriam, 1901 – Nicaragua through Panama.
P. c. cougar Kerr, 1792 – NE USA.
P. c. greeni Nelson & Goldman, 1931 – E Brazil.
P. c. hippolestes Merriam, 1897 – C USA.
P. c. improcera Phillips, 1912 – NW Mexico (S Baja California).
P. c. incarum Nelson & Goldman, 1929 – Andean Peru.
P. c. kaibabensis Nelson & Goldman, 1931 – W USA (Nevada & Utah).
P. c. mayensis Nelson & Goldman, 1929 – S Mexico through El Salvador.
P. c. missoulensis Goldman, 1943 – NW Canada through NW USA (Idaho & Montana).
P. c. oregonensis Rafinesque, 1832 – NW USA (Oregon and Washington).
P. c. osgoodi Nelson & Goldman, 1929 – C Bolivia.
P. c. patagonica Merriam, 1901 – S Argentina (E side of Lago Pueyrredón).
P. c. pearsoni Thomas, 1901 – Patagonian Argentina and Chile.
P. c. puma Molina, 1782 – C Chile and adjacent Argentina.
P. c. schorgeri Jackson, 1955 – Midwestern USA
P. c. soderstromi Lönnberg, 1913 – Andean Ecuador.
P. c. stanleyana Goldman, 1936 – S USA (Texas) and adjacent Mexico.
P. c. vancouverensis Nelson & Goldman, 1932 – SW Canada (Vancouver I).

Descriptive notes. Head-body 86–155 cm, tail 60–97 cm. Average weight ranges from 53–72 kg for adult males, and 34–48 kg for adult females. An exceptionally large male weighed 120 kg. Mass at birth is about 0·6 kg. Growth rates are similar for both males and females. Puma are large, slender cats, tawny above and whitish below. Melanism has been reported rarely in South America, but not in North America. Kittens are buff-colored, with rows of irregularly-shaped black spots until 9–12 months old. The tail of the adult is a long and sweeping "J" that is tipped in dark brown to black hair. Puma have proportionally the longest rear legs in the Felidae. Hair length, color, and texture vary geographically throughout the species' range in the Western Hemisphere. Individuals from colder, higher altitudes tend to have thicker and longer hair than those from more tropical climates. Dentition follows the typical felid pattern of prominent canines, modest incisors, and sharp carnassial cheek teeth for shearing tendons and bones. Puma exhibit a range of vocalizations, which are infrequently heard but may be associated with mating behavior. These include bird-like chirps that appear to be used by females to communicate with kittens, and the more stereotypical scream, which is likely related to mating behavior. Unlike the great cats, the Puma is unable to roar, a product of reduced larynx and hyoid apparatus. The prevalence of a crooked tail, atrial septal defects, a dorsal whorl of hair, and other anomalies in the Florida subspecies (*coryi*) is likely a product of reduced population size and several generations of inbreeding. Interestingly, all of these anomalies were absent from young born of matings between Texas female Pumas and Florida Panther males. Seven Texas female Pumas were inserted into the Florida Panther population as part of a genetic augmentation effort in 1995; five of these females were known to have reared at least two litters each.

Habitat. The Puma is usually associated with remote, rugged terrain where there is cover for stalking and ambush-hunting, secure places to establish natal dens, and at least one species of abundant deer-sized prey. It has been suggested that viable populations of Puma are impossible without at least one species of deer-sized prey. Its extensive distribution throughout the Western Hemisphere, from sea level to more than 4000 m elevation, suggests a tolerance of environmental conditions that is rare among mammals. Habitat use can be highly seasonal where prey species such as Elk migrate altitudinally in response to snowfall, or can be annually static, for example, in subtropical southern Florida, where prey species have stable annual home ranges. Specific habitat preferences are as variable as the regions in which the Puma lives, and range from mixed conifer and curlleaf mountain mahogany vegetation in rugged topography in Wyoming to subtropical hardwood hammocks, pine flatwoods, and palm forests in southern Florida. Female Puma locate secretive natal dens in boulder piles, dense vegetation, or other natural structures that provide some protection from the elements and reduce detection by potential predators. In Florida these sites tended to be at least one km from a paved road, and were usually located within dense thickets of saw palmetto (*Serenoa repens*), which provided vertical cover, horizontal cover, and reduced temperatures compared to outside air. Where the species is dependent upon forest, occupied areas tend to be at least 20,000 ha without major roads. The species increasingly is found in landscape patches that have been fragmented by expanding human activity and infrastructure such as highways, ranches, produce farms, human settlements, and extractive industries. In these areas, remnant landscape connections and restored habitat corridors can be important demographic linkages. In Florida and California dispersing individuals are tolerant of habitat that may include canals, highways, relatively open terrain, and other features that are usually recognized as barriers by resident adults.

Food and Feeding. The Puma's extensive distribution is reflected in a diverse list of prey. In general, Puma from temperate climates eat larger prey than Puma from tropical climates, and solitary adults tend to eat larger prey than females with kittens. The smaller prey size of Puma in the tropics may be the result of niche separation with the larger, socially dominant Jaguar. Puma are ambush hunters; they utilize cover to closely approach potential prey before an attack is made. Common prey in North America include Elk, White-tailed Deer, Mule Deer, Wild Boar, Collared Peccary, porcupines, rabbits, and hares. In South America common prey include vizcacha, Guanaco (*Lama guanicoe*), brocket deer, Pampas Deer (*Ozotoceros bezoarticus*), pudu (*Pudu*), agouti, armadillo, and porcupine. Domestic stock is occasionally taken throughout the species' range, and exotic species such as Wild Boar and European Hare can be important dietary components even where larger prey are available. In marginal habitat such as in the Everglades of southern Florida, atypical prey such as alligator (*Alligator mississipiensis*) and North American River Otter may be taken. This is the result of inherently low populations of White-tailed Deer in the Everglades region. Puma routinely remove the entrails of large prey before caching and burying their kills with leaves and other debris for future use. The use of such kills may last from one to 27 days. Humans can alter the abundance and spatial use patterns of Puma and their prey through hunting and other activities. Historically, Puma predation on humans has been rare, although in recent years there has been an apparent increase in encounters, especially involving juvenile or underweight cats. Many of these attacks have occurred in the urban-wilderness interface where the likelihood of an encounter increases with presence of humans in occupied peripheral Puma habitat.

Activity patterns. Puma are primarily crepuscular and nocturnal and do the bulk of traveling and hunting at night. This pattern appears related to the activity of their prey and the concealment offered by darkness. In Florida, activity peaks occurred from 01:00–07:00 h and 18:00–22:00 h. Females with kittens tended to leave their natal dens to hunt at 22:00 h and return to them at 08:00 h. Activity patterns of females at natal dens were similar to those of solitary adults, but exhibited less difference between activity peaks and nadirs.

Movements, Home range and Social organization. Puma exist in a system of dynamic land tenure: resident adults have prior rights to home ranges, and residency is dependent upon the death or departure of other residents. Annual home range size varies from 50 to more than 1000 km^2 and appears to be related to primary productivity and prey abundance. Movement distances greater than 20 km in a 24-hour period have been recorded. Male home ranges are generally more than twice as large as female home ranges, and tend to incorporate as many females as possible within a territory boundary that is not continually defended. Males tend to use their larger home ranges evenly across seasons, whereas female movements are related to reproductive condition and the presence of kittens. Females restrict their movements to the immediate vicinity of natal dens for about two months, after which time kittens join their mothers at kills. Aggressive encounters between males appear to be contests for breeding rights and often result in the death or injury of at least one of the combatants. The basic social unit of this solitary species is the female-kitten group, which lasts for 10–24 months. Independence of offspring may be related to onset of estrus in the female and subsequent sexual encounters with adult males. In Florida, independence of juveniles was preceded by encounters between the mother and an adult male in 63% of 27 documented instances. Females are philopatric and tend to establish home ranges adjacent to those of their mothers. In Florida, dispersal distances ranged from six to 32 km in females and from 24 to 224 km in males. In Wyoming, a male dispersed 274 km. Females are capable of long-distance dispersal, but seldom do so. Translocated individuals have been known to return to capture locations from more than 470 km away.

Breeding. Puma reproduction can occur year-round, varies regionally, and, if seasonal, appears to be linked to the reproductive patterns of primary prey. For example, in Florida, reproduction has occurred in every month, but most litters are born in the spring, after the pulse of White-tailed Deer fawn production. Gestation varies from 92–96 days, following a bout of copulations that may last several days. Adult males may be aspermatic for portions of the year. In Florida, despite poor sperm quality, reduced genetic variability seems insufficient to limit population growth. Litter size averages two and ranges from one to four. Earliest documentation of first reproduction in the species is 18 months for females. Males generally begin breeding after three years, although sexual maturity is likely attained at or before two years.

Status and Conservation. The Puma is listed on Appendix II of CITES with the subspecies *coryi*, *costaricensis*, and *cougar* listed on Appendix I. Classified as Least Concern on *The IUCN Red List*. In North America Puma inhabit less than 50% of their original range, primarily due to the loss of habitat and intensive human activities. A similar pattern likely pertains in Central and South America where deforestation is occurring at a rapid pace. In North America legal status varies: the Puma is an unregulated predator in Texas; a hunted species with distinct seasons in Nevada, Montana, and Alberta, Canada; a non-hunted species in California and Manitoba, Canada. The Puma is fully protected in Florida. Races *cougar* and *schorgeri* are probably extinct whereas *coryi*, *costaricensis*, and *brownii* are listed as threatened or endangered by the US Fish and Wildlife Service. In South America Puma hunting is prohibited in Argentina, Brazil, Bolivia, Chile, Colombia, Costa Rica, French Guiana, Guatemala, Honduras, Nicaragua, Panama, Paraguay, Surinam, Venezuela, and Uruguay; it is unprotected in Ecuador, El Salvador, and Guyana. The Puma can be hunted in Mexico and Peru. Small population size has resulted in reduced genetic variability and maladaptive physiological traits such as atrial septal defects in *coryi*. However, there is no evidence that such phenotypic characters have negatively affected demographics in the population. Efforts to save the Florida Puma include experimental translocations and genetic introgression via the transport of female Puma from Texas. The Puma, like other large carnivores, is an effective conservation flagship because it requires large areas, exhibits top-down regulation, and can be popular with the public. A landscape approach to the conservation of this species will be important in maintaining both large and small populations because the species occurs at inherently low densities. Successful management and recovery strategies for Puma will require local and regional planning to balance expanding human populations and infrastructure development with habitat restoration. Land management policies that enhance prey populations and offer the Puma interconnected reserve systems are needed. Efforts to create blueprints for such large-scale conservation include Paseo Pantera (Wildlife Conservation Society) in Central and South America and the Florida Ecological Network.

Bibliography. Ackerman *et al.* (1986), Anderson (1983), Ashman *et al.* (1983), Azevedo (2008), Banfield (1974), Barone *et al.* (1994), Beier (1993, 1995), Belden & Hagedorn (1993), Creel (2006), Culver, Hedrick *et al.* (2008), Culver, Johnson *et al.* (2000), Cunningham *et al.* (1999), Dalrymple & Bass (1996), Etling (2001), Fuller, K.S. *et al.* (1987), Gay & Best (1995), Gonyea (1976), Hoctor *et al.* (2000), Holt (1994), Iriarte *et al.* (1990), Kelly *et al.* (2008), Kilgo *et al.* (1998), Kurtén (1973), Laing & Lindzey (1993), Logan & Irwin (1985), Logan & Sweanor (2001), Logan *et al.* (1986), Maehr (1990, 1997), Maehr & Caddick (1995), Maehr & Cox (1995), Maehr & Moore (1992), Maehr, Belden *et al.* (1990), Maehr, Land & Roof (1991), Maehr, Land, Roof & McCown (1989), Maehr, Land, Shindle *et al.* (2002), Maehr, Roof *et al.* (1989), McIvor *et al.* (1995), Murphy *et al.* (1999), Pierce *et al.* (2000), Pimm *et al.* (2006), Rabb (1959), Romo (1995), Rosas-Rosas *et al.* (2003), Ruth *et al.* (1998), Scognamillo *et al.* (2003), Seidensticker *et al.* (1973), Sunquist & Sunquist (2002), Thompson & Stewart (1994), Toweill *et al.* (1988), Van Dyke *et al.* (1986), Wilson, D.E. & Reeder (2005), Wilson, P. (1984), Yáñez *et al.* (1986), Young & Goldman (1946).

Plate 9 ➤

ssp *manul*

28

29

ssp *ferrugineus*

30

PLATE 9

inches 10
cm 25

31

ssp *bengalensis*

32

ssp *borneoensis*

ssp *euptilurus*

ssp *iriomotensis*

Genus *OTOCOLOBUS*
Brandt, 1842

28. Pallas's Cat *Otocolobus manul*
French: Manul / **German**: Manul / **Spanish**: Manul
Other common names: Manul, Steppe Cat

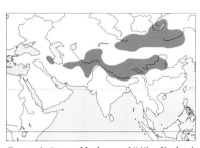

Taxonomy. *Felis manul* Pallas, 1776, S of Lake Baikal, Russia.
Three subspecies recognized.
Subspecies and Distribution.
O. m. manul Pallas, 1776 – Lake Baikal region S through Mongolia to N & NW China.
O. m. ferrugineus Ognev, 1928 – Kazakhstan S to Iran and Pakistan, including lowlands S of the Caucasus and W of the Caspian Sea to Armenia.
O. m. nigripectus Hodgson, 1842 – Kashmir to Nepal, the Tibetan highlands, and E to C & SW China.
Descriptive notes. Head-body 46–65 cm, tail 20·6–31 cm; weigh 2·5–4·5 kg. Coat color variable from silvery-buff to orange red. Winter coat is grayer and less patterned than summer coat. A compact, short-legged felid with long, dense fur. Thick, bushy tail marked with five or six narrow black rings and a broad black tip. Small, rounded ears are set low on the sides of the broad head. Backs of ears are buff, grayish, or rust. Forehead and top of head marked with black spots. Two parallel black stripes extend downward from eyes to the cheeks. Race *ferrugineus* is often reddish and has the fewest stripes and *nigipectus* has the most pronounced stripe pattern.
Habitat. Steppe and semi-desert areas with rock outcrops and talus slopes. Not usually found in areas with continuous snow cover, or in areas where snow depths exceed 10 cm, as it has difficulty moving in loose, deep snow. Dens, which may be in a rock crevices, marmot burrows, or under a boulder, are used year round. High altitude steppe up to 3000–4000 m.
Food and Feeding. Diet consists mainly of pikas, gerbils, voles, and hamsters, ground squirrels, hares, sandgrouses, and partridges. Stalks or ambushes prey near rocks and burrows. Not adapted to running.
Activity patterns. Hunts mainly at dusk and in the early morning. Often seen basking outside its den during the day.
Movements, Home range and Social organization. Nothing known.
Breeding. Birth dens found in rock crevices or abandoned burrows of foxes and marmots. Dens contain bedding composed of plants, rodent skins, feathers, and prey remains. Mating occurs in February and March, accompanied by frequent vocalizations. Period of sexual receptivity is short, 26 to 42 hours. Gestation about 66–75 days, and 4–6 kittens are born in April and May. Kittens weigh 80–90 g at birth, 500–600 g at two months of age.
Status and Conservation. CITES Appendix II. Classified as Near Threatened on *The IUCN Red List*. Widely distributed but uncommon. Hunting prohibited in most countries in its range but the species is still illegally hunted for its pelt. Habitat destruction and poisoning to control pika populations also threaten it. Unstudied in the wild until recently, when they were captured and radio-collared as part of a veterinary study to characterize parasite load and physiologic and genetic parameters.

Bibliography. Brown & Munkhtsog (2000), Heptner & Sludskii (1992a), Mellen (1993), Murdoch *et al.* (2006), Nowell & Jackson (1996), Roberts (1977), Schauenberg (1978), Sunquist & Sunquist (2002), Wang Zongyi & Wang Sung (1986), Weigel (1972).

Genus *PRIONAILURUS*
Severtzov, 1858

29. Rusty-spotted Cat *Prionailurus rubiginosus*
French: Chat rougeâtre / **German**: Rostkatze / **Spanish**: Gato indio

Taxonomy. *Felis rubiginosus* Geoffroy Saint-Hilaire, 1831, Pondicherry, India.
Three subspecies recognized.
Subspecies and Distribution.
P. r. rubiginosus Geoffroy Saint-Hilaire, 1831 – India.
P. r. koladivinus Deraniyagala, 1956 – dry zone of Sri Lanka.
P. r. phillipsi Pocock, 1939 – wet zone of SW Sri Lanka.
Descriptive notes. Head and body 35–48 cm, tail 15–29·8 cm. Adult males heavier (1·5–1·6 kg) than adult females (1·1 kg). One of the smallest felids. The short, smooth fur is gray with a reddish tinge, patterned with lines of small, rusty-colored spots, which may form stripes along the top of the head, back and flanks. Throat, chest, and belly are white and marked with dark spots and bars. Ears are small and rounded. Tail may be marked with faint rings. Often mistaken for domestic cat.
Habitat. Forest scrub, grasslands, rocky areas, hill slopes, and tea plantations. Also reported from agricultural areas and close to human habitation. In India is thought to be absent from the wetter montane forests of the Western Ghats. However, in Sri Lanka is found in humid mountain forests to 2100 m.
Food and Feeding. Little known. Diet thought to consist mainly of birds, small mammals, insects, lizards, and frogs. Also preys on domestic poultry. Excellent tree climber, but probably hunts mostly on the ground.
Activity patterns. Primarily nocturnal.
Movements, Home range and Social organization. In captivity, this cat is extremely active, and walks rapidly with quick darting movements. No information from the wild.
Breeding. Birth dens found in hollow logs and under rocks. Estrus lasts about five days and one or two young are born after a gestation of 66–70 days. Kittens weigh about 60–77 g at birth. Fur is dark brown with a slight reddish tinge marked with blackish spots; the characteristic rusty spots appear later.
Status and Conservation. CITES Appendix I (Indian population), CITES Appendix II (Sri Lankan population). Classified as Vulnerable on *The IUCN Red List*. Unstudied in the wild. Distribution in India is extremely disjunct, confusing, and based on few specimens. Until recently the species was thought to be confined to west-central and southern India and Sri Lanka. In 1975 a single record from Jammu and Kashmir extended the species range more than 1600 km north from Bombay.

Bibliography. de Alwis (1973), Chakrabarty (1978), Chavan *et al.* (1991), Jerdon (1874), Mellen (1993), Nowell & Jackson (1996), Patel (2006), Pathak (1990), Phillips (1984), Sterndale (1884), Sunquist & Sunquist (2002), Tehsin (1994).

30. Flat-headed Cat *Prionailurus planiceps*
French: Chat à tête plate / **German**: Flachkopfkatze / **Spanish**: Gato cangrejero

Taxonomy. *Felis planiceps* Vigors & Horsfield, 1827, Sumatra, Indonesia.
Monotypic.
Distribution. Peninsular Thailand and Malaysia, and islands of Sumatra and Borneo.
Descriptive notes. Head-body 44·6–52·1 cm, tail 12·8–16·9 cm; weights of males and females similar 1·5–2·5 kg. Fur is thick and soft, dark roan-brown on flanks and reddish-brown on top of the head. Underparts are mottled white. Many body hairs tipped with white or gray. Two prominent whitish streaks on each side of face, which is noticeably paler in color than body. Muzzle and chin are white. Appearance is more mustelid-like than cat-like, with short legs, elongated and flattened head, small, rounded, low-set ears, and a short tail. Eyes are large and set close together. Teeth pointed: first two upper premolars are large and sharp, adaptations for gripping slippery prey. Webbing on feet well-developed.
Habitat. Has not been studied in the wild. Most collection records are from riparian habitats. There are also incidental observations in logged primary and secondary forest, freshwater swamp forest, and secondary forest/scrub habitat within coastal lowland floodplains, and in mature secondary forest. Also recorded from oil palm and rubber plantations, suggesting some tolerance for human-altered landscapes.
Food and Feeding. Morphological specializations (teeth, claws, eyes) and a few behavioral observations of captive animals suggest that its diet is composed largely of fish. Captives readily play in water, submerge their heads to seize pieces of fish, and adults seen to grope along bottom of pan of water with their forepaws spread wide, much like raccoons. Captive adults also killed rats and mice with a nape bite. In the wild, diet probably includes fish, frogs, crustaceans, and small mammals.
Activity patterns. Thought to be nocturnal.
Movements, Home range and Social organization. No information.
Breeding. Gestation 56 days, litter size 1–2.
Status and Conservation. CITES Appendix I. Classified as Endangered on *The IUCN Red List*. There is no information on status or abundance, but appears to be rare and elusive. Species may be vulnerable because its distribution tied to watercourses. These habitats are often the first to be developed.

Bibliography. Bezuijen (2000), Guggisberg (1975), Lekagul & McNeely (1991), Lim & Rahman bin Omar (1961), Muul & Lim (1970), Nowell & Jackson (1996), Payne *et al.* (1985), Pocock (1932b), Schaffer & Rosenthal (1984), Sunquist & Sunquist (2002).

31. Fishing Cat *Prionailurus viverrinus*
French: Chat viverrin / **German**: Fischkatze / **Spanish**: Gato pescador

Taxonomy. *Felis viverrinus* Bennett, 1833, India.
Two subspecies recognized.

On following pages: 32. Leopard Cat (*Prionailurus bengalensis*).

Subspecies and Distribution.
P. v. viverrinus Bennett, 1833 – Sri Lanka, India, mainland SE Asia, and Sumatra.
P. v. rizophoreus Sody, 1936 – Java.
Descriptive notes. Head-body 57–115 cm, tail 24·1–40 cm; weight 5–16 kg, adult males are larger than adult females. A powerful looking, stocky, short-legged cat with a relatively short, thick tail. Fur is short and coarse, olive gray patterned with rows of dark spots. In some places the spots merge into streaks or lines. The face is elongated and two dark stripes extend across the cheeks from the eye to below the ear. The ears are small and set low on the sides of the head. The backs of ears have a central white spot. Tail is marked with 5–6 black rings; tail tip is black. Toes have moderately well-developed webs. The claw sheaths are not large enough to cover the retracted claws.

Habitat. Typically associated with wetlands such as marshes, reed beds, oxbow lakes, mangrove areas, and swamps. However, in the Nepalese lowlands three radio-collared individuals spent most of their time in dense grasslands, sometimes well away from water.

Food and Feeding. Teeth are not specially modified for catching fish and its diet probably includes any small to medium-sized vertebrate it can catch. There are records of fishing cats killing frogs, snakes, rodents, Small Indian Civets, Chital fawns, small pigs, coots, ducks, sandpipers, and a variety of domestic animals such as goats, calves, poultry, and even dogs. They are powerful swimmers. They often hunt for fish while fully immersed in water and have been seen catching fish by plunging their heads under water. They also flick or scoop fish out of the water with their paws. One report describes catching waterfowl by swimming underwater and seizing their legs from beneath.

Activity patterns. Thought to be primarily nocturnal but little is known of their behavior in the wild.

Movements, Home range and Social organization. In the only telemetry study to date, two adult females used areas of 4–6 km². A subadult male's range measured about 16–22 km².

Breeding. There are a few observations of kittens in the wild in April and May, suggesting that mating occurs in January and February. Two birth dens were found in dense patches of reeds. Gestation lasts about 63–70 days and litter size varies from 1–4; mean litter size is 2·6. Kittens weigh about 170 g at birth. One female attained sexual maturity at 15 months.

Status and Conservation. CITES Appendix II. Classified as Endangered on *The IUCN Red List*. The conversion of wetland and floodplain habitats to agriculture has reduced the habitat of the species throughout its range.

Bibliography. Bhattacharyya (1992), Jayewardene (1975), Lekagul & McNeely (1991), Mellen (1993), Mukherjee (1989), Nayerul & Vijayan (1993), Nowell & Jackson (1996), Sunquist & Sunquist (2002), Ulmer (1968).

32. Leopard Cat *Prionailurus bengalensis*

French: Chat du Bengale / **German**: Bengalkatze / **Spanish**: Gato bengalí

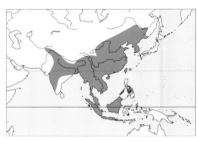

Taxonomy. *Felis bengalensis* Kerr, 1792, Bengal, India.

Taxonomy in need of reevaluation, especially the subspecific distinctness of island forms. Race *iriomotensis* described as separate species, but key characters found to be polymorphic in *P. bengalensis* and genetic analysis suggest subspecific status; race *euptilurus* considered a distinct species based on comparisons between Russian specimens and those from South-east Asia, but these distinctions do not hold when intervening Chinese populations. Race *alleni* possibly not distinct from *chinensis* and *borneoensis* not distinct from *sumatranus*. Twelve subspecies recognized.

Subspecies and Distribution.
P. b. bengalensis Kerr, 1792 – Indian and Indochinese region and Malay Peninsula.
P. b. alleni Sody, 1949 – Hainan I.
P. b. borneoensis Brongersma, 1935 – Borneo.
P. b. chinensis Gray, 1837 – China, except for NE, and Taiwan.
P. b. euptilurus Elliot, 1871 – Manchurian region, Korean and Russian Far East.
P. b. heaneyi Groves, 1997 – the Philippines (Palawan).
P. b. horsfieldi Gray, 1842 – Sub-Himalayan region E of Indus River.
P. b. iriomotensis Imaizumi, 1967 – Japan (Iriomote I.).
P. b. javanensis Desmarest, 1816 – Java and Bali.
P. b. rabori Groves, 1997 – the Philippines (Negros, Cebu & Panay).
P. b. sumatranus Horsfield, 1821 – Sumatra and Nias I.
P. b. trevelyani Pocock, 1939 – Kashmir.

Descriptive notes. Head-body 45–75 cm, tail 19·5–31·5 cm; weight 1·7–7·1 kg. Adult males larger than females and there is considerable geographic variation in size. Cats from Russia and northern China are two to three times larger than from Borneo and southern portions of Asia. Coat color and pattern also show significant variation across the geographic range. Individuals from northern areas have long, full coats

that are a pale silvery gray, whereas the background coat color of cats living near the equator is yellow ocher or brownish. Black spots mark the body and limbs, sometimes coalescing to form lines. There are often two to four rows of elongated lines along the back. The tail is spotted and the tip is black. Muzzle is white and the backs of the ears have a white central spot. Feet are long and narrow, with well-developed webbing between the toes.

Habitat. The broadest distribution of all small Asian felids, extending from southern India to the islands on the Sunda Shelf and north to the Russian Far East. They are found in a great variety of forest types, from lowland tropical evergreen rainforest and rubber and oil palm plantations at sea level to moist temperate broadleaf and dry coniferous forests in the Himalayas at 3000 m. Also does well in successional habitats, shrub forest, farmlands, and on coastal islands. It is rarely found in cold steppe grasslands or arid areas. In Russia is commonly associated with river valleys, forested ravines and coastal habitats where the cover is deciduous broadleaf forest. Their small feet are not well adapted for moving in deep snow and they avoid areas where snow depth exceeds 10 cm. Radio-collared cats in Thailand's Huai Kha Khaeng Wildlife Sanctuary rarely visited the dry deciduous dipterocarp forest, a fire-maintained habitat with little understory vegetation; they preferred mixed deciduous and dry evergreen forest habitats, especially those associated with watercourses. These habitats not only offered more cover but they also harbored more prey. Similarly, radio-tagged cats in Tabin Wildlife Reserve, Sabah, used the oil palm plantations just outside the Reserve more than expected, presumably because of the high density of Whitehead's Rats, the cats' principle prey.

Food and Feeding. Feeds on a variety of small prey, including rodents, reptiles, birds, amphibians, crabs, and insects. They are excellent swimmers and captives spend much time playing in water. Small birds were the principal prey in Pakistan; secondary prey included wood mice (Muridae) and flying squirrels. In Kaeng Krachan National Park, Thailand, small mammals, principally *Rattus* spp. and *Mus* spp. were the dominant prey; incidential prey included Tree Shrews and hares. Based on an analysis of 230 scats, on Tsushima Island, Japan, fed largely on murid rats (72·6%), but they also ate moles, birds, amphibians, and insects. On Iriomote Island, 95 prey species were identified in 849 scats. Rats were the dominant prey, but flying foxes, skinks, and birds were also important. Incidental prey included amphibians, crabs, and insects. In Tabin Wildlife Reserve, Sabah, murid rats, especially Whitehead's Sundaic Maxomys and the Sundaic Arboreal Niviventer, formed the bulk of the diet, although lizards, snakes, and frogs were also important, particularly in the wet season. On Peninsular Malaysia, forest and field rats (Muridae) were the major prey, but the remains of lizards (Varanidae), snakes (Xenopeltidae), tree shrews, and crabs were also identified in stomachs.

Acitivity patterns. Radio-collared individuals in Tabin Wildlife Reserve, Sabah, were nocturnal, but levels of nighttime activity were significantly higher in the dry season than in the wet season. While the levels of nocturnal activity were reduced in the wet season, their levels of daytime activity were significantly higher than in the dry season. The activity patterns of radio-collared individuals in Thailand were arrhythmic, which was attributed to them foraging extensively on both nocturnal and diurnal prey.

Movements, Home range and Social organization. In the dry season at Tabin Wildlife Reserve, Sabah, radio-tagged males traveled an average of 1·72 km per night compared to 1·27 km for females; average distances traveled per night in the wet season decreased to 1·06 km and 0·87 km, respectively. Males traveled faster and farther than females, but for both sexes, movement rates were higher in the first half of the night than in the second half. Movement rates for females tended to be slower because their travels were frequently punctuated with long periods of no movement, during which they were presumably sitting and waiting for prey. All observations (n = 67) in Tabin were of solitary individuals. The home ranges of four resident males varied from 2·64 to 3·8 km². The ranges of two resident females measured 1·93 and 2·25 km². Ranges of resident males overlapped those of one or more females. In Thailand, the mean home range size in Huai Kha Khaeng Wildlife Sanctuary was 4·33 km² (range 1·5–7·5 km²) and in Kaeng Krachan National Park it was 3·38 km² (range 2·3–5·4 km²). On Tsuchima Island, Japan, the mean home range size was 0·83 km². Differences in home range sizes are in part related to body size, as cats in Thailand are larger than those on the islands of Borneo and Tsuchima. The effects of differences in resource levels and other environmental conditions among the sites on home range sizes are not known. Some differences in home range sizes may also be due to different methods of analysis. The density in Tabin was estimated at 37·5 adults/100 km², which is comparable to the density on Iriomote Island of 34/100 km².

Breeding. In the northern portion of its range, is a seasonal breeder, in Russia kittens are born in May. For those living closer to the Equator, births may occur in any month. Gestation lasts 60–70 days and litter size is typically 2–3 young. Young weigh 75–130 g at birth and open their eyes at 10–15 days of age. By the time they are two weeks old, kittens have doubled their birth weight. Permanent canines erupt at about four weeks, which coincides with the young beginning to eat solid food. This new diet results in rapid weight gain and by 13 weeks of age the young have increased their birth weight tenfold. At nine months the young are nearly adult size. In captivity, sexual maturity occurs as early as eight months, and one female produced her first litter at 13–14 months of age.

Status and Conservation. Listed on CITES Appendix II, except for populations in India, Thailand, and Bangladesh, which are listed on CITES Appendix I. Classified as a species of Least Concern on the *The IUCN Red List*. Heavily hunted in many parts of its range and its pelt figures prominently in the fur trade. The Chinese govern-

ment has set an annual harvest quota of 150,000 individuals, but the actual harvest is probably higher. There are also estimated stockpiles of more than 800,000 pelts in Chinese fur company warehouses. Leopard Cat coats are frequently sold in Nepal and Kashmir. Where it is not persecuted, appears to be able to coexist with humans. It seems to be an adaptable species, and has been found in secondary forest, successional vegetation, tea, coffee, rubber, and oil palm plantations.

Bibliography. Acharjyo & Mishra (1983), Dathe (1968), Dobroruka (1971), Frese (1980), Grassman (1998a, 2000), Grassman, Tewes, Silvy & Kreetiyutanont (2005), Hemmer (1979), Inoue (1972), Lim (1999), Lim & Rahman bin Omar (1961), Lu Houji & Sheng Helin (1986), Nowell & Jackson (1996), Rabinowitz (1990), Rajaratnam (2000), Rajaratnam et al. (2007), Roberts (1977), Santiapillai & Supraham (1985), Schauenberg (1979a), Singh (2005), Sunquist & Sunquist (2002), Wang Zongyi & Wang Sung (1986), Yasuma (1981, 1988).

PLATE 10

inches 12

cm 30

ssp *chaus*

33

ssp *nilotica*

ssp *nigripes*

34

ssp *kutas*

ssp *thomasi*

ssp *margarita*

35

ssp *thinobia*

ssp *lybica*

36

37

ssp *silvestris*

ssp *ornata*

Genus *FELIS*
Linnaeus, 1758

33. Jungle Cat *Felis chaus*
French: Chat des marais / **German**: Rohrkatze / **Spanish**: Gato marismeño
Other common names: Swamp Cat, Reed Cat

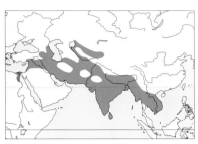

Taxonomy. *Felis chaus* Schreber, 1777, Russia, Terek River, north of Caucasus. Six subspecies recognized.
Subspecies and Distribution.
F. c. chaus Schreber, 1777 – SE Turkey, Jordan, Israel, Lebanon, Irak, Syria, Iran, and N to the Caucasus Mountains, adjoining Russia, and E through region of Caspian and Aral Seas to W China.
F. c. affinis Gray, 1830 – Sub-Himalayan region.
F. c. fulvidina Thomas, 1929 – Cambodia, Laos, Vietnam, also Myanmar and Thailand.
F. c. kelaarti Pocock, 1939 – S India & Sri Lanka.
F. c. kutas Pearson, 1832 – N India, Pakistan, and Bangladesh.
F. c. nilotica de Winton, 1898 – Egypt.
Descriptive notes. Head-body 61–85 cm, tail 20–31 cm. Adult males heavier (5·7–12 kg) than adult females (2·6–9 kg). Coat plain and unspotted, varying in color from reddish to sandy brown to tawny gray. Black tips on guard hairs impart a slightly speckled appearance. Tail tip is black. Face is long and slim, muzzle white; white lines above and below eyes. Ears long, rounded, set close together, and tipped with tuft of black hairs. Backs of ears are reddish brown. Melanistic individuals reported from Pakistan and India. Northern subspecies larger and heavier than those from southern Asia.
Habitat. Prefers tall grass, thick bush, riverine swamps, and reed beds. Few records from dense jungle. Sometimes found in association with man-made fish ponds, reservoirs, and sprinkler-irrigated landscapes. Also survives in drier, open forests, and even sandhill desert and steppe habitats. Adaptable species. Rarely found above 1000 m elevation.
Food and Feeding. Mammals are the principal prey. Smaller species include voles, gerbils, jirds (Gerbilinae), muskrats, jerboas, and ground squirrels. Other mammals include hares, Coypu (Myocastoridae), and the occasional Chital fawn. Birds rank second in importance, with ducks, coots, pheasants, partridges, peafowl, and jungle fowl, sparrows, and domestic poultry being prominent in the diet. Other prey include frogs, lizards (Agamidae, Lacertidae), snakes (Colubridae, Viperidae), and turtles. Minor elements include insects, fish, and turtle eggs. Stalk-and-ambush hunters, capture most prey on ground, but can climb and leap well.
Activity patterns. Nocturnal, but also regularly seen hunting at dawn and dusk.
Movements, Home range and Social organization. Little information available, but snow tracking in Tajikistan and Uzbekistan estimated movements of 3–6 km per night.
Breeding. Mating and births vary by latitude and seasonal temperature. Most young born December-June after gestation of 63–66 days. Den sites in burrows, hollow trees, reed beds, and dense thorn bushes. Litter size usually three. Young independent by nine months of age.
Status and Conservation. CITES Appendix II. Classified as Least Concern on *The IUCN Red List*. The most common felid in many parts of its geographic range. Species thrives in agricultural landscapes. Have been heavily exploited for their pelts in some parts of their range.

Bibliography. Acharjyo & Mohapatra (1977), Duckworth *et al.* (2005), Eaton (1984), Guggisberg (1975), Hemmer (1979), Heptner & Sludskii (1992a), Johnsingh (1983), Mellen (1993), Mukherjee (1989), Mukherjee *et al.* (2004), Niethammer (1966), Nowell & Jackson (1996), Roberts (1977), Schauenberg (1979b), Sunquist & Sunquist (2002).

34. Black-footed Cat *Felis nigripes*
French: Chat à pieds noirs / **German**: Schwarzfußkatze / **Spanish**: Gato de pies negros
Other common names: Small Spotted Cat, Anthill Tiger

Taxonomy. *Felis nigripes* Burchell, 1824, Kuruman, South Africa.
Two subspecies recognized.
Subspecies and Distribution.
F. n. nigripes Burchell, 1824 – Namibia through the Kalahari to NE South Africa.
F. n. thomasi Shortridge, 1931 – S South Africa (Eastern Cape Province).
Descriptive notes. Head-body 36–52 cm, tail 12·6–20 cm; weight 1–2·45 kg, adult males distinctively larger than adult females. The smallest cat in Africa. Small stocky cat with broad head and large, widely spaced, rounded ears. The nose is very small and varies from red to black in color. Eyes are dark yellow to light greenish. The soft fur grows longer and denser during winter. The margins of the eyes, ears and mouth are white. There are two black cheek stripes running from the corner of the eyes and from below the eyes to the edge of the face. On the back of the neck there are four black bands, two running along the back and onto the shoulder. The body color varies from cinnamon buff to tawny or off-white. There are bold black or rust-tinged bands or rings on the shoulders and high on the legs, up to five on the hindlegs and two on the front, and distinct spots of the same color on the body. The throat has two or three black to reddish stripes that are either solid or broken up. The underparts are pale buff or white. The tail is short (less than 40% of head-body length) and narrowly black-tipped; the backs of the ears are the same color as the body. The hair on the undersides of the front paws and back legs is black. The skull is high and rounded. The auditory bullae are exceptionally large, their total length being 25% of the total skull length, and their width, at the widest point 18%. Races not well defined, possibly representing a geographical cline from the smaller, paler nominate, with more bleached ground color and less distinctive brown striping, to the larger, more vividly colored *thomasi* with jet black bands and spots.
Habitat. Inhabits dry, open savanna, grasslands, and Karoo semi-desert (savanna biome) with sparse shrub and tree cover with a mean annual rainfall of between 100–500 mm annually; absent from the driest and sandiest parts of the Namib and Kalahari Deserts. Seems to avoid rocky terrain and bushy country. Presence of South African Spring Hare burrows and *Trinervitermes* termitaria for shelter may be crucial since 98% of 184 resting places in central South Africa were in abandoned South African Spring Hare burrows. In some areas frequently uses hollowed out termitaria; hence the common name "anthill-tiger." Also rests under rock slabs.
Food and Feeding. Opportunistic carnivore, taking everything it can overpower. Of seven stomachs collected in Botswana four contained murid rodents, three spiders, and one each elephant shrews, reptiles, insects, and birds. In central South Africa 43 vertebrate prey species identified. 14 mammal species comprised 72% of the total prey mass consumed. Most important, with 39% of prey mass, were murids; 21 species of birds (26%), mainly larks, with eggs of various species taken; eight species of frogs and reptiles (Gekkonidae, Scincidae, Colubridae); prey up to the size of hares, mongooses and pigeons, sandgrouse, and bustards taken. A minimum of ten invertebrate species were eaten, some as small as the alates of harvester termites. Average prey size is 24 g. In central South Africa on average males kill larger prey; the smaller and more agile females are more successful in catching small birds. In summer both sexes concentrate on abundant small rodents. In winter a higher proportion of larger (over 100 g) birds and mammals are taken. Three different hunting styles identified: "fast-hunt" when moves in swift bounds at 1–2 km/h trying to flush prey from cover; "slow-hunt" involving a slow stalk at an average speed of 0·5–0·8 km/h, while looking and listening carefully; and "sit-down", waiting at a rodent den system for up to two hours. About 70% of the night is spent moving. Birds are sometimes snatched from the air. Hunting success very high, about one vertebrate prey animal caught every 50 minutes and 10–14 rodents or small birds caught per night, representing 200–300 g of food or about 20% of the body weight; record intakes can reach 450 g per night. Excess food is cached and scavenged readily. Independent of water but will drink occasionally when water is available.
Activity patterns. Nocturnal and crepuscular; when moving during daylight birds mob them. Hunting occurs throughout the night in all weather conditions and temperatures. Are occasionally shadowed by Marsh Owls, which catch flushed prey animals. Small body size allows the cat to hunt and rest in open arid areas. Its auditory bullae are exceptionally well-developed, enhancing hearing ability in areas with little vegetation cover. Considered to be the southern representative of the Sand Cat, which has similar proportions. Sight is acute for crepuscular and nocturnal hunting.
Movements, Home range and Social organization. Nightly travel distance is between 4·5 and 16 km (mean = 8 km). Males have larger cumulative home ranges (17·6 km²) than females (9·5 km²) and their ranges overlap those of 1–4 females. Intra-sexual overlap is marginal. Home range size is likely to vary between regions according to local resource availability. Solitary, except during mating; the only other prolonged social contact are females with dependent kittens. Communicate mainly through urine spray marking; frequency of female spraying fluctuates strongly during the year, depending on the stage of reproductive cycle, with high frequency before mating, low when pregnant, and no spraying when rearing kittens. Males spray intensively prior to mating, up to 585 sprays per night. Scent rubbing and possibly claw-raking may have signalling function. Feces are rarely covered or deposited on middens. Vocal communication, a loud meowing sound, repeated up to ten times in quick succession, mostly from males looking for females during mating season. Females rarely call in estrus. Soft calls used by males courting females and by females calling kittens. Females give special alarm call, with ears depressed, to kittens. The adult sex ratio in the wild was four males to six females. Birth sex ratio is 1·16:1 in captivity. Captive individuals may live up to 16 years; however data from the wild indicate 4–6 years as the average.
Breeding. Females have an estrous cycle of 54 days. Mate often, 6–10 copulations during 36-hour female estrous period; resident male guards females and chases and fights with intruding males. Gestation is 63–68 days; up to two litters in the spring and summer season, coinciding with the rains and high availability of food. No litters in winter. Litter size 1–4, but usually two. Birth weight 60–90 g. Kittens born in hollow termite mound ("ant hill"), or South African Spring Hare burrow; mother leaves kittens for two hours on night of birth and resumes her nocturnal hunting schedule after four days, returning infrequently to suckle kittens. Kittens moved frequently after the first

On following pages: 35. Sand Cat (*Felis margarita*); 36. Chinese Mountain Cat (*Felis bieti*); 37. Wildcat (*Felis silvestris*).

week; they develop rapidly, opening eyes at 3–9 days, first take solid food at 30 days, weaned within two months. Female carries prey items to them for feeding and teaching kittens to hunt live prey. Kittens independent after 3–4 months, but remain within mother's range for extended periods. Sexual maturity (in captivity) is seven months for females and nine months for males.

Status and Conservation. CITES Appendix I. Classified as Vulnerable on *The IUCN Red List*. South African red data book: rare; very inconspicuous, shy, difficult to census; 8 adults/60 km^2 in central South Africa; in low quality habitat densities probably lower; species may be expanding in some areas; threats include expansion of human settlement and arable agriculture, use of poison, desertification, and overgrazing with bush encroachment. May be susceptible to locust poisoning. Farmers setting "coyote-getters" and poisoning carcasses during control operations targeting other predators may affect since they readily scavenge. Night calling and shooting aimed at Black-backed Jackal also impacts this species in the central Karoo. Cats also fall victim to dogs, used to chase or dig out jackals during problem animal operations. Young or sick individuals and kittens are vulnerable to Black-backed Jackal and Caracal predation. Kittens and possibly adults may fall victim to large nocturnal raptors such as eagle-owls (*Bubo africanus, B. capensis, B. lacteus*); both wild and captive individuals often die of kidney failure (amyloidosis), indicated by high urea concentrations in the blood.

Bibliography. Burchell (1824), Leyhausen & Tonkin (1966), Mellen (1989), Molteno *et al.* (1998), Nowell & Jackson (1996), Olbricht & Sliwa (1995, 1997), Power (2000), Roberts (1926), Shortridge (1931, 1934), Skinner & Smithers (1990), Sliwa (1994a, 1994b, 1994c, 1995, 1997, 1998, 2004, 2006), Sliwa & Schürer (2000), Smithers (1971, 1986), Stuart (1981, 1982), Stuart & Wilson (1988), Sunquist & Sunquist (2002), Visser (1977).

35. Sand Cat *Felis margarita*

French: Chat des sables / **German**: Sandkatze / **Spanish**: Gato de las arenas

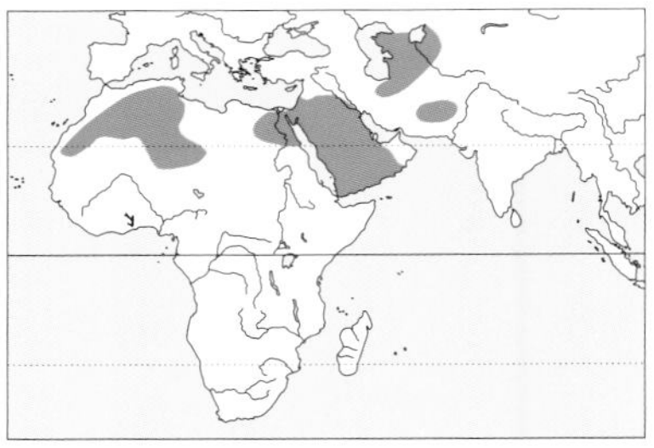

Taxonomy. *Felis margarita* Loche, 1858, Sahara, Algeria.

Four subspecies recognized.

Subspecies and Distribution.

F. m. margarita Loche, 1858 – Sahara.

F. m. harrisoni Hemmer, Grubb & Groves, 1976 – Egypt, Israel, Arabian Peninsula.

F. m. scheffeli Hemmer, 1974 – Pakistan.

F. m. thinobia Ognev, 1926 – deserts E of the Caspian Sea.

Descriptive notes. Head-body 39–52 cm, tail 23·2–31 cm; weight 1·35–3·4 kg. Adult males larger than adult females. A small cat; size and build like the Wildcat but ears larger, broad, and set low on sides of head without apical tufts; head is flat and broad, flattening the Sand Cat's profile, which may aid the cat in detecting movements of subterranean prey and protect inner ears from wind-blown sand. Eyes yellow amber, greenish to yellow-bluish. Nose pad black; vibrissae white and up to 8 cm long. Limbs of medium length. Paws broader than in the Wildcat; palms and soles covered with dense mat of fine black hair (about 10 mm), completely concealing the pads, which may facilitate walking on soft sand, muffling sound, or protecting soles from hot ground. Claws are blunt, due to lack of sharpening surfaces and digging habits: claw impressions often visible in spoor. Pelage soft and dense, in winter with abundant soft woolly underfur, giving a solid appearance despite its small size; coloration is strikingly pallid; typical camouflage for sand-dwelling (eremial) species. Back is pale sandy isabelline, finely speckled with black over the shoulders and with silvery gray on the upper flanks; poorly differentiated spinal band. Crown of head is pale sandy marked with ill-defined striations; face broad due to well-developed beard; dark reddish-fulvous stripe runs from anterior edge of eyes backwards across cheeks. Backs of ears rufous tawny with extensive apical black spot. Chest and belly white; faint buffy wash on the lower throat; limbs are white internally; externally they are marked by at least two black elbow bars extending around the leg; thighs with black barring; flank pattern with 7–8 indistinct reddish-brown vertical stripes, broken up into spots with black in places. Tail 50% of body length, tipped with black and varying number of subterminal tail rings; baculum less than 3 mm. Distinctive skull with large forward facing orbits; rostrum short and broad; wide zygomatic arches and prominent sagittal crest; exceptionally large inflated auditory bullae to increase hearing abilities in areas with little vegetation cover. Nominate race from Algeria and Niger tend to be brighter in color and have more distinct markings than other subspecies. Size small in both sexes, skull relatively narrow with relatively small bullae, small carnassials, 2–6 tail rings; *harrisoni* has broader skull, relatively larger tympanic bullae and larger carnassials than nominate, also dorsal pelage is paler and the ear patch is relatively small and less dark, pelage pattern is quite sharply marked and paws are very white, 5–7 tail rings; *thinobia* slightly bigger than the other subspecies and stronger reduction of dark markings, tail rings 2–3 up to six in kittens; *scheffeli* males larger in size, females small; skull broad with very large bullae, but smaller carnassials than *thinobia*, color similar to *thinobia*, but also more strongly marked individuals, more than eight tail rings, at least in kittens. Different races become gradually larger from West to East, with the smallest one nominate in Africa. Probably the ancestral form most closely resembled the nominate; from this a radiation of more specialized forms arose, with *thinobia* and *scheffeli* acquiring a more intensely eremial pattern of skin and *harrisoni* of skull.

Habitat. Undulating stabilized dune areas, dry river beds "wadi", and steppe with sparse grass and shrub cover; also uses shifting sand dunes and may be found in rocky deserts "hammada". Absent from heavier vegetated valleys within the desert, and rare in shifting sand dunes. Recorded up to 1200 m. Mean annual rainfall in habitat is 20–300 mm.

Food and Feeding. Mainly on small desert rodents, including Spiny Mice, gerbils, jerboas, but also young of Cape Hare (*Lepus capensis*); it will also hunt larks and consume reptiles such as skinks , geckoes, and snakes (Viperidae, Colubridae). Also eats insects; capable of rapid digging to extract prey items. May cover kills with sand and return later to feed. Independent of drinking water, they can satisfy their moisture requirements from their prey, but drink readily if water is available. Scats are covered with sand.

Activity patterns. Nocturnal, although during the winter may be active during the day. Ambient temperatures may range from 58°C to −25°C. In the Aravah Valley, Israel, were active throughout the night.

Movements, Home range and Social organization. A male in the Aravah Valley, Israel, hunted and travelled on average 5·4 km/night during nine nights. Dens are in disused fox warrens, and in rodent (*Rhombomys*) or hedgehog burrows enlarged by the cats. Several used burrows interchangeably. Race *thinobia* lives in shallow burrows in the sand, constructed among the roots of saltbushes or *Caligonum* plants. Nominate race may use burrows excavated by the Fennec, which is ecologically similar. A den in Niger of 150 cm length went down in a straight line to 60 cm deep and had a tunnel diameter of 15 cm. Home range size is likely to vary between regions according to resources available to the animals, and possibly competition from other sympatric carnivores such as Red Fox , and Wildcat, which consume similar prey. Ranges of males overlap; in Israel one male had a 16 km^2 home range. Only density estimates are from telemetry study in southern Israel, where four adult cats roamed in a relatively small area. They are a solitary species. Males uttered a distinctive sharp call, like a small dog, from hilltops—possibly related to mating. In captivity both sexes vocalized upon first introduction.

Breeding. Mating occurs from November–February. One female had an estrous cycle of 46 days. Gestation 59–67 days; young are born from January–April. Litter size 2–5, but usually three. Young grow rapidly, and may become independent as early as four months. Sexual maturity at 9–14 months. During the reproductive season, pairs share the same burrows. Captives may live up to 13 years. Most Sand Cats presently in captivity are *harrisoni* or are hybrids between *harrisoni* and *sheffeli*.

Status and Conservation. CITES Appendix II. Listed as Near Threatened on *The IUCN Red List*, and probably still widespread. Race *scheffeli* placed as Endangered by the USA Endangered Species Act and *The IUCN Red List*. However, striking paucity of records from N Africa. Threats include expansion of human settlement, disturbance, and introduction of feral and domestic dogs and cats, or the Red Fox, resulting in direct competition, predation, and disease transmission. Difficult to census and thus often reported as rare. In low-quality habitat, such as shifting sand dunes, densities might be very low. May be killed in traps in oases targeting foxes and jackals. Some individuals are surprisingly tame when encountered. They are placid animals and tame easily. Kittens are probably vulnerable to Red Fox and eagle owl (*Bubo bubo ascalaphus*) predation. Adults fall victim to Golden Jackal, especially when Jackals hunt in pairs, and probably to domestic dogs; captive individuals are highly susceptible to disease of the respiratory tract.

Bibliography. Abbadi (1993), Boitani *et al.* (1999), De Smet (1989), Dragesco-Joffé (1993), Gasperetti *et al.* (1985), Goodman & Helmy (1986), Harrison & Bates (1991), Hemmer (1974a, 1974b, 1977), Hemmer *et al.* (1976), Heptner,V.G. & Sludskij (1992b), Heptner, W.G. (1970), Huang *et al.* (2002), Hufnagl (1972), Kingdon (1990), Kowalski & Rzebik-Kowalska (1991), Mellen (1989, 1993), Nowell & Jackson (1996), Sausman (1997), Schauenberg (1974), Sunquist & Sunquist (2002).

36. Chinese Mountain Cat *Felis bieti*

French: Chat de Mongolie / **German**: Graukatze / **Spanish**: Gato chino de montaña

Other common names: Chinese Desert Cat, Pale Desert Cat

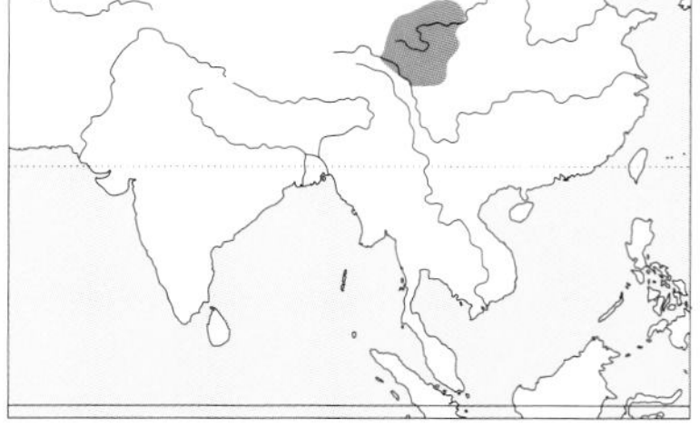

Taxonomy. *Felis bieti* Milne-Edwards, 1892, Sichuan, China.

Proposed races *chutuchta* and *vellerosa* are placed in present spcies by some authors while others consider that they belong to *F. silvestris*. Monotypic.

Distribution. As yet not well defined but reported from Quinghai, Sichuan and Gansu, in C China.

Descriptive notes. Head-body 68·5–84 cm, tail 32·1–35 cm. A wild-caught male weighed 9 kg, a female 6·5 kg. Like a stocky domestic cat with relatively short legs. Nearly uniform coloration, generally lacking any stripes or spots on flanks. Coat pale yellowish-gray in winter, somewhat darker and marked with blown flecks in summer. Faint, dark stripes on outside of hind- and forelimbs. Ears are adorned with short dark tufts and are yellow-gray on the back. Fur on soles of feet is long and protrudes between the pads. Tail is marked with 5–6 dark gray bands and tail-tip is black.

Habitat. While its name suggests it is an inhabitant of mountainous terrain, a recent survey in western Sichuan Province, China, found it was restricted to high elevation steppe grasslands. There was no evidence that the cat lived in true desert or forested mountains. Has been recorded from elevations of 2500–4100 m.

Food and Feeding. Rodents such as White-tailed Pine Voles and Mole Rats are the main prey. Pikas and birds (Phasianidae) are also taken.

Activity patterns. Nocturnal in captivity and thought to be nocturnal-crepuscular in the wild. Rests in burrows during the day.

Movements, Home range and Social organization. Nothing known.

Breeding. Mating occurs from January–March and most young are born in May. Birth dens are in burrows, typically situated on south-facing slopes. Litter size is probably 2–4.
Status and Conservation. CITES Appendix II. Classified as Vulnerable on *The IUCN Red List*. There is no information on status or abundance. Unstudied in the wild. Fully protected in China, but pelts of this species are commonly found in markets.
Bibliography. Allen (1938), Anon. (1986), Chen *et al.* (2005), Corbet (1978), Gao *et al.* (1987), Groves (1980), Guggisberg (1975), Haltenorth (1953), He *et al.* (2004), Hemmer *et al.* (1976), Liao (1988), Nowell & Jackson (1996), Sunquist & Sunquist (2002), Tan Bangjie (1984), Wang Sung (1990), Wang Zongyi & Wang Sung (1986).

37. Wildcat *Felis silvestris*

French: Chat sauvage / **German**: Wildkatze / **Spanish**: Gato montés
Other common names: Asiatic Steppe Wildcat, Desert Cat (Asian races)

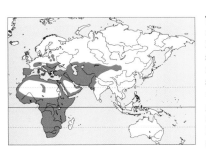

Taxonomy. *Felis silvestris* Schreber, 1777, no locality = Germany.
Race *lybica* often thought to be a separate species. *F. catus* considered to be the domesticated form from this species. Recent studies place present species closer to *F. margarita* and consider *F. catus* as a sister group to *lybica*. Proposed races *chutuchta* and *vellerosa*, now merged with *F. bieti*, have been sometimes placed in present species. Has been argued that *lybica* was a lapsus for *libyca*, but there is no clear internal evidence that the name was misspelled. Nineteen subspecies recognized.

Subspecies and Distribution.
F. s. silvestris Schreber, 1777 – Europe E to the Carpathian Mts and the River Dnieper N of the Black Sea.
F. s. brockmani Pocock, 1944 – Somalia.
F. s. cafra Desmarest, 1822 – Zimbabwe, S Mozambique and South Africa.
F. s. caucasica Satunin, 1905 – Caucasus Mts and Turkey.
F. s. caudata Gray, 1874 – deserts E Caspian Sea to NW China (Xinjiang) and Mongolia.
F. s. foxi Pocock, 1944 – Senegal to Lake Chad.
F. s. gordoni Harrison, 1968 – Batinah coast of Oman.
F. s. grampia G. S. Miller, 1907 – N Scotland.
F. s. griselda Thomas, 1926 – Kalahari region to S Angola.
F. s. iraki Cheesman, 1920 – Arabian Desert regions.
F. s. lybica Forster, 1780 – desert regions of N Africa to Sudan and N Niger.
F. s. mellandi Schwann, 1904 – SC Africa.
F. s. nesterovi Biurla, 1916 – Mesopotamian region to SW Iran.
F. s. ocreata Gmelin, 1791 – Ethiopian highlands.
F. s. ornata Gray, 1830 – India. Probably W through Iran.
F. s. pyrrhus Pocock, 1944 – N Angola and SW Zaire.
F. s. sarda Lataste, 1885 – coastal Maghreb region of Morocco and Algeria.
F. s. tristrami Pocock, 1944 – Palestine and Red Sea coast of Arabia.
F. s. ugandae Schwann, 1904 – E Africa.
Descriptive notes. Wildcats are found in Africa, Asia, and Europe, and their size, coat color, and pattern of markings vary somewhat from continent to continent. In Africa the size range is: head-body 40·6–66·5 cm, tail 24·1–36·8 cm; weight 2·4–6·4 kg. Asiatic Wildcats tend to weigh less than their African counterparts: head-body 47–74 cm, tail 21·9–36 cm; weight 2–6 kg. The following measurements are recorded from Europe: head-body 54·7–65·5 cm (males), 47·3–57·5 cm (females), tail 27·6–32·6 cm (males), 25·7–32 cm (females); weight 3·77–7·26 kg (males), 2·35–4·68 kg (females). Larger and more robust than domestic cats and have relatively longer legs. Adult males are slightly larger and heavier than adult females. In Africa the fur color and markings are highly variable, ranging from grayish to reddish, with or without small spots. The fur is soft, and the hairs often have a pale subterminal band and black tip, giving the pelage a slightly speckled appearance. Spots sometimes coalesce to form transverse stripes or black bars, especially prominent on the legs. The long, thin tail often ends with two or three blackish rings and a black tip. The head is narrow, sometimes with rufous or dark lines. The ears are rounded and widely separated, with short dark tufts; the backs of the ears are a bright red-brown. The chin is white, the underparts are pale orange-buff to whitish, and there is a line of darker hair down the spine from the shoulder to base of tail. Soles of feet are black. In general, Wildcats that live in dryer areas tend to be pale or tawny colored and those from humid areas tend to be darker and more heavily spotted and striped. Lightly built and long-legged. When sitting upright the long front legs raise the body to an almost vertical position. The long legs, narrow chest, and high shoulder blades impart a cheetah-like appearance to its motion. The Wildcats of India, Pakistan, and neighboring Russian are pale sandy, gray, or isabelline in color. The spot pattern is variable: the spots can be large, small, distinct, blurred, black, brown, or grayish. In some cats the spots along the back form a dark line. The tail is long, thin, and spotted near the base but ringed toward the black-tipped end. In Wildcats from Mongolia the spots are fused to form unbroken lines. One or two dark bands circle the upper fore- and hindlegs. The underparts are whitish and unspotted. The backs of the ears are yellowish-buff or khaki, and there is a characteristic tuft of dark hair on the tip of each ear. The relatively long limbs, long tail, and long body distinguish the Wildcat from its domestic relatives. In Europe, the background coat color varies from yellowish-brown to buff gray and even silvery. The coat is marked with a variable pattern of "tabby" stripes. There are usually four broad nape stripes, a single dorsal stripe, which ends at the root of the tail, and 3–5 rings on the bushy tail, which has a blunt, black tip. Body stripes are variable; they are most distinct in the west and there is a cline to the east where almost no striping is apparent. Melanism, flavism, and white spotting have been recorded very rarely, and may result from introgressive hybridization with domestic cats. The skull is similar to that of domestic cat, but it has a significantly greater cranial volume, differently-shaped nasals and interparietal suture, and a well-developed angular process on the mandible.
Habitat. In Africa, Wildcats are found in a variety of habitat types from sea level to about 3000 m, but appear to be absent from tropical rain forest and from areas that receive less than 100 mm of annual rainfall. Some cover for hunting and rest sites may be important, but cats in Ngorongoro Crater were seen to use the open grasslands, where they rely on holes dug by other animals to escape from larger carnivores. In Botswana Wildcats were seen at night in open woodlands and grasslands. In Zimbabwe's Hwange National Park, the cats were more commonly seen in drier woodland and scrub habitats than in areas close to water. A radio-tagged Wildcat in Kenya was frequently located in woodlands and grasslands; riverine forest and agricultural lands were infrequently used. Wildcats in Israel prefer open Mediterranean forest in hilly areas. The Wildcat also occurs on the outskirts of villages and towns, thus bringing it into contact with domestic cats. Wildcats in Asia inhabit thickets of *Acacia, Maytenus, Capparis, Tamarix*, and *Prosopis* in the desert in western Rajasthan, India; in Pakistan the cats are sparsely distributed in the desert regions of south-west Baluchistan and scattered throughout the dryer hilly regions on the western bank of the Indus. In Turkmenistan, Tajikistan, and Uzbekistan these cats live in tamarisk, saxaul, and saltwort thickets and shrub vegetation. In Kazakhstan, Wildcats are found in the bush and reeds fringing lakes and rivers; in the foothills of the Tian Shan Mountains they use bushy areas up to 2000 m. Wildcats use natural caves for shelter or excavates their own burrows. In Europe Wildcats are typically found in broad-leafed and mixed woodlands, particularly in mainland Europe. Coniferous forest use is probably marginal. They are also found in Mediterranean maquis scrubland, riparian woodland, and along the edges of marshes and coasts (but not in marsh edges and coasts in Scotland). They avoid very high mountains, exposed coasts, and intensive agricultural, urban, and industrial habitats, and are not found where snow covers more than 50% of the terrain, is more than 20 cm deep, or remains for 100 days or more each year. Where large-scale deforestation has occurred (e.g., in Scotland), Wildcats have adapted to living in the foothills of mountains and on moorland where rough grazing occurs, and are often associated with forest and cropland. They require some kind of cover to lie up in when inactive. Forestry plantations may provide important habitat in the early stages. They are frequently seen hunting in grasslands adjacent to woodland in Europe.
Food and Feeding. Murids rodents are the dominant prey in most areas in Africa, although larger prey such as spring hares, rabbits, and possibly young antelope are sometimes taken. May also be serious predators of poultry. In Zimbabwe and Botswana about three-quarters of all stomachs examined contained murid rodents. Birds, principally doves, quail, and weavers, ranked second. Incidental prey included lizards, skinks, and snakes. In a semi-desert area of Botswana a common prey identified in stomachs was hunting spiders (Solifugidae). In the Namib Desert the remains of small mammals were found in more than 90% of scats; insects occurred in 70% of scats. Similar percentages of small rodents and insects were found in Wildcat feces from Karoo National Park, South Africa. In the Sahara Wildcats were seen 15 km from the nearest waterhole, suggesting they can do without drinking water. In Asia the cats feed principally on rodents, but will take other prey opportunistically, including insects, lizards, snakes, birds, and are known to raid domestic poultry pens. The prey along the Ili River, Kazakhstan, consisted largely (81%) of hares, muskrats, gerbils, House Mice, and jerboas. In western Rajasthan, the Wildcat's diet was largely jirds (Muridae) and hares, but it was also seen hunting a variety of ground-foraging birds (doves, partridge, sandgrouse, peafowl, pigeons). Snakes, including cobras, saw-scaled vipers, and sand boas were also killed, as were geckos, scorpions, and large beetles. In mainland Europe Wildcats feed predominantly on mice and voles, but in Scotland, rabbits and other lagomorphs are by far the most important prey (up to 70% by frequency in the east). Studies in Scotland have shown that predation on birds, especially game birds, is insignificant. Primarily terrestrial hunter, but can climb well if pursued. They may hunt in trees for rats in flooded forest in Caucasus. Hunt either by waiting in ambush for prey, e.g., outside rabbit burrows, or hunt opportunistically when patrolling home ranges. Moving slowly and quietly along trails and paths, looking and listening for prey. Once prey is detected, creeps forward, patiently, using every piece of cover to get as close as possible before making its attack. Prey seized with the claws and pinned to the ground, or held with the paws until the killing bite delivered. Prey may be cached either by hiding it under vegetation, in holes and trees, or by covering it with debris.
Activity patterns. Secretive, and most reports suggest they are strictly nocturnal, although in areas where undisturbed sometimes seen in early morning and late afternoon. In Pakistan reportedly shelter underground or in dense cover during the heat of the day and emerge at night to hunt. In Turkmenistan described as crepuscular, but in Uzbekistan found active at any time of the day in all seasons. In the northern part of their European range, often also active during daylight in winter, but strictly nocturnal in summer. May remain inactive for up to 28 hours during heavy snowfall or rain and strong winds.
Movements, Home range and Social organization. Little known of social habits in Africa, most sightings are of solitary animals. Anecdotal information suggests animals are highly territorial. The home range of a radio-collared adult male in Kenya was 1·6 km² over the short time followed. In contrast, the home ranges of a radio-tagged male and female Wildcat in the United Arab Emirates measured 28·7 km2 and 52·7 km2, respectively. While the male's range was smaller than that of the female, he was only tracked

for 1·5 months compared to 14 months for the female. The male did, however, travel farther per night than the female, 8·64 km/night and 4·86 km/night, respectively. Over the 14 months she was tracked, the female was located to 42 dens, all of which were burrows made by Red Foxes. In Asia, also, outside of mating associations, are solitary. In south-west Tajikistan the area used for hunting was thought to cover about 3–4 km². In a steppe habitat of Uzbekistan, two animals occupied an area of 10 km². In eastern Scotland, where rabbits were abundant, mean annual home range size was 1·75 km² for both sexes; in western Scotland, where rabbits were scarce, home ranges were much larger (9–10 km² for males and 8–10 km² for females). Home ranges of males in Scotland may overlap with one or more of those of females, but there is usually little intrasexual overlap. Social groupings comprise mostly mothers with kittens, but also dispersing siblings and males with females in estrus. Communication mainly by scent marking, including spraying urine and depositing feces in prominent places near trails on trees, vegetation, and boulders. Feces may be combined with anal sac-gland secretions. Trees and saplings may be scratched using forepaws, leaving a visual marker and an olfactory sign from interdigital gland secretion.

Breeding. Mating is noisy, marked by much screeching and yowling. In the northern Sahara, breed in winter. In southern and East Africa, small young found in all months of the year, but tend to be born during the wet season, which coincides with peaks in rodent abundance. In Central Asia, mating takes place in January–February, and in Rajasthan, in November–December and March–April. In southern Sind, Pakistan, breeding may occur at any season of the year. The female is in heat for about four days; ovulation occurs a day after copulation. Wildcats are induced ovulators. Females come into estrus every six weeks unless conception occurs. Gestation lasts from 56 to 65 days. Typically two or three kittens (maximum five) born, furred and blind, in a well-concealed location. Kittens have been found in hollow trees, underground burrows, rocky crevices, and dense grass. The young first emerge from the natal den at one month and are weaned and introduced to hunting between 3–4 months. In captivity, a female introduced her young to live prey when they were 60 days old, and two days later, the male kittens were killing mice on their own. By the fourth day the female kitten did likewise. In the wild a female was seen bringing injured gerbils to the den for her young to try to kill. Kittens are independent by 5–6 months. Females reach sexual maturity at ten months and males at about twelve months. In captivity, signs of sexual activity were observed in a female who was just over nine months of age and gave birth to a single kitten (80 g) when was eleven months old. In the wild a female born in April was pregnant when caught in late January. In captivity two year-old males attempted to mate with a female who was showing signs of coming into estrus, but in the wild the testes of males were not developed until the cats were 21–22 months of age. In Europe most mating occurs January–March, although the breeding season

may extend December–July. Estrus lasts for 2–9 days; if no conception occurs, recycle in about 14 days. Most births occur in April and May after a gestation period of 60–68 days, but births may extend March–August. Usually only one litter per year, but may have a second if a litter is lost early. Litter sizes in capitivity range from 1–8 (average of 3·4) and in the wild, from 1–7. At birth, kittens weigh 65–163 g (and usually do not survive at less than 90 g). Lactation lasts for 6–7 weeks but may continue sporadically for up to four months. The eyes open at 7–13 days, the kittens begin walking at 16–20 days, playing at 4–5 weeks, and follow their mother at twelve weeks of age. Milk teeth are fully erupted by 42–49 days and permanent dentition is complete by 175–195 days. In captivity females may breed when they are a year old. Males show sign of sexual activity at 9–10 months, but may not mate successfully until established in home range. The young disperse when they are from 4–5 months to ten months old. Wildcats are full-grown by 18–19 months of age.

Status and Conservation. In Asia, CITES Appendix II. In Europe, CITES Appendix II. Listed as species of Least Concern on *The IUCN Red List*, with subspecies *grampia* Vulnerable. In Africa, show tolerance to wide range of environmental conditions and may have benefited from agricultural activities that increased rodent densities. Have historically been trapped in Asia in large numbers for the fur trade, but currently there appears to be little international trade in their pelts. Their population status in most of Asia is not known, but in some areas is reported to be rare. An estimated 90% of its habitat in India has reportedly been lost. Are killed for raiding poultry sheds, and some are killed by domestic dogs. Threats in Europe include fragmentation of habitats and exposure to toxic agricultural chemicals and domestic cat diseases. Persecution and hunting for fur are still important causes of mortality in some areas, e.g., in eastern Europe and Scotland. Road accidents are also a significant cause of mortality. In a study in eastern Scotland, 42% of mortality was due to human causes, mostly persecution and road accidents. On all three continents, the biggest threat to the species is hybridization with domestic cats. This has produced a significant hybrid swarm in some areas (e.g., Scotland). It is unclear whether hybridization will ultimately result in the loss of the genetic integrity of the species, but it has affected legal protection in Scotland.

Bibliography. Amori *et al.* (1999), Beaumont *et al.* (2001), Chavan (1987), Corbett (1979), Daniels, Balharry *et al.* (1998), Daniels, Golder *et al.* (1999), Dragesco-Joffé (1993), Easterbee *et al.* (1991), Estes (1991), Fuller *et al.* (1988), Gasperetti *et al.* (1985), Guggisberg (1975), Hemmer (1999), Heptner & Sludskii (1992a), Jenkins *et al.* (1964), Kingdon (1971-1982), Kitchener (1998), Kitchener & Daniels (2008), McOrist & Kitchener, (1994), Mellen (1993), Mendelssohn (1989), Meyer-Holzapfel (1968), Nowell & Jackson (1996), Palmer & Fairall (1988), Piechocki (1990), Pocock (1944, 1951), Roberts (1977), Sapozhenkov (1961), Scott *et al.* (1993), Sharma (1979), Smithers (1968, 1983), Stahl & Artois (1991), Stahl & Leger (1992), Stuart (1977, 1981), Sunquist & Sunquist (2002), Tonkin & Kohler (1981), Volf (1968), Wilson (1975).

CLASS MAMMALIA

ORDER CARNIVORA

SUBORDER FELIFORMIA

Family PRIONODONTIDAE (LINSANGS)

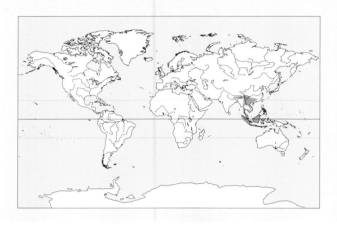

- Small mammals with slender, genet-like aspect, pointed muzzle, elongated neck, and tail almost as long as the head and body; spotted coat pattern and a pair of large stripes on the nape.
- 61–84·9 cm.

- South-east Asia.
- Moist and evergreen forests, including montane forests up to 2700 m.
- 1 genus, 2 species, 4 taxa.
- No species threatened; none Extinct since 1600.

Systematics

The Prionodontidae is a monogeneric family, represented by two distinct species, the Banded Linsang (*Prionodon linsang*) and the Spotted Linsang (*P. pardicolor*).

The taxonomy of the genus *Prionodon* has been very confused. It was first allocated as a "section Prionodontidae" within the genus *Felis* because of morphological similarities with the Felidae. Indeed, their dentition, notably characterized by a vestigial M_1, compressed carnassials, a P_4 almost without talonid, a reduced crushing function of the molars, a vestigial M^1, and a lack of M^2 (in most cases), is cat-like. The purely "flesh-cutting" felid teeth are approached, although canines are smaller, slender, and form a straight vertical line. In addition, linsangs share with felids the absence of perineal scent glands and metatarsal pads, and the presence of deeply grooved pads and fully retractile (sheathed) claws.

The dentition, basicranium, and auditory anatomy of *Prionodon* are very similar to a feliformian fossil from the Upper Oligocene of Eurasia, *Palaeoprionodon*. *Palaeoprionodon* is one of the possible ancestral feliformian morphotypes, together with another Oligocene genus, *Stenoplesictis*, and the extant genus *Nandinia*. It shares several symplesiomorphies with *Prionodon*, including a rudimentary ectotympanic (bulla chamber likely enclosed by a cartilaginous caudal entotympanic in *Palaeoprionodon*), a ventral process of the petrosal promontorium forming a small flange on the medial margin of the petrosal, and double-rooted P_1 and P^1. The morphological similarity between *Palaeoprionodon* and *Prionodon* is reinforced by their dentition, including narrow molars and the absence of M^2. Recently, *Prionodon* was on this basis included in the Viverridae under the subfamily Prionodontinae, as part of a cline between plesiomorphic and modern morphotypes, from *Palaeoprionodon* to *Poiana* (the "African linsang" or oyan) and *Genetta*.

The genus *Prionodon* also shows coat pattern and cranial shape similarities with the "African linsang" or oyan (*Poiana* spp.), which led traditional classifications to include the Linsangs within the Viverridae. They were, however, ranked as a distinct sub-familial taxon (Prionodontinae or Prionodontini) given their noticeable divergences with *Poiana*, including the separation of the hypoglossal foramen from the posterior lacerate foramen, the independent paraoccipital process, the absence of perineal scent glands, and the lack of metatarsal pads.

Recent molecular investigations have clarified the taxonomic status of *Prionodon*, revealing that the Linsangs are the sister-group of extant felids and thus constitute their own family, the Prionodontidae. Those results document an exceptional case of morphological convergence between *Poiana* and *Prionodon*, suggesting that the genome of the feliformians conserved its potential ability of expression for a peculiar adaptive phenotype (i.e. hypercarnivory, arboreality and spotted coat pattern in tropical forests) throughout evolution. They thus confirmed how changeable dental, hair ultrastructure, and coat characters can be within the Carnivora. They also suggested that traits previously considered useful for diagnosing fossils, such as the structure of the auditory bulla and the relative length of metacarpal bones, are subject to convergence. A study using morphological characters within a molecular phylogenetic framework showed that *Prionodon* consisted of a mosaic of shared homoplasies to which *Eupleres* (cranial characters), *Nandinia* (postcranial characters), and *Poiana* (dental characters) mainly contributed. Conversely, morphological similarities between the Linsangs and felids (e.g. hypercarnivory, foot structure) are likely to represent symplesiomorphies. In this context, *Palaeoprionodon* rather represents a lineage at the base of the clade (Prionodontidae, Felidae), or an early offshoot of the Prionodontidae. Divergence time estimates derived from molecular-based methods have yielded values of c. 42 million years (Eocene) for the split between Prionodontidae and Felidae, and c. 13 million years (Miocene) for the cladogenesis between the two species of Linsangs. The clade formed by those two species is supported by a strict, diagnostic synapomorphy, namely the fusion into one straight keel of the two spinous processes of the sacral vertebrae.

Morphological Aspects

Linsangs resemble a slender genet, with a pointed muzzle and an elongated neck, hypercarnivorous dentition, a tail almost as long as the head and body, spotted coat pattern and a pair of large stripes on the nape.

Habitat

The Linsangs inhabit moist and evergreen forests over a wide range in South-east Asia, including montane forests up to 2700 m. They are also recorded in ecotones or mosaics of natural forests and cultivated zones, and may be found in agroecosystems.

Communication

Poorly known. Although perineal glands are absent, scent marking through neck, shoulder, and flank rubbing exists. Territory is marked with urine and feces. Few oral sounds have been re-

Banded Linsangs *have beautiful soft fur, which is unfortunate because this leads to them being hunted. Deforestation is an even greater threat. Slim and graceful, linsangs move like cats, have claws that retract into sheaths like cats, and have teeth like cats. Their family, the Prionodontidae, split from the Felidae some 42 million years ago and began to evolve into the two species recognized today about 13 million years ago. Most information about their diets comes from examining stomach contents and knowing what captives will eat. Banded Linsangs were found to eat fish and eggs as well as chicks and mice, but refused fruits. Spotted Linsangs refused fish, eggs, and fruits.*

Prionodon linsang
Photo: Kenneth W. Fink

corded; adults may snarl and emit whistling noises when confronted by other animals. When scared, they emit a squeak accompanied by a "drumming" on the ground with one forepaw.

Food and Feeding

Linsangs are primarily carnivorous. They have been reported to feed on rodents, frogs, lizards, snakes, small birds, cockroaches, and even carcasses. Captive specimens always refused fruits. Foraging may occur both in trees and on the ground. Small rodents are killed with a bite to the neck, whereas larger prey may be held in the jaws and killed with a series of crunching bites. The forepaws are rarely used for manipulating prey items during feeding.

Breeding

Linsangs give birth once or twice a year, between February and August, to two young per litter. At birth, Banded Linsang

Spotted Linsangs, *like Banded Linsangs, can descend from trees headfirst. They are thought to be primarily arboreal, but camera traps have caught them foraging on the ground. When frightened, they squeak and drum one forepaw on the ground. Females have one or two litters of two cubs per year. The cubs' eyes are fully open by three weeks of age, and they are adult size at four months. Females remain with their mothers until maturity, but males leave after weaning.*

Prionodon pardicolor
Huong Son, Ha Tinh, Vietnam.
Photo: Darrin Lunde/AMNH

cubs were about 40 g and 16 cm from head to tail; weight was doubled at day 18 and eyes were wide open between 18 and 21 days; adult size was reached at four months. The mother never carried her young in her mouth. Maximum longevity in captivity is almost eleven years.

Movements, Home range and Social organization

Due to their secretive, nocturnal, and solitary way of life, there is a lack of data on the eco-ethology of Linsangs in the wild.

Relationship with Humans

Linsangs are small and secretive, and no direct interaction with humans has been reported. They may be occasionally hunted for fur across their range. Continuous degradation of their forested habitats may affect populations in several parts of their range.

Status and Conservation

Although hard data are scarce, both species of Linsangs appear widely distributed but mostly uncommon throughout their range. They are listed on CITES under Appendices I (Spotted Linsang) and II (Banded Linsang), but are considered of Least Concern on *The IUCN Red List*. Protected across almost all their range, major threats remain habitat loss and, to a lesser extent, hunting for fur.

General Bibliography

Azlan (2003), Boitani *et al.* (2006), Choudhury (2002), Duckworth (1997), Duckworth *et al.* (1999), Gangloff (1975), Gaubert & Cordeiro-Estrela (2006), Gaubert & Veron (2003), Gaubert, Wozencraft *et al.* (2005), Hardwicke (1821), Hodgson (1847), Hunt (1998, 2001), IUCN (2008), Kuznetzov & Baranauskas (1993), Lim (1973), Louwman (1970), Nowak (1999), Pham-chong-Ahn (1980), Pocock (1915d, 1933c, 1935), Radinsky (1975), Schreiber *et al.* (1989), Sunquist (1982), Taylor (1988), Tizard (2002), Van Rompaey (1993, 1995), Wurster & Benirschke (1968).

Genus *PRIONODON*

Horsfield, 1822

1. **Banded Linsang** *Prionodon linsang*

French: Linsang rayé / **German**: Bänderlinsang / **Spanish**: Linsang rayado

Taxonomy. *Viverra linsang* Hardwicke, 1821, Malacca, Malaysia. [restricted by Robinson & Kloss (1920) to "Malacca".]

Two subspecies recognized, *linsang* includes *maculosus* and *gracilis* includes *hardwichii*, *fredericae*, and *interliniurus*.

Subspecies and Distribution.

P. l. linsang Hardwicke, 1821 – S Myanmar, Peninsular Malaysia, Sumatra, and S Thailand.

P. l. gracilis Horsfield, 1822 – Bangka I, Belitung I, Borneo, and Java.

Descriptive notes. Head-body 37·9–45 cm, tail 33–37·5 cm; weight 590–800 g. Ratio head-body/tail slightly superior to one. Two pairs of mammae. Adult males may be slightly larger than females, but size overlap between the two genders is considerable. Has a genet-like aspect, with head and neck more elongated; pointed muzzle; nose pad brownish pink. Extremely slender; captive individual reported to escape through bars 4 cm apart. Ears are medium-sized, broad at the base and rounded. Iris is dark brown to black, and pupil is vertical. Pelage is short and very soft. Coat color is relatively uniform across the body, and varies from pale yellowish to white. Individual variation exists in spot markings. Back exhibits two main pairs of lines of very large dark spots that fuse into five more or less clearly delineated transversal stripes. The characteristic pair of nucchal stripes in continuation with the second row of spots is wider than in Spotted Linsang. A line of thin spots starting behind the shoulders forms a broken medio-dorsal stripe that is vertically crossing the transversal stripes. Smaller spots are irregularly distributed on the flanks, shoulders and thighs. The rest of the hindlimbs and the forepaws are not spotted. Five claws fully retractile; presence of sheaths. Hindfeet digitigrade, forefeet plantigrade; hallucal lobe small and remote; absence of metatarsal pads. Tail is almost as long as head and body; thickly furred, with short hair; exhibits seven to nine broad dark rings. Confused annealing pattern at the whitish tip, with the last bright ring often interspersed with a thin dark ring. Perineal glands are absent. Rostrum is moderately elongated; sagittal crest forms a large, flat stripe that fuses with the frontal bone. Caudal entotympanic bone more ventrally inflated—compared to the ectotympanic bone—than in Spotted Linsang. Dental formula: I 3/3, C 1/1, P 4/4, M 1/2 = 38. M^2 may sometimes exist under vestigial condition. Chromosome number: 2n = 34. In *gracilis*, average body size and skull length are smaller.

Habitat. Primary–secondary evergreen and mixed deciduous forests, up to 2700 m (e.g. Jang Plateau, Java). May be found in ecotonal habitats and disturbed forests; few records in human-inhabited places. Its distribution could be shaped by moisture gradients and their topographical variations.

Food and Feeding. Primarily carnivorous. Stomach contents in continental Malaysia and Borneo included rodents (long-tailed rats, spiny-furred rats, ground squirrels), lizards, frogs, birds and cockroaches. Captive individuals were fed with minced meat, mice, chicks, fresh fish, eggs, cottage cheese, and occasionally birds and ox liver; fruits were always refused. May hunt both in canopy and on the ground; direct observations always made on the ground. Great dexterity when chasing small birds. Rodents are killed with a bite to the neck; may combine grasping and killing into one movement, and proceed to a series of crunching bites from the seized part of the body to the head while the prey is maintained between the jaws. Forepaws are rarely used for manipulating preys during feeding; however, an individual was seen pulling off flesh pieces while maintaining the prey with its forepaws (head was eaten first).

Activity patterns. Mostly nocturnal, but may be active during daytime. Presumably arboreal, but probably uses the ground to move and forage. Individuals in continental Malaysia were seen moving among tree branches 3–8 m high but were always trapped on the ground. Nests in hollows of dead trees, under roots of large trees, or in tree holes above ground level. A nest entrance was around 13 cm in diameter and 45 cm in depth; the inside was covered with leaves and contained bits of dry sticks. Good climber and jumper; semi-digitigrade, with plantigrade forefeet and digitigrade hindfeet; uses a "head-first" vertical descent of trees. Has a cat-like gait, and often stands on its hindlegs. In captivity, observed sleeping with tail curled around forepaws and head; frequent sharpening of the claws; self grooming and face washing very similar to genets.

Movements, Home range and Social organization. Almost unknown. Probably solitary. Newly-born captive kittens emit shrill and vibrating cries when handled; adults may snarl and make sharp, whistling noises when other animals are confronted. A captive male frequently urinated while walking, marking about 1 m around. Neck and shoulders, and subsequently flanks, are rubbed against objects for marking.

Breeding. Litters of two cubs, apparently once a year, between February and August. Dens reported in hollow trees; may raise young on the ground. Young with same coloration as adults except at nose (pink) and undersides (white). At birth, captive cubs weighed 40 g and measured 16 cm from head to tail. Weight was doubled at day 18;

eyes were wide open between 18 and 21 days. Young were 275 g and 40 cm at eight weeks; equalled adult size at four months; at this age, they had the same color as their parents but their undersides were still whiter. The mother never carried her young in her mouth. In the wild, females stay with their mother until maturity, but males leave after weaning. A captive specimen lived up to ten years and eight months.

Status and Conservation. CITES Appendix II. Classified as Least Concern on *The IUCN Red List*. Widespread distribution over the Sundaic region at all elevations but records are scarce, especially at northern edge (Myanmar, Thailand) and in Java. Major threats are deforestation and, to a lesser extent, hunting/trade for fur. Most of the skins kept in museums were collected from natives. Protected by national laws in Myanmar, Thailand, Malaysia (only partially protected in Sarawak) and Indonesia.

Bibliography. Azlan (2003), Banks (1949), Boitani *et al.* (2006), Davis (1958), Gangloff (1975), Hardwicke (1821), Jones (1982), Lim (1973, 1976), Louwman (1970), Nowak (1999), Pocock (1915d, 1933c, 1935), Sody (1936, 1949), Schreiber *et al.* (1989), Taylor (1988), Van Rompaey (1993), Wells *et al.* (2005).

2. Spotted Linsang   *Prionodon pardicolor*

French: Linsang tacheté / **German**: Fleckenlinsang / **Spanish**: Linsang manchado

Taxonomy. *Prionodon pardicolor* Hodgson, 1842, "Sikim... Sub-Hemalayan mountains". [Sikkim, India].
Two subspecies recognized, *pardicolor* includes *pardochrous*, and *perdicator*.
Subspecies and Distribution.
P. p. pardicolor Hodgson, 1842 – Bhutan, NE India, N Myanmar, and Nepal.
P. p. presina Thomas, 1925 – Cambodia, S China, Laos, N Thailand, and Vietnam.
Descriptive notes. Head-body 31–45 cm, tail 30–39·9 cm; weight 550–1220 g. Ratio head-body/tail slightly superior to one. Two pairs of mammae. Adult males are larger than and may be twice as heavy as females. Has a genet-like aspect, with head and neck more elongated, pointed muzzle; nose pad brownish pink. Ears are medium-sized, broad at the base and rounded. Iris is dark brown to black. Pelage is short and very soft. Coat color is relatively uniform across the body, and varies from pale gray to yellow rufous on the back and flanks; ventral pelage pale gray to pale yellow. Individual variation exists in spot markings. Back exhibits two main pairs of lines of large dark spots rarely fused, and a characteristic pair of large nucchal stripes in continuation with the second row of spots. A line of thin spots starting behind the shoulders forms a broken medio-dorsal stripe. Small spots are irregularly distributed on the flanks, shoulders and thighs. The rest of the hindlimbs and the forepaws are not spotted. Five claws fully retractile; presence of sheaths. Hindfeet digitigrade, forefeet plantigrade; hallucal lobe small and remote; absence of metatarsal pads. Tail is almost as long as head and body; thickly furred, with short hair; exhibits 7–9 broad dark rings. Confused annealing pattern at the whitish tip, with broad, distal rings

often interspersed with thin ground-colored rings. Perineal glands are absent. Rostrum is moderately elongated; sagittal crest forms a large, flat stripe that fuses with the frontal bone. Caudal entotympanic bone poorly inflated ventrally when compared to the ectotympanic bone. Dental formula: I 3/3, C 1/1, P 4/4, M 1/2 = 38. The brain weighs about 9 g. Geographic variations in coat pattern have been described. In *presina*, size is greater, dorsal spots are smaller and less regularly distributed, ground color—especially on the belly—is paler, and dark rings on the tail are narrower.
Habitat. Primary and secondary moist forests, up to 2700 m (e.g. Nepal, Assam). Also recorded in mosaics of lowland riverine/sal forests and grassland (Nepal), mixed bamboo forests along mountain rivers (Vietnam), and disturbed evergreen forest (Thailand, Laos).
Food and Feeding. Primarily carnivorous. Stomach contents in Vietnam showed remains of rodents, frogs, snakes and small birds. A captive female of 600 g ate around 100 g of meat per day, of which 76·5% was digested. Several authors have mentioned that the favorite food is passerine birds, which may be preyed upon either in trees or hiding in the grass. However, it is not known whether foraging more frequently occurs in trees or on the ground; a captive individual always ate on the ground. Small rodents are killed with a bite to the neck, whereas larger preys (e.g. rats) are leaped upon and finished whilst lying side-by-side on the ground. Reported to feed on carcasses killed by other predators. A captive specimen refused fish, eggs and fruits.
Activity patterns. Most of the active period (about eight hours) takes place during the night. Presumably arboreal, but from recent camera-trap records, may frequently use the ground to move and forage. A captive specimen was reported to spend most of its time at heights up to 1 m, although wild individuals were sighted higher in the canopy. Shelter in trees. Good climber; springs and climbs in the manner of cats; semi-digitigrade, with plantigrade forefeet and digitigrade hindfeet; uses a "head-first" vertical descent of trees. Jumps may reach 1 m high.
Movements, Home range and Social organization. Almost unknown. Probably solitary. A female captive specimen marked territory with urine and feces. When scared, may emit a squeak accompanied by a "drumming" on the ground with one forepaw.
Breeding. Litters reported to be of two cubs, once or twice a year, between February and August (three litters in one year has been reported once in captivity). Dens are located in tree holes.
Status and Conservation. CITES Appendix I. Classified as Least Concern on *The IUCN Red List*. Widespread distribution over South-east Asia but individuals rarely sighted, especially in Myanmar, Thailand and Cambodia. Recent records from camera-trapping however suggest that the species is not uncommon in some parts of its range (e.g. Yunnan, China). Major threats are habitat loss (e.g. slash and burn shifting cultivation) and hunting for fur. Most of the skins kept in museums were collected from natives. Listed on Category II of the China Wildlife Protection Law; totally protected in India, Myanmar, Nepal, Thailand, and Vietnam.

Bibliography. Boitani *et al.* (2006), Choudhury (1997a, 1997b, 2002), Duckworth (1997), Duckworth *et al.* (1999), Hodgson (1842, 1847), Kuznetzov & Baranauskas (1993), Pham-chong-Ahn (1980), Pocock (1915c, 1933c, 1935), Radinsky (1975), Ramakantha (1994), Schreiber *et al.* (1989), Sunquist (1982), Taylor (1988), Tizard (2002), Van Rompaey (1995).

CLASS MAMMALIA

ORDER CARNIVORA

SUBORDER FELIFORMIA

Family VIVERRIDAE (CIVETS, GENETS AND OYANS)

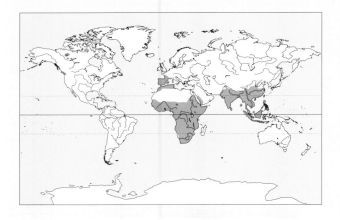

- Small- to medium-sized mammals; body shape is long and slender, with a pointed face, small ears, fairly short legs, and a long tail.
- 65–180 cm.

- Old World tropics throughout Asia and Africa, also southern Europe.
- Found mainly in forests, although some species also live in more open habitats such as savannah and grassland.
- 14 genera, 34 species, at least 79 extant taxa.
- 1 species Critically Endangered, 1 species Endangered, 9 species Vulnerable; none Extinct since 1600.

Systematics

Today, 34 species of civets, genets, and oyans are recognized throughout Asia and Africa, although further taxonomic research may change this number. One species, the Common Genet (*Genetta genetta*), also occurs in Europe, but it may have been introduced to this region during historical times. Based on similarities with the miacids and fossil feliforms of the Oligocene and Miocene, the Viverridae was traditionally viewed as an ancestral group leading to the other feliforms (cats and hyenas). After recent studies, the Viverridae is now viewed as an ancient family of the mesocarnivores that branched off early within the feliform lineage.

The classification of this family was traditionally based on morphological features: the anterior and posterior chambers of the auditory bullae, the foramens at the base of the skull, the dentition, the plantar pads on the feet, and the anal and perineal glands (a scent pouch that lies between the genitals and the anus). Using these features, several authors grouped the civets, genets, linsangs, and mongooses, within the Viverridae, whereas others considered the mongooses as a separate family, the Herpestidae. Recent molecular studies have confirmed that the mongooses should be placed in a separate family; in fact they are closer to the hyenas (Hyaenidae) than to the Viverridae.

Several authors also questioned the relationships of other species traditionally included in the Viverridae, highlighting their unusual features. The African Palm Civet has a cartilagineous entotympanic bone; the Spotted Linsang and Banded Linsang both have a very similar morphology to an Oligocene feliform (*Paleoprionodon*), very cat-like dentition, and do not have a perineal scent gland. The African oyans (*Poiana*) are very similar to the Asian linsangs, but also share some morphological features with the genets (*Genetta*). The previously considered Malagasy viverrids (the Fosa, Falnanouc, and Spotted Fanaloka) were also questioned, particularly the Fosa, which has large plantigrade feet (similar to those of the palm civets) and a viverrid-like basicranium, but has cat-like dentition. The other Malagasy carnivores were traditionally placed in the mongoose family.

The Viverridae has now been redefined by reassessing morphological features and by using new molecular techniques

Subdivision of the Viverridae

Figure: Toni Llobet

VIVERRIDAE

VIVERRINAE

terrestrial civets
6 species
(*Viverricula, Civettictis, Viverra*)

PARADOXURINAE

palm civets and Binturong
7 species
(*Arctogalidia, Macrogalidia, Arctictis,
Paguma, Paradoxurus*)

GENETTINAE

genets and oyans
17 species
(*Poiana, Genetta*)

HEMIGALINAE

palm civets and Otter Civet
4 species
(*Cynogale, Chrotogale, Hemigalus,
Diplogale*)

FAMILY
SUBFAMILY

(comparing the differences in the base pairs of mitrochondrial and nuclear genes). The African Palm Civet is now believed to be an early offshoot within the feliform branch and is placed in a separate family, the Nandiniidae. The Asian linsangs have recently been shown to be a sister group to the cats (Felidae) and are now separated into their own family, the Prionodontidae. It appears that the morphological similarities between the Asian linsangs and African oyans were due to convergent evolution towards a certain morphotype; the African oyans are in fact closely related to the genets. A recent study has also revealed that the Malagasy viverrids form a monophyletic group with the Malagasy mongooses; all the Malagasy carnivores are now placed in their own family, the Eupleridae, a sister group to the mongoose family (Herpestidae). Around 18 to 24 million years ago, an African ancestor (closely related to the mongooses) colonized Madagascar and diversified into mongoose-like, civet-like, and cat-like carnivores on the island, in the absence of any other representatives of the Carnivora.

These studies not only resulted in a new classification of the Viverridae, with the exclusion of some viverrid-like taxa from this family, but they also highlighted the difficulties of using traditional morphological features to define systematic relationships within the feliform carnivores. Dental and basicranial features, such as the auditory bullae, were found to be convergent features or primitive generalized characters in this group. In contrast, some soft anatomy features, such as perineal glands and the morphology of the plantar pads, were shown to be reliable characters to establish relationships. In consequence, the classification of fossil taxa has proved to be very problematic and the origin and evolutionary history of the Feliformia is still not fully resolved.

On the grounds of molecular systematics, morphological divergence, and divergence time estimates, the Viverridae has now been divided into four subfamilies: Genettinae (genets and oyans); Hemigalinae (palm civets and Otter Civet); Paradoxurinae (palm civets and Binturong); and Viverrinae (terrestrial civets).

The subfamily Viverrinae is monophyletic and comprises six species of large, digitigrade terrestrial civets. The African Civet (*Civettictis civetta*) is found in Africa; the Malay Civet (*Viverra tangalunga*), Large Indian Civet (*Viverra zibetha*), Large-spotted Civet (*Viverra megaspila*), Malabar Civet (*Viverra civettina*), and the Small Indian Civet (*Viverricula indica*) all occur in Asia. This group probably originated in Eurasia, with an African Civet ancestor emigrating to Africa during the Middle Miocene. The Small Indian Civet is a sister taxon to the other terrestrial civets; it is the smallest viverrine species and shows some distinctive features. The rare Malabar Civet, endemic to the Western Ghats in India, is very similar to the Large-spotted Civet and

was believed to be conspecific by some authors, but is now recognized as a valid species. In 1997, a new terrestrial civet species, the Taynguyen Civet (*Viverra tainguensis*), was described in Vietnam. However, insufficient evidence has been presented to show that the Taynguyen Civet is a distinct species: it shows many similarities with the Large Indian Civet, and the morphological features considered as diagnostic for the Taynguyen Civet can be observed in the Large Indian Civet in different parts of its range.

The systematic relationships within the Genettinae have been debated for a long time. This subfamily comprises 17 species of slender, semi-arboreal, semi-digitigrade genets and oyans, all found in Africa (except for the Common Genet, which is also found in Europe and on the Arabian peninsula). The Central African Oyan (*Poiana richardsonnii*) and Leighton's Oyan (*Poiana leightoni*), now recognized as two species, were believed to be either close to the genets or the Asian linsangs. Their morphology is peculiar, with a small rounded skull and no second upper molar. Moreover, the presence of a perineal gland in oyans is debated. Recent molecular studies have shown *Poiana* to be a sister group to the genet clade (*Genetta*). Another unusual genettine, the Aquatic Genet (*Genetta piscivora*), has a uniform brown pelage, naked feet, a piscivorous dentition, and a dorsal position of the nostrils. All these features are linked to its presumed adaptation to a semi-aquatic way of life, and were sufficiently unique that it was originally placed it in its own genus, *Osbornictis*. Molecular studies now show that it is in fact a derived genet and should be placed within the genus *Genetta*.

The classification of the remaining genets (*Genetta*) has been fraught with complex taxonomic and species delimitation problems and has long been debated. Species boundaries were difficult to assess using traditional morphological characters (cranial measurements and coat patterns), with the similar species of the large-spotted genet complex being the most problematic. Morphological analyses suggested that this complex should be divided geographically into three groups that correspond to valid species: west of the Volta River (*G. pardina*), east of the Volta River (*G. maculata*), and the coastal area of South Africa (*G. tigrina*). *G. maculata* was also thought to comprise several valid species. Other debated genets were several "forest forms" of the large-spotted genets, the servaline genets, and the Feline Genet *Genetta felina*, which has been considered a subspecies of the Common Genet. Recent molecular and morphological studies have proposed that at least 17 *Genetta* species should be recognized (including the aquatic genet), but the validity of some species still needs to be confirmed.

The current consensus is that the first species to branch off the genet tree were the Hausa Genet (*G. thierryi*), and Abyssinian Genet (*G. abyssinica*), followed later by the Giant Genet (*G.*

*The subfamily Viverrinae comprises six species of terrestrial civets, one found in Africa and five in Asia. The **Small Indian Civet** is a sister taxon to the other viverrine civets (Viverra). It is the smallest species within this subfamily and shows some distinctive features: the black and white neck-stripes are narrower and more variable than in the Viverra civets, and it lacks an erectile dorsal crest. Eleven subspecies are distributed across the Indian subcontinent, Indochina, China, Thailand, Peninsular Malaysia, and Indonesia. The variations in the pattern of lines of spots along the back do not seem to correlate with geographic origin.*

Viverricula indica
Photo: Michael & Patricia Fogden

victoriae). The servaline genets are now confirmed to be two species, the Servaline Genet (*G. servalina*) and Crested Genet (*G. cristata*). The Aquatic Genet and Johnston's Genet (*G. johnstoni*) are closely related and are characterized by distinct morphology. The small-spotted genet complex is a paraphyletic group and consists of two species, the Common Genet and the Feline Genet; the Feline Genet is in fact more closely related to the Angolan Genet (*G. angolensis*) than to the Common Genet. The large-spotted genet complex is monophyletic and comprises at least five species: Rusty-spotted Genet (*G. maculata*), Cape Genet (*G. tigrina*), Pardine Genet (*G. pardina*), King Genet (*G. poensis*), and the newly described Bourlon's Genet (*G. bourloni*). Two other forms within this complex, *letabae* and *schoutedeni*, have been proposed as valid species, but further research is required to confirm their status. Hybridization between some genet species has been detected, which has important evolutionary and conservation implications.

The subfamily Hemigalinae is monophyletic and comprises at least four species that are found in South-east Asia. Their relationships are poorly known. Two species of Otter Civet have been described: the Otter Civet (*Cynogale bennettii*) in the Sundaic region and Lowe's Otter Civet (*Cynogale lowei*) in North Vietnam and southern China. However, the description of Lowe's Otter Civet is based on an immature animal that was bought in a village in North Vietnam (its actual origin is unknown). Although some skins have been reported from villages in China, no further specimens have been found to confirm its status or its presence in the Indochina region. The semi-aquatic Otter Civet has a distinct morphology and is a sister taxon to the rest of this group. The Banded Palm Civet (*Hemigalus derbyanus*), Owston's Palm Civet (*Chrotogale owstoni*), and Hose's Palm Civet (*Diplogale hosei*) were all grouped in the genus *Hemigalus* by some authors, on the basis of their similar morphology, but this is not supported by recent molecular studies, at least for Owston's Palm Civet (Hose's Palm Civet has not yet been included in a molecular phylogeny because of the difficulties in obtaining DNA samples). Although Owston's Palm Civet has a restricted range in Vietnam, Laos, and China, recent genetic analyses have shown two distinct populations.

The subfamily Paradoxurinae is monophyletic and comprises at least seven species of Asian arboreal civets, including the Masked Palm Civet (*Paguma larvata*) and the Binturong (*Arctictis binturong*), the largest civet species. The taxonomic relationships of this group are not yet fully resolved. The Small-toothed Palm Civet (*Arctogalidia trivirgata*) has a peculiar dentition, is very arboreal, and males do not possess a perineal gland.

These features led some authors to consider the Small-toothed Palm Civet as a primitive offshoot of the Viverridae and placed it in a monotypic subfamily, the Arctogalidiinae. It is now considered to be a sister taxon to the other paradoxurine species; the absence of a perineal gland in males may be a secondary loss rather than a primitive feature. *Paradoxurus* is the only polytypic genus within the Paradoxurinae. The number of species in this genus is still uncertain; the Mentawai Palm Civet (*Paradoxurus hermaphroditus lignicolor*) may either be a subspecies of the Common Palm Civet (*Paradoxurus hermaphroditus*) or a distinct species. The Common Palm Civet has a large distribution throughout Asia and varies in size, coat pattern, and color throughout its range; at least thirty subspecies have been described. The other *Paradoxurus* species, the Brown Palm Civet (*Paradoxurus jerdoni*) and Golden Palm Civet (*Paradoxurus zeylonensis*) were also described mainly on the basis of coat color and pattern, and could either be different morphotypes of Common Palm Civet or valid species. A recent molecular study revealed significant genetic distances between the Brown Palm Civet and the Common Palm Civet, which suggests that the Brown Palm Civet is a valid taxon; this is also supported by its distinctive morphology (brown uniform color, no spots, no facial pattern, the hairs on the neck are reversed, and there is a large parastyle on the upper carnassial). The Golden Palm Civet, endemic to Sri Lanka, and the Sulawesi Palm Civet (*Macrogalidia musschenbroekii*), endemic to Sulawesi, have yet to be investigated by molecular studies. The morphological features of the Sulawesi Palm Civet suggest that it may be a sister taxon to *Arctictis*, *Paguma*, and *Paradoxurus*.

Although the fossil record of the Viverridae is quite poor, current evidence suggests that this family appeared in Eurasia around 30–35 million years ago, with the four subfamilies emerging around 25 million years ago (Late Oligocene to Early Miocene). Viverrid fossils are mainly identified on the basis of cranial features (the structure of the basicrania and auditory bullae) and dentition. Fossils recognized by some authors as viverrids include *Paleoprionodon* (Early Oligocene, 30–34 million years ago, France and Mongolia), *Herpestides* (Aquitanian, 21–23 million years ago, France), *Viverra* (subgenus *Viverrictis*), *Jourdanictis*, and *Semigenetta* (13–20 million years ago, Europe and China). The earliest African fossils are from the Early to Middle Miocene and include *Stenoplesictis* or *Semigenetta* (19·6 million years ago) and *Orangictis* (17·5 million years ago). Large viverrids (exceeding the size of the African Civet) were a diverse group during the Plio-Pleistocene, in both Africa and Eurasia.

Before 21 million years ago, South-east Asia was covered by dry and seasonal vegetation, but this later changed to predominately rainforest. The climatic and paleogeographic changes that occurred during the recent Ice Ages may have affected the diversification and distribution of the Asian civet species on the Sunda shelf (an area comprising the Thai/Malay Peninsula south of the Isthmus of Kra, Sumatra, Borneo, Palawan, Java, and other Indonesian islands). During the Pleistocene, the dispersal of species was associated with changing sea levels and the establishment of land bridges. During glacial maximums, sea levels were much lower than today and all the land areas of the Sunda shelf were connected into one large landmass, across which species could move freely (up until about 10,000 years ago when higher sea levels once more physically separated the islands). However, despite the Late Pleistocene existence of land connections between Borneo, Java, Sumatra, and the Malay Peninsula, the present day distribution of some civet species indicates that there may have been barriers to animal movement, and that dispersal between different areas was restricted. Some species may have not used land bridges because of ecological barriers: during the glacial periods, the climate was drier, colder, and more seasonal, and open habitats (such as tree savannah) covered some areas in the Sundaic region, whereas other areas remained forested. Physical barriers may also have affected species distribution: during the last glacial maximum, large rivers on the northern Sunda shelf separated the landmasses between Java and Borneo, and between Peninsular Malaysia and Borneo.

Sulawesi is an island bounded by deep ocean trenches, which has remained isolated from the Asian and Australasian continents even when sea levels dropped during the Ice Ages. This severely restricted the dispersal of animal and plant species across these continents, resulting in many unique species evolving in this region. Sulawesi has an impoverished mammalian carnivore fauna, comprising just three species of civets: the endemic Sulawesi Palm Civet, the Malay Civet, and the Common Palm Civet. The latter two species may have been introduced by humans.

A phylogeographic study of the Binturong has shown that mainland populations are separated by the Isthmus of Kra on Peninsular Thailand, a recognized geographic barrier for Indochina and Sundaic mammalian faunas. Geographical barriers may also have affected the distribution of Asian viverrids between the Indian and Indochina sub-regions: the Brahmaputra River in Bangladesh (Small-toothed Palm Civet and the Large Indian Civet) and the Salween River in Myanmar (Large-

spotted Civet, Masked Palm Civet, and Binturong). In India, the Malabar Civet and Brown Palm Civet are both endemic to the Western Ghats, and the Golden Palm Civet is endemic to Sri Lanka.

The collision that occurred between Africa and Asia at least 20–27 million years ago ago allowed for faunal and floral exchanges between these two continents (via the Arabian microplate). An additional Africa-Eurasia migration route was the connection between south-western Europe and North Africa. These routes may have persisted until the Early Pliocene, after which the Arabian Peninsula desertified and the strait of Gibraltar opened. During the Miocene, two independent viverrid migration events occurred from Asia to Africa, possibly through the forested corridors on the Arabian Peninsula. One took place between the Late Oligocene and the Middle Miocene (the genet group) and the other during the Middle Miocene (an African Civet ancestor).

The African genets evolved from a *Poiana*-like ancestor that inhabited rainforests. Around eight million years ago, the Hausa Genet was the first species to split from the genet tree and inhabit open habitats. A period of rainforest expansion at the

The subfamily Genettinae comprises 17 species of slender, semi-arboreal, semi-digitigrade genets and oyans. All are found in Africa, except the **Common Genet**, which is also found in Europe (where it may have been introduced) and on the Arabian Peninsula. The classification of the Genettinae has been fraught with complex taxonomic problems. The different species are difficult to assess using traditional morphological characters, such as cranial measurements and coat patterns. Hybridization between some genet species has also been detected. Recent molecular and morphological studies have proposed that at least 17 Genetta species should be recognized, but the validity of some of these species still needs to be confirmed. High intra-specific variability within the Common Genet makes clear distinctions between populations difficult to assess and over 30 subspecies have been described, although only five are recognized here. The Common Genet is part of the "small-spotted genet complex", a paraphyletic group that also includes the **Feline Genet**, (which some have considered a subspecies of the Common Genet). The Feline Genet is a medium-sized genet, with long guard hairs. Found in largely arid habitats, its coat color is whitish-gray.

Above: *Genetta genetta*
Vizcaya, Spain.
Photo: José Luis Gómez de Francisco

Below: *Genetta felina*
South Africa.
Photo: Roland Seitre

beginning of the Pliocene (5·3 million years ago) coincided with an emergence of additional savannah species (through geographical isolation) and a divergence of rainforest species. Equatorial Africa at that time was warmer and more humid, and rainforest covered a larger area than today. From the Middle Pliocene onwards, climatic changes resulted in rainforest contraction, which favored the speciation of genets across a wide range of open habitats (especially during major arid periods between 3·2–3 million years ago). Most of the extant genets appeared during the cooling and drying periods of the Pleistocene, with the two forest species, the Crested Genet and the Servaline Genet, splitting during the Late Pliocene–Middle Pleistocene, perhaps due to isolation in forest refuges.

Although recent studies have redefined the Viverridae and greatly clarified many of the relationships within this group, several issues still remain to be resolved. The systematics of the civets, genets, and oyans, is difficult to study: many viverrids are rare in the wild, so obtaining fresh DNA samples is extremely difficult, and some species are very poorly represented in museum collections. Moreover, their evolutionary history has been difficult to understand because viverrid fossils are rare and largely unstudied. In particular, the evolution of the genets seems very complex and has been influenced by many factors.

Morphological Aspects

Viverrids are small carnivore species, ranging from the 0·6 kg African oyans to the 20 kg Binturong. Sexual dimorphism is not very evident in many species and generally males and females appear to be similar in size. The general body shape is long and slender, with a pointed face, small ears, fairly short legs, and a long tail. The body form ranges from the digitigrade terrestrial civets, to the semi-digitigrade semi-arboreal genets, and oyans, to the plantigrade arboreal palm civet species; the terrestrial civets tend to be more compact with a shorter tail. The different body forms are clearly related to life on the ground and/or in trees. In the digitigrade species, where the animal stands and moves on its toes, the limb bones are elongated and the metapodials in the feet are long and often closely bound together. These adaptations increase the stride length for efficient movement on the ground and help absorb stresses while travelling at speed. In the arboreal plantigrade species, where the whole foot is used in locomotion, the metapodials are shorter and more spreading, the digits are arranged fanwise, the limbs are generally shorter and heavier, and there is a greater lateral mobility at the wrist and ankle. These adaptations allow for efficient movement through trees. A long tail in an arboreal species also helps provide balance while travelling along branches; the Binturong is unusual in that it is the only viverrid species in which the tail is prehensile.

Viverrid coat patterns vary considerably between species. The primary function of coat coloration in a small carnivore is concealment, from both predators and prey; a small carnivore is vulnerable to attack from a larger predator and it needs to remain undetected by its potential prey. Forest species tend to have darkish coats, often with mottling, spots or stripes, that are difficult to see in an uneven pattern of light and shade. This irregular patterning is extremely cryptic, even in relatively open terrain. Several viverrid species, such as the Binturong and Aquatic Genet, have a uniform coat and tail, with no spots or stripes (or only indistinct markings). The Binturong's coat is also very shaggy, with long dark hairs. The genets, oyans, and terrestrial civets, have a basic coat pattern of dark spots (which in some species are arranged in lines or join up to form longitudinal stripes), and a tail with alternating dark and pale rings. The dark mid-dorsal stripe in some of these species has a crest of long erectile hairs that can be raised when the animal is alarmed or excited. The Banded Palm Civet and Owston's Palm Civet are unusual in that they have a coat pattern with large transverse bands across their backs.

Coat color in mammals is under complex genetic control and color mutations in viverrids have been reported: melanism in the African Civet and genets, and both albino and melanistic specimens in the Common Palm Civet. Geographical variation in the pelage has also been found for many species across their range, notably in the Common Palm Civet. Temporary changes

in viverrid coat color may occur during seasonal molts, when the new shorter hair gives a different appearance. In the Banded and Owston's palm civets, the pelage changes color as young animals reach maturity. Generally, both sexes have a similar coat color and pattern. However, in male Owston's Palm Civets the ventral pelage is bright orange-red, whereas in the female it is pale yellow (except for an orange area around the vulva).

Many viverrids, such as the Common Palm Civet and African Civet, have well-defined facial markings that resemble the "bandit" mask of the Northern Raccoon. The Masked Palm Civet has a black face with a white longitudinal band and white patches around the eyes; Owston's and Banded palm civets have dark longitudinal stripes along the nose and through each eye. A number of hypotheses have been suggested to account for these distinctive markings. They are an anti-glare device; they help maintain group cohesiveness; they elicit grooming; they influence mate choice; they enhance the size of the teeth or the body; they provide disruptive coloration. The most favored hypothesis is that they act as a warning signal of a viverrid's fighting abilities and thus help deter predation by larger carnivores.

The terrestrial civets have a conspicuous black and white neck pattern that may serve to orient bites between individuals to a relatively safe part of the body. For instance, the play fighting of young African Civets is very prone to turn vicious and as soon as this happens they fence for position and bite predominantly at the side of the neck, an area of the body where there are no vital structures near the surface. As hypothesized for facial masks, these neck stripes could also serve as a warning signal to larger predators. Interestingly, in a few viverrids, such as the Brown Palm Civet and Golden Palm Civet, the hair on the neck does not slope backwards but is instead directed forward. The reason for this is not known, but one suggestion is that it is related to grooming, perhaps between a mother with young or a male and female during mating, when the neck hair is licked forward.

Viverrids have an elongated snout, with well-developed vibrissae (whiskers) on the muzzle (mystacial), above the eyes (superciliary), on the cheeks (genal), and below the chin (inter-ramal); these vibrissae are particularly long in the Otter Civet. Viverrids also have carpal vibrissae on the wrists. The rhinarium is generally quite large and in the palm civets the median groove reaches the upper part of the nose. In the Otter

The **Rusty-spotted Genet** is part of the "large-spotted genet complex", which is monophyletic and includes at least four other species: Cape Genet, Pardine Genet, King Genet, and the newly described Bourlon's Genet. The species boundaries between the genets of this complex are very difficult to assess using traditional morphological characters. For instance, the Rusty-spotted Genet has been considered conspecific with the Cape Genet. Some morphological analyses suggested that this complex should be divided geographically into three groups that correspond to valid species: west of the Volta River (Pardine Genet), east of the Volta River (Rusty-spotted Genet), and the coastal area of South Africa (Cape Genet).

Genetta maculata
Rubondo Island National Park, Tanzania.
Photo: Günter Ziesler

Civet and Aquatic Genet, the nostrils are located on the dorsal surface. It is not known how well viverrids can smell, but in the African Civet at least, the sense of smell appears to be acute and clearly plays an important part in its life. As soon as it wakes up, it points its nose upwards and sniffs the air, while moving the head gently up and down through a small arc. During mating, male African Civets have been observed to make the grimace known as flehmen, which is commonly seen in cats. While sniffing a female's perineal region or her urine, the male's lips are pulled up, the nose is wrinkled and drawn back, and the head is raised. This action brings odors into contact with the Jacobson's organ, a pouch lined with receptor cells in the roof of the mouth. It is not known how universal the flehmen response is among the viverrids, but it has also been observed in some genets and in Binturongs.

Viverrids are generally nocturnal, so they tend to have large eyes: a large eye with a wide aperture allows more light to enter at night. There is also a reflective layer, the tapetum lucidum,

outside the receptor layer of the retina. Light that has passed through the retina without being absorbed is reflected back again and so has a second chance of stimulating a receptor. When a bright light is shone in the eye, the resulting "eyeshine" is the reflected light that has not been absorbed on the return journey and which passes back to the observer. Viverrids have vertically slit pupils, an adaptation that allows almost compete closure of the pupils in bright light. It appears that viverrids are either color blind or only able to distinguish a few colors, and in general, it seems that these visual cues are unimportant to the animal. The Cape Genet is unable to discriminate yellow, green, and blue from gray, but the Small Indian Civet is able to distinguish red and green. However, special training was required and normally the Small Indian Civet responded preferentially to brightness clues.

The ears of viverrids are generally round, with the skin of the outside rim folded to form a small purse called a bursa. The ears can be directed forward or rotated laterally in response

As a member of the monophyletic Paradoxurinae subfamily of Asian arboreal palm civets, the **Binturong** is the largest civet species, and the only viverrid in which the tail is prehensile. It is also a little unusual in having a shaggy, uniform coat and tail, with no spots or stripes. The general coat color is black, but the tip of the guard hairs can be white, giving a grizzled appearance in some individuals. The ears are black and rounded, with a white rim. Largely arboreal, Binturongs can climb trees with ease, but progress slowly and deliberately, using their tails for balance and to hold branches for support. On the ground, they are plantigrade. Their feet have five digits, and very large metacarpal and metatarsal pads covered with coarse skin.

Arctictis binturong
Sarawak, Borneo.
Photo: Art Wolfe

to auditory stimuli, but they cannot be folded back. Almost nothing is known about the hearing sensitivity of viverrids, but the upper limit of the Common Palm Civet has been recorded around 70 kHz, far above that of humans (around 16 kHz). Sensitivity to high frequencies is very useful for detecting the high-pitched sounds and rustles of small prey.

Viverrids have five toes on each foot, although the first digits in some species are much reduced and they do not appear in any tracks. Like the felids, viverrids have retractable claws (although it is not known for certain if this is a universal feature). At rest, the claws are held retracted by ligaments and in order to use them the animal must extend the terminal phalanges and protract the claw, using muscular action (it is therefore more accurate to say that the claws are protractable). In cats, there is a sheath of skin that protects the claw when retracted (except in the Cheetah). A few viverrids are also known to have protective skin sheaths (although not as well-developed as in the cats), but there are absent in many species. Several viverrids have been described as having semi- or partially retractable claws, but it is unclear if this refers to their limited retractability or to whether there is no fleshy sheath around each retracted claw (giving them a more exposed, protracted appearance at rest), or both. Several arboreal viverrids, such as the Common Palm Civet and Sulawesi Palm Civet, have a fleshy web between the toes.

The structure of the feet and footpads is variable within this family and reflects adaptations for living on the ground and/or in trees. The usual structure of the footpads is five digit pads, five plantar pads (one for each digit, but they can be indistinct), and two metapodial pads (metacarpal pads on the forefeet and metatarsal pads on the hindfeet—these can be large in arboreal viverrids, but are reduced or absent in the terrestrial species). Arboreal viverrids are plantigrade and have large flexible feet that allow them to grip trunks and branches while moving and climbing through trees. Some palm civets are arboreal and have short metapodials and long, wide metapodial pads that reach the plantar pads. The bottom of the foot is naked and in some species there are depressions between the pads that are covered by coarse horny tubercles. The surfaces of the footpads are rough, except in the Small-toothed and Sulawesi Palm Civets. The third and fourth digit pads are fused in some paradoxurine species, which is possibly linked to their ability to walk along branches. In the semi-arboreal genets and oyans, the metatarsal pads are long and very narrow, but they do not reach the plantar pads. The metatarsal pads are fairly short in the Banded Palm Civet, perhaps indicating a more terrestrial

lifestyle; however, little is known about the habits of this species. The terrestrial civets are digitigrade, with elongated metapodials; the metacarpal pads are reduced and the metatarsal pads are reduced or absent.

Viverrids have a unique perineal scent gland that produces a very odorous substance and which is used for scent marking. It consists of a compact mass of glandular tissue that lies between the anus and the genitals and which opens onto a naked or sparsely haired area. The secretion of the perineal gland is called civet and contains a chemical called civetone, a macrocyclic compound (9-cis cycloheptadecenone). This thick secretion is yellowish in color and has a strong musky odor due to the array of saturated and unsaturated cyclic ketones and alcohols. It turns brown with age and can retain its odor for at least three months. A perineal gland is present in both sexes of viverrids, except in the male Small-toothed Palm Civet. It is uncertain if the male Sulawesi Palm Civet has this gland (although there is a small naked area between the anus and scrotum) and the presence of perineal glands in the African oyans is also debated. A perineal gland has been described in the African Palm Civet (which is no longer considered a viverrid); however, the structure and position of this gland seem to be different from that of the true viverrids.

The structure of the perineal gland varies among viverrid species. In the Paradoxurinae, this gland is simple, consisting of a patch of glandular tissue that is divided into right and left halves, with numerous small openings to the overlying area of naked skin. The position of this naked area varies from species to species and may be flat or folded to form two small storage pockets. The perineal glands are similar in the Hemigalinae: the glandular area delivers its secretion into a longitudinal depression in the Banded Palm Civet and into a number of shallow pits (not surrounded by labia) in the Otter Civet. In the genets, the perineal gland is a longitudinally folded muscular pad that appears as two densely furred labia. When the muscles of the gland contract, the labia and inner surface can be everted to form a raised, creased, oval-shaped pad that is covered with a fine layer of white hair. The gland secretion is deposited by the underlying glandular tissue into the creases, where it accumulates and eventually spreads over the pad surface. The perineal gland reaches it highest development in the Viverrinae. In the terrestrial civets, it forms a double-pocketed invagination, which is visible externally as two large swellings. Inside each gland is a large hair-lined pouch, in which the secretory portion is surrounded by striated muscle that compresses the

*Many viverrids have well-defined facial markings that resemble the "bandit" mask of the Northern Raccoon. In the northern parts of its range, the **Masked Palm Civet** has a black face with a white longitudinal band from the nose to the nape, and white patches above and below the eyes. Among the various hypotheses to account for these distinctive facial markings (they are an anti-glare device, help maintain group cohesiveness, enhance the apparent size of the teeth or the body, or provide disruptive coloration), the most favored hypothesis is that they may act as a warning signal of a small carnivore's fighting abilities, helping deter predation by larger predators.*

Paguma larvata
Sichuan, China.
Photo: Pete Oxford/naturepl.com

The **Common Palm Civet** has a large distribution throughout Asia and varies in size, coat pattern, and color across its range. The number of subspecies of the Common Palm Civet is debated, and at least 30 have been described. The coat color is gray, grayish-brown, or rusty, with brown or black body spots and stripes. The head pattern is very variable, but generally consists of a dark mask, with white or pale gray patches below the eyes, on the forehead, and at the bases of the ears. Facial variations include: a muzzle with white nose patches; ear and forehead patches that are fused; face patches that are very small; and facial patterns that are absent or very faint. The pattern of rows of spots on the flanks is also variable, and can be obscure in some populations. For instance, on Borneo and the Philippines, the whole body can be dark brown or black, and the stripe and spot pattern is indistinguishable. Albino and melanistic specimens have also been reported. Temporary changes in viverrid coat color may occur during seasonal molts, when the new shorter hair gives a different appearance. In the northern parts of the Common Palm Civet's range, the length of the guard hair seems to vary seasonally; when the pelage is long, the coat pattern tends to be faint. Paradoxurus is the only polytypic genus within the subfamily Paradoxurinae, and the number of species in this genus is still uncertain. The other Paradoxurus species, the Brown Palm Civet and the Golden Palm Civet, were described mainly on the basis of coat color and pattern, and could either be different morphotypes of the Common Palm Civet or valid species. However, a recent molecular study revealed significant genetic distances between the Brown Palm Civet and the Common Palm Civet, which suggests that the Brown Palm Civet is a valid taxon. Similarly, the Mentawai Palm Civet may either be a subspecies of the Common Palm Civet or a distinct species.

Paradoxurus hermaphroditus
Pulau Ubin, Singapore.
Photo: Norman Lim

MILY VIVERRIDAE
ivets, Genets and Oyans

In the **Brown Palm Civet**, the hairs on the neck are directed forward, a feature that also occurs in the Golden Palm Civet, but not in the Common Palm Civet. The reason for this characteristic is not known, but one suggestion is that it is related to grooming, perhaps between a mother with young or a male and female during mating, when the neck hair is licked forward. The coat color is a uniform brown, but is darker on the head, neck, shoulders, legs, and tail; there are paler patches in front of the ears. The Brown Palm Civet is endemic to the Western Ghats, India.

Paradoxurus jerdoni
Valparai, Tamil Nadu, India.
Photo: Kalyan Varma

gland. An oblong opening between the pouches is kept closed by a pair of labia that are everted when the secretion is being applied.

Viverrids have anal glands, but they are not as well-developed as in other carnivores. The anal sacs are located under the skin of the anal region and open directly into the rectum. They are composed of an epithelial lining with sebaceous glands, connective tissue, and a thick layer of muscle. The Large Indian Civet is unusual in that a depressed area of naked skin surrounds the anal area. The yellowish secretion of the anal gland does not have the characteristic odor of the perineal gland secretion and consists of cholesterol esters, monoester waxes, cholesterol, and fatty acids. Viverrids cannot mark objects directly with the anal glands; instead the secretion is added to the feces. The role of this secretion in viverrids is un-

clear; the odor from African Civet scats was actually found to be more dependent on the food consumed than on its anal gland secretion.

Most viverrids have an elongated, narrow, flat skull, but the oyans (and to a lesser extent the genets) have a shorter snout and a more rounded skull. The rostrum is quite short and the maxillo-turbinals are relatively small, with simple branchings. This does not mean that olfactory acuity is reduced, as the olfactory epithelium extends only over the posterior turbinals; the function of the maxillo-turbinals is in fact to warm and moisten the incoming air. The orbital ring is far from complete; the post-orbital and jugal processes are short or sometimes rudimentary. The auditory bullae have two chambers, as in other feliforms, but viverrids have a characteristic elongated caudal entotympanic bone (the posterior chamber) that extends ante-

Two species of **Otter Civet** have been described: the Otter Civet in the Sundaic region, and Lowe's Otter Civet in North Vietnam and southern China; however, this latter species is only known from the type specimen, and its validity is doubtful. The Otter Civet has a distinct morphology and is a sister taxon to the other species within the subfamily Hemigalinae. It has a large snout, with the nostrils opening upwards. The ears are small and round; both ears and nostrils can be closed when the head is submerged. The facial vibrissae are very long and numerous. The Otter Civet has very specialized dentition, with sharp, blade-like premolars and wide, crushing molars, which is presumably related to its aquatic diet.

Cynogale bennettii
Malaysia.
Photo: Roland Seitre

Owston's Palm Civet and Banded Palm Civet are unusual among viverrids in that they have a coat pattern with large transverse bands across their backs. Other forest viverrid species tend to have darkish coats, with mottling, spots, or stripes. Owston's Palm Civet has four large black bands across the back that resemble long triangles, with their bases on the back and the apex towards the abdomen. This pelage pattern is very similar to that of Banded Palm Civet, but Owston's Palm Civet has black spots on the sides of the neck, forelimbs, thighs, and flanks. Both of these species have dark longitudinal stripes along the nose and through each eye. Generally, both sexes have a similar coat color and pattern. However, in male Owston's Palm Civets, the ventral pelage is bright orange-red, whereas in the female it is pale yellow, except for an orange area around the vulva. In both species, the pelage changes color as young animals reach maturity. On the basis of their similar morphology, Owston's Palm Civet, Banded Palm Civet, and Hose's Palm Civet were all grouped in the genus Hemigalus by some authors, but this is not supported by recent molecular studies (at least not for Owston's Palm Civet). Although Owston's Palm Civet has a restricted range in Vietnam, Laos, and China, recent genetic analyses have show two distinct populations that mig be considered subspecies.

Chrotogale owstoni
Vietnam.
Photo: Roland Seitre

Some palm civets have feet adapted for an arboreal existence. But in the **Banded Palm Civet**, the metatarsal foot pads are fairly short, perhaps indicating a more terrestrial lifestyle; its diet also suggests that it forages on the forest floor. However, the Banded Palm Civet is believed to be partly arboreal, and it climbs well in captivity. Very little is known about the habits of this species in the wild.

Hemigalus derbyanus
Sarawak, Borneo.
Photo: Art Wolfe

riorly. The back of the auditory bulla is completely covered by a wide paroccipital process and there is no bony auditory tube. The basicranium and the foramens are quite similar to other feliforms, and the alisphenoid canal is present.

Viverrid dentition is diversified and is linked to their wide range of diets. They generally have 40 teeth, with a typical dental formula of three incisors, one canine, four premolars and two molars on each side of the upper and lower jaws (I 3/3, C 1/1, P 4/4, M 2/2). The oyans lack the second upper molar. The small incisors are mainly used for nipping food items, such as the flesh from carcasses, and the canines are used to grasp and kill prey by piercing the neck or skull. The characteristic carnassial teeth (the fourth upper premolar and the first lower molar) are specially adapted to cutting through flesh with a scissor-like action. In viverrids, the upper carnassial has a protocone set anteriorly, a long blade-like metacone, a high pointed paracone, and a characteristic weak parastyle. The lower carnassial has a well-developed trigonid (with three cusps of similar size) and a well-developed talonid. The premolars, depending on their particular shape, may either aid in holding prey or, like the molars, be used mainly for crushing food items, particularly plant material. Viverrids with a high carnivorous component in their diet (the terrestrial civets and genets) have carnassial teeth with developed sharp blades, while others (the arboreal palm civets) have developed crushing teeth, suitable for eating fruit and other plant material. The Otter Civet and Aquatic Genet both have very specialized dentition; the Otter Civet has sharp, blade-like premolars and wide crushing molars. Presumably, these features are related to their aquatic diet. Johnston's Genet has teeth that suggest it specializes in eating insects.

The milk dentition provides a juvenile animal with the necessary equipment for dealing with solid food, but since the jaws are not adult size, further teeth (particularly the molars) must develop later. The milk dentition and the permanent set are each a functional unit and the transition from one to the other must take place without disrupting the functioning of the dentition as a whole. Permanent canines do not emerge directly beneath their milk precursors, but a little in front or alongside them, and the milk teeth are not shed until after the permanent ones have erupted sufficiently to be functional. Malay Civets that are approximately nine months old have permanent canines that are just emerging in front of the milk teeth. In the Rusty-spotted Genet, the first canines appear at four weeks and are shed after the permanent canines have fully erupted, at around 10–11 months. The eruption sequence for the pre-

molars and molars has only been recorded for the Common Palm Civet (upper jaw: P^1, P^2, M^1, P^4, P^3, M^2; lower jaw: P_1, P_2, M_1, P_3, P_4, M_2).

The post-cranial skeleton does not differ much from other feliform carnivores. The relative size of the metacarpal and metatarsal bones varies according to the mode of locomotion, being longest in the terrestrial species. Some skeletal adaptations exist in the arboreal species to allow a greater flexibility of the joints. The number of caudal vertebrae varies according to the length of the tail, which itself is related to arboreal habits: there are 26 in genets, 28 in *Paradoxurus*, and 32 in the Binturong. The Binturong is unusual within the viverrids in having a prehensile tail with a higher number of caudal vertebrae, a longer proximal caudal region, and more robust distal caudal vertebrae (with expanded transverse processes). These features allow for enhanced flexion-extension of the proximal part of the tail, and increase the strength and flexibility of the distal end of the tail.

A baculum (a small bone within the penis) is present in most known viverrids, but is said to be absent in the palm civets *Paguma* and *Paradoxurus*. It is short in most viverrid species, except in the Asian terrestrial civets (*Viverra* and *Viverricula*). This penis bone is found throughout the Carnivora (except the Hyaenidae) and may help in penetrating the vaginal orifice and providing vaginal stimulation. In its simplest form it is a rod-like structure, grooved below for the passage of the urethra and the corpus spongiosum. The baculum varies among species, each showing distinctive characters, although the function and significance of the different shapes and sizes are not entirely clear.

Habitat

The Viverridae live mainly in forests, although some species also live in more open habitats such as savannah and grassland. They are found mainly in the Old World tropics throughout Asia and Africa; the Common Genet also occurs in Europe (but humans may have introduced this species into this region) and some Asian civet species have been introduced to several islands throughout South-east Asia. The Viverridae are not found in the American continents, which suggests that during their evolutionary history they were unable to traverse colder northern latitudes and enter the New World through the Bering land bridge. They also do not occur in the Australasian region (New Guinea, Australia, and New Zealand).

Viverrids groom themselves in a cat-like manner. They lick and nibble their fur, clean their faces with tongue-moistened paws, and, like this **Binturong***, scratch themselves with their hindpaws. Other cat-like behavior includes scratching their claws on suitable surfaces (to prevent them from becoming too long), and stretching by first humping the back and extending the forelegs, then arching the back and extending the hindlegs.*

Arctictis binturong
Photo: Roland Seitre

Viverrids are found over a wide elevation range, from sea level up to around 3800 m. Some species, like the Banded Palm Civet, appear to be more common in lowland forests, while others, such as the Masked Palm Civet, may be more common at higher altitudes.

The Viverridae probably evolved from a forest-living ancestor, which explains why many species are found in forests today. Climatic changes that caused expansions or contractions of forest and open habitats had an impact on viverrid evolution, particularly in Africa. African genets evolved from a rainforest ancestor and diversified during a period of rainforest expansion at the beginning of the Pliocene. From the Middle Pliocene onwards, cooling/drying events and rainforest contraction led to a further diversification of genet species in both open habitats and rainforest.

The habitat preferences of most viverrid species are not very well known. For many species, we only know where they occur from museum specimens and anecdotal information provided by local people and field researchers. Recent spotlighting surveys (using a powerful electric torch at night to detect eyeshine) and camera-trapping (automatic camera systems) are now providing more information. Radio-tracking studies can provide detailed information about habitat preferences, but so far few studies have been done on viverrids. Using Geographical Information System (GIS) data and computer modelling, we can also make some predictions about the potential range of a species, giving us a greater insight into their distribution and a means to direct future survey efforts.

The impacts of forest loss and fragmentation on viverrids are not well known. There is a high demand for timber and land throughout the tropics; forests are fast disappearing and the land converted to other uses such as growing crops and expanding urban areas. Lowland forest is particularly vulnerable and little remains in some countries. Studies on tropical rainforest fragmentation have shown that the diversity and abundance of plant and animal species is influenced by the size of the habitat, with larger areas usually containing a greater number of species. Species that are severely impacted by habitat fragmentation are those with specialist habitat requirements or large home ranges.

The Western Ghats mountain range in India underwent considerable habitat fragmentation and degradation between 1920 and 1990, with an estimated four-fold increase in the number of forest fragments and an 83% reduction in the size of the surviving patches. A recent study in this region found that the endemic, arboreal, and predominately frugivorous Brown Palm Civet was more common in medium-sized rainforest fragments (adjoining coffee plantations that still had some native tree cover) than in more isolated smaller and larger rainforest fragments. In contrast, the omnivorous Small Indian Civet was more abundant in rainforest fragments than in relatively undisturbed, large contiguous tracts of rainforest. This species may be unaffected by forest fragmentation because of its ability to use modified habitats in the surrounding landscape, whereas the Brown Palm Civet probably suffers from forest fragmentation because it cannot survive in areas that are devoid of continuous tree cover and which have insufficient fruit resources.

Little is also known about the impact of habitat degradation on viverrid species, such as selective logging in tropical rainforests. Selective logging is the predominant method of commercial timber exploitation in South-east Asia. In a logged forest on Borneo, several civet species were found to persist in the logged area, but in significantly lower numbers than in an adjacent undisturbed forest. The predominately carnivorous civet species (particularly invertebrate feeders) were more adversely affected by logging than the omnivorous civets; moderate habitat disturbance may have a positive effect on frugivorous viverrids if opening up a forest results in an increase in these food resources.

Generally, we do not yet know the long-term consequences of logging for viverrid species and how vital it is to have adjacent areas of undisturbed habitat. Current evidence suggests that forest-dependent species with specialist diets are the most severely impacted by habitat loss and disturbance. Omnivorous, habitat generalists may be more tolerant of these changes and be capable of exploiting human-modified environments. It is clear, however, that we need more field studies to understand how each viverrid species tolerates habitat changes. Until we know more, we cannot assume that survey records of a species in disturbed habitats indicate that a self-sustaining population exists in these areas. These animals may be sink populations or dispersers from nearby undisturbed habitats; forest-dependent species may use non-forest habitats when dispersing to another forested area. Records in disturbed areas may be frequent if they are close to primary forest and form part of an individual's home range. Some forest viverrids, such as the Malay Civet and the Large Indian Civet, have been found in non-forest habitats, such as plantations, but it appears that they still need nearby forests to be able to utilize these open areas.

Several species of genet inhabit open habits such as savannahs and open woodland, and the Small Indian Civet is frequently found in grassland, scrub, and plantations. But it is not well known how these species utilize these open areas or how important ground cover is for providing refuges, particularly during the day. The Aquatic Genet and the Otter Civet show many specialized adaptations for a semi-aquatic life and they are both found near streams and swampy areas, where they probably forage in water. Riverine forest habitat is vulnerable to logging pressures and it appears these specialized viverrids may have low tolerance to habitat disturbance. A few viverrids, notably the Common Palm Civet, have been able to exploit human-modified environments and are often found in plantations and around villages.

Habitats that provide suitable den/resting sites are very important for civets, genets, and oyans. Nocturnal, solitary-living viverrids are vulnerable while resting during the day and a female with young needs a secure site to raise her offspring. Viverrids are preyed upon by snakes, raptors, and other larger carnivores, and are therefore likely to choose den/resting sites that minimize exposure to predation. These sites may also be chosen to provide protection from the elements. For example, tree-shaded areas are cooler places to sleep in on a hot, sunny day and will also provide shelter when it rains. Terrestrial civet species, such as the Malay Civet, choose den sites in dense cover on the ground, such as under large piles of tree branches and foliage in treefall areas. Many genets use burrows and other holes in the ground, or sleep on branches in trees. Arboreal species, such as the Common Palm Civet, prefer tall trees covered in tangled vines. Viverrids seem to regularly change their rest sites, although some are re-used several times. A female with young may use the same natal den for up to several weeks, and only move her young to another site when they are fairly

well-developed or if the original den site has been compromised in some way.

Communication

Communication between animals requires a signal to be sent, a receiver to detect the information, and the ability to process and utilize the information detected. The sensory capabilities of the receiver are therefore an important component, and viverrids are considered to possess good eyesight, hearing, and smell, although how acute these senses are is poorly known.

There are three main ways that viverrids can communicate with each other: visual, vocal, and olfactory. Civets, genets, and oyans, are solitary species, so visual and vocal communication will be most prevalent when a male and female come together during the breeding season, and when a female has young. The repertoire of viverrid calls and visual signals is unlikely to be extensive or complex as compared to the more sociable carnivore species, but unfortunately we know very little about how viverrids communicate with each other in the wild; most of our knowledge comes from observing captive animals.

The main means of communication with conspecifics appears to be scent marking, primarily using the secretion from the perineal gland. Olfactory signals have the advantage of being persistent, lasting days to weeks, compared to visual or auditory communication, which are instantaneous. Scent marks may attract or repel other individuals and can be responded to when the animal that made them is far away, out of earshot, as well as out of sight; scent also works in the dark.

The scent marks left by viverrids play an important role in territory marking and during the breeding season. The perineal secretions may be mixed with urine (and vaginal fluid in

*Habitats that provide suitable rest sites are very important. When resting, many terrestrial genets make their dens in burrows, within crevices in rocks, in hollow logs, or among piles of branches and foliage. Others, like the partly arboreal **Banded Palm Civet**, may sleep on branches in trees. Arboreal civet species, like the Common Palm Civet, prefer tall trees covered in tangled vines. Many nocturnal viverrids, such as the Banded Palm Civet, are preyed upon by snakes, raptors, and other larger carnivores, and are thus vulnerable while resting during the day. They are therefore likely to choose rest sites that minimize exposure to predation. Tree-shaded resting places also provide shelter from rain and the direct heat of the sun. Viverrids change their rest sites regularly, often daily, although some may be used several times. However, a female with young will use the same natal den for several weeks, and only move her young to another site when they are fairly well-developed, or if the original den site has become unsafe.*

Hemigalus derbyanus
Malaysia.
Photo: Gerald Cubitt/NHPA

*Most viverrids appear to be
nocturnal, but often this has
been assumed from opportunistic
observations of animals seen
foraging or sleeping, or from
comparisons with similar species.
The* **Common Genet** *is one of
the few viverrid species to have
been studied using radio tracking
collars, and was found to be
primarily nocturnal. In Spain,
a male and female were found
to be most active from sunset
to midnight, and the male had
a secondary peak of activity
just before sunrise. However,
the activity patterns of some
individuals studied varied: one
male was found to be exclusively
nocturnal, whereas genets in the
south-east, although also primari
nocturnal, were active almost a
third of the time during the day.*

Genetta genetta
Madrid, Spain.
Photo: José Luis Gómez de Francisco

females) and together may carry information about sex and other individual characteristics, thus identifying the owner and its breeding condition. In the Small Indian Civet, scent marking activity increases during the breeding season, which supports the notion that scent marking gives information on the reproductive status of the animal. The place chosen for setting a mark will obviously affect the likelihood of its being noticed by a conspecific. Scent marks appear not to be randomly distributed and are generally set on much-frequented pathways and other important places, such as territorial boundaries. Because scents gradually evaporate, the difference between a fresh mark and an old one may be detectable and give an indication when an animal was last present in an area.

When a terrestrial civet marks a vertical object, the animal backs up to it, everts the lips of the perineal gland and presses it against the surface, leaving a double mark corresponding to the opening of the gland. On a suitable flat surface, the African Civet will deposit a line of such marks, all on one level, and each quite distinct. In genets, females have been observed using a squatting position to press the perineal gland against a low-lying object, and males can use a handstand position to deposit scent on an elevated surface; both sexes also use the reversed quadrupedal method to scent-mark. In all positions, the perineal gland is everted before or as it is pressed to the object and may be accompanied by rhythmic movements of the pelvis. The small and simple perineal glands that are present in the arboreal viverrid species are simply rubbed along a branch.

Some viverrids, such as the Common Genet, are also known to scent-mark by flank rubbing, which consists of rubbing the cheek, neck, and dorsal parts of the flank against unscented vertical surfaces (these body regions have a higher density of sebaceous glands). Males are able to recognize the physiological state of females from sniffing the scent marks left by flank rubbing. Flank rubbing increases during agonistic encounters and is often associated with visual threat signals, such as piloerection of the dorsal crest and the tail.

Urine and feces can be used as scent marking substances and also as visual signals. As sex hormones are excreted in urine, it may carry information about the reproductive condition of an individual; captive male African Civets, Binturongs, and genets have been observed to flehm after sniffing the urine of females. Feces are normally coated with mucus that is secreted by the gland cells of the large intestine, but the secretions of the anal sacs can also be added. The anal sacs of viverrids are not as well-developed as in other carnivore species, so the role played by scent in their feces is not clear, and may have a lesser importance than the secretions of the perineal gland. The type of food eaten can also give feces a distinctive odor.

In a solitary species that ranges over a large area, the value of feces in information transfer may be greater if they are concentrated in one particular spot than if they are widely distributed. African Civets and genets are known to concentrate their feces in specific latrine sites, which are often found in conspicuous places, and thus seem to play an important role in marking their territories. The latrines of the Common Genet are often on rocks or cliffs. African Civets deposit their feces at latrines sites (also called civetries) adjacent to paths and roads, some of which are used frequently, even if the accumulation of scats is removed. These civetries are also located in hollows, near the edges of clearings, in thickets, in grassland, and in dense reed beds. They are sometimes communal and used by a number of individuals.

The visual signals made by an individual are non-persistent and stop when it finishes making them or moves out of visual range. They only carry over short distances and their main use is in face-to-face encounters, not only between individuals of the same species, but also between different species (for example, when viverrids encounter larger predators). Many viverrids have well-marked facial masks, or stripes on the head, or a conspicuous neck pattern, and these markings may play an important role in visual communication. Small carnivore species, though predators themselves, coexist with larger carnivores that could potentially kill them. However, small carnivores can be formidable opponents to larger predators, especially if they are quite close in size, and these masks could warn of their ability to counterattack. Also, these colorations could warn larger predators of the obnoxious smells that can be produced from the perineal scent gland. However, they cannot spray these secretions like skunks, and offensive and defensive behavior using these secretions has not been seen in viverrid species, nor it is known if larger predators are deterred by their smells. African Civets that were kept in captivity did not emit civet from their perineal glands when alarmed. Arboreal masked species, such as the Common Palm Civet, can seek refuge in trees and can thus avoid fighting with larger carnivores, particularly ground species. Clearly, the function of these markings in masked viverrid species is not fully understood.

Several species of viverrids have long dark hairs that form a crest along the back, which can be raised when the animal is

When resting, **Binturongs** usually
ie curled up, with the head tucked
under the tail, or, as shown here,
draped over a branch or fork
in the tree with head and limbs
lolling. More than half the day
may be spent resting. But even
when apparently asleep or relaxed,
Binturongs, like other viverrids,
remain alert. Their preferred rest
sites are in the upper branches of
tall trees. An animal's activity
pattern is often associated with
foraging. For instance, to feed
upon exclusively nocturnal prey,
a carnivore must also be active at
night. Small carnivore species may
also need to adjust their activity
patterns to reduce encounters with
arger mammalian carnivores that
might kill them. In contrast to
the nocturnal pattern of activity
shown by most civets and genets,
the Binturong has been found to
be arrhythmic, and is active both
day and night. In Thailand,
Binturongs were observed feeding
at night, but individuals were
also seen feeding between dawn
and early afternoon. In Sabah,
Binturongs were seen almost as
often by day as by night. Though
said to feed on small vertebrates
and invertebrates, Binturongs
are believed to be predominantly
ugivorous, and so are presumably
less constrained by the activity
patterns of prey species.

Arctictis binturong
Thailand.
Photos: Roland Seitre

dent of the continued presence of the marker. Several cat species are known to mark trees in this way, but it is not known if many viverrids also do this. Claw marks made by Sulawesi Palm Civets have been found on trees and it has been said that the Rusty-spotted Genet also scratches trees.

Vocal signals can be received over considerable distances and may be particularly useful when thick cover and darkness limit visibility; the roar of a lion at night is a well known example. However, viverrids are usually quiet and when they are seen moving or feeding at night they do so silently. Viverrids are generally quite small and are thus vulnerable to attacks from larger predators, so advertising their presence using loud vocal sounds would increase their predation risk (particularly the terrestrial civet species). On sensing danger, African Civets have been observed to move off quietly without vocalization or at most with a low "wuff". Moving silently while foraging also helps to minimize detection by live prey. Vocal communication in viverrids thus appears to be more important over a short range, between individuals, in face-to-face encounters.

The vocal repertoire of civets, genets, and oyans, is not well known, except from observations made with a few captive animals. The "cough" sound is made with the mouth closed; it comprises one or a series of repeated sounds, which is sometimes mistaken for a sneeze (a true sneeze, however, has a longer duration and is often accompanied by a characteristic head motion). The "cough" can be imitated by saying "ha-ha-ha" with the lips closed, and has a clicking quality in the Small Indian Civet. This is a common contact call emitted by terrestrial viverrid species; it can be made by all individuals from the day of birth and continues through life. It is frequently heard from kittens that find themselves alone; a littermate at once responds by repeating the call and then moves to join the other. As infants grow older and become more assured in their environment, their calling becomes less frequent and the response to it is less predictable and automatic. A mother uses this call to summon the kittens and they respond in the same way as they do to each other. However, when a kitten calls and the mother replies, she does not go to the calling youngster, but merely waits for it to come to her. These contact calls ensure that the litter does not get dispersed, that the young can find their mother, and that she can summon them to her when necessary. Among adults, this call is used in any situation where contact with a conspecific is desired. For example, during mating a male uses it while following a female in estrus and also prior to copulations.

"Hissing", "snorting", or "spitting" are threat or avoidance sounds that are normally heard when a terrified animal is ap-

The main means of communication within viverrids appears to be scent marking, primarily using the secretion from the perineal gland. In contrast to visual signals, scent works in the dark, which may be particularly important for nocturnal species such as **Owston's Palm Civet**. Olfactory signals also have the advantage of being persistent, lasting days to weeks, compared t visual or auditory communicatic which are instantaneous. Scent marks may attract or repel other individuals, and can be responde to when the animal that made them is far away. Scent marks play an important role in territor marking, and during the breedin season. Perineal secretions may b mixed with urine and/or vagina fluid, identifying the sex of the owner and its breeding condition

Chrotogale owstoni
Vietnam.
Photo: Roland Seitre

alarmed. In the African Civet, these crest hairs can reach 10·5 cm. When erected they form a dramatic knife-edge effect, increasing the height of the animal. Piloerection of the dorsal crest occurs mainly as a defensive threat and is accompanied by a sideways turn of the body so that the erect hair and increase in body size are fully visible to the opponent. This defensive posture involves mixed motivations: a tendency to escape combined with a readiness to attack if further molested. Intimidating behavior in Common Genets is very cat-like, with an arched-back stance, erection of the dorsal crest and tail hairs, hissing, and an open mouth showing the teeth.

A visual signal that involves marking an object, such as making scrapes on the bark on a tree, will last long and is indepen-

The behavior of **African Civets** suggests that scent and sound are more important than sight in alerting them to the presence of prey. This seems reasonable in a species that hunts by night. The African Civet takes mainly smal prey such as rodents, reptiles, amphibians, insects, and birds and their eggs, which are likely to be concealed among the dense ground cover of their favored habitats. Even if a food item is clearly visible, an African Civet will sniff around and move slow toward the source of the smell.

Civettictis civetta
Kruger National Park, South Africa.
Photo: Getaway/D. Rogers/
Photo Access

proached. These sounds are often explosive and may be associated with head darting. Viverrids in traps will give a low threatening growl if they are approached too closely and, if sudden movements are made, a loud coughing spit. "Whining" is a characteristic call of infants, emitted in response to temperature changes, hunger, and other sources of discomfort and pain. It is phonetically rendered "wee" or "wew" and is first produced within minutes after birth; it acquires a lower frequency as the animal matures, and is rarely produced in adults. "Screaming" is a sound frequently emitted by animals in pain, sometimes heard while engaged in wrestling, fighting, biting, and clasping. Young animals seem to be unable to respond to pain or trauma with a sound more forceful than a loud whine. "Purring" is composed of continuous, rapid, low intensity clicks, produced during both inspiration and expiration, with the mouth closed. It often occurs while an infant sucks milk (the eyes may or not be closed), and is very quiet during the first week. Some tame genets continued to purr until they were six months old, but purring is thought not to occur in adults (although female Owston's Palm Civets are said to purr during mating). A "meowing" sound, much like that of a domestic cat, is often made by females during copulations and by distressed infants. "Growling" is a prolonged low rumbling noise, often associated with hissing. It is a defensive threat sound and is commonly heard from a female in defense of her young. "Humming" has been recorded in some viverrids, such as the Masked Palm Civet and has a lower sound intensity than growling. It usually begins at a low frequency, then rises slowly and steadily to a higher pitch, and may last from several seconds to at least half a minute. Viverrids that make this sound do not growl, but humming is usually not produced under circumstances conducive to growling, so the function of this sound is unclear. Masked Palm Civets have also been heard to "neigh" and Common Palm Civets make a "whinny" call. Neighing is produced with a partly opened mouth and is uttered with a single sustained expiration. It is composed of a rapid series of brief, high-pitched sounds that gradually rise and fall, and is best rendered as "yip-yip-yip-yip". It is feasible that these arboreal palm civet species use these calls in establishing territorial boundaries, for their brief, loud, and repetitive sound properties make them easily detectable over relatively long distances. The perineal gland in these species has low secretory rates and produces relatively weak scents, so vocal communication may have taken over some of the role of territorial marking. Arboreal species are also less vulnerable to predation, so it is less critical that an animal betrays its position through sound.

Food and Feeding

Viverrids have a varied diet, but little is known about the feeding habits of many species. As most viverrids are shy and elusive animals there have been few direct observations of civets, genets, and oyans, foraging in the wild. Most of our information on the food eaten by different species comes from identifying the remains in scats and in the stomach contents of dead viverrids. These results are often expressed as frequency of occurrence or percentage volume, or a combination of both. Dietary studies are fraught with biases and other complications, so unless correction factors are applied to give more accurate estimates, interpretations of these findings can give misleading conclusions for which food items are the most important in the diet of an animal. Different recording methods also complicate comparisons between different studies.

The paradoxurine palm civets are mainly frugivorous and feed on a wide range of fruits, but they also eat small vertebrates and invertebrates. Common Palm Civets eat the fruit of at least 35 plant species; they are also notorious for feeding on fermented palm sap, known as toddy, which have earned these civets the popular local name "Toddy Cat". The Small-toothed Palm Civet is probably more frugivorous than the other species of palm civets; its teeth are very small and have no shearing blades. The terrestrial civets are omnivorous: they feed on small vertebrates, invertebrates, and fruits. They are renowned as rat killers and may have been introduced to different parts of the world for this reason. However, they can also prey on chickens and eat crops, so they are often considered pests. The genets are mainly carnivorous, feeding on small vertebrates and invertebrates, but they may also include fruit in their diet; Johnston's Genet is thought to be largely insectivorous and the Aquatic Genet is presumed to eat mostly fish. Field studies on Common Genets have shown seasonal and geographical variations in their diet; they appear to be opportunistic predators and eat the most available food. The Banded Palm Civet is thought to be mainly carnivorous, while its close relative, the Owston's Palm Civet, feeds mainly on earthworms. Quite often, grass is found in viverrid scats and stomach contents, even in the more carnivorous civet and genet species. Even cats, which are strict meat-eaters, are known to ingest grass at times. Grass may provide trace elements and vitamins, help disgorge indigestible material, or help void parasites.

Observations of captive civets and genets have given us some insight as to how they hunt and eat different types of food. The behavior of African Civets suggests that scent and sound are more important than sight in alerting them to the presence of

*The **Rusty-spotted Genet** forages both in trees and on the ground. It is mainly carnivorous, with prey including small mammals, birds and their eggs, snails, centipedes, millipedes, spiders, scorpions, insects, crustaceans, fish, amphibians, and reptiles. There are also reports of Rusty-spotted Genets killing poultry. However, in some parts of its range, fruits, seeds, and berries can be important foods. One study in Kenya investigated seed dispersal in the Rusty-spotted Genet; fruits and seeds of more than 40 species were found in their scats. With their carnivorous dentition, these genets are almost unable to chew seeds, and after passing through the gut, many seeds are still viable and will germinate.*

Genetta maculata
Semliki National Park, Uganda.
Photo: Greg & Yvonne Dean/
WorldWildlifeImages.com

When a viverrid is hunting live prey, the animal is stalked and then pounced upon. It is often approached cautiously and slowly until a favorable position is reached for the final rush. Before being killed, prey is bitten several times, or sometimes shaken. The paws are not used in prey capture; instead the prey is seized by the mouth and secured with the teeth, like this **Rusty-spotted Genet** is doing with a grasshopper. Insects and other small active prey such as lizards are quite easily captured in the mouth. With larger vertebrate prey, viverrids usually kill with repeated bites; seldom do they inflict an accurately oriented killing bite on the neck, like the cats. Though mainly carnivorous, genets appear to be opportunistic predators, and eat the most easily available food; a few studies have shown that there are seasonal and geographical variations in their diet. There is little evidence that the Rusty-spotted Genet feeds on carrion, although some specimen stomachs from South Africa did contain maggots. Similar to the strictly carnivorous cats, which are known to ingest grass on occasion, grass is often found in viverrid scats and stomach contents, even in the more carnivorous civet and genet species. Grass may provide trace elements and vitamins, help disgorge indigestible material, or help void parasites.

Genetta maculata
N Zambia.
Photo: Steve Robinson/NHPA

Carnivores have characteristic carnassial teeth—the modified fourth upper premolars and first lower molars—that cut through flesh with a scissor-like shearing action. These carnassials are generally not well-developed in the more frugivorous viverrids and so they cannot easily cut through tough meat. Unable to dismember large prey simply by slicing pieces off, these species hold the prey down with the forepaws, and tear off pieces by gripping with the incisors and pulling upwards. In the **Small Indian Civet**, *the heads of vertebrates are chewed and other parts of the body are merely crushed. Mammals, snakes, and large lizards are eaten from the head down, but small prey, such as mice, can be taken into the mouth whole.*

Viverricula indica
Keoladeo Ghana National Park,
Bharatpur, India.
Photo: Nayan Khanolkar

prey, which seems reasonable in a species that hunts by night and takes mainly small prey that is easily concealed by vegetation. Even if a food item is clearly visible, an African Civet will sniff around and move slowly toward the source of the smell. If a small piece of meat is concealed in a clump of grass, an African Civet passing by will stop, sniff, and then search around until it finds the food.

When a viverrid is hunting live prey, the animal is stalked and then pounced upon. It is often approached cautiously and slowly until a favorable position is reached for the final rush to the kill. The paws are not used in prey capture; instead the prey is seized by the mouth and secured with the teeth. African Civets use their paws to scrape out an insect or a frog from a refuge only if efforts to reach the prey with the mouth have failed, and they soon give up if they are not immediately successful.

Various methods have been observed when attacking live prey. A "run-away bite" is a quick nip aimed at any part of the prey's body, followed by instant release and retreat; this a typical initial attack on intimidating prey. Before this bite is delivered, the animal may make a quick snap in the direction of the prey without actually contacting it. The "bite-and-throw" is where the prey is held just long enough to be thrown aside with a quick movement of the head. This is usually the second stage in an attack on intimidating prey and it is often accompanied by a quick leap in the air, with all four legs leaving the ground at once. In a "bite-and-shake" attack, the grip is retained and the prey is shaken to break the vertebrate. This shaking is sufficient to smash the backbone and rupture the major blood vessels of a small rodent. After shaking, the prey may be thrown aside with considerable force, or it may merely be dropped. African Civets frequently use the shaking technique with snakes; a snake is powerless to strike back while being shaken and once its vertebral column has been broken in several places, it is virtually helpless. When attacking a snake, the initial run-away bites and bites-with-throwing are usually directed towards the tail. This may injure the snake slightly and prevent its escape. The civet's withdrawal after a bite is so fast that the snake has no chance to turn and strike. Sometimes the civet will leap in the air with all four feet clear of the ground; a procedure that takes it clear of any attack the snake might make. Once the stage of bite-and-shake is reached, the snake is helpless while being shaken, and when its back is broken in a few places, it can no longer raise its head from the ground and is powerless to strike.

A fourth attack method is the "killing bite" in which the jaws bite home firmly. Unlike cats, viverrids seldom inflict an accurately oriented killing bite on the neck of the prey and usually kill it with repeated bites. These are made quickly, without ever withdrawing the teeth fully, so that although there may be no more than four punctures in the skin (where the canines originally entered), the area beneath is severely mauled. If the prey has been seized in an unfavorable location on the body, "snapping" may be used to shift the grip forwards towards the head (the teeth are fully withdrawn between successive closures of the jaws). With small prey, such as a mouse or small lizard, a killing bite is lethal, regardless of where the prey is seized. When dealing with larger animals, an aimed killing bite is sometimes directed at the skull; a civet or genet will pause for a moment before attacking and look carefully at the prey before biting in this way. With rats and snakes, the aimed head bite is sometimes used as the coup-de-grace, administered after the prey has been disabled by preliminary attacks. This head bite can be single or repeated, depending on the hardness of the prey's skull, and it is also sometimes accompanied by shaking. The death of any prey item is sometimes assured by giving it a head bite before starting to eat.

Birds are killed in much the same way as mammals: one or two undirected bites combined with shaking are sufficient to break the back, and the final kill is usually a head bite. Bird eggs are held between the forepaws, then bitten open and licked out cleanly. Insects and aquatic prey (such as small fishes and frogs) are usually captured with the mouth; African Civets do not hesitate to put their faces in water to catch small fish, seizing them with a scooping bite. To subdue large prey that is difficult to handle, such as a rat, a genet will hold it with the forefeet while biting it, then roll over onto its side and rake the prey with the claws of the hindfeet.

The terrestrial civets are poor climbers, but African Civets have been observed clambering along low stout branches of fig trees to get at ripening fruit. Otherwise, they rely on the natural fall of ripe fruit or on other mammals and birds knocking it to the ground. African Civets may attack prey as large as hares, although they are clumsy killers. They have been observed to eat as much as 2 kg in one night and be able to go without food for as long as two weeks.

Post-killing behavior consists of nosing the prey and poking at it with the paw. This usually lasts for no more than half a minute, but two captive genets were observed to sit for a considerable period watching the prey for movement, before starting to eat. Without very specialized carnassials (as in the cats), civets and genets cannot easily cut through anything tough. Large prey cannot be dismembered simply by slicing pieces off with the carnassials, so instead, it is held down with the forepaws and pieces are torn off by gripping with the incisors and pulling upwards. Once a bit of meat has been taken into the mouth, it is chewed for some time, alternately using the left and right sides of the jaw. A dead bird is not plucked, but is held down and the flesh

The **Common Genet** forages at night; this individual is hunting for rodents near a farm's corn store. While small mammals make up the main part of their diet, the Common Genet also eats other small vertebrates (including birds, reptiles, amphibians, and fish), invertebrates (mainly insects), eggs, fruits, and sometimes grass. Field studies have shown seasonal and geographical variations in the diet. For example, in a wooded area of south-west France, rodents, insectivores (including shrews and moles), and occasionally a few mustelids, like Least Weasel and Ermine, provided the bulk of the diet, with a much smaller contribution from passerine birds, and insects. While the percentage of small mammals in the diet remained stable throughout the seasons, more birds were eaten during winter, and fewer during spring. In north-west Portugal, rodents were the main prey, followed by insectivores and, particularly in the spring, birds. Reptiles were consumed mostly in the spring, and fruit in the summer. However, in riparian and montane forest in north-east Algeria, arthropods predominated in the diet. On Cabrera, a small shrubby covered island in the Balearics, one study found that mammals made up a relatively small proportion of the diet, (relative to arthropods and reptiles), although another study on the same island found mammals and birds to be the most significant food items. Larger mammals, such as rabbits, are occasionally preyed upon in many areas, and there are records of Common Genets having eaten bats.

Genetta genetta
Raimat, Catalonia, Spain.
Photos: Jordi Bas

A few viverrids, notably the **Common Palm Civet***, have been able to exploit human-modified environments. Like other paradoxurine palm civets, the Common Palm Civet is mainly frugivorous, eating the fruit of at least 35 plant species. They can be found in plantations and gardens around villages, and are sometimes killed as pests by fruit farmers. When fruit is out of season, the Common Palm Civet's diet shifts to small vertebrates and invertebrates. One source of fruit is Bengal coffee. Coffee beans that have passed through the digestive tract of the Common Palm Civet are collected and sold as the most prized and expensive coffee in the world: "kopi luwat" or civet coffee.*

Paradoxurus hermaphroditus
Keoladeo Ghana National Park,
Bharatpur, India.
Photo: Gertrud & Helmut Denzau

pulled from the body using the incisors. Initially, there is some difficulty in getting rid of the feathers in the mouth, but once a few bits of skin have been torn away and the flesh exposed, further pieces can be torn off more easily. With experience, African Civets become adept at getting rid of the tail and wing feathers, by plucking the meat from the feathers, rather than vice versa. Genets have been reported to eat almost every part of a dead bird, including the beak and legs. Mammals, snakes and large lizards are eaten from the head down, but small prey species, such as mice, can be taken into the mouth whole. Fruit is swallowed with minimal chewing. Civets drink with a noisy dog-like lapping, in contrast to the silent lapping characteristic of cats; they appear to take mouthfuls of water, rather than using the tongue alone to convey fluid into the mouth.

In the African Civet, eating may be preceded or punctuated by scent rubbing on the food: the civet lowers its body and rubs the chin, the side of the neck, and the shoulder along the food item. It may then stand and repeat the whole procedure. Rubbing is performed by both sexes and even young kittens will rub on their first encounters with meat or fish, usually before trying to eat. Rubbing is performed with particularly strong-smelling animal food, but vegetable foods are never rubbed. The significance of this scent rubbing, which is particularly widespread amongst the Canidae, is obscure. It seems not to be connected with claiming ownership of food and there is no tendency for one animal to avoid taking food rubbed by the other.

Breeding

Viverrids are usually very secretive, and consequently we know little about their breeding behavior, although the trapping of pregnant females and young animals has given us some indication of when some species may breed. Most of our information on mating and breeding behavior has come from observing captive animals, particularly some of the genets and terrestrial civet species.

During the breeding season, viverrid females are in estrus for several days, although in some species, such as the Binturong, estrus may last as long as two weeks. Females appear to be polyestrous and capable of producing several litters a year. They may also be induced ovulators, in which the rupture of the follicle and release of ova is induced by mating. Viverrids are solitary; for most of the year adult males and females live apart and must come together to breed. Regular cycling, a relatively

long receptive period, and ovulation triggered by copulation, all increase the chances that a successful fertilization will occur.

In captivity, births may not be seasonal and often there are more than two litters a year. Female African Civets come into estrus again when their young are about three and a half months old, although if a litter is lost a female will come into estrus within a fortnight. Although captive studies have indicated that several litters a year are possible, it is not known what the actual situation may be in the wild for many viverrid species. However, we do know that some species appear to have definite breeding periods and it is likely that these coincide with seasonal changes and high food availability. A female has high energy demands while she is pregnant and needs to find food for both herself and her young while she is raising them, so breeding might be expected to take place when there is an abundance of food. Some viverrid species, however, seem to have a non-seasonal breeding pattern, particularly in areas where there are no obvious changes in seasons and/or availability of food resources.

During estrus, a female advertizes her receptivity and attracts a mate through scent marking, apparently using both her perineal gland secretions and urine, which presumably contains hormonal cues that indicate her reproductive status. During this period, she is very active and calls frequently. The male responds by sniffing the scent marks left by the female and often flehmns while checking these smells. During the first phases of mating, the male makes calls and follows the female closely, often approaching her to sniff her posterior region. The female initially keeps turning away and flees with her hindquarters kept low. Eventually she answers the male's calls and allows him to come into close contact. She holds her tail up, and crouches with her hindquarters raised and tail deflected sideways. The male then mounts, usually with his forelegs placed on either side of the female's shoulders, sometimes grasping her on the neck. Coupling lasts a few minutes, during which both animals may meow like cats. After the male dismounts, the female may growl and try to bite him. Copulation does not always result in successful intromission and several mountings may be attempted over a period of hours and days. In a natural situation, the male leaves soon after mating and the female is left to raise the young on her own. Maternal-only care is the norm. Depending on whether the species is arboreal or terrestrial, a pregnant female chooses a secluded site in a tree or on the ground in which to give birth. These natal den sites can be in hollow trees, within dense vegetation, in disused holes, within the shelter of

Although said to feed on small
vertebrates and invertebrates,
the **Binturong** is believed to be
predominantly frugivorous, as
shown here feeding on wild figs
from the strangler fig tree. Its teeth
are comparatively small, with the
shearing blades of the carnassials
reduced. Figs were found to be the
main food item in one specimen
stomach collected from Borneo, and
in a scat collected from a trapped
animal in Thailand. Binturongs
have also frequently been observed
in fig trees, and one individual
was photographed eating fallen
jackfruit in Sumatra.

Arctictis binturong
Gunung Palung National Park,
Borneo.
Photo: Tim Laman

rocks, or in other places that afford substantial cover. Gestation periods range from 45 to 99 days. Litter sizes may be as many as six in some species, such as the Binturong, but two seems to be a common number.

Viverrids that are predominately carnivorous have complex foraging and feeding behavior (catching live prey requires high cognitive ability, skill, and experience), and this necessitates that their young have a relatively long dependency period. Post-weaning, the young must be provisioned with food and must learn to hunt and capture prey themselves. The more frugivorous viverrid species may have prolonged lactation periods to ensure that the infants receive sufficient nourishment while gaining foraging experience (but with little maternal assistance).

The young are usually born fully furred and blind; their eyes open during the first two weeks. For the first day or so, infants are only capable of flexing their bodies and pulling themselves forward using their forelimbs; their movement is minimal and is focused on locating the mother's nipple. The young suckle several times an hour during the first few days, but this rate decreases as they become older. By day two or three, an infant's jaws can execute sustained bites with considerable pressure, and repeated biting movements resembling nibbling can be observed. The mother lies on her side to feed the young and they use a combination of paws and snout to stimulate the flow of milk. Kittens will usually only suckle from one particular teat, although teat ownership may be slower to establish when compared with the domestic cat. The mother will groom her young by licking their bodies and will consume their urine and feces.

After the first few days, infants are able to crawl. On successive days, their coordination improves and they are then capable of supporting themselves and walking for brief periods, although their hindlegs may tend to drag in the early stages. In genets (at least), the claws cannot be retracted during the first couple of weeks and can easily snag on rough surfaces, but they clearly help an infant cling on slopes. Once walking becomes steady, other locomotor patterns appear, and by 20–30 days, infants are capable of trotting, running, galloping, and jumping. Between 30–40 days, young genets can stand on two legs, and by 32–40 days, they can climb up and down steeply inclined surfaces.

Very young kittens in a den will spit defensively in response to any strange object that approaches them rapidly. When outside, young African Civets will move under cover and then freeze when suddenly alarmed. Occasionally they will try to climb to a high point, such as an old fence post. This seems an unusual type of escape behavior for a terrestrial species, but it may be a trait that has been retained from an arboreal ancestor, in which this type of response would be normal.

Indications of play appear during the first couple of weeks. The role of play is not fully understood, but it often comprises elements of fighting and simulated mating behavior, similar to that exhibited by adults during mating. Playing with food items may help improve subsequent foraging and hunting abilities. Once explorations outside the den have started, play becomes much more active and includes running, chasing, and jumping at each other, followed by biting and wrestling. Play behavior becomes less frequent as the infants near sexual maturity, and in three-month-old African Civets, elements of sexual behavior appear when wrestling, often ending in mounting attempts. Play with live prey has not been observed in young African Civets, but the shaking and throwing of a corpse (which often follows an adult kill), appears to be playful.

At around four to six weeks of age, the milk teeth are almost fully erupted and young viverrids can take solid food. At this stage meat can be eaten readily. In African Civets, small lizards are too tough for six-week olds to chew up, but they can hold them down with the forepaws and tear pieces off with their incisors. Young African Civets attempt to catch insects during the second month, and by eight weeks, they are capable of killing a mouse when offered. Their first few experiences with live prey are often timid, but they quickly gain confidence with each new kill. Is not known if a mother viverrid provides her young with any opportunities to gain experience in killing and hunting live prey, but captive female African Civets have been observed sharing food with their kittens. No regurgitation of food by the mother for the young has been observed.

Physical and reproductive maturity is attained between nine months and two years in the majority of viverrid species. Young viverrids are vulnerable to a variety of predators, in particular snakes, raptors, and larger carnivores. Unfortunately, there is insufficient information to determine mortality rates. Under favorable conditions (particularly in zoos), civets and genets have the potential to live between ten and twenty years.

Once they are independent, young viverrids leave their mother and disperse to establish their own place to live, but little is known about the dispersal of young in viverrid species. In some solitary carnivores, young females may not disperse far and may actually establish a home range that overlaps part of their mother's, whereas young males often disperse over large distances.

The **Sulawesi Palm Civet** has larger premolars and molars than other palm civets, but these teeth lack shearing blades. Nearly half of the food items found in scats examined in the Lore Lindu National Park, Sulawesi, consisted of rodents. The diet also included the Sulawesi Dwarf Cuscus, birds, grass, and palm fruit. The Sulawesi Palm Civet is known to raid villages for pigs and chickens, and is sometimes killed in retaliation. Captive Sulawesi Palm Civets catch and kill chickens by seizing them with the forepaws and biting them on the head. Feeding begins at the head, and the entire carcass is eaten, including the feet and nearly all of the feathers. Sulawesi has an impoverished carnivore fauna comprising just three civet species. The Sulawesi Palm Civet is endemic, and the Common Palm Civet and the Malay Civet have been introduced. The latter two species also occur on Borneo, where there is a large carnivore guild.

Macrogalidia musschenbroekii
Lore Lindu National Park, Sulawesi.
Photos: Alain Compost

Movements, Home range and Social organization

Viverrid movements are mainly concerned with finding food, patrolling and scent marking territorial boundaries, and searching for mates during the breeding season. The main gaits when moving along the ground are the walk, gallop, and trot. The walk varies from a leisurely progression to a speed equalling moderately energetic human walking. The gallop usually appears as an escape response (if the animal is alarmed) and is also used during sexual chasing. Civets can jump well and when galloping can bound over obstacles up to half a metre high. The trot is seen mainly as a transitional phase between the walk and the gallop and does not appear as an important gait in its own right.

The arboreal palm civets are excellent tree climbers, but the terrestrial civet species are poor climbers (although the African Civet has been observed clambering along low, stout branches of fig trees to get at ripening fruit). Genets are very capable tree climbers, able to traverse along a branch in an inverted position and to ascend and descend vertical surfaces, often using "vertical looping" (the spine is arched and the fore- and hindfeet alternatively slid forward), with or without the assistance of the claws.

Generally, viverrids are poor diggers; the terrestrial civets have blunt-clawed digitigrade feet that are suited neither for digging nor climbing. Other postures and movements of viverrids include sitting and standing on hindlegs (often seen in genets), crouching, and resting or sleeping on their side. The African Civet usually sleeps lying on its side, with the body either fully extended and the head resting on one cheek, or curled up, with the head near the base of the tail. Another posture commonly adopted when resting, but not deeply asleep, is to lie on the belly with the forepaws tucked neatly under the chest, the neck fully extended, and the chin resting on the ground. Viverrids groom themselves in a cat-like manner; they lick and nibble their fur, and clean their face with tongue-moistened paws. Also like cats, they scratch their claws on suitable surfaces (to prevent them from becoming too long) and stretch by first humping the back and extending the forelegs, then by arching the back and extending the hindlegs.

Information on viverrid movements is scarce, but they are capable of covering quite large distances within a day; Common Genets can travel over 8 km in 24 hours. Young civets, genets, and oyans, will eventually leave their mother and disperse to find their own place to live. The dispersal distances are likely to vary among species and between the sexes, but this information is unknown for viverrids.

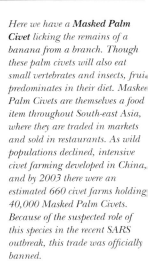

*Here we have a **Masked Palm Civet** licking the remains of a banana from a branch. Though these palm civets will also eat small vertebrates and insects, fruit predominates in their diet. Masked Palm Civets are themselves a food item throughout South-east Asia, where they are traded in markets and sold in restaurants. As wild populations declined, intensive civet farming developed in China, and by 2003 there were an estimated 660 civet farms holding 40,000 Masked Palm Civets. Because of the suspected role of this species in the recent SARS outbreak, this trade was officially banned.*

Paguma larvata
Cuc Phuong National Park, Vietnam.
Photo: Matthew Maran/naturepl.com

Most viverrids appear to be nocturnal, but often this has been assumed from limited anecdotal information or from comparisons with similar species that have been studied to some extent. Information from field surveys and opportunistic observations of animals seen foraging, found sleeping, or moving through the undergrowth or in trees, has given us some indication of when an animal is active or when it rests, but this often does not give the whole picture. Radio-telemetry studies can provide detailed information on activity and movement patterns, but unfortunately few such studies have been done on viverrids. In contrast to most of the civets and genets, the Binturong has been found to be arrhythmic, active both day and night. Both nocturnal and diurnal activity has also been reported for the Otter Civet in Sumatra and for the Abyssinian Genet in Ethiopia. For the latter species, it was suggested that this diurnal activity was a locally adaptive response to the activity patterns of rodent prey at high altitudes, and that this

Civets drink with a noisy dog-like lapping, in contrast to the silent lapping characteristic of cats. They appear to take mouthfuls of water, rather than using the tongue alone to convey fluid into the mouth. **Common Palm Civets** *are also notorious for drinking the fermented sap from tapped coconut palms ("toddy"), earning them the popular local name "Toddy Cat". They also feed on the nectar of* Bombax ceiba *and sap from the stems of* Vallaris solanacea.

Paradoxurus hermaphroditus
Dachigam National Park,
Jammu-Kashmir, India.
Photo: Joanna Van Gruisen/Ardea

might also minimize direct competition with African Wildcats (*Felis silvestris*). Malay Civets on Sulawesi are most active during the night from 18:00–07:00 h, but they are also quite active throughout the day.

An animal's activity is often associated with foraging, the timing and duration of which is usually a function of food availability. Nocturnal activity in Malay Civets on Sulawesi, for instance, would increase encounter rates with prey such as rodents, which are strictly nocturnal. Small carnivore species may also adjust their activity patterns to reduce encounters with larger mammalian carnivores that may kill them. Interspecific killing among mammalian carnivores may account for up to 68% of known mortalities in some species. Carnivores killed two out of five radio-tracked Common Palm Civets in Nepal. The absence of large nocturnal predators on Sulawesi, such as Tigers or Leopards, may contribute to the high frequency of nocturnal activity that is observed in the Malay Civet.

As far as is known, all viverrid species are solitary; for most of the time they have very little contact with conspecifics, except during the breeding season and when a female has young. Solitary living indicates both an absence of strong selection pressures for cooperation (such as increased foraging efficiency, improved young production, and more successful predator defense) and the presence of factors promoting solitariness (such as prey characteristics and hunting methods). Viverrids generally take animal prey that is much smaller than themselves and which can be subdued alone. In this situation, the presence of conspecifics in their immediate surroundings would have a negative effect on foraging efficiency, through disturbance of prey or through depletion of local food resources.

Information on home ranges and spatial organization can be provided by radio-telemetry studies, in which individuals are captured and fitted with radio collars and then tracked over many months, recording their position on a regular basis. Unfortunately very few telemetry studies have been done on viverrids.

A number of factors affect home range sizes, including body size, sex, age, habitat quality, diet, the availability of food resources and den sites, and climate (rainfall, temperatures, and seasonal patterns). Even within a species, home range sizes can be highly variable depending on the prevalence of these factors in different areas. For example, the home ranges of Common Genets varied from 0·3 to 1·7 km² in Ethiopia, and from 0·7 to 14·7 km² in Spain. A wide variation in home range sizes was also found for Common Palm Civets at different study sites in Nepal and Thailand, possibly due to differences in habitat productivity.

Large animals have high energy demands and thus require larger home ranges than smaller individuals. The largest civet species, the Binturong, can weigh as much as 20 kg and have a home range of up to 20·5 km², whereas ranges as small as 0·06 km² have been recorded in the 3 kg Brown Palm Civet. However, other factors, such as the type of diet (e.g. carnivorous or frugivorous), can mitigate this general body-size/home range relationship.

For home ranges to be exclusive and non-overlapping, an animal's food resources must be evenly distributed and stable. If these resources vary in space and time, home ranges must be larger to provide sufficient food at all times. A larger area may contain a surplus of food for most of the year, which may then allow several animals to utilize the same area; in this situation, a system of overlapping ranges may develop. In Nepal, the overlap of home ranges in Common Palm Civets is minimal when food is abundant and uniform, but increases when food is most clumped. Home range overlaps are substantial for Binturongs in Thailand, which indicates a lack of territories. In south-east Sulawesi, there is little overlap of intra-sexual home ranges in the Malay Civet, which indicates that this species has exclusive home ranges in this region, but there are considerable overlaps of home ranges of both sexes in East Sabah, suggesting that the Malay Civet is not territorial on Borneo. These findings suggest that for some species food abundance and distribution may vary in space and time (and maybe in different areas), which would then account for overlapping home ranges.

Male spatial organization is influenced by the availability of food and receptive females. To maximize their reproductive success, males can either stay in one area and try to monopolize a number of females or they can roam and compete over access to every female that comes into estrus. A system of non-overlapping male ranges is the best tactic when females are highly concentrated and evenly distributed. In this situation, a male may control a number of females and secure matings with them. Viverrid females rear young by themselves, so their reproductive success is closely correlated with the availability of food. However, little is known about the spatial organization of viverrid species. In Common Genets, there is low intra-sexual overlap of home ranges (i.e. male ranges are separate, as are female ranges), but male ranges overlap with female ranges.

Male and female viverrids are generally similar in body size, so we might expect similar home range sizes for both sexes. However, other factors may cause differences in range sizes between the sexes. On Sulawesi, male Malay Civets were found to be heavier than females, but their home ranges were not signif-

Viverrids appear to be polyestrous and captive studies have indicated that they are capable of producing several litters a year. However, it is not known what the actual situation may be in the wild for many viverrid species. Some species do appear to have definite breeding periods, and it is likely that these coincide with high food availability, to meet the high energy demands of the pregnant and nursing female. Studies of the **Common Genet**, for example, indicate that in Kenya there may be two breeding seasons, from March to May and from September to December, which correspond to the wet seasons. In Europe and North Africa, Common Genets mate in spring and autumn; birth peaks are in April–June and in September–November. Once the female in estrus has allowed the interested male into close contact, she holds her tail up, and crouches with her hindquarters raised and tail deflected sideways. The male then mounts, usually with his forelegs placed on either side of the female's shoulders, sometimes grasping her on the neck. Coupling lasts a few minutes, during which both may meow like cats. After the male dismounts, the female may growl and try to bite him. Copulation does not always result in successful intromission and several mountings may be attempted over a period of hours or days. The male leaves soon after mating, and the female is left to raise the young on her own. She chooses a secluded site in which to give birth. Natal den sites can be in hollow trees, amongst dense vegetation, in disused holes, within the shelter of rocks, or in other places that afford substantial cover. Common Genets favor burrows, rocky crevices or, as shown here, holes in trees. Viverrid gestation periods range from 45 to 99 days; in the Common Genet, it is from 70 to 77 days.

Genetta genetta
Spain.
Photo: Juan José Hinojosa/FLPA

*Little is yet known about breeding in the **Cape Genet**. In the Rusty-spotted Genet, which was previously considered conspecific with the Cape Genet, there are records of dens with three young, and of two female specimens each containing three fetuses. Litter size in the Common Genet is from one to four; the most common number is two. In some viverrid species, such as the Binturong, there may be as many as six in a litter. The young are born fully furred and blind, with closed ears. Very young kittens in a den will spit defensively at any strange object that approaches them rapidly. Early movement is confined to locating the mother's nipple. After a few days the infants can crawl; coordination and locomotor skills then improve rapidly.*

Genetta tigrina
Helderberg Nature Reserve,
Western Cape, South Africa.
Photo: Peter Steyn/Ardea

icantly larger even though they presumably had higher energy demands. However, it appeared that during the study period, female Malay Civets had dependent young and thus their energy requirements (and hence home ranges) were greater than expected from their body size.

The presence of competitors may also affect viverrid home range sizes. Sulawesi has an impoverished carnivore fauna comprising just three civet species: the endemic Sulawesi Palm Civet and two possibly introduced species, the Malay Civet and Common Palm Civet—both of which also occur on Borneo, where there is a large carnivore guild. The lack of competition for food from other mammalian carnivores on Sulawesi may mean that there is increased prey available for these three Sulawesi civets, allowing them to meet their daily energy requirements within smaller home ranges than on Borneo. The home range sizes of female Malay Civets in south-east Sulawesi were found to be significantly smaller than those of female Malay Civets on Borneo.

Human factors can also have an influence on ranging behavior and spatial organization. Access to supplemental food at human garbage dumps can result in a high degree of range overlap between individuals. On Borneo and Sulawesi, trails and roads are an important resource for the Malay Civet. African Civets also make great use of paths and roads, along which they move slowly and purposefully.

In many regions, several viverrid species are sympatric (occur in the same area), and this is accommodated through niche partitioning, which minimizes inter-specific competition for resources, particularly food. This can happen through spatial separation (different microhabitats, terrestrial or arboreal, elevation) and/or differences in diet and activity periods. For example, on Peninsular Malaysia, the Malay Civet is terrestrial, the Common Palm Civet is arboreal, and the arboreal Masked Palm Civet appears to be more common at higher altitudes.

Relationship with Humans

Viverrids have had a long relationship with humans and play a small but significant role in our economy and culture, at least at a local and regional level. Although not as well known as the felids and canids, they are fascinating animals in their own right.

The substance produced by the perineal scent glands, a thick greasy secretion called civet (or civet oil), has played a significant role in the perfume industry. Its scent at high con-

centrations can be nauseating, but it is very attractive in minute traces. It is also used as an exaltant, enhancing and prolonging the smell of other, more delicate fragrances. Civet has been used in the production of perfume for centuries and was reportedly presented as a gift to King Solomon by the Queen of Sheba in the 10th century BC. The terrestrial civets found in Asia, and Africa, have a large, muscular, perineal gland, which in the African Civet can accumulate up to 15 g of civet per week. Several thousand African Civets are kept on farms in Ethiopia (and maybe in other parts of Africa), although exact

*At around 4–6 weeks of age, the milk teeth are almost fully erupted, and most young viverrids can take solid food. Young **Binturongs** start to eat solid food at the age of 6–8 weeks. By 20–30 days, young viverrids can run and jump. Their play behavior often comprises elements of fighting and simulated mating. Playing with food items may help improve subsequent foraging and hunting abilities. Once exploration outside the den has started, play becomes much more active and includes running, chasing, and jumping at each other, followed by biting and wrestling. Play behavior becomes less frequent as the infants near sexual maturity.*

Arctictis binturong
Photo: Rod Williams/naturepl.com

numbers are not known. One estimate is that 180 civet farmers hold more than 2700 animals, with up to 60 civets per farm. Although there is no legislation governing civet farming a permit is needed to capture civets, but the vast majority of farmers do not apply for one. The civets are captured and housed in small cylindrical cages made from sticks woven together with twine. The civet oil is taken every 9–15 days. For extraction, the sticks are removed from one end of the cage and the hindlegs of the civet are pulled out so that the perineal gland at the base of the animal's tail is exposed. The gland is opened up and squeezed until the musk exudes, which can take several minutes. The animal is often distressed and injuries can easily happen. The civets are kept in a dark room in which a smouldering fire maintains high temperatures during the day, as farmers believe this increases the amount of civet produced. Attempts to breed African Civets on these farms have not been successful, so to replenish those that die, new animals are taken from the wild. Civet farms (for civet oil extraction) also exist in Asia, notably India, but these are less extensive than in Africa. Some civet species may have been introduced to some parts of the world for the purpose of civet production. Although many manufacturers have now stopped using civet oil in favor of synthetic musks, fairly large quantities are still being produced. Over 13,000 kg of civet was exported from Ethiopia between 1985 and 1996.

Civet oil is also used in pharmacology, traditional medicine, and in incense sticks. It is reputed to reduce perspiration and cure some skin diseases, and to have anti-asthmatic, anti-inflammatory, and aphrodisiac properties. Civet is also used for flavoring tobacco; several tobacco shops in France are still named "La Civette". The indigenous people of southern India traditionally use civet oil from Small Indian Civets for respiratory ailments and as a cure against pimples and discoloration of the face. It is also applied over the body of couples on the day of a wedding, believing that it will act as a sexual stimulant and accelerate the chances of pregnancy. Members of the royal family used civet oil during traditional smoking. Some communities also use the perineal glands of viverrids. The entire glandular area of a civet is first removed with a knife. After the civet oil is squeezed from the gland (and preserved for future use) it is then dried with smoke or placed in the sun. Once dried, it is cut into small pieces, rolled in tobacco leaves with ganja (a narcotic), and smoked. Dried or smoked perineal glands were also a major gift item given annually by Indian communities to

the Maharaja, and were burned with other incense to perfume the palace.

In southern India, Small Indian Civets are farmed for their civet oil. The Sri Venkateswara temple in Tirumala (Andhra Pradesh) maintains a colony of Small Indian Civets, from which the perineal gland secretion is used in religious rituals. This species is protected in India, so it is illegal to keep them captive. If permission is granted by a government agency, owners have to follow certain guidelines. An investigation of civet holdings in Kerala (India) found over 40 units, most of which had up to three civets each. Only two of these units had permission to keep civets. There is no captive breeding and the majority of civets are taken from the wild; any animals born in captivity come from mothers who were in their late pregnancy when trapped. Females may not yield any perineal secretions during pregnancy and lactation so there is little incentive for civet owners to breed civets. Most animals are kept in individual wooden cages, with a reed pole fixed vertically in the center to facilitate scent marking by perineal gland rubbing. The butter-like secretion turns brownish when exposed to air and light and is scraped off the pole at least twice a week, sometimes daily, using a scalpel or a piece of coconut leaf. Each animal can produce 2–6 g of civet per month. To increase the quantities for selling, civet owners mix the secretion with white vaseline, butter, finely ground poovan pazham (a variety of plantain) and even civet feces. Selling collected secretion is easy as there is a high demand. The secretory output of the perineal glands ceases after seven or eight years; when old animals are no longer productive, they are either set free or killed and eaten. Since there is no captive breeding, owners trap new civets from the wild in order to replace old, diseased, and dead animals (over 20% of civets die in captivity after a few months).

Viverrids are hunted for food (bushmeat) throughout Africa and Asia. In some regions, particularly in Africa, bushmeat is an important source of protein for village communities. In Ghana, a study showed that 75% of the population depended on wild animal protein, and that wild fauna made up 62% of the animal protein eaten by the rural population. In Guinea, the amount of bushmeat sold in a town of 30,000 inhabitants was about 131 tons a year, involving 21 species of mammals. Antelopes, deer, pigs, and primates, are the most sought-after prey, but the usual methods of hunting are not very selective and most animals are caught according to their frequency. Local hunters use dogs, spears, traps, and snares. Blowpipes

The viverrids were last assessed for The IUCN Red List in 2008. Several species have moved into higher threat categories, reflecting increasing extinction risks. The **Large-spotted Civet** is now classified as Vulnerable. It is known only from a few records, and almost nothing is known about its habits. The Large-spotted Civet is mainly found in tall forest below 300–400 m. Unfortunately, this habitat is suffering ongoing loss and degradation throughout South-east Asia. This species is also vulnerable to hunting, particularly with snares. This occurs in much of its range, with snare trapping found even in some protected areas.

Viverra megaspila
Thailand.
Photo: Roland Seitre

and poisoned darts are also used to catch arboreal animals. Meat from small carnivores, including civets, genets, and mongooses, can be up to 15% of the bushmeat consumed in some communities. It is therefore no wonder that viverrids can play a prominent role in their myths and culture.

In China, civet meat is considered a delicacy and in recent years there has been an increase in demand. In order to supply this high demand, civet farms have been created, housing thousands of Masked Palm Civets. Reliable figures are difficult to obtain but recent information indicates that as many as 40,000 to 60,000 Masked Palm Civets are being kept in 400 to 660 farms. The civets are kept in small wire cages, stacked together in long rows. Four civets (one male and three females) are usually kept in each cage and fed with food pellets and provided with water. Pregnant females are isolated to allow them to give birth. Their newborns are then housed in tiny cages. An adult male can weight up to 8 kg and be sold for about

US$ 120; females sell for up to US$ 50 each. Sale for pets can fetch even higher prices. When sold for food, even the skin is eaten, but apparently the fur is not used.

Farmed civets are sold alive in the Guangdong and Guangxi markets in southern China, and also exported to Hong Kong. Due to the recent SARS (Severe Acute Respiratory Syndrome) epidemic, the Chinese government has attempted to control this industry by closing farms, destroying and releasing animals, and banning the sale of meat in markets and restaurants. However, it remains to be seen if these measures will have an impact on civet farming and trade in civet meat. Civets are also sold for their meat in the markets and restaurants of northern Vietnam and Laos. The indigenous people of southern India also consider civet meat to be tasty and nutritious, and believe that eating it helps regain a person's lost vigor and vitality. Although it is illegal, they hunt Common Palm and Small Indian Civets using traps and bows. Trained dogs are also used to lo-

Forest loss, fragmentation, and degradation appear to be the primary threats to forest-dependent viverrids. Between 1985 and 1997, there were forest losses of 59% in the northern peninsular of Sulawesi, 72% in the central peninsular, and 67% in the south-eastern peninsular. The **Sulawesi Palm Civet** is possibly threatened by this loss and fragmentation of its forest habitat, particularly at lower elevations. It was classified as Vulnerable on The IUCN Red List in 2008. Protected under Indonesian law, the species has recently been recorded in Rawa Aopa National Park, Tanjung Peropa Wildlife Reserve, and Mangolo Recreation Forest.

Macrogalidia musschenbroekii
Lore Lindu National Park, Sulawesi.
Photo: Alain Compost

cate civets that have taken shelter in holes and under bushes; they are then smoked out and killed.

Over the last fifty years, hunting for regional and international markets has increasingly outweighed subsistence hunting. Numerous species are now targeted for the huge illegal trade in wildlife for food, traditional medicines, skins and bones, and pets. The increased use of guns has made it easier to hunt wary and arboreal animals, particularly at night, when electric torches are also used. Wire-snares and other traps are effective in catching animals, but are unselective in what they catch, and non-targeted animals are also taken and often killed. Wildlife traders have penetrated into the remotest areas and actively encourage the hunting of animal species for which there is a demand. In some countries, professional hunters from outside are a major threat, such as Vietnamese hunters in Laos. The last twenty years has seen the development of a colossal trade in live animals and animal parts throughout South-east and Central Asia. China, in particular, has long been a major market for wildlife products and Oriental communities throughout the rest of the world also provide additional markets.

Although viverrids are traded for food in local and international markets, there does not appear to be a large demand for their fur, unlike the fur trade in felids and mustelids for the fashion industry. Skins of viverrids are found in markets, but they are mainly sold for local uses. For instance, the Bakumu people, who live near Kisangani (Zaire), use viverrid skins for adorning spiritual dancers' costumes and the hats of village chiefs.

There is a large trade in animals as pets, and this includes some viverrid species. It is possible that some civet species were introduced as pets to some island areas in South-east Asia. For instance, the Common Palm Civet (which is often kept as pet) has only been recorded from the vicinity of the two major port towns on Sulawesi, suggesting that this was a human introduction. In Medan (North Sumatra), one of South-east Asia's major centers for domestic and international wildlife trade, a five-year study of the pet industry recorded 300 bird species, 34 species of mammals, and 15 reptile species. Many of these are exported by sea and air to Malaysia, Singapore, Thailand, and other global destinations. Also, many animals are imported to Indonesia from other Asian countries, including China. Local hunters may specifically target animals that are in high demand, and plantation and forest workers may supplement their income by opportunistically catching mammals to sell as

pets (and for other uses). Most of this wildlife trade is illegal, violating Indonesian wildlife laws; CITES permits and international laws are also often ignored and not enforced. The Common Palm Civet was the most frequent viverrid observed for sale, with 264 animals recorded during the monthly surveys; the actual number sold over the five-year survey period was obviously far greater than this figure. Masked and Small-toothed Palm Civets also were found for sale in the markets, although in lower numbers.

Since many civets (especially the terrestrial species) eat rodents, some species may have been introduced to agricultural areas to catch rats, and thus may play an important economic role in controlling mammalian pests wherever crops are grown. The Malay Civet may have been introduced to Sulawesi (and other nearby islands) for this reason. Early human settlers introduced the Small Indian Civet to Madagascar around 2000 years ago. Unfortunately, the downside is that introduced viverrids are often considered pests as they sometimes raid crops and prey on small livestock, such as chickens. Whether they have a significant impact is not known, but many farmers deliberately kill these animals to minimize damage to their crops and to reduce livestock losses. Civets and genets foraging in plantation areas may also be inadvertently killed when they ingest pesticides and herbicides, either directly or via contaminated food and ground water.

Since many viverrids feed heavily on fruits (particularly some palm civet species), they may have an important ecological and economic role in dispersing plant seeds. In Kenya, one study investigated seed dispersal in the Rusty-spotted Genet by collecting seeds from scats, which were then germinated in bags filled with soil. Although this species is mainly carnivorous across much of its range, fruit can be an important component of its diet in some areas. With their carnivorous dentition, these genets are almost unable to chew seeds and are thus unlikely to destroy them; after passing through the gut, many seeds were viable and germinated. It was found that these genets dispersed less than 10% of the total number of available seed species; however, this did not take into account any spat-out seeds and seeds that were too big to be swallowed. Although genets may only play a minor role in dispersing seeds, compared to the more frugivorous viverrid species, some genets are not limited to one habitat type and could be important seed dispersers in disturbed and exposed sites, such as rocky areas.

The Masked Palm Civet has played a role in the recent SARS epidemic, which was associated with a new coronavirus (SARS CoV). The outbreak of this disease started in November 2002, in southern China, and quickly spread to other places around the world. Early investigations revealed that the first human cases involved people closely associated with animals and food activities, such as wild animal traders in markets and cooks working in restaurants specialising in wild animals. A SARS-like CoV strain, clearly related to the SARS virus, was discovered from wild animals found in a Shenzhen market. Three small carnivore species tested positive for this virus strain, the Masked Palm Civet, the Raccoon Dog, and the Chinese Ferret-badger. The SARS-like CoV was then isolated and sequenced from the Masked Palm Civet. This virus has been found in farmed civets in China, but it is possible that it entered China from neighboring countries through the wild animal trade. The origin of the SARS virus, the true wild reservoir host, and the role of carnivore species in the virus epidemiology, is still unknown, and further research is being undertaken.

"Kopi luwak" or civet coffee is made from coffee cherries that have been eaten by and passed through the digestive tract of the Common Palm Civet. It is said to be the finest coffee in the world and is certainly the most expensive, selling for up to US$ 270 per kilo. These civets eat the ripe berries and excrete partially-digested beans in their feces, which are then harvested for sale. The inner bean of the berry is not digested, but it is believed that enzymes in the civet's stomach improve the coffee's flavor by breaking down the proteins that give coffee its bitter taste. The beans are excreted by the civets and then collected by locals to be sold to dealers. The beans are washed and given only a light roast so as to not destroy the complex flavors that have developed through the digestive process. It is produced in Indonesia, the Philippines, Vietnam, and the coffee estates of south India, and is sold mainly in Japan and the USA.

Status and Conservation

Viverrids are among the least known of the Carnivora; many species are rarely observed and most have never been studied. Very little is known about their natural history and a few species are only known from museum skins. Until recently, the taxonomy of this family was poorly understood and heavily debated, with great uncertainty about the taxonomic status and distribution of many species and subspecies; the genets, for instance, have been notorious for their taxonomic difficulties.

All the viverrids were last assessed for *The IUCN Red List* in 2008. A few species were moved into higher threat categories, which reflects the increasing extinction risks for many viverrid species. The Malabar Civet was at one point declared as probably extinct, but after the discovery of skin specimens in the late 1980s and early 90s confirmed that it still exists, it has now been declared Critically Endangered. Other viverrids, such as the Ot-

Very little is known about the conservation status and ecological requirements of any of the species of palm civet classified as Vulnerable on The IUCN Red List. *One of these,* **Hose's Palm Civet,** *is almost completely unknown. There are fewer than 20 museum specimens, and this species has been recorded only in a handful of scattered localities, within a very restricted range. Ascertaining the exact geographic range of a species is important to determine if it includes well-managed areas of sufficient size. Some species may be confined to small areas within a seemingly homogenous forest and understanding the factors that explain this mosaic-like distribution is crucial for implementing conservation measures.*

Diplogale hosei
Bukit Retak,
Ulu Temburong National Park,
Borneo.
Photo: Yasuma Shigekil

ter Civet, are listed as Endangered, and several civets, including Hose's, Banded, Owston's, and Sulawesi Palm Civets, are classified as Vulnerable. However, the reality is that there is so little information about civets, genets, and oyans, that it is difficult to accurately assess the extinction risks for most viverrids.

The most important reason for the decline of viverrid species appears to be habitat destruction. Forest loss, fragmentation, and degradation, are the primary threats to forest-dependent viverrids. Fragmentation of forests results in a sub-division of populations into smaller units, and smaller populations have a higher extinction risk from intrinsic and extrinsic factors (disease, climatic changes, fire, etc.). Fragmentation may also restrict dispersal and gene flow between isolated groups, resulting in a higher occurrence of inbreeding. Inbreeding can result in the loss of important alleles that confer resistance to infectious diseases, and also allows harmful recessive genes to be expressed. Logging roads allow greater access for hunters, which can lead to increases in hunting pressure. Forest degradation, such as selective logging, can also have serious consequences for forest species. Although not as destructive as clear cutting, it can dramatically alter the structure of a forest, affecting the availability of food resources and suitable den sites. Remaining forests need to be protected and conserved through the implementation of management plans, and habitat corridors connecting these forest patches should also be protected and maintained. Protected areas should be managed in ways that take into account the needs of viverrids as well as more charismatic animal species, which are often given priority.

A number of viverrid species are heavily hunted, whether targeted or accidentally. Hunting pressures for some species appear to be increasing and may be unsustainable, particularly if their habitat is also being destroyed or altered. The demands for viverrid meat, skins, and other body parts, need to be eliminated or considerably reduced. Existing protection laws need to be enforced and new ones implemented. All the threats that impact viverrid species need to be identified and assessed.

Genetic introgression occurs when a species is introduced within the range of closely related species or subspecies, which are capable of hybridizing with the introduced form. Depending on the success of the colonizing species, this process can have a significant, rapid impact on the gene pool of the original population. Even a small degree of genetic introgression can lead to the loss of the distinctiveness of a taxon or contribute to its extinction through the elimination of adaptive genetic characters. For instance, the Common Palm Civet is quite commonly taken from the wild and kept as a pet, and is exported and imported throughout Asia. Unfortunately, some of these places may already have endemic subspecies of the Common Palm Civet; the extent to which these might have been affected by hybridization with escaped pets is unknown.

Considering the lack of data on the distribution and conservation status of most viverrid species, field surveys investigating these aspects are important for identifying the sites and the problems on which conservation activities should concentrate. Ascertaining the exact geographic range of a species is especially important to determine if its distribution includes well-managed areas of sufficient size. Even when a reserve is known to be within the range of an endangered species, it must be verified that the species actually occurs within the protected area, and that the area contains a viable population. Ecological research on tropical rainforest animals has shown that many species are distributed patchily, both across landscapes and at smaller spatial scales; sometimes a species is confined to small areas in a seemingly homogenous forest. Understanding the factors that explain this mosaic-like distribution pattern is crucial for implementing conservation measures.

Most viverrid species have never been studied by scientists in the wild. Field research of these elusive, nocturnal and solitary small carnivores, in difficult and remote environments, poses many practical and logistical challenges. But these studies are vital for determining their ecological requirements for long-term conservation measures. To formulate population viability models and predict extinction risks for viverrids we need to know a great deal about their ecology and natural history. A better understanding of the social structure of a species and its dispersal patterns is essential for estimating the minimum population sizes needed for preserving genetic variability. The reasons for peculiar distribution patterns, and the factors that impact population sizes, also require investigation. For instance, some species that have been recorded over large areas may only be found in low numbers locally or in a few isolated populations; dependence on a rare and patchily distributed habitat type, specialization on certain food items, or competition with other species, are some possible explanations. Field research into feeding ecology and breeding behavior can also help improve techniques for captive management.

Taxonomic revisions are necessary in order to provide a systematic framework and to define important units for conservation purposes and for answering scientific questions. Animal protection laws are usually applied to defined entities, such as recognized species or subspecies, so defining these entities is crucial. For quite a long time, viverrids were an overlooked

*Zoo-based captive breeding programs for the **Binturong**, which is classified as Vulnerable on The IUCN Red List, are managed by the European Studbook Programme, and a Population Management Plan in American zoos. Such captive breeding programs can benefit from molecular studies, which can help define subspecies and populations that may have adaptations to local conditions (such as climate, competitors, predators, parasites, and pathogens). Molecular studies can also help evaluate the genetic diversity of captive populations for breeding purposes, as was recently investigated in the Binturong.*

Arctictis binturong
Photo: Kenneth W. Fink

*There is a scarcity of recent records for the **Otter Civet**, and little is known about current populations. It is classified as Endangered on The IUCN Red List. The Otter Civet is found near streams and wetland areas in lowland forest. Logging and conversion of both lowland and peat swamp forests to oil palm plantations has probably reduced populations, and its riverine habitats are increasingly polluted and disturbed. Field surveys and ecological studies are needed to ascertain its current distribution, to monitor populations, and to determine its tolerance to habitat disturbance, especially where riverine forest remains in a mosaic of logged lowland forest.*

Cynogale bennettii
Photo: Roland Seitre

group and the focus of little taxonomic research. Recent molecular and morphological studies have clearly shown the value of such research in establishing valid species. But further work is needed to resolve certain issues and to define important subspecies and populations. Subspecies may have particular adaptations to the local climate or to different competitors, predators, parasites, or strains of pathogens. Molecular studies also provide a tool for identifying the geographic origin of viverrid species that are taken for the wildlife trade and sold in markets (as was shown in a recent study on the Owston's Palm Civet). Captive breeding programs can also benefit from molecular studies, which may help define conservation units (species, subspecies, and populations) and help evaluate the genetic diversity of captive populations for breeding purposes; this was recently investigated in the Binturong.

Captive breeding can be a powerful tool in ensuring the survival of an endangered species, particularly where short-term protection of the animal and its natural habitats is not likely to be successful. Unfortunately, viverrids are so poorly known that it is not possible to say how many are so seriously endangered that their survival can only be ensured by captive breeding. There has also been a general neglect of this family in zoos. However, keeping animals in zoos raises many ethical and welfare issues, and many people and animal organizations oppose zoos on these grounds. Even within the conservation community there is considerable debate about how great a role captive breeding should form part of a conservation strategy for ensuring the survival of a species. Many conservationists argue that captive breeding should be seen as supporting, not substituting conservation efforts in the wild, and should only be used as a last resort. They highlight the potential difficulties of captive breeding programs. For instance, conditions in captivity are different from those that a species has to live with in the wild, and there is a risk that captive breeding over several generations may select animals that would not be able to reproduce if subject to natural selection. Also, the management of captive populations could lead to changes in a species' genetic structure, and we do not know the consequences of such changes and their impact on long-term fitness. To maintain sufficiently large captive populations requires appreciable investments of funds and expertise. Also, most zoos and breeding centers are independent institutions that are run as businesses and this can influence which animals are held in collections and breeding programs.

Captive breeding programs have been developed for the Binturong and Owston's Palm Civet, and other viverrid species have been bred in zoos. However, as far as is known, no reintroduction programs have been planned. Unfortunately for most species, our knowledge of their habitat requirements and threats is not sufficiently known to undertake successful reintroductions.

Keeping civets in captivity, either for extracting their perineal gland secretions or for their meat, raises many ethical and welfare issues. There are also conservation implications since taking animals from the wild may deplete local populations and threaten their survival. Many wildlife organizations consider this practice, and the deplorable conditions in which civets are often kept, as totally unacceptable, and several are trying to get this banned through education campaigns, lobbying governments, and encouraging direct action (such as urging consumers not to buy products containing civet oil). However, some will argue that civet farming is an important part of the traditional beliefs and practices of indigenous people and provides a significant economic benefit for local communities. Others point out that civet farming could be sustainable through captive breeding and with good husbandry practices. Perhaps creative "win-win" solutions could be a way forward, especially if they incorporate local people and their traditional practices in wildlife management and conservation efforts. For example, since civets scent-mark prominent signposts in their natural habitats, it might be possible to collect the civet oil from these marked sites. If so, this valuable resource could be gathered without disturbing the animals, thus benefiting both humans and viverrids.

General Bibliography

Balakrishnan & Sreedevi (2007a, 2007b), Colon (1999, 2002), Colyn *et al.* (2004), Corbet & Hill (1992), Cosson *et al.* (2007), Crawford-Cabral (1993), Engel (1998b), Estes (1991), Ewer (1973), Ewer & Wemmer (1974), Garbutt (2007), Gaubert & Begg (2007), Gaubert & Cordeiro-Estrela (2006), Gaubert & Veron (2003), Gaubert, Fernandes *et al.* (2004), Gaubert, Taylor, Fernandes *et al.* (2005), Gaubert, Taylor & Veron (2005), Gaubert, Tranier *et al.* (2004), Gaubert, Veron & Tranier (2002), Gaubert, Wozencraft *et al.* (2005), Gittleman (1989, 1996), Gupta (2004), Heydon & Bulloh (1996), Hunt (1996, 2001), IUCN (2008), Jennings *et al.* (2006), Meijaard (2003), Moutou (2004), Mudappa *et al.* (2007), Patou *et al.* (2008), Pocock (1915e, 1915f, 1915g, 1915h, 1933a, 1933b, 1933c, 1933d, 1934a, 1934b, 1934c, 1939), Pugh (2008), Schreiber *et al.* (1989), Skinner & Chimimba (2005), Veron (1994, 1995, 1999), Veron & Catzeflis (1993), Veron & Heard (2000), Veron, Gaubert *et al.* (2006), Veron, Heard *et al.* (2004), Veron, Laidlaw *et al.* (2004), Walston & Veron (2001), Wemmer (1977), Wozencraft (1984, 2005), Yoder *et al.* (2003), Youlatos (2003).

PLATE 12

inches   12
cm   30

1

ssp *civetta*

ssp *schwarzi*   2

3

4

5

6

Subfamily VIVERRINAE
Genus *VIVERRICULA*
Hodgson, 1838

1. Small Indian Civet *Viverricula indica*

French: Civette indienne / **German**: Kleine Indische Zibetkatze / **Spanish**: Civeta india pequeña
Other common names: Lesser Oriental Civet

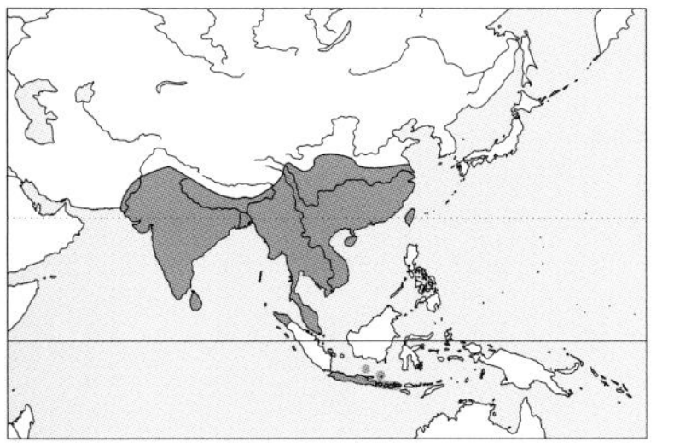

Taxonomy. *Viverra indica* Geoffroy Saint-Hilaire, 1803, India.
Often named *V. malaccensis*, but this name is now not considered valid. The number of subspecies is debated, but some authors recognize eleven subspecies.
Subspecies and Distribution.
V. i. indica Geoffroy Saint-Hilaire, 1803 – S peninsular India.
V. i. atchinensis Sody, 1931 – Sumatra.
V. i. baliensis Sody, 1931 – Bali.
V. i. baptistae Pocock, 1933 – Bangladesh to NE India (Assam), and Bhutan.
V. i. deserti Bonhote, 1898 – Pakistan through C India to Nepal.
V. i. klossi Pocock, 1933 – Malaysia.
V. i. mayori Pocock, 1933 – Sri Lanka.
V. i. muriavensis Sody, 1931 – Java.
V. i. taivana Schwarz, 1911 – Taiwan.
V. i. thai Kloss, 1919 – Myanmar and Thailand through Indochina to China.
V. i. wellsi Pocock, 1933 – NW India.
It has been introduced to Madagascar, Zanzibar Island, the Comoro Islands, and Socotra Island for the production of civet or to be used as rat catchers; its presence on some of the Indonesian islands (Bali, Bawean, Kangean, Lombok, and Sumbawa) could also have resulted from introductions.
Descriptive notes. Head–body 48·5–68 cm, tail 30–43 cm, hindfoot 8·5–10 cm, ear 3·9–5 cm; weight 2–4 kg. A small terrestrial civet, with no erectile dorsal crest, a short muzzle, and ears set close on the forehead. The coat color is gray, tawny, or brown. The body is covered by small brown or black spots on the flanks, which tend to run as three to five longitudinal lines on the back. This pattern of lines and spots is variable and does not seem to be correlated with geographic origin. The black and white neck-stripes are narrower and more variable than in the *Viverra* civets. There are white patches on both sides of the muzzle and white spots between the eyes, but these are not clearly defined. The tail has six to nine dark rings and a white tip. The feet are dark brown or black and have five digits; however, the hallux and pollex are reduced and elevated. The metacarpal pads are reduced to one small lobe and the metatarsal pads are absent. The perineal gland is larger in males. This gland opens into specialized pouches; the inner pockets are enclosed by antero-posteriorly elongated lips (these are everted when the gland secretion is applied). There are at least two pairs of teats. The skull is low and elongated, with well-developed post-orbital processes. The posterior chamber of the auditory bullae is well-developed. Dental formula: I 3/3, C 1/1, P 4/4, M 2/2 = 40. The first upper premolars are reduced and the lower premolars have well-developed cusps. The largest teeth are the carnassials.
Habitat. Semi-evergreen and deciduous forest, mixed deciduous forest, bamboo forest, scrubby areas, grasslands, and riverine habitat. Also found near plantations and human settlements. Reported up to 1200 m in north-east India. In Thailand, a radio-collared male moved in an area consisting of 62% dry deciduous forest, 25% dry evergreen forest, and 13% mixed deciduous forest. In Thailand, out of 29 individuals live-trapped, 16 captures were in open shrub habitat, ten were semi-evergreen/mixed deciduous forest, and four were in grassland; camera-trapping produced 14 photographs, with 13 photos from semi-evergreen/mixed deciduous forest, and one from open shrub habitat. In India (Western Ghats), Small Indian Civets were found to be more abundant in rainforest fragments than in relatively undisturbed large tracts of rainforest.
Food and Feeding. Omnivorous; feeds largely on small vertebrates and invertebrates (particularly insects). In China, the most common prey was rodents (80%) and insects (23%). In southeastern China, the frequency of occurrence of food items in 44 scats was 89% rodents, 39% insects, 21% birds, 14% fruit, 9% leaves, 5% shrews, 5% acorns, 2% crustaceans, and 2% paddy rice. In Taiwan, the percentage of occurrence was 95% insects, 67% earthworms, 58% plants, 40% mammals, 16% amphibians, and 11% reptiles; the occurrence of birds, fish, crustaceans, chilopods, gastropods, and arachnids, were all less than 10%. There was some variation in the diet due to seasonal availability; insects were consumed more in the summer and less in the winter, and plants were consumed more in the spring and summer. The contents of seven stomachs from India comprised rats, babblers, frogs, scorpions, crabs, crickets, centipedes, millipedes, beetles, seeds, berries (*Zizyphus oenoplia* and *Aporusa lindleyana*), pineapple, and grass. The stomachs of Small Indian Civets captured near human habitations contained boiled rice and fish bones. The heads of vertebrates are chewed and other parts of the body are merely crushed.
Activity patterns. Nocturnal: activity during the night has been recorded by camera-traps, field sightings, and radio-telemetry. In Thailand, a radio-collared male was active over 50% of the time between 16:30 h and 04:30 h, with a peak of activity between 19:30 h and 01:30 h. The highest monthly activity level was in the rainy month of February. In Myanmar, two Small Indian Civets showed peak activity from 19:30–22:00 h, and from 00:30–03:00 h. In southeastern China, two males were active over 50% of the time between 18:00 h and 05:00 h. In Thailand, rest sites were located in trees and on the ground, all in mixed deciduous forest. In southeastern China, daybeds were on the ground, under bushes or among tall grass, and were often adjacent to each other. They were used once (43%) or twice (29%), but four were used 6–10 times each. In Myanmar, Small Indian Civets rested on the ground, within dense shrub cover, or less often, in a hole in the ground; 60% of the sites were used only once, although one was re-used 15 times over a period of 250 days.
Movements, Home range and Social organization. Solitary, single individuals have been observed in the field and recorded by camera-traps. Terrestrial, but is said to climb well. In southeastern China, the resting home range of a male was 2·3 km^2. The mean distance moved between consecutively used daybeds was 613 m. In Thailand, the home range of a male was 3·1 km^2; his core home range was 1·1 km^2, and the mean daily movement was 500 m. In India (Nilgiri Biosphere Reserve), the home range of a male was 2·2 km^2; the distance between successive daytime locations ranged from 193 m in September to 2260 m in October. In Myanmar, the mean distance moved between consecutive resting sites was 214 m. Scent marking activity, using the secretions from the perineal gland, occurs in both sexes, but is more frequent in males. They mark any object, but vertical objects seem to be preferred. Scent marking varies between days and season. In captivity, it occurs mainly at night, with three peaks at 18:00–19:00 h, 21:00–23:00 h, and before dawn. Scent marking is more common in the spring, during the breeding season. Vocal communication in captive civets includes: a scream (given by the female during fights with a male); threat calling (given under stress and when an animal is terrified); courtship calling, "da da da" (given by the male as an estrus female approaches).
Breeding. In China, captive Small Indian Civets had two breeding periods. Breeding occurred mostly between February and April; and less frequently in August and September. In southern India, breeding in captive civets occurred during March to May and October to December. When the female is in estrus, both the male and female increase scent marking, inter-individual contacts, and locomotor activity (which is highest between 20:00 h and 21:00 h). Scent marking increases in the male first and then in the female, with a peak during estrus; it decreases after copulations. The male also sniffs the posterior quarters of a female in estrus. Courtship commences with a series of "duk-duk-duk" calls from the male. During the first mounting attempts, the female responds with a sharp scream and bites the male. This often ends in a fight, in which both animals can be injured on the nape and tail. Courtship calls resume after 5–30 minutes. After three or four such attempts, the female runs around the cage, often touching and slightly pushing the male. The male follows and sniffs at the perineal region of the female and finally she lies down, allowing the male to mount; the body of the female is fully extended, with the hindlegs slightly raised. The male mounts with the forepaws placed on either side of the female's shoulders. He grips the hair on her nape and begins pelvic thrusts. After some time, the female makes a low cat-like call and the male then dismounts. Immediately after dismounting, the female growls and tries to bite the male; they then go to separate corners of the cage. During the first ten days after copulation, females are less active than before, but their appetite increases. Scent marking decreases to a base level and stops around 20 days after a successful mating. Females do not resume scent marking until two months after the parturition date. Movements of the fetuses within a pregnant female are noticeable from the sixth week of pregnancy. Females do not eat on the day of parturition. The mean gestation period is 67 ± 2 days. The litter size varies from two to five, with two being the most common. The mother nurses the young three to four times every hour during the first week after parturition, but this decreases to once every hour by the second week, to once every two hours by the third week, and to two to three times a day by the seventh week. The mother licks the whole body of her offspring and eats their excreta. If alarmed, she will hold a kitten in her mouth, gripping the fur on its nape. At birth, the newborn civets are blind and covered with fur; their weight ranges from 90 to 110 g. They immediately cluster beside the belly of the mother and crawl to reach a teat. Their eyes open on the fifth day and from the eighth day onwards they can walk slowly. They start eating solid food by four weeks of age. Scent marking behavior is first observed when they are eight weeks old, but perineal gland secretions are not noted until they are eight months old. The body weight is 180–200 g by the end of the second week, 250–300 g by the end of the fourth, 400–500 g by the end of the eighth week, and 1 kg by ten weeks. They reach adult size at six months of age.
Status and Conservation. Classified as Least Concern on *The IUCN Red List*. The Small Indian Civet is considered unthreatened due to its widespread distribution and generalist habitat and food preferences. However, it is not fully understood how habitat disturbance may affect this species, and more ecological studies are needed. Small Indian Civets are hunted for their meat and scent, and are particularly vulnerable to snare trapping. They are also farmed in India to extract their perineal gland secretion for medicinal purposes. These farmed civets are not captive-bred, but are trapped in the wild, and this could be causing declines in local populations. Field surveys are needed to monitor populations, especially in areas where their numbers may be depressed due to high trapping pressures.
Bibliography. Austin & Tewes (1999b), Ayyadurai *et al.* (1987), Balakrishnan & Sreedevi (2007a, 2007b), Chuang & Lee (1997), Corbet & Hill (1992), Duckworth (1997), Gaubert (2003b), Gupta (2004), Jha (1999),

On following pages: 2 African Civet (*Civettictis civetta*); 3. Malabar Civet (*Viverra civettina*); 4. Large-spotted Civet (*Viverra megaspila*); 5. Malay Civet (*Viverra tangalunga*); 6. Large Indian Civet (*Viverra zibetha*).

Kumar & Umapathy (2000), Lekagul & McNeely (1991), Medway (1969), Mohan (1994), Mudappa (2001), Muddapa *et al.* (2007), Pocock (1933a, 1933b, 1939), Rabinowitz (1991), Sheng & Xu (1990), Stuart & Stuart (1998), Su & Sale (2007), Veron (1999), Wang & Fuller (2001, 2003b), Wang *et al.* (1976), Wozencraft (1984, 2005), Xu & Sheng (1994).

Genus *CIVETTICTIS*

Pocock, 1915

2. African Civet *Civettictis civetta*

French: Civette d'Afrique / **German**: Afrikanische Zibetkatze / **Spanish**: Civeta africana

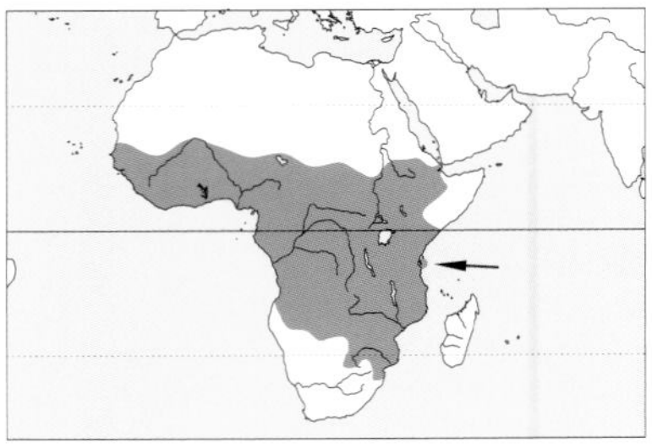

Taxonomy. *Viverra civetta* Schreber, 1776, Guinea.

Six subspecies are recognized.

Subspecies and Distribution.

C. c. civetta Schreber, 1776 – S Mauritania and Senegal E to Ethiopia and Somalia, and S to Gabon.

C. c. australis Lundholm, 1955 – Zambia and E Botswana to Malawi and Mozambique, and S to South Africa and Swaziland.

C. c. congica Cabrera, 1929 – S Sudan, DR Congo and Rwanda, S to Angola and N Zambia.

C. c. pauli Kock, Künzel & Rayaleh, 2000 – Djibouti.

C. c. schwarzi Cabrera, 1929 – S Somalia, Kenya, Uganda, and Tanzania (including Zanzibar I).

C. c. volkmanni Lundholm, 1955 – NE Namibia and N Botswana.

Descriptive notes. Head–body 67–84 cm, tail 34–46·9 cm, hindfoot 12·3–13·9 cm, ear 5·4–5·8 cm; weight 7–20 kg. In South Africa, females are larger and heavier than males, but there is a large overlap. A large terrestrial civet, with large hindquarters and an erectile dorsal crest. The pelage is coarse, with long thick guard hairs. The coat color varies from white to yellow to reddish-buff. The body spots are brown to black and are arranged in irregular lines along the body. Melanistic individuals have been reported from some areas, including up to one third of the population in the Congo Basin. The head is broad, with a pointed muzzle and small rounded ears. There is a black band across the face and white patches between the eyes and ears and on the sides of the muzzle. The forehead is whitish or grayish; the ears are white at the front and black at the back, with a white tip. The neck has conspicuous large black and white bands. The hairs along the dorsal crest increase in length from the forehead and reach their maximum on the posterior back, where the maximum length reaches 10–12 cm. The tail is dark on the dorsal surface and marked with five diffuse white rings; the tip is broadly black. There are five digits on each foot, although the hallux and pollex are set back and do not appear in prints. The claws are long and curved, and slightly retractile. The metacarpal and metatarsal pads are reduced and fused, and form a small rounded bi-lobed pad. The perineal gland is well-developed, forming a double-pocketed invagination. This gland is visible externally as paired swellings (each about 30 mm long and 19 mm wide), with an oblong opening about 25 mm long that is kept closed by a pair of labia (which are everted when the secretion is applied). Inside each gland there is a large hair-lined sac; the secretion from the glands enters a space that functions as a storage reservoir. Up to 15 g of civet oil can be extracted each week from captive animals. Anal glands are present, but are simple; they are situated in the wall of the rectum and open directly into the rectum. There are two pairs of teats. The skull is heavily built with developed crests, especially in males. The auditory bullae are large and oval, with the posterior chamber rounded and swollen. The paroccipital process is well-developed and extends beyond the bullae ventrally. The post-orbital constriction is not well marked and the post-orbital processes are short and blunt. Dental formula: I 3/3, C 1/1, P 4/4, M 2/2 = 40. The canines are short and heavily built. The carnassials and post-carnassial teeth are well-developed; the molars are blunt and broad, adapted for crushing.

Habitat. Forest and open habitats (particularly with dense ground cover). Often associated with riverine habitat in drier regions and sometimes found in plantations and near human settlements. Found up to 1700 m. In Ethiopia, a radio-tracked male used *Hagenia* and *Juniper* forests (62% of the time), bush (19%), grassland (11%), and farmland (8%).

Food and Feeding. Omnivorous: invertebrates, fruits, small vertebrates, eggs, and grass. In Zimbabwe, an examination of 27 stomachs revealed that during the warm, wet summer months (October to April), 70% contained insects, (predominantly grasshoppers and beetles), followed by 40% fruits, 30% rodents (Muridae, mainly multimammate mice *Mastomys* spp., and the Angoni Vlei Rat, *Otomys angoniensis*), 30% reptiles, 20% amphibians, 20% myriapodes, 20% grass, and 10% birds. In the colder, dryer months (May to September), the highest percentage of occurrence was 57% fruits, followed by 43% insects, 43% Muridae, 21% birds, 21% grass, 14% reptiles, and 7% amphibians. Animal prey also included Scrub Hare (*Lepus saxatilis*), Banded Mongoose, Common Slender Mongoose, Smith's Bush Squirrel (*Paraxerus cepapi*), South African Spring Hare (*Pedetes capensis*), and helmeted guineafowl (*Numida meleagris*). Carrion of Impala (*Aepyceros melampus*), Greater Kudu (*Tragelaphus strepsiceros*), Bushbuck (*T. scriptus*), and Blue Wildebeest (*Connochaetes taurinus*) was also eaten. A similar diet has been reported in West and East Africa, but aquatic organisms (crabs, snails, and mudskippers) were also eaten. In Nigeria, stomach contents contained rodents, reptiles, insects, birds, amphibians, gastropods, and plants. In the Central African Republic, the frequency of occurrence in scats was 97% arthropods, 73% fruits, 30% rodents, 3% reptiles, and 3% birds. In Zaire, scats contained eleven fruit species (Arecaceae, Burseraceae, Moraceae, Myristicaceae, and Sapindaceae); seasonal variations were observed and a wider diversity of fruits was consumed during the rainy season. A civet feeding on a fruiting tree immediately exploited a nearby outbreak of millipedes. Their behavior in captivity suggests that they detect their prey mainly by scent and sound, rather than vision. Animal prey is seized by the mouth, the paws are not usually used in the capture and the killing bite is often directed at the head. Various methods have been observed when attacking live prey: run-away bite (a quick nip aimed at any part of the prey's body, followed by instant release and retreat); bite-and-throw (the prey is held long enough to be thrown quickly aside with a quick movement of the head); bite-and-shake (the grip is retained and the prey is shaken to break the vertebrae); killing bite (the jaws bite home firmly).

Activity patterns. Predominantly nocturnal, with peaks in activity one to two hours before sunset until midnight, and around sunrise. Occasionally seen in the morning or afternoon on overcast days. In Ethiopia, diurnal rest sites were in dense vegetation on the ground, mostly in an area of dense *Juniper* forest (nine out of eleven sites). In Zaire, African Civets selected dens close to fruit-bearing trees and moved away when the fruiting season was over.

Movements, Home range and Social organization. Solitary, although groups consisting of an adult and young have been observed. Terrestrial; they are poor climbers, but are known to clamber along low stout branches to get at ripening fruit. In Ethiopia, a radio-collared sub-adult male had a home range of 11·1 km²; the core area was 0·4 km², centered on *Hagenia* and *Juniper* forests. On one occasion, this male was found within 20 meters of a White-tailed Mongoose. African Civets deposit their feces in latrines (civetries); these are usually located along game trails and in clearings and may play a role in marking territories. Some are used frequently and then abandoned for periods of several months. They tend to use the same sites, even when the accumulation of scats is removed. In Zimbabwe, latrines were found in *Asparagus* thickets, in grassland, and in the cover of dense reed beds. In Zaire, four latrines were separated by several kilometres; each one was used by a single civet. These latrines were in natural hollows in the ground left by uprooted trees (35–65 cm deep and 60–170 cm wide), and all were close to a river (8–30 m). Urine may also play a role in scent marking: captive males have been observed to sniff a female's urine, which prompted them to flehm. African Civets scent-mark objects with their perineal gland secretion (called civet), both on the ground and on vertical surfaces. In South Africa, they were found to mark trees (50%), rocks (29%), shrubs (19%), and herbs (10%); the mean height of marks above ground was 35 cm. They mark trees and shrubs that bear fruits eaten by them and also at or near civetries. Scent marks retain a strong musk odor for one month and are still detectable after four months. To mark a tree, the civet backs up, raises its tail, and presses the everted perineal gland against the trunk. Both sexes scent-mark, but males do it more frequently than females (the perineal gland is larger in the male). Captive females mark horizontal surfaces more than vertical ones; the opposite is true for males. Young animals scent-mark only in the squatting posture, whereas adults only perform the backing-up technique. African Civets do not emit perineal civet when alarmed, but they do sometimes mark when anxious or feeling insecure. Their senses of smell and hearing are acute (particularly for high pitched sounds). When at ease and alert, they move with the head held higher than the shoulder and the legs well extended. When anxious or in fear, they lower their head and flex the legs; the whole body sags, the eyes are narrowed, and the erectile crest is depressed. In a defensive threat, the dorsal crest is erected, the head is directed toward the source of alarm, and the body is turned sideways so that the change in size is visible to the opponent. An appeasement posture has been observed in captive civets and consists of lying down on one side. Although generally silent, several distinct vocalizations have been detected in captive animals: growl (frequently emitted by a female in defense of her kittens); cough-spit (when a terrified civet is approached); and scream (heard during serious fights). There are three different types of meow: a distress meow from kittens; a cat-like meow (made by the female during copulation); and the female sex call (emitted by the female before and during estrus). The most frequent vocalization is the contact call: a short sound, usually repeated three or four times, and sounds like "ha-ha-ha" emitted with the mouth closed.

Breeding. Breeding seems to occur throughout the year in West Africa, but there may be favored breeding seasons in East Africa (March to October) and southern Africa (August to January). Sexual maturity is attained at around twelve months. Females are polyoestrous and can have two or three litters a year; the estrus period appears to last up to six days. Natal den sites are in holes made by other animals or in cavities under tangled roots. Breeding behavior has been observed in captivity. As the female comes into estrus, the male and female became more aggressive, the male gives more contact calls, and both sexes increase their locomotor activity. The male makes several mounting attempts before the female accepts him; she will often move away and sometimes turn to snap at the male. When the female is receptive, she shows this by breaking into a run and inciting the male to pursue her. After several unsuccessful mounting attempts, the female finally lies down (with her hindquarters slightly raised) and permits the male to mount. The male places his forelegs on both sides of the female's shoulders and makes treading movements with his hindlegs on each side of her flanks. Pelvic thrusting then takes place, during which the male bites the female's fur between the shoulders. During copulation, the female gives a long meow; the male dismounts after forty seconds. After copulating, each civet licks its genitals. Copulations take place at

night. Gestation is 60 to 81 days. Litter size in captivity ranges from one to four. The young are born with short dark soft fur; the neck stripe is present, but is pale grayish and less conspicuous than in the adult. The facial pattern is indistinct, but the white muzzle marks are present. The perineal gland in the young is genet-like; the pouch is marked by an area of pale hairs, in the center of which the naked lips of the gland are visible. In female young, there is a patch of naked skin around the anus and a hairless isthmus links the lips of the gland. At one month old, the dark hairlines that traverse the adult pocket start to appear. Growth of the pocket conceals the naked lips, which are then only visible when everted. The eyes are open at birth or within the first few days. Newborns can crawl at birth; at five days they can stand on their hindlegs. They start to play at 14 days and to explore outside the den at 17–18 days. The mother licks her young all over, with special attention to the perineal region, and consumes the urine and feces voided in response to this stimulation. The young are not given the opportunity to urinate independently before they are 25 days old. They are dependant on the mother's milk for up to six weeks; they usually suckle from the posterior teats and it seems that each young always uses the same one. They start eating solid food in their second month and weaning occurs at around 14 to 16 weeks. In the second month, the young begin to catch insects and at 42 days the mother provides solid food. Mouth suckling (the young lick their mother's mouth) is exhibited immediately before the mother begins to provide solid food. Weights of young are: 162 g at six days; 440–540 g at 17 days; 480–550 g at 21 days; and 680–810 g at 33 days. During the fifth month, the young begin to mark vertical objects with the backing-up technique, the perineal gland secretion becomes strongly scented, and males first flehm in response to female urine.
Status and Conservation. Classified as Least Concern on *The IUCN Red List*. Considered common and widespread, and is not thought to be threatened. However, some local populations could be threatened by hunting and civet farming. African Civets are hunted and sold in markets for bushmeat and for their skins. They are also kept on farms in Ethiopia for the purpose of extracting their perineal secretions for the perfume industry. Although exact numbers are not known, one estimate is that there are 180 civet farmers holding over 2700 African Civets. They are not bred on these farms and to replenish those that die, new animals are taken from the wild. There is still not much known about this species across its range and field studies are needed.
Bibliography. Admasu *et al.* (2004b), Angelici (2000), Angelici, Luiselli, Politano & Akani (1999), Colyn *et al.* (2004), Duckworth (1995), Ewer & Wemmer (1974), Guy (1977), Hoppe-Dominik (1990), Jacob & Schliemann (1983), Kock *et al.* (2000), Mallinson (1969), Pendje (1994), Pocock (1915e), Randall (1977, 1979), Ray (1995, In press), Ray & Sunquist (2001), Sillero-Zubiri & Marino (1997), Skinner & Chimimba (2005), Stuart & Stuart (1998), Veron (1999), Wozencraft (2005).

Genus *VIVERRA*
Linnaeus, 1758

3. Malabar Civet *Viverra civettina*
French: Civette de Malabar / **German**: Malabar-Zibetkatze / **Spanish**: Civeta malabar
Other common names: Malabar Large-spotted Civet

Taxonomy. *Viverra civettina* Blyth, 1862, Southern Malabar, India.
Has been considered a subspecies of the Large-spotted Civet (*V. megaspila*). Monotypic.
Distribution. SW India (Western Ghats).
Descriptive notes. Head–body 76–85 cm, tail 30–40 cm, hindfoot 13–15 cm; weight 6·6–8 kg. A large terrestrial civet, very similar to the Large-spotted Civet. The coat is gray or tawny, with large black spots on the flanks, thighs, and hindlegs. There are conspicuous black and white bands on the throat and sides of the neck. A black crest of erectile hairs runs along the back and continues as a dorsal black line to the tip of the tail; the length of the crest hairs is up to 50 mm. The tail has five or six incomplete dark rings; the tip is black. The feet have five digits, but the hallux and pollex are reduced. There are small rounded metacarpal pads and small metatarsal pads; the area around the plantar pads is naked. There are two pairs of teats. The posterior chamber of the auditory bulla has a pyramidal shape. Dental formula: I 3/3, C 1/1, P 4/4, M 2/2 = 40. The cheek teeth are larger than in the Large-spotted Civet.
Habitat. Lowland swamp and riparian forests, but may also be found in cashew plantations.
Food and Feeding. Nothing known.
Activity patterns. Reported to be nocturnal and to rest in scrub forests and cashew plantations during the day.
Movements, Home range and Social organization. Thought to be terrestrial and solitary.
Breeding. Nothing known.
Status and Conservation. Classified as Critically Endangered on *The IUCN Red List*. Schedule I of the Indian Wildlife (Protection) Act. The Malabar Civet is extremely rare and is listed as a priority species for conservation by the IUCN/SSC Small Carnivore Specialist Group. It has been recorded mostly in the coastal district, from Kanyakumari in the south to Honnavar in the north. There are only two reports of its occurrence at higher elevations, in the High Wavy Mountains and Kudremukh. In 1972, the IUCN

declared that the Malabar Civet was "possibly extinct". However, in the 1970s there were two possible sight records of this species, one in the Kudremukh area, Karnataka, and the other in Tiruvella, Kerala. Skins of recently killed civets were obtained in Elayur, Kerala (in 1987), and near Nilambur, northern Kerala (in 1990). Loss and degradation of habitat is a serious threat; it is likely that surviving populations exist in the remaining lowland forests and sub-optimal habitats along the foothills and lower slopes of the Western Ghats. Another major threat is hunting for meat. Various conservation measures have been proposed: greater protection of remaining populations and habitats, captive breeding, field surveys, and ecological studies.
Bibliography. Ashraf (1990), Ashraf *et al.* (1993), Hutton (1949), Karanth (1986), Kumar & Rai (1991), Kurup (1987, 1989), Pocock (1933a, 1939), Prater (1980), Rai & Kumar (1993), Schreiber *et al.* (1989), Wozencraft (2005).

4. Large-spotted Civet *Viverra megaspila*
French: Civette à grandes taches / **German**: Großfleck-Zibetkatze / **Spanish**: Civeta moteada

Taxonomy. *Viverra megaspila* Blyth, 1862, Prome, Myanmar.
The Malabar Civet (*V. civettina*) was previously included in *V. megaspila*, but they are now believed to be separate species. Monotypic.
Distribution. S China and Mainland SE Asia to Peninsular Malaysia.
Descriptive notes. Head–body 72–85 cm, tail 30–36·9 cm, hindfoot 13–13·8 cm, ear 4·5–4·8 cm; weight 8–9 kg. A large civet with conspicuous black and white bands on the throat and sides of the neck. The coat varies from gray to buff, with large black spots on the flanks, thighs, and hindlegs. A black crest of erectile hairs runs along the back and continues as a dorsal black line to the tip of the tail; the length of the crest hairs varies from 50 to 100 mm (mean 60 mm). The basal half of the tail has four or five incomplete dark rings; the terminal end is more or less completely dark. The head is more massive, and the muzzle is longer and more swollen, than in the Large Indian Civet. The feet are brown; there are small rounded metacarpal pads and no metatarsal pads. There are two pairs of teats. The skull resembles that of the Large Indian Civet, but has larger auditory bullae, a more inflated post-orbital constriction, and smaller post-orbital processes located behind the midpoint of the total length of the skull. The long axis of the sub-orbital foramina is horizontal. The dentition is similar to that of the Large Indian Civet, but with a longer maxillary toothrow and smaller canines and incisors. Dental formula: I 3/3, C 1/1, P 4/4, M 2/2 = 40. Differs from the Malabar Civet by having smaller cheek teeth.
Habitat. Primary evergreen and deciduous forest, and disturbed forest. Found up to 520 m, but most records are from below 300 m.
Food and Feeding. Nothing known.
Activity patterns. Camera-trapping data and sightings indicate that it is nocturnal.
Movements, Home range and Social organization. Terrestrial and solitary.
Breeding. Nothing known.
Status and Conservation. Classified as Vulnerable on *The IUCN Red List*. Listed as Threatened in the 1989 IUCN *Action Plan for the Conservation of Mustelids and Viverrids*. Known only from a few records and almost nothing is known about its habits. Habitat loss poses a major threat. Throughout South-east Asia, large areas of lowland forest have been cleared or degraded, through logging and conversion to other land uses. This species is also vulnerable to hunting, particularly with snares. This occurs in much of its range, with snare trapping found even in some protected areas. Field surveys and ecological studies are needed to determine its distribution and to learn more about its natural history and conservation requirements. Lowland forests need to be protected, hunting pressures reduced, and the threats to this species monitored.
Bibliography. Corbet & Hill (1992), Duckworth (1994, 1997), Khounboline (2005), Lekagul & McNeely (1991), Lynam *et al.* (2005), Pocock (1933a), Schreiber *et al.* (1989), Wozencraft (2005).

5. Malay Civet *Viverra tangalunga*
French: Civette malaise / **German**: Malaiische Zibetkatze / **Spanish**: Civeta malaya

Taxonomy. *Viverra tangalunga* Gray, 1832, West Sumatra.
Two subspecies are recognized, but a systematic revision is needed.
Subspecies and Distribution.
V. t. tangalunga Gray, 1832 – Peninsular Malaysia, Sumatra, Borneo, several Indonesian islands (Amboina I, Banggi I, Langkawi I, Rhio-Lingga Archipelago, Bangka I, Karimata I & Sulawesi), and the Philippines; also two records from Java, but no evidence of native population.
V. t. lankavensis Robinson & Kloss, 1920 – Malaysia (Langkawi I).
Descriptive notes. Head–body 54–77·3 cm, tail 26–39·5 cm, neck circumference 18–23·1 cm, hindfoot 8·2–11·6 cm, ear 2·5–4·8 cm; weight 3–7 kg. A fairly large civet with conspicuous black and white bands on the throat and sides of the neck. The coat varies from ash-gray to yellowish-gray, with numerous small black spots on the flanks, thighs, and

---

hindlegs. A black line runs along the back to the tip of the tail; there is a series of spots arranged in a row on each side of the dorsal median stripe. The face is gray, with a white patch on each side of the muzzle. There is a white patch below each eye, the rhinarium is large with a deep groove, and the ears are rounded. The chin is blackish brown. The tail has 10–15 dark brown or black rings, alternating with pale rings. The legs are blackish. The feet have five digits, but the hallux and pollex are reduced; the claws are retractable, and there are no metatarsal pads. There are two pairs of teats. Skull similar to that of *Viverra zibetha*, but smaller. Dental formula: I 3/3, C 1/1, P 4/4, M 2/2 = 40.

Habitat. Primary and disturbed forest, up to 1100 m. Also found in plantations and near villages that are adjacent to forest.

Food and Feeding. Omnivorous. Diet includes invertebrates (beetles, crabs, scorpions, and millipedes), fruit, small mammals (rodents and insectivores), birds, frogs, snakes, and lizards. May enter forest camps and villages looking for food scraps. Forages on the ground. A male civet was observed foraging using three capture techniques: pausing to listen, then plunging its head into the undergrowth; running over a short distance to grab prey; sniffing up and down vegetation before snapping at small prey.

Activity patterns. Mainly nocturnal, with activity peaks immediately after dark and shortly before dawn. In Sabah, the mean activity from 18:00–07:00 h was 81%; on Sulawesi it was 94%. Malay Civets were more active during the day on Sulawesi (57%) than in Sabah (21%). Rest sites are within dense cover on the ground.

Movements, Home range and Social organization. Generally solitary. Terrestrial, but can climb trees. In Sarawak, a male had a home range of 0·5–0·7 km². In Sabah, in an unlogged forest, the mean home range size for males was 0·93 km², and 0·80 km² for females; in a logged forest, the mean home range size for males was 1·59 km², and 1·05 km² for females. On Sulawesi (Buton Island), the mean home range size for males was 0·86 km², and 0·50 km² for females. In Sabah, there was considerable home range overlap in both sexes, indicating that this species was not territorial; however, there was low intra-sexual overlap on Sulawesi. In Sabah, the density of Malay Civets was lower in logged forest (1 per 1·1 km²) than unlogged forest (1 per 0·5 km²); minimum daily travel distance ranged from one to 9·7 km. On Sulawesi, the mean minimum distance covered in 24 hours was 415 m for males, and 286 m for females. A male civet has been observed scent marking using three methods: after protracted sniffing at a site, the civet elevated its tail, reversed into an upright tree trunk, and swayed its posterior from side to side; as it meandered about it paused momentarily, dipped and pressed its anal region onto the ground, raised it again and moved on; the side of the head and neck was rubbed against vegetation. Feces are found in latrines on the ground, generally in cavities and depressions.

Breeding. On Peninsular Malaysia, a female appeared to be denning in October and November one year, and in August the following year. Two juvenile civets (about one month old) were caught in late August. At about nine months old, two young civets were not yet adult size and weight; the adult canines were just erupting in one individual. In Sabah, juveniles were captured between March and May.

Status and Conservation. Classified as Least Concern on *The IUCN Red List*. Considered to be common, however, the exact population status in the wild is unknown. Its presence on some islands in South-east Asia possibly resulted from introduction. Although Malay civets seem able to tolerate habitat disturbance, forest loss and degradation could be a threat to this species, and their ability to survive in disturbed habitats and forage in plantation areas may be influenced by the proximity of undisturbed forest. They are hunted and snared for food. Malay Civets are often considered pests as they prey on small livestock and raid fruit orchards, and may be deliberately killed in retaliation. Malay Civets foraging in plantation areas may also be inadvertently killed if they ingest pesticides, either directly or via contaminated food and ground water.

Bibliography. Colon (1996, 1999, 2002), Corbet & Hill (1992), Jennings *et al.* (2006), Kitchener *et al.* (1993), Macdonald & Wise (1979), Meiri (2005), Nowak (1999), Nozaki *et al.* (1994), Veron (1999, 2001), Wozencraft (2005).

6. Large Indian Civet *Viverra zibetha*

French: Grande Civette / **German**: Indische Zibetkatze / **Spanish**: Civeta india grande

Taxonomy. *Viverra zibetha* Linnaeus, 1758, India.

The validity of the Taynguyen Civet (*V. tainguensis*) is debated and has been considered a synonym of *V. zibetha*. Six subspecies are recognized.

Subspecies and Distribution.

V. z. zibetha Linnaeus, 1758 – SW China (Xizang) to Nepal and NE India.

V. z. expectata Colbert & Hooijer, 1953 – China.

V. z. sigillata Robinson & Kloss, 1920 – Thailand and Peninsular Malaysia.

V. z. hainana Wang & Xu, 1983 – China (Hainan I).

V. z. pruinosus Wroughton, 1915 – Myanmar.

V. z. surdaster Thomas, 1927 – Cambodia, Laos and Vietnam.

Introduced to the Andaman Islands.

Descriptive notes. Head–body 75–85 cm, tail 38–49·5 cm, hindfoot 10·9–14·0 cm, ear 4·7–5·2 cm; weight 8–9 kg. A large civet with conspicuous black and white bands on the throat and sides of the neck. The coat is pale gray or fawn, with indistinct dark spots or a mottling of black or dark brown on the flanks, thighs, and hindlegs; this pattern varies throughout its range. The coat length varies according to the season, at least in northern areas. The face is grayish with white patches on each side of the muzzle. A black crest of erectile hairs runs along the back and ends at the base of the tail; the length of the crest hairs reaches 90 mm in China, 70 mm in Nepal, north-east India and Bengal, but is less than 55 mm in Peninsular Malaysia. The tail has five or six complete dark rings, alternating with complete white rings. The forefeet are dark brown, the hindfeet are medium brown, and the claws are retractable. The metacarpal pads are rounded and small; there are no metatarsal pads. There are at least two pairs of teats. The skull is long and low, with moderate crests, a low, flat zygomatic arch, and a marked depression between the nasal bones. The post-orbital processes are small and are located in front of the midpoint of the skull. The sub-orbital foramina are relatively small, with the long axis vertical. The mandibular ramus has a vertical posterior edge. The auditory bullae are small, shorter than the width across the occipital condyles. In comparison with the Large-spotted Civet, the dentition is more robust, with longer and stronger canines and incisors and a smaller first upper premolar. Dental formula: I 3/3, C 1/1, P 4/4, M 2/2 = 40.

Habitat. Primary evergreen and deciduous forest, disturbed forest, and within plantations adjacent to forest. Found up to 1600 m. In Thailand, a radio-collared male moved within an area that comprised 52% dry evergreen forest, 35% mixed deciduous forest, 10% hill evergreen forest, and 3% dry dipterocarp forest.

Food and Feeding. Omnivorous. Diet said to include small mammals, birds, eggs, lizards, snakes, frogs, insects, crabs, fish, fruit, and roots. Forages on the ground.

Activity patterns. Primarily nocturnal, with a peak in activity between 19:30 h and 22:30 h. Rests during the day within dense cover on the ground.

Movements, Home range and Social organization. Generally solitary. Terrestrial, but apparently can climb trees. In Thailand, an adult male had a home range of 12 km², with a mean daily movement of 1·7 km.

Breeding. Said to breed throughout the year, with two litters per year. Litter size is one to four. Newborns are black, with white markings on the lip, ear, throat and tail, and their eyes are closed. The eyes open at ten days and weaning commences at about one month.

Status and Conservation. Classified as Near Threatened on *The IUCN Red List*. Considered common in some parts of its range, but is not well known and more field studies are needed. Habitat loss and degradation could be a threat to this species; it is hunted and snared for food in Vietnam and China.

Bibliography. Agrawal *et al.* (1992), Austin & Tewes (1999b), Azlan (2003), Corbet & Hill (1992), Duckworth (1997), Lekagul & McNeely (1991), Long & Hoang (2006), Medway (1969), Nowak (1999), Pocock (1933a), Rabinowitz (1991), Veron (1999), Walston & Veron (2001), Wozencraft (2005).

Plate 13 ➤

7

8

9

10

11

12

13

14

ssp *genetta*

ssp *dongolana*

ssp *pulchra*

PLATE 13

inches 10

cm 25

Subfamily GENETTINAE

Genus *POIANA*

Gray, 1865

7. Leighton's Oyan *Poiana leightoni*

French: Poiane de Leighton / **German**: Westafrikanischer Linsang / **Spanish**: Oyán occidental

Other common names: West African Linsang, Leighton's Linsang

Taxonomy. *Poiana leightoni* Pocock, 1908, Liberia.
Has been considered a subspecies of the Central African Oyan (*P. richardsonii*). Monotypic
Distribution. Ivory Coast and Liberia. Its presence in SE Guinea requires confirmation.
Descriptive notes. Head–body 30–38 cm, tail 35–40 cm; weight 500–700 g. A small, slender genet-like carnivore. The dorsal pelage is soft and very short. The coat color is yellowish-fawn; the ventral pelage is white. There are large irregular spots on the back and flanks, and much smaller spots on the fore- and hindlimbs, and on the flanks near the belly; these spots are more or less arranged into four to five longitudinal rows and form longitudinal stripes on the neck. A dark, sometimes interrupted, mid-dorsal stripe runs from between the shoulders to the base of the tail. There are ten to twelve chevron-shaped dark tail-rings (narrower laterally and ventrally). Dental formula: I 3/3, C 1/1, P 4/4, M 1/2 = 38.
Habitat. Rainforest.
Food and Feeding. Diet is said to include insects, birds, and plants.
Activity patterns. Nothing known.
Movements, Home range and Social organization. Said to build a round nest of green material in trees, at least two meters from the ground.
Breeding. Nothing known.
Status and Conservation. Classified as Data Deficient on *The IUCN Red List*. Known only from a dozen museum specimens; the most recent records are two skins collected in 1988 from eastern Liberia. Major threats to this species are not known, but it is probably being affected by ongoing habitat loss in the upper Guinean forests. This is a priority species for survey work in order to determine its current range and population status, and to investigate its ecology.
Bibliography. Gaubert (2003b), Rosevear (1974), Schreiber *et al.* (1989), Van Rompaey & Colyn (In press j), Wozencraft (2005).

8. Central African Oyan *Poiana richardsonii*

French: Poiane de Richardson / **German**: Zentralafrikanischer Linsang / **Spanish**: Oyán

Other common names: African Linsang, Richardson's Linsang

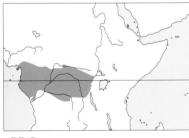

Taxonomy. *Genetta richardsonii* Thomson, 1842, Bioko Island, Equatorial Guinea.
Has been considered conspecific with Leighton's Oyan (*P. leightoni*). Two subspecies are recognized.
Subspecies and Distribution.
P. r. richardsonii Thomson, 1842 – Cameroon, Central African Republic, Equatorial Guinea (and Bioko I), Gabon, and PR Congo.
P. r. ochracea Thomas & Wroughton, 1907 – DR Congo.
Descriptive notes. Head–body 32·1–40 cm (males), 34·6–39·5 cm (females), tail 35·2–40·2 cm (males), 34·0–38 cm (females), hindfoot 5·7–6·4 cm (males), 5·7–6·1 cm (females), ear 2·9–3·7 cm (males), 3–3·4 cm (females); weight 510–750 g (males), 455 g (females). A small, slender genet-like carnivore, with a short, soft pelage. The coat color is yellowish- to reddish-brown, with small, brownish-black spots of various shapes and sizes on the back and flanks, coalescing into stripes on the neck. These spots do not form longitudinal lines and are very small on the thighs and forelimbs. There is a dark mid-dorsal line, sometimes interrupted or absent. The ventral pelage is pale gray and unspotted. The head has a pointed muzzle, a gray rhinarium, wide rounded ears, and large yellowish-brown eyes. The feet are grayish, unmarked, and with hairy soles (except for the digital pads and a narrow bare line on the plantar surface). The tail has 9–14 alternating broad and narrow black bands, interspersed with pale rings. Dental formula: I 3/3, C 1/1, P 4/4, M 1/2 = 38.
Habitat. Lowland and montane forest.
Food and Feeding. Said to eat rodents, birds, insects, fruits, and other plant matter.
Activity patterns. Thought to be nocturnal. Has been observed sleeping on thick tangled vines in trees. On Bioko Island, at 17:10 h, an individual was observed walking in a dry, rocky streambed with little vegetation, before it fled to the forest.

Movements, Home range and Social organization. Thought to be arboreal.
Breeding. A lactating female has been noted in October.
Status and Conservation. Classified as Least Concern on *The IUCN Red List*. A poorly known species and field studies are needed. There are no known major threats, but it may be undergoing localized decline due to forest loss and hunting for bushmeat and skins.
Bibliography. Bates (1905), Carpaneto & Germi (1989b), Halternorth & Diller (1985), Harrington *et al.* (2002), Rosevear (1974), Van Rompaey & Colyn (In press i), Wozencraft, (2005).

Genus *GENETTA*

Cuvier, 1816

9. Abyssinian Genet *Genetta abyssinica*

French: Genette d'Éthiopie / **German**: Äthiopien-Genette / **Spanish**: Gineta abisinia

Other common name: Ethiopian Genet

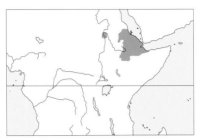

Taxonomy. *Viverra abyssinica* Rüppell, 1835, Gondar, Ethiopia.
Was previously placed in the subgenus *Pseudogenetta* with the Hausa Genet (*G. thierryi*). Monotypic.
Distribution. Djibouti, Eritrea, Ethiopia, Somalia, and Sudan.
Descriptive notes. Head–body 40·8–43 cm, tail 38–40·3 cm; weight 1·3–2 kg. A small genet with short legs and a moderately long tail. The pelage is soft, with short straight hair. The coat color varies from pale creamy-gray to yellow; the underparts are pale gray. Two distinct color forms have been reported: pale (in the lowlands) and dark (in the highlands). The forehead is gray, with a thin dark vertical line on the muzzle. The dark facial mask is well marked and there are pairs of supra- and sub-ocular white spots. The nuchal stripes are well defined; the spots on the side of the neck merge into two dark lines. The dark mid-dorsal line is split longitudinally by a pale line of hairs; there is no dorsal crest. The dorsal spots are fused into five longitudinal black stripes. The spots on the lower flanks are also elongated and look more like stripes than spots. The tail has seven to nine pale rings, alternating with dark rings; the tip of the tail is dark. The fore- and hindlimbs are pale gray with dark spots, the feet are pale gray and unspotted. The central depression of the sole of the foot is hairless. The skull is small. The premaxillary-frontal contact is absent. The posterior chamber of the auditory bulla is not ventrally inflated and has a continuous curve line on the external side. Dental formula: I 3/3, C 1/1, P 4/4, M 2/2 = 40. The maxillary-palatine suture is anterior to the main cusp of P³.
Habitat. Montane dry forest (dominant vegetation includes tree heath *Erica arborea*, curry bush *Hypericum revolutum* and Abyssinian rose *Rosa abyssinica*), montane heather moorland, Afro-alpine grassland, and steppe and sub-desert areas on lowland plains. Found up to 3750 m.
Food and Feeding. Appears to be predominately carnivorous. In the Ethiopian highlands, the analysis of 25 scats showed that small vertebrates (mostly rodents) were the main prey items, with smaller quantities of insects and fruit. Compositional differences between habitats were found, suggesting opportunistic consumption of the most available food sources. In the Afro-alpine areas, 15 scats consisted mainly of rodents (*Arvicanthis* and *Lophuromys* genera), with small quantities of birds (passerines), insects (Coleoptera), and fruit. In a savannah-woodland area, ten scats revealed that rodents and birds were also the main prey items, but more insects and fruit were consumed than at the higher altitude.
Activity patterns. Believed to be mainly nocturnal; one individual was seen at 18:10 h. However, some observations of diurnal activity have been reported: sightings at 13:10 h, 14:30 h and 16:00 h were recorded in the Ethiopian Highlands. It has been suggested that this diurnal activity is a local adaptive response to the activity patterns of rodent prey at high altitudes, and that this might also minimize direct competition with African Wildcats.
Movements, Home range and Social organization. Possibly solitary: the few reported sightings have been of single individuals. Latrine sites were found in Afro-alpine and montane savannah-woodland complexes (an average of 30 droppings was found in each). One latrine was found on a rocky ledge at 3750 m, in an area covered by high-grass steppe, scattered giant lobelias, and globe thistle. Two were found within an Afro-alpine area at 3680 m; they were in rocky holes at the base of an escarpment, in an area of steep slopes, medium to high-grass steppe, and scattered lobelias. Another latrine was found on a rocky ledge in dry massif at 2150 m, in an open shrubby-grassy area, dominated by several acacia species.
Breeding. Nothing known.
Status and Conservation. Classified as Least Concern on *The IUCN Red List*. Listed as Threatened in the 1989 IUCN *Action Plan for the Conservation of Mustelids and Viverrids*. Known from fewer than 20 museum specimens and a handful of sightings. Considered rare and is likely to be threatened by habitat loss due to agriculture and livestock pres-

On following pages: 10. Angolan Genet (*Genetta angolensis*); 11. Bourlon's Genet (*Genetta bourloni*); 12. Crested Genet (*Genetta cristata*); 13. Feline Genet (*Genetta felina*); 14. Common Genet (*Genetta genetta*).

sures. There is a need for further fieldwork to better understand its habitat requirements, population status, and ecology.

Bibliography. Crawford-Cabral (1981), Diaz & Van Rompaey (2002), Gaubert (In press b), Gaubert, Taylor & Veron (2005), Gaubert, Veron & Tranier (2002), Schreiber et al. (1989), Wozencraft (2005), Yalden et al. (1996).

10. Angolan Genet *Genetta angolensis*

French: Genette d'Angola / **German**: Angola-Genette / **Spanish**: Gineta angoleña

Other common names: Miombo Genet

Taxonomy. *Genetta angolensis* Bocage, 1882, Caconda, Angola.
Monotypic.
Distribution. Angola, DR Congo, Malawi, Mozambique, Tanzania, and Zambia.
Description. Head–body 46·5–47·8 cm (males), 44–45·5 cm (females), tail 40–43 cm (males), 38–39 cm (females), hindfoot 8·7–9·8 cm (males), 8–9 cm (females), ear 4·7–5·4 cm (males), 5·1–5·8 cm (females); weight 1·3–2 kg. The coat color is pale ocher, with brownish or grayish tones; melanistic individuals are quite common. The throat and chest are blackish, and the ventral pelage varies from creamy white to dirty white. The stripes and spots on the body vary from different hues of brown to black. The nuchal stripes run as two parallel lines from the nape to the shoulders, where they diverge and enlarge towards the elbows; they are not so conspicuously marked as in other genet species. Below them, a pair of thinner stripes and small spots are scattered on the shoulders and sides of the neck. A third pair of thinner, parallel stripes runs down the neck between the nuchal stripes, extending to about one fourth of the mid-dorsal line, where they vanish or diverge as the first row of flank spots. The black mid-dorsal line is continuous and is flanked on each side by four rows of oblong to squared spots, and by a few small-scattered spots below. There is a dorsal erectile crest. The face has a dark mask and a pair of white sub-ocular spots. The tail has seven to nine black rings, alternating with pale rings; the intervening white spaces are pigmented with a brownish tinge on the dorsal midline. The width of the pale rings relative to the dark rings in the middle of the tail is 50–75%; the tip of the tail is dark. The hindlimbs and forelimbs are black; there are white hairs on the metacarpals and metatarsals. The posterior parts of the feet are dark. There are two pairs of teats. The posterior chamber of the auditory bulla is not ventrally inflated and has a continuous curve line on the external side. The ratio between the inter-orbital constriction and frontal width is 1·00 ± 0·12. Dental formula: I 3/3, C 1/1, P 4/4, M 2/2 = 40.
Habitat. Open miombo woodland (*Brachystegia*), interspersed with savannah.
Food and Feeding. The stomach contents of a specimen from the Kafue National Park (Zambia) contained remains of grasshoppers, insects, unidentified fruit, and grass.
Activity patterns. Appears to be nocturnal.
Movements, Home range and Social organization. Has been seen foraging on the ground at night.
Breeding. Nothing known.
Status and Conservation. Classified as Least Concern on *The IUCN Red List*. There are no known major threats: its habitat has only seen minor change and there appears to be little hunting pressure. Field studies of this poorly known species are needed.
Bibliography. Crawford-Cabral (in press), Crawford-Cabral & Pacheco (1992), Crawford-Cabral & Fernandes (2001), Gaubert, Taylor & Veron (2005), Gaubert, Veron & Tranier (2002), Halternorth & Diller (1985), Schlawe (1980), Wozencraft (2005).

11. Bourlon's Genet *Genetta bourloni*

French: Genette de Bourlon / **German**: Bourlon-Genette / **Spanish**: Gineta guineana

Taxonomy. *Genetta bourloni* Gaubert, 2003, Sérédou, Cercle de Macenta, Guinea.
On the basis of morphological characters and molecular studies, some individuals of the large-spotted genet complex (which were previously attributed to the Pardine Genet *G. pardina*) have now been identified as representing *G. bourloni*. Monotypic.
Distribution. Guinea, Ivory Coast, Liberia, and Sierra Leone. A specimen collected from Oda in Ghana in 1946 has been attributed to this species, but its true origin is in question.
Descriptive notes. Head–body 49·5 cm, tail 41 cm; weight 1·5–2 kg. Similar to Pardine Genet, but differs by the more grayish coloration, the very dark spots that partly coalesce on the rump, and almost half of the tail is dark. The coat color is pale yellowish-gray; the underparts are whitish-yellow to gray. The pelage is relatively short and rough. The face has a well-marked mask, sub- and supra-ocular white spots, and a thin dark line on the muzzle. The nuchal stripes are well defined. The mid-dorsal line is dark and wide, and begins after the shoulder; there is no dorsal erectile crest. The dorsal spots are completely dark, elongated, and partly fused on the rump. The tail has five to seven pale rings; almost half of the tail is dark. The fore- and hindlimbs are dark and well

spotted. The upper parts of the forefeet are spotted, whereas the hindfeet are unspotted. The under parts of the feet are dark. The skull has a very large posterior extension of the frontal bones, which almost completely overlaps the dorsal region of the inter-orbital constriction. The posterior chamber of the auditory bullae is inflated, with a broken curve line on the external side. The ratio between the inter-orbital constriction and frontal width = 1·00 ± 0·2. Dental formula: I 3/3, C 1/1, P 4/4, M 2/2 = 40.
Habitat. Rainforest.
Food and Feeding. Nothing known.
Activity patterns. Nothing known.
Movements, Home range and Social organization. Nothing known.
Breeding. Nothing known.
Status and Conservation. Classified as Near Threatened on *The IUCN Red List*. Described in 2003 and known only from 29 museum specimens. Habitat loss is likely to be a major threat, particularly if this species is restricted to rainforest as suspected; forest loss in the Upper Guinea forests has been quite severe. Hunting is also a likely threat, as skins have been seen in bushmeat markets. Fieldwork is needed to better understand its habitat requirements, population status, and ecology.
Bibliography. Crawford-Cabral (1981), Gaubert (2003a, In press c), Gaubert, Fernandes et al. (2004), Gaubert, Taylor & Veron (2005), Wozencraft (2005).

12. Crested Genet *Genetta cristata*

French: Genette à crête / **German**: Niger-Genette / **Spanish**: Gineta crestada

Taxonomy. *Genetta cristata* Hayman, 1940, Cameroon.
Previously included as a subspecies of the Servaline Genet (*G. servalina*). Hybridization between *G. cristata* and *G. servalina* may be occurring in a sympatric zone: central Cameroon, northern Gabon, and the PR Congo. Monotypic.
Distribution. Cameroon, Nigeria, and possibly Gabon and the PR Congo.
Descriptive notes. Head–body 49·5–62·2 cm, tail 43·1–43·2 cm, ear 8·6–9·5 cm; weight c. 2·5 kg. The coat color ranges from pale buff to pale ocher, darkening to ocher on the shoulders and the middle line of the back. The throat is a light ash-gray; the remaining underparts a mixture of buff and gray, paling to ash-gray in the genital region. The black mid-dorsal line is composed of relatively long hairs; it begins after the shoulder and runs to the base of the tail. There is a dorsal erectile crest. The large dark brown to black spots on the dorsal pelage run in longitudinal rows, with the top three rows being the most uniform. These spots become smaller and more randomly spaced towards the ventral pelage, where the chest and throat have only a few small spots; there are no spots between the hindlegs. The hair covering the scrotum in the male is dark brown. The face has a dark mask and a pair of supra- and sub-ocular white spots. The tail has eight to ten pale rings alternating with dark rings. The width of the pale rings relative to the dark rings in the middle of the tail is 50–75%; the tip of the tail is pale gray. The forelimbs and hindlimbs are boldly spotted. The forelegs are pale on the innermost side and dark gray above, with scattered small spots. The inner hindlegs are dark gray, unspotted, and have a grayish patch over the upper metatarsal region. The feet are dark. There is one pair of teats. The auditory bulla has a ventrally inflated posterior chamber, with a continuous curve line on the external side. The premaxillary-frontal contact is present and the ratio between the inter-orbital constriction and frontal width is 1·00 ± 0·12. Dental formula: I 3/3, C 1/1, P 4/4, M 2/2 = 40.
Habitat. Deciduous forest, where there are areas of scrub and dense understory vegetation. Also recorded in secondary and montane forest. Found up to at least 1000 m. In Nigeria, its presence was positively correlated to primary dry forest and bush-mango plantations inside the forest, and to a lesser extent secondary dry forest and primary flooded forest. Suburban areas, pineapple plantations, bushlands, and oil palm plantations, had a negative influence. Ecological niche modelling has expanded the potential range to at least 500 km south and 180 km west from what was previously known. Its apparent absence east of the Congo and Oubangi rivers might be due to lack of survey effort, low dispersal abilities, or riverine geographical barriers.
Food and Feeding. In Nigeria, the percentage occurrence of prey items in eleven stomachs was: 51% insects, 20% mammals, 9% reptiles, and 6% plant matter. In terms of biomass, small mammals were the most important prey items, followed by arthropods; there is a 70% overlap in diet with the sympatric Rusty-spotted Genet, indicating strong interspecific competition for food between these two species. Two captive genets were observed pursuing and pouncing on small insects, frogs, and lizards.
Activity patterns. Captive individuals were crepuscular, resting throughout the day.
Movements, Home range and Social organization. Captive animals are agile climbers, spending the majority of their time in high places. They defecated and urinated in one place. They also scent-marked while urinating, slowly moving the pelvis from side-to-side, and rolled and rubbed themselves in smells or substances to which they were attracted. Four vocalizations were noted: a purr and growl; a long meow; a short squeak; and a short sneeze/cough/grunt (used as a contact call).
Breeding. In Nigeria, one-week-old juveniles were captured in late August and mid-October, and two embryos were found in a female collected in December.
Status and Conservation. Classified as Vulnerable on *The IUCN Red List*. Habitat loss may be a major threat: the Cross River State forests are rapidly being converted into farms or wastelands and the Niger Delta is exploited as an oil-production area. May

also suffer from high hunting pressure. This species is a high priority for further survey work in order to better understand its ecology, distribution, and population status.

Bibliography. Angelici & Luiselli (2005), Gaubert, Fernandes *et al.* (2004), Gaubert, Papes & Peterson (2006), Gaubert, Taylor & Veron (2005), Gaubert, Veron & Tranier (2002), Heard & Van Rompaey (1990), Rosevear (1974), Van Rompaey & Colyn (In press e), Wozencraft (2005).

13. Feline Genet *Genetta felina*

French: Genette féline / **German**: Südliche Kleinfleckgenette / **Spanish**: Gineta felina
Other common names: South African Small-spotted Genet

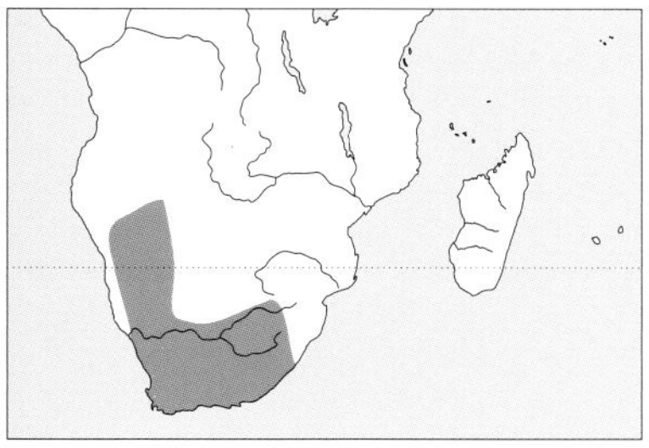

Taxonomy. *Viverra felina* Thunberg, 1811, South Africa.
Has been considered a subspecies of the Common Genet (*G. genetta*). Monotypic.
Distribution. Namibia and South Africa. One possible specimen in Angola and one in Zambia require confirmation.
Descriptive notes. Head–body 47·5–56·5 cm (males), 43–55 cm (females), tail 41–49·4 cm (males), 41–47 cm (females), hindfoot 7·3–9·5 cm (males), 7–8·8 cm (females), ear 4–5·6 cm (males), 4–5·2 cm (females); weight 1·5 to 2·4 kg (males), 1·4 to 2 kg (females). A medium-sized genet with long guard hairs. The coat color is whitish-gray; the ventral pelage varies from whitish or pale yellowish-gray to gray. The nuchal stripes are well defined. The mid-dorsal line is black and continuous; there is a dorsal erectile crest. The face has a dark mask and a pair of supra- and sub-ocular white spots. The tail has eight to ten pale rings alternating with dark rings. The pattern of rings is confused at the beginning of the tail and the width of the pale rings relative to the dark rings in the middle is 200%; the tip of the tail is pale. The hindlimbs and forelimbs are the same color as the coat and are spotted. The hindfeet are covered by a dark "sock" and the posterior part of the forefeet is completely dark. There are two pairs of teats. The auditory bulla has a broken curve line on the external side. The posterior extension of the frontal bones overlaps about 50% of the dorsal region of the inter-orbital constriction. The ratio between the inter-orbital constriction and frontal width is 1 ± 0·12. Dental formula: I 3/3, C 1/1, P 4/4, M 2/2 = 40.
Habitat. Woodland savannah, grassland, thickets, dry vlei areas, and the border of deserts. In South Africa, it occurs in areas with scrub, bush cover, or rocky outcrops.
Food and Feeding. In South Africa, the stomach contents of 25 genets contained rodents (*Rhabdomys pumilio*, *Otomys* sp., *Desmodillus auricularis*, *Mus minutoides*), insects (Orthoptera and Coleoptera), birds, arachnids, frogs, reptiles, shrews, and plants (grass, leaves, and grapes). Also reported to feed on carrion.
Activity patterns. Appears to be nocturnal: seen during a night survey in South Africa.
Movements, Home range and Social organization. Said to be solitary.
Breeding. In South Africa, pregnant females with two fetuses were recorded in September and October. Newborn weight is 70 g. A young female taken in mid-July weighed 500 g and one young animal collected in June weighed 715 g.
Status and Conservation. Classified as Least Concern on *The IUCN Red List*: included in *G. genetta*. A poorly known species: field surveys, ecological studies, and assessments of any threats are needed.

Bibliography. Delibes & Gaubert (In press), Gaubert, Fernandes *et al.* (2004), Gaubert, Taylor & Veron (2005), Skinner & Chimimba (2005), Stuart (1981), Wozencraft (2005).

14. Common Genet *Genetta genetta*

French: Genette commune / **German**: Kleinfleckgenette / **Spanish**: Gineta común
Other common names: Common Small-spotted Genet

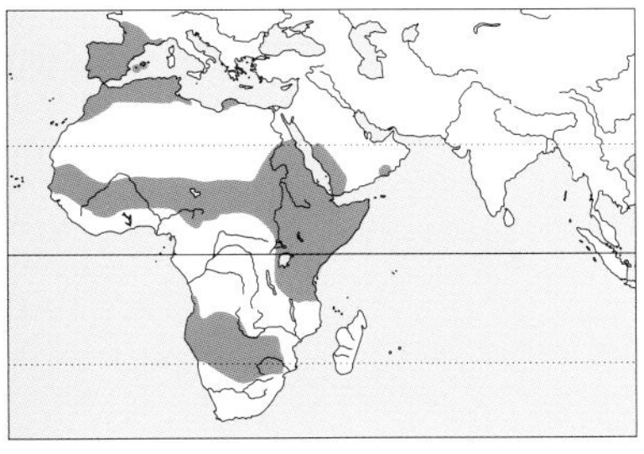

Taxonomy. *Viverra genetta* Linnaeus, 1758, El Pardo, near Madrid, Spain.
Some authors have included the Feline Genet (*G. felina*) as a subspecies of *G. genetta*; *G. felina* is treated here as a separate species. High intra-specific variability within the Common Genet makes clear distinctions between populations difficult to assess and over thirty subspecies have been described. A taxonomic revision is needed, but five subspecies are recognized here.
Subspecies and Distribution.
G. g. genetta Linnaeus, 1758 – SW Europe and N Africa from Morocco to Libya.
G. g. dongolana Hemprich & Ehrenberg, 1833 – E, NE & C Africa.
G. g. grantii Thomas, 1902 – SW Arabian Peninsula in Saudi Arabia and Yemen, and Oman.
G. g. pulchra Matschie, 1902 – Angola, Namibia, Botswana, W Zambia, and NE South Africa.
G. g. senegalensis Fischer, 1829 – W Africa.
Descriptive notes. Head–body 46·5–52 cm (males), 46·5–49 cm (females), tail 42–51·6 cm (males), 40–51·6 cm (females), hindfoot 8–9·7 cm (males), 8·2–9·1 cm (females), ear 4–6 cm (males), 4·2–6·5 cm (females); weight 1·6–2·6 kg (males), 1·4–2·3 kg (females). A medium-sized genet, with a slender body and a long tail. The coat color ranges from whitish-gray to pale yellow-rufous; the underparts are whitish, pale yellowish-gray or gray. The pelage has relatively long guard hairs. In the arid parts of its range, the pelage is shorter and the coat color and spots are lighter. The head is small, with a pointed muzzle and small, upstanding round ears. The facial mask is relatively well marked, with a dark line on the muzzle and contrasting white sub- and supra-ocular white spots. The nuchal stripes are well defined. There is a thin, dark mid-dorsal line with long erectile hairs (up to 7·5 cm), which begins after the shoulder and runs to the base of the tail. The dark dorsal spots merge into longitudinal lines. The tail is relatively long, with eight to ten pale rings alternating with dark rings; the tip of the tail is whitish. The pale rings and the dark rings are the same width, although the margins of the rings are often not clearly distinguishable due to the overlapping long guard hairs of the preceding ring. The fore- and hindlimbs are spotted; the upper parts of the feet are lightly spotted. The underparts of the hindlimb and feet are dark. There are five digits on each foot; the first digits are slightly set back and do not mark in the print. The central depression of the forefeet is hairy. The forefeet have reduced metacarpal pads and the hindfeet bear two very narrow, elongated metatarsal pads. The claws are sharp, curved, and retractile. The perineal gland opens into a longitudinal Y-shaped slit. There are two pairs of teats. The baculum in the male is well-developed. The skull is medium-size and ovoid, with a strong sagittal crest. The rostrum is narrow and elongated. The inter-orbital constriction is weakly marked and the zygomatic arches are lightly built. The post-orbital processes of the frontal and jugal bones are almost totally absent. The auditory bullae are elongated, with the anterior chambers only slightly smaller than the posterior chambers. The premaxillary-frontal contact is absent and the posterior extension of the frontal bones is moderate, overlapping about 50% of the dorsal region of the inter-orbital constriction. The ratio between the inter-orbital constriction and frontal width is 1 ± 0·12. Dental formula: I 3/3, C 1/1, P 4/4, M 2/2 = 40. The upper canines are elongated, curved and sharp, and the second upper molar and the second lower molars are small. The presence and development of the inner cusp of the third upper premolar is variable. The maxillary-palatine suture is at the same level as the main cusp of P^3.
Habitat. Occurs in a wide range of habitats. Often associated with trees and bushes, but can also be found in rocky, treeless areas. Seems to avoid dense rainforest and very arid zones, but can be found in close proximity to human dwellings. In Morocco, the Common Genet is found in forests and bushy areas (mainly in the mountains), rocky ravines (preferably vegetated and near water), and in the Sahara fringe (where it is common in oases and other productive areas). In Algeria, it is found in riparian forests at sea level and up to 2000 m in the Djurjura Mountains, where it occupies all types of habitats (most abundant in old forests of *Quercus ilex* and *Cedrus atlantica*). In West Africa, it occurs in wooded savannahs. In the Ethiopian Highlands, a radio-collared female was found in woodland (84% of the time), bush (9%), farmland (5%), and grassland (2%). In Tanzania, Common Genets were camera-trapped in lowland forest. In the Serengeti, they are strongly associated with trees and thickets and are frequently seen on escarpments, rocky outcrops, and other hills. In Botswana, they are found in all the major vegetation associations (including riverine forests and open, dry scrub savannahs): 47 genets were captured in *Acacia* woodland or scrub, 16 in mopane (*Colophospermum mopane*) woodland or scrub, twelve in *Terminalia-Bauhinia* scrub, nine in unspecified riverine forests, nine in open grassland (with scattered bushes and trees), and lower numbers in other habitats. The Common Genet does not occur in open habitats unless there is some adjacent scrub cover or isolated patches of trees with underbrush, which suggests that scrub cover or woodland is an essential habitat requirement. In some places, the Common Genet can penetrate into deserts along seasonal watercourses. In Arabia, it is said to inhabit dry ravines in hills and mountains. In Europe, it is especially abundant in oak forests (*Quercus* spp.) and is also common in olive groves (*Olea europaea*), riparian copses, ash groves (*Fraxinus* spp.), pine forests, rocky areas, and scrublands, but is rare or absent in open areas, marshes, and agricultural fields. Common Genets prefer to live at low altitudes, especially in northern areas, which suggests that cold temperatures may restrict its distribution: in central Spain, genets were scarce on plateaux and the upper parts of mountains (not found above 1400 m), but were widely distributed in lower mountain areas. They were present in areas with abundant scrub cover and high mean temperatures. In northern Spain, three radio-collared males showed a strong preference for holm oak forest; pine plantations were avoided, eucalyptus plantations were used according to availability, and other habitats such as meadows, gardens, and crops near houses, were used opportunistically by two of the three genets.
Food and Feeding. Feeds mainly on small mammals, but also eats other small vertebrates (including birds, reptiles, amphibians, and fish), invertebrates (mainly insects), eggs, fruits, and sometimes grass. Field studies have shown seasonal and geographical variations in the diet (frequency of occurrence of food items). In south-west France (woodlands with rocky areas): 73% small mammals, including rodents (mainly *Apodemus sylvaticus*, *Clethrionomys glareolus*, *Arvicola sapidus*, *Pitymys and Microtus* spp.), insectivores (*Sorex* spp., *Talpa europaea*, *Crocidura russula*, and *Neomys fodiens*), and occasionally a few mustelids Least Weasel and Ermine. Other prey items included: 10% birds (mainly passerines), 9% insects (Coleoptera and Orthoptera), 1% amphibians, 0·7% reptiles, 0·6% European Rabbits (*Oryctolagus cuniculus*), 0·2% fish, and a few eggs. Plant remains included 13% grass, and 10% fruits and berries. Some seasonal variations were observed. The percentage of small mammals in the diet remained stable, but more birds were eaten during winter and fewer during spring, and the consumption of fruits followed the fruiting season, being consumed mainly in the summer and autumn. In north-west France (marshy forest): 71% small mammals, 18% birds, 8% arthropods, and 2% rabbits. In north-west France (broad-leaved forest with pastures):

59% small mammals, 26% birds, 7% arthropods, 3% rabbits, 0·7% reptiles, and 0·4% amphibians. In north-west Spain (broad-leaved forest and riparian forest): 67% small mammals, 18% arthropods, 8% birds, 4% amphibians, and 2% reptiles. In north-east Spain (riparian forest): 34% arthropods, 30% small mammals, 10% reptiles, 7% birds, 4% rabbits, and 1% amphibians. In central Spain (holm oak and broad-leaved forests): 36% arthropods, 30% birds, 28% small mammals, 7% reptiles, 4% amphibians, and 0·2% rabbits. In southern Spain (Mediterranean shrubs): 65% small mammals, 16% birds, 8% arthropods, 7% amphibians, 4% rabbits, and 3% reptiles. In central Portugal: 58% mammals (42% rodents, 8% insectivores, 8% rabbits), 15% arthropods, 11% birds, 2% reptiles, 1% gastropods, 0·7% eggs, 9% fruits and 2% plants. Small mammals were consumed more in the autumn and winter, birds and fruits in the spring and summer. In north-west Portugal, rodents were the main prey (particularly *Apodemus sylvaticus* and *Microtus agrestis*), followed by insectivores and birds (particularly in the spring). Reptiles were consumed mostly in the spring and fruits in the summer. On Mallorca (Mediterranean forest): 47% small mammals, 25% arthropods, 23% reptiles, 4% rabbits, 3% birds, and 1% amphibians. Another study on Mallorca (Mediterranean forest): 91% mammals, 39% plants, 20% birds, 18% arthropods, and 8% reptiles. On Ibiza (Mediterranean shrubs): 45% small mammals, 19% reptiles, 18% arthropods, 10% amphibians, 6% birds, and 0·7% rabbits. Another study on Ibiza (Mediterranean shrubs): 92% mammals, 42% plants, 32% birds, 18% reptiles, and 12% arthropods. On Cabrera Island (Mediterranean shrubs): 46% arthropods, 40% reptiles, 16% small mammals, 11% amphibians, 5% birds, and 2% rabbits. Another study on Cabrera Island (Mediterranean shrubs): 70% mammals, 48% birds, 31% plants, 26% reptiles, and 21% arthropods. In Morocco (oak forest): 72% small mammals, 19% arthropods, 4% birds, 3% reptiles, 1% amphibians, and 2% fruits. In north-east Algeria (riparian forest): 64% arthropods, 23% small mammals, 7% amphibians, 3% reptiles, 1% birds, 0·6% fish, and 2% fruit. In north-east Algeria (Mediterranean montane forest), 62% arthropods, 20% small mammals, 12% birds, 3% reptiles, and 1% amphibians. In Zimbabwe: 66% insects (Coleoptera, Orthoptera and Isoptera), 51% rodents (*Mastomys* spp., *Mus* spp., *Tatera* spp., *Rattus rattus*, *Saccostomus campestris*, and *Steatomys pratensis*), 31% arachnids, 10% birds, 10% reptiles, 3% shrews (Soricidae), 3% amphibians, and 3% Myiaodia. In Botswana: 73% insects (Orthoptera, Isoptera, Coleoptera, and Lepidoptera), 53% arachnids, 50% rodents (*Mastomys* spp., *Mus* spp., *Tatera* spp., *Rattus rattus*, *Saccostomus campestris*, *Steatomys pratensis*, *Gerbillurus paeba*, *Thallomys paedulcus*, *Otomys angoniensis*, and *Aethomys* spp.), 18% reptiles, 6% birds, 5% Myriapodia, 1% shrews (Soricidae), 1% Chiroptera, 1% dormice (Muscardinidae), and 5% fruits. Foraging takes place at night.

Activity patterns. Primarily nocturnal. In Senegal, 25 nocturnal observations were recorded between 20:00–22:30 h. In Botswana, the earliest sightings were just after dark at 19:00 h, with activity recorded until 02:00 h. In Ethiopia, a radio-tracking study showed that Common Genets were nocturnal; four genets were also seen at night. In Spain, a radio-collared male was exclusively nocturnal; a young female was active 65% during the night, but was also active 19% of the time during the day. Both genets showed greater activity from sunset to midnight and the male had a secondary peak of activity just before sunrise. In south-east Spain, radio-collared genets were primarily nocturnal, but were active 29% of the time during the day. Rest sites are in trees (hollow trunks and branches), hollow logs, dense thickets and bushes, rocky areas, and holes in the ground. In Ethiopia, a female genet used several diurnal resting sites, most of them in trees. In Spain, a young female and an adult male both used areas with high ground cover for resting. The diurnal resting sites were located in dense thickets (86% in the young female, 36% in the male) and in treetops (14% and 64%, respectively). When both were available, they usually selected thickets. In treetops, they generally used old bird nests, pine-needle tufts, and dry pine branches, 4–15 m above the ground. Rest sites changed each day. The mean distance between consecutive daybeds was 277 m for the female and 2175 m for the male.

Movements, Home range and Social organization. Solitary, although pairs have occasionally been observed. Common Genets are proficient climbers, but most of their activity appears to be on the ground. In Tanzania, one marked individual was observed using an area of 0·25 km². In Ethiopia, a radio-collared juvenile female had a home range of 0·34 km² and a lactating female had a range of 0·62 km²; both ranges closely overlapped with each other. In southern Ethiopia, a female had a home range of 1·7 km², with a core area of 0·2 km² (centered on *Hagenia* and *Juniperus* woodlands). In southwestern Spain, a young female had a home range of 1·4 km²; she used 0·2 km² in the first month, 0·7 km² the second, and 1·2 km² in the third, suggesting that she was increasing her home range as she got older. The radio-collared male in this study appeared to be a dispersing individual as he covered an area of 50 km². The mean daily distance travelled in 24 hours was 2978 m for the female and 8050 m for the male. Two types of movement were detected: a zig-zag run (associated with searching for food and hunting) and a more or less straight-line run (travelling). Further studies in southwestern Spain, revealed a mean home range size of 7·8 km² for eight individuals (range 0·73–14·71 km²); there was a large inter-sexual and a low intra-sexual overlap of ranges. The mean distance travelled was 2·78 km/day; the mean distance between consecutive resting sites was 0·73 km. The density of adults was estimated to be 0·33 individuals/km². In northern Spain, three males had home ranges of 2·12, 3·39, and 10·16 km². In north-east Spain, the mean annual home range size was 1·13 km² in males and 0·72 km² in females; resting home range sizes were nine times lower than overall home range sizes. Home range sizes changed with the seasons and were smallest in the summer (0·41 km² in males and 0·29 km² in females) and largest in the spring (0·79 km² in males and 0·56 km² in females). Core areas represented 27% of the total home range in males and 19% in females. Intra-sexual home range overlap was lower than inter-sexual overlap; there was no overlap of core areas. The minimum density was 0·98 individuals/km². Common Genets deposit their feces in latrines, which are either elevated (on rocks and in trees) or on the ground. More than one individual may use the same latrine and a large number of feces can be found in them. They are more frequently located on the edges of home ranges. In Spain, the number of feces in 27 latrines ranged from one to 27, with seven containing only one scat. More than one individual appeared to use these latrines. Feces were found in trees (44% on main trunks, 22% on secondary trunks, 15% on raptor nests, and 7% on branches), on thickets or hedges (7%), and on the ground (4%). Feces on trees were situated on average 4·2 m high. Each genet tended to deposit feces all over the surface of the latrine (never over fresh feces, but over old ones). Scattered feces were also found on the ground. Within the study area, Common Genets inhabited mesic scrubland patches and preferentially deposited their feces on the edges of these patches. The number of feces in latrines was highest in February–March and November–December, and lowest in April–August. Among 15 latrines, only five were continuously used for at least four months and only one was always used. All were close to resting sites and when these were deserted the latrines were no longer used. In central Spain, fecal sites were in areas with high rock and shrub cover, habitats that provided good feeding places and refuges. In south-west Portugal, the selection of latrine and scent marking sites was driven by the availability of shelter and food: latrines were more often in habitat with high understory cover. Latrines were usually located on conspicuous structures: old-growth trees were the dominant latrine sites. In south-west France, latrines were often located on rocks and were found to contain ten to 65 feces, but those with higher numbers were rare and isolated feces were also found. Common Genets also use the secretion from their perineal gland and urine as a means of communication. While scent marking, they adopt a handstand posture or a flexion of the hindlegs. In captivity, scent marking behavior increased in the male and decreased in the female during the breeding season; it increased again in the female after mating, but decreased again before parturition. Captive males and females sniffed the scent marks of unknown genets more than those of known genets (of the opposite sex). They also spent more time sniffing marks of other genets than their own marks. The Common Genet also scent-marks by flank rubbing, which consists of rubbing the cheek, neck and dorsal parts of the flank against unscented vertical surfaces; these body regions have a higher density of sebaceous glands. Males are able to recognize the physiological state of females from sniffing scent marks left by flank rubbing. Flank rubbing increases during agonistic encounters and is generally associated with visual threat signals, such as piloerection of the dorsal crest and the tail. Intimidating behavior in Common Genets is very cat-like, with an arched-back stance, erection of the dorsal crest and tail hairs, hissing, and an open mouth showing the teeth.

Breeding. There may be two breeding seasons in Kenya, from March to May and September to December, which correspond to the wet seasons. One adult female was found lactating in southwestern Ethiopia at the end of November and a pregnant female was recorded in Zambia in February. Most pregnant females were detected in Botswana from October to February. Elsewhere in southern Africa, pregnant females have been taken in September, October, and January. In Europe and North Africa, mating mainly occurs in the spring and autumn; birth peaks are in April to June and September to November. Breeding behavior has been mainly observed in captivity. Several days before mating, the male and female increase their uro-genital marking activity; the male emits contact calls, and sniffs the ano-genital region and flanks of the female. Copulations occur at night, last two or three minutes, and are repeated up to five times. Gestation is 70 to 77 days. Natal den sites are in hollow trees, burrows, and rocky crevices. Litter size is one to four; the most common number is two. Newborns are covered with hair and have closed ears and eyes. Weight at birth is 60 to 85 g; the young are 300 g at one month, 450 g at two months, 900 g at four months, and 1500 g at eight months. They nurse during the first four months and start eating solid food when they are about 45 days old. They start to pursue prey at twelve weeks and have acquired their predator skills by the 18th week. They are sexually mature at around 19–24 months.

Status and Conservation. Classified as Least Concern on *The IUCN Red List*. Possibly introduced to Spain during historical times and has spread to France and Portugal. Individuals have also been recorded in Belgium, Germany, Holland, Italy, and Switzerland.The populations on Ibiza Island, sometimes considered a distinct subspecies (*G. g. isabelae*), were classified as Vulnerable on the *The IUCN Red List*. Listed on Appendix III of the Bern Convention and on the EU Habitats and Species Directive, Annex V. The Common Genet is not considered threatened because of its wide distribution and its generalist habitat and food preferences. However, it is eaten by people in some African localities and the body parts are used for medicinal purposes. In southern Africa, they have been reported for sale in city markets.

Bibliography. Admasu *et al.* (2004b), Alcover (1982), Aymerich (1982a), Camps-Munuera & Llober (2004), Carvalho & Gomes (2004), Clevenger (1995, 1996), Crawford-Cabral (1981), Cugnasse & Riols (1984), Delibes & Gaubert (In press), Delibes *et al.* (1989), Dobson (1998), Duckworth (1995), Espirito-Santo *et al.* (2007), Gangloff & Ropartz (1972), Gaubert, Fernandes *et al.* (2004), Gaubert, Taylor, Fernandes *et al.* (2005), Gaubert, Taylor & Veron (2005), Hamdine *et al.* (1993), Ikeda *et al.* (1983), Larivière & Calzada (2001), Livet & Roeder (1987), Lodé *et al.* (1991), Mitchell-Jones *et al.* (1999), Palomares (1993a), Palomares & Delibes (1988, 1994, 2000), Roeder (1978, 1980), Roeder & Thierry (1994), Roeder *et al.* (1989), Rosalino & Santos-Reis (2002), Sillero-Zubiri & Marino (1997), Skinner & Chimimba (2005), Taylor (1969, 1970b), Virgos & Casanovas (1997), Virgos, Casanovas & Blazquez (1996), Virgos, Llorente & Cortes (1999), Virgos, Romero & Mangas (2001), Waser (1980), Wozencraft (2005), Zuberogoitia & Zabala (2004), Zuberogoitia *et al.* (2002).

Plate 14 ➤

PLATE 14

inches 10

cm 25

15. Johnston's Genet *Genetta johnstoni*

French: Genette de Johnston / **German**: Liberia-Genette / **Spanish**: Gineta de Nimba

Taxonomy. *Genetta johnstoni* Pocock, 1908, Liberia. Monotypic.

Distribution. Ghana, Guinea, Ivory Coast, Liberia, and Sierra Leone.

Descriptive notes. Head–body 47–51·4 cm, tail 46·2–49·5 cm, hindfoot 8·5–9 cm, ear 4·5–4·6 cm; weight 2·2–2·6 kg. A slender genet with a thick soft coat and elongated face. Both sexes are similar in color and size. The coat color ranges from yellowish-ocher to yellowish-gray; the ventral pelage varies from yellowish-gray to buff. The dark, continuous mid-dorsal line strongly contrasts with the surrounding blackish to rufous-brown spots. The pattern of nuchal stripes varies. A dorsal crest is sometimes apparent. The large dorsal spots are generally aligned in three rows. The first two rows often coalesce into complete or partial lines, especially at the rump. The spots on the flank, thigh and shoulder, are smaller and darker. The face has a dark mask and there are supra- and sub-ocular white spots. The eyes are large, with vertical pupils, and the ears are elongated. The tail has eight to nine pale rings alternating with dark rings; the dark rings broaden from the proximal part of the tail. The width of the pale rings relative to the dark rings in the middle of the tail is less than 20%; the tip of the tail is pale. The hindlimbs and forelimbs are dark brown. The perineal gland is 30–40 mm long and 15–20 mm wide, with a tripartite structure. There is one pair of teats. In sub-adults, the coat is densely spotted and the pattern is irregular, but the mid-dorsal line is clearly marked. The skull is elongated and narrow, with a flattened mandible and reduced jugal teeth. The posterior extension of the frontal bones is large, almost completely overlapping the dorsal region of the inter-orbital constriction. The auditory bulla has a continuous curve line on the external side. The ratio between the inter-orbital constriction and frontal width is 1·00 ± 0·12. Dental formula: I 3/3, C 1/1, P 4/4, M 2/2 = 40.

Habitat. Rainforest. Frequently observed in wetland areas, including swamp forest and riverine habitat. One specimen was collected from an area of moist woodlands and savannah in Guinea.

Food and Feeding. Dentition suggests an insectivorous diet.

Activity patterns. Radio-tracking data indicates it is mainly nocturnal. During the day, it sleeps in tree holes or on large branches in the canopy. Over a period of one month, a radio-collared female returned before dawn each day to sleep in the canopy of the same tree (approximately 20 m high); a collared male was found sleeping in different trees each day over a period of several weeks.

Movements, Home range and Social organization. Mainly solitary, but pairs are occasionally seen.

Breeding. In the Ivory Coast, an adult female showed signs of having recently finished lactation in late July. Juvenile genets were observed in early June; however, species identity was uncertain. Unknown if breeding is seasonal. The number of young has not been recorded, but the presence of only two teats suggests that a litter size greater than two is unlikely.

Status and Conservation. Classified as Vulnerable on *The IUCN Red List*. Considered a rare species with a restricted range. Habitat loss could be a serious threat: intensive deforestation resulting from agriculture, logging and mining pressures, has reduced the once continuous Upper Guinean forest zone to a few remaining blocks of intact forest. Hunting may also be affecting populations, even within protected areas; they are taken by commercial and local hunters for meat and skins. Field surveys and ecological studies are needed to determine its distribution, to monitor populations, and to implement conservation measures.

Bibliography. Dunham & Gaubert (In press), Gaubert, Taylor & Veron (2005), Gaubert, Tranier *et al.* (2004), Gaubert, Veron, Colyn *et al.* (2002), Gaubert, Veron & Tranier (2002), Gaubert, Volobouev *et al.* (2004), Kuhn (1960), Lamotte & Tranier (1983), Rosevear (1974), Wozencraft (2005).

16. Rusty-spotted Genet *Genetta maculata*

French: Genette à grandes taches / **German**: Großfleckgenette / **Spanish**: Gineta de manchas grandes

Other common names: Central African Large-spotted Genet

Taxonomy. *Viverra maculata* Gray, 1830, Ethiopia.

The name *G. rubiginosa* has been also used for this species, but this is now considered invalid. Has been considered conspecific with the Cape Genet (*G. tigrina*) and Pardine Genet (*G. pardina*), and was sometimes also designated under the name *G. tigrina*. Recent morphometric and molecular studies have suggested that race *letabae* is a separate species, but this requires further investigation. Four subspecies are recognized.

Subspecies and Distribution.

G. m. maculata Gray, 1830 – Ethiopia and Eritrea.

G. m. letabae Thomas & Schwann, 1906 – W, C & E Africa, also in Angola, NE Namibia, Botswana, and SW Zambia.

G. m. mossambica Matschie, 1902 – Mozambique and South Africa.

G. m. zambesiana Matschie, 1902 – Malawi and Zimbabwe.

Descriptive notes. Head–body 44·3–52·1 cm (males), 41·1–49·9 cm (females), tail 41·4–53·5 cm (males), 39·5–54 cm (females), hindfoot 8·1–9·8 cm (males), 8–9·3 cm (females), ear 4·1–5 cm (males), 4·1–6·5 cm (females); weight 1·4–3·2 kg (males), 1·3–2·5 kg (females). A slender genet with a short, soft pelage. Both sexes are similar in color and size. The coat color is extremely variable: sandy-gray, pale yellow, rufous-gray, or gray-yellow. The ventral pelage is whitish-gray to pale yellow. The nuchal stripes are well defined. The continuous mid-dorsal line is the same color as the body spots; it begins after the shoulder and runs to the base of the tail. There is no dorsal crest. The spots are black to rufous-brown and variable in size and shape; the first two dorsal rows are round or square and sometimes coalesce at the rump. The face has a well-marked mask, a thin dark vertical line on the muzzle, and white sub- and supra-ocular spots. The tail has seven to nine pale rings alternating with dark rings. The width of the pale rings relative to the dark rings in the middle of the tail is 50–75%. The elongated dark tail tip is due to the suffusion of dark hairs in the last two pale rings. The hindlimbs and forelimbs are well spotted. The posterior region of the hindlimbs is densely covered in dark hairs. This coloration extends to the bottom of the hindfeet and borders the toes. The upper parts of the forefeet and hindfeet are the same color as the coat and are lightly spotted. The central depression of the forefeet is hairy. There are two pairs of teats. In juveniles, the coat is densely spotted, with a very irregular pattern. The skull is of medium size, with a thin sagittal crest and a narrow inter-orbital constriction. The posterior extension of the frontal bones is very narrow. The posterior chamber of the auditory bulla is not ventrally inflated and has a broken curve line on the external side. The maxillary-palatine suture is at the same level as the main cusp of P^3. The ratio between the inter-orbital constriction and frontal width is lesss than 1 ± 0·07. Dental formula: I 3/3, C 1/1, P 4/4, M 2/2 = 40.

Habitat. Primary and secondary rainforest, woodland savannah, savannah-forest mosaic, and montane forest. Also occurs in cultivated areas, farmlands, and suburbs. Said to prefer wet habitats such as swamps and riparian areas. In Nigeria, it was positively correlated with derived savannah, oil palm plantations, and other altered habitats, whereas it was negatively correlated with various types of forests. In south-east Africa, it only occurs in areas with a mean annual rainfall exceeding 450 mm. In Ethiopia and Eritrea, it is found in wet forest, woodlands, and humid grassland. In Tanzania, it was camera-trapped in both open and closed lowland forests from 280 to 1470 m. It can live at high altitudes, such as the Simien Mountains (Ethiopia) and Mount Kilimanjaro (Tanzania).

Food and Feeding. Mainly carnivorous, although in some parts of its range, fruits, seeds, and berries can be important foods. Animal prey includes small mammals, birds (and eggs), terrestrial and aquatic gastropods, bivalves, centipedes, millipedes, spiders, scorpions, insects, crustaceans, fish, amphibians, and reptiles (including lizards and snakes). The frequency of occurrence of food items in the diet has been determined in several places throughout its range. In Zambia, scats contained 100% rodents (including *Mastomys denniae*, *Mastomys* sp., *Grammomys dolichurus*, *Otomys* sp., and *Mus minutoides*), 67% invertebrates, 67% insects (including Orthoptera), 39% grass, 33% amphibians, 11% insectivores (*Crocidura* sp.), and 6% reptiles. In Zimbabwe, stomach contents contained 68% murids (including *Mastomys* sp.), 40% insects (Coleoptera, Orthoptera, Isoptera, Lepidoptera and Hymenoptera), 15% birds, 9% arachnids, 8% reptiles, 8% wild fruits, 3% shrews, 3% centipedes, 2% amphibians, 1% lagomorphs and 1% fish. In Botswana, the diet comprised 90% insects (Coleoptera, Orthoptera, and Isoptera), 47% murids (including the Pouched Mouse *Saccostomus campestris*), 27% arachnids, 17% wild fruits, 10% centipedes, 7% birds, and 1% reptiles, amphibians and other arthropods. In Kenya, the relative occurrence of food items found in scats was 74% seeds and fruit (more than 40 species) versus 82% arthropods and 44% other food remains (small mammals, reptiles, birds, snails, and leaves). In Nigeria, stomach contents contained small mammal species (*Praomys tullbergi*, *Cricetomys* sp., *Mus musculoides*, *Lemniscomys striatus*, *Hybomys univittatus*, *Dendromus* sp., *Crocidura nigeriae*, *Crocidura poensis*, and *Crocidura* sp.), insects (including Orthoptera and Coleoptera), birds, eggs, reptiles, fruits, seeds, centipedes, and spiders; there was a 70% overlap in diet with the sympatric Crested Genet, indicating strong interspecific competition for food between these two species. In South Africa (*Pipistrellus capensis* and genera *Eptesicus*, *Scotophilus*, and *Rhinolophus*) and Somalia (genus *Tadarida*). There are reports of Rusty-spotted Genets killing poultry: in Zimbabwe, stomach contents included domestic fowl (pheasants, young peafowl, pigeons, and chickens). There is little evidence that carrion is eaten, although some stomachs from South Africa did contain maggots. Rusty-spotted Genets forage both in trees and on the ground. Prey is caught by careful stalking, followed by a pounce. Before being killed, its prey is bitten several times or sometimes shaken.

Activity patterns. Mainly nocturnal. In Kenya and Ethiopia, radio-collared genets were more active between sunset and sunrise than during daylight hours. Rest sites include trees, hollow logs, under tree roots, in disused Aardvark (*Orycteropus afer*) or spring hare burrows, under boulders, rock overhangs, caves, and man-made shelters. Resting sites are reused by both sexes.

On following pages: 17. Pardine Genet (*Genetta pardina*); 18. Aquatic Genet (*Genetta piscivora*); 19. King Genet (*Genetta poensis*); 20. Servaline Genet (*Genetta servalina*); 21. Hausa Genet (*Genetta thierryi*); 22. Cape Genet (*Genetta tigrina*); 23. Giant Genet (*Genetta victoriae*).

Movements, Home range and Social organization. Generally solitary, except pairs are seen during the breeding season. A radio-tracking study in Kenya (June–August), found mean home ranges of 5·9 km^2 for three males and 2·8 km^2 for two females; male ranges overlapped those of females. Males may move at 3 km/hour. Often seen on the ground, but also regularly observed climbing in trees; it can descend headfirst and uses its tail as a balancing organ. Uses regular latrine sites; some ground latrines are shared by other genet and mongoose species. Territories are marked using the perineal gland secretion, urine, and feces (with anal gland secretions). Tree scratching also may play a role in marking. A threatening attitude is achieved by arching the back and erecting the hairs on the back and tail.
Breeding. Two breeding peaks have been reported from Kenya: a main peak from October to December and another between March and May. In southern Africa, it appears that the breeding season extends from August to March. In South Africa, three young were found in February and two pregnant females, both with three fetuses, were recorded in November. Three two-week-old kittens were found in a hollow tree in northern Namibia in October. In Botswana, a female was found lactating during February and in Zimbabwe births were recorded from August to February. In Zambia, four-week-old juveniles were taken in October and November. Breeding behavior has been observed in captivity. A courting male, after sniffing the vulva of the female, exhibits a facial grimace (flehmen). He follows the female closely and produces grumbling and coughing calls. During the early stages of courtship, the female keeps turning away from the male, with her tail and hindquarters low, and flees. She eventually answers the male's calls and allows him to come into close contact. Each partner then sniffs the other's face and genitals, and they rub their cheeks. The female holds her tail up and crouches with raised hindquarters and tail deflected sideways. The male then clasps the female on the groin area, with his chest and belly resting on her lower back. As the female curves her spine, intromission occurs with pelvic thrusting. The male may sometimes bite the neck of the female during the final seconds of copulation, which usually lasts five minutes. Coupling pairs often meow. After copulating, the female may anal-drag and roll on her back, and both partners lick their genitals. Gestation is 70–77 days. Litter size appears to be two to five. Births take place in hollow trees, nests of leaves, and under roofs in urbanized habitats. Neonates are blind; they are covered with hair and have a discernable coat pattern. The eyes open at ten days and the first set of canines erupts at four weeks. These are shed after the permanent canines have erupted, at around 10–11 months. The mother licks her kittens ano-genitally and consumes their excrement. The young begin to take solid food at about six weeks, and may start to kill and eat live vertebrates at about 28 weeks. At approximately eight weeks of age, the young start running, jumping, rolling, and playing fighting games.
Status and Conservation. Classified as Least Concern on *The IUCN Red List*. Considered unthreatened as it has a wide range and occurs in a number of habitats. However, it may be declining in some areas due to hunting: it is found in bushmeat markets and is frequently trapped. Rusty-spotted Genets have a bad reputation as poultry thieves and farmers sometimes poison or trap them in retaliation.
Bibliography. Angelici (2000), Angelici & Gaubert (In press), Angelici & Luiselli (2005), Angelici, Luiselli & Politano (1999), Angelici, Luiselli, Politano & Akani (1999), Carpenter (1970), Crawford-Cabral & Fernandes (1999, 2001), Crawford-Cabral & Pacheco (1992), De Luca & Mpunga (2005), Duckworth (1995), Engel (1998a, 1998b, 2000), Estes (1991), Fernandes & Crawford-Cabral (2004), Fuller *et al.* (1990), Gaubert & Wozencraft (2005), Gaubert, Fernandes *et al.* (2004), Gaubert, Taylor, Fernandes *et al.* (2005), Gaubert, Taylor & Veron (2005), Gaubert, Tranier, Veron *et al.* (2003), Gaubert, Volobouev *et al.* (2004), Gaubert, Veron & Tranier (2001, 2002), Grimshaw *et al.* (1995), Grubb (2004), Ikeda *et al.* (1982), Kingdon (1971-1982, 1997), Maddock & Perrin (1993), Pienaar (1964), Rautenbach (1982), Rowe-Rowe (1971), Skinner & Smithers (1990), Smithers (1971), Smithers & Wilson (1979), Stuart (1990), Stuart & Stuart, M.D. (1997, Stuart & Stuart, T. (2003), Taylor (1969), Waser (1980), Wemmer (1977), Wozencraft (2005), Yalden *et al.* (1996).

17. Pardine Genet *Genetta pardina*

French: Genette pardine / **German**: Pardelgenette / **Spanish**: Gineta pardina
Other common names: West African Large-spotted Genet

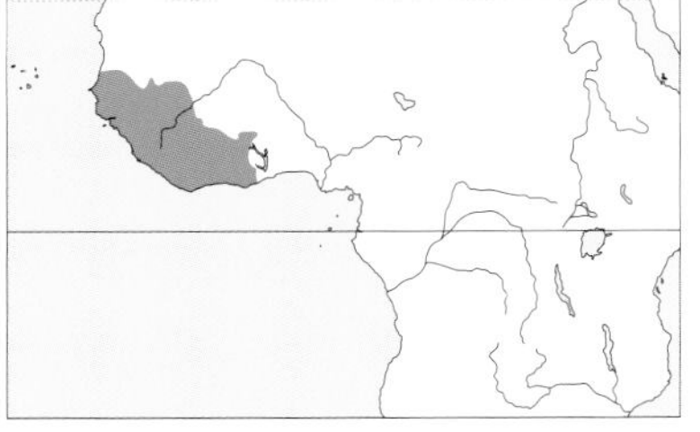

Taxonomy *Genetta pardina* Geoffroy Saint-Hilaire, 1832, Senegal.
Has been considered conspecific with *G. maculata* and *G. tigrina*. Several forms related to *G. pardina* or to *G. maculata* have been debated and some are now recognized as separate species (*G. bourloni* and *G. poensis*). Other forms (such as *schoutedeni* and *letabae*) have also been suggested as distinct species by morphometric and molecular studies, but these need further investigation. Monotypic.
Distribution. W Africa from Senegal and Mali to Burkina Faso and Ghana.
Descriptive notes. Head–body 41–55·3 cm (males), 41–53 cm (females), tail 39–49 cm (males), 42–45 cm (females), hindfoot 9–10 cm (males), 8·8–9·5 cm (females), ear 3·9–4·7 cm (males), 4–4·5 cm (females); weight up to 3·1 kg. A heavily built genet with a short, rough pelage. Both sexes are similar in color and size. The coat color varies from yellowish-gray to pale or sandy-gray; the ventral pelage is whitish-yellow or gray. The nuchal stripes are well defined. The wide, dark mid-dorsal line begins after the shoulder and runs to the base of the tail. There is no dorsal crest. The dorsal spots are dark brown or rufous brown, elongated and squared, not coalesced, and are bordered by dark rings. The first two rows form a line of separated spots, equal in width to the dorsal line. The face has a well-marked mask, a thin dark vertical line on the muzzle, and white sub- and supra-ocular spots. The ears are broad-based and slightly rounded. The tail has six to seven pale rings alternating with dark rings. The width of the pale rings relative to the dark rings in the middle of the tail is less than 20%; the tip of the tail is dark. The hindlimbs and forelimbs are the same color as the coat and are well spotted. The upper parts of the forefeet are spotted, whereas the upper parts of the hindfeet are unspotted. The underparts of the feet are dark-brown. There are two pairs of teats. In juveniles, the pattern of spots is similar to adults, but the spots on the flank, thigh and shoulder, are smaller and darker. The skull is large, with a thin sagittal crest. The posterior chamber of the auditory bulla is ventrally inflated and has a broken curve line on the external side. The premaxillary-frontal contact is absent. The posterior extension of the frontal bones overlaps c. 50% of the dorsal region of the inter-orbital constriction. The maxillary-palatine suture is at the same level as the main cusp of P^3. The ratio between the inter-orbital constriction and frontal width is less than 1 ± 0·12. Dental formula: I 3/3, C 1/1, P 4/4, M 2/2 = 40.
Habitat. Primary and secondary rain forests, gallery forests, and moist woodlands. Also occurs in forest plantations, bushlands, and suburban areas.
Food and Feeding. Diet thought to include rodents, invertebrates, and fruit. A specimen collected in the Ivory Coast contained remains of the brush-furred rat (*Lophuromys* sp.), insects, palm fruits, and grass.
Activity patterns. Appears to be nocturnal.
Movements, Home range and Social organization. Considered solitary.
Breeding. In the Ivory Coast, two one-month-old juveniles were found in April and one sub-adult male in June. Another sub-adult specimen, estimated to be five to six months old, was collected in July.
Status and Conservation. Classified as Least Concern on *The IUCN Red List*. Assumed to be common within its range and there are no known major threats. However, Pardine Genets have been recorded from bushmeat markets, so hunting pressure may have an impact on local populations.
Bibliography. Anon. (1960), Ansell (1978), Bourlière *et al.* (1974), Coe (1975), Coetzee (1977), Crawford-Cabral (1970, 1973, 1981), Crawford-Cabral & Fernandes (2001), Crawford-Cabral & Pacheco (1992), Gaubert (2003a), Gaubert & Dunham (In press a), Gaubert, Fernandes *et al.* (2004), Gaubert, Taylor, Fernandes *et al.* (2005), Gaubert, Taylor & Veron (2005), Grubb *et al.* (1998), Haltenorth & Diller (1985), Hoppe-Dominik (1990), Jones (1966), Rahm (1961), Rosevear (1974), Sillero-Zubiri & Marino (1997), Wozencraft (2005).

18. Aquatic Genet *Genetta piscivora*

French: Genette aquatique / **German**: Wassergenette / **Spanish**: Gineta acuática

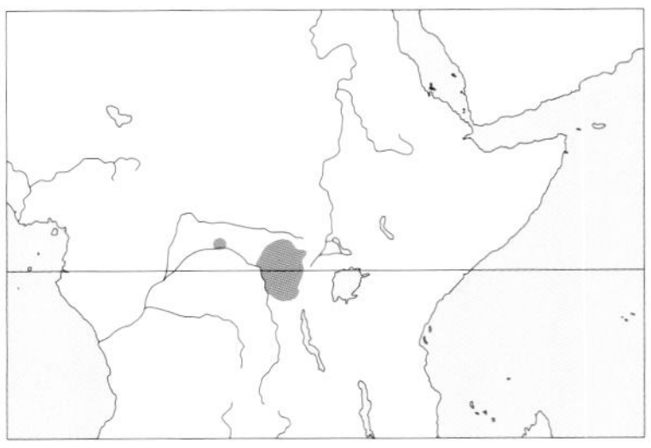

Taxonomy. *Osbornictis piscivora* J. A. Allen, 1919, Niapu, Zaire.
Monotypic.
Distribution. DR Congo.
Descriptive notes. Measurements from two adult males (respectively): Head–body 44·5–49·5 cm, tail 34–41·5 cm, hindfoot 8·3–9 cm, ear 6 cm; weight c. 1·5 kg. A slender unspotted genet, with a black bushy tail and strongly contrasting facial markings. The pelage is long and dense, especially on the tail. The coat is chestnut-red to dull red, without spots or bands; some individuals have a dark mid-dorsal stripe. An indistinct line of whitish hairs runs along the midline of the abdomen. There is a pair of elongated whitish spots between the eyes. The front and sides of the muzzle, and the sides of the head below the eyes, are whitish. The ears are blackish and edged with long whitish hairs. The rhinarium is small and without a median sulcus. The chin and throat are white. The tail is black and without rings. The palms and soles of the feet are bare, and the hindfeet have distinct elongated metatarsal pads. The skull is long and lightly built, and the teeth are relatively small and trenchant. The premaxillary-frontal contact is absent and the dorsal region of the frontal bone is concave. The ratio between the inter-orbital constriction and frontal width is less than 1 ± 0·12. The posterior extension of the frontal bone is very narrow and the posterior chamber of the auditory bulla has a continuous curve line on the external side. The premaxillary-maxillary suture is at the same level as P^1 and the maxillary-palatine suture is at the same level as the main cusps of P^3–M_1 (reduced). Dental formula: I 3/3, C 1/1, P 4/4, M 2/2 = 40.
Habitat. Rainforest. Nearly all specimens were trapped near small rivers and some were collected in forests dominated by limbali trees (*Gilbertiodendron*). Found from 460 to 1500 m.
Food and Feeding. Thought to be semi-aquatic and to primarily eat fish; natives say that fish is the favored prey. The stomach of one specimen contained bones of a small fish and an entire catfish (Clariidae) about 10 cm in length. The dentition may be adapted to dealing with slippery prey and the bare palms may be an adaptation for feeling and handling fish in muddy holes. Also reported to feed on crustaceans, but this is considered unlikely by some authors. Two captive adults never ate frogs, tadpoles, or crabs, but a young animal tried to eat all three. None showed any interest in moths or beetles that flopped into the pools in their enclosure. Small pools, or slowly flowing brooks, were approached with an extremely slow, gliding stalk. As the animal moved slowly along the water's edge, the surface was alternately tested with the vibrissae and patted with the forefoot. The wrist was bent back almost to the vertical and the surface struck with a downward pivoting action. Insect-eating fish such as barbel

(*Barbus*, up to 30 cm), catfish (*Clarias*), squeaker (*Synodontis*), and *Labio* were caught with a rapid, open-mouthed strike, and carried away.

Activity patterns. Thought to be crepuscular and nocturnal.

Movements, Home range and Social organization. Considered solitary. Has been caught in snare-traps set on the ground.

Breeding. A pregnant female was collected in late December with a single foetus, which was about 15 mm in length. A captive male made very aggressive tom-cat-like meows when pursuing a female and trying to mate. A chuffing call is used between individuals.

Status and Conservation. Classified as Data Deficient on *The IUCN Red List*. Mostly known from museum specimens (around 30) and considered among the rarest of the African carnivores. Has been given complete protection by the DR Congo government. Major threats are unclear, but Aquatic Genets are hunted for bushmeat by Bambuti pygmies. This species is a high priority for field studies to better understand its ecology, distribution, and population status.

Bibliography. Carpaneto & Germi (1989b), Gaubert, Taylor & Veron (2005), Gaubert, Tranier et al. (2004), Gaubert, Veron & Tranier (2001), Hart & Timm (1978), Van Rompaey (1988), Van Rompaey & Colyn (in press f), Verheyen (1962), Wozencraft (2005).

19. King Genet *Genetta poensis*
French: Genette royale / **German**: Königsgenette / **Spanish**: Gineta real

Taxonomy. *Genetta poensis* Waterhouse, 1838, Fernando Po.

Has been considered conspecific with *G. pardina*. Monotypic.

Distribution. Liberia, Ivory Coast, Ghana, Equatorial Guinea (Bioko I), and PR Congo.

Descriptive notes. Head–body 60·2 cm, tail 41·5 cm; weight 2-2·5 kg. A heavily built genet with a short, rough pelage. The coat varies from pale yellowish-gray to yellow; the ventral pelage is whitish-yellow to gray. The nuchal stripes are not clearly defined. The continuous mid-dorsal line is dark and begins after the shoulder. There is no dorsal crest. The dorsal spots are elongated and squared, completely dark, and coalesced in various parts of the body. The face has a well-marked mask, sub- and supra-ocular white spots, and a thin dark vertical line on the muzzle. The ears are broad-based and slightly rounded. The tail is thickly furred, with four to six pale rings; the proximal half is dark. The hindlimbs and forelimbs are dark and well spotted. The forefeet and hindfeet are spotted above and dark below. The skull is large, with the insertion of the masseter muscles always forming a narrow elevated crest. The premaxillary-frontal contact is present and the posterior extension of the frontal bones is narrow. The posterior chamber of the auditory bulla has a broken curve line. The ratio between the inter-orbital constriction and frontal width is less than 1 ± 0·12. Dental formula: I 3/3, C 1/1, P 4/4, M 2/2 = 40.

Habitat. Rainforest.

Food and Feeding. Nothing known.

Activity patterns. Nothing known.

Movements, Home range and Social organization. Nothing known.

Breeding. Nothing known.

Status and Conservation. Classified as Data Deficient on *The IUCN Red List*. Only known from ten museum specimens, with no records since 1946. Urgent survey work is required to confirm if it still survives in the wild. Hunting pressure is a threat, as most of the museum skins were collected from local hunters or bushmeat markets.

Bibliography. Crawford-Cabral (1981), Gaubert (2003a, 2003b, In press d), Gaubert, Taylor & Veron (2005), Gaubert, Tranier et al. (2004), Grubb et al. (1998), Rosevear (1974), Schlawe (1981), Wozencraft (2005).

20. Servaline Genet *Genetta servalina*
French: Genette servaline / **German**: Serval-Genette / **Spanish**: Gineta servalina

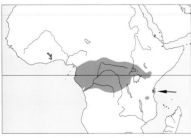

Taxonomy. *Genetta servalina* Pucheran, 1855, Gabon.

G. cristata was previously included as a subspecies of *G. servalina*, but is treated here as a valid species. Hybridization between *G. servalina* and *G. cristata* may be occurring in a sympatric zone: in central Cameroon, northern Gabon, and the PR Congo. Five subspecies are recognized.

Subspecies and Distribution.

G. s. servalina Pucheran, 1855 – Cameroon, Central African Republic, Equatorial Guinea, and Gabon.

G. s. archeri Van Rompaey & Colyn, 1998 – Zanzibar I.

G. s. bettoni Thomas, 1902 – DR Congo, Kenya, Rwanda, Burundi, Uganda, and Sudan.

G. s. lowei Kingdon, 1977 – S Tanzania.

G. s. schwarzi Crawford-Cabral, 1970 – PR Congo.

Descriptive notes. Head–body 49–51 cm (males), 44·5–49·5 cm (females), tail 45–46·5 cm (males), 36·8–48·5 cm (females), hindfoot 8·7–9·2 cm (males), 8–9·5 cm (females), ear 4·6 cm (1 male), 4–4·2 cm (females); weight 2·3 kg (females). The coat

color ranges from gray to ocherous yellow. The dark mid-dorsal line is discontinuous and there is no dorsal crest. The large black spots on the dorsal pelage run in longitudinal rows, with the top three rows being the most uniform. These spots become smaller and more randomly spaced towards the ventral pelage. The chest and throat have only a few small spots. The face has a dark mask and a pair of supra- and sub-ocular white spots. The tail has eight to twelve pale rings alternating with dark rings. The width of the pale rings relative to the dark rings in the middle of the tail is less than 20%; the tip of the tail is pale. The forelimbs and hindlimbs are boldly spotted. The forelegs are pale on the innermost side, with some scattered small spots, and dark gray above with small round spots. The inner hindlegs are dark gray, unspotted and have a grayish patch over the upper metatarsal region. The feet are dark. There is one pair of teats. The posterior chamber of the auditory bulla is inflated ventrally and has a continuous curve line on the external side. The premaxillary-frontal contact is present. The ratio between the inter-orbital constriction and frontal width is more than 1 ± 0·12. Dental formula: I 3/3, C 1/1, P 4/4, M 2/2 = 40.

Habitat. Primary and secondary forest, woodland savanna, savannah-forest mosaic, and gallery forest. Also found in wet forest, high-altitude bamboo forest, and coral rag thicket. Found up to at least 3500 m. Ecological niche modelling has predicted a potential broad distribution: the whole rainforest zone (Upper and Lower Guinean Blocks and Congo Basin); degraded lowland rainforest (N Cameroon, Central African Republic, DR Congo, Uganda, and Kenya); deciduous forest and woodlands (Tanzania); mangroves (Mozambique and Nigeria); and the deciduous forest and woodlands of southern Africa (Angola, Zambia, and Mozambique).

Food and Feeding. In the Central African Republic, the frequency of occurrence of prey items in 35 scats was: 77% mammals (mostly shrews and rodents), 71% arthropods (termites, beetles, and orthopterans), 14% reptiles and amphibians (snakes, lizards, and anurans), 6% birds, and 3% fruit. One individual has been observed scavenging a duiker (*Cephalophus* spp).

Activity patterns. Thought to be nocturnal.

Movements, Home range and Social organization. Considered solitary, but has been seen in pairs. Hunts on the ground and at low level in bushes. Feces are often deposited under overhanging rocks.

Breeding. Births have been reported in Uganda from February to August.

Status and Conservation. Classified as Least Concern on *The IUCN Red List*. Considered common, but is not well known and field studies are needed. Re-discovered in the Udzungwa Mountains National Park (Tanzania), after a gap of nearly 70 years. There are no known major threats, but may be undergoing localized declines in some regions due to hunting for bushmeat and skins.

Bibliography. Brink et al. (2002), Charles-Dominique (1978), De Luca & Mpunga (2002, 2005), Gaubert, Papes & Peterson (2006), Gaubert, Taylor & Veron (2005), Gaubert, Tranier et al. (2004), Gaubert, Veron & Tranier (2002), Goldman & Winther-Hansen (2003), Ray & Sunquist (2001), Taylor (1970b), Van Rompaey & Colyn (1998, In press g), Wozencraft (2005).

21. Hausa Genet *Genetta thierryi*
French: Genette de Thierry / **German**: Haussa-Genette / **Spanish**: Gineta Hausa
Other common names: Thierry's Genet, Villiers's Genet

Taxonomy. *Genetta thierryi* Matschie, 1902, Borgou, Togo.

The type specimen of *G. rubiginosa* is actually *G. thierryi*. Was sometimes considered a subspecies of *G. tigrina* or *G. maculata*. Monotypic.

Distribution. W Africa from Senegal to Nigeria and Cameroon.

Descriptive notes. Head–body 44·3–45 cm, tail 40–43 cm, hindfoot 6–7·5 cm, ear 3·5–4 cm; weight 1·3–1·5 kg. A small genet with a short pelage and no dorsal crest. Both sexes are similar in color and size. The coat varies from yellow-brown and pale gray to pale beige; the ventral pelage is grayish-white. The nuchal stripes are either irregular or marked by two thin parallel lines. The continuous mid-dorsal line is rufous-brown; it starts after the shoulder and is usually split longitudinally by a line of pale hairs, at least in the upper part. The dorsal spots are rufous-brown, elongated, and aligned in two rows; the row flanking the mid-dorsal line partially coalesces just before the rump. The spots of the flank, thigh and shoulder, are smaller and darker. The facial mask is lightly marked. The muzzle and forehead are pale gray, with a thin dark vertical line on the muzzle. The sub-ocular white spots are well marked, but the supra-ocular spots are absent. The ears are rounded. The tail is narrow, but the base is thicker and has longer hairs. There are usually eight or nine pale rings alternating with dark rings, but the markings are indistinct due to brownish or rufous extensions of the dark rings. The width of the pale rings relative to the dark rings in the middle of the tail is 100%. Dark hairs cover the last pale ring; the tip of the tail is dark. The forelimbs, lower hindlimbs, and feet are unspotted and are the same color as the coat. The line bordering the outer side of the forefoot pads and inner side of the hindfoot pads is brown. The central depression of the forefoot is hairless. There are two pairs of teats. In juveniles, the general coloration is darker and the pattern of spots is irregular. The mid-dorsal line is present and the markings of the tail are identical to the adult. The skull has an elongated post-orbital process. The posterior chamber of the auditory bulla is ventrally inflated and has a continuous curve line on the external side. The premaxillary-frontal contact is absent.

The maxillary-palatine suture is anterior to the main cusp of P^3. The ratio between the inter-orbital constriction and frontal width is 1 ± 0.12. Dental formula: I 3/3, C 1/1, P 4/4, M 2/2 = 40.

Habitat. Moist and dry savannahs, with open woodlands. Also found in moist woodlands (Guinea-Bissau), rainforest (Sierra Leone, Ghana, and Ivory Coast), and dry wooded steppes (Senegal).

Food and Feeding. Nothing known.

Activity patterns. A few observations suggest it is nocturnal.

Movements, Home range and Social organization. Nothing known.

Breeding. In Mali, two sub adults (8–10 months old) were collected in early November. Thought to bear young in holes dug in the ground or amongst rocks. A juvenile was found asleep in a dead tree in the Ivory Coast.

Status and Conservation. Classified as Least Concern on *The IUCN Red List*. Considered rare and is poorly known. There may be no major threats; however, this species has been reported from bushmeat markets throughout its range and there is some international traffic for the skins or as pets. Field surveys and ecological studies are needed.

Bibliography. Bourlière *et al.* (1974), Crawford-Cabral (1981), Gaubert & Dunham (In press b), Gaubert, Taylor & Veron (2005), Gaubert, Tranier *et al.* (2004), Gaubert, Veron & Tranier (2002), Halternorth & Diller (1985), Rosevear (1974), Wozencraft (2005).

22. Cape Genet *Genetta tigrina*

French: Genette tigrine / **German**: Südliche Großfleckgenette / **Spanish**: Gineta manchada
Other common names: South African Large-spotted Genet

Taxonomy. *Viverra tigrina* Schreber, 1776, Cape of Good Hope, South Africa.

Has been considered conspecific with *G. maculata*. Two subspecies are recognized.

Subspecies and Distribution.

G. t. tigrina Schreber, 1776 – South Africa (Southern region of Western Cape to Eastern Cape Provinces).

G. t. methi Roberts, 1948 – South Africa (S of Umzigaba River, Pondoland), and Lesotho.

Descriptive notes. Head–body 46–58 cm (males), 42·7–56 cm (females), tail 39–45·9 cm (males), 38·5–43·2 cm (females), hindfoot 8–9 cm (males), 7·7–8·5 cm (females), ear 3·6–5·5 cm (males), 3·9–4·3 cm (females); weight 1·6–2·1 kg (males), 1·4–1·9 kg (females). Both sexes are similar in color and size. The coat is whitish-yellow or gray; the ventral pelage is gray to whitish-gray. The nuchal stripes are well defined. The continuous black mid-dorsal line begins behind the shoulder; there is a short dorsal erectile crest. There are large spots on the thigh and shoulder. The face has a well-marked mask, a thin dark vertical line on the muzzle, and white sub-ocular spots; the white supra-ocular spots are less contrasting. The tail has seven to eight pale rings alternating with dark rings. The width of the pale rings relative to the dark rings in the middle of the tail is 50–75%. Dark hairs cover the last pale ring; the tip of the tail is dark. The hindlimbs are dark, with a thin row of pale hairs on the anterior surface. The posterior part of the forelimbs is dark. The upper parts of the forefeet and hindfeet are lightly spotted. There are two pairs of teats. The skull has a thin sagittal crest. The posterior chamber of the auditory bulla is flattened in comparison with the anterior chamber and has a continuous curve line on the external side. The maxillary-palatine is anterior to the main cusp of P^3. The ratio between the inter-orbital constriction and frontal width is 1 ± 0.05. Dental formula: I 3/3, C 1/1, P 4/4, M 2/2 = 40.

Habitat. Forests, lowland and mountain fynbos (heathland); often associated with dense vegetation cover. Frequents riparian zones and is sometimes found in scrub and open grasslands.

Food and Feeding. Diet includes rodents (Namaqua Micaelamys, *Micaelamys namaquensis* and Southern African Vlei Rat, *Otomys irroratus*), birds (Egyptian goose *Alopochen aegyptiacus* and Columbidae), insects (Coleoptera and Orthoptera), spiders, pill millipedes, freshwater crabs, earthworms, and plants (seeds, leaves, and grass). Also seen feeding in rubbish dumps. In the Eastern Cape Province, 372 scats contained invertebrates (arthropods, myriapods molluscs, and annelids), vertebrates (small mammals, birds, reptiles, and fish), fruit, and other plants. By volume, the dominant food items were insects and grass. There was some variation in diet between habitats and seasons,

which appeared to be dependent on prey availability. Birds appeared under-represented in the diet, but peaked during the winter and spring.

Activity patterns. Appears to be nocturnal: active at night during a survey in the former Cape Province. One individual has been observed resting during the day in a hollow oak tree, three metres above the ground

Movements, Home range and Social organization. Appears to be solitary, but females may be accompanied by a mate or the young of a recent litter. Home ranges in Kwa-Zulu-Natal were 50–100 ha.

Breeding. Possibly gives birth to young from January to February: a lactating female caught in January had recently given birth. A juvenile male collected in March weighed 300 g and was estimated to be six weeks old.

Status and Conservation. Classified as Least Concern on *The IUCN Red List*. Considered common, with no known major threats. However, it is sometimes killed by farmers in retaliation for preying on small domestic stock and poultry, so in some areas trapping, poisoning, and shooting may be having an affect on local numbers.

Bibliography. Coetzee (1977), Crawford-Cabral (1981), Crawford-Cabral & Pacheco (1992), Gaubert (2003a, In press d), Gaubert, Taylor & Veron (2005), Meester *et al.* (1986), Roberts *et al.* (2007), Schlawe (1981), Stuart (1981, 1990), Wozencraft (2005).

23. Giant Genet *Genetta victoriae*

French: Genette géante / **German**: Riesengenette / **Spanish**: Gineta gigante

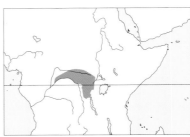

Taxonomy. *Genetta victoriae* Thomas, 1901, type locality debated: Uganda or Zaire. Monotypic.

Distribution. DR Congo and W Uganda.

Descriptive notes. Head–body 55–60 cm, tail 41·3–49 cm, hindfoot 9·2–10·5 cm, ear 4·5–5·1 cm; weight 2·5–3·5 kg. A large genet. Both sexes are similar in color and size. The coat color ranges from yellowish to ochraceous-white; the ventral pelage is paler. There is a pair of wide nuchal stripes and a nuchal crest. The dark mid-dorsal line is discontinuous, but has long hairs that give it a continuous appearance; these hairs form an erectile dorsal crest. The dorsal spots are small and randomly distributed. The face has a dark mask and a pair of supra- and sub-ocular white spots. The tail has about six pale rings alternating with dark rings. The width of the pale rings relative to the dark rings in the middle of the tail is less than 20%; the tip of the tail is dark. The hindlimbs and forelimbs are brown to black. There is one pair of teats. The posterior chamber of the auditory bulla is ventrally inflated, with a continuous curve line on the external side. The premaxillary-frontal contact is present and the maxillary-palatine suture is just behind the main cusp of P^3. The ratio between the inter-orbital constriction and frontal width is less than 1 ± 0.12. Dental formula: I 3/3, C 1/1, P 4/4, M 2/2 = 40.

Habitat. Rainforest. Ranges up to 2000 m. Ecological niche modelling has predicted potential suitable regions in lowland forests in Cameroon, southwestern Central African Republic, northern Gabon, and north-western PR Congo (plus a small area of swamp forest between the PR Congo and the DR Congo). Deciduous forest and woodlands in southern DR Congo and Angola, and patches of deciduous forest and woodland in Tanzania, northern Zambia, and Uganda, also offer possible habitat. Its apparent absence west of the Congo and Oubangi rivers might be due to lack of survey effort, low dispersal abilities, or riverine geographical barriers.

Food and Feeding. Nothing known.

Activity patterns. Appears to be nocturnal: a single animal was observed trotting along a forest road at about 22:30 h, and a captive individual was only active at night. Reported to sleep in hollow trunks of dead trees or among vines.

Movements, Home range and Social organization. Thought to be solitary.

Breeding. Nothing known.

Status and Conservation. Classified as Least Concern on *The IUCN Red List*. A poorly known species and field studies are needed. There are no known major threats, but it is hunted for bushmeat and skins, which are used to make hats and other ceremonial objects.

Bibliography. Carpaneto & Germi (1989b), Gaubert, Taylor & Veron (2005), Gaubert, Papes & Peterson (2006), Kingdon (1971-1982), Schreiber *et al.* (1989), Van Rompaey & Colyn (In press h), Wozencraft (2005).

Plate 15 ➤

24

25

27

26

ssp *whitei*

ssp *binturong*

28

29

30

PLATE 15

inches 12
cm 30

31

32

33

34

Subfamily PARADOXURINAE

Genus *ARCTOGALIDIA*

Merriam, 1897

24. Small-toothed Palm Civet *Arctogalidia trivirgata*

French: Civette à trois bandes / **German**: Streifenroller / **Spanish**: Galidia
Other common names: Three-striped Palm Civet

Taxonomy. *Paradoxurus trivirgatus* Gray, 1832, type locality restricted to "Java, Buitenzorg".

Three subspecies are recognized here, but a systematic revision is needed. Some authors believe that the Small-toothed Palm Civet should be split into two species, one north of the Isthmus of Kra and one in the Sundaic region. Three subspecies recognized.

Subspecies and Distribution.

A. t. trivirgata Gray, 1832 – Peninsular Thailand and Malaysia, Sumatra, and Borneo; also found on several small Indonesian Is.
A. t. leucotis Horsfield, 1851 – NE India (Assam), Bangladesh, China (Yunnan), and Mainland SE Asia to the Isthmus of Kra.
A. t. trilineata Wagner, 1841 – Java.

Descriptive notes. Head–body 43·2–53·2 cm, tail 46·3–66 cm, hindfoot 7·5–9·5 cm, ear 4·2–5 cm; weight 2–2·5 kg. A small civet with a long tail; smaller on Borneo, and the pelage varies in color and pattern between different populations. The coat color varies from gray to dark brown; the underparts are grayish-white or creamy buff. The under fur on the back and sides is reddish brown. There are three dark dorsal stripes (narrow rows of spots) and a median white band on the nose (which can be missing or inconspicuous, particularly in Bornean individuals). The head and feet are darker than the body. The tail is dark brown or black and is paler at the base; there can also be faint dark rings at the base of the tail in some individuals. The skin and hairs on the tip of the ear are white in populations north of the Isthmus of Kra (subspecies *A. t. leucotis*). The rhinarium has a deep groove in the front and on its upper surface. The feet have five digits and smooth plantar pads; the metapodial pads are large and covered with smooth skin. The area between the metatarsal pads is naked and covered by coarse skin; the heel is hairy. On the hindfoot, the third and fourth digit pads are close together, but are not fused as in other paradoxurine species. The perineal scent gland is absent in the male. In the female, this gland is simple and consists of a small naked area in front of the vulva, surrounded by a flap of naked skin; the gland does not reach the anus and the principal secreting area is located in front of the vulva. There are two pairs of teats. The skull has long post-orbital processes; the post-orbital process of the zygomatic arch rises sharply to form part of the lower rim of the orbit. The sagittal crest is low and incomplete in some specimens, but the occipital crests are well-developed. The auditory bullae have a distinctive fusion of the bones of the anterior and posterior chambers. Dental formula: I 3/3, C 1/1, P 4/4, M 2/2 = 40. The teeth are small, round, and widely separated. The protocone of the upper carnassial is medial to the paracone and the shearing blades of the molars are absent.

Habitat. Primary semi-evergreen forest; a few records are from degraded forest in Laos. Found up to 1500 m. In Vietnam, an adult was observed in primary hill forest at 770 m and two sightings were in lowland, semi-evergreen forest. In Cambodia, a male was observed in a small area of semi-evergreen forest at 150 m and in Thailand individuals were seen in dry evergreen forest. In central Sumatra, a skull was found in primary forest at 800 m. On Borneo, one individual was trapped in primary forest at 600 m.

Food and Feeding. Believed to be omnivorous, feeding on small vertebrates, invertebrates, and fruits. On Borneo, two stomachs contained 90% fruits and arthropods; another stomach collected in Myanmar contained remains of squirrels. Has been observed feeding on figs.

Activity patterns. Appears to be nocturnal: sightings have been recorded in the early morning hours and during the night. Said to rest during the day in the upper branches of tall trees.

Movements, Home Range and Social organization. Appears to be solitary, although pairs have been seen. Arboreal: mainly observed in the crown of trees and rarely on the ground. It is an excellent climber and uses its tail for balance while walking on thin limbs. In Thailand, individuals were seen in trees, 10–25 m from the ground, and a pair was seen feeding in a fig tree. In Vietnam, individuals were observed in trees, 15–50 m above the ground, and in Cambodia, a single male was seen feeding in a fig tree. In Laos, several sightings were recorded in the canopy, but none were seen on the ground.

Breeding. A female with two embryos has been reported; in captivity, litter size ranged from one to three, with two litters a year. A captive female had her first estrus period at 17 months and then at six-month intervals. Gestation is 45 days.

The young are born blind; their eyes open at eleven days. They are weaned after two months.

Status and Conservation. Classified as Least Concern on *The IUCN Red List*, the Javan subspecies *trilineata* has been recorded only in Gunung Halimun, Gunung Gede and Ujung Kulon National Parks, and is classified as Endangered by *The IUCN Red List* and is considered Threatened in the 1989 IUCN *Action Plan for the Conservation of Mustelids and Viverrids*. Habitat loss and degradation could be a serious threat: in South-east Asia, there has been loss and degradation of primary forests through logging and conversion to non-forest land-uses. On Borneo, the overall density of civets in logged forests was found to be significantly lower than in primary forests. Small-toothed Palm Civets are hunted in the Indochina region, and they are seen in local markets and outside restaurants. However, they may be less vulnerable to traps and snares set on the ground than more terrestrial civet species. Field surveys are needed to determine their current distribution and to monitor populations. As this is a very arboreal species, it is unlikely to be detected by camera-traps set close to the ground; spotlighting at night appears to be a more appropriate detection method. Ecological studies also are needed.

Bibliography. Borissenko *et al.* (2004), Corbet & Hill (1992), Davis (1962), Duckworth (1997), Goldman (1982), Holden (2006), IUCN (2008), Lekagul & McNeely (1991), Long & Hoang (2006), Medway (1969), Meiri (2005), Payne *et al.* (1985), Pocock (1915f, 1933c, 1939), Rabinowitz (1991), Schreiber *et al.* (1989), Van Bemmel (1952), Veron (1999), Walston & Duckworth (2003), Wells *et al.* (2005), Wozencraft (1984, 2005).

Genus *MACROGALIDIA*

Schwarz, 1910

25. Sulawesi Palm Civet *Macrogalidia musschenbroekii*

French: Civette des Célèbes / **German**: Sulawesi-Roller / **Spanish**: Civeta de las Célebes
Other common names: Giant Palm Civet

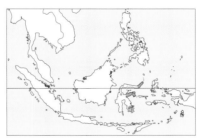

Taxonomy. *Paradoxurus musschenbroekii* Schlegel, 1879, Menado-Kinilo, Celebes. Monotypic.

Distribution. Sulawesi.

Descriptive notes. Head–body 65–71·5 cm, tail 44·5–54 cm, hindfoot 10·1–11·1 cm, ear 3·9–4·1 cm; weight 3·9–6·1 kg. A large palm civet with a long tail. The coat color is light brownish-chestnut to dark brown on the upperparts; the underparts are yellowish-brown, with a reddish breast. There are lighter patches above and below the eyes, in front of the ears, and on the edge of the upper lip. The eyes are large, with light brown irises and vertical pupils; the rhinarium is large and similar to that of the Binturong. There are two longitudinal rows of indistinct dark dorsal spots on either side of the midline that converge anteriorly. The tail has seven to eleven indistinct pale yellowish rings. The feet have five digits, retractile claws, rudimentary skin sheaths over the claws (digits 2–5), and a fleshy web connecting the toes; the metapodial pads are large and smooth. The naked depression between the long metatarsal pads is wider distally than proximally, and is covered with coarse, horny tubercules. The feet are flexible and can be rotated to allow headfirst descents from trees. The perineal gland in the female is a shallow semi-circular depression behind the vulva; the secretion tinges the surrounding hairs an orange color. The male lacks a noticeable perineal gland, although there is a small naked area between the anus and scrotum. There are two pairs of teats. The skull has a near parallel-sided palate and its general shape is similar to the Common Palm Civet. Dental formula: I 3/3, C 1/1, P 4/4, M 2/2 = 40. The premolars and molars are larger than in other palm civets and lack shearing blades. The first upper and lower premolars are small and deciduous in old age.

Habitat. Primary forest, up to 2600 m; also recorded in grassland and near farms.

Food and Feeding. Appears to be omnivorous: the percentage occurrence of food items in 47 scats found in the Lore Lindu Reserve was: 47% rodents, 4% Sulawesi Dwarf Cuscus (*Strigocuscus celebensis*), 2% birds, 2% grass, and palm fruit (including 45% *Arenga* spp., 15% *Pandanus* sp.). Captive animals caught and killed chickens by seizing the chicken with the forepaws and biting it on the head. Feeding began at the head and the entire carcass was eaten, including the feet and nearly all the feathers. They chewed fruit with their heads tilted upwards.

Activity patterns. Appears to be nocturnal: has been camera-trapped at night and captive animals were reported to be mainly active at night.

Movements, Home range and Social organization. Appears to be solitary: the few recorded camera-trap photographs have been of single individuals. Arboreal, but has been camera-trapped and snared on the ground. Captive animals have demonstrated that they are skilful climbers; they can walk upside down across the mesh of a cage and can ascend and descend along trunks by vertical looping (synchronous movements of the fore and hindfeet, accompanied by arching of the back as the body is contracted and extended). Sulawesi Palm Civets claw-mark smooth-barked trees; scratches

On following pages: 26. Binturong (*Arctictis binturong*); 27. Masked Palm Civet (*Paguma larvata*); 28. Common Palm Civet (*Paradoxurus hermaphroditus*); 29. Brown Palm Civet (*Paradoxurus jerdoni*); 30. Golden Palm Civet (*Paradoxurus zeylonensis*); 31. Otter Civet (*Cynogale bennettii*); 32. Owston's Palm Civet (*Chrotogale owstoni*); 33. Banded Palm Civet (*Hemigalus derbyanus*); 34. Hose's Palm Civet (*Diplogale hosei*).

extending up to 2·7 m above the ground have been found on trees up to 65 cm in circumference. They do not appear to deposit scats on prominent logs or rocks, but simply leave them on the ground.

Breeding. Nothing known.

Status and Conservation. Classified as Vulnerable on *The IUCN Red List*. Listed as Threatened in the 1989 IUCN *Action Plan for the Conservation of Mustelids and Viverrids*. Protected under Indonesian law. Recently recorded in Rawa Aopa National Park, Tanjung Peropa Wildlife Reserve, and Mangolo Recreation Forest. Possibly threatened by habitat loss and fragmentation, particularly at lower elevations; between 1985 and 1997, there were forest losses of 59% in the northern peninsular, 72% in the central peninsular, and 67% in the southeastern peninsular. Known to raid villages for pigs and chickens and are sometimes killed in retaliation. Little is known about this species and field surveys, ecological studies, and assessments of threats are needed.

Bibliography. Corbet & Hill (1992), Dammerman (1939), Groves (1976), Lee *et al.* (2003), Pocock (1933c), Schlegel (1879), Schreiber *et al.* (1989), Veron (1999, 2001), Wemmer & Watling (1986), Wemmer *et al.* (1983), Wozencraft (1984, 2005).

Genus ARCTICTIS
Temminck, 1824

26. Binturong *Arctictis binturong*
French: Binturong / **German**: Binturong / **Spanish**: Binturong

Taxonomy. *Viverra binturong* Raffles, 1822 [presented orally in 1820, often incorrectly ascribed as 1821], Malacca, Malaysia.
The number of subspecies is debated and up to nine have been recognized; the subspecies on Palawan Island, the Philippines (*whitei*) has been considered a distinct species by some authors. There is no recent taxonomic revision, but a molecular study has suggested a separation of the Sundaic and northern populations.

Distribution. E Nepal, NE India (Sikkim, Assam & Arunachal Pradesh), Bhutan, Bangladesh, S China (Yunnan, Guangxi), Mainland SE Asia, Peninsular Malaysia, Indonesia (Sumatra, Java, Nias, Bangka, Bintan & Kundur Is), and the Philippines (Calauit & Palawan Is).

Descriptive notes. Head–body 61–96·5 cm, tail 50–84 cm, hindfoot 11·8–18 cm, ear 4·9–5·2 cm; weight 9–20 kg. The largest civet species, with a long shaggy coat. The general color is black; the tip of the guard hairs can be white, giving a grizzled appearance in some individuals. The head is black, grayish, or almost white; the grayish color of the head can also extend behind the shoulder. The ears are black and rounded, with a white rim and long tufts of hairs on the dorsal surface and at the tip. The mystacial vibrissae are white. The rhinarium has a median groove within a shallow depression; this groove extends onto the dorsal surface. The tail is long and prehensile. The feet have five digits and very large metacarpal and metatarsal pads covered with coarse skin. The forefeet have large metacarpal pads, which are neither well defined nor well separated from the plantar pads. On the hindfeet, the divisions between the plantar pads, metatarsal pads, and the medial depression also are not well defined. The naked area on the foot extends to the back of the heel, which is covered by horny pointed papillae. On the hindfoot, the third and fourth digit pads are fused at their base. The claws are strong, sharp and retractile, but are unguarded by lobes of skin. There are two pairs of teats. The perineal gland is simple and consists of a pair of haired labia. The skull is large and not constricted in the post-orbital area. Dental formula: I 3/3, C 1/1, P 4/4, M 2/2 = 40. The teeth are quite small, with the shearing blades of the carnassials reduced, and the incisors well separated.

Habitat. Primary and secondary forest, including grassland/forest mosaic. Found up to 1500 m on Borneo, and from 700 to 2500 m on Sumatra. In north-east India, it is restricted to dense tropical and subtropical forests up to 2000 m.

Food and Feeding. Said to feed on small vertebrates, invertebrates, and fruits, but is believed to be predominantly frugivorous. Figs were found to be the main food item in one specimen stomach collected from Borneo and in a scat collected from a trapped animal in Thailand; Binturongs have been observed in fig trees frequently. One individual was photographed eating fallen jackfruit (*Artocarpus heterophyllus*) in Sumatra.

Activity patterns. In Thailand, radio-collared Binturongs were found to be arrhythmic; they were active 47% of the time and had activity peaks between 04:00–06:00 h and 20:00–22:00 h. Also in Thailand, two Binturongs were observed feeding at night (00:30 h and 03:30 h), but several diurnal field observations were also reported: feeding animals were seen between dawn and early afternoon, with a peak active period from 06:30–08:00 h. In Sabah, Binturongs were seen almost as often by day as by night. On Sumatra, sightings were frequently reported during the day, but they were also camera-trapped at night. A captive female and two males showed an arrhythmic activity pattern: moving, feeding, and agonistic behavior were highest from 09:00–12:00 h, resting was highest from 00:00–03:00 h, and reproductive activities were more frequent from 03:00–06:00 h. Another captive male from Vietnam was found to be strictly nocturnal. Rest sites are in the upper branches of tall trees; when resting, it lies curled up, with the head tucked under the tail.

Movements, Home range and Social organization. Solitary, but sometimes females are seen with young. Arboreal, but will descend to the ground. Binturongs can climb trees with ease, but progress slowly and deliberately, using their long prehensile tails for balance and to hold branches for support. On the ground, they are plantigrade and walk along on the soles of their feet. In Thailand, five radio-collared males had a mean annual range size of 6·2 km² (range 4·7 to 7·7 km²); wet season ranges were larger. The home range overlaps were substantial (mean= 35%) indicating a lack of territories. The mean one-day movement distance was 688 m. In another study in Thailand, the home range of a female was 4·0 km², and 20·5 km² for a male (with a core area of 3·5 km²). Captive Binturongs utter high-pitched whines and howls, rasping growls, and a variety of grunts and hisses when excited.

Breeding. Breeding seems to occur throughout the year, at least in captivity. Captive females are non-seasonally polyoestrous and may give birth to two litters annually; however, there is a pronounced birth peak from January to March. Litter size is one to six, most commonly two. Gestation is 84 to 99 days. Observations in captivity have shown that copulations usually take place in trees. Captive males and females had their first copulations between 13 and 48 months old. Both sexes remain fertile until 15 years old; the maximum lifetime productivity is estimated to be 23 young. The mean estrous cycle is 83 days. Copulations are observed during a period of up to 15 days, suggesting a long estrous period. During estrus, females increase their activity and calling; this call consists of a single blowing sound (made by expelling air through the nose) that is also emitted by males in adjacent cages. During encounters, the male follows the restless female, frequently sniffing both her and the cage. After mutual sniffing, the male investigates the female's perineal region and often exposes this area by pulling her tail aside with his forepaws; males often flehmen after licking the perineal region of the female. The female indicates her receptivity by emitting a coarse purring sound and incites the male to follow her by trotting briskly. She will then lie down and the male mounts by either standing on the female's back, clasping her around the mid body with his forepaws, or by standing and straddling the female with his forelegs. Thrusting occurs in bouts and frequently alternates with periods of back licking; the female emits a continuous loud coarse purring noise during copulations. The female terminates copulations by quickly departing. The male remains at the copulation site and licks his penis; the female licks her perineal gland and vulva. After a pause, the female walks around the cage and initiates another mounting sequence. Mean newborn birth weight is 319 g, which is about 3% the weight of the mother. The young start to eat solid food at the age of six to eight weeks.

Status and Conservation. CITES Appendix III (India). Classified as Vulnerable on *The IUCN Red List*. Classified as Critically Endangered on the China Red List. Habitat loss and degradation could be a major threat: in South-east Asia, there has been forest loss and degradation through logging and conversion to non-forest land-uses. On Borneo, the overall density of civets (including the Binturong) in logged forests was found to be significantly lower than in primary forests. In the Philippines, Binturongs are harvested for the pet trade. Hunting is a threat, particularly snaring, as they descend to the ground occasionally; in Vietnam, a Binturong was found in a snare-trap. There has been an increased demand for civet meat in Chinese and Vietnamese markets; it is considered particularly tasty in parts of Laos and civets are also taken for human consumption in southern areas. Binturongs are found in markets in Laos and skins are traded to Vietnam. They are hunted in north-east India, as civet oil is believed to have aphrodisiac properties. Field surveys, ecological studies, and assessments of threats are needed. In order to manage captive breeding programs of this species, there is a Population Management Plan in American zoos and a European Studbook Programme in European zoos.

Bibliography. Arivazhagan & Thiyagesan (2001), Austin (2002), Austin & Tewes (1999b), Azlan (2003), Corbet & Hill (1992), Cosson *et al.* (2007), Duckworth (1997), Esselstyn *et al.* (2004), Grassman, Tewes & Silvy (2005), Heydon & Bulloh (1996), Holden (2006), Jha (1999), Lekagul & McNeely (1991), Long & Hoang (2006), Nettelbeck (1997), Payne *et al.* (1985), Pocock (1915f, 1933c, 1939, 1945), Rozhnov (1994), Story (1945), Veron (1999), Wemmer & Murtaugh (1981), Wozencraft (2005).

Genus PAGUMA
Gray, 1831

27. Masked Palm Civet *Paguma larvata*
French: Civette masquée / **German**: Larvenroller / **Spanish**: Paguma

Taxonomy. *Gulo larvatus* C. E. H. Smith, 1827, type locality not known (possibly S China).
The number of subspecies is debated and up to sixteen have been considered. A taxonomic revision is needed, but six subspecies are recognized here.

Subspecies and Distribution.
P. l. larvata C. E. H. Smith, 1827 – China (and Taiwan & Hainan Is), Cambodia, Laos, Myanmar, and Vietnam.
P. l. annectens Robinson & Kloss, 1917 – Peninsular Malaysia and Thailand.
P. l. grayi Bennett, 1835 – Bhutan, India, Nepal, and Pakistan.
P. l. leucocephala Gray 1865 – Borneo.

P. l. leucomystax Gray, 1837 – Sumatra.
P. l. tytlerii Tytler, 1864 – Andaman Is.
A possible sighting in western Java in 1993; however, there are no other records for this island. Introduced to Japan.
Descriptive notes. Head–body 50·8–87 cm, tail 50·8–63·6 cm, hindfoot 9·5–10·4 cm, ear 4·6–5 cm; weight 3–5 kg. A large palm civet. The coat color varies from gray, light brown, or blond to dark brown; the underparts are paler. There are no stripes or spots on the body and tail. The facial mask generally consists of a median white stripe from the nose to the top of the head, bordered by large black patches on both sides. Below each eye is a small white patch and above there is a large white mark that extends to the base of the ear and beyond. In the northern regions, the white band on the nose can extend beyond the forehead to the neck and shoulders. In the Sundaic region, the facial mask can be almost absent or yellowish, with no distinct patches, or black and white pattern. The rhinarium is large and deeply grooved up to its dorsal surface. The distal end of the tail may be darker than the basal part, and sometimes has a whitish-yellow tip. The feet have five digits and are blackish. The metapodial pads are large and wide. The plantar and metacarpal pads on the forefeet are clearly separated by ridges. The metatarsal pads on the hindfeet are long and partly fused anteriorly to the plantar pads; the depression in between is naked and covered by horny papillae. On the hindfoot, the third and fourth digit pads are fused at the base. There are two pairs of teats. The perineal gland is simple: it consists of a pair of thickened ridges of skin that form the walls of a longitudinal fossa (the external parts of the ridge are hairy and the inner sides are naked). The skull is quite similar to the Common Palm Civet, but is larger and wider. Dental formula: I 3/3, C 1/1, P 4/4, M 2/2 = 40. The teeth are small and low, and the blades on the carnassials are reduced. The premolars are small and separated from each other.
Habitat. Primary evergreen and deciduous forest, and in disturbed habitats. Found up to 2500 m. In Thailand, a radio-collared female moved in an area that constituted 67% dry evergreen forest, 30% mixed deciduous forest, and 3% dry deciduous dipterocarp forest.
Food and Feeding. Omnivorous: fruit, small vertebrates, and insects. In southeastern China, the frequency of occurrence of food items in 37 scats was: 38% Chinese berry (*Abelia chinensis*), 27% rodents, 24% unidentified fruit, 22% kiwi fruit, 22% beetles, 19% persimmon fruit (*Diospyros* spp), 3% birds, and 3% grass. In Japan, where it has been introduced, 38 stomach contents contained 73% fruit, 56% leaves, 40% arthropods, 21% other plant items, 13% molluscs, 8% mammals, 8% fish, 5% birds, and 3% reptiles. Fruits and mammals were the highest food items by weight.
Activity patterns. Mainly nocturnal. Field sightings and camera-traps have recorded activity during the night. In Thailand, radio-collared Masked Palm Civets were active over 50% of the time between 16:30 h and 04:30 h, with a peak of activity between 19:30 h and 22:30 h. In southeastern China, five radio-tracked individuals were also found active over 50% of the time between 18:00 h and 05:00 h; their activity declined throughout the morning, reaching the lowest point at 12:00 h, then remained moderately low until 18:00 h. Reported to sleep in tree holes or on branches in large trees. In southeastern China, rest sites were in burrows, mainly the abandoned dens of Malayan Porcupines (*Hystrix brachyura*); numerous daybeds were used, either once (59%), twice (14%), three times (11%), or several times (some up to 17).
Movements, Home range and Social organization. Solitary and arboreal, but does spend some time on the ground. In Thailand, an adult male had a home range of 5·9 km² and an adult female had a home range of 3·7 km²; the mean daily movement was 840 m for the male and 620 m for the female. In southeastern China, the resting home ranges of three adult males were 1·8, 3·5 and 4·1 km², and 1·9 and 2·9 km² for two adult females; the mean distance moved between consecutive daybed locations was 429 m for males and 404 m for females.
Breeding. Based on captive animals, it appears that there are two breeding seasons, early spring and late autumn, although some authors suggest that this species is polyoestrous. Estrus lasts one to 13 days (mean five days) and gestation is 51 to 56 days. Litters of up to four have been reported. Neonates are born blind and open their eyes when around nine days old. They are mature at 10–22 months.
Status and Conservation. Classified as Least Concern on *The IUCN Red List*. Masked Palm Civets may be threatened by habitat loss and degradation, hunting, the food trade, and the SARS epidemic. They are traded throughout South-east Asia and are commonly sold in food markets and restaurants in China, Vietnam, and Laos. They are farmed on a large scale in China for the meat trade. In the 1960s, the annual take from the wild was 80,000 to 100,000 in China. During the 1990s, civet farming developed intensively, as wild populations became scarce. By 2003, there were 660 farms in China holding 40,000 Masked Palm Civets. The SARS-like coronavirus has been isolated in this species and it may have played a role in the recent SARS epidemic (although there is no evidence that it is the natural reservoir of this virus); it is yet unclear what the ramifications will be of any recent control methods for this disease. The impacts of habitat loss and degradation on Masked Palm Civet populations are largely unknown, but on Borneo, it was found that the overall density of civet species in logged forest was significantly lower than in primary forest. May also be at risk from snare trapping; on Sumatra, they are commonly caught in snares set for Muntjac. Field surveys, ecological studies, and monitoring of threats are needed.
Bibliography. Azlan (2003), Bell *et al.* (2004), Brooks & Dutson (1994), Corbet & Hill (1992), Duckworth (1997), Goldman (1982), Grassman (1998c), Guan *et al.* (2003), Heydon & Bulloh (1996), Holden (2006), Jha (1999), Jia *et al.* (2000, 2001), Jiang *et al.* (2003), Keiji (1998), Lekagul & McNeely (1991), Long & Hoang (2006), Medway (1969), Meiri (2005), Moutou (2004), Payne *et al.* (1985), Pocock (1915f, 1933d, 1934a, 1934b, 1934c), Rabinowitz (1991), Saksaki (1991), Tan (1989), Torii (1986), Veron (1999), Wang & Fuller (2001, 2003), Yu *et al.* (2003), Wozencraft (2005).

Genus *PARADOXURUS*

Cuvier, 1821

28. Common Palm Civet *Paradoxurus hermaphroditus*

French: Civette hermaphrodite / **German**: Fleckenmusang / **Spanish**: Musang

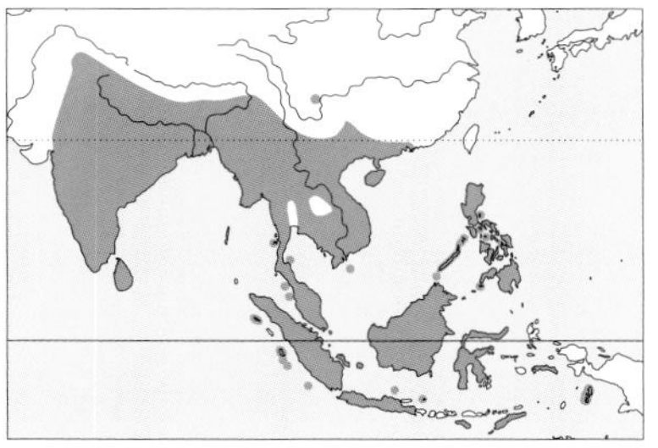

Taxonomy. *Viverra hermaphrodita* Pallas, 1777, type locality unknown.
The number of subspecies is debated and over thirty have been described; a taxonomic revision is needed. Included here is the Mentawai Palm Civet (*P. lignicolor*), endemic to the Mentawai Islands, which is sometimes considered a separate species.
Distribution. Pakistan, India, Sri Lanka, and Nepal to China, Mainland SE Asia, Peninsular Malaysia, Sumatra, Java, Borneo, the Philippines, and many associated small islands. Also scattered records in Sulawesi, Moluccan Is, Timor, and the Aru Is, probably resulting from introductions. Presence uncertain in Papua New Guinea. Introduced to Japan in the late 1800s.
Descriptive notes. Head–body 42–71 cm, tail 33–66 cm, hindfoot 7–9 cm, ear 4·1–4·9 cm; weight 2–5 kg. Smaller on islands, notably Borneo. A small civet with a dark mask and long tail. The coat color is gray, grayish-brown or rusty; the body spots and stripes are brown or black. The head pattern is very variable, but generally consists of a dark mask, with white or pale gray patches below the eyes, on the forehead, and at the bases of the ears. Variations include: a muzzle with white nose patches, ear and forehead patches that are fused, facial patches that are very small, and facial patterns that are absent or very faint. The rhinarium is large and has a deep groove in the middle. There are black spots along the back that merge to form three lines, which run longitudinally from the shoulders to the base of the tail. The spots on the flanks are well separated, but tend to be in rows. This pattern is variable and can be obscure in some populations; on Borneo and the Philippines, the whole body can be dark brown or black, and the stripe pattern is indistinguishable. In the northern parts of the range, the length of the guard hairs seems to vary seasonally; when the pelage is long, the coat pattern tends to be faint. Some individuals have faint rings at the base of the tail, and the tail tip can sometimes be white or yellow. The feet have five digits. The metapodial pads are large and not well separated from the plantar pads. They cover the whole sole and the area between them is naked. On the hindfoot, the third and fourth digit pads are fused at their base. The perineal gland is simple and consists of a naked elongated area. There are three pairs of teats, but the third pair is reduced. The skull is long and low, with prominent post-orbital processes, low crests, a rising rather than flat zygomatic arch, and a marked post-orbital constriction. The posterior chamber of the auditory bullae is ovoid and extends anteriorly, covering largely the anterior chamber. Dental formula: I 3/3, C 1/1, P 4/4, M 2/2 = 40. The carnassials have reduced shearing blades. Sometimes the upper carnassial is short and triangular, with a strong post-lingual cingulum; it also can be elongated and narrower, with a reduced post-lingual cingulum. The shape of the premolars and molars is variable. The first premolars are reduced; the second and third premolars are rather simple and pointed. The teeth of old individuals are often very worn.
Habitat. A wide range of habitats, including evergreen and deciduous forest (primary and secondary), plantations, and around human dwellings and settlements. Found up to 2400 m. In Thailand, one radio-collared male moved through an area that constituted 44% dry dipterocarp forest, 30% mixed deciduous forest, and 26% dry evergreen forest; another male moved within 55% dry dipterocarp forest, 32% dry evergreen forest, and 12% mixed deciduous forest.
Food and Feeding. Mainly frugivorous, but also eats small vertebrates and invertebrates. On Borneo, specimen stomachs contained 90% arthropods and 45% fruits and leaves (no vertebrate remains were found). In Nepal, 193 scats contained 85% fruits; insects, molluscs, small reptiles, birds, and small mammals were also included in the diet. The major source of fruit was *Coffea benghalensis* (from mid-December to February) and *Bridelia stipularis* (in March and April). All scats contained fruits during the fruiting seasons. When ripe fruits were not available, the diet shifted to small vertebrates and invertebrates. Field observations showed that they also fed on the nectar of *Bombax ceiba* and sap from the stems of *Vallaris solanacea*. In India, scats contained 83% fruits (including 23% papaya, *Carica papaya*), rodents (Roof Rats *Rattus rattus*, House Mice *Mus musculus*, and Indian Gerbils *Tatera indica*), and insects (beetles and cockroaches). Common Palm Civets sometimes drink the juice (called "toddy') from tapped coconut palms, hence the local colloquial name "Toddy Cat" for this species.
Activity patterns. Nocturnal. Camera-traps and field sightings have recorded this species as active during the night. In Thailand, radio-collared individuals were active over 50% of the time between 16:30 h and 04:30 h, with a peak between 19:30 h and 01:30 h. In Nepal, an adult female was active 79% of the time during the hours of darkness, and five other radio-tracked individuals were active from 18:00–04:00 h; they were more active on darker nights, and none of them left their resting sites when there was a full moon. Common Palm Civets rest in trees, choosing the tallest and largest tree in their immediate area at the onset of daylight. They rest more often in trees covered with dense vines (63%) than in trees with holes (21%) or without vines or holes (16%). Trees with vines or holes were used for several consecutive days, but those without these features were not. Common Palm Civets are also known to sleep in buildings. They rest alone, except for females with young. In Myanmar, rest sites were usually in tall trees (greater than 10 m in height) that had dense tangles of climbing plants (e.g.

lianas). In shrubby areas, rest sites are in a tangle of shrubs (sometimes surrounding a tall tree), 2–3 m above the ground. About 45% of rest sites were used once only; one site was used 55 times over a period of 294 days.

Movements, Home range and Social organization. Solitary. Mainly arboreal, but can be active on the ground. In Nepal, a radio-collared adult female had a home range of 0·12 km². In another study in Nepal, three males had home ranges of 0·17, 0·17, and 0·20 km², and two females had home ranges of 0·06 and 0·12 km². Home ranges were smaller during February and June, when the fruits of *Coffea benghalensis* and *Murraya koeniggii* were abundant, and largest in March to May, when ripe fruits were clumped or scarce. There was considerable overlap of home ranges among adjacent civets, but this changed according to food availability; more overlap was observed when ripe fruiting trees were at low density or clumped in distribution. In Thailand, the home ranges of two males were 4·2 and 17 km²: a shift in the range of the latter male occurred during the study. Mean daily movements were from 660 m to 1 km. In another study in Thailand, two males had home ranges of 1·1 and 3·4 km², and a female had a home range of 1·4 km². The mean daily movement was 0·43 km for males and 0·48 km for the female. Common Palm Civets deposit scats on the ground and on tree branches.

Breeding. Breeding seems to occur throughout the year, although young are more frequently seen between October and December. Litter size is two to five. The female often gives birth in a hollow tree. In Nepal, a female palm civet was captured in May with five young, estimated to be a week old; they were found in a den within a hollow tree. In captivity, gestation is 61 to 63 days. The eyes of neonates are closed and they weigh 69–102 g. They attain sexual maturity at 11–12 months.

Status and Conservation. CITES Appendix III (India). Classified as Least Concern on *The IUCN Red List*. *P. h. lignicolor* (Mentawai Islands, Indonesia) is classified as Vulnerable. The subspecies *kangeanus* (Kangean Islands, Indonesia) and *P. h. lignicolor* are listed as Threatened in the 1989 IUCN *Action Plan for the Conservation of Mustelids and Viverrids*. Although widespread and considered common (even in disturbed habitats), on Borneo, it was found that the overall density of civets (including this species) in a logged forest was found to be significantly lower than in a primary forest. Common Palm Civets are often considered pests by fruit farmers and are killed. They are also trapped and traded for meat. Common Palm civets are kept as pets and used as rat catchers, which may explain why they were introduced to several areas. They may be under threat on the Mentawai Islands due to forest loss from commercial logging. Field surveys and ecological studies are needed to ascertain their distribution and conservation status, particularly on small islands on which they are known to occur.

Bibliography. Abegg (2003), Austin & Tewes (1999b), Azlan (2003, 2005), Bartels (1964), Blanford (1885a, 1885b), Corbet & Hill (1992), Davis (1962), Dhungle & Edge (1985), Duckworth (1997), Goldman (1982), Grassman (1998c), Groves (1984), Heydon & Bulloh (1996), Holden (2006), Joshi, Smith & Cuthbert (1995), Krishnakumar & Balakrishnan (2003), Krishnakumar et al. (2002), Lekagul & McNeely (1991), Long & Hoang (2006), Medway (1969), Payne et al. (1985), Pocock (1915f, 1933d, 1934a, 1934b, 1934c), Rabinowitz (1991), Schreiber et al. (1989), Su & Sale (2007), Veron (1999, 2001), Wozencraft (1984, 2005).

29. Brown Palm Civet *Paradoxurus jerdoni*

French: Civette de Jerdon / **German**: Jerdon-Musang / **Spanish**: Musang indio
Other common names: Jerdon's Palm Civet

Taxonomy. *Paradoxurus jerdoni* Blanford, 1885, Tamil Nadu Province, Palni Hills, Kodaikanal, S India.
Two subspecies are recognized.
Subspecies and Distribution.
P. j. jerdoni Blanford, 1885 – SW India (Western Ghats).
P. j. caniscus Pocock, 1933 – S India (Palni Hills, Tamil Nadu).
Descriptive notes. Head–body 51–61·5 cm, tail 44–50 cm; weight 2·0–4·3 kg. The coat color is a uniform brown, but is darker on the head, neck, shoulders, legs, and tail; there are paler patches in front of the ears. The pelage can be slightly grizzled and the long tail sometimes has a white or pale yellow tip. The hairs of the neck are directed forward, a feature that also occurs in the Golden Palm Civet, but not in the Common Palm Civet. The feet have five digits. The metapodial pads are large and not well separated from the plantar pads; they cover the whole sole and the area between them is naked. On the hindfoot, the third and fourth digit pads are fused at the base. The perineal gland is simple and consists of a naked elongated area. The skull is very similar to that of the Common Palm Civet. Dental formula: I 3/3, C 1/1, P 4/4, M 2/2 = 40 teeth. The upper carnassial retains a major portion of the metastylar blade and has a large parastyle, but does not have a posterolingual cingulum.

Habitat. Evergreen forest; occasionally in coffee plantations. Reported from 500 to 1300 m.

Food and Feeding. Mainly frugivorous. In the Kalakad-Mundanthurai Tiger Reserve, 1013 scats contained 91% seeds, fruits and flowers, 11% invertebrates (insects, millipedes, centipedes, snails, and crabs), and 4% vertebrates (small mammals, birds, and reptiles). There were also small quantities of grass and beeswax. The fruits of 53 native plants and four exotic species were consumed. There was considerable variation in the diet throughout the year: the highest consumption of animal prey occurred during the dry season and was related to the low availability of fruits, but there were other peaks in prey consumption that did not correspond to lower fruit availability.

Activity patterns. Nocturnal. Radio-collared individuals were active 80% of the time

between dusk and dawn (18:00–06:00 h). All sightings were at night. Daytime rest sites were on 19 tree species (mainly *Syzygium* spp. and *Mangifera indica*), within nests of Indian Giant Squirrels (*Ratufa indica*) (40%), tree hollows (30%), vine tangles (18%), and on the forks of branches (3%). Most daybeds were not reused. Rest site trees were tall and wide, within mature forest stands (where there was good canopy contiguity).

Movements, Home range and Social organization. Appears to be solitary: out of 14 sightings, all were of single individuals, except one observation of two together on the same tree. Although they are predominantly arboreal and can be observed moving long distances through the canopy, they have been sighted, trapped and camera-trapped, on the ground. The home ranges of three adult males were 0·10, 0·33 and 0·56 km². The home range for a sub-adult male was 0·18 km², and 0·07 km² for a juvenile male. The home ranges of two adult females were 0·06 and 0·17 km². There were spatial overlaps between some home ranges (up to 33%), although on a short temporal scale (during the same month) there were very little or no overlaps.

Breeding. Females with one and two young have been seen.

Status and Conservation. CITES Appendix III. Classified as Least Concern on *The IUCN Red List*. Listed as Threatened in the 1989 IUCN *Action Plan for the Conservation of Mustelids and Viverrids*. The major threat is forest loss and degradation in the Western Ghats: Brown Palm Civets were found to be more common in medium-sized fragments adjoining coffee plantations than in more isolated smaller and larger fragments. Remaining isolated and disturbed rainforest patches on private lands should be identified and incorporated into an overall habitat conservation plan. Regular and systematic monitoring, using suitable field methods, should be implemented to ascertain population trends and distribution. More ecological studies are also needed.

Bibliography. Ashraf (1990), Ashraf et al. (1993), Blanford (1885a, 1885b, 1886), Corbet & Hill (1992), Ganesh (1997), Ganesh et al. (1998), Gupta (1997), Mudappa (2001, 2006), Mudappa et al. (2007), Pocock (1939), Rajamani et al. (2002), Ramachandran (1990), Schreiber et al. (1989), Wozencraft (1984, 2005).

30. Golden Palm Civet *Paradoxurus zeylonensis*

French: Civette de Ceylan / **German**: Goldmusang / **Spanish**: Musang dorado

Taxonomy. *Viverra zeylonensis* Pallas, 1777, Sri Lanka.
Monotypic.
Distribution. Sri Lanka.
Descriptive notes. Head–body 50·2–58 cm, tail 43·7–52·5 cm; weight 3·6 kg. A small civet with a tail as long as the body. The pelage is golden brown, rusty red or beige; there are sometimes three indistinct brown dorsal stripes. The face may be paler, and the tail more yellowish, than rest of the body. The tip of the tail is often white or yellow. The hairs on the neck are directed forward, as in the Brown Palm Civet. The feet and perineal glands are believed to be identical to those of the Common Palm Civet. Dental formula: I 3/3, C 1/1, P 4/4, M 2/2 = 40. The upper third molar is narrow and has no lingual lobe. The upper carnassial does not have a distinct parastyle and the posterolingual cingulum is absent.

Habitat. Lowland to montane forest and dense monsoon forest.

Food and Feeding. Believed to be omnivorous, feeding on fruits and possibly small vertebrates and insects.

Activity patterns. Appears to be nocturnal, based on field sightings and camera-trapping data. Said to spend the day in large hollow tree branches.

Movements, Home range and Social organization. Believed to be solitary. Arboreal but has been trapped and camera-trapped on the ground.

Breeding. Litter size is reported to be two or three. Births may occur in October and November.

Status and Conservation. Classified as Vulnerable on *The IUCN Red List*. Listed as Threatened in the 1989 IUCN *Action Plan for the Conservation of Mustelids and Viverrids*. A poorly known species, vulnerable due to its very restricted range. It has been recorded in Uda Walawe National Park, the Sinharaja Forest area, Wasgomuwa and Yala National Parks. Deforestation is a threat: lowland forests have almost totally disappeared from Sri Lanka. It is also hunted for its meat. Field surveys within National Parks and other established reserves are needed to obtain population estimates. A greater protection status for other forested areas is also needed (particularly lowland forests). Research into the species' ecological and conservation requirements are a high priority. In 2005, the National Zoological Gardens of Sri Lanka initiated a breeding and conservation programme.

Bibliography. Corbet & Hill (1992), Hoffman (1990), IUCN (2008), Jayasekara et al. (2003), Pocock (1939), Schreiber et al. (1989), Wozencraft (1984, 2005).

Subfamily HEMIGALINAE

Genus CYNOGALE

Gray, 1837

31. Otter Civet *Cynogale bennettii*

French: Civette loutre / **German**: Otterzivette / **Spanish**: Civeta pescadora

Taxonomy. *Cynogale bennettii* Gray, 1837, Sumatra.

Included here is Lowe's Otter Civet (*C. lowei*), which is only known from the type specimen, a poorly preserved juvenile skin from north Vietnam. Monotypic.

Distribution. Myanmar, Thailand, Peninsular Malaysia, Singapore, Sumatra, and Borneo. There is one skin from N Vietnam (Tonkin, the type locality of *C. lowei*) and a possible skin record in China (S Yunnan). However, there have been no further confirmed records from these two areas.

Descriptive notes. Head–body 57·5–68 cm, tail 12–20·5 cm, hindfoot 10·2–11·1 cm; weight 3–5 kg. A dark brown civet, with a short tail and a grizzled appearance (the tips of the guard hairs are gray). The underparts are a paler brown and not speckled. The chin and corners of the mouth are white, and there are whitish spots on each cheek and above the eyes. The head has a large snout, with an expanded upper lip; the facial vibrissae are very long and numerous. The rhinarium is deeply grooved on its anterior surface, with the nostrils opening upwards on top of the muzzle. The ears are small and round; both the ears and nostrils can be closed when the head is submerged. There are two pairs of teats. The feet have five digits and are webbed; they have small metapodial pads and the area surrounding these pads is naked. The perineal gland is simple, consisting of an area of naked skin and openings (a pair of small depressions in the female and a series of median pores in the male). The skull is long and low, with only a slight sagittal crest and a flat zygomatic arch; there is a very slight post-orbital process and a low ascending ramus. Dental formula: I 3/3, C 1/1, P 4/4, M 2/2 = 40. The canines are only a little longer than the premolars. The premolars are set close together and are triangular in shape, with high, pointed crowns; the molars are broad with low cusps.

Habitat. Primary lowland dry forest, swamp forest, bamboo forest, and secondary forest. It has been recorded as high as 1200 m in Borneo, but most records are from lowland forest. The majority of field observations and camera-trap records are in the vicinity of water, near streams and swampy areas.

Food and Feeding. Thought to be semi-aquatic and is said to feed on aquatic prey (small vertebrates and invertebrates).

Activity patterns. May be nocturnal: several field observations were at dusk, at night, and in the early morning, and one camera-trap in Riau Province (Indonesia) recorded an Otter Civet at 03:20 h. However, camera-trapping in the Way Kambas National Park (Sumatra) recorded Otter Civets as active at all times of the day.

Movements, Home range and Social organization. Terrestrial, but there is one camera-trap photograph showing an Otter Civet climbing a tree. Mainly solitary, but photographs of mothers with young have been recorded: of 59 camera-trap pictures in Sumatra, 53 were of single individuals, four were of two individuals, and two were of three individuals.

Breeding. Females with two and three embryos have been recorded, and camera-traps have photographed females with one and two young. In captivity, the litter size has been reported to range from two to three.

Status and Conservation. CITES Appendix II. Classified as Endangered on *The IUCN Red List*. Listed as Threatened in the 1989 IUCN *Action Plan for the Conservation of Mustelids and Viverrids*. Most museum specimens are from 1826 to 1940. There is a scarcity of recent records, especially from Peninsular Malaysia and Thailand, and little is known about current populations. As it is found primarily in lowland forest, particularly near streams and wetland areas, the loss of lowland forest within its range has probably reduced populations of this species and threatens its persistence. Riverine habitats are increasingly being polluted and disturbed. Selective logging may also be responsible for its apparent rarity: in northern Borneo, the abundance of civets was significantly lower in logged forest than in primary forest, with the most specialized civets (such as the Otter Civet), being less tolerant of logged forests than generalist civet species. Conversion of peat swamp forests to oil palm plantations is an additional threat. Field surveys and ecological studies are needed to ascertain its current distribution, to monitor populations, and to determine its tolerance to habitat disturbance.

Bibliography. Chen (1988), Corbet & Hill (1992), Davies & Payne (1982), Goldman (1982), Harrison (1974), Heydon & Bulloh (1996), Heydon & Ghaffar (1997), Lekagul & McNeely (1991), Payne *et al.* (1985), Pocock (1915g, 1933c), Schreiber *et al.* (1989), Sebastian (2005), Veron (1999), Veron *et al.* (2006), Wozencraft (1984, 2005), Yasuma (1994).

Genus *CHROTOGALE*
Thomas, 1912

32. Owston's Palm Civet *Chrotogale owstoni*
French: Civette d'Owston / **German**: Fleckenroller / **Spanish**: Hemigalo chino

Taxonomy. *Chrotogale owstoni* Thomas, 1912, Yen Bay on the Songhoi River, Vietnam. No subspecies are recognized, but there may be two distinct geographic clades. Monotypic.

Distribution. S China (Yunnan & Guangxi), Laos, and Vietnam.

Descriptive notes. Head–body 56–72 cm, tail 35–47 cm, ear 4–6 cm; weight 2·5–4·2 kg. A slender civet with a pointed muzzle and large pointed ears. The coat color var-

ies from nearly white to buff; the pelage is washed by orange in adults. The underparts are whitish, but are also orange around the belly, especially in the male. There are four large black bands across the back, which resemble long triangles (with their bases on the back and the apex towards the abdomen). This pelage pattern is similar to the Banded Palm Civet, but differs from *Hemigalus* by the presence of black spots on the sides of the neck, forelimbs, thighs, and flanks. The muzzle is long and pointed; the ears and eyes are large. The face has a narrow black stripe that runs along the midline from the nose to the nape, and two broad black stripes that start at the muzzle, encircle each eye, and pass backwards over the base of the ear to the neck. There are whitish patches under and above each eye. Two broad stripes run from the neck back to the shoulders. The terminal two-thirds of the tail is black; there are two faint black rings at the base. There are two pairs of teats. The feet have five digits; the metatarsal pad covers half the foot. The skull is long and low. Dental formula: I 3/3, C 1/1, P 4/4, M 2/2 = 40. The lower incisors are projecting and the canines are thin and curved.

Habitat. Primary deciduous and evergreen forest, bamboo forest, and degraded forest. Found from lowland to montane areas and in scrubby and humid habitats (near streams, lakes, and rivers).

Food and Feeding. Specimen stomach contents and information from captive animals suggest that earthworms are the major food item in the diet (65–100% of the total content), but it may also include small vertebrates, insects, and fruit.

Activity patterns. Observations and camera-trap photographs indicate that this species is nocturnal. Den and rest sites are said to be under large tree trunks, in dense bushes, in tree holes, amongst rocks, or in the ground.

Movements, Home range and Social organization. Terrestrial, but can climb well. Considered solitary, except during the breeding season.

Breeding. Information is known only from captive animals. The breeding season appears to be mainly from January to early March, during which both sexes increase flank rubbing, scent marking, and vocalizations. When the female comes into estrus, the male becomes excited and spends much of the time following the female and attempting to mount her. She does not accept mating immediately, but initially avoids the male mounting by moving forward or sometimes turning and snapping at him. All mating behavior happens in darkness. During copulation, the female lies flat on the ground with her body extended. The hindpart of her body rises slightly and the tail is raised up high to expose the vulva; she will often purr in this position. The male firmly places his forelegs on either side of the female's shoulders and his hindlegs on either side of the female's flanks, and begins to make thrusting movements. Copulations last for two to three minutes, after which each animal makes a low meow sound and the male dismounts. There are numerous copulations during the night (at least eight and as many as 15). Gestation is between 75 and 87 days. Litter size varies from one to three. Most births occur at night; newborn weight is around 80–135 g. The young are born blind; their eyes open between four and fifteen days. From birth, they are able to purr, mew, growl, and "chuff" (a call that is used by kittens to summon their mother and between siblings). The young are capable of walking at 10–14 days and start exploring their environment at four to six weeks. Between eight and eleven weeks, they start eating solid food, particularly worms. They are weaned at around 12–18 weeks. The young reach full size at two years and sexual maturity at around 18 months; the first breeding season may occur at 21 months.

Status and Conservation. CITES Appendix II. Classified as Vulnerable on *The IUCN Red List*. Listed as Endangered on the China Red List and as Threatened in the 1989 IUCN *Action Plan for the Conservation of Mustelids and Viverrids*. Owston's Palm Civet is threatened by habitat loss and fragmentation, and illegal hunting for food, medicines, and trophies. Due to its restricted distribution and high level of threats, this species is of conservation concern. In 1995, a captive-breeding program was established at Cuc Phuong National Park, Vietnam (the Owston's Palm Civet Conservation Program); there have been successful births since 1997, and in 2004 three breeding pairs were exported to England. Field surveys and ecological studies are needed to ascertain its current distribution, to monitor populations, and to determine its tolerance to habitat disturbance.

Bibliography. Adler (1991), Corbet & Hill (1992), Dang & Anh (1997), Dang & Evghenjeva (1990), Dang, Anh & Huynh (1992), Dang, Anh, Nhu & Chan (1991), Duckworth (1997), Heard (1999), Long & Hoang (2006), Pocock (1933c), Roberton & Muir (2005), Rozhnov *et al.* (1992), Schreiber *et al.* (1989), Streicher (2001), Tan (1989), Veron (1999), Veron & Heard (2000), Veron, Heard *et al.* (2004), Veron, Laidlaw *et al.* (2004), Wozencraft (2005).

Genus *HEMIGALUS*
Jourdan, 1837

33. Banded Palm Civet *Hemigalus derbyanus*
French: Civette de Derby / **German**: Bänderroller / **Spanish**: Hemigalo cebrado

Taxonomy. *Paradoxurus derbyanus* Gray, 1837, Peninsular Malaysia. There has been no recent taxonomic revision, but three subspecies are recognized here, including *minor* and *sipora* from the Mentawai Islands.

Subspecies and Distribution.
H. d. derbyanus Gray, 1837 – Myanmar, Thailand, Peninsular Malaysia, Sumatra, Siberut I, and Borneo.
H. d. minor G. S. Miller, 1913 – South Pagai I.
H. d. sipora Chasen & Kloss, 1928 – Sipora I.
Descriptive notes. Head–body 41–56·5 cm, tail 23·5–37·5 cm, hindfoot 7·5–8·2 cm, ear 3·6–5·5 cm; weight 1–3 kg. A small slender civet. The coat color is grayish to pale rufous brown on the upperparts; the underparts are lighter and lack markings. There are four to eight large black bands across the back, which resemble long triangles (with their bases on the back and the apex towards the abdomen). The muzzle is long and pointed; the ears and eyes are large. The rhinarium is large and deeply grooved both along the front and above (the upper edge appears biconvex). The face has a narrow black stripe on the midline from the nose to the nape, and two broad black stripes that start at the muzzle, encircle each eye, and extend over the base of the ear to the neck. There are whitish patches under and above each eye. Two broad stripes, sometimes broken into shorter stripes or spots, run back from the neck and curve downwards to the elbow. The hairs on the neck are reversed and point forward. The terminal two-thirds of the tail is black; there are two faint black rings at the base. The limbs and feet are the same color as the body; there are a few faint bands on the upper forelimbs. There are five digits on each foot, with claws that are fully retractable (but lack sheaths). The metatarsal pads are well-developed and extend to one third the length of the foot. The metacarpal pads are also well-developed; the internal one is long and narrow and touches the external metacarpal pad, which is a little longer and thicker. The space between the plantar pads and the metacarpal/metatarsal pads is naked. The perineal scent gland consists of a pair of longitudinal folds that are covered by silky hairs; between them is an oval depression, which deepens at the front. There are three pairs of teats. The skull is long and narrow, with a constricted post-orbital area and a very low crest. The zygomatic arch is relatively flat and the post-orbital processes are short and blunt. The auditory bullae have a posterior chamber that is ovoid and elongated, and which expands anteriorly. Dental formula: I 3/3, C 1/1, P 4/4, M 2/2 = 40. The first upper and lower premolars have one root and no accessory cusps. The carnassials and molars are multi-cusped.
Habitat. Primary and disturbed rainforest, particularly lowland areas. In western Sumatra, has been camera-trapped in primary lowland forest at 150 m and 800 m. Found up to 1200 m on Borneo.
Food and Feeding. Carnivorous (particularly insects and earthworms). In Thailand, specimen stomachs contained insects, and in Malaysia, the remains of crabs, molluscs, frogs, lizards, and giant rats where found in two stomachs. On Borneo, the frequency of occurrence of prey items found in twelve stomachs was: 65% insects (including Orthoptera, Coleoptera, Lepidoteran larvae, and ants), 22% earthworms, 9% other arthropods (spiders, pedipalps, centipedes, millipedes, and crabs), 2% molluscs, and 1% amphibians (toads and frogs). No fruits or other plants were found, except fragments of dead leaves and pieces of rotten wood. Based on its diet, it appears to forage mainly on the forest floor and along stream banks.
Activity patterns. Data from camera-traps and field observations indicate it is nocturnal. In captivity, is active when the enclosure is in the dark. Said to rest in hollow logs or in tree holes.
Movements, Home range and Social organization. Appears to be terrestrial: has been captured and camera-trapped on the ground, three specimens were shot along forest streams, and its diet suggests that it forages on the forest floor. However, it is also believed to be partly arboreal: it climbs well in captivity, one live animal was found in a hole in a large tree, and another was trapped 8 m above the ground. Captive animals have been observed scent marking by rubbing the perineal gland onto a solid surface; this was more common in males than females. While in a defensive, agitated, or startled state, a civet may squirt an oily spray from the perineal gland (from a standing position and with a sudden quick lift of the tail).
Breeding. A pregnant female with one foetus was recorded from Borneo in February. In captivity, litter size has been reported as one to two. One newborn female weighted 125 g and measured 25 cm. Newborns are scarcely able to crawl, their eyes are closed, and the ears are folded. The eyes open between eight and twelve days. The young start walking at around 18 days and can climb trees at four weeks. At four months, one young female weighed 1050 g and was 76 cm long. At ten weeks, the young start to eat on their own. At six months, they are adult-sized. The adult orange buff coloration on the neck and belly appears when the young civets are sexually mature.

Status and Conservation. CITES Appendix II. Classified as Vulnerable on *The IUCN Red List*. The Mentawai subspecies are listed as Threatened in the 1989 IUCN *Action Plan for the Conservation of Mustelids and Viverrids*. Habitat loss and degradation are major threats. In South-east Asia, there has been loss and degradation of forests (particularly lowland forests), through logging and conversion to other land-uses. Although the Banded Palm Civet has been recorded in disturbed forests, on Borneo, the overall density of civets (including this species) in a logged forest was found to be significantly lower than in a primary forest. Hunting and trade could also be threats. Field surveys, ecological studies, and assessments of threats are needed.

Bibliography. Corbet & Hill (1992), Davis (1962), Dinets (2003), Gangloff (1972, 1975), Goldman (1982), Heydon & Bulloh (1996), Holden (2006), Kowalczyk (1989), Lekagul & McNeely (1991), Lim (1973, 1991), Louwman (1970), Payne *et al.* (1985), Pocock (1915h, 1933c, 1939), Ratnam *et al.* (1995), Schreiber *et al.* (1989), Veron (1999), Veron, Laidlaw *et al.* (2004), Wozencraft (2005).

Genus *DIPLOGALE*
Thomas, 1912

34. Hose's Palm Civet *Diplogale hosei*
French: Civette de Hose / **German**: Schlichtroller / **Spanish**: Hemigalo de Borneo

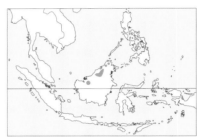

Taxonomy. *Hemigale hosei* Thomas, 1892, Mount Dulit, N. Borneo.
Monotypic.
Distribution. Borneo.
Descriptive notes. Head–body 47·2–54 cm, tail 29·8–33·5 cm, hindfoot 7·4–8·1 cm, ear 3·6 cm, weight 1·3 kg. A slender civet with a long pointed muzzle and large ears. Similar in body shape to the Banded Palm Civet, but with a dark brown or blackish coat and no stripes and bands; the underparts are white or slightly brownish-white. There are whitish patches on the side of the muzzle, above and below the eyes, and on the side of the cheeks. The whiskers are long (greater than 150 mm). The rhinarium is bilobed and the nostrils diverge and open to the side. The tail is black and the inner sides of the limbs are grayish. The feet have five digits and are partly webbed, with patches of short hair between the footpads. There is one pair of teats. The skull is quite similar to that of the Banded Palm Civet. The posterior chamber of the auditory bullae is ovoid, extends anteriorly, and partly covers the anterior chamber. Dental formula: I 3/3, C 1/1, P 4/4, M 2/2 = 40. The first upper and lower premolars are two-rooted and have accessory cusps. The second upper premolar has a small postero-internal cusp.
Habitat. Primary rainforest, montane broadleaf forest, and mature mixed-dipterocarp forest. Specimens and sighting records are from 450 m to 1700 m.
Food and Feeding. One specimen stomach was said to contain various small insects.
Activity patterns. Possibly nocturnal: one individual was seen at 22:00 h in Brunei, another individual was observed at 03:00 h on Mount Kinabalu (Sabah), and a third was camera-trapped at 22:00 h. A captive female emerged only at night and rested during the day.
Movements, Home range and Social organization. Possibly terrestrial and solitary: the few reported records are of single individuals on the ground. A captive female was trapped on the ground and was never seen climbing on the branches within her cage.
Breeding. Nothing known.
Status and Conservation. Classified as Vulnerable on *The IUCN Red List*. Listed as Threatened in the 1989 IUCN *Action Plan for the Conservation of Mustelids and Viverrids*. An almost completely unknown species with a very restricted range; there are fewer than 20 museum specimens. Hose's Palm Civet has been recorded only in a handful of scattered localities in Sabah (Mount Kinabalu National Park and Kinabatangan Wildlife Sanctuary), Brunei (Ulu Temburong National Park), and north-eastern Sarawak (Mount Dulit). In 1997, an adult female was live-trapped in Brunei (at 1500 m) and kept in captivity for about 2½ months. Field surveys, ecological studies, and assessments of any threats are needed.

Bibliography. Chapron *et al.* (2006), Corbet & Hill (1992), Dinets (2003), Francis (2002), IUCN (2008), Payne *et al.* (1985), Pocock (1933c), Schreiber *et al.* (1989), Van Rompaey & Azlan (2004), Wells *et al.* (2005), Wozencraft (2005), Yasuma (2004).

CLASS MAMMALIA
ORDER CARNIVORA
SUBORDER FELIFORMIA

Family HYAENIDAE (HYENAS)

- Medium- to large-sized mammals with round or pointed ears relatively large in comparison to body size, exceptionally powerful jaw muscles, hindquarters long and sloping; somewhat dog-like in overall appearance, very muscular.
- 85–185 cm.

- Africa and Middle East to India.
- Mainly savannas, but other semi-arid and desert regions to edges of forests, both tropical and temperate zones.
- 4 genera, 4 species, at least 5 extant taxa.
- All Lower Risk; none Extinct since 1600.

Systematics

The family Hyaenidae contains only four living species, and is therefore one of the smaller families of mammalian carnivores. Members of this family first appeared in Europe during the Early Miocene (23–16 million years ago), but soon radiated extensively, dispersing into Asia, and later also into Africa. Only one extinct hyaenid (*Chasmaporthetes*) ever inhabited North America, and no hyaenids ever occurred in South America or Australia. At the peak of hyaenid diversity in the Late Miocene (12–6 million years ago), at least 24 different species concurrently roamed Eurasia and Africa. Members of the hyena family once occupied a wide array of ecological niches. The earliest hyaenids were small and resembled modern mongooses and civets. Some of these early forms were insectivorous, others were omnivorous, and

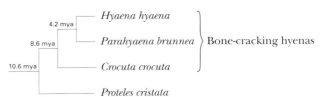

Figure 1:
Phylogeny of the extant Hyaenidæ Relationships & divergence times (mya=million years ago) from Koepfli et al. (2006).

many occupied niches like those occupied today by members of the canid family. Although most hyaenids were terrestrial, one early form apparently was arboreal. The largest hyaenid ever to walk the earth (*Pachycrocuta*) was the size of a modern lion.

Today there are only four extant species, each assigned to its own genus. These are the Brown Hyena (*Parahyaena brunnea*), the Striped Hyena (*Hyaena hyaena*), the Spotted Hyena (*Crocuta crocuta*), and the Aardwolf (*Proteles cristata*). The Aardwolf, the sole member of the subfamily Protelinae, is the only surviving representative of the once-large clade of dog-like hyenas. The other three species are assigned to the subfamily Hyaeninae, which includes all the extinct and extant bone-cracking hyenas. Bone-cracking forms appeared relatively late in the history of the hyena family, during the late Miocene.

Although extant hyenas are rather dog-like in many aspects of their appearance, the family Hyaenidae actually belongs to the Carnivore suborder Feliformia, which also contains cats, mongooses, civets, and their allies. Hyenas are thus more closely related to cats and other Feliform taxa than to Caniform carnivores such as dogs or bears. Fossil data suggest that members of the family Hyaenidae last shared a common ancestor with their closest Feliform relatives in the Oligocene, 25–29 million years ago. Recent molecular data further suggest that the sister group to the Hyaenidae is a Feliform clade containing the mongooses (family Herpestidae) and the Fossa (genus *Cryptoprocta*), a small, civet-like Malagasy carnivore.

All four extant genera of hyaenids apparently originated in Africa, their ancestors having arrived earlier from Eurasia via the Gomphothere land bridge at what is now Saudi Arabia. The genera *Hyaena*, *Parahyaena*, and *Crocuta* all first appear in the fossil record in the late Pliocene, but the Aardwolf does not appear until the Pleistocene. Although Brown Hyenas are known from the Pleistocene in East Africa they occur only in southern Africa today. After originating in Africa and finding refuge there during the glacial periods of the Pleistocene, Striped Hyenas dispersed out of Africa sometime within the last 130,000 years, and these animals today occur at low density in patches throughout much of Africa, and Asia as far east as Nepal and India.

Although every conceivable relationship among the four extant hyaenid species has been proposed, the best supported phylogenetic hypothesis is shown in Figure 1. Recent molecu-

*The **Striped Hyena** is the least studied, least known of the four species in the Hyaenidae. Each of the four is in a separate genus. They all resemble dogs, but genetic analysis places them in the suborder Feliformia, with cats (Felidae), mongooses (Herpestidæ and civets (Viverridae), rather than in the Caniformia with dog: (Canidae) and bears (Ursidae). This hyena's somewhat ragged ear might be the result of a food fight.*

Hyaena hyaena
Photo: Roland Seitre

Subdivision of the Hyaenidae

Figure: Toni Llobet

HYAENIDAE

PROTELINAE

HYAENINAE

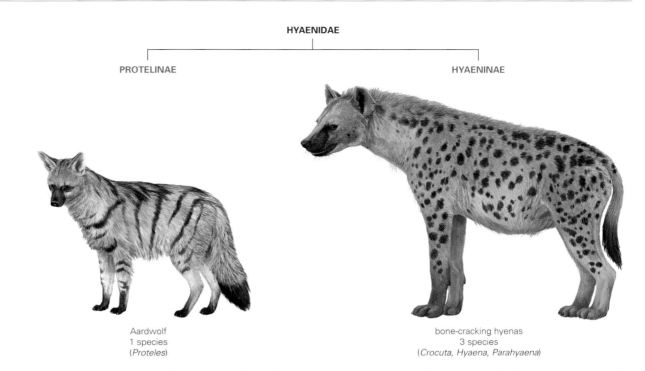

| FAMILY |
| SUBFAMILY |

Aardwolf
1 species
(*Proteles*)

bone-cracking hyenas
3 species
(*Crocuta, Hyaena, Parahyaena*)

lar data clearly indicate that, in relation to non-hyaenid carnivores, the extant hyaenids form a monophyletic clade in which *Parahyaena* and *Hyaena* are most closely related, *Crocuta* appears as the sister taxon to the lineage containing *Parahyaena* and *Hyaena*, and *Proteles* forms the most basal lineage in the group. *Proteles* apparently diverged from the clade containing the three bone-cracking forms around 10·6 million years ago. *Crocuta* and its sister taxon diverged approximately 8·6 million years ago, and *Hyaena* and *Parahyaena* last shared a common ancestor roughly 4·2 million years ago.

Morphological Aspects

Hyaenids are medium to large in size, 10–80 kg. They have bushy tails, and three of the four species have stripes or spots on their coats (the Brown Hyena is the exception). The ears are either rounded or pointed. A mane is best developed in Striped and Brown Hyenas, and least well-developed in Spotted Hyenas. The forelegs are longer than the hindlegs, so that the back slopes downwards to the base of the tail. The stance is digitigrade and the claws are short, blunt and non-retractile. The Aardwolf has five toes on each foot whereas the other hyenas have only four.

Hyaenids, both living and extinct, are distinguished by specific features of the skull: they all possess a posteriorly expanded ectotympanic bone and a reduced caudal endotympanic bone. The skulls of extant hyaenids also lack alisphenoid canals, and their auditory bullae are divided, although the septum is not easily visible. Each of these animals has a well-developed tapetum lucidum, which enables them to see well at night. Another feature common to all extant hyaenids is the presence of anal

*Hyenas make their hair stand on end for a variety of reasons, often to appear larger and fiercer before attacking or fleeing from a rival or enemy. With their very long hair, **Brown Hyenas** offer the most impressive display of this behavior. All hyenas have longer forelegs than hindlegs, and all have patterned leg fur. This is the only species lacking spots or stripes on the shoulders and back. Brown Hyenas have long, pointed ears and use their acute sense of hearing, as well as their sense of smell, when they are foraging. Males are very slightly larger than females.*

Parahyaena brunnea
Kalahari Gemsbok National Park,
South Africa.
Photo: Eliot Lyons/naturepl.com

Spotted Hyenas are easily
distinguished from other members
of the Hyaenidae family by their
large size, spotted coats, and
rounded, rather than pointed, ear.
They are also the noisiest of the
four species. Spotted Hyenas are
sometimes known as "laughing
hyenas" because one of their
vocalizations, used for submission
sounds like a human giggle.
Spotted Hyenas are the only ones
whose calls can be heard at long
distances. Their "whoops," can
often be heard during the night
in parts of rural Africa.

Crocuta crocuta
Kruger National Park, South Africa.
Photo: Greg & Yvonne Dean/
WorldWildlifeImages.com

pouches, which the animals evert to mark objects within their territories with pungent secretions called "paste". Anal pouches are generally equally well-developed in males and females. In contrast to other carnivores, male hyaenids lack a baculum.

The three species of bone-cracking hyenas are characterized by massive skulls, strong jaws, and large, robust premolar teeth used to break open bone in order to consume the marrow within. In the bone-cracking hyaenids, the high sagittal crest on the dorsal surface of the skull increases the attachment area for the powerful temporalis muscles, which permit these animals to break open large bones. The bone-cracking forms possess a complex multidimensional structure in their tooth enamel, which makes the enamel resistant to fracture, and a vaulted forehead, which functions to dissipate stresses generated by bone-cracking at the third premolar tooth. By contrast, the skull of *Proteles* is quite delicate, its teeth lack specialized enamel, and its cheekteeth are small and peg-like, although

its canines are sharp and fairly large. The incisors of hyaenids are unspecialized, except that the third incisor on each side is larger than the others. The dental formula of *Proteles* is I 3/3, C 1/1, P 3/2–1, M 1/1–2 = 28–32; that of bone-cracking hyenas is I 3/3, C 1/1, P 4/3, M 1/1 = 34. Modern bone-cracking hyenas have at most 34 teeth, fewer than the number found in most other carnivores.

The molar teeth have been greatly reduced in the bone-cracking hyaenids. Reduction of the posterior-most teeth frees space along the tooth row for enlargement of the premolars, protects the blade-like carnassial teeth from wear during bone-cracking, permits the jaw musculature to generate maximal bite force at the premolar teeth, and permits larger bones to be positioned in the mouth between the main bone-cracking teeth. All extant and many extinct bone-cracking hyaenids show severe reduction or loss of the post-carnassial molars. Among the living hyaenids, the molars are reduced in *Hyaena*,

The **Aardwolf** is by far the smalles
member of the Hyaenidae family
and the only one not famed for
its ability to crack bones. A true
insectivore, its skull is delicate an
its cheek teeth are reduced to pegs,
but it has large canine teeth it
uses for fighting and defense. The
Aardwolf is the only hyena with
five toes on each foot; the others
have four. Aardwolves live on ope
plains and in bush, but do not
inhabit forests or deserts.

Proteles cristata
South Africa.
Photo: Clem Haagner/Ardea

Adult **Spotted Hyenas** sleep on the ground rather than in dens, often snoozing in thickets that provide a little shade in hot weather. Although they have excellent night vision, they are almost as likely to be active during the day as at night. These friendly faces hide jaws of incredible strength: a Spotted Hyena can crack open the leg bone of a Giraffe or rhinoceros. Bite force is measured in units called Newtons. Cracking the long bone of a zebra or a wildebeest, something Spotted Hyenas do routinely, requires 7000–9000 Newtons. A Giraffe or rhino leg bone requires an even more powerful bite. To put the Spotted Hyena's jaw power in perspective, domestic dogs of about the same size have a maximum bite force of less than 1400 Newtons.

Crocuta crocuta
Amboseli National Reserve, Kenya.
Photo: Martin Harvey/DRK

The Giraffe will not risk drinking
while the **Spotted Hyenas** are
relaxing in the water. The zebras
are watchful, but not worried.
Clearly the hyenas are not hungry.
Spotted Hyenas often play or
simply cool off in water. They
are even known to cache extra
food in ponds. Although they
prey on zebras, in this situation,
the zebras could easily gallop to
safety if necessary. Spotted Hyenas
often hunt singly or in pairs, but
to bring down a zebra, several
hyenas usually hunt together: the
most common predator to prey
ratio is nine hyenas to one zebra.
Spotted Hyenas use a variety of
habitats, from mountain forests
to woodlands to swamps to
savannah.

Crocuta crocuta
Etosha National Park, Namibia.
Photo: Greg & Yvonne Dean/
WorldWildlifeImages.com

Spotted Hyena greetings involve
lifted hindlegs and mutual sniffing
and sometimes licking of each
others' underparts. Cubs know
and use this greeting ritual when
they are only four weeks old. Both
sexes greet clan members this way,
although an adult female does not
usually greet an adult male unless
the male enjoys high status in the
pack. Brown Hyenas and Striped
Hyenas also engage in "greeting
ceremonies," sniffing each others'
faces, necks, and especially anal
regions when they meet.

Crocuta crocuta
Masai Mara National Park, Kenya.
Photo: Günter Ziesler

Aardwolves eat as many as
300,000 termites a night. Both
predator and prey spend the day
underground, and both emerge
at night, the termites in huge
numbers, and the Aardwolf to
lick them from the ground with its
broad tongue coated with sticky
saliva. Aardwolves eat a genus of
termite, Trinervitermes, which
other mammals avoid, because
the soldier termites secrete a toxic
chemical. Young Aardwolves have
been seen vomiting after feeding.
Apparently their bodies have to
learn to tolerate this chemical.

Proteles cristata
Selinda Concession, Botswana.
Photo: Daryl Balfour/NHPA

further reduced in *Parahyaena*, and usually gone altogether in *Crocuta*. Furthermore, most bone-cracking hyaenids have their carnassial teeth oriented more strictly in a sagittal plane than do most other species of carnivores. More sagittal orientation of the carnassial teeth tends to shift the shearing component of the dentition away from the bone-cracking component and thereby reduces wear on the shearing blades needed to open carcasses. In order to crack bones efficiently with minimal risk of tooth breakage, a tooth should have a conical or pyramidal shape and a very broad base. The upper and lower third premolars are the primary bone-cracking teeth in hyaenids. Reinforcement of the enamel in these teeth is provided by a complex three-dimensional micro-structure of the enamel characterized by zig-zag bands.

Those hyaenids most highly specialized for bone-cracking have a substantially wider palate and a broader rostrum than do more generalized forms, including the Aardwolf. The specialized bone-cracking forms also have shorter skulls and high, vaulted foreheads that permit smooth transition of stresses at the top of the skull. In carnivores with straight foreheads, such as the Aardwolf, stresses generated at the upper third premolar are, instead, actually compounded at the top of the skull, potentially leading to displacement of the bones of the skull relative to each other. A vaulted forehead, together with a single, uninterrupted tract of bone along the force trajectories emanating from the bone-cracking teeth, helps dissipate the enormous compressive forces generated during bone-cracking. This mechanical adaptation permits a stronger premolar bite.

Vaulting of the forehead is produced by anterior enlargement of the frontal sinus directly dorsal and caudal to the eye orbits. Interestingly, the frontal sinus in extant bone-cracking hyaenids is also elongated posteriorly. It extends deep into the parietal bone, and lies over the entire brain case. A greatly elongated frontal sinus is also apparent in the skull of the first known bone-cracking hyena, *Adcrocuta eximia*, which is now extinct. This pneumatized skull roof is unique in the entire history of the order Carnivora. Pneumatization of the skull enhances the ability to resist bending, and together with the vaulted forehead, plays a critical role in dissipating stress smoothly and evenly away from the facial region.

There appears to be a predisposition among hyaenids to exhibit unusual traits in their genitalia. Spotted Hyenas have been of interest to humans since the time of Aristotle because the female's genitalia are very heavily "masculinized". These virilized genitalia are unique among mammals: female Spotted Hyenas have no external vagina, so urination, penile intromission, and parturition take place through the clitoris, which is fully erectile and closely resembles the penis of the male. Furthermore, the female's vaginal labia are fused and filled with connective tissue to form a structure that looks remarkably like the scrotal sac of the male. It was long assumed that early androgen exposure must be responsible for the virilized appearance of the female genitalia. However recent experiments involving intensive treatment of pregnant female hyenas with anti-androgens have shown this not to be the case. Formation of the penile clitoris of the female Spotted Hyena is, in fact, an androgen-independent event, although androgens secreted by the fetal testes are responsible for sex differences between the penis and the clitoris that are essential for successful reproduction. For example, androgens produced by the fetal testes alter the shape of the glans of the male's phallus, making it more pointed at the tip than the blunt, barrel-shaped tip of the fe-

An adult Blue Wildebeest weighs
about three times as much as an
adult **Spotted Hyena**, yet a hyena
hunting alone can bring down a
wildebeest. A young one like this
is even easier prey. Unlike felids,
which kill and then dismember
prey, hyenas rip the living animal
apart. When a large ungulate such
as a wildebeest is killed, as many
as 30 clan members arrive quickly
to feast. Although they are known
as scavengers, Spotted Hyenas are
frequent and successful predators.
Only about a third of their meals
are scavenged, at most, and up to
95% of their diet may be comprised
of prey they kill themselves.

Crocuta crocuta
Masai Mara National Park, Kenya.
Photo: Günter Ziesler

male's pseudopenis. The pointed glans in the male facilitates intromission during copulation attempts.

Striped Hyenas also have been found recently to exhibit transient genital anomalies during the first two years of life. These anomalies are characterized by a convergence in genital appearance among young males and females between one and 18 months of age. However, this convergence is entirely gone by the time the animals reach adulthood, and the appearance of the adult genitalia in Striped Hyenas is unremarkable. Nevertheless, this recent finding indicates that Spotted Hy-

enas exhibit an extreme elaboration of a preexisting trait they shared homologously with Striped Hyenas.

Habitat

Since the Late Miocene, the geographic range of the family Hyaenidae has shrunk considerably. Hyaenids now occur only in Africa and the Middle East to India and Nepal. Nevertheless, modern hyaenids occupy a vast range of habitat types including deserts, thick bush, swamps, montane forests, and open savannas. These animals are currently very important and influential inhabitants of most African and some Asian ecosystems. The Brown Hyena occurs in open woodland savanna, and bushveld in southern Africa, but also occupies extreme desert habitat along the south-western coast of Africa. Striped Hyenas inhabit arid and semi-arid desert regions, but they also occur in grasslands, open woodlands, and scrub regions, usually in rugged mountainous terrain. Aardwolves are found mainly on open grassy plains or in bush country, but they occupy most habitat types in eastern and southern Africa except forests and deserts. Spotted Hyenas occupy an extraordinarily diverse array of habitats in sub-Saharan Africa, including savanna, bushveld, desert, swamps, woodland, and montane forest up to 4000 m of elevation.

General Habits

All extant hyaenids are largely nocturnal, although crepuscular activity is common in some species, and Spotted Hyenas in many areas are often active on cool or rainy days. Members of the family Hyaenidae fill a surprisingly wide array of ecological niches, ranging from specialized insectivore (the Aardwolf) to large predator (the Spotted Hyena). The hyena family is also remarkable for its social diversity, which surpasses that of much larger families such as canids and felids. Aardwolves generally form monogamous pairs for breeding, but are otherwise solitary. Brown Hyenas live in small family groups. Spotted Hyenas live in large, complex societies that more closely resemble the societies of old-world monkeys than those of any other carnivore species. Striped Hyenas have been far less well studied than the other members of this family, so their social lives remain poorly understood. In some areas they appear to

Many mothers admonish their
children, "Chew your food; don't
wolf it down," but a better phrase
might be "Don't hyena it down."
Spotted Hyena eat as much as
possible as quickly as possible,
competing fiercely with each other
for every bite. An entire wildebeest
can disappear in 13 minutes.
Even the bones, in this case of an
infant gazelle, will be completely
consumed and digested.

Crocuta crocuta
Serengeti National Park, Tanzania.
Photo: Kevin Schafer

be largely solitary, and in other parts of their range, they are known to form small polyandrous groups containing one female and multiple males. Elsewhere these animals may even form small family groups much like those of Brown Hyenas. Spotted, Striped, and Brown Hyenas engage in "greeting ceremonies" when an individual encounters a group-mate from which it has been separated for some hours. These ceremonies involve mutual sniffing of the face, neck, and anal regions, during which the anal pouch is often protruded. During greeting ceremonies both participating hyenas may be standing or one may be lying down and exposing its anogenital region while its partner stands and sniffs this area.

Communication

Because all extant hyaenids are most active at night, they rely heavily on chemical communication. All hyaenids mark their living spaces with fecal middens, called latrines, and with deposits from their anal scent glands. Deposition of scent secre-

Spotted Hyenas *digest bones so
completely that only inorganic
components show up in their fece.
In fact, they digest every part of
an ungulate except the hooves,
hair, and keratin on the outside
of antelope horns. They eat both
freshly killed prey and carrion.
The bacteria in carrion do not see
to trouble their digestive or immu
systems.*

Crocuta crocuta
Kalahari Gemsbok National Park,
South Africa.
Photo: J & B Photographers/
Photo Access

tions on particular substrates in the animals' environments
is called "pasting". The frequency with which hyaenids paste
varies greatly within and among species. When they come into
close physical proximity with other members of their species,
all of the hyaenids also communicate directly with one another
by erecting their manes and tails, as well as through a rich repertoire of facial expressions. In many respects, the body language of hyaenids is much like that seen in canids. The size of
the vocal repertoire, as well as the importance of vocal communication in social life, varies enormously among the Hyaenidae.
Aardwolves have a very small repertoire of vocal signals and are
generally silent. By contrast, Spotted Hyenas emit a large array of distinctive sounds, and engage in a great deal of long-
distance communication. In fact, they are often referred to as
"laughing hyenas" because of their submissive vocalization that
sounds much like hysterical human giggling. Their long-distance vocalizations, called "whoops", are the most commonly
heard sounds during the night in most parts of rural Africa.
Like Aardwolves, Striped and Brown Hyenas have relatively
small vocal repertoires, and have no long-distance call.

Food and Feeding

The four extant hyena species occupy three different feeding
niches. Aardwolves are strict insectivores, Striped and Brown Hyenas feed mainly on carrion, and Spotted Hyenas are efficient
predators that feed mainly on medium and large-size antelope
they kill themselves. Food storage is practiced commonly by all
the bone-cracking hyaenid species; food items may be stored in
tall bushes, clumps of grass or marsh vegetation, under water,
or at the base of dense shrubby vegetation. Although hyenas
and Aardwolves may spend considerable time with conspecifics
each day, they are strictly solitary foragers except for Spotted
Hyenas, which may hunt alone or in large groups.

Although the Aardwolf is the only surviving member of the
once-large clade of dog-like hyenas, in contrast to its meat-
eating ancestors, it is highly specialized for feeding exclusively
on harvester termites in the genus *Trinervitermes*. The Aard-

wolf licks termites from the soil surface using its broad, sticky
tongue, and can consume hundreds of thousands of termites
in a single night. Even mated pairs of Aardwolves always forage
solitarily; only unweaned young accompany a foraging adult.

Brown Hyenas are primarily scavengers of a wide array of
vertebrate remains, including both large bones and dried flesh.
This diet is supplemented by fruits, insects, and birds' eggs, and
they also occasionally hunt small mammals like spring hare or
Springbok lambs. Their hunting behavior is unspecialized and
opportunistic, focuses exclusively on small animal targets, and
is usually unsuccessful. Like Brown Hyenas, Striped Hyenas
are primarily scavengers of a wide array of vertebrate remains,
supplemented by fruits, insects, small vertebrates, and occasionally garbage from human settlements. Striped Hyenas also
apparently hunt small vertebrates. Hunts involve opportunistic
chases and grabs at prey.

The Spotted Hyena is still widely regarded as a scavenger
that picks up leftovers at the kills of other carnivores (Cheetah, Leopard, Lion) or feeds on carrion. However, this is not
correct: all studies demonstrate that the Spotted Hyena is an
efficient predator in its own right. Although they do scavenge
opportunistically, they kill as much as 95% of the food they eat.
The Spotted Hyena is impressively versatile in its choice of prey,
as its food varies greatly among ecosystems. In addition, it has
developed a wide diversity of hunting techniques.

The bone-cracking hyenas are capable of eating and digesting all parts of their prey except hair, hooves, and the keratin
sheath on antelope horns. Bones are digested so completely
that only the inorganic components are excreted in the hyena's fecal material. The calcium content of fecal material is
13.6±5.1 mg/g stool in Spotted Hyenas and 14.3±7.6 mg/g
in Brown Hyenas. In fact, the feces of the Spotted Hyena are
usually bright white with powdered bone matrix when they dry.
The immune system of carrion-eating hyenas appears to cope
unusually well with bacteria they may ingest from this diet.

The bone-cracking hyenas can generate enormous bite
forces. Spotted Hyenas have been seen breaking open the leg
bones of giraffes, rhinoceroses, and hippopotamuses, bones
that can exceed 7 cm in diameter. A bite force in the range

These **Brown Hyenas** have found a treasure: an unguarded nest of ostrich eggs. Ostriches lay their eggs communally in a shallow pit scraped in the ground by the male. The eggs, which are huge, are incubated around the clock for up to 45 days. Brown Hyenas are able to bite the eggs open, whereas Spotted Hyenas, although they have even stronger jaws, kick the eggs until one breaks. A Brown Hyena who found an abandoned ostrich nest containing 26 eggs, ate three of them and spent four hours carefully carrying 14 eggs away from the nest. Brown Hyenas are primarily scavengers who forage alone at night, often traveling considerable distances searching for carrion. They also eat insects, fruits, eggs, and the occasional small mammal. They are opportunistic but not skilled hunters, and most of their hunts end in failure.

Parahyaena brunnea
W Namibia.
Photos: Martin Harvey/DRK

Spotted Hyenas *are remarkably versatile when it comes to their pr preferences, as their food sources vary greatly among ecosystems. They are opportunistic and able exploit a wide variety of different prey types, from caterpillars to elephants, modifying their hunti behavior to take advantage of the prey species that are most abundant or easiest to catch. Th can change seasonally in some localities, like in Lake Nakuru National Park, which provides breeding and feeding grounds for many thousands of flamingos, which are attracted to the lake's abundance of algae. As seen here, a hyena may charge into th shallow water and take advanta of the resulting chaos of the lesser flamingos taking flight to try to catch one that is not quite as fas to flee.*

Crocuta crocuta
Above: Lake Nakuru National Park,
Kenya.
Photo: Elliott Neep/FLPA

Below: Lake Nakuru National Park,
Kenya.
Photo: Tony Crocetta/NHPA

dog of roughly the same weight as an adult Spotted Hyena was 1394 Newtons.

Breeding

Aardwolves breed seasonally in southern Africa, but the time of breeding appears to be less restricted in more northern parts of their range. Breeding appears to occur throughout the year in Brown, Spotted, and Striped Hyenas, although reproduction in Striped Hyenas has never been studied in the northernmost parts of the species' range, where seasonal breeding would be most likely. Mating in all hyaenid species appears to be promiscuous, even among Aardwolves, which are socially monogamous. Brown and Striped Hyenas live in small groups, whereas Spotted Hyenas live in large groups of up to 80 individuals. Hyena social groups are referred to as "clans". Female Brown and Spotted Hyenas prefer to mate with males not born in their natal clans. All hyaenids maintain their young in underground dens or caves. The period of infant dependency is exceptionally long in the bone-cracking hyaenids, but not in the Aardwolf. This suggests that delayed wearing among the Hyaenine species allows sufficient time for development of the massive feeding apparatus required for bone-cracking.

Aardwolves live in socially monogamous pairs, but both males and females are known to mate promiscuously with individuals other than their partners. Despite this promiscuity, Aardwolf partners defend territories that contain enough termite mounds to support the pair and their juvenile offspring, and both parents participate in care of the young. Pair bonds may last 2–5 years. Litter size is 1–4 cubs. The gestation period is 90–91 days, and weaning occurs when the cubs are about four months old.

Brown Hyenas live in small clans ranging in size from a single female and her cubs to approximately 14 animals. Larger clans consist of extended families that include a female, her adult offspring of both sexes, and an immigrant male. Brown Hyenas of both sexes mate with multiple partners. Both nomadic and immigrant males may mate, and all adult females in a clan may reproduce, although the matriarch apparently produces more cubs than other female clan members. Females may nurse each other's young, but they give priority to their own offspring. Although females are responsible for most parental care, adult males and subadults are also known

of 7000–9000 Newtons is required to break open the much smaller long bones of the prey species hyenas more commonly consume, such as wildebeest and zebra. Therefore an adult Spotted Hyena is almost certainly able to apply bite forces exceeding 9000 Newtons. A 13-month old hyena in the wild was able to generate bite forces of nearly 3000 Newtons, even though this animal was not even half grown, and was still nursing. In contrast, the largest bite force measured in a domestic

The cub shown here will soon ha[ve]
a spotted coat like its mother's.
Spotted Hyenas are born with
black fur. They begin molting
at 5–6 weeks of age and have
adult coats when they are 4–5
months old. Clans raise their cub[s]
communally. The communal den
can be a noisy place, with as man[y]
as 30 offspring of different ages,
from up to 20 litters, in residence
Females use deep, groaning
vocalizations to call their cubs
out of the den and loud "whoops
to locate wandering cubs. Cubs
whoop when they want to nurse,
whine for attention, and squabb[le]
noisily with each other. Adults
do not typically bring meat to the
den to provision cubs, and males
do not help with child-rearing. I[n]
contrast, when Brown Hyena cub[s]
are about four months old, adult[s]
begin bringing food to the den, a[nd]
before they are a year old, the cub[s]
are trying to forage on their own.
Brown Hyena cubs two years of a[ge]
have been seen bringing food to t[he]
den for younger cubs.

Crocuta crocuta
Masai Mara National Park, Kenya.
Photo: Suzi Eszterhas/naturepl.com

Spotted Hyenas live in clans that can have as many as 80 members. Clans are largest where prey is plentiful and may number only about ten where it is scarce. Females spend their lives in the clan where they were born, and inherit and keep their mother's social status, whereas most males disperse after they reach puberty. This social system has the advantage of spreading genes among clans, preventing inbreeding. Immigrant males have to ingratiate themselves into a clan. They are even submissive to resident cubs. Clear hierarchies within clans determine an individual's access to food and other resources. Scientists have observed similarly complex matrilineal societies in troops of baboons, but not in other carnivores.

Crocuta crocuta
Masai Mara National Park, Kenya.
Photo: Günter Ziesler

to help provision den-dwelling cubs with carrion. All group members cooperate to defend a common territory and also aid in rearing young by bringing food to the den. The Brown Hyena is polyestrous but does not become pregnant during lactation. The gestation period is about 97 days, and mean litter size is 2·3 (range: 1–5 cubs). The cubs are weaned at 12–14 months of age.

Striped Hyenas of both sexes appear to mate with multiple partners. Both male and female parents may provision den-dwelling cubs with food, and subadults also are reported to do so in some populations. The gestation period lasts 90–91 days,

and litter size ranges from 1–4 cubs. Young Striped Hyena cubs nurse for over one year.

Female Spotted Hyenas give birth through their penis-like clitoris. During parturition, the posterior surface of the peniform clitoris tears to permit the passage of the young. Age at first parturition ranges from two to six years depending on female social rank and local food availability. All females in a clan reproduce, although high-ranking females produce cubs at shorter intervals than do low-ranking females, and the cubs of high-ranking females enjoy better survivorship. Females usually give birth in an isolated natal den, where the cubs are main-

Spotted Hyenas nurse their cubs for more than a year, and sometimes for as long as two years. Each female nurses only her own offspring. Spotted Hyena milk is rich in fat and has the highest protein content of all terrestrial carnivores. This, and the long nursing period, represents a huge energy investment on the part of the mother. Weaning is a risky process: cub mortality is highest at that time, and about half of all Spotted Hyena cubs die before puberty.

Crocuta crocuta
Amboseli National Reserve, Kenya.
Photo: Martin Harvey/DRK

247

Spotted Hyena cubs are born in
an isolated natal den and carried
to the clan's communal den when
they are 2–5 weeks old. At birth,
their eyes and ears are open, their
canine and deciduous teeth are
fully erupted, and they are so well
coordinated that if there is more
than one in the litter, they begin
squabbling with each other almost
immediately. Their wrestling
matches are more than just play:
the dominant cub controls access
to the female's milk supply. Brown
Hyena cubs are not nearly as
precocial. They are toothless at
birth and their eyes do not fully
open for about two weeks. Striped
Hyenas, too, are born with their
eyes and ears closed and can barely
crawl. Their teeth start to erupt
when they are three weeks old. At a
month of age, they are eating meat.

Crocuta crocuta
Masai Mara National Park, Kenya.
Photo: Günter Ziesler

tained for the first few weeks of life. However, all clan females subsequently bring their young together and raise them at a communal den, which may contain up to 30 cubs of different ages from up to 20 litters. Female Spotted Hyenas almost invariably nurse only their own cubs, and they reject other cubs' attempts to suckle. Cubs are seldom provisioned at dens, and when this occurs, it is performed exclusively by mothers. The average age of weaning is about 14 months. Male Spotted Hyenas do not participate in parental care. Although males occasionally remain in their natal groups to breed, most disperse after puberty, and reproductively successful males are usually immigrants. Males invest heavily in developing amicable relationships with clan females; males that have developed such relationships may be favored as mates, and thus father more cubs than other males.

Movements, Home range and Social organization

All hyaenids engage in fairly large movements while foraging, marking territorial borders, or searching for potential mates. The nightly distance traveled by foraging Aardwolves is 1·5–9·1 km, with a mean of 4·2 km. Their travel speed is 2·3 km/h when not feeding and 1 km/h when feeding intensively. Aardwolves defend territories 1·5–3·8 km² with territory size varying negatively with termite density.

Although the Brown Hyena utilizes carrion as a food resource instead of termites, it also covers large distances in its daily search for food. In the southern Kalahari, Brown Hyenas spend 80% of the hours of darkness moving around in search of food, and they cover an average of 31·1 km per night, with the maximum recorded distance traveled being 54·4 km. Although clan members forage solitarily, they join together to defend a common territory. In the Kalahari, clan territories varied in size from 170 to 480 km², and along the desert coast of Namibia, where clans contain 12 or 13 individuals, group

territories may be 220–980 km². In the Transvaal agricultural area of South Africa, the range of a translocated adult male was only 49 km², suggesting that agricultural development may sometimes be advantageous to the Brown Hyena.

Like Brown Hyenas, Striped Hyenas spend most of their waking hours traveling. In the Serengeti, the greater part of their nocturnal activity is spent searching for food or moving between established foraging sites. Striped Hyenas cover a total of 7–27 km (mean 19 km) per night, either following established animal tracks or zig-zagging cross-country. Home range sizes of one female and one male in the Serengeti were 44 km² and 72 km² respectively. Home range size for a single female in the Negev Desert in Israel was approximately 61 km². Her home range partially overlapped those of two other individuals. In Kenya, the mean home range size for 12 males was 82 km², and for eight females was 71 km², with no significant difference in home range sizes between the sexes. In the Laikipia region of Kenya, no adult females were found to have significant home range overlaps, although groups of up to three males and one female exhibited almost complete overlap in home ranges. In a different region of Kenya, home ranges of some females overlapped extensively.

Spotted Hyenas show remarkable plasticity in their use of space. In most parts of Africa, they restrict their foraging to the clan's territory, which remains constant in size throughout the year. This pattern is seen not only in prey-rich areas, but also in areas of intermediate and low prey density. The key determinant appears to be the year-round presence of suitable numbers of resident prey. Where densities of resident prey are generally low but migratory herbivores are available, Spotted Hyenas are known to adopt strikingly different foraging patterns. In the Serengeti, they commute long distances from their defended territory to migratory herds. In Etosha National Park, Namibia, they defend territories that expand and contract seasonally, as migratory herds change locations. In the Kalahari, Spotted Hyenas traveled average distances of 42 to 80 km between consecutive meals. In one population in Botswana, they regularly walked up to 28 km between the clan's territory

*Cubs and their mothers recognize each other through a combination of vocal, olfactory, and visual clues. **Spotted Hyena** clanmates use these same clues to know who belongs within the clan's territory and who should be chased to the border. Territories are marked with scent, including pungent, yellowish anal gland secretions known as "paste," which are deposited on stalks of grass. Brown Hyenas paste as well, using two different secretions, one white and one black. Spotted Hyenas are the most social of the four species of hyaenids. Brown Hyenas live in small family groups. Aardwolf adults lead somewhat solitary lives except when they come together to breed and raise their young. Striped Hyenas, about whom the least is known, are variously reported to live in small groups of one female and several males, small family groups like Brown Hyenas, or to be primarily solitary.*

Crocuta crocuta
Serengeti National Park, Tanzania.
Photo: Winfried Wisniewski/FLPA

and a permanent source of water. In the Serengeti, lactating females may travel 2880–3680 km per year as they commute between the den and distant aggregations of migratory prey.

Relationship with Humans

More myths have arisen in regard to hyaenids than to any other carnivores in Africa or Asia. They are portrayed in a negative light in Western art and literature, they are mocked and derided in films, and they are often feared and hated by people living sympatrically with them. This dark public image, born largely of ignorance, is one of the most serious obstacles to the conservation of hyaenids.

In the past, other carnivores were responsible for most hyena mortality, but this situation is rapidly changing as human populations expand and encroach on the remaining wilderness areas in Africa and Asia. The extent to which humans kill hyenas in Asia is not known. However, in many parts of Africa, humans now kill more hyenas than any natural mortality source. They do this both intentionally and unintentionally. For example, in many rural parts of Africa, small farmers put wire nooses in small openings in their corral fences. If a hyena gets caught in the snare, the tribesmen rush out and spear or club it to death.

Hyenas of all types are commonly killed on motorways. They are sometimes hit while crossing roads, but the danger is exacerbated by the fact that they often feed on roadkill, which puts them directly in the path of oncoming cars. In addition, hyenas are most likely being killed intentionally or inadvertently in war zones in Africa and Asia. We have no way to estimate the mortality to Striped Hyenas caused by explosives, etc, in war-torn parts of the Middle East, but this may be considerable. The same is likely to be true for Striped and Spotted Hyenas in areas of conflict in Somalia and Ethiopia. Hyenas are also often unintentional victims of bush-meat hunting. Members of a number of African tribes make their living by capturing herbivores in snares and selling the meat. They usually set their snares along the narrow trails that herbivores take through dense vegetation. Hyenas use these same trails, and are often captured inadvertently. Some manage to escape by biting through the wire snare. Others are killed when the hunters come by to check their traps. Some cut themselves free but die later as the snare slowly tightens and strangles them.

Sometimes hyenas are killed to obtain body parts used in aphrodisiacs and medicines. These are actually unlikely to have any medicinal value at all beyond a minor placebo effect. Young hyenas are also captured for sale as pets in Africa and especially in Asia. In fact, hyenas do not make good pets. As adults, they can be highly destructive of furniture and other objects, and their powerful teeth and jaws can do a great deal of damage to their owners. Finally, and most significantly, many people believe that hyenas, including Aardwolves, are regular livestock predators and are therefore not worthy of conservation efforts. This false impression must be corrected for there to be any public enthusiasm for protecting these fascinating creatures.

Spotted Hyenas do occasionally kill humans or livestock. Humans can be attacked while sleeping unprotected in the bush, and livestock are usually taken at night when a hyena penetrates a fenced enclosure. Because of such incidents of livestock depredation, people in some parts of Africa saturate the carcass of a goat or cow with fast-acting poison and put it out for hyenas to feed on during the night. This can result in the deaths of large numbers of hyenas, and also in the deaths of other sympatric carnivores such as cheetahs and jackals. Many ranchers keep rifles close at hand and kill any hyenas seen on their property. Sport hunting is not a major source of hyena mortality, but some are shot each year in Africa by sport-hunters.

Status and Conservation

Both Brown and Striped Hyenas are currently classed by *The IUCN Red List* as Near Threatened. Although little information is available about remaining numbers of Aardwolves, particularly in the northern parts of their range, the Aardwolf is currently listed as Least Concern. *The IUCN Red List* also currently classifies the Spotted Hyena as Least Concern. All extant hyaenids occur at low densities and have large home ranges, characteristics which tend to increase the chance of fragmentation of remaining populations into small, non-viable units.

Because Aardwolves are often overlooked, their numbers may be somewhat underestimated. However, a tentative estimate sets the total worldwide population at a minimum of several thousand individuals. Although Aardwolves are sometimes harvested for food and are purposefully or accidentally

Striped Hyenas are found across a wide geographical range, but usually in small, isolated populations. Their numbers are declining everywhere except, perhaps, in Ethiopia and Kenya. Less carrion is available: there are fewer large predators whose kills can be shared, and carcasses of domestic animals are no longer commonly left out for hyenas to find. Striped Hyenas are thought to rob graves and attack humans and livestock, and are consequently feared and persecuted. Humans also hunt them for body parts for traditional medicine. Some are killed by Lions, while others are killed by vehicles while feeding on roadkill. Like Brown Hyenas, Striped Hyenas are classified as Lower Risk: Near Threatened on The IUCN Red List, *but in most of Africa where sufficient data exist, they are believed to be threatened. There is less concern about the status of Aardwolves and Spotted Hyenas.*

Hyaena hyaena
Israel.
Photo: David Hosking/FLPA

killed in predator control programs, these mortalities appear to be of little significance in areas with well-established populations. The greatest threat to this species appears to be from insecticides. Spraying these poisons could significantly reduce Aardwolf populations, and could even lead to local extinctions, particularly when repeat sprayings occur at brief intervals.

The global population of Brown Hyenas is thought to be fewer than 10,000 individuals, with one estimate putting the total at 5000 to 8000. In South Africa the Brown Hyena is considered to be rare. A major threat is the false belief that they often threaten domestic livestock. In fact, the impact of the Brown Hyena on domestic animals is usually very small. An individual hyena occasionally becomes a livestock predator, and removal of that individual usually solves the problem. Brown Hyenas are habitual scavengers, and finding one or more of these animals eating a carcass is not proof that they killed it.

The Striped Hyena has already been extirpated in many parts of its range, and its populations are generally declining. A major reason is the decline in natural and domestic sources of carrion, which in turn is a result of declining populations of large predators (Wolves, Cheetahs, Leopards, Lions, and Tigers) and their prey, and changing livestock husbandry practices. Carcasses of domestic animals are now seldom left where hyenas can find them. Striped Hyenas are feared because of real and imagined attacks on humans, which include predation on people sleeping outside, snatching of children, and grave robbery. They are also widely hunted for body parts that are used as aphrodisiacs or other kinds of traditional medicine, and killed because of suspected or real damage inflicted on agricultural produce and livestock. They are widely poisoned and hunted using baited traps, pits, or with the help of dogs. A tentative estimate of the total worldwide population is 5000 to 14,000 individuals. The Striped Hyena is considered threatened in all parts of its African range where data are sufficient to evaluate its local status, with the exceptions of Ethiopia and Kenya.

The total world population size of the Spotted Hyena is currently well above 10,000 individuals, and several subpopulations exceed 1000 individuals. The rapid decline of populations outside conservation areas due to persecution and habitat loss makes the species increasingly dependent on the continued existence of protected areas.

Habitat loss is having a major impact on the ranges of all four extant members of the hyena family. In recent decades there has been a shocking range contraction as more and more land has become unsuitable for hyena habitation. Recent work has found that human activity also has significant negative effects on the behavior and physiology of Spotted Hyenas. In the future it might be possible to monitor these behavioral and physiological changes in hyena populations to anticipate and avoid population crashes.

Hyenas deserve protection. They are fascinating animals, and they perform valuable services in the ecosystems they inhabit. Aardwolves consume termites, which can be terribly destructive, and the three species of bone-cracking hyenas all facilitate energy transfer and cycling of nutrients between biotic and abiotic portions of their habitats.

Hyenas are also essential indicators of ecosystem health throughout much of their range. Spotted Hyenas are keystone predators in most places where they occur. A keystone predator is an animal feeding at the highest trophic level in its ecosystem, whose removal from that ecosystem results in a cascade of deleterious events, leading ultimately to habitat destruction.

Spotted Hyenas, by far the most abundant large carnivores on the African continent, appear to have the greatest behavioral plasticity of any large carnivore, and they are relatively easy to monitor because they are often active during the day. Often they can survive under conditions no other large carnivore can tolerate, so their disappearance from an ecosystem indicates that the habitat has become very severely degraded, perhaps irreversibly. Where these hyenas still occur, their behavior and physiology can be monitored to reveal indications of deleterious trends. If such trends can be identified and quantified, they can potentially be halted or reversed. This is particularly important in Africa, where loss of large carnivores would remove an important incentive for tourism. Loss of this badly-needed revenue would deprive many developing nations in sub-Saharan Africa of an essential source of foreign exchange.

General Bibliography

Buckland-Wright (1969), Buglass *et al.* (1990), IUCN (2008), Joeckel (1998), Koepfli *et al.* (2006), Kruuk (1972), Kurtén & Werdelin (1988), Mills (1990), Rensberger & Stefen (2006), Rensberger & Wang (2005), Rohland *et al.* (2005), Rosevear (1974), Skinner & Ilani (1979), Stefen (1995, 1997), Tanner *et al.* (2008), Wagner, Frank *et al.* (2007), Watts & Holekamp (2007), Werdelin (1989), Werdelin & Solounias (1991).

PLATE 16

inches ⊢————————————⊣ 15
cm ⊢————————————⊣ 38

1

2

3

4

Subfamily PROTELINAE

Genus *PROTELES*

Geoffroy Saint-Hilaire, 1824

1. Aardwolf *Proteles cristata*

French: Protèle / **German**: Erdwolf / **Spanish**: Proteles

Taxonomy. *Viverra cristata* Sparrman, 1783, Eastern Cape Province, South Africa.
Although previously placed in its own family (Protelidae), it is now considered a member of the family Hyaenidae. The Aardwolf belongs to the subfamily Protelinae, of which it is the only extant member. They occur in two distinct populations separated by about 1500 km. However, studies of the extent of genetic and morphological differences between these groups have not been conducted. Two subspecies are recognized.
Subspecies and Distribution.
P. c. cristata Sparrman, 1783 – E African coast (S Egypt, Sudan, Eritrea, Djibouti, Ethiopia,

Somalia, Kenya, NE Uganda to C Tanzania).
P. c. septentrionalis Rothschild, 1902 – most of S Africa (S Angola, S Zambia, SW Mozambique, Namibia, Botswana, Zimbabwe, Swaziland, Lesotho, and South Africa).
Descriptive notes. By far the smallest of the four hyaenid species. Head-body 55–80 cm, tail 20–30 cm, height at shoulder 45–50 cm; weight (adult) 8–12 kg with seasonal variation, and reported as high as 14 kg. No sexual size dimorphism. Superficially similar in appearance to the Striped Hyena, with dark vertical stripes on a buff, yellowish-white or rufous body, and irregular horizontal stripes on the legs. However, the Striped Hyena is more than twice as large with less regular striping. The Aardwolf's coat is about 2·5 cm long, with longer hairs along the mane and in the bushy tail. The neck is long and the throat is a pale gray-white. The legs are long and slender and the striping terminates in black at the feet. As in the Striped and Brown Hyena, the Aard-

wolf has long, pointed ears and a long erectile mane extending the length of its body. Like the other hyaenids, *Proteles* has a sloping back with the forelegs longer than the hindlegs, and a well-developed anal gland used for scent marking. Females have two pairs of teats. Uniquely among the hyaenids, *Proteles* has a number of adaptations for feeding exclusively on termites, including a long, spatulate tongue with large and varied papillae, and a large submaxillary gland which produces copious amounts of sticky saliva. Very small peg-like cheek teeth are widely spaced along the jaw margins, yet large canines have been retained for use in territorial disputes with other Aardwolves and defense against jackals. Their skulls also feature a relatively broad, nearly parallel-sided palate, and extraordinarily large tympanic bulla.

Habitat. Aardwolves are primarily found on open, grassy plains or in bush country, but can live in a range of habitats with rainfall between 100–800 mm. They are most common where rainfall is 100–600 mm. They do not occur in forests or pure desert and are independent of drinking water. The northern subspecies occurs in grasslands and tree savannas of the Somali-Masai Arid Zone and the southern subspecies in the Southern Savanna and South-west Arid Zone.

Food and Feeding. Aardwolves are solitary foragers and feed almost exclusively on *Trinervitermes* termites, usually on one species in each particular region: *T. bettionianus* in East Africa, *T. rhodesiensis* in Zimbabwe and Botswana and *T. trinervoides* in South Africa. These termites are largely avoided by other termite-eating mammals due to the noxious terpenoid chemicals secreted by the soldier termites, to which the Aardwolf is uniquely tolerant. In addition to the lack of competition, Aardwolf preference for this termite genus is likely due to the fact that these termites regularly congregate at night in large aboveground foraging parties. The termites are licked directly from the soil surface, and are easily obtainable in large quantities. Also, unlike true harvester termites, *Trinervitermes* forage throughout the year, making them a dependable year-round food source. Due to the small size of *Trinervitermes* and the wide dispersion of colonies, female Aardwolves must forage for at least six hours a night, during which up to 300,000 termites/night (1–2 kg) are consumed. Foraging Aardwolves travel approximately 1 km/h, with their ears cocked forward and head bent slightly down, following an erratic zig-zag route. Because they often approach termite colonies from downwind, and approach with directed movement before termites could be seen, it appears that termite foraging parties are detected at least partially by smell. However, the hearing of the Aardwolf is particularly acute and is assumed to play a role in colony detection. The average time spent foraging at individual termite patches was 20–28 seconds in East Africa, but in drier Namibian grassland, Aardwolves spent an average of 1·8 and 9·2 minutes at each patch in consecutive years of observation. In South Africa, a newly weaned four-month old cub spent an average of only eleven seconds at each patch, and juveniles frequently are seen vomiting after feeding on *Trinervitermes*, indicating that tolerance to the chemical secretions of *Trinervitermes* soldiers increases with age. Even adult Aardwolves maintain some aversion to the terpene chemicals, because they will avoid feeding on mounds under repair, where typically only dense concentrations of soldiers are found at the surface. Other surface-foraging termites, particularly *Hodotermes* and *Microhodotermes* (South Africa), *Odontotermes* and *Macrotermes* species (East Africa), make up a larger proportion of the diet when *Trinervitermes* are seasonally uncommon or unavailable, as during winter (May–August) in South Africa, and during the rainy season in East Africa. However, these species forage aboveground in much smaller parties (10–20 individuals vs. 4000 in *Trinervitermes*) and the reduced winter availability of *Trinervitermes* in South Africa results in a significant seasonal reduction in Aardwolf body weight and field metabolic rate. Aardwolves here were found to consume only one-sixth the number of termites in winter that they did in summer. Winter is also the highest period of mortality in Aardwolf cubs, which are 7–10 months old at this time, further indicating that this is a period of significant energetic stress. Other termites found in fecal samples have included *Odontotermes*, *Macrotermes*, and *Lepidotermes* that are not surface-foraging species and therefore not important components of the Aardwolf diet. Occasional additional food items include ants and Coleopterans, yet the Aardwolf appears to be surprisingly inefficient at foraging on non-termite insects. Due to the high degree of specialization of its tongue for licking small arthropods, and the almost complete degeneration of its cheek teeth, it is thought that they are unable to handle larger food items, making the species highly dependent on *Trinervitermes*. This dependence is supported by the absence of Aardwolves from Zambia and central and western Africa, where surface foraging *Trinervitermes* are either uncommon or available only a small part of the year. Aardwolves defecate in middens (also called latrines). The first defecation occurs when they exit the burrow in the evening and is typically very large, weighing up to 1 kg. Defecations are typically covered with soil. This practice of concentrating and burying their faeces, which retains some of the terpene smell of the soldier termites, has been suggested as a way of reducing the probability that an Aardwolf will mistake its own faeces for a termite colony when it is foraging. Up to 20 middens may be located in a territory.

Activity patterns. Predominantly nocturnal, in South Africa Aardwolves are generally active for 8–9 hours a day in summer but only 3–4 hours a day in winter. In summer, they generally leave the den within an hour after sunset and return 1–4 hours before sunrise. However, during winter, some diurnal activity may be observed. Aardwolves typically become active up to an hour before sunset and return to their dens after 3–4 hours of foraging. A higher proportion of their time is spent feeding in winter than in summer, and a relatively large portion of the activity of both males and females in winter (12·6%) consists of breeding activities (e.g. courtship/copulation). Inactive hours during the day are spent in underground dens, which provide refuge from temperature extremes and predators, particularly Black-backed Jackals. Dens also function importantly in cub-rearing. Nighttime rest periods are also often spent near or inside dens. A territory may include up to ten different den holes, which are typically spring hare burrows that have been enlarged by Aardwolves.

Movements, Home range and Social organization. A social unit, which occupies a well-defined territory throughout the year, consists of a male-female pair and their most recent offspring. All natal animals disperse from the territory, usually 1–2 months before birth of the next litter. Pair bonds are fairly stable lasting 2–5 years. Males without mates (due to death or abandonment by females) establish pair bonds with adjacent females and may abandon their original territories. Territory size ranges from 1·5 km^2 in East Africa to 3·8 km^2 in South Africa, and appears to be negatively related to the density of available termite mounds. Territories in the Northern Cape Province of South Africa generally supported 3000 termite mounds with an average of 55,000 termites/mound. Aardwolf density reaches 1 adult/km^2 in optimal habitat. Territories are maintained primarily by scent marking, which is concentrated along territory boundaries, but direct interactions between neighboring residents also occasionally occur. Both males and females actively defend territorial boundaries. Chasing and fighting, with manes raised, occurs between same-sex individuals defending territories. Intruders encountered within the territory are usually chased to the boundary and mutual avoidance is generally practiced along boundary areas. If physical contact occurs both combatants drop to their carpals and bite at each others' necks. Although territorial behavior is exhibited by males and females, it differs between mating (June and July in South Africa) and non-mating seasons. Direct fights between Aardwolves appear restricted to the mating season. Whereas females tend to stay within territory boundaries year round, male behavior undergoes a marked change at the start of the mating season. After an approximately one-month "scouting" period at the beginning of the mating season, when males make frequent extra-territorial movements, yet largely refrain from pasting outside the territory, they begin more aggressive extra-territorial pasting. Their movements outside the territory continue to increase, peaking in frequency about a week before females come into estrus. These excursions are suggested to be advertizements of quality to both males and females in surrounding territories. Males engage in consecutive over-markings by pasting on particular grass stalks; the less aggressive, and apparently less fit, individual will eventually cease pasting, thus "losing" the contest. During pre-estrus females also increase their rate of pasting, primarily along territory boundaries and just outside them, apparently to encourage visits by extra-pair males. Visiting males during this period frequently "flirt" with resident females and chase or fight males that they encounter. "Flirting" typically involves the male running toward the female, then veering off and prancing past with his tail raised. However, by the time the female is in estrus (lasting 1–3 days) she is typically left with only her resident male, and potentially an aggressive neighbor. As in Striped Hyenas, there have been cases in which two male Aardwolves shared a territory with a female, both males mating with her and both guarding her cubs, but this appears to be exceptional and rare. Aardwolves are remarkably antisocial outside the breeding season. Members of resident mixed-sex pairs feed alone and typically ignore each other when they meet. Unlike the other three hyaenids, Aardwolves usually do not engage in greeting ceremonies between familiar individuals, with the exception of an occasional muzzle to muzzle sniff between mother and cub. In South Africa, nightly distance traveled by foraging females ranged from 1·5 to 9·1 km (average 4·2 km). Summer travel distances ranged from 8–12 km per night, whereas winter distances were highly variable (from less than 3 km to more than 24 km) depending on whether males were conducting extra-territorial mating forays. Travel speed is 2·3 km/h when not feeding, and about 1 km/h when feeding intensely. Aardwolves return to underground burrows during the day. There are typically 5–6 dens per territory. Dens are used for only 1–2 months at a time, and mates rarely use the same dens concurrently. Because Aardwolves rarely interact, the primary form of communication is olfactory. Like the other three hyaenids, the Aardwolf engages in scent marking behavior called pasting, during which a strong-smelling, yellowish-orange secretion (which quickly turns black) is deposited onto grass stalks from an extruded anal gland, located just above the anus. In addition to marking frequently at dens and latrines, which generally are not associated with territory boundaries, Aardwolves appear to use pasting as a means of territory defense. Boundary marking occurs most frequently, and is most concentrated along borders where neighboring Aardwolves maintain territories. Pasting is generally frequent, occurring about twice every 100 m of travel, and about 200 times per night, with males pasting more than females. Based on experiments with translocated scent marks, information conveyed in scent marks appears to include the sex, female reproductive state, and individual identity, at least in the case of resident neighbors, partners, and self-recognition. Outside the mating season, pasting outside territory boundaries is rare if not nonexistent, but this behavior, particularly by males, changes notably during mating periods. Even though direct interactions are rare, Aardwolves possess an impressive visual display, during which the hairs along the mane are erected, resulting in a near doubling of the apparent size of the animal. This is used in intraspecific aggressive interactions involving territory defense and in interspecific defensive interactions. Although generally a silent species, the most comprehensive analysis of the vocal repertoire of *Proteles* identified nine distinct sound types: "purr", whine, jaw click, lip smack, growl, snarl, bark, squeal, and a whizzing sound which was only documented in one individual. Agonistic vocalizations are relatively diverse and increase in intensity in the following order: lip smack/jaw click, growl, snarl, bark. Squeals are heard only in cubs and appear to represent begging to mothers. The whine elicits a variety of reactions depending on the addressee and addressor, but likely functions as an appeasing

On following pages: 2. Spotted Hyena (*Crocuta crocuta*); 3. Striped Hyena (*Hyaena hyaena*); 4. Brown Hyena (*Parahyaena brunnea*).

or reassuring sound. As in striped and brown hyenas, Aardwolves lack a loud, long-distance vocalization like the whoop of spotted hyenas.

Breeding. Monogamous, yet during the mating season extra-pair copulations can be common (40% in South Africa). Strictly seasonal breeding in the Northern Cape where most mating occurs during the first two weeks of July. Females give birth every year in early October to 1–4 cubs (average of 2·5), after a 90-day gestation period. In more northern parts of the range, breeding seasons appear to be less restricted. Estrus lasts 1–3 days but females may cycle again within two weeks if fertilization does not occur. Copulation lasts from 1–4·5 hours during which multiple ejaculations occur. Copulations may be interrupted by extra-pair males and in some cases females copulate with these new males. Cubs are born in a den and rarely emerge above ground during the first month. By three months, cubs have begun making short excursions from the den, usually accompanied by an adult. Weaning occurs around four months, and by this time cubs begin foraging alone within the territory. After weaning, cubs spend little time with their parents, are independent by about seven months, and are excluded from the territory soon after, usually by one year of age. Cubs grow quickly, reaching adult body mass by 3·6 months. This is likely an adaptation to maximize survival of cubs through their first winter, when cub mortality is highest. Sexual maturity is reached by 1·8 years. Each resident breeding male guards the female's cubs during the period of den dependence. This is energetically costly as it typically leaves the males only 2–3 hours of foraging time before sunrise, compared to at least six hours for females. Due to the frequency of extra-pair copulations, cuckoldry appears to be an established aspect of the mating system ("overt cuckoldry"), and males are likely to frequently help raise litters of mixed paternity or sired entirely by other males. Currently this appears to be unique among mammals.

Status and Conservation. Listed as a species of Least Concern on *The IUCN Red List*. Due to their shy and nocturnal nature, Aardwolves are probably more common than usually believed. That notwithstanding, Aardwolves in southern Africa generally occur outside of protected areas, and the primary threat in these locations is indirect poisoning aimed at locust outbreaks. Poisoning events can result in the death of up to half the local adult population and all the cubs. Within protected areas, the most important mortality sources are severe drought and predation on cubs by Black-backed Jackals. Human-caused mortality also occurs as a result of direct persecution from farmers suspecting Aardwolf involvement in lamb predation, harvesting of Aardwolves as a food source, and indirect persecution during organized hunting for jackals. Aardwolves may also be killed by vehicles during the night. However, all these other mortality sources appear insignificant relative to poisoning, jackal predation and drought. Across its range, habitat fragmentation and isolation may be the most serious threat to long-term population viability; however, its dependence on habitat preferred for use in livestock grazing makes extensive habitat loss improbable.

Bibliography. Anderson, M.D. & Richardson (2005), Anderson, M.D. *et al.* (1992), Cooper & Skinner (1979), Kingdon (1971-1982), Koehler & Richardson (1990), Koepfli *et al.* (2006), Kruuk & Sands (1972), Mills & Hofer (1998), Peters & Sliwa (1997), Richardson (1985, 1987a, 1987b, 1987c, 1990, 1991), Richardson & Bearder (1984), Richardson & Levitan (1994), Skinner & Van Aarde (1986), Sliwa & Richardson (1998), Smithers (1983), Sparrman (1783), Van Jaarsveld (1993), Van Jaarsveld *et al.* (1995), Werdelin & Solounias (1991), Williams *et al.* (1997).

Subfamily HYAENINAE
Genus *CROCUTA*
Kaup, 1828

2. Spotted Hyena   *Crocuta crocuta*
French: Hyène tachetée / **German**: Tüpfelhyäne / **Spanish**: Hiena manchada

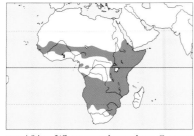

Taxonomy. *Canis crocuta* Erxleben, 1777, Guinea, Aethiopia; restricted to "Senegambia".
The earliest members of the genus *Crocuta* first appear in the fossil record of Africa in the early Pliocene, dated at roughly 3·7 million years ago. However, members of this genus soon dispersed out of Africa, and based on fossils from the period of its greatest range expansion in the Pleistocene, the genus *Crocuta* occupied virtually all of Europe and Asia, as well as most of sub-Saharan Africa. When exactly modern *C. crocuta* arose is not entirely certain, but this species is clearly very recent. *C. crocuta* does not appear in the fossil record until sometime after 990,000 years ago, and probably substantially closer to the present, perhaps within the last 250,000 years. Modern Spotted Hyenas can be distinguished from members of the genus *Crocuta* found in the fossil record based on body size, limb length and stoutness, the length and shape of particular skull bones, and unique characteristics of the cheek teeth. In contrast to earlier members of the genus, including the Cave Hyenas of Europe and Asia (*C. spelaea*), modern Spotted Hyenas have a post-cranial skeleton that is modified for cursorial hunting. Currently only one subspecies is recognized despite substantial variation in coloration and body mass throughout sub-Saharan Africa. For example, individuals from southern Africa are larger than those from eastern Africa. Monotypic.

Distribution. Most of Africa S of the Sahara Desert, except in lowland tropical rainforests. Spotted Hyenas have been extirpated from many areas of southern Africa.

Descriptive notes. Largest of the four hyaenid species. Head-body 125–160 cm, tail 22–27 cm, height at shoulder 77·3–80·7 cm; weight 45–55 kg and up to 86 kg. Females approximately 10% larger than males, although size distributions for males and females overlap. Degree of sexual dimorphism in body size varies geographically, being most pronounced in southern Africa. Its general color is sandy, ginger, or dull gray to reddish-brown, with black or dark brown spots on the back, flanks, rump, and legs. Spots may turn brown and fade with age. The fur is shorter in this species than in the other extant hyaenids. The head is large, rounded and powerful, with a short and blunt muzzle. In contrast to the other extant hyaenids, all of which have pointed ears, Spotted Hyenas have ears with rounded tops. The tail ends in a black, bushy tip, with approximately 12 cm of hair extending beyond the end of the tail bone. Like the other hyaenids, the Spotted Hyena has a sloping back because the forelegs are longer than the hindlegs, and a well-developed anal gland used for scent marking. The mane in this species is more poorly developed than in other hyaenids. The feet have four toes. Females usually have only two teats. The Spotted Hyena has long been considered a hermaphrodite in many parts of Africa because the external genitalia of the female are very similar to those of the male. The female has a peniform clitoris that is only a few mm shorter than the male's penis, and is fully erectile. The sexes can be distinguished by the shape of the penile glans: the male glans is pointed whereas that of the female is blunt. A single urogenital canal traverses the enlarged clitoris; through this canal the female urinates, copulates and gives birth. There is no external vaginal opening as the outer labiae are fused to form a structure that resembles the scrotal sac of the male. The female's pseudo-scrotum has a bi-lobed appearance; the testes of the adult male make the scrotal sac larger and give it more distinctly rounded bulges. Thus scientists who study these animals can distinguish males from females even when the animals are lying down.

Habitat. Spotted Hyenas occupy an extraordinarily diverse array of habitats, including savanna, semi-desert, swamps, woodland, and montane forest up to 4000 m of elevation, but are absent in lowland tropical rainforests, in alpine areas at high elevation, and in extreme desert conditions. Although they require water for drinking, they are able to make do with very little water, and seldom require access to it. Even lactating females can survive without water for over one week. The highest population densities reported for this species occur on the prey-rich plains of Kenya and Tanzania, and surprisingly, in the forests of the Aberdare Mountains in Kenya. In these areas, densities of Spotted Hyenas exceed one animal per square kilometer.

Food and Feeding. The foraging behavior of Spotted Hyenas is remarkably flexible. Long believed to feed mainly on carrion, these animals are in fact efficient predators that kill 60% to 95% of their prey themselves. On average across populations in which the relative proportions of hunted and scavenged foods have been documented, two-thirds of their diet is derived from kills they make themselves, and only one third from scavenged food items. In addition to being able to obtain food either by hunting or scavenging, Spotted Hyenas exhibit extraordinary plasticity with respect to their prey preferences. Spotted Hyenas have catholic tastes, they are extreme opportunists, and they are able to exploit a vast array of potential prey types, ranging from caterpillars to elephants; they may also occasionally consume some plant material. However, in most parts of Africa, Spotted Hyenas derive the large majority of their food intake from only a small subset of the prey species available to them locally. In most environments, they focus on the local medium- and large-sized ungulates, capture of which yields the greatest caloric return while demanding the least effort and the fewest risks. Thus, in eastern Africa, Spotted Hyenas prey most frequently on Blue Wildebeest, zebra, gazelles and Topi. In the arid parts of southern Africa, they prey most frequently on Gemsbok. In Kruger National Park, their most common prey is Impala, and in western Africa, common prey includes Red-fronted Gazelles and Hartebeest. Foraging behavior varies with the prey currently sought. Spotted Hyenas search for gazelle fawns by wandering upwind through open grassland in a zig-zag pattern. They may dig for crocodile eggs along large rivers, and snap flying termites out of the air with their jaws. When hunting, Spotted Hyenas modify their behavior to take advantage of the most abundant prey species, or the species that is easiest to catch; these change seasonally in some localities with the migratory movements of particular ungulate species. Instead of using felid-like stealth as a primary hunting tactic, Spotted Hyenas rely on their extraordinary endurance for success in hunting. They can run at speeds of up to 55 km/h, but at slightly lower speeds, they can maintain a chase for several kilometres. If the antelope being chased becomes winded, and turns to defend itself with its horns, the Hyenas rush in and start tearing off pieces of the prey animal's flesh. Like canids, Spotted Hyenas kill their prey by disembowelling and dismembering them rather than by using a particular killing bite. Spotted Hyenas may hunt either solitarily or in groups; in the latter case group size varies with the type of prey sought. Mean hunting group sizes among Hyenas in Kenya are 1·2 for Topi, 1·7 for Impala, 2·08 for Thompson's Gazelle, 2·92 for Blue Wildebeest, and 9·1 for zebra. Thus only zebra hunts involve large groups of hunters, and most hunting parties contain only one or two Hyenas. Ungulates such as Topi and Blue Wildebeest weigh roughly three times as much as an adult Hyena, but solitary Hyenas routinely kill these antelope. Although hunting group size is often surprisingly small among Spotted Hyenas, the feeding groups formed by these animals are often very large once a prey animal has been killed. The noise produced by feeding Hyenas often draws members of the clan that were not involved in the hunt to the kill site. Feeding competition among the Hyenas present at a kill is usually very intense. In East Africa, often more than 30 Hyenas can be observed trying to feed from a single carcass. Because of this intense competition, each individual Hyena consumes as much food as possible in a very short period of time. A group of 20–30 hungry Hyenas can reduce an adult Blue Wildebeest to nothing more than a pile of rumen contents in only 13 minutes. It is estimated that an adult Spotted Hyena can consume a mass of food equal to 25%–30% of its body weight, and individual Hyenas have been observed to ingest up to 18 kg of meat and bone in one hour. However, as a result of limited access to carcasses, average food intake ranges only from 1·5 to 3·8 kg per day. Spotted Hyenas sometimes engage in kleptoparasitism, which is the aggressive acquisition of a fresh carcass from other predators. They have been observed displacing jackals, Striped Hyenas, Leopards, Cheetahs, and African Wild Dogs from kills. However Spotted Hyenas most frequently compete for kills with Lions. Spotted Hyenas and Lions occur sympatrically in many areas of Africa, and in most of these habitats, bi-directional food stealing has been observed between these two species. Dominance relations between Spotted Hyenas and competing species are not absolute but depend on the numerical presence of both parties. For instance, Lions usually displace Spotted Hyenas at kills. However, if Hyena group size is large and the ratio of Spotted Hyenas to female and subadult Lions exceeds four to one, Hyenas are often able to displace Lions from kills unless a male Lion is present. A single Spotted Hyena can usually dominate a Cheetah, Leopard, Striped Hyena, Brown Hyena, any species of jackal, or an African Wild Dog. Spotted Hyenas have been observed caching surplus food in thickets and under water in ponds. These animals are very comfortable in water; they often play in seasonal pools, and lie in shallow water or wet mud to keep cool on hot days. Compared to the other bone-cracking hyenas, Spotted Hyenas rarely carry food to their young at dens. This appears to be because the risk of having one's food stolen, even by much smaller hyenas, is very high at dens, particularly for low-ranking individuals.

Activity patterns. Spotted Hyenas are predominantly nocturnal and crepuscular, although they may be active at midday when temperatures permit. Dens are typically modified holes dug by Aardvarks, although caves are used as den sites in some areas. Only cubs live in dens; adults sleep above ground, often in thickets, particularly when midday temperatures are high. Although Spotted Hyenas are active for roughly one third of each 24-hour cycle, their activity is not continuous. Instead, activity occurs in bouts interspersed with periods of rest. Hyenas in Kenya that were followed for complete 24-hour cycles spent 32% of their time active, but 53% of their active time occurred during hours of darkness.

Movements, Home range and Social organization. On average, Spotted Hyenas in Kenya move 928 m per hour when active, and typically travel over 12 km during each 24-hour period, with males moving more than females. In Serengeti, daily movements may be much greater than this, as resident hyenas often commute 30–40 km in order to feed on migratory herbivores. Spotted Hyenas live in social groups, called clans, which contain from ten to eighty members. Large clans contain multiple matrilines of related females and their offspring, as well as a number of adult immigrant males that are generally unrelated to one another. Small clans may contain only a single matriline and a single breeding male. Clan size appears to be determined by abundance of local prey animals; where these are plentiful, as on the prey-rich plains of eastern Africa, clans are typically very large, but in desert areas of southern Africa, clans may be tiny. Clans are fission-fusion societies. That is, all clan members know each other individually, occupy a common territory, and rear their cubs together at a communal den, yet they also spend much of their time alone or in small sub-groups. Spotted Hyena clans bear little resemblance to canid packs or Lion prides, but they are remarkably similar in their size, structure, and complexity to the societies of cercopithecine primates. Like troops of baboons and macaques, Hyena clans typically contain individuals from multiple overlapping generations, and clans are structured by clear linear dominance hierarchies in which an individual's rank determines its priority of access to food and other resources. In contrast to the situation characteristic of other hyaenids and most other mammals, female Spotted Hyenas are socially dominant to all adult immigrant males. Rank relationships among female clan-mates are usually stable for periods of many years. Average relatedness among females from different matrilines within a clan is extremely low. Like most primates, Spotted Hyenas produce tiny litters at long intervals, and their offspring require an unusually long period of nutritional dependence on the mother. Young Hyenas typically nurse for well over a year, and because it takes them years to become proficient at hunting and feeding, their mothers continue to help them gain access to food at ungulate kills long after weaning. Similar to female baboons, the social status of a female Hyena is determined not by her size or fighting ability, but by her mother's social rank. Indeed, the acquisition of social rank during early development occurs in a pattern identical to that seen in many monkey species, a pattern called "maternal rank inheritance" by primatologists even though no literal inheritance occurs involving genetic transfer of status from mother to offspring. Instead, in both Hyenas and baboons, maternal rank "inheritance" involves a great deal of important social learning that occurs during a protracted juvenile period. Young Hyenas initially direct their aggressive behaviors equally at higher- and lower-ranking individuals. But this changes rapidly during the first year of life as cubs learn to direct aggression only at animals lower in rank than their own mother. When youngsters become involved in disputes with group-mates, the mother intervenes on their behalf against all individuals lower-ranking than herself. Interventions by high-ranking mothers are more frequent and more effective than those by low-ranking females. In addition, like young baboons, Hyena cubs are often joined in fights by coalition partners who may be either kin or unrelated animals. Along with maternal interventions, coalition formation functions importantly in rank acquisition. Thus the mechanisms by which youngsters acquire their social ranks are virtually identical in Hyenas and old-world monkeys. Patterns of competition and cooperation among Spotted Hyenas are also remarkably like those found in baboons. Although Hyenas compete intensively for food, they also rely heavily on cooperative interactions with group-mates, particularly their close kin, to acquire and defend both their social rank and such key resources as food and territory. Young Spotted Hyenas of both sexes "inherit" the social rank of their mother early in life, and retain their maternal rank as long as they remain in the natal clan. However, whereas females remain in their natal group throughout their lives, virtually all males disperse after puberty to join a new clan. When a male immigrates into a new group, he enters as the lowest-ranking Hyena in the dominance hierarchy; he

behaves submissively to all Hyenas he encounters in the new territory, regardless of their size, fighting ability, or social rank. This results in a society in which adult females and their cubs are dominant to all adult male immigrants. A male Hyena loses his maternal social rank and its associated feeding privileges when he disperses. In their new clans, immigrant males sometimes invest a great deal of time and energy in developing amicable relationships with resident adult females, as males engaging in these amicable relationships may enjoy a high probability of siring cubs. Due to the female's male-like genitalia, coercive sex is impossible, so female choice of mates is an important sexually selected force in this species. Mate choice by female Spotted Hyenas apparently drives males to disperse: females strongly prefer to mate with immigrants, and they appear to discriminate against adult natal males. Therefore, almost all offspring are sired by immigrant males. Immigrants queue for status within the male hierarchy of the new clan; the highest-ranking males are those that immigrated first into the clan. Males rise in rank only when higher-ranking immigrants die or engage in secondary dispersal; roughly 40% of immigrants disperse again, although the potential benefits of secondary dispersal are unknown. Clan members defend group territories from neighboring Hyena groups. Territory size ranges from roughly 20 km² in East Africa to approximately 1500 km² in the desert regions of southern Africa, and is negatively related to the density of available prey. Territorial behavior is exhibited by both sexes, although females engage in these activities more frequently than males. Intruders encountered within the territory are usually chased to the territory boundary. Border clashes with neighboring clans, called "clan wars", are most commonly observed in habitats containing high densities of Hyenas, where intrusion pressure is most intense. Territorial behavior is rarely observed among Spotted Hyenas inhabiting the vast desert regions of southern Africa, where prey are sparse, clan size is small, intrusion pressure is low, and the home ranges of resident hyenas are enormous. In some parts of Africa, where densities of resident prey may be low but where migratory herbivores are available as prey, Spotted Hyenas are known to adopt patterns of space-use that differ strikingly from those seen in areas with year-round resident prey. Specifically, Spotted Hyenas may frequently commute long distances from their defended territory to herds of migratory prey. In the unusual "commuting system" exhibited by Spotted Hyenas in the Serengeti, individuals travel long distances north or south from their centrally-located clan territories in order to feed on migratory herbivores. Intruders are tolerated by territory residents when the intruders are merely passing through, although residents behave aggressively toward intruders found hunting or feeding. In Namibia, Spotted Hyenas defend territories that expand and contract in size seasonally, as migratory prey change locations. Territory boundaries are visited sporadically by multiple clan members performing border patrols, during which boundaries are marked by pasting. A strong-smelling, yellowish buttery secretion is deposited from the anal glands onto grass stalks during border patrols. Spotted Hyenas also commonly paste deep inside their territories, although the frequency with which this occurs is generally far less than in the other hyaenid species. The paste transmits information about an individual's identity, sex, reproductive state, and clan membership. Young Hyenas engage in pasting behavior long before there is any paste in their anal sacs, suggesting that this behavior enables cubs to acquire group odors from sites where clan-mates had pasted earlier. Spotted Hyenas engage in ritualized greeting ceremonies in which two individuals stand parallel and face in opposite directions. Both individuals usually lift the hindleg nearest to the other and sniff or lick the anogenital region of the other. The unique aspect of their greetings is the prominent role of the erect "penis" in animals of both sexes. This is used to signal submission. Greetings occur between hyenas of all ages and both sexes, although greetings between adult females and adult males are uncommon and restricted to high-ranking males. Cubs can erect their penis or clitoris and engage in greeting ceremonies as early as four weeks after birth. Spotted Hyenas recognize their group mates based on visual cues, odors, and individually distinctive vocalizations. These animals are well known for their rich vocal repertoire. They emit deep groans to call their cubs out of dens, high-pitched whines to beg for food or milk, and cattle-like lowing sounds to bring group-mates to a common state of high arousal. The sound most frequently heard during the night throughout much of sub-Saharan Africa is the long-distance vocalization of the Spotted Hyena, called a whoop. This loud call can be heard over several kilometers. Whoops clearly serve a variety of functions. They can be rallying calls to gather scattered clan members together to defend territory boundaries, food resources, the communal den, or clan-mates in danger. Mothers whoop to locate their wandering cubs, and hungry cubs whoop to call their mothers so they can nurse. Spotted Hyenas sometimes whoop to recruit hunting partners. Whoops are also used as a form of individual display, particularly by males of high rank. Adult males whoop more frequently than females, and high-ranking males whoop more often than lower ranking males. Finally, Spotted Hyenas are well known for their laugh or giggle, which sounds much like maniacal human laughter. This vocalization is a signal of submission. A submissive individual giggles to signal to another Hyena that it accepts a lower status.

Breeding. Females bear young throughout the year in most parts of Africa, although there are distinct birth peaks and troughs in some populations. Both sexes mate promiscuously with multiple partners. Courtship by male Spotted Hyenas is unusual among mammals because it appears to reflect such extreme conflicting desires to approach the female and also to flee from her. Males often engage in approach-avoid and bowing displays, both of which appear to reflect strong motivational conflict and hesitancy on the part of the male. Their behavior suggests that interactions with females may be unusually risky for males in this species, and that males fear females. In general, the female seems to take little notice of the male hyena's sexual advances. Estrus lasts 1–3 days, but the length of the female's cycle, and whether ovulation is spontaneous or induced, are not known. Copulation involves multiple mounts, intromissions, and ejaculations. Female receptivity is indicated by inhibited aggression toward the male and by assumption of a distinctive receptive stance in which the female lowers her head and keeps her mouth near the ground. The only behavior indicative of a female's interest in mating is that she may follow a male. Some males who sire cubs form consortships with females, but others do not, suggesting that individual male Hyenas may adopt multiple alternative reproductive tactics to attract and acquire mates. That is, male Hyenas may sometimes "shadow" or "guard" their mates, but intensive mate-guarding is not required to ensure that a male will sire the cubs of a particular female. Females have been observed mating with one to four males within a single estrous period, and multiple paternity has been documented to occur in 25–30% of twin litters. Many copulations among *Crocuta* appear to be infertile. Female Spotted Hyenas are exposed to high concentrations of androgens *in utero*, and this early androgen exposure may have negative effects on female fertility by altering ovarian histology or other mechanisms. It has recently been determined that early androgen exposure is not necessary for formation of the female's peniform clitoris. Females give birth through their penis-like clitoris. During parturition, the clitoris tears to permit the passage of the young, creating a large bleeding wound on the posterior surface that may take weeks to heal. Females usually produce litters of two, although singletons are also common, and triplets are observed occasionally. Cubs weigh roughly 1 kg at birth. They are born with their eyes open, their deciduous canine and incisor teeth fully erupted, and they are capable of remarkably coordinated movement immediately after birth. They are thus relatively precocial compared to cubs in other hyaenid species or in most other carnivores. Their coats are pure black at birth; cubs start to molt at 5–6 weeks of age, and the natal coat is completely replaced by an adult-colored, spotted pelage by 4–5 months of age. The spots never change except to fade a bit with age. Cubs are usually born in an isolated natal den and are transferred to the clan's communal den when they are 2–5 weeks old. They remain at the communal den until they are 8–12 months old, and then begin traveling around the clan's territory, initially with their mothers and later alone. As in the other bone-cracking hyenas, weaning occurs surprisingly late, usually around 13–14 months of age, but twin litters borne by low-ranking females may be nursed as long as two years. Fifty percent of cubs die before puberty, and mortality rates are generally highest immediately after weaning. Males reach reproductive maturity at around two years of age, and most females start bearing young in their third or fourth year. However, age at first parturition varies between two and six years. All females in a clan reproduce, and females rear their young together in the communal den. Therefore occupied dens may contain up to 30 young of different ages from up to 20 litters. Females nurse only their own cubs and usually reject approaches by other cubs. The milk of Spotted Hyenas has the highest protein content (mean 14·9%) recorded for any terrestrial carnivore, a fat content (mean 14·1%) exceeded only by that of palaearctic bears and the sea otter, and a higher gross energy density than the milk of most other terrestrial carnivores. Due to the high energy content of their milk, and the long nursing period, Spotted Hyenas have the highest energetic investment per litter of any carnivore. Reproductive success in both sexes is related to dominance status, although this relationship is stronger among females than males. High-ranking females enjoy greater reproductive success than low-ranking females because they have longer reproductive life spans and shorter inter-birth intervals, and because their cubs experience lower mortality than do cubs of low-ranking females. Sex ratios among adults are usually slightly female-biased. Reproductive success among males varies with intra-sexual rank, although alpha males fare more poorly than would be expected based on social status alone. As most males disperse from their natal clan when they are at least two years old, most breeding males are immigrants. Spotted Hyenas are sometimes referred to as the "Cain and Abel" of the animal world because of the common belief that they routinely kill their siblings shortly after birth. Although littermates do engage in aggressive interactions within minutes after birth, and although this can result in obvious scarring of the subordinate littermate, these aggressive interactions seldom result in the death of a sibling. These early fights quickly lead to the establishment of a dominance relationship that allows the dominant cub to control access to the mother's milk. Siblicide in the Spotted Hyena is facultative in that it occurs only in some twin litters rather than routinely. The purpose of the early fighting is to establish an unambiguous dominance relationship within the litter. It appears that the relative costs and benefits of killing one's sibling vary with current socio-ecological conditions: a cub that kills its sibling may obtain significant benefits if its mother is unable to support multiple cubs. However, mothers can usually support two cubs in many parts of Africa without undue difficulty.

Status and Conservation. Listed as Least Concern on *The IUCN Red List*. The total world population of the Spotted Hyena is well above 10,000 individuals, several subpopulations exceed 1000 individuals and its range well exceeds 20,000 km². The rapid decline of populations outside conservation areas due to persecution and habitat loss makes the species increasingly dependent on the continued existence of protected areas. Spotted Hyenas have been extirpated in Algeria and Lesotho, and they are listed as threatened in Benin, Burundi, Cameroon, Mauritania, Niger, Nigeria, Rwanda, and Sierra Leone. The largest remaining populations are found in Kenya, Tanzania, South Africa, and Namibia. Most adult mortality is caused directly by lions and humans, although disease is an important mortality source in some areas. Human-caused mortality is common even inside protected areas. Spotted Hyenas may attack livestock, particularly where natural prey are usually or seasonally sparse. Often in response to confirmed or assumed livestock depredation, Spotted Hyenas are shot, snared, speared, or poisoned in many parts of their range by ranchers and pastoralists. Spotted Hyenas are also commonly killed on motor-ways. Habitat fragmentation and reduction are also having significant negative effects on the size of many Spotted Hyena populations. Finally, one of the most important threats to the conservation of Spotted Hyenas is their negative public image. Many people apparently believe these animals are not worth conserving. Educating the public about these complex and fascinating animals is expected to have a substantial positive effect on conservation efforts.

Bibliography. Bearder (1977), Bearder & Randall (1978), Binder & Van Valkenburgh (2000), Binford *et al.* (1988), Boydston, Kapheim & Holekamp (2006), Boydston, Kapheim, Van Horn *et al.* (2005), Boydston, Morelli & Holekamp (2001), Cooper (1989, 1990, 1991, 1993), Cooper *et al.* (1999), Cunha *et al.* (2005), Di Silvestre *et al.* (2000), Drea & Frank (2003), Drea, Coscia & Glickman (1999), Drea, Place *et al.* (2002), Drea, Vignieri, Cunningham & Glickman (2002), Drea, Vignieri, Kim *et al.* (2002), Drea, Weldele *et al.* (1998), East & Hofer (1991a, 1991b, 2001, 2002), East, Burke *et al.* (2003), East, Hofer & Wickler (1993), Eloff (1964, 1975), Engh, Esch *et al.* (2000), Engh, Funk *et al.* (2002), Frank (1986a, 1986b, 1994, 1997), Frank & Glickman (1991, 1994), Frank, Davidson & Smith (1985), Frank, Glickman & Licht (1991), Frank, Glickman & Powch (1990), Frank, Glickman & Zabel (1989), Frank, Holekamp & Smale (1995), Frank, Weldele & Glickman (1995), Gasaway *et al.* (1989, 1991), Glickman, (1995), Glickman, Cunha *et al.* (2006), Glickman, Frank *et al.* (1993), Golla *et al.* (1999), Hamilton *et al.* (1986), Harve (1992), Hayward (2006), Henschel & Skinner (1987, 1990a, 1990b, 1991), Henschel, & Tilson (1988), Hofer & East (1993a, 1993b, 1993c, 1995, 1996, 1997, 2003, 2008), Hofer, Campbell *et al.* (1996), Hofer, East & Campbe (1993), Holekamp & Smale (1990, 1993, 2000), Holekamp, Boydston & Smale (2000), Holekamp, Boydston Szykman *et al.* (1999), Holekamp, Sakai & Lundrigan (2007), Holekamp, Smale, Berg & Cooper (1997), Holekamp, Smale & Szykman (1996), Holekamp, Szykman *et al.* (1999), Höner, Wachter, East & Hofer (2002), Höner Wachter, East, Streich *et al.* (2007), Koepfli *et al.* (2006), Kolowski & Holekamp (2006), Kolowski *et al.* (2007), Kruuk (1972, 1977), Lewis & Werdelin (2000) Licht *et al.* (1992), Lindeque & Skinner (1982), Matthews (1939), Mills, (1985, 1989, 1990), Mills & Gorman (1987), Mills & Hofer (1998), Neaves *et al.* (1980), Pienaar (1969), Pournelle (1965), Rensberger (1999), Rohland *et al.* (2005), Rosevear (1974), Sillero-Zubiri & Gottelli (1992a, 1992b), Skinner, Funston *et al.* (1992), Skinner, Henschel & Van Jaarsveld (1986), Smale, Frank & Holekamp (1993), Smale, Holekamp & White (1999), Smale, Nunes & Holekamp (1997), Sutcliffe, (1970), Szykman, Eng *et al.* (2001), Szykman, Van Horn *et al.* (2007), Theis, Greene *et al.* (2007), Theis, Heckla *et al.* (2008), Tilson & Hamilton (1984), Tilson & Henschel (1984, 1986), Tilson, von Blottnitz & Henschel (1980), Trinkel & Kastberg (2005), Trinkel *et al.* (2004), Van Horn, McElhinny & Holekamp (2003), Van Horn, Wahaj & Holekamp (2004), Van Horn, Engh *et al.* (2004), Van Jaarsveld *et al.* (1988), Wachter *et al.* (2002), Wahaj & Holekamp (2006), Wahaj, Place *et al.* (2007), Wahaj, Van Horn *et al.* (2004), Watts (2007), Werdelin & Solounias (1991), Whateley (1980, 1981), Whateley & Brooks (1978).

Genus *HYAENA*

Brisson, 1762

3. Striped Hyena *Hyaena hyaena*

French: Hyène rayée / **German**: Streifenhyäne / **Spanish**: Hiena rayada

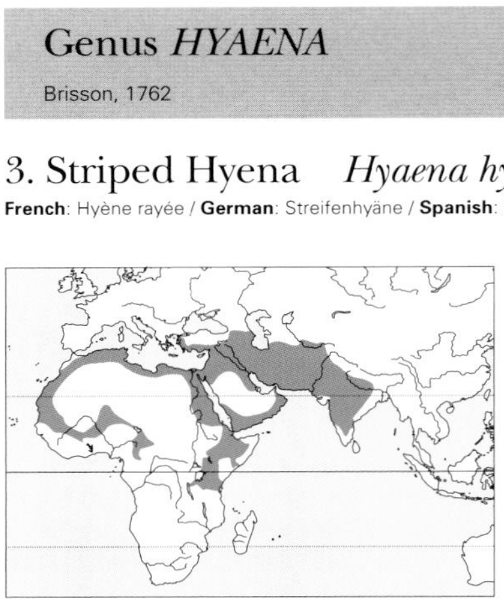

Taxonomy. *Canis hyaena* Linnaeus, 1758, India.

Of the extant hyaenids, the Striped Hyena is most closely related to the Brown Hyena, and its lifestyle, reproduction, and social behavior more closely resemble those of Brown Hyenas than those of Spotted Hyenas or Aardwolves.

Some authorities provisionally recognize five subspecies, distinguished mainly by differences in size and pelage (*hyaena* from India, *barbara* from NW Africa, *dubbah* from NE Africa, *sultana* from the Arabian Peninsula, and *syriaca* from Syria, Asia Minor and the Caucasus). However, other authorities argue that current morphological data and other evidence do not support multiple subspecies.

Distribution. The Striped Hyena has a very large range, covering much of Africa and western Asia. Although they do not occur in the central Sahara, these animals occur at low density in patches throughout eastern, western and northern Africa, including Algeria, Benin, Burkina Faso, Cameroon, Chad, Djibouti, Egypt, Ethiopia, Ghana, Kenya, Libya, Mali, Nigeria, Mauritania, Morocco, Niger, Senegal, Tanzania, and Tunisia. Striped Hyenas also occur in the Middle East and Central Asia. Middle Eastern and Asian countries included in the modern distribution of the Striped Hyena are Afghanistan, Armenia, Azerbaijan, Georgia, India, Iran, Iraq, Israel, Jordan, Lebanon, Nepal, Oman, Pakistan, Saudi Arabia, Tajikistan, Turkey, Turkmenistan, Uzbekistan and Yemen. The current distribution of this species is patchy, and usually appears to occur in small, isolated populations.

Descriptive notes. The Striped Hyena is the smallest of the three bone-cracking hyaenids, but is substantially larger than the Aardwolf. Head-body 100–115 cm, tail 30–40 cm, shoulder height between 66–75 cm; weight 26–41 kg (males) and 26–34 kg (females). Among the provisional subspecies, body mass and body size are only well studied in *syriaca* in Israel and *dubbah* in Kenya. In these populations, there was no significant sexual dimorphism in body size. However, in one recent study in Israel, sexual dimorphism accounted for 39% of the variation in adult body size. Like the other hyaenids, the Striped Hyena has a sloping back because the forelegs are longer than the hindlegs, and has well-developed anal glands used for scent marking. Large ducts from the anal glands open into an anal pouch dorsal to the anus. As in the other bone-cracking Hyenas, the head, neck, and shoulders are relatively massive and powerful. The fur is pale gray or straw-colored, with black vertical stripes on the sides of the body. Like the Brown Hyena, the Striped Hyena has longer fur than the Spotted Hyena, giving it a rather shaggy appearance. The Striped Hyena has a black muzzle and a black patch on the throat. It has five to nine vertical stripes on the flanks, two cheek stripes and clear black transverse and horizontal stripes on all four legs. The head is roundish with a pointed muzzle and long, pointed ears. It has a gray or blond mane that run along its dorsal midline from the ears to the tail; the mane can be erected to increase the animal's apparent size by over 30%. The mane in this species is more pronounced than that in any other hyaenid, with hairs up to 20 cm long. The black and white tail is long and bushy, with hair that is generally coarse and long. Females have two or three pairs of teats, but if they have three, only the caudal two pairs are functional. Juvenile females have well-defined labia-like folds anterior to the vagina. These ridges are hairless and darker and rougher than the surrounding tissue. Juvenile males have smaller, smooth, hairless skin folds along the middle septum close to, but anterior to, the scrotum. Unlike Spotted Hyenas, these genital characteristics are not severe enough to confuse sexing of juveniles, and adult genitalia appear normal. Subspecies descriptions are based on limited data except for *syriaca* in Israel and *dubbah* in Kenya. In general animals living in the northern parts of the range tend to be slightly larger than those living in southern regions. Variation in pelage color appears slight, although the Lebanese population is reported to have a reddish coat color, and hyenas on the Arabian Peninsula are described as having a yellow mark below the eyes and a mixed gray and black dorsal crest.

Habitat. In most of its range the Striped Hyena occurs in rugged, arid habitat or light thorn bush country. These animals drink regularly where water is available, but they can also survive in many waterless areas. In North Africa they prefer open woodlands and bushy and mountainous regions. The central Arabian and Sahara Deserts are not suitable habitat. In central Asia, Striped Hyenas avoid high altitudes and dense thickets and forests. The maximum elevations recorded are 2250 m in Iran, 2500 m in India and 3300 m in Pakistan. In the Caucasus region, Turkmenistan, Tadzhikistan, and Uzbekistan, prime habitats include savannah and semi-desert regions up to an elevation of 2100 m, mountain areas with strong relief, valleys with abundant caves or other resting sites, and riverine areas. The Striped Hyena avoids areas with minimum temperatures of less than –15°C to –20°C and more than 80–120 days of frost per year. In Israel, Striped Hyenas are present even close to dense human settlements. In West Africa, they occur in dry scrub savanna and Sahel woodland, particularly in the belt of *Acacia raddiana* woodland that extends from Senegal to Chad. In eastern Africa, Striped Hyenas are found in a variety of habitats ranging from open savanna to rugged, bush-covered mountain terrain.

Food and Feeding. The diet of Striped Hyenas apparently varies considerably from one part of their range to another, but these animals are clearly scavengers with catholic tastes. They are primarily carrion-eaters; their diet consists mainly of dried flesh and bones from carcasses of large vertebrates. They scavenge carrion and the remains of kills made by other predators, including Spotted Hyenas, Cheetahs, Leopards, Lions, and Tigers. The Hyena's massive cheek teeth and supporting musculature easily permit the gnawing and breaking of bones, as well as the carapaces of tortoises and turtles. Striped Hyenas have also been reported to consume a wide variety of invertebrates, vegetables, fruit, garbage, and small vertebrates that the Hyenas hunt themselves. In central Kenya, analysis of bone fragments and hairs from fecal samples indicated that hyenas regularly consume small mammals and birds that are unlikely to be scavenged. The limited available diet data may underestimate the importance of active hunting in the lives of these animals. In various parts of eastern Africa, Striped Hyenas are reported to supplement their diet with *Balanites* fruits. The proportion of scavenged and killed prey items in the diet is still a matter of debate as there has been no detailed research on these Hyenas' food intake. Some authors suggest that only individuals from the three larger subspecies, *barbara*, *syriaca* and *hyaena*, kill large prey, including livestock, as there is no evidence that the smaller subspecies, *dubbah* and *sultana*, attack large herbivores. In Turkmenistan the Striped Hyena has been reported feeding on Wild Boar, Kulan, porcupine, and particularly tortoises. In Uzbekhistan and Tadzhikistan, seasonal abundance of oil willow fruits (*Eleagnus angustifolia*) is reflected in the diet; in the Caucasus region the diet includes abundant grasshoppers. In Israel the Striped Hyena feeds on garbage, carrion, and fruits, particularly dates and melons. In eastern Jordan, the main sources of food are carcasses of feral horses and water buffalo and refuse from local villages. The Striped Hyena can drink water of very variable quality, from fresh water to soda and salt water, but it may also satisfy its water requirements with melons or other fruits. Very little is currently known about the hunting behavior of Striped Hyenas, but those few hunts that have been observed involved simple chases and grabs at prey. Seasonal influxes of Striped Hyenas follow migrations of large herds of domestic and wild ungulates in Turkmenistan, suggesting that the Hyenas cover long distances on foraging trips. In Egypt they are known to move along ancient caravan roads where the chance of locating dead camels is high. In Serengeti and in southern Kenya, they spend most of the night actively searching for food or moving between established foraging sites. Striped Hyenas apparently can remember the locations of fruiting trees, garbage dumps and other established feeding sites, although the routes taken to re-visit such food sources are seldom repeated on consecutive foraging trips. They are also able to locate tortoises in their hiding places during periods of aestivation and hibernation. Striped Hyenas frequently cache bones or pieces of skin, using their snouts to push these items deep into clumps of grass or stands of dense shrubs. They may also carry food items back to their dens. Bone collections are common at den sites used by Striped Hyenas, although it is often unclear whether these collections represent scavenged or killed prey, and whether the bones collected play a significant nutritional role in the lives of these animals. Several studies have inferred diet by combining data from bone collections and fecal samples. In central Kenya, however, bone collections indicated a much broader range of prey than did scat analysis, and significant portions of bone assemblages were very old bones unlikely to represent material scavenged from fresh kills. From fecal analysis alone, several researchers have found remains of prey items that are more likely to have been scavenged than hunted, and larger mammals are represented far less often in the analysis of hairs in fecal material than would be expected based only on bone collections at dens. Striped Hyenas appear to be strictly solitary foragers, although multiple individuals occasionally gather at rich food sources such as large carcasses or refuse pits. These animals are sometimes found in small groups while resting, but there is no indication that they ever forage cooperatively. Genetic relatedness among members of groups seen feeding together has not been investigated. Foraging activity in Kenya and Tanzania is restricted to hours of darkness except during rain or unusually cloudy weather. Under those circumstances, Striped Hyenas may return to previously visited kills or carcasses, but do not embark on full foraging forays. In many areas, and for many centuries, Striped Hyenas have been described as raiding human graves and carrying away bones. Fruit and vegetable crop raiding by Striped Hyenas is currently considered a serious problem in some parts of Israel. While foraging, Striped Hyenas zigzag across the landscape and do not appear to follow set routes, even when returning to the same food source on multiple nights. Minimum mean distance travelled per night is 19 km at speeds of 2–4 km/h, occasionally trotting at speeds of up to 8 km/h, or running at a maximum of 50 km/h. Overall, the evidence indicates that Striped Hyenas are solitary foragers for which carrion, insects, fruits and vegetable matter represent significant portions of the diet.

Activity patterns. The Striped Hyena is almost strictly nocturnal, although it does occasionally engage in some activity after dawn and before dusk. Some authorities suggest Striped Hyenas may be most strictly nocturnal in areas characterized by relatively intensive anthropogenic activity, and where they are directly persecuted by humans.

Movements, Home range and Social organization. In Serengeti, Striped Hyenas travel an average of 19 km per night (range 7–27 km), either following established animal tracks or zig-zagging cross-country. A similar pattern was observed in southern Kenya, where Striped Hyenas followed by human observers covered large distances, but stopped frequently to paste or to investigate grass clumps, carcasses, and other things found on the ground along the way. Home range sizes of one female and one male in the Serengeti were 44 km^2 and 72 km^2 respectively. There was little evidence of territorial behavior. Home range size was calculated for a single female in the Negev Desert in Israel to be approximately 61 km^2; this range partly overlapped those of two other individuals. In the Laikipia District of Kenya, the mean home range size for 12 males was 82 km^2, and for eight females was 71 km^2, with no significant difference in home range sizes between sexes. No evidence of territorial defense has been recorded in any studied population, but in some populations these hyenas are known to scent-mark frequently within their home ranges while traveling, and also to defecate in "latrines" near feeding sites and along travel routes. Striped Hyenas are the least well-studied of the extant hyaenids, and their social behavior is very poorly understood. They are most often reported to be solitary. Nevertheless, there appears to be considerable variability with respect to patterns of social grouping among Striped Hyena populations. In some areas, such as central Asia, these animals are reported to form short-term monogamous pair bonds for breeding, with a resulting family unit that may endure for several years. Such family units may sometimes contain offspring from multiple litters. Under these circumstances, both parents and the older offspring may be observed provisioning den-dwelling cubs. Typical group sizes are one or two in all subspecies, but groups of up to seven have been reported in Libya. In Israel, Striped Hyenas are generally solitary, but occasionally several are seen together at a carcass, including both males and females, or females with large cubs. Age-specific foraging data are extremely limited, but cubs have occasionally been observed accompanying their mothers on foraging trips away from the den by 6–12 months of age. Otherwise, foraging is strictly solitary. Almost invariably described as solitary in sub-Saharan Africa, it was recently discovered that Striped Hyenas in the Laikipia District of Kenya are behaviorally solitary but exhibit a polyandrous system of space use. These animals form groups of up to four adults; each group contains one adult female and one to three adult males. Females in both wild and captive populations appear to be highly intolerant of one another, starting around the time they reach puberty. The overall adult sex ratio in the Laikipia population was three males to two females. Members of these groups share a common home range and may be found resting together during daylight hours. The home ranges of group-mates exhibit 85% overlap, whereas their ranges overlap only 22% with those of animals in other groups. Individual group members spend more than 90% of their time alone. Adult male group-mates included both closely-related and distantly related individuals. In contrast to spatial patterns of relatedness documented in other carnivores, pairs in non-adjacent groups tended to be more closely related genetically than pairs living in adjacent groups. This was true for females as well as males. As these animals are usually found alone, very little has been recorded regarding direct social interactions except for captive situations. In this species, males are slightly larger than females, and males also appear to be socially dominant to females in resource competition. The long dorsal hairs of the mane may be erected to enhance the apparent size of the individual during confrontations with conspecifics. Both mane and tail hairs are erected when the animal assumes a defensive posture, but also when it adopts an aggressive stance. The mane is also commonly bristled whenever the animal pastes. When Striped Hyenas fight they bite at the throat and legs, rather than at the mane. During an agonistic interaction, the subordinate individual may hunch its body, lower its mane, and swing or turn its head from side to side whereas the dominant animal remains bristled and stands erect. The Striped Hyena exhibits a number of visual displays, the most striking of which is the erection of the mane and bristling of the tail like a bottle brush. The mane and tail thus serve as signalling devices during social interactions. When members of the same social group meet after being separated, they engage in "meeting ceremonies", which involve investigation and licking of the mid-back region and sniffing of the nose and extruded anal pouch. The tail is often held vertically during meeting ceremonies. Meeting ceremonies may also involve repeated pawing of the throat of the greeting partner. The well-developed anal pouch is inverted during scent marking, called pasting, and also during greetings. In scent marking, the anal pouch produces a pungent yellow to beige paste which is deposited at nose-height on grass stalks, stones, tree-trunks, or sticks. Foraging Striped Hyenas pause to paste at frequent intervals, and these scent marks appear to be deposited throughout the home range rather than exclusively at its borders. Pasting has also been observed at large carcasses in the wild, and, in captivity, on food bowls. Some Striped Hyena vocalizations resemble those of Spotted Hyenas, although calls emitted by Striped Hyenas tend to be much softer, and the sounds carry shorter distances. The vocal repertoire of the Spotted Hyena is also far more elaborate than that of the Striped Hyena. Most of its vocalizations are uttered in the presence of conspecifics. Cubs whine while they are nursing. Giggling or yelling may occur when a Striped Hyena is frightened or being chased by another predator. A long, drawn-out lowing sound sometimes accompanies the defensive posture, and growling may occur during fighting or play-fighting with conspecifics.

Breeding. Females are polyestrous and breed throughout the year. Estrus is reported to last one day. No detailed descriptions of sexual behavior in the wild have been reported, but during matings in captivity, females may mate several times at intervals of at least 15 minutes. In the wild, litter size varies from one to four (median of three), after a gestation period of 90–91 days. Average litter size in captivity is 2·4, with a range of one to five. Parturition is preceded by intensive digging behavior by the female. Cubs weigh approximately 700 g at birth; they have adult-like markings but lack manes, and instead have only black spinal stripes. They are born with eyes and ears closed, and they are barely able to crawl, so they are far more altricial than Spotted Hyena cubs at birth. Their eyes first open after five to nine days, and cubs may emerge from the den at around two weeks of age. Deciduous teeth start to erupt on day 21. Cubs begin to eat meat at the age of 30 days. In the wild cubs are known to nurse for over one year. They reach reproductive maturity during the second year of life. The mating system is promiscuous or polyandrous. In the Laikipia population in Kenya, females appear to mate with both group males and males that reside elsewhere. It is not known whether sires contribute in any way to parental care in this population, but lactating females are usually found alone at dens with their cubs, males do not spend significant periods of time at dens, and females appear to be solely responsible for care of young. Multiple paternity in this population occurred in half of sampled litters, and extra-group males sired roughly one third of the cubs born to group females. Striped Hyenas usually use caves, ravines or other sheltered rocky places as dens, although earthen dens may also be used. Den entrances are fairly narrow and may be hidden by large boulders. Two dens were measured in the Karakum Desert. The entrances were 0·67 m and 0·72 m wide. The dens sloped downward 3 m and 2·5m and were 4·15 m and 5 m long, with no lateral extensions or special chambers. These simple constructions contrast with much more elaborate dens found in Israel, which can exceed 27 m in length.

Status and Conservation. Listed as Near Threatened on *The IUCN Red List*. Despite their broad distribution, the basic biology of Striped Hyenas, including their abundance in most parts of their range, remains very poorly known. Throughout its range, the Striped Hyena occurs at low densities. There have been only two local estimates of Striped Hyena density in Africa, and it is considered either threatened or data deficient throughout its African range. In Serengeti and Laikipia, density was estimated to be 0·02 per km² and 0·03 adults per km², respectively. Remarkably little information is available on the species. This is undoubtedly due to its shy, nocturnal, mostly solitary nature, its apparent affinity for rugged terrain, its generally negative reputation, and frequent confusion with, or lack of differentiation from, Spotted Hyenas where the two species overlap. Most adult mortality is directly caused by Lions and humans. Striped Hyenas, particularly those inhabiting areas where natural prey are usually or seasonally sparse, may attack livestock, and as a result they are shot, snared, speared, or poisoned in many parts of their range by ranchers and pastoralists. It appears that the Striped Hyena is already extinct in many localities, and that populations are generally declining. The major reasons for this decline appear to be decreasing natural and domestic sources of carrion due to declines in the populations of other large carnivores and their prey, and changes in livestock practices. Moreover, the low densities and associated large home ranges of these animals are likely to increase the chances that populations will become fragmented into small, non-viable units. This must be considered a key problem if these animals are to be protected. The Striped Hyena evokes many superstitious fears because of putative and documented cases of grave-robbing and attacks on humans. In addition, its body parts are widely exploited as aphrodisiacs, and are utilized in folk medicine. Striped Hyenas are often killed because of suspected or real damage inflicted on agricultural produce and livestock, and they are often shot by livestock ranchers. These animals have also been widely hunted through poisoning, baiting traps, pits, or with the help of dogs. The Striped Hyena does sometimes cause damage to crops, and may sometimes also attack domestic animals, predominantly goats, sheep, dogs, and poultry. In many cases of damage to livestock, it is unclear whether the targeted individual was adult or young, healthy or sick, so Striped Hyenas may be blamed for livestock mortality for which they are not truly responsible. In any case, the records suggest that attacks on livestock by Striped Hyenas usually occur at very low frequencies. Tentative estimates of the total worldwide population size range from 5000 to 14,000 individuals. Fragmentation into many subpopulations is suspected even though the actual degree of fragmentation is unknown. In addition, habitat loss and declining population size are occurring at unknown rates. The Striped Hyena is considered threatened in all parts of its African range where data are

sufficient to evaluate the local status, except in Ethiopia and Kenya, where it is considered at lower risk. As we currently know so little about the biology of this species, one of the most pressing conservation concerns is to study these animals in a number of different locales. In addition to knowing very little about their behavioral ecology, we also know virtually nothing about their abundance and population dynamics. Before we can make management decisions in the best interest of Striped Hyenas, we need more information. Fortunately, studies of these animals are currently underway in East Africa, India, and the Middle East.

Bibliography. Bouskila (1984), Davidar (1990), Hofer (1998), Horwitz & Smith (1988), Kerbis-Peterhans & Horwitz (1992), Koepfli *et al.* (2006), Kolska (1991), Kruuk (1976), Leakey *et al.* (1999), Macdonald (1978), Mendelssohn (1985), Mills & Hofer (1998), Pocock (1934d), Rieger (1978, 1979a, 1979b, 1979c, 1981), Skinner & Ilani (1979), Skinner *et al.* (1980), Van Aarde *et al.* (1988), Wagner (2006, In press), Wagner, Creel *et al.* (2007) Wagner, Frank & Creel (2008), Wagner, Frank, Creel & Coscia (2007), Werdelin & Solounias (1991), Yom-Tov & Geffen (2006).

Genus *PARAHYAENA*
Hendey, 1974

4. Brown Hyena *Parahyaena brunnea*

French: Hyène brune / **German**: Braune Hyäne / **Spanish**: Hiena parda

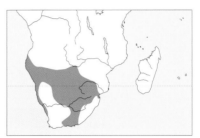

Taxonomy. *Hyaena brunnea* Thunberg, 1820, South Africa, Western Cape Province, Cape of Good Hope.

Formerly classified as *Hyaena brunnea*, but a recent molecular analysis assigns this species to a separate genus from that of the Striped Hyena. Along with Striped and Spotted Hyenas, the Brown Hyena belongs to the subfamily Hyaeninae. Monotypic.

Distribution. Namibia, Botswana, W & S Zimbabwe, S Mozambique, Swaziland, W Lesotho, and South Africa. Records from the SW of Angola are all before 1970.

Descriptive notes. Head-body 110–136 cm; average 123 cm (males), 117 cm (females), tail 18·7–26·5 cm, average height at shoulders 79 cm (males) and 74 cm (females), weight (adult) varies somewhat regionally, ranges from 28 to 47·5 kg and averages about 40 kg. Most studies show some sexual size dimorphism, but it is often minimal, with males slightly heavier and longer than females. Has a typical hyena appearance with front legs longer and more robust than the rear legs, a broad head and short muzzle, thick neck and short tail. Like the Striped Hyena it has large pointed ears and course shaggy fur that is longest along the back and on the tail. The general color is dark brown with lighter tawny hair on the neck and shoulders. The legs are banded with dark horizontal stripes and the front feet are large and well-developed for digging. Like the Spotted and Striped Hyenas, the Brown Hyena possesses the bone-crushing third premolar that is unique to this family. In contrast to Spotted Hyenas, there is no masculinization of the female genitalia in Brown Hyenas. Females have two to six pairs of teats, but only the two most caudal pairs are functional.

Habitat. Brown Hyenas are found in a variety of relatively arid habitats from open desert or semi-desert in the Namib and Kalahari, to dry open scrub and woodland savannah, mopani scrub and tree savannah, as well as the bushveld of the northern Transvaal. They do not need drinking water and inhabit areas where annual rainfall may be even lower than 100 mm, up to about 650 mm.

Food and Feeding. These hyenas forage alone at night and do not cooperate in hunting or in feeding, although group members tolerate each other at large food items. Although not competent hunters, Brown Hyenas are extremely efficient scavengers with an omnivorous diet. They are opportunistic feeders on a range of vertebrates, primarily mammals, the vast majority of which are scavenged, often from the kills of other carnivores. Fruits, insects and reptiles can be important supplementary foods when carcasses are rare. In one population 58 different food items were identified from fecal analysis. Brown Hyenas in the southern Kalahari spent 30% of their feeding time eating carrion, 28% on vegetable matter, 4·5% on small mammals, 1·5% on birds' eggs, and 29% on unknown items. Only 5·8% of food they were seen eating was killed by the hyenas themselves. In the central Kalahari 35·9% of all observed feeding bouts were on fresh scavenged kills, 33·9% on old carcasses, 16% on their own kills, and 12·5% on vegetative food sources. Brown Hyenas do not depend on standing water. In the central Kalahari, no free water or rain is typically found for eight months of the year. Although they will drink on a daily basis when water is present, much of the water during dry seasons is obtained from Cucurbitaceae fruits such as the tsama melon, gemsbok cucumber, and Hookeri melon, which can compose significant proportions of the diet in these seasons. Brown Hyenas inhabiting the Namibian coast feed almost exclusively on subadult Brown Fur Seals. The majority of these seals are thought to be scavenged, although Brown Hyenas have been seen hunting seal pups. In fact, hunting efficiency on seal pups during the peak pupping season can be as high as 47%, and an average of almost five seals per day may be killed from a single colony. Small rodents and seabirds make up the rest of this unique diet. Elsewhere hunting attempts by Brown Hyenas are opportunistic and directed at small mammals such as

Springbok lambs, spring hares, Bat-eared Foxes, and ground nesting birds. The hunting technique of the Brown Hyena is unspecialized, rarely successful (except in the case of Brown Fur Seal pups), and may include a brief lunge at a surprised prey, a prolonged chase of up 1 km, or an attempt to dig up a burrowed animal. The percent of observed hunting attempts that were successful was 4·7% in the southern Kalahari and 13·7% in the central Kalahari. The hyenas generally feed where they find food, but food from larger carcasses is frequently cached nearby in a clump of grass or under a bush. Considerable time is often spent at carcasses removing limbs for this purpose and one animal may remove and cache up to three legs before any competitors arrive. Sites where food is cached are scent-marked and may be re-visited over multiple days. In a remarkable example of food caching in the southern Kalahari, a Brown Hyena arrived at an abandoned ostrich (*Struthio camelus*) nest with 26 eggs, which are prized food items. The hyena spent four hours carrying 14 eggs distances of 150–600 m from the nest, some of which it simply dropped in the open. It ate only three eggs during this period. Brown Hyenas also carry food back to cubs at the den. This provisioning of cubs can result in significant bone accumulations at den sites. In the southern Kalahari the average distance moved between significant meals was 7·2 km, and the average nightly distance traveled was 31·1 km. During the dry season, nightly movements were longer and were recorded as high as 54·4 km. During the wet season movements were reduced and ranged from 10–20 km. In Namibia, daily distances traveled ranged from 15–47 km. When foraging, Brown Hyenas move at a pace of about 4 km/h, often walking in a zig-zag pattern, probably to maximize their chance of coming across food items. They use smell to locate much of their food, as evidenced by frequent sniffing and moving upwind toward food sources. Their hearing appears to be acute as well and is likely also used in foraging. The Brown Hyena is subordinate at kills to Spotted Hyenas, Lions and African Wild Dogs, although it appears to dominate Leopards in most situations. While they always dominate Cheetahs, they compete heavily with the much smaller Black-backed Jackal, which is often able to steal scraps from hyenas at carcasses. There is some evidence that, where they are sympatric, Brown Hyenas avoid areas frequented by Spotted Hyenas, potentially to avoid direct aggression and competition. For example, dens in the southern Kalahari were rarely found in the prey-rich riverine habitat where most Spotted Hyena dens occurred. Although their presence at livestock carcasses has resulted in much antagonism toward, and persecution of, Brown Hyenas by livestock owners, predation on livestock by these animals appears to be done by a small number of individuals. However, these hyenas, which typically target cow calves and sheep, can account for a large number of kills. Removal of these problem individuals appears effective at halting stock losses.

Activity patterns. Primarily a nocturnal animal, although activity is occasionally observed during the day, particularly on cool, cloudy days during the rainy season. There are typcally two peaks of activity, from 19:30 h to 24:00 h and 2:30 h to 6:00 h, with a rest period in between. Radio-collared adults in the southern Kalahari were active for 42·6% of the 24 h period, and 80.2% of the period between 18:00 h and 06:00 h. In Namibia, three males with satellite collars spent an average of 57·1–72·3% of 24 h active. Brown Hyenas typically rest during the day in a hole, or under a large tree or bush.

Movements, Home range and Social organization. Approximately 65% of Brown Hyenas in a population are members of small social groups called clans, with the remaining individuals living as nomads. Clan size ranges from 4–14 individuals, including cubs, and clans defend large stable territories. In the southern Kalahari far-ranging nomadic males (8% of the adult population) were the only males observed to breed with clan-living females, yet in the central Kalahari, breeding also occurs with resident immigrant males. In the southern Kalahari territories averaged 308 km² (range: 215–461 km²) with never more than 20% overlap between territories. Brown Hyena density there was calculated to be 1·8 hyenas/100 km². In the central Kalahari territories averaged 170 km², but varied greatly with annual rainfall, reaching a maximum of 400 km². In Namibia, where Brown Hyenas depend almost entirely on Brown Fur Seals along the coast, territories of two clans in one study were 31·9 km² and 220 km². In another study the home ranges of three males ranged from 420–1460 km², with the largest home range being an inland location. Density in this latter Namibian study ranged from 1·0–2·9/100 km². In general, group size appears to be correlated with food abundance and quality within the territory, whereas territory size is influenced by the distribution of food resources. Territories are maintained primarily through scent marking behavior (called "pasting") and aggression toward intruders. Clan structure appears to vary across regions, but always includes 1–5 breeding females and their subadult offspring. In the central Kalahari, groups often also include at least one adult resident immigrant male. Mean clan size in the southern Kalahari was 3·7 adults and subadults, and total clan size ranged from 4–14. In the central Kalahari, a well-studied clan contained 13 members including cubs. Because adult females and their offspring are the core of a social group, the majority of clan members are related. However, dispersal from and immigration into the clan occurs. Although subadults of both sexes may disperse from their natal clan, males do so more often than females and most males disperse by 36–40 months of age. In two reported cases of female emigration in the central Kalahari, the number of resident adult females was at its zenith (five) and the dispersing females both were targets of severe aggression from other resident females prior to dispersal. In both cases, dispersal appeared to be prompted by conflicts with established adults of the same sex. The central Kalahari and southern Kalahari locales also apparently differ with respect to clan social hierarchies. In the central Kalahari a linear within-sex dominance hierarchy was apparent, and at carcasses with more than one hyena, rank determined priority of access to food. Although immigrant males were dominant to all natal males, the highest ranking male and female appeared to be of equal status. Adult females were typically dominant to natal males of less than 36 months of age. These natal males were tolerated until about 24 months, when aggression gradually increased until their dispersal. However, in one case, a natal male remained in the clan and eventually dominated the clan females. In the southern Kalahari no dominance hierarchy was apparent, with no sex, age-class, or individual consistently winning fights or monopolizing food resources in clans. Differences in the breeding systems and the existence or lack of a hierarchy are thought to be related to significant differences in Brown Hyena density in the two locales. In the central Kalahari, 37·81% of observations involve the association of two or more hyenas. In the southern Kalahari contact between group members appears to be less frequent. Although there is typically aggression between hyenas of the same sex from different groups when they meet, the level of aggression within clans appears to vary between the southern and central Kalahari. In the central Kalahari, neck-biting appears to be used to maintain rank relationships within the clan and is observed with some frequency, while in the southern Kalahari, fighting within the clan is rare, with clan members seldom interacting at all. Here, the only aggression observed is between same-sex members of neighboring clans, and this is extremely infrequent. Interestingly, in the southern Kalahari, where resident males do not breed with clan females, these males show little aggression to nomadic males, who are responsible for mating with group-living females, suggesting that Brown Hyenas can differentiate between neighboring males and nomadic males. When they meet after being separated, Brown Hyenas from the same group engage in a greeting ceremony in which each animal in turn crouches and presents its extruded anal pouch to the other. This is accompanied by a lowering of the ears and a "grin" (teeth exposed by pulling lips up and corners of the mouth back) by the subordinate animal when it is greeting a dominant. Greetings can last as long as five minutes. Two additional behaviors that appear to be important in Brown Hyena society are neck-biting and muzzle-wrestling. Neck-biting is a purely agonistic interaction (though cubs may engage in it during play) and is primarily intrasexual. In the southern Kalahari, this behavior is largely restricted to interactions between members of neighboring clans, whereas in the central Kalahari, it can be seen more frequently between clan members and is thought to function in maintenance of a dominance hierarchy. Neck-biting behavior is a ritualized, somewhat elaborate interaction in which dominant and subordinate animals are clear from the start. The submissive animal approaches a standing dominant individual grinning and with its mane and tail raised. Either before or at its approach, the dominant seizes the neck of the subordinate, holding the skin and hair of the neck with its incisors and one or both canines, and vigorously shakes the victim from side to side. This type of interaction typically lasts less than five minutes, and only rarely does the subordinate flee at its conclusion. Muzzle wresting may be observed anywhere in the territory and is exhibited by all clan members. However, adults rarely engage in this behavior with other adults, though they will do so with cubs with some frequency. Most muzzle-wrestling occurs between cubs and subadults. The two participants stand face to face, and attempt to bite each other on the jowls or along the side of face. Their heads pitch rapidly from side to side with mouths open, and they often growl softly throughout. One or both hyenas may be crouched on their carpals, and in some cases one may lie beneath the other. This behavior is clearly less aggressive than neck biting and may often be play, although it can escalate into true aggression. There is no clear loser, and animals typically remain with each other after muzzle-wrestling, which may last from a few minutes to an hour. The most striking visual display of the Brown Hyena is pilo-erection of the long hairs along its neck and back, which is observed in situations calling for either an attack or flight response. Despite its rather elaborate social interactions, Brown Hyenas spend the vast majority of their time alone, and the primary form of communication between hyenas is olfactory. They convey information to conspecifics with latrines, which have accumulations of feces, and grass stalks on which they have deposited a strong-smelling white secretion and a smaller black secretion. Both secretions are deposited during pasting from an extruded anal scent pouch located between the rectum and base of the tail. Although all four hyaenid species paste, the deposition of two different secretions is unique to Brown Hyenas. Whereas the lipid-rich white secretion is discernible to the human nose for well over 30 days, the more watery black secretion appears unscented after a few hours. This black secretion is thought to convey information relating to the time elapsed since it was deposited, and therefore signal that a hyena has recently foraged in the area. It is suggested that this allows other group members to avoid unproductive areas, and minimizes competition between group members for limited resources. The longer-lasting white secretion is thought to function in territory marking and defense. Pasting is done throughout a clan's territory. Although most pasting occurs in the central part of the territory, where residents spend most of their time, frequency of pasting and over-pasting (deposition on an existing mark) is highest when individuals visit territory boundaries. Very little pasting is done by residents when they are outside of their territory. Pasting during traveling/foraging movements can be quite frequent, with ten individuals averaging a paste every six minutes. However, this is highly variable, with some individuals pasting only once or twice during a night-time observation period. Males and females do not differ in rate of pasting during their travels. At the den, adults and subadults frequently paste soon after arriving and before departing. At least in the southern Kalahari, the perimeter of hyena territories is thought to be too large to make strict border marking possible or effective. Instead, marks are scattered throughout the residents' territory. This is known as hinterland marking. Given the frequency of pasting, and how widely pastes are deposited across a territory, simulations indicate that in the southern Kalahari, hinterland marking is effective. Intruders would likely encounter resident paste marks very soon after entering a territory. Indeed, individual hyenas are estimated to deposit some 29,000 paste marks in a year. Experiments with translocated pasted grass stalks indicate that hyenas can distinguish between pastes of group and non-group members and that over-pasting is more commonly done on pastings from non-group hyenas. Chemical analysis of white and black paste suggests that the scent of these substances probably varies between individuals, allowing for identification of the paster. In the southern Kalahari, latrines are not as regularly spaced as pastings, and show a clumped distribution, largely around primary foraging areas that occur along the territory border. Latrines are often associated with landmarks such as trees, bushes or roads, and those along the border are visited more frequently than those in the interior. The vocal repertoire of the Brown Hyena is relatively small, as in the Striped Hyena, and consists of eight vocalizations: a yell, a hoot, two whines and four growls, none of which functions as a long-distance communication. Some authors group these into five calls, the squeal/whine, squeak, scream, yell, and growl/grunt. The squeal is a shrill sharp cry emitted by a juvenile or other subordinate while approaching to greet or beg food from a dominant individual. The squeak is a hoarse rasping cry of abject submission associated with carpal crawling. A scream is a high-pitched, cackling shriek given by a hyena whose neck is being bitten. The yell is a loud, abrupt high-pitched call associated with defensive threat. A growl/grunt is low-pitched, breathless and throaty, and is given while muzzle-wrestling. All but the growl appear to indicate submission or appeasement in social contexts of varying intensity.

Breeding. Brown Hyenas are polyestrous, non-seasonal breeders. Litters range from 1–4 cubs with a modal litter size of three. Estrus lasts approximately one week but mating in captivity occurs over a 15–day period. Based on six observed mating bouts in the southern Kalahari, mating associations consist of multiple copulation attempts over a 5–90 minute period, and may be preceded by extended courtship, during which both animals may show aggression and there are mutual approaches and retreats. Gestation in captivity was 96 days. Interbirth intervals appear to range widely. In the southern Kalahari they were as short as a year and as long as 41 months apart, although lost litters in the interim could not be ruled out. Cubs are born with their eyes closed and their ears bent forward. Their fur is similar in color to that of adults. Their eyes begin to open at eight days and are completely open at 14 days. Unlike Spotted Hyenas, Brown Hyena cubs are born without teeth. As in the other bone-cracking hyaenids, den dependence is long and weaning occurs late. Cubs from 0–3 months of age rarely leave the den hole except when their mother or another adult is present. During this period, mothers attend the den frequently, often at sunrise and sunset and cubs rely completely on their mother's milk. At four months, visits by the mother become less frequent, with mothers visiting about once a night, but suckling periods are longer. At this time, mothers and other group members begin bringing food to the den for the cubs. Weaning normally occurs at 12-16 months of age, yet weaning conflicts have been observed at ten months. Starting at ten months, cubs begin extensive, and very often solitary, foraging movements away from the den. Length of den residence is variable however, ranging from 8–15 months. Regardless of their dependence on the den, by 16 months weaning has occurred and full adult dentition is present. As they mature, subadults themselves begin to bring food back to the den for younger cubs. This has been observed in subadults as young as 22 months. Adult size is reached at 30 months. The earliest breeding recorded in the wild is 35 months; breeding continues until at least ten years of age. Cubs are raised in underground, sometimes extensive, tunnels, always small enough to prevent adults and potential predators from entering. They are easily distinguished by accumulations of bones, hair, feathers, horns, pieces of hide, and hyena feces. In the southern Kalahari Brown Hyena dens appear to be used only rarely by multiple females at once, and cubs are typically raised in the same den in which they are born. However, communal denning appears to be common in the central Kalahari, with cubs of multiple females, and of different ages, raised together at a single den location. In this system, cubs are born in a solitary den and transported to the communal den sometime before they are four months of age. Throughout their development, den moves are common and cubs may reside at as many as seven different dens, though distances between dens are typically not large. In the central Kalahari, where a social rank system is evident, dominant females enjoy greater reproductive success in terms of number of surviving offspring, yet the number of litters does not vary based on rank. There appears to be variation, both regionally and temporally, in the mating system of Brown Hyenas. In one system, females breed only with nomadic males that range over wide areas without defended territories or family groups. In the other, females breed not only with nomadic males but with resident immigrant males as well. These residents are members of the clan and assist in territory defense, yet their tenure, at least in the central Kalahari, is rela-

tively short (less than three years). In this area, where both nomadic males and resident immigrant males are present, dominant clan males were observed to copulate with resident females more frequently than nomadic males. In the southern Kalahari, the only mating observed involved nomadic males, and no resident males, either immigrant or natal, were observed to mate. Although males known to be natal showed little sexual interest at all in any resident females, researchers were unable to observe immigrant males long enough to ascertain sexual interest in resident females. The source of the variation in the mating system of Brown Hyenas is unclear, although it may be related to dispersion of food. In the central Kalahari, where both systems were observed over time, mating with nomadic males was restricted to the dry season, when resident clan males would likely have difficulty maintaining contact with clan females (some were separated by 22 km). Because territories are very large in the southern Kalahari and only breeding with nomadic males is seen, the food dispersion theory is further supported. Individual reproductive patterns in males are also likely to be influenced by individual status and the behavior of other males in the population. In either case, natal males are never observed to mate with females in their natal clan. Communal care of cubs is better developed among Brown Hyenas than in any of the other three hyaenid species. Non-parental aid in cub rearing includes communal suckling (although preference in nursing one's own cubs has been shown), food provisioning, den maintenance, defense against predators, play, and adoption of orphans. Subadult and adult females of all social ranks and reproductive states bring food items to the den for cubs. However, the extent of involvement in provisioning by adult males seems to vary by region. In the central Kalahari, subadult males provision cubs, but to a lesser degree than females, and they only bring food to closely related cubs. Neither immigrant nor natal adult males were seen provisioning cubs. It has been suggested that this is because males do not benefit from an increased group size, as they are likely to emigrate from their natal clan. In the southern Kalahari, however group-living males and females, both adult and subadult, were observed to provision cubs regularly. Average distance in this population from which food was carried back to the den was 6·4 km.

Status and Conservation. Listed as Near Threatened on *The IUCN Red List*. In 1994 the species was down-listed from Appendix I status, which was afforded the species in 1975, to Appendix II by the IUCN and it has since been deleted from CITES listing altogether. It is generally considered to be widespread yet rare. The total population is estimated to be 5000 to 8000, but this may be an underestimate due to the secretive nature and nocturnal habits of this animal. It is estimated that areas in excess of 1000 km² are required to maintain a viable population of Brown Hyenas. These populations currently exist in the Kalahari Gemsbok National Park, South Africa and the adjacent Gemsbok National Park, Botswana, the Central Kalahari Game Reserve, Botswana, and the coastal regions of the southern Namib Desert. These are also the sites of the primary research projects that provide much of what we know about this species in the wild. Much of the habitat where Brown Hyenas occur outside protected areas is used for livestock ranching, and the hyenas are heavily persecuted (shot, poisoned, trapped, and hunted with dogs) in these areas because they are assumed to be livestock predators. This persecution, and habitat loss and fragmentation, are the primary threats to persistence of Brown Hyena. Because they are scavengers, many livestock carcasses where they are seen feeding are likely not to have been killed by Brown Hyenas. Although the species can be involved in depredation, this is usually restricted to a few individuals. Regardless, management of Brown Hyenas on ranchlands must address livestock losses. Typically, removal of individual problem hyenas ends the depredation. Because there is evidence that Brown Hyenas may be limited by the presence of Spotted Hyenas and perhaps other large predators, which are often absent from ranches, these ranchlands have the potential to be developed as Brown Hyena conservation areas, given proper management and conservation education efforts. Brown Hyenas are uncommon in captivity and traditionally do not breed well in confinement. Due to difficulties in captive breeding, the international studbook was discontinued in 1993 and as of 1995 there were only 16 specimens in nine collections. There is no known illegal trade in the species.

Bibliography. Eaton (1976), Gorman & Mills (1984), Maddock (1993), Mills (1982a, 1982b, 1982c, 1983a, 1983b, 1984a, 1990), Mills & Hofer (1998), Mills & Mills (1978, 1982), Mills *et al.* (1980), Owens, D.D. & Owens (1979a, 1979b, 1984, 1996), Owens, M.J. & Owens (1978), Schultz (1966), Shoemaker (1983), Siegfried (1984), Skinner (1976), Skinner & Ilani (1979), Skinner & Van Aarde (1981), Skinner *et al.* (1995), Stuart & Shaughnessy (1984), Wiesel (2006).

CLASS MAMMALIA

ORDER CARNIVORA

SUBORDER FELIFORMIA

Family HERPESTIDAE (MONGOOSES)

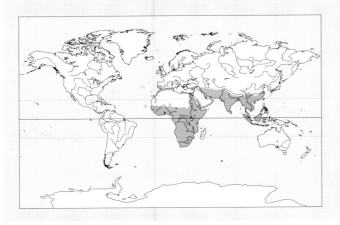

- Small-sized mammals with relatively uniform morphology characterized by a long face and body, short legs, small rounded ears, and long, tapering bushy tails.
- 34–151 cm.

- Old World tropics throughout Asia and Africa, also Middle East and southern Europe.
- Found in habitats ranging from open areas, such as deserts, savannah, and grasslands, to closed forest, over a wide elevation range, from lowlands to montane areas.
- 15 genera, 34 species, at least 84 extant taxa.
- 2 species Vulnerable; none Extinct since 1600.

Systematics

Today, 34 species of mongooses are recognized, although further taxonomic research may change this number. Twenty-five species are found in Africa and nine species in Asia. Mongooses are feliform carnivores that were traditionally included in the Viverridae (civets, genets, and oyans), but were later recognized as a separate family, the Herpestidae. This separation has now been confirmed by molecular studies; in fact, the mongooses are now shown to be closely related to the Hyaenidae (hyenas).

Phylogenetic relationships among the mongooses have been studied using morphological features, chromosomal data, and allozymes, and more recently by sequencing DNA and comparing the differences in the base pairs of mitochondrial and nuclear genes. The Herpestidae previously included the Malagasy mongooses, which were grouped in the subfamily

Galidiinae. Recent molecular studies have found that the Madagascar mongooses and the other Malagasy carnivores (such as the Fosa) are closely related to each other; together they form a monophyletic group that is an offshoot of the Herpestidae. All Malagasy carnivores are now placed in a separate family, the Eupleridae, a sister-group of the Herpestidae. The monophyly of the Madagascar Carnivores and their close relationship to the mongooses is supported by several morphological features, such as the presence of an anal pouch and a narrow paroccipital process (a bony process at the back of the skull that partly covers the caudal section of the auditory bullae). Around 18–24 million years ago, an African ancestor, close to the mongooses, colonized Madagascar and diversified into mongoose-like, civet-like, and cat-like carnivores on the island, in the absence of any other representatives of the Carnivora.

Within the Herpestidae, two subfamilies are now currently supported by morphological and molecular data, the Herpestinae (large, solitary mongooses) and the Mungotinae (small, social mongooses).

The subfamily Mungotinae comprises eleven mongoose species: Alexander's Cusimanse (*Crossarchus alexandri*), Angolan Cusimanse (*Crossarchus ansorgei*), Common Cusimanse (*Crossarchus obscurus*), Flat-headed Cusimanse (*Crossarchus platycephalus*), Pousargues's Mongoose (*Dologale dybowskii*), Ethiopian Dwarf Mongoose (*Helogale hirtula*), Common Dwarf Mongoose (*Helogale parvula*), Liberian Mongoose (*Liberiictis kuhni*), Gambian Mongoose (*Mungos gambianus*), Banded Mongoose (*Mungos mungo*), and the Meerkat (*Suricata suricatta*). As far as is known, all these mongooses are social and despite their differences share certain behavioral characteristics that may have been present in a common ancestor. The common belief that social mongooses only live in open habitat is not true, as some species live in forests (the cusimanses and the Liberian Mongoose), but the molecular phylogeny of the mongoose family suggests that sociality was initially favored by the opening up of forest habitats.

The Meerkat was recognized as a very distinct species and was previously placed in a separate subfamily (Suricatinae) on the basis of its peculiar morphology, but is now recognized as the sister-taxon to the clade containing all the other social mongooses.

The phylogenetic relationship of the poorly-known Liberian Mongoose was previously unclear, although it was suspected to be close to the cusimanses. A molecular phylogenetic study has now shown that the Liberian Mongoose is closely related to the other small social mongooses, but that it is closer to the Banded Mongoose than to the cusimanses. Recently, it has been observed foraging in groups of four to six individuals (though larger groups have also been seen), thus confirm-

*Thirty-four species of mongooses are recognized, although future taxonomic research may change this number. Mongooses were first included in the Viverridae (civets, genets and oyans), but they were later recognized as a separate family, and recent molecular studies have shown them to be closely related to the Hyaenidae (hyenas). The **Marsh Mongoose** is a member of the subfamily Herpestinae, which comprises 23 large, solitary mongoose species. The Marsh Mongoose is more closely related to the Long-nosed Mongoose than to the Herpestes mongooses.*

Atilax paludinosus
Photo: J & B Photography/
Photo Access

Subdivision of the Herpestidae

Figure: Toni Llobet

HERPESTIDAE

HERPESTINAE

MUNGOTINAE

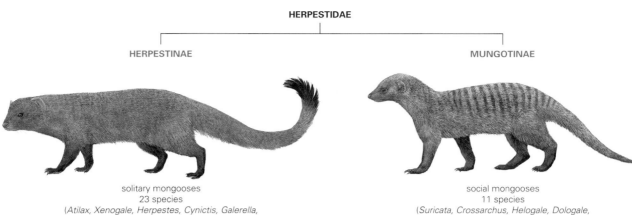

FAMILY
SUBFAMILY

solitary mongooses
23 species
(*Atilax, Xenogale, Herpestes, Cynictis, Galerella, Ichneumia, Paracynictis, Bdeogale, Rhynchogale*)

social mongooses
11 species
(*Suricata, Crossarchus, Helogale, Dologale, Liberiictis, Mungos*)

ing that this species displays the social behavior characteristics shared by the members of this subfamily. However, it does not share the dental formula of the small social species and has smaller cheek-teeth in relation to the size of the skull; it is also slightly larger than the other social mongooses. These differences may be adaptations to a diet specialized in earthworms.

The cusimanses (genus *Crossarchus*) have been shown by molecular studies to be the sister group of the dwarf mongooses (genus *Helogale*). The systematic position of Pousargues's Mongoose (which is believed to be close to these species) remains to be studied within a molecular phylogeny, as no genetic sample has yet been made available. Pousargues's Mongoose possesses the morphological features that characterize the social mongoose clade (notably small size, general body shape, tooth formula, and shape and size of the claws of the forefeet), but there is as yet no information on its social organization.

The subfamily Herpestinae comprises 23 mongoose species: Marsh Mongoose (*Atilax paludinosus*), Bushy-tailed Mongoose (*Bdeogale crassicauda*), Jackson's Mongoose (*Bdeogale jacksoni*), Black-footed Mongoose (*Bdeogale nigripes*), Yellow Mongoose (*Cynictis penicillata*), Angolan Slender Mongoose (*Galerella flavescens*), Somalian Slender Mongoose (*Galerella ochracea*), Cape Gray Mongoose (*Galerella pulverulenta*), Common Slender Mongoose (*Galerella sanguinea*), Small Indian Mongoose (*Herpestes auropunctatus*), Short-tailed Mongoose (*Herpestes brachyurus*), Indian Gray Mongoose (*Herpestes edwardsii*), In-

dian Brown Mongoose (*Herpestes fuscus*), Egyptian Mongoose (*Herpestes ichneumon*), Javan Mongoose (*Herpestes javanicus*), Collared Mongoose (*Herpestes semitorquatus*), Ruddy Mongoose (*Herpestes smithii*), Crab-eating Mongoose (*Herpestes urva*), Stripe-necked Mongoose (*Herpestes vitticollis*), White-tailed Mongoose (*Ichneumia albicauda*), Selous's Mongoose (*Paracynictis selousi*), Meller's Mongoose (*Rhynchogale melleri*), and the Long-nosed Mongoose (*Xenogale naso*). Although this subfamily is thought to comprise solitary species, almost nothing is known about the social behavior of many of the species within this group (particularly the Asian mongooses). A few field studies have revealed that some herpestine species have more complex social systems and inter-individual contacts than expected.

The relationships within the Herpestinae are poorly understood and many species have not yet been included in any molecular studies due to the difficulty of obtaining DNA samples. But molecular data shows that the genus *Herpestes* is not monophyletic, with the Egyptian Mongoose closely related to the species of *Galerella* and not to the other *Herpestes* species.

The genus *Galerella* has a confusing history with controversy over the number and identity of species within. Many authors have placed four of the African *Herpestes* (*flavescens, pulverulenta, sanguinea,* and *ochracea*) in the genus *Galerella*, based on allozyme and morphological data; however, this was not supported by one craniometric study. The first molecular phylogeny of the

The relationships within the Herpestinae are poorly understood. Molecular studies can help resolve species identification in situations where this is difficult to do on the basis of their morphology. The very similar **Small Indian Mongoose** *and Javan Mongoose were often considered conspecific, but a recent molecular study has shown that they should be considered separate species, being as distant from each other as they are from the Indian Gray Mongoose. Many mongoose species have not yet been included in any molecular studies due to the difficulty of obtaining DNA samples.*

Herpestes auropunctatus
India.
Photo: Iain Green/NHPA

The **Indian Gray Mongoose** is a member of the Herpestes genus, along with nine other mongoose species. Like the Marsh Mongoose, the sole member of the genus Atilax, and the mongooses in the Galerella genus, male Herpestes mongooses have one fewer chromosome than the female. Instead of the normal X and Y sex chromosomes, the Y chromosome is attached to an autosome (non-sex chromosome). Females have the usual two X sex chromosomes. This peculiar phenomenon does not occur in the other herpestine genera, and may help clarify the relationships of these mongooses. The translocation of a sex chromosome onto an autosome is very rare, and unlikely to have occurred several times, so it is possible that these mongooses share an ancestor in which this event occurred. The Indian Gray Mongoose is diurnal like many other species. Studies have revealed that some diurnal mongooses may have good color vision, which would help them find and recognize prey. Both the Indian Gray Mongoose and the Egyptian Mongoose have retinas with a central area composed almost entirely of cones, the receptor cells which are involved in color vision and which are able to function at high light intensities. The Indian Gray Mongoose can distinguish several colors from gray.

Herpestes edwardsii
Keoladeo Ghana National Park, Bharatpur, India.
Photo: Günter Ziesler

Herpestidae revealed that two species of *Galerella* (*pulverulenta* and *sanguinea*) are closely related to each other, but are distant enough to be considered distinct species. However, further research is needed to know whether these two species form a monophyletic group with the other *Galerella* species (*flavescens* and *ochracea*).

The Long-nosed Mongoose, previously included within the genus *Herpestes*, and currently the only member of the genus *Xenogale*, is now shown to be closer to the Marsh Mongoose (genus *Atilax*) than to any *Herpestes* species. These two mongooses share several morphological and ecological features, but there are sufficient differences to justify placing them in separate genera.

The systematics of the African Bushy-tailed and Black-footed mongooses (genus *Bdeogale*) have also been debated and they are currently separated into three species. A recent molecular study found that the genetic divergence between the Bushy-tailed Mongoose and the Black-footed Mongoose is similar to that found between other mongoose species, which justifies their status as separate species. The Sokoke Bushy-tailed Mongoose subspecies (*Bdeogale crassicauda omnivora*) has been considered a separate species on the basis of size and coat color characteristics, but the systematic status of this mongoose requires confirmation. Jackson's Mongoose has been considered either as conspecific with the Black-footed Mongoose or a separate species; its systematic status has not yet been investigated within a molecular phylogeny.

The Yellow Mongoose was considered to be closely related to the social mongooses on the basis of its morphology and social behavior. However, molecular studies have now shown that it should be included within the solitary mongoose subfamily (Herpestinae). Recent ethological studies have revealed that although this species can be observed in small groups, it does not exhibit some of the social behavior of the true social mongooses, like babysitting and group foraging. This is a gregarious species, but its colony size and social structure were overestimated. Also, the morphological features that prompted several authors to consider the Yellow Mongoose close to the small social mongooses appear to be the result of convergence in ecological and behavioral characteristics (open habitat, insectivorous diet, and communal burrows). In fact, the Yellow Mongoose shares morphological characters with the White-tailed Mongoose and these two species recently have been shown by molecular data to be related closely to each other and to the Bushy-tailed Mongoose, Black-footed Mongoose, and Meller's Mongoose.

Selous's Mongoose was also considered to be part of the Mungotinae, but it has now been shown by molecular analyses to be in the Herpestinae, and is probably closely related to the Yellow Mongoose.

Meller's Mongoose was believed to be related to the cusimanses and the Meerkat. It was then considered to be close to the White-tailed Mongoose and the Bushy-tailed Mongoose; this was recently confirmed by a molecular study, which also included the Yellow Mongoose within this group. The body shape of Meller's Mongoose is very similar to the White-tailed Mongoose, but it differs from other members of this clade by the absence of a groove on the upper lip, a distinctly snubby nose, and by the flatness of its molars.

The systematic position and taxonomic status of the Asian mongoose species (genus *Herpestes*) remains largely unconfirmed by molecular studies. However, it has been shown that they do not group with the African member of the genus, the Egyptian Mongoose. The very similar Small Indian Mongoose and Javan Mongoose were often considered conspecific, but a molecular study has now shown that they should be considered separate species, being as distant from each other as they are from the Indian Gray Mongoose. This finding highlights how little these species have been studied and that molecular studies can help resolve species identification in situations where this is difficult on the basis of their morphology.

Within the Herpestinae, some mongooses display a rare and interesting characteristic among mammals: the translocation of a sex chromosome onto an autosome. In males, instead of the normal X and Y sex chromosomes, the Y chromosome is attached to an autosome. Females have the usual two X sex chromosomes and as a consequence they have one more chromosome than males. As far as is known, this translocation occurs only in the genera *Herpestes*, *Galerella*, and *Atilax*. In the Indian Gray Mongoose, Javan Mongoose, and the Crab-eating Mongoose, the diploid chromosome number is 35 in males and 36 in females; the same is found in the Marsh Mongoose. A higher number of chromosomes is found in the Egyptian Mongoose and in the *Galerella* species, but still the male has one less chromosome than the female. This phenomenon does not occur in the other herpestine genera *Bdeogale*, *Cynictis*, and *Ichneumia*, which have the same number of chromosomes as those in the Mungotinae (a diploid number of 36). Whether it occurs in *Rhynchogale* and *Xenogale* is not known. This peculiar characteristic in *Herpestes*, *Galerella*, and *Atilax* may help clarify the relationships of these mongooses, as the translocation of a sex chromosome onto an autosome is a very rare event and is unlikely to have occurred several times. It is possible that the mongooses having this characteristic share an ancestor in which this event occurred.

The systematic status and validity of many mongoose subspecies are debated and taxonomic revisions are needed. Further genetic and morphological studies will help clarify species subdivisions and may highlight the role that geographic and ecological barriers have played. Some island or isolated popula-

Most of the Herpestes *mongooses are Asian. The only African member of the genus is the* **Egyptian Mongoose**. *But molecular analyses have now shown that the Egyptian Mongoose is more closely related to the species of* Galerella, *which are all African, than to the other* Herpestes *species. Despite its name, the Egyptian Mongoose is found throughout Africa, and into parts of the Middle East and Turkey. It also occurs in Spain and Portugal, where it was probably introduced.*

Herpestes ichneumon
Maa'gan Michael, Israel.
Photo: Yossi Eshbol/FLPA

Climatic changes over the last few million years, particularly the recent ices ages, may have affected the diversification and distribution of the Asian mongooses throughout South-east Asia. For example, the **Javan Mongoose** *is found on Sumatra and Java, but not on Borneo. During glacial periods, the climate was drier, colder, and more seasonal, and open habitats covered some areas, whereas other areas remained forest covered. This may have formed ecological barriers preventing the Javan Mongoose from using the land connections that existed between Borneo, Sumatra, and Java.*

Herpestes javanicus
Viti Levu, Fiji.
Photo: Roland Seitre

tions may be threatened, so it is imperative that we verify their taxonomic status.

The herpestid fossil record is very poor, making it difficult to retrace their evolutionary history. The first fossil considered as a herpestid is *Leptoplesictis*, which lived in Africa during the early Miocene (c. 17–18 million years ago) and in Europe during the middle Miocene. Some authors believe that the early mongooses originated in southern Asia. However, herpestids are unknown in Asia before the late Miocene. The collision that occurred between Africa and Asia at least 20–27 million years ago allowed for faunal and floral exchanges between these two continents, via the Arabian microplate. An additional Africa-Eurasia migration route was the connection between south-western Europe and North Africa. During the Miocene, mongoose species could have migrated from Asia to Africa, and vice versa. These routes may have persisted until the Early Pliocene, after which the Arabian Peninsula desertified and the strait of Gibraltar opened. Unambiguous fossilized modern mongoose genera have recently been found in late Miocene deposits in Pakistan (7–9·5 million years ago) and in Africa (around seven million years ago).

During the last few million years, climate changes caused expansions and contractions of forest and open habitats, which resulted in the diversification of African mongoose species. Some fossils of the early Pliocene (around five million years ago) of Africa have been attributed to the genus *Herpestes*. Representatives of the genera *Crossarchus*, *Cynictis*, *Helogale*, *Herpestes*, and *Mungos* have been found in the Late Pliocene (1·8–3·5 million years ago) of South Africa, and fossils of *Atilax* and *Suricata* occur in the early Pleistocene (0·8–1·8 million years ago).

The paleogeographic and climatic changes over the last few million years, particularly the recent ices ages, may have affected the diversification and the distribution of the Asian mongooses throughout South-east Asia. For example, the Javan Mongoose is found on Sumatra and Java, but not on Borneo. During glacial periods, the climate was drier, colder, and more seasonal, and open habitats covered some areas, whereas other areas remained forest covered. This may have formed ecological barriers that prevented the Javan Mongoose from using some of the land connections that existed between Borneo, Sumatra, and Java. Physical barriers also may have affected the distribution of some species over the Sunda shelf. During the last glacial maximum, large rivers flowed between Java and Borneo, and between Peninsular Malaysia and Borneo, separating

the landmasses. Unfortunately, with a very scarce fossil record, dispersal events of mongooses are difficult to date and link to climatic changes and palaeobiogeographical events.

Morphological Aspects

Mongooses are slender, small carnivores, ranging from the 200 g Common Dwarf Mongoose to the 5 kg White-tailed Mongoose. They have a relatively uniform morphology and are characterized by their small size, long face and body, short legs, small rounded ears, and long, tapering bushy tails. They all share a number of anatomical features, such as the structure of the auditory bullae, specialized ear cartilage, and the presence of an anal pouch. Mongooses are digitigrade (stand and move on their toes) and are mainly terrestrial; there have been a few observations of mongooses climbing in trees, but they are generally considered poor tree-climbers. All species swim well when forced to do so and a few species are semi-aquatic, such as the Marsh Mongoose in Africa and the Crab-eating Mongoose in Asia.

Mongooses generally have a uniform pelage with long coarse hairs; these hairs are ringed with different colors in some species, giving a grizzled aspect to the coat. The pelage color varies from light gray or yellow to brown or black, and the feet, legs, tail, or tail tip are often a different hue. Considerable variation in coat color can occur within a species across its range; this may be correlated with soil color, suggesting that camouflage is important for survival. The tail is particularly short in the Short-tailed Mongoose, where it is less than half the length of the head and body. In many other mongooses, it is as long as the head and body, as in the Indian Gray Mongoose or the Ruddy Mongoose. The tail is particularly bushy in some of the larger species, such as the Bushy-tailed Mongoose, and in the White-tailed Mongoose the tail is a different color than that of the body: it is entirely white throughout most of the species' range, although some West African populations possess a black tail. No mongoose species has spots and only a few have stripes on the body; the Banded Mongoose and Meerkat have dark transverse stripes across the back, and the Stripe-necked, Crab-eating, Collared, Liberian, and Gambian mongooses all have a colored band on the side of the neck, from the ear to the shoulder. It has been suggested that this neck stripe may act as a warning to other predators, because mongooses can ex-

Mongooses are digitigrade; that is, they stand and move on their toes. They are primarily terrestrial, although some may occasionally climb trees. These include the Common Cusimanse, Liberian Mongoose, Banded Mongoose, and, shown here, the **Ruddy Mongoose***, which has been observed hunting, feeding, and resting in trees. In the Ruddy Mongoose and many other mongooses, the tail is as long as the head and body. However this can vary: in Sri Lanka, the Ruddy Mongoose's tail varies from 75% to 90% of the head and body length, whereas it is 90% to 110% of the head and body length in India.*

Herpestes smithii
Yala National Park, Sri Lanka.
Photo: Rolf Kunz

pel a malodorous secretion from their anal glands. This stripe may also play a bite-directing role in intra-specific encounters, which can occur between a mother and play-fighting young or adult males and females during courtship. This mark is then assumed to direct bites to a specific region where there are no vital structures.

The snout is fairly long, with well-developed vibrissae (whiskers) on the muzzle (mystacial), above the eyes (superciliary), on the cheeks (genal), and below the chin (inter-ramal), although these are somewhat reduced in the more fossorial (burrowing) Meerkat. Sebaceous glands producing a honey-like substance have been found at the base of the genal vibrissae in the Indian Gray Mongoose. This feature may be present in other mongoose species; the Common Dwarf Mongoose, the Marsh Mongoose, and the Common Cusimanse have been observed rubbing their cheeks on various objects. The rhinarium is quite large in some species. It is not known how well mongooses can smell, but Meerkats have been observed to make the grimace known as flehmen, commonly seen in cats: the lips are pulled up, the nose is wrinkled and drawn back, and the head is raised. This response is evoked by strong-smelling substances; flehming might serve to bring odors into contact with the Jacobson's organ (a pouch lined with receptor cells in the roof of the mouth). It is not known how developed or universal the flehmen response or Jacobson's organ are among the herpestids.

Mongoose ears are small and rounded, and lack a bursa (a folded purse of skin on the outer rim), a feature that is typically found in other carnivores. In the Yellow Mongoose, which has the largest ears of any mongoose, a small depression at the posterior margin may represent a vestigial bursa. The ears of the fossorial mongooses, such as the Meerkat, can be closed by the apposition of the ear ridges: the posterior ridges are moved forward and the superior ridge is moved downward so that both contact the anterior ridge.

Most carnivores, particularly nocturnal species, have eyes with a reflective layer outside the receptor layer of the retina called the tapetum lucidum. Light that has passed through the retina without being absorbed is reflected back again and so has a second chance of stimulating a receptor. When a bright light is shone in the eye the resulting "eyeshine" is produced by reflected light that has not been absorbed, which then passes back to the observer. The nocturnal Marsh Mongoose and

White-tailed Mongoose have very obvious eyeshine, whereas in the Common Cusimanse (which is largely diurnal, but will forage after dark), eyeshine is present but less striking. The diurnal Yellow Mongoose and Meerkat are said to lack a tapetum and several other diurnal species also may lack this feature. Several mongoose species are known to have horizontal, elongated oval pupils and this may be characteristic of the Herpestidae as a whole. This feature has the advantage of extending the visual field in the horizontal plane, which may be of value to short-legged, terrestrial mongooses. Studies of color vision in carnivore species have revealed that some mongooses (at least the diurnal species) may have good color vision, which would be expected in those species that search for food by day and where color may help in recognizing and distinguishing different prey types. Color vision is mediated by receptor cells

Mongooses generally have a uniform pelage, with long coarse hairs that may be ringed with different colors in some species, giving a grizzled aspect to the coat, as in the **Crab-eating Mongoose***. Considerable variation in coat color can occur within a species across its range. In the Crab-eating Mongoose, its coat color varies from gray to blackish-brown. In some mongoose species, variations in coat color may be correlated with soil color, suggesting that camouflage is important for survival.*

Herpestes urva
Photo: Ian Beames/Ardea

within the eye called cones, which are able to function at high light intensities. Both the Egyptian Mongoose and the Indian Gray Mongoose have retinas with a central area composed almost entirely of cones, and the Indian Gray Mongoose is able to distinguish several colors from gray. Another feature of the carnivore eye is a well-developed nictitating membrane, which in many species can be pulled right across the eye and protects or cleans the eye surface.

Most mongoose species have feet with five digits; however, the pollex and hallux are missing in the Meerkat, Black-footed Mongoose, Bushy-tailed Mongoose, and Selous's Mongoose; only the hallux is missing in the Yellow Mongoose. This characteristic may indicate that these species are more cursorial than the other mongooses. Mongoose feet are long and narrow, with the long toes closely bound together. The metacarpal and metatarsal pads are not very distinct and the surface of the foot is mostly naked or covered with a few hairs on the posterior section. The claws are not retractable and are often long and curved, particularly in the small social species that live in burrows. Many mongooses use their claws for digging, and although they become worn down they remain reasonably sharp; the claws on the forefeet grow much faster than those on the hindfeet. The Marsh Mongoose has soft naked palms and long, sensitive, unwebbed fingers, which are used to find food in turbid water or soft mud. Except for the Marsh Mongoose and the Short-tailed Mongoose, mongooses—most notably the Long-nosed Mongoose—have partly-webbed feet, but the web is often reduced in some species.

Mongooses have anal glands, as do most carnivore species. The anal sacs are located under the skin of the anal region and open directly into the rectum through a short canal or duct. The secretion of the anal gland has a characteristic odor and consists of cholesterol esters, monoester waxes, cholesterol, and fatty acids. In the mongooses, the skin around the anus is invaginated to form an anal pouch, usually closing to form a transverse line. The ducts of the anal sacs open into this pouch; when the secretion is to be applied the pouch is everted to expose the openings, which may lie on either side of the anus or distinctly above it. In some species the lining of the pouch itself also contains enlarged cutaneous glands, which are uniformly distributed in the Marsh Mongoose, whereas in the social mongooses *Helogale*, *Mungos*, and *Suricata*, the lining of the pouch is folded into pockets, in which the secretion of the anal glands is presumably stored. An anal pouch also is found in the Madagascar Carnivores and the hyenas.

Most mongooses have a small, low skull, with a fairly short muzzle (compared to civets and genets). The post-orbital processes of the jugal and frontal bones are long in all mongooses, and in *Cynictis*, *Galerella*, *Ichneumia*, *Paracynictis*, and *Suricata*,

these processes reach each other and close the orbit completely. The shape of the skull is very peculiar in the Meerkat, being round and short, with the orbits placed in a more forward-looking position, giving them greater binocular vision and ability to judge distances. Meerkats are diurnal, live in open habitats, and detect predators by standing or sitting on their haunches and moving their head from side to side.

The auditory bulla (a bony case surrounding the middle ear) of feliform carnivores has two chambers separated by a bilaminar septum. The ectotympanic bone forms the anterior chamber, which expands laterally into a well-developed bony tube (the external auditory meatal tube); the caudal entotympanic bone forms the posterior chamber. The anterior chamber is inflated and much enlarged in some mongooses (such as the Yellow Mongoose and Selous's Mongoose), in which it has a characteristic "C" shape, and is larger than the posterior chamber. In the other mongooses, the anterior chamber is also well-inflated, but remains smaller than the posterior chamber. The posterior chamber is inflated ventrally and laterally in mongooses, but it does not extend toward the anterior region, unlike the civets, for instance. The caudal part of the auditory bullae is cupped by the paroccipital apophysis, which is narrow enough that the mastoid process is exposed when viewing the skull from its caudal side. This is different from the viverrids, in which the paroccipital apophysis is wider and covers the posterior of the bullae and the mastoid process. The Madagascar Carnivores display the same condition as the mongooses, supporting the close relationship of the Madagascar Carnivores to the Herpestidae.

Mongooses generally have 40 teeth, with a dental formula of three incisors, one canine, four premolars, and two molars on each side of the upper and lower jaws (I 3/3, C 1/1 P 4/4, M 2/2). The first upper and lower premolars are absent in some genera (*Crossarchus*, *Dologale*, *Helogale*, and *Mungos*, total = 36 teeth), and the first lower premolars are often absent in some individuals of *Herpestes* and *Galerella* (total = 38 teeth). In the Marsh Mongoose, the small first premolars are sometimes present but are commonly absent, so that the number of teeth in this species is 36, 38, or 40. The small incisors are mainly used for nipping food items, such as the flesh from carcasses, and the canines are used to grasp and kill prey by piercing the neck or skull. The characteristic carnassial teeth (the fourth upper premolar and the first lower molar) are specially adapted to cutting through flesh with a scissor-like action. The premolars, depending on their particular shape, may either aid in holding prey or, like the molars, be used mainly for crushing food items. All mongooses have a somewhat varied diet and in each species the teeth are modified according to the relative importance of different types of food. In many species the dentition

*No mongoose species has spots, and only a few have stripes on the body. The **Stripe-necked Mongoose**, Crab-eating Mongoose, Collared Mongoose, Liberian Mongoose, and Gambian Mongoose all have a colored band on the side of the neck, from the ear to the shoulder. It has been suggested that this neck stripe may act as a warning to other predators because mongooses can expel a malodorous secretion from their anal glands. The stripe may also direct play bites and courtship bites to an area where there are no vital organs.*

Herpestes vitticollis
Sri Lanka.
Photo: Joanna Van Gruisen/Ardea

Mongoose ears are small and rounded, and lack a bursa (a folded purse of skin on the outer rim), which is a feature typical of other carnivores. In the **Yellow Mongoose**, which has the largest ears of any mongoose, a small depression at the posterior margin may represent a vestigial bursa.

The eyes of most carnivores, particularly nocturnal species, have a cell layer called the tapetum lucidum, which reflects light back, causing their eyes to shine in headlights. The diurnal Yellow Mongoose, and the Meerkat, are said to lack a tapetum, and several other diurnal mongoose species may not have this feature. The Yellow Mongoose was considered to be closely related to the social mongooses, such as the Meerkat, on the basis of its morphology and social behavior. However, molecular studies have now shown that it should be included within the solitary mongoose subfamily (Herpestinae). Its similarities to the small, social mongooses appear to be the result of convergence in ecological and behavioral characteristics (open habitat, insectivorous diet, and communal burrows). In fact, the Yellow Mongoose shares morphological characters with the White-tailed Mongoose, and these two species have recently been shown by molecular data to be closely related to each other, as well as to the Bushy-tailed Mongoose, Black-footed Mongoose, and Meller's Mongoose. Despite its name, the Yellow Mongoose's coat color ranges from dark tawny to grayish-yellow. This wide color variation has resulted in the description of up to twelve subspecies, which are now mostly considered invalid.

Cynictis penicillata
Kalahari Gemsbok National Park,
South Africa.
Photo: Tony Heald/naturepl.com

The genus Galerella *has a
confusing history and contains
a debated species composition.
The first molecular study of the
Herpestidae revealed that two
species, the* **Cape Gray Mongoos**
*and the Common Slender
Mongoose, are closely related to
each other, but are distant enoug
to be considered distinct species.
Further research is needed to kno
whether these two species form a
monophyletic group with the othe
two* Galerella *species, the Angol
Slender Mongoose and the
Somalian Slender Mongoose. Th
formerly recognized subspecies of
the Cape Gray Mongoose are no
regarded as synonymous with the
Angolan Slender Mongoose.*

Galerella pulverulenta
Cape Town, South Africa.
Photo: David Hosking/FLPA

shows adaptations relating to a carnivorous or insectivorous diet: the cusps of the premolars and molars are sharp, the canines are long, and the carnassials are well-developed. For example, the Yellow Mongoose is an efficient killer of small vertebrate prey and has long canines and a relatively well-developed carnassial shear. The Meerkat, which feeds largely on insects, has sharp-cusped, interlocking teeth, but the carnassial shear is very poorly developed. In the Marsh Mongoose the teeth, particularly the posterior premolars, are very robust and capable of breaking through the shells of crabs. Meller's Mongoose and the Bushy-tailed Mongoose have an insectivorous diet and their premolars and molars are large and low, with rounded cusps, which is an adaptation for crushing and grinding.

A baculum (a small bone within the penis) is present in herpestids. This penis bone is found throughout the Carnivora (except the Hyaenidae) and may help in penetrating the vaginal orifice and providing vaginal stimulation. In its simplest form, it is a rod-like structure, grooved below for the passage of the urethra and the corpus spongiosum. The baculum varies among species, each showing distinctive characters, although the function and the significance of the different shapes and sizes are not entirely clear.

Habitat

The Herpestidae are principally distributed in Asia and Africa, and occupy a latitudinal band from Spain to South Africa. Different mongoose species are associated with certain habitat types, on a macro (geographic or biome) and micro (localized) scale. The biomes (gross ecosystem/habitat types) occupied by the herpestids include chaparral, hot desert, thorn forest, tropical evergreen forest, tropical deciduous forest, savannah, temperate grassland, and temperate evergreen forest. Within these biomes, the Herpestidae occupy a diverse range of ecosystems, from dry arid habitats (e.g. the Meerkat and Ethiopian Dwarf Mongoose) to riparian habitats (e.g. the Marsh Mongoose and Crab-eating Mongoose). They are found in habitats ranging from open areas, such as savannah/grasslands (e.g. the Meerkat), to closed forest (e.g. the cusimanse species and Liberian Mongoose). In particular, three genera, *Herpestes*, *Bdeogale*, and *Crossarchus*, are principally occupants of forest habitats, along with the Liberian and Long-nosed Mongooses. The black form of the Angolan Slender Mongoose (*Galerella flavescens nigrata*) is said to be petrophilic (restricted to rocky habitats); its color

a camouflage adaptation to its shadowy habitat. The remaining mongoose species are generally inhabitants of more open terrain.

Mongooses occur over a wide elevation range, from lowlands to montane areas, with records for the Crab-eating Mongoose up to 2000 m, the Indian Gray Mongoose to 2100 m, the Stripe-necked Mongoose to 2133 m, and the Ruddy Mongoose to 2200 m. A relic population of Alexander's Cusimanse occurs on Mount Elgon, Uganda at 2900 m, and Jackson's Mongoose has been observed at 3300 m.

Mongooses are primarily terrestrial, although some may occasionally climb trees (e.g. the Common Cusimanse, Liberian Mongoose, and Banded Mongoose), and some occasionally take to the water (e.g. the Marsh Mongoose and the Crab-eating Mongoose). There are no truly arboreal or aquatic members of the herpestid family.

Habitat type and mongoose gross morphology appear to be correlated. The open-terrain mongooses, such as the Common Dwarf Mongoose, Ethiopian Dwarf Mongoose, Meerkat, and Yellow Mongoose, are relatively small sized, with body weights ranging from around 200 g to 900 g. Their body shape is generally low-slung, with a long body and relatively small, short head and muzzle. The forest mongooses, such as the cusimanses and the Liberian Mongoose, are larger, weighing between 450 g and 2·3 kg. Their body shape is fatter, and their head relatively larger, with a proportionally longer muzzle. The specific selective pressures leading to these morphological associations with habitat type are unclear.

The sensory faculties of mongooses also appear to be adapted to their habitat. The spectral quality of the large, bright green tapetum lucidum in the eye of the Small Indian Mongoose matches the spectral radiometric measures of its typically grassy environment. The diurnal open-habitat mongooses, the Common Dwarf Mongoose and Meerkat, are said to have acute long-distance vision, enabling them to detect and recognize potential aerial predators kilometres away. Mongoose behavior is also related to habitat in the riparian mongooses; the Marsh Mongoose and Crab-eating Mongoose are said to be good swimmers.

The vegetation characteristics of different habitats can influence mongoose density. A survey of carnivore abundance in the Kalahari showed that Meerkat density decreases with increasing shrub cover. Yellow Mongoose numbers increase with increasing shrub cover up to 10–18%, but then decrease at higher shrub densities. For the Yellow Mongoose, the amount

Over 40 subspecies of the **Common Slender Mongoose** have been described, mostly on the basis of unreliable characters, such as size and coat color. Of these, the Somalian Slender Mongoose is now considered a valid species. The others are not considered valid here, but this may be changed by further studies, including genetic analyses. The coat color is quite varied, from almost black to bright red, but most frequently is grizzled brown-grayish. The grizzled appearance derives from individual hairs having very light bands alternating with dark ones. The Common Slender Mongoose is a better climber than most mongooses, but its feet are adapted to life on the ground. Mongoose feet are long and narrow, with the long toes closely bound together. The surface of the foot is mostly naked or covered with a few hairs on the posterior section. Most mongoose species have feet with five digits.

Although the Common Slender Mongoose does have five digits on each foot, the first one is reduced. Its heel pads are not haired, and a narrow web connects the digits. Mongoose claws are not retractable and are often long and curved, particularly in the small, social species that live in burrows. Many mongooses use their claws for digging, and although they become worn down they remain reasonably sharp; the claws on the forefeet grow much faster than those on the hindfeet. The Common Slender Mongoose is capable of digging its own dens, but often prefers to usurp them from other animals.

Galerella sanguinea
Namibia.
Photo: David Hosking/FLPA

*Mongooses range in size from the 200 g Common Dwarf Mongoose to the 5 kg **White-tailed Mongoose**. As in some other large mongooses, the White-tailed Mongoose's tail is bushy. In contrast to the dark body color, its tail is entirely white throughout most of the species' range, although some West African populations possess a black tail. The tail is apparently used in visual signaling: a threatened individual will erect its fur and tail as well as vocalize. It has relatively long legs, and its skeleton is taller and more dog-like than that of other herpestids.*

Ichneumia albicauda
South Luangwa National Park, Zambia.
Photo: Philip Perry/FLPA

of shrub cover presents a trade-off between burrow protection (a positive effect of cover) and prey availability (a negative effect of cover). Slender Mongooses are relatively unaffected by shrub cover. These findings have important implications for habitat management and mongoose conservation, as overgrazing leads to increased shrub encroachment on savannah rangelands.

Food availability and predation pressure within a habitat are the principal two factors that are instrumental in determining the presence, density, and social organization of the Herpestidae. The type and density of food available is determined to a large degree by habitat type. Riparian habitats are associated with aquatic prey, e.g. crustacea, amphibia, and fish. Open habitats are associated with higher invertebrate densities and bush habitats tend to support higher densities of small vertebrates.

The spatial use of an area generally differs between mongoose species and is often dependent upon habitat variables. For instance, the riparian Marsh Mongoose has home ranges that tend to be long and thin, following a stream or river. Mongoose species are often sympatric (overlapping in geographic range), and this is accommodated via niche partitioning. Different mongoose species occupy different ecological niches, principally by adapting to or preferring a differing habitat or diet. For example, a study of two similarly-sized sympatric herpestids in a coastal area of South Africa, the Cape Gray Mongoose and Yellow Mongoose, found that these species occupy different habitat and dietary niches. The Cape Gray Mongoose prefers bush habitat, where its vertebrate prey is abundant. The Yellow Mongoose prefers open habitat, where its invertebrate prey is abundant. Although mongoose species can often be partitioned via habitat preference, there is also evidence of flexibility and broad habitat tolerance in the absence of herpestid competition. The successful introduction of the Small Indian Mongoose to a variety of new locations and habitats is testament to this.

The openness of a habitat type may have a great impact, not just on food availability, but also on the vulnerability of a mongoose species to predation. This is one possible argument for the evolution of sociality within the mongooses, as the majority of social species inhabit open terrain. However, the forest-living cusimanses and the Liberian Mongoose are also considered to be social species, which calls the importance of open habitat into question. Nevertheless, mongoose species occupying open habitats are likely to be more vulnerable to predators, and this can have important implications for survival, reproductive success, and population density. For example, population fluctuations in the Banded Mongoose in open grassland are potentially linked to predation pres-

sure. Banded Mongoose densities are substantially higher in Uganda (18 individuals/km²) than Tanzania (2 individuals/km²). This difference may reflect higher food availability and/or a lower density of large predators in Uganda. Alternatively, the difference in population density may be linked to differences in habitat structure. High amounts of rain in Uganda promote vegetation growth, a more complex vegetated habitat, and thereby likely reduced vulnerability of Banded Mongooses to predators. As predation pressure is thought to be a major selective pressure favoring the evolution of sociality within the group-living herpestids, it would be interesting to know whether predation pressure in forest habitats is relatively high, and if not, what other factors favor group living in some forest mongoose species.

Den availability is also an important habitat variable affecting the presence and density of mongooses. For instance, Common Dwarf Mongoose distribution is affected by termite mound availability. In this species, termite mounds are used not only as dens for sleeping at night, but also for rearing young during their first month of life, and as look-out posts and refuges from predators. Common Dwarf Mongooses occur at a higher density in areas where there are more termite mounds, which reflects not just a habitat preference, but a selective advantage: groups that occupy areas with high termite mound density experience lower mortality and increased reproductive success. In fact, a high density of shelter sites is the best determinant of Common Dwarf Mongoose density, and they only occur in areas that lack termite mounds if there are suitable alternatives available, e.g. rock kopjes. Den/rest site availability is also of importance to the White-tailed Mongoose and the Common Cusimanse, as they may be unable to excavate their own dens. Other mongoose species, however, can modify their habitat to create suitable den, resting, or refuge sites: Meerkat group members are actively involved in the digging and maintenance of dens and boltholes, and Yellow Mongooses also dig their own dens.

Mongooses potentially play a major role in ecosystem dynamics. Those species that dig dens or dig to forage may have a large impact on their habitat, and could be considered as ecosystem engineers, contributing to the complexity of the environment and aiding in the mixing of soil. For example, the Liberian Mongoose, while foraging for earthworms, may affect seedling recruitment and mortality through its disturbance of the soil. In the Serengeti (Tanzania), the small carnivore guild preys on beetles, ants, and termites. These invertebrates play a major role in the ecosystem: dung beetles recycle nutrients into the soil, ants utilize a diversity of resources, and termites consume grass. Mongooses may also have a significant impact

Within the Herpestidae, there are two subfamilies that are supported by morphological and molecular data: the Herpestinae (large, solitary mongooses) and the Mungotinae (small, social mongooses). There are eleven species in the Mungotinae, including the **Meerkat**. The common belief that social mongooses only live in open habitat is not true. Some species, such as the cusimanses and the iberian Mongoose, live in forests. However, the evolutionary history of the mongooses suggests that the velopment of sociality was indeed initially favored by the opening up of forest habitats. As far as is known, all the Mungotinae mongooses are social, and despite their differences, share certain havioral characteristics that may have been present in a common ancestor. The Meerkat was previously placed in a separate subfamily (Suricatinae) on the basis of its peculiar morphology, but is now recognized as a sister taxon to the clade containing all the other social mongooses. The shape of the skull is very peculiar in the Meerkat, being round and short, with the orbits of the eyes placed in a more forward-looking position, giving them greater binocular vision and ability to judge distances. The eye sockets make up more than 20% of the total skull length. Meerkats are diurnal, live in open habitats, and detect predators by standing or sitting on their haunches and moving their head from side to side. They are also able to close eir ears, an adaptation found in other burrowing mongooses.

Suricata suricatta
Kalahari, Namibia.
Photo: Monika Dossenbach

on population numbers of agricultural pests, by preying on invertebrate and small vertebrate species.

The high densities of some herpestids also support the notion that they can have a large impact on ecosystem dynamics. Some species of mongooses are abundant in Africa, and can occur at local densities higher than other carnivore families. In the Serengeti, the guild of Common Dwarf, Banded, Slender, and White-tailed Mongooses reach densities an order of magnitude higher than other Serengeti carnivores, reaching five Common Dwarf Mongooses per km², two Banded Mongooses per km², five Common Slender Mongooses per km², and four White-tailed Mongooses per km².

Competition for resources is likely to be higher between closely related species than distantly related ones. The high diversity of mongooses in some areas is therefore of great interest. Coexistence suggests some form of resource partitioning, which may occur through temporal, spatial (e.g. habitat), or dietary means. A radio-tracking study of a four-species herpestid assemblage (Egyptian, Slender, Marsh, and Banded Mongooses) in South Africa found differential habitat selection. The Egyptian Mongoose was found to prefer open habitat, the Common Slender Mongoose selected forest habitat, the Marsh Mongoose was associated with water and adjacent forest, and the Banded Mongoose appeared to select scrub forest. Such restricted habitat utilization in the absence of other mongoose species is unlikely.

Mongoose species overlap with other carnivores, with which they may compete for prey (e.g. civets, genets, and foxes) or may be in danger of becoming prey (e.g. Leopards, Lions, and hyenas). The co-occurrence of these other carnivore species may well affect presence, density, and habitat use by herpestids. In the Serengeti, there appears to be a negative correlation between White-tailed Mongoose density and Bat-eared Fox and Aardwolf densities.

A number of mongoose species are found near or within human settlements. In some cases, they adapt well and utilize human garbage as a supplemental food source. The Indian Gray, Cape Gray, Small Indian, Banded, and White-tailed mongooses are all observed near human settlements. In addition, Cape Gray, White-tailed, and Banded Mongooses are all known to use buildings, woodpiles, and other human structures as dens. In contrast, the Stripe-necked Mongoose and Ansorge's Cusimanse are rarely seen near human settlements. Although supplemental food may attract (and benefit) mongooses, there can be negative effects from a close association with humans. For example, 45 White-tailed Mongooses were killed in one year

by domestic dogs in a Ugandan town. Also in Uganda, Banded Mongooses foraging in garbage dumps experience higher encounter rates with potential predators, including marabous (*Leptoptilos crumeniferus*), Nile monitors (*Varanus niloticus*), and even Common Warthogs (*Phacochoerus africanus*).

Communication

Communication by definition requires a signal to be sent, a receptor or receiver to detect the information, and the ability to process and utilize the information detected. Sensors are therefore as important as signals when it comes to communication. Herpestids are considered to possess good sight, hearing, and smell. Unfortunately little is known of mongoose morphology and physiology with regard to these sensory modalities. However, herpestids, particularly the social species, possess a relatively well-developed ability to communicate with conspecifics through behavioral displays, sound, and scent.

Compared to sound and scent, visual communication (excluding secondary visual communication by visually marking the environment) can only be used effectively when individuals are at relatively close range. Posturing appears to be involved in dominance and subordination behavior in a number of species, particularly the social mongooses. In the Meerkat, Common Dwarf Mongoose, Banded Mongoose, and Yellow Mongoose, interactions within groups often include one individual standing erect, indicating dominance, while another assumes a lowered, crouching, or cowering posture, indicating subordination. Tail position is also thought to indicate emotional state and dominance in some species, and it is notable that some mongooses have an obvious color difference on the tail or the tail tip, which may be involved in highlighting signals. The nocturnal White-tailed Mongoose has a white tail that contrasts with its dark body, although some West African populations have a black tail. This mongoose arches its tail when it is scent marking and when it is close to conspecifics. In the Yellow Mongoose, which has a conspicuous white tail tip, tail position can apparently indicate "neutrality" (straight tail with decline toward tip), "danger" (erect S-shape), "satisfaction" (horizontal between base and tip with downward kink in mid-tail), and "uncertainty" (horizontal between base and tip with upward kink in mid-tail). Such visual signalling of status or emotional state is probably used by the majority of mongooses when interacting at close range with other individuals. In the social mongooses, it is likely that posture also plays a role in intergroup communi-

The smallest of the mongooses, the **Common Dwarf Mongoose**, is found in a wide range of habitats, and its coat color varies geographically, from yellow to black. The coat color is uniform both above and below, with no difference between the sexes. The open-terrain mongooses, such as the Common Dwarf Mongoose, Ethiopian Dwarf Mongoose, Meerkat, and Yellow Mongoose, are all relatively small-sized, with body weights ranging from around 200 g to 900 g. Their body shape is generally low-slung, with a long body and relatively small, short head and muzzle.

The forest mongooses, such as the cusimanses and the Liberian Mongoose, are larger, weighing between 450 g and 2·3 kg. Their body shape is fatter, and their heads are relatively larger, with a proportionally longer muzzle. The specific selective pressures leading these morphological associations with habitat type are unclear. Common Dwarf Mongooses are associated with termite mounds, which they use both as dens and as lookout posts. Like Meerkats, they are able to spot potential predators great distances. Group members, principally subordinate males, take turns standing guard, and give a "watchman's song" to inform the group that they are on duty. Alarm calls convey information on predator type and urgency: for instance, calls are shorter and higher in pitch, the more immediate the danger. Warning vocalizations appear to be instinctive; Common Dwarf Mongoose young will produce them in response to objects moving overhead.

Helogale parvula
Above: Chobe National Park, Botswana.
Photo: Terry Carew/Photo Access

Below: Waterberg Plateau National Park, Namibia.
Photo: Dick Forsman

cation. In the Meerkat "war dance", individuals piloerect, arch the back, stiffen their legs, erect the tail, and rock back and forth from their front to their back legs. The bunching and to-and-fro movements of Meerkat, Common Dwarf Mongoose, and Banded Mongoose groups when attempting to repel a terrestrial predator, may also be a form of deceptive signalling—appearing as a large super-organism to repel the predator.

Because of the shy, solitary nature of the majority of mongoose species and the fact that they do not advertize their presence by vocalizing, as Lions or Gray Wolves do, information on their vocalizations is scant. The mechanics of vocalization are also unknown. Are they produced via inhalation or exhalation? Is the principal structure the larynx, pharynx, oral, or nasal cavity? Nevertheless, field and captive studies have provided some information on the vocalizations produced by various species and their role in communication.

Vocalizations are often accompanied by characteristic signalling behaviors. For example, in Banded Mongooses, a "spit" is often accompanied by a lunge and a "growl" by a hunched body shape. As such, vocalizations are often associated with context, and likely contain referential and emotional information. As with other mammalian groups, social mongoose species tend to have a wider vocal repertoire and make greater use of vocalizations than do solitary species. However, there is also a surprising vocabulary of vocalization in asocial mongooses. Most species appear at the very least to have distinct vocalizations for aggression, alarm, and pain, although the last is reported to be absent in the Common Dwarf Mongoose, Meerkat, and Common Cusimanse.

Twelve distinct vocal categories have been identified for the Small Indian Mongoose, including weep, squawk, honk, ruck-a-ruck, pant, spit, bark, chuck, scream, and growl. The White-tailed Mongoose mutters while digging for insects, growls, grunts, or barks if threatened, and screams if hurt. The vocal repertoire of captive Marsh Mongooses includes bark-growl threats, excitement bleats, and moan/bleats that may fulfill a contact role. The Egyptian Mongoose has seven distinct vocalizations: an alarm call, consisting of a deep sharp growl that causes other individuals to flee; a contact call of short duration, repeated by group members to maintain contact during foraging; a growl associated with food defence, mating, and territorial defence; a bark/spit given during mating or fighting; and a pain call of a short, sharp, vigorous nature. None of these, except the pain call, is used when alone. Vocalizations in the Yellow Mongoose include an alarm bark eliciting others to run to a bolthole, a growl emitted in defence of food items, a purring during copulation, and a high-pitched scream during fights.

Vocalizations are best understood in the social species; the Banded Mongoose, Common Dwarf Mongoose, and Meerkat. These species all give a regular contact call while foraging. These short-pulse duration "soft" calls are emitted by each group member every few seconds (average frequency is 0·26 calls per second during active periods for the Common Dwarf Mongoose). They are apparently unsynchronized, and likely serve to maintain group cohesion while foraging. Contact calls enable each individual to remain with the group without constantly having to check visually, and may also enable individual recognition. In the Common Dwarf Mongoose, contact calls (around 1·6 kHz) differ in base frequency among individuals. Lead or "moving out" calls are given by the dominant female in Common Dwarf and Banded Mongooses, and elicit the group to follow. Growls and spits are used in defence of resources when another group member approaches or attempts to steal the resource. Shrill "war" cries are used to alert group members to a rival group and to elicit recruitment, bunching, and charges. Short sharp alarm calls, given upon sighting a potential predator, elicit rapid evasive behavior. "Worry" calls warn group members of lower intensity danger, and bring the group together when vigilance is necessary. In the Banded Mongoose, worry calls are harmonic with a fundamental frequency of 0·4–0·7 kHz; they occur either singly or in a volley. They are associated with an alert head-up posture and are principally made when there are secondary cues (scent) indicating other Banded Mongoose groups or predators.

Young mongooses also vocalize. Once they are weaned, pups of all species spend weeks or months following and being provisioned by adults. In the Common Dwarf Mongoose, Meerkat, and Banded Mongoose, pups give a "begging" call while they follow foraging adults. Field studies of Meerkat and Banded Mongoose pup vocalizations document two distinct call types: a "begging" call emitted continuously over long periods of time and a more intense, high-pitched "give-me-food" call given when a nearby adult finds a food item. These calls remind the foragers of the presence and needs of the pup, and pups that call at a higher frequency and volume are more likely to be provisioned by an adult. It is likely that similar begging occurs in the asocial mongoose species. In addition to begging calls, pups can also give simple warning calls from an early age. Warning vocalizations appear to be instinctive, as Common Dwarf Mongoose young have an innate warning vocalization toward objects moving overhead.

The adult alarm calls of both the Common Dwarf Mongoose and Meerkat are acoustically distinct, depending on the predator type (i.e. they provide semantic information), with calls also indicating the signaller's perception of urgency (providing emotional information). In the Common Dwarf Mongoose, alarm calls are shorter and higher in pitch the more immediate the danger, and carry information on predator type and urgency. There are two main call types. Pulsed calls indicate the predator's distance from the mongoose on guard duty. Frequency modulated calls indicate a predator's above-ground elevation, identity, and the level of danger. Pulsed calls always precede frequency modulated ones. The alarm calls direct group response, which relates to predator type. Ground predator warnings elicit recruitment and group attack, and aerial predator warning calls elicit scatter behavior. In the Meerkat, different alarm calls are given for terrestrial mammal predators (e.g. Black-backed Jackal), aerial raptors (e.g. martial eagle *Polemaetus bellicosus* and tawny eagle *Aquila rapax*), and snakes (e.g. cape cobra *Naja nivea* and puff adder *Bitis arietans*). The response of group members to these calls also differs, confirming that responders can differentiate between calls and extract relevant information from them. When a Meerkat gives a mammal predator call, the group will run to the nearest bolthole and look around. In response to a Meerkat giving an avian predator call, group members will crouch and freeze and look to the sky. In response to a Meerkat snake alarm call, individuals approach the caller—an appropriate response facilitating recruitment to mob the snake. The snake alarm call is also used for indicating secondary cues such as the hair, urine, or feces of a predator or another Meerkat group. Again, a recruitment response is appropriate to these situations. If a danger is perceived as being very close, the signaller gives a "high-urgency" variation of the specific alarm call. This is a harsher, noisier sound than low urgency variants, which are clearer and more harmonic. Individuals respond to the degree of urgency, responding most strongly to high-urgency calls. Whether asocial species exhibit such an informative level of alarm calling and interpretation is unknown, but it is unlikely, as such a complex system would seem to require sociality for its evolution.

Mongooses can also respond to alarm calls given by other species. Meerkats respond to the alarm calls of fork-tailed drongos (*Dicrurus adsimilis*) and yellow-billed hornbills (*Tockus leucomelas*). Banded Mongooses respond with increased vigilance to the alarm calls of numerous other species, but particularly plovers (*Vanellus* spp.). These are likely examples of opportunistic eavesdropping, the mongooses using information not directly intended for them. However, Common Dwarf Mongooses form mutual associations with hornbills (*T. flavirostris* and *T. erythrorhynchus*) and benefit from alarm calls signalling the presence of raptors, including some raptor species that prey on mongooses, but not hornbills.

Both the Common Dwarf Mongoose and Meerkat use a coordinated vigilance system, in which group members take turns going "on-guard", standing on an elevated termite mound or tree to watch for predators. Guards will give an alarm call upon sighting a predator. The coordinated vigilance system in these species depends upon effective communication to maintain efficiency of coverage, a necessity in a predator-rich environment. In both species, the individual on guard gives a specific call, the "watchman's song" to inform other group members which mongoose is on guard, with individuals periodically swapping roles. There is a guard on duty more often in predator-rich areas, and effective guarding reduces mortality within the group. By definition, this level of coordinated vigilance cannot occur in the asocial mongooses, and it demonstrates the high levels of cooperation and communication that have evolved in some of the social mongoose species, which rival the higher primates in the complexity of their social organization. In contrast to canids and felids, mongooses do not appear to use vocalization in territorial advertizement or in mate attraction, probably due to their smaller size and greater vulnerability. Instead, scent is used for these purposes.

For a family whose ancestry lies in a solitary, nocturnal lifestyle, it is not surprising that olfaction plays a major role in communication. Scent marks have the advantage of being persistent (lasting days to weeks), whereas visual and auditory communication are instantaneous. Additionally, in contrast to visual communication, scent works in the dark. Scent signals, like other forms of communication, can serve to attract or repel other individuals, or in the case of communal marking (in the social species) to represent membership. Scent signals can be deposited via anal or cheek marking, feces, and urine.

Herpestids are distinguished from viverrids by the more complex morphology of their anal scent glands. Like hyenids, mongooses possess an anal pouch. The chemical content of herpestid scent marks is poorly known and the relevance of component compounds to communication even less well understood. However, there is some information on the chemical composition of Egyptian and Small Indian Mongoose anal secretions.

Some social mongoose species rival the higher primates in the complexity of their social organization. **Meerkats** *live in groups, typically of 4–9 individuals, with up to 49 recorded. They defend a home range, with a mean size of around 5 km². Meerkat groups have around five dens within their home range; they generally occupy a different den every few days, but may use a den for longer periods when pups are present. Meerkat groups are highly social, with individuals grooming and marking each other to maintain group bonding. Members cooperate in rearing young and repelling predators. Communal latrines are used to mark the group's territory.*

Suricata suricatta
Kalahari, Namibia.
Photo: M. Delpho/CD-Gallery

When threatened by a predator, social mongooses may bunch together and move like a single "super organism". Even the tiny **Common Dwarf Mongoose** effectively utilizes group defensive behavior. A study of groups in the Taru Desert found that 83% of interactions with ground predators resulted in the repulsion of the predator, with no mongoose mortality. Common Dwarf Mongoose groups have rescued members that had been captured by an aerial predator. A Common Dwarf Mongoose was carried almost 2 m into the air after it bit the leg of a marabou that had swallowed a pup. Group "huddles" can also be more relaxed, as shown here, likely associated with communal marking, grooming, or resting.

Helogale parvula
Masai Mara National Park, Kenya.
Photo: Jonathan & Angela Scott/ NHPA

The anal glands produce odoriferous carboxylic acids that differ fundamentally between the two species, being long-chain in the Egyptian Mongoose and short-chain in the Small Indian Mongoose. In the Egyptian Mongoose, male secretions include a major component not present in females. While it is unclear whether anal gland secretions play a role in individual recognition in the Egyptian Mongoose, the relative concentrations of acids in the Small Indian Mongoose differ among individuals, and enable individual recognition. It appears that the bacterial microflora in the anal pockets might produce the different inter-individual concentrations. In the Small Indian Mongoose, there are at least four species of bacteria in the anal pockets, producing different digestive products and therefore combinations of carboxylic acid. The diversity and/or relative proportions of different bacteria species likely differ between individual mongooses, and therefore so will their anal pouch odor.

Individual scent discrimination among adults is also likely in the Marsh Mongoose. This mongoose demonstrates different responses to anal gland secretions and scats, and the response differs depending on the sex of the individual that left the scent. Anal gland secretions are also individually recognisable in the Common Dwarf Mongoose. In this species, male anal gland secretions contain vitamin E, the role of which is unknown. Common Dwarf Mongooses can also differentiate between anal gland secretions based upon the age of the secretion: the component carboxylic acids have different volatilities and evaporate at different rates, so the chemical signal changes over time. The Common Dwarf Mongoose anal gland secretion is detectable for 20–25 days under laboratory conditions, which is close to the 18–26 days it takes a group to complete a circuit of their territory, suggesting that it is useful in marking territorial boundaries. An anal mark, therefore, has the potential to provide information on the sex and identity of the marker, and the timing of its deposition.

Anal marking is commonly used to mark prominent objects within the home range, or to mark other individuals. It is usually achieved via a horizontal dragging of the anus along the ground or other object, but the scent can also be deposited on vertical objects using a characteristic handstand (*Crossarchus, Helogale, Herpestes, Atilax*) or cocked leg (*Suricata*). These different methods of application may be due to the structure of the anal glands. In *Crossarchus*, the anal glands open into a series of dorsal longitudinal grooves. In *Suricata*, they are horizontally elongate and situated on either side of the anus. Some spe-

cies, e.g. the Egyptian Mongoose, Crab-eating Mongoose, and Marsh Mongoose, can forcefully eject the anal gland secretion under stress, although whether this is a defensive or physiological reaction is unknown.

In the social mongooses, dominant individuals commonly scent-mark more often than subordinates. In the Common Dwarf Mongoose, the frequency and order of anal and cheek marking is correlated with rank, the dominant female marking most. In the Meerkat, the dominant male and female mark four to five times more frequently than subordinates. Anal gland secretions are used in the social mongooses to mark other group members, and to mark their home range (using fecal, urine, and cheek marking as well), which is often a communal event, with all group members contributing to a "group mark". In the social mongooses, even if individual anal marks differ, communal marking will produce a combined "group smell".

There is little information on cheek gland secretions, although cheek marking is noted in a number of species, e.g. the Common Dwarf Mongoose, Yellow Mongoose, and Marsh Mongoose. In the Common Dwarf Mongoose, cheek gland secretions persist for only two days and contain no individual signature, but elicit a hostile response when presented to a conspecific.

Fecal marking is often localized in latrines, in which feces are deposited in a small area (typically 0·5–6 m²) within the home range. In Meerkats, the highest density of latrines is in the group's central core area. This core-marking strategy (versus a more dispersed latrine distribution) may maximize the probability of transient groups and prospecting males (who are looking for females) finding a latrine. This strategy may also be linked to the unfeasibility of patrolling the entire boundary against unpredictable intruders (transient groups and prospecting males). Marking of core areas, or marking near the most recently used rest site, is common, and known to also occur in the Common Dwarf, Egyptian, Yellow, and White-tailed mongooses. Each Meerkat group also usually shares one latrine with each neighboring group, and this probably plays a role in monitoring the status of nearby territories and groups. Latrines likely play an important role in Meerkat mate defence, because the frequency of group marking at latrines increases during the breeding season, especially when prospecting males are encountered.

The ability of mongooses to identify and interpret olfactory signs is demonstrated by the Banded Mongoose. In this species,

Den availability is an important habitat variable affecting the presence and density of mongooses. For instance, **Common Dwarf Mongoose** distribution is affected by termite mound availability. Termite mounds are used not only as dens for sleeping at night, but also for rearing young during their first month of life, and as look-out posts and refuges from predators. Common Dwarf Mongooses occur at a higher density in areas where there are more termite mounds, which reflects not just a habitat preference, but a selective advantage: groups that occupy areas with high termite mound density experience lower mortality, and increased reproductive success. In fact, a high density of shelter sites is the best determinant of Common Dwarf Mongoose density, and they only occur in areas that lack termite mounds if there are suitable alternatives available, such as rock kopjes. Other mongoose species can modify their habitat to create suitable dens. Meerkat group members are actively involved in the digging and maintenance of dens and boltholes, and **Yellow Mongooses** also dig their own dens. Mongooses that dig dens or dig to forage may have a large impact on their habitat, and potentially play a major role in ecosystem dynamics. They could be considered as ecosystem engineers, contributing to the complexity of the environment, and aiding in the mixing of soil. Yellow Mongooses are solitary foragers, but spend the night in their communal dens, and cooperate in raising young, like those shown here.

Above: *Helogale parvula*
Chobe National Park, Botswana.
Photo: Clem Haagner/Ardea

Below: *Cynictis penicillata*
Chobe National Park, Botswana.
Photo: Daryl Balfour/NHPA

groups respond to the scent of feces and urine from another group by worry calling, inspecting (sniffing), and overmarking (defecating, urinating, or anal marking). Their acute olfactory sensory and cognitive abilities are well demonstrated by their different intensity of responses, depending upon the familiarity and location of a scent. Scat samples of neighbors placed near the center of the focal group's home range elicit a longer duration inspection than similar scats placed at the periphery of their home range, suggesting that centrally-located scats are seen as a greater threat of territorial incursion. Experiments also demonstrate that Banded Mongooses can discriminate between neighboring groups, treating scats from a neighbor group as familiar if placed on the side of their home range where they would normally encounter that group, but treating them as strangers if placed on the opposite side of their home range. These responses are related to the perceived higher threat-level of neighbors versus transients. Whether such a high degree of recognition and spatial memory occurs in solitary species is unknown.

The communication role of scent marking is also apparent in the White-tailed Mongoose, which deposits scats at latrines that may be used by several adults. This species urinates and anal marks at increased frequency when there is another mongoose nearby, and at territorial boundaries. In the Yellow Mongoose, subordinate adults mark more than dominants, and mark more at border areas and outside the territory. Subordinates are the animals most involved in territorial defence, and are also the ones most likely to disperse or cross territorial borders to mate with neighbors. Marking clearly plays a role in territorial advertizement, and it likely also plays a role in sexual advertizement. Feces and urine contain hormone traces, particularly estrogen in females, which can inform others of their reproductive status. This is probably why more individual and group interactions occur during estrous periods, in the Banded and Yellow Mongooses.

Food and Feeding

Herpestids are primarily carnivorous, but the diet can be very variable between and within species. By nature of their small body size and inability to take relatively large prey, the animal component of mongoose diet is restricted to invertebrates and small vertebrates (principally rodents, small lizards, frogs, and toads). Plant material, such as fruit, is also consumed by some species but generally to a limited extent.

As active predators of invertebrates and small vertebrates, mongooses have to use their senses to locate and capture prey. Herpestids are generally considered to have good senses of

sight, hearing, and smell, and all are probably used, but the relative importance of these senses in foraging likely differs depending upon the habitat, food type, and activity period (i.e. diurnal versus nocturnal). The Small Indian Mongoose has a relatively small cornea, nonspherical lens, and a retina with a high cone to rod proportion (25–40% of photoreceptors are cones, comparable to diurnal primates). These are all characteristics of a diurnal-adapted eye, matching this species' lifestyle. Their eyes also possess a high accommodative ability, which is probably beneficial in tracking fast-moving prey in a congested habitat. Anecdotal observations on other diurnal species, the Meerkat and Common Dwarf Mongoose, indicate an ability to detect and differentiate between raptor species that are kilometres away. These diurnal herpestids thus appear to possess acute vision, which may also be used in the detection of food. Information is lacking on the eyesight of nocturnal species, but observations of eyeshine in some mongooses, notably the White-tailed Mongoose and Marsh Mongoose, indicate the presence of a tapetum lucidum (a reflective layer outside the retina that reflects back unabsorbed light), a structure usually associated with nocturnal vision. Unfortunately, there is little structural or functional information available on the auditory or olfactory senses of mongooses, but the latter would appear to be well-developed in view of the wide use of olfactory communication within the Herpestidae.

The skull structure and dentition of mongooses reflects their principal diet of insects and small vertebrates. Species with a more vertebrate-based diet tend to have a robust skull structure, reflecting the greater force required to kill and process vertebrate prey; insectivorous species tend to have a less robust skull. In many mongoose species, the structure of the premolars, molars, and carnassials is adapted to crushing. However, the carnassial shear is well-developed in the more carnivorous species. In the Marsh Mongoose, which specializes in crushing crustaceans, the teeth (especially the posterior premolars) are particularly robust. In contrast, in the Liberian Mongoose, which is thought to specialize in eating earthworms, the teeth are said to be relatively small and the jaw structure weak. Herpestid canines are relatively long, strong, and recurved. They are generally larger and stronger in the more carnivorous species, and are important in delivering the killing bite. The non-retractable claws of herpestids are not sharp for prey capture, like felid claws, but are generally used for digging.

Seven mongoose species appear to be principally vertebrate feeders (Cape Gray, Egyptian, Indian Gray, Jackson's, Javan, Stripe-necked, and Ruddy). Seventeen species are primarily invertebrate feeders (Common Dwarf, Marsh, Bushy-tailed, Black-footed, Yellow, White-tailed, Liberian, Banded, Gambian, Selous's, Meller's, and Long-nosed Mongooses, Meerkat, Alex-

Serious aggression within a group is rare in social mongooses like the **Common Dwarf Mongoose**, although play fighting in juveniles (as in the photo above) is a normal part of development. Quarrels over food items are common, but are usually settled in favor of the owner. Growls and spits are used to defend resources from other group members. However, there is an age-related dominance hierarchy in males and females. The dominant female takes precedence over all other group members in access to food and frequency of anal marking, and can displace others from a foraging site. The male dominance hierarchy becomes obvious during estrus, when males compete for access to females. Posturing appears to be involved in dominance and subordination behavior in a number of species, particularly the social mongooses. In the Common Dwarf Mongoose, Meerkat, Banded Mongoose, and Yellow Mongoose, interactions within groups often include one individual standing erect, indicating dominance, while another assumes a lowered, crouching, or cowering posture, indicating subordination. Tail position is also thought to indicate emotional state and dominance in some species, and it is notable that some mongooses, such as the White-tailed Mongoose, have an obvious color difference on the tail or the tail tip, which may be involved in highlighting signals. Interactions between individual White-tailed Mongooses are generally tolerant. Fights between Angolan Slender Mongooses can occur close to an abundant resource such as carrion. However, there is little data on intra-species aggression and other social interactions in the large, solitary mongoose species.

Above: *Helogale parvula*
Photo: Walter Rohdich/FLPA

Below: *Helogale parvula*
Kruger National Park, South Africa.
Photo: Alan Weaving/Ardea

ander's, Angolan, Common, and Flat-headed Cusimanses). In ten mongoose species, the principal dietary component is unclear, unknown, or variable (Slender, Angolan Slender, Somalian Slender, Small Indian, Short-tailed, Crab-eating, Ethiopian Dwarf, Pousargues's, Indian Brown, and Collared). Within the Herpestidae, mongoose scats or stomachs have been recorded to contain mammal, bird, reptile, amphibian, fish, crustacean, mollusc, insect, spider, scorpion, myriapod, isopod, millipede, fruit, and seed remains.

Habitat type and mongoose diet are understandably correlated. In the riparian Marsh Mongoose, the major components of the diet are crustacea (e.g. crabs) and amphibia, but in drier areas (or during drier spells) they switch to more terrestrial prey. Their diet also differs between coastal and inland areas. They feed principally on amphipods and shore crabs at coastal sites, and on frogs, rodents, birds, crabs, or fish, at inland river sites. A comparison of the diet and habitat selection of two similarly-sized sympatric herpestids in a coastal area of South Africa found diet and habitat use to be correlated. The mainly insectivorous Yellow Mongoose used the open short-grass plains, where invertebrate prey was found at a higher density than in the bush habitat. The mainly carnivorous Cape Gray Mongoose was exclusively found in bush habitat, where its small rodent prey was more abundant than in the short-grass habitat. In contrast, a study of scats of two sympatric, open-terrain, insectivorous mongoose species in South Africa, the Common Dwarf and Banded Mongoose, found substantial dietary overlap (72–82%) of prey categories, although Banded Mongooses ate more myriapods. How these species can coexist using the same food resources is unclear. The same question arises concerning the Common Dwarf Mongoose and the closely related Ethiopian Dwarf Mongoose, although little is known of the diet of the latter.

Banded Mongoose individuals groom themselves, and this can occupy a significant part of the day. A study of another species, the Yellow Mongoose, in a coastal area of South Africa found that individuals spent 11% of the day grooming, more time than was spent traveling (9%). The rest of the time was spent foraging (49%) and being inactive (28%). Banded Mongooses in Uganda and the Masai Mara groom Common Warthogs, from which they probably remove and eat ectoparasites.

Mungos mungo
Etosha National Park, Namibia.
Photo: Ann & Steve Toon/NHPA

Within a species, individuals may adjust their diet to the most available food, depending upon habitat and season. A study of Egyptian Mongoose scats in Spain found this species to be an opportunistic predator, consuming the most abundant prey available in each area and season. Similarly, the diet of the Yellow Mongoose has been shown to differ between arid and coastal regions in South Africa, with a much higher percentage of rodents eaten at the coastal site. The diversity of diets in the different populations of the Small Indian Mongoose, which has been introduced to numerous island and mainland locations, further demonstrates the dietary flexibility within a species. Their diet varies from principally insects in the Rajasthan Desert, St. Croix Island, and Puerto Rico, to vertebrates on Mauritius, to mainly plant material (fruits) on Korcula Island, Croatia. On Viti Levu, Fiji, the diet varies between habitats, from principally crabs in mangrove forests, to rats in cane-fields, to cockroaches in urban areas.

Major seasonal changes in diet have been recorded for some mongoose species. The White-tailed Mongoose switches from termites and ants in the dry season to dung beetles in the wet season. A study of Yellow Mongoose scats in a coastal area of South Africa found them to be almost exclusively insectivorous from July to September, the scats containing no reptiles and almost no rodent prey during this period; with a high percentage of reptile and mammal prey at other times of the year. Yellow Mongooses became almost exclusively insectivorous from July to September. The diet of the Crab-eating Mongoose similarly varies seasonally, dominated by insects in summer and autumn, crustaceans in winter, and reptiles in late spring and early summer. In the Common Slender Mongoose, the diet shifts from principally insects in May to September to small vertebrates in October to April.

Prey availability may also affect the timing and success of reproduction. In most species, the birth of young coincides with the rainy season, which is likely to support high prey densities. For example, in the Common Dwarf Mongoose, lactation is timed to coincide with the months of highest invertebrate densities.

Diet and prey density should be expected to affect home range size. However, a comparison of the mainly insectivorous Yellow Mongoose, and the mainly carnivorous Cape Gray Mongoose found no significant difference in home range size or population density. Food also has implications for home range use. Mongooses rarely forage in the same area on consecutive days, and this is likely to minimize prey disturbance and depletion. Temporarily avoiding an area gives the prey an opportunity to recover, making the area productive when next visited.

Home range size, and movements within a home range, may be reduced when more food is available. Individuals will localize their movements, and even abandon territoriality, to take advantage of temporary bonanza-like resources. For several days, three Common Slender Mongooses were observed feeding together on fly larvae from a giraffe carcass. Up to seven Angolan Slender Mongooses were observed feeding upon adult, larval, and pupal sarcophagid flies on a Greater Kudu (*Tragelaphus strepsiceros*) carcass, with a radio-collared male reducing his home range use by 66% to concentrate on this food resource. Similar observations have been recorded for more permanent supplemental food sources. Whilst most observations of Egyptian Mongoose populations suggest it to be a solitary species, social groups of several individuals were observed to form at garbage dumps in Israel. In Uganda, Banded Mongoose groups concentrated their home range use on the garbage dumps.

Diet may affect foraging times and distances travelled. However, a comparison of the daily distance covered and the distance covered per hour between two similarly-sized sympatric herpestids, the mainly insectivorous Yellow Mongoose and the mainly carnivorous Cape Gray Mongoose, found no significant differences. Common Dwarf Mongoose groups forage for on average five hours per day and Meerkats spend five to eight hours per day foraging. In these species, better-fed individuals make higher contributions to group activities (digging, vigilance, babysitting, and provisioning). In the social mongooses, the group tends to leave a babysitter with the young while the group forages. However, rarely do suckling females babysit, as they need to forage in order to fulfil the heavy energetic demands of lactation.

Almost all mongooses are terrestrial or subsurface foragers. They are active feeders: rarely will a mongoose sit and wait for prey. Generally they explore with their attention oriented towards the ground. The more carnivorous members of the family (e.g. the Egyptian Mongoose and the Common Slender Mongoose) will trot along and pounce upon or chase small vertebrate or invertebrate prey that are disturbed. Others, like the White-tailed Mongoose, stop frequently as they trot to pick invertebrates off vegetation or out of dung piles. The social insectivorous mongooses spread out as a loose group to forage, each individual scratching at the surface and periodically stopping to dig. The cusimanses are said to root around in the litter of the forest floor with their long snouts. The Marsh Mongoose tends to forage in mud or shallow water, using its dexterous forefeet to root around for prey.

The killing bite in mongooses tends to be oriented to the skull of vertebrates, and this likely limits the relative size of

*Grooming is one of the activities that helps maintain group bonds in social mongoose species like the **Meerkat**. The group sleeps together overnight in a subterranean den, emerging in the early morning and returning before sunset. They usually start the day by sunbathing at the den and end the day relaxing by the den. In Meerkat and Common Dwarf Mongoose groups, the dominant breeders make the lowest contribution to babysitting and feeding the young. Non-breeding helpers contribute by babysitting, grooming, provisioning, and protecting the pups.*

Suricata suricatta
Kalahari, Namibia.
Photo: Martin Harvey/DRK

vertebrate prey that they can tackle. A skull-directed killing bite has been recorded in the Common Dwarf, Slender, Small Indian, and Cape Gray mongooses, the Common Cusimanse, and the Meerkat, and is likely typical of all mongoose species. Observations of the Egyptian, Slender, and Marsh mongooses suggest that a neck bite may be used on larger prey. Mongooses tend to kill and eat invertebrates starting from the head.

The herpestids have a characteristic method of dealing with hard prey items. This was first described in the Banded Mongoose: an individual picked up and clasped a pill millipede (*Sphaerotherium* sp.) in its forepaws, oriented itself so that its rear was facing a rock or other hard object, and threw the millipede between its rear limbs onto the hard surface, cracking or smashing the prey, and making it more accessible. This method

of cracking hard prey items has similarly been described in the Common Cusimanse, Slender, Egyptian, White-tailed, Common Dwarf, Cape Gray, and Crab-eating mongooses. Observations on the Marsh Mongoose suggest that this species throws hard objects down to the ground vertically, from a standing position, rather than horizontally through the hindlegs; the Crab-eating Mongoose has also been observed to use this method. The throw-and-smash method is used for a variety of hard prey items, including dung beetles, birds' eggs, crabs, and molluscs.

Mongooses are perhaps most famed for their ability to kill snakes, immortalized in traditional fables about the Small Indian and Indian Gray mongooses. The speed and agility of the mongoose is said to be instrumental in their ability to avoid being bitten and to overcome a snake, and at least some mon-

*Mongooses that are active in the daytime tend to rest in the shade during the hottest part of the day. This **Banded Mongoose** may be trying to cool itself by flattening its body against the cool, shaded surface of a road, or it may just be "chilling out". Mongooses may also seek shade in rock crevices and termite mounds, or within dens, where temperatures are more stable and comfortable than the hot and cold extremes on the surface.*

Mungos mungo
Hwange, Zimbabwe.
Photo: N. Greaves/Photo Access

goose species are highly resistant to snake neurotoxins (e.g. the Egyptian Mongoose). However, snake remains are rarely found in the scats or stomach of mongooses. Other dangerous or toxic prey types eaten by mongooses include scorpions and Myriapods (centipedes and millipedes). The Small Indian Mongoose has been observed eating toads, including their toxic parotid glands.

The percentage of vertebrate to invertebrate prey has implications for sociality in the mongooses. Because vertebrates are relatively low-density prey, and are mobile, sensitive to disturbance, and slow to renew, they are not appropriate for group foraging. In contrast, invertebrates tend to be relatively high-density prey, and are immobile, not very sensitive to disturbance, and rapid to renew, and therefore enable group foraging. Small vertebrate renewal rates are likely to be in the order of 0·07 per 24 hours, whereas the renewal rate for invertebrates is an order of magnitude higher, approximately 0·7 per 24 hours. The group-living social mongooses all exhibit a predominantly insectivorous diet. That is not to say that an insectivorous diet promotes sociality (there are numerous asocial insectivorous mongoose species), but that it allows it where other factors, principally predation pressure, provide a selective pressure for grouping.

Group cooperative hunting occurs in some of the social canids (such as Gray Wolves) and the only social felid (the Lion), enabling larger prey to be taken, but cooperative hunting does not usually occur in the social mongooses. A possible exception may be the occasional excavation of European Rabbit (*Oryctolagus cuniculus*) breeding dens by two or three Egyptian Mongooses, as has been observed in Spain. However, it was unclear whether prey capture in these cases was coordinated. There is also an observation of two Small Indian Mongooses hunting crabs (*Metapograpsus messor*) together, with one turning over stones and the other attacking the crab. Even in the social mongooses, the Common Dwarf Mongoose, Meerkat, and Banded Mongoose, there is no record of cooperative prey capture or of a group bringing down large prey. These species are predominantly insectivorous and their cooperative nature generally does not extend to sharing food. Individuals respond aggressively to approaches by others when they are feeding or digging a foraging hole.

In mongooses, food is shared with young pups. In the majority of species, this is done by the mother, but in social mongooses, adult males and females (breeders and non-breeders) can all provision pups with food items. As the pups gain the skills required to forage independently they are fed less. The time needed to reach foraging independence is variable, but

usually is from between three months in the Meerkat and Banded Mongoose to up to a year in the Egyptian Mongoose.

Scavenging is not uncommon in the Herpestidae. The Angolan Slender Mongoose has been recorded feeding upon a Greater Kudu carcass. The Stripe-necked Mongoose has been observed scavenging on Sambar (*Rusa unicolor*) and Indian Hare (*Lepus nigricollis*). The Indian Gray Mongoose has also been observed feeding on carrion. The occurrence of large mammal material in the scats and stomach of some species also suggests scavenging, as mongooses are unlikely to be able to

The predominantly insectivorous
Yellow Mongoose is an
opportunistic feeder. In the more
arid parts of its range, dangerous
or toxic prey, such as scorpions and
spiders, can be significant items in
the diet. It will also hunt rodents,
birds, reptiles, and amphibians. In
South Africa, the Yellow Mongoose
uses open habitats, where
invertebrate prey is found at a
higher density, whereas the mainly
carnivorous Cape Gray Mongoose
is exclusively found in bushy areas
where small rodent prey is more
abundant.

Cynictis penicillata
Kalahari Gemsbok National Park,
South Africa.
Photo: Ann & Steve Toon/NHPA

prey actively on larger mammals. For example, the analysis of scats collected in rainforest from the Long-nosed Mongoose and Marsh Mongoose revealed ungulate remains: Blue Duiker (*Philantomba monticola*) in the former and Water Chevrotain (*Hyemoschus aquaticus*) in the latter. Cape Porcupines (*Hystrix africaeaustralis*) have also been found in Long-nosed and Cape Gray Mongoose scats. There is also a record of a group of Banded Mongooses stealing food regurgitated by a pair of Black-backed Jackals for their pups.

Numerous mongoose species (including the White-tailed, Yellow, Small Indian, Cape Gray, Egyptian, Angolan Slender, and Banded mongooses) are known to readily feed on human garbage. In the Banded Mongoose, access to supplemental food at garbage dumps can improve body condition, but it can also lead to increased interaction with potential predators. In the case of the Angolan Slender Mongoose, access to supplemental food likely led to a Dassie Rat (*Petromus typicus*) population crash due to the increased mongoose population. These examples highlight the potential effects of anthropogenic waste disposal on ecosystem and mongoose population dynamics. Occasionally mongooses prey on domestic livestock, and this can bring them into conflict with humans. Small Indian Mongooses and Marsh Mongooses have been observed taking fowl.

There is little information on the drinking habits of herpestids; it therefore seems that mongooses drink rarely, and some species may not need to drink at all, likely fulfilling their water requirement from the prey that they eat. There are observations of Banded Mongooses drinking irregularly and apparently opportunistically, and of Common Dwarf Mongooses drinking available water.

Breeding

The mongoose family incorporates a variety of social and breeding systems and strategies for care of young. In general, mongooses are polygamous, each male mating with multiple females during estrus (the fertile period), and females mating with multiple males (at least in some of the social species). Current evidence suggests that induced ovulation takes place in the Herpestidae, in which the rupture of the follicle and release of the ova is induced by mating. Although observations in the wild are few, information from captivity and limited free-living species suggest that females are receptive (in estrus) for a a number

of days and are polyestrous, cycling regularly. These traits likely resulted from solitary lifestyles of ancestral Carnivora, in which individuals ranged relatively widely and alone in search of prey. This presented problems for successful matings; regular cycling, a relatively long receptive period, and ovulation triggered by copulation, all improve the probability of successful fertilizations.

The majority of herpestids are solitary. In these species, males and females live alone, the female advertizes her receptivity via scent marking, and male home ranges generally overlap a number of female home ranges. In the group-living mongooses, finding a mate is not such a problem and estrous periods are often accompanied by fights and intergroup copulations: both males and females may leave their home range in order to mate with neighboring individuals and this may be facilitated by hormonal cues in female urine.

During estrus, males remain in close association with potential mates for a period of hours or days. Copulation itself may involve chasing, playing or fighting prior to the male mounting the female, which usually involves the male clasping the female with his forelimbs forward of the female's pelvis and thrusting his pelvic region. He may also grasp the nape of the female's neck in his mouth. There is no copulatory lock as occurs in canids. A copulation event is extremely variable in duration within species and may last from a few seconds to a few minutes (for example, in the Common Dwarf Mongoose, median copulation duration is 21 seconds, with a maximum of nearly 11 minutes). Copulation does not always result in successful intromission and a male is likely to copulate a number of times with a female during her estrus, and a female may mate with more than one male. Small Indian Mongoose males are known to lose weight and condition during the mating season, which is likely due to their increased energy expenditure.

Herpestids are typically polyestrous, with females producing one or more litters per year (up to five in the Banded Mongoose in equatorial regions, where it breeds year-round). Births in most species occur in the wet season, when prey densities are higher than during the dry season. A study on the Small Indian Mongoose found that the onset of estrus might be induced by a lengthening photoperiod.

Gestation varies from 42 days (Small Indian Mongoose and Yellow Mongoose) to 80 days (Marsh Mongoose). The interbirth interval is dependent upon the season, but Banded Mongooses are able to enter estrus within one week of parturition of the previous litter. The interbirth interval of Meerkats and the Yellow

The teeth of the **Marsh Mongoose**, particularly the rear premolars, are very robust and capable of breaking through the shells of crabs and molluscs. Marsh Mongooses share their range and habitat with otters, and there is some overlap in diet, but the Marsh Mongoose is less dependent upon aquatic prey. In drier areas (or during drier spells) they switch to more terrestrial food items. Marsh Mongoose home ranges tend to be long and thin, following a stream or river. They are both crepuscular and nocturnal, foraging in vegetation alongside streams, in mud, or in shallow water. They are excellent swimmers, but do not swim readily. Marsh Mongooses are extremely dexterous compared to other herpestids. They reach into cracks, mud, and rocks with their forelimbs to root around for prey, and stand up and use their forelimbs to throw hard-shelled prey items, such as crabs or mussels, downwards against rocks. Some prey, including crabs, snakes, and large rodents, are seized in the jaws and flicked sideways prior to being given a killing bite. Small crabs are eaten whole; larger crabs are turned upside down, the foreclaws are bitten off, the meat eaten, and the carapace discarded. Upturned carapaces on riversides indicate the presence of Marsh Mongooses; otters normally crunch up the crab carapaces.

Atilax paludinosus
Serengeti National Park, Tanzania.
Photo: Bruce Davidson/naturepl.com

Beetles are a major item in the diet of the **Banded Mongoose**. Herpestids have a characteristic method of dealing with hard prey items like beetles, which was first described in the Banded Mongoose. An individual clasped a pill millipede in its forepaws, oriented itself so that its rear was facing a rock or other hard object, and threw the millipede between its rear limbs onto the hard surface, cracking or smashing it. This method of cracking hard prey items has similarly been described in other mongooses, such as the Common Cusimanse and Crab-eating Mongoose.

Mungos mungo
Queen Elizabeth National Park, Uganda.
Photo: Anup Shah/naturepl.com

Mongoose similarly suggests that estrus occurs while the female is still suckling a litter. Lactation is energetically costly in mammals, and female Small Indian Mongooses are at their poorest body condition when lactating or immediately after lactation.

In most species, females have four to six teats and the maximum litter size per female is six (although up to eight have been recorded in the Meerkat). Nevertheless, litter size is variable even within a species. In most cases, females give birth in a den, such as a burrow. Solitary mongooses tend to have small litters of one to three pups that remain in the den for approximately ten weeks. In contrast, social mongoose females average a pre-natal litter size of three to four, with pups emerging from the den at around four weeks. Herpestid pups are born blind and deaf, sparsely furred, and dependent upon parental or alloparental care. Information is limited, but weight at birth varies from 20 g (Banded Mongoose) to 125 g (Marsh Mongoose). The eyes open at around two weeks and the young are generally weaned between four and eight weeks. If the young are moved, they are generally picked up by the nape of the neck by the adult.

Maternal-only care is the norm, but little is known of offspring care in solitary species. Alloparental care (assistance in the care of young by other females and males) only occurs in the social mongoose species. The larger litter sizes and reduced period of dependence in the social mongooses may be due directly to the care and food provided by alloparents (helpers), which lower the energetic demands upon the mother. By freeing time and resources for the mother, helpers may allow her to invest more in feeding her young.

In the intensively studied social mongooses, reproductive suppression occurs in the Meerkat and Common Dwarf Mongoose, but apparently not in the Banded Mongoose. In the first two species usually only the dominant male and female breed with numerous subordinates not breeding. In Banded Mongoose groups, almost all individuals breed (over 80% females conceive) and up to ten females give birth in the same den, on the same day. Births are also highly synchronized if reproductive suppression fails in the Common Dwarf Mongoose, and females in a group will then give birth on the same day. In Meerkat groups, they give birth within a week of each other. Infanticide may occur when subordinate females breed, which may be a method of controlling reproduction where pre-conception suppression has failed. In the Yellow Mongoose, females within a group can give birth approximately four to ten days apart.

Hormones and pheromones are likely to play a role in the synchronization of parturition in the social mongoose species.

Both aggression and hormonal (or psychological) suppression by dominant individuals are implicated in the failure of subordinates to breed successfully. Where subordinates are relatives of the dominant (opposite-sex) individual, their "reluctance" to breed may reflect inbreeding avoidance. Interestingly, although glucocorticoid secretion (released in response to stress) is known to suppress reproduction in some mammal species, it is the dominant individuals that show elevated glucocorticoid concentrations in Common Dwarf Mongoose and Meerkat groups.

In the Common Dwarf Mongoose and Meerkat, the dominant breeders make the lowest contribution to babysitting and feeding the young. Non-breeding helpers contribute by babysitting, grooming, provisioning, and protecting the pups, and in the case of some females, by allonursing (producing milk and allowing suckling). Contributions to care are likely to have a hormonal basis, and prolactin has been shown to precede babysitting in male Meerkats. Banded Mongooses also provide care to offspring that are not their own, although in this species, the majority of caregivers may also be breeders. Apparently, they contribute care to the communal litter rather than specifically to their own offspring. There are a number of possible benefits to caring for the young of others: relatives may gain indirect fitness benefits by helping to rear related young, and allocarers may benefit via tolerance by dominants (payment of rent), by maintaining or increasing group size (with possible benefits in intergroup competition), or by gaining experience in the care of young.

Young mongooses generally remain in a den from birth until emergence. In most cases the young are suckled in the den during this period, although above-ground suckling is occasionally observed. In contrast to larger carnivores, such as canids and hyenids, which exhibit regurgitation or food-bringing, food provisioning at the den does not occur (except in the Yellow Mongoose, where large prey items—rodents, bats, reptiles, and large arachnids—are delivered to the den after weaning). In the social mongooses, the young remain dependent upon group members until they are three to four months old, at which point they are no longer provisioned and are able to procure food independently. In the solitary mongooses, cohabitation between a mother and her offspring lasts for approximately six months, but the time of foraging independence is unknown. Physical and reproductive maturity is probably reached between nine months and two years in the majority of species.

The complex nature of mongoose foraging and feeding behavior necessitates a relatively long period of dependence.

The eggs of ground nesting birds form a regular, but small, part of the diet of many mongoose species, which stumble across them while they forage. The eggs may be broken in the jaws—as this **Banded Mongoose** is doing—or cracked by throwing them against a hard surface. A few mongoose species are persecuted for taking domestic poultry and their eggs—though allegations that the Yellow Mongoose also takes newborn lambs are considered to be false. As well as a few eggs, the diet of the **Indian Gray Mongoose** is said to include rats, mice, snakes, lizards, frogs, insects, scorpions, centipedes, fruits, and roots. The remains of rodents, grey francolins, and desert monitors were found in a specimen stomach from Rajasthan, India. Another stomach contained termites and scorpions. The Indian Gray Mongoose has also been seen feeding on carrion. Scavenging is not uncommon in the Herpestidae, as evidenced by the occurrence, in scats and stomachs, of the remains of mammals too large for mongooses to prey upon. The Angolan Slender Mongoose has been recorded feeding upon a Greater Kudu carcass, and the Stripe-necked Mongoose has been observed scavenging on Sambar. Even in the social mongooses, like the Common Dwarf Mongoose, Meerkat, and Banded Mongoose, there is no record of cooperative prey capture, or of a group bringing down large prey. A possible exception may be the occasional excavation of European Rabbit breeding dens by two or three Egyptian Mongooses, as has been observed in Spain. However, it was unclear whether prey capture in these cases was coordinated.

Above: **Mungos mungo**
Etosha National Park, Namibia.
Photo: Malcolm Schuyl/FLPA

Below: **Herpestes edwardsii**
Zainabad, Gujarat, India.
Photo: Otto Pfister

The diet of opportunistic foragers like mongooses can vary both geographically and seasonally. **Yellow Mongooses** ar predominantly insectivorous, but will also eat vertebrates, includin lizards. In central South Africa, the analysis of 95 stomachs foun more rodents than insects. In the Western Cape, the occurrence of rodents varied during the year, according to the fluctuating rode populations. Yellow Mongooses usually forage individually, but have been seen in pairs or in sme groups. Foraging typically occurs during early morning and late afternoon. However in the Easte Cape, they have been observed feeding throughout the day.

Cynictis penicillata
Suikerbosrand Nature Reserve, South Africa.
Photo: Ian Merrill

Catching prey requires greater cognitive ability, skill, and experience than grazing or browsing. Post-weaning, the young must be provided with food while they learn to capture prey themselves. Observations on the social mongooses suggest that group members teach pups the foraging skills they need. During the early post-weaning phase an adult will kill, break up, and give food to the young, but over time the adult gradually reduces its prey processing, first by not breaking it up, then by not killing it, then by not grabbing the prey, and finally by not completing a dig. The young are therefore taught to forage step by step. Post-weaning information is lacking for the solitary mongooses.

Pups also likely compete for access to food. In the Banded Mongoose pups actively defend their adult "escort" against other pups to monopolize food provisioned. Young mongooses also play, and their play appears to include behaviors similar to fighting and mating. However, studies of the Meerkat suggest that play does not increase social cohesion, reduce aggression, or provide a mode of bonding with future dispersal partners, nor does play fighting improve subsequent fighting ability. The role of play therefore remains uncertain.

In the solitary mongooses, both male and female young disperse, although in some cases, there is female philopatry (females remain within the natal home range). Dispersers usually benefit by reducing the probability of inbreeding, but can suffer increased mortality during dispersal. In the White-tailed Mongoose, female offspring remain on the natal territory for an extended period. Among the social mongooses, females are generally philopatric, and male-biased dispersal occurs in the Meerkat and Common Dwarf Mongoose. The mode of dispersal may differ between the sexes and between individuals. In the Meerkat, females may be evicted by the dominant female, and males generally prospect before voluntarily emigrating to join another group. In the Common Dwarf Mongoose, both females and males may leave voluntarily. In the Banded Mongoose, either sex can emigrate voluntarily to join a group of opposite sex individuals, or they may be aggressively evicted from their natal group. Takeovers have also been recorded in all these species, where individuals of one sex displace the same-sex dominant individuals from another established group. In all three species, individuals have been recorded joining neighboring groups, but they may also disperse over substantially longer distances (e.g. over 20 km in the Banded Mongoose).

Being relatively small, mongooses are vulnerable to a variety of predators, especially snakes, raptors, and carnivorous mammals (including other mongooses). In particular, the mortality of young can be relatively high. Predators of adult Banded Mongooses include african rock pythons (*Python sebae*), and martial eagles. Marabou storks and monitor lizards have been observed taking pups. Meerkat predators include Black-backed Jackals, martial eagles, tawny eagles, and for pups, pale chanting-goshawks (*Melierax canorus*) and snakes. As the smallest of the mongooses, the Common Dwarf Mongoose is vulnerable to a great many predators, including Egyptian Mongooses, Slender Mongooses, Black-backed Jackals, desert monitor (*Varanus griseus*), eastern chanting-goshawks (*Melierax poliopterus*), and brown snake eagles (*Circaetus cinereus*), with marabous recorded killing pups. A Cape Gray Mongoose was observed being killed by a Caracal.

Survival rates vary between species and locations. In the Egyptian Mongoose in Spain, annual adult survival rates vary between 0·13 and 0·60; in the Banded Mongoose adult survival is 0·65–0·86, in the Common Dwarf Mongoose, 0·68–0·74, and in the Meerkat 0·68. Although mortality can be high, mongooses have the potential to be relatively long lived under favourable conditions. A captive Cape Gray Mongoose lived to over 20 years, and in the wild, a male Common Dwarf mongoose reached 14 years.

Movements, Home range and Social organization

The herpestids occupy a diversity of habitats and dietary niches; consequently there is a large variation in their home range sizes, movements, and degree of sociality. The ancestral mongoose was likely a forest animal that lived a solitary, nocturnal life. The majority of the 34 extant species in the Herpestidae are solitary. In many solitary carnivore species, the spatial organization involves each female defending a territory from other females, and each male defending a territory from other males. However, spatial organization in the Herpestidae is variable, with several species forming social groups.

Information on mongoose home ranges is scarce. There is often substantial variation in home range sizes between and within species due to habitat characteristics, den/rest site availability, predation pressure, diet, group size, and climate. For example, in the Small Indian Mongoose, which has been introduced to a number of island and mainland locations, home

Mongooses are perhaps most famed for their ability to kill snakes, as immortalized in traditional Indian fables about the **Indian Gray Mongoose** and the Small Indian Mongoose, and in the character of Rikki-Tikki-Tavi in Rudyard Kipling's Jungle Book. The speed and agility of the mongoose is said to be instrumental in its ability to avoid being bitten and to overcome a snake, and some mongoose species are highly resistant to snake neurotoxins. Mongooses are seen in staged fights with snakes in many Asian towns and villages, often as tourist attractions. When the mongoose is fighting, its hair is erected so that it can appear twice its natural size, and the combination of piloerection and agility may reduce the probability of a direct hit. Vipers of comparable size may be much more effective against mongooses than cobras, and fights staged in the West Indies involving the Small Indian Mongoose and a viper more often than not end in the victory of the viper. Despite the traditional association of mongooses with snakes, snake remains are rarely found in the scats or stomachs of mongooses. In fact, being small, mongooses, especially young ones, are likely to fall prey to snakes, such as rock pythons. Large groups of Meerkats and Banded Mongooses will attempt to repel rather than kill pythons or cobras. They bunch together and engage in to-and-fro behavior; the large size and mobility of this apparent "super organism" ideally scaring off the predator. If the snake does not retreat, it is often the mongooses that will flee.

Herpestes edwardsii
Tamil Nadu, India.
Photos: Daniel Heuclin/NHPA

ranges vary from 0·014 to 1·10 km². Even within a study site, there can be great variation between individuals.

Habitats with higher food densities generally support smaller home ranges or larger group sizes. In the White-tailed Mongoose, home ranges varied from 0·39 to 1·23 km² in the Serengeti (Tanzania), and in Bale (Ethiopia), they varied from 1·11 to 4·27 km². The Tanzania study was in an area high in beetle density, and the Ethiopian study was in an area that likely had a lower density of beetles. The maximum home range in the Ethiopian study was probably the largest home range recorded for a solitary mongoose, with only the group-living Meerkat occupying larger home ranges (up to 10 km², but averaging 5 km²).

Generally male home ranges are substantially larger than female home ranges (up to four times in the Yellow Mongoose and thirteen times larger in the Small Indian Mongoose). This intersexual dichotomy is primarily due to female territories being based on defensible food resources, whereas male territories are based upon both food and females as limiting resourc-es. In the Small Indian Mongoose, there is a substantial overlap of home ranges within the sexes, with a mean intra-sexual overlap of 84% for males and 37% for females, although there is little overlap in core ranges. Similarly, in the Cape Gray Mongoose, males do not appear to maintain exclusive territories. In contrast, in the White-tailed Mongoose, although female home ranges overlap (35–81% overlap), the ranges of males do not (less than 3% overlap). In the Egyptian Mongoose in Spain, female home ranges overlap substantially, but core areas are almost exclusive; male Egyptian Mongoose home ranges barely overlap, but do overlap several females.

An individual's or group's use of a home range is affected by food availability. Mongooses have been observed to use different parts of their range on different days, and this is likely a general trait that allows prey replenishment. Access to supplemental food (such as human garbage) can also affect home range, either by decreasing it or allowing others to use the supplemental food within the home range. This has been observed in the Small Indian, Banded, and Cape Gray mongooses, which use anthropogenic food, and the Angolan Slender Mongoose, which sometimes feeds around carcasses.

Home ranges may be reduced when young are in the den. A female Small Indian Mongoose and Banded Mongoose groups reduce their home ranges when they have dependent young. Body size may also affect home range size. For the Egyptian Mongoose in Spain, home range size has been shown to be related to body mass, with a negative correlation within females, but a positive correlation within males. This suggests that larger females occupy areas richer in resources, whereas larger males range further and overlap with more females.

Mongoose movements are mainly concerned with finding food and with territorial patrol. Prospecting for mates during the mating season also contributes to activity and movements. A study of Egyptian Mongooses in Spain showed an activity budget of 70% resting, 21% foraging, 6% eating, and 3% walking. A study of the Yellow Mongoose in a coastal area of South Africa found that individuals spent 49% of the day foraging, 28% inactive, 11% grooming, 9% travelling, 1% digging at the den, and 1% in social interaction.

Information on mongoose movements is scarce, but they are capable of moving fast and covering great distances within a day, and can probably cross their home range within a 24-hour period. Recorded movement measurements range from 21·4 m/s (Marsh Mongoose) to 4·2 km/h (White-tailed Mon-

*When monitor lizards are found in the stomachs of mongooses, they are usually assumed to have been scavenged. However, this **Ruddy Mongoose** has attacked a monitor lizard as large as itself, and far larger than the type of prey a mongoose would usually attempt to kill. The killing bite in mongooses tends to be oriented to the skull of vertebrates, and this probably limits the relative size of vertebrate that they can tackle, although observations of some species suggest a neck bite may be used on larger prey. Monitor lizards are known to prey upon mongoose pups and it could be that this Ruddy Mongoose is attacking the lizard in defense of its young.*

Herpestes smithii
Sri Lanka.
Photo: Monika Dossenbach

*The killing method of the **Small Indian Mongoose** is very efficient: it drives the canines into the brain and vertebral column of rodents, birds, and snakes. The Small Indian Mongoose has been introduced to many places (mainly islands) to control snakes and agricultural pests. Most of its dietary information comes from these introduced populations, but it is reported to eat rodents, snakes, insects, centipedes, and scorpions within its native range. Centipedes and scorpions are bitten and repeatedly tossed before being consumed. Two individuals were reported working together to hunt crabs in Pearl Harbor, Hawaii.*

Herpestes auropunctatus
Keoladeo Ghana National Park,
Bharatpur, India.
Photo: Bernard Castelein/
naturepl.com

Although the staple foods of the **Cape Gray Mongoose** are generally small mammals or insects, it has been recorded feeding on larger mammals, such as Scrub Hares and Cape Porcupines, and has even been known to attack and kill young Cape Grysbok by tearing at the nose and mouth. However, because it scavenges, it is uncertain to what extent large prey in the diet is the result of active predation. Larger prey are stalked; the killing bite is delivered to the head, and the prey then held firmly on the ground with the front feet and torn apart.

Galerella pulverulenta
Photo: Peter Steyn/Photo Access

goose) and distances covered in a day range from 1 km (Common Dwarf Mongoose) to 6 km (Meerkat). However, as with home range size, day range is likely to vary as much within a species as between species, depending on habitat. For example, Banded Mongooses travel 2–3 km per day in the Queen Elizabeth National Park (Uganda), but up to 10 km in the more arid Serengeti (Tanzania).

The majority of mongooses are solitary and a major factor influencing this is their diet. The density of small vertebrates is generally insufficient to support a group of mongooses. In addition, vertebrate prey is generally mobile and sensitive to disturbance; individuals foraging alone are less likely to scare off potential prey. In mongoose species for which invertebrates are a more important component of the diet, sociality is more common. Invertebrates are much less sensitive (and therefore less disturbed) by multiple foragers, and the invertebrate renewal rate within a harvested patch is relatively rapid. It is therefore less costly to forage in the company of conspecifics for inver-

tebrate-feeders than for vertebrate-feeders. It is notable that although the Yellow Mongoose is mainly insectivorous, this species, in which individuals den together but forage alone, has a relatively high proportion of small vertebrate prey in its diet.

In the solitary mongooses, the only extended period of cohabitation is between a mother and her offspring (for a period of a few months). However, recent field studies have revealed that some solitary mongoose species have more complex social systems and inter-individual contacts than expected. For instance, the Yellow Mongoose is semi-social, with individuals denning together but foraging alone. The Slender, Cape Gray, and Small Indian mongooses have been observed to exhibit semi-social tendencies in some populations, with males sometimes forming associations. Groups have sometime been recorded in Egyptian Mongooses, but these almost never consist of same-sex adults (except for a study of an isolated population in Israel).

Three mongoose species have so far been confirmed to be fully social, regularly denning and foraging together as a

Although absent from truly arid areas, **Banded Mongooses** drink irregularly, sparingly, and apparently opportunistically, and may go several days without visiting a water source. They drink by lapping up the water with their tongue. In general, not much is known about the drinking habits of herpestids. Thus, it appears that mongooses rarely drink, and perhaps some species may not need to drink at all, probably getting the water they need from the prey that they consume. In addition to observations of Banded Mongooses at water sources, Common Dwarf Mongooses have also been seen drinking available water.

Mungos mungo
Lengwe National Park, Malawi.
Photo: Johannes Ferdinand

The majority of mongoose species
live solitary lifestyles, which
presents problems for successful
mating. Although observations
from the wild are few, studies of
wild and captive species suggest
that females are receptive (in
estrus) for a few days and are
polyestrous, cycling regularly. The
traits, together with ovulation
triggered by copulation, all impro
the probability of successful
fertilizations. During estrus, ma
Egyptian Mongooses remain in
close association with potential
mates for a period of hours or da;
Mating occurs over two months i
the spring.

Herpestes ichneumon
Israel.
Photo: Yossi Eshbol/FLPA

group: the Meerkat, Banded Mongoose, and Common Dwarf Mongoose. The four cusimanse (*Crossarchus*) species, and four other mongooses (Pousargues's, Ethiopian Dwarf, Liberian, and Gambian) are also believed to be fully social, but scientific documentation is limited or lacking. The social mongooses are characterized by small body size (less than 2 kg), diurnality, and insectivory. Diurnality and the use of small, rapidly renewing prey differentiates the social herpestids from other small carnivore species.

The Meerkat, Banded Mongoose, and Common Dwarf Mongoose are known to live in social groups that share a home range, which they jointly defend. Group sizes vary, but commonly range from 3–30, and contain adult males and females, and young.

Within a Meerkat group, there is a dominance hierarchy, with dominant males and females regularly displacing subordinates from disputed sites. Most subordinate adults are related to the dominant female, but immigrant males are also commonly present. Generally only the dominant pair breeds: dominant females produce 75% of litters and dominant males father 80% of pups within the group.

Within Banded Mongoose groups, males are closely related and females are closely related, but the breeding adults are not related to each other. There is generally little evidence of a dominance hierarchy. However, a male dominance hierarchy becomes obvious during estrus, when males compete for access to females. Dominant males guard females and aggressively repel subordinate males who attempt to sneak copulations. There is no sign of female competition for access to males. However, there is a hierarchy in "mate-guarding", with older females mate-guarded first, and younger females mate-guarded later. Females may escape their mate-guard and mate with other males within and outside their group. The overall result is that most males and females copulate with numerous partners, and about 75% of the females in a group give birth, often on the same day.

In the Common Dwarf Mongoose, there is an age-related dominance hierarchy in males and females. The dominant female dominates all other group members. The male dominance hierarchy only becomes obvious during estrus, when males compete for access to females. Early in the dominant female's estrous cycle, the dominant male guards her, maintaining exclusive proximity and copulation rights, and aggressively repelling subordinate males, who attempt to sneak copulations. Later in estrus, the dominant male will mate with subordinate females and the dominant female then mates with

other males. However, despite the fact that all group members may copulate, dominant females produce 73% of all litters. If subordinate females do breed, they are usually synchronized with the dominant female, giving birth on the same day. Most offspring born to subordinate females fail to survive, probably due to infanticide by the dominant female.

Cooperative hunting is a common explanation for sociality in large carnivores (such as Gray Wolves and Lions), but different selection pressures favor sociality in the Herpestidae, which lack cooperative prey capture. Sociality in mongooses requires high food availability to facilitate grouping. That the diet of the social mongooses consists principally of rapidly renewable invertebrate prey supports this. However, the primary selective pressure favouring group living may be protection from predators. Being relatively small, mongooses are very vulnerable to a diversity of predators, in particular snakes, raptors, and larger carnivorous mammals. Open habitat increases vulnerability to predation and, with the exception of the forest-living cusimanses and Liberian Mongoose, the social mongooses occupy open savannah-type habitat. Grouping of individuals can reduce individual predation rates, via coordinated vigilance (as exhibited by Common Dwarf Mongooses and Meerkats) and defensive aggregations (Common Dwarf Mongooses, Meerkats, and Banded Mongooses bunch to repel predators). Even the tiny Common Dwarf Mongoose effectively utilizes group defensive aggregation. A study of groups in the Taru Desert found that 83% of interactions with ground predators resulted in predator repulsion, with no mongoose mortality. In the truly social species, there is also evidence of an Allee effect, with increased individual mortality at smaller group sizes. This reflects the adaptive significance of grouping and the dependence of individuals upon one another to maximize inclusive fitness in these species. Large groups of Meerkats and Banded Mongooses will attempt to repel (rather than kill) pythons or cobras. They bunch together and engage in to-and-fro behavior; the large size and mobility of the apparent "super-organism" ideally scaring off the predator. However, if the snake does not retreat, it is often the mongooses that will flee. A group of Banded Mongooses was seen rescuing a group member from the talons of a martial eagle. Banded Mongooses have also been observed leaping up to a meter in the air in an attempt to bite airborne marabous that have grabbed a pup. Similarly, groups of Common Dwarf Mongoose have successfully rescued members that had been captured by an aerial predator. A Common Dwarf

*Copulations in the **White-tailed Mongoose** occur during consortships that last for several hours. In the Herpestidae, copulation may involve chasing, playing, or fighting, prior to the male mounting the female, which usually involves the male clasping the female with his forelimbs forward of the female's pelvis and thrusting his pelvic region. He may also grasp the nape of the female's neck in his mouth. There is no copulatory lock as in dogs, which prevents immediate withdrawal by the male. A male is likely to copulate a number of times with a female during her estrus, and a female may mate with more than one male.*

Ichneumia albicauda
Photo: Roland Seitre

Mongoose was carried almost two meters into the air after it bit the leg of a marabou that had swallowed a pup. There is even an instance of a group of Common Dwarf Mongooses rescuing a crested francolin (*Francolinus sephaena*) by attacking an eastern chanting-goshawk.

The social mongooses often display an impressive level of cooperation (such as babysitting and provisioning young, invalid care, predator deterrence). Interspecific cooperation also occurs in some species. Liberian Mongooses are often found in association with Sooty Mangabeys (*Cercocebus atys*) and flee in response to the monkeys' anti-predator warning calls. Hornbills (*Tockus flavirostris* and *T. erythrorhynchus*) regularly forage with Common Dwarf Mongooses in Kenya, the latter benefiting from the birds' alarm calls. Banded Mongooses in Uganda and the Masai Mara groom Common Warthogs, from which they are likely to remove and eat ectoparasites. The Cape Gray Mongoose has been observed in association with the african marsh harrier (*Circus ranivorus*) during foraging, and a Yellow Mongoose was observed in cooperative vigilance with a group of Meerkats. Common Cusimanses have been observed playing with Mona Monkeys (*Cercopithecus mona*).

Irrespective of the importance of diurnality to the evolution of sociality in the mongooses, activity periods within the family Herpestidae cover the entire spectrum. In addition to the diur-

*Gestation in **Meerkats** is around 70 days. There are 3–7 pups in the litter. They are born with eyes and ears closed, and short hair, and each pup weighs between 25 g and 36 g. The eyes open at 10–14 days. Meerkat pups remain in the subterranean den until they are 3–4 weeks old. Mating in Meerkats is rarely observed because it occurs in the subterranean den. The Meerkat exhibits a despotic social system: generally only the dominant pair breeds. When a second or subordinate female conceives, it is usually followed by infanticide or den desertion.*

Suricata suricatta
Photo: Ángel M. Sánchez

In most mongoose species, the young are suckled in the den, although above ground suckling is occasionally observed, as in the case of this **Yellow Mongoose** and its pup. Lactation in the Yellow Mongoose lasts 6–8 weeks. Litter size is 1–5, and most commonly two; Yellow Mongooses have three pairs of mammae. Some females may have two litters per year. The interbirth interval of the Yellow Mongoose suggests that estrus occurs while the female is still suckling a litter. Lactation is energetically costly in mammals, and females are at their poorest body condition during and just after lactation.

Cynictis penicillata
Etosha National Park, Namibia.
Photo: B & L Worsley/Photo Access

nal social (and semi-social) mongooses, there are numerous diurnal solitary species (Angolan Slender, Collared, Crab-eating, Egyptian, Indian Gray, Javan, Long-nosed, Ruddy, Short-tailed, Slender, Small Indian, and Stripe-necked). Pousargues's Mongoose is also diurnal, but of unknown social status. There are also numerous nocturnal species (Black-legged, Bushy-tailed, Indian Brown, Jackson's, Meller's, Selous's, and White-tailed) and one crepuscular species, the Marsh Mongoose. This range of activity patterns highlights the adaptability, great diversity, and niche coverage of the mongoose family.

Within the Herpestidae, mongoose species occupy a variety of habitats and dietary niches, and display different activity patterns, resulting in a variety of social organizations. Unfortunately, there are many gaps in our knowledge regarding the behavioral ecology of the majority of herpestid species and field research is needed into their breeding biology, ranging behavior, and social organization.

Relationship with Humans

Mongooses have had a long history of association with people, particularly within the region stretching from Northern Africa to India. This is not surprising, as some mongooses are often found in close proximity to humans, exploiting the increased food availability provided by garbage dumps, and preying on the other animal species associated with people, such as mice, rats, and cockroaches. With their perceived characteristics of courage, cunning, strength, ferocity, and curiosity, mongooses have played a significant role in human culture since early times and are featured in many religious myths, legends, and stories.

Ancient Egyptians believed that mongooses break crocodile eggs and that without the mongoose the number of crocodiles would be so great that no one would be able to approach the Nile. The sun-god *Re* once transformed himself into a mongoose to fight *Apophis*, the serpent of the netherworld. The mongoose god in the mortuary temple of *Amenemhet III* (1991–1786 BC) represented the spirits of the netherworld. In Letopolis, the mongoose god was equated with the falcon-god *Horus* and in Heliopolis with the creator-god *Atum*. Mongooses were thus venerated in ancient Egypt (at least from 2500 BC) and considered a sacred animal. They were often embalmed in large numbers, and mummies of mongooses have been found inside small bronze statues of the lion-headed goddess *Uto*. Many Egyptian Mongoose mummies were discovered at Tanis.

Often these mummies were packed in small coffins, the lids of which were decorated with either paintings or models of the living animal. The ancient Greeks and Romans were also familiar with mongooses.

Mongooses were also the objects of artwork, and they appeared as bronze figures, on coins, or as figurines of human beings with mongoose-like heads. Representations of the Egyptian Mongoose can be found on the walls of tombs and temples of Thebes and Saqqara; the earliest date from the Old Kingdom (2800–2150 BC). The greatest number of mongoose representations that were left by the ancient Egyptians date from the Greco-Roman period (after 332 BC), when the cult of sacred animals was at its height. These include small bronzes that may have been produced in large numbers. Some of these are of a mongoose walking, with the legs in such a position that all four can be seen from the side. Others show the animal in the sitting position with the sun disc and the uraeus (or sacred asp) on its head.

Mongooses feature prominently in Middle and Far Eastern religions, frequently as guardians of wealth. In Hindu mythology, the mongoose is regarded as the natural foe of the *nagas* (serpents) and a guardian of the jewels and treasures lying under the earth. Mongooses were conceived of having wrested the wealth from the possession of the serpents; hiding the treasures in their stomachs was considered a good repository of riches and a suitable tribute to the god of wealth. *Kubera* (the son of a sage) was given immortality by *Brahma* and made god of wealth and guardian of all the treasures of the earth. In the 1st century BC, *Kubera* is sculptured with a mongoose-shaped purse (probably made from mongoose skin) in his left hand, and is later depicted holding a mongoose in his hands. In Buddhist mythology, *Kubera* is known as *Jambhala* and is often sculpted with a mongoose in his left hand; the mongoose, when pressed, disgorges streaks of wealth or rounded coins from its mouth. Similar artwork has been found in the Greco-Buddhist art of Ghandhara, in Tibet (*Hariti*, as the "bestower of wealth" presses a mongoose to her left breast), Nepal (god of *Mahkala*), and China (*To-wen* is seen holding a mongoose).

Rudyard Kipling granted mongooses an everlasting place in literature when he wrote the story of *Rikki-Tikki-Tavi* in the *Jungle Book* (1894). In this tale, an English family, having moved to a bungalow in India, discovers a young mongoose half drowned from a storm and decides to keep it as a pet. The young mongoose, called Rikki-Tikki, soon finds himself confronted by two dangerous cobras, Nag and Nagaina. Nag plans to kill the hu-

In most mongoose species, females have four to six teats, and the maximum litter size per female is six, although up to eight have been recorded in the **Meerkat**. In cial species, the care of the young is shared. Meerkat pups suckle milk from numerous females. Allosuckling also occurs in social species of other families of the Carnivora, for example, Lions. If more than one female Meerkat within a group gives birth, the births usually occur within one week. However, females that have not given birth also suckle the pups. Non-pregnant subordinate females are often evicted by the dominant female during the late stages of her pregnancy, but are allowed to return to the group fter the birth of her pups. During the period in the den, one or more individuals will remain with the young to "babysit" the pups, while the group forages. The babysitter usually changes every day. These babysitters guard the pups from predators, and also probably help keep the pups warm. Breeder adults do atively little babysitting, whereas non-breeding subordinates make higher individual contributions. The larger litter sizes and reduced period of dependence in the social mongooses may be due directly to the care and food provided by the elpers (alloparents), which lower the energetic demands upon the mother. Pup survival is higher in ups with more helpers. Although any litters fail completely within the first month, 70% of Meerkat ups are estimated to survive from weaning to independence.

Suricata suricatta
Photo: Kenneth W. Fink

Pups of social mongooses such a.
Banded Mongooses *emerge from*
the den at around four weeks.
If the young are moved, they are
generally picked up by the nape
the neck by the adult. In seasona
climates, births are restricted to t
wetter months and are presumal.
correlated with invertebrate prey
availability. Female Banded
Mongooses in dry regions have
one or two litters a year; females
in wetter equatorial regions can
have up to five. The age at whic
females first reproduce is also
geographically variable, recorded
at two years in the Serengeti and
under one year in Uganda. Estr
can occur within six days of giv
birth, enabling females to concei
and gestate while suckling the
current litter of pups.

Mungos mungo
Masai Mara National Park, Kenya.
Photo: Dave Richards

man family so that the snakes can have free run of the garden. He goes into the house to kill the "big man", but falls asleep while waiting. Rikki grabs the snake by the head and Nag thrashes about furiously. The man then comes and fires a shotgun at the snake, blowing him in two pieces. Nag is thrown on the rubbish heap, where Nagaina mourns for him and vows vengeance. Rikki, well aware of her threat, searches for Nagaina's eggs and manages to destroy most of the brood. Nagaina finds the family at the dinner table and threatens to kill the family's son. Alerted to the crisis, Rikki races to his family with the last egg. Once there, Rikki shows the egg to distract Nagaina long enough for the man to pull the boy to safety. Nagaina snatches the egg and flees to her hole while Rikki pursues her inside. After a long wait, Rikki comes out of the hole in triumph having killed Nagaina. Rikki then spends the rest of his days defending the family garden, where no snake would dare enter.

Similar stories are known in many earlier variations and are reflected in a number of classical tales from India. The best-known source of Indian stories is from the five books of the *Panchatantra*, which possibly dates from as early as 100 BC. The better known of the two mongoose fables occupies all of Book V and is called "*Hasty Action*" or "*The Brahman and the Mongoose*". In one version of this tale, there was a Brahman family. One day a son was born to them and on that very day a female mongoose living in the house gave birth to a young one, but the mother mongoose died the same day. The Brahman lady reared the young mongoose along with her own son, feeding them both with her own milk. One day she left her son sleeping and went out to fetch water. While the child was left alone, a cobra came out of a hole in the room. The mongoose fought with the cobra to save his human brother and cut the cobra to pieces. After saving his brother, he joyfully went outside to meet his mother. But the mother, on her return, saw blood on his mouth and thought the mongoose must have killed her son. She threw a pitcher full of water at the mongoose and killed him. She then found her baby still sleeping in his room and a cobra, cut into pieces, lying by his side. She then realized her mistake and repented, crying that she had killed her son the mongoose.

Mongooses also appear in other stories in Middle and Far Eastern cultures and variations based on all these fables began to circulate in Europe from as early as the 20th century. The mongoose is mentioned in early Indian medical books such as the *Charak Sanhita* (c. 100 AD) and *Susrata*. An old Indian belief is that when bitten by a cobra, the mongoose goes to the jungle to look for a plant known as mungo root (*Ophiorrhiza mungos*), which it eats as an antidote to the venom. More recently, Meerkats have become extremely popular thanks in part to television wildlife documentaries and cartoons, and the blockbuster Disney movie "The Lion King", in which the character Timon, Simba's friend, is a Meerkat.

For millennia, mongooses have been famous for killing reptiles, particularly venomous snakes; the ancient Egyptians, for instance, kept mongooses to kill snakes. Aristotle recorded that "the Egyptian ichneumon, when it sees the serpent called the asp, does not attack until it has called in other ichneumons to help; to meet the blows and bites of their enemy the assailants beplaster themselves with mud, by first soaking in the river and then rolling on the ground". Other authors such as Pliny the Elder, Aelian, and Strabo made similar remarks, although these were sometimes embellishments of other accounts and often inaccurate. Mongooses are seen in staged fights with snakes in many Asian towns and villages, often as tourist attractions. Several accounts of these staged fights have been described, for example, one between a spectacled cobra (*Naja naja*) and an Indian Gray Mongoose. At the start of this fight, the mongoose uttered a strident cry and walked up to the cobra with its tail bristling. For a second they faced each other, and, as the towering snake opened its jaws and drew back its hood to strike, the mongoose darted in and sprang for the lower jaw, simultaneously gripping the cobra's body with all four legs as it bit. The snake writhed, sometimes taking the mongoose aloft with it, and as they struggled the mongoose worked its jaws with a crunching action, its snout always keeping contact with the snake. This initial struggle lasted about five seconds after which the mongoose broke loose. The cobra was crippled by the bites and could not raise itself to its former height, and its lower jaw hung broken on the right side. The mongoose then made repeated attacks; each lasting about five seconds, during which it invariably targeted the snake's head and not the body. In the early stages, the mongoose attacked with a quick rush from the side, but once it had slowed the cobra down it sprang straight in regardless of danger. It would spring inside the cobra's striking circle and wait (sometimes up to eight seconds) until the dazed cobra opened its jaws to strike, when it would jump up, sieze the jaw and continue biting. This particular fight lasted about 35 minutes and was then stopped, but had it continued it seemed certain that the cobra would have been killed. The mongoose had sustained two gashes in its upper lip, which were likely to be fang marks, but

Handbook of the Mammals of the World.

The communal breeding
practices in **Common Dwarf
Mongooses** reveal a classic case
of a despotic social system of
"high reproductive skew": the
dominant females produce 73%
of all litters, even though there
are twice as many subordinate
females. Subordinate reproduction
is suppressed hormonally and
behaviorally. If subordinates do
breed, it is usually synchronized
with the dominant female, and
they give birth on the same day.
However, most offspring born
to subordinates do not survive,
probably due to infanticide by the
dominant female. After the birth
of a communal litter, pups stay in
the den until they are about 3–4
weeks old and subordinate females
usually babysit them while the rest
of the group forages.

Helogale parvula
Lake Manyara National Park,
Tanzania.
Photo: Günter Ziesler

otherwise it showed no ill effects. Mongooses are not immune to cobra venom, but they are more resistant than other mammals.

Other accounts of staged fights between mongooses and snakes emphasize that it is the speed and agility of the mongoose that is chiefly responsible for its success. When the mongoose is fighting, its hair is erected so that it often appears twice its natural size, and this often causes the snake to strike short. Vipers of comparable size may be much more effective against mongooses than cobras and fights staged in the West Indies between the Small Indian Mongoose and vipers more often than not end in the victory of the viper.

Some species of mongooses have been used as biological control agents and introduced to various places throughout the world. The Egyptian Mongoose is found in Spain and Portugal, but is generally not considered native and perhaps was intentionally introduced into Europe from Northern Africa during the early Middle Ages. The Indian Gray Mongoose was introduced to Japan in 1910 to control vipers, and may also have been introduced to Mauritius. The Small Indian Mongoose has been introduced to many places (mainly islands) to control snakes and agricultural pests, particularly rodents. It was first introduced into the West Indies during the 1870s for the purpose of controlling rats in sugar cane plantations and to control venomous snakes. From then on, it was introduced into many other places including the Hawaiian Islands, Adriatic Islands, Mauritius, and Japan. These introductions demonstrated the risks of biological control: mongooses not only killed selected pest species, but also devastated native endemic species not adapted to coping with efficient predators. Although the Small Indian Mongoose quickly become very numerous and reduced the number of rats on most of the islands, in many areas there was a shift in public opinion quite soon after they were introduced, and many people then considered that this mongoose was causing more harm than good: the Small Indian Mongoose not only preyed on indigenous birds, reptiles, and amphibians, thus threatening their survival, it also became notorious for killing poultry.

Some mongoose species prey opportunistically on domestic poultry and many sheep farmers believe that they are important predators of lambs (although this may be based more on myth than fact). Not surprisingly, mongooses are often persecuted where they are thought to contribute to poultry or livestock losses and this may be why the number of Egyptian Mongooses kept in North African villages has decreased. Mongooses are also sometimes persecuted because of their possible role in the spread of rabies. In Puerto Rico, there were only 21 cases of ra-

bies in dogs and farm animals from 1911 to 1933. From 1933 to 1950, this island was considered to be one of the few rabies-free areas in the world. However, in 1950, it was discovered that the Small Indian Mongoose was an important reservoir and vector of rabies on Puerto Rico. This was apparently the first time that rabies had been reported in a species of *Herpestes*. In South Africa, the Yellow Mongoose has been recognized as a vector of the disease since 1928. Meerkats have also been controlled as a rabies vector and in East Africa, the Common Slender Mongoose is said to be very prone to rabies.

Over the last fifty years, hunting for regional and international markets has increasingly outweighed subsistence hunting. Numerous animal species are now targeted for the huge illegal trade in wildlife for food, traditional medicines, skins, bones, and pets. Wire-snares and other traps are very effective in catching animals, but are unselective in what they catch, and non-targeted animals are also taken and often killed. Wildlife traders have penetrated into the remotest areas and actively encourage the hunting of species for which there is a demand. Together with other small carnivores, mongooses are a source of protein (bushmeat) for many local communities, especially in South-east Asia and Africa. The contribution to total diet is substantial in some communities, especially where the breeding of domestic animals is problematic because of tripanosomiasis and other parasites. In Ghana, a study showed that 75% of the population depended on wild animal protein and that the wild fauna made up 62% of the animal protein of the rural population. In Guinea, the amount of bushmeat sold at a town market (30,000 inhabitants) was about 131 tons a year, involving 21 savannah species of mammals. Antelopes, deer, pigs, and primates are the most sought after prey, but the usual methods of hunting are not very selective and most animals are caught according to their frequency. Local hunters use dogs, spears, traps, and snares. Small carnivore meat (including mongooses) can make up to 15% of all the bushmeat consumed in some African communities. In the Democratic Republic of the Congo, a study showed that the Angolan Cusimanse was the most frequently killed mammal, accounting for 6% of all mammal bushmeat. Five mongoose species (Egyptian, Long-nosed, Slender, and Marsh mongooses, and Common Cusimanse) were found in a survey of bushmeat markets within south-eastern Nigeria.

There does not appear to be a large demand for mongoose fur, unlike the fur trade in felids and mustelids for the fashion industry. Skins of mongooses are found in local markets, but it appears that they are mainly sold for local uses: their hair is

In the social mongooses, the your
remain dependent upon group
members until they are 3–4 mont
old, at which point they are no
longer provisioned, and are able
to procure food independently.
In contrast to larger carnivores,
such as canids and hyenids,
which exhibit regurgitation or foo
bringing, food provisioning at
the den does not occur, except in
the Yellow Mongoose, where large
prey items such as rodents, bats,
reptiles, and large arachnids, are
delivered to the den after weaning
When **Meerkat** pups emerge from
the den and begin accompanying
the foraging group, helpers provi
care by carrying and provisionin
pups, and defending them again
predators. Provisioning involves
dropping or leaving whole or
partial prey items. In contrast to
the social behavior of the Banded
Mongoose, there is no pup
escorting system, and pups move
between group members begging
for food. Pups emit two types of
begging calls, a constant repeat
call and a high-pitched "give-me-
food" call when an adult finds
a prey item. There are a number
of possible benefits to caring for
the young of others: relatives may
gain indirect fitness benefits by
helping to rear related young, an
allocarers may benefit from being
tolerated by the dominant males
and females ("payment of rent"),
by maintaining or increasing
group size (with possible benefits
in intergroup competition), or by
gaining experience in the care of
young. In addition to predation
by snakes, jackals, and eagles,
Meerkat pups may be killed by
neighboring Meerkat groups.

Suricata suricatta
Tswalu Kalahari Reserve,
South Africa.
Photo: Marguerite Smits Van Oyen/
naturepl.com

used for making shaving brushes, paint brushes, and good luck charms.

Mongooses are kept as pets either as companions, to protect houses from dangerous animals (such as snakes, scorpions, and spiders), or to reduce mice and rat populations. Mongoose skulls found in houses at Merkes, Babylon, suggests that even in these early times (c. 600 BC) mongooses were household pets. The mongoose species that are most readily tamed and become the most satisfactory pets are those that are gregarious and diurnal, such as the Meerkat, the Banded Mongoose, and the Common Dwarf Mongoose. Their need for social contact is so great that they quickly come to accept a human as a substitute companion. However, some of the solitary species, such as the Small Indian Mongoose, can also make a pleasing pet if they are caught young enough. They often become attached to the people they know and will attack strangers. They can learn to recognize their pet names and will come if a reward is likely to follow. Unlike dogs, but like cats, they appear to do only those things that please them.

Today, mongooses are still kept as pets, particularly in tropical Asia. Throughout Asia, there is a large demand and trade in animals as pets and this includes mongoose species. In Medan, North Sumatra, one of South-east Asia's major centers for domestic and international wildlife trade, a five-year study of the pet industry recorded 300 bird species, 34 species of mammals, and 15 reptile species. The Small Asian Mongoose was frequently observed for sale, with a total of 324 animals recorded during the monthly surveys; the actual number sold over the five-year survey period was obviously far greater than this figure. Many of these animals are exported by sea and air to Malaysia, Singapore, Thailand, and other global destinations. Also, many animals are imported from other Asian countries, including China. Plantation and forest workers may supplement their income by opportunistically catching mammal species to sell as pets (and other uses) in local markets or to wildlife dealers. Other hunters may specifically target animals that are in high demand. Most of this wildlife trade is illegal, and local wildlife laws, CITES permits, and international laws are usually ignored and not enforced.

Status and Conservation

Some species of African mongooses, such as the Banded Mongoose, occur over a wide area, are found in a broad range of habitats, and appear to tolerate human-modified environ-

ments. Although these species appear to be unthreatened, many other herpestids have never been studied and very little is known about their ecology, natural history, and conservation status. For instance, the Liberian Mongoose was only discovered by western scientists in 1958 and the Angolan Cusimanse was known from only two specimens until 1984.

The herpestids were recently assessed for *The IUCN Red List* in 2008. The majority of mongoose species are currently listed as Least Concern; only the Indian Brown Mongoose, Liberian Mongose, Sokoke Bushy-tailed Mongoose (*Bdeogale crassicauda omnivora*)—a debated subspecies of Bushy-tailed Mongoose—are classified as threatened. However, the reality is that there is generally so little information that it is difficult to accurately assess the extinction risks for most of the herpestid species. Thus, the current biggest threat to mongoose conservation is our lack of knowledge of their distribution, ecology, and population sizes. Field surveys are urgently needed to investigate these aspects and to identify the sites and the problems on which conservation activities should concentrate. Ascertaining the exact geographic range of a species is especially important in order to determine if its distribution includes well-managed areas of sufficient size. Even if reserves are known to be within the range of an endangered species, it must be verified that they actually occur within these protected areas, and that these areas contain viable populations. Ecological research on tropical rainforest animals has shown that many species are patchily distributed, both across landscapes and at smaller spatial scales; sometimes a species is confined to small areas in a seemingly homogenous forest. Understanding the factors that explain this mosaic-like distribution pattern is crucial for implementing conservation measures.

Most herpestid species have never been studied by scientists in the wild. Field research in difficult and remote environments poses many practical and logistical challenges, but is vital in order to determine ecological requirements for long-term conservation measures. To formulate population viability models and predict extinction risks for herpestids, we need to know a great deal about their ecology and natural history. The reasons for peculiar distribution patterns and the factors that impact population sizes also require investigation. For instance, some species that have been recorded over large areas may only be found in low numbers locally or in a few isolated populations; dependence on a rare and patchily distributed habitat type, specialization on certain food items, prey abundance and distribution, or competition with other species, are some possible explanations.

Banded Mongooses are truly communal breeders, with up to ten females in a group giving birth, often on the same day, in the same den. Such birth synchrony may reduce infanticide by reducing the ability of males and females to discriminate between offspring. After they emerge from the den at weaning, at around 3–4 weeks, most pups have an adult escort, who cares for it for the next 4–8 weeks. This escort is unlikely to be the pup's parent. The pup closely follows its escort, fending off other pups, and begging for the food items the escort provides. Pups that associate most often with an escort are more likely to survive. Males generally do more babysitting and escorting than females.

Mungos mungo
Masai Mara National Park, Kenya.
Photo: Dave Richards

Young mongooses play, and their play appears to include behavior similar to fighting—as these **Meerkat** pups are doing—and mating. However, studies of the Meerkat suggest that play does n increase social cohesion, reduce aggression, or provide a mode of bonding with future dispersal partners, nor does play fighting improve subsequent fighting ability. The role of play therefore remains uncertain. Social play is part of the daily repertoires of activities of adult **Common Dwa Mongooses**, Banded Mongooses, and Meerkats—the three social mongoose species that have been studied in detail. The four cusimanse species and four other mongoose species, Pousargues's Mongoose, Ethiopian Dwarf Mongoose, Liberian Mongoose, and Gambian Mongoose, are also believed to be fully social, bu scientific documentation is limite or lacking. Play behavior is said be common in captivity and in t wild in the Common Cusimanse

Above: **Suricata suricatta**
Kalahari Gemsbok National Park,
South Africa.
Photo: Nigel J. Dennis/NHPA

Below: **Helogale parvula**
Masai Mara National Park, Kenya.
Photo: Dave Richards

Field research into a species feeding ecology and breeding behavior can help improve techniques for captive management. A better understanding of the social structure of a species and its dispersal patterns is essential for estimating the minimum population sizes needed for preserving genetic variability.

Forest-dependent herpestid species may be threatened by forest loss, fragmentation, and degradation. Fragmentation of forests results in a sub-division of species populations to smaller units and smaller populations have a higher extinction risk from intrinsic and extrinsic factors (e.g. disease, climatic changes, fire). Fragmentation may also restrict dispersal and gene flow between isolated groups, resulting in a higher occurrence of inbreeding. Inbreeding can result in the loss of important alleles that confer resistance to infectious diseases and also allow harmful recessive genes to be expressed. Logging roads allow hunters greater access and lead to increases in hunting pressure. Forest degradation, such as selective logging, can also have serious consequences for forest species. Although not as destructive as clear cutting, it can dramatically alter the structure of a forest, affecting the availability of food resources and suitable den sites. Remaining forests need to be protected and conserved through the implementation of management plans, and habitat corridors connecting these forest patches should also be protected and maintained. The management of protected areas needs critical analysis in order to incorporate the requirement of herpestid species; often more charismatic well-known animal species are given priority and there may be conflicts of interest.

All the threats that impact herpestids need to be identified and assessed. For instance, a number of mongoose species are hunted, whether targeted or accidentally. The impacts of hunting on mongoose species are largely unknown, but for some this may be unsustainable, particularly if their habitat is also being destroyed or altered. The demands for herpestid meat and skins need to be eliminated or considerably reduced. Existing protection laws need to be enforced and new ones implemented. The impact of the pet trade on certain mongoose species is also unknown and needs to be assessed, monitored, and control measures implemented if necessary.

One mongoose species, the Small Indian Mongoose, is considered a pest on many of the islands where is has been introduced and poses a severe threat to other native animal species. Attempts to eradicate this mongoose on some of these islands have been made; for example, the Territorial Government in the Virgin Islands authorized payment of a bounty (10 cents for males and 15 cents for females), and in the ten years from 1940 to 1950, bounty payments were made on about 7000 mongooses. The Governments of Trinidad, St Kitts, Antigua, Barbados, and St Vincent also paid bounties for its destruction.

In Trinidad, 30,026 mongooses were paid for in 1928, 32,650 in 1929, and 21,231 during the first eight months of 1930. Some people also advocated poisoning campaigns, hunting mongooses for sport, and even suggested that inhabitants should eat mongooses, saying that their flesh is very appetizing and is like that of a rabbit or squirrel in appearance. Despite all these killing methods and suggestions, these eradication campaigns at best have only controlled mongoose numbers.

Until recently, the taxonomy of this family was poorly understood, with great uncertainty about the taxonomic status and the distribution of many species and subspecies. Taxonomic revisions are necessary in order to provide a systematic framework and to define important units for conservation purposes and for answering scientific questions. Animal protection laws are usually applied to defined entities (most commonly a recognized species) and incorporating difficult taxonomic issues, such as subspecies, into this protective scheme is crucial. For quite a long time, herpestids were an overlooked group and the focus of little taxonomic research. Recent molecular and morphological studies have clearly shown the value of such research in establishing valid species. But further work is needed to resolve certain issues and to define important subspecies and populations. Subspecies may have particular adaptations to the local climate, or to different competitors, predators, parasites, or strains of pathogens. Molecular studies also provide a tool for identifying the geographic origin of some species taken for the wildlife trade and sold in markets. Captive breeding programs may also benefit from molecular studies, which may help define conservation units (species, subspecies, and populations) and help evaluate the genetic diversity of captive populations for breeding purposes.

Captive breeding can be a powerful tool in ensuring the survival of an endangered species, particularly in cases where in the short term the protection of the animal and its natural habitats is not likely to be successful. Unfortunately, herpestids are generally so poorly known that it is not possible to say whether any are endangered to such an extent that even their short-term survival can only be ensured by captive breeding. Although some mongoose species, such as the Meerkat and Banded Mongoose, are very popular exhibits in zoos, there has been a general neglect of the lesser-known species. Keeping animals in zoos raises many ethical and welfare issues and many people and animal organizations oppose zoos on these grounds. Even within the conservation community there is considerable debate on how much of a role captive breeding should play part of a conservation strategy for ensuring the survival of a species. Captive breeding should be seen as supporting, not substituting, conservation efforts in the wild and perhaps should only be used

as a last effort to save a species, but there are several problems connected with this approach. Since conditions in captivity are different from the natural environment that a species has to live with in the wild, captive breeding over several generations poses the risk of unintentionally selecting animals for further breeding which would not be capable of reproduction if subject to the conditions of natural selection. Management of captive populations could lead to changes in a species genetic structure and we do not know the consequences of these changes and their impact on long-term fitness. The genetic and demographic implications of keeping a species in captivity over many generations, and the need to maintain a sufficiently large population, require an appreciable investment of funds and expertise. Also, most zoos and breeding centers are independent institutions that are run as businesses and this can influence which animals are held in collections and breeding programs. Finally, for most

mongoose species our knowledge of their habitat requirements and threats may not be sufficiently known to undertake successful reintroductions.

General Bibliography

Admasu *et al.* (2004a), Aeschlimann (1965), Al-Khalili (1984, 1990), Allen (1911), Allen & Loveridge (1927), Al-Safadi (1995), Angelici (2000), Angelici, Luiselli & Politano (1999), Angelici, Luiselli, Politano & Akani (1999), Ansell (1960c, 1969, 1974), Asher *et al.* (1998), Austin & Tewes (1999b), Avenant & Nel (1992, 1997), Azzaroli & Simonetta (1966), Baker (1988a, 1988b, 1988c, 1989, 1992a, 1992b, 1998), Baker & Meester (1986), Baker & Ray (In press), Baldwin (1954), Baldwin *et al.* (1952), Barchan *et al.* (1992), Bdolah *et al.* (1997), Bechthold (1939), Bell (2007), Ben Yaacov & Yom Tov (1983), Bequaert (1922), Beynon & Rasa (1989), Blaum, Rossmanith, Fleissner & Jeltsch (2007), Blaum, Rossmanith, Popp & Jeltsch (2007), Brotherton *et al.* (2001), Buskirk *et al.* (1990), Cant (1998, 2000, 2003), Cant & Gilchrist

*The **Liberian Mongoose** was only discovered by western scientists in 1958. An earthworm and soil invertebrate specialist, its foraging is restricted to riverine wetland areas and swamp forest. Possible threats include deforestation due to agriculture, logging, and mining. It is heavily hunted for food throughout its range, and may also be vulnerable to pesticides, as worms are known to accumulate toxins at levels dangerous to mammalian predators. Although it is found in secondary forests, it is thought that the lack of suitable den sites may restrict its distribution. It is classified as Vulnerable on* The IUCN Red List.

Liberiictis kuhni
Photo: Kevin Schafer

(In press), Cant *et al.* (2001, 2002), Cardillo *et al.* (2004), Carlson, Manser *et al.* (2006), Carlson, Nicol *et al.* (2003), Carlson, Russell, *et al.* (2006), Carlson, Young *et al.* (2004), Caro & Stoner (2003), Carpaneto & Germi (1989a, 1989b), Cavallini (1992a, 1992b, 1993), Cavallini & Nel (1990a, 1990b, 1995), Cavallini & Serafini (1995), Chan *et al.* (1992), Choudhury (1997a, 1997b, 2000), Christopher & Jayson (1996), Chuang & Lee (1997), Clutton-Brock, Brotherton, O'Riain, Griffin, Gaynor, Kansky *et al.* (2001), Clutton-Brock, Brotherton, O'Riain, Griffin, Gaynor, Sharpe *et al.* (2000), Clutton-Brock, Brotherton, Russell *et al.* (2001), Clutton-Brock, Brotherton, Smith *et al.* (1998), Clutton-Brock, Gaynor, Kansky *et al.* (1998), Clutton-Brock, Gaynor, McIlrath *et al.* (1999), Clutton-Brock, Hodge *et al.* (2006), Clutton-Brock, Maccoll *et al.* (1999), Clutton-Brock, O'Riain *et al.* (1999), Clutton-Brock, Russell & Sharpe (2003, 2004), Clutton-Brock, Russell, Sharpe, Brotherton *et al* (2001), Clutton-Brock, Russell, Sharpe & Jordan (2005), Clutton-Brock, Russell, Sharpe, Young *et al.* (2002), Coblentz & Coblentz (1985), Coetzee (1977), Colyn (1984), Colyn & Van Rompaey (1990, 1994a, 1994b), Colyn, Dudu & Mankoto Ma Mbaelele (1987), Colyn, Dufour & Van Rompaey (2000), Corbet & Hill (1992), Corn & Conroy (1998), Couturier & Dutrillaux (1985), Crawford-Cabral (1989, 1996), Creel (1996, 2001, 2005, In press), Creel & Creel (1991) Creel & Waser (1994, 1997), Creel, Creel *et al.* (1992), Creel, Monfort, Creel *et al.* (1995), Creel, Monfort, Wildt & Waser (1991), Creel, Wildt & Monfort (1993), De Luca & Ginsberg (2001), De Luca & Mpunga (2005), De Luca & Rovero (2006), De Vos *et al.* (1956), Decker *et al.* (1992), Doolan & Macdonald (1996a, 1996b, 1997, 1999), Duckworth (1997), Duckworth & Robichaud (2005), Earle (1981), Eisner (1968), Eisner & Davis (1967), Engel & Van Rompaey (1995), Engeman *et al.* (2006), Estes (1991), Ewer (1963, 1973), Flynn *et al.* (2005), Fredga (1972), Gilchrist (2001, 2004, 2006a, 2006b, 2008), Gilchrist & Otali (2002), Gilchrist & Russell (2007), Gilchrist *et al.* (2004), Goldman, C.A. (1984, 1987, In press), Goldman, C.A. & Dunham (In press), Goldman, H. & Winther-Hansen (2003), Gorman (1975, 1976a, 1976b, 1979), Gorman *et al.* (1974), Gregory & Hellman (1939), Griffin *et al.* (2003), Grzimek (1972), Haque (1989), Hays (1999), Hays & Conant (2003, 2007), Hays & Simberloff (2006), Hedges (1997), Hefetz *et al.* (1984), Hendey (1974), Hinton & Dunn (1967), Hiscocks & Perrin (1991a, 1991b), Hoagland & Kilpatrick (1999), Hoagland *et al.* (1989), Hodge (2003, 2005), Hoffmann, J.C. *et al.* (1984), Hoffmann, M.H. & Taylor (In press), Hollen & Manser (2006, 2007), Hunt (1996), Ikeda *et al.* (1982), IUCN (2008), Jordan *et al.* (2007), Keane, Creel & Waser (1996), Keane, Waser *et al.* (1994), Kingdon (1971-1982, 1997), Kingdon & Van Rompaey (In press), Krystufek & Tvrtkovic (1992), Kumar & Umapathy (2000), Kutsukake & Clutton-Brock (2006a, 2006b), La Rivers (1948), Lekagul & McNeely (1991), Lim (1992), Long & Hoang (2006), Louw & Nel (1986), Lynch (1980), Maddock & Perrin (1993), Madhusudan (1995), Manser (1998, 1999, 2001), Manser & Avey (2000), Manser & Bell (2004), Manser, Bell & Fletcher (2001), Manser, Sey-

farth & Cheney (2002), Markotter *et al.* (2006), Masi *et al.* (1987), Mason & Rowe-Rowe (1992), Messeri (1983), Moran (1984), Moran & Sorensen (1986), Moran *et al.* (1983), Morley (2004), Moss *et al.* (2001), Mudappa (1998, 2001, 2002), Mudappa *et al.* (2007), Muller, C.A. (2007), Muller, C.A. & Manser (2007), Muller, E.F. & Lojewski (1986), Mulligan & Nellis (1975), Nader & Al-Safadi (1991), Neal (1970a, 1970b, 1971), Nellis (1989), Nellis & Everard (1983), Nellis & Small (1983), Nellis *et al.* (1989), Nowak (1999), Ogura, Kawashima *et al.* (2000), Ogura, Nonaka *et al.* (2000, 2001), Ogura, Otsuka *et al.* (2000), O'Riain *et al.* (2000), Otali & Gilchrist (2004), Palomares (1991, 1993a, 1993b, 1994), Palomares & Delibes (1992, 1993), Pearson & Baldwin (1953), Peigné *et al.* (2005), Perez *et al.* (2006), Petter (1969, 1974), Pilsworth (1977), Pimentel (1955), Pocock (1916b, 1916d, 1919, 1937, 1941a), Prakash (1959), Prater (1980), Purves *et al.* (1994), Quinn & Whisson (2005), Rasa (1973a, 1973b, 1973c, 1976, 1977a, 1977b, 1979, 1983a, 1983b, 1984, 1985, 1986a, 1986b, 1987a, 1987b, 1989a, 1989b, 1994), Rasa *et al.* (1992), Rathbun (2004), Rathbun & Rathbun (2006), Rathbun *et al.* (2005), Ray (1995, 1997, 1998), Ray & Sunquist (2001), Roberts (1977), Rood (1974, 1975, 1978, 1980, 1983a, 1983b, 1986, 1987, 1989, 1990), Rosevear (1974), Ross-Gillespie & Griffin (2007), Rowe-Rowe (1978a), Rowe-Rowe & Somers (1998), Roy (2002a, 2002b), Russell, Brotherton *et al.* (2003), Russell, Carlson *et al.* (2004), Russell, Sharpe *et al.* (2003), Russell, Young *et al.* (2007), Sale & Taylor (1970), Santiapillai *et al.* (2000), Sasaki (1991), Savage & Russell (1983), Scantlebury *et al.* (2002), Schoener (1974), Schwarz (1947), Seaman (1952), Seaman & Randall (1962), Sharpe (2005a, 2005b, 2005c, 2007), Sharpe & Cherry (2003), Sharpe *et al.* (2002), Shekar (2003), Shetty *et al.* (1990), Sillero-Zubiri & Bassignani (2001), Simberloff *et al.* (2000), Simmons (1995), Simpson (1964, 1966), Skinner & Chimimba (2005), Smits van Oyen (1998), Somers & Purves (1996), Stains (1983), Stephens *et al.* (2005), Stone & Keith (1987), Struhsaker & McKey (1975), Stuart & Stuart (1998, In press a, In press b, In press c), Tan (1989), Taylor, M.E. (1969, 1972, 1975, 1986, 1987, In press a, In press b, In press c, In press d), Taylor, M.E. & Dunham (In press), Taylor, M.E. & Goldman (1983), Taylor, P.J. *et al.* (1991), Thevenin (1943), Thornton & McAuliffe (2006), Thulin *et al.* (2006), Tomich (1969), Tvrtkovic & Krystufek (1990), Van Rompaey (1978, 1991, 2000), Van Rompaey & Colyn (1992, In press a, In press b, In press c), Van Rompaey & Jayakumar (2003), Van Rompaey & Kingdon (In press), Van Rompaey & Powell (1999), Van Rompaey & Sillero-Zubiri (In press), Van Staaden (1994), Veron (1995), Veron & Catzeflis (1993), Veron, Colyn *et al.* (2004), Veron, Patou *et al.* (2007), Vilella (1998), Viljoen (1980), Waser (1980, 1981), Waser & Waser (1985), Waser, Elliott *et al.* (1995), Waser, Keane *et al.* (1994), Wells (1989), Wells *et al.* (2005), Wenhold & Rasa (1994), Whitfield & Blaber (1980), Williams (1951), Wozencraft (2005), Yalden, Largen & Kock (1980), Yalden, Largen, Kock & Hillman (1996), Yoder *et al.* (2003), Young & Clutton-Brock (2006).

PLATE 17

inches

cm

Subfamily HERPESTINAE

Genus *ATILAX*

Cuvier, 1826

1. Marsh Mongoose *Atilax paludinosus*

French: Mangouste des marais / **German**: Sumpfmanguste / **Spanish**: Mangosta negra
Other common names: Water Mongoose

Taxonomy. *Herpestes paludinosus* Cuvier, 1829, Cape of Good Hope, South Africa. Ten subspecies are recognized.
Subspecies and distribution.
A. p. paludinosus Cuvier, 1829 – S South Africa.
A. p. macrodon J.A. Allen, 1924 – Central African Republic through Congo republics to Rwanda and Burundi.
A. p. mitis Thomas, 1902 – Ethiopia.
A. p. mordax Thomas, 1912 – S Tanzania.
A. p. pluto Temminck, 1853 – Senegal to Nigeria.
A. p. robustus Gray, 1865 – Chad and Sudan.
A. p. rubellus Thomas & Wroughton, 1908 – Malawi, Mozambique, and Zimbabwe.
A. p. rubescens Hollister, 1912 – N Tanzania, Kenya, and Uganda.
A. p. spadiceus Cabrera, 1921 – Cameroon to Gabon.
A. p. transvaalensis Roberts, 1933 – N South Africa to Angola and Zambia.
Descriptive notes. Head-body 51·4 cm (males), 48·7 cm (females), tail 31–41 cm (males), 33–40 cm (females), hindfoot 11–11·5 cm (males), 10·7–11·8 cm (females), ear 3–4·5 cm (males), 3·2–3·7 cm (females); weight 2·9–4 kg (males), 2·4–4·1 kg (females). Females are slightly smaller than males. The pelage is shaggy, grizzled dark reddish-brown to black, with white, red, or russet annulations on the guard hairs. The guard hairs are 3·2–5 cm long, longest at the rump; the underfur is 1·5–2·5 cm long. Relatively broad head, small eyes with horizontal pupils, and broad, round ears. Hair long and thick in front of ears, protecting inner ear from water, but short around the mouth. A slit down the black rhinarium divides upper lip. Relatively long body with short legs. Tail approximately 66% of head-body length. The five-toes on each foot are unwebbed, enabling toes to spread. Feet have soft, naked pads and short, curved, non-retractible claws. Longest foreclaw about 11 mm. Hindfoot claws shorter and less curved. Plantar surfaces naked. There are two to three pairs of mammae. Convex baculum in male (c.18 mm in adults). Cheek glands present. Broad skull: zygomatic breadth less than 50% condylobasal length. Supraoccipital crest is flange-like and meets well-developed sagittal crest (up to 4 mm high) to form T-shape. Brain case pear-shaped. Marked post-orbital constriction. Eye sockets small relative to skull length (20% of condylobasal length). Relatively short rostrum. Broad lower jaw. Posterior ear bullae more prominent than anterior. Dental formula: I 3/3, C 1/1, P 3–4/3–4, M 2/2 = 36–40. Upper jaw incisors larger than lower, outer incisors larger than inner for both jaws. Carnassials adapted to crushing rather than slicing. Heavy canines, upper possess blade-like processes on front and back, lower curved. Sharp canines and stout premolars and carnassials adapted to crushing shellfish.
Habitat. Coincident with riparian habitats, such as swampy and streambed areas. In Dzanga-Sangha forest, Central African Republic, restricted to swamp forest adjacent to streams. Also occurs in estuarine and marine habitats, as well as freshwater areas. Ranges farther from watercourses during dry periods. Found from sea level up to 2500 m.
Food and Feeding. Opportunistic, with diet dependent upon prey availability. Marsh Mongooses are sympatric with Spotted-necked and African Clawless otters and there is some overlap in diet, but this species is less dependent upon aquatic prey. Prey composition differs between areas. In South Africa, the most frequent food types eaten varied across seven regions, but overall the frequency of prey types (as percentage composition in scats) was: Crustacea (23%), Insecta (17%), Mammalia (13%), Amphibia (9%), Mollusca (8%), and Aves (8%). In Zimbabwe, food types (as percentage of stomach contents) were: Amphibia (29%), Crustacea (24%), Mammalia (24%), Insecta (19%), and Pisces (5%). In the Central African Republic, the most abundant prey types (as frequency of occurrence in scats) from a rainforest study were: Coleoptera (86%), Amphibia (82%), Orthoptera (74%), and Crustacea (67%). Marsh Mongooses forage alongside or in shallow water. They are excellent swimmers, but do not swim readily. They reach into cracks, mud, and rocks with their forelimbs to search for prey, and stand up and use their forelimbs to throw hard-shelled prey items, e.g. crabs or mussels, downwards against rocks. Some prey, e.g. crabs, snakes, and large rodents, are seized in the jaws and flicked sideways prior to being given a killing bite. Small crabs are eaten whole; larger crabs are turned upside down, the foreclaws are bitten off, the meat eaten, and the carapace discarded. Upturned carapaces on riversides indicate the presence of *Atilax* (otters normally crunch up the crab carapace). Marsh Mongooses are extremely dexterous compared to other herpestids. They occasionally prey on poultry.
Activity patterns. Crepuscular and nocturnal. Two studies, both in Natal (South Africa), produced conflicting results: one found them to forage mostly in the early morning and late afternoon, whereas the other (using telemetry) found them to be nocturnal. A telemetry study in Central African Republic found males to be crepuscular. Day beds are located on relatively high areas surrounded by deep mud or water.
Movements, Home range and Social organization. Solitary, although occasionally two are seen together. Home range sizes are generally linear in shape, due to fidelity to watercourses. One radio-collared adult male in the Central African Republic travelled up and down a stream around 5 km in length; its home range was estimated at 54 ha. In South Africa, the home range of a male was 131 ha and that of a female was 204 ha. The Central African Republic study showed that the male could spend up to seven days without visiting the edges of his territory, and documented a mean traveling speed of 21·4 m/s. Marsh Mongooses defaecate in latrines in exposed, open areas alongside streams. They may be territorial, communicating with conspecifics through sound, scent marking (with urine and anal and cheek glands), and with behavioral displays. Scats and anal gland secretions may be used in individual discrimination among adults; the response to marks made by the same and the opposite sex differ. May eject strong-smelling anal fluid when stressed. A variety of vocalizations have been noted, including bark-growl threats, excitement bleats, and moan/bleat vocalizations (which may fulfill a contact role).
Breeding. In southern Africa, breeding is seasonal and occurs in the summer. Mating takes place from as early as August through to February. There is no evidence of a breeding season in West Africa. In captivity, estrus lasts approximately nine days, gestation is 69–80 days, litter size is two to three (mean of six litters: 2·5), and birth weight ranges from 78–125 g. Sex ratio at birth is unbiased. The young are born blind and softly furred (black). The eyes open at 9–14 days, and the young are weaned at 30–60 days. Two females in the wild carried one and two fetuses. Longevity in captivity is just over 19 years.
Status and Conservation. Not CITES listed. Classified as Least Concern in *The IUCN Red List*. Pesticides have been found in scats, but not at dangerous concentrations. Widespread and relatively common and therefore unlikely to become threatened in the near future. However, continued destruction and conversion of swamplands to arable land is a concern. Also commonly occurs as bushmeat.

Bibliography. Angelici (2000), Avenant & Nel (1997), Baker (1988a, 1988b, 1988c, 1989, 1992a, 1992b, 1998), Baker & Meester (1986), Baker & Ray (In press), Estes (1991), Kingdon (1971-1982, 1997), Louw & Nel (1986), Maddock & Perrin (1993), Markotter *et al.* (2006), Mason & Rowe-Rowe (1992), Nowak (1999), Purves *et al.* (1994), Ray (1997), Ray & Sunquist (2001), Rowe-Rowe (1978a), Rowe-Rowe & Somers (1998), Skinner & Chimimba (2005), Somers & Purves (1996), Whitfield & Blaber (1980), Wozencraft (2005).

Genus *XENOGALE*

J. A. Allen, 1915

2. Long-nosed Mongoose *Xenogale naso*

French: Mangouste à long nez / **German**: Langnasenichneumon / **Spanish**: Mangosta hocicuda

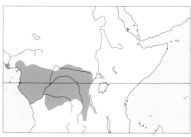

Taxonomy. *Herpestes naso* de Winton, 1901, "Cameroon River, West Africa", Cameroon.
Has been previously placed in *Herpestes* and in *Xenogale*, but recent molecular studies have shown that it is more closely related to the Marsh Mongoose (*Atilax paludinosus*) than to *Herpestes* spp., and is here placed in the genus *Xenogale*. Three subspecies have been described: *naso*, *almodovari*, and *microdon*, but a morphometric study has shown that none can be distinguished on the basis of cranial or external features. Monotypic.
Distribution. SE Nigeria, Cameroon, Central African Republic, Equatorial Guinea, Gabon, PR Congo, and DR Congo.
Descriptive notes. Head-body 43–60·9 cm (males), 40–58 cm (females), tail 32–42·5 cm (males), 32–42·5 cm (females), hindfoot 9·6–11·2 cm (males), 8·5–11·3 cm (females), ear 2·5–4 cm (males), 3–3·8 cm (females); weight 1·9–4·5 kg (males), 2–3·4 kg (females). A large dark-colored mongoose, with a long muzzle and nose. The long, rough dorsal pelage is brownish-black, speckled with yellow or orange; the hairs have dark and light rings, giving a grizzled aspect, but the overall appearance of the body color is black. The dorsal hairs are 50–60 mm long; the underfur is grayish-brown to orange-brown. The ventral pelage is sparser and paler. The head is grayish and more grizzled than the body; the muzzle is long with a black rhinarium. The eyes have a very dark brown iris, and the ears are round, broad, and low set. The tail is tapered and has long black hairs. The fore- and hindlimbs are deep brown to black. The feet have five digits, long claws, and are partly webbed; the soles are hairy up to the pads. The skull is long and fairly narrow; the egg-shaped braincase terminates posteriorly in a broad, flange-like supra-occipital crest. In mature specimens there is a distinct sagittal crest. The rostrum is relatively longer

On following pages: 3. Small Indian Mongoose (*Herpestes auropunctatus*); 4. Short-tailed Mongoose (*Herpestes brachyurus*); 5. Indian Gray Mongoose (*Herpestes edwardsii*); 6 Indian Brown Mongoose (*Herpestes fuscus*); . Egyptian Mongoose (*Herpestes ichneumon*); 8. Javan Mongoose (*Herpestes javanicus*); 9. Collared Mongoose (*Herpestes semitorquatus*); 10. Ruddy Mongoose (*Herpestes smithii*); 11. Crab-eating Mongoose (*Herpestes urva*); 12. Stripe-necked Mongoose (*Herpestes vitticollis*).

and broader than that of the Egyptian Mongoose, and the inter-orbital breadth is relatively wider in the Long-nosed Mongoose. Dental formula: I 3/3, C 1/1, P 4/4, M 2/2 = 40. There is a posterior-lingual cusp on P_4, a long talonid on M_1, and a large M^2 and M_2.

Habitat. Found in forests near swamps, streams, and streambeds. A radio-tracking study in the Central African Republic showed that this species spent most of its time in upland mixed-species forest; stream habitat was very important and they generally avoided stands of open understorey "molapa" forest (*Gilbertiodendron dewevrei*). Recorded up to 640 m.

Food and Feeding. The diet is mainly arthropods and small mammals. In the Central African Republic, the frequency of occurrence of food items in 346 scats was: beetles (72%), orthopterans (68%), mammals (52%, including 23% rodents, 19% shrews, 6% ungulates, 5% porcupines, 0·9% pangolins, 0·6% primates, 0·3% bats, and 0·3% Hyraxes), termites (41%), ants (20%), millipedes (17%), fruits (8%), frogs and toads (8%), snakes (8%), birds (7%), butterflies and moths (5%), lizards and skinks (4%), spiders, scorpions and larvae (4%), bees and wasps (2%), crustaceans (0·6%), and fish (0·3%). Mammal prey greater than 5 kg was rarely taken; Blue Duikers (*Philantomba monticola*) were the most common large prey found in scats. Fluctuations in rodent availability had no effect on the occurrence of shrews in the diet. Among eight co-existing carnivores in the Central African Republic, Long-nosed Mongooses had the second highest niche breadth. In Nigeria, two stomachs contained a centipede, a snail, and some remains of fruits and berries. Long-nosed Mongooses are said to carry snails to a particular spot and to break them by throwing them backwards with the forepaws against a tree or a rock.

Activity patterns. Diurnal. In the Central African Republic, radio-collared individuals were active 74% of the time during the day (06:00–18:00 h) and active 17% of the time at night (18:00–06:00 h). Movement peaks occurred at midday (12:00 h), with smaller peaks at 08:00 h and 15:00 h. The location of nocturnal resting sites varied from day to day. One specimen was found within a hollow log. There is no evidence of latrine-use; however, scats are occasionally found in the same spot where one had been found previously.

Movements, Home range and Social organization. Terrestrial and solitary, but sometimes observed in pairs. In the Central African Republic, the home ranges of two adult males were 0·93 and 0·12 km², and 0·71 km² for a sub-adult male. The home range for an adult female was 1 km², and 0·24 km² for a sub-adult female. A male followed over 24 hours travelled 2324 m and covered 71% of its home range during this period. Another male moved 4605 m, but visited only 29% of its home range.

Breeding. A litter of three has been reported. A two- to three-month-old juvenile was found in mid-March in Nigeria, and one juvenile West African specimen was collected at the end of May. The young reach adult size at around seven months of age and permanent dentition is attained at one year.

Status and Conservation. Classified as Least Concern in *The IUCN Red List*. May be threatened by forest loss and fragmentation. This species is hunted for food in Cameroon and Nigeria and may be rare in the Niger Delta. In the Central African Republic, it appeared to be the most abundant carnivore species in the Dzanga-Sangha forest reserve. Field surveys, ecological studies, and assessments of threats are needed.

Bibliography. Angelici, Luiselli & Politano (1999), Angelici, Luiselli, Politano & Akani (1999), Colyn & Van Rompaey (1994b), Perez *et al.* (2006), Ray (1995, 1997, 1998), Ray & Sunquist (2001), Rosevear (1974), Van Rompaey & Powell (1999), Veron, Colyn *et al.* (2004), Wozencraft (2005).

Genus *HERPESTES*

Illiger, 1811

3. Small Indian Mongoose *Herpestes auropunctatus*

French: Mangouste tachetée / **German**: Goldstaubmungo / **Spanish**: Meloncillo chico

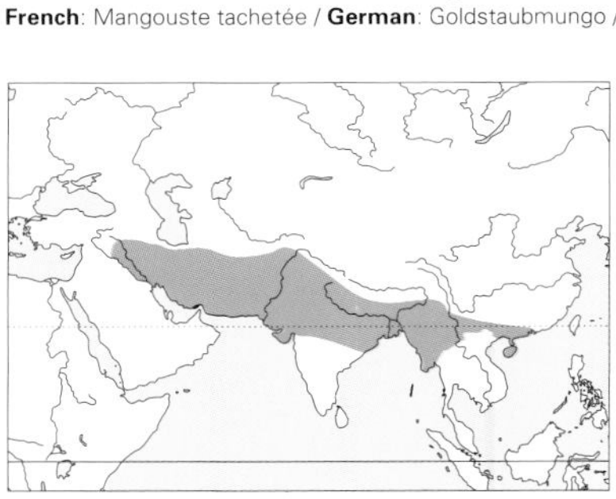

Taxonomy. *Mangusta auropunctata* Hodgson, 1836, central Nepal.

Some authors considered the Small Indian Mongoose and the Javan Mongoose (*H. javanicus*) conspecific under the name *H. javanicus* or *H. auropunctatus*. Recent molecular studies suggest that they should be treated as separate species. Five subspecies have been recognized in *H. auropunctatus*, but the taxonomy needs clarification as some populations (notably from southern China) have not been confirmed as belonging to this species or to *H. javanicus*. Included here is *H. palustris*, which has been considered either a separate species or a synonym of *H. auropunctatus*.

Distribution. SW Asia from Iraq and Iran to Afghanistan, Pakistan, India, Nepal, and Bhutan; also Bangladesh, Myanmar and S China (including Hainan I). Introduced to Antigua, Barbados, Beef Island, Buck Island, Carriacou, Croatia, Cuba, Fiji, French Guiana, Goat Island, Grenada, Guadeloupe, Guyana, Hawaii, Hispaniola, Jamaica, Japan, Jost Van Dyke, La Desirade, Lavango, Mafia (Tanzania), Marie Galante, Martinique, Maui, Mauritius, Molokai, Nevis, Oahu, Puerto Rico, St. Croix, St. John, St. Kitts, St. Lucia, St. Martin, St. Thomas, St. Vincent, Surinam, Tortola, Trinidad, Vieques, and Water Island. Introduction was unsuccessful in the Dominican Republic. The Small Indian Mongoose or the Javan Mongoose is said to occur on Hong Kong since the 1980s and to have been also introduced to some Indonesian islands (particularly Ambon).

Descriptive notes. Head-body 25–37 cm, tail 19·2–29 cm; weight 305–662 g. There is sexual dimorphism, males being larger than females (particularly in introduced populations), for example on St Croix Island (Caribbean): Head-body 22·2–44·6 cm (males), 21·4–38·5 cm (females). The smallest of the Asian mongooses, with a slender body and short legs. The coat color varies from buff to rufous or dark yellowish gray; the hairs have white and dark rings, giving a grizzled appearance. The muzzle is pointed, the rhinarium is blackish, the eyes are small with a brown iris, and the ears are short. The tail is muscular at the base and tapers throughout its length. There are five digits on each foot, with long, sharp, non-retractile claws. The soles are naked. There is an anal pouch in which the ducts of the anal glands open laterally to the anus. The anal glands have a diameter of about 5 mm and a mean weight of 10 mg/100 g of body weight. The secretion from these glands contains volatile fatty acids, with some differences between males and females. There are three pairs of teats. A claw-shaped baculum is present in the male and ranges in size from 5–15 mm. The skull is elongated and narrow, with a long brain case. The post-orbital bar encloses the orbit. The sagittal crest is weak, but the lambdoidal crest is developed. The posterior chamber of the auditory bulla is slightly inflated and projects no more than the anterior chamber. Dental formula: I 3/3, C 1/1, P 4/4, M 2/2(3) = 40–42 (the presence of a third lower molar is rare). The canines are long and slightly recurved. The first premolars are small, and the other cheek teeth are well-developed and trenchant.

Habitat. Forest, scrub, and open habitats. Also found close to human habitations. On Mauritius, a radio-tracking study found that this species favored woodland and scrub regions over other habitat types, and preferred riverine and dense forest at larger spatial scales.

Food and Feeding. Omnivorous. Most of the dietary information comes from introduced populations, but it is reported to eat rodents, snakes, insects, centipedes, and scorpions in its native range. The diet appears to vary according to the season and the locality. Two specimen stomachs collected in the Rajasthan desert, India, contained remains of insects (*Helicopric bucephalus, Anthic sexguttata, Blap orientalus, Onthophagus longicornis*, and *Grylus sagillatus*) and a scorpion. In 56 stomachs from Puerto Rico, 315 food items were recorded, with the following frequency of occurrence: insects (56%), reptiles (17%), myriapods (12%), arachnids (8%), mammals (3%), crustaceans (1%), asteroids (starfish) (1%), amphibians (1%), and plants (11%). On St. Croix Island, 36 stomachs contained insects (83%), toads (14%), mice *Mus musculus* (14%), rat *Rattus rattus* (14%), crabs (11%), birds (3%), poultry (3%), lizards *Anolis* (0·5%), fruit (11%), and other plant material (6%). On Viti Levu, Fiji, an analysis of 4404 scats showed that the diet varied with the habitat: crabs were the main food in mangrove forests, rats in cane-fields, and cockroaches in urban areas. In Hawaii, a preponderance of cockroaches in the diet was reported. In the Caribbean, the Small Indian Mongoose was observed eating toads (including the parotid glands, which are normally noxious to predators), and the eggs and young of the hawksbill sea turtle (*Eretmochelys imbricata*) and leatherback turtle (*Dermochelys coriacea*). In Mauritius, 458 stomachs contained 46% rodents and shrews, 20% Tail-less Tenrecs (*Tenrec eucaudatus*), 20% invertebrates, 18% refuse, carrion and plants, 15% reptiles and amphibians, and 6% birds; there were seasonal changes in the diet, with more insects eaten during the wet season and more reptiles taken during the dry season. During the winter on Korcula Island, Croatia, 184 food items were identified in 126 scats: the frequency of occurrence was 66% plants (mostly the fruits of juniper *Juniperus oxycedrus* and strawberry tree *Arbutus unedo*), 38% mammals (mainly wood mice *Apodemus sylvaticus* and rats *Rattus* sp.), 23% arthropods (mainly Coleoptera and a few Orthoptera), 14% birds (mostly passerines), and 1% reptiles. Compared to introduced populations in tropical areas, individuals on Korcula Island ate more fruits and less insects and reptiles. The killing method is efficient; the canines are driven into the brain and vertebral column of rodents, birds, and snakes. Centipedes and scorpions are bitten and repeatedly tossed before being consumed. Two individuals were reported working together to hunt crabs (*Metapograpsus messor*) in Pearl Harbor, Hawaii; one turned over a stone, allowing the other to attack the crab. Individuals are reluctant to enter water more than a few centimetres deep.

Activity patterns. Diurnal activity is reported from observations in India and Pakistan and in regions where it has been introduced. In the Caribbean, most activity was between 10:00 h and 16:00 h, although they were seldom active on rainy days. Rest sites in Mauritius are mostly in fallen trees and holes in tree root systems. In India, they are reported to use burrows that they dig themselves.

Movements, Home range and Social organization. Information mainly comes from introduced populations. While this species tends to be solitary, individuals frequently have been seen close to each other in introduced areas. Home ranges on St. Croix were 2·2 ha for females and 4·2 ha for males; home ranges overlapped both within and between sexes, but the overlap of core areas was minimal. On Oahu Island, Hawaii, the mean home range was 1·4 ha for seven females and 19·2 ha for five males (during the breeding season); the mean intra-sexual overlap of home ranges was 84% for males and 37% for females, with a large overlap between male and female ranges. Each male moved from den to den on successive nights and on some occasions two or three males shared a sleeping den. Females also moved den sites, except when they produced pups (they showed den fidelity during the 20 to 22 days after parturition). It appeared that males formed social coalitions, at least during the breeding season. The high population density in this introduced population suggested an abundance of resources, which may favor social behavior. Other studies report home range sizes of 22 to 39 ha in the Fiji Islands and 25 to 100 ha on Hawaii. On Puerto Rico, the home ranges of twenty mongooses were 3·2 to 19·4 ha. On Mauritius, the home ranges of 14 individuals were 25 ha to 110 ha, with considerable overlap between individuals. On two islands in Hawaii, both males and females showed natal dispersal in the fall, and males also dispersed during the breeding season. Population densities vary from less than ten to several hundred animals per km². The Small Indian Mongoose scent-marks using the secretions from its anal glands by wiping objects with its anal pouch. Males and females scent-mark their home range and are able to distinguish the scent marks of other individuals. This species has a large vocal repertoire of twelve distinct calls, which is unusually rich for an asocial species. The vocalizations are extremely varied and include weep, squawk, honk, ruck-a-ruck, pant, spit, bark, chuck, scream, and growl. Small Indian Mongooses can scratch and dig vigorously and have considerable manipulative dexterity. Gaits include walk, trot and gallop. They can climb, but are rarely observed far above the ground.

Breeding. Breeding data comes mainly from captive animals. Ovulation is induced by copulation. The estrous cycle is about three weeks, with estrus lasting three to four days. Gestation is approximately 49 days. The mean litter size is two and ranges from one to five. There are two to three litters a year. The timing of reproduction may be related to day length, as most pregnancies seem to occur prior to the summer solstice. In Mauritius, breeding is timed to avoid the driest times of the year. The beginning of estrus in captive females is revealed by restlessness and increased scent marking. Several males may attend a female, and they commonly scream, bark, and chase each other. Both sexes are polygamous and may copulate several times a day in the absence of estrus, and more frequently during estrus. Females in the late stage of pregnancy show antagonism toward males. Births occur at night, shortly after sunset. Nesting material is not used. Birth weight is about 21 g. Newborns are covered with light gray hairs, which are sparse on the abdomen. The incisors and the eruptive cones of the canines are visible, and the claws are well-developed. The eyes are closed and will open between 17 and 20 days. Mewling vocalizations are emitted when the young are disturbed. At two weeks, the incisors are fully in place and the canines have erupted. At 22 weeks, all the permanent teeth are in place. Two-thirds of the adult body mass is attained at four months and sexual maturity is reached at one year. The first excursion out of the den occurs at about four weeks and the young follow the mother on hunting trips at six weeks. Spermatogenesis in the male begins when the weight reaches 400 g; the baculum reaches adult size and mass at five months or when the weight reaches 500 g.

Status and Conservation. Listed on CITES Appendix III in India. Classified as Least Concern in *The IUCN Red List*. Vulnerable in China.The Small Indian Mongoose is considered unthreatened in its native range as it occurs in many different types of habitats. However, these mongooses are often captured and sold as pets, and there is some commercial trade in China, India, and Nepal, which may constitute a threat in some parts of its native range. This species has been introduced to several tropical oceanic islands for rodent control in plantations or to control vipers. Unfortunately, introduced populations have also preyed on the endemic fauna on some islands and may have caused the extinction of several species of birds, mammals, and reptiles. They eat the eggs and young of some endangered sea turtles and have also been identified as the vector of different diseases, notably rabies and leptospirosis. There have been mainly unsuccessful attempts to eliminate this species on several islands where they have been introduced.

Bibliography. Allen (1911), Baldwin (1954), Baldwin *et al.* (1952), Bechthold (1939), Buskirk *et al.* (1990), Cavallini & Serafini (1995), Chan *et al.* (1992), Corbet & Hill (1992), Corn & Conroy (1998), De Vos *et al.* (1956), Gorman (1975, 1976a, 1976b, 1979), Gorman *et al.* (1974), Haque (1989), Hays (1999), Hays & Conant (2003, 2007), Hoagland & Kilpatrick (1999), Hoagland *et al.* (1989), Krystufek & Tvrtkovic (1992), La Rivers (1948), Morley (2004), Mulligan & Nellis (1975), Nagayama *et al.* (2001), Nellis (1989), Nellis & Everard (1983), Nellis & Small (1983), Ogura, Kawashima *et al.* (2000), Ogura, Nonaka *et al.* (2000, 2001), Ogura, Otsuka *et al.* (2000), Ogura, Sakashita & Kawashima (1998), Pearson & Baldwin (1953), Pimentel (1955), Pocock (1919, 1937, 1941a), Prakash (1959), Prater (1980), Quinn & Whisson (2005), Roberts (1977), Roy (2002a, 2002b), Seaman (1952), Seaman & Randall (1962), Shekar (2003), Simberloff *et al.* (2000), Stone & Keith (1987), Thulin *et al.* (2006), Tomich (1969), Tvrtkovic & Krystufek (1990), Veron *et al.* (2007), Vilella (1998), Wells (1989), Wozencraft (2005).

4. Short-tailed Mongoose *Herpestes brachyurus*

French: Mangouste à queue courte / **German**: Kurzschwanzmungo / **Spanish**: Meloncillo colicorto

Taxonomy. *Herpestes brachyurus* Gray, 1837, Malacca, Malaysia.

Hose's Mongoose *H. hosei* from Borneo is known only from one specimen (an adult female) collected from Sarawak in 1893. This was treated as a separate species on the basis of a less rounded coronoid process of the lower mandible, but has also been considered an aberrant specimen of the Short-tailed Mongoose, and is here considered as a synonym of *H. brachyurus*. The Collared Mongoose (*H. semitorquatus*) has also been considered a subspecies of *H. brachyurus*, but is now generally accepted as a valid species. Several subspecies of the Short-tailed Mongoose have been proposed, but a taxonomic revision is needed. The subspecies *javanensis* was described from a menagerie specimen labelled from Java, but there are no other records from this island. Four subspecies are recognized here.

Subspecies and Distribution.

H. b. brachyurus Gray, 1837 – S Thailand, Peninsular Malaysia, and Singapore.

H. b. palawanus J.A. Allen, 1910 – the Philippines (Palawan & Calamian Is).

H. b. rajah Thomas, 1921 – Borneo.

H. b. sumatrius Thomas, 1921 – Sumatra.

Descriptive notes. Head-body 35–49 cm (males), 36·8–46 cm (females), tail 19·3–24·5 cm (males), 17·2–25 cm (females), hindfoot 7·5–9·6 cm (males), 7·9–9·3 cm (females), ear 2–3·2 cm (males), 2·8–3·2 cm (females); weight 1–3 kg (males), 1·2–2·5 kg (females). The general coat color is dark brown, finely marked with orange or yellow speckling. The head is paler and more olive-brown, the forelegs and lower half of the hindlegs are dark brown, the cheeks and throat rusty yellowish-brown, and the chest and belly are brown. The tail is short, usually less than 55% of the head-body length, and tapers from the base to the tip. The eyes are reddish-brown with a horizontal, oval pupil; the ears are small, and the nose is large and reddish-orange. There are five digits on the fore- and hindfeet, although the first digits are much smaller than the rest. The claws are long. The posterior chamber of the auditory bulla is less flat than in the Javan Mongoose and extends to well below the occipital condyle. Dental formula: I 3/3, C 1/1, P 4/4, M 2/2 = 40. The cuspids are sharp and the carnassial shear is well-developed.

Habitat. Primary and disturbed forest; often found close to rivers and small streams. Occasionally recorded in plantations adjacent to forest. Found at low elevations on Peninsular Malaysia, but has been recorded up to 1280 m on Borneo.

Food and Feeding. Reported to feed on small vertebrates, invertebrates, eggs, fruits, and roots. The stomach content of one individual from north Borneo included fragments of insects (scarab beetle, orthopterans), spider, crab, and a reptile egg. Another Bornean specimen, collected from the banks of a stream, was found to be full of cockroaches.

Activity patterns. Diurnal.

Movements, Home range and Social organization. Solitary. Terrestrial, but has been reported as having limited climbing ability.

Breeding. Nothing known.

Status and Conservation. Classified as Least Concern in *The IUCN Red List*. Threats to this species are unknown, but this species may be eaten in some parts of Sarawak. Field surveys, ecological studies, and assessments of possible threats are needed.

Bibliography. Corbet & Hill (1992), Davis (1962), Esselstyn *et al.* (2004), Medway (1969), Payne *et al.* (1985), Schwarz (1947), Van Rompaey (2000), Wells (1989), Wozencraft (2005).

5. Indian Gray Mongoose *Herpestes edwardsii*

French: Mangouste d'Edwards / **German**: Indischer Mungo / **Spanish**: Meloncillo gris

Taxonomy. *Ichneumon edwardsii* Geoffroy Saint-Hilaire, 1818, Madras, East Indies. Five subspecies are recognized, but a taxonomic revision is needed.

Subspecies and Distribution.

H. e. edwardsii Geoffroy Saint-Hilaire, 1818 – SE India and Sri Lanka.

H. e. carnaticus Wroughton, 1921 – SW India (Karnataka).

H. e. moerens Wroughton, 1915 – Bangladesh, Bhutan, C & NE India, and Nepal.

H. e. montanus Bechthold, 1936 – Saudi Arabia to NW India.

H. e. pallens Ryley, 1914 – W India (Gujarat).

A few old museum specimens are reported from Peninsular Malaysia, where it is said to have been introduced, but it has not been recorded there since the beginning of the 20th century.

Descriptive notes. Head-body 35·5–45 cm, tail 32–45 cm, hindfoot 7–9 cm, ear 2·2 cm; mean weight 1·4 kg. Males are heavier and larger than females. A small mongoose, with a slender body, short legs, pointed muzzle, and short ears. The coat color is tawny or yellowish-gray; light and dark rings on the body hairs give the coat a grizzled appearance. A reddish coloration, particularly on the extremities (muzzle, feet, and tail), is variable, but is more frequent in the northern part of its range. The underparts are covered with short orange-brown hairs. The upperparts of the feet and limbs are reddish-brown. The tail is tipped with white or yellowish-red, never black. The hairs at the base of the tail are long, reaching up to 55 mm. The tail length is 90 to 100% of the Head-body. The posterior chamber of the auditory bulla is not much inflated. Dental formula: I 3/3, C 1/1, P 4/4, M 2/2 = 40.

Habitat. Dry secondary forests, thorn forests, disturbed areas, plantations, and near human settlements. Recorded up to 2100 m. Frequents open, shrubby areas.

Food and Feeding. The diet is said to include rats, mice, snakes, lizards, frogs, insects, scorpions, centipedes, birds' eggs, fruits, and roots. Has been seen feeding on carrion. The remains of grey francolins (*Francolinus pondicerianus*), rodents, and desert monitor (*Varanus griseus*) were found in a specimen stomach from Rajasthan, India. Another stomach contained termites and scorpions.

Activity patterns. Mainly diurnal, although may be active during dusk. Rests under rocks, bushes, and in holes at the base of trees or in the ground.

Movements, Home range and Social organization. Mainly solitary, but mating pairs and females with young have often been seen. A male radio-tracked for three months in the Nilgiri Biosphere Reserve, India, had an overall home range of 15·5 ha. Adopts a defensive posture when attacked by rolling into a ball, it places its head between its legs and under its bushy tail, and erects the long hairs on its back, thereby shielding its body with the parts that have the longest hairs (on the tail and the sacral and lumbar regions of the back). In captive individuals, vocal communications started at daybreak and reached a maximum by dusk; no vocalizations were heard at night. Juveniles were

the most vocal, subordinates moderately, and dominants the least, which suggested that vocalizations played a role in social ranking.
Breeding. Two to three litters may be produced in a year. Gestation is 56–68 days. Births may occur in May–June and October–December; in central India litters were seen during June and July. Litter size is two to four. The young are helpless and blind at birth, but develop rapidly. They remain with the mother for up to six months if she does not mate again. A female was reported to mate for the first time at nine months old.
Status and Conservation. CITES Appendix III (India). Classified as Least Concern in *The IUCN Red List*. Often captured and sold as pets. Some tribes from northern India capture these mongooses for their skins, which they sell in local markets in Nepal. Also in demand for the wildlife trade: the meat is eaten by several tribes and the hair is used for making shaving brushes, paint brushes, and good luck charms. This species is captured by the Jogi tribes in Pakistan, who stage fights with cobras. Field surveys, ecological studies, and monitoring of threats are needed.
Bibliography. Al-Khalili (1984, 1990), Choudhury (2000), Christopher & Jayson (1996), Corbet & Hill (1992), Ewer (1973), Hinton & Dunn (1967), Kumar & Umapathy (2000), Pocock (1941a), Prater (1980), Roberts (1977), Sasaki (1991), Shekar (2003), Shetty *et al.* (1990), Veron *et al.* (2007), Wells (1989), Wozencraft (2005).

6. Indian Brown Mongoose *Herpestes fuscus*

French: Mangouste de Malabar / **German**: Indischer Kurzschwanzmungo /
Spanish: Meloncillo pardo

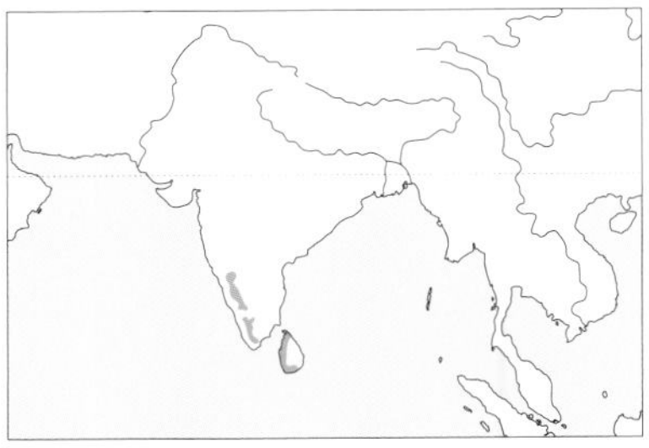

Taxonomy. *Herpestes fuscus* Waterhouse, 1838, India.
Some authors previously considered the Indian Brown Mongoose conspecific with the Short-tailed Mongoose (*H. brachyurus*). Four subspecies are recognized.
Subspecies and Distribution.
H. f. fuscus Waterhouse, 1838 – SW India (Western Ghats).
H. f. phillipsi Thomas, 1924 – Sri Lanka (Central Province).
H. f. rubidior Pocock, 1937 – Sri Lanka (Western Province).
H. f. siccatus Thomas, 1924 – N Sri Lanka (Northern Province).
Descriptive notes. Head-body 33–48 cm, tail 19·8–33·6 cm, hindfoot 6·5–8·7 cm; weight c. 2·7 kg. A large, heavily built mongoose. The coat color is blackish-brown, speckled with yellow or tawny, and the feet are almost black. The tail is bushy and conical, about 60–70% the length of the head and body. The posterior chamber of the auditory bulla is less flat than in the Javan Mongoose and extends to well below the occipital condyle. Dental formula: I 3/3, C 1/1, P 4/4, M 2/2 = 40.
Habitat. Dense forest and adjacent areas. On Sri Lanka, found in lowland forest, central hill country, and the dry zone. In south-west India, also occurs in tea and coffee plantations at elevations from 900 to 1400 m.
Food and Feeding. Nothing known.
Activity patterns. Appears to be nocturnal, based on a few camera-trap photographs and sightings.
Movements, Home range and Social organization. Terrestrial. Appears to be solitary.
Breeding. Said to breed in burrows beneath rocks and tree roots, and to have three to four young.
Status and Conservation. Classified as Vulnerable in *The IUCN Red List*. Specific threats to this species are not known, but habitat loss, fragmentation, and degradation could have major impacts on populations. It seems to be rare to uncommon; in India it is found in Virajpet in south Kodagu and Ooty in the Nilgiri Hills, Tiger Shola in the Palni Hills, High Wavy Mountains in Madurai, Kalakkad-Mundanthurai in the Agasthyamalai range, Valparai plateau in the Anaimalai Hills, and Peeramedu in Kerala. Field surveys, ecological studies, habitat protection, and monitoring of threats are urgently needed.
Bibliography. Corbet & Hill (1992), IUCN (2008), Madhusudan (1995), Mudappa (1998, 2001, 2002), Mudappa *et al.* (2007), Pocock (1941a), Prater (1980), Wozencraft (2005), Yoganand & Kumar (1995).

7. Egyptian Mongoose *Herpestes ichneumon*

French: Mangouste d'Égypte / **German**: Ichneumon / **Spanish**: Meloncillo
Other common names: Large Gray Mongoose, Ichneumon

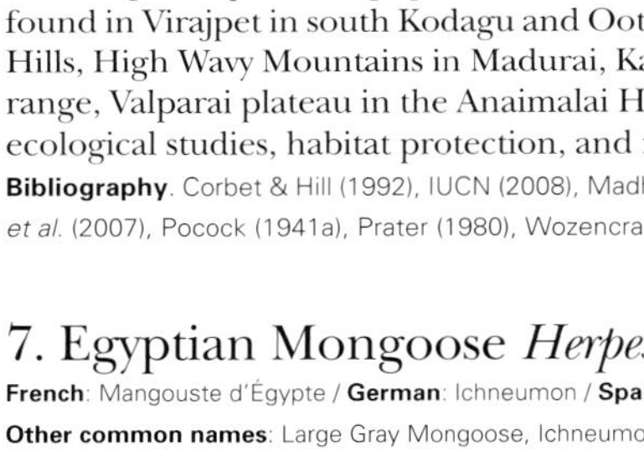

Taxonomy. *Viverra ichneumon* Linnaeus, 1758, Egypt.
Up to ten subspecies are recognized, but a taxonomic revision is needed.
Distribution. Iberian Peninsula, N Africa, and the Middle East in S Turkey, Syria, Lebanon, Jordan, and Israel; in Sub-Saharan Africa from Senegal and Gambia to E Africa in Sudan, Ethiopia, Somalia, and Kenya and then S to Gabon, Angola, N Namibia, N Botswana, N Zimbabwe, Mozambique, and South Africa. Occurrence in Europe (Portugal and Spain) likely due to introduction from North Africa.
Descriptive notes. Head-body 55·7–61 cm (males), 50–58 cm (females), tail 44·7–61 cm (males), 43·5–56·3 cm (females), hindfoot 9·5–11·5 cm (males), 8·9–11·4 cm (females), ear 2·5–3·8 cm (males), 3–4·2 cm (females); weight 2·6–4·1 kg (males) 2·2–4·1 kg (females). Grizzled gray body, with darker head, and black on the lowe limbs. Coarse guard hairs up to 80 mm on rump, tapering to 40 mm toward tail tip but tail tip hairs up to 13 cm. Shorter hair on underparts. Hairs annulated with fiv to six black and white alternating bands and white tip. Soft underfur of variable colo but generally gray at fore and red to yellow toward flank. Long-bodied, with relativel short legs. Long head with pointed muzzle and short rostrum. Long tail (longer tha head-body) ends in long black-tassled tip. Short, rounded ears, partially covered b hair. Five digits, with short first digit situated behind plantar pad. Claws long (up to 1 mm) and curved. Scent glands lie either side of the anus, opening into a pouch, an are surrounded by two rows of sebaceous glands. Females normally possess three pair of mammae (sometimes two pairs). Long, narrow skull with zygomatic arch breadt less than half skull length. Ovoid, elongate brain case. Well-developed supraoccipita crest, rising to 7 mm. Sagittal crest not well-developed. Anterior chambers of ear bu lae larger than posterior. Zygomatic arches strong. Long postorbital processes. Denta formula: I 3/3, C 1/1, P 4/4, M 2/2 = 40. Outer upper incisors are larger than inner less obvious in lower jaw. Lower canines more recurved than upper. Carnassials hav high cusps suggesting crushing rather than slicing action.
Habitat. Flat, grassy, open riparian areas, alongside rivers, dams, lakes, and swamps A study in South Africa found this species to preferentially occupy open habitat an avoid forest. In Spain, individuals appear to prefer vegetative to open habitat.
Food and Feeding. A study of scats in Spain suggested opportunistic predation, wit Egyptian Mongooses consuming the most abundant prey available in each area an season. Percentage of food types from 105 scats collected in south Western Cap (South Africa): unidentified rodents (17%), Coleoptera (12%), green grass (12%) Orthoptera (10·5%), *Rhabdomys pumilio* (rodent, 5·5%), *Otomys irroratus* (roden 5·5%), dry grass (4·5%), seed (4·5%), unidentified bird (4·2%), unidentified snak (3·7%), terrestrial Gastropod (2·4%), *Bitis arietans* (snake, 2·1%), bird egg (1·3%) fish (1%), *Bathyergus suillus* (rodent, 1%), unidentified shrews (1%), *Praomys verraux* (rodent, 0·8%), felid (0·5%), unidentified lizard (0·5%), *Mabuya* species (0·5%) scorpion (0·5%), solifugid (0·5%), *Cryptomys hottentotus* (rodent, 0·3%), *Myosorex va ius* (0·3%), *Chrysochloris asiatica* (0·3%), *Procavia capensis* (0·3%), crab (0·3%), spide (0·3%), millipede (0·3%), and freshwater Gastropod (0·3%). Percentage occurrenc of food types from 19 stomachs collected in Zimbabwe: Muridae (63%), Aves (37%) Amphibia (16%), Reptilia (16%), and Insecta (16%). European Rabbits (*Oryctolag cuniculus*) form the staple prey in Spain, with lizards, insects (including beetles), bird (*Anas platyrhynchos*), rats (*Rattus rattus*) and tortoises (*Testudo graeca*) also recorded. Ap parently resistant to snake venom (neurotoxins). Powerful digger. The name "Ichneu mon" is thought to be derived from the Greek word for "tracker" in relation to the ability to find and dig out crocodile eggs. Adults kill small prey with a bite to the head and large prey with a bite to the neck, eating from the head. Hunts alone, although i Spain, two or three individuals were observed simultaneously excavating rabbit breec ing dens. Occasional food sharing of rabbit prey was also observed in Spain.
Activity patterns. Mainly diurnal (in South Africa and Spain), but some nocturnal a tivity recorded in South Africa, and a group studied in Israel was crepuscular (this ma have been induced by vulnerability to dogs). A study of a Spanish population showe the activity budget to comprise 70% resting, 21% foraging, 6% eating, and 3% walking
Movements, Home range and Social organization. Solitary, although occasionally see in pairs and larger groups (up to five in Spain, including pups). Larger groups though to be polygynous, made up of one male and several females (up to three in Israel) with their pups. In Israel, individuals with access to a garbage dump formed territo rial social groups, with four groups found occupying a total range of 3 km². In Sout Africa, home ranges varied from 0·30 to 0·45 km². In Spain, mean home range was 3· km², and density reached 2 individuals/km² (density negatively correlated with th presence of Iberian Lynx). The home range of a radio-collared male was elongated i shape, following the border of a marsh. Female home ranges overlapped substantiall but core areas were almost exclusive. Male home ranges showed minimal overlap, bu tended to overlap numerous females' home ranges (one male overlapped four femal ranges, another five females). Home range size was correlated with body mass, nega tively in females and positively in males. In Spain, male daily home range size average 2·3 times that of females, but there was no difference in male and female multi-da home range size. An adult male travelled from 0·6 to 6·4 km per day. Latrines are use by all family members, and tend to be found near resting sites in preferred habitats Individuals anal-mark stones along trails by squatting or anal dragging. The anal glan secretion is composed of complex long-chain carboxylic acids. Sex-specific compo nents differentiate male and female secretions. Seven distinct vocalizations have bee described: a deep, sharp growling alarm call that elicits fleeing in other individual a short, repeated contact call given by individuals during foraging; a growl associate with defence of food, territory or mate; a bark or spit given during mating or fighting and a short, sharp, vigorous pain call. The pain call is the only vocalization made b solitary individuals. Underground dens (dug by European Rabbits or European Badg ers), thickets and tree hollows, are used as nocturnal and day rest sites in Spain.
Breeding. Sexual maturity is reached at over one year of age. During the breeding se son, males increase frequency of contact with females. Mating occurs over two month in the spring. Females usually have only one litter per year but will produce a secon litter if the first is lost or if the rodent population is high. Gestation lasts approximate 60 days. Litter size averages 2·7 in Spain and 3·3 (range = 1–4) in captivity, in Israe The female reared the pups alone in Spain, but in Israel, group members shared b bysitting. The pups' eyes open at approximately 21 days. Weaning occurs between fou to eight weeks. Pups are mobile at four weeks, first emerge around six weeks, and show first hunting behavior at ten weeks. In Israel, pups suckled from any breeding femal

in the group. Adults provision pups until they are a year old, when the young may disperse. In Spain, annual adult survival rate varied between 0·13 and 0·60. In Israel, only 3% of individuals survived to two years, with hunting and road kills accounting for 69% of mortality. The oldest known individual in captivity lived to over 20 years. Predators in Spain include the Iberian Lynx; domestic dogs kill mongooses in Israel.

Status and Conservation. Classified as Least Concern in *The IUCN Red List*. Wide distribution suggests this species is unlikely to become threatened in the foreseeable future. However dependence upon riparian habitats leaves them vulnerable to drainage and ground water extraction. Subject to predator control in Portugal, where it has recently increased its distribution northwards, and increased in local population densities (as in Spain). The Egyptian Mongoose's behavioral ecology is relatively well known from Spain, but is understudied in its native Africa.

Bibliography. Angelici (2000), Bdolah *et al.* (1997), Beltrán (1991), Beltrán *et al.* (1985), Ben Yaacov & Yom Tov (1983), Dobson (1998), Hefetz *et al.* (1984), Maddock & Perrin (1993), Nowak (1999), Palomares (1991, 1993a, 1993b, 1994), Palomares & Delibes (1992, 1993), Skinner & Chimimba (2005), Wozencraft (2005).

8. Javan Mongoose *Herpestes javanicus*

French: Mangouste de Java / **German**: Kleiner Mungo / **Spanish**: Meloncillo de Java
Other common names: Small Asian Mongoose

Taxonomy. *Ichneumon javanicus* Geoffroy Saint-Hilaire, 1818, Java.
Some authors considered the Javan Mongoose and the Small Indian Mongoose (*H. auropunctatus*) conspecific. Recent molecular studies suggest that they should be treated as separate species. Three subspecies have been recognized in *H. javanicus*, but the taxonomy still needs clarification as some populations (notably from southern China) have not been confirmed as belonging to this species or to *H. auropunctatus*. Information on the Small Indian Mongoose has often been published under the name *H. javanicus*.

Distribution. Mainland SE Asia, Peninsular Malaysia, and Sumatra. The Javan Mongoose or the Small Indian Mongoose is said to occur on Hong Kong (since the 1980s), and to have been introduced to some Indonesian islands.

Descriptive notes. Head-body 30–41·5 cm, tail 21–31·5 cm, hindfoot 6–7 cm, ear 1·8–3·1 cm; weight 0·5–1 kg. A small mongoose, with a slender body and short legs. The coat color varies from buff to dark brown; the hairs have dark brown and white rings giving a grizzled appearance. The head is reddish and the legs are the same color as the body or slightly darker. The muzzle is pointed, the rhinarium is blackish, and the eyes and ears are small. The tail is muscular at the base and tapers throughout its length. There are five digits on each foot, with long, sharp non-retractile claws. The soles are naked. There is an anal pouch; the ducts of the anal glands open laterally to the anus. There are three pairs of teats. The skull is elongated and narrow, with a long brain case. The post-orbital bar encloses the orbit. The sagittal crest is weak, but the lambdoidal crest is developed. The posterior chamber of the auditory bulla is slightly inflated and projects no more than the anterior chamber. Dental formula: I 3/3, C 1/1, P 4/4, M 2/2 = 40. The canines are long and slightly recurved. The first premolars are small and the other cheek teeth are weakly developed and trenchant.

Habitat. Dry dipterocarp forest, grassland, open areas, and secondary vegetation. Has been observed in scrubby areas, lowland forests, and mixed deciduous forests in Laos, and was seen in Java entering a paddy field on the edge of a swamp forest. Trapped and camera-trapped in open grassland in Khao Yai National Park (Thailand). Several field observations were close to water.

Food and Feeding. The diet is said to include rats, birds, reptiles, frogs, crabs, and insects.

Activity patterns. Current evidence suggests that this species is diurnal: one sighting and camera-trap picture were recorded in Thailand during the daytime and it has been observed during the day in Laos and Java.

Movements, Home range and Social organization. Appears to be solitary, although a pair was seen running through a field in Thailand.

Breeding. Said to breed throughout the year and to produce litters of two to four.

Status and Conservation. Classified as Least Concern in *The IUCN Red List*. Protected in Peninsular Malaysia and Thailand and listed as Vulnerable in the Chinese Red List. Hunted or snare trapped and sold for meat in markets in China, Laos, Thailand, and Vietnam. Field surveys, ecological studies, and assessment of threats are needed.

Bibliography. Austin & Tewes (1999b), Bechthold (1939), Chan *et al.* (1992), Corbet & Hill (1992), Duckworth (1997), Lekagul & McNeely (1991), Lim (1992), Nellis (1989), Simberloff *et al.* (2000), Veron *et al.* (2007), Wells (1989), Wozencraft (2005).

9. Collared Mongoose *Herpestes semitorquatus*

French: Mangouste à collier / **German**: Halsbandmungo / **Spanish**: Meloncillo de collar

Taxonomy. *Herpestes semitorquatus* Gray, 1846, Borneo.
The Collared Mongoose has sometimes been considered a subspecies of the Short-tailed Mongoose (*H. brachyurus*), but is now generally accepted as a valid species. Two subspecies were recognized: one on Borneo and one on Sumatra, but a taxonomic revision and a verification of specimen records are needed.

Distribution. Borneo. Said to occur on Sumatra, but this is based only on two old museum specimens.

Descriptive notes. Head-body 40–45·5 cm, tail 25·8–30·3 cm, hindfoot 8·2–9·3 cm; weight c. 3–4 kg. The coat color is reddish-brown, with fine yellow markings on the back. The lower parts of the legs are blackish-brown. The underside of the head and neck are yellowish; there is a whitish stripe on the side of the neck, from the ear to the shoulder; the color above the stripe is dark and is lighter below. Dorsal hairs are short (10–20 mm). The tail is yellowish and is more than 60% of the head and body length. The posterior chamber of the auditory bulla is less flat than in the Javan Mongoose and extends to well below the occipital condyle. Dental formula: I 3/3, C 1/1, P 4/4, M 2/2 = 40.

Habitat. Primary rainforest, disturbed forest, and plantations. On Borneo, recorded from lowland areas up to 1200 m.

Food and Feeding. Nothing known.

Activity patterns. Appears to be manly diurnal, based on recent camera-trapping data.

Movements, Home range and Social organization. Terrestrial. Appears to be solitary.

Breeding. Nothing known.

Status and Conservation. Classified as Data Deficient in *The IUCN Red List*. Virtually nothing is known about this species. Field studies and assessments of possible threats are urgently needed.

Bibliography. Corbet & Hill (1992), Davis (1962), Payne *et al.* (1985), Schwarz (1947), Wells *et al.* (2005), Wozencraft (2005).

10. Ruddy Mongoose *Herpestes smithii*

French: Mangouste roussâtre / **German**: Indischer Rotmungo / **Spanish**: Meloncillo rojo

Taxonomy. *Herpestes smithii* Gray, 1837, Bombay (?), India.
Two subspecies are recognized.
Subspecies and Distribution.
H. s. smithii Gray, 1837 – India.
H. s. zeylanius Thomas, 1921 – Sri Lanka.
Descriptive notes. Head-body 39–47 cm, tail 35·1–47 cm, hindfoot 8–8·6 cm; weight c. 2·7 kg. The coat color is brown, with a rufous tinge on the underparts. On Sri Lanka, the tail length varies from 75 to 90% of the head and body, whereas it is 90 to 110% of the head and body in India. The tip of the tail is black. The feet are darker than the body and are webbed up to the last joint. The soles of the hindfeet are naked. Dental formula: I 3/3, C 1/1, P 4/4, M 2/2 = 40.

Habitat. Dry forests, dry thorn areas, disturbed forests, and open areas. Recorded up to 2200 m. On Sri Lanka, it appears to be confined mostly to the lowland forests of the dry and intermediate zones.

Food and Feeding. Has been seen feeding on birds (including doves, partridges, and quails), reptiles (rat snake), and the Long-tailed Climbing Mouse (*Vandeleuria oleracea*).

Activity patterns. Appears to be mainly diurnal.

Movements, Home range and Social organization. Terrestrial, but sometimes hunts, feeds, and rests in trees. Solitary, but has occasionally been seen in pairs and sometimes in groups of four or five animals. Out of 78 sightings in Rhuna National Park (Sri Lanka), 92% were solitary individuals and 8% were pairs (adult males and females).

Breeding. Nothing known.

Status and Conservation. CITES Appendix III (India). Classified as Least Concern in *The IUCN Red List*. This species is hunted and snared. Habitat loss, fragmentation, and degradation may have an impact on populations. Very little is known about this species and field studies and assessments of possible threats are urgently needed.

Bibliography. Christopher & Jayson (1996), Corbet & Hill (1992), Hinton & Dunn (1967), Madhusudan (1995), Mudappa (1998, 2001), Pocock (1916b, 1941a), Prater (1980), Santiapillai *et al.* (2000), Shekar (2003), Wozencraft (2005), Yoganand & Kumar (1995).

11. Crab-eating Mongoose *Herpestes urva*

French: Mangouste crabière / **German**: Krabbenmanguste / **Spanish**: Meloncillo cangrejero

Taxonomy. *Gulo urva* Hodgson, 1836, Nepal.
Four subspecies are recognized, but a taxonomic revision is needed.
Subspecies and Distribution.
H. u. urva Hodgson, 1836 – Nepal through Indochina to Peninsular Malaysia.
H. u. annamensis Bechthold, 1936 – Vietnam.
H. u. formosanus Bechthold, 1936 – Taiwan.

H. u. sinensis Bechthold, 1936 – S China (and Hainan I).

Descriptive notes. Head-body 44–55·8 cm, tail 26·5–34 cm, hindfoot 9–10·9 cm, ear 2·9–3·5 cm; weight 3–4 kg. A fairly large mongoose, with long guard hairs (dorsal hairs are 40–50 mm long) and a white neck stripe. The coat color varies from gray to blackish-brown, with individual hairs ringed black and white. The chin is white, the throat is grayish, the chest is dark brown, and the belly is a lighter brown. The top of the head is pale grayish-brown, finely speckled with white. The muzzle is pale yellowish; the nose is flesh-colored with a deep vertical groove. The ears are short, broad, and rounded, and are covered with very short grayish hairs. The color of the iris varies from egg-yellow to deep brown. There is a white stripe that starts at the corner of the mouth and runs along the neck to the shoulder; the stripe is about 9–10 cm long and 8 mm wide at the base. The limbs are brown to black. The feet have shallow interdigital webs and strong claws; the naked sole on the hindfoot only extends about two-thirds the distance to the heel. The tail is bushy and tapering, and averages 63% the length of the head and body; it is the same color as the body, but becomes progressively ocherous (sometimes reddish) towards the tip. The anal glands on each side of the anus are about the size of a cherry and produce an aqueous fetid secretion (which can be squirted out with great force). There are three pairs of teats. The skull is large and heavy, but with relatively small crests. The posterior chamber of the auditory bulla is less flat than in the Javan Mongoose and extends to well below the occipital condyle. Mature individuals have a complete occipital bony orbit, although this may be incomplete in immature mongooses. Dental formula: I 3/3, C 1/1, P 4/4, M 2/2 = 40. The lower first premolar is inconspicuous and may be lacking in immatures; the last lower molar is small, but complex.

Habitat. Evergreen and deciduous forest, scrubby areas, and plantations. Also reported to inhabit wetlands, forest streams, and small marshes inside forests. Often found near pools and streams. Recorded up to 2000 m.

Food and Feeding. In northern Taiwan, the percentage occurrence of food items in scats was: 96% insects, 74% crustaceans, 65% amphibians, 48% reptiles, 18% earthworms, 17% gastropods, 14% chilopods, and less than 10% mammals, plants, birds, fish, and arachnids. In terms of overall volume, crustaceans (29%) and insects (28%) were the highest, followed by amphibians (16%) and reptiles (14%). The diet appeared to vary with changes in the availability of food in different habitats and seasons; Crab-eating Mongooses ate more insects in summer and autumn, more crustaceans in winter, and more reptiles in late spring and early summer. In south-eastern China, the percentage occurrence of food items in scats was: 65% rodents, 48% beetles, 45% snakes, 44% crabs, 10% clams, 8% birds, 8% grass, and 7% cherokee rose fruit. A few other mammals, amphibians, frogs, fish, locusts, snails, centipedes, and fruits were found at low occurrence (less than 6%). Crab-eating Mongooses hunt along the banks of streams, feeling under stones, and in rock crevices, and scratch, dig and sniff at the ground. They are supposed to be good divers and swimmers and do not hesitate to enter water. Crabs and molluscs are taken with the forepaws and either lifted and smashed on a rock or thrown between the hindlimbs to a hard surface behind.

Activity patterns. Diurnal according to recent evidence (radio-tracking, camera-trapping, and sightings), whereas previously it had been said to be nocturnal. Between 10:00 h and 18:00 h, a radio-collared female had a mean activity level of 56%. Rests in holes in the ground and in rock crevices. In south-eastern China, daybeds were underground dens (within a foothill region, adjacent to farmland).

Movements, Home range and Social organization. Terrestrial and solitary, but has been seen in groups of up to four individuals. The home range of a radio-collared female in south-eastern China was at least 100 ha (located only seven times).

Breeding. The large testicle size of males caught in March–early April suggests that this is one possible breeding period. Gestation is 50 to 63 days and litter size is two to four.

Status and Conservation. CITES Appendix III (India). Classified as Least Concern in *The IUCN Red List*. Very little is known about the ecology, population status and threats to this species, and more field surveys and ecological studies are needed. In Taiwan, people hunt this mongoose for meat and villagers across Laos trap it when they can. Coats made of pelts are widely sold at Chinese markets and live animals have been seen for sale as pets in a market in Cambodia. Pelts and meat of Crab-eating Mongooses are also sold along the Yunnan–Vietnam border.

Bibliography. Choudhury (1997a, 1997b, 2000), Chuang & Lee (1997), Corbet & Hill (1992), Duckworth (1997), Duckworth & Robichaud (2005), Lekagul & McNeely (1991), Lim (1992), Long & Hoang (2006), Pocock (1941a), Tan (1989), Wang & Fuller (2001, 2003b), Wells (1989), Wozencraft (2005).

12. Stripe-necked Mongoose *Herpestes vitticollis*

French: Mangouste à cou rayé / **German**: Halsstreifenmungo / **Spanish**: Meloncillo indio

Taxonomy. *Herpestes vitticollis* Bennett, 1835, Travancore, South India.
Two subspecies are recognized.

Subspecies and Distribution.
H. v. vitticollis Bennett, 1835 – SW India and Sri Lanka.
H. v. inornatus Pocock, 1941 – W India (Karnatka).

Descriptive notes. Mean measurements for Sri Lanka: head-body 48·9 cm (males), 46·4 cm (females), tail 32·5 cm (males), 30·4 cm (females); weight up to 3·1 kg (males), up to 1·7 kg (females). Mean measurements for India: head-body 52·9 cm (males), 47·4 cm (females), tail 31·5 cm (males), 29·7 cm (females); weight up to 3·4 kg (males), up to 2·7 kg (females). A large mongoose, with long guard hairs and a neck stripe. The head is iron-gray to purplish-brown, finely speckled with yellow, darkest on the forehead and paler on the sides. The front part of the body is reddish-yellow, grizzled with brown; the rear part is orange-red and lightly grizzled. A black band runs from behind the ears along the sides of the neck to the shoulders. The ears are rounded and covered with short, fine, reddish-brown hairs. The chin and throat are the same color as the cheeks, but are less grizzled. The under-surface of the neck and chest are brownish-yellow and the belly is orange-yellow, but is not abruptly defined from the color of the chest. The underfur is sparse and pale yellow-brown. The dorsal hairs are 50–60 mm long. The hairs on the sides are greater than 60 mm long; they are banded with black and gray, and end in long orange-red tips. The general color of the tail is orange-red except for the 9-cm-long black tip; the hairs at the base of the tail are about 8 cm long, but decrease in length towards the tip. The forelegs, front of the hindlegs, and tarsus are dark purplish-brown. There are five toes on the fore- and hindfeet. The skull is large, has a flattened and expanded frontal region, a narrow long muzzle, powerful teeth, and an auditory bulla with a pronounced projection of the posterior chamber. Dental formula: I 3/3, C 1/1, P 4/4, M 2/2 = 40.

Habitat. Evergreen and deciduous forest. Seen in swampy clearings and along watercourses, and also in plantations and open scrub. In Sri Lanka, its distribution may encompass lowland dry forest; it is rarely sighted in disturbed areas or close to human settlements. Recorded up to 2133 m.

Food and Feeding. The diet is reported to include small mammals, birds, birds' eggs, reptiles, insects, and roots. It has also been suggested that crabs, frogs, and fish may be part of the diet, due to its habit of hunting by the banks of rivers and frequenting swamps and flooded rice fields. This species has been observed scavenging on Sambar (*Rusa unicolor*) and Indian Hare (*Lepus nigricollis*), and seen foraging in soft, damp soil and swamps.

Activity patterns. Appears to be mainly diurnal.

Movements, Home range and Social organization. Usually solitary, but also seen in pairs.

Breeding. Litter size may be two or three. On Sri Lanka, a female was observed in May suckling three young on a dry patch of earth, under an overhanging mass of rocks.

Status and Conservation. CITES Appendix III (India). Classified as Least Concern in *The IUCN Red List*. This species is hunted for meat and for its fur, but the chief threat may be habitat loss. In India, it is rare in the northern part of its range, and most abundant in southern Kerala, the Nilghiri and Palni plateaus, the High Wavy Mountains, and in the Anamalai Hills. In Sri Lanka, is fairly common in the higher hills of the Central Highlands, but seems to be declining. The species is not uncommon in the low-country along the banks of the Menik Ganga (Sri Lanka's Dry Zone), and is present, but not common, in the Kalutara District (Western Province). May be particularly vulnerable due to its restricted distribution. Field surveys, ecological studies, and assessments of threats are urgently needed.

Bibliography. Hinton & Dunn (1967), IUCN (2008), Madhusudan (1995), Pocock (1941a), Prater (1980), Van Rompaey & Jayakumar (2003), Wozencraft (2005), Yoganand & Kumar (1995).

Plate 18 ➤

13

ssp *nigrata* 14 ssp *shortridgei*

PLATE 18

inches

cm

pale gray morph

15

16

dark brown
morph

dark morph

bright red morph

17

grizzled brown-grayish
morph

ssp *albicauda* 18

19

black tailed morph

20 ssp *omnivora*

ssp *crassicauda*

21

22

23

Genus CYNICTIS
Ogilby, 1833

13. Yellow Mongoose *Cynictis penicillata*
French: Mangouste fauve / **German**: Fuchsmanguste / **Spanish**: Mangosta dorada

Taxonomy. *Herpestes penicillatus* Cuvier, 1829, type locality "Cape" (South Africa). The wide color variation has resulted in the description of up to twelve subspecies, which are now mostly considered invalid. Three subspecies are recognized here.
Subspecies and Distribution.
C. p. penicillata Cuvier, 1829 – South Africa, and Lesotho.
C. p. bradfieldi Roberts, 1924 – S Angola, N Botswana, Namibia, and W Zimbabwe.
C. p. coombsii Roberts, 1929 – S Botswana and Northern Transvaal.
Descriptive notes. Head-body 26·5–46 cm, tail 15–29·2 cm, hindfoot 6·1–7·8 cm, ear 2·4–3·9 cm; weight 715–900 g. Males and females are similar in size. A tawny to grayish-yellow colored mongoose, with a long bushy tail. The tail color is similar to the dorsal pelage. The ears are relatively large and project above the line of the head; their anterior margins are pallid, with a tuft of pale hairs partially covering the ear opening. Body size and pelage color are highly variable geographically. Southern specimens are larger-sized, with a dark tawny (reddish-brown) dorsal pelage; the ventral pelage, legs, chin, and throat are pale buffy cream; the tail ends in a pure to dirty-white tail-tip. Northern specimens are distinctly smaller, with a grizzled dorsal pelage; the ventral pelage, legs, chin, and throat, are pure creamy-white; the tail is without a white tip. There are five digits on the forefoot, four on the hindfeet. The sole of the hindfoot is more hairy, the forefoot palm is naked to the wrist. Cheek glands are present and used for marking of objects. There are three pairs of mammae. The skull is pear-shaped with a post-orbital bar complete in adults. The rostrum is short and broad, the zygomatic arches are weak, and the supra-occipital crest little more than a slight ridge. Dental formula: C 3/3, I 1/1, P 4/4, M 2/2 = 40; the upper and lower P_1 are sometimes absent (especially the latter).
Habitat. Found in semi-arid, open habitats, from sparse bushland to grasslands and semi-deserts. Avoids dense bushes, woodlands, deserts, and mountains. Requires the presence of soft or sandy soils for digging dens, although it often occupies existing dens of South African Ground Squirrels (*Xerus inauris*) or Meerkats.
Food and Feeding. Predominantly insectivorous, preferring Isoptera (termites: *Hodotermes*, *Trinervitermes*, *Microhodotermes*), Coleoptera (beetle larvae and adults), and Orthoptera (locusts and grasshoppers). However, Yellow Mongooses are opportunistic feeders and will also hunt rodents, birds, reptiles, amphibians, and arachnids (scorpions and spiders). The diet varies both geographically and seasonally. In Botswana, the percentage occurrence of prey items in 54 stomachs was: 92% insects, 15% small mammals (murids), 13% scorpions, 11% reptiles, 4% Myriapoda, 2% birds, and 2% amphibians. In the former Transvaal (South Africa), the percentage occurrence of prey items in 76 stomachs was: 87% invertebrates (mostly termites and locusts) and 28% vertebrates (including mammals, birds, and amphibians). In the Western Cape (South Africa), the percentage occurrence in 332 scats was: 90% insects (mostly Isoptera), 40% rodents (including Bush Vlei Rat *Otomys unisulcatus*, Four-striped Grass Mouse *Rhabdomys pumilio*, Pygmy Mouse *Mus minutoides*), 12% birds, and 13% reptiles; the occurrence of rodents varied during the year according to the fluctuating population densities of rodents. In the Karoo (South Africa), 86 scats contained: 100% insects (mostly Coleoptera and Orthoptera), 10% birds, and 3% rodents. In the Free State (South Africa), the percentage occurrence in 156 stomachs was 74% Isoptera; 48% Orthoptera, 42% Coleoptera, 22% Lepidoptera; vertebrates and other invertebrate groups occurred at much lower percentages. In central South Africa, the analysis of 95 stomachs found rodents to have a higher occurrence than insects. Yellow Mongooses are also known to feed occasionally on fruits and carrion (such as Common Duiker *Sylvicapra grimmia* and South African Spring Hare *Pedetes capensis*). They may also eat hens and their eggs, but anecdotal reports of preying on newborn lambs are considered false. Yellow Mongooses usually forage individually, but they have been seen in pairs or in small groups. Foraging typically occurs during the early morning and late afternoon. On the west coast of South Africa, a radio-tracking study indicated that 37% of the time was spent foraging. In the Eastern Cape, they have been observed feeding throughout the day, except during the hottest days of the summer.
Activity patterns. Mainly diurnal. During the night they rest in dens, which they enter around sunset and exit shortly after sunrise. Yellow Mongooses occasionally rest around midday for variable periods of time. They can become active at night, especially in cases of exceptional food availability (e.g. termites swarming).
Movements, Home range and Social organization. Yellow Mongooses are solitary foragers, but spend nights in communal dens and cooperate in raising their young. Mean group size varies from 1–13, but is usually three or four. The group typically comprises a dominant male, with separate hierarchies for the subordinate females and males.

Juveniles are the lowest ranking. To assess dominance status, two individuals approach one another and sniff each other's facial glands. The dominant individual rises higher on its feet while biting the subordinate's neck. The subordinate lies on its side and may emit a high-pitched scream. A dominant individual marks a subordinate by straddling it from above and using the anal glands in a standing position. In one colony, the dominant male marked colony members on a daily basis. In another colony, the dominant male was not involved in dominance interactions, but high-ranking subordinates deferred to the dominant males, and in turn dominated lower ranking members. In South Africa (West Coast National Park), the mean home range of three males was 1 km² (range = 0·7 to 1·2), and 0·3 km² for four females (range = 0·1–0·5). Overlap among males was substantial and individual home ranges overlapped those of several females, while the ranges of females in different burrows showed almost no overlap. Males and females move similar distances per hour (mean = 292 m/h and 228 m/h, respectively); males move an average of just over 3 km per day. Yellow Mongooses are partly nomadic, and may rotate the use of several burrow systems on different nights, within a much larger territory. Defecation takes place in latrines close to burrows or along a group territory. The anal glands are used in scent marking home ranges and allomarking between colony members. The dominant pair and juvenile females concentrate their markings mainly around the burrow. Objects may also be marked by means of the cheek gland, often preceded by wiping the entire side of the body on the ground or side-swiping. All members of the group help mark, although most marking is done by younger, subordinate individuals. Five vocalizations have been recognized: a high-pitched scream (uttered during fighting); a low growl (when an individual was disturbed at a food source); an even lower growl (when approached in a live trap); a short barking sound (alarm call); and a soft purring uttered during copulation.
Breeding. There is no reproductive suppression in a colony so that more than one female can breed simultaneously. Mating starts in early July. When females are in estrus, males purr, "caw", and scream, while following the females around and attempting to mount. Estrus females will allow copulation over a two-day period, after which males are vocally rebuffed with bites to the head and neck. Two observed copulations lasted 37 and 45 minutes. During copulation, the male purrs, while the female bites or licks the male's ears and neck. Gestation is 60–62 days. Birth season is probably from August to January (until March in Botswana). Litter size is one to five, most commonly two; some females may have two litters per year. The young are born in nesting chambers in the burrows. Adult "helpers" (some of the previous year's offspring that remain in the natal group) provision young at their dens for the first four weeks, carrying back large prey items (rodents, bats, reptiles, and large arachnoids). The young first accompany adults on foraging expeditions at about eight weeks of age. Lactation lasts six to eight weeks, and young are nutritionally independent at 16–18 weeks of age.
Status and Conservation. Classified as Least Concern in *The IUCN Red List*. A carrier of rabies throughout South Africa, which has led to extermination campaigns (usually through the use of burrow gassing). Also persecuted in the past because it was believed to be a predator of newborn lambs. Its wide distribution, high densities (6–7 individuals per 100 ha have been recorded in suitable areas), catholic diet, and tolerance to human-induced changes to habitat, are all positive factors for the long-term conservation of this species.

Bibliography. Avenant & Nel (1992), Blaum, Rossmanith, Fleissner & Jeltsch (2007), Cavallini (1993), Cavallini & Nel (1995), Coetzee (1977), Earle (1981), Ewer (1973), Fredga (1972), Gregory & Hellman (1939), Hendey (1974), Hinton & Dunn (1967), Lynch (1980), Nowak (1999), Pocock (1916b), Rasa *et al.* (1992), Rosevear (1974), Skinner & Chimimba (2005), Taylor (1993), Taylor & Meester (1993), Taylor, Campbell, van Dyke *et al.* (1990), Taylor, Campbell, Meester & Van Dyck (1991), Wenhold & Rasa (1994).

Genus GALERELLA
Gray, 1865

14. Angolan Slender Mongoose *Galerella flavescens*
French: Mangouste flavescente / **German**: Kaokoveld-Schlankichneumon / **Spanish**: Mangosta angoleña
Other common names: Kaokoveld Slender Mongoose, Black Mongoose, Larger Red Mongoose

Taxonomy. *Herpestes gracilis* var. *flavescens* Bocage, 1889. "Benguella", Namibia. Formerly classified as a subspecies of the Common Slender Mongoose (*G. sanguinea*) or of the Cape Gray Mongoose (*G. pulverulenta*). Three subspecies of uncertain status (*annulata*, *nigrata*, and *shortridgei*) have been described. Pending revision, all should be considered here as synonyms of *G. flavescens*.
Distribution. SW Angola and NW Namibia.
Descriptive notes. Head-body 33·5–35·5 cm (males), 31–33 cm (females), tail 32·5–36·2 cm (males), 34–34·5 cm (females), hindfoot 6·9–7·2 cm (males), 6·4–6·6 cm

On following pages: 15. Somalian Slender Mongoose (*Galerella ochracea*); 16. Cape Gray Mongoose (*Galerella pulverulenta*); 17. Common Slender Mongoose (*Galerella sanguinea*); 18. White-tailed Mongoose (*Ichneumia albicauda*); 19. Selous's Mongoose (*Paracynictis selousi*); 20. Bushy-tailed Mongoose (*Bdeogale crassicauda*); 21. Jackson's Mongoose (*Bdeogale jacksoni*); 22. Black-footed Mongoose (*Bdeogale nigripes*); 23. Meller's Mongoose (*Rhynchogale melleri*).

females, ear 2·7–2·8 cm (males), 2·4–2·5 cm (females); weight similar to that of the Common Slender Mongoose. A small mongoose, with a long slender body and long tail (equal to body length). Variable body and tail color, generally either reddish (from chestnut to yellow; *shortridgei*) or dark brown to black (*nigrata*). Skull length 63–68 mm (males larger than females). Skull larger than the Common Slender Mongoose and smaller than the Cape Gray Mongoose.

Habitat. Appears to select arid areas, with limited bushy cover, but avoids true deserts (such as the Namib and surrounding areas). The black form (*nigrata*) seems to strongly select scattered granite boulders, avoiding areas in between.

Food and Feeding. Preys on a variety of small rodents, birds, reptiles, and insects. Also feeds on sarcophagous arthropods in and around carrion, and fleshy seeds when available.

Activity patterns. Appears to be diurnal.

Movements, Home range and Social organization. Normally seen singly, sometimes in groups of two or three. Up to five observed within 30 m of a kudu carcass. Intraspecific fights can occur close to an abundant resource such as carrion. In the Erongo Mountains (Namibia), the home range of a radio-tracked male was 145 ha.

Breeding. Nothing known.

Status and Conservation. Classified as Least Concern in *The IUCN Red List*. No significant threats are known and occurs in a number of protected areas.

Bibliography. Crawford-Cabral (1996), Rathbun (2004), Rathbun *et al.* (2005), Taylor (In press b), Taylor & Goldman (1993).

15. Somalian Slender Mongoose *Galerella ochracea*

French: Mangouste d'Abyssinie / **German**: Somalia-Schlankichneumon / **Spanish**: Mangosta somalí

Taxonomy. *Herpestes ochraceus* Gray, 1848. "Abyssinia", exact locality unknown.
The Somalian Slender Mongoose has been classified as a subspecies of the Common Slender Mongoose (*G. sanguinea*), and only recently has been recognized as a distinct species. Monotypic.

Distribution. Ethiopia, Somalia, and NE Kenya.

Descriptive notes. Head-body 25·4–29 cm (males), tail 22–27·3 (males), hindfoot 5–5·6 cm (males), ear 2·5–2·8 cm (males); weight similar to that of the Common Slender Mongoose. A small mongoose, with a long slender body and long tail (85–90% of body length). Variable hair color, from dark brown to pale gray, sometimes reddish. No black tail tip (in contrast with the Common Slender Mongoose). Skull length 53–61 mm (males larger than females); smaller than most Slender Mongooses. Auditory bullae relatively large. Dental formuala: I 3/3, C 1/1, P 4/3, M 2/2 = 38.

Habitat. Appears to select dry areas. Found up to 600 m in Ethiopia.

Food and Feeding. Nothing known.

Activity patterns. Apparently diurnal.

Movements, Home range and Social organization. Nothing known.

Breeding. Nothing known.

Status and Conservation. Classified as Least Concern in *The IUCN Red List*. Assumed to be fairly common, but this is a very poorly known species and is in need of further studies.

Bibliography. Azzaroli & Simonetta (1966), Taylor (In press c), Taylor & Goldman (1993), Yalden, Largen & Kock (1980), Yalden, Largen, Kock & Hillman (1996).

16. Cape Gray Mongoose *Galerella pulverulenta*

French: Mangouste du Cap / **German**: Kap-Schlankichneumon / **Spanish**: Mangosta de El Cabo

Taxonomy. *Herpestes pulverulentus* Wagner, 1839, type locality "Cape", exact locality unknown.
The Cape Gray Mongoose has been placed in the genus *Galerella* o *Herpestes* by different authors. Traditionally, six subspecies were recognized: *ruddi*, *nigrata*, *shortridgei*, *basutica*, *annulata*, and the nominate form, although skull morphological analyses failed to reveal any quantitative distinctiveness. *G. nigrata*, *annulata*, and *shortridgei* are now regarded as synonyms of *G. flavescens*. Three subspecies are recognized here.

Subspecies and Distribution.
G. p. pulverulenta Wagner, 1839 – Namibia, South Africa (Western, Eastern and Northern Cape & Free State).
G. p. basutica Roberts, 1936 – E Lesotho to South Africa (W KwaZulu-Natal).
G. p. ruddi Thomas, 1903 – South Africa (extreme NW portion of the species range).

Descriptive notes. Head-body 34–42 cm (males), 33–35·5 cm (females), tail 20·5–34 cm (both sexes), hindfoot 5·9–7·5 cm (males), 5·2–7·5 cm (females), ear 1·5–3·6 cm (both sexes); weight 680–1250 g (males), 491–900 g (females). A small mongoose, with short legs and a long, bushy tail (c. 90% of head and body length). The body and

tail are grizzled gray (from light gray to dark brownish-gray); the underparts are less grizzled. The muzzle and legs are darker. The head is pointed. The ears are slightly darker, small, close to the head, and partly covered by a band of longer hairs. The rhinarium is small, with a central depression that continues downwards and divides the haired section of the upper lip. The tip of the tail is sometimes inconspicuously shaded brown (the hair on the tail is short: less than 20 mm). Individual guard hairs are black or gray, with four to six white to yellowish bands. There are five digits on each foot, with the first one reduced. The heel pad is not haired and the claws are not very long. Females have three pairs of mammae. Skull length usually more than 67 mm (males) and less than 63 mm (females), with ovoid braincase and short rostrum. Dental formula: I 3/3, C 1/1, P 3/4, M 2/2 = 38. The outer incisors are slightly larger than the inner ones. The lower canines are distinctly curved. In the upper jaw, the first molar is small, and the second molar is very small.

Habitat. Found in a wide range of habitats, in forested as well as non-forested areas, but generally avoids open spaces. Occurs mainly in Karoo and Karroid bushveld, and sclerophyllous bush, and is often associated with refuge areas such as dense bushes and rocky outcrops, but avoids open fields with short vegetation. More common in dry than in wet areas (especially areas with a warm temperate climate), but is absent from the driest parts of the region (Kalahari thornveld; rainfall below 20 cm). Sometimes found close to human settlements. Recorded from sea level (around the Western Cape) to 1900 m (KwaZulu-Natal).

Food and Feeding. An opportunistic predator, its diet includes a wide range of prey from termites and grasshoppers to snakes and rodents. Nevertheless, the staple foods are generally small mammals or insects. In the West Coast National Park (Western Cape), murids predominated in the diet (90%), with insects (5%) forming a secondary food resource. Vlei rats and Four-striped Grass Mouse appear to be favored murid prey. It has been recorded feeding on larger mammals such as Scrub Hares (*Lepus saxatilis*) and Cape Porcupine (*Hystrix africaeaustralis*), and has even been known to attack and kill Cape Grysbok (*Raphiceros melanotis*) lambs by tearing at the nose and mouth. However, because it scavenges, it is uncertain to what extent large prey in the diet is the result of active predation. They have been observed to associate with small raptors (African marsh harrier *Circus ranivorus*) while foraging. Usually moves from bush to bush, inspecting potential foraging sites like holes and rodent nests. It seems to rely mainly on sight and smell for food searching. It scratches the soil in search of invertebrates, but is not an avid digger. Insects caught on the ground are held down with the front feet and then taken directly in the mouth. Larger prey are stalked, the killing bite delivered to the head. Small mammals are chewed in the side of the mouth. Insects are thoroughly masticated. Larger and tougher prey is held firmly on the ground with the front feet and torn apart. Cape Gray Mongooses can break eggs by throwing them against a vertical surface.

Activity patterns. Predominantly diurnal; activity is more common at sunset and sunrise, but is reduced in bad weather and at high temperatures. Occasionally rests for variable lengths of time around midday.

Movements, Home range and Social organization. Normally seen singly, but groups of up to five have been recorded (more often in summer and early autumn, after parturition). Of 163 sightings, 151 were of single animals, seven were of pairs, and five were of groups of three. Groups typically consist of one or two adults and juveniles. Males may show some sociality, with stable pairs composed of a large and a small individual. In the West Coast National Park (Western Cape), home range sizes of three males were 55–92 ha; a female had the smallest range (30·6 ha); another female, a juvenile, ranged more widely (359 ha), possibly dispersing. Home ranges overlapped widely, both within and between sexes. In the Vrolijkheid Nature Conservation Station (Little Karoo region, South Africa) the mean home range size of four animals was between 5–36 ha, and there appeared to be considerable overlap in home ranges. While foraging, individuals usually move 50–100 m every 15 minutes, and travel on average, 4 km during the course of a day's foraging.

Breeding. Seasonal breeders, probably at the end of winter (August to December). Lactating females have been found in August, and in November to February. Litter size is one to three. Rock crevices, farm outbuildings, fodder stores, and woodpiles are used for rearing young.

Status and Conservation. Classified as Least Concern in *The IUCN Red List*. No significant conservation threats are known. Human development is unlikely to have an impact, as they seem to adapt easily to living close to houses.

Bibliography. Cavallini (1992a), Cavallini & Nel (1990a, 1990b, 1995), Lynch (1981, 1983), Skinner & Chimimba (2005), Stuart (1991), Watson & Dippenaar (1987).

17. Common Slender Mongoose *Galerella sanguinea*

French: Mangouste svelte / **German**: Rotes Schlankichneumon / **Spanish**: Mangosta esbelta

Taxonomy. *Herpestes sanguineus* Rüppell, 1835. "Kordofan", Sudan, exact locality unknown.
Variously placed in the genus *Galerella* or *Herpestes*. A large and variable number of subspecies (over forty) have been described, mostly on the basis of unreliable characters (mostly pelage color and size). Of these, the Somalian Slender Mongoose (*G. ochracea*) is now considered a valid species. The others are not considered valid here, but this may be changed by further studies, including genetic analyses.

Distribution. Widely distributed, ranges from the sub-Saharan belt, from Senegal to the Red Sea Coast in Sudan, and S to South Africa, also occurs on Zanzibar I.

Descriptive notes. Head-body 32–34 cm (males), 27–33 cm (females), tail 19·4–31 cm (males), 21·2–29 cm (females), hindfoot 4·5–7 cm (males), 4·4–6 cm (females),

ear 1·4–2·8 cm (males), 1·5–2·5 cm (females); weight 363–789 g (males), 277–565 g (females). Males are larger than females. A small and slender mongoose, with short legs and a long body and tail. The pelage color is very varied, from almost black to bright red, but most frequently grizzled brown-grayish. The tip of the tail is darker or black. The grizzled appearance derives from individual hairs being annulated, with very light bands alternating with dark ones. These bands are narrower on the head (where the hair is shorter) than on the body and tail. The ventral surface is lighter and less grizzled. The face is pointed, and the ears are small and close to the head. The rhinarium is small, and usually pinkish-brown to light brown, with a depression that continues in a slit that divides the hair on the upper lip. The iris of the eye is bright orange. Each foot has five digits, with the first one reduced; the heel pad is not haired, and a narrow web connects the digits. There are two to three pairs of mammae. Skull length 60–70 mm (males), 59–68 mm (females), with ovoid braincase and a short and broad rostrum. Dental formula I 3/3, C 1/1, P 3/4, M 2/2 = 38. Upper canines almost straight, lower distinctly curved. The first upper premolars are very small and sometimes absent.

Habitat. Found in a variety of habitats, mostly arid and sub-arid areas, but is absent from true deserts (Sahara and Namib). Usually absent from forests, but may occur in forest fringes and penetrate into forests along roads. Sometimes found close to villages. When in sympatry with closely related species (the Somalian Slender Mongoose and the Angolan Slender Mongoose), it seems to select bushier, less arid habitat. Ranges from sea level up to the Ethiopian Plateau (2700 m).

Food and Feeding. Diet includes a wide variety of small mammals and invertebrates. Insects (grasshoppers, termites, beetles, and ants) are found very frequently in stomachs and feces, but vertebrates are often more important as a percentage of total biomass consumed. Vertebrate prey includes reptiles (e.g. agamas, skinks, and snakes) and rodents of various genera (*e.g. Mastomys, Rhabdomys, Pelomys*). Wild fruits are consumed. Carrion is eaten, along with associated sarcophagous insects. Possibly owing to the climbing ability of this species, wild birds are also occasionally consumed. In a sample of 60 stomachs from Botswana and Zimbabwe, the percentage occurrence of prey items was: 73% insects, 27% lizards (including southern tree agama *Acanthocercus atricollis* and the variable skink *Trachylepis varia*), and 25% murids (including the East African Pelomys (*Pelomys fallax*). Based on observations of captive mongooses, eggs seem a preferred food item and are broken open by smashing them against a hard surface. Common Slender Mongooses are implicated in killing domestic birds. The diet seems to follow seasonal variation in availability; insects are more frequently consumed during wet and warm periods, than in dry and cold ones, when more small mammals are eaten. While hunting, Common Slender Mongooses move around continuously. They have been observed chasing and pouncing on rodents, and flushing grasshoppers and catching them in flight.

Activity patterns. Mainly diurnal, with a peak in activity before sunset.

Movements, Home range, and Social organization. Although normally seen singly, males show some tendency to associate; two males may occupy the same territory, and stable, larger coalitions (up to four individuals) may defend a territory from other males. Home ranges are 50–100 ha for males and 25 ha for females; however, these are based on visual observations and are likely to be underestimates. Female home ranges (and possibly also male ranges) seem exclusive. A better climber than most mongooses. Dens (either self-dug or usurped from other animals) may be used for shelter.

Breeding. Seasonal breeders; births seem to be concentrated in the wet season (October–November and February–April in East Africa, October to March in eastern South Africa). Females may have two litters per year. Gestation probably lasts 60–70 days. Litter size is two to four. Dens are used for breeding and are changed frequently. Weaning occurs at around eight weeks. Juveniles disperse before six months of age. Dispersal may be male-biased. Young attain adult size and sexual maturity by the time they are one year old. Survival rate is 0·63 for young and 0·8 for adults. The oldest individuals found in the wild were eight years old.

Status and Conservation. Classified as Least Concern in *The IUCN Red List*. No significant threats known. Very widespread and common (densities of up to six individuals/km² have been recorded).

Bibliography. Coetzee (1977), Hinton & Dunn (1967), Nowak (1999), Petter (1969), Pocock (1916b), Rood (1986), Sale & Taylor (1970), Skinner & Chimimba (2005), Taylor (1969, 1975), Waser, Elliott *et al.* (1995), Waser, Keane *et al.* (1994).

Genus *ICHNEUMIA*
Geoffroy Saint-Hilaire, 1837

18. White-tailed Mongoose *Ichneumia albicauda*

French: Mangouste à queue blanche / **German:** Weißschwanzichneumon / **Spanish:** Mangosta coliblanca

Taxonomy. *Herpestes albicaudus* Cuvier, 1829, southern Africa and Senegal.
Six subspecies are listed here, but their validity is questionable.

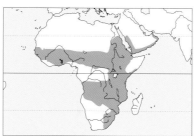

Subspecies and Distribution.
I. a. albicauda Cuvier, 1829 – Senegal to E Sudan, Eritrea, and N Somalia; also Arabian Peninsula.
I. a. dialeucos Hollister, 1916 – N Kenya, S Somalia, and S Ethiopia.
I. a. grandis Thomas, 1890 – S Angola, Zambia, S Tanzania to South Africa.
I. a. ibeana Thomas, 1904 – DR Congo to C Kenya.
I. a. loandae Thomas, 1904 – N Angola and S DR Congo.
I. a. loempo Temminck, 1853 – W Africa (Guinea).

Descriptive notes. Head-body 47–69 cm, tail 34·6–47 cm (males), 39·2–48·5 cm (females), hindfoot 13–14·7 cm (males), 13–14·8 cm (females), ear 4·2–5 cm (males), 3·7–5 cm (females); weight 2·9–5·2 kg (males), 3·1–5 kg (females). No obvious sexual dimorphism. This is probably the heaviest mongoose; Zimbabwe individuals substantially heavier than those in Tanzania. Slender, long-legged, and tall. Variable pelage, but generally dark with coarse, sometimes silvery body fur; grayish head and black legs. On the dorsum, coarse, black-tipped guard hairs extend beyond the thick, woolly, pale undercoat. The guard hairs are short on the head (10 mm) and increase in length to 90 mm toward the rump. Some of these hairs are black, but most have a broad black tip and two silvery bands separated by a black band. The underfur is substantially shorter and off-white. The tip of the tail is white. The guard hairs on the tail are shorter towards the tip. Near the rump, they are white-tipped with a broad black ring; close to the tip, they become pure white. The tail is black-tipped in West African populations. The ventral pelage is pale brown. The tip of the muzzle is dusky brown and the cheeks are whitish. The upper lip is divided by a groove from nose to mouth; the lip is deeper than in most mongooses, extending as far as the blackish rhinarium. The ears are large and squarish. The skeleton is more dog-like than that of other herpestids, reflecting this mongoose's more cursorial lifestyle and digitigrade locomotion. Fore- and hindfeet have five toes. The forefeet have long (13 mm), strong, curved claws; the claws are shorter and less curved on hindfeet. The hallux and pollex are reduced and set back from the plantar pad. The forelimbs are naked to the wrist. The hindlimbs have hair from behind the first digit to the heel. Conspicuous anal scent pouches are used in marking. There are two to three pairs of abdominal mammae. The frontal region of the skull is expanded and more elevated than the parietal region. Postorbital processes well-developed. Sagittal and lambdoidal crests well-developed. Braincase broadest at zygomatic arch. Front chambers of ear bullae small relative to hindchambers. Condylobasal 10·9–11·9 cm. Dental formula: I 3/3, C 1/1, P 4/4, M 2/2 = 40. Heavy dentition. Lower canines recurved, upper canines slightly recurved. Lower molars have high cusps, especially at front of teeth.

Habitat. Found in a wide range of habitats, principally grassland, woodland, and farmland, but not in swamps, tropical rainforest, desert, or above 4000 m.

Food and Feeding. Predominantly insectivorous, feeding on surface invertebrates. However, White-tailed Mongooses are opportunistic and occasionally take small vertebrates, berries and fruits. They feed mainly on termites and ants in the dry season, and dung beetles in the rainy season. When foraging, they use a rapid zig-zag trot with occasional brief stops. In suburban settings, they raid garbage cans. Examination of 65 stomachs collected in Zimbabwe contained the following diet components: 86% Insecta, 31% Amphibia, 18% Muridae, 15% Reptilia, 6% Oligochaeta, 6% fruit, 5% Aves, 1·5% Myriapoda, 1·5% Scorpiones, 1·5% Solifugae, and 1·5% Soricidae.

Activity patterns. Nocturnal, particularly active during first third of the night, with more frequent activity on darker nights. White-tailed Mongooses use daytime resting sites in termite mounds, rocks, or buildings, changing sites from day to day. Their ability to dig dens is apparently limited. Their habit of foraging on roads at night makes them vulnerable to injury or death.

Movements, Home range and Social organization. Mainly solitary (79–91% of records; the remainder are male–female pairs). In Ethiopia, the mean male home range was 3·17 km² (range = 1·11–4·27); one female home range was 2·61 km². In Tanzania, the mean male home range was 0·97 km² (range = 0·80–1·23), mean female home range was 0·64 km² (range = 0·39–1·18), and density was up to 4 individuals/km². Home ranges in Kenya were reported to be up to 8 km². Walking pace was recorded at 4·2 km/h. Males did not share ranges with other males, but their ranges overlapped substantially with those of females. Some female ranges were exclusive, but others were apparently shared with other females. In Ethiopia, male-male overlap was less than 3%, whereas male-female overlap was 35–81%. In high-density populations, there appears to be male-biased dispersal; females remain on the maternal home range, but forage independently. This leads to the formation of female clusters or clans. Individuals cover approximately a quarter of the entire home range each night. Females sometimes share day-rest sites with juveniles or other females. Rest site availability may limit population size. There is little social interaction. Interactions between individuals are generally tolerant, with little attention paid; occasional aggression is directed at members of a neighboring clan. White-tailed Mongooses are quite vocal for a solitary species. They mutter while digging for insects, and if threatened, may growl, grunt, or bark. The tail is apparently used in visual signalling: a threatened individual will erect its fur and tail as well as vocalize. Individuals scent-mark with anal gland secretions, urine, and dung. They deposit scats at den and central middens (one or two per territory), which may be used by several adults. Urination is usually accompanied by an arching of the tail.

Breeding. Copulations occur during consortships that last for several hours. Litter size averages 1·4 (rarely three or four). Females rear young alone. The young apparently share the maternal home range for at least four months post-weaning. Longevity up to ten years in captivity.

Status and Conservation. Not CITES listed. Classified as Least Concern in *The IUCN Red List*. Their wide geographical distribution, relatively wide habitat utilization, and ability to forage in human garbage, suggest it is a robust species. Distribution and population densities are likely limited by suitable den site availability.

Bibliography. Admasu *et al.* (2004a), Al-Safadi (1995), Dehghani *et al.* (2008), Estes (1991), Ikeda *et al.* (1982), Kingdon (1971-1982, 1997), Skinner & Chimimba (2005), Taylor (1972, In press d), Waser (1980), Waser & Waser (1985), Wozencraft (2005).

Genus *PARACYNICTIS*
Pocock, 1916

19. Selous's Mongoose *Paracynictis selousi*
French: Mangouste de Selous / **German**: Trugmanguste / **Spanish**: Mangosta de Selous

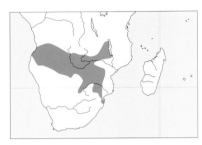

Taxonomy. *Cynictis selousi* de Winton, 1896, Essex Vale, Matabeleland, near Bulawayo, Zimbabwe.
Four subspecies are recognized.
Subspecies and Distribution.
P. s. selousi de Winton, 1896 – W Mozambique, NE South Africa (Limpopo & Mpumalanga Provinces), and Zimbabwe.
P. s. bechuanae Roberts, 1932 – E Botswana.
P. s. ngamiensis Roberts, 1932 – Angola, Zambia, Malawi, N Namibia, and N Botswana.
P. s. sengaani Roberts, 1931 – S Mozambique and South Africa (NE KwaZulu-Natal).

Descriptive notes. Head-body 39–47 cm, tail 28–43·5 cm, hindfoot 10·3–12·4 cm, ear 3·9–5 cm; weight 1·4–2·2 kg. A small mongoose with a grizzled gray coat, black feet, and a white-tipped tail. The upperparts are grayish to tawny-gray; the coat is grizzled, with white rings on the guard hairs. The underparts are also gray to tawny-gray, but paler than the upperparts. The underfur is thick; the hairs are dark at the base and buffy to buffy-gray at the tip. The soft guard hairs are short on the head (15 mm) and increase in length toward the rump (40 mm); on the tail they are shorter at the base (50 mm) and are longer toward the tip (up to 10 cm). The tail is white for a short section towards the tip and is about 40% of the total body length. The muzzle is pointed, with a small rhinarium that has a small medium depression in front; the groove continues downwards to divide the upper lip. The ears are large and are partially covered in front by long hairs. The upperparts of the limbs are black or dark brown. There are four digits on each foot. The claws on the forefeet are slightly curved and about 8–10 mm long; on the hindfeet they are straight. The soles of the feet are hairy. There are three pairs of teats (although a specimen with two pairs has been reported). The skull is elongated; the braincase is ovoid and narrows slightly to the inter-orbital constriction. The post-orbital bar is complete and the rostrum is short and broad. The supra-occipital crests are well-developed and are up to 5–6 mm in height. The sagittal crest is present, but not well-developed. The zygomatic width is half the length of the skull. The auditory bullae are large; the two chambers are of equal size. The coronoid process of the lower jaw is not very high. Dental formula: I 3/3, C 1/1, P 4/4, M 2/2 = 40. The upper canines are short, rounded and slightly recurved; the lower are strongly recurved. The first premolars are small and not always present. The cusps of the upper carnassials are well-developed. The cusps on the trigonid of the lower carnassial are high.

Habitat. Savannah grassland and woodland; absent from forest, desert, and semi-desert. Found in *Acacia* scrub and woodland (with a sandy substrate), open habitats (on cultivated land or where bush clearing has taken place), and on floodplains and grasslands (with short grass and scanty cover). Not dependent on the availability of water and is known from areas with a mean annual rainfall of 400 to 1000 mm.

Food and Feeding. The diet is reported to include insects, mice, reptiles, amphibians, and eggs. The analysis of 51 stomach contents from Botswana and Zimbabwe showed that insects had the highest percentage occurrence, including 43% Orthoptera (mainly grasshoppers and crickets), 43% Isoptera (termites, including *Hodotermes mossambicus* and *Macrotermes falciger*), 37% Coleoptera adults (dung beetles Scarabaeidae, ground beetles Carabidae, weevils Curculionidae, water beetles Dysticidae, and click beetles Elateridae), 27% Coleoptera larvae (including ground beetles Tenebrionidae, dung beetles Scarabaeidae, and click beetles Elateridae), 10% Lepidoptera (Pieridae butterflies, Noctuidae moths, caterpillars of hawk moths Sphingidae, lace wings Neuroptera, and Formicidae). Other food items were: 22% hunting spiders (Solifugidae, notably *Solpuga monteiroi*), 18% scorpions (*Opisthophthalmus wahlbergi* and *Parabuthus granulatus*), 8% Aranea, and 8% Myriapods (*Scolopendra morsitans*). Among the vertebrates eaten were: 16% Muridae (Common African Fat Mouse *Steatomys pratensis* and the Climbing Mouse *Dendromus* sp.), 14% reptiles (the Cape gecko *Pachydactylus capensis*, the spiny agama *Agama hispida*, Wahlberg's snake-eyed skink *Panaspis wahlbergi*, the ornate sandveld lizard *Nucras taeniolata*, the striped skink *Mabuya striata*, the shield-nose snake *Aspidelaps scutatus*, Peters' thread snake *Leptotyphlops scutifrons*, the Cape wolf snake *Lycophidion capense*, and Bibron's burrowing asp *Atractaspis bibronii*), 8% amphibians (toads *Bufo* sp., Delalande's burrowing frog *Tomopterna delalandii*, and Bocage's burrowing frog *Leptopelis bocagii*), and 4% birds (remains of eggs). Selous's

Mongooses are avid diggers and excavate for beetle larvae among litter or at the bases of tufts of grass. They move with the head low and nostrils close to the ground, which suggests that they locate their prey by smell. It is believed that they have good hearing, which may assist them in locating subterranean food.

Activity patterns. Reported to be nocturnal. During the day they rest in burrows.

Movements, Home range and Social organization. Normally solitary, although sometimes recorded in pairs. They excavate burrows in sandy ground. Burrows may have one or two entrances, which are often under the shelter of a low bush, but at other times are out in the open. In Kwazulu-Natal, a burrow had passages and chambers down to a depth of 1·5 m. Under stress, Selous's Mongooses may go into any available hole and have been observed entering South African Spring Hare and Aardvark (*Orycteropus afer*) burrows. They can rise on their legs and hold their head high to look for danger.

Breeding. Births may occur in the warm wet months, from August to March, and litter size appears to be up to four. Pregnant females with three and four fetuses have been reported in Botswana in February and September, and during August in Zimbabwe. Two juveniles weighing 450 g were found in December and January; another juvenile weighing 900 g was found in February. In Namibia, a pregnant female was captured in October.

Status and Conservation. Classified as Least Concern in *The IUCN Red List*. Appears to be uncommon across its range, but its habitat is not considered to be vulnerable and there are thought to be no major threats to this species. Field surveys and ecological studies are needed.

Bibliography. Kingdon (1997), Nowak (1999), Skinner & Chimimba (2005), Stuart & Stuart (In press b), Wozencraft (2005).

Genus *BDEOGALE*
Peters, 1850

20. Bushy-tailed Mongoose *Bdeogale crassicauda*
French: Mangouste à queue touffue / **German**: Buschschwanzmanguste / **Spanish**: Mangosta coligruesa

Taxonomy. *Bdeogale crassicauda* Peters, 1852, "Tette", Mozambique.
Some authors consider the Sokoke Bushy-tailed Mongoose race *omnivora* as a distinct species. Five subspecies are recognized.
Subspecies and Distribution.
B. c. crassicauda Peters, 1852 – DR Congo, Malawi, Mozambique, Zambia, and Zimbabwe.
B. c. nigrescens Sale & Taylor, 1970 – Kenya (Lukenya Hill).
B. c. omnivora Heller, 1913 – coastal forests of Kenya and extreme NE Tanzania.
B. c. puisa Peters, 1852 – NE Mozambique and E Tanzania.
B. c. tenuis Thomas & Wroughton, 1908 – Tanzania (Zanzibar I).
A few recent records from Yemen, but these need confirmation.

Descriptive notes. Head-body 40–50 cm, tail 18–30 cm, hindfoot 7–9·4 cm, ear 2–3·9 cm; weight 1·3–2·1 kg. A medium-sized dark mongoose, with a bushy tail (about 60% of the head and body length). The head and body are yellowish-brown or dark brown, with a grizzled appearance due to the white rings on the guard hairs; in some parts of its range this speckled appearance is not present. The guard hairs are 5 mm on the forehead; they increase in length towards the rump, where they reach about 45 mm. The underparts are sparsely haired, and the hairs are not annulated, except under the throat, and to a lesser extent, on the belly. The underfur is dense and grayish-buff; in some specimens, it tends to show through the guard hairs, particularly on the flanks, which gives a paler gray appearance to these parts. The muzzle is blunt, with a large rhinarium divided by a naked median groove that continues downward and divides the upper lip. The ears are short and wide and the eyes have a horizontal pupil with a grayish-brown iris. The tail is covered with long dark hairs (up to 60 mm). The limbs are black or dark brown. The fore- and hindfeet have four digits; the hallux and pollex are missing. The digits have stout, curved claws, which on the forefoot are 8–9 mm long and usually show considerable wear; on the hindfoot they measure up to 10–11 mm. The hindfeet have hairs up to the back of the plantar pads; the forefeet have a short naked section behind the pads. There are two pairs of teats and the baculum in the male is 15 mm long. The skull is elongated, with the zygomatic width 50% of the total length. The braincase is ovoid and broadest at the level of the jaw articulation; it narrows to the postorbital constriction, which averages 85% of the inter-orbital width. The post-orbital bar is never complete. The rostrum is long (31% of the length of the skull), but the nasal bones are well behind the incisors. The supra-occipital crest is well developed, reaching 4 mm in adults. The sagittal crest is high at the back of the braincase and the zygomatic arches are heavily built. The anterior chambers of the auditory bullae are not inflated. Dental formula: I 3/3, C 1/1, P 4/4, M 2/2 = 40. The upper canines are nearly straight, with sharp cutting edges; the lower canines are recurved. The first premolars are small and peg-like, the second premolars have a normal shape, and the third and fourth premolars are broader than in other herpestid species. The two molars are broad and rectangular. The dentition clearly indicates an adaptation to crushing rather than to slicing.

Habitat. Wooded grasslands, *Acacia* and *Brachystegia* woodlands, montane and bamboo forests, coral-rag thicket, and groundwater forests. In Kenya, it is recorded at the base of hills with rocky outcrops and boulders, where the vegetation is grassland with scattered shrubs and trees (especially *Acacia* sp. and *Commiphora africana*), and also rambling herbs on the hillsides (*Cissus quadrangularis*, *Sarcostemma* spp., and *Ficus* spp.). Along the Kenyan and Tanzanian coasts, the Bushy-tailed Mongoose is found in thick rainforest; in Kenya, one individual was observed approximately 300 m from the forest edge, along a dirt road, between a large open grassland area (with bush and small patches of forest) and a plantation of pine (*Pinus caribaea*). Also found in lowland forest (between 300 and 750 m) and montane forest (up to 1850 m) in the Udzungwa Mountains (Tanzania). In Mozambique, it occurs on the floodplains of the lower Shire and Pungwe Rivers, where on the drier, raised areas, there is an association of *Acacia* woodland. In NE Zimbabwe, it is found on granite koppies up to 1500 m, and in the eastern regions, on the fringes of lowland forest at 230 m. In Zimbabwe, it occurs in *Brachystegia* woodland, low-elevation riverine associations, and mopane woodland.

Food and Feeding. Appears to be predominately insectivorous, but also eats other invertebrates, small mammals, and reptiles. In seven stomach contents from Zimbabwe, the frequency of occurrence of food items was: 86% insects (termites, *Macrotermes falciger*, *Odontotermes badius*, *Trinervitermes rhodesiensis*, Orthoptera, and Coleoptera), 57% reptiles (variable skink *Mabuya varia*, Kirk's rock agama *Agama kirkii*, and the brown house snake *Lamprophis fuliginosus*), 29% amphibians (red toad *Bufo careens*, the striped toad *B. pusillus*, Bocage's burrowing frog *Leptopelis bocagii*, the savanna ridged frog *Ptychadena superciliaris*, and the Mozambique ridged frog *P. mossanbica*), 29% murids (*Mastomys* sp.), 29% millipedes, 14% spiders (baboon spider *Harpactira* sp.), 14% scorpions, 14% gastropods (*Laevicaulis natalensis*), and 14% grass. Other reports have stated that this species feeds on insects, particularly ants and termites, and that the diet includes caterpillars, crickets, grasshoppers, beetles, dragonflies, and spiders. In Kenya, an individual was observed foraging on either queen termites or male driver ants (*Dorylus* sp.). On Zanzibar Island, it is said to prey on large land snails, which it smashes against coral outcroppings, stones or tree trunks. Beetle and crab remains have been found in a specimen stomach and scats in East Africa.

Activity patterns. Camera-trapping data indicates nocturnal activity. An individual was spotted in Kenya walking along a road at 18:50 h.

Movements, Home range and Social organization. Solitary, although pairs have been photographed by camera-traps.

Breeding. In Kenya, newborns and a female with a fetus were recorded in November and December.

Status and Conservation. Classified as Least Concern in *The IUCN Red List*; Sokoke Bushy-tailed Mongoose *B. c. omnivora* is classified as Vulnerable and is considered Threatened in the 1989 IUCN Action Plan for the Conservation of Mustelids and Viverrids. *B. c. tenuis* has been placed on the list of species that are illegal to hunt on Zanzibar Island. The Bushy-tailed Mongoose is said to be rare with a patchy distribution; the causes of its rarity are unknown. However, it was the most photographed carnivore species in a camera-trapping survey in the Udzungwa Mountains, Tanzania. In Kenya, the population in the Arabuko-Sokoke Forest is under threat from habitat loss due to illegal logging, and the Shimba Hills population is potentially under threat from afforestation with non-native pine species. Field surveys, ecological studies, and assessments of threats are needed.

Bibliography. Allen & Loveridge (1927), Al-Safadi (1995), De Luca & Mpunga (2005), Engel & Van Rompaey (1995), Goldman & Winther-Hansen (2003), Kingdon (1971-1982), Nader & Al-Safadi (1991), Perez *et al.* (2006), Pocock (1916b), Sale & Taylor (1970), Schreiber *et al.* (1989), Simmons (1995), Skinner & Chimimba (2005), Stuart & Stuart (1998), Taylor (1986, 1987, In press a), Williams (1951), Wozencraft (2005).

21. Jackson's Mongoose *Bdeogale jacksoni*

French: Mangouste de Jackson / German: Jackson-Manguste / Spanish: Mangosta masai

Taxonomy. *Galeriscus jacksoni* Thomas, 1894, Mianzini, Masailand, Kenya.
Some authors consider *B. jacksoni* conspecific with the Black-footed Mongoose (*B. nigripes*), but others believe that there are sufficient skin and skull differences to consider them as two separate species. Monotypic.

Distribution. Kenya (Aberdares & Mt Kenya), Tanzania (Udzungwa Mts), and SE Uganda.

Descriptive notes. Head-body 50·8–57·1 cm, tail 28·3–32·4 cm, hindfoot 8·6–10·8 cm, ear 2·3–3·5 cm; weight 2–3 kg. A large mongoose with a bushy tail. The long, dense dorsal pelage is grizzled black and white; the legs are dark brown or black, and the tail is white. The dorsal hairs have black and white rings and are 20 mm long. The underparts are light gray and the under fur is dense and woolly. The muzzle and chin are brownish-white, and the cheeks, throat, and the sides of the neck are yellowish. The muzzle is blunt and the ears are round and broad. The rhinarium is large with a median groove running down to the upper lip, which is divided by a naked groove. The fore- and hindfeet have four digits: the hallux and pollex are missing. The claws are thick and strong, and the soles are naked. Dental formula: I 3/3, C 1/1, P 4/4, M 2/2 = 40.

Habitat. Montane forest and bamboo zones, but also lowland forest. Found up to 3300 m.

Food and feeding. Rodent remains of rodents of the genera *Dasymys* and *Otomys* have been found in stomachs. In the Aberdare Mountains (Kenya), the volume of food items in 40 scats was over 50% rodents (*Otomys* sp., *Dasymys* sp., and *Praomys* sp.) and 40% insects (army ants *Anona* sp., beetles, caterpillars, and weevils), with millipedes, snails, lizards, and eggs also part of the diet. About 80% of the juveniles' diet was rodents (*Otomys* sp., *Lophuromys* sp., *Mus* sp., *Praomys* sp.), but beetles, lizards, birds, and a few ants were also included.

Activity patterns. Appears to be nocturnal. In the Udzungwa Mountains National Park (Tanzania), 25 camera-trap photographs were recorded during the night; 73% of these were taken between 19:00 h and midnight.

Movements, Home range and social organization. Possibly solitary, but often seen in pairs and occasionally in groups of four.

Breeding. Nothing known.

Status and Conservation. Classified as Near Threatened in *The IUCN Red List*. Listed as Threatened in the 1989 IUCN Action Plan for the Conservation of Mustelids and Viverrids. Occurs in isolated populations and appears to be rare. Given its apparent dependence on forest habitat, the main threat to this species is likely to be ongoing forest loss within its range. Field surveys, ecological studies, and assessments of any threats are urgently needed.

Bibliography. De Luca & Mpunga (2005, 2006), IUCN (2008), Kingdon (1971-1982, 1997), Pocock (1916b), Schreiber *et al.* (1989), Van Rompaey & Kingdon (In press), Wozencraft (2005).

22. Black-footed Mongoose *Bdeogale nigripes*

French: Mangouste à pattes noires / German: Schwarzfußmanguste / Spanish: Mangosta calzada
Other common names: Black-legged Mongoose

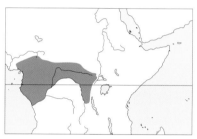

Taxonomy. *Bdeogale nigripes* Pucheran, 1855, Gabon.
Some authors consider *B. nigripes* to be conspecific with Jackson's Mongoose (*B. jacksoni*), but others believe that there are sufficient skin and skull differences to consider them as two separate species. Monotypic.

Distribution. SE Nigeria, Cameroon, Central African Republic, DR Congo, Equatorial Guinea, Gabon, and PR Congo. Also reported from Angola, but this is rejected by some authors.

Descriptive notes. Head-body 46–63 cm (males), 45–65 cm (females), tail 30–38·5 cm (males), 29–40 cm (females), hindfoot 9·4–11·5 cm (males), 9·4–11·3 cm (females), ear 3–3·9 cm (males), 3·3–3·7 cm (females); weight 2–4·8 kg. A large, short-haired gray mongoose, with dark-colored legs. The pelage is usually grayish-white, but can sometimes be brownish-red; the hairs have white and brown rings, tipped with white. The color of the underparts varies from grayish-white to dark brown. The underfur is dense and short with yellow to brown hairs 10–12 mm long; the guard hairs are 20 mm or less in length. The forehead and muzzle are short-haired and are lighter colored than the body. The muzzle is blunt, with a large rhinarium divided by a median groove that continues on the upper lip as a naked strip. The ears are short and wide. The color of the throat and belly varies from grayish-white to dark brown. The tail is white to yellowish, moderately bushy, and slightly tapering. The legs and the feet range from light brown to brownish-black. The fore- and hindfeet have four slightly webbed digits; the hallux and the pollex are missing. The soles are hairy up to the pads. There are two pairs of teats. The skull is the largest of all West African mongooses and is long and relatively narrow, the zygomatic breadth being almost exactly half of the condylobasal length. The braincase is ovoid and has a sharp sagittal crest; the occipital crest is broad and flange-like. The frontal region is slightly elevated and smoothly rounded, and the post-orbital constriction is markedly less than the inter-orbital breadth. The posterior part of the skull is notably short. The front section of the auditory bulla is small, the posterior chamber is well inflated. Dental formula: I 3/3, C 1/1, P 4/4, M 2/2 = 40. The molars are as broad as long, giving a squarish appearance, and are low-cusped, suggesting that they have a crushing rather than slicing function.

Habitat. Primary rainforest, up to a least 1000 m.

Food and Feeding. In the Central African Republic, 86% of scats contained arthropods; the frequency of occurrence of other food items in scats was: 48% mammals (including 19% insectivores, 14% rodents, and 10% squirrels), 14% reptiles and amphibians, and 5% fruit. Termites and driver ants (*Dorylus* and *Myrmecaria* sp.) were found in three out of nine specimen stomachs collected from the PR Congo.

Activity patterns. Said to be nocturnal, but there are some reports of diurnal observations. Rests in holes between the roots of big trees and in the dens of African Brush-tailed Porcupines (*Atherurus africanus*).

Movements, Home range and Social organization. Believed to be solitary, but has been seen in pairs.

Breeding. In West Africa, breeding may occur at the beginning of the dry season: three captured juveniles were born between early November and early January. According to the Mbuti pygmies of the DR Congo, there are usually one or two young; a female and one young were collected in early December in the Ituri Forest.

Status and Conservation. Classified as Least Concern in *The IUCN Red List*. Numbers may be declining as a result of forest loss and fragmentation (from logging, mining, and slash and burn farming), and to a lesser degree from bushmeat hunting. Field surveys, ecological studies, and assessments of threats are needed.

Bibliography. Bequaert (1922), Carpaneto & Germi (1989a, 1989b), Crawford-Cabral (1989), Kingdon (1997), Perez *et al.* (2006), Ray & Sunquist (2001), Rosevear (1974), Van Rompaey & Colyn (In press a), Wozencraft (2005).

Genus *RHYNCHOGALE*
Thomas, 1894

23. Meller's Mongoose *Rhynchogale melleri*

French: Mangouste de Meller / **German**: Meller-Manguste / **Spanish**: Mangosta crestada

Taxonomy. *Rhynogale melleri* Gray, 1865, Kilosa, Tanganyika Territory, Tanzania.
Two subspecies are recognized.
Subspecies and Distribution.
R. m. melleri Gray, 1865 – DR Congo, Tanzania, Malawi, N & C Mozambique, Zambia, Zimbabwe, and possibly NE Botswana.
R. m. langi Roberts, 1938 – S Mozambique, Swaziland, and South Africa (Limpopo & Mpumalanga Provinces).
Descriptive notes. Head-body 44–50 cm, tail 28–41·2 cm, hindfoot 9·5–10·6 cm, ear 3·1–4·3 cm; weight 1·8–2·8 kg. A medium to large brown mongoose with a bushy tail. The general coloration is grayish to pale brown, the head is paler, and the feet are darker. The pelage is coarsely grizzled; the hard, wiry, guard hairs have white, buffy, brown, or dark brown rings. The underparts are generally lighter in color than the dorsal pelage. The underfur is dense and fine; the hairs are gray, gray-brown, or ashy-gray at the base, tinged with brown at the tip. The hairs are 8–10 mm long on the head, increasing in length toward the rump, where they reach 40–45 mm long. The muzzle is blunt and swollen, the rhinarium has no central groove and the upper lip is not divided. The color of the tail is variable: in black-tailed individuals the tail is white or brownish-white at the base and the remainder is black, and in white-tailed individuals the tail hairs have black and white rings, with white tips. At the tip of the tail the hairs are up to 12·5 cm long in black-tailed forms, but in white-tailed forms the hairs barely reach 9 cm. The tail length is slightly less than 50% of the total body length. The lower parts of the limbs are darker than the dorsal coat and are not grizzled. There are five digits on each foot, but the hallux is much reduced. The claws on the forefeet are short, curved, sharp, and about 8 mm long; the claws of the hindfeet are heavier and less curved. The sole of the hindfoot is hairy. The anus and anal glands open into a circular pouch that closes with a transverse slit. There are two pairs of teats. The skull is lightly built and elongated; the width is half of the total length and is highest at the midpoint of the zygomatic arches. The ovoid braincase is widest just behind the glenoid articulations and narrows forward to the post-orbital constriction. The post-orbital constriction is broad (70% of the braincase width). The skull is enlarged at the point where the sagittal crest divides, and the eye sockets are set in a forward position. The post-orbital bar is not closed; the post-orbital processes are long, but do not reach each other. The zygomatic arches are thin and weak, and the coronoid process is of medium height, suggesting that the jaw muscles are not very large. The supra-occipital crest slopes backwards, rising to about 5 mm in height; the sagittal crest is low. The rostrum is short and broad. The anterior chamber of the auditory bulla is much smaller than the posterior chamber, which is round and rises to a high apex. The palate is broad and the cheeck teeth are set in a curved row. Dental formula: I 3/3, C 1/1, P 4/4, M 2/2 = 40. The upper canines are thin, sharp, and curved; the lower canines are more curved and heavier. The first premolars are very small. The upper carnassials are broad and molariform and the fourth lower premolars are broad, with high cusps. The trigonid of the lower carnassial has three high cusps; the second lower molar is similar, but with lower cusps. The teeth appear to be adapted to grinding more than slicing.

Habitat. Savannah, open woodland, and grassland (with termitaries). Recorded in Mwanihana bamboo forest at 1850 m in Tanzania. In Zimbabwe and Malawi, it is found in open *Brachystegia* woodland and is associated with open grassland and vlei area where particular species of termites are found. Recorded from mountainous areas and on low-lying granite soils in the Kruger National Park (South Africa).

Food and Feeding. Mainly insectivorous, particularly termites. In Zimbabwe, 23 stomachs all contained termites (*Macrotermes falciger*, *M. natalensis*, and *Hodotermes mossambicus*). The frequency of occurrence of other food items was: 13% Orthoptera (grasshoppers), 4% Myriapoda (a centipede *Scolopendra morsitans*), 4% Coleoptera (black beetles), 4% reptiles (Peters's thread snake *Leptotyphlops scutifrons*), and 4% amphibians (a frog). Most of the stomachs contained small pieces of grass. In eastern Zambia a specimen stomach contained termites and two centipedes. Fruits were reported in stomachs collected in Malawi.

Activity patterns. Nocturnal activity has been recorded by camera-traps in Tanzania.

Movements, Home range and Social organization. Believed to be solitary.

Breeding. Births may take place in November and December. Litter size appears to be to up to three: a female with three fetuses was found in November. In Zimbabwe, a female and two young were taken from an Aardvark (*Orycteropus afer*) burrow in January. In Zambia, in December, a litter of two newborn young was found in a cave and a pregnant female had two fetuses.

Status and Conservation. Classified as Least Concern in *The IUCN Red List*. Considered uncommon, but is present in several protected areas and its preferred habitat is extensive. There are no obvious major threats. However, in Tanzania and Zambia, there has been considerable expansion of the human population and domestic dogs, which could represent a significant local threat. Field surveys and ecological studies are needed.

Bibliography. Ansell (1960b, 1969, 1974), De Luca & Mpunga (2005), Kingdon (1971-1982, 1997), Perez *et al.* (2006), Skinner & Chimimba (2005), Stuart & Stuart (In press c), Thevenin (1943), Wozencraft (2005).

Plate 19 ➤

PLATE 19

inches

cm

Subfamily MUNGOTINAE

Genus *SURICATA*

Desmarest, 1804

24. Meerkat *Suricata suricatta*

French: Mangouste suricate / **German**: Erdmännchen / **Spanish**: Suricata
Other common names: Suricate, Slender-tailed Meerkat, Gray Meerkat

Taxonomy. *Viverra suricatta* Schreber, 1776, Cape of Good Hope, South Africa. Three subspecies are recognized.
Subspecies and Distribution.
S. s. suricatta Schreber, 1776 – Botswana, South Africa, possibly Lesotho, and Kalahari Desert in Namibia.
S. s. iona Cabral, 1971 – SW Angola.
S. s. marjoriae Bradfield, 1936 – Namibia (Namib Desert).
Descriptive notes. Head–body 24·5–29 cm (males), 26–28·5 cm (females), tail 20·5–24 cm (males), 19–23 cm (females), hindfoot 6·3–7·4 cm (males), 6·5–7·4 cm (females), ear 2·1 cm (18–26) (males), 1·8 cm (17–20) (females); weight 626–797 g (males), 620–969 g (females). Females become significantly larger and heavier upon assuming dominant status, averaging 750 g; non-dominant females average 710 g. The Meerkat is a small mongoose, with a relatively large pointed muzzle. It has coarse, pale-gray, tan, or silvery-brown fur, with dark transverse bands across the back, and black eye patches. The underparts are paler than the dorsum; the coat color is darker in the southern part of the species' range. The fur on the tail is short, sparse on the underside, and yellowish with a black tip. The guard hairs are 15 mm at shoulder, increasing to 30–40 mm at the rump, decreasing to 20 mm at base of the tail and tapering to 12 mm at tail tip. The dorsal guard hairs are light at the base, have two dark rings separated by a light band, and a silvery tip. The small, rounded ears can close to keep dust out while the animal digs: the posterior and superior ear ridges move forward and down. The tail is slender, not bushy, and the legs are thin. The muscular forelimbs have four digits, each with long claws (15 mm). The hindfeet also have four digits, with shorter claws (8 mm). The feet are naked to the wrist/ankle. There are three pairs of mammae. Meerkats lack cheek glands. The skull is high, broad, and rounded. Hindchambers of ear bullae larger relative to anterior. Closed orbital space. Relatively large eye sockets (more than 20% total skull length). Supra-orbital crest represented by low ridge. Saggital crest not present. Light zygomatic arches. Dental formula: I 3/3, C 1/1, P 3/3, M 2/2 = 36. Outer upper incisors larger than other incisors. Upper canines straight, slightly flattened on inside. Lower canines distinctly recurved. Broad molars with sharp cusps. Poorly developed carnassial shear adapted for insectivory.
Habitat. Open semi-arid areas, scrub, rangeland, and grassland. Subterranean dens are used, which tend to be extensive, with multiple entrances and chambers. The temperatures within dens are more stable and comfortable than the hot and cold extremes on the surface. Meerkats are good diggers, and are likely to excavate some dens themselves, but usually occupy dens dug by other small mammals. Dens may be shared with South African Ground Squirrels or Yellow Mongooses.
Food and Feeding. Insectivorous diet, especially Coleoptera (beetles), Arachnids (scorpions and spiders), and Myriapoda (centipedes) larvae. Occasionally vertebrates (including lizards and small snakes) are consumed. Frequency of occurrence of food types from 23 stomachs collected from Botswana: Coleoptera larvae (91%), Scorpiones (35%), Coleoptera adults (17%), Orthoptera (17%), Myriapoda (13%), Reptilia (13%), and Isoptera (9%). Frequency of occurrence of prey items in 98 stomachs collected from Orange Free State (South Africa): Coleoptera (58%), Lepidoptera (pupae and larvae) (43%), Isoptera (40%), Orthoptera (34%), Diptera (pupae, larvae) (23%), Arachnida (21%), Hymenoptera (15%), Dermaptera (12%), Chilopoda (10%), Dictyoptera (10%), Diplopoda (9%), Amphibia (5%), Reptilia (5%), Aves (2%), and Hemiptera (1%). Meerkats move as a loose group, with individuals foraging independently. Individuals generally walk, sniffing and scraping at the ground surface, and often stop and dig intensively for prey—sometimes disappearing from view in the deep hole they have dug. Potential food items, foraging holes and scrapes, are generally defended from approach by others, except for adults sharing food with young pups.
Activity patterns. Diurnal. A group sleeps together overnight in a subterranean den, emerging in early morning and returning before sunset. During the day the group forages together, usually resting in a shady area around midday. They usually start the day by sunbathing at the den and end the day relaxing by the den. Their behavioral repertoire includes foraging, resting, vigilance (including standing erect), self and allogrooming, social play, scent marking, and vocalization.
Movements, Home range and Social organization. Meerkats live in social groups that share a home range, which they jointly defend. Mean group size is 4·2 to 8·5 individuals (range = 3–20), with up to 49 recorded. Mean home range size is 5 km² (range = 1–10 km²). Population density varies from 0·32–1·69 individuals/km². Home ranges

are defended, with larger groups usually displacing smaller groups. A group can cover up to 6 km in a day. Groups have around five dens within their home range; they generally occupy a different den every few days, but may use a den for longer periods when pups are present. Groups also have up to 1000 boltholes on their territory that they run to when danger threatens. Group encounters often result in chases or fights. When a fight occurs it is usually accompanied by piloerection, erection of the tail, tiptoe body stance, and a "war dance". Groups are highly social, with grooming and marking utilized to maintain group bonding. Groups contain adult males and females, and the young of the dominant pair; the adult sex ratio is approximately equal. Within a group, most subordinate adults are related to the dominant female, but immigrant males are also commonly present. There is evidence of a dominance hierarchy, with dominant males and females regularly displacing subordinates from disputed sites, and marking four to five times more frequently. In addition, subordinate approaches and allogrooming are characterized by "creeping" behavior. Aggression over food items is common, but usually settled in favor of the owner. The group works as a whole in rearing young and repelling predators. Vocal communications include contact calls, emitted every few seconds, which maintain group cohesion while foraging. Growls and spits are used to defend resources from approach by another group member. Short, sharp alarm calls elicit rapid evasive behavior. These are most frequently given by individuals who are "on guard", standing erect on a raised mound or dead tree. Group members take turns going "on guard" and give a "watchman's song" to inform the group that they are sentries. Alarm calls carry specific information on predator type (aerial or terrestrial) and urgency. "Worry" calls warn group members of lower intensity danger. Pups emit two types of begging call, a constant repeat call and a high-pitched "give-me-food" call when an adult finds a prey item. Olfactory communication is used for both intra- and inter-group communication. Group members scent-mark by wiping each other and objects (e.g. rocks) with their anal gland. Such marking is often done communally, with all group members involved in synchronous bouts of scent marking. Urine and feces are also apparently used in communication, with individuals overmarking excretion sites. These "signals" from other groups often elicit excited and aggressive responses. Communal latrines are used to mark territory. Dominant individuals usually mark a territory.
Breeding. Females rarely conceive before they are two years old. The Meerkat is believed to be an induced ovulator and births are restricted to the wetter, warmer months (presumably correlated with invertebrate prey availability). Mating is rarely observed, occurring in the subterranean den, but mate-guarding by the dominant male has been observed. The Meerkat exhibits a despotic social system of high reproductive skew: generally only the dominant pair breeds. Dominant females produce 75% of litters and dominant males father 80% of pups within the group. In some cases this is due to inbreeding avoidance. When a second or subordinate female conceives, it is usually followed by infanticide or den desertion. Non-pregnant subordinate females are often evicted by the dominant female during the late stages of her pregnancy, but are allowed to return to the group after the birth of the dominant female's pups. The number of litters per female per year varies from one to three, with dominant females producing more litters per year (mean 2·8) than subordinates (mean 0·9). The gestation period is approximately 70 days. Mean fetal litter size is 4·1 (range = 1–8); litter size at birth is three to seven. If more than one female gives birth within a group, the births usually occur within one week. The interbirth interval can be as little as 73 days, indicating that females can conceive within 4–12 days of parturition. The young are born with eyes and ears closed and short hair. Pup weight at birth is 25–36 g. Eyes open at 10–14 days. Following birth of the litter, pups are retained in the subterranean den until they are three to four weeks of age. The sex ratio of the pups at emergence from the den is approximately equal. During the period in the den, one or more individuals will remain at the den to "babysit" the pups, while the group forages. The babysitter usually changes every day. These babysitters guard the pups from predators and also probably help keep the pups warm. Breeder adults do relatively little babysitting; non-breeding subordinates (helpers) make higher individual contributions. Allosuckling occurs: pups suckle milk from numerous females, including females that have not given birth. Weaning occurs at around two months of age (49–63 days). When the pups emerge from the den and begin accompanying the foraging group, helpers provide care by carrying and provisioning pups and defending them against predators. Provisioning involves dropping or leaving whole or partial prey items. In contrast to the social behavior of the Banded Mongoose, there is no pup escorting system and pups move between group members begging for food. Nevertheless, pup survival is higher in groups with more helpers. Although many litters fail completely within the first month (21%), 70% of pups are estimated to survive from weaning to independence. Annual survival rate for pups is 0·20, with adult annual survival rate a low 0·68. Annual survival rates of group members older than pups are dependent upon predator density. Predators likely include snakes (e.g. cape cobra *Naja nivea*), mammalian carnivores (e.g. Black-backed Jackal), and raptors (e.g. martial eagle *Polemaetus bellicosus*, bateleur eagle *Terathopius ecaudatus*, tawny eagle *Aquila rapax*, and pale chanting-goshawk *Melierax canorus*). In addition, pups are killed by neighboring Meerkat groups. There is no sex-bias to dispersal, but dispersal mode differs between the sexes. Subordinate females are forceably evicted by the dominant female, but males tend to leave voluntarily and prospect for females in other groups. Meerkats can live to over eight years in wild, and over twelve years in captivity.

Status and Conservation. Not CITES listed. Classified as Least Concern in *The IUCN Red List*. A common species that appears to be unthreatened. Historically killed in rabies control efforts that mainly targeted the Yellow Mongoose. May be beneficial to farmers in controlling pest Lepidoptera species.

Bibliography. Brotherton *et al.* (2001), Carlson, Manser *et al.* (2006), Carlson, Nicol *et al.* (2003), Carlson, Russell *et al.* (2006), Carlson, Young *et al.* (2004), Clutton-Brock, Brotherton, O'Riain, Griffin, Gaynor, Kansky *et al.* (2001), Clutton-Brock, Brotherton, O'Riain, Griffin, Gaynor, Sharpe *et al.* (2000), Clutton-Brock, Brotherton, Russell *et al.* (2001), Clutton-Brock, Brotherton, Smith *et al.* (1998), Clutton-Brock, Gaynor, Kansky *et al.* (1998), Clutton-Brock, Gaynor, Mcllrath *et al.* (1999), Clutton-Brock, Hodge *et al.* (2006), Clutton-Brock, Maccoll *et al.* (1999), Clutton-Brock, O'Riain *et al.* (1999), Clutton-Brock, Russell & Sharpe (2003, 2004), Clutton-Brock, Russell, Sharpe, Brotherton el al. (2001), Clutton-Brock, Russell, Sharpe & Jordan (2005), Clutton-Brock, Russell, Sharpe, Young *et al.* (2002), Decker *et al.* (1992), Doolan & Macdonald (1996a, 1996b, 1997, 1999), Estes (1991), Griffin *et al.* (2003), Hodge *et al.* (2007), Hollen & Manser (2006, 2007), Jordan *et al.* (2007), Kingdon (1997), Kutsukake & Clutton-Brock (2006a, 2006b), Lynch (1980), Manser (1998, 1999, 2001), Manser & Avey (2000), Manser & Bell (2004), Manser, Bell & Fletcher (2001), Manser, Seyfarth & Cheney (2002), Moran (1984), Moran & Sorensen (1986), Moran *et al.* (1983), Moss *et al.* (2001), Muller & Lojewski (1986), O'Riain *et al.* (2000), Ross-Gillespie & Griffin (2007), Russell, Brotherton *et al.* (2003), Russell, Carlson & Clutton-Brock (2004), Russell, Clutton-Brock *et al.* (2002), Russell, Sharpe *et al.* (2003), Russell, Young *et al.* (2007), Scantlebury *et al.* (2002), Sharpe (2005a, 2005b, 2005c, 2007), Sharpe & Cherry (2003), Sharpe *et al.* (2002), Skinner & Chimimba (2005), Stephens *et al.* (2005), Thornton & McAuliffe (2006), Van Staaden (1994), Young & Clutton-Brock (2006), Young, Carlson & Clutton-Brock (2005), Young, Carlson, Monfort *et al.* (2006).

Genus *CROSSARCHUS*
Cuvier, 1825

25. Alexander's Cusimanse *Crossarchus alexandri*
French: Mangouste d'Alexander / **German**: Kongo-Kusimanse / **Spanish**: Cusimansé del Congo

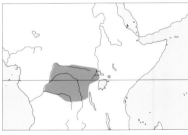

Taxonomy. *Crossarchus alexandri* Thomas & Wroughton, 1907, Ubangi, Democratic Republic of the Congo (formerly Zaire). Two subspecies were recognized by Goldman in 1984, who proposed *minor* as restricted to eastern DR Congo and Uganda. However, subsequent research has discounted the subspecies status of this population and returned this species to monotypic status.

Distribution. DR Congo and Uganda.

Descriptive notes. Head–body 35–44 cm, tail 22·5–31·7 cm, hindfoot 7·5–9·1 cm, ear 1·9–2·8 cm; weight 1–2 kg. Largest member of the genus *Crossarchus*. Dark thick shaggy fur. Crest from head to tail (6–8 cm long between neck whorls). Conspicuous whorls of hair present on neck. Dorsal guard hairs 40–50 mm, gradually lengthening from nape to rump. Crest and whorl hair length similar to surrounding guard hairs. Snout-like nose is longest of the cusimanses (rostrum 34–36% of condylobasal length). Face has short fur. Five digits on fore- and hindfeet. Well-developed claws on forefeet. Ectotympanic bullae inflated less than entotympanic bullae. Alexander's Cusimanse is sympatric with the subspecies *nigricolor* of the Angolan Cusimanse in the DR Congo, but is larger (head–body more than 36·4 cm, condylobasal more than 74 mm, post-dental palate length subequal to width). Condylobasal 74–81·1 mm. Rostrum 25·7–31·9 mm. Zygomatic breadth 35·4–43·4 mm. Dental formula: I 3/3, C 1/1, P 3/3, M 2/2 = 36.

Habitat. Lowland and montane rainforest, damp valley bottoms, and seasonally flooded swamp forest. Said to utilize cultivated and inhabited land (in contrast to Angolan Cusimanse). Relict population believed to live on Mount Elgon (1500–2900 m).

Food and Feeding. Believed to feed on invertebrates and vertebrates of the forest floor and in rotting logs, feeding mainly on earthworms, slugs, snails, and beetles, with some fruit.

Activity patterns. Believed to be diurnal, although reports of at least some nocturnal activity at Kivu (DR Congo).

Movements, Home range and Social organization. Social. Up to 20 animals in a group. Groups believed to rove, with no fixed dens. Contact calls with grunts and twitters whilst foraging. Will climb trees.

Breeding. Nothing known.

Status and Conservation. Not CITES listed. Classified as Least Concern in *The IUCN Red List*. Not endangered, with the exception of a relict population on Mount Elgon (possibly threatened by hunting). Heavily hunted for bushmeat in the DR Congo. Very little is known about this species and scientific studies, particularly on ecology and behavior, are needed.

Bibliography. Coetzee (1977), Colyn & Van Rompaey (1990, 1994a), Colyn *et al.* (1987), Ewer (1973), Goldman (1984, 1987), Kingdon (1997), Van Rompaey & Colyn (1992, In press b), Wozencraft (2005).

26. Angolan Cusimanse *Crossarchus ansorgei*
French: Mangouste d'Ansorge / **German**: Angola-Kusimanse / **Spanish**: Cusimansé de Angola
Other common names: Angolan Mongoose, Ansorge's Cusimanse

Taxonomy. *Crossarchus ansorgei* Thomas, 1910, Ndalla Tando, Angola.
Two subspecies are recognized.

Subspecies and Distribution.
C. a. ansorgei Thomas, 1910 – N Angola.
C. a. nigricolor Colyn & Van Rompaey 1990 – DR Congo (Congo River Basin).

Descriptive notes. Head–body 32–36 cm, tail 20·8 cm (male), 22·1 cm (female), hindfoot 7 cm (male), 6 cm (female), ear 2·4 cm (male); weight 0·6–1·5 kg (males). Dark shaggy fur with dense brown under fur. *C. a. ansorgei* is reddish-brown, with annulated hairs, a dark crown and pale face but lacks a facial stripe. *C. a. nigricolor* is black and has white flashes on the cheeks from the corner of the mouth to the neck below the ear. The face is pale. There is some white or yellow speckling on the upper body and a dark dorsal line from the nuchal crest to the base of the tail. Its snout-like nose is the shortest of the cusimanses (rostrum 31·5% of condylobasal length, compared to 34–36% for other cusimanses). Short rounded ears, capable of closing via movement of posterior ridges. Pupils are horizontally elongated. Relatively short tail and short legs. Five digits on fore- and hindfeet. Well-developed claws on forefeet. Area between digital and plantar pads naked, with naked heel on hindfeet. No obvious sexual dimorphism (except male tail more bushy than female). The subspecies *nigricolor* of the Angolan Cusimanse is sympatric with Alexander's Cusimanse in DR Congo, but is smaller (head–body ≤ 34·2 cm, condylobasal ≤ 67 mm, postdental palate length half width). Skulls show no sexual dimorphism in size. Condylobasal 59·4–65·9 mm. Rostrum 18·1–21 mm. Zygomatic breadth 31·2–35·3 mm. Ectotympanic bullae inflated less than entotympanic bullae. Skull bullae more inflated than Alexander's Cusimanse. Dental formula: I 3/3, C 1/1, P 3/3, M 2/2 = 36.

Habitat. Deciduous rainforest. Apparently never visits agricultural or human-inhabited land (in contrast to sympatric Alexander's Cusimanse).

Food and Feeding. Believed to be strictly carnivorous (based upon captive observations). Feeds on invertebrates and vertebrates of the forest floor and in rotting logs eating mostly insects, larvae, eggs, and small vertebrates.

Activity patterns. Believed to be diurnal.

Movements, Home range and Social organization. Social. Groups of up to 20 or more appear to rove, with no fixed dens.

Breeding. Nothing known.

Status and Conservation. Not CITES listed. Classified as Data Deficient in *The IUCN Red List*. In the IUCN/SSC Action Plan for the conservation of Mustelids and Viverrids (1989) listed as "known or likely to be threatened". Appears to be locally abundant but is commonly hunted and consumed, and is frequently found in bush-meat markets. Most frequently killed mammal (6% of all hunted mammal species) in the Ubila River region (DR Congo). In Angola only a single specimen has been collected, in 1908, north of the Cuanza River. Least known species within the genus *Crossarchus*.

Bibliography. Coetzee (1977), Colyn (1984), Colyn & Van Rompaey (1990, 1994a), Colyn *et al.* (1987), Ewer (1973), Goldman (1984, 1987), IUCN (2008), Kingdon (1997), Schreiber *et al.* (1989), Van Rompaey & Colyn (1992, In press c), Wozencraft (2005).

27. Common Cusimanse *Crossarchus obscurus*
French: Mangouste brune / **German**: Dunkelkusimanse / **Spanish**: Cusimansé del Niger
Other common names: Cusimanse, Long-nosed Cusimanse

Taxonomy. *Crossarchus obscurus* Cuvier, 1825, Sierra Leone.
Separation from *C. platycephalus* is based upon skull morphology, but with some doubts. Monotypic.

Distribution. W Africa in Guinea, Sierra Leone, Liberia, Ivory Coast, and Ghana.

Descriptive notes. Head–body 30–37 cm, tail 14·6–21 cm, hindfoot 6–7·3 cm, ear 2–2·6 cm; weight 0·45–1 kg. Similar in size to Flat-headed Cusimanse, but lacks crest of hair between the ears and neck on the midline (in Flat-headed Cusimanse), and lacks whorls of hair present on the neck of Alexander's Cusimanse. Dark shaggy brown to black fur; pale underfur. Fur on head and face is shorter and lighter. Dense under fur is lighter than the dorsal guard hairs. Dorsal guard hairs 10–15 mm at nape, gradually lengthening towards rump (30–35 mm). Long, snout-like nose ends substantially beyond lower lip. No longitudinal groove on upper lip. Short, rounded ears, capable of closing via movement of posterior ridges. Pupils are horizontally elongated. Relatively short tail and short legs. Well-developed claws on forefeet. Five digits on fore- and hindfeet. Hindfoot soles naked except last third toward heel. No obvious sexual dimorphism. There are three pairs of mammae. Cheek glands present. Skull long and narrow with elongate rostrum. Condylobasal 64·8–75 mm. Rostrum 22·2–26·7 mm. Zygomatic breadth 32·2–37·9 mm. Ectotympanic bullae inflated less than entotympanic bullae. Dental formula: I 3/3, C 1/1, P 3/3, M 2/2 = 36.

Habitat. Dense undergrowth of rainforest and riparian forest, but also in logged forest and plantations. Ranges from sea level to 1000 m (in Sierra Leone) and 1500 m in Mount Nimba (Guinea).

Food and Feeding. Feeds on invertebrates and vertebrates of the forest floor and in rotting logs. Invertebrate prey includes snails (Gastropoda), earthworms (Oligochaeta), spiders (Arachnida), crabs (Decapoda), woodlice (Isopoda), centipedes (Chilo poda), millipedes (Diplopoda), grasshoppers and crickets (Orthoptera), cockroaches (Blattaria), beetles (Coleoptera), mason wasp larvae (Eumenidae). Vertebrate prey includes frogs, snakes, lizards (including eggs), birds (including eggs and nestlings), and small mammals (up to size of Greater Cane Rat *Thryonomys swinderianus*). Fruits and berries are also consumed. Forages by scratching and rooting using claws and snout. Small mammals are killed with a bite to back of the neck. Invertebrate prey apparently shaken before consumption.

Activity patterns. Believed to be mainly diurnal, but some night activity reported. Forages in dense vegetation. May excavate own burrows. Has been observed to spend the night above-ground in trees.

Movements, Home range and Social organization. Social. Groups of up to 20 or more appear to rove, with no fixed dens, sleeping in burrows, under logs or in dense vegetation. Some climbing and shallow water foraging observed. Said to wander through their home range, rarely seen for more than a few days in the same place. Elaborate vocal repertoire; group members keep in contact with contact chirps, churrs, and twitters. Substantial difference in chemical composition between male and female anal sac secretions (female secretions contain compounds absent in male). Both sexes scent-mark using cheek and anal glands. Play behavior said to be common in captivity and wild.

Breeding. Polyestrous in captivity. Apparently induced ovulation. The male initiates copulation by first mounting the female with his forelegs forward of her pelvic region, then grasps the female at back of the neck and begins thrusting. Litter size two to four (usually four). Up to three litters per year in captivity. Mean gestation for three captive litters was 58 days. Altricial young, born with underfur, but eyes closed (head and body 9–10 mm). In captivity, eyes opened at twelve days and weaning occurred at three weeks. Young are probably sexually mature at approximately nine months. Longevity nine years in captivity. Predators likely include large carnivores and raptors (e.g. the crowned hawk eagle, *Stephanoaetus coronatus*).

Status and Conservation. Not CITES listed. Classified as Least Concern in *The IUCN Red List*. Apparently common within its range, but heavily hunted and vulnerable to hunting dogs. The Common Cusimanse is one of the least known of the social mongooses and field studies are required (current information principally based upon captive animals).

Bibliography. Coetzee (1977), Colyn & Van Rompaey (1990), Decker *et al.* (1992), Ewer (1973), Goldman (1984, 1987), Goldman & Dunham (In press), IUCN (2008), Kingdon (1997), Van Rompaey & Colyn (1992), Wozencraft (2005).

28. Flat-headed Cusimanse *Crossarchus platycephalus*

French: Mangouste à tête plate / **German:** Kamerun-Kusimanse / **Spanish:** Cusimansé de Camerún

Other common names: Cameroon Cusimanse

Taxonomy. *Crossarchus platycephalus* Goldman, 1984, Eseka, Cameroon.
Some uncertainty regarding differentiation from *C. obscurus*. Differentiation based mainly upon skull morphology (broader skull in *C. platycephalus*). Monotypic.
Distribution. Benin and Nigeria to Cameroon, Central African Republic, Equatorial Guinea, PR Congo, and probably Gabon.

Descriptive notes. Head-body estimated 30–36 cm, tail 15·6–21 cm, hindfoot 6·1–7·6 cm, ear 2–2·6 cm; weight 0·5–1·5 kg. Dark shaggy brown to black fur. Dorsal guard hairs 10–15 mm at nape, gradually elongating towards rump (30–35 mm). Long, snout-like nose. Short, rounded ears. Well-developed claws on forefeet. Short legs and relatively short tail. Flatter (broader) skull than the Common Cusimanse and nuchal hair crest on midline between ears and neck (30–40 mm long hair). No obvious sexual dimorphism. Condylobasal 65·2–75·6 mm. Rostrum 22·8–26·8 mm. Zygomatic breadth 34·8–41·7 mm. Dental formula: I 3/3, C 1/1, P 3/3, M 2/2 = 36.
Habitat. Tropical rainforest and associated riparian forest.
Food and Feeding. Feeds on invertebrates and vertebrates of the forest floor and in rotting logs.
Activity patterns. Believed to be diurnal.
Movements, Home range and Social organization. Social. Groups appear to rove with no fixed dens.
Breeding. Two females collected in Cameroon had three and five embryos.
Status and Conservation. Not CITES listed. Classified as Least Concern in *The IUCN Red List*. Apparently widespread, but patchily distributed. Hunted as bushmeat. Almost nothing is known of its ecology and field studies are needed.
Bibliography. Colyn & Van Rompaey (1990, 1994a), Ewer (1973), Goldman (1984, 1987, In press), Kingdon (1997), Van Rompaey & Colyn (1992), Wozencraft (2005).

Genus *HELOGALE*
Gray, 1862

29. Ethiopian Dwarf Mongoose *Helogale hirtula*

French: Mangouste d'Éthiopie / **German:** Somalia-Zwergmanguste / **Spanish:** Mangosta etíope

Other common names: Somali Dwarf Mongoose, Desert Dwarf Mongoose

Taxonomy. *Helogale hirtula* Thomas, 1904, Gabredarre, Kebridar, Ethiopia.
Previously considered by some authors to comprise two subspecies, *hirtula* (Somalia, Ethiopia, N. Kenya) and *percivalli* (C & W Kenya). However, a lack of specimens to support subspecific designations makes these doubtful and this species is considered monotypic here.
Distribution. Djibouty, S Ethiopia, S & C Somalia, N & C Kenya, and NE Tanzania.

Descriptive notes. Head-body 20–27 cm, tail 15–18 cm; weight 220–354 g. Overall grizzled gray color with yellowish face and underparts. Compared to Common Dwarf Mongoose, the color is less red, and Ethiopian Dwarf Mongoose has brown-black digits and its coat is longer and shaggier. The head is short but pointed, with small, rounded ears. Elongated, low body on short legs. Long claws on forefeet. No obvious sexual dimorphism. Dental formula: I 3/3 C 1/1 P 3/3 M 2/2 = 36. Cheek teeth relatively heavy compared to those of Common Dwarf Mongoose.
Habitat. Principally arid, semi-desert grassland, scrub, bush, and dry open woodland, but not closed forest. Occurs at elevations up to 600 m in Ethiopia. Not water-dependent. Uses termitaria and rocky outcrops for dens.
Food and Feeding. Nothing known.
Activity patterns. Diurnal.
Movements, Home range and Social organization. Said to be social.
Breeding. Nothing known.
Status and Conservation. Not CITES listed. Classified as Least Concern in *The IUCN Red List*. Distribution believed to be patchy and densities are unknown. Due to its small body size, open habitat, and diurnal lifestyle it is likely vulnerable to a wide array of predators. There is no quantitative data on its behavior or ecology and field studies are needed. Sympatric with Common Dwarf Mongoose throughout its range.
Bibliography. Caro & Stoner (2003), Kingdon (1997), Kingdon & Van Rompaey (In press), Wozencraft (2005), Yalden *et al.* (1996).

30. Common Dwarf Mongoose *Helogale parvula*

French: Mangouste naine / **German:** Zwergmanguste / **Spanish:** Mangosta enana

Other common names: Dwarf Mongoose.

Taxonomy. *Herpestes parvulus* Sundevall, 1847, Transvaal, South Africa.
Seven subspecies are recognized, but a revision is needed.
Subspecies and Distribution.
H. p. parvula Sundevall, 1847 – NE South Africa, Mozambique, and Zimbabwe.
H. p. ivori Thomas, 1919 – NE Mozambique and Tanzania.
H. p. mimetra Thomas, 1926 – NW Botswana and N Namibia.
H. p. nero Thomas, 1928 – C Namibia.
H. p. ruficeps Kershaw, 1922 – Zambia (Southern Province & Kafue area).
H. p. undulata Peters, 1852 – N & E Africa from Ethiopia and Sudan to Malawi.
H. p. varia Thomas, 1902 – C Africa from Angola to Uganda.
Descriptive notes. Head–body 16–22·7 cm (males), 18·5–23 cm (females), tail 15·2–18·3 cm (males), 14·2–18·8 cm (females), hindfoot 4·1–5·1 cm (males), 4·1–4·9 cm (females), ear 1·5–2·1 cm (males), 1·4–2·1 cm (females). Weight 223–341 g (males), 213–341 g (females) for Botswana population; Serengeti (Tanzania) population heavier: weight 265–415 g (males), 221–395 g (females). No obvious sexual dimorphism. Smallest of the mongooses. Body covered with smooth hair. Uniform coat color varies geographically from yellow to dark brown. Hair on head is short (2–3 mm), gradually increasing towards tail, reaching 15 mm on rump, 18 mm on tail. Individual guard hairs are dark with whitish annulations, one near the tip, and the other closer to the body. Dense underfur; dark at base, lighter near tip (in lighter morphs). Hair on underparts is sparser than on upper body, but similar in color. Domed head with pointed muzzle. Ears small and rounded. Rhinarium tiny with shallow depression between nostrils. Tail approximately half overall length. Five digits. Foreclaws elongated (up to 10 mm) and strong for digging, hindclaws shorter (up to 8 mm). There are three pairs of abdominal mammae. Anus and anal gland openings enclosed in anal subcircular pouch. Pear-shaped brain case. Postorbital bars incomplete. Supraorbital crest well-developed. Low, ridged sagittal crest. Relatively heavy zygomatic arches. Front chambers of ear bullae slightly larger than hind. Short rostrum (1/4 total skull length). Eye sockets relatively small in diameter (one fifth of total skull length). Dental formula: I 3/3, C 1/1, P 3/3, M 2/2 = 36. Sharp, strong teeth, especially canines. Carnassials not adapted for slicing. Relatively large upper canines reaching below base of lower canines. Molars have high cusps, an adaptation to insectivory. Outer upper incisors larger than inner.
Habitat. Found in a wide range of habitats, principally in savannah, tree savannah, woodland, and dry bush. Also occurs in forests. Associated with termitaria, which are used as dens. In Zimbabwe, not found above 1100 m.
Food and Feeding. Predominantly insectivorous diet, especially Coleoptera (beetles) and termites, but also Myriapoda (centipedes), larvae, and occasional small vertebrates (including small mammals, geckos, snakes, and birds). Common Dwarf

Mongooses move as a group, but individuals spread out to forage while the group is moving. Examination of 160 scats from Natal (South Africa), found the following frequency of occurrence of food types: Coleoptera (79%), Orthoptera (64%), Myriapoda (34%), Arachnida (21%), Seeds (12%), Isoptera (8%), Hemiptera (8%), Lepidoptera (4%), and Mammalia (1%). Frequency of occurrence of food types in 27 stomachs collected from the northern area of southern Africa: Insecta (undetermined) (44%), Coleoptera adults (37%) and grubs (33%), Orthoptera (33%), Isoptera (33%), Araneae (11%), Muridae (4%), Myriapoda (4%), Reptilia (4%), Scorpiones (4%), and Solifugae (4%). Observed to crack crested francolin (*Francolinus sephaena*) eggs by grasping the eggs in their forelimbs and throwing them backwards through the hindlimbs onto a rock or other hard surface. Small vertebrates (e.g. mice or snakes) are killed with a bite through the back of the head. Large insects are generally eaten starting with the head.

Activity patterns. Diurnal. Groups sleep together overnight in subterranean dens (usually termite mounds), emerging in the early morning and returning to the den before sunset. During the day, the group forages together, often resting around midday. Their repertoire of behaviors includes foraging, resting, vigilance (including standing upright), self and allogrooming, social play, scent marking, and vocalization.

Movements, Home range and Social organization. Lives in cohesive groups. Group size averages 8·9 (range = 2–21) in the Serengeti (Tanzania), and 12·3 (range = 2–32) in the Taru Desert (Kenya). Group members forage and sleep together, and share a home range. Termite mounds (*Macrotermes* and *Odontotermes* species) and rock crevices are commonly used as subterranean dens for sleeping at night and for shade and protection during the day. Up to 200 termitaria are available within a territory, and groups favor areas with high termitaria density. Groups generally occupy a different den every night, but use a den for longer periods when babysitting pups. Mean home range size varies from 0·27 to 0·96 km², and mean population density ranges from 3·9 to 30·9 individuals/km². Daily foraging distances of up to 1 km have been recorded. Larger groups travel farther than smaller groups, but reduce foraging distance when travelling with small pups. Home ranges are defended. When two groups meet, the smaller group will generally retreat, without any physical aggression, but skirmishes can occur. Groups are highly social, with heterosexual mutual grooming common. Groups contain adult males and females and young of the dominant breeding pair. There is no consistent sex ratio bias amongst adults or pups. Intragroup aggression is rare, but there is an age-related dominance hierarchy in males and females. The dominant female dominates all other group members in access to food and frequency of anal marking, and can displace others from a foraging site. The male dominance hierarchy becomes obvious during estrus, when males compete for access to females. Subordinates exhibit a submissive crouching stance on approach of a dominant. Group members cooperate in rearing young, repelling predators, and rescuing group members from predators. They communicate vocally. Short nasal "peeps", emitted every few seconds, serve to maintain group cohesion while foraging. Lead or "moving out" calls, given by the dominant female, elicit the group to follow. Shrill "tsiii" war cries are used to alert group members to a rival group and makes the group bunch and charge; a standard deployment has the dominant male leading and the dominant female at the rear. Alarm calls convey information on predator type and urgency. Repeated "tchee" alarm calls warn the group of a predator, and a close approach of a predator is signalled with an alarm "chitter", as they run to cover. Alarm calls are shorter and higher in pitch, the more immediate the danger. Group members, principally subordinate males, take turns standing guard, and give a "watchman's song" to inform the group that they are on duty. Guards use posts (elevated objects). Group members follow a predictable rota of guard duty. Common Dwarf Mongooses are known to form mutualistic associations with hornbills (*Tockus flavirostris* and *T. erythrorhynchus*), which prey upon disturbed invertebrates. The mongooses benefit from the hornbills' alarm calls for raptors. Interestingly, the hornbills give alarm calls to raptor species that prey on mongooses, but not hornbills. Olfactory communication is also used in intra- and inter-group communication. Group members scent-mark each other and the den site with their anal or cheek glands. This marking is often done communally, particularly after intergroup encounters. Male anal gland secretions contain vitamin E (absent in female secretions), suggesting they play a sex-specific role.

Breeding. In seasonal climates, births are restricted to the wetter months, which is likely to be correlated with invertebrate prey availability. Dominant females can produce up to four litters per year. The age of first conception for females is rarely under two years. Estrus in a group is synchronized and occurs for one to seven days. Estrus can occur within two to four weeks of parturition, enabling females to conceive and gestate while suckling the current litter of pups. During estrus, males compete for access to females and females solicit copulation from males. Early in the dominant female's estrous cycle, the dominant male guards her, maintaining exclusive proximity and copulation access and aggressively repelling subordinate males, who attempt to sneak copulations. Later in estrus, the dominant male will mate with subordinate females. The dominant female then mates other males. Almost all individuals mate, virtually everyday during estrus. However, in spite of the fact that all group members copulate, the Common Dwarf Mongoose is a classic example of a species exhibiting a despotic social system of high reproductive skew: dominant females produce 73% of all litters, despite being outnumbered by subordinates 1:2. Subordinate reproduction is suppressed both behaviorally and hormonally. There is no evidence of inbreeding avoidance; individuals mate randomly without regard to relatedness, even though most males and females within groups are usually closely related. The gestation period is approximately seven weeks. Litter size varies from two to six, with two to three being the most common. When subordinate females do breed, they are usually synchronized with the dominant female, giving birth on the same day. Most offspring born to sub-

ordinate females fail to survive, probably due to infanticide by the dominant female. Following birth of the communal litter, pups are kept in the subterranean den until they are approximately three to four weeks old. During this period, one or more individuals (usually subordinate females) will remain at the den to "babysit" the pups while the group forages (the babysitter changes daily). These babysitters guard the communal litter from predators and groom and warm the pups. Some subordinate females nurse the dominant female's pups without giving birth themselves, lactating due to a physiological pseudopregnancy. Weaning occurs around 40–45 days. When the pups emerge from the den and begin accompanying the foraging group, adults provide care by carrying, grooming, guarding, and provisioning pups. Subordinates (mainly females) usually provide more care than the parents. Pups beg for food from adults. Provisioning involves carrying food to young and dropping or leaving whole or partial prey items. There appears to be an escort system, where each pup forms a one-to-one association with an adult (its escort) that it closely follows and who feeds it, similar to the system seen in the Banded Mongoose. Pup survival is higher in groups with more helpers, principally because efficient vigilance reduces predation (of both adults and pups). With its small body size, open habitat, and diurnal lifestyle the Common Dwarf Mongoose is vulnerable to a variety of predators. Annual survival rate of emergent pups is 0·41 and adult annual survival rate is between 0·68 and 0·74. Pup predation is likely driven by snakes (e.g. cobra), monitor lizards, larger mongoose species (Banded Mongoose and Egyptian Mongoose), and raptors, in particular the eastern chanting goshawk (*Melierax poliopterus*) and brown snake eagle (*Circaetus cinerus*). Predation is 260% higher in smaller groups, with guards suffering the highest predation rate. In the wild, males can live up to ten years and females 14 years. In captivity, an individual is recorded to have lived for over twelve years. Invalid care has been recorded, where the group remains in proximity to and provisions a sick or injured adult. Males and females commonly transfer between groups voluntarily or via takeovers. Females are more likely to remain in their natal group than males. Voluntary dispersers are usually young adults, who increase their probability of attaining a dominant breeding position via emigration. Single-sex and mixed-sex transient groups also occur. In contrast to the Banded Mongoose and Meerkat, emigration from groups does not appear to involve intra-group aggression (excluding takeovers).

Status and Conservation. Not CITES listed. Classified as Least Concern in *The IUCN Red List*. A widely distributed species that can occur at high densities. Unlikely to become threatened in the foreseeable future.

Bibliography. Beynon & Rasa (1989), Caro & Stoner (2003), Creel (1996, 2001, In press), Creel & Waser (1991, 1994, 1997), Creel, Creel *et al.* (1992), Creel, Monfort, Creel *et al.* (1995), Creel, Monfort, Wildt & Waser (1991), Creel, Wildt & Monfort (1993), Decker *et al.* (1992), Estes (1991), Hiscocks & Perrin (1991a, 1991b), Keane, Creel & Waser (1996), Keane, Waser *et al.* (1994), Kingdon (1971-1982, 1997), Messeri (1983), Pilsworth (1977), Rasa (1973a, 1973b, 1976, 1977a, 1977b, 1979, 1983a, 1983b, 1984, 1985, 1986a, 1986b, 1987a, 1987b, 1989a, 1989b, 1994), Rood (1978, 1980, 1983a, 1986, 1987, 1990), Skinner & Chimimba (2005), Waser *et al.* (1995), Wozencraft (2005).

Genus *DOLOGALE*
Thomas, 1926

31. Pousargues's Mongoose *Dologale dybowskii*

French: Mangouste de Dybowski / **German**: Listige Manguste / **Spanish**: Mangosta centroafricana
Other common names: Savannah Mongoose

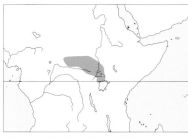

Taxonomy. *Crossarchus dybowskii* Pousargues, 1893, "Ubangi, Congo Belge", Central African Republic.
Monotypic.

Distribution. Central African Republic, NE DR Congo, S Sudan, and W Uganda. Possibly also occurs in the PR Congo.

Descriptive notes. Head-body 25–33 cm, tail 16–23 cm; weight 300–400 g. A very small grizzled mongoose, with short, fine fur. The head and neck are black, grizzled with grayish-white; the back, legs, and tail are paler, being more brownish. The underparts are reddish or pale gray. The muzzle is not elongated and does not have a groove on the upper lip. The throat displays a prominent reverse "cow-lick" of fur. The claws are robust. Dental formula: I 3/3, C 1/1, P 3/3, M 2/2 = 36. The teeth are weak.

Habitat. Savannah-forest mosaic, montane forest grasslands, and the thicketed shores of Lake Albert. Said to rest in holes in trees and termite mounds.

Food and Feeding. The digging claws and unspecialized teeth suggest that the diet may include fossorial invertebrates and small burrowing vertebrates.

Activity patterns. Said to be at least partly diurnal.

Movements, Home range and Social organization. The few records are of single individuals.

Breeding. A litter of four was reported from the DR Congo.

Status and Conservation. Classified as Data Deficient in *The IUCN Red List*. Listed as Threatened in the IUCN Action Plan for the Conservation of Mustelids and Viverrids (1989). This species is known from just 31 museum specimens and a handful of possible sightings; there have been no positive records for more than two decades. Field surveys, ecological studies, and assessments of any threats are urgently needed.

Bibliography. Cardillo *et al.* (2004), Kingdon (1971-1982, 1997), Nowak (1999), Schreiber *et al.* (1989), Stuart & Stuart (In press a), Wozencraft (2005).

Genus *LIBERIICTIS*
Hayman, 1958

32. Liberian Mongoose *Liberiictis kuhni*
French: Mangouste du Libéria / **German**: Liberia-Kusimanse / **Spanish**: Mangosta de Liberia

Taxonomy. *Liberiictis kuhni* Hayman, 1958, Kpeaplay, NE Liberia.
Monotypic.
Distribution. Ivory Coast and Liberia.
Descriptive notes. Head-body 43·2–46·8 cm, tail 19·7–20·5 cm; weight 2·3 kg. No sexual dimorphism has been reported. A medium-sized mongoose, with a dark brown pelage, a pale throat, and two dark stripes on the sides of the neck (bordered by faint white ones). Head elongated, with a long snout; ears small and round. The tail is bushy, gradually tapering towards the tip. Legs are gradually darker toward the extremities. Dental formula I 3/3 C 1/1 P 4/4 M 2/2 = 40. Teeth are relatively small and mandibles weak.
Habitat. Primary and secondary evergreen forest, and swamp forest; found near streambeds with deep sandy soils.
Food and Feeding. Field observations and scat analyses suggest that the Liberian Mongoose is an earthworm specialist, primarily eating large species of the family Megascolecidae. In the Ivory Coast (Tai National Park), 32 scats all contained earthworms. However, remains of caecilians (subterranean amphibians) were found in four scats, suggesting that small vertebrates may also be taken if encountered while digging for worms. Insect larvae and fruits were also consumed. Foraging is restricted to riverine wetland areas and swamp forest. Individuals dig for earthworms and other soil invertebrates by alternately using the front feet to excavate the earth, and then sticking the muzzle into the soil. Sand is often ingested with food items. Foraging activities in a streambed or swamp forest may result in considerable disturbance of the soil. Groups return to the same area to forage approximately once every three to four weeks. Has been reported to climb palm trees to forage for beetle larvae.
Activity patterns. Appears to be diurnal. Group members sleep together at night in hollow logs, under fallen trees, or occasionally in termite mounds; den sites are rarely used on consecutive nights.
Movements, Home range, and Social organization. Terrestrial and social. Individuals travel and forage alone or in groups of four to six animals, though larger groups have been observed. Adult males are often observed alone; a radio-collared male frequently travelled between three stable groups, joining them for one to three days at a time. Groups are very quiet, communicating with soft grunting sounds. They are often found in association with Sooty Mangabeys (*Cercocebus atys*) and respond to the monkeys' anti-predator warning calls by quickly dispersing and running into thick vegetation or under fallen trees. In the Ivory Coast, an aggressive encounter was observed with a group of Common Cusimanse; four Liberian Mongooses initiated the encounter and displaced the larger group of ten Common Cusimanses by advancing and giving threatening growls.
Breeding. Limited observations suggest that births coincide with the middle of the rainy season (May to September), when invertebrates are probably most available.
Status and Conservation. Classified as Vulnerable in *The IUCN Red List*. Listed as Threatened in the 1989 IUCN Action Plan for the Conservation of Mustelids and Viverrids. This species was unknown until recently; it was first described in 1958 from eight skulls and the first live animal was caught in 1989. Possible threats include deforestation from agriculture, logging, and mining. It is heavily hunted for food throughout its range with dogs, shotguns, and snares, and may also be vulnerable to the heavy use of pesticides in forest plantations, as worms are known to accumulate toxins at levels dangerous to mammalian predators. Although it is found in secondary forests, it is thought that the lack of suitable den sites may restrict its distribution. Field research is urgently required to determine its distribution and to understand the threats facing this species.
Bibliography. Schlitter (1974), Schreiber *et al.* (1989), Taylor & Dunham (In press).

Genus *MUNGOS*
Geoffroy Saint-Hilaire & Cuvier, 1795

33. Gambian Mongoose *Mungos gambianus*
French: Mangouste de Gambie / **German**: Gambia-Manguste / **Spanish**: Mangosta de Gambia

Taxonomy. *Herpestes gambianus* Ogilby, 1835, Cape St. Mary, Gambia.
Monotypic.
Distribution. W Africa from Senegal and Gambia to Nigeria.

Descriptive notes. Head-body 30–45 cm, tail 23–29 cm; weight 1–2·2 kg. No obvious sexual dimorphism. Short face. Brownish-gray fur with a distinctive black streak at the sides of the white neck from ear to foreleg. Fur coarse. Bushy tail that tapers at the black tip. Five digits on feet, with strong claws on the forefeet. Three pairs of mammae. Dental formula: I 3/3, C 1/1, P 3/3, M 2/2 = 36.
Habitat. Semi-moist savannah and grassland, semi-desert, and woodland.
Food and Feeding. Mainly invertebrates (with some vertebrates).
Activity patterns. Diurnal.
Movements, Home range and Social organization. In Senegal, mixed-sex groups average 6·7 individuals (range = 1–40). Twitters continuously while foraging.
Breeding. Nothing known.
Status and Conservation. Not CITES listed. Classified as Least Concern in *The IUCN Red List*. Apparently widespread and common, but almost nothing known of its ecology and field research is needed. Sometimes considered a pest to farmers and is sold as bushmeat.
Bibliography. Colyn *et al.* (2000), Ewer (1973), Kingdon (1997), Sillero-Zubiri & Bassignani (2001), Van Rompaey (1991), Van Rompaey & Sillero-Zubiri (In press), Wozencraft (2005).

34. Banded Mongoose *Mungos mungo*
French: Mangouste rayée / **German**: Zebramanguste / **Spanish**: Mangosta rayada

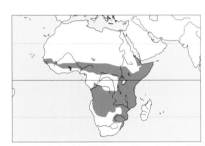

Taxonomy. *Viverra mungo* Gmelin, 1788, origin uncertain (later attributed to Gambia, but subsequently suggested to be Cape Province, South Africa).
Up to fifteen subspecies have been named, but a revision is needed.
Distribution. Senegal and Gambia E to Eritrea and Somalia and then SW to PR Congo, Angola, and NE Namibia, and S to E South Africa.
Descriptive notes. Head-body 30–40 cm (males), 33–38·5 cm (females), tail 17·8–31 cm (males), 19–24·5 cm (females), hindfoot 5·3–9 cm (males), 5·3–8·4 cm (females), ear 2·1–3·6 cm (males), 2–2·7 cm (females); weight 0·89–1·88 kg (males), 0·99–1·74 kg (females). No obvious sexual dimorphism. Medium-sized; body covered with coarse hair. Coat color varies geographically from whitish-gray to dark brown, with 10–15 dark bands across the back from the shoulders to the base of the tail. The guard hairs are short on the head (6 mm), lengthen toward the rump (45 mm in eastern specimens, 35 mm in western specimens), and are shorter on the tail. The individual guard coat hairs are light-colored at the base, with two broad black bands interspersed with light bands and a narrow dark tip. In reddish-brown mongooses, the lighter-colored bands are red-brown. The underfur is fine and short, with a dark base and light tip; there is apparently no undercoat on the rear. Long head with a pointed muzzle. Rhinarium short and lacks split. Ears small and rounded. Five digits on fore- and hindfeet; hallux and pollex reduced. Front claws are elongated (20 mm—except first digit, which is 8 mm) and strong for digging. Hindclaws shorter (14 mm) and less curved than front claws. Three pairs of mammae. Pear-shaped braincase. Postorbital bars incomplete. Zygomatic arches thin. Short, broad rostrum. Supraoccipital crest not well-developed (less than 1·5 mm high). No sagittal crest. Dental formula: I 3/3, C 1/1, P 3/3, M 2/2 = 36. Sharp strong teeth, especially canines. Outer incisors larger than inner. Upper canines slightly recurved. Lower canines distinctly recurved. Cheek teeth possess low, rounded cusps. Carnassials adapted to crushing, not slicing.
Habitat. Found in a wide range of habitats, principally in savannah and woodland. Also seen in towns and villages. Absent from desert, semi-desert, and montane regions. Preferentially use termitaria as dens; otherwise dens are sited in gulleys or thickets. Dens have multiple entrances and chambers.
Food and Feeding. Insectivorous diet, especially Coleoptera (beetles) and Myriapoda (centipedes) larvae. Occasionally vertebrates (including eggs, mice, rats, frogs, lizards, and small snakes) are consumed. Frequency of occurrence of food types in 120 scats from Uganda: Diplopoda (96%), Coleoptera (88%), Formicidae adults (69%) and pupae (23%), Gryllidae (44%), Isoptera (33%), Dermaptera (23%), larvae (unidentified) (20%), Blattidae (13%), Acrididae (10%), Acarina (8%), pupae (unidentified) (7%), Hemiptera (6%), Tettigoniidae (5%), Lepidoptera (2%), Araneae (3%), and Gastropoda (2%). Frequency of occurrence of food types in 113 scats from Natal (South Africa): Myriapoda (70%), Coleoptera (92%), Orthoptera (57%), Isoptera (33%), Hemiptera (29%), Arachnida (21%), Seeds (20%), Mammalia (7%), Lepidoptera (7%), and Blattodea (5%). Frequency of occurrence of food types in 14 stomachs from Zimbabwe and Botswana: Insecta (71%), Reptilia (43%), fruits (36%), Amphibia (7%), Araneae (7%), Myriapoda (7%), Scorpiones (7%), and Solifugae (7%). Human garbage dumps also utilized. Banded Mongooses move as a group, but individuals forage independently within the moving group. Individuals generally walk, sniffing and scraping at the ground, and often stop and dig intensively for prey. Dung of large herbivores (especially African Elephant, *Loxodonta africana*) is popular for foraging,

due to the relatively high density of beetles. Individuals often crack hard-shelled prey (e.g. dung beetle, pill millipede, or egg) by holding it in their front paws, whilst balancing on their hindlimbs, and throwing it between the hindlegs onto a rock or other hard surface. Prey and foraging sites such as holes, scrapes, and dung are generally defended from conspecifics, except for adults provisioning or sharing food with young pups. There is a report of a group stealing food regurgitated by a pair of Black-backed Jackal for their pups.

Activity patterns. Diurnal. Groups sleep together in subterranean dens, emerging in early morning and returning before sunset. During the day the group forages together, usually resting in a shady area around midday. The behavioral repertoire includes foraging, resting, vigilance (including standing on the hindlegs), self and allogrooming, social play, scent marking, and vocalizing.

Movements, Home range and Social organization. Banded Mongooses live in cohesive groups, which share a home range. In Uganda (Queen Elizabeth National Park), mean group size is 15 individuals (range = 9–28), mean home range size is 0·9 km² (range = 0·6–2), mean population density is 18 individuals/km² (range = 7–36), and daily foraging distances are 2–3 km. In Tanzania (Serengeti), mean group size is 15 (range = 4–29), mean population density is two individuals/km², and daily foraging distances are up to 10 km. A group size of 41 was recorded in Somalia, and 75 from South Africa (Kruger National Park). Group size, home range size, population density, and daily foraging distances depend upon habitat type and food density, and therefore vary geographically. Groups have up to 40 dens within their home range. They generally occupy a different den every few days, but use a den for longer periods when babysitting pups. Concentrated food sources (e.g. garbage dumps) can support larger groups and smaller core areas within the home range. Home ranges are defended. A smaller group will generally retreat, without physical aggression, but skirmishes can occur and individuals have been killed during such encounters. Groups respond more intensely to scats of neighboring groups than to scats from more distant groups, suggesting that neighbors pose a greater threat. Groups are highly social. Grooming and marking maintain group bonds. Groups contain adult males and females and their young. The adult sex ratio is male-biased. Within a group, males are closely related and females are closely related, but the breeding adults are not related to each other. There is generally little evidence of a dominance hierarchy. However, a male dominance hierarchy becomes obvious during estrus, when males compete for access to females. Aggression over food items is usually settled in favor of the owner. Group members cooperate in rearing young and repelling predators; one group was seen rescuing a member from the talons of a martial eagle. One case of invalid care has been reported. Group members communicate vocally. Contact calls, emitted every few seconds, serve to maintain group cohesion while foraging. "Lead" calls are used by individuals to elicit the group to follow them; "pup-follow" calls encourage pups to follow the adults. Shrill chirruping "war" cries alert group members to a rival group and encourage them to charge at the invaders. Growls and spits are used to defend resources if another group member approaches. Short, sharp alarm calls elicit rapid evasive behavior; "worry" calls warn group members of lower-intensity danger. A "lost" call indicates distress when an individual is separated from the group. Individuals also respond to the alarm calls of other species, in particular plover (*Vanellus* spp.). Olfactory communication is also used in intra- and inter-group communication. Group members scent-mark each other and objects (e.g. rocks), by wiping them with the anal gland. This marking is often done communally, with all group members involved in an orgy of scent marking. Urine and feces are also apparently used in communication, with individuals overmarking excretion sites. An olfactory "signal" from another group often elicits an excited and aggressive response. In addition to allogrooming, Banded Mongooses in Uganda and Masai Mara, Kenya, have been seen grooming Common Warthogs (*Phacochoerus africanus*); they are probably removing ectoparasites, which they eat.

Breeding. In seasonal climates, births are restricted to the wetter months (presumably correlated with invertebrate prey availability). Females in dry regions have one or two litters a year; females in wetter equatorial regions can have up to five. The age at which females first reproduce is also geographically variable, recorded at two years in the Serengeti and under one year in Uganda (the earliest record being just over eight

months). Estrus can occur within six days of parturition, enabling females to conceive and gestate while suckling the current litter of pups. This minimizes the interbirth interval, so females can produce four or even five litters per year. During estrus, males compete for access to females. Dominant males guard females and aggressively repel subordinate males who attempt to sneak copulations. There is no sign of female competition for access to males. However, there is a hierarchy in mate-guarding, with older females mate-guarded first, and younger females mate-guarded later. Each female is guarded for two to three days. Females may escape their mate-guard and mate with other males within and outside their group. The overall result is that most males and females copulate with numerous partners. About 75% of the females in a group give birth. Gestation lasts approximately nine weeks. Mean litter size is 3·2 (range = 1–6). Litter size and fetus size are smaller in younger, smaller females. Abortion and miscarriage are rare. Banded Mongooses are truly communal breeders, with up to ten females in a group giving birth, often on the same day, in the same den (there is rarely more than a few days between births). Such birth synchrony may reduce infanticide by reducing the ability of males and females to discriminate between offspring. Although infanticide occurs, it appears to be a rare event. Alternatively, synchronous parturition may be a strategy to economize pup care, by enabling communal care of the young for a minimal period. A female may either abort her litter or give birth to it over different days—an extremely unusual behavior for a mammal. Birth weight of pups is 20–50 g. Pups are born blind and with short fur. Their eyes open at around ten days. The sex ratio of pups at emergence from the den is male-biased. Pups stay in the subterranean den until they are weaned, at around three to four weeks of age. During this period, one or more individuals will remain at the den to "babysit" the pups while the group forages. The babysitter usually changes every day. These babysitters guard the communal litter against predators. On the rare occasions when pups are observed out of the den during this period, pups suckle from numerous females. When the pups emerge from the den and begin accompanying the foraging group, adults provide care by carrying, grooming, playing with, and provisioning pups. Provisioning involves dropping or leaving whole or partial prey items. Adults also provide protection: pups shelter under the belly of the nearest adult when frightened. Most pups have an adult escort, who cares for it for four to eight weeks; this escort is unlikely to be the pup's parent. The pup closely follows its escort, fending off other pups, and begging for the food items the escort provides. Pups that associate most often with an escort are more likely to survive. Males generally do more babysitting and escorting than females. Due to their relatively small body size, open habitat, and diurnal lifestyle, pups and adults are vulnerable to a wide array of predators. In Uganda, pup mortality is high, with 20% of litters failing completely within the first month. Only 18% of pups are estimated to survive from birth to independence. Adult survival is substantially higher (annual survival rate 0·86). Comparable annual survival rates from Serengeti are 0·46 for pups and between 0·65 and 0·69 for adults. Pups are heavily preyed upon by marabous (*Leptoptilus crumeniferus*) and Nile monitors (*Varanus niloticus*); predators on adults include snakes (especially the rock python *Python sebae*), mammalian carnivores (e.g. Leopards) and raptors (e.g. martial eagle). Dispersal can occur via forced eviction of single-sex sub-groups by group members or via voluntary emigration (also of single-sex sub-groups). Dispersers are usually young adults. There is no clear sex bias to dispersal, although females appear to be evicted and males appear to voluntarily emigrate more often. Banded Mongooses can live to over ten years in the wild, and twelve years in captivity.

Status and Conservation. Not CITES listed. Classified as Least Concern in *The IUCN Red List*. As a species with wide habitat tolerance and distribution, and one that adapts well to human habitation, it is unlikely to become threatened in the foreseeable future.

Bibliography. Bell (2007), Cant (1998, 2000, 2003), Cant & Gilchrist (In press), Cant *et al.* (2001, 2002), Caro & Stoner (2003), De Luca & Ginsberg (2001), Eisner (1968), Eisner & Davis (1967), Estes (1991), Gilchrist (2001, 2004, 2006a, 2006b, 2008), Gilchrist & Otali (2002), Gilchrist & Russell (2007), Gilchrist *et al.* (2004, 2008), Hiscocks & Perrin (1991a, 1991b), Hodge (2003, 2005), Kingdon (1971-1982, 1997), Masi *et al.* (1987), Messeri (1983), Muller (2007), Muller & Manser (2007), Neal (1970a, 1970b, 1971), Otali & Gilchrist (2004), Rood (1974, 1975, 1983b, 1986), Simpson (1964, 1966), Skinner & Chimimba (2005), Smits van Oyen (1998), Van Rompaey (1978), Viljoen (1980), Waser *et al.* (1995), Wozencraft (2005).

CLASS MAMMALIA
ORDER CARNIVORA
SUBORDER FELIFORMIA

Family EUPLERIDAE (MADAGASCAR CARNIVORES)

- Small to medium mammals with elongated bodies; external features vary, heads range from elongated and angular to flat and rounded, legs from short to long.
- 51–150 cm.

- Madagascar.
- Forested habitats (dry deciduous, rainforest, and montane); also sub-desert and above forest line.
- 7 genera, 8 species, 13 taxa.
- 1 species Endangered, 3 species Vulnerable; none Extinct since 1600.

Systematics

This family of eight living and at least one more still undescribed species is restricted to Madagascar, and all the native carnivores on Madagascar are in the family Eupleridae. The family has a complicated taxonomic history. Recent molecular research has brought considerable insight into the origin and evolutionary history of these animals. They represent a monophyletic lineage endemic to the island. Patterns of geographic variation in certain species still need to be worked out. Over the course of the taxonomic history of the endemic Madagascar Carnivores, these mammals have been placed in a number of families, at least in part associated with morphological resemblances to other, extralimital members of the order. These similarities, which we now understand to be cases of convergence, include euplerids that are cat-like and were considered to be Felidae (*Cryptoprocta*), civet-like species that were classified as Viverridae (*Fossa* and *Eupleres*), and mongoose-like mammals included in the Herpestidae (*Galidia, Galidictis, Salanoia*, and *Mungotictis*). However, the earliest fossils assignable to the order Carnivora are Paleocene, and are about 63 million years old. Madagascar separated from the African mainland 170–155 million years ago, which would indicate that carnivorans were not present on the island when the landmasses split. Given the time sequence, felids, vivverids, and herpestids would have had to colonize Madagascar, crossing water to do so, on at least three separate occasions. While this is theoretically possible, it is difficult to imagine that carnivorans dispersed to Madagascar from Africa across the 400 km Mozambique Channel by swimming or floating on rafts in three separate dispersal events. Recently, an Antarctic–African corridor was proposed, but the close land connections associated with this hypothesis would have been severed before the inferred period of carnivoran evolution. If carnivorans began evolving 63 million years ago, as the fossil record indicates, and Madagascar was already an island in its current position, over-water dispersal is the only explanation for the presence of Carnivora on Madagascar.

The recent placement of the native Madagascar Carnivores into the family Eupleridae, based on molecular phylogenetic research, helps to resolve, in part, enigmas in dispersal history. Given the monophyly of this group, it would mean that on only one occasion the ancestor of the modern euplerids crossed the Mozambique Channel, either by swimming or rafting. This ancestral mammal successfully colonized the island and then underwent an adaptive radiation nearly unparalleled amongst living carnivorans. This evolutionary trajectory resulted in animals that mirror the body forms of Carnivora found elsewhere in the world. The former classification, which placed the species we now recognize as the Eupleridae in three different families of Carnivora, is best explained by character convergence in their differentiation on Madagascar. Grouping all Madagascar Carnivores in a single family has considerable support on molecular phylogenetic grounds, but no anatomical characters unite the euplerids. For the most part, the natural history, distribution, and conservation status of members of this family are still poorly known.

```
                          EUPLERIDAE
              ┌──────────────┴──────────────┐
          EUPLERINAE                    GALIDIINAE
```

Subdivision of the Eupleridae

Figure: Toni Llobet

Civet-like Madagascar Carnivores
3 species
(*Cryptoprocta, Eupleres, Fossa*)

Mongoose-like Madagascar Carnivores
5 species
(*Galidia, Galidictis, Mungotictis, Salanoia*)

FAMILY
SUBFAMILY

Falanoucs have relatively massive bodies, large feet, and long, thin claws that touch the ground when they walk. Their claws are better suited for scratching than for serious digging, and are not adapted for climbing, but can be used to lash at predators. When searching for worms, slugs, and other invertebrates, Falanoucs hunter slowly and quietly through the forest and nearby marsh habitat. To prepare for the cold dry season, they deposit a considerable amount of fat in the tail. Their teeth are similar to those of the Aardwolf; a case of two mammals evolving separately to feed on similar prey.

Eupleres goudotii
Montagne d'Ambre National Park, N Madagascar.
Photo: Pete Oxford/naturepl.com

Although the demonstration of monophyly in the Madagascar Carnivores helps to resolve the enigma of multiple dispersals of these animals to Madagascar, such a dispersal would have had to occur at least once. It remains difficult to fathom how this could have happened, how the ancestor of the euplerids was able to swim or raft on floating vegetation to the island. At minimum, a group or a pregnant female would have had to make this journey. Certain physiological or behavioral traits have been proposed to explain how a non-flying, medium to small-sized vertebrate could have colonized the island. One proposed trait is the ability of some mammals to store fat and undergo aestivation or even hibernation: perhaps the colonizer survived by being holed up in the cavity of a floating tree or burrowed into a mat of floating vegetation. In the living euplerids, species in the genus *Fossa* can store considerable reserves of fat, up to 25% of the typical body mass. *Eupleres* can store up to 800 g of subcutaneous fat in the tail, estimated to represent about 20% of its average body weight. Although there is no evidence that these animals aestivate, these fat reserves allow them to pass through periods of food scarcity. If the accumulation of body fat is a character found in the earliest members of this radiation, this may explain how such a crossing would have been physiologically or energetically plausible.

The first described species in what is now recognized as the Eupleridae, was the Spotted Fanaloka (*Fossa fossana*), followed by the Broad-striped Vontsira (*Galidictis fasciata*). Subsequently, as natural history specimens from Madagascar made their way to Europe, four of the remaining six living species were named in the first half of the 19th century and one in the second half. The most recently described member of this family is the Grandidier's Vontsira (*Galidictis grandidieri*) in 1986.

To a large extent, the generic classification of Madagascar Carnivores has been stable over the past century, but a considerable number of species names, other than those currently in use, were proposed. The complicated questions of synonymy have been largely worked out by R. Albignac and W. C. Wozencraft. However, several issues remain, principally associated with polytypic species complexes. These include: the broadly distributed Ring-tailed Vontsira (*Galidia elegans*), which is divided into three morphologically distinct geographic forms; the Falanouc (*Eupleres goudoti*), which has two very distinct geographic forms that probably warrant separation into different species; the Broad-striped Vontsira which is divided into two poorly defined subspecies; and the Narrow-striped Boky (*Mungotictis decemlineata*), which has two morphologically distinct subspecies that probably deserve separation. Some preliminary phylogeographic studies have shown, for example, that the northern Ring-tailed Vontsiras are genetically divergent from populations in central and east-southern Madagascar. These types of studies, based on recently obtained tissue

samples and associated specimens, should help to resolve most of these questions within the next few years.

Although our purpose here is not to provide a detailed review of the higher level systematics of endemic Madagascar Carnivores over the past two centuries, certain aspects are rather interesting, particularly from the perspective of phylogenetic inference of different characters and their utility in interpreting the evolutionary history of these animals. For example, Fosa (*Cryptoprocta ferox*) was at one time placed in its own family, Cryptoproctidae, and at others, in several different ways within the Felidae, the Viverridae, and Herpestidae. An extreme case, in this regards, was the placement of Falanouc within the Insectivora by an early 19th century taxonomist.

One of the earliest comprehensive classifications of the Carnivora was that of Gray, using toe and tail morphology and fur patterns. He placed Spotted Fanaloka in the genet tribe (Genettina); Ring-tailed Vontsira and Brown-tailed Vontsira (*Salanoia concolor*) in a tribe endemic to Madagascar (Galidiina); Fosa within a monospecific tribe (Cryptoproctina); Broad-striped and Grandidier's Vontsiras within the herpestid tribe (Herpestina); and Falanouc in a tribe of morphologically diverse carnivores (Crossarchina). His work was followed, early in the 20th century, by numerous detailed anatomical studies of Carnivora by Pocock, who often treated Malagasy animals and proposed closely-related genera.

Gregory and Hellman presented a very detailed analysis of skull and dental characters of fossil and living Carnivora. They used a mixture of different classifications, including, in part, Pocock's configuration of the Viverridae: the Fossinae and Euplerinae within the section Hemigalida; the Galidictinae within the section Galidictida; and the Cryptoproctinae within the section Cryptoproctida in the family Felidae. Numerous aspects of the classification of Madagascar Carnivores remained unresolved. For example, these authors noted that Fosa maintains numerous viverroid characters on the one hand and feloid characters on the other, and stands in "the border zone between the Viverridae and the Felidae".

In Simpson's classification of mammals, published in 1945, he placed all of the Madagascar Carnivores, as well as numerous other members of this order, in the superfamily Feloidea. His Feloidea included the earlier concept of the Aeluroidea and also the family Viverridae, and was divided as follows: subfamily Hemigalinae—*Fossa* in the tribe Fossini and *Eupleres* in the tribe Euplerini; subfamily Galidinae—*Galidia, Galidictis, Mungotictis,* and *Salanoia;* and subfamily Cryptoproctinae—*Cryptoprocta.* The fact that these different animals were classified as being in different subfamilies, with different African and Asiatic tribes separating them, implied their not sharing a common recent evolutionary history. Simpson explicitly stated this point: "It appears probable, however, that Malagasy viverrids do represent more

Fosa, *the largest extant species of Eupleridae, is a formidable predator, with carnassial teeth capable of slicing through meat much like scissors cutting paper. It is an agile climber, able to chase arboreal prey, using its long tail for balance. With its blunt nose, rounded ears, long whiskers, flexible ankle joints, and sleek, muscular body, it resembles a New World felid, the Puma. Fosas and their fellow Madagascar Carnivores fill ecological roles similar to those filled elsewhere by mongooses (Herpestidae), civets (Viverridae), and felids (Felidae). However, scientists no longer group them with any of these families of mammals that occur elsewhere in the world. Molecular studies confirm the close relationship of all native carnivorans on the island with each other and support placing them in a single family, Eupleridae, even though no single anatomical feature is common to all of them. Fosas have short, soft fur. The fur on the underside of a adult male is often stained orange by secretions from his glands. Males are larger than females. T whiskers on the Fosa pictured below are notably black near the bridge of its nose and white lower on its jowls.*

Cryptoprocta ferox
Above: Kirindy National Park,
W Madagascar.
Photo: Pete Oxford/naturepl.com

Below: Madagascar.
Photo: Terry Whittaker/FLPA

Although largely terrestrial, **Ring-tailed Vontsiras** can climb nearly vertical tree trunks and navigate thin vines and branches. Partially webbed feet make them good swimmers, and they are sometimes seen in streams, presumably hunting aquatic prey. They stay in or near forests, occurring across a wide elevational range and a broad range of forest types. Family groups mark their territories with urine and musk and maintain contact through whistling vocalizations. Ring-tailed Vontsiras in the north differ genetically from those in central and south-eastern Madagascar. These animals were once known as Ring-tailed Mongooses, a name that reflected confusion about their evolutionary history.

Galidia elegans
Madagascar.
Photo: Konrad Wothe/FLPA

than one mainland stock, as the classification suggests, although this is not certainly established". Simpson's classification was followed by numerous other systematists for nearly five decades, until molecular phylogenetic studies revealed that indeed the endemic Madagascar Carnivores come from a common ancestor.

A study of Viverridae neuroanatomy, based on the examination of endocasts, provided the following conclusions with respect to the native carnivorans of Madagascar: *Fossa* and *Eupleres* showed characters atypical of the family or subfamily Hemigalinae and *Galidia*, *Galidictis*, and *Salanoia* (subfamily Galidiinae), and *Cryptoprocta* (subfamily Cryptoproctinae), showed characters similar to herpestines. The character states associated with the brain anatomy of these different Madagascar Carnivores provided little resolution of the phylogenetic history of what was considered several subfamilies of the Viverridae. Subsequently, this enigma, too, was resolved partially by placing these animals in a separate family endemic to Madagascar.

The next major step in understanding the phylogenetic history and relationships of the native Madagascar Carnivores has been molecular genetic work conducted in different laboratories. These studies reveal what Simpson hinted at, that the island's native carnivorans are not members of the Viverridae, Herpestidae, or Felidae, but represent a unique monophyletic and endemic radiation. Hence, the earlier difficulty in the family or subfamily placement of these animals was associated with extensive convergence that, in part, masked their real evolutionary history. Rather consistently across most of these studies, *Cryptoprocta* and *Fossa* appear to be basal within the radiation. The position of *Eupleres* and *Salanoia* is not completely resolved, and *Galidia*, *Galidictis*, and *Mungotictis*, the "mongoose-like" members of the group, form a more derived internal clade. The sister group to the Eupleridae is the Herpestidae, with the Hyaenidae as the next group out to the combined Eupleridae–Herpestidae clade. This probable higher-level relationship has been supported by subsequent molecular phylogenetic studies using expanded taxa sampling and different genes. When different types of morphological characters were superimposed on the molecular data set, the original phylogenetic signal was in most cases not recoverable. This explains why centuries of systematic studies using morphology were unable to resolve the evolutionary history of the Madagascar Carnivores.

These molecular phylogenies formed the basis of Wozencraft's placement of the native Madagascar Carnivores in the endemic monophyletic family Eupleridae, composed of the subfamilies Euplerinae (*Cryptoprocta*, *Eupleres*, and *Fossa*) and Galidiinae (*Galidia*, *Galidictis*, *Mungotictis*, and *Salanoia*). We follow this classification in the species accounts.

Previous taxonomic associations of the euplerids with other groups of carnivorans were incorporated into their vernacular names, so, for example, that *Fossa* was referred to as the Malagasy Civet and *Galidia* as the Ring-tailed Mongoose. Now that we know that there are no native viverids, herpestids, or felids in Madagascar, we are proposing new vernacular names in the species accounts that follow, often based on those used in Malagasy, the language of Madagascar, to replace the inappropriate names used in the past.

The fossil record of vertebrates on Madagascar can be divided into two distinct periods: up until the late Cretaceous; and after the late Pleistocene and early Holocene (Quaternary). This 65 million year gap in information, which falls during the period many modern animals are presumed to have colonized Madagascar, considerably limits insights into the evolutionary history of the island's vertebrates. Hence, the known fossil record from Madagascar provides no clues as to what happened during this important period in geological time.

Subfossil remains found in Quaternary paleontological and archeological deposits provide some indication that recent changes have occurred in Madagascar's native Carnivora fauna. A species of *Cryptoprocta*, the Giant Fosa (*C. spelea*), which was notably larger than its existing congener, *C. ferox*, has gone extinct over the last few thousand years. At some sites remains of both taxa have been found, but due to a lack of stratigraphic control, it is not known if these two species were temporally sympatric. The specific factors that led to the demise of *C. spelea* are proposed to have been a combination of climate change and human pressures, including the transformation of the island's landscapes. Another interesting find in subfossil deposits was bones of Grandidier's Vontsira. This living species was named in 1986 on the basis of some old museum specimens. If the subfossil remains had been studied before the modern remains in the museum collection were described, *Galidictis grandidieri* would have been originally named as an extinct taxon.

Since human colonization of the island some 2500 years ago, three species of Carnivora have been introduced to the island: domestic dogs, and Wildcats, and the Small Indian Civet.

The **Spotted Fanaloka** *was
originally thought to be a species
of civet (Viverridae), and was
formerly called the Malagasy Civ
These nocturnal animals use a
variety of habitat types, but are
most common in eastern humid
forests. They shelter in hollow
tree trunks or under rocks rather
than using ground dens. They
have a strong, musky smell and
communicate with anal, neck, a
cheek gland secretions more than
vocally. A scientific mystery: how
did the ancestors of Madagascar
eight species of Carnivora get to
the island? Madagascar split
from the continent of Africa befo
carnivores evolved and is separa
from the mainland by a body of
water too wide for swimming or
floating to have been likely. The
ability of certain species of eupler
to accumulate large fat deposits
may have been an important
adaptation to survive long perio
of rafting across the sea.*

Fossa fossana
Ranomafana National Park,
SE Madagascar.
Photo: Greg & Yvonne Dean/
WorldWildlifeImages.com

Morphological Aspects

Inherent in the convoluted systematic history of the native Madagascar Carnivores, now recognized as endemic Eupleridae, is the lack of morphological characters that can be used to define the family. This is notably different from other Carnivora groups, such as the Felidae, where there are very clear external and anatomical characters that naturally unite them. Members of the Eupleridae show extraordinary patterns of convergence to felids, civets, and mongooses, and hence based on morphology, it is not possible to define this family. Other than the molecular genetic studies mentioned in the Systematics section, the only aspect that unifies them is their occurrence on Madagascar. In general, members of this family do not show differences in pelage coloration between the sexes, although in some there is sexual dimorphism in body size.

The largest living species is the Fosa, which approaches the body size of a small Puma. Males are larger (6·2–8·6 kg) than females (5·5–6·8 kg). These animals have a sleek muscular body, long torso, tail length nearly equivalent to head-body length, and semi-retractable claws. The muzzle is relatively short, as are the rounded ears. The body fur is notably short and fine, and with uniform, pale, reddish-brown upperparts and dirty cream underparts. Adult males often have an orange-colored underside, associated with gland secretions. Falanouc has one of the more peculiar body forms in the family. It has a relatively massive, elongated torso; a short and tapered tail, often rounded with fat deposits; long and narrow rostrum; and short and rounded ears. It has proportionately large feet, particularly the forelimbs, with non-retractable thin claws that touch the ground when it walks giving the animal a slow and sauntering gait.

Narrow-striped Bokys
*communicate through scent,
but also send visual signals by
erecting their fluffy tails. They a
gregarious and have a complex
social system, sometimes living
in small groups led by an alpha
female. The Narrow-striped Bok
is a good climber, but spends
most of its foraging time on the
ground, scratching with its long
claws in sandy soil or rotten woo
for invertebrates, especially inse
larvae. It also eats reptiles, birds
and mammals, some hunted an
some scavenged, and is itself pre
upon by the Fosa.*

Mungotictis decemlineata
Kirindy National Park, Madagascar.
Photo: Jason Gilchrist

Within the "mongoose-like" euplerids in the genera *Galidia*, *Salanoia*, *Galidictis*, and *Mungotictis*, there are some parallels in morphology. These include an elongated body, relatively short feet, and a fluffy furred tail that is two-thirds to one-half the body length. Each genus has distinct tail fur coloration. *Galidia* possesses a somber dark or reddish-chestnut body, fulvous throat and head grizzled with black, and nearly black venter, feet, and flanks. The tail is marked with five to seven alternating dark reddish-brown and blackish bands. In body shape and form, *Salanoia* is very similar to *Galidia*, but with a uniform dark pelage, pale-tipped hairs that give an agouti appearance, and a uniformly dark brown, slightly bushy tail. Broad-striped Vontsira has an overall grayish-beige dorsum, the central portion of which is marked with distinct dark brown longitudinal bands that are wider or equal in width to the grayish-beige interlines. The distal two-thirds of the tail is a unicolored whitish, the head grizzled grayish-brown, and the venter distinctly paler. Grandidier's Vontsira has the same basic fur coloration of its congener, but it is slightly larger and the dorsal black lines are narrower. Narrow-striped Boky tends to have an even more pointed snout and cylindrical body than the other mongoose-like forms. Its dorsum is a grizzled gray mixed with light brown or beige and characterized by eight to ten broadly-spaced thin longitudinal stripes. Amongst these mongoose-like forms there is mixed evidence of sexual dimorphism. In the genus *Galidictis* males and females have the same body coloration, but in *G. grandidieri*, males are heavier than females; the same seems to be true of *Galidia*. Based on current data, there is no evidence of sexual dimorphism in *Salanoia* or *Mungotictis*.

The foot structure in members of the mongoose-like group shows some interesting adaptations. In *Galidia*, the hindfeet are longer than the forefeet, and it has well-developed and naked footpads. There is notable webbing between the toes, and the claws are non-retractable. These adaptations allow the animal to be agile while walking or running on the ground, dexterous while climbing trees, and a good swimmer. In Grandidier's Vontsira, the feet are notably elongated, the claws long and non-retractable, and there is webbing between the toes. This species lives in areas of rock and sand and the modifications of the limbs are presumed adaptations for these conditions. In contrast, Broad-striped Vontsira, which occurs in areas of hard-packed soils, has shorter limbs and claws and less-developed toe-webbing. Finally, Narrow-striped Boky lives in areas with sandy soils and has both toe webbing and elongated claws.

The "civet-like" Spotted Fanaloka has short legs, a pointed snout, a large rounded body, and a bushy tail. The dorsal pelage is brownish, with two mostly-continuous black mid-dorsal lines; these are bordered by a row of partially-broken stripes that merge into spots on the flanks. The tail is brown with concentric rings and spots. There is no evidence of sexual dimorphism in size, mass, or pelage coloration.

Habitat

Members of the family Eupleridae are strictly or largely forest-dwelling animals; most taxa are not known to cross open, non-forested habitats. They occur in all of the natural forest types on Madagascar from humid forests that receive more than 6 m of annual precipitation to sub-desert formations receiving less than 400 mm, and from lowland spiny bush to mountain areas above forest line. Given the habitat preferences of euplerids to natural forests, their continued long-term existence is closely tied to the conservation of Madagascar's forest ecosystems.

Some species have broad geographical distributions that encompass a range of forest ecosystems. Others are restricted to a very specific forest type. An example of the former is Ring-tailed Vontsira. It occurs across a considerable elevational range, which in the east includes lowland and littoral forests as well as high altitude montane forest (up to 1950 m). This species inhabits transitional humid-deciduous forests in the northwest, and deciduous forests in the west-central Madagascar. An excellent example of a habitat-specific species is Grandidier's Vontsira, only known from a small area of spiny bush along a limestone plateau in the extreme south-west.

Fosa will move across several kilometers of land that lacks natural forest, and is the principal exception to the strict forest-dwelling habitats of the Eupleridae. Ring-tailed Vontsira can also be seen foraging at the forest edge or in secondary forest, but it is not known to occur more than a few hundred meters away from the ecotone of these habitats. The final exception is Falanouc, which can be found at certain sites with natural marsh habitats, but these tend to be in close proximity to forests.

Species richness is highest in the eastern humid forests, where up to five species of Eupleridae occur along the slopes of certain mountains. It must be emphasized that few data are available from many portions of this vast zone, and records and observations are often limited. For example, on the Andohahela Massif in the south-east, with its summit just under 2000 m, five species of Eupleridae are known. At this site in the lowland forests (up to 800 m), there are four species (Ring-tailed Vontsira, Broad-striped Vontsira, Fosa, and Spotted Fanaloka). In the montane section (1200–1500 m) of this elevational gradient, species diversity remains the same, but with Fosa dropping out and Falanouc filling in. Towards the summit of the massif, at 1875 m, only Ring-tailed Vontsira and Fosa have been recorded. Fosa presumably has a continuous distribution across the slopes of this massif; Falanouc tends to occur in zones with wet to moist soils, particularly marshes.

Brown-tailed Vontsira is only known from lowland and littoral forest formations in the central-east and north-east, habitats that have been greatly modified by humans over the past century; this modification certainly resulted in a contraction of this animal's distribution. Presumably, Brown-tailed Vontsira once occurred on the now-deforested lowland slopes of certain massifs, and up to six species of Eupleridae would have occurred across some elevational gradients.

The elevational patterns on other forested massifs in the east are similar to the patterns mentioned above for Andohahela. In general, Ring-tailed Vontsira occurs across the gamut of forest types from lowland to montane formations, as does Fosa, which occurs above forest line to the summits of the highest peaks on the island (2600 m). The areas above forest line on the Andringitra Massif, where Fosa has been studied, witness extreme weather conditions. Daily temperatures span more than 40 °C, and temperatures dip well below freezing during the cold and dry months. In addition, this zone has periodic snowfall.

In contrast, the western and south-western dry forests have lower species richness than the eastern humid forests, but perhaps higher densities of native carnivores. The number of euplerids occurring in the dry forests does not exceed two taxa at any given site. Fosa occurs across this zone, and broadly co-exists with three species of Galidinae—Ring-tailed Vontsira in the north, Narrow-striped Boky in the central-west, and Grandidier's Vontsira in the south-west. The reasons for the non-overlapping distributions of the Galidinae species that co-exist with Fosa across this area have not yet been studied, but presumably have to do with habitat gradients and the available prey base. Interestingly, the Tsiribihina River separates the northern limit of Narrow-striped Boky and the southern limit of Ring-tailed Vontsira.

The littoral forests of the east, which occur on sandy soils, hold three species of Eupleridae (Fosa, Ring-tailed Vontsira, and Spotted Fanaloka), in notably low densities. Further, there is evidence that Brown-tailed Vontsira occurred or still occurs in the littoral forest of Tampolo, north of Toamasina.

No euplerids have been properly documented on the offshore islands of Isle Sainte Marie, Nosy Mangabe, and Nosy Be, which were connected to the main island of Madagascar during periods of the Quaternary with lower sea levels. Given that the natural forests of these islands have been greatly reduced in the past few centuries, it is difficult to know whether the absence of euplerids is the result of human perturbation of habitats or is associated with the natural distribution patterns of these animals.

In the northern and north-western forests, several zones of which are transitional between mesic and dry habitats, the distribution of the Eupleridae seems to be more complex. For example, in certain limestone areas of Ankarana, three species of euplerids, Fosa, Spotted Fanaloka, and Ring-tailed Vontsira, can be found, and presumably, a fourth species, Falanouc, might also occur in portions of the zone with moist soils. In these areas, Fosa moves between dry and moist forested and non-forested habitats. The smaller euplerids are generally associated with mesic forests occurring in canyons.

Ring-tailed Vontsira is the most conspicuous native carnivoran on the island, and occurs in virtually all of the natural forest formations except for the southern portion of the western deciduous forest and the southwestern spiny bush. Broad-striped Vontsira is found in the eastern humid forests, across an elevation range from lowland forest to montane forest at about 1500 m. Most records are from relatively intact forests. Falanouc and Spotted Fanaloka tend to be most common in forested areas with watercourses or marshy habitats.

Grandidier's Vontsira has the smallest known distribution of any species of euplerid, occurring in the rugged limestone Mahafaly Plateau. This notably arid zone receives less than 400 mm average annual precipitation and daily temperatures can exceed 40 °C. The distribution of this carnivoran is largely restricted to the western base and flank of the plateau, a zone of water resurgence associated with an underground aquifer. It is not known whether this species is obliged to drink water daily,

*The **Spotted Fanaloka** feeds on a variety of prey species. It does much of its foraging in shallow water, searching for aquatic organisms. Its diet includes amphibians, crustaceans, eels, and crabs, and it also preys on various terrestrial invertebrates and vertebrates. It eats insects all year, but consumes many more mammals in the dry season than in the wet season. The Spotted Fanaloka is the only Madagascar Carnivore other than the Falanouc known to accumulate substantial fat deposits before the start of the cold dry season. The fat is stored in the tail and allows the animal to survive periods of food scarcity without aestivating or hibernating.*

Fossa fossana
Ranomafana National Park,
SE Madagascar.
Photo: Jiri Lochman/
Lochman Transparencies

Ring-tailed Vontsiras are true
omnivores and are notorious
raiders of human food supplies
and camp trash. Excellent
climbers, they have been seen as
high as 15 m above the ground,
probing into tree crevices and
epiphytes with their noses and
claws in search of invertebrates
and small vertebrates. Slugs,
insects, frogs, and chameleons are
all important dietary components.
Ring-tailed Vontsiras also enter
streams in search of frogs and other
aquatic prey. They have been seen
watching silently at the edge of
a small stream and then leaping
into the water and seizing prey,
presumably a fish, frog, or crayfish.
Various diurnal forest birds mob
Ring-tailed Vontsiras, presumably
because these mammals steal eggs
and young birds from nests.

Galidia elegans
Ankarana Special Reserve,
NW Madagascar.
Photo: Jiri Lochman/
Lochman Transparencies

but the prey base near these water sources is higher in density and diversity than in surrounding areas without water.

Communication

No formal studies have been conducted on inter- and intra-specific patterns of communication in members of the Eupleridae, nor have recordings of their vocalizations under natural situations been made that have been followed by laboratory analysis. Euplerids are often difficult to follow in the forest, particularly the nocturnal species, and hence are not conducive to this type of study. However, observations have been made in the wild and in captivity of vocal and olfactory communication in these animals, and a number of studies have been conducted on how lemurs use vocal communication as a deterrent to predation by euplerids, particularly Fosa.

Fosa seems to be relatively silent. Most of its vocalizations are associated with mating activities. Olfactory signals are the common means for this generally solitary animal to communicate, by scent marking prominent objects with body gland secretions. Occasionally a short raspy or guttural "roar", which is apparently a type of contact call or perhaps one of intimidation or defense, can be heard in the forest. Before copulation, the female gives a series of "mewing" calls that seem to stimulate the male to mount her. Young animals emit a "purring" sound when nursing or in contact with their mother.

Falanouc seems to be largely silent. Captive animals have been noted to give two types of vocalizations: a sort of spitting call connected with agonistic encounters; and a hiccupping sound associated with mother-infant interactions. However, olfactory communication is important, particularly during the breeding season, when individuals use different glands to mark territories and for other kinds of signals. Both males and females rub their anal glands on prominent objects (low vegetation and prominent rocks) and rub the neck gland on vertical surfaces.

Spotted Fanaloka apparently does not have a large vocal repertoire. It uses a muffled "growl" during agonistic encounters and a cry for adult-young communication. It has a strong, distinctive musky smell and olfactory signaling is important. Neck, cheek and anal glands become well-developed during the breeding season and their secretions are used in olfactory communication.

Ring-tailed Vontsira is rather vocal and its auditory signals have been classified into four types: a whistle-like contact call between family members, often given while moving through the forest; a specific prey capture call; growl and "shrill" screams as intimidation, attack, or defense; and a copulation vocalization. In aggressive encounters between individuals, particularly adult males, the dominant individual is pacified by a submissive display and associated vocalization. When the dominant animal approaches, the submissive animal assumes a prostrate posture and gives a loud, high-pitched "screech". Trapped animals produce a two-part threat call, a guttural growl followed by a raspy "spit". Adults regularly scent-mark their home range using urine and a form of musk produced by their perineal, cheek, and sub-mandibular glands.

Virtually nothing is known about communication in *Galidictis*. Both species, Broad-striped and Grandidier's Vontsiras, often can be observed at night with their distinct white tail held in a vertical position; this is presumed to be some form of signaling.

Food and Feeding

The vast majority of euplerids are carnivorous, although a variety of non-animal matter is consumed and some probably scavenge carrion. The smaller species tend to feed more on invertebrates than vertebrates, or on small-bodied animals. There are also records of euplerids feeding on domestic animals, mostly chickens. However, in at least some cases reported by people living in the countryside, the actual predator was the introduced Small Indian Civet. Certain taxa show considerable seasonal, altitudinal, and regional variation in their dietary regime, presumably associated with shifts in the local prey base. Over the past years, numerous studies have been conducted on the dietary regime of many species of Madagascar Carnivores, the majority based on scat analysis, which forms the basis of much of current knowledge.

Using dental characters and adult body mass, the Eupleridae can be divided into three dietary classes. Dietary class one, includes animals weighing more than 5 kg and having carnas-

sial teeth (Fosa); dietary class two includes animals weighing 1·5–3 kg and with reduced teeth that have conical cusps (Falanouc); and dietary class three includes animals weighing less than 2 kg and having carnassial teeth of different cutting or crushing abilities (Spotted Fanaloka, Ring-tailed Vontsira, Broad-striped and Grandidier's Vonsiras, Narrow-striped Boky, and Brown-tailed Vontsira).

Fosa, with its considerable strength, broad footpads, long tail, and semi-retractable claws, is the largest, best known, and most powerful living predator on the island. It is capable of bringing down both terrestrial and arboreal prey. This animal, which can be active sporadically throughout the day and night, is the only member of dietary class one. Its diet shows considerable variation based on bioclimatic parameters associated with geographical region and elevation. Both nocturnal and diurnal lemurs are regular elements in its diet. In dry deciduous forests, primates comprise over 80% of the biomass and nearly 60% of prey based on relative frequency. Larger diurnal lemur species are disproportionately represented and smaller nocturnal species are under-represented in the Fosa diet as compared to the lemurs' frequency in the local forest ecosystems. Fosa has been labeled a "lemur specialist", but this is a misnomer for several reasons, one of which is that across its range, it also takes a wide variety of non-primate prey and shows remarkable dietary plasticity.

Fosa is known to take animals nearly its own body weight, such as 6 kg *Propithecus* lemurs. Further, bone fragments of cows and Bush-pigs have been recovered in their scats; whether these food items were hunted or scavenged is impossible to discern. In high mountain zones above the forest line (1950 m), there is a dramatic decrease in the average body mass of individual prey to 40 g. These small prey items are mostly shrew tenrecs (Tenrecidae). In contrast, the average body mass of individual prey is 480 g in the northern humid forests and 1140 g in dry deciduous forests.

Dietary class two contains a single member, Falanouc, with its tiny conical and flattened cusps that are adapted to a soft-bodied invertebrate diet. It has been suggested that this species uses its claws for digging out prey, primarily earthworms, from soil or rotten wood, and the prey is immobilized with the jaws and teeth. However, its long, thin claws are not adapted for this type of rigorous and abrasive activity. Falanouc also feeds on slugs, insects, frogs, and chameleons, and there are unconfirmed reports that it consumes vegetable matter. Across portions of its range, this species occurs in sympatry with mem-

bers of dietary classes one and three, but there is clearly little overlap in the types of prey taken by these different animals. Falanouc shows numerous dentary and dietary convergences to the Aardwolf of the hyena family.

Falanouc stores up to 800 g of subcutaneous fat in the tail, or about 20% of its average body weight. This takes place before the start of the cold and dry season (June to August), a period when availability of ground invertebrates, such as worms, is notably reduced near the soil surface. We are unaware of any research that has investigated if these fat reserves are used during aestivation or possibly hibernation, but such reserves certainly would help active animals survive periods of decreased food availability.

Dietary class three comprises several genera of smaller euplerids with carnassial teeth, and several of these occur in sympatry in the humid forests. Based on limited information, there is little evidence for specialization, and most are dietary generalists. The possible exception to this is the nocturnal and digitgrade Spotted Fanaloka, which seems to have a propensity for aquatic organisms (e.g. amphibians, crustaceans, crabs, etc.), which it hunts in shallow water; it also takes various terrestrial invertebrates and vertebrates. There is a strong seasonal component to prey choice: 96% of the wet season diet is composed of insects, reptiles, and amphibians and 94% of the dry season diet of insects, crabs, and mammals. Spotted Fanaloka is the only member of the Eupleridae other than Falanouc known to accumulate substantial fat deposits in its tail before the start of the cold dry season; these can reach 25% of the normal body mass and allow the animal to survive periods of food scarcity. There is no evidence that this species aestivates or hibernates.

The largely diurnal or crepuscular and notably omnivorous Ring-tailed Vontsira occurs in sympatry over a portion of its range with the nocturnal species Spotted Fanaloka and Broad-striped Vontsira, and the diurnal Brown-tailed Vontsira. Ring-tailed Vontsira feeds on a wide variety of vertebrates and invertebrates, taking animals of at least 200 g, as well as raiding the nests of birds for eggs and young. One of the remarkable aspects of Ring-tailed Vontsira is that with its semi-digitgrade gait and notably fleshy footpads, it is able to climb nearly vertical tree trunks, relatively thin horizontal branches, and lianas. These animals have been observed in trees up to 15 m off the ground, searching for invertebrate and small vertebrate prey by probing with their rostrums and digging with their claws in hollows and epiphytic plants. They also enter small streams to hunt aquatic animals, presumably fish, frogs, and perhaps cray-

Especially during the breeding season, **Spotted Fanalokas** *advertise by leaving anal gland secretions on prominent rocks and low vegetation, and by rubbing their neck and cheek glands on vertical surfaces. They sniff each other prior to mating. Females have one pair of mammae, and give birth to a single young. The neonate is remarkably precocious: its eyes are open and it can crawl within a day. By day three its incisor teeth are erupting and it can walk. Young Spotted Falanokas begin to eat solid food after about a month and are weaned by two and a half months of age.*

Fossa fossana
Ratmafahana, SE Antananarivo,
Madagascar.
Photo: M. Watson/Ardea

fish; the partially webbed feet help with propulsion in water. At long-term research camps in the forest, Ring-tailed Vontsira quickly become habituated to the presence of people and regularly raid food supplies and camp trash. Rural villagers report that Ring-tailed Vontsira feed on poultry, which indeed may be true in a few cases, but this species does not venture far from the forest edge. In certain areas, there may be some dietary overlap with Spotted Fanaloka, but given the temporal niche separation of these animals, as well as notable differences in carnassial blade length and other tooth parameters, this may be limited.

No quantitative information is available on the diet of Broad-striped Vontsira. This member of dietary class three is largely terrestrial and notably secretive. It probably consumes rodents and small lemurs, and perhaps other land vertebrates such as reptiles and amphibians. It does raid, at least on occasion, food supplies in forest camps. Given that this species is not known to leave the cover of natural forest, its reputation as a chicken thief in villages needs to be substantiated.

The other eastern humid forest-dwelling species of dietary class three is Brown-tailed Vontsira. Few details are available on its diet. It digs in rotten wood with its claws and extracts beetle larvae. Brown-tailed Vontsira is known to climb 5–10 m off the ground in trees where it is presumed to forage on invertebrate prey. A comparative study of this species and Ring-tailed Vontsira at a lowland site in the eastern humid forest noted several differences in prey type and habitat utilization that might reduce competitive interactions between them. Both species are diurnal-crepuscular. The more diminutive body size and reduced carnassial blade surfaces in the teeth of Brown-tailed Vontsira may help partition the available prey base. In many ways, the general size and cranial and dental (carnassial) morphology of Brown-tailed Vontsira is similar to Narrow-striped Boky, which occurs in the central portion of the western deciduous forests.

Amongst dietary class three euplerids, two species, Narrow-striped Boky and Grandidier's Vontsira, are found in the dry forest formations of west-central and south-western Madagascar. The strictly terrestrial and diurnal/crepuscular Narrow-striped Boky is a consumer of invertebrates, largely insect larvae. It digs these out of the soil or rotten wood; they constitute a large percentage of its diet during the extended dry season. Narrow-striped Boky also takes snails and vertebrates, including reptiles, birds and mammals. Lemur taxa have been identified from scat remains, including Red-tailed Sportive Lemur

(*Lepilemur ruficaudatus*); this species weighs up to 850 g and is presumed to have been scavenged. Bone remains of the rodent Votsovotsa (*Hypogeomys antimena*), which can weigh over 1 kg, have been found in the fecal remains of Narrow-striped Boky and was also probably scavenged. Fosa is the only other euplerid whose range overaps that of Narrow-striped Boky, and these two animals have notably different diets.

Little has been published about the food habits of the nocturnal Grandidier's Vontsira, but based on a current study some details are known. It feeds predominantly on invertebrates, particularly large hissing cockroaches (*Gromphadorhina*), and, to a lesser extent, locusts and beetles. Amongst vertebrates, the rock-dwelling lizard *Oplurus*, some geckos, some birds (including *Coua* spp.), and small mammals (rodents, tenrecs, and on rare occasions, bats) all constitute elements of its diet. Throughout the reduced distributional range of this species, the only sympatrically occurring native Carnivora is Fosa, which has a very different diet.

Breeding

Available information on euplerid reproductive biology is limited, and most data are from captive animals. The major exception is Fosa, and to a lesser extent Ring-tailed Vontsira, for which there is information from wild populations. Virtually nothing is known about breeding in Broad-striped, Grandidier's, or Brown-tailed Vontsiras from wild or captive animals.

In the western dry forests, which have a much more pronounced dry season than the eastern humid forests, copulation in Fosa occurs between September and December and young are born in December and January. In Narrow-striped Boky copulation is in August. It has been proposed that there is not a fixed reproductive season in Grandidier's Vontsira, which lives in the most arid portion of the region.

In the east, copulation in Fosa has been observed in October; hence, its breeding season apparently overlaps with western populations. Spotted Fanaloka is a seasonal breeder, with coitus occurring in August and September and births from October to December. The reproductive season is less defined in Ring-tailed Vontsira, with mating generally taking place between July and November. The reported gestation period for Fosa is 42–49 days, although 90 days has been cited; that of Spotted Fanaloka is 80–89 days; Ring-tailed Vontsira 75 days; and Narrow-striped Boky is 90–105 days, with another estimate

Fosas *copulate on tree branches. The female signals her willingne to mate by giving a series of mewing calls, which apparently prompts the male to mount her. Meanwhile, as many as eight otl males wait at the base of the tree, behaving aggressively toward eac other. Over the course of several days, after mating with the first male, the female will mate with one or more of the others. During copulation, the female holds ont the branch with her front claws, and the male grasps her with his front paws. He may lick or bite her neck: there are visible scars from mating on the neck of the female below. Gestation lasts six or seven weeks. Fosas usually have two offspring; all other euplerids mate on the ground and almost always give birth to a single young, except for the Falanouc, which also sometimes has two. Adult Falanoucs are on about half the size of Fosas, but have proportionately bigger, more precocious babies. Their young are born with their eyes open, ca walk in a day or two, can climb after a month, and are weaned c about nine weeks. In contrast, F neonates are blind and toothless, their eyes do not open for two or three weeks. They first leave the natal den when they are four or five months old, are independen at about a year, and attain sexu maturity at three or four years of age. A female Fosa has three pairs of mammae; all of the othe Madagascar Carnivores have ju one pair. There is no solid evider that the males in any of these species help care for the young.*

Cryptoprocta ferox
Above: W Madagascar.
Photo: Pete Oxford/DRK

Below: Ankarana Special Reserve,
NW Madagascar.
Photo: Jiri Lochman/
Lochman Transparencies

Galidia elegans
Ankarana Special Reserve,
NW Madagascar.
Photo: Jiri Lochman/
Lochman Transparencies

of 74 days. These numbers confirm how little is known about reproduction in the Eupleridae.

Considerable detail exists on Fosa reproduction, based largely on observations in the wild. Copulation generally takes place on a horizontal tree branch. For other euplerids, it takes place on the ground. The trees employed by Fosa for these mating sessions are often reused for years, and with remarkable precision as to the annual dates of the event. The female lies with her belly down on the branch and grasps it with her front claws, the hindlimbs are tucked underneath her, and she extrudes the genital opening. She then utters a series of mewing calls, which incites the male to mount her from behind, slightly to one side. He grasps the female with his forelimbs around her waist, often licking her neck, and then penetration occurs. During coitus, there is a copulatory tie, which is difficult to break if the mating session is interrupted. Copulation is repeated several times with a single male and the sequence can last from one to 14 hours. Up to eight males have been observed around a mating tree, and considerable antagonistic interactions occur between them as they compete for access to the receptive female. Over the course of several days, a female will copulate with more than one male.

Before copulating, a male Ring-tailed Vontsira pursues the female with increasing intensity and both animals mark prominent objects with the cheek and sub-mandibular glands. At the same time, the male sniffs the female's urogenital region. Copulation takes place after the female solicits the male by lowering and quivering the anterior portion of the body and slowly treading the hindquarters. Neck-biting does not seem to occur in this species. Individual coitus bouts usually last 10–30 seconds and involve 7–12 copulations during a period of 15–80 minutes.

Some details on mating behavior in Narrow-striped Boky also are available. Soon after sunrise, the male arrives at the burrow entrance of the female and waits for her to exit; when she does, she displays aggressive behavior towards him. These agonistic interactions decrease over the course of an hour, and eventually the male mounts the female. The pair copulates up to three times.

Litter size across euplerids is one, the exceptions being Fosa with at least two young and Falanouc with two young on occasion. In Ring-tailed Vontsira, females may have up to two litters per year, each being a single young. An individual of Grandidier's Vontsira had two placental scars, presumably reflecting litter size. All species of euplerids have one pair of inguinal

mammae, with the exception of Fosa, which has three pairs (inguinal, ventral, and pectoral). No information is available for Brown-tailed Vontsira.

At birth, Fosa weigh less than 100 g, have fine light-colored fur, and are blind and toothless. Development is slow, with the eyes opening about 2–3 weeks after birth. At that point, the young become more active and there is a notable darkening of the fur color. Fosa cubs leave the natal den for the first time around 4·5 months of age, become independent of their mother at about one year, and reach sexual maturity at 3–4 years. In contrast, Falanouc, which has an adult body mass less than half that of Fosa, has neonates weighing 150 g and their eyes are open at birth. They walk after 1–2 days, climb into vegetation after a month, and are weaned at about nine weeks. In Spotted Fanaloka, young are born weighing about 100 g and with their eyes open, start to crawl on day one, walk on day three, and are weaned within 2·5 months. Galidiinae neonates are distinctly more precocious than Fosa, weighing 40–50 g in Ring-tailed Vontsira and 50 g in Narrow-striped Boky. In Ring-tailed Vontsira the eyes open on day four, the incisors erupt on day eight and the premolars on day 21. Walking commences on day twelve, weaning takes place at 2–2·5 months, and the young start hunting at three months. Young Narrow-striped Boky are even more precocious than Ring-tailed Vontsira, walking within a day of being born. Their incisors erupt by day four and they eat solid food within 15 days, although they continue to nurse for about two months. By day 45, they are agile climbers. They are actively hunting within three months. Sexual maturity is reached at two years.

Movements, Home range and Social organization

Relatively precise details are available on these topics for a few species of Eupleridae (*Cryptoprocta*, *Fossa*, and *Galidia*), based largely on radio-collar or capture-mark studies. Further field research on the island's carnivorans is essential to fill in details of their natural history. Such data are important in determining parameters associated with the conservation status of several critical taxa.

Densities of Fosa in dry deciduous forests of central western Madagascar are estimated to be one animal per 4 km². Females have home ranges of up to 13 km², and males up to 26 km². Individual home ranges showed some overlap. Those of females tend to be separate from one another, but this may in part be associated with seasonal differences in prey and water availability. Based on a long-term study in this habitat, the adult sex ratio was estimated to be 1:1.

At a site in the eastern humid forest, the density of Spotted Fanaloka was high, with 22 animals trapped in an area of about 2 km²; ten of these animals were recaptured. This two-week field project took place during the cold season, when food resources are presumed to be limited. At the same site, four radio-tracked individuals (males and females) yielded home range estimates 0·073 to 0·522 km².

Estimated home range size in eastern humid forest-dwelling Ring-tailed Vontsira, extrapolated from trapping studies, was 20 to 25 ha/individual. In the same area, a short-term capture-mark-release study estimated the density index to be 37 animals per km², which may be a slight overestimation. Preliminary results of a trapping study in Grandidier's Vontsira indicate that minimum densities are about five animals per km². For the other species of Eupleridae, no quantified studies are available, although the home range of Falanouc has been proposed to be "very large".

On the basis of recapture or re-sightings of marked animals, some minimum estimates can be provided for individual movements. Fosa: in dry deciduous forest, one individual moved a straight-line distance of over 7 km in 16 hours; Ring-tailed Vontsira: an animal in eastern humid forest marked at 810 m elevation was observed several days later at 1200 m, a straight-line distance of about 2·5 km; and Grandidier's Vontsira: in the spiny bush along a rugged limestone plateau, during a single night an animal moved 1·5 km direct-line distance.

We are unaware of any species of Eupleridae in which the male provides parental care to his presumed offspring. The only exception to this may be Ring-tailed Vontsira, in which male-female groups can be seen with smaller individuals, presumably their young. In most euplerids, males live alone during the non-breeding season, and observed groups are generally females with their young of the year. The exception to this appears to be Grandidier's Vontsira, in which groups of several males have been observed.

Members of the Eupleridae have a variety of types of sites where they sleep and raise their young. Fosa live in under-ground dens, rock crevices, or hollows in large tree trunks or termite mounds, and often such sites are used for birthing and raising young. It has been noted that Falanouc live in dens; however, given their thin claws, they may not be physically able to dig these structures themselves. This species is known to sleep at the base of trees and, at least in sub-adults, in tree branches 1·6 m off the ground. Spotted Fanaloka apparently does not occupy ground dens, but lives in tree trunk hollows and rock shelters. Ring-tailed Vontsira is capable of excavating its own burrows, which apparently can be complicated structures with numerous openings. The dens are in zones with exposed hard-packed soils; den sites include burrows under large trees and in carved-out soil fissures along riverbanks or in the hollow bases of large standing trees or downed hollow logs. In areas with exposed rocks, Ring-tailed Vontsira makes its lairs in rock crevices and subterranean passages. Another member of the Galidiinae, Grandidier's Vontsira, generally places its dens in the labyrinth of holes and caves in karstic limestone, generally in areas of exposed rock without vegetation. Some of these lairs are several meters deep, where these nocturnal animals can escape the intense heat of the day. J. Jeglinski found one Grandidier's Vontsira den in a hollow tree about 3 m off the ground.

Relationship with Humans

With the possible exception of Grandidier's Vontsira and Brown-tailed Vontsira, local people in the countryside of Madagascar consume all euplerids as bush meat. Recent field research has indicated that for certain species, this type of pressure is far greater than previously recognized. Virtually all non-domestic carnivorans are considered by people living near forested areas as vermin because they are thought to prey on domestic animals, particularly fowl. However, euplerids other than Fosa and perhaps Ring-tailed Vontsira are forest-dwelling, and there is a low possibility of their gaining access to domestic fowl. The real predator is probably the Small Indian Civet. In some cases, euplerid body parts are used for medicinal and supernatural potions.

We know little about the transmission of diseases from domestic introduced animals, particularly cats and dogs, to euplerids. These diseases might include anthrax, canine distemper, canine parvovirus, feline calicivirus, and toxoplasmosis, which have been isolated from Fosa. It is assumed that euplerids have no natural immunities to these diseases. The direct impact of introduced carnivores on the native species is unknown, but there is some evidence of competition for prey and of outright predation on the smaller euplerids. The Wildcat was introduced to Madagascar in the 19th century, and viable wild populations are not uncommon in natural forest habitats, particularly in drier formations in the west and southwest. The introduced Small Indian Civet tends to inhabit heavily degraded and open areas or at the forest edge, and possibly has less direct impact on native carnivorans than domestic dogs and Wildcats that enter the forest.

Status and Conservation

One species, the Giant Fosa is currently known only from sub-fossil remains and is believed to have survived at least into the recent geological part.

As mentioned earlier, the distribution of all extant members of the Eupleridae is associated with the remaining native vegetation of Madagascar, with most species being forest-dependent. Hence, their long-term future is ultimately linked with the protection of the natural forest ecosystems of the island. Over the past half century, Madagascar has lost nearly 40% of its natural forest cover and there has been extensive reduction in the size of remaining forest blocks. Recent action taken by the Malagasy Government to curb this level of habitat destruction includes the "Plan Durban", which is intended to increase conservation zones three-fold and bring about 10% of the island into the protected areas program. This initiative is well advanced and there is considerable promise that it will be largely met by 2009.

There are other factors to consider when assessing the long-term future of Madagascar Carnivores. In contrast to

*The **Fosa** is better known than the other euplerids, although much remains to be learned, including good estimates of its actual population. It has a wide distribution and can apparently persist in some degraded forest habitats. Individuals can travel several kilometers in a day to move from one patch of forest to another. However, the Fosa is under pressure from many directions and is listed as Vulnerable on* The IUCN Red List. *It is hunted for bush meat, it is persecuted because of reputation for preying on domestic fowl, and it gets diseases brought into the forest by cats and dogs. Habitat destruction is the major threat both to the Fosa and its prey base: trees are cut for charcoal and firewood, cattle graze in the forest, and tracts of remaining natural habitat are slashed and burned for subsistence crops.*

Cryptoprocta ferox
Madagascar.
Photo: Pete Oxford/naturepl.com

*The **Narrow-striped Boky** is listed
s Vulnerable on The IUCN Red
List. It lives in dry deciduous
forests that are being cleared at an
alarming rate for cultivated land
nd pasture. Of the eight species of
Carnivora living on Madagascar,
only one of them is not of
immediate concern. Grandidier's
Vontsira is Endangered with
a range of less than 500 km²,
more or less representing a single
location. Fosa and Brown-tailed
Vontsira are listed as Vulnerable,
and Spotted Fanaloka, Broad-
striped Vontsira, and Falanouc are
listed as Near Threatened. Since
most species are dependent on the
forest, their long-term future is tied
to the protection of the natural
forest ecosystems of Madagascar.
The Malagasy Government has
started programs to stop the high
levels of habit destruction and to
address the underlying causes of
the devastation.*

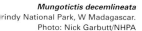

Mungotictis decemlineata
Kirindy National Park, W Madagascar.
Photo: Nick Garbutt/NHPA

most other biodiversity hotspots around the world, where commercial exploitation of forests or the replacement of forest with commercial agriculture are the driving forces behind the devastation, Madagascar's biological crisis is rooted in its socio-economic problems. Most forest clearance is the result of subsistence-level activities, including slash-and-burn agriculture and the creation of pasture for cattle. Bringing cattle into native forest ecosystems can have a drastic negative impact on the understory vegetation, which in turn influences the distribution and population dynamics of the animals euplerids prey upon. Further, considerable areas of natural forest are being cut for charcoal and firewood. The Malagasy Government has launched a series of projects to try to ameliorate the underlying causes of habitat devastation.

One of the key problems in determining the conservation status of most Eupleridae is the lack of detailed information on their distribution and population dynamics. Recent biological exploration of forested areas of the island, particularly nocturnal and trapping surveys in unknown or poorly known zones, has added considerable new information about these animals. Only one species, Fosa, is sufficiently well known to begin population assessment exercises. The basic natural history of taxa such as Broad-striped Vontsira and Brown-tailed Vontsira are largely unknown and conclusions about their conservation status based on current information are preliminary at best. The lack of detailed information and the hiatus between published information available to policy makers and unpublished knowledge of specialists creates a serious problem in the validation of the conservation status of these animals. For example, Fosa and Falanouc were listed in *The IUCN Red List* in 2007 as Endangered; however, the result of a Species Survival Commission/ IUCN workshop held in 2001 and attended by specialists working on Madagascar Carnivores gave the status of these species as Vulnerable. In the intervening six years, there has not been a drastic reduction in the populations of these animals nor has there been a massive amount of new field information; the way data are interpreted, emotional issues, and the politics of conservation have clearly had an important bearing on the designated status of these animals. *The IUCN Red List* released in 2008 includes the Grandidier's Vontsira as Endangered; the Fosa, Narrow-striped Boky, and Brown-tailed Vontsira as Vulnerable; and the Falanouc, the Spotted Fanaloka, and Broad-striped Vontsira as Near Threatened. Three taxa appear on Appendix II of the CITES treaty (Fosa, Falanouc, and Spotted Fanaloka). One of the eight living species is listed in *The IUCN Red List* as

Endangered: Grandidier's Vontsira, and three as Vulnerable: Fossa, Narrow-striped Boky, and Brown-tailed Vontsira.

The types of pressures having a direct impact on the populations of euplerids are not consistent across taxa. For example, Fosa has a broad distribution on the island, is able to traverse several kilometers of non-forested habitats, persists in disturbed habitats, and lives in natural habitats above forest-line. For this animal, forest habitat reduction certainly constrains available habitat and prey resources, but human persecution associated with Fosa's reputation for preying on domestic stock also has a major impact on populations. This is in contrast to Narrow-striped Boky, for example, which is strictly forest-dwelling, has higher densities in less disturbed habitats, and has a relatively small distribution intimately linked to a formation of dry deciduous forests in central lowland western Madagascar, which is being cleared at a considerable rate. The entry of roads and mineral seismographic and drilling test trails deep into previously pristine forested habitats is followed by homesteaders and their associated domestic animals (cattle and dogs), local loggers, and other anthropogenic perturbations, which have direct impacts on this carnivoran. Grandidier's Vontsira, described slightly more than two decades ago, presents a different set of considerations. This species has a small distribution in the extreme south-west of the island, apparently limited by natural ecological parameters rather than by direct anthropogenic factors. Further, a significant portion of its range falls within an existing protected area that will be extended in the near future by the Durban Plan. The future of this species rests on maintaining the protected area and minimizing human pressures, which are currently not that prevalent within this zone. Finally, little is known about the genetic structure of euplerid populations, and this information is critical to the development of long-term conservation programs.

General Bibliography

Beaumont (1964), Bennett (1833, 1835), Burney *et al.* (2004), Couturier *et al.* (1986), Doyère (1835), Flower (1869), Flynn (1998), Flynn & Nedbal (1998), Flynn *et al.* (2005), Friscia *et al.* (2007), Gaubert & Cordeiro-Estrela (2006), Gaubert & Veron (2003), Gaubert, Wozencraft *et al.* (2005), Golden (In press), Goodman & Ramanamanjato (2007), Goodman & Rasolonandrasana (2001), Goodman *et al.* (1993), Gray (1864), Gregory & Hellman (1939), Harper *et al.* (2007), IUCN (2008), Kappeler (2000), Lamberton (1930), Masters *et al.* (2006), Petit (1935), Petter (1974), Pocock (1915c, 1915d, 1915e, 1916a, 1916b, 1916c), Poux *et al.* (2005), Radinsky (1975), Razafimahatratra (1988), Scheumann *et al.* (2007), Simpson (1945), Veron (1995), Veron & Catzeflis (1993), Wozencraft (1993, 2005), Yoder & Flynn (2003).

PLATE 20

inches

cm

1

2

ssp *elegans*

4

ssp *dambrensis*

3

5

6

7

8

Subfamily EUPLERINAE
Genus *CRYPTOPROCTA*

Bennett, 1833

1. Fosa *Cryptoprocta ferox*

French: Fossa / **German**: Fossa / **Spanish**: Fosa
Other common names: Fossa, Tratraka, Kintsala

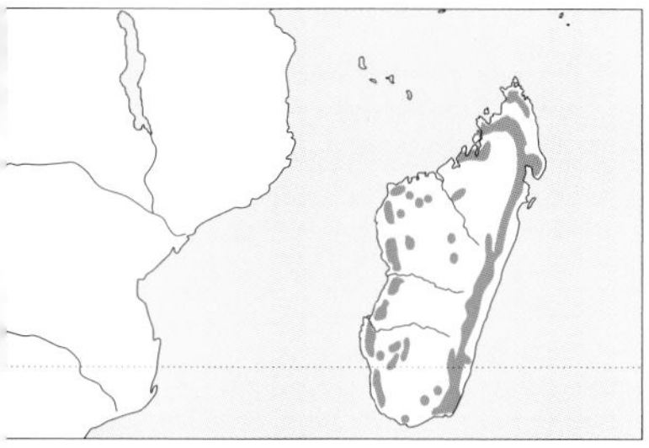

Taxonomy. *Cryptoprocta ferox* Bennett, 1833, Madagascar.
The interpretation of the systematic position of *C. ferox* has varied over the years, because these animals possess characteristics seemingly diagnostic of the families Herpestidae, Viverridae, and Felidae. The ambiguities in understanding the evolution of this genus are now partially resolved. Apparently, all native Madagascar Carnivores represent a monophyletic endemic lineage derived from a single colonization of the island. They are now placed in the family Eupleridae. *Cryptoprocta typicus* is a synonym of *C. ferox*. A notably larger form of this genus, *C. spelea*, was identified from bone remains recovered from Holocene sites. At some of these sites remains of both *C. spelea* and *C. ferox* have been found, but due to a lack of stratigraphic control it is unknown if they were temporally sympatric. The name *C. antamba* applied to some subfossil remains appears to be a teratological *C. spelea*. In different parts of Madagascar, people living in the countryside note the presence of two forms of *Cryptoprocta*—*fosa mainty* or "black *Cryptoprocta*" and *fosa mena* or "reddish *Cryptoprocta*"; the red form is said to be smaller. In the extreme south-west there are reports of a whitish morphotype. It remains unclear whether the differentiation of these forms is simply folklore or is associated with some general pattern of variation (age, sex, geographic) in extant *C. ferox*. Monotypic.

Distribution. Madagascar.

Descriptive notes. Head-body 70–80 cm, tail 65–70 cm, hindfoot 12–12·8 cm; weight 6·2–8·6 kg (males) and 5·5–6·8 kg (females). Sexually dimorphic, with males being larger. There have been previous reports of individuals weighing up to 20 kg; either these measurements are incorrect or perhaps from unnaturally heavy captive animals. There is some indication of geographic variation in external measurements across the range of this species, but this needs further substantiation, as sample sizes are not extensive. This animal resembles a small Puma, with a sleek muscular body, long torso, and tail length nearly equivalent to head-body length. Fosa has a relatively short muzzle and short rounded ears. The pelage is fine and relatively dense, generally with uniform, pale, reddish-brown upperparts and dirty cream underparts. In some individuals, particularly males, the venter is colored orange from gland secretions.

Habitat. Fosa is largely forest-dwelling. It is known from near sea level to 2600 m elevation. It occurs in all of the different natural forest types on Madagascar from the wettest (greater than 6000 mm of annual rainfall) to the driest zones (less than 400 mm). This species appears to have higher population densities in the lowland western dry deciduous forests than in the lowland eastern rainforests. Densities decrease with increasing elevation in both sectors. Fosas are also found in the remaining forested islands in the central highlands. They are known on the Andringitra Massif from about 750 m (lower limit of the forest) to 2600 m (above forest line); this latter zone has extreme meteorological conditions with daily temperatures in August ranging from –11°C to 30°C. Previous reports of this species on the off-shore island of Ile Sainte Marie are erroneous: the locality was Sainte Marie de Marovoay, not far from Mahajanga.

Food and Feeding. The Fosa's large size, considerable strength, carnassial teeth, broad paw pads, highly flexible ankle joints, and semi-retractable claws make it a formidable carnivore, the top predator of Madagascar. In captivity these animals eat 800–1000 g of meat per day. Wild populations have a broad dietary regime, at least in part associated with local prey availability. There appears to be no differences between the sexes in dietary regime. Fosa has been reported to feed on mammals, birds, snakes, lizards, freshwater turtles, and insects. In recent years several analyses of scats have been conducted to determine the diet of this animal, across the different biomes it inhabits. The scats of Fosa are easy to recognize; they form thin 10–14 cm long and 1·5–2·5 cm wide rolls, with at least one of the ends twisted. Most examples are gray in color; they often contain hair and mammalian bone fragments. At the majority of sites, mammals are the most important prey. Both by number of individuals and biomass, lemurs are regular elements in the Fosa's diet; the larger diurnal species of lemurs are at least in part taken from their arboreal sleeping sites. In the dry deciduous forests of Kirindy Centre de Formation Professionnelle Forestière (CFPF), primates comprise over 80% of the biomass and nearly 60% based on relative frequency of the prey taken. In the dry deciduous forests of Ankarafantsika, larger lemur species (*Eulemur* spp. and Verreaux's Sikafa *Propithecus verreauxi*) are over-represented in the diet of Fosa as compared to their relative local densities, while notably smaller species (mouse lemurs *Microcebus* spp. and Lesser Dwarf Lemur *Cheirogaleus medius*) are under-represented. At this site there are notable seasonal shifts in the types of lemurs taken by Fosa. Fosas also take a wide variety of non-primate prey and clearly have considerable dietary plasticity. They are known to feed on other Eupleridae; Fosa was a serious problem in a study of the Spotted Fanaloka, where it followed trap lines and preyed on captured individuals. Bone remains of Narrow-striped Boky have been found in its scats. Fosa can be a voracious chicken predator. During the dry season in western deciduous forests there is a notable increase in the number of chicken remains in scats. Towards a 2000 m summit in the south-east, small tenrecs of the genera *Microgale* and *Oryzorictes* (Oryzorictinae), all with adult body mass of less than 35 g, were found in Fosa scats. Above the tree line in the high mountain zone of Andringitra, birds, rodents, and shrew tenrecs (*Microgale*) are important components of this animal's diet; to a lesser extent, their diet includes frogs and crabs. Further, at this site the average prey body mass is only 40 g, including vertebrates weighing less than 10 g. This contrasts with an average prey body mass of 480 g in the humid forests of the north and 1140 g in the western dry deciduous forests. Some of the prey animals found in the Andringitra scats recovered above tree line were of forest-dwelling animals, indicating that these Fosas have notably large home ranges and do not rely completely on the prey base available above the forest. Fosas are known to take prey nearly their own weight, such as 6 kg lemurs of the genus *Propithecus*, but assertions that the Fosa is a lemur specialist, with these animals representing more than 50% of its diet, cannot be supported across its complete geographic range. Bone fragments of even larger animals, such as cows and bush pigs (*Potamochoerus*), have been found in Fosa scats and it is presumed that these are scavenged. Fosas have also been cited as feeding on the 1 kg endemic and endangered rodent Votsovotsa *Hypogeomys antimena*, which is known only from a limited area in central western Madagascar; heavy predation pressure and poor recruitment of young into the breeding population have been cited as reasons for the rodent's rarity. However, based on the analysis of Fosa scat obtained within this rodent's range, it represents a small proportion of the Fosa's diet. Fosa is notably adapted for hunting both on the ground and in trees. It is often seen foraging solitarily, but during the austral spring breeding season has been observed hunting communally; these foraging parties are presumably of male-female pairs. At other times of the year, mothers and their young hunt together. One Fosa will chase lemurs in trees, scaling the trunks and leaping from tree to tree, forcing the lemurs to the ground, where its hunting partners easily catch them. The Fosa's semi-retractable claws help it grip trees and its long tail, which is not prehensile, acts as a balancing device.

Activity patterns. In the eastern and more mesic portions of the island, Fosa demonstrate highly irregular periods of activity during the day and night and is best considered cathemeral. Two radio-collared individuals showed periods of peak activity soon after dawn, in the mid-afternoon, and late at night. The same general pattern has been found in drier forests in western Madagascar. Solitary individuals do not use the same sleeping sites on a regular basis, but females with young frequent the same den.

Movements, Home range and Social organization. In recent years several studies using radio collars on these animals have been conducted in the dry deciduous forests of western Madagascar. In the Kirindy (CFPF) Forest, north of Morondava, densities have been estimated at one animal per 4 km^2; females had home ranges of up to 13 km^2 and males up to 26 km^2. The home ranges of different individuals were not necessarily mutually exclusive, but those of females tended to be separate from one another. Home ranges showed seasonal variation, with notable expansion during the dry season; this is apparently related to food and water availability. The adult sex ratio is 1:1. Animals have been documented to move a straight-line distance of over 7 km in 16 h. On the basis of limited radio-tracking data from the eastern humid forests, home ranges overlapped by approximately 30%. Fosa make few vocalizations, most associated with mating. Olfactory communication seems to be common throughout the year, by scent marking prominent objects such as rocks and trees, or the ground, with a secretion from the anal and chest glands, as well as genitalia. Outside the breeding season, it is rare to find adults together, except for females with their young. Female Fosa show transient masculization: individuals 1–2 years old have an enlarged, spiny clitoris, which is physically supported by a bone-like structure, the os clitoridis, and visually resembles a penis. In these females the masculization does not appear to be associated with a pseudo-scrotum. In adult females the length of the os clitoridis decreases as body length increases. This change is not linked in juvenile (masculinized) and adult (nonmasculinized) females to different levels of hormones (testosterone, androstenedione, dihydrotestosterone). Two different hypotheses have been proposed to explain transient masculization in this species: reduced sexual harassment of juvenile females by adult males or reduced aggression from territorial females.

Breeding. Most details of reproduction in wild populations are from the western dry deciduous forests. Copulation occurs between September and December and young are born in December and January. There are conflicting reports of the gestation period in Fosa, ranging from 6–7 weeks to approximately 90 days. Whether certain of these details are applicable to eastern populations will require further field research. Reported observations of copulation in the eastern humid forest were in October. Pairs copulate on horizontal tree branches, generally about 20 cm in diameter and up to 20 m off the ground; there are also reports of intromission on the ground. Mating sites are generally near water sources. Numerous males remain in close vicinity to the receptive female. The female lays belly-down, grasps the substrate with the claws of her forelimbs, with the hind limbs tucked underneath her, and extrudes the genital opening a few centimeters. She gives a series of mewing vocalizations, which seems to stimulate the male to mount her. He mounts from behind, slightly to one side, grasps the female around the waist

On following pages: 2. Falanouc (*Eupleres goudotii*); 3. Spotted Fanaloka (*Fossa fossana*); 4. Ring-tailed Vontsira (*Galidia elegans*); 5. Broad-striped Vontsira (*Galidictis fasciata*); 6. Grandidier's Vontsira (*Galidictis grandidieri*); 7. Narrow-striped Boky (*Mungotictis decemlineata*); 8. Brown-tailed Vontsira (*Salanoia concolor*).

with his forelimbs, and often licks her neck. There is a copulatory tie, which is difficult to break if the mating session is interrupted. Copulation is repeated several times with a single male and the mating bout can last from one to 14 hours; males often remain close to the females for up to an hour after the sequence has finished. The trees where these annual mating sessions take place are often reused for years, and with remarkable precision as to the date the season commences. As many as eight males can be found around the mating site. With considerable vocalizing, there are antagonistic interactions among them as they compete to have access to the receptive female. Females seem to choose the males they mate with. Their choices are apparently not correlated with morphometric parameters in males, nor do they determine the length of an intromission bout. Over the course of several days a given female will mate with more than one male. In one case, documented by Claire Hawkins, a receptive female remained in the branches of a tree for a week, mating with numerous males. The female was then replaced by another receptive female, who mated with some of the males that had serviced the previous female as well as with newly arriving males. The litter size is generally two, although up to six young have been recorded. Birthing sites include concealed underground dens, rock crevices, or hollows in large tree trunks or termite mounds. Females raise their young alone and have three pairs of nipples—one inguinal, one ventral, and one pectoral. The neonates, weighing less than 100 g at birth, have almost white fur and are blind and toothless. Cub development is slow, with the eyes opening about 2–3 weeks after birth. Thereafter they become more active and there is a notable darkening of the fur to a pearl gray color. Litters are of mixed sexes, contrary to some previous assertions. The cubs leave the natal den for the first time around 4·5 months of age and become independent of their mother at about one year. The Fosa gets its permanent teeth at about 1·5 years and the young are sexually mature at 3–4 years of age.
Status and Conservation. CITES Appendix II. Listed in *The IUCN Red List* as Vulnerable. This species has a broad distribution across much of the forested portions of the island, including a wide variety of vegetational formations and elevational range. On the basis of current information, densities tend to be higher in less-disturbed forests. This species persists in some degraded habitats, which might be related to the considerable distances it can travel on a daily basis. Some Malagasy natives consume this species as bush meat. Fosas are known to prey on domestic fowl and other livestock, but the extent of this predation may be exaggerated. A number of diseases and viruses have been isolated from wild and captive Fosa. Several of these (anthrax, canine distemper, canine parvovirus, feline calicivirus, and *Toxoplasma gondi*) presumably were transmitted by dogs and cats that live in forested habitats and are in contact with Fosa. A combination of factors ranging from habitat destruction to hunting pressure has affected the remaining populations of Fosa across its range. Little is known about the genetic structure of wild populations, which is certainly a critical question in the development of long-term conservation programs.
Bibliography. Albignac (1970, 1972, 1973, 1975, 1984), Blancou (1968), Conservation Breeding Specialist Group (SSC/IUCN) (2002), Decary (1950), Dollar (1999a, 2006), Dollar *et al.* (2006), Garcia & Goodman (2003), Golden (2005, In press), Goodman (2003a), Goodman & Pidgeon (1999), Goodman & Raselimanana (2003), Goodman, Ganzhorn & Rakotondravony (2003), Goodman, Kerridge & Ralisoamalala (2003), Goodman, Langrand & Rasolonandrasana (1997), Goodman, Rasoloarison & Ganzhorn (2004), Grandidier & Petit (1932), Hawkins (1998, 2003), Hawkins & Racey (2005, 2007), Hawkins *et al.* (2002), Hugh-Jones & de Vos (2002), IUCN (2007), Karpanty & Wright (2006), Kaudern (1915), Kerridge *et al.* (2003), Köhncke & Leonhardt (1986), Köhncke & Schliemann (1977), Laborde (1986), Ljungquist (1930), Louvel (1954), Nicoll & Langrand (1989), Piertney *et al.* (2000), Powzyk (1997), Rahajanirina (2003), Rasamison (1997), Rasoloarison *et al.* (1995), Rasolonandrasana (1994), Schreiber *et al.* (1989), Sommer *et al.* (2002), Vosseler (1929), Wemmer & Wozencraft (1984), Willis (1895), Wright *et al.* (1997), Yoder *et al.* (2003), Youlatos (2003), ZICOMA (1999).

Genus *EUPLERES*

Doyère, 1835

2. Falanouc *Eupleres goudotii*

French: Euplère de Goudot / **German**: Ameisenschleichkatze / **Spanish**: Falanuc
Other common names: Fanaloka, Ridarida, Amboa Laolo

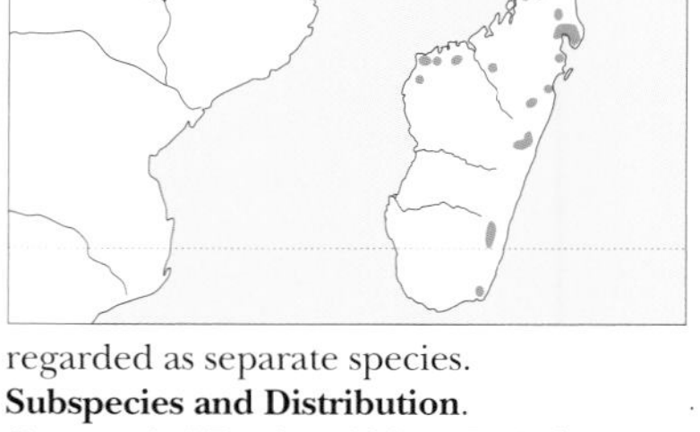

Taxonomy. *Eupleres goudotii* Doyère, 1835, "Tamatave" [= Toamasina].
The two currently recognized subspecies of *Eupleres* show numerous morphological features that readily separate them, including foot structure, pelage coloration, and cranial and dental characters. They are apparently allopatric in their distributions. Further research into the level of differentiation of these two forms will probably indicate that they should be regarded as separate species.
Subspecies and Distribution.
E. g. goudotii Doyère, 1835 – E Madagascar.
E. g. major Lavauden, 1929 – W & NW Madagascar.
Descriptive notes. In the nominate form, *E. g. goudotii*: head-body 45·5–49·5 cm, tail 22–24 cm, hindfoot 8–8·2 cm, ear 4–4·4 cm; weight 1·6–2·1 kg. *E. g. major*: head-body 51·5–65 cm, tail 24–25 cm, hindfoot 8·1–9·2 cm, ear 4·7–5 cm; weight 2·8–4·6 [with heavy fat] kg. This species has an elongated, massive body, a long, narrow rostrum, prominent ears, notably large feet, and a short, rounded and tapered tail. Non-retractable claws on the forelimbs are very well-developed. When walking, the claws touch the ground, which gives the animal a slow and sauntering gait. In the nominate subspecies, the dense and soft body and tail fur are a uniform reddish-brown and the venter a brownish-beige. *Eupleres g. major* is darker in color, with the dorsum and tail a dark brown grizzled with gray, and the thighs and underparts often have an orangish tinge.
Habitat. The nominate form occurs across the eastern portion of the island at elevations from about 50 to 1600 m. Based on current limited data, it seems to prefer tracts of upland humid forest with natural aquatic habitats, and areas of marshland dominated by *Cyperus* and *Raphia*. There are a few observations of this animal in dense mesic forests away from aquatic and marshland habitats. On Montagne d'Ambre in the far north, this species can be seen with some regularity in an open grassy field that is seasonally flooded, close to irregularly used human habitations, and within 50 m of the forest edge. Even less is known about the habitat of the W and NW form, *E. g. major*. This animal appears to have a relatively limited distribution, with most records coming from the Sambirano Region. However, it has been recorded as far south as the Baie de Baly near Soalala. Its preferred habitat has been cited as undisturbed forest areas and wetlands with *Raphia* and *Afromomum*; there is little in the way of undisturbed lowland forest in the Sambirano Region and the two cited plant genera are probably introduced to Madagascar. Much remains to be learned about this animal's habitat requirements and distribution. This species might occur on the Manongarivo Massif, but two separate expeditions to different portions of this mountain found no evidence that it did. The geographical distribution of the two subspecies needs further research. The nominate form has been reported from the Tsaratanana Massif, a portion of which falls within the Sambirano Domain, a zone that has been cited as the stronghold of *E. g. major*. The previously cited record of this species on Ile Sainte Marie, an offshore island in the east, is actually from Sainte Marie de Marovoay, in the west, near a large marsh system and not far from the Ankarafantsika reserve.
Food and Feeding. The dentition of Falanouc is notably reduced, with tiny conical and flattened cusps, adapted to a soft-bodied invertebrate diet. This animal shows numerous convergent parallels to the Aardwolf (*Proteles*) of the hyena family. Its primary food appears to be earthworms, but is also known to feed on slugs, insects, frogs, and chameleons. In captivity it will consume small bits of meat. Local people report that Falanouc feeds on the fruits of *Afromomum*. Its long claws are used for scraping food items from shallow soil or rotten wood; prey is immobilized with the jaws and teeth.
Activity patterns. On the basis of the few observations of this species, it is best considered cathemeral. Individuals of this apparently largely terrestrial and solitary species have been observed or camera-trapped in the middle of the night, during the day, and in the early morning. When threatened, rather than fleeing, Falanouc can maintain a freezing position for up to one hour. The long thin front claws are used against potential predators with a lashing action. This species is known to store up to 800 g of subcutaneous fat in the tail, estimated to represent about 20% of its average body weight. Accumulation of tail fat takes place before the cold and dry season (June to August), when accessible food, particularly invertebrates such as worms, is notably reduced. It is not known if these fat reserves are used as the energy source for some form of aestivation-hibernation, but they certainly would allow the animal to survive seasonal periods of decreased food availability. Individuals have been observed in July in the eastern humid forest, indicating that at least in this zone they are active during the cold and dry season.
Movements, Home range and Social organization. Virtually no information. All known observations in the wild are of solitary individuals or females with their offspring. The home range of this animal has been proposed to be "very large," but no numeric estimates are available. This species seems to be largely silent. In captivity only two vocalization types were noted, a sort of spitting call connected with agnostic encounters and a hiccupping sound associated with mother-infant interactions. Olfactory communication is important, particularly during the breeding season, when individuals use different glands to mark territories and for other kinds of signals. Both males and females can be seen rubbing the anal gland on low vegetation and prominent rocks, and, to a lesser extent, rubbing the neck gland on vertical surfaces. It has been proposed that Falanoucs can dig their own dens in the soil; however, their long, thin claws are not really adapted for this type of activity. Animals captured by Roland Albignac did not show abraded claws. This species probably occupies previously existing burrows and holes, rather than digging these from scratch. It apparently sleeps at the base of trees, sometimes using those protected by dense vegetation. Sub-adults are known to sleep in tree branches up to 1·6 m off the ground; this behavior is unrecorded in adults.
Breeding. Few details are available on reproduction in the wild and the following is largely from captive animals. Copulation, which has yet to be observed, presumably takes place between August and September. The only recorded births were in mid-November, and each litter comprised a single young, although there are reports of litters of two. Females have one pair of inguinal mammae. Neonates weigh 150 g, their eyes are open, and the pelage is noticeably darker than that of adults. Within one or two days the young are able to walk normally and after a month they climb to arboreal sleeping sites. They are weaned at about nine weeks. The age of sexual maturity is unknown. In captivity these animals are apparently very susceptible to stress and difficult to maintain, but successful breeding has occurred at least on three occasions.
Status and Conservation. CITES Appendix II. Listed in *The IUCN Red List* as Near Threatened; however, the result of a Conservation Breeding Specialist Group workshop sponsored by the IUCN/SSC held in 2001 and attended by specialists working on Madagascar Carnivores gave the status of this species as Vulnerable. Given the secretive nocturnal habits of Falanouc and that few field researchers venture into marshlands, its apparently preferred habitat, little information is available to assess its conservation

status. In total, there are fewer than 20 recent locality-based records of this animal, and estimates of the total adult population are impossible to make. In the 1990 and 1994 Red Data Books it was listed as Vulnerable, but on the basis of several human-related pressures, its status has been elevated to Endangered. These factors include ongoing habitat loss and degradation, hunting pressure for bush meat, and introduced species. Problems with introduced species have been cited as competition or outright predation from feral or hunting dogs and the Small Indian Civet, but no data have been published verifying this interaction. Virtually all terrestrial mammals on Madagascar are subject to some form of hunting pressure, often localized, and it is not clear that Falanouc is preferred bush meat.

Bibliography. Albignac (1973, 1974, 1984), Conservation Breeding Specialist Group (SSC/IUCN) (2002), Dollar (1999b, 2006), Goodman & Pidgeon (1999), Goodman & Soarimalala (2002), Goodman, Ganzhorn & Rakotondravony (2003), Grandidier & Petit (1932), Hawkins (1994), IUCN (2007), Kaudern (1915), Nicoll & Langrand (1989), Schreiber et al. (1989).

Genus FOSSA
Gray, 1865

3. Spotted Fanaloka *Fossa fossana*
French: Fossane / **German**: Fanaloka / **Spanish**: Fosana
Other common names: Malagasy Civet, Tombokatosody, Tomkasodina, Tambosadina, Kavahy, Fanaloka

Taxonomy. *Viverra fossana* Müller, 1776, Madagascar.
The specific name of this animal has varied in the literature: *Fossa fossa, F. daubentoni*, and *F. majori* are all synonyms of *F. fossana*. Monotypic.
Distribution. Madagascar.
Descriptive notes. Head-body 40–45 cm, tail 22·1–26·4 cm, hindfoot 8·4–9·3 cm, ear 4·4–4·8 cm; weight of adult males 1·5–1·9 kg and adult females 1·3–1·75 kg. These weights are probably at the lower end of the normal range, as trapping occurred during the winter, when food may have been in short supply. This animal, with its short legs, pointed snout, bushy tail, and large body is very reminiscent of a civet; hence the misleading and formerly used English common name "Malagasy Civet". The dense dorsal pelage ranges from tan to light brown. There are two nearly continuous black mid-dorsal lines. These are bordered by a row of partially-broken stripes. Below them is a row of spots on the flanks; there are also scattered spots on the flanks. The throat, lower neck, and balance of venter vary in color from cream to pale orange. The tail is medium brown with a series of concentric rings and spots.
Habitat. This species occurs in a variety of habitat types, but seems most common in humid eastern forests from near sea level to about 1300 m. In this habitat it is usually found in areas with watercourses. It is known to occur in forested limestone canyons in the Réserve Spéciale d'Ankarana, a dry deciduous forest with no permanent ground water, and has been found resting on sand in littoral forests in the vicinity of Tolagnaro. It also has been seen in the transitional dry-humid forests of the Sambirano and the isolated humid forest of Montagne d'Ambre.
Food and Feeding. In the eastern humid forests of Madagascar, Spotted Fanaloka feeds on various prey, but seems to specialize on aquatic organisms such as amphibians, crustaceans, crabs, eels, and perhaps invertebrate larvae, which it readily hunts in shallow water. It also feeds on terrestrial insects, reptiles, small birds, rodents, and tenrecids. In a study of scat remains recovered at humid forest sites in the south-east, prey items included three species of rodent (two introduced); up to six species of tenrecids; crabs; snakes; frogs; millipedes; various types of beetles; grasshoppers; and a lizard. There are notable seasonal shifts in its diet. At the end of the wet season, insects, reptiles, and amphibians make up 96% of the diet, and during the dry season insects, crabs, and mammals compose 94%. This species also has been trapped with fruit bait.
Activity patterns. Spotted Fanaloka is nocturnal and digitigrade. It stores fat in the tail before the start of the cold dry season, when many forest organisms in its prey base become scarce. These fat deposits can reach 25% of the normal body mass and allow the animal to survive periods of food scarcity. There is no evidence that this species aestivates or hibernates.
Movements, Home range and Social organization. Few details are available and most come from the region of Vevembe. Here Spotted Fanaloka density was high: 22 animals were trapped in an area of about 2 km² during the last two weeks of July 1999. Ten of these animals were recaptured during the two-week period and the rest may have been non-territorial transients. This study occurred during the cold dry season, which is presumably a lean period for food. Preliminary analyses of four individuals radiotracked from mid-July to the end of September 1999 provided home range estimates for males and females of 0·07 to 0·52 km². This study ended at the start of the mating season, when males remain close to females in small core areas of their established territory, presumably to guard against the intrusion of unpaired males. Spotted Fanaloka is not known to occupy ground dens, but rather to live in tree trunk hollows and rock shelters. Spotted Fanaloka apparently does not have a large vocal repertoire. It uses a muffled growl during agonistic encounters and a cry for adult-young communication. It has a strong, distinctive musky smell and olfactory signaling is important. Glands on the neck and cheeks and an anal gland, particularly well-developed during the breeding season, are used in olfactory communication and to mark territories.
Breeding. Spotted Fanaloka is a seasonal breeder, with copulation occurring in August and September and births from October to December. The gestation period, based on captive animals, is 80–89 days. Females have one pair of inguinal mammae. The single young weighs about 100 g at birth and is developmentally precocious. The tail rings and back markings are more distinct than in adults. Neonates are born with their eyes open. They start to crawl within a day after birth and are walking on day three. The incisors erupt by day three and the premolars on day five. The ears open on day eight. The young eat solid food after about a month and are weaned within 2·5 months. They are adult size after one year.
Status and Conservation. CITES Appendix II. Listed in *The IUCN Red List* as Near Threatened. However, the result of a Conservation Breeding Specialist Group workshop sponsored by the IUCN/SSC in 2001 and attended by specialists working on Madagascar Carnivores gave the status of this species as Least Concern. It has been suggested that its strongholds are in the Mananara and Masoala portions of the east. Biological exploration of this vast region of eastern Madagascar in the past few decades has made it clear that Spotted Fanaloka has a broad distribution in the relatively intact portions of this zone, as well as in a few other formations. Unlike some other small species of Eupleridae, such as Ring-tailed Vontsira, Spotted Fanaloka does not seem to occur in, or have the ability to colonize, secondary forest habitats. In the countryside, Spotted Fanalokas are considered vermin because of their purported predation on chickens. Villagers kill them and other carnivores caught raiding fowl and also set traps in the forest baited with rats or mice. People also hunt them for food. As habitat degradation and human persecution of this species continues, their status of Vulnerable is unlikely to improve. Little is known about the genetic structure of wild populations across the island, which is certainly a critical question in the development of long-term conservation programs.

Bibliography. Albignac (1971a, 1972, 1973, 1984), Conservation Breeding Specialist Group (SSC/IUCN) (2002), Duckworth & Rakotondraparany (1990), Golden (2005), Goodman & Pidgeon (1999), Goodman, Kerridge & Ralisoamalala (2003), IUCN (2007), Jenkins & Carleton (2005), Kerridge et al. (2003), Sovey et al. (2001), Wemmer (1971), ZICOMA (1999).

Subfamily GALIDIINAE
Genus GALIDIA
Geoffroy Saint-Hilaire, 1837

4. Ring-tailed Vontsira *Galidia elegans*
French: Galidie à queue annelée / **German**: Ringelschwanzmungo / **Spanish**: Galidia de cola anillada
Other common names: Ring-tailed Mongoose, Vontsira, Vontsira Mena, Kokia, Vontsika

Taxonomy. *Galidia elegans* Geoffroy Saint-Hilaire, 1837, Madagascar, subsequently restricted to the region of "Tamatave" [= Toamasina].
The relationships between the subspecies have not been examined in a modern phylogeographic sense and in certain cases the characters used to separate them are ambiguous. The subspecific status of certain geographically intermediate populations remains unresolved (e.g. Sambirano Basin, lake region to the west of Bemaraha, and the forests near Daraina). Captive hybrids between these different geographical forms produce fertile young. Three subspecies recognized.
Subspecies and distribution.
G. e. elegans Geoffroy Saint-Hilaire, 1837 – E Madagascar (from the region surrounding the Andapa Basin S to Tolagnaro).
G. e. dambrensis Tate & Rand, 1941 – N Madagascar (originally described from Montagne d'Ambre, but animals at Ankarana are also referable to this form).
G. e. occidentalis Albignac, 1971 – CW Madagascar (limestone regions of Bemaraha, Namoroka & Kelifely).
Descriptive notes. Measurements of the nominate form *elegans*: head-body 30–38 cm, tail 26–29·1 cm, hindfoot 6–7·2 cm, ear 2·8–3 cm; weight 655–965 g. The external measurements of the other subspecies largely overlap. There is some indication of sexual dimorphism in body size based on measurements made at Ranomafana in the eastern humid forest—eight adult males averaged 992 g (range 900–1085 g) and two adult females weighed 760 and 890 g respectively. The body form is typically mongoose-like (hence the inappropriate English common name "Ring-tailed Mongoose" that has been used in the past), with relatively short feet and a fluffy furred tail that is slightly more than two-thirds of the body length. The nominate form is the darkest, with body coloration a somber dark or reddish-chestnut, throat fulvous, top and sides of the head fulvous grizzled with black, and venter, feet and flanks nearly black. There is considerable variation in the pelage coloration of this subspecies, particularly with regard to the venter. The tail is marked with five to seven alternating dark reddish-brown and nearly black bands. The ears are noticeable, but not prominent, and are edged with a light-colored border. The other recognized subspecies tend to be paler

than the nominate form, without dark venters, but the characters generally used to differentiate them are highly variable. *Galidia e. dambrensis* tends to have five dark tail rings. Ring-tailed Vontsira have relatively large feet, with well-developed and naked footpads. There is also webbing at the bases of the toes. The hindfeet are longer than the forefeet, and the claws are not retractable. These various adaptations allow the Ring-tailed Vontsira to walk and run on the ground, climb trees, and swim.

Habitat. This species is the most conspicuous native carnivoran on the island, and occurs in most types of natural forest formations with the exception of the southern portion of the western deciduous forest and the south-western spiny bush. Populations in eastern Madagascar are known from littoral forests on sandy substrates and close to sea level, through the complete range of eastern humid forests up to the forest line at 1950 m. The Ring-tailed Vontsira can be seen short distances from relatively intact forest, in secondary forest and even in clearings. In the far northern end of the island, *G. e. dambrensis* occurs in the distinctly humid forests of Montagne d'Ambre, which grow on lateritic soils, from about 650 m to the summital zone at 1475 m, as well as in areas of mixed mesic-dry deciduous forest within the exposed karst of Ankarana. *Galidia e. occidentalis* is known from widely separated zones of limestone and occurs in canyons and zones with relatively mesic habitat. Animals recorded at Tsimembo, in close proximity to Bemaraha and outside of the limestone zone, are presumably of this subspecies.

Food and Feeding. This species is omnivorous, feeding on a wide variety of small mammals (rodents, tenrecs, and lemurs), aquatic animals (fish and frogs), reptiles (including large snakes), invertebrates (crabs, crayfish, snails, worms, pill millipedes, and insects, including larvae), as well as bird eggs. It has been recorded digging rodents weighing up to 200 g out of burrows, and feeding on different species of lemur, the largest being Eastern Wooly Lemur *Avahi laniger*, which weighs on average 1·2 kg. It is not clear whether Ring-tailed Vontsira caught the *Avahi* or stole it from a bird of prey. On several occasions, Ring-tailed Vontsira have been observed resting silently at the edge of small streams, then leaping into the water and seizing prey that was presumed to be fish, frogs, or crayfish. The partially webbed forefeet help with aquatic propulsion to subdue prey. Ring-tailed Vontsiras are camp pests; once accustomed to the presence of humans they do not hesitate to raid food supplies or scavenge in camp trash. They are reputed by rural villagers to feed on poultry. This vontsira has a semi-digitgrade gait and notably fleshy footpads that aid it in climbing nearly vertical tree trunks, fine horizontal branches, and lianas. This species has the ability to jump from horizontal to vertical vegetation. The population at Montagne d'Ambre (*dambrensis*) often searches for food in trees, up to 15 m off the ground. Here animals frequently can be seen probing in tree holes and epiphytic plants for invertebrates and small vertebrates, which they consume immediately upon capture. In the eastern central lowland, at Betampona, nearly 13% of all observations were in arboreal situations, generally less than 5 m off the ground, although in one case an animal was found at around 12 m. Various diurnal forest birds will mob this carnivore, presumably because of its habit of stealing eggs and young birds from nests. In the eastern humid forests, Ring-tailed Vontsira is sympatric with other relatively small carnivores, particularly the slightly larger Broad-striped Vontsira and the slightly smaller Brown-tailed Vontsira. Temporal niche separation may reduce competition between Ring-tailed Vontsira, which is diurnal, and *Galidictis*, which is nocturnal. Few details are available on the diet of the latter species to evaluate this hypothesis. A comparative study at Betampona, where the largely diurnal Brown-tailed Vontsira and Ring-tailed Vontsira co-occur, noted a number of differences between them in prey type and habitat utilization.

Activity patterns. Recent work on radio-collared Ring-tailed Vontsira has demonstrated that they are not exclusively diurnal, as previously thought, but are occasionally active during the night. Ring-tailed Vontsiras tend to have bouts of activity in the early morning and late afternoon. They are generally considered to be terrestrial, but are agile climbers of trees.

Movements, Home range and Social organization. Roland Albignac conducted fieldwork on this species in several different forest types and consistently estimated home range size, extrapolated from trapping studies, to be 20 to 25 ha. On the basis of a short-term capture-mark-release study in humid forest in the Ranomafana National Park, the density index was estimated to be 37 animals per km^2, which may be a slight overestimation. An animal marked in the humid forest in the extreme south-east at 810 m elevation was observed several days later at 1200 m, a straight-line distance of about 2·5 km. In some zones it can reach noticeably high densities. For example, at 1000 m on Montagne d'Ambre, it was very common in the mid-1990s. During the course of seven days of trapping at this locality, with 20 carnivore traps set each day, more than 28 Ring-tailed Vontsira were captured in a relatively limited area. This forested site has high densities of introduced *Rattus*, which the Ring-tailed Vontsira feed upon. Little is published about the social organization of this species in the wild, but based on field studies it appears to live, at least seasonally, solitarily or in small groups of three to four individuals. The small groups presumably are composed of a male-female pair and their sub-adult young. Aggressive encounters between individuals, particularly adult males, often include a distinctive submissive display by the non-dominant animal. The submissive animal bends the front limbs so the chest practically touches the ground, the ears are folded backwards, the teeth exposed, and the snout is pointed up, almost touching the face of the dominant animal. When the dominant individual approaches, the submissive animal gives a loud, high-pitched screeching vocalization. Trapped animals produce a two-part threat call, a guttural growl followed by a raspy spitting sound. This species is rather vocal and its auditory signals have been classified into four types: a whistle-like contact call between family members, often given while moving through the forest; a specific prey capture call; growl and shrill screams as intimidation, attack or defense calls; and a copulation vocalization. Adults regularly scent-mark within their home range using urine and a form of musk produced by their perineal, cheek, and sub-mandibular glands. Dens of this species have been found in a variety of settings, and it is capable of digging its own burrow systems. In exposed sedimentary rock zones, such as the Bemaraha Plateau, lairs have been found in rock crevices and subterranean passages. In the humid forests of the east, dens tend to be in the ground under large trees, in carved-out soil fissures along riverbanks, or in the hollow bases of large standing trees or downed hollow logs. Often the dens have numerous openings. They are not necessarily used by the same individuals on consecutive nights.

Breeding. Mating in the eastern forests generally takes place between July and November. The gestation period is about 75 days and litter size is one. Females have one pair of inguinal mammae. Before copulation the male pursues the female with increasing intensity and both animals mark prominent objects with the cheek and sub-mandibular glands. Males frequently sniff the females' urogenital region. Copulation takes place after the female solicits the male by lowering and quivering the anterior portion of the body and slowly treading the hindquarters. Neck biting was not observed in this species. Individual copulation bouts usually last 10–30 seconds and the complete sequence of 7–12 copulations takes place during a period of 15–80 minutes. Neonates are fully furred, generally weigh between 40 and 50 g, and have the same pelage coloration as adults. The auditory canal is open at birth, the eyes open on day 4, the incisors erupt on day 8, and the premolars on day 21. Walking commences at day 12. Weaning takes place at approximately 2 to 2·5 months and the young start to hunt small prey at three months; they retain the deciduous dentition until seven months. After the young become active, they can be seen foraging in the forest with their parents; they probably remain with their parents for up to one year, when they reach adult size. They reach reproductive age at two years. There is some evidence that in some portions of this species' range, females may reproduce twice in good years. This might explain pairs being observed with two young of different sizes.

Status and Conservation. Listed in *The IUCN Red List* as Least Concern. The result of a Conservation Breeding Specialist Group workshop sponsored by the SSC/IUCN held in 2001 and attended by specialists working on Madagascar Carnivores gave the status of *G. e. elegans* and *G. e. occidentalis* as Least Concern and that of *G. e. dambrensis* as Vulnerable. Continued reduction of forest cover across this species' range is a major pressure on existing populations. Perhaps of less importance is the utilization of body parts of this animal, particularly in the southern portions of its range, for various medicinal and supernatural potions, as well as its being hunted for bush meat. It can be found at the ecotone between forest and anthropogenic zones, where it is in contact and conflict with people and their domestic animals. Ring-tailed Vontsira are considered poultry raiders and are hunted and persecuted. Their bad reputation may not be deserved, since Ring-tailed Vontsira is a conspicuous diurnal animal. In general, given the wide distribution of Ring-tailed Vontsira on Madagascar and their relatively high densities in certain areas, they are among the less threatened native Carnivora on the island. Further, they occur in regenerating forests, cross open areas between forest fragments, and are seen where there are non-native trees in close proximity to native forests.

Bibliography. Albignac (1969, 1973, 1984), Britt & Virkaitis (2003), Carlsson (1910), Conservation Breeding Specialist Group (SSC/IUCN) (2002), Decary (1950), Dunham (1998), Golden (2005), Goodman (1996a, 2003a, 2003b), Goodman & Pidgeon (1999), IUCN (2007), Jenkins & Carleton (2005), Larkin & Roberts (1979), Pocock (1915a), Rand (1935), Ryan *et al.* (1993), Tate & Rand (1941), Wesener & Sierwald (2005).

Genus *GALIDICTIS*

Geoffroy Saint-Hilaire, 1839

5. Broad-striped Vontsira *Galidictis fasciata*

French: Galidie à bandes larges / **German**: Breitstreifenmungo / **Spanish**: Galidia bandeada

Other common names: Broad-striped Malagasy Mongoose, Vontsira Fotsy, Bakiaka Betanimena, Bakiaka Belemboka

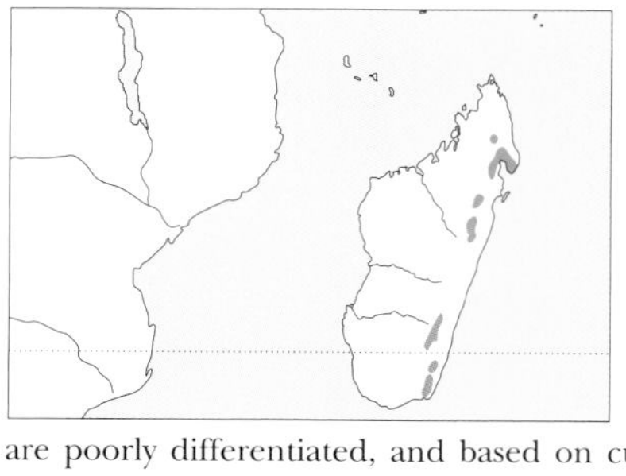

Taxonomy. *Viverra fasciata* Gmelin, 1788, type locality presumed to be Madagascar, erroneously listed by Gmelin as "India". Pocock revised this genus and recognized two species occurring in the eastern humid forest: *G. eximius* in the north and *G. ornatus* in the south. Subsequently, Albignac reduced these to one species and recognized *G. eximius* as *G. f. fasciatus* and *G. ornatus* as *G. f. striata*. These two geographic forms are recognized here, but are poorly differentiated, and based on current evidence probably do not warrant recognition.

Subspecies and Distribution.

G. f. fasciata Gmelin, 1788 – C & SE Madagascar (at least as far N as the Kianjavato region).

G. f. striata Geoffroy Saint-Hilaire, 1826 – CE Madagascar (from near Brickaville and N to the Sihanaka Forest E of Lac Alaotra).

Descriptive notes. Head-body 30–34 cm, tail 24·9–29·3 cm, hindfoot 6·9–7·4 cm, ear 3–3·2 cm; weight 520–745 g. The body form is mongoose-like, with relatively short feet and a furred unicolored tail that is a little less than one-half of the body length. The dorsal pelage is an overall grayish-beige that extends to the feet and proximal portion of tail. The head is a grizzled grayish brown, and the venter is distinctly paler. The distal two-thirds of the tail is a distinct creamy-white. The dorsum is marked from the nape to the base of the tail with distinct dark brown longitudinal bands that are wider or equal in width to the grayish-beige interlines.

Habitat. Broad-striped Vontsira occurs in the eastern humid forests of the island, across an elevation range from lowland forest to montane forest at about 1500 m. It is not known from littoral forests on sandy substrate. Recent exploration of the eastern humid forest indicates that it has a much broader geographic range than previously recognized, from at least Masoala in the north to Andohahela in the south. Reports from the mountains surrounding the Andapa Basin need further verification. Most records are from relatively intact forests, but it has been reported from degraded forested habitats. A previous report of this species in a salt marsh is a mistaken record of Grandidier's Vontsira.

Food and Feeding. No quantitative information is available on the diet of this species, but it has been inferred to feed largely on rodents and small lemurs, and perhaps on reptiles and amphibians. It is known to raid forest camp food reserves on occasion, but its reputation as a chicken thief in villages needs to be verified based on scat analysis.

Activity patterns. Very few details are available. This species is largely terrestrial and secretive. Individuals have been trapped on large downed logs and observed climbing in trees up to 1·5 m above the ground. During field inventories, it is trapped as often as it is seen, further attesting to its secretive habits.

Movements, Home range and Social organization. No precise details available. It has never been found in high densities in carnivore surveys and it is poorly known by people living near the forest edge. This might be because it is nocturnal and seems not to venture outside of the forest. At several sites, local informants claimed to be familiar with "vontsira fotsy", but further questioning made it clear that they confused this species with the Small Indian Civet (*Viverricula indica*), an introduced carnivore with superficially similar pelage that occurs in open areas and at the forest edge.

Breeding. It has been proposed that the social life of Broad-striped Vontsira is similar to that of Ring-tailed Vontsira, but few details are available on its reproductive activities and seasonality. A female captured in the south-east in November 1995, did not show signs of reproductive activity and the following day at the same site a sub-adult was trapped. Females have a single pair of inguinal mammae. Males with scrotal testes have been captured between late October and late November.

Status and Conservation. Listed in *The IUCN Red List* as Near Threatened. This species has a broad distribution in the eastern humid forests of Madagascar, including montane forest habitat that remains relatively untouched as compared to lowland forests. Presumably it is widely distributed and occurs at relatively low densities.

Bibliography. Albignac (1973), Barden *et al.* (1991), Goodman (1996a, 1996b, 2003a, 2003c), Goodman & Pidgeon (1999), Grandidier & Petit (1932), Hawkins *et al.* (2000), IUCN (2007), Nicoll (2008), Pocock (1915a, 1915b), Schreiber *et al.* (1989), Wozencraft (1986).

6. Grandidier's Vontsira *Galidictis grandidieri*

French: Galidie de Grandidier / **German**: Großer Breitstreifenmungo / **Spanish**: Galidia de Wozencraft

Other common names: Grandidier's Mongoose, Votsotsoke

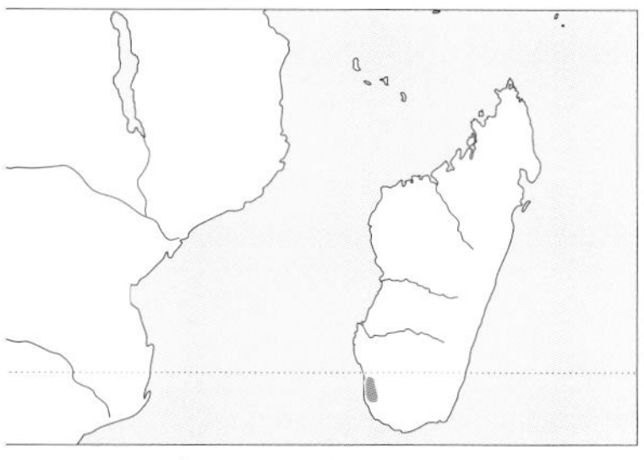

Taxonomy. *Galidictis grandidiensis* Wozencraft, 1986, Madagascar.

Galidictis grandidiensis was subsequently emended to *G. grandidieri*. After the recent description of this species based on two modern specimens, one of which had precise collection information, subfossil remains were identified from a cave about 50 km south of this site. If the subfossil remains had been studied before the recent description of this taxon, it would have been named as an extinct taxon. Monotypic.

Distribution. Extreme SW Madagascar.

Descriptive notes. Head-body 45–48 cm, tail 30–32·6 cm, ear 9–9·5 cm, hindfoot 3·9–4·5 cm; weight 1–1·5 kg. Recent fieldwork of J. Jeglinski and colleagues has provided additional body mass data: one adult male weighed 1723 g and four adult females had a mean weight of 1494 g. Other than body mass, there is no evidence of sexual dimorphism in this species. The body is typically mongoose-like, with a relatively long pointed snout. The bushy tail lacks rings and is a little less than one-half of the head and body length. The dorsal and ventral pelage is dark grayish-beige, the tail white, and the rostrum and feet grizzled reddish-brown. The distal portions of the ears are covered with a fine layer of short fur. Eight dark brown longitudinal stripes on the dorsum, all roughly parallel and about 5–7 mm wide, run from behind the ears and converge at the base of the tail. The 8–12 mm spaces between the stripes are white and slightly wider than the stripes but with considerable variation between individuals. The feet are notably elongated and there is webbing between the toes. The hindfeet are longer than the forefeet. The claws are long and non-retractable.

Habitat. This species occurs in the rugged limestone zone to the south of the Onilahy River known as the Mahafaly Plateau, which is aligned along a north–south axis. It is known from an elevational range of 35 to 145 m. This portion of the island receives on average less than 400 m of rainfall per year and daily temperatures can exceed 40°C. Soon after its original description in 1986, Grandidier's Vontsira was "rediscovered" in the portion of the Mahafaly Plateau just to the east of the coastal plain comprising the large alkaline Lac Tsimanampetsotsa; one of the type specimens was collected at this site. Grandidier's Vontsira can be found in two distinct local xerophytic vegetational communities: at the base of the plateau, which is dominated by *Didierea madagascariensis* (Didiereaceae) and a variety of Euphorbiaceae and Burseraceae; and in the spiny bush formation on the exposed limestone escarpment on the western portion of the Mahafaly Plateau. At numerous sites on the lower western side of the plateau, there is the resurgence of an underground aquifer along a north–south geological fault. Considerable portions of the upland and eastern portions of the plateau are without water sources for tens of kilometers. Most of the recent sightings of this species are at sites along this fault line, where there are natural water sources. While it is unknown if *Galidictis* is obliged to drink water on a regular basis, the prey base near these water sources is higher in density and diversity than surrounding areas without water.

Food and Feeding. Little is known about the food habits of this Vontsira. During an ornithological expedition to Lac Tsimanampetsotsa in 1929, this carnivore was found soon after dark digging up the carcasses of skinned birds. On the basis of some unpublished scat analyses of material collected at Lac Tsimanampetsotsa, it feeds predominantly on invertebrates. By far the most common was hissing cockroaches (*Gromphadorhina*). Other prey types include locusts, scorpions, and rarely, vertebrates. There is some evidence that it might feed on radiated tortoise (*Geochelone radiata*) and perhaps carrion.

Activity patterns. Grandidier's Vontsira is strictly nocturnal, becoming active shortly after sunset and returning to its den well before dawn. It was thought to be exclusively terrestrial, but recent observations of J. Jeglinski indicate that it climbs in trees.

Movements, Home range and Social organization. Few details are currently available, but an ongoing radio-tracking study by researchers from the University of Hamburg should fill in numerous details. Preliminary results, based on a trapping study, indicate that minimum densities are about five animals per km^2. Current data indicate that the home range of males is relatively large and probably overlapping between individuals, resulting in lower density than the females. In one case, an animal moved during a single night 1·5 km direct-line distance. Solitary individuals and groups of two are frequently observed. More rarely, groups of up to five are seen. Observations of single animals are most likely predominantly of males; pairs are generally of females with their offspring; and sightings of three or more animals are disproportionately of males. In male groups, aggressive interactions can be observed and the females generally initiate these encounters towards the males. Easily visible at night, the white tail probably has an important signaling function. This species places its dens in the labyrinth of holes and caves in the karstic limestone making up the Mahafaly Plateau. These are generally located in areas of exposed rock without vegetation and generally associated with nearby latrine sites. In a few known cases, the crevices reach depths of several meters, where these animals can escape the intense day heat. One den was found in a hollow tree about 3 m off the ground. On the basis of a radio-tracking study, during a period of 16 consecutive days, a female with juvenile utilized seven different dens aligned along the limestone cliff across a maximum distance of 1 km. Current evidence seems to indicate that the same burrow is not necessarily used on consecutive days. There is no evidence that this species excavates burrows, but given the rocky substrate it lives on, this is not unexpected. Latrine sites are notably conspicuous and found near prominent features of the landscape (e.g., hill crests, prominent rocks, and outcrops).

Breeding. Few details available. It has been proposed that there is not a fixed reproductive season in this species, and they breed throughout the year. During a rapid survey at Lac Tsimanampetsotsa in November 1989, a number of captured females were in different stages of reproduction, including lactating, pregnant, and in estrus; sub-adults of different ages were also trapped. Thus, it was concluded that this species breeds throughout the year. However, given the high degree of seasonality of meteorological patterns, particularly rainfall, it is assumed that the prey base of Grandidier's Vontsira would show notable fluctuations. These patterns might be partially offset in places by the permanent water sources along the fault line. Recent data document some seasonality in the testicle volume of adult males, which suggests some seasonality in reproduction. However, females were observed during the same period with offspring of notably different sizes, which supports the hypothesis that reproductive activity is not seasonal. A specimen collected in March had two placental scars, which would indicate a litter size of up to two. Females have one pair of inguinal mammae.

Status and Conservation. Listed in *The IUCN Red List* as Endangered. However, the result of a Conservation Breeding Specialist Group workshop sponsored by the IUCN/SSC held in 2001 and attended by specialists working on Madagascar Carnivores gave the status of this species as Threatened. The calculated surface area of the narrow band of habitat where Grandidier's Vontsira has been observed is 442 km^2, of which 118 km^2 falls within the Parc National de Tsimanampetsotsa. On the basis of preliminary trapping data from different areas along the Mahafaly Plateau, a rough estimate of 6–8 individuals per km^2 has been advanced. This translates to a population within its known distribution of approximately 2650–3540 animals. Recently, based on more extensive trapping data, an estimate of five individuals per km^2 has been suggested, which provides an estimate of about 2200. A significant portion of its range is in a zone of relatively undisturbed spiny bush habitat at the western edge of the Mahafaly Plateau and in a region that has been proposed for an extension of the Parc National de Tsimanampetsotsa. This zone is relatively free of heavy anthropogenic pressure, other than browsing by cattle, which occurs mostly at the foot of the plateau, and some exploitation of forest resources for local utilization (construction wood and medicinal plants).

Bibliography. Conservation Breeding Specialist Group (SSC/IUCN) (2002), Goodman (1996b), Goodman, Ganzhorn & Rakotondravony (2003), Goodman, Raherilalao *et al.* (2002), IUCN (2007), Mahazotahy *et al.* (2006), Rand (1935), Wozencraft (1986, 1987, 1990).

Genus *MUNGOTICTIS*

Pocock, 1915

7. Narrow-striped Boky *Mungotictis decemlineata*

French: Galidie à dix raies / **German**: Schmalstreifenmungo / **Spanish**: Galidia rayada

Other common names: Narrow-striped Mongoose, Boky, Boky-boky

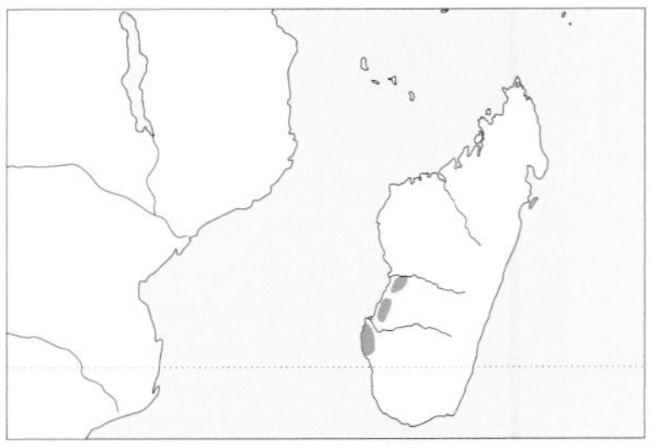

Taxonomy. *Galidia decemlineata* Grandidier, 1867, "à la côte ouest de Madagascar". The previous statement that the type locality is the "east coast of Madagascar" is incorrect.

An animal from the Toliara region was described as *Galidictis vittata*. This species was subsequently transferred to the genus *Mungotictis* by Pocock, which contained two species: *M. vittatus*, which was preoccupied by *G. vittata*, and *M. substriatus*, which was renamed as *M. lineatus*. To further complicate the situation, Pocock was apparently unaware of the description of *Galidia decemlineata*, the senior synonym that replaced *vittatus* (sensu Gray, 1848). Finally, R. Albignac divided the species into two geographic forms, *M. d. decemlineata* and *M. d. lineata*, but the single specimen he referred to the latter form was actually of Grandidier's Vontsira. The name *M. d. lineata* has been retained for the south-western population, which until 2005 was only known from a single specimen associated with *M. lineatus*. *M. d. lineata* is maintained here as a geographical form. Several measurement and pelage coloration characters separate this population from those occurring farther north. These differences may warrant the two geographical forms being recognized as full species; molecular studies should help to resolve this point. Two subspecies recognized.

Subspecies and Distribution.

M. d. decemlineata Grandidier, 1867 – CW Madagascar (Menabe region).

M. d. lineata Pocock, 1915 – SW Madagascar (S of the Mangoky River). The previous records of this form in the Lac Tsimanampetsotsa area are misidentified specimens of Grandidier's Vontsira.

Descriptive notes. Adults of the nominate form from the central Menabe region, *M. d. decemlineata*: head-body 26·4–29·4 cm, tail 19·1–20·9 cm, hindfoot 6–6·2 cm, ear 2·4–2·5 cm; weight of adult males is 475–625 g, adult females is 450–740 g, and juveniles 350–490 g. No apparent sexual dimorphism in external measurements. Measurements of an adult female *M. d. lineata* include: head-body 33·5 cm, tail 21·5 cm, hindfoot 5·9 cm, ear 2·5 cm. The Narrow-striped Boky's long, pointed snout, cylindrical body, short legs, and long bushy tail easily distinguish this relatively small animal from other Madagascar Carnivores. The dorsal pelage coloration of the nominate form is a grizzled gray mixed with light brown or beige and is characterized by eight to ten broadly-spaced, thin longitudinal stripes running from the nape to the base of the tail. The venter and legs are monochrome pale brownish-beige to pale orangish-brown. The ears are short and rounded. The light gray tail is without stripes or rings. There is webbing between the toes and the claws are long. *Mungotictis d. lineata* has a darker dorsum and the back stripes are darker and more distinct. They start as well-defined stripes higher on the nape and just behind the ears. The venter is distinctly darker than the nominate form's and approaches a russet color.

Habitat. In the central and northern portions of its distribution, the Narrow-striped Boky occurs at elevations from near sea level to 400 m in dry deciduous forests on sandy substrate. Baobab trees are often the dominant vegetation. These forested zones tend to have relatively intact habitat, with a dense understory and notably homogenous vegetational structure and floristic composition. The Tsiribihina River forms its northern distributional limit. This species tends to be distinctly more common in the larger areas of native forest and is uncommon, absent or extirpated from smaller and degraded forest blocks. In 2004, an individual referable to *M. d. lineata* was captured on the southern bank of the Manombo River at approximately 400 m above sea level and in dry deciduous forest. On both banks of the river, thin alluvial soils support a 25–50 m wide band of disturbed gallery forest immediately adjacent to the flood plain. Beyond this, the gallery forest gives way to dry deciduous forest, with a taller canopy layer.

Food and Feeding. Narrow-striped Boky is primarily insectivorous. In one study 69 of 71 scats contained insects. Particularly during the extended dry-cold season, it feeds largely on insect larvae, which are extracted by digging them out from soil or rotten wood. This species is also known to feed on a variety of vertebrates, including reptiles, birds, and small mammals (tenrecs, shrew-tenrecs, native rodents, and lemurs), as well as other invertebrates such as snails. Scat analyses found a variety of primate remains, including Gray Mouse Lemur (*Microcebus murinus*), Lesser Dwarf Lemur, Giant Mouse Lemur (*Mirza coquereli*), and Red-tailed Sportive Lemur (*Lepilemur ruficaudatus*), of which the Red-tailed Sportive Lemur, weighing close to 850 g, is the largest and was probably scavenged. Remains of the rodent Votsovotsa, which can weigh over 1 kg, also were found and presumably were also the result of scavenging. There are records of this species cooperatively hunting prey such as mouse-lemurs, adults of which weigh more than 50 g. Based on local folklore, Narrow-striped Boky is reputed to feed on large boas and regularly on wild honey. There is no evidence of extensive fat storage before the onset of the dry season.

Activity patterns. Narrow-striped Boky is largely diurnal, but on occasion can be active at night. This species is considered scansorial; it mainly moves on the ground but can climb and descend trees, including vertical surfaces. It has been reported to swim, but no recent confirmation of this behavior is available.

Movements, Home range and Social organization. Earlier studies, largely of Narrow-striped Boky in captivity, concluded that they were not particularly social but tend to live in couples. Recent research in the wild indicates that they are notably gregarious and have a complex social system with some particularly interesting intricacies. In a telemetry study conducted in the Kirindy forest Centre de Formation Professionnelle Forestière by L. Razafimanantsoa, 26 animals (20 adults and six sub-adults) were captured and marked in an area of about 90 ha. These animals belonged to different groups and included dispersing solitary individuals. A good proportion of the marked animals were not seen again in the study area, which was occupied by two different groups. The first group was composed of two adult females, an adult male, a sub-adult female, and one of the previous season's young; the second group was two adult females and a sub-adult male. The home range of the first group was calculated as about 18 ha and the second group 13 ha. These figures are notably smaller than previous inferred estimates of 20–25 ha. The ranges of the two groups overlapped over an area of about 1·5 ha. In the overlap zone, group members intensively scent-marked using glandular secretions and no aggressive interactions were observed between them. Based on these radio-tracking studies, individual Narrow-striped Boky can traverse a distance of 2200 m in a single day, of which two-thirds is covered during the morning. This species often can be observed in groups with three to five adults, and depending on the season, with numerous sub-adults. Groups of more than ten individuals have been observed and, in certain areas, the age and sex ratio remains stable over the course of years. As a group moves through the forest, the alpha female plays the role of "leader". After mating, the males will generally leave the female group for several months. Lone individuals can be observed, particularly towards the end of the dry season, and these are presumed to be solitary males. During the mating period, males were tolerant of visiting males and even allowed them to copulate with group females. Some marked males visited the female groups frequently both during and outside the mating period, and this social configuration has been referred to as a "super-group". Narrow-striped Bokys appear to have a limited vocal repertoire. After birth, the young emit a shrill call that is very similar to a communication call between adult males and females, and can be transcribed as "bouk-bouk". Almost certainly, the Malagasy name of this animal is the onomatopoeic form of this vocalization. The Narrow-striped Boky often erects its fluffy tail, which is undoubtedly for visual communication. Narrow-striped Boky has well-developed jaw, neck, and anal glands that it uses to mark vertical vegetation, tree trunks, and the ground. This animal uses three different types of night shelters, depending on the season: partially collapsed and abandoned ant burrows during the dry, cold season; hollows in fallen dead trees at the beginning of the rainy, warm season; and cavities up to 10 m above the ground in standing dead or living trees during the rainy, warm season. Underground burrows are at least partially excavated, with a single tunnel entrance terminating as a chamber. This carnivore is known to share tree hollows with a variety of nocturnal lemurs, but the species are not in direct contact, as they occupy different portions of the cavity. Groups regularly move between different resting shelters, generally along the periphery of their home range, which may help to reduce ectoparasite loads. Narrow-striped Bokys are preyed upon by Fossa.

Breeding. In the Kirindy (CFPF) Forest, mating takes place in August. In the early morning, soon after sunrise, the male arrives at the burrow entrance of the female and waits for her to exit. At the onset of each encounter, females are vocal and aggressive towards the males. These agonistic interactions decrease over the course of an hour, and eventually the male can mount the female. They then copulate up to three times, and in each case, the period of intromission decreases. Subsequently, the male leaves the group for several months. The alpha-female is apparently receptive before any other females of the same group. The gestation period is estimated to be between 90 and 105 days; however, a recent estimate of 74 days has been advanced. Females give birth to a single baby weighing about 50 g, and there appears to be some synchrony between females living in the same group. At birth, neonates already have their ears and eyes open; their fur coloration is slightly lighter than that of adults. The young appear to be particularly precocious, walking within a day of being born. The incisors erupt by four days, and they eat solid food within 15 days, although they continue to nurse for about two months. They are agile climbers by 45 days and are actively hunting within three months. Soon after birth, the young are placed in communal crèche sites, with an opening small enough that adult Narrow-striped Boky cannot enter. The young exit the site and feed when they are called by their mothers; they nurse three times a day the first week after birth. In late afternoon, before sunset, mothers take their respective babies from the crèche to a night shelter. Sexual maturity is apparently reached at two years of age.

Status and Conservation. Listed in *The IUCN Red List* as Vulnerable; however, the result of a Conservation Breeding Specialist Group workshop sponsored by the IUCN/SSC held in 2001 and attended by specialists working on Madagascar Carnivores gave the status of *decemlineata* as Threatened and that of *lineata* as Data Deficient. On the basis of a recent trapping survey of the central portion of the Menabe region, the local population is estimated to be 2000–3400 adults and that of the S Menabe region (to the northern bank of the Mangoky River) as 6400–8650 adults. In the central Menabe, the area of occupancy was estimated as 900 km² and the extent of occurrence as 1524 km². For the southern Menabe population, the figures are 1871 km² and 8729 km² respectively. No comparable information is available on the population of *lineata* occurring south of the Mangoky River. The factors limiting the distribution of this species are associated with forest cover, but at a series of sample sites, the abundance of *decemlineata* was not correlated with variables such as soil structure, litter depth, or nvertebrate abundance. It has been proposed that building access roads for logging or other forms of exploitation greatly increases threats to this animal, including predation or harassment by dogs, and the destruction of the forest understory by domestic ivestock. Further, in certain portions of this species' range people hunt it for bush neat. The dry deciduous forests of western Madagascar are under the most severe human pressures of any natural forest formation on the island. The recently trapped *M. l. lineata* specimen was obtained in a region known as the Mikea Forest, spanning the zone from the Fiherenana River north to the Mangoky River. In this region there are several species of locally restricted endemic animals, including two recently described species of small mammals discovered during a 2003 expedition to the zone. The occurrence of *M. d. lineata* in this forest block helps to underscore the need to protect it. Initial steps have been taken to place a portion of the southern Mikea Forest, the zone between the Manombo and Fiherenana Rivers, into a conservation area.

Bibliography. Albignac (1971b, 1972, 1973, 1976, 1984), Conservation Breeding Specialist Group (SSC/IUCN) (2002), Goodman (2003a), Goodman & Raselimanana (2003), Goodman, Thomas & Kidney (2005), Hawkins, F.A. *et al.* (2000), Hawkins, C.E. & Racey (2007), IUCN (2007), Nicoll & Langrand (1989), Pocock (1915b), Rabeantoandro (1997), Rasolonandrasana (1994), Razafimanantsoa (2003), Schreiber *et al.* (1989), Woolaver *et al.* (2006), Wozencraft (1986).

Genus *SALANOIA*
Gray, 1865

3. Brown-tailed Vontsira *Salanoia concolor*

French: Galidie unicolore / **German**: Schlichtmungo / **Spanish**: Galidia parda
Other common names: Brown-tailed Mongoose, Salano, Vontsira Boko, Tabiboala, Fanaloka

Taxonomy. *Galidia concolor* Geoffroy Saint-Hilaire, 1837, Madagascar.
The specific names *olivacea* and *unicolor* are synonyms. Monotypic.
Distribution. E Madagascar. Records from the extreme south-east, in Andohahela, or from the far north, at Montagne d'Ambre, are not considered valid.
Descriptive notes. Head-body 35–38 cm, tail 16–20 cm, hindfoot 6·6–7 cm, ear 2·9 cm; weight 780 g. In numerous ways this species is similar to Ring-tailed Vontsira, with which is sympatric, but is uniformly darker. It has a short dark dorsal pelage, with pale-tipped hairs giving an agouti appearance. The underside, including the inner thighs, is reddish-brown merging to a whitish-gray around the chin and mouth. The uniform dark brown and slightly bushy tail is shorter than the head and body. No sexual differences have been noted in coloration or size.

Habitat. The known range is in the eastern humid forest across an elevational range from near sea level to around 1000 m. Previous information indicated that it was relatively common in the region of Mananara and the Masoala Peninsula. However, few recent details are available about its distribution and it remains the least known native carnivore in Madagascar.

Food and Feeding. Little information is available. At the Réserve Spéciale de Betampona, a lowland eastern humid forest in east-central Madagascar, Brown-tailed Vontsira was observed on eight occasions feeding on beetle larvae that it extracted from rotten wood with its sharp straight claws. It was also observed foraging in leaf litter. This species is also known to climb in trees 5–10 m off the ground, where it presumably forages for invertebrates in a fashion similar to Ring-tailed Vontsira. It is reputed by rural villagers to feed on poultry; however, given its apparent arthropod diet and slightly reduced dentition, this is questionable. These poultry raids may actually be conducted by the similar-looking Ring-tailed Vontsira. On the basis of a comparative study conducted at Betampona, where Brown-tailed Vontsira and Ring-tailed Vontsira occur in sympatry, a number of differences were noted in prey type and habitat utilization that might reduce competitive interactions between them. Certain dietary and morphological and behavioral aspects of Brown-tailed Vontsira are notably similar to Narrow-striped Boky of the central western dry deciduous forests.

Activity patterns. Current evidence indicates that this species is strictly diurnal, being active in the early morning and with another bout of activity in the late afternoon. When foraging, Brown-tailed Vontsira will occasionally emit guttural squeaks and growls, but it is often silent. If alarmed it produces loud growls and at the same time erects the tail fur.

Movements, Home range and Social organization. Little is known about the social organization of this species. At Betampona, it was frequently observed singly or in pairs. There are records of groups of three individuals; generally one is notably smaller than the other two and presumed to be their offspring. It has been estimated that family groups occupy home ranges of approximately 20 ha, but this needs to be verified with field studies.

Breeding. Infants are born between November and January and it is suspected that young remain with their parents for one year after birth.

Status and Conservation. Listed in *The IUCN Red List* as Vulnerable. At Betampona, close to 93% of observations of Brown-tailed Vontsira were in intact forest, often on ridge tops, and the balance were in areas of secondary vegetation and cultivated zones. In 1876 Audebert made a collection of animals in the Mahambo, north of Toamasina, which included Brown-tailed Vontsira. This site, which no longer has any natural forest, is within a few kilometers of the station Forestière de Tampolo, where rapid biological inventories took place in 1997 and 2004. On two occasions a small, terrestrial, diurnal Carnivora that had the characteristics of Brown-tailed Vontsira was observed in the Tampolo littoral forest. Further, this species is well known to local research assistants working at the station. It seems that remnant populations can withstand certain levels of human habitat degradation, at least in the short-term.

Bibliography. Albignac (1973), Britt (1999), Britt & Virkaitis (2003), Conservation Breeding Specialist Group (SSC/IUCN) (2002), Goodman, Soarimalala & Ratsirarson (2005), Grandidier & Petit (1932), IUCN (2007), Schreiber *et al.* (1989), Wozencraft (1986), ZICOMA (1999).

CLASS MAMMALIA
ORDER CARNIVORA
SUBORDER CANIFORMIA
Family CANIDAE (DOGS)

- Small to quite large mammals with triangular heads, long, pointed muzzles, well-developed jaws, and prominent, roughly triangular pointed ears; muscular, deep-chested body, long and slender limbs, and bushy tail.
- 45·8–182 cm.

- Cosmopolitan, all regions except Antarctica and many oceanic islands.
- Occur in all major habitats, spanning tropical forests, woodland, savannah, deserts, alpine heathlands, and the Arctic; found at all altitudes from sea level to over 5000 m.
- 13 genera, 35 species, at least 172 extant taxa.
- 3 species Critically Endangered, 3 species Endangered; 1 species and 5 subspecies Extinct since 1600.

Systematics

The Canid family is characterized by a great flexibility of diet, opportunistic and adaptable behavior, and complex social organization with much variation within and between species. The contemporary Canidae is the most widespread family of extant Carnivora, with at least one species present on all continents except Antarctica. There are 35 living canids, 36 if we treat the Dingo (considered here a subspecies of the Gray Wolf *Canis lupus dingo*) as a separate species. Recognition of the eastern North American wolf form (*Canis lycaon*) would add another species.

The distribution of Canid species may be highly restricted—almost the entire Darwin's Fox (*Pseudalopex fulvipes*) population occurs only on one island (the smallest geographic range of any living canid) and Island Fox (*Urocyon littoralis*) subspecies occur on one island each, whereas other species span several continents. Red Foxes (*Vulpes vulpes*) and Gray Wolves (*Canis lupus*), for example, have the most extensive natural range of any land mammal (with the exception of humans and perhaps some rodents). The Red Fox has the widest geographical range of any member of the order Carnivora, covering nearly 70 million km² across the entire Northern Hemisphere from the Arctic Circle to North Africa, Central America, and the Asiatic steppes; and it was introduced to Australia in the 1800s. In the USA, its range was also extended through several introductions of European Red Foxes by settlers, starting in the mid-1700s. The Gray Wolf has a similar distribution, occurring widely throughout North America, Asia, and parts of Europe.

The kaleidoscope of species diversity has changed over the last century: there are places in North America where the Gray Wolf and Red Fox have been replaced by what amounts to their "ecological average", the Coyote (*Canis latrans*), once confined to mainly arid areas in western North America and now found in every state, province, and country north of Panama. Coyotes flourished throughout most of the USA in the early 1900s following the extirpation of Gray Wolves.

Small canids such as foxes may have limited dispersal ability and be less able to traverse topographic barriers. Moreover, due to shorter dispersal distances, small canids may show a more pronounced pattern of genetic differentiation with distance and population subdivision. The small arid-land foxes of North America are habitat specialists and relatively poor dispersers. In California, for example, the Kit Fox of the San Joaquin Valley (*Vulpes macrotis mutica*), whose range is circumscribed by the coastal mountain range to the west and the Sierra Nevada mountain range to the east, is protected by the USA Endangered Species Act. Populations to the east of the Rocky Mountains are collectively referred to as Swift Foxes (*V. velox*), and

those to the west as Kit Foxes. However, the two forms hybridize in north-central Texas and are recognized as conspecific by some authors.

The highest diversity of canids occurs in South America, Africa, and Asia. South America harbors eleven species, nine of which are endemic to the continent; these are mainly *Pseudalopex* foxes. In Africa, 13 species are present, including eight endemics ranging in size from the Cape Fox (*Vulpes chama*) to the African Wild Dog (*Lycaon pictus*). Of twelve canid species found in Asia, three are Asian endemics: the Indian Fox (*Vulpes bengalensis*), Tibetan Fox (*V. ferrilata*) and Dhole (*Cuon alpinus*). Two species, the Golden Jackal (*Canis aureus*) and Arctic Fox (*Alopex lagopus*) are present on three continents, and the Red Fox and Dingo reached Australia and Oceania with assistance from humans.

Five canid species are endemic to a single country. These are the Red Wolf *Canis rufus* (reintroduced in the south-eastern USA); the Ethiopian Wolf, *C. simensis* (Ethiopia); Darwin's Fox (Chile); the Island Fox (USA); and the Hoary Fox, *Pseudalopex vetulus* (Brazil). One other, the Sechuran Fox, *P. sechurae*, is a near-endemic to Peru. Most of these country endemics are, not surprisingly, threatened. The last surviving 500 Ethiopian Wolves, for example, are confined to seven isolated mountain ranges in the Ethiopian highlands, at elevations of 3000–4500 m above sea level, and critically endangered Island Foxes are geographically restricted to six of the eight Channel Islands of California.

The genera *Canis* and *Vulpes* are both found in North America, Europe, Africa, and Asia (and were introduced to Australia). Of the remaining eight canid genera, six are restricted to only one continent: *Chrysocyon* (South America), *Otocyon* (Africa), *Pseudalopex* (South America), *Speothos* (South America), *Cuon* (Asia), and *Lycaon* (Africa). The genus *Urocyon*, which includes Northern Gray Fox (*U. cinereoargenteus*) and Island Fox, is restricted to North and South America. *Nyctereutes*, represented only by the Raccoon Dog (*N. procyonoides*), was formerly restricted to Asia, but has also been introduced to Europe.

Africa, Asia, and South America support the greatest diversity of canids, with more than ten species each. Red Foxes are sympatric with 14 other canids (from three geographical regions), Golden Jackals with 13 (from two regions), and Gray Wolves with eleven (from three regions). Within any one location, however, canid diversity is usually limited from one to five species. Sudan is the country with the highest number of canids (ten species), followed by USA (nine species) and Ethiopia (eight species).

Within the Carnivora, canids fall into the Suborder Caniformia, or dog-like forms. The Caniformia are divided into two major groups that share a close genetic relationship: Superfamily Cynoidea, which includes Canidae, and Superfamily Arctoidea, which includes the Ursidae, Ailuridae, Procyonidae, and Mustelidae, as well as the aquatic Pinnipedia and the extinct Amphicyonidae.

The ancient divergence of dogs from other carnivores is estimated by molecular clock calculations as 50 million years before present. This value is consistent with the first appearance of the family in the Eocene, although it is somewhat more ancient than the date of 40 million years suggested by the fossil record. There are three major groups (subfamilies) in the family Canidae: Hesperocyoninae, Borophaginae, and Caninae. Of these, two are represented by fossil forms only. The Hesperocyoninae is the most ancient group of all canids, and its basal member, *Hesperocyon*, gave rise to the two more advanced subfamilies, Borophaginae and Caninae.

The Canidae can broadly be divided into two distinct lineages that diverged between five and nine million years ago. Fox-like canids are generally small in size and have a low diploid chromosome number (2n = 36–66). Wolf-like canids (wolves, coyotes, jackals, dogs) are medium-sized to large and typically have a diploid chromosome number of 2n = 74–78. Evolutionary relationships within the family Canidae have been reconstructed using comparative karyology, allozyme electrophoresis and mitochondrial DNA protein coding sequence data. Assuming an approximate molecular clock, the modern Canidae originated about ten to twelve million years ago and were followed by the divergence of wolf and fox like canids about six million years ago. By the latest Pleistocene (300,000–10,000 years ago), most living species or their close relatives had emerged, along with the extinct North American Dire Wolf, (*Canis dirus*).

The living Canidae are divided into five distinct groupings. They include the wolf-like canids as a monophyletic group that consists of the Coyote, Gray Wolf, Red Wolf, Ethiopian Wolf, and Jackals (*Canis* spp.) as well as the Dhole. Basal to *Canis* and *Cuon* is the African Wild Dog. Within this clade the Gray Wolf, Coyote and Ethiopian Wolf form a monophyletic group, with the Golden Jackal as the most likely sister taxon. The Black-backed jackal (*C. mesomelas*) and Side-striped Jackal (*C. adustus*) are sister taxa, but they do not form a monophyletic group with the Golden Jackal and Ethiopian Wolf.

Although the African Wild Dog preys mainly on larger animals, as do the Gray Wolf and Dhole, it is not closely related to

either species but is sister to the clade containing these species. This phylogeny implies that the trenchant heeled carnassial, a particular dentition now found only in *Speothos*, *Cuon*, and *Lycaon*, evolved at least twice or was primitive and lost in other wolf-like canids and the Maned Wolf (*Chrysocyon brachyurus*).

The South American canids are not a monophyletic group and likely owe their origin to three separate invasions. The Bush Dog (*Speothos venaticus*) and Maned Wolf (*Chrysocyon*) clade groups with the wolf-like canids rather than with the South American foxes. The large sequence divergence between the Bush Dog and Maned Wolf, and between these taxa and the South American foxes, suggests that they diverged from each other 6–7 million years ago, well before the Panamanian land bridge formed about 2–3 million years ago. Thus, three canid invasions of South America best explain the phylogenetic distribution of the extant species. These invasions are today represented by, respectively, the Bush Dog, the Maned Wolf, and the South American foxes. Furthermore, within the South American foxes, the Crab-eating Fox (*Cerdocyon thous*) and the Short-eared Dog (*Atelocynus microtis*) are ancestral (6–3 million years ago). Divergence values between them and other South American foxes suggest they may have diverged before the opening of the Panamanian land bridge as well. The fossil record supports the hypothesis that the Crab-eating Fox had its origin outside of South America, as the genus has been described from late Miocene deposits of North America (3–6 million years ago). *Pseudalopex* (*Lycalopex* for some authorities) foxes evolved fairly recently (2·5–1 million years) and, perhaps together with *Atelocynus* might have a South American origin. They are intermediate in appearance between the popular images of foxes and canids such as wolves and coyotes, and were referred to as Fox-tailed Wolves by the 19th century British taxonomist J. E. Gray. Further, the generic distinction given to *Pseudalopex* and *Lycalopex* does not reflect much genetic differentiation, and in the absence of appreciable morphologic differences, the genetic data suggest these species should be assigned to a single genus.

The Red Fox group is a fourth grouping in the genetic tree consisting of other fox-like taxa, including *Vulpes* and *Alopex*. The Arctic Fox, *Alopex lagopus*, is a close sister to the Kit Fox and Swift Fox, with all three species sharing the same unique karyotype and having only recently evolved (mid-Pleistocene; half a

The contemporary Canidae is the most widespread family of extant carnivora, with at least one species present on all continents, except Antarctica. There are 35 living species. The **Dhole** is one of the three endemic Asian species, out of twelve canids found in Asia. One of the group of wolf-like canids, along with the Coyote, Gray Wolf, Red Wolf, Ethiopian Wolf, and the jackals, the Dhole is more closely related to the jackals than the wolves. The Dhole is the only surviving member of the genus Cuon; Cuon species were common in South America several million years ago.

Cuon alpinus
Kanha National Park, India.
Photo: Jorge Sierra

The modern Canidae originated
about 10–12 million years ago.
The wolf-like and fox-like canids
diverged about six million years
ago. The **Gray Wolf** is the larges
of the canids, and its adaptabili
to differing climes has resulted
in many widely varying forms.
Depending on the subspecies,
mature male wolves may be 2
m long including the tail, can
stand more than 1 m high at
the shoulder, and weigh up to
62 kg. The typical adult is the
size of a large German shepherd
dog, weighing about 38 kg and
standing 70 cm at the shoulder.
The smallest Gray Wolves inhab
desert and semi-desert areas nea
the southern border of their rang
Medium-sized wolves tend to be
found in forested areas in the
central portions of their range.
Wolves in Arctic regions are the
largest, illustrating Bergmann's
rule, which describes this kind o,
size gradient from the Equator t
the North Pole. The Gray Wolf
shows marked variation in color
ranging from nearly pure white
through gray to black; the most
common coat color is gray flecke
with black. The palest-colored
wolves tend to inhabit desert an
Arctic regions. In North Americ
and Russia, wolves are often
brown or black, but black wolves
are extremely rare in Europe.
In winter, the fur is longer and
bushier.

Canis lupus
Above: Saudi Arabia.
Photo: Roland Seitre

Below: Quttinirpaaq National Park
Canada.
Photo: Staffan Widstrand

Lycaon pictus
Gauteng, South Africa.
Photo: W. H. J. Sator/CD-Gallery

million years). Basal to *Vulpes* is Fennec Fox (*V. zerda*), suggesting an early divergence of that lineage, and which is sometimes placed in its own genus, *Fennecus*. Blanford's Fox (*Vulpes cana*) and the Fennec Fox are considered by others as sister taxa, and represent an old radiation (four million years).

Finally, three lineages have long and distinct evolutionary histories and are survived today by the monospecific genera *Nyctereutes* (Raccoon Dog) and *Otocyon* (Bat-eared Fox), and *Urocyon* (Island Fox, *U. littoralis* and Northern Gray Fox, *U. cinereoargenteus*), which appear basal to other canids in all molecular and karyological trees. The two *Urocyon* species are closest to the ancestors of all canids. Although morphologically resembling the classic vulpine fox, they are not genetically related to any of the other foxes. The three genera diverged early in the history of the family, approximately eight to twelve million years ago.

The taxonomy of wild canids is largely uncontroversial, although there is some disagreement regarding the use of the generic names *Pseudalopex* or *Lycalopex* for the South American genera. The validity of the Red Wolf as distinct from the Gray Wolf has also been questioned. Some recent genetic evidence suggests that Red Wolves and Gray Wolves in southern Ontario are so genetically similar that they represent a separate species, *C. lycaon*. The classification of the Dingo and New Guinean Singing Dog, which some authorities consider a Dingo and others consider a separate species (*Canis hallstromi*), is also debated.

The now extinct Falkland Islands Wolf (*Dusicyon australis*) was first described by Charles Darwin during his visit to the southern archipelago. Based on skull and teeth measurements, these wolf-like foxes were more similar to *Canis* than *Pseudalopex*, but their extermination by pelt-hunters by 1880 sadly relegated them to the status of a biological mystery. Some maintain that *D. australis* descended from a domestic canid, pointing out that it had a white-tipped tail, rather than the black one of all surviving *Pseudalopex* species. Another possibility is that it was related to the genus *Cuon*, of which only the Dhole survives (*Cuon* species were common in South America several million years ago).

Among the living families within the Suborder Caniformia, Canidae is the most ancient. Canids originated more than 40 million years ago in the late Eocene in North America from a group of archaic carnivorans, the Miacidae. Modern canids still maintain some features that are primitive among all carnivorans. Canids were confined to the North American continent during much of their early history, playing a wide range of predatory roles that encompassed those of the living canids, procyonids, hyaenids, and possibly felids. Two archaic subfamilies, Hesperocyoninae and Borophaginae, thrived in the middle to late Cenozoic from about 40–2 million years ago. Living canids all belong to the final radiation, Subfamily Caninae, which achieved its present diversity only in the last few million years. By the latest Miocene (about 7–8 million years ago), members of the Subfamily Caninae were finally able to cross the Bering Strait into Asia, commencing an explosive radiation and giving rise to the modern canids of the Old World. The family blossomed in the Oligocene (19 genera) and exploded in the Miocene (42 genera), later declining to the 13 genera recognized today. At the formation of the Isthmus of Panama, three million years ago, canids arrived in South America and quickly established themselves as one of the most diverse groups of carnivorans on the continent. With the aid of humans, *Canis lupus* was transported to Australia late in the Holocene, giving rise to the modern Dingo. Since that time, canids have become truly worldwide predators, unsurpassed in distribution by any other group of carnivorans.

North America remained a center for canids through the Pliocene, producing the Coyote as an endemic form. After their arrival in Eurasia, *Canis* underwent an extensive radiation and range expansion, yielding the wolves, Dhole, African Wild Dog and fossil relatives on the Eurasian and African continents. During the Pleistocene, elements of the larger canid fauna invaded mid-latitude North America—the last invasion of which was the appearance of the Gray Wolf south of the glacial ice sheets in the late Pleistocene (about 100,000 years ago).

The vulpines' major center of radiation was in the Old World. *Vulpes* species were widespread and diverse in Eurasia during the Pliocene, resulting from an immigration event independent of that of the *Canis* clade. Red Fox and Arctic Fox appeared in North America only in the late Pleistocene, evidently

Body shape does not vary dramatically in canids, with most species fitting into either a vulpine (fox-like) or wolf-like morphotype, although some variation exists. The **Maned Wolf** is very distinctive, however, having extremely long limbs in relation to its body, and very long fur, which is reddish-orange in color. It has been described as like a Red Fox on stilts, and is as tall as the largest Gray Wolves, though much lighter in weight at around 20·5–30 kg. Its common name comes from the mane-like strip of black fur running from the back of the head to the shoulders, averaging 470 mm in length. The Maned Wolf was originally placed in the wolf-like genus, Canis, but is now included in a genus of its own, Chrysocyon. South America has eleven species of canid, nine of which are endemic to the continent. However, the South American canids are not a monophyletic group (a group descended from a common ancestor), and probably owe their origin to three separate invasions of the continent by ancestor species. These invasions are today represented by the Bush Dog, the Maned Wolf, and the South American foxes. The Maned Wolf and Bush Dog clade is grouped with the wolf-like canids, rather than with the South American foxes. The large DNA sequence divergence between the Bush Dog and the Maned Wolf, and between these taxa and the South American foxes, suggests that they diverged from each other 6–7 million years ago, well before the Panamanian land bridge formed about 2–3 million years ago.

Chrysocyon brachyurus
Serra da Canastra National Park, Brazil.
Photo: Tui de Roy/
Roving Tortoise Photos

as a result of an immigration back to the New World. Preferring more wooded areas, the Northern Gray Fox (*Urocyon*) has remained in southern North America and Middle America. Records of the Gray Fox clade indicate a fairly continuous presence in North America throughout its existence, with intermediate forms leading to the living species *U. cinereoargenteus*. Morphologically, the African Bat-eared Fox *Otocyon megalotis* of today is closest to the *Urocyon* clade, although molecular evidence suggests that the Bat-eared Fox lies at the base of the fox clade or even lower. If the morphological evidence has been correctly interpreted, then the Bat-eared Fox must represent a Pliocene immigration event to the Old World independent of other foxes.

The only canid to go extinct in North America at the end of Pleistocene was the Dire Wolf (*Canis dirus*), together with two bears and three cats, all of which were very large. The Gray Wolf, Coyote, and several foxes survived. What can be learned by examining the winners and losers in the late Pleistocene about the causes of current predator declines? Examination of the losers reveals that they tended to be larger and more adapted for hypercarnivory (i.e. dietary specialization). Remarkably, two of the species that went extinct, the Dire Wolf and Saber-toothed Cat (*Smilodon fatalis*), were five times more common in the Rancho La Brea tar pit deposits of California than the next most common carnivore, the Coyote, suggesting that they were dominant predators at this time, comparable to the numerically dominant African Lion and Spotted Hyena of extant African ecosystems. The extinction of the apparently successful Dire Wolf and Saber-toothed Cat appears to be linked to the decline of their prey, which included the Mammoth.

The directional trend toward the evolution of large, hypercarnivorous forms apparent in groups of dog-like carnivores may be a fundamental feature of carnivore evolution. The likely cause is the prevalence of interspecific competition among large, sympatric predators. Interspecific competition tends to be more intense among large carnivores because prey are often difficult to capture and can represent a sizable quantity of food that is worth stealing and defending. Hypercarnivory appears late in the history of the Caninae and represents at least several independent radiations in South America, North America, and the Old World. The South American radiation of large hypercarnivorous canids occurred at a time (2·5–0·01 million years ago) when cat-like predators were rare or absent. It followed

the elevation of the Panamanian land bridge around 2–3 million years ago, which allowed movement between the previously separated continents. The canids that first entered South America found a depauperate predator community. Between 2·5 million years ago and 10,000 years ago, 16 new species of canids appeared in South America, at least seven of which had trenchant heeled carnassials and clearly were adapted for hypercarnivory. All of these South American hypercarnivorous canids, except the Bush Dog, went extinct at the end of the Pleistocene. In the Old World, the evolution of hypercarnivorous canines occurred within the last four million years and did not coincide with an absence of cats. Wolf-like hyaenids were the dominant dog-like predators of the Old World Miocene, reaching a diversity of 22 species between nine and five million years ago, but then declining dramatically to just five species by about four million years ago. Their decline may have opened up ecospace for the large canids and favored the evolution of hypercarnivory.

Morphological Aspects

Canid anatomy is adapted for the cursorial pursuit of prey in relatively open environments, and often characterized by tall, lithe bodies, a bushy tail, long limbs, and digitigrade, four-toed feet. Canids typically have triangular heads with long, pointed muzzles, well-developed jaws, and prominent, roughly triangular pointed ears. In some desert species the ears may be very large, an extreme case being the Fennec Fox, which has the largest ear to body ratio of any carnivore.

The Canidae are quite variable in size, ranging from the Fennec Fox, weighing less than 1 kg, to the Gray Wolf, which may weigh over 60 kg. Most fox species weigh 1·5–9 kg and most of the remaining canids weigh 5–27 kg. Sexual dimorphism, when present at all, is usually minimal, with males slightly larger than females, but similar in color. Geographical variability in body size can be explained to some degree by differences in availability of food, with small canids (e.g. Fennec Fox and other desert foxes) usually associated with arid and less productive habitats in which only a small body mass can be supported year round, whereas larger canids (e.g. African Wild Dog, Dhole, and Ethiopian Wolf) often are associated with habitats in which prey is abundant.

The **Bush Dog** is one of the least dog-like canids in appearance. It has a long body with short legs, a short tail, and a broad face with a short muzzle and small, rounded ears. This body type is well-suited for life in the tropical forests it occupies, and probably represents an adaptation that lets it pursue burrowing prey and navigate efficiently through dense vegetation. Its feet are webbed, suggesting semi-aquatic habits; it is generally found near water, particularly small streams. It is among the least known of all canids, with even the most basic information on distribution and biology lacking.

Speothos venaticus
Ilha Solteira, São Paulo, Brazil.
Photo: Haroldo Palo Jr/NHPA

Within the South American foxes, the **Crab-eating Fox** *is an ancestral species. The fossil record supports the hypothesis that this fox had its origin outside of South America, as the genus* Cerdocyon *has been described from late Miocene deposits of North America from 3–6 million years ago. All its immediate relatives are extinct and the Crab-eating Fox is now the only living member of its genus. It is a medium-sized canid, weighing 4·5–8·5 kg, with a short, narrow head. Its coarse, bristly coat varies in color across its range and within populations, from silver-gray to almost black.*

Cerdocyon thous
Tuparro National Park, Colombia.
Photo: Otto Pfister

The Gray Wolf is the largest of the canids, and its adaptability to differing climes has resulted in many widely varying forms. Depending on the subspecies, mature male wolves may be 2 m long including the tail, can stand more than 1 m high at the shoulder, and weigh up to 62 kg. The typical adult wolf, however, is the size of a large German shepherd dog, weighing about 38 kg and standing 70 cm at the shoulder. The smallest Gray Wolves inhabit desert and semi-desert areas near the southern border of their range. Medium-sized wolves tend to be found in forested areas in the central portions of their range. Wolves in Arctic regions are the largest, illustrating Bergmann's rule, which describes this kind of size gradient from the Equator to the North Pole.

The Red Fox also shows immense variation in adult body size across its distribution, with weight ranging from 3–14 kg and head and body lengths ranging from 45–90 cm. Island Foxes are the smallest North American canids (1·8–2 kg), representing a dwarf form of the mainland Northern Gray Fox. This reduction in body size is likely a consequence of an insular existence. Island Foxes are at least 30% smaller, and typically have fewer caudal vertebrae (15–22), than the Northern Gray Fox (21–22).

Body shape does not vary dramatically in canids, with most species fitting into either a vulpine or a wolf-like morphotype, although some variation exists. The Maned Wolf, for example, is unusually distinctive, having extremely long limbs in relation to its body. Meanwhile, the Bush Dog is one of the least dog-like canids in appearance. Considered by indigenous peoples to be one of the best hunters in the forest, the Bush Dog has a small compact body, squat legs, a short tail and a broad-face with small, rounded ears. This body type is well suited for life in the tropical forests it occupies and probably represents an adaptation that lets it pursue burrowing prey and efficiently navigate through dense vegetation. Its feet are webbed, suggesting semi-aquatic habits. A similar partial interdigital membrane in the feet of the Short-eared Dog of the western Amazonian lowlands suggests that it, too, may be at least partly aquatic.

Perhaps with the exception of the aptly named Maned Wolf, canid pelage is relatively short, with dense underfur mixed with longer guard hairs. Coat color is generally tawny brown or gray, but black, white and shades of ocher also occur. The underparts are usually paler than the rest of the body. The tail is generally bushy, often with a white or black tip and a darker, bristly patch covering the dorsal supra-caudal scent gland near the base.

Desert foxes are all very pale in color, with the Pale Fox (*Vulpes pallida*) being the palest. Reddish coats are also common amongst canids, reaching their brightest expression in Red Foxes, Ethiopian Wolves, Dholes, and Red Wolves. The Gray Wolf shows marked variation in color, ranging from white through gray to black; the most common pelage is gray flecked with black. The palest-colored wolves tend to inhabit desert and Arctic regions. In North America and Russia, wolves are often brown or black, but black wolves are extremely rare in Europe.

Some foxes also exhibit different color morphs. Arctic Foxes, for example, exhibit two distinct morphs, "blue" and "white". The "blue" color morph is the rarer of the two, occurring in less than 1% of the continental population, although in some regions, especially on islands and along coastal areas, it can be relatively common. Each morph also changes by season, with "blue" molting from brown in summer to paler brown tinged with a blue sheen in winter. "White" remains nearly pure white in winter, while in summer it changes to brown and pale gray. Red Foxes also exhibit color morphs, including red, silver (black with variable amount of silver "frosting" on guard hairs), and cross (grayish brown with long black guard hairs on back and shoulders).

There is little difficulty in recognizing living canids from their dentition, which is relatively uniform and unspecialized. Canids have an unreduced dental formula that is closest to the ancestral morphotype of Carnivora, namely three incisors, one canine, four premolars and three molars in each half-jaw. Other Carnivora families generally have fewer teeth. The most prominent feature of canine dentition is the presence of shearing carnassial teeth, formed by the upper fourth premolar and the lower first molar (P^4/M_1), which are the main meat-slicing teeth in the Carnivora. Crushing molars are well-developed and the largest teeth in all species. The canine teeth are long and sharply pointed in all species. From this moderately conservative carnivorous plan, many large canids evolved toward a hypercarnivorous (highly carnivorous) niche with a tendency to increase the size of the carnassial pair at the expense of the molars behind. For example, the Dhole has lost the last molars. Alternatively, canids may tend toward a hypocarnivorous (slightly carnivorous) dental pattern, with development of the molars for grinding, at the expense of the carnassial shear. The Bat-eared Fox is unique among living, terrestrial eutherians in

The foxes of the genus
Pseudalopex *are restricted to*
South America and evolved as
recently as 2·5–1 million years
ago. They are intermediate in
appearance between the popular
images of foxes and canids like
wolves and coyotes. The **Culpeo**
is the largest of the Pseudalopex
foxes, with females weighing up
to 10 kg, the males being typically
1·5 times as heavy. In Chile, the
Culpeo and the closely-related
South American Gray Fox eat
the same prey in comparable
quantities, but vary in size with
latitude throughout their range.
Average body length of the Culpeo
increases from 70 cm to 90 cm
from north to south, while that
of the South American Gray Fox
decreases.

Pseudalopex culpaeus
Bolivia.
Photo: Pete Oxford/naturepl.com

Despite its stocky body and short
legs, the **Northern Gray Fox** *is*
unusual amongst the canids
in being a notable tree climber.
Urocyon *is currently considered*
a basal genus within the Canidae,
and has only two surviving
members, the Northern Gray Fox
and the Island Fox, restricted to
North and South America. The two
Urocyon *species are closest to the*
ancestors of all canids. Although
morphologically resembling the
classic vulpine fox, they are not
genetically related to any of the
other foxes. The Northern Gray
Fox clusters genetically with two
other ancient lineages, the Raccoon
Dog and the Bat-eared Fox, but the
exact relationship is unclear.

Urocyon cinereoargenteus
Adams County, SW Ohio, USA.
Photo: Dave Maslowski/
Maslowski Productions

having four to five functional lower molars, and unique among modern canids in having three to four upper molars, yielding a dentition of 46 to 50 teeth, the largest number for any non-marsupial land mammal.

Larger carnivores tend to dominate smaller ones and so selection should favor the evolution of large body size, which in turn selects for a highly carnivorous diet because of energetic considerations. Killing and consuming large prey is best done with a hypercarnivorous dentition and so the evolution of large body size and hypercarnivory are often linked, although this does not preclude the less common evolution of hypercarnivory at sizes less than 20 kg, which has occurred in certain fossil forms (subfamily Hesperocyoninae) and the modern Arctic Fox and Kit Fox.

In contrast to the relatively short face of Felids and Mustelids, a typical canid skull is elongated (although relatively shorter in *Canis* than in *Vulpes* and *Pseudalopex*), and a complex cerebral cortex indicates that canids are probably intelligent. The typical skull has wide zygomatic arches, bony orbits that do not form a complete ring, and temporal ridges that may be united in a sagittal crest along the top of the skull. Jaw muscles attach to the sagittal crest, resulting in powerful jaw-closing, adapted for seizing, biting, and holding prey. The auditory bullae in a canid skull are relatively large; they and the rest of the middle ear region are key anatomical features defining canids. The canid basicranial characteristics have remained more or less stable throughout their paleontological history, allowing easy identification in the fossil record when these structures are preserved.

The Canidae are cursorial and digitigrade, adapted for long-distance travel over horizontal ground. They run on their toes or the small palmar pad. They have long, slender limbs, compact feet with four functional toes, and blunt, non-retractible claws. A vestigial fifth toe (pollex or dew claw) on the front feet occurs on all canid species except the African Wild Dog. Other adaptations to running, which make African Wild Dogs and most *Canis* species formidable long-distance runners, include the fusion of the wrist's scaphoid and lunar bones, and the locking of radius and ulna in the front leg to restrict rotation. Another distinctive morphological feature of canids is the presence of a well-developed grooved penis bone (baculum). During mating, most species engage in a copulatory tie that may last an hour or more.

Unusual amongst the canids, Northern Gray Foxes are notable tree climbers, able to climb branchless, vertical trunks to heights of 18 metres, and to jump vertically from branch to branch. Blanford's Fox and the Arctic Fox are the only canids known regularly to climb cliffs. Compared with other small canids, Blanford's Fox has a relatively long, bushy tail, which is probably an important counter-balance during jumps and

As its name suggests, the **Raccoon Dog** is not unlike a raccoon in general appearance, with a black facial mask, small rounded ears, pointed muzzle, and long hair on its cheeks. Uniquely among canids it hibernates in winter, especially areas like southern Finland, where winters are harsh. In autumn and winter, it becomes very fat and has thick fur, giving an impression of a round animal with short, thin legs. In summer when the fur is thin and fat reserves are small, the animal looks much slimmer. Its weight varies considerably, from 3 kg to 12·5 kg. The head and body length is from 50 cm to 75 cm, with the relatively short, thickly furred tail adding a further 15–23 cm. Raccoon Dogs do not bark, but growl when menaced. In Japan their vocalizations are higher in tone than those of a domestic dog, and resemble the sounds of a domestic cat. The Raccoon Dog lineage probably diverged from other canids as early as 7–10 million years ago. Some features of the skull resemble those of South American canids, especially the Crab-eating Fox, but genetic studies have revealed that they are not close relatives. Native to East Asia, the Raccoon Dog has been widely introduced within Central and Eastern Europe, the Baltic States, and Scandinavia, and has been seen as far west as France.

Above: *Nyctereutes procyonoides*
Photo: Luis Casiano

Below: *Nyctereutes procyonoides*
Finland.
Photo: Kerstin Hinze/naturepl.com

may function like a parachute in some instances. The jumping ability of Blanford's Fox is astonishing: these foxes are able to climb vertical, crumbling cliffs by a series of quick leaps. Their small feet and naked pads provide sure footing even on the narrow ledges of a vertical wall. Their sharp, curved, and semi-retractile claws enhance traction on the more difficult vertical ascents. Other canid "athletes" include Red Foxes, which can launch into pouncing aerial strikes on mice, and the short-legged Bush Dog, which cartwheels into handstands to project its scent marks.

The Arctic Fox has many physical adaptations to the Arctic environment. Its fur has the best insulative properties of any terrestrial mammal; it does not need to increase metabolic rate to maintain homoeothermy under any naturally-occurring temperature. Other physiological adaptations for energy conservation include the ability to reduce resting metabolic rate, body-core temperature and food intake during winter. Arctic Foxes change from summer to winter pelage, adjusting their insulating capabilities and enhancing their camouflaging potential. They further conserve body heat by having fur on the soles of their feet (Linnaeus thus named the species *lagopus*, literally hare-foot), small ears, short noses, and the ability to reduce blood flow to peripheral regions of their bodies. In autumn, Arctic Fox weight may increase by more than 50% as fat is deposited for insulation and reserved energy. When travelling long distances, the Arctic Fox falls into an energy-efficient short gallop, similar to that of the Wolverine. Surprisingly, for Arctic Foxes, the energetic cost of running is lower in winter than in summer, and is also lower during starvation than when feeding ad lib.

At the other end of the temperature range, the physiology and behavior of Fennec Foxes are adapted to extremely high temperatures. They are the only carnivore of the Sahara living completely away from water sources. The Fennec Fox starts to shiver at temperatures less than 20°C, and neatly wraps its tail like a stole around its nose and feet when cold. It starts to pant only when the temperature exceeds 35°C, and its jaws open to a full pant only at 38°C; it curls its tongue up so as not to waste even a precious drop of saliva. When the animal pants, its resting rate of 23 breaths per minute rockets to a maximum of 690 breaths per minute.

The Fennec Fox has the largest ear-to-body ratio in the family. Its butterfly-like ears constitute 20% of the body surface and, when the temperature soars, it dilates the blood vessels in its ears and feet, increasing the amount of heat radiated to the outside. If the air temperature climbs higher than its normal body temperature of 38·2°C, the Fennec Fox lets its body heat up to 40·9°C, thus reducing the water it has to "waste" in sweating. In addition, the Fennec Fox has well-developed nasal turbinates that limit water loss during respiration and efficient kidneys that filter extremely high concentrations of urea with little water loss. The Fennec Fox also saves energy by having a metabolism that functions at only 67% of the rate predicted for such a small animal. Similarly, its heart rate of 118 beats per minute is 40% lower than could be expected for its body size. In addition to aiding heat dissipation, the ears enable the Fennec Fox to locate prey, including insects and small vertebrates.

Although not quite to the same extent, the ability of Rüppell's Foxes (*V. rueppellii*), and to a lesser extent Sechuran Foxes, to survive in a hyper-arid environment, where opportunities to drink are extremely rare, appear to be facilitated by various ecological, behavioral and physiological adaptations. A diet rich in plant material, fruits and roots, likely provides much of their moisture requirements. Nocturnal activity patterns and denning during daylight hours combine with morphological adaptations such as small size, hair on feet, and large ears to help with thermoregulation.

All canids have excellent senses of smell and hearing. Sight is less acute in some species, although good. The keen sense of smell probably coevolved with scent marking as the dominant means of communication. Most canids have a well-developed vomeronasal organ that allows them to "smell" chemical cues present in scent marks. Sensitive hearing helps many species detect food. Bat-eared Foxes, for example, use their exquisite sense of hearing to find insect prey up to several inches below ground. Hearing also improves predator detection, which is especially important during pup rearing. Many of the smaller canids, including most of the foxes, are nocturnal and are able to see in very low light conditions. Some of the larger canids, such as African Wild Dogs, which are crepuscular, are unable to see as well at night, but will occasionally hunt during periods with ample moonlight.

Bat-eared Foxes *have small, slim bodies, long bushy tails, and very large ears, which give them their common name. They have 46–50 teeth, the largest number for any non-marsupial land mammal. The milk dentition is typically canid, with unreduced carnassials. In adults, the carnassial shear is lost. If morphological evidence has been correctly interpreted, the African Bat-eared Fox represents a Pliocene immigration event to the Old World independent of other foxes. Morphologically, the Bat-eared Fox of today is closest to the* Urocyon *clade.*

Otocyon megalotis
Namibia.
Photo: David Hosking/FLPA

Some foxes have different color morphs. The **Arctic Fox**, for example, exhibits two distinct morphs, "blue" and "white". Eac morph also changes by season, with "blue" molting from brown i summer, to paler brown tinged w a blue sheen in winter. "White" remains nearly pure white in winter, while in summer it chang to brown and pale gray. The "blue" morph comprises less than 1% of the population throughou most of its continental range, bu 25–30% in Norway, Sweden, and Finland, and 65–70% in Iceland. The proportion of "blue morphs also increases in coastal areas and on islands such as Mednyi Island, Russia, and St. Paul Island, Alaska, where it can reach up to 100%. Within each morph, there is considerable variation in appearance. In Sweden, sand-colored foxes are occasionally seen in summer, but they appear to be of the "white" morph without brown pigment. I Iceland, cinnamon colored foxes of both morphs occur. The Arctic Fox evolved in the mid-Pleistocen only half a million years ago. It has many physical adaptations the Arctic environment. Its fur h the best insulative properties of a terrestrial mammal, and it does not need to increase its metabolic rate to maintain a stable body temperature under any naturally occurring temperature. To save energy in winter, it is able to red its resting metabolic rate, body co temperature, and food intake. In autumn, Arctic Foxes may increa their weight by more than 50% they build up fat reserves for ener and insulation. They also have on the soles of their feet.

Above: *Alopex lagopus*
Hudson Bay, Nunavut, Canada.
Photo: Wayne Lynch/DRK

Below: *Alopex lagopus*
Photo: M. Watson/Ardea

Canids are adapted for running. Most have long, slender limbs, like the **Red Fox**, and compact feet with four functional toes. The Red Fox has the widest geographical range of any member of the order Carnivora, covering nearly 70 million km² across the entire Northern Hemisphere from the Arctic Circle to North Africa, Central America, and the Asiatic steppes. It has also been introduced to Australia. The largest fox in the genus Vulpes, Red Fox shows enormous geographical variation in size. For example, Red Foxes are substantially smaller in the Middle East deserts than in Europe, and they are also smaller in North America.

Vulpes vulpes
Hamilton County, SW Ohio, USA.
Photo: Dave Maslowski/
Maslowski Productions

Several canid species have adapted to harsh conditions, like the **Corsac Fox**, which survives in the bleak stony steppes of Central Asia. To cope with the extremes of climate, its summer fur is short and sparse, and its winter fur is dense, soft, and silky. It chooses open habitats, avoiding dense vegetation. In winter, it also avoids areas where the snow is deeper than around 15 cm, preferring areas where snow is either shallower, or highly compressed. The Corsac Fox is typically vulpine in appearance, with a skull that is similar in shape to the Red Fox, but smaller, shorter, and wider, and with more robust canine teeth.

Vulpes corsac
Photo: Eric Soder/NHPA

Habitat

Although canids evolved in relatively open spaces, their great adaptability has enabled them to flourish in most conditions. Today they occur in all major habitats, spanning tropical forests, woodland, savannah, deserts, mountains, alpine heathlands, the Arctic, and even cities. Wild canids are found at all altitudes from sea level to over 5000 m, and are present in all continents except Antarctica and many oceanic islands.

The Arctic, alpine tundra, and boreal forests harbor the lowest canid diversity, and canids there tend to occur at a much lower density that those found in temperate grasslands and tropical habitats. The Arctic Fox is an opportunistic predator and scavenger found throughout the Arctic, alpine tundra and subarctic maritime habitats of Eurasia, North America, the Canadian archipelago and Greenland. In most inland areas, however, they are heavily dependent on fluctuating populations of rodents such as lemmings (*Lemmus* spp. and *Dicrostonyx* spp.). Arctic wolves also show a remarkable ability to adapt to harsh Arctic conditions, relying on Snowshoe Hares (*Lepus americanus*) and Muskoxen (*Ovibos moschatus*) for sustenance.

Most canids tend to be generalists. Red Foxes, for example, are recorded in habitats as diverse as tundra, desert, and forest, as well as in city centers (including London, Paris, and Stockholm). Coyotes are the most versatile of all canids. Their plasticity in behavior, social ecology, and diet allows them not only to exploit, but to thrive, in almost all environments modified by humans. South American Gray Foxes (*Pseudalopex griseus*) generally inhabit plains and low mountains, but have been reported to occur as high as 4000 m, spanning very different climatic regimes, from remarkably hot and dry areas such as the Atacama coastal desert in northern Chile (less than 2 mm average annual rainfall, 22°C mean annual temperature) to the humid regions of the temperate Valdivian forest (over 2000mm, 12°C) and the cold Tierra del Fuego.

Ethiopian Wolves are somewhat unusual among canids in that they are a very localized endemic species, confined to a handful of isolated pockets of Afro-alpine grasslands and heathlands above the tree-line at about 3200 m and up to 4500 m. They favor open areas with short vegetation, where they feed almost exclusively on Afro-alpine rodents such as Ethiopian African Mole Rats (*Tachyoryctes macrocephalus*) and Murinae grass rats (*Arvicanthis* spp., *Otomys* spp.), which provide a very rich resource, sometimes reaching up to 3000 kg of prey biomass per km².

Temperate grasslands, shrublands, and montane habitats are home to a more diverse array of canids, with over 20 canid species favoring these open habitats. Only four South American species, the Bush Dog, Short-eared Dog, Hoary Fox, and Crab-eating Fox, are essentially restricted to tropical forest. The first three rank among the least known of all canids, with even the most basic information on distribution and biology lacking. The limited distribution information available suggests that the Short-eared Dog, a true Amazonian species, may be locally common, but absent through large parts of its range.

Geographical variability in body size can be explained to some deg by differences in food availability with small canids like **Rüppell's Fox** and **Fennec Fox** usually associated with arid and less productive habitats, in which only a small body mass can be supported year round. The typica habitat of Rüppell's Fox includes sand and stone deserts. They can live in areas without any availab water, for example on the fringes of the Arabian Empty Quarter and in the western Sahara. This ability to survive in a hyper-arid environment is supported by various ecological, behavioral, and physiological adaptations. The Rüppell's Fox's diet is rich in plant material, which probably provides much of the moisture it requires. Rüppell's Foxes are mos nocturnal, spending the hottest hours of the day in their dens. Their large ears, and the hair-covered soles of their feet, help the regulate their body temperature. However, the most extreme adaptations to hot and arid climate are seen in the Fennec Fox for which sand dunes appear to ideal habitat. It has the largest e to-body ratio of any canid, with i ears constituting 20% of the bod surface. When the temperature soars, it dilates the blood vessels in its ears and feet to increase the amount of heat radiated to the outside. It also has kidneys that filter extremely high concentration of urea with little water loss. It saves energy by having a metabolism that functions at only 67% of the rate predicted for suc a small animal, and its heart rate is 40% lower than could be expected for its body size. When th temperature exceeds 35°C, it star to pant, and its breathing rate rockets from 23 breaths per minu when at rest, to a maximum of 6 breaths per minute.

Above: **Vulpes rueppellii**
Awserd, Western Sahara.
Photo: Rafael Armada

Below: **Vulpes zerda**
Morocco.
Photo: Graham Hatherley/
naturepl.com

The tiny Darwin's Fox is mostly restricted to temperate forests of Chile's Pacific coast, notably Chiloé Island.

Several canid species have adapted to the harsh conditions of deserts and semi-deserts with little vegetation, no free-standing water and sparse prey. There are three species, the Fennec, Rüppell's, and Pale Foxes, present in the Sahara and Sahel, with a fourth, Blanford's Fox, present in the deserts and mountains of Western Asia. Sechuran Foxes live in the coastal desert of Peru and Ecuador. All these foxes are nocturnal and make extensive use of burrows during the day to survive in a hyper-arid environment. The Red Fox is also able to survive in dry habitats, and tends to outcompete Rüppell's Foxes everywhere except in the harshest desert areas. Other fox species, such as the Corsac Fox (*Vulpes corsac*) and Tibetan Fox survive in the bleak stony steppes of Central Asia.

Closely related, sympatric species may show differences in habitat preferences and some level of partitioning. Golden Jackals inhabit relatively arid regions and dry grassland (but may be found in forested areas in Asia); the Side-striped Jackal prefers moist woodland and riverine forest; the Black-back Jackal shows a preference for dry grassland and *Acacia* woodland.

The reduction of suitable habitat because of urban spread, agriculture, and resource-extraction is the greatest threat facing canids throughout the world. Even protected areas are often inadequate to maintain genetically viable populations of canids that have large home range requirements. Even when suitable habitat is available, the persistence of canids is also dependent upon ecosystem factors such as prey availability and interspecific competition, which may or may not be influenced by human actions.

General Habits

Many of the smaller canids are nocturnal, whereas most of the social, larger species tend to be diurnal, although diurnal habits may change due to human impact. As a result of human persecution, Coyotes became substantially less diurnal after decades of intensive control activity, and Ethiopian Wolves revert to more nocturnal habits when persecuted. Gray Wolves have adopted more secretive and nocturnal activity patterns in parts of Europe where they coexist with people. Red Foxes are more diurnal where undisturbed and are dramatically more approachable beyond those parts of Europe and North America

where they have been persecuted. Jackal species are nocturnal, with peaks of activity during the early morning and evening, but where human disturbance is low they may be active during the day.

As its name suggests, the Raccoon Dog is not unlike a raccoon in general appearance, and, uniquely among canids, hibernates in winter, especially in areas like southern Finland, where winters are harsh. There is some evidence that during hibernation, Raccoon Dogs may incubate the rabies virus and hence cause the disease to persist from one season to the next in places where Red Fox densities are so low that it might otherwise die out.

Competition, hostility, and aggression between sympatric canids are important forces in their biology. Indeed, intraguild aggression, as an expression of competition, emerges as a commonplace of carnivore communities. Aggression and killing between different canid species has been widely documented. Gray Wolves kill Coyotes and Red Foxes; Coyotes kill Red Foxes, Swift Foxes, and Kit Foxes; and Red Foxes kill Kit Foxes and Arctic Foxes. In Africa, Black-backed Jackals torment and kill Cape Foxes, and African Wild Dogs kill Bat-eared Foxes.

Red Foxes are a determinant of the geographical range of the Arctic Fox in Europe. One study found that Arctic Foxes seldom bred within 8 km of a Red Fox den, and when they did, in most cases the Red Foxes killed their young. Red Foxes may thus be excluding Arctic Foxes from high quality, low elevation breeding habitat. In Ontario, Red Foxes existed only in the interstices between Coyote territories, and in California, it appears that Red Foxes increased when Coyotes declined following urbanization. Another notable example of inter-specific hostility is that of the Coyote and Gray Wolf. Within ten years of the Gray Wolf's arrival on Isle Royale, Coyotes had disappeared. Population densities of Gray Wolves and Coyotes appear to be inversely related, as are those of Coyotes and Red Foxes. Consequently, although wolves sometimes also kill Red Foxes, they are more numerous where the Gray Wolves are found, benefiting from a corresponding decrease in Coyotes.

Oddly, and against the generality that larger canids are hostile to smaller ones, Black-backed Jackals dominate the larger Side-striped Jackals. And while in some canid communities there is evidence of character displacement, in parts of Kenya where Black-backed, Golden, and Side-striped Jackals coexist, they become more rather than less similar in size. The generality of inter-guild competition in canid ecology is vividly illus-

traditional explanation for pack living has been that carnivores
nt together to overwhelm prey too large or challenging to be hunted lone. An alternative explanation could be that only where prey is large can packs be large. **Dholes** *usually live in packs of 5–10 dividuals, but groups of as many as 25 (including juveniles) have en regularly recorded. Packs may contain significantly more males han females, perhaps a reflection of female-biased dispersal. Group size and composition may vary under different environmental conditions. Groups have a strong hierarchical structure, with a dominant male and female. Pack members regularly play together, engaging in mock-fights, and mutual grooming.*

Cuon alpinus
India.
Photo: Iain Green/NHPA

*Howling is common in **Coyotes**,
Gray Wolves, jackals, and other
medium and large canids. It
provides an immediate, long-ran
message that indicates the presen
of an individual or pack in a
particular area. Howling plays
a role in territorial maintenance
and pack spacing by advertising
boundaries and signaling the
presence of alpha animals that
will confront intruders and defen
the territory. Howling by one pac
may stimulate howling in adjace
packs. Because of this, researcher
in some areas use artificial calls
estimate the density of species like
Coyotes and Gray Wolves.*

Canis latrans
Montana, USA.
Photo: Jurgen & Christine Sohns/FL

trated by the plight of Island Foxes on the California Channel Islands. Predation by golden eagles (*Aquila chrysaetos*) is probably responsible for the recent catastrophic declines of five of the six populations of Island Foxes. The presence of feral pigs enabled eagles to colonize the islands, increase in population size, and over-exploit the fox.

Direct competition may also have affected the distribution and sizes of *Pseudalopex* species. In central and southern Chile both the Culpeo (*Pseudalopex culpaeus*) and the South American Gray Fox eat rodents, birds, birds' eggs, and snakes in comparable quantities. However, the two species vary in size with latitude throughout their range. Average body length of the Culpeo increases from 70 to 90 cm and that of the Gray Fox decreases from 68 to 42 cm from north to south. Where the two species are of similar size, the Culpeo inhabits higher altitudes of the Andes, so reducing competition. Farther south, where the altitude decreases, bringing the species into apparently direct competition, the much smaller size of the Gray Fox predisposes it to hunting smaller prey than the Culpeo, and so again, competition is reduced.

Communication

The canids are a highly variable taxonomic group in terms of behavior, ecology, shape and form. As such, they have developed a wide range of ways to communicate, including scent marking, vocalizations, and various visual expressions. Communication may be more or less complex, depending on the species, and provides key information within and between social groups, over a variety of distances and time frames.

Canids are perhaps best known for their exquisite sense of smell. In most species, this allows them to detect minute traces of scent in the environment, scents that are often imperceptible to humans. The canid ability to detect chemical signals such as pheromones or the volatiles from scent-gland secretions probably co-evolved with the development of a variety of scent glands and the pervasiveness of scent marking as a primary means of communicating. Interactions with conspecifics, whether members of the same or a different social group, often can be dangerous and even result in injury or death. Scent marking provides a relatively safe and passive means of communicating information.

Defined in its most basic form as the application of animal odor to the environment, scent marking occurs in many ways. Scents can be applied through glandular secretions. Most canids have a variety of glands, including anal glands, that can, but do not always, discharge pungent secretions with feces. Anal gland secretions cover feces and provide a relatively long-lasting mark for some species. Shorter-term secretions can come from tail glands; for example, from the supracaudal or "violet" gland that is often identified in foxes by a small area covered by black hairs near the root of the tail. This gland discharges volatiles into the air. Inter-digital glands on the feet also provide shorter-term signals by releasing scents as the animal moves along a path or when it scratches the ground. Some species also have facial glands, sometimes on the lips, cheeks, or along the angle of the jaw, that are used to rub scents onto particular objects or substrates.

Scent marking by most species predominantly occurs through the application of urine or feces. Urine marks, in particular, often contain chemical compounds that convey specific messages and occur frequently in some species. Red Foxes use "token" urine marks—or short squirts of urine—to mark conspicuous objects frequently throughout their range. Similarly, Kit Foxes may use short urine marks at rates of up to 30 per hour, and packs of Ethiopian Wolves have been observed marking with urine at rates of up to twelve signs per kilometer of distance traveled. Scent marking with feces also occurs. Some species deposit feces singly on or near conspicuous objects or locations. Coyotes and Wolves, for example, often mark at the intersection of trails or paths, Red Foxes may mark on tree stumps or dirt clods, and Maned Wolves tend to mark sites such as insect mounds. Several species also mark on latrines or piles of multiple feces that are continually remarked. Latrine use has been documented in the Island Fox, Northern Gray Fox, Kit Fox, and Swift Fox, as well as larger species like the Raccoon Dog, Golden Jackal, Dhole, Maned Wolf, and Ethiopian Wolf.

Scent marking, whether through urine, feces, or glands, can have several functions, depending on the species. It can have reproductive functions, such as synchronizing mating activities. It can indicate the precise timing of estrus through hormonal traces in urine. Female Bush Dogs increase marking frequency during the proestrus and estrus periods, often over-marking male marks and adopting an unusual hand-stand posture to do so. In captivity, a receptive female Bush Dog remark-

Direct interactions with other canids of the same species can be ingerous. Scent marking provides relatively safe and passive means of communicating information. Scent marking by most species predominantly occurs through the application of urine or feces. Urine marks, in particular, often contain chemical compounds that convey specific messages. Packs of **Ethiopian Wolves** *have been observed marking with urine at rates of up to twelve signs per kilometer of distance traveled. All pack members, independent of social rank, regularly scent-mark objects along territory boundaries with raised-leg urinations and scratches.*

Canis simensis
Bale Mountains National Park,
Ethiopia.
Photo: Martin Harvey/DRK

ably scent-marked 81 times in one hour after being introduced to a pair of males. In more social species, like the Gray Wolf and African Wild Dog, scent marking also may indicate individual status or suppress the reproductive activities of others in a group or pack through chemical cues and behaviors associated with marking.

Scent marking often functions to demarcate and maintain territories. Carefully placed scent marks at territory boundaries can provide a passive indication to others that a particular territory is occupied. Some of the larger canid species, including Coyotes and Gray Wolves, are well known to "signpost" territory boundaries to advertize ownership. Ethiopian Wolves also tandem mark territory boundaries during regular patrols, where all pack members actively contribute.

Scent marking also may improve foraging efficiency, by providing chemical signals indicating that a particular food patch has been exploited. Red Foxes, for example, mark depleted food resources such as emptied caches or inedible food remnants to provide a "book keeping system" of resources not worthy of re-inspection. Book keeping, also observed among Coyotes and Gray Wolves, may be particularly important during periods of food shortage.

Most canids have a variety of glands, including anal glands, which can discharge pungent secretions with feces, providing a relatively long-lasting scent mark for some species. Shorter-term secretions can come from tail glands or inter-digital glands on the feet. Some canids also have lands on the lips, cheeks, or along the angle of the jaw, that are used to rub scents onto objects, as this **South American Gray Fox** *seems to be doing. Scent marking can serve a wide variety of purposes, depending on the species. It can have reproductive functions, demarcate and maintain territories, provide individual, group, or species recognition, serve as an alarm signal, give spatial references, and allow an individual to assess competitors.*

Pseudalopex griseus
Monumento Natural Bosques
Petrificados, Patagonia, Argentina.
Photo: Francisco Erize

Living in packs benefits foraging efficiency, breeding success, and survivorship in medium and larg canids like **Gray Wolves**, but it also increases the possibility of aggressive encounters between pa members. As well as using scent and vocalizations, wolves, like other canids, also communicate through visual expressions. Some expressions, such as baring the teeth and retracting the lips, or the position of the tongue, may indicate aggression or submission, depending on the situation. The position of the tail ears, and overall body can also indicate dominance, submission, aggression, distress, or warning. Some canids "raise their hackles" by erecting hairs along the spine or around the neck and shoulder. Submissive behavior may include rolling on the back and exposing vulnerable parts such as the thro. By ritualizing these encounters, threat of real injury is minimized However, fights between packs ov territory can lead to serious injur and death. Many combinations of body language are also used to indicate social status. During scent marking by Gray Wolves, certain positions, such as raised-leg urinations, are only used by dominant individuals. Lone or unpaired Gray Wolves (both mal and female), and subordinates, different postures.

Above: *Canis lupus*
Yellowstone National Park, Wyomir
USA.
Photo: Juan Carlos Muñoz

Below: *Canis lupus*
Photo: Bernd Zoller/Imagebroker/FL

Black-backed Jackals are territorial, and use feces and urine to demarcate their territorial boundaries. Intruders are aggressively expelled by territory holders. Water sources are shared with intruders, but the intruders perform submissive behavior to territory holders, even to their pups. The monogamous mated pair is the basis of the Black-backed Jackal's social structure, and if one member of a pair dies, the other will often lose its territory. Groups of between eight and ten Black-backed Jackals can gather at large herbivore carcasses, and such aggregations are accompanied by aggressive behavior between territorial individuals.

Canis mesomelas
Kalahari, South Africa.
Photo: J&B Photographers/
Photo Access

Other roles of scent marking include providing individual, group, or species recognition, signaling alarm, providing spatial references, assessing competitors, and possibly conveying information about relative population size.

Vocalizations provide another effective form of communication, and are often used in conjunction with scent marking or other forms of communication. Vocalizations vary and may include barks, yelps, howls, chitters, and whistles. Depending on the species, vocalizations may include long distance calls that for some larger species transmit well over 10 km, or subtler, softer, shorter distance calls that occur between individuals in a social group. In some species, the vocal repertoire is vast, while in others, only few vocalizations, if any, have been documented. Red Foxes, for example, have been described using over 30 different vocalizations, ranging from yips to barks and screams. By comparison, some of the smaller, more solitary fox species such as Blanford's Fox seldom vocalize.

Vocalizations often provide similar functions and complement scent marking and other forms of communication. Among several canids, vocalizations serve territorial functions. Howling is common in Gray Wolves, Coyotes, jackals, and other medium and large-sized species, and provides an immediate, long-range message that indicates the presence of an individual or pack in a particular area and maintains a territory presence. Howls also provide a spatial reference to the receiver about the caller's location, which is useful in preventing potentially injurious or fatal encounters. Howling generally occurs by dominant individuals in most species and may invoke response howls from individuals on neighboring territories. Because of this, researchers in some areas use artificial calls to estimate the density of some species like Gray Wolves and Coyotes.

Several canids use other types of vocalizations for territorial purposes. Arctic Foxes, for example, commonly emit sequences of barks (i.e. several short barks in rapid succession) when they are patrolling territorial boundaries, and in response to barking by neighbors. Playback experiments have shown that Arctic Foxes are more likely to respond with territorial behavior and longer bouts of barking to barks from neighbors or strangers than to barks from fellow group members. These calls are individually specific, allowing foxes to distinguish the calls of other group members or neighbors. Swift Foxes and a number of other species, such as the Bush Dog and Red Fox, also have individual specific barking calls.

Vocalizations serve many intragroup functions. In some species, especially foxes, vocalizations are used in courtship, to attract a mate or potential mate, or mate guarding. Vocalizations may also be used to strengthen group cohesion. African Wild Dogs, for example, engage in elaborate pre-hunt rallies in which pack members race around greeting one another while emitting distinctive, high-pitched "chittering" calls. During hunts, when pack members spread out over large distances, wild dogs use another vocalization, a "hoo" call, to establish contact with each other and reconvene. Contact calls are used by other species as well, including the Dhole, which emits a short repeated "whistle" call during hunting to contact pack members and possibly coordinate cooperative hunting. Similarly, Bat-eared Foxes call each other to rich food patches with a low whistle. Canid vocalizations also may indicate distress, warning, submission (i.e. to reduce potential intraspecific aggression), or status within the group.

Canids also communicate through visual expressions. Facial expressions are commonly used by Red Foxes to convey messages to other members of a social group. Bat-eared Foxes also rely on a variety of facial expressions to communicate with group members. Some expressions, such as baring the teeth and retracting the lips or the position of the tongue may indicate aggression or submission, depending on the situation or behavioral context.

Posture conveys a variety of similar information. The position of the tail, ears, and overall body can indicate dominance, submission, aggression, distress, or warning. Some canids erect hairs along the spine or around the neck and shoulders (i.e., raised hackles) during agonistic displays. Many combinations of body language are also used to indicate social status. During scent marking by Gray Wolves, for example, certain types of positions, such as raised-leg urinations, are only used by dominant individuals. Lone or unpaired Gray Wolves (both male and female) and subordinates use different postures.

Food and Feeding

Canid diets are among the most versatile in carnivores, varying from strictly carnivorous to some that contain less than 5% protein. Canids can be divided into small (under 6 kg), medium, and large (over 13 kg) species, and there are some general dif-

*Interference competition at kills c...
be considerable. This single* **Gold**
Jackal *is heavily outnumbered by*
vultures, and may lose its kill.
The outcome of such competition
generally appears to be affected b
group size and habitat type. The
social organization of large cani
is extremely flexible and depends
the availability and distribution
of food resources. In Israel, a
large pack of Golden Jackals
habitually stole food from a smal
pack, suggesting that strength in
numbers has concrete energetic a
territorial advantages.

Canis aureus
Rift Valley, Kenya.
Photo: Günter Ziesler

ferences in diets in each size group. Most of the smaller species are opportunistic omnivores, eating anything from mammals to birds, reptiles, insects, fruit, and carrion. Larger, group-living species such as Gray Wolves, Dholes, and African Wild Dogs may be more strictly carnivorous, preying on medium to large-sized mammals that often exceed their own body size. The Maned Wolf, which lives in South America's savannas, is unusual for a large canid in feeding mostly on rodents and fruit.

Packs of Gray Wolves are among the dominant meat-eaters in the Northern Hemisphere. Dhole packs fill this role in southern Asia, and African Wild Dogs command a mighty pres-

ence in sub-Saharan Africa. All three species consume a wide range of foods, mostly obtained by killing animals larger than themselves. Large hoofed animals such as Moose (*Alces*), Red Deer/Elk (*Cervus elaphus*), Reindeer/Caribou (*Rangifer tarandus*), Muskox, Bison (*Bison*), sheep, and goats are the primary prey of Gray Wolves. Though wolves are quite capable of killing healthy adult animals, more than 60% of their prey consists of young, weak, or older animals. Wolves are keen observers of behavior and are able to detect subtle weaknesses not evident to the human eye. Healthy, vigorous prey often escape Gray Wolf predation by fighting back, and on occasion wolves are

"Intraguild" predation is an
enormous force in canid ecology.
Predators like this **Gray Wolf**
can be killed and eaten by larger
predators. For example, Lions a
responsible for 43% of African
Wild Dog mortality in South
Africa's Kruger National Park.
Predation by golden eagles is
probably responsible for the decli
of five of the six populations of
Island Foxes. Aggression and
killing between different canid
species has also been widely
documented. Gray Wolves kill
Coyotes and Red Foxes; Coyotes
Red Foxes, Swift Foxes, and Kit
Foxes; and Red Foxes kill Kit Fo
and Arctic Foxes.

Canis lupus
Denali National Park and Preserve,
Alaska, USA.
Photo: Mark Newman/FLPA

killed by Moose, Bison, or Elk. Wolves may also eat voles, Beavers, and hares, and where available, fish, berries, and carrion. Arctic wolves may subsist on small mammals and birds when their primary prey, Reindeer, migrate to their summer range.

African Wild Dogs epitomize cursorial pack-hunting, with large bands of as many as 20 dogs displaying a cunning ability to orchestrate sophisticated hunts and identify susceptible prey. The hunting abilities of Asian Dholes are less well known, since they favor forest, where observation is not straightforward. Their preferred prey includes deer, Gaur (*Bos frontalis*), Banteng (*Bos javanicus*), and other large bovids. They rely on sound to coordinate kills in thick forest.

Coyotes are opportunistic, generalist predators that eat a variety of food items ranging from fruit and insects to prey larger than themselves, including both wild and domestic ungulates. Their Old World equivalents, the three jackal species, are skilful hunters of small birds and mammals up to the size of hares or newborn antelopes, and readily eat insects and fruit. Indeed, jackals are adept at locating any rich source of food, so their diet is catholic, varying a great deal between seasons.

Although most canids of comparable size are opportunistic hunters, there is a specialist among them. Just shy of 20 kg in weight, the Ethiopian Wolf has an unusual diet. It feeds almost exclusively upon the diurnal rodents of Ethiopia's high-altitude Afro-alpine grasslands. In the Bale Mountains, diurnal rodents accounted for 96% of all prey occurrences in feces, with 87% belonging to three endemic species: the Ethiopian African Mole Rat *Tachyoryctes macrocephalus* (up to 930 g in weight), Blick's Grass Rat *Arvicanthis blicki*, and the Black-clawed Brush-furred Rat *Lophuromys melanonyx*. Although the Ethiopian Wolf is preeminently a solitary hunter, it can also hunt cooperatively, and small packs may chase and kill Ethiopian Highland Hare *Lepus starcki*, Rock Hyrax *Procavia capensis*, lambs, and small antelopes.

Although usually found near large herds of hoofed mammals, such as zebra (*Equus*), wildebeest (*Connochaetes*), and African Buffalo (*Syncerus caffer*), the Bat-eared Fox is the only canid to have largely abandoned mammalian prey in favor of insects. The teeth of the Bat-eared Fox are relatively small, but numerous, with four to eight extra molars. A step-like protrusion on the lower jaw anchors a large muscle used for rapid chewing.

Insects abound where large ungulates are numerous, so the Bat-eared Fox depends on other mammals for provision of its food despite the insectivorous nature of its diet. Colonies of harvester termites (*Synthermes* spp. and *Cornitermes* spp.), which can make up 70% of the fox's diet, live underground, but large numbers surface to forage for grasses; the grasses occur mainly where large ungulates feed. Dung beetles eat the dung of ungulates and lay their eggs in dung balls, which the female beetles bury. Bat-eared Foxes eat both adults and larvae, which they locate by listening for the sound of the grub as it gnaws its way out of the dung ball. The diet of Brazil's Hoary Fox also appears to be predominantly insectivorous. Ground-dwelling harvester termites were recorded in 87% of Hoary Fox feces.

Apart from these termite specialists, there are no proven differences in fox species' diets other than those imposed by the availability of prey. The few fox species that have been studied have been found to be opportunistic, eating whatever food was locally available. Red Foxes have very diverse diets, ranging from small hoofed mammals, rabbits, hares, rodents, and birds to invertebrates such as beetles, grasshoppers, and earthworms. In season, fruit such as blackberries, apples, and the hips of the Dog Rose can form as much as 90% of the Red Fox diet. If given the choice, however, Red Foxes prefer arvicoline rodents, such as Field Voles, to members of the family Muridae, such as Field Mice. However, being true opportunists, they will cache even less-favored prey for future use, and have a good memory for the location of these larders. Red Foxes may also catch fish, wading stealthily through shallow marshes. Arctic Foxes will take sea birds, rock ptarmigan (*Lagopus muta*), shore invertebrates, fruit, and berries, together with carrion they find while methodically beachcombing. They time their shore visits to coincide with the receding tide, when fresh debris is stranded. Blanford's Foxes eat chiefly insects and fruit, consuming more fruit during the hot summer, which compensates for deficiencies in body water.

Scavenging is widespread among canids, and most species will readily help themselves to carrion whenever the opportunity arises. A group of jackals squabbling over an antelope carcass recently abandoned by Lions or Spotted Hyenas is a common sight in many of Africa's national parks. Even so, jackals are less dependent on carrion than is popularly believed,

scavenging only 6–10% of their diet. Scavenging can be a vital part of other species' diets. For example, Arctic Fox productivity can be determined by access to seals killed by Polar Bears. In Iceland the reproductive success of Arctic Fox pairs could be correlated to the length of tidal beach they had available to comb for food. As a side note, large, wolf-like canids are unique among carnivores in that they are able to carry food in their stomachs and regurgitate it for their offspring. Unlike their lupine relatives, no vulpine (fox-like) canid has been reported to regurgitate. Instead, they carry and cache their food. From this we might deduce that regurgitation is a trait of the lupine

canids, evolved only after their split six million years ago from the early vulpines.

The similar foraging behaviors of different fox species could lead to severe competition for food, and affect their geographical distribution. Red and Arctic Foxes were once thought to be separated by the latter's remarkable tolerance to cold temperatures. Yet Red Foxes are sometimes found in even colder places than Arctic Foxes, indicating that the two species are probably separated by food competition. Red Foxes are up to twice as heavy, and correspondingly need more food. In the far north, where prey is sparse, Red Foxes cannot match the Arctic Fox

on energy gain versus expenditure. In areas where both species can subsist, however, the Red Fox's greater size enables it to intimidate the Arctic Fox, in effect determining the southern limit of the latter's range.

Vertebrate prey must be actively pursued, and canids are uniquely adapted to cursorial pursuit, which they often combine with group efforts to achieve high hunting success. While large canids may resort to pack hunting, with a tendency for larger packs to hunt larger prey, medium-sized species are more versatile. Coyotes hunt small mammals alone, even when pack size is large. When preying on larger ungulate prey, cooperation among pack members may facilitate the capture of prey, but is not essential. Age, habitat, wind, and snow conditions all influence the ability of Coyotes to capture small mammals. And environmental factors are equally important to the success of an attack on adult ungulates. The number of Coyotes is not as important as whether the alpha pair or younger individuals are involved in the attack. In areas with an ungulate prey base in winter, resource partitioning and competition for a carcass may be intense, even among members of the same pack.

Side-striped jackals have been observed bumping up against bushes or stamping the ground to disturb locusts, beetles, and grasshoppers, which are subsequently snapped up. Jackals are expert rodent hunters. They use their acute hearing to pinpoint prey in long grass, then leap into the air, pounce on the rodent with their forefeet, and deliver a killing bite. When larger mammalian prey such as hares or newborn antelope is available, jackals will often cooperate with their mates in order to make a catch. While one member of a pair chases the prey, the other may harass would-be protectors or else cut off the prey as it tries to zigzag. When hunting gazelle fawns or Spring Hares (*Pedetes capensis*), jackals that cooperate are two to three times more successful than those that hunt alone.

All foxes are opportunistic foragers, using hunting techniques that vary from stealth to dash-and-grab. Most foxes hunt solitarily. Although their paths may cross many times each night, foxes within a group may forage mainly in different parts of the territory, with dominant animals generally monopolizing the best habitat. All vulpine foxes catch rodents with a characteristic "mouse leap," springing a meter off the ground and diving, forepaws first, onto the prey. This aerial descent may be a device to counter the vertical jump used by some mice to escape predators. Fennecs have not been seen using the "mouse

leap" hunting strategy typical of most foxes, but reportedly dig to find insects and small vertebrates. Fennecs, like most other foxes, do cache food by burying it. Food caching is rare or absent in Blanford's Fox.

Red Foxes catch earthworms that have ventured out of their burrows on warm, moist nights by crisscrossing pastures at a slow walk and listening for the sound of the worms' bristles rasping on the grass. Once a worm is detected, the fox poises over it before plunging its snout into the grass. Worms that manage to retain a grip in their burrows are not pulled and broken, but gently pulled taut by the fox after a momentary pause, just like fishermen collecting bait.

Although much larger in size, Ethiopian Wolves often resemble foxes in their foraging antics, leaping and hammering their reinforced snouts into rodent burrows to shock and pin down their quarry. Ethiopian Wolves often forage among cattle, using the herd as a mobile hide as a tactic to ambush rodents out of their holes. Wolves explore rich food patches by walking slowly, frequently stopping to investigate holes or listen to the rodents underground. Once the prey is located, the Ethiopian Wolves alternate short, stealthy steps with short periods of immobility, until the quarry is grabbed with the mouth after a short dash. A stalk can last up to one hour when the quarry is a Ethiopian African Mole Rat, although these more often are dug out from as deep as one meter below ground. Wolves may also run in zig-zags across rat colonies picking up the scampering rodents.

Bush Dogs are also unusual because they are small-sized, but live in large family groups and hunt cooperatively. Due to their tropical forest habits they have received little study, yet some opportunistic observations reveal their peculiar natural history. Bush Dogs hunt large forest rodents such as Paca (*Agouti paca*) and Agouti (*Dasyprocta* spp.), and hunting as a pack they can take prey considerably larger than themselves, such as Capybaras (*Hydrochaeris hydrochaeris*), brocket deer (*Mazama* spp.), greater rheas (*Rhea americana*), and possibly even South American Tapirs (*Tapirus terrestris*). They are quite vocal and keep in contact while foraging in forest undergrowth where visibility is poor by means of frequent whines, which may be an adaptation to maintain group cohesion. Bush Dogs put their social coordination to good use when hunting, and readily share their quarry. It is said that they use each other's bodies to lever bones from a carcass, and will slice off chunks of meat from prey held in a compan-

*This **Arctic Fox** is getting its rest during the day, in order to hunt and scavenge at night. Despite being primarily nocturnal, however, the Arctic Fox exhibits flexible activity patterns, often in accordance with main prey species. The basic social unit of the Arctic Fox is the breeding pair. However, on Mednyi Island, Russia, there are permanent Arctic Fox groups comprising up to six adults, and complex social systems have also been observed on other islands. Home ranges of group members generally overlap widely with each other, but very little with those of neighboring groups. Temporary groups of non-breeding individuals are also sometimes formed.*

Alopex lagopus
Quttinirpaaq National Park, Canada.
Photo: Staffan Widstrand

Primarily nocturnal, the **Sechura**
Fox *is a generalist omnivore that
preferentially consumes vertebrate
prey or carrion. However, feces
collected during late winter
and early spring in the inland
Sechuran Desert contained main
the remnants of undigested
seeds and seed pods. Following
El Niño rains, fox droppings
revealed a dramatic dietary shift
to grasshoppers and mice as these
prey became more abundant. Rac
telemetry tracking found that
the phases of the moon did not
influence their nocturnal activity
pattern, perhaps because the foxe
were consuming seeds and seed
pods rather than hunting.*

Pseudalopex sechurae
Chaparri Ecological Reserve,
Lambayeque, Peru.
Photo: Tui de Roy/
Roving Tortoise Photos

ion's mouth. Bush Dog packs have reportedly pursued amphibious prey into water, where the dogs swim and dive with agility.

Almost all extant carnivores that weigh more than 21 kg take prey as large as or larger than themselves. A traditional explanation for pack-living has been that carnivores hunt together to overwhelm prey too large or challenging to be hunted alone. However, statements such as that Serengeti's Black-backed Jackals were more successful in killing gazelle fawns when they cooperated in deflecting the mother's defenses have never been substantiated. Coyotes occur in large groups in areas where they prey on Elk and Mule Deer (*Odocoileus hemionus*), implying a group hunting explanation for sociality. Similarly, their method of hunting has been used to explain the pack behavior of Gray Wolves and Dholes. However, an alternative explanation could be that only where prey is large can packs be large. Perhaps the explanation for sociality in canids is to be found elsewhere. Wolves on Isle Royale illustrate the downside of cooperative hunting; daily intake of food per wolf per day declined with larger pack sizes. Another description of Gray Wolf pack hunting reveals that in the absence of scavengers, members of larger packs secure relatively reduced foraging returns and would therefore do best by hunting in pairs or alone.

Using an energetic model, it has been demonstrated that large body size brings with it constraints on foraging time and energetic return. Large carnivores cannot sustain themselves on relatively small prey because they would expend more energy in hunting than they would acquire. By taking prey as large as or larger than themselves, they achieve a greater return for a given foraging bout. Although even a single African Wild Dog can kill large prey, there is evidence that the hunting success of African Wild Dogs increases with pack size, at least up to four adults. Large hunting parties need more kills to meet the requirements of each hunter, so hunting success per dog may decrease above a certain group size, with this effect apparently more marked when hunting gazelle. Thus, hunting in large, but not too large, groups will provide the optimal ratio of benefit to cost.

Energetic constraints may shape canid behavior. Measurements of the energy consumption of African Wild Dogs demonstrated that hunting is so expensive that a reduction in the measured hunting success would lead to an exponential increase in the time needed to break even energetically. For example, if that deterioration resulted in a loss of 25% of their kills to

Spotted Hyenas, the dogs' daily hunting time requirements will push up from three and a half hours to twelve hours a day.

Irrespective of the possible advantage of collaborating to make a kill, larger groups of Coyotes are more successful at defending, or indeed stealing, carcasses from neighboring packs. Similarly, in Israel, a large pack of Golden Jackals habitually stole food from a smaller pack, suggesting that strength in numbers has concrete energetic and territorial advantages.

Interference competition at kills can be considerable and canids may also be the scavengers' victims. The outcome of such competition generally appears to be affected by group size and habitat type. A lone Gray Wolf might lose two-thirds of a moose kill to scavengers, but a pack of ten wolves would lose only 10%. The greater food-sharing costs in larger packs of Gray Wolves are more than offset by the reduced losses to scavengers. Wolves occasionally scavenge at rubbish dumps, even when wild prey is available. In Romania and Italy they even have been known to scavenge from rubbish bins in or near towns and cities. Coyotes in suburban areas are adept at exploiting human-made food resources and will readily consume dog food or rubbish. Ethiopian Wolves occasionally will take carrion and feed on carcasses. There is a local belief that they follow mares and cows about to give birth to eat the afterbirth, giving origin to their local name of Horse's Jackal.

Predation as an expression of intra-guild competition is an enormous force in canid ecology. Perhaps that is why African Wild Dogs are scarce where Spotted Hyenas and Lions thrive, especially in open habitats where the Lions and Hyenas can easily detect feeding dogs. Wild Dogs tend to actively avoid these large predators; Lions are responsible for 43% of their natural mortality in South Africa's Kruger National Park. Heavy predation by Lions and kleptoparasitism by Spotted Hyenas are important factors to which large packs of wild dogs seem likely to be adapted. More pairs of eyes and ears increase the dogs' chances of detecting danger, allowing large packs to avoid dangerous encounters. Wild Dog packs will mob potential predators if their pups are threatened. A pack can drive off jackals, Spotted Hyenas, and Leopards, and larger packs will even mob Lions.

African Wild Dogs can defend a carcass from Spotted Hyenas if they outnumber the hyenas, although each dog is about a third to a quarter of the body weight of a hyena. Larger packs of African Wild Dogs are able to repel marauding hyenas for longer periods of time, meanwhile dismembering the carcass

All canids have an excellent sense of smell, allowing them to detect minute traces of scent in the environment. When **South American Gray Foxes** were studied in Torres del Paine National Park, Chile, the most common foraging behavior consisted of slow walking, with abrupt, irregular turns through low vegetation. Prey appeared to be located by sound, sight, and smell. Foraging occurs mostly in open areas. Although hunting groups of up to five individuals have been reported, South American Gray Foxes mostly hunt alone, except perhaps at the end of the breeding season, when juveniles may join the parents in search of food.

Pseudalopex griseus
Torres del Paine National Park, Chile.
Photo: Luis Miguel Ruiz Gordón

and bolting it down. Packs of Dholes are reported to be capable of driving a Tiger, which is ten times the size of a Dhole, from a kill. Bat-eared Foxes form larger groups to mob hyenas than they do to mob jackals, and these small canids will even join forces to mob Leopards.

Breeding

Wild canids tend to be territorial, relying on scent marking from urine and feces to demarcate their home ranges and communicate with conspecifics. Marking is involved in establishing and maintaining pair bonds and dominance hierarchies, and may provide an indication of a female's reproductive state. Black-backed Jackal pairs defend their territory from other jackal pairs by leaving urine and feces on conspicuous objects. Unrelated jackals within this area are chased away vigorously, especially during the breeding season.

Canid females are monoestrous, with ovulation seasonal and spontaneous. In wolf-like canids, typically only one female in each family group or pack rears young annually, whereas among the vulpine species, more than one female may breed.

The foraging techniques of the **Bat-eared Fox** depend on prey type, but food is often located by walking slowly, with its nose close to the ground and its large ears cocked forward. Prey is detected mostly by sound, and often excavated by digging. Colonies of harvester termites, which can make up 70% of the fox's diet, live underground, but large numbers surface to forage for grasses. In the Serengeti and elsewhere, dung beetles are the main food in the rainy season, when termites are less active. Dung beetles lay their eggs in balls of dung, which they bury. Bat-eared Foxes eat both adults and larvae, which they locate by listening for the sound of the grub as it gnaws its way out of the dung ball.

Otocyon megalotis
Photo: Jurgen & Christine Sohns/FLPA

Adaptable and opportunistic omnivores, **Red Foxes** have very diverse diets, including small hoofed mammals, rabbits, hares, rodents, mammalian insectivores (such as this mole), birds, and invertebrates such as beetles, grasshoppers, and earthworms. Foxes typically kill birds and mammals up to about 3.5 kg. They also scavenge. Deer and she carcasses may be the major food source in upland areas in winter, and in urban areas they will eat discarded food and other refuse. They cache food that is in excess of their requirements, and have a highly developed memory for locations of hoards.

Vulpes vulpes
Brown County, SW Ohio, USA.
Photo: Dave Maslowski/Maslowski Productions

When a female's progesterone levels go up, the dominant male will develop an interest, following the female assiduously and attempting to mate. The pair often stays together for several days. Once a female is in estrus and receptive, a short courtship begins. The male attempts to mount, often at right angles, and the female makes short dashes away and then back to her partner. In many wolf-like canids, several males may attend a female in estrus and competition and aggression may ensue. In Gray and Ethiopian Wolves, males from neighboring packs may be aware of the female's receptivity, raising the possibility of extra-pair copulations. Such an out-breeding mechanism may help reduce the risk of inbreeding between closely-related individuals. Circumstantial evidence suggests that inbreeding is the norm amongst Bat-eared Foxes, where, through natal philopatry, seven out of fifty-four females were mounted by their father, and one by her brother.

When the male finally mounts, he grips the female with his forelegs. Intromission often leads to a copulatory lock or "tie". This is facilitated by a ring of erectile tissue called the bulbus glandus on the dog's penis. The male often turns and male and female remain in a back-to-back position until the ring reduces in diameter, allowing the tie to end. Fennecs have an exceptionally long copulatory tie that can last 2 hours 45 min.

Most canids species have a single annual estrous cycle, and are thus considered monoestrous. Females usually reach sexual maturity at the age of one year. In wolves, the age at first ovula-

In most inland areas, the **Arctic Fox** is heavily dependent on rodents, as seen here by this individual with a mouthful of lemmings. Changes in Arctic Fox populations have been observed to follow those of their main prey. Populations of lemmings, which can form up to 85% of the Arctic Fox's diet in summer, tend to peak every 3–4 years, before crashing, and Artic Fox litter size varies with such food availability. For example, on Wrangel Island, Russia, in years with high lemming abundance, up to 19 pups per litter have been observed. Arctic Fox productivity can also be determined by access to seals killed by Polar Bears. When food is abundant, they cache food for later use.

Alopex lagopus
Greenland.
Photo: M. Watson/Ardea

Foxes are opportunistic foragers, using hunting techniques that vary from stealth to dash-and-grab. Vulpine foxes such as the **Arctic Fox** *catch rodents with a characteristic "mouse leap", springing a meter off the ground and diving, forepaws first, onto the prey. This aerial descent may be a device to counter the vertical jump used by some mice to escape predators. Similar foraging behaviors between fox species can lead to severe competition for food, and affect their geographical distribution. In areas where both Red Foxes and Arctic Foxes can subsist, the Red Fox's greater size enables it to intimidate the Arctic Fox, in effect determining the southern limit of the latter's range.*

Alopex lagopus
Hudson Bay, Manitoba, Canada.
Photos: Stephen J. Krasemann/DRK

tion varies from about ten months to around 22 months. Social suppression of reproduction is common, and thus reproduction is often delayed. For example, in the larger wolf-like species, the female may first reproduce at the age of two years. However, once a female has cycled, anestrus is rare, and reproductive failure is generally attributable to lack of copulation. The onset of reproduction may be associated with environmental factors, probably related to physiological condition, which in turn reflects the availability of resources. Many temperate species tend to reproduce in late-winter, early-spring. Scent marking may provide the mechanism for neighboring females to monitor their reproductive condition reciprocally, which might lead to estrus synchronization. This has been observed in Ethiopian Wolves, where neighboring packs reproduce synchronously, but out of synch with packs 20 km away.

Some generalizations about canid breeding biology are possible. These can be categorized according to three canid size classes. Small canids (under 6 kg) are either largely monogamous (e.g. Blanford's, Swift, and Kit Foxes) or form small, loose-knit groups with a female-biased sex ratio. Young males tend to emigrate, and females stay in their natal range as helpers until a breeding opportunity arises (e.g. Red and Arctic Foxes). Medium-sized canids (6–13 kg) in general have an equal adult sex ratio and emigration rate. Both sexes may be helpers, and both sexes also disperse (e.g. all jackals, Coyotes, and Crab-eating Foxes). In contrast, most larger canids (over

Studies of predatory behavior in canids, like this **Red Fox**, *show that habitat, wind, and snow conditions all influence their ability to capture small mammals. The depth of snow can affect hunting success, restricting access to rodents and giving them more opportunities to escape, Different canids have different techniques for catching rodents. Jackals use their acute hearing to pinpoint prey in long grass, then leap into the air, pounce on the rodent with their forefeet, and deliver a killing bite. Ethiopian Wolves use cattle as mobile hides to ambush rodents out of their holes, or run in zig-zags across rat colonies, picking up the scampering rodents.*

Vulpes vulpes
Berlin, Germany.
Photo: Bruno D'Amicis

Most large canids are social, and often feed on prey larger than themselves. The **Maned Wolf** is the largest canid in South America, and in contrast to what would be predicted by body size alone, it is primarily solitary, and relies on a diet consisting principally of fruits and small- to medium-sized vertebrates, particularly rodents, as this individual is probably pursuing. The Maned Wolf sometimes also eats armadillos and Pampas Deer. Hunting technique include stalking with a final pounce, digging after burrowing animals, leaping into the air to capture flying birds and insects, and sprinting after fleeing deer. Approximately 21% of all hunting attempts end with the successful capture of prey.

Chrysocyon brachyurus
Serra da Canastra National Park, Brazil.
Photo: Mark Jones/
Roving Tortoise Photos

13 kg) exhibit an adult sex ratio skewed towards males, female emigration and male helpers (e.g. Ethiopian Wolves, Dholes, African Wild Dogs, and the Bush Dog, which is an atypically diminutive member of this category).

Canid female body mass is positively correlated with gestation, neonate mass, litter size, and litter mass. Larger canids tend to have large litters of relatively small, dependant pups. The prolonged dependency of their litters requires more male postpartum investment competition among females for males as helpers, therefore driving the system towards polyandry. Smaller canids produce smaller litters of more precocial neonates that require less parental investment. The lesser demand for paternal investment enables males to invest in additional females, resulting in polygyny.

An alternative view is that much of the variation in canid size, social structure, and litter size can be explained better by environmental variation in the availability of food. For example, Red and Arctic Foxes and Gray Wolves exhibit decreases in litter size when prey abundance is low. Large canids are often associated with habitats in which prey are at least very abundant (e.g. Ethiopian Wolves) and more generally, abundant and large (e.g. African Wild Dog and Gray Wolf), and group living permits them to have smaller, more numerous pups. Smaller canids generally eat smaller, more scattered foods and thus live in smaller groups. Fennecs and other small foxes usually are associated with arid and poor habitats in which only a small body mass can be supported year round. They have to work harder to gather extra food for the young, and therefore are less able to defend them. This may have pushed them to have more advanced pups, and fewer of them. In San Joaquin Kit Foxes, for instance, density and growth rates fluctuate widely under variable environmental conditions, tracking primary productivity determined by rainfall a year earlier. Pregnancy rates are similar from year to year, but neonatal survival is reduced in years of low precipitation. Reproductive success and litter size tend to be low during periods of low food availability. Sex ratios at birth are also male-biased, but ratios are female-biased when fox abundance is low and the population is increasing. A study of Red Foxes on Round Island, Alaska, provides another example: it showed a shift from 71% polygyny when food was superabundant to 100% monogamy when prey abundance declined, and a concomitant decrease in litter size. It suggests that an increase in food availability permits an increase in litter size, and males can afford to breed with more than one female only when prey is especially abundant.

Coyote group size may depend on relative prey size. In habitats where Mule Deer and Elk are important prey items, Coyote pups delay dispersal and form larger groups. Where small rodents are the main prey, group size tends to be smaller and dispersal occurs earlier. However, there are populations that feed on high-density rodents in habitats in which dispersal is difficult, and these Coyotes form larger groups. Smaller packs would theoretically have to increase the number of hunts (and the associated costs and risks) to raise the same number of pups as do larger packs.

Conception in canids is followed by a gestation of approximately 62 days. Known gestation periods are 60–63 days for the Red Fox and 51 days for the Fennec. In the wild the number of young at birth is seldom known, but litter sizes typically range from 2–13. Fox litter sizes are normally from one to six, the average for the Red Fox varying with habitat from four to eight. The maximum number of fetuses found in a Red Fox vixen was twelve. African Wild Dogs have very large litters averaging 10–11, and occasionally as large as 21, and Arctic Foxes may produce very large litters of up to 19. The large Maned Wolf is an exception, averaging two hefty pups. Larger canids tend to have the largest litters and largest pups.

Females have 6–16 mammae, with five pairs typical for *Canis*, and six or seven pairs typical for Dholes. Canids have their young in underground natal dens, dug beforehand by the female, and sometimes reused in future years. Den sites seem to be selected for shelter and protection and often offer good visibility to guard for intruders. Fox cubs are generally born in burrows dug by the vixen or appropriated from other species, or rock crevices. Litters of Red Foxes have also been found in hollow trees, under houses, or simply in long grass. Fennec Fox dens may be huge, covering up to 120 m², with as many as 15 different entrances. Pups are born blind and pretty helpless, only able to crawl and nurse. The female usually spends the first day or two with the young, keeping them warm and fed. For the first two to three weeks females suckle the pups underground, and the pups do not venture outside. Other adults are

*Although most medium-sized canids are opportunistic hunters, the **Ethiopian Wolf**, which can grow to just under 20 kg, is a specialist, feeding almost exclusively on the diurnal rodents of Ethiopia's high altitude Afroalpine grasslands. It is preeminently a solitary hunter, but it can also hunt cooperatively. Small packs have been seen chasing and killing young antelopes, lambs, and hares. Ethiopian Wolves often resemble foxes in their foraging antics, leaping in the air, and hammering their reinforced snouts into rodent burrows to shock and pin down their quarry. Once the prey is located, they move with short, stealthy steps, alternating with short periods of immobility, sometimes with their bellies pressed flat to the ground. The quarry is grabbed with the mouth after a short dash. A stalk can last from seconds to up to an hour, the longer time being especially true if the quarry is an Ethiopian African Mole Rat, although these are more often dug out from as much as 1 m deep. In such cases, the effort varies from a few scratches at a rat hole to the total destruction of a set of burrows, leaving mounds of earth up to 1 m high. Kills are often cached and later retrieved. In Ethiopia's Bale Mountains, almost 90% of the diet belongs to three endemic species: the Ethiopian African Mole Rat, which can weigh up to 930 g, Blick's Grass Rat, and the Black-clawed Brush-furred Rat. Ethiopian Wolves will also take carrion or feed on carcasses; in fact, a sheep carcass is the most successful bait for attracting wolves. The local name "jedalla farda" (the horse's jackal) refers to wolves' habit of following mares and cows about to give birth, so they can eat the afterbirth.*

Canis simensis
Bale Mountains National Park, Ethiopia.
Photos: Martin Harvey/NHPA

African Wild Dogs live and hunt in packs. Although they mostly hunt medium-sized antelopes, they will also take small prey such as hares opportunistically. But these make a very small contribution to their diet. They will also give chase to larger species than their usual prey, such as Common Eland and African Buffalo, but rarely kill these species. In some areas, warthogs and small antelopes, like dik-diks, duikers, and Steenbok, are important prey items. Pack size varies from a pair to as many as 30 adults and yearlings, although typically packs include between four and nine adults, along with yearlings and pups.

Lycaon pictus
Okavango Delta, Botswana.
Photo: Patricio Robles Gil

kept out of the natal den by the female, although the dominant dog often hovers around the entrance and ventures in if given the chance.

Lactation is very demanding on the female. Her energetic requirements may double or triple during the first few weeks of the litter. During this period, females intensify their hunting efforts and rely heavily on food provisioning by the dominant male and other group members. Bat-eared Foxes are an exception in that all adult females in a group produce young and suckle communally (but see allosuckling below). Lactation may last for 5–9 weeks, with most litters beginning to be weaned to solid foods in their second month.

Canid pups have a prolonged period of dependency and are commonly tended by both parents. The collaborative care of young may be a more fundamental and ubiquitous feature of canid society than the much vaunted cooperative hunting. For example, non-breeding female Red Foxes guard and play with cubs, may even tend littermates in several dens, and sometimes feed them at least as diligently as does their mother. The original list of species for which non-breeding "helpers" feed and tend the young—Red and Arctic Foxes, Jackals, Gray Wolves, Ethiopian Wolves, and African Wild Dogs—has expanded almost in direct proportion to the number of species studied, revealing alloparental care as a widespread canid trait. Provisioning the mother during pregnancy and lactation allows her to guard her young more continuously and lets her direct more energy into gestation and lactation.

In addition to provisioning, in many social canid species, non-breeding pack members will babysit diligently. Non-breeding females tend to be particularly attentive to the pups. Babysitters chase potential avian and mammal predators away, ensure the pups do not stray, and warn them to go into the den if danger threatens. Thanks to babysitters, African Wild Dog mothers—often by their status experienced hunters—can return to hunting three weeks after parturition, eight weeks before their pups can follow the pack. Pack size may improve anti-predator behavior, and small packs may not be able to afford babysitters since it may affect their hunting success. In Serengeti there seems to be a threshold of two pups per adult, below which pup guarding becomes much less likely. This translates to a pack-size of five, assuming the pack produces one litter of ten pups, which is the average litter size. This suggests that there is a cost to pup-guarding when fewer adults are in charge of more pups. In Zimbabwe pup guarding was significantly

more likely in larger packs (88% of 167 hunts), whereas packs of fewer than five individuals left a guard in only 34 % of their hunts. Hunts that took place during the night, when pups are more vulnerable, invariably involved a guard remaining with the pups, whereas during 39% of diurnal hunts pups were left alone. In Ethiopian Wolves, although the breeding female and putative father spent more time at the den on average than did other wolves, the proportion of time for which pups were left unattended was inversely correlated to the number of non-breeding helpers in the pack. In social wolf-like species, guarding may also protect pups from visiting conspecifics from neighboring packs, preventing infanticide. On Mednyi Island in the Bering Sea, the cubs of Arctic Foxes may be attended at the den by various adults, and the more of these guards present at a den, the more likely one of them is to launch an attack on a passing intruder. Such attacks occurred in 43% of the 54 cases where only one animal was present at the den, but in 88% of the 66 cases where two or more animals were present.

Wolf-like canids are the only carnivores to regurgitate food to their young, and males and females also provision pregnant and lactating mates or even fellow group members. African Wild Dogs, Gray Wolves, Ethiopian Wolves, Dholes, Coyotes, and jackals swallow kills and then regurgitate for the young pups in the den. African Wild Dogs cram three days worth of food, at least 4 kg of meat, into their stomachs for transportation to their pups. This is a practice that facilitates transport and prevents loss of food to kleptoparasites such as hyenas, which might steal food carried by mouth. In contrast, vulpine canids do not regurgitate, but most fox species bring solid foods to the den. Blanford's Foxes are apparently an exception: they have never been observed carrying food to the young, and it appears that any direct contribution to the pups' survival by any individual other than the mother is probably minimal.

Food provisioning by the parental pair may be increased with one or several non-breeder helpers. This alloparental care appears self-evidently helpful. The classic demonstration that this is so is that pup survival to weaning increases with the number of helpers among Red Foxes, Black-backed Jackals, Coyotes, and African Wild Dogs. Wolf helpers appear to increase the survival of the young only when food is abundant. When food is scarce, offspring in large wolf groups actually survive less well. However, demonstrating that assiduous helping in canids, or other conspicuously helpful carnivores, translates into improved reproductive success has proven difficult. Young male

In winter, **Gray Wolves** hunt in packs, although in summer they hunt singly, in pairs, or in small groups. Although this pack seems to be strategizing its attack, when the chase begins, it could range from 100 m to more than 5 km. The main prey of the Gray Wolf consists of large ungulates such as deer, Reindeer, and Wild Boar. Though wolves are quite capable of killing healthy adult animals, more than 60% of their prey consists of young, weak, or older animals. Wolves are keen observers of behavior, and are able to detect subtle weaknesses not evident to the human eye. Healthy, vigorous prey often escape Gray Wolf predation by fighting back, and on occasion, wolves are killed by Moose, American Bison, or Elk.

Canis lupus
ellowstone National Park, Wyoming, USA.
Photo: William Campbell/DRK

Ethiopian Wolves remain in their natal territories and never disperse, joining other pack members in providing solid food to the pups. Although there is no detectable increase in pup survival, increased numbers of helpers lets the Ethiopian Wolf mothers work less hard at provisioning pups. Breeders tend to contribute significantly more food than non-breeders, and females more than males, although African Wild Dog and Gray Wolf males may provide more solid foods to pups per capita than do females. African Wild Dog pups are entirely dependent upon adults for meat until they are about twelve months old, so their survival depends on helpers.

Although pup survival is generally correlated with pack size, further analyses of the impact of pack size on pup survival among African Wild Dogs in the Serengeti illustrate some complexities. A positive correlation was found to exist between pup survival to one year of age and pack-size in the Serengeti. Although yearlings are not yet experienced hunters, their presence contributes to foraging efficiency. Generally the alpha dogs lead the hunt, but yearlings nonetheless contribute in several ways to cooperative hunting, by helping prevent kleptoparasitism, by increasing the speed at which the carcass is devoured, by increasing the ratio of dogs to Spotted Hyenas, and by regurgitating meat to the begging pups back at the den. A related phenomenon to babysitting the dominant female's offspring may be the care of invalid animals. Adult Red Foxes have been seen feeding an injured adult, and a helper was observed rearing the pups of an ailing mother. Among African Wild Dogs, incapacitated and older members of the pack are tolerated at kills, and may be fed by regurgitation. A possibly related behavior may be adoption of unrelated pups, which has been recorded in Wild Dogs.

The most extreme form of alloparental behavior is allo-suckling, or lactation by females other than a litter's mother, which has been seen in Red, Indian, Bat-eared, and Arctic Foxes, as well as Gray Wolves and Ethiopian Wolves, South American Gray Foxes, Coyotes, and African Wild Dogs. In a Bat-eared Fox group, two females may both regularly rear litters and nurse them communally. This also has been observed occasionally in Red Foxes. More remarkably, sometimes females appear to lactate spontaneously. This has been seen in Ethiopian Wolf females following an aborted pregnancy or pseudo-pregnancy (the latter widely reported in domestic dogs). Although the mechanism remains uncertain, five of eight allosuckling Ethiopian wolves had shown no visible signs of pregnancy. Lactation

and allosuckling can also occur if a subordinate female loses her pups through the dominant's infanticide, as reported for African Wild Dogs and Ethiopian Wolves. A subordinate female Ethiopian Wolf's attempt to leave her pack and breed independently failed after the dominant female killed the pups; the subordinate and her helpers then returned and assisted at the dominant's den. Alternatively, a female may lose her own pups due to inexperience or induced by social repression. In one case, a formerly successful breeding female Red Fox nursed the pups of the new dominant.

Among African Wild Dogs it has been suggested that communal suckling allows two mothers to alternate rest periods, which enable them to participate in hunts sooner. This might also increase pup survival by allowing the transfer of both females' maternal antibodies to both litters. Measuring the benefit, if any, of having two suckling females in a group of canids has been confounded by the fact that benefits of the extra milk supply may be offset by behavioral tension between the mothers. Allosuckling may at times seem maladaptive with communally nursing Bat-eared Foxes, Mednyi Island Arctic Foxes, and Ethiopian Wolves weaning fewer pups than those of neighboring females without allonurses. Similarly, the death of a subordinate Bush Dog's litter appeared to be due to over-anxious mothering. These examples raise the possibility that in addition to infanticide by dominant females, a second mechanism leading to litter reduction in communally breeding canids may be mis-mothering: in effect, a "tug-of-love" over the pups. Therefore, the evidence that allosuckling in canids is helpful is far from conclusive. The rate of survival to weaning of pups nursed by two females is at times significantly worse than those nursed by only one, but there may be a longer term reward in that those pups may show greater reproductive success as adults.

Dominant canid females typically reproductively suppress their subordinates to monopolize their own breeding opportunities. This has been reported for Gray Wolves, African Wild Dogs, Ethiopian Wolves, and most small canids. Indeed, reproductive suppression was recorded in at least 44% of 25 species for which there was information, and is thus conspicuous by its absence in Bat-eared Foxes. For example, female Gray Wolves can breed as yearlings but rarely do so in the wild before the age of three. Subordinate female wolves rarely have offspring and generally lose those they do have. The degree of suppression, however, varies both among and within species, and sub-

*African Wild Dog hunts appear t'
be highly coordinated, and they a'
often preceded by a sort of "social
rally". During chases, African
Wild Dogs may run at speeds of u
to 60 km/h, and they are adapted
to cope with the heat stress that
this involves. Group living allow.
African Wild Dogs to capture
large prey such as Impala, Greate'
Kudu, and Blue Wildebeest.
Although even a single African
Wild Dog can kill large prey, there
is evidence that their hunting
success increases with pack size,
at least up to four adults. Large
parties need more kills to meet
the needs of each individual,
so hunting success per dog may
decrease above a certain group
size. Thus, hunting in large, but
not too large, groups will provide
the optimal ratio of benefit to cost.
African Wild Dogs hunt mainly
during the early morning and ea.
evening hours. They may also hu'
when the moon is bright.*

Lycaon pictus
Masai Mara National Park, Kenya.
Photo: Stefan Meyers/Ardea

ordinates of Red Foxes, Gray Wolves and African Wild Dogs do reproduce, albeit at lower rates than dominants. Red Fox subordinate females do not usually breed in high density populations where interactions with the dominant vixen are high, although they may breed more successfully in other populations. At 40% of 25 African Wild Dog dens in the Kruger National Park, more than one female produced pups, yet only about 9% of all pups examined genetically were offspring of the subordinates.

It is important to distinguish between the suppression of endocrine cycles and that of reproductive behavior. Dominant males may directly prevent subordinates from mating within the pack, although multiple paternity has been reported in Ethiopian Wolves and African Wild Dogs, often as a result of sneaky matings. Although dominant female Ethiopian Wolves appear to mate only with the dominant male in their group, they will mate with males of any status from neighboring groups, doing so more often than with the alpha male in their own pack. Such complications in mating systems may be widespread. Territorial male Red Foxes make frequent excursions beyond their territories during the mating season, and itinerant males make incursions into territories. Female reproductive suppression and helpers are most prevalent among larger canids, which tend to eat larger prey and hunt in packs. As energetic costs increase and the reproductive tactic is to produce more young per litter, there is a higher incidence of alloparental behavior and reproductive suppression. Increased reproductive output in canids may be an evolutionary consequence of selection that favors reproductive suppression as a means of recruiting helpers.

Pups venture outside the den at two to three weeks of age, and become bolder exploring the surroundings as time goes by. Vixens start to bring live prey back to the den and pups are allowed to play with it before the prey is killed by the adult. Among the larger wolf-like canids, pups are introduced to solid foods at about two months of age, and they alternate using the den and playing. Their resting area surrounds the natal den and expands as the pups get older. The pups begin to follow their mother or babysitters on foraging trips, and engage in play resembling adult foraging techniques. By the time they are three months or older most canid young follow hunting adults. As they get older they begin to practice hunting skills, stalking and chasing small prey such as birds and small rodents. The adults in attendance gradually provide different prey items to enable the young to hone their foraging and killing skills. Larg-

er, social canids remain dependent on adults for longer than vulpine species, receiving solid foods from adults consistently until they are six months old, and being regularly provisioned at least until they are one year of age. Yearling male Ethiopian Wolves often steal solid foods from their younger siblings.

Most canids, like most carnivores, disperse from their natal home range at sexual maturity, following a decline in affiliative behavior by the breeding pair. They leave their natal ranges to join other social groups, find mates and establish their own home ranges. Wolf-like canids generally disperse at two years old, whereas most foxes do so in their first winter. The mechanism of dispersal in canids, and what triggers it, are poorly understood. Although a general assumption of dispersal, supported by some Red Fox data, has been that parents aggressively drive the subordinate youngsters of a generation away, for Coyotes it has been argued that it is actually the most robust individuals that disperse.

There remain huge gaps in understanding canid dispersal and its interaction with mating and social systems, largely because a proper study of dispersal would require studying individuals during pre-dispersal, dispersal and settlement phases. A monumental radio-tagging study revealed that a greater proportion of male yearling Red Foxes dispersed, and dispersed farther, than did females. The bee-line distances of dispersing foxes, while varying greatly among populations, tended to cross a rather constant number of territories.

Studies of 300 radio-tagged Gray Wolves from 25 contiguous packs in Minnesota, USA, gave some sense of the mysteries of canid dispersal. The time between emigrating and settling for these animals varied from one week to twelve months, averaging less than a month for females and more than four months for males. One female travelled some 4117 km^2 before settling. Her descendents illustrate every variant of dispersal: one female dispersed, paired, lost her litter and returned to her natal territory permanently; another lost her litter and returned, but dispersed again a few weeks later; some spent days separated from the pack but within the natal territory before departing; one female lived this way for months; one male returned home intermittently for a year while courting a neighboring female; some Gray Wolves moved to adjoining territories; some moved far away.

There is no sex bias in dispersal distance or tendency among Gray Wolves, although genetic evidence suggests either that males engage in more long-range dispersal, or suffer

*Social hunting in **African Wild Dogs** is coordinated so that after one dog has made the first grab of a wildebeest or other prey species, other pack members join and help drag the quarry to the ground. On some occasions, one pack member may restrain the head of the prey by biting its nose and holding on to it, while others make the kill. Individuals may also chase and bring down prey alone. Hunting success is high in comparison with other large carnivore species. For example, in the Serengeti, 70% of 133 African Wild Dog hunts ended in a kill. Measurements of the energy consumption of African Wild Dogs demonstrated that hunting is so expensive that a reduction in hunting success would lead to an exponential increase in the time needed to break even energetically. For example, if they lost of 25% of their kills to Spotted Hyenas, the dogs' daily hunting time requirement would push up from three and a half hours to twelve hours a day. This is perhaps one reason that African Wild Dogs are scarce where Spotted Hyenas and Lions thrive, especially in open habitats where the Lions and hyenas can easily detect feeding dogs. But African Wild Dogs can defend a carcass if they outnumber the hyenas, or repel the hyenas for long enough to dismember the carcass and bolt it down, even though each dog is only a third to a quarter of the body weight of a Spotted Hyena.*

Lycaon pictus
Above: Masai Mara National Park, Kenya.
Photo: Jonathan & Angela Scott/NHPA

Below: Serengeti National Park, Tanzania.
Photo: Fritz Pölking/DRK

greater mortality en route, than do females. Further down the spectrum lie Ethiopian Wolves, with predominantly female dispersal, and African Wild Dogs, where usually groups of sibling females disperse. Sometimes male groups disperse later and go farther than the females.

Dispersal is generally assumed to be dangerous and of uncertain outcome. Dispersing animals are drawn to a hunted population of Alaskan wolves, even though survival there is low. Where the costs of dispersal are high, such as in Ethiopian Wolves, which are effectively restricted to "islands" of Afro-alpine grasslands, individuals may be more disposed to seek the benefits of remaining in larger groups. Dispersing Crab-eating Foxes tend to settle in territories at the borders of their natal range, but return intermittently to their original territory in amicable company with their parents. Of four dispersing males, two subsequently returned to their natal group following the deaths of their mates. Both neighborhood relatedness and return from dispersal may be widespread among canids (e.g. Gray Wolves, African Wild Dogs, and Bat-eared Foxes).

*Hunting **Dholes** often drive deer into water, where they swim out to surround and capture them. They are communal hunters, occasionally forming packs of ove 30 animals, but they more often hunt in groups of fewer than ten. They may also hunt alone or in pairs, taking smaller prey. Certai individuals may take particular roles in the hunt, such as leading the chase or taking the first grab at the prey. Some Dholes may lie in ambush while others drive pre towards them. Their preferred pre includes deer and large bovids lik Gaur and Banteng.*

Cuon alpinus
Periyar National Park, India.
Photo: Gertrud & Helmut Denzau

Movements, Home range and Social organization

Wild canids are among the most cosmopolitan groups of mammals, and have adapted to living in a variety of landscapes from deserts to grasslands to rugged mountain environments. Throughout the world, canids exhibit a wide range of behavioral adaptations and as such have been the focus of intensive study in some areas. Variation in ranging behavior and social organization, in particular, have been key to understanding the biology of the family and, in many regions, to solving complex conservation issues.

Most species of canids are territorial. By definition, territories are defensible areas containing important resources like food and space, and are typically established and maintained through scent marking, vocal communication, and direct encounters with conspecifics. Among mammals, home range size

*The diet of the **Black-backed Jackal** depends on food availability, and may be restricte according to what other carnivor it is competing with. When large mammalian prey, such as hares newborn antelopes, are available, jackals will often cooperate with their mates in order to make a catch. While one member of a pair chases the prey, the other ma harass would-be protectors, such this mother gazelle, or else cut off the prey as it tries to zig-zag. Whe hunting gazelle fawns or spring hares, jackals that cooperate are two to three times more successful than those that hunt alone. In Botswana, they occasionally form "packs" in order to hunt adult Impala, and there are records of them taking other adult antelope*

Canis mesomelas
Masai Mara National Park, Kenya.
Photo: Elliott Neep/FLPA

and spatial movements often scale allometrically with body size (and hence metabolic needs), with small species occupying smaller ranges and moving shorter distances than larger species, which live in larger ranges and travel greater distances. This pattern is shown by canids, although variation exists within and between species, and ranging patterns are not always predictable from the scaling of metabolic needs alone. In many cases, range size variations may be attributed to the availability and dispersion of key food and habitat resources. Resource differences have also been shown to affect a species' sociality and shape its relationships with conspecifics and other species and communities.

Among small canids, which are represented mainly by the foxes (22 species in six genera; 61% of all canid species), most species tend to be nocturnal, live in well-defined territories, and organize in small family groups that usually consist of a monogamous pair and a small number of philopatric offspring. The desert-dwelling foxes, such as the Kit Fox, Fennec, and Blanford's Fox, are characteristic of this group.

Kit Foxes are active exclusively at night, feeding on Kangaroo Rats and other nocturnal rodents. They occupy a variety of landscapes from urban environments and agricultural lands to undisturbed desert. They live in small groups often composed of a breeding pair and one or two offspring (usually females) that share a territory. Kit Fox home ranges vary from 2–12 km², depending largely on the quality of habitat. In urban environments, where food resources are generally rich, ranges tend to be smaller than in less productive, food-poor regions. Other small canids show a similar trend. Raccoon Dogs living in urban areas of Japan, where food resources are plentiful, occupy ranges as small as 0·07 km², but elsewhere, in regions with less plentiful resources, home ranges as large as 10 km² have been recorded. Similarly, the ranges of Red Foxes in urban environments in Britain averaged 0·18 km², whereas the ranges of those living in less productive environments, such as the Canadian tundra, were as large as 34·2 km². Golden Jackals show similar variation. In Israel, ranges near clumped food sources such as garbage dumps and feeding sites were smaller than those recorded in locations where food was less abundant and more scattered.

Although small fox species tend to be monogamous, at least some exhibit flexibility in their breeding and social systems. In the Kit Fox, which has typically been regarded as a monogamous species, reports of litters with multiple paternity indicate that polygamy occurs in some populations. Multiple paternity has been also been documented in other small foxes traditionally considered monogamous, including the Island Fox and Swift Fox. Flexible sociality has provided the ubiquitous Red Fox with the ability to adapt to a variety of landscapes and environmental conditions. In an extreme example, Red Foxes in Alaska shifted from 71% polygyny during a period when food was highly abundant to 100% monogamy when food became dramatically scarce. The social flexibility of Red Foxes has also been noted in other environments, such as the deserts of Saudi Arabia, where prey resources are generally limited and highly dispersed. Although in a different size class, Coyote sociality may also be affected by prey size or prey biomass; in populations where they rely chiefly on rodents as prey, Coyotes tend to live in pairs or trios, whereas in populations where Elk and deer are available, large packs of up to ten individuals may form.

Among the medium and large-sized canids, most species have evolved to live in groups or packs. Group living benefits foraging efficiency, breeding success, and survivorship, but it also brings in a suite of energetic constraints and behavioral disadvantages. Thus the formation of groups in large canids represents an intricate balance of trade-offs. African Wild Dogs are among the most social canids, known for their conspicuous visual and auditory displays during group interactions. Wild dogs live in packs composed of a breeding pair, several adults, yearlings, and pups, and new packs may form when same-sex groups emigrate from their natal ranges. An average pack includes four to nine adults, two to six yearlings, and five to eleven pups. Wild dog packs are dynamic and may fluctuate rapidly in numbers, with packs of as many as 30 adults reported, but with lonely pairs also known to raise families on occasion. Five adults has been suggested by some as the magic minimal pack size required for successful reproduction. One advantage of group living in Wild Dogs is increased survival of pups that are raised cooperatively by all members of a pack. Group living also allows African Wild Dogs to efficiently capture large prey such as Impala (*Aepyceros melampus*), Greater Kudu (*Tragelaphus strepsiceros*), and Blue Wildebeest (*Connochoates taurinus*), and defend kills from other predators like Spotted Hyenas and jackals. Wild Dogs range over large areas in search of prey. They occupy home ranges

*The diet of the **Dhole** shows its preference for medium to large ungulates, although it also includes food items such as rodents, birds, and plant material, like the diets of many other canids. Dholes also scavenge, though possibly only when prey is scarce, like during the dry season. Although Dholes are found in a wide variety of vegetation types, tropical dry and moist deciduous forest may represent optimal habitats, based on the regions thought to hold the largest Dhole populations. Ungulate biomass, particularly that of deer species, is highest in these vegetation types when compared to others in the same region. Dholes rely on sound to coordinate kills in thick forest: a repetitive whistle-like contact call may allow dispersed pack members to identify one another and to re-group.*

Cuon alpinus
Nagarhole National Park, Karnataka, India.
Photo: Khalid Ghani/NHPA

Gray Wolves *usually eat most of the carcass of their prey, leaving only the larger bones, and chunks of hide. When there is surplus food, wolves will cache either regurgitated chunks or large pieces. When hunting large prey, they first attack the rump, but they may go for the head, shoulders, flanks, or rump of smaller prey. Wolves may also eat voles, beavers and hares, and where available, fish, berries, and carrion. Arctic wolves may subsist on small mammals and birds when their primary prey, Reindeer, migrate to their summer range. Wolves occasionally scavenge at rubbish dumps, even when wild prey is available, and in Romania and Italy they have been known to visit rubbish bins in towns and cities. Wolves are generally considered less social than African Wild Dogs. Pack hunting has positive and negative aspects. Wolves on Isle Royale, Michigan, USA, illustrate the downside of cooperative hunting; the daily intake of food per wolf per day declined with larger pack sizes. Another description of Gray Wolf pack hunting reveals that in the absence of scavengers, members of larger packs secure relatively reduced foraging returns and would therefore do better by hunting in pairs or alone. On the other hand, the greater food sharing costs in larger packs of wolves can be more than offset by the reduced losses to scavengers. A lone Gray Wolf might lose two-thirds of a moose kill to scavengers, but a pack of ten wolves would lose only 10%.*

Canis lupus
Denali National Park, Alaska, USA.
Photo: Martin W. Grosnick/Ardea

that are defended infrequently but aggressively against neighboring packs. Ranges are much larger than would be expected on the basis of their body size (c. 25 kg) and have been recorded from 150 km² in South Africa's Kruger National Park to nearly 2500 km² in the Serengeti National Park in Tanzania.

Gray Wolves, the largest of the canids (c. 60 kg), also live in packs, but are generally considered less social than African Wild Dogs. In the boreal winter, wolves largely hunt in packs, which are usually families, but in summer, they hunt singly, in pairs, or in small groups. This distinction is not so clear in wolf populations living at lower latitudes. Packs include a dominant breeding pair and philopatric offspring and may include up to 36 individuals, although smaller size packs of 5–12 individuals are more common. Territories may be as small as 75 km² and as large as 2500 km², depending on prey density, and are actively maintained through howling, scent marking, and intraspecific killing.

The Dhole or Asian Wild Dog is another large (c. 15 kg), group-living canid. Dholes organize in packs of 4–15 adult members and up to ten pups, but most packs contain fewer than ten animals. Packs usually have a dominant breeding pair that mates yearly, producing pups that are cooperatively raised by other pack members. Dholes occupy smaller ranges compared with most other large canids. Their ranges probably vary as a function of prey density, composition, and distribution. Home range size has been reported from 12–83 km². Dholes have been described as the whistling hunters, for the high-pitched vocalizations they use while hunting in packs. Their vocalizations probably have a role in coordinating the chase and kill. Although Dholes are considered typical pack hunters, they are occasionally observed hunting alone or in pairs.

Unique among the larger canids is the Ethiopian Wolf, a highland specialist restricted to isolated mountain ranges in central Ethiopia. Ethiopian Wolves live in discrete and cohesive social units. These family packs share and defend an exclusive territory packed with rodent prey. Packs usually consist of 3–13 adults which congregate for social greetings and border patrols at dawn, noon, and evenings, and rest together at night. During the morning and early afternoon hours, however, packs break up and the wolves forage individually. Their diet consists almost entirely of diurnal rodents of the high-altitude Afro-alpine grassland community, such as the Ethiopian African Mole Rat; they rely on an unusually high rodent biomass, which may

reach 2500 kg of potential prey per km². As a result of these riches, annual pack home ranges are smaller than would be predicted for a carnivore of this size, averaging a mere 6 km². In areas with relatively lower prey biomass ranges may be larger (c. 13 km²) and family sizes smaller. Packs engage in regular "patrols" of territory borders that often involve high rates of scent marking. Unlike Gray Wolves, all members of the pack a year or older contribute actively to scent marking, and tandem-marking, where the wolves actually queue up for the opportunity to spray a particular spot, is quite common.

At c. 25 kg, the elegant, long-legged, Maned Wolf is the largest canid in South America. It lives mainly in tall grasslands, shrublands, and open canopy woodlands of Brazil, Bolivia, Paraguay, and Argentina. Territories range from 5–105 km² according to the habitat and food availability. In contrast to what would be predicted by body size alone, Maned Wolves are primarily solitary, relying on an omnivorous diet consisting principally of fruits and small to medium-sized vertebrates. Maned Wolf pairs appear to be facultatively monogamous, like many of the smaller fox species. Pairs form, mate, and raise young together during the reproductive period, but during other times of the year, pairs are rarely seen.

Dispersal of individuals from a natal group is an important component of the social organization and ranging behavior of canids, as the young attempt to find mates and establish territories. The ethology, triggers, and mechanisms of dispersal in most canid species remain poorly understood. Dispersal may be male biased—as in the Red Fox and other vulpines—or female biased—as in the Ethiopian Wolf—or exhibit no sex bias—as in African Wild Dogs. In some canid species trends in dispersal vary by region. Dispersal in African Wild Dog populations from East Africa, for example, has been reported to be female biased. In Botswana, Wild Dog males disperse later, in larger groups, and farther than females. Most canids disperse from their natal home range at sexual maturity. Gray Wolves, for example, generally disperse at two years of age, whereas most foxes do so in their first winter, although variations in dispersal patterns exist. Dispersal tends to bring forward conflicts of interest within family groups: youngsters may happily wait for a favorable opportunity to make a move, but their parents or siblings may forcefully precipitate their departure.

Some individuals may disperse for very large distances, and their wandering can last for long periods. The time between

The **Arctic Fox** is an opportunist predator and scavenger. Reindeer remains are frequently found in the feces of these small foxes. In coastal areas, Arctic Foxes will comb beaches methodically for carrion, timing their visits to coincide with the receding tide, when fresh debris is stranded. In Iceland, the reproductive success Arctic Fox pairs could be correlate to the length of tidal beach they had available to comb for food. Foxes living near ice-free coasts have access to inland prey, and also sea birds, seal carcasses, fish and marine invertebrates, leadin to relatively stable food availabili and a more generalist feeding strategy.

Alopex lagopus
Svalbard.
Photo: Jordi Bas

emigrating and settling among Gray Wolves, for instance, varies from a week to a year, but averages less than a month for females and more than four months for males. Data suggest that the younger the animal the farther it disperses. Most often, dispersing wolves establish territories or join existing packs, which may be near their natal pack or some 50 to 100 km away. Directional dispersal is a strategy that may take the disperser into a new population or to the very edge of the species' range. Wolves of both sexes have dispersed to areas up to 886 km away, some crossing highways and circumventing large lakes and cit-

ies. The record-holder is a female wolf that was part of an extensive study of radio-tagged wolves in Minnesota: she travelled 4117 km before settling.

Dispersal may not happen at all in some family groups in certain years, if dispersal opportunities are tightly constrained and a high degree of philopatry is exhibited. While this is rare, it often reflects the cost of dispersal. In other cases, as with the Ethiopian Wolf, there may be no empty niches for youngsters to disperse to. Most prime Ethiopian Wolf habitat is already occupied. The wolves occupy small islands of Afro-alpine habitat

Scavenging is very common in canid species, and most will take advantage of carrion when they come across it. The **Red Fox** scavenges in both rural and urban areas. In rural areas of Europe and Canada, it feeds on deer and sheep carcasses, which may be important food sources in winter in upland areas. In urban areas, the Red Fox may scavenge on bird-feeding tables, compost piles, and refuse. It is generally a solitary forager, but individuals may forage close to each other where resources are found clumpe together. Foraging in the Red Fox is predominantly nocturnal and crepuscular. However, it can be more diurnal in areas where the species is undisturbed.

Vulpes vulpes
Belianske Tatra, Slovakia.
Photo: Bruno D'Amicis

Although it is an opportunistic predator, the **Culpeo** is considered more carnivorous and a consumer of larger mammalian prey than the other South American foxes. Its diet includes wild ungulates, domestic sheep (in northern Patagonia), European Hares and European Rabbits, as well as small mammals, lizards, birds, and insects. Culpeos are also consumers of fruits and berries, and are thought to disperse seeds of a variety of plant species. Highest fruit consumption occurs when small mammals are the least abundant. Culpeos tend to forage alone and their foraging activity may be influenced by the nocturnal habits of their main prey, but also by persecution.

Pseudalopex culpaeus
Colca Canyon, Peru.
Photo: Tui de Roy/
Roving Tortoise Photos

and in some populations live at saturation density. Thus dispersal occurs rarely, indicating the potential for inbreeding, as most offspring remain philopatric. Two-thirds of female wolves dispersed at, or shortly before sexual maturity (two years). Some became floaters and hovered in wedges of space between established territories until a breeding opportunity arose. Males, on the other hand, very seldom disperse, and are recruited into closely knit, multi-male philopatric packs.

Dispersal in general is a risky business to the individual animal, often resulting in a higher risk of mortality than if it stayed put. Dispersal can also be energetically costly. Among Kit Foxes, where males are generally more likely to disperse than females, 62% of pups died within ten days of departure from their natal home ranges, although survival tended to be higher for dispersing than for philopatric males. Most dispersal movements in Kit Foxes are probably less than 10 km, although some individuals in Utah, USA, dispersed as far as 64 km and dispersals of over 100 km have been observed in California. Dispersal distances for the Swift Fox are similar to those for the Kit Fox, but slightly longer on average. Swift Foxes translocated

Black-backed Jackals and Brown Hyenas are the only large terrestrial carnivores on the coast of the southern Namib Desert, where seal colonies can provide the main food source. During the seal birth season, stillborn pups and placentas provide rich pickings, but the jackals will still attack live pups. The pups are protected only by their mothers, but they move slowly on land, and so are easy prey for the jackals. The jackals kill the pups (which can weigh almost as much as the jackals themselves), by holding the throat until they suffocate. Before the seal pups are born, jackals have also been observed taking yearling seals.

Canis mesomelas
Skeleton Coast, Namibia.
Photo: Kevin Schafer

from Wyoming to Colorado had dispersal distances of 27 km for adults and 19 for juveniles, whereas average dispersal distances for naturally-dispersing Swift Foxes in Colorado, Kansas, and Canada were less than 15 km.

Relationship with Humans

Wild canids have had a long relationship with people, and canids can be traced back to the earliest recorded history as objects of worship. The human-canine relationship has varied from fear, persecution, and exploitation to the domestication of man's best friend. Today many wild canids are thriving, and often find themselves in conflict with humans due to their predisposition for attacking livestock. Some of the more charismatic species are now sought out by growing numbers of wildlife tourists.

The Golden Jackal features in the mythology and cultural history of several ancient civilizations. The ancient Egyptians worshipped the jackal-headed god Anubis as keeper of the dead, the association perhaps originating with the common presence of jackals near abbatoirs and cemeteries. The Greek gods Hermes and Cerberus were probably derived from the Golden Jackal. There is no animal more enshrined in the myths of northern cultures than the Gray Wolf. Aesop's fables celebrated its cunning, while the story of Rome's legendary founders Romulus and Remus was only one of many telling of children raised by wolves. Folklore undoubtedly demonizes the wolf, but in the last half-century myriad biological studies have given a more sympathetic view of these mighty predators, which are slowly making their way back from near-extinction a few decades ago.

The Indian Fox is featured in several tales from the ancient Jataka texts and the Panchatantra, where it is depicted as a clever and sometimes cunning creature. The Raccoon Dog, or Tanuki, which owes its name to an uncanny resemblance to the Northern Racoon, has often appeared in Japanese folklore. In Brazil, the night cry of the Maned Wolf is believed to portend changes in the weather. Adaptable and opportunistic foragers, Red Foxes have a long association with humans in Europe and Asia. They have been hunted at least since the 4th century BC. They are wily characters in the popular tales of many cultures, reflecting both their wide distribution and their resourceful behavior.

It is not just the image of wild canids as predators and competitors that influenced our ancestors. Humans have used their skins for clothing, bedding, and shelter, and other body parts for medicinal and shamanistic purposes. Canids have been exploited for subsistence, commercial profit, and hunting for sport. Much of the pioneering history and economies of northern latitudes was built on trade in fur, much of it originally worn by foxes and wolves. The extent of commercial exploitation has fluctuated, depending on supply and demand for furs, which are still used today, although not with the same assiduity. Until the advent of fur-farming in the 20th century, the fur trade concentrated on wild populations, notably of Coyote, Red Fox, and Arctic Fox. Very large shipments also originated from three of South America's Southern Cone foxes. Such intensive hunting often impacted the density and demography of these populations. In some areas today, trapping is largely done by farmers trying to reduce predation on livestock or poultry. However, even for these people, the sale of fur can be economically important, for example, representing up to a quarter of the annual income of some ranch-hands in Patagonia.

Arctic Foxes remain the most important terrestrial game species in the Arctic, mainly because of their exceptional fur. Fortunately with the decline of the fur hunting industry, the threat of over-exploitation has also declined for most Arctic Fox populations. Raccoon Dogs have been raised for fur in Japan and exported, mostly to the USA before World War II, and their fur is still used in Japan. The Russians introduced Raccoon Dogs into the European part of the former Soviet Union to establish a valuable new fur animal in the wild. Trapping is legal throughout much of the Northern Gray Fox's range, with 90,604 skins taken during the 1991/1992 season in the USA alone, although there is no evidence that trapping has adversely affected Northern Gray Fox numbers, which appear stable throughout their range. Although arguably hunting can increase the value of many canid species, their exploitation is becoming increasingly controversial.

The versatility of many canids enables them to flourish in human landscapes such as farmland and even in cities, where they may prey on game species and domestic livestock. This

*Among the hunting techniques used by the **Black-backed Jackal** is dash-and-grab, shown in this successful ambush on a flock of pigeons. Black-backed Jackals are relatively unspecialized canids, well-suited for an opportunistic lifestyle in a wide variety of habitats. When the jackals occur in the same areas as other carnivores using the same prey base, food resources are partition Black-backed Jackals preferential use either open grassland, when sympatric with Side-striped Jackal, or wooded savannah, when sympatric with Golden and Side-striped Jackals. In western Zimbabwe, Black-backed Jackals aggressively displaced Side-striped Jackals from the grassland habitat where spring hares are found.*

Canis mesomelas
Etosha National Park, Namibia.
Photo: Martin Harvey/DRK

Although they will eat plant material and insects, the **Black-acked Jackal** has a well-developed carnassial shear, with a longer premolar cutting blade than other jackal species, an indication of a greater tendency towards meat-eating. As seen here, its upper canines are long, curved, and pointed, and they have a sharp ridge on their posterior faces. Of the other jackal species, the Side-triped Jackal is more omnivorous, with a seasonal diet that can at times consist entirely of insects or fruit. Side-striped Jackals may be less predatory than other species, although in the dry months they turn their attention to small mammals up to the size of South African Spring Hares, and they may compete with Black-backed ckals for gazelle fawns. Similarly, Golden Jackals will eat a great deal of fruit and other vegetable oods when in season. But Golden Jackals have also been observed to hunt young, old, and infirm ungulates that are sometimes 4–5 times their body weight. Although Golden Jackals are able to hunt alone, cooperative hunting in small packs of 2–4 individuals is often more successful, and permits them to kill larger prey, including antelope fawns and langur monkeys. Single Golden ackals typically hunt smaller prey like rodents, hares, and birds up to the size of flamingos. Where Golden Jackals overlap with Black-backed Jackals, resources may be partitioned not just according to habitat, but also by time of day, ith Golden Jackals almost entirely nocturnal, while Black-backed Jackals may also be active in the arly morning and late afternoon.

Canis mesomelas
Etosha National Park, Namibia.
Photo: Martin Harvey/DRK

Coyotes are supreme generalist predators, consuming food types in relation to their availability, such as salmon during their spawning run. As well as killing newborn young and scavenging larger carcasses, they occasionally kill adult ungulates. Cooperation among pack members may facilitate the capture of larger prey but is not essential. The number of Coyotes is not as important as which individuals are involved in the attack. Success depends on the presence of the alpha Coyote pair; younger animals generally do not participate. Coyotes hunt small mammals alone. In suburban areas, they readily consume refuse and pet food.

Canis latrans
Yellowstone National Park,
Wyoming, USA.
Photo: Tom & Pat Leeson/Ardea

brings them into conflict with humans far beyond the borders of protected areas. Throughout history, wild canids have been seen as competitors for humans' wild prey. In Britain, the practice of predator control to protect game species resulted in the development of large, privately owned sporting estates in the 19th century. An estimated 70,000 Red Foxes are killed by some 3500 professional game-keepers in Britain every year to preserve game birds for sport shooting. In the royal hunting preserves of medieval Europe, Gray Wolves were killed to protect deer. Many deer hunters in Europe and North America believe that competition with canids reduces their hunting opportunities, and today deer hunters are among the most vocal opponents to Gray Wolf reintroduction. In Alaska, Gray Wolves and Brown Bears were blamed for low Moose and Reindeer (Caribou) densities and thus for reduced hunting quotas. The public harvest of Gray Wolves in Alaska to increase deer numbers for hunting received a very positive response from sport hunters, but has been vehemently opposed by conservationists. However, there are times when canid predation upsets conservationists, such as when Red Foxes kill rare avocets (*Recurvirostra avosetta*) or cap-

Here considered a **Gray Wolf** *subspecies, Dingoes (Canis lupus dingo),* shown in the photo, evolved from a primitive dog transported to Australasia. Over 170 prey species have been identified, ranging from insects to buffalo, with the main prey in Australia composed of magpie geese, Common Wombats, European Rabbits, kangaroos, rats and mice, and lizards, including monitor lizards, as seen here. Comparison of kangaroo and emu populations inside and outside the "dingo fence" in South Australia suggests Dingoes limit and probably regulate these prey species. Dingoes may have displaced by competition both the Thylacine and the Tasmanian Devil.

Canis lupus
Nadgee Nature Reserve,
New South Wales, Australia.
Photo: Jean-Paul Ferrero/Auscape

Arctic Foxes forage singly, presumably the most efficient foraging technique in view of the species' main prey base of rodents and birds. When food is abundant, they cache supplies for later use. Active the year round, Arctic Foxes are primarily nocturnal, but exhibit flexible activity patterns, often in accordance with their main prey species. In Alaska, seasonal migrations are reported, when individuals leave breeding grounds in autumn, travel to the coast, and return in late winter or early spring. Large-scale emigrations have been recorded in Canada, northern Scandinavia, and Russia. These may result from drastic reductions in food supplies, such as a population crash in lemmings.

Alopex lagopus
Churchill, Manitoba, Canada.
Photo: Gerard Lemmo

ercaillie (*Tetrao urogallus*) in Britain, or California's Island Foxes kill San Clemente shrikes (*Lanius ludovicianus meamsi*), or Javan Dholes kill Banteng, Asia's threatened wild cattle.

Because of their broad range of sizes, canid species can fill dramatically different ecological roles, and killing them can have varying impacts on their communities. The removal of Gray Wolves and Brown Bears from the Yellowstone ecosystem 150 years ago, for example, triggered a cascade effect by allowing increased density of Moose. The resulting increased foraging on vegetation negatively affected the diversity of migrant birds. Coyotes play a keystone role—their removal can lead to an abundance of mesopredators, including Northern Gray Foxes, and in turn, to a reduction in the abundance and diversity of prey such as small rodents and Black-tailed Jackrabbits (*Lepus californicus*).

Predation on domesticated animals, from chickens to cattle, is the root of a deeply ingrained antipathy towards wild canids throughout the world. Hoary Foxes in Brazil are killed indiscriminately as predators of domestic fowl, though they may not deserve this reputation: sympatric Crab-eating Foxes are formidable poultry raiders. The ability of large canids, such as Gray Wolves, African Wild Dogs, Dingoes, Dholes, and Coyotes to kill large prey means they can cause substantial economic damage through depredation on livestock. Although larger canids attract particular wrath, the collective damage of smaller species such as jackals and foxes may be greater, exacerbated by changes in husbandry over the last century that preclude once-traditional livestock-guarding practices. Where stock-guarding traditions have vanished, re-colonization by wolves now provokes furious public complaint.

Livestock depredation by canids is highly variable in space and time. For example, 50% of sheep producers in the USA reported annual losses to Coyotes that were less than 5% of their stocks, but nearly a quarter reported losses greater than 15%. Coyote predation may be affected by sheep breed, sheep and predator management practices, and environmental conditions. Similarly, in Britain, lamb losses to Red Foxes are typically estimated to be 1–2% of lambs born, though reported loss for individual flocks can reach 15%. The risk posed by Arctic Foxes to lambs in Iceland increases with distance from the farmstead, and it has been suggested that only a minority of Red Foxes in Britain try to or have the opportunity to kill lambs.

Region-wide culling of common canids such as Coyotes, Dingoes, Culpeos, and Red Foxes over large areas has been widespread in the past, but largely ineffective, with most of these species thriving despite tremendous hunting pressure.

However, some canids can be out-gunned by high levels of culling. The Falkland Islands Wolf or Malvinas Fox disappeared in 1876 due to the activity of fur traders and poisoning by settlers to control sheep predation, worsened by the wolves' unwary behavior. Intensive culling has also had an impact on Gray Wolves in North America, but less so on Coyotes, though the historical near-absence of Coyotes in the prairie pothole region has been attributed to culling. A contraction in sheep farming in many areas is changing control practices. Argentine Patagonia was devoted to sheep ranching during most of the 20th century. Culpeos were reported to kill 7–15% of lambs annually. The annual tally in Culpeo skins averaged 15–20,000 during the 1970s and 1980s. In the last two decades ranches have switched to cattle production and the sheep stock has halved, leading to reduced hunting pressure on Culpeos. This in turn has resulted in 24–40% of lamb stock killed per year on the remaining sheep ranches and native Indian reservations. In the USA, the number of sheep declined by 75% in the 50 years prior to the 1980s, likewise concentrating Coyote predation on the isolated ranches that still raise sheep, requiring a switch from regional to local control.

Some of the larger canids may occasionally maul or even kill people, although these attacks are rare. Healthy Gray Wolves have caused no human deaths in North America for a century, unlike Pumas or Brown Bears. In contrast, there are many documented cases of Wolves killing people in Eastern Europe and Russia, although with few fatal attacks during the 20th century. In India there is good evidence that where Gray Wolves come into contact with children working as shepherds, they actively select them as prey, and 273 children have been reported killed by wolves in the last 20 years. African Wild Dogs are feared across Africa as ruthless killers, but their attacks on humans are rare or non-existent. No attack by Dholes has been documented. Coyote attacks on people are also known, although rarely fatal. In the UK, a few cases of Red Foxes in urban areas biting or scratching infants have been reported in the press in recent years.

Archaeological evidence suggests that the dog was the first animal species to be domesticated, toward the end of the Ice Age. The earliest known archaeological indication of domestication comes from a single canine jawbone unearthed at a late Palaeolithic grave at Oberkassel in Germany. The jaw is more

foreshortened than that of a wolf, with the teeth more closely packed together; this find is dated at 14,000 years BC. There are several other finds some 2000 years later in western Asia, notably at Natufian in Palestine and Palegawra in Iraq. These seem to be followed by a rapid expansion of domestication, with dog remains found in the southern tip of South America by 8500 BC. The Gray Wolf is generally accepted as the most likely ancestor of today's domestic dogs, which are thus known to science as a subspecies—*Canis lupus familiaris*. The Gray Wolf

entered into domestic partnership with man before any other animal species and before the cultivation of plants for food. Indeed, recent molecular evidence suggests that dogs may have been domesticated as long as 100,000 years ago. Various theories, which center on our ancestors' deliberate use of wolves for practical purposes such as food, hunting, guarding, and tidying carrion and refuse around settlements, have been advanced. It is equally likely, however, that domestication came about by accident, with hunter-gatherer societies capturing and raising young wild animals as pets.

Primitive Dingo-like feral dogs were associated with nomadic hunter-gatherer societies of Africa, Asia, and Europe, and later with sedentary agricultural population centers. Austronesian-speaking people transported Dingoes from mainland Asia to Australia and Pacific islands as long as 11,000 years ago, either for food or companionship. The Dingoes of South-east Asia are often referred to as Pariah Dogs. Australian aborigines may have used Dingoes for warmth at night, as food, or as guards, but probably not for hunting. There is no use for Dingoes today, but they feature strongly in the Aborigines' folklore. Europeans did not discover the Dingo in Australia until the 17th century, and taxonomists originally thought it was a feral domestic dog, before its long journey alongside people from Asia was pieced together.

Human introduction of alien carnivores can have a catastrophic impact on resident faunas, either through predation or competition, and often results in extinctions, extirpation or range contractions. Dingoes may have displaced by competition both the Thylacine (*Thylacinus cynoecephalus*) and the Tasmanian Devil (*Sacophilus harrisi*). Comparison of kangaroo and emu (*Dromaius novaehollandiae*) populations inside and outside the "dingo fence" in South Australia suggests that Dingoes limit and probably regulate these prey species. Similarly, Red Fox control by culling in the wheat-belt of Western Australia allowed two Black-flanked Rock Wallaby (*Petrogale lateralis*) populations to increase by 138% and 223%, compared with 14% and 85% declines at nearby sites without fox control.

Many ground-nesting seabirds are dependent on predator-free islands for nesting, and introduced foxes can decimate them. The Arctic Fox has had a large impact on several Arctic seabird colonies on islands where the fox has been introduced or invaded naturally. In California, introduced Red Foxes are threatening rare clapper rails (*Rallus longirostris*) and Salt-marsh Harvest Mice (*Reithrodontomys raviventris*). They also kill endangered San Joaquin Kit Foxes.

*In season, fruit such as blackberries, apples, and the hips of the dog rose can form as much as 90% of the diet of the **Red Fox**. Although versatile opportunists, Red Foxes do have preferences, favoring arvicoline rodents, such as voles, over rats and mice. However, they will cache even less-favored prey for future use, and have a good memory for the location of these larders. Red Foxes will scent-mark depleted food resources, such as emptied caches inedible food remnants, to provide a "book keeping system" of resources not worthy of re-inspection.*

Vulpes vulpes
Minehead, Somerset, UK.
Photo: John Daniels/Ardea

*The fruit Solanum lycocarpum, known as wolf apple or lobeira, grows throughout much of the range of the **Maned Wolf** and is a primary food source. The seeds which have passed through the wolf's digestive tract have been found to have a higher germination rate, and germinating seeds are frequently seen in wolf feces. The wolf thus plays an important part in propagating one of its main food sources. Other canids which have been found by experimental germination to disperse plants by means of their feces include Crab-eating Fox, Short-eared Dog, Darwin's Fox, and Sechuran Fox.*

Chrysocyon brachyurus
Serra da Canastra National Park, Brazil.
Photo: Tui de Roy/
Roving Tortoise Photos

The **Bush Dog**, seen here drinking, is a forest dweller, occurring generally near water sources, particularly small streams. At the opposite extreme are foxes like the Fennec Fox and the Sechuran Fox, which can survive in environments with no standing water, perhaps obtaining all they need from their food, or by licking condensation from vegetation. Also living in deserts, Blanford's Foxes consume more fruit during the hot summer, which compensates for deficiencies in body water.

Speothos venaticus
Photo: Neil Lucas/naturepl.com

Cross-breeding with domestic dogs represents a growing threat to wolf-like canids. In Australia, the proportion of pure wild Dingoes has declined from about 49% in the 1960s to about 17% in the 1980s. Today, pure Dingoes occur only as remnant populations in central and northern Australia and throughout Thailand.

Hybridization is also a problem for Ethiopian Wolves in the Bale Mountains, where females occasionally mate with male dogs. A single litter may have both a wolf and dog as fathers, and hybrid pups remain in the natal pack and behave largely as wolves. Limited hybridization between Gray Wolves and dogs has been detected in Bulgaria, Italy, Latvia, Scandinavia, and Spain, and it is likely to be most frequent near human settlements where Gray Wolf density is low, habitats are fragmented, and feral and domestic dogs are common.

The Red Wolf is intermediate in size between the Coyote and Gray Wolf, and has been considered a fertile hybrid between the two species. Hybridization with Coyotes or Red Wolf × Coyote hybrids is the primary threat to the Red Wolf's persistence in the wild. A recent analysis of Coyotes in the south-east-

Most canids have a single annual estrous cycle, and are thus monoestrous. In Zimbabwe, **Side-striped Jackal** mating occurs mostly during June and July. Once a female is in estrus and receptive, and her progesterone levels go up, the male will develop an interest. A short courtship begins, with the male following the female assiduously, and attempting to mate. Scent marking is involved in establishing and maintaining pair bonds. Jackal pairs defend their territory from other jackal pairs by leaving urine and feces on conspicuous objects. Unrelated jackals within this area are chased away vigorously.

Canis adustus
Moremi Game Reserve, Botswana.
Photo: Daryl Balfour/NHPA

*Mating in the **Red Fox** occurs
between December and February
in the Northern Hemisphere and
June to October in Australia. The
onset of breeding is correlated with
day length, and so starts earlier
at more southerly latitudes. When
after courtship, the female finally
allows the male to mount, he grips
her with his forelegs. Intromission
often leads to a copulatory lock
or "tie", which is facilitated by
a ring of erectile tissue called
the bulbus glandus on the dog's
penis. The male often turns, and
the male and female remain in a
back-to-back position, as seen here
until the ring reduces in diameter,
allowing the tie to end.*

Vulpes vulpes
India.
Photo: Gertrud & Helmut Denzau

ern USA suggests an ancient coyote-domestic dog hybridization event when the first Coyotes were expanding into eastern habitats formerly occupied by Red Wolves.

A further reason for canid-human conflict is that canids can be vectors of diseases that are harmful to people and their domestic animals. Paradoxically, their susceptibility to infection derives from the fact that domestic dogs and wild canids share receptivity to rabies, canine distemper, leishmaniasis, and sarcoptic mange, among other pathogens. Rabies is a serious infection that has a major impact on human lives, particularly in developing countries, with 30,000 people estimated to die annually from rabies in India alone. Of 534 human deaths investigated worldwide in 1995, 89% were attributed to domestic dog bites, 6% to bats, and less than 3% to other wildlife. Wild canids such as Red Foxes in Western Europe may be self-sustaining rabies reservoirs, but in most places wild populations occur at densities too low for rabies to persist without cross-species infection. Instead, domestic dogs may provide the vehicle for rabies to reach their wild relatives, affecting populations of rare Ethiopian Wolves and African Wild Dogs.

Most recent recorded attacks by wild canids on humans involve rabid animals. With the eradication or reduction of rabies, the incidence of Gray Wolf attacks has dropped disproportionately in eastern Europe, but cases are still occasionally reported from Asia and the Middle East. In Argentina, rabies in wild canids has been reported only recently, with cases of Crab-eating Foxes and Culpeos that attacked people. The tolerance of some foxes to human encroachment may bring them into close contact with domestic dogs. These contacts can occur in towns and involve Red Foxes, which are susceptible to rabies, mange, or hydatids in towns, or in Amazonian villages, with Crab-eating Foxes susceptible to leishmaniasis. Leishmaniasis is a disease of humans and domestic dogs resulting from infection by a protozoan carried by sandflies. Wild canids also acquire the infection, and may be additional reservoirs for human infection. Canine distemper, another pathogen that causes high mortality among wild canids, has affected Island Foxes and African Wild Dogs in recent years.

Trapping, shooting, gassing, and poisoning of foxes, Coyotes, and Gray Wolves has been widely practiced in Eurasia and North America in attempts to control rabies, with possible regional conservation implications. During a campaign to control rabies in Alberta, Canada, 50,000 Red Foxes, 35,000 Coyotes, 4200 Gray Wolves and many other carnivores were killed in an 18-month period. Vaccination has been used with great

success to control rabies in Western Europe and North America. This has the advantages of being more humane and not disrupting the population dynamics and spatial organization of the host species. Rabies has been nearly eradicated in Western Europe through a mass aerial vaccination targeting Red Foxes with oral baits, with up to 60% of foxes immunized.

There is no doubt that public perception of many carnivore species is beginning to change. Some large carnivores are major attractions for tourists. High-profile and visible canid species such as African Wild Dogs, Gray Wolves, Ethiopian Wolves, Dholes, and Maned Wolves may be capable of supporting, at least partially, a sustainable tourist trade. However, many other canids are frustratingly secretive. Although the big cats were the main draw to a national park in Zimbabwe when visitors of all nationalities were polled, African Wild Dogs ranked top for Zimbabweans, and second among South Africans, indicating an appreciation for their natural history. Visitors to Yellowstone in the USA take pleasure in the expectation of seeing or hearing Gray Wolves, and more than 20,000 have observed Gray Wolves there since 1995. Ethiopian Wolves are the chief attraction at the Bale Mountains National Park in southern Ethiopia, and Maned Wolves are a highlight of tourism to the protected grasslands of Argentina and Brazil. Nonetheless, expectations of revenue should not be exaggerated. For example, in Ethiopia's Bale Mountains, where income from tourism is often given as a justification to the local community for the presence of a park, the number of tourists visiting each year is only in the hundreds, many use their vehicles rather than local guides or horses, and the sums reaching the local community are not great. Furthermore, the susceptibility of tourism to fluctuations in the global economy and to political instability makes it unwise to base conservation entirely on economic values.

Thanks to changing public opinion, legal protection and habitat recovery, the Gray Wolf is returning to areas in Europe and North America where it was long ago hunted to extinction. Other canids currently have an improving conservation status. Of these, several are medium-sized opportunists that have extended their distributions recently, sometimes aided by the removal of larger carnivores and sometimes because they flourish in new environments. There are urban populations of Red Foxes, Coyotes, and even Kit Foxes. In contrast, other canid species, such as the Ethiopian Wolf, Red Wolf, Darwin's Fox, and the Island Fox, are threatened and restricted in distribution and numbers.

Fox cubs are generally born in burrows dug by the vixen, or appropriated from other species. Fox litter sizes are normally from one to six. In the **Swift Fox**, the cubs are born after a relatively short gestation of 51 days. Swift Foxes are among the most burrow-dependent canids, using their burrows throughout the year. The distribution and density of dens are considered important components of Swift Fox habitat requirements, particularly in terms of evading Coyote predation or Red Fox competition. Swift Foxes excavate their own dens, or modify the burrows of other species.

Dens serve several functions, such as providing a refuge from predators, and protection from extreme climate conditions, both in summer and winter, as well as shelter for raising the young. Kit Foxes also use their dens all year round, and have multiple dens. Although they can excavate their own dens, preferring loose-textured soils, Kit Foxes frequently occupy and modify the burrows of prairie dogs, kangaroo rats, ground squirrels, and American Badgers. Occasionally, they will den in man-made structures such as culverts and pipes, but the young are almost always born in earthen dens. Other burrow-dependent foxes include Fennec Fox: dens may be huge, covering up to 120 m^2, with as many as 15 different entrances. Another African desert-dwelling species, the Pale Fox, digs extensive burrows, 2–3 m deep and up to 15 m in length, often under sandy tracks or near villages. They line the inner chambers with dry vegetation. However, Blanford Foxes studied in Israel appeared to use only natural cavities, and never dug burrows.

Vulpes velox
Canada.
Photos: Roland Seitre

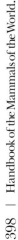

Coyotes *make their dens in brush-covered slopes, on steep banks, under rock ledges, in thickets, and inside hollow logs. They may also use the dens of other animals. Dens can have more than one entrance, and interconnecting tunnels. The same den may be used from year to year. Canid young have a long period of dependency, and denning and pup rearing are the focal points of Coyote families for several months, until the pups are large and mobile. The pups are born blind and helpless after a gestation of around 63 days. Litter size averages six, but may be affected by population density and food availability during the previous winter, and can be as few as one and as many as nine. In northern latitudes, litter size changes in response to population cycles in Snowshoe Hares. Litter size has been found to increase after cold, snowy winters, when more ungulate carcasses are available to ovulating females. Birth weight per pup is 240–275 g. Their eyes open at about 14 days, and they emerge from the den at about three weeks. The young are cared for by their parents and other associates, usually siblings from a previous year, and they may also be suckled by females other than their mother. The Coyote pups are weaned at 5–7 weeks of age.*

Canis latrans
Kalispell, Montana, USA.
Photo: Tom & Pat Leeson/DRK

Although they most commonly give birth once annually, **Fennec Foxes** can produce more than one litter per year under some conditions. Fennec Foxes mate in January and February. The copulatory tie is exceptionally long, lasting as much as two hours and 45 minutes. After a gestation of 50–52 days, they give birth in March and April to litters of 1–4 pups. Fennecs and other small foxes associated with arid and poor habitats, in which only a small body mass can be supported, have to work harder to gather food for the young, and therefore are less able to defend them. This may have pushed them to have more advanced pups, and fewer of them.

Vulpes zerda
Israel.
Photo: Yossi Eshbol/FLPA

Status and Conservation

Wild canids tend to be opportunistic, and a majority of species range widely across multiple habitat types, including human-dominated landscapes. As a result, canids are often in conflict with humans, raising a wide variety of conservation issues. Some of the larger species, such as Gray Wolves, African Wild Dogs, and Coyotes, have been persecuted heavily due to their predation on livestock, and more rarely for the perceived risk of attacks on humans. Some smaller species, notably Arctic Foxes and South American foxes, have been subject to heavy harvesting by the fur trade. In the past, blanket culling of some common canids such as Dingoes, Coyotes, Culpeos, and Red Foxes was widespread but largely ineffective, with most of these species thriving despite tremendous hunting pressure. More recently, the impact of diseases on small populations of some wild canid species has become apparent.

The current status of wild canids is mixed. Although some threatened species have declined in numbers and distribution, most canids have remained widespread, and a few species have even expanded in distribution. Coyotes, for example, are now more common and more widely distributed than ever before, inhabiting much of North and Central America, reaching as far south as Panama. Golden Jackals have spread into Western Europe and are becoming a regular sight in countries where they were previously unknown, such as Bulgaria, Italy, and Aus-

African Wild Dog litters average 10–11 pups, but litters as large as 21 have been recorded. Each African Wild Dog pack includes a dominant pair that breeds each year. Subordinate females may breed on some occasions, but their pups rarely survive. Parental care involves all pack members and such alloparental care is vital: small packs of less than four members rarely manage to raise any pups. The most extreme form of such group care is allosuckling, when pups are suckled by females other than their mother. This has also been seen in other large canid species, including Gray Wolves, Coyotes, Ethiopian Wolves, African Wild Dogs, and South American Gray Foxes, and Red, Indian, Bat-eared, and Arctic Foxes. In Ethiopian Wolves, females which have shown no previous sign of pregnancy may lactate spontaneously.

Lycaon pictus
Kruger National Park, South Africa.
Photo: Wendy Dennis/FLPA

tria. Gray Wolves are another success story, slowly but steadily recolonizing parts of Western Europe and some parts of the USA where they had once been eradicated.

The IUCN/SSC Canid Specialist Group evaluated the conservation status of all 35 canid species for *The IUCN Red List*. The group listed one species, the Pale Fox, as Data Deficient and six species as threatened under the categories Critically Endangered and Endangered, while four species were consider as Near Threathened. In general, threatened canids are either naturally rare, with limited distributions, or have become threatened by human factors such as habitat loss, persecution, and disease transmission. One species, the Falkland Islands Wolf, became extinct in the 19th century, out-gunned by high levels of culling facilitated by the fox's apparent naïveté to humans.

The Critically Endangered Darwin's Fox is one of the rarest canids, with a total population of a few hundred. Darwin's Fox was known until recently only from the Island of Chiloé, off the coast of south Chile, where it was collected by Charles Darwin during his HMS *Beagle* voyage. A small population has also been recorded in Nahuelbuta National Park in mainland Chile. A forest dweller, Darwin's Fox is known for killing poultry and raiding garbage dumps, apparently with little fear of people (and domestic dogs), and has even been observed entering houses at night in search of food. The Chiloé Island population remains relatively secure. The presence of domestic dogs in Nahuelbuta may pose the greatest threat to the species by acting as vectors of lethal diseases or by direct attacks.

Island Foxes, also listed as Critically Endangered, are rare and highly range-restricted. Island Foxes are endemic to the six largest of the eight Channel Islands off southern California. Each island population differs in genetic structure and is considered a separate subspecies. Island Fox numbers fell within a decade from approximately 6000 individuals to fewer than 1500 in 2002. Two populations in the southern Channel Islands have declined by an estimated 95% since 1994, and consist of only 17 and fewer than 30 individuals, respectively. The remaining Island Foxes are especially vulnerable to the introduction of canine diseases, including distemper, necessitating more stringent control of domestic dogs brought in by visitors. On the northern Channel Islands, the primary threat is an unusually high level of predation by golden eagles. These birds are recent arrivals to the islands, preying on introduced pigs.

The other Critically Endangered canid is the Red Wolf, which once ranged across most of the south-eastern USA. There is some debate as to whether Red Wolves should be considered a distinctive species or a fertile hybrid between Coyotes and Gray Wolves. One recent line of genetic evidence suggests that it is a unique taxon, while another proposes that Red Wolves and Gray Wolves in southern Ontario (*Canis lupus lycaon*) are so genetically similar that they represent a separate canid species, *C. lycaon*. The Red Wolf was declared Extinct in the Wild by 1980 following years of direct persecution by humans. It was reintroduced into eastern North Carolina, and is now common within the reintroduction area of roughly 4000 km². Road kills account for 25% of known Red Wolf deaths in the reintroduced population, but hybridization remains the primary threat. Models suggest the current population may be lost within 12–24 years if current levels of hybridization continue.

Of the three wild canids listed as Endangered, African Wild Dogs are arguably the best known but least understood by people in their range. Formerly distributed throughout much of sub-Saharan Africa with the exception of rainforests, wild dogs have disappeared from most of their former range—25 of the former 39 range countries no longer support populations—and current population estimates suggest that as few as 5000 free-ranging wild dogs remain. Wild dogs are rarely seen, even where they are common, and it appears that populations have always existed at very low densities. Competition with larger predators has a major impact on their behavior and biology, with Lions being a major cause of natural mortality in many areas. However, more than half of the mortality recorded among adults is a direct result of human activities, even in some of the largest and best-protected areas. Although the status of African Wild Dogs in South Africa, Botswana, Zimbabwe, and Tanzania is well documented, virtually nothing is known of the remnant populations in West Africa, Angola, Sudan, and Central African Republic.

The Dhole, also known as the Asian Wild Dog, is another Endangered canid. In recent decades, Dholes have dwindled in numbers with the shrinking of their native forests. With the

Collaborative care of young may be a more fundamental and ubiquitous feature of canid society than cooperative hunting. Alloparenting may enable animals that have not yet bred to gain parenting skills; lack of experience may explain the rather unorthodox way in which this adult **Gray Wolf** is holding the pup. The original list of species in which non-breeding "helpers" feed and tend the young—Gray Wolves, Red and Arctic Foxes, Jackals, Ethiopian Wolves, and African Wild Dogs—has expanded almost in direct proportion to the number of species studied. Non-breeding pack members help provide food for both pregnant and lactating mothers and pups. They also babysit diligently, chasing away predators, ensuring the pups do not stray, and warning them to go into the den if danger threatens.

In social wolf-like species, guarding may protect pups from animals from neighboring packs, preventing infanticide. However, demonstrating that assiduous helping in canids, or other conspicuously helpful carnivores, translates into improved reproductive success, has proven difficult. Wolf helpers appear to increase the survival of the young only when food is abundant. When food is scarce, offspring in large wolf groups actually survive less well.

Canis lupus
Photo: Herbert Kehrer/Imagebroker/
FLPA

Small canids are either largely
monogamous, or form small,
loose-knit groups with a female-
biased sex ratio. **Tibetan Foxes**
are usually seen alone or in male-
female pairs, although one family
of three adults and two juveniles
has been observed. Most aspects
of the Tibetan Fox's reproductive
and social behavior remain largely
unknown. Mating is thought to
occur in February, with 2–5 young
born in May. Their burrows are
typically located at the base of
boulders, along old beach lines, or
low down on slopes. There may be
one to four entrances to a den.

Vulpes ferrilata
Ladakh, India.
Photo: Gertrud & Helmut Denzau

exception of an isolated study in south India which began to reveal the fascinating natural history of these whistling hunters, we know very little about them. Dholes provide a harrowing example of another feature of community ecology affecting canid conservation, namely the dilemma of endangered predators killing endangered prey. The rare Dholes of Java, a distinct subspecies locally known as Ajag, prey upon the calves and cows of the Endangered Banteng, a rare wild cow, threatening its population in east Java. The San Clemente Island Fox provides another perplexing example. The foxes kill or disturb the Critically Endangered San Clemente loggerhead shrike; to protect these birds, wildlife managers trap and remove the foxes.

Ethiopian Wolves, the rarest living dogs, with a total adult population of less than 500, are restricted to seven isolated mountain pockets. The low levels of genetic variation in the Ethiopian Wolf reflect a long history of population declines due to a gradual post-Pleistocene warming of the continent, compounded by more recent habitat fragmentation and losses to subsistence agriculture. However, a greater and more immediate concern is the vulnerability of the remaining populations to diseases such as rabies. The Wolves' last remaining stronghold in the Bale Mountains has been threatened by recurrent rabies epidemics. Ethiopian Wolves were listed as Critically Endangered, but recent recovery of their numbers in Bale and better information on other remote, isolated popula-

Ethiopian Wolf pups are born
in a den dug by the female in
open ground, under a boulder,
or inside a rocky crevice. Two to
seven pups emerge from the den
after three weeks. At this time, the
charcoal gray natal coat begins
to be replaced by the reddish fur
typical of the species. Among
the larger wolf-like canids, pups
are introduced to solid foods at
about two months of age, and
they alternate using the den and
playing. Their resting and play
area surrounds the natal den and
expands as the pups get older. The
only detailed information on the
reproductive habits of Ethiopian
Wolves comes from four years of
observations of nine wild packs in
the Bale Mountains.

Canis simensis
Bale Mountains National Park,
Ethiopia.
Photo: Martin Harvey/DRK

The young of large social canids like **Gray Wolves** remain dependent on adults for longer than vulpine species, receiving solid foods from adults consistently until they are six months old, and being regularly provisioned at least until they are one year of age. Yearlings may steal solid food from their younger siblings. Breeders tend to contribute significantly more food than non-breeders, and females more than males, although African Wild Dog and Gray Wolf males may provide more solid foods to pups per capita than do females. Wolf-like canids are the only carnivores to regurgitate food for their young, swallowing meat from kills in order to bring it back to pups at the den. Foxes do not regurgitate, but most fox species carry solid foods to the den. Blanford's Foxes are apparently an exception: they have never been observed carrying food to the young, and it appears that any direct contribution to the pups' survival by any individual other than the mother is probably minimal. Male Blanford's Foxes have been observed grooming and accompanying two- to four-month-old juveniles, but have not been seen feeding them or the female.

Canis lupus
Photo: Duncan Usher/Ardea

403

tions in North Ethiopia have permitted their reclassification as Endangered.

Inbreeding depression may occur in canids and may conceivably influence the persistence of a population, although there are no clearcut examples of this happening. Loss of genetic variation in small populations may also influence the ability of a population to adapt to changing conditions. Ethiopian Wolf females cunningly avoid inbreeding through mate choice, decreasing the rate at which genetic variation might be lost and potentially mitigating the effects of inbreeding. In parts of Bale Mountains, Ethiopian Wolves have been observed to hybridize with domestic dogs, but this threat seems to be restricted to an area where the wolves coexist with shepherds and their dogs.

The group living, pack hunting Bush Dog has one of the largest distributional ranges of the South American canids, occurring in vast areas of cerrado and rainforest habitats. Intriguingly, the species is never abundant and seems to be naturally rare independent of human disturbance. Rapid habitat conversion and human encroachment in those habitats, however, are causes for concern for this Near Treathened species, considered by some as the ultimate forest hunter. Another Amazonian dweller, the Short-eared Dog, is similarly listed as Near Threatened by the rapid advance of the deforestation arc on the Amazon. Sechuran Foxes in northern Peru, and Maned Wolves complete the list of species likely to become formally threatened in the near future.

Maned Wolves inhabit the grasslands and scrub forests of central South America, where they are threatened by the drastic reduction of habitat due to conversion to agriculture and pastureland. Their low reproductive output, with litters averaging only two pups, makes them particularly vulnerable to anthropogenic mortality. Maned Wolves are targeted as killers of small livestock and poultry, and are often killed by domestic dogs and in some areas by vehicles on highways. Native folklore contributes to local peoples' attitudes, which range from tolerance to fear and dislike. Although it is one of the largest carnivores in the grasslands, the species is apparently not well known to a large segment of the population.

Gray Wolves were considered seriously threatened in the 1970s, when their plight was brought to global attention. There are some 300,000 Gray Wolves worldwide today, and they are making a healthy recovery in many areas where they were extirpated or near extinction not long ago. Dramatic demographic declines or population bottlenecks have been documented for some Gray Wolf populations that now contain less genetic vari-

ation. For example, the Italian Gray Wolf population declined dramatically in the 18th and 19th centuries due to habitat loss and predator-control programs. By the 1970s, only about 100 wolves were left in the Apennine Mountains of central Italy. These wolves showed a single mitochondrial haplotype, which represents lower diversity than that of other Old World populations. Scandinavian wolves likewise declined over the past few hundred years to the point of near extinction in the 1970s. However, a new group of wolves was discovered in southern Sweden in the early 1980s, and this is thought to be the founding stock of the current Scandinavian population, estimated to be about 100 individuals in 2000.

Gray Wolves on Isle Royale, Michigan, in the USA have levels of average relatedness approaching inbred captive populations, and could conceivably suffer a decrease in fitness that would eventually affect population persistence. High levels of gene flow likely characterized Old World populations in the past, so there is reason to restore past levels of gene flow in parts of Europe, either through habitat restoration and protection along dispersal corridors or through translocation.

The Mexican Gray Wolf subspecies (*Canis lupus baileyi*) is one of the most threatened, and was functionally extinct in the wild due to habitat loss and an extensive extermination campaign in the first half of the 20th century. Recovery efforts led by the US Fish and Wildlife Service resulted in successful wolf reintroductions in Arizona and New Mexico, and populations are beginning to be restored in northern Mexico.

Ancestral Dingoes were associated with nomadic hunter-gatherer societies in South-east Asia and later with sedentary agricultural population centers where the animals were tamed and subsequently transported around the world. Today they are considered vermin throughout most of their range. Bounties for Dingo skins and scalps exist in some regions of Australia, and Dingo meat is sold in several food markets in Asia. Dingoes are rare in New Guinea and possibly extinct as there have been no confirmed sightings for about 30 years. They are common in Sulawesi and throughout northern and central Thailand, they are considered rare in the Philippines and are probably extinct on many islands.

A major cause of Dingo mortality in Australia is a cycle involving Dingo population density, food supply, and human control. When food becomes scarce for a large population of Dingoes, they disperse to pastoral and agricultural areas where there are fewer Dingoes. There, intense human control measures (poisoning, trapping, or shooting) create vacant areas

*Lactation in the **Red Fox** lasts for four weeks, and the pups are fully weaned at 6–8 weeks. Short after the pups begin to venture outside, the vixen starts to bring live prey back to the den, and the pups are allowed to play with it before it is killed by the adult. By the time they are three months or older, most canid young follow adults on foraging trips, and engage in play resembling adult foraging techniques. As they get older they begin to practice hunti skills, stalking and chasing smal prey such as birds and small rodents. The adults in attendanc gradually provide different prey items to enable the young to hone their foraging and killing skills.*

Vulpes vulpes
Collsuspina, Catalonia, Spain.
Photo: Jordi Bas

Male **Bush Dogs** exhibit a high
degree of parental care towards
their pups. This can also include
food supplementation to females
prior to birth and throughout
nursing. Lactation lasts
approximately eight weeks. Infant
Bush Dogs whine, grunt, growl,
and bark; these vocalizations
are thought to either elicit care or
reduce aggression. Confined to
tropical forests where they are hard
to observe, Bush Dogs have received
little study. The Bush Dog mating
season is unknown, although pups
have been found in the wet season.

Speothos venaticus
Photo: Gerard Lacz/FLPA

and perpetuate the dispersal-mortality cycle. Dingoes have been eliminated in most of south-eastern Australia through such human control and loss of habitat, and this situation is maintained with a 5614 km barrier fence.

The Blanford's Fox was discovered in the Middle East, including in isolated parts of the Arabian Peninsula, only two decades ago, and more recently the species has been recorded in Egypt. Populations are also thought to exist in Iran, Afghanistan, and Pakistan, although little is known about its status in those countries. Restricted to cliffs and rocky areas, habitat loss is of limited concern for the well-studied Israeli populations.

Development in other areas, such as along the Dead Sea coast, may pose a threat to its survival. Surveys in the rugged terrain of eastern Egypt, eastern Sudan, Eritrea and North Ethiopia, however, may unveil a more extended African distribution for this long-tailed cliff specialist.

Among the species that are listed as Least Concern, the Coyote is one of the most widespread today. As suggested by molecular analyses, Coyote numbers decreased from about 3·7 million breeding females (about 18 million Coyotes) in the late Pleistocene to 460,000 breeding females (2·2 million Coyotes) in the recent past. There are now about seven million Coyotes.

From four weeks old, **African
Wild Dog** pups are fed with meat
regurgitated by adults. The pups
are entirely dependent upon adults
for meat until they are about twelve
months old. African Wild Dogs
cram three days worth of food,
at least 4 kg of meat, into their
stomachs for transportation to
their pups. This is a practice that
facilitates transport, and prevents
loss of food to kleptoparasites such
as hyenas, which might steal food
carried by mouth. In the Serengeti,
a positive correlation was found
between pup survival to one year
of age and pack size. Subordinates
and yearlings contribute by
increasing the speed at which prey
is devoured, thereby reducing the
chance that it will be stolen by
hyenas or Lions, and by taking
meat back to the pups.

Lycaon pictus
Namibia.
Photo: Martin Harvey/DRK

Arctic Foxes *mate in late winter and early spring, so that pup rearing takes place during the snow-free period from June to September. Lactation generally lasts 8–10 weeks. During this time, the male provides food for the female, but as meat forms an increasing proportion of the pups diet, the roles of the parents become more similar, and the female takes an active part in hunting and provisioning the pups. Non-breeding foxes, usually yearlings from the previous litter, may also help. With such a small window for pup rearing, growth is fast, a weight gain after weaning has been recorded at 30–34 g per day.*

Alopex lagopus
Svalbard.
Photo: Jordi Bas

The difference in abundance estimates for the recent past and today may reflect reduced Gray Wolf numbers, resulting from habitat loss and direct persecution, which allowed Coyotes to expand their distribution and the number of Coyotes to increase. This relationship illustrates the role of intra-guild competition in determining the status of some canid populations. It is well established that Coyotes kill both San Joaquin Kit Foxes and Swift Foxes restored to Canada. On the other side of the world, Red Foxes may be the main cause for local extinction of the Rüppell's Fox in Israel, where it was the most abundant vulpine in the Negev Desert up until the 1960s. Red Fox numbers increased as the human population and associated agriculture expanded; this, in turn, coincided incriminatingly with a sharp decline in Rüppell's Foxes.

Ignorance of distribution and abundance, and even taxonomic status, makes it hard to be confident about the conservation status of many of the lesser known canid species. In several cases—the Bush Dog and the Short-Eared Dog paramount amongst them—repeated but failed attempts to find them and survey their populations give grounds for pessimism. A similar situation applies to the Pale, Ruppell's, and Fennec Foxes of the Sahara, whose distribution and status can only be guessed from scant reports.

Despite their widespread distribution, Indian Foxes are nowhere abundant. They occur at densities as low as 0·04km^2 throughout their range. Their populations undergo major fluctuations due to prey availability. In some areas, such as Tamil Nadu, anthropogenic mortality of Indian Foxes is high, with

*Modified termite mounds, and other convenient shelters such as Aardvark burrows, often with multiple entrances, are the preferred natal dens of **Black-backed Jackals**. The same den site may be used from year to year. Pups first emerge from the den at three weeks, are weaned at 8–9 weeks, and are completely independent of the den at 14 weeks. Alloparental care is well documented, and consists of feeding pups by regurgitation, and guarding them when the parents are foraging. O "helper" may increase the average number of pups surviving per mated pair from one to three, and two such helpers further increase survival to four pups.*

Canis mesomelas
Masai Mara National Park, Kenya.
Photo: Günter Ziesler

Young **Coyotes** join in the howling that helps maintain territories and pack spacing. Coyotes have a dominance hierarchy within each pack, which influences order of access to food resources. In captivity, pups show early development of aggressive behavior, and engage in dominance fights when 19–24 days old. The process of establishing hierarchy within litters appears to last up to four and a half months. The pups reach adult weight by about nine months, and juveniles usually disperse during autumn and early winter. Dispersal of individuals from the natal group is an important component of the social organization and ranging behavior of canids, as the young attempt to find mates and establish territories. Most canids disperse from their natal home range at sexual maturity. Gray Wolves, for example, generally disperse at two years of age, whereas most foxes do so in their first winter, although variations in dispersal patterns exist. Dispersal tends to bring forward conflicts of interest within family groups: youngsters may happily wait for a favorable opportunity to make a move, but their parents or siblings may forcefully precipitate their departure. However, in Coyotes, dispersal seems to be voluntary, as social pressures intensify during winter, when food becomes limited.

It has been argued that it is actually the most robust Coyotes that disperse. Pups, yearlings, and non-breeding adults of lower social rank may disperse from the natal site into adjacent areas, or farther afield. The eventual home range size is influenced by social organization, with transients using larger areas, and residents occupying distinct territories.

Canis latrans
Minnesota, USA.
Photo: Roland Seitre

*From the age of around three months, most canid young, like these **Red Foxes**, follow hunting adults. In Red Foxes, sexual maturity is reached at 9–10 months of age. Juveniles may disperse at 6–12 months. Studies indicate that adult Red Foxes aggressively drive the youngsters away. Males typically disperse farther than females, and dispersal distances range from less than 5 km to more than 50 km, although distances of up to 394 km have been recorded in the USA. The basic Red Fox social unit is a pair, but groups with up to six members, usually one adult male and 2–5 females, probably related, may share a territory.*

Vulpes vulpes
Tso-Kar, Ladakh, India.
Photo: Otto Pfister

humans (frequently using dogs) killing foxes for their flesh, teeth, claws and skin. In the 20th century several catastrophic population declines of Corsac Foxes were recorded, during which hunting of Corsacs in the former Soviet Union was completely banned for some periods.

Wherever the relationship lies on the spectrum from exploitation to conflict, a human dimension underlies almost all canid conservation problems. Thus biologists working with the Sechuran Fox in northern Peru argue that its future lies on the one hand in reducing predation by the foxes on poultry, and on the other, persuading people not to make amulets out of pieces of fox. Little is known of Tibetan Foxes other than that their furs regularly turn up at local markets in Tibet; market

surveys may help document the extent of trade and its possible impact on wild populations. However, prejudices cannot be changed until they are identified and then—if possible—debunked. That is why, for example, surveys of the attitudes of local people to Maned Wolves are considered a priority. Some problems, such as road kills, cannot simply be talked out of existence—they require action. Hence the positioning of road signs to protect Ethiopian Wolves, and efforts to study how the impact of urban development and highways on San Joaquin Kit Foxes can be mitigated.

Another expression of the human dimension is the emergence of disease as an important threat to wild canids, and the role wild canids play as vectors. Rabies, canine distemper, an-

*One of three wild canids classified as Endangered on The IUCN Red List, **African Wild Dogs** were formerly distributed throughout much of sub-Saharan Africa, but have disappeared from 25 of the former 39 range countries. Estimates suggest that as few as 5000 remain. They survive mainly in small isolated populations, which makes them vulnerable to potentially catastrophic events. Rabies, probably spread from domestic dogs, caused the extinction of African Wild Dogs in the Serengeti ecosystem on the Kenya/Tanzania border in 1990–1991. Although they are legally protected across much of their range, more than half the mortality of adults is caused directly by human activities.*

Lycaon pictus
Masai Mara National Park, Kenya.
Photo: Pete Oxford/DRK

thrax, and other pathogens have caused dramatic die-offs and even local extinctions of several canid populations, notably Island Foxes, Ethiopian Wolves, and African Wild Dogs. Infectious pathogens cannot persist in small, isolated populations, but may be transmitted by closely related species such as domestic dogs. The threat of rabies to Ethiopian Wolves was demonstrated all too dramatically in 1991, when three quarters of a known population perished. Conservation priority since has been given to protecting the wolves from disease by vaccinating domestic dogs within the wolf's range against rabies and canine distemper.

One hope of many canid conservationists is that people formerly hostile to canids will come to value them. This aspiration is behind developments in tourism around African Wild Dogs on game farms in South Africa. This tourism ties in nicely with the conservation strategy for African Wild Dogs in South Africa. Because no sufficiently large piece of land remains in the country that can support a self-sustaining, unmanaged African Wild Dog population, a constellation of smaller, satellite (mostly private) reserves has been managed for small dog populations to function as a natural meta-population. This involves intervention to manage movements of individuals between these sub-populations to obviate the adverse effects of crowding and inbreeding. Steps are taken to minimize the damage done by the dogs to commercially valuable game and to maximize the revenue generated by the dogs themselves.

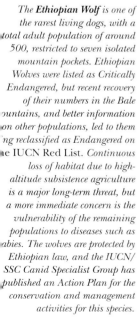

Extinct in the Wild by 1980, the
Red Wolf was reintroduced into
eastern North Carolina by the
US Fish and Wildlife Service in
1987. It is now listed as Criticall
Endangered on The IUCN Red
List. The Red Wolf is now comm
within the reintroduction area of
roughly 6000 km². Road kills ha
accounted for 25% of known Re
Wolf deaths in the reintroduced
population, but hybridization wi
Coyotes remains the primary thre
However, similar hybridization h
been observed in the population
of suspected Red Wolf-type wolves
in Algonquin Provincial Park,
Ontario, Canada. If these wolves
are shown to be Red Wolf-type
wolves, this will nearly triple the
known number of Red Wolf-type
wolves surviving in the wild.

Canis rufus
SE USA.
Photo: Tom & Pat Leeson/Ardea

This intriguing concept brings into stark relief the degree of human involvement needed to restore the African Wild Dogs in South Africa.

Protected areas are a fundamental tool of nature conservation, although most appear inadequate to ensure the long-term persistence of most large canid species. The persistence of several carnivore species, including Gray Wolves, Dholes, and African Wild Dogs, was compared with reserve sizes within the species' historical ranges. These large canids persisted in reserves above certain critical sizes, which researchers identified as varying from 723 km² for Dholes to 3606 km² for African

Wild Dogs. A far more important and difficult question is what size protected area is necessary to maintain a viable population. Past estimates of minimum reserve sizes to protect large canid populations have never been more precise than the "several thousand km²" suggested for Gray Wolves and the 10,000 km² suggested for African Wild Dogs. The shape of a protected area can affect its efficiency in protecting animal populations and it was suggested that the magnitude of the edge effect is related to a species' ranging behavior: when a species is wide-ranging, a relatively larger proportion of the population is exposed to the edge effect, compared to a species with smaller home ranges.

Endemic to the six largest Chann
Islands off southern California,
where each island population
differs in genetic structure and is
considered a separate subspecies,
the **Island Fox** is listed as Critica
Endangered on The IUCN
Red List. It is vulnerable to
diseases like canine distemper,
and to predation by golden eagle
Population numbers fell from
approximately 6000, to fewer the
1500 in 2002. Two populations
in the southern Channel Islands
have declined by an estimated
95% since 1994, and consist of
17 and fewer than 30 individua
respectively. This prompted
biologists to bring all remaining
individuals into captivity.
Attempts at captive breeding ha
been only modestly successful.

Urocyon littoralis
Santa Catalina Island,
California, USA.
Photo: B. Peterson/Ardea

The Critically Endangered **Darwin's Fox** *has a total population of a few hundred individuals. Known until recently only from the Island of Chiloé, off the coast of south Chile, a small population has also been recorded in Nahuelbuta National Park in mainland Chile. The island population, being protected in Chiloé National Park, appears to be relatively safe. The mainland population is reported to be vulnerable, and its survival uncertain. Mainland foxes are exposed to risks in winter when they move to lower, unprotected private areas in search of milder conditions. Domestic dogs in Nahuelbuta may pose the greatest threat, by acting as vectors of lethal diseases, or by direct attacks.*

Pseudalopex fulvipes
Nahuelbuta National Park, Chile.
Photo: Daniel González Acuña

Protected areas may be an effective conservation tool for small canids, but they cannot be expected to ensure large canid survival unless they encompass enormous areas—as large as entire regions. This approach has been proposed for North America, but it seems unrealistic for most of the rest of the world. Generally, conservation, especially of species living at low density and on large home ranges, can be achieved only through the integrated management of a reserve network and coexistence with humans on unprotected land.

Protected areas will continue to be a primary tool for canid conservation only if they are an integral component of conservation strategies that extend over the populations' entire range and include all aspects of the animal/human interface. Since lasting conservation of canid populations, especially the large ones, cannot be achieved within the small scale of most protected areas, the challenge is to adopt a broader perspective and expand projects temporally and spatially to include all ecological and socio-economic components. The Carpathian Large Carnivore Project currently active in Romania for Gray Wolf, Brown Bear, and Lynx conservation is one of the best examples of an integrated conservation development project (ICDP) involving canids and it shows the potential of adopting this approach.

International treaties such as the Convention on International Trade in Endangered Species (CITES) provide a mechanism for species conservation across international boundaries. At a national level, legislation is needed to justify government action, provide funding, and implement projects. In the USA, the Endangered Species Act of 1973 has been a fundamental tool for the conservation of many species, including the San Joaquin Kit Fox—threatened by habitat loss and degradation, rodenticides, and expanding populations of non-native Red Foxes—and for reintroducing Gray Wolves into Yellowstone National Park. Strategic conservation planning at species and/or national levels is the purpose of the IUCN/SSC Canid Specialist Group. Three notable examples are the Action Plans for Canids, for the African Wild Dog, and for the Ethiopian wolf. These Action Plans provide the comprehensive vision and the general framework under which any management action should be planned and implemented to be most effective.

The role of reintroductions in canid conservation, using either captive breeding or translocations, has been much debated and its applicability has been somewhat controversial. Reintroductions have been attempted with African Wild Dogs,

Wolves, Red Wolves, and Kit and Swift Foxes. Captive-bred or wild caught African Wild Dogs have been released in South Africa, Namibia, Zimbabwe, and Kenya. However, nine of the ten attempts have failed to produce wild offspring. Gray Wolf reintroductions of five and four animals, in Alaska and Michigan respectively, failed, but a translocation of 107 wolves in Minnesota to minimize livestock depredation was successful. A more recent reintroduction of Canadian Wolves to Yellowstone National Park in the USA has been effective, as released wolves have survived, reproduced, and the population has increased. A reintroduction of San Joaquin Kit Foxes in California failed, with annual fox mortality rates of 97%, primarily because of Coyote predation.

Captive breeding will not be necessary or appropriate for many species, but it has been essential to the recovery of two North American canids. The Red Wolf and Mexican Wolf, considered Extinct in the Wild, were successfully bred and reintroduced into the wild. Captive breeding has also played a role in the conservation and population management of other North American canids. Two subspecies of Island Foxes, for example, experienced population crashes, which prompted biologists to capture and bring all remaining individuals into captivity. Attempts to breed them in captivity have been only modestly successful, however. The release of 942 Swift Foxes in Canada between 1983 and 1997 is the most extensive canid reintroduction program to date. Although the released foxes had to face high levels of Coyote predation, this effort is largely considered successful.

General Bibliography

Asa & Valdespino (2003), Bekoff (1978b), Berta (1984), Biben (1983), Brady (1981), Bueler (1973), Cabrera (1931), Carbyn, Armbruster & Mamo (1994), Carbyn, Fritts & Seip (1995), Clutton-Brock *et al.* (1976), Coetzee (1977), Corbett (1995), Creel & Creel (2002), Dragesco-Joffé (1993), Eisenberg (1989), Emmons & Feer (1997), Ewer (1973), Geffen, Mercure *et al.* (1992), Gittleman (1989), Gittleman & Harvey (1982), Hall (1981), Haltenorth & Diller (1980), Heptner & Naumov (1992), IUCN (2008), Kingdon (1971-1982, 1997), Kleiman (1972), Langguth (1975), Macdonald (1979b), Malcolm & Marten (1982), Mech (1970), Mech & Boitani (2003), Mercure *et al.* (1993), Mivart (1890a), Moehlman & Hofer (1997), Nowak (1979, 1999, 2002), Ralls *et al.* (2007), Redford & Eisenberg (1992), Roemer & Wayne (2003), Sillero-Zubiri, Gottelli & Macdonald (1996), Sillero-Zubiri, King & Macdonald (1996), Skinner & Smithers (1990), Van Gelder (1978), Wayne (1993), Wayne *et al.* (1997), Woodroffe & Ginsberg (1998), Zunino *et al.* (1995).

ssp *lupus*

ssp *arctos*

ssp *cubanensis*

1

dark morph

ssp *occidentalis*

ssp *pallipes*

ssp *dingo*

PLATE 21

inches 16
cm 40

Genus *CANIS*

Linnaeus, 1758

1. Gray Wolf *Canis lupus*

French: Loup gris / **German**: Wolf / **Spanish**: Lobo
Other common names: Wolf, Timber Wolf, Tundra Wolf, Arctic Wolf

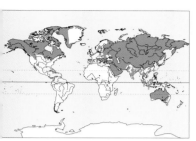

Taxonomy. *Canis lupus* Linnaeus, 1758, Sweden.
There have been two recent proposals for major taxonomic changes to the Gray Wolf in North America. One proposal, used in this account, reduces twenty-four North American subspecies to five. The other proposal is that molecular genetics data supports the theory that the Gray Wolves in eastern North America now classified as the subspecies *lycaon* evolved in North America and not in Eurasia. *Canis lycaon* has been proposed as the name of the Gray Wolf believed to have evolved in North America. Australasian Dingoes *dingo*, which evolved from a primitive dog transported to Australia by Asian seafarers about 4000 years ago, are here considered as a Gray Wolf subspecies. Earlier listed as *C. antarcticus* or *C. familiaris dingo*. Today, the wild Dingo population comprises Dingoes, feral dogs, and hybrids of the two. The two Japanese subspecies of Gray Wolf from Hokkaido (*hattai* Kishida, 1931) and Honshu (*hodophilax* Temminck, 1839) are extinct. Eleven extant subspecies are recognized currently.
Subspecies and Distribution.
C. l. lupus Linnaeus, 1758 – Asia, Europe.
C. l. albus Kerr, 1792 – N Russia.
C. l. arctos Pocock, 1935 – Canadian High Arctic.
C. l. baileyi Nelson & Goldman, 1929 – Mexico, SW USA (extinct in the wild).
C. l. communis Dwigubski, 1804 – C Russia.
C. l. cubanensis Ognev, 1923 – E-C Asia.
C. l. dingo Meyer, 1793 – SE Asia and Australasia.
C. l. lycaon Schreber, 1775 – SE Canada, NE USA.
C. l. nubilus Say, 1823 – E-C Canada and C USA.
C. l. occidentalis Richardson, 1829 – Alaska, NW Canada.
C. l. pallipes Sykes, 1831 – Middle East and SW Asia to India.
Descriptive notes. Head-body 100–130 cm for males and 87–117 cm for females, tail 40–52 cm for males and 35–50 cm for females. The Gray Wolf is the largest wild canid, weighing up to 62 kg. The general appearance and proportions are not unlike those of a large German Shepherd dog, except the legs are longer, feet larger, ears shorter, the eyes are slanted, the tail is curled, the winter fur is longer and bushier, and the Wolf has chin tufts in winter. The fur is thick and usually mottled gray, but can vary from nearly pure white, red, or brown to black. Dental formula I 3/3, C 1/1, PM 4/4, M 2/3 = 42.
Habitat. All northern habitats where there is suitable food, with highest densities where prey biomass is highest. In west Asia and north-east Africa present in very arid environments. Dingoes are found in all habitats from tropical alpine moorlands to tropical wetlands and forests to arid hot deserts.
Food and Feeding. Extremely variable, but main prey consists of large ungulates (Moose *Alces* sp., Reindeer *Rangifer tarandus*, deer, Wild Boar *Sus scrophra*, etc.). Gray Wolves will also eat smaller prey items, livestock, carrion, and garbage. In winter, they hunt in packs, but in summer they hunt singly, in pairs, or in small groups. Chases ranging from 100 m to more than 5 km are the rule. Generally Gray Wolves end up with, or tend to select, older individuals, juveniles (under 1 year) or debilitated animals, or those in otherwise poor condition. Average daily food consumption varies from 2·5–6·3 kg or more per day, and kill rates vary accordingly. Wolves first attack the rump of larger prey, but the head, shoulders, flanks, or rump of smaller prey. Usually they eat most of the carcass, leaving only the larger bones and chunks of hide. When there is surplus food, wolves will cache either regurgitated chunks or large pieces. Dingoes, eat a diverse range of prey types and over 170 species have been identified ranging from insects to buffalo, with the main prey in Australia composed of magpie geese (*Anseranas semipalmata*), Agile Wallabies (*Macropus agilis*), Red Kangaroos (*Macropus rufus*); Wallaroos (*Macropus robustus*), wallabies (*Wallabia bicolor, Macropus rufogriseus*), possums (*Trichosurus vulpecula, Pseudocheirus peregrinus*), Common Wombats (*Vombatus ursinus*), European Rabbits (*Oryctolagus cuniculus*), rodents (*Rattus villosisimus, R. colletti, Mus musculus*) and lizards (*Ctenophorus nuchalis*). In Asia, Dingoes live commensally with humans in most regions and their main food items are rice, fruit, and other table scraps provided by people or scavenged.
Activity patterns. Mostly nocturnal or crepuscular, but activity periods may extend well into daylight hours in areas where they are free from persecution. Predominantly diurnal in the Arctic summer.
Movements, Home range and Social organization. Gray Wolves live in packs, which mostly comprise family groups. The dominant pair breeds, and other maturing females are reproductively suppressed unless food is abundant. Packs may include up to 36 individuals, but smaller size packs (5–12) are more common. They occupy territories of 75–2500 km² depending on prey density. Territories are maintained by howling, scent marking, and direct killing. Dingoes are usually seen alone, but when undisturbed most individuals belong to discrete and stable packs of 3–12 Dingoes occupy territories throughout the year. The largest recorded home ranges (90–300 km²) occur in the deserts of south-western Australia. Elsewhere they range from 10–113 km². Some Dingoes disperse, especially young males; the longest recorded distance for a tagged Dingo is about 250 km.
Breeding. Mating takes place from January to April, depending on latitude. Gestation is nine weeks. Dens are in holes, caves, pits, hollow logs, protruding tree roots or fallen trees. Litter size is 1–11 (mean 6). Duration of lactation is 8–10 weeks. Age at sexual maturity is 22–46 months, occasionally ten months. Dingoes breed once each year, with litters of 1–10 (mean 5) usually whelped in winter (May to July). Pups usually become independent at 3–6 months.
Status and Conservation. CITES Appendix II, except populations from Bhutan, India, Nepal, and Pakistan, which are listed on Appendix I. Classified as Least Concern on *The IUCN Red List*. Current legal protection varies from well enforced and complete protection to concerted efforts to control certain populations. Because of the diversity in climate, topography, vegetation, human settlement, and development of the Wolf's range, Gray Wolf populations in various parts of the original range vary from extinct to relatively pristine. Population densities vary from approximately 0·08 to 0·008 individuals per km². Population status is fully viable across Canada and Alaska, but Gray Wolves have been extinct in Newfoundland since 1911. Threatened in Greenland (Denmark). Endangered in north-west USA, and viable, increasing or reintroduced in other USA range states. Highly endangered in Mexico. Rare and threatened to fully viable in Europe, stable to fully viable in north and Central Asia, highly endangered to viable/declining in the Middle East, and declining to endangered in southern Asia. Dingoes are listed as Vulnerable on *The IUCN Red List*, but are considered a pest throughout much of the remaining range. The Gray Wolf's original worldwide range has been reduced by about one-third, primarily in developed areas of Europe, Asia, Mexico, and the USA, by poisoning and deliberate persecution due to predation on livestock. Since about 1970, legal protection, land-use changes, and rural human population shifts to cities have arrested Gray Wolf population declines and fostered natural recolonization in parts of Western Europe and the USA, and reintroduction in the western USA. Continued threats include competition with humans for livestock, especially in developing countries, exaggerated fears by the public concerning the threat and danger of wolves, and fragmentation of habitat, with resulting areas becoming too small to maintain viable populations in the long term.

Bibliography. Boitani (1995), Carbyn *et al*. (1995), Corbett (1995, 2004), Corbett & Newsome (1987), Daniels & Corbett (2003), Fuller (1989), Harrington & Paquet (1982), Koler-Matznick *et al*. (2000), Mech (1970, 1974, 2002), Mech & Boitani (2003, 2004), Mech *et al*. (1998), Nowak (1995), Wilson *et al*. (2000), Young & Goldman (1944).

2

3

ssp *latrans*

ssp *texensis*

4

5

6

7

PLATE 22

inches 16

cm 40

2. Red Wolf *Canis rufus*

French: Loup roux / **German**: Rotwolf / **Spanish**: Lobo rojo

Taxonomy. *Canis rufus* Audubon & Bachman, 1851, Texas, USA.
The taxonomic status of the Red Wolf has been debated widely. Recent genetic and morphological evidence suggests the Red Wolf is a unique taxon, and not a hybrid of Gray Wolf and Coyote, as previously suggested. Three subspecies were initially recognized: *rufus* (Audubon & Bachman, 1851), *gregoryi* (Goldman, 1937), and *floridanus* (Miller, 1912), of which only one, *gregoryi*, is believed to have survived. Genetic methodologies have not been applied to sub-specific designation, and current disagreement about the relatedness of wolves in eastern North America, if resolved, may alter currently accepted subspecific classification of *C. rufus*.

Distribution. Red Wolves exist only as a reintroduced population in E North Carolina, USA.

Descriptive notes. Head-body 104–125 cm for males and 99–120·1 cm for females, tail 33–46 cm for males and 29·5–44 cm for females; weight 22–34·1 kg for males and 20·1–29·7 kg for females. Generally appears long-legged and rangy with proportionately large ears. Intermediate in size between the Coyote and the Gray Wolf. The Red Wolf's almond-shaped eyes, broad muzzle, and wide nose pad contribute to its wolf-like appearance. The muzzle tends to be very pale in color with an area of white around the lips extending up the sides of the muzzle. Coloration is typically brownish or cinnamon with gray and black shading on the back and tail. A black phase occurred historically but is probably extinct. The dental formula is I 3/3, C 1/1, PM 4/4, M 2/3 = 42.

Habitat. Very little is known about Red Wolf habitat because the species' range was severely reduced by the time scientific investigations began. Given their wide historical distribution, Red Wolves probably utilized a large suite of habitat types at one time. The last naturally occurring population utilized the coastal prairie marshes of south-western Louisiana and south-eastern Texas. However, many agree that this environment probably does not typify preferred Red Wolf habitat. There is evidence that the species was found in highest numbers in the once extensive bottomland river forests and swamps of the South-east. Red wolves reintroduced into North Carolina, and their descendants, have made extensive use of habitat types ranging from agricultural lands to pocosins, which are forest/wetland mosaics with an understory of evergreen shrubs. This suggests that Red Wolves are habitat generalists and can thrive in most settings where prey populations are adequate and persecution by humans is slight. This generalization is supported by one study in which low human density, wetland soil type, and distance from roads were the most important predictors of potential wolf habitat in North Carolina.

Food and Feeding. Mammals such as Coypu (*Myocastor coypus*), rabbits (*Sylvilagus* spp.), and rodents (*Sigmodon hispidus*, *Oryzomys palustris*, *Ondatra zibethicus*) are common in south-eastern Texas and appear to have been the primary prey of Red Wolves historically. Presently in North Carolina, White-tailed Deer (*Odocoileus virginianus*), Northern Raccoons, and rabbits are the primary prey species for the reintroduced population (86% of the diet). While it is not uncommon for Red Wolves to forage individually, there is also evidence of group hunting by pack members. Also, resource partitioning among members of a pack sometimes occurs. In one study of pack feeding, rodents were consumed more by juveniles than adults, and use of rodents diminished as the young wolves matured.

Activity patterns. Mostly nocturnal with crepuscular peaks of activity. Hunting usually occurs at night or at dawn and dusk.

Movements, Home range and Social organization. Red Wolves normally live in extended family units or packs, typically including a dominant breeding pair and their offspring from previous years. Dispersal of offspring tends to occur before individuals reach two years of age. Group size in the reintroduced population ranges from a single breeding pair to twelve individuals. Red Wolves are territorial, and like other canids, appear to scent-mark boundaries to exclude non-group members from their territory. Home range size (46–226 km²) varies with habitat availability.

Breeding. Red Wolves typically reach sexual maturity by 22 months of age, though breeding at ten months may occur. Mating usually takes place between February and March, gestation lasting 61–63 days. Peak whelping dates occur from mid-April to mid-May, producing litters of 1–10 pups. In a given year, a dominant pair produces one litter per pack. During the denning season, pregnant females may establish several dens. Some dens are shallow surface depressions located in dense vegetation for shelter at locations where the water table is high; other dens are deep burrows, often in windrows between agricultural fields or in canal banks. Dens have also been found in the hollowed out bases of large trees. Pups are often moved from one den to another before leaving the den altogether, and den attendance by male and female yearlings and adult pack members is common.

Status and Conservation. CITES not listed. Classified as Critically Endangered on *The IUCN Red List*. Extinct in the Wild by 1980, the Red Wolf was reintroduced by the US Fish and Wildlife Service in 1987 into eastern North Carolina. The Red Wolf is now common within the reintroduction area of roughly 6000 km². However, the species' abundance outside this area is unknown. Hybridization with Coyotes or Red Wolf/ Coyote hybrids is the primary threat to the species' persistence in the wild. While hybridization with Coyotes was a factor in the Red Wolf's initial demise in the wild, it was not detected as a problem in North Carolina until approximately 1992. Indeed, the region was determined to be ideal for Red Wolf reintroductions because of a purported absence of Coyotes. However, during the 1990s the Coyote population apparently became well established in the area. In the absence of hybridization, recovery of the Red Wolf and subsequent removal of the species from the USA Endangered Species List is deemed possible. It is noteworthy that similar hybridization has been observed in the population of suspected Red Wolf-type wolves in Algonquin Provincial Park, Ontario, Canada. If these wolves are ultimately shown to be Red Wolf-type wolves, this will enhance the conservation status of the species and nearly triple the known number of Red Wolf-type wolves surviving in the wild. Human-induced mortality (vehicles and gunshot) can be significant. However, the threat this represents to the population is unclear. Most vehicle deaths occurred early in the reintroduction and were likely due to naive animals.

Bibliography. Carley (1975), Goldman (1937), Hahn (2002), Kelly (2000), Kelly, Beyer & Phillips (2004), Kelly, Miller & Seal (1999), Nowak (1979, 2002), Paradiso & Nowak (1971, 1972), Parker (1986), Phillips & Henry (1992), Phillips, Henry & Kelly (2003), Phillips, Smith *et al.* (1995), Riley & McBride (1972), Shaw (1975), US Fish & Wildlife Service (1990), Wilson & Reeder (2005).

3. Coyote *Canis latrans*

French: Coyote / **German**: Kojote / **Spanish**: Coyote
Other common names: Brush Wolf, Prairie Wolf

Taxonomy. *Canis latrans* Say, 1823, Nebraska, USA.
The ancestral Coyote, *C. lepophagus*, is believed to have become widespread throughout North America by the late Pliocene. In the north-eastern USA, the eastern Coyote may be a subspecies with some introgression of wolf and dog genes. Nineteen subspecies have been recognized. However, the taxonomic validity of some subspecies is questionable.

Subspecies and Distribution.
C. l. latrans Say, 1823 – S Canada and USA (Great Plains region).
C. l. cagottis Hamilton-Smith, 1839 – SE Mexico.
C. l. clepticus Elliot, 1903 – Mexico (N Baja California) and USA (S California).
C. l. dickeyi Nelson, 1932 – Costa Rica, El Salvador, W Honduras, Nicaragua, and Panama.
C. l. frustror Woodhouse, 1850 – USA (Missouri, Kansas, parts of Oklahoma & E Texas).
C. l. goldmani Merriam, 1904 – Belize, Guatemala, and S Mexico.
C. l. hondurensis Goldman, 1936 – E Honduras.
C. l. impavidus J. A. Allen, 1903 – W Mexico.
C. l. incolatus Hall, 1934 – Alaska and NW Canada.
C. l. jamesi Townsend, 1912 – Mexico (Tiburon I, Baja California).
C. l. lestes Merriam, 1897 – SW Canada and W USA (Intermountain Region & NW).
C. l. mearnsi Merriam, 1897 – NW Mexico and SW USA.
C. l. microdon Merriam, 1897 – NE Mexico and S USA (S Texas).
C. l. ochropus Eschscholtz, 1829 – W USA (W coast).
C. l. peninsulae Merriam, 1897 – Mexico (S Baja California).
C. l. texensis Bailey, 1905 – S USA (W Texas & New Mexico).
C. l. thamnos Jackson, 1949 – N-C Canada and E USA.
C. l. umpquensis Jackson, 1949 – USA (NW coast).
C. l. vigilis Merriam, 1897 – SW Mexico.
Coyotes did not originally occur on the USA E coast or Florida. They (probably *thamnos*) have expanded into the area with the clearing of forests and been introduced to Florida and Georgia (subspecies unknown).

Descriptive notes. Head-body 74–94 cm for males and 74–94 cm for females, tail 29–36·3 cm for males and 26–34·3 cm for females; weight 7·8–15·8 kg for males and 7·7–14·5 kg for females. Slender appearance with a long, pointed nose, large pointed ears, slender legs with small feet, and a bushy tail. Size varies geographically, although adult males are heavier and larger than adult females. Coyotes range in color from pure gray to rufous; melanistic Coyotes are rare. Fur texture and color varies geographically: northern subspecies have long coarse hair. Coyotes in the desert tend to be fulvous in color, while Coyotes at higher latitudes are darker and grayer. The belly and throat are paler than the rest of the body and have a mantle of darker hair over the shoulders. The tip of the tail is usually black. Hairs are about 50–90 mm long, mane hairs tend to be 80–110 mm long. Pelage during summer is shorter than in winter. The dental formula is I 3/3, C 1/1, PM 4/4, M 2/3 = 42.

Habitat. Coyotes utilize almost all available habitats throughout their range including prairie, forest, desert, mountain, and tropical ecosystems. Their ability to exploit human resources also allows them to occupy urban areas. Water availability may limit distribution in some desert environments.

Food and Feeding. Opportunistic, generalist predators that eat a wide variety of food items, ranging from fruit and insects to small mammals to large ungulates and live-

On following pages: 4. Ethiopian Wolf (*Canis simensis*); 5. Golden Jackal (*Canis aureus*); 6. Side-striped Jackal (*Canis adustus*); 7. Black-backed Jackal (*Canis mesomelas*).

stock, typically consuming items in relation to availability. Livestock and wild ungulates are often consumed as carrion, but predation on large ungulates (native and domestic) does occur. Predation on neonates of native ungulates can be high during fawning. Coyotes in suburban areas are adept at exploiting human-made food resources and will readily consume refuse, pet food or other human-related items. Studies of predatory behavior show that Coyote age, habitat, and wind and snow conditions all influence their ability to capture small mammals. Coyotes hunt small mammals alone, even when pack size is large. When preying on native ungulates, cooperation among pack members may facilitate the capture of prey, but is not essential. Environmental factors are important to the success of an attack on adult ungulates, as is the presence of the alpha Coyote pair, and younger animals generally do not participate. The number of Coyotes is not as important as which individuals are involved in the attack. The outcome is also affected by the ability of the quarry to escape into water, its defensive abilities, and its nutritional state. In areas with an ungulate prey base in winter, competition with other sympatric carnivores for a carcass may be intense and there can even be competition among members of the same pack.

Activity patterns. Coyotes may be active throughout the day, but they tend to be more active during the early morning and around sunset. Activity patterns change seasonally (e.g. during winter, when there is a change in the food base in some areas) or in response to human disturbance and persecution.

Movements, Home range and Social organization. The basic social unit is the bonded alpha pair, which may breed for up to 10–12 years. Associate animals often remain in the pack and possibly inherit the pack or displace members of the breeding pair and become alphas themselves. Associates participate in territorial maintenance and pup rearing, but not to the extent of the alpha pair. Other Coyotes exist outside of the resident packs as transient or nomadic individuals. Transients travel alone over larger areas and do not breed, but will move into territories when vacancies occur. One factor that may affect Coyote sociality is prey size or prey biomass. In populations where rodents are the major prey, Coyotes tend to be in pairs or trios. In populations where Elk and deer are available, large packs of up to ten individuals may form. Coyotes are territorial, with a dominance hierarchy within each resident pack. The dominance hierarchy influences access to food resources within the pack. In captivity, pups show early development of aggressive behavior and engage in dominance fights when 19–24 days old. The process of establishing hierarchy within litters appears to last up to 4·5 months. Territoriality regulates Coyote numbers as packs space themselves across the landscape in relation to available food and habitat. Home range size varies with energetic requirements, physiographic makeup, habitat, and food distribution. Home range size is influenced by social organization, with transients using larger areas, and residents occupying distinct territories. Only packs (2–10 animals) maintain and defend territories, both by direct confrontation and indirectly with scent marking and howling. Fidelity to the home range is high and may persist for many years. Shifts in territorial boundaries may occur in response to the loss of one or both of the alpha pair. Pups, yearlings, and non-breeding adults of lower social rank may disperse from the natal site into adjacent areas or farther afield. Dispersal seems to be voluntary, as social and nutritional pressures intensify during winter when food becomes limited. Juveniles usually disperse during autumn and early winter. Pre-dispersal forays may occur. Coyotes communicate using auditory, visual, olfactory, and tactile cues. Studies have identified different types of vocalizations, seasonal patterns, and the influence of social status on vocalization rates. Howling plays a role in territorial maintenance and pack spacing by advertising boundaries and signaling the presence of alpha animals that will confront intruders and defend the territory. Scent marking contributes to territory maintenance and is performed mostly by alpha individuals. Scent marking may also be an indicator of sexual condition, maturity, or synchrony.

Breeding. Both males and females show annual cyclic changes in reproductive anatomy and physiology. Females are seasonally monoestrous, showing one period of estrus per year between January and March, depending on latitude. Courtship behavior begins 2–3 months before copulation. Copulation ends with a copulatory tie lasting up to 25 minutes. The percentage of females breeding each year varies with local conditions and food supply. Usually, about 60–90% of adult females and up to 70% of female yearlings produce litters. Gestation lasts approximately 63 days. Litter size averages six (range 1–9) and may be affected by population density and food availability during the previous winter. In northern latitudes, litter size changes in response to population cycles in Snowshoe Hares (*Lepus americanus*). Litter size has been found to increase after cold, snowy winters, when more ungulate carcasses are available to ovulating females. Coyotes may den in brush-covered slopes, steep banks, under rock ledges, thickets, and hollow logs. Dens of other animals may also be used, and may have more than one entrance and interconnecting tunnels. The same den may be used from year to year. Denning and pup rearing are the focal point of Coyote families for several months, until the pups are large and mobile. Pups are born blind and helpless in the den. Birth weight is 240–275 g. Their eyes open at about 14 days and they emerge from the den at about three weeks. The young are cared for by the parents and other associates, usually siblings from a previous year. Pups are weaned at about 5–7 weeks of age and reach adult weight by about nine months.

Status and Conservation. CITES not listed. Classified as Least Concern on *The IUCN Red List*. Coyotes are abundant throughout their range, which may be expanding due to their ability to successfully live in human-modified landscapes. Elimination of Wolves may also have facilitated Coyote expansion. Density varies geographically with food and climate, and seasonally due to mortality, changes in pack structure, predator density and food abundance. Coyotes are considered a pest species in many regions. Control programs temporarily reduce numbers on a short-term basis, but Coyote populations are generally stable in most areas and free of threats throughout their range. Conservation measures have not been needed to maintain viable populations. Coyotes adapt to human environments and occupy most developed habitats, including urban and agricultural areas. Hybridization with dogs and Gray Wolves may be occurring in some areas.

Bibliography. Andelt (1985, 1987), Bekoff (1978b), Bekoff & Diamond (1976), Bekoff & Gese (2003), Bekoff & Wells (1986), Bekoff *et al.* (1981), Camenzind (1978), Gese & Bekoff (2004), Gese & Grothe (1995), Gese *et al.* (1996a, 1996b, 1996c), Gier (1968), Kitchen *et al.* (2000a, 2000b), Knowlton *et al.* (1999), Laundré & Keller (1984), O'Donoghue *et al.* (1997), Richens & Hugie (1974), Thurber & Peterson (1991), Todd & Keith (1983), Wayne & Lehman (1992), Young & Jackson (1951).

4. Ethiopian Wolf *Canis simensis*

French: Loup d'Abyssinie / **German**: Äthiopien-Wolf / **Spanish**: Lobo etíope

Other common names: Simien Fox, Simien Jackal, Abyssinian Wolf, Abyssinian Red Fox

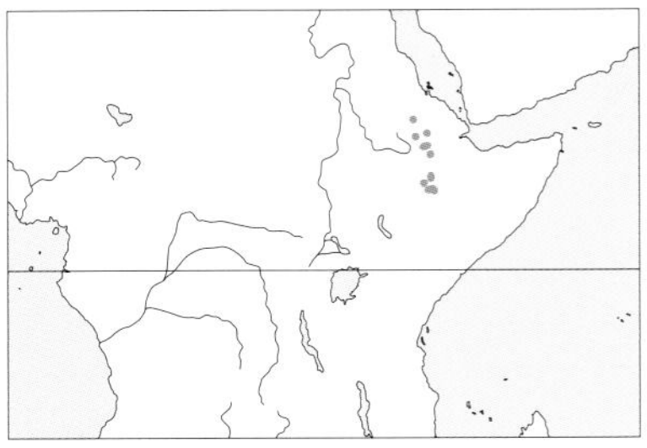

Taxonomy. *Canis simensis* Rüppell, 1835, Ethiopia.

Originally placed in the genus *Simenia*, *C. simensis* was noted to be the most distinct species in the genus *Canis*, and was considered to bear close affinity to *C. adustus* and *Dusicyon* spp. The Ethiopian Wolf is not closely linked to the *Vulpes* group, despite having been called the Simien or Simenian Fox. Its other name of Simien or Ethiopian Jackal suggests a close relationship with jackals. Other, previously used vernacular names included Abyssinian Wolf and Red Fox, making clear the difficulty naturalists had in cataloguing this species. Phylogenetic analysis using mitochondrial DNA sequencing suggested that *C. simensis* is more closely related to *C. lupus* and *C. latrans* than to any African canid, and that the species may have evolved from a Wolf-like ancestor crossing to northern Africa from Eurasia as recently as 100,000 years ago. There are fossils of wolf-like canids from the late Pleistocene in Eurasia, but unfortunately no fossil record of *C. simensis* itself. Microsatellite and mitochondrial DNA variability in *C. simensis* is small relative to other canid species, suggesting small population sizes may have characterized its recent evolution. Two subspecies are recognized.

Subspecies and Distribution.

C. s. simensis Rüppell, 1835 – NW of Ethiopia's Rift Valley.

C. s. citernii de Beaux, 1922 – SE of Ethiopia's Rift Valley.

Descriptive notes. Head-body 92·8–101·2 cm for males and 84·1–96 cm for females, tail 29–39·6 cm for males and 27–29·7 cm for females; weight 14·2–19·3 kg for males and 11·2–14·2 kg for females. A medium-sized canid with a reddish coat, distinctive white markings, long legs, and an elongated muzzle, resembling a Coyote in conformation and size. Males weigh 20% more than females. The face, ears and upper parts of the muzzle are red. Ears broad, pointed, and directed forward; the pinnae are thickly fringed with long white hairs growing inward from the edge. Palate, gums, and naked borders of the lips entirely black. Characteristic facial markings include a white ascending crescent below the eyes, and a small white spot on the cheeks. The throat, chest, and underparts are white, the ventral part of the neck with a distinctive white band. Pelage is soft and short, ocher to rusty red, with a dense whitish to pale ginger underfur. The boundary between the red coat and the white markings is sharp and well defined. The contrast of white markings against the red coat increases with age and social rank in both sexes; the female's coat is generally paler than the male's. The long, slender legs are reddish outside, with inner aspect white. There is a short rufous colored stripe at the base of the tail, which becomes a black stripe leading to a thick brush of black-tipped guard hairs. The skull is very flat in profile, with only a shallow angle between frontals and nasals. The neuro-cranium is low and narrow, thick, and almost cylindrical. Its width is 30% of the total skull length. Facial length is 58% of the total skull length. The inter-parietal crest is slightly developed, and the coronal ridge is linear. Teeth small and widely spaced, especially the premolars. The dental formula is I 3/3, C 1/1, PM 4/4, M 2/3 = 42; m3 occasionally absent. Sharply pointed canines average 19 mm in length (14–22 mm); carnassials (P^4 and M_1) are relatively small.

Habitat. A very localized endemic species, confined to isolated pockets of Afro-alpine grasslands and heath lands, where they prey on Afro-alpine rodents. Suitable habitats are above the tree-line, from about 3200 to 4500 m, with some wolves present in montane grasslands at 3000 m. However, subsistence agriculture extends up to 3500–3800 m in many areas, restricting the wolves to higher ranges. Rainfall at high altitude varies between 1000 and 2000 mm/year, with one pronounced dry period from December to February/March. Wolves utilize all Afro-alpine habitats, but prefer open areas with short herbaceous and grassland communities where rodents are most abundant, along flat or gently sloping areas with deep soils and poor drainage in parts. Prime habitats in the Bale Mountains are characterized by short herbs (*Alchemilla* spp.) and grasses, and low vegetation cover, a community maintained in continuous succession as a result of Ethiopian African Mole Rat (*Tachyoryctes macrocephalus*) burrowing activity. Other good habitats include tussock grasslands (*Festuca* spp., *Agrostis* spp.), high-altitude shrubs dominated by *Helichrysum* spp., and short grasslands in shallow soils. In northern parts of the range, plant communities characterized by a matrix of "*guassa*" tussock grasses (*Festuca* spp.), "*cherenfi*" bushes (*Euryops pinifolius*) and giant lobelias (*Lobelia rhynchopetalum*) sustain high rodent abundance and are preferred by wolves. Ericaceous moorlands (*Erica* and *Phillipia* spp.) at 3200–3600 m are of marginal value, whereas open moorlands containing patches of herbs and grasses offer relatively good habitat.

Food and Feeding. Ethiopian Wolves feed almost exclusively upon diurnal rodents of the high-altitude Afro-alpine grassland community. In the Bale Mountains, diurnal rodents accounted for 96% of all prey occurrences in feces, with 87% belonging to three Bale endemic species: the Ethiopian African Mole Rat (300–930 g), Blick's Grass Rat (*Arvicanthis blicki*), and the Black-clawed Brush-furred Rat (*Lophuromys melanonyx*). Other prey species include the Ethiopian Vlei Rat (*Otomys typus*), Ethiopian Buff-spotted Brush-furred Rat (*Lophuromys flavopunctatus*), Ethiopian Highland Hare (*Lepus starcki*), and occasionally goslings and eggs. On occasion, wolves were observed feeding on Rock Hyrax (*Procavia capensis*), and young of Bush Duiker (*Sylvicapra grimmia*), Common Reedbuck (*Redunca redunca*), and Mountain Nyala (*Tragelaphus buxtoni*). Sedge leaves (*Carex monostachya*) are occasionally ingested, probably to assist digestion or control parasites. Where the Ethiopian African Mole Rat is absent (i.e. *Gaysay* montane grassland in Bale and Menz), it is replaced in the wolf diet by the smaller Northeast African Mole Rat (*Tachyoryctes splendens*). Similarly, in northern Ethiopia *Arvicanthis abyssinicus* and *Lophuromys flavopunctatus* replace their respective endemic relatives (*A. blicki* and *L. melanonyx*) from Bale. Elsewhere, *O. typus*, a rare prey item in Bale and Menz, was identified as the commonest prey in droppings collected in the other five populations. The same study confirmed that wolves are specialized hunters of diurnal rodents throughout their distribution, but that there is also some degree of variation in diet composition along climatic-induced gradients. Although the Ethiopian Wolf is primarily a solitary rodent hunter, it can also hunt cooperatively. Occasionally, small packs have been seen chasing young antelopes, lambs, and hares and making kills. Ethiopian Wolves will take carrion or feed on carcasses; in fact, a sheep carcass is the most successful bait for attracting wolves. The local name "jedalla farda"—the horse's jackal—refers to wolves' habit of following mares and cows about to give birth so they can eat the afterbirth. In areas of grazing in Bale, wolves were often seen foraging among herds of cattle, a tactic that may aid in ambushing rodents out of their holes, by using the herd as a mobile hide. Wolves carefully explore rich food patches by walking slowly and pausing frequently to investigate holes or to localize the rodents by means of their excellent hearing. Once the prey is located they move with short, stealthy steps alternating with short periods of immobility, sometimes with belly pressed flat to the ground. The quarry is grabbed with the mouth after a short dash. A stalk can last from seconds to up to an hour, especially if the quarry is an Ethiopian African Mole Rat. Occasionally, wolves run in zig-zag through rat colonies, grabbing the rodents in passing. Digging prey out is common and is the favored technique to catch Ethiopian African Mole Rats. In such cases, hunting effort varies from a few scratches at a rat hole to the total destruction of a set of burrows, leaving mounds of earth often up to one meter high. Sometimes, digging serves to reach a nest of grass rats. Kills are often cached and later retrieved.

Activity patterns. In Bale, wolves are mostly diurnal. Packs congregate for social greetings and border patrols at dawn, around midday and in the evening, and rest together at night, but break up to forage individually in the morning and early afternoon. Peaks of foraging activity suggest a synchronization with the aboveground activity of rodents. There is little nocturnal activity, wolves seldom moving far from their evening resting site. They may become more crepuscular and nocturnal where human interference is severe.

Movements, Home range and Social organization. Ethiopian Wolves live in packs of 3–13 adults, in discrete and cohesive social units that share and defend an exclusive territory. Annual home ranges of eight packs monitored for four years averaged 6 km², with some overlap. Home ranges in an area of lower prey biomass averaged 13·4 km² (n = 4). Overlap and aggressive encounters between packs were highest during the mating season. Dispersal movements are tightly constrained by the scarcity of suitable habitat. Males do not disperse and are recruited into multi-male philopatric packs; some females disperse at two years of age and become "floaters", occupying narrow ranges between pack territories until a breeding vacancy becomes available. Breeding females are typically replaced after death by a resident daughter. Pack adult sex ratio is biased toward males 1·8:1, with small family groups closer to 1:1. Wolves commonly advertize and maintain their territories by scent marking territory boundaries with urine posts, scratching, feces (deposited on conspicuous sites like mounds, rocks, and bushes), and by means of vocalizations. All pack members, independent of social rank, regularly scent-mark objects along territory boundaries with raised-leg urinations and scratches. Aggressive interactions with neighboring packs are common, highly vocal, and always end with the smaller group fleeing from the larger. Vocalizations can be grouped into two categories: alarm calls, given at the scent or sight of humans, dogs, or unfamiliar wolves; and greeting calls, given at the reunion of pack members and to advertize pack size, composition, and position. Alarm calls start with a "huff" (rapid expulsion of air through mouth and nose), followed by a quick succession of high-pitched yelps and barks. These sounds can also be made as contact calls, and often attract nearby pack mates. Greeting calls include a threatening growl, a high-frequency whine of submission, and intense "group yip-howls". Lone and group howling are long-distance calls used to contact pack members, and can be heard up to 5 km away. Howling by one pack of wolves may stimulate howling in adjacent packs. Communal calls muster pack members before a border patrol.

Breeding. The only detailed information available on the reproductive habits of these animals comes from four years of observations of nine wild packs in the Bale Mountains. Pre-copulatory behavior by the dominant female includes an increased rate of scent marking, play-inducing and food-begging behavior towards the dominant male, and agonistic behavior towards subordinate females. The receptive period is synchronized in sympatric females to less than two weeks. Courtship may take place between adult members of a pack or with members of neighboring packs. After a brief courtship, which primarily involves the dominant male permanently accompanying the female, wolves copulate over a period of three to five days. Copulation involves a copulatory tie lasting up to 15 minutes. Other males may stand by a tied pair with no signs of aggression. Females exert mate preference, discouraging mating attempts from all but the pack's dominant male, either by defensive snarls or moving away. Females are receptive to any visiting male from neighboring packs, and one study found that 70% of matings (n = 30) involved males from outside the pack. The dominant female of each pack gives birth once a year between October and January. Only about 60% of females breed successfully each year. During breeding and pregnancy, the female coat turns pale yellow and becomes woolly, and the tail turns brownish, and loses much of its hair. Gestation lasts 60–62 days (based on the time from last day of mating to parturition). Pups are born in a den dug by the female in open ground, under a boulder or inside a rocky crevice. Neonates are born with their eyes closed. The natal coat is charcoal gray with a buff patch in chest and inguinal regions. Two to seven pups emerge from the den after three weeks. At this time, the dark natal coat begins to be replaced by the pelage typical of the species. Pups are regularly moved between dens up to 1300 m apart. In eight out of 18 observed natal dens, a subordinate female assisted the mother in suckling the pups. At least 50% of extra nursing females showed signs of pregnancy and may have lost or deserted their own offspring before joining the dominant female's den. Five and six placental scars were counted in the uteri of two of these females. Development of the young takes place in three stages: early nesting (weeks 1–4), when the young are entirely dependent on milk; mixed nutritional dependency (weeks 5–10), when milk is supplemented by solid foods regurgitated by all pack members until pups are completely weaned; and post-weaning dependency (week ten to six months), when the pups subsist almost entirely on solid foods supplied by helpers. Adults have been observed providing food to juveniles up to one year old. Juveniles join adults in patrols as early as six months of age, but do not urinate with a raised leg until eleven months, if male, or 18 months, if female. Yearlings attain 80–90% of adult body mass, and full adult appearance is reached at two years. Both sexes become sexually mature during their second year.

Status and Conservation. CITES not listed. Classified as Endangered on *The IUCN Red List*. Full official protection under Ethiopia's Wildlife Conservation Regulations of 1974, Schedule VI. Killing a wolf carries a sentence of imprisonment for up to two years. There is an estimated global population of 500 adults, of which more than half live in the Bale Mountains, where wolf density is high for a social carnivore of its size, ranging from 0·1 adults/km² (ericaceous heath lands and barren peaks) to 1–1·2 adults/km² (short Afro-alpine herbaceous communities). Elsewhere overall wolf density is lower; e.g. transect data from the region of Menz estimated wolf density at 0·2 animals per km². Recent comprehensive surveys indicate high abundance figures in North Wollo (0·20 sightings per km), intermediate in Arsi and Guna (0·10–0·11 and 0·10–0·14, respectively), and lower in South Wollo and Simien (0·08–0·13 and 0·06–0·11, respectively). These results were supported by counts of wolf signs (diggings and droppings) and interviews with local residents. Continuous loss of habitat due to high-altitude subsistence agriculture is the major threat. Sixty percent of all land above 3200 m has been converted into farmland, and all wolf populations below 3700 m are particularly vulnerable to further habitat loss, especially in small and relatively flat areas. Habitat loss is exacerbated by over-grazing of highland pastures by domestic livestock, and in some areas habitat is threatened by proposed development of commercial sheep farms and roads. Human persecution triggered in the past by political instability is currently less severe and is associated with conflicts over livestock losses. Recent wolf population decline in Bale is mostly due to disease epizootics, with road kills and shootings as secondary threats. Rabies is a potential threat to all populations. Most of these threats are exacerbated by the wolves' specialization to life in the Afro-alpine ecosystem. In Bale, the Ethiopian Wolf hybridizes with domestic dogs. Although hybrids are currently confined to the Web Valley in West Bale, they may threaten the genetic integrity of the wolf population. Following hybridization, a population may be affected by outbreeding depression or reduction in fitness, although to date this does not seem to have taken place in Bale. To date there is no indication of hybridization taking place outside West Bale.

Bibliography. Ashenafi *et al.* (2005), Clutton-Brock *et al.* (1976), Gottelli & Sillero-Zubiri (1992), Gottelli, Marino *et al.* (2004), Gottelli, Sillero-Zubiri *et al.* (1994), Haydon, Laurenson & Sillero-Zubiri (2002), Haydon, Randall *et al.* (2006), Marino (2003, 2004), Marino *et al.* (2006), Sillero-Zubiri & Gottelli (1994, 1995a, 1995b), Sillero-Zubiri & Macdonald (1997, 1998), Sillero-Zubiri & Marino (2004), Sillero-Zubiri, Gottelli & Macdonald (1996), Sillero-Zubiri, Johnson & Macdonald (1998), Sillero-Zubiri, King & Macdonald (1996), Sillero-Zubiri, Malcolm *et al.* (2000), Sillero-Zubiri, Tattersall & Macdonald (1995a, 1995b).

5. Golden Jackal *Canis aureus*

French: Chacal doré / **German**: Goldschakal / **Spanish**: Chacal dorado
Other common names: Asiatic Jackal, Common Jackal

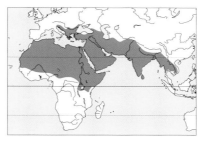

Taxonomy. *Canis aureus* Linnaeus, 1758, Iran.
As many as twelve subspecies are distinguished across the range. However, there is much variation and populations need to be re-evaluated using modern molecular techniques.

Distribution. Widespread in N and NE Africa, occurring from Senegal on the W coast of Africa to Egypt in the E, in a range that includes Morocco, Algeria, Tunisia, and Libya in the N to Nigeria, Chad, and Tanzania in the S. They have expanded their range from the Arabian Peninsula into Western Europe, to Bulgaria, Austria, and NE Italy and E into Turkey, Syria, Iraq, Iran, Central Asia, the entire Indian subcontinent, then E and S to Sri Lanka, Myanmar, Thailand, and parts of Indochina.

Descriptive notes. Head-body 76–84 cm for males and 74–80 cm for females, tail 20–24 cm for males and 20–21 cm for females; weight 7·6–9·8 kg for males and 6·5–7·8 kg for females. Medium-sized canid, considered the most typical representative of the genus *Canis*. Approximately 12% difference in body weight between sexes. Basic coat color is golden but varies seasonally from pale creamy yellow to a dark tawny hue. The pelage on the back is often a mixture of black, brown, and white hairs, giving the appearance of a dark saddle similar to that of Black-backed Jackals. Jackals inhabiting rocky, mountainous terrain may have grayer coats. The belly and underparts are a lighter pale ginger to cream. Unique paler markings on the throat and chest make it possible to differentiate individuals. Melanistic and piebald forms are sometimes reported. The tail is bushy with a tan to black tip. The legs are relatively long, and the feet slender with small pads. Females have four pairs of mammae. The skull is more similar to Coyote and Gray Wolf than to Black-backed Jackal, Side-striped Jackal, or Ethiopian Wolf. The dental formula is I 3/3, C 1/1, PM 4/4, M 2/3 = 42.

Habitat. Tolerance of arid zones and an omnivorous diet enable Golden Jackals to live in a wide variety of habitats. These range from the Sahel to the evergreen forests of Myanmar and Thailand. Golden Jackals occupy semi-desert, short to medium grasslands and savannahs in Africa, and forested, mangrove, agricultural, rural, and semi-urban habitats in India and Bangladesh. Golden Jackals are opportunistic and will venture into human habitation at night to feed on garbage. They have been recorded at elevations of 3800 m in the Bale Mountains of Ethiopia and are well established around hill stations at 2000 m in India.

Food and Feeding. An omnivorous and opportunistic forager, the Golden Jackal's diet varies according to season and habitat. According to one study in east Africa, although they consume invertebrates and fruit, over 60% of Golden Jackal diet consisted of rodents, lizards, snakes, birds (from quail to flamingoes), hares, and Thomson's Gazelle (*Eudorcas thomsoni*). In India, over 60% of the diet comprised rodents, birds, and fruit in Bharatpur, while in Kanha over 80% of the diet consisted of rodents, reptiles, and fruit. In Sariska Tiger Reserve, India, scat analysis (n = 36) revealed that Golden Jackal diet included mainly mammals (45% occurrence, of which 36% was rodents), vegetable matter (20%), birds (19%), and reptiles and invertebrates (8% each). Golden Jackals often ingest large quantities of vegetable matter, and during the fruiting season in India they feed intensively on the fruits of *Ziziphus* sp., *Carissa carvanda*, *Syzigium cuminii*, and pods of *Prosopis juliflora* and *Cassia fistula*. Single jackals typically hunt smaller prey like rodents, hares, and birds. They use their hearing to locate rodents in the grass and then leap in the air and pounce on them; they also dig out Indian Gerbils (*Tatera indica*) from their burrows. They have been observed to hunt young, old, and infirm ungulates that are sometimes 4–5 times their body weight. Although Golden Jackals are able to hunt alone, cooperative hunting in small packs of 2–4 individuals is often more successful and permits them to kill larger prey, including antelope fawns and langur monkeys (*Presbytis pileata* and *P. entellus*). Groups of 5–18 Golden Jackals have been sighted scavenging on carcasses of large ungulates, and there is a report of similar aggregations on clumped food resources in Israel. In several areas of India and Bangladesh, jackals subsist primarily by scavenging on carrion and garbage. They also cache food.

Activity patterns. Golden Jackals are mainly nocturnal, but have flexible activity patterns and may be active during the day. During Blackbuck (*Antilope cervicapra*) calving peaks in Velavadar National Park, India, for example, jackals were observed searching throughout the day for calves in hiding, searches intensifying during the early morning and late evening.

Movements, Home range and Social organization. The social organization of Golden Jackals is extremely flexible and depends on the availability and distribution of food resources. The basic social unit is the breeding pair, which is sometimes accompanied by its current litter of pups and/or by offspring from former litters. In Tanzania breeding pairs usually form long-term bonds, and both members mark and defend their territories, hunt together, share food, and cooperatively rear the young. Of a total of 270 recorded jackal sightings in the Bhal and Kutch areas of Gujarat, India, 35% consisted of two individuals, 14% of three, 20% of more than three, and the rest of single individuals. Average group sizes have been reported as 2·5 (Serengeti, Tanzania) and 3 (Velavadar National Park, India). Scent marking by urination and defecation is common around denning areas and on intensively used trails, and is thought to play an important role in territorial defense. Recent telemetry data from the Bhal area in India suggest that most breeding pairs are spaced well apart and likely maintain a core territory around their dens. Feeding ranges of several Golden Jackals in the Bhal overlapped. Jackals were observed to range over large distances in search of food and suitable habitat, and linear forays of 12–15 km in a single night were not uncommon. Non-breeding members of a pack may stay near a distant food source like a carcass for several days prior to returning to their original range. Recorded home range sizes vary from 1·1–20 km², depending on the distribution and abundance of food resources. Greeting ceremonies, grooming, and group vocalizations are common social interactions. Vocalizations consist of a complex howl repertoire beginning with two to three simple, low-pitched howls and culminating in a high-pitched staccato of calls. Jackals are easily induced to howl. A single howl usually evokes responses from several jackals in the vicinity. In the presence of large carnivores, Golden Jackals often emit a warning call that is very different from their normal howling repertoire. In India, howling is more frequent between December and April, a time when pair bonds are being established and breeding occurs, perhaps suggesting a role in mate attraction, mate guarding, or territory defense.

Breeding. Reproductive activity occurs from February to March in India and Turkmenistan, and from October to March in Israel. In Tanzania, mating typically occurs from October to December, with pups being born from December to March. Timing of births coincides with abundance of food supply; for example, at the beginning of the monsoon season in northern and central India, and with the calving of Thomson's Gazelle in the Serengeti. Females are typically monoestrous, but there is evidence in Tanzania of multiple litters. Gestation lasts about 63 days. Mean litter size has been recorded as 5·7 (range 1–8) in Tanzania. In the Bhal area in India average litter size was 3·6 (range 2–5). In Tanzania, two pups on average have been recorded emerging from the den at three weeks of age. Golden Jackals in India excavate their dens in late April to May, mainly in natural and man-made embankments, usually in scrub habitat. Rivulets, gullies, road and check-dam embankments are prime denning habitats, and drainage pipes and culverts are also used. Dens may have 1–3 openings and typically are about 2–3 m long and 0·5–1 m deep. In Tanzania both parents and "helpers" (offspring from previous litters) provision and guard the new pups, which results in higher pup survival. The male also feeds his mate during her pregnancy, and both the male and "helpers" (i.e. other social group members) provision the female during the period of lactation.

Status and Conservation. CITES Appendix II (India). Classified as Least Concern on *The IUCN Red List*. Jackals are on Schedule III of India's Wildlife Protection Act (1972) and are afforded the least legal protection (mainly to control trade of pelts and tails). However, no hunting of any wildlife is permitted under the current legal system in India. Fairly common throughout its range, although considered to be steadily declining except in protected areas. High densities are observed in areas with abundant food and cover. Known density estimates for parts of India enable a minimum population estimate of over 80,000 Golden Jackals for the Indian sub-continent. Population estimates for Africa are not available, but densities in the Serengeti National Park have been recorded as high as 4 adults/km². Traditional land use practices such as livestock rearing and dry farming are conducive to the survival of jackals and other wildlife but are being steadily replaced by industrialization and intensive agriculture; similarly wilderness areas and rural landscapes are being rapidly urbanized. Jackal population adapt to some extent to these changes and may persist for a while, but will eventually disappear from such areas. There are no other known threats, except for local policies of extirpation and poisoning.

Bibliography. Coetzee (1977), Fuller *et al.* (1989), Genov & Wassiley (1989), Golani & Keller (1975), Golani & Mendelssohn (1971), Jaeger *et al.* (1996), Jerdon (1874), Jhala & Moehlman (2004), Kingdon (1971-1982), Kruuk (1972), van Lawick & van Lawick-Goodall (1970), Macdonald (1979a), Moehlman (1983, 1986, 1989), Moehlman & Hofer (1997), Mukherjee (1998b), Newton (1985), Poche *et al.* (1987), Prater (1980), Rosevear (1974), Sankar (1988), Schaller (1967), Sillero-Zubiri (1996), Stanford (1989).

6. Side-striped Jackal *Canis adustus*

French: Chacal rayé / **German**: Streifenschakal / **Spanish**: Chacal rayado

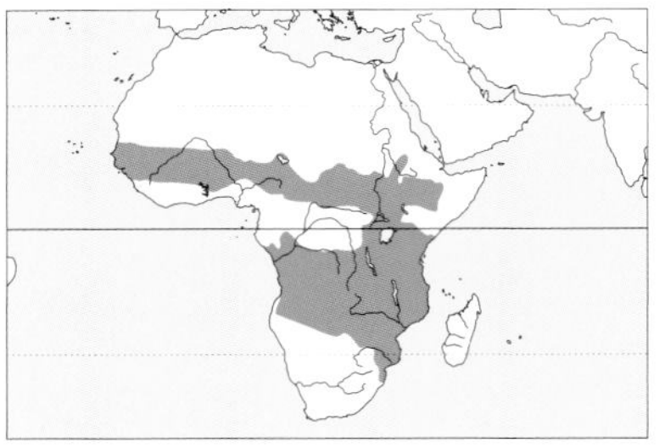

Taxonomy. *Canis adustus* Sundevall, 1847, South Africa.

Concensus is lacking regarding number of subspecies, variously given as between three and seven. Many authorities have pointed out that, as with the Black-backed Jackal, subspecies are hard to distinguish and the differences may be a consequence of individual variation.

Distribution. W, C and S Africa; replaced in the arid SW and NW of the continent by the Black-backed Jackal and in N Africa by the Golden Jackal.

Descriptive notes. Head-body 65·5–77·5 cm for males and 69–76 cm for females, tail 30·5–39 cm for males and 31–41 cm for females; weight 7·3–12 kg for males and 7·3–10 kg for females. Medium-sized canid, overall gray to buff-gray in color, with a white side stripe blazed on the flanks, and a diagnostic white tip to the tail. Head is gray-buffy, ears dark buffy. The back is gray, darker than the underside, and the flanks are marked by the indistinct white stripes running from elbow to hip, with black lower margins. The boldness of markings, in particular the side stripes, varies greatly among individuals; those of juveniles are less well defined than those of adults. The legs are often rufous-tinged, and the predominantly black tail nearly always bears the distinctive white tip, possibly a "badge" of the species' nocturnal status. The female has two pairs of inguinal teats. Skull flatter than that of Black-backed Jackal, with a longer and narrower rostrum, a distinct sagittal crest, and zygomatic arches of lighter build. As a result of the elongation of the rostrum, the third upper premolar lies almost in line with the others and not at an angle as in the Black-backed Jackal. The dental formula is I 3/3, C 1/1, PM 4/4, M 2/3 = 42.

Habitat. Occupies a range of habitats, including broad-leaved savannah zones, wooded habitats, bush, grassland, marshes, montane habitats up to 2700 m, abandoned cultivation and farms. Tends to avoid open savannah, thickly wooded areas, and arid zones, but does enter the equatorial forest belt in the wake of human settlement. Side-striped Jackals frequently occur near rural dwellings and farm buildings, and penetrate suburban and urban areas. Where Side-striped Jackals occur sympatrically with Golden and Black-backed Jackals, they may avoid competition by ecological segregation. In such areas of sympatry, Side-striped Jackals usually occupy areas of denser vegetation, and Black-backed and Golden Jackals dominate in the more open areas.

Food and Feeding. Omnivorous, with a diet that is responsive to both seasonal and local variation in food availability. On commercial farmland in the Zimbabwe highveld hey eat mainly wild fruit (30%) and small (less than 1 kg) to medium-sized (more than 1 kg) mammals (27% and 23%, respectively). The remainder of their diet comprises birds, invertebrates, cattle cake, grass, and carrion. In wildlife areas of western Zimbabwe, Side-striped Jackals feed largely on invertebrates during the wet season and small mammals up to the size of Spring hares (*Pedetes capensis*) during the dry months of the year. They scavenge extensively from safari camp rubbish dumps and occasionally from large carnivore kills (although they are often out-competed for this resource by Black-backed Jackals). In the Ngorongoro Crater, Side-striped Jackals have been recorded competing with Black-backed Jackals for Grant's Gazelle (*Nanger granti*) fawns. Their diet may consist exclusively of certain fruits when in season. Apparently less predatory than other jackals, although according to one authority this may not hold when prey is highly available. The species forages solitarily, although in western Zimbabwe family groups have been observed feeding together on abundant resources, and as many as twelve have been counted at kills or scavenging offal outside towns. Jackals have been described foraging opportunistically, exploiting food-rich habitats by random walks, and they display an amazing ability to find food where none seems obvious to the human observer.

Activity patterns. Primarily nocturnal, but can employ extremely flexible foraging strategies in areas where they are persecuted. May also adapt activity pattern to reduce competition when in sympatry with Black-backed Jackals.

Movements, Home range and Social organization. Side-striped Jackals occur solitarily, in pairs and in family groups of up to seven individuals. The basis of the family unit is the mated pair, which has been known to be stable over several years. In game areas of western Zimbabwe, home ranges varied seasonally from 0·2 km² (hot dry season) to 1·2 km² (cold dry season), whereas in highveld farmland, home ranges were seasonally stable and in excess of 4 km² (a third of the yearly total range). Sub-adults disperse from the natal territory, up to 12 km in Zimbabwe's highveld farmland and 20 km in game areas. In highveld farmland, territories are configured to encompass patches of grassland where resources are most available, and the structure of the habitat mosaic appears an important factor. Home ranges overlap by about 20% in highveld farmland and 33% in game areas. The residents use the core territory almost exclusively. Vocal repertoire is broad, including an explosive bark, growls, yaps, cackles, whines, screams, a croaking distress call, and a hooting howl. Calling occurs all year round, but is especially common between pair members during the mating period. Jackals from neighboring territories sometimes answer each other. Captive pups have been heard calling at eight weeks, but may start earlier.

Breeding. In Zimbabwe, mating occurs mostly during June and July, and the gestation period is about 60 days. Litters of 4–6 pups are born from August to November, coinciding with the onset of the rainy season. Pup mortality is thought to be high. Abandoned Aardvark (*Orycteropus afer*) holes or excavated termitaria are common den sites, with the den chamber occurring 0·75–1 m below the surface and 2–3 m from the entrance. The same pair may use such dens in consecutive years. After the pups are weaned, both parents assist in rearing them, returning at two- to three-hour intervals through the night to feed the pups on food that is probably regurgitated. The pups are aggressive towards each other, as evidenced by the degree of wounding observed. Year-old offspring remain in the parental territory while additional offspring are raised. It appears likely that alloparental care as observed in other jackals also occurs in this species, which may be more social than previously thought.

Status and Conservation. CITES not listed. Classified as Least Concern on *The IUCN Red List*. No legal protection outside protected areas. Regional estimates of population abundance are not available, but from work undertaken in two diverse habitats in Zimbabwe, it seems reasonable to assume the species is common and to estimate a total population in excess of three million. The species appears well capable of exploiting urban and suburban habitats, a factor which may help to ensure its persistence. It is likely that the population is at least stable. Side-striped Jackals are persecuted because of their role in rabies transmission and their putative role as stock killers. In areas of high human population density, snaring may be the commonest cause of death in adult jackals. It is unlikely that this persecution has an effect on the overall population, but indiscriminate culling through poisoning could affect local abundance. The species' dietary flexibility and ability to co-exist with humans on the periphery of settlements and towns suggests that populations are only vulnerable in cases of extreme habitat modification or intense disease epidemics.

Bibliography. Atkinson (1997a, 1997b), Atkinson & Loveridge (2004), Atkinson, Macdonald & Kamizola (2002), Atkinson, Rhodes *et al.* (2002), Estes (1991), Fuller *et al.* (1989), Kingdon (1997), Loveridge (1999), Loveridge & Macdonald (2001, 2002, 2003), Moehlman (1979, 1989), Rowe-Rowe (1992b), Skinner & Smithers (1990), Smithers (1971, 1983), Smithers & Wilson (1979), Stuart & Stuart (1988).

7. Black-backed Jackal *Canis mesomelas*

French: Chacal à dos noir / **German**: Schabrackenschakal / **Spanish**: Chacal dorsinegro

Other common names: Silver-backed Jackal

Taxonomy. *Canis mesomelas* Schreber, 1775, Cape of Good Hope, South Africa.

Different authors have recognized between two and six subspecies. However, considering the regional variation in the species, only two geographically isolated subspecies are recognized here.

Subspecies and Distribution.

C. m. mesomelas Schreber, 1775 – S Africa.

C. m. schmidti Noack, 1897 – E Africa.

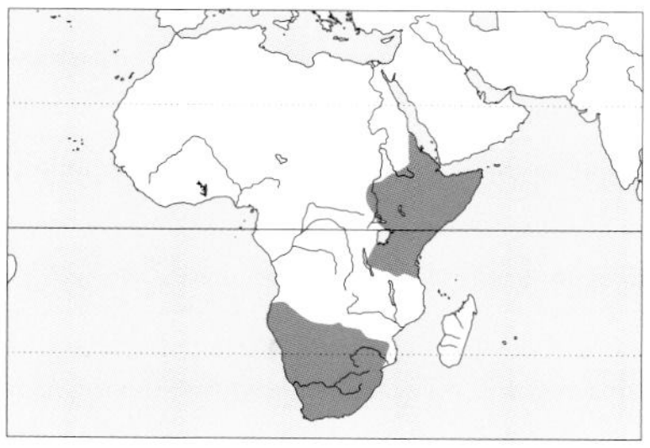

Descriptive notes. Head-body 69–90 cm for males and 65–85 cm for females, tail 27–39·5 cm for males and 26–38·1 cm for females; weight 5·9–12 kg for males and 6·2–9·9 kg for females. Males are slightly larger and heavier than females. Somewhat fox-like in appearance, with a long, pointed muzzle. Diagnostic features include the dark saddle, black bushy tail and reddish flanks and limbs. The ears are large, erect, pointed, and constantly mobile. The overall body color is rufous brown, most intense on the ears, rump, and flanks. A black stripe midway up each flank slopes obliquely from behind the shoulder to the top of the rump; the dark saddle is broadest at the shoulders and tapers to a narrow point at the base of the tail. Anterior to this stripe, just behind the shoulder, is a small vertical stripe, diffuse in some individuals. Above the side markings, the back is marbled black and white giving an overall silver appearance in mature animals. Juveniles and sub-adults have similar markings, but these are drabber and only gain their full intensity at around two years of age. In the drier west and Namib coast in southern Africa the winter coat is a deep reddish brown (especially in males). The bushy tail is dark brown to black with a distinctive black sub-caudal marking. The markings, especially the side and shoulder stripes, are unique and can be used to identifiy individuals. Skull elongated, braincase pear-shaped, rostrum narrow, supra-occipital crest well-developed, bullae rounded, zygomatic arches broad and well-developed, and post-orbital bars incomplete. Dental formula is I 3/3, C 1/1, PM 4/4, M 2/3 = 42. Outer upper incisors larger, more pointed, and more caniniform than others. Upper canines long, curved, and pointed, with a sharp ridge on their posterior faces.

Habitat. Black-backed Jackals are found in a wide variety of habitats including arid coastal desert, montane grassland, arid savannah and scrubland, open savannah, woodland savannah mosaics, and farmland. In general they show a preference for open habitats, tending to avoid dense vegetation. In KwaZulu-Natal, South Africa, they are recorded from sea level to more than 3000 m in the Drakensberg Mountains, and in localities receiving more than 2000 mm of rainfall. Where more than one jackal species occurs in sympatry the selection of habitat is partitioned. Black-backed Jackals preferentially use either open grassland (when sympatric with Side-striped Jackal) or wooded savannah (when sympatric with Golden and Side-striped Jackals). In western Zimbabwe, habitat partitioning was mediated by aggressive encounters in which Black-backed Jackals displaced Side-striped Jackals from grassland habitats.

Food and Feeding. Generalist feeders. Diet varies according to food availability. When the jackals occur in sympatry with other carnivores using the same prey base, food resources are partitioned. Dietary items typically include small- to medium-sized mammals (e.g. murids, spring hares, young ungulates), reptiles, birds and bird eggs, carrion, and human refuse, as well as invertebrates and plants. In coastal areas, Black-backed Jackals will eat beached marine mammals, seals, fish, and mussels. Invertebrates such as termites and insects are also commonly eaten. Pairs and small groups are often seen foraging together. Groups of between eight and ten aggregate at large carcasses of herbivores, and more than 80 have been recorded at seal colonies on the Namib Desert coast. Such aggregations are accompanied by aggressive behavior between territorial individuals. However, in the south-western Kalahari, where antelope carcasses are uncommon, groups of up to 15 pairs can feed in succession without much overt aggression. Mated jackal pairs will often cooperate in the capture of prey, resulting in a higher success rate. In Botswana, they occasionally form "packs" in order to hunt adult Impala (*Aepyceros melampus*), and there are also records of their taking adult antelope. On the Namib Desert coast they patrol beaches for beached marine refuse and move along sheltered paths between food-rich patches; the tops of coastal hummocks are used as feeding sites. In this environment, they frequently follow Brown Hyenas (*Parahyaena brunnea*), from a distance in the hope of securing the odd food item. Their large, mobile ears are used to locate invertebrate and small mammalian prey, which are then captured with a leap followed by an accurate pounce, in a similar manner to Red Foxes.

Activity patterns. Mostly nocturnal, but activity periods may extend well into daylight hours in areas where they are free from persecution.

Movements, Home range and Social organization. The monogamous mated pair, which appears to be a life-long association in most cases, is the basis of social structure, and if one member of a pair dies the other often will lose its territory. Black-backed Jackals are territorial and use feces and urine to demarcate their territorial boundaries. Territories are spatially and temporally relatively stable, and intruders are aggressively expelled by territory holders. Water sources are shared with intruders, but the intruders perform submissive behavior to territory holders, even to their pups. Density and group size is dependent on food biomass and dispersion. In South Africa, home range size averaged 18·2 km² (n = 14). In the more arid south-western Kalahari, adult ranges varied from 2·6–5·2 km² (n = 7) and mean sub-adult ranges were 6·3 km² (n = 4). In Zimbabwe, home ranges were largest in the cold, dry season (c. 1·0–1·3 km²) and smaller in the hot dry season (c. 0·3–0·6 km²), while in the Rift Valley in Kenya, home ranges varied from 0·7–3·5 km². Home ranges are universally defended and mutually exclusive for pairs, with the exception of a population on the Namibian coast for which average home range size varied from 7·1–24·9 km² (n = 4). A high-pitched, whining howl is used to communicate with group members and is often used to call the group together in the early evening; this may also function in territorial advertisement. Howling often stimulates the same behavior in adjacent territories or in nearby individuals. A three- to five-syllable alarm call, consisting of an explosive yelp followed by a series of shorter high-pitched yelps, is used when disturbed and may be frantic and prolonged when the jackals are mobbing a Leopard

(*Panthera pardus*). A low-pitched, gruff bark is used to warn pups of intruders near the den, and whines are used to call to pups. Also noted is use of a "clattering distress call" and a loud yelp when alarmed. Interestingly, Black-backed Jackals are much less vocal where they occur alongside the Golden Jackal, which is the only jackal species heard to howl in East Africa.

Breeding. Mating is accompanied by increased vocalization and territoriality in both sexes. Dominant individuals within a territory constantly harass same-sex subordinates to prevent them from mating. In southern Africa mating generally occurs from late May to August, and following a gestation period of about 60 days, births occur from around July to October. It has been suggested that summer births are timed to coincide with the reproductive season of important rodent prey, and winter births with an increase in the availability of ungulate carcasses at the end of winter. Litter size is typically between one and six, and pups are born in modified termitaria or other convenient burrows, often with multiple entrances. The same den sites may be used from year to year. Pups first emerge from the den at three weeks, are weaned at 8–9 weeks, and are completely independent of the den at 14 weeks. Alloparental care is well documented and consists of feeding pups by regurgitation and guarding them when the parents are foraging. One "helper" may increase the average number of pups surviving per mated pair from one to three, and two such "helpers" further increase survival to

four pups. Pups reach sexual maturity at about eleven months, and even at this early age they can disperse at distances of more than 100 km.

Status and Conservation. CITES not listed. Classified as Least Concern on *The IUCN Red List*. No legal protection outside protected areas. Regional estimates of abundance are not available. However, Black-backed Jackals are generally widespread, and in Namibia and South Africa they are common in protected areas where suitable habitat occurs. Also occur in many livestock-producing areas, where they are considered vermin; however, despite strenuous control measures in many farming areas of southern Africa, this species is still relatively abundant. Snaring and road accidents may be the commonest cause of jackal mortality in areas of high human density. Black-backed Jackals are persecuted as livestock killers and as carriers of rabies. Population control efforts appear largely ineffective and probably only succeed in producing a temporary reduction in local numbers.

Bibliography. Avery *et al.* (1987), Bernard & Stuart (1992), Bothma (1971a, 1971b), Bothma *et al.* (1984), Coetzee (1977), Dreyer & Nel (1990), Ferguson (1980), Ferguson *et al.* (1983), Fuller *et al.* (1989), Hiscocks & Perrin (1988), Kaunda (2000), Kaunda & Skinner (2003), Kingdon (1997), Kok (1996), Lamprecht (1978), van Lawick & van Lawick-Goodall (1970), Loveridge (1999), Loveridge & Macdonald (2001, 2002), Loveridge & Nel (2004), McKenzie (1990), Meester *et al.* (1986), Moehlman (1978, 1979, 1983, 1987), Nel & Loutit (1986), Oosthuizen *et al.* (1997), Pienaar (1969), Rowe-Rowe (1982, 1983), Stuart (1976).

Plate 23 ➤

winter

ssp *alpinus*

8

ssp *hesperius*

PLATE 23

inches

cm

9

color variants

11

color variants

10

12

13

Genus *CUON*
Hodgson, 1838

8. Dhole *Cuon alpinus*

French: Dhole / **German**: Asiatischer Wildhund / **Spanish**: Cuón
Other common names: Asiatic Wild Dog

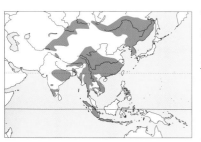

Taxonomy. *Canis alpinus* Pallas, 1811. Amur region, former USSR.

The genus *Cuon* is post-Pleistocene in origin, and related more closely to the extant jackals than to wolves. Although initially placed in the subfamily Simocyoninae, together with *Lycaon pictus* and *Speothos venaticus*, analysis of morphological, ecological and behavioral characteristics across 39 canid species showed that *Cuon* was actually more similar to *Canis*, *Dusicyon*, and even *Alopex*, the resemblance with *Speothos* or *Lycaon* being based solely on skull and dental characteristics. Analysis of sequences from mitochondrial DNA provided further evidence for the taxonomic distinctiveness among *Speothos*, *Cuon*, and *Lycaon*. Eleven subspecies have been recognized, although many of those forms are doubtful. Three subspecies recognized here.

Subspecies and Distribution.
C. a. alpinus Pallas, 1811 – C Russia and W China southward through India to Bhutan and Bangladesh.
C. a. hesperius Afanas'ev & Zolotarev, 1935 – E Russia, China, and SE Asia.
C. a. sumatrensis Hardwicke, 1821 – Sumatra and Java.

Descriptive notes. Head-body 88–135·5 cm and tail 32–50 cm; weight 15–20 kg for males and 10–13 kg for females. Large canids, usually with a reddish or brown coat and a darker, bushy tail (sometimes with a white tip). Sexual dimorphism is not very distinct. Ears triangular, about half the length of the face, with rounded tips. The pinnae are usually whitish-fawn on the inside and reddish-brown on the outside. The muzzle is brown, relatively short, and slightly convex in profile. Nose black and eyes slightly hooded; irises are amber. The dorsal and lateral pelage is red to brown and the foreneck, chest, and undersides are often whitish or pale ginger colored. In the south and south-west of the Dhole's range, their fur is shorter and rusty-red colored. In the north and north-east, the fur is longer, brownish-red, or yellowish-brown. The legs are notably shorter in some alpine regions and the coat is a yellowish-gray color in Himalayan regions. In Thailand, the coat is more uniformly brown, lacking the paler throat and chest. The toes are red, brown, and/or white; the hairless foretoe pads (on all feet) are joined at the base (near the main pad) unlike most domestic dogs. Dentition is unique within the Canidae, having one fewer lower molar teeth (I 3/3, C 1/1, PM 4/4, M 2/2 = 40), with the heel of the lower carnassial M_1 crested and with a single cusp (all other canids within the range of Dhole have two cusps). There are usually six or seven pairs of mammae.

Habitat. Dholes are found in a wide variety of vegetation types, including primary, secondary, and degraded forms of tropical dry and moist deciduous forest; evergreen and semi-evergreen forests; dry thorn forests; grassland–scrub–forest mosaics; and alpine steppe (above 3000 m). They are not recorded from desert regions. In India, tropical dry and moist deciduous forest may represent optimal habitats, based on the regions thought to hold the largest Dhole populations. Ungulate biomass, particularly that of cervid species, is highest in these vegetation types when compared to others in the same region. Important factors that may influence habitat selection include the availability of medium to large ungulate prey species, water, the presence of other large carnivore species, human population levels, and suitability of breeding sites (i.e. in terms of proximity to water, presence of suitable boulder structures, and sufficient prey).

Food and Feeding. Diet includes beetles, rodents, birds, and occasionally grass and other plants like many other canids. However, Dholes hunt mainly vertebrate prey, with a preference for medium to large ungulates. They are also known to scavenge and occasionally have been observed eating carrion (e.g. Asian Elephant (*Elephas maximus*) and Gaur (*Bos frontalis*) carcasses). It has been suggested that such scavenging only occurs during periods of prey scarcity, particularly during the dry season. Grass is ingested, but may serve an anti-helminthic function rather than a nutritional one. Dholes are communal hunters, occasionally forming packs of over 30 animals, but are more often found in hunting groups of fewer than ten animals. Depending on prey availability, Dholes may also hunt alone or in pairs, taking smaller prey such as deer fawns or hares. During hunts, some Dholes may lie in ambush while others drive prey towards them. Dholes often drive deer into water, where they swim out to surround and capture them. It is common for certain individuals to take particular roles in the hunt, such as leading the chase or taking the first grab at the prey.

Activity patterns. Primarily a crepuscular forager, but can hunt at any time of the day or night.

Movements, Home range and Social organization. Dholes usually live in packs of 5–10 individuals, but groups of as many as 25 (including juveniles) have been recorded on a regular basis. Their ability to regurgitate small quantities of meat at will and thus transport food to pack-mates and neonates facilitates communal breeding, providing food for the pups, the mother, and other adult helpers that remain at the natal den. Group size and composition may vary under different environmental conditions, but most of the current data are from India. Packs have been reported to contain significantly more males than females, perhaps a reflection of female-biased dispersal. Pack members regularly play together, engaging in mock-fights, rolling, and allo-grooming. Social rank is established by pushing and holding, but rarely by aggressive biting. Groups have a strong hierarchical structure, with a dominant male and female who are the main breeders. Pack members over-mark each other's feces and urine on latrines throughout the group's range. The ranges of neighboring packs often exhibit little overlap, though interactions between groups occur and can be either friendly or hostile. In India, reported home range size ranged from 40 to 83 km². In Thailand, two radio-collared adult male Dholes occupied home range sizes of 12 km² and 49·5 km². Dholes have a broad and unusual vocal repertoire that includes whines, mews, squeaks, growls, growl-barks, chattering calls, and screams. This large range of alarm calls may have evolved to alert pack members to danger from predators (e.g. Leopard, Tiger, Humans), and could serve to intimidate adversaries. A repetitive whistle-like contact call may allow dispersed pack members to identify one another and to re-group. Maintaining group cohesion in this way is likely to be highly adaptive in areas with other large predators.

Breeding. Dholes give birth once a year and have a gestation period of about nine weeks. Mating periods vary in different locations, occurring between November and April (dry season) in India, and January to May (end of the wet season) in East Java. Females are seasonally polyestrous with a cycle of 4–6 weeks. The dominant pair engages in vigorous play and marking, culminating in a copulatory tie. Usually only the dominant female breeds, but exceptions have been noted. Subordinate males sometimes show sexual interest in the alpha female and may contribute to the paternity of the litter. Litter sizes vary dramatically, even within the same pack in different years. The largest litter size recorded is twelve, with only one lactating female in the group. In captivity, newborn pups can weigh 200–350 g, although by the age of ten days their body weight can double, and they have a total body length of about 340 mm. Pups suckle from the mother until they are about three weeks old, when they start to receive regurgitated meat from other pack members. Weaning occurs by about 6–7 weeks, although in captivity this can happen as late as 8–9 weeks. All adults take part in guarding, feeding, grooming, and playing with the pups. By about three months, the pups accompany the adults on hunts; however, the pack may not be fully mobile until about eight months. Dholes reach adult size by about 15 months. In captivity, Dholes of both sexes can reproduce at two years of age. Den types range from earthen burrows to rocky caverns.

Status and Conservation. CITES Appendix II. Listed as Endangered on *The IUCN Red List*. Latest estimates state that fewer than 2500 mature individuals remain in the wild. Current wildlife decrees in Cambodia give the Dhole protection from all hunting. A new forestry law is under preparation, and a proposal to list the species for full protection is under discussion. India's 1972 Wildlife Act affords legal protection, specifying that permission is required to kill any individual unless in self-defense or if an individual is a man-killer. The creation of Project Tiger Reserves in India has provided some protection for Dhole populations. In the former Soviet Union, Dholes received the status of "protected animal" in 1974; however, the poisoning and shooting of Gray Wolves may inadvertently affect any remnant Dhole populations. The Dhole is legally protected in Vietnam. Knowledge of Dhole abundance is limited to estimates of the number of packs within a few protected areas in southern and central India, where Dholes are generally thought to be abundant. Abundance is relatively lower in West Bengal, Assam, and Arunachal Pradesh. In the rest of north-eastern India, Dholes are currently extinct or close to extinction. No remotely comparable information on density is available for any part of South-east Asia, and there are no empirical data on trends in this region. Threats include depletion of prey base, habitat loss and transformation, persecution by cattle grazers, and disease.

Bibliography. Clutton-Brock *et al.* (1976), Cohen (1977, 1978), Davidar (1973, 1975), Durbin (1998), Durbin *et al.* (2004), Fox (1984), IUCN (2008), Johnsingh (1979, 1982, 1983), Paulraj *et al.* (1992), Thenius (1954), Venkataraman (1998), Venkataraman *et al.* (1995), Wayne *et al.* (1997).

Genus *LYCAON*
Brookes, 1827

9. African Wild Dog *Lycaon pictus*

French: Lycaon / **German**: Afrikanischer Wildhund / **Spanish**: Licaón
Other common names: Painted Hunting Dog

Taxonomy. *Hyaena picta* Temminck, 1820, coastal Mozambique.

The former placement of *Lycaon* in its own subfamily, the Simoncyoninae, is no longer recognized, and recent molecular studies have supported the separation of this species into its own genus. The African Wild Dog has been grouped with Dhole and Bush Dog, but the morphological similarities among these species are no longer considered to indicate common ancestry. Genetic and morphological studies initially suggested the existence of separate subspecies in eastern and southern Africa. However, no geographical boundaries separated these proposed subspecies, and dogs sampled from

On following pages: 10. Maned Wolf (*Chrysocyon brachyurus*); 11. Bush Dog (*Speothos venaticus*); 12. Crab-eating Fox (*Cerdocyon thous*); 13. Short-eared Dog (*Atelocynus microtis*).

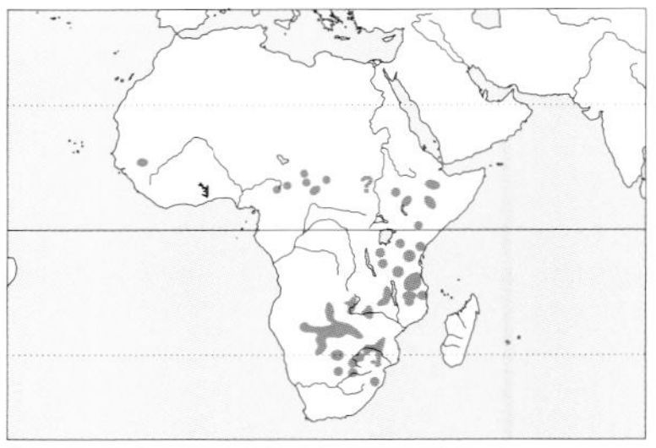

the intermediate area showed a mixture of southern and eastern haplotypes, indicating a cline rather than distinct subspecies.

Distribution. Sub-Saharan Africa; virtually eradicated from W Africa, and greatly reduced in C and NE Africa. The largest populations exist in Botswana, Tanzania, and Zimbabwe, which account for approximately half of the estimated number of African Wild Dogs remaining in the wild. Other populations occur in Central African Republic, Ethiopia, Kenya, Mozambique, Namibia, South Africa, Sudan, and Zambia. Potential small populations (less than 100 individuals) may exist in Cameroon, Chad, Senegal, and Somalia.

Descriptive notes. Head-body 84·5–138·5 cm for males and 93–141 cm for females, tail 32–42 cm for males and 31–37 cm for females; weight 21–34·5 kg for males and 18–26·5 kg for females. Males are slightly heavier than females, and are easily recognized by the conspicuous penis sheath. A large but lightly built canid, with long, slim legs and large, rounded ears. The coloration of the pelage is distinctive but highly variable, a combination of irregular black, yellow-brown, and white blotches on the back, sides, and legs. African Wild Dogs in north-eastern Africa are predominantly black, with small white and yellow patches. Dogs in southern Africa are lighter, with a mix of brown, black, and white. Pelage coloration is unique to each animal, and can thus be used to identify individuals. Head yellow-brown with a black mask, black ears, a black line following the sagittal crest, and a white-tipped tail. Hair is generally very short on the limbs and body and longer on the neck, sometimes giving a shaggy appearance at the throat. Females have six to eight pairs of mammae. The dental formula is I 3/3, C 1/1, PM 4/4, M 2/3 = 42. As with *Cuon* and *Speothos* departure from the typical form of dentition within the Canidae is apparent in the lower carnassial, where the inner cusp of the talonid is missing so that instead of forming a basin, this part of the tooth forms a subsidiary blade. This is indicative of a highly carnivorous diet.

Habitat. Wild Dogs occupy a range of habitats including short-grass plains, semi-desert, bushy savannahs, and upland forest. Early studies in Tanzania's Serengeti led to a belief that Wild Dogs were primarily an open-plains species, but they reach their highest densities in thicker bush (e.g. central Tanzania, western Zimbabwe and northern Botswana). Several relict populations also occupy dense upland forest (e.g. Harenna Forest, Ethiopia; Ngare Ndare Forest, Kenya). Wild Dogs have been recorded in desert, although they appear unable to expand into the southern Kalahari or into montane habitats; they occur in some lowland forest areas. It appears that their current distribution is limited primarily by human activities and the availability of prey, rather than the loss of a specific habitat type.

Food and Feeding. Wild Dogs mostly hunt medium-sized antelope. In most areas their principal prey are Impala, Greater Kudu (*Tragelaphus strepsiceros*), Thomson's Gazelle, and Blue Wildebeest (*Connochaetes taurinus*). They will give chase to larger species, such as Common Eland (*Tragelaphus oryx*) and African Buffalo (*Syncerus caffer*), but rarely kill these species. Warthogs (*Phacochoerus* spp.), dik-diks (*Madoqua* spp.), Steenbok (*Raphicerus campestris*), and duikers (Cephalophini) are important prey items in some areas. African Wild Dogs also take small prey opportunistically, such as hares, lizards, and bird eggs, but these make a very small contribution to their diet. African Wild Dogs live and hunt in packs. Hunts appear to be highly coordinated and are often preceded by a "social rally". During chases, African Wild Dogs may run at speeds of up to 60 km/h, and are specially adapted to cope with the heat stress that this involves. After one dog has made the first grab of an antelope or other prey species, other pack members join and help drag the quarry to the ground. In some hunts, one pack member may restrain the head of the prey by biting its nose and holding on while others make the kill. Individuals may also chase and bring down prey alone. Hunting success is high in comparison with other large carnivore species (e.g. in the Serengeti, 70% of 133 African Wild Dog hunts ended in a kill). Social hunting gives each pack member a higher foraging success rate (measured as kg killed per km chased) relative to hunting alone. African Wild Dogs very rarely scavenge.

Activity patterns. African Wild Dogs are mainly crepuscular and hunt during the early morning and early evening hours. They may also hunt occasionally at night when moonlight is ample. Activity appears to be limited by ambient temperature and availability of light.

Movements, Home range and Social organization. African Wild Dogs are intensely social, living in close association with each other in a pack. Pack size varies from a pair to as many as 30 adults and yearlings, although typically packs include between four and nine adults along with yearlings and pups. Packs form when small same-sex subgroups (usually littermates) leave their natal groups and join subgroups of the opposite sex. Occasionally, new packs form by fission from larger groups, males and females emigrating together. Because African Wild Dogs are obligate social breeders, the pack, rather than the individual, should be considered the basic unit within the population. African Wild Dogs have large home ranges, for example 620 to 2460 km² in Serengeti, which are much larger than would be expected on the basis of their body size. Ranges in other areas, however, are typically between 400 and 600 km². Ranges are defended infrequently but aggressively against neighboring packs, and African Wild Dogs may thus be considered territorial, especially as such areas are scent-marked. During the breeding season, when they are feeding young pups at a den, packs are confined to relatively small core areas (50–200 km²), but outside the denning period they range widely. As a result, the large home ranges of this species translate into low population densities. African Wild Dogs dispersing from their natal packs may travel distances exceeding hundreds of kilometers. African Wild Dogs have a complex communication system that includes unique vocalizations.

Breeding. Each pack includes a dominant pair that breeds each year. Subordinate females may breed on some occasions, but their pups rarely survive. Parental care involves all pack members. Such alloparental care is vital: small packs (less than four members) rarely manage to raise any pups. Cooperative care may even extend to caring for adopted pups. Whelping occurs once per year, and gestation lasts 71–73 days. Wild Dogs have large litters, averaging 10–11 pups, but litters as large as 21 have been recorded. Pup sex ratios are male-biased in some populations. The pups each weigh approximately 300–350 g and are born in an underground den, which they use for the first three months of life. The dens are often those of Aardvarks, sometimes modified by warthogs or Spotted Hyenas. The mother is confined to the den during early lactation, and is reliant on other pack members to provision her during this time. Pack members feed the mother and pups (from four weeks of age) by regurgitating solid pieces of meat. Some also "babysit" the pups and chase predators off while the remainder of the pack is away hunting. Pups are generally fully weaned by eight weeks but continue to use a den for refuge until 12–16 weeks of age. They reach sexual maturity in their second year of life, but social suppression can mean that few animals breed at this age, or indeed at any age.

Status and Conservation. CITES not listed. Classified as Endangered on *The IUCN Red List*. Estimated population size is 3000 to 5500 remaining in the wild. Legally protected across much of its range. However, this protection is rarely enforced and Wild Dogs are extinct in several countries despite stringent legal measures. African Wild Dogs survive mainly in small isolated populations in reserves and protected areas, which makes them more prone to extinction and less likely to recover from potentially catastrophic events (i.e. outbreaks of epidemic disease). More than half of the mortality of adults is caused directly by human activities, even in some of the largest and best protected areas. African Wild dogs using protected areas often range outside borders and into areas used by people. Here they encounter a myriad of threats including high-speed vehicles, guns, snares, and poisoning, as well as domestic dogs, which can be reservoirs of potentially lethal diseases. Rabies, in particular, probably spread from domestic dogs, caused the extinction of African Wild Dogs in the Serengeti ecosystem on the Kenya/Tanzania border in 1990–91 and is suspected to have caused the deaths of several packs in northern Botswana in 1995 and 1996. Canine distemper may also affect African Wild Dog populations, although exposure may not always be fatal. The status of African Wild Dogs in several areas, including West and Central Africa, remains largely unknown.

Bibliography. Creel & Creel (1995, 2002), Creel, Creel, Mills & Monfort (1997), Creel, Creel, Munson *et al.* (1997), Fanshawe & Fitzgibbon (1993), Fanshawe *et al.* (1997), Frame *et al.* (1979), Fuller, Kat *et al.* (1992), Fuller, Mills *et al.* (1992), Ginsberg & Woodroffe (1997), Girman *et al.* (1997), Malcolm & Marten (1982), Malcolm & Sillero-Zubiri (2001), McCreery & Robbins (2001), McNutt (1996a, 1996b), Mills & Biggs (1993), Robbins (2000), Taylor *et al.* (1971), Van Heerden (1981), Woodroffe, Ginsberg & Macdonald (1997), Woodroffe, McNutt & Mills (2004).

Genus *CHRYSOCYON*

C. E. H. Smith, 1839

10. Maned Wolf *Chrysocyon brachyurus*

French: Renard à crinière / **German**: Mähnenwolf / **Spanish**: Aguaraguazú

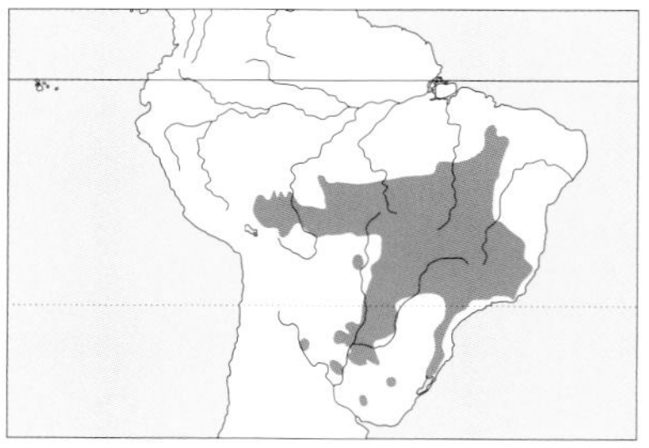

Taxonomy. *Canis brachyurus* Illiger, 1815. Type locality not specified, but later restricted to Paraguay.

The species was originally placed in the genus *Canis*, but is now widely included in the monotypic genus *Chrysocyon*. Monotypic.

Distribution. Grasslands and scrub forest of C South America, from NE Brazil through the Chaco of Paraguay into Rio Grande do Sul State, Brazil, W to Bolivia and Peru border, and S into Uruguay and Argentina to the 30° S parallel.

Descriptive notes. Head-body 95–115 cm and tail 38–50 cm; weight 20·5–30 kg. The Maned Wolf is hard to confuse with any other canid due to its long, thin legs, long reddish orange fur, and large ears. The English common name comes from the mane-like strip of black fur running from the back of the head to the shoulders, averaging 470 mm in length. Muzzle black, throat white, inner ears white, forelegs black, and most of distal part of hindlegs black. An average of 44% of the tail is white at the distal end, but the extent of white varies from 17–66% of the tail length. No underfur present. The adult dental formula is I 3/3, C 1/1, PM 4/4, M 2/3 = 42.

Habitat. Favors tall grasslands, shrub habitats, woodland with an open canopy "cerrado", and wet fields (which may be seasonally flooded). Some evidence indicates that they may prefer areas with low to medium shrub density. Maned Wolves are also seen in cultivated areas and pastures. Daytime resting areas include gallery forests, cerrado, and marshy areas near rivers. There is some evidence that they can utilize cultivated land for hunting and resting, but additional studies are essential to quantify how well the species tolerates intensive agricultural activity.

Food and Feeding. Omnivorous, consuming principally fruits and small- to medium-sized vertebrates. Numerous studies document a broadly varied diet of c. 50% plant and c. 50% animal material. The fruit *Solanum lycocarpum* grows throughout much of the range and is a primary food source; other important items include small mammals (Caviidae, Muridae, Echimydae) and armadillos (Dasypodidae), other fruits (Annonaceae, Myrtaceae, Palmae, Bromeliaceae, and others), birds (Tinamidae, Emberizidae, and others), reptiles, and arthropods. Although the frequency of plant and animal items found in fecal samples is approximately equal, the biomass of animal items is usually greater than that of plant items. Certain items, such as rodents and *Solanum*, are consumed year round, but diet varies with food availability. At least occasionally, Pampas Deer (*Ozotoceros bezoarticus*) are also consumed. In one study, deer occurred in 2·4% of 1673 fecal samples analyzed. Strategies for hunting animal prey include stalking with a final pounce, digging after burrowing animals, leaping into the air to capture flying birds and insects, and sprinting after fleeing deer. Approximately 21% of all hunting attempts end with the successful capture of prey, and the strategies do not differ in their success rates. Maned Wolves have been recorded feeding on Coypu that were caught in traps set by hunters, and have been observed scavenging opportunistically on road-kill carcasses.

Activity patterns. Nocturnal and crepuscular. May forage for up to eight consecutive hours.

Movements, Home range and Social organization. Maned Wolves appear to be facultatively monogamous. Pairs are not often seen together, although researchers have observed pairs resting, hunting, and traveling together. Home ranges of pairs in Serra da Canastra National Park averaged 25·2 km^2 (21·7–30 km^2, n = 3 pairs). Home ranges studied elsewhere are larger, averaging 57 km^2 (15·6–104·9 km^2, n = 5) in Águas Emendadas Ecological Station and 49·0 km^2 (4·7–79·5 km^2, n = 5) in Emas National Park. Home range boundaries appear stable over time and are defended against adjacent pairs. Termite mounds are preferentially used as urine-marking sites, and more marks are placed on the upwind side of objects than on the downwind side. Floater individuals without territories appear to move along territory boundaries and do not scent-mark. The most frequently heard vocalization is a loud roar-bark, which may occur during any time of the day or night throughout the year.

Breeding. Females enter estrus once per year for approximately five days. Peak breeding season is from April to June. There are numerous published accounts of breeding behavior in captivity, but little information is available from wild populations. In captivity, the frequency of vocalizations (roar-bark) and scent marking increases during the weeks prior to mating, and the amount of time a pair spends in close proximity increases significantly during the estrous period. Courtship is characterized by frequent approaches, mutual anogenital investigation, and playful interactions. Mounting may occur frequently during estrus; successful breeding includes a copulatory tie that may last several minutes. In Emas National Park, Brazil, a breeding pair observed at night for approximately three and a half hours foraged together and vocalized frequently whenever one partner was out of sight. The male marked with urine or feces wherever the female marked. A breeding display lasting ten minutes concluded in a two-minute copulatory tie, after which the pair continued to forage together. Gestation length is approximately 65 days, the majority of births occurring from June to September, during the dry season. One female gave birth to three pups in a bed of tall marsh grass. At 45 days of age the pups had not yet left the den and weighed 2 kg (females) and 2·25 kg (males). All dens found in the wild have been above ground, sheltered by natural features such as shrub canopies, rock crevices, gullies, and dry mounds in marshy, tall-grass areas. In captivity, an analysis of 361 births indicated that parturition peaks in June (winter), and the average litter size is three (range 1–7). Birth weights average 390–456 g (n = 8). In captive animals, nursing bouts begin to decline after the first month, and weaning is complete at c. 15 weeks. Pups begin consuming solids regurgitated by the parents at about four weeks of age; regurgitation has been recorded up to seven months after birth. Females with 7–14-week-old pups have been observed hunting for continuous periods of eight hours over 3 km from their den sites and pups. Pups stay in the mother's home range for approximately one year, when they begin to disperse. Juveniles attain sexual maturity at around the same time, but usually do not reproduce until the second year. One of the many unknown aspects of Maned Wolf behavior is the role the male plays in rearing pups. Pups have been seen accompanied by two adults, and a female with pups was seen accompanied by a male many times. In captivity, males increase pup survival rates and are frequently observed regurgitating to pups and grooming them. Nonetheless, direct confirmation of male parental care in the wild is still lacking.

Status and Conservation. CITES Appendix II. Classified as Near Threatened on *The IUCN Red List*. Current global population is estimated to number c. 13,000 mature individuals. Maned Wolves are protected by law in many parts of their range, but enforcement is frequently problematic. Protected in Argentina (classified as "endangered" on the Red List) and included on the list of threatened animals in Brazil. Maned Wolves exist in low densities throughout their range, although in some areas of central Brazil, they appear to be more common. The most significant threat to Maned Wolf populations is habitat reduction, especially for agricultural conversion. The cerrado, for example, has been reduced to about 20% of its original area, and only 1·5% is currently protected. In addition, habitat fragmentation causes the isolation of sub-populations. Road kills represent one of the main causes of mortality of Maned Wolves in Brazil, especially for young individuals and sub-adults. Highways border many of the Conservation Units of the Brazilian cerrado, and drivers often do not respect speed limits. Reserves close to urban areas often have problems with domestic dogs, which pursue and may kill Maned Wolves and can also be an important vector of disease. Diseases may represent a significant cause of mortality in the wild, but there is very little information available on the health of wild populations. Domestic dogs also possibly compete with the Maned Wolf for food. Maned Wolves are not viewed as a serious threat to livestock, although they may occasionally be shot when caught raiding chicken pens. Hunting them is prohibited in Brazil, Paraguay, and Bolivia.

Bibliography. Azevedo & Gastal (1997), Bartmann & Nordhoff (1984), Beccaceci (1992), Bernardes *et al.* (1990), Bestelmeyer (2000), Bestelmeyer & Westbrook (1998), Brady (1981), Brady & Ditton (1979), Cabrera (1958), Carvalho & Vasconcellos (1995), Chebez (2008), Dietz (1984, 1985), Fonseca *et al.* (1994), IUCN (2008), Jácomo (1999), Juarez & Marinho (2002), Langguth (1975), Mones & Olazarri (1990), Motta-Júnior (1997), Motta-Júnior *et al.* (1996), Ratter *et al.* (1997), Richard *et al.* (1999), Rodden, Rodrigues & Bestelmeyer (2004), Rodden, Sorenson *et al.* (1996), Santos (1999), Silveira (1968, 1999), Van Gelder (1978).

Genus *SPEOTHOS*

Lund, 1839

11. Bush Dog *Speothos venaticus*

French: Chien des buissons / **German**: Waldhund / **Spanish**: Zorro vinagre

Other common names: Vinegar Dog, Savannah Dog

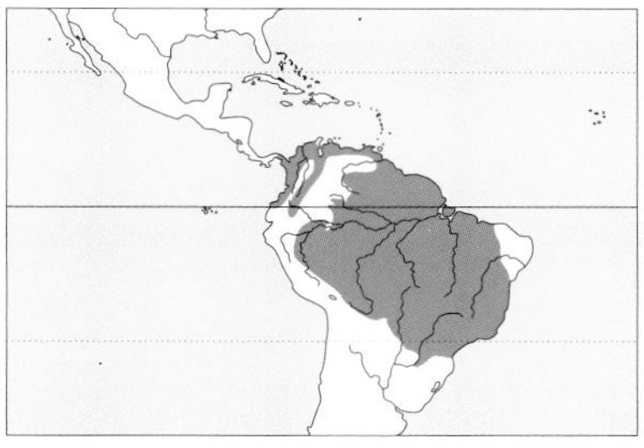

Taxonomy. *Cynogale venatica* Lund, 1842, Minas Gerais, Brazil.

S. pacivorus, an extinct species, is known only from fossil deposits in Lagoa Santa caves in Minas Gerais, Brazil, and may not have existed past the Holocene. Three subspecies are recognized.

Subspecies and Distribution.

S. v. venaticus Lund, 1842 – Argentina (Misiones), Bolivia, N & C Brazil, Colombia, Ecuador, the Guianas, Paraguay, Peru, and Venezuela.

S. v. *panamensis* Goldman, 1912 – Panama.

S. v. wingei Ihering, 1911– SE Brazil.

Descriptive notes. Head-body 57·5–75 cm, tail 12·5–15 cm; weight 5–8 kg. Characterized by a long body, a short and sometimes stubby tail, and short legs. Broad face with short muzzle, small rounded ears, brown eyes. Head and neck are generally reddish-tan or tawny, gradually darkening to black or dark brown hindquarters and legs. The underside is also dark and some individuals may show a pale white throat or chest patch. Coat patterns can be highly variable, from almost all black to very light blonde. Feet are partially webbed and tracks are nearly identical to those of the domestic dog. Bush Dogs are one of three canid species with trenchant heel dentition, a unicuspid talonid on the lower carnassial molar that increases the cutting blade length. Dental formula is I 3/3, C 1/1, PM 4/4, M 2/2 = 40.

Habitat. The Bush Dog is a forest dweller, occurring generally near water sources, particularly small streams, and near available prey populations, especially Lowland Paca (*Cuniculus paca*). Bush Dogs have been observed in lowland (below 1500 m) forested habitats, including primary and gallery forest, semi-deciduous forest, and seasonally flooded forest. Observations have also been recorded from cerrado habitat in Brazil and Paraguay and pampas (wet savannah) edge/riparian areas, and as far as 5700 m from forest habitat. Occasionally reported from secondary forest, ranchland, and fragmented cerrado ranchland.

Food and Feeding. Primarily carnivorous, Bush Dogs mainly hunt large rodents such as Lowland Pacas and agoutis (*Dasyprocta* spp.). Their diet often includes other small mammals (e.g. rats, *Oryzomys* spp. and *Proechimys* spp., rabbits, *Sylvilagus brasiliensis*, opossums, *Didelphis* spp. and the Nine-banded Armadillo *Dasypus novemcinctus*). Other prey items include teju lizards (*Tupinambis* sp.), snakes, and possibly ground-nesting birds. Bush Dogs can engage in group hunting to take prey considerably larger than themselves, such as Capybaras (*Hydrochoeris hydrochaeris*), and rheas (*Rhea americana*), deer (*Mazama* spp.), and even South American Tapir (*Tapirus terrestris*). Bush Dogs hunt in packs of 2–8 animals (mean 4·5) employing a variety of cooperative hunting strategies. Prey is pursued relentlessly by the pack, even into deep water. In Bolivia the dogs hunt *Mazama* deer by attacking the legs until the animal tires and falls. Olfaction may play a large role when foraging. Some individuals may enter the burrow of a prey species while other pack members wait at possible escape routes.

Activity patterns. Mostly diurnal; the pair and any family members spend the night in a den.

Movements, Home range and Social organization. Bush Dogs are considered the most social of the small canids, reportedly living in groups ranging from 2–12 individuals, with most observed groups including 2–6 members. The ability of a pack to hunt cooperatively appears to be a primary benefit of the Bush Dog's social organization. Estimated home range is between 4·6 and 4·7 km^2. A monogamous pair-bond is likely with the offspring from multiple years living with the pair. Urine-marking may be important for the formation and maintenance of pair-bonds. Bush Dogs tend to be associated with strong smell, lending evidence that urine is a particularly effective intra-specific communication medium. Males extrude the penis and move laterally, creating a spray rather than a stream, and females drag their ano-genital region over a surface or display either a forelimb handstand or a squat. The raised posture allows urine to be deposited some 150 mm higher than the spray of the male. Adult Bush Dog vocalizations have been classified as whines, repetitive whines, pulsed vocalization, screams, barks, and growls. Infants whine, grunt, growl, and bark; these vocalizations are thought to either elicit care or reduce aggression. The elaborate set of close-contact calls assists in communicating subtle changes in mood as well as changes in location.

Breeding. The Bush Dog mating season is unknown, although pups have been found in the wet season. Captive females have two estrous cycles per year. Estrus is aseasonal and likely influenced by social factors. Dominant females appear to suppress the estrus of daughters. Gestation in captivity is 67 days, and mean litter size is 3·8 (range 1–6). Lactation lasts approximately eight weeks. Males exhibit a high degree of parental care that includes food supplementation to females prior to birth and throughout nursing. Bush dogs appear to be sexually mature by one year.
Status and Conservation. CITES Appendix I. Classified as Near Threatened on *The IUCN Red List*. Currently, the population is estimated to number fewer than 15,000 mature individuals. Appears naturally rare throughout its range, independent of human disturbance. Hunting and trade is regulated in Argentina, Bolivia, Brazil, and Venezuela, and is prohibited elsewhere in the range. Perceived threats include habitat conversion and human encroachment. Bush dogs are occasionally killed in Bolivia and Ecuador as predators of chickens, and road kills have been documented in Brazil.
Bibliography. Aquino & Puertas (1997), Beccaceci (1994), Berta (1984), Brady (1981), Cabrera (1961a), Chebez (2008), Defler (1986a), Deutsch (1983), Drüwa (1983), Emmons (1998), Gittleman & Harvey (1982), IUCN (2008), Kleiman (1972), Macdonald (1996b), Peres (1991), Porton (1983), Porton *et al.* (1987), Silveira *et al.* (1998), Strahl *et al.* (1992), Van Humbeck & Perez (1998), Zuercher & Villalba (2002), Zuercher *et al.* (2004).

Genus *CERDOCYON*

C. E. H. Smith, 1839

12. Crab-eating Fox *Cerdocyon thous*

French: Renard crabier / **German**: Savannenfuchs / **Spanish**: Zorro cangrejero
Other common names: Savannah Fox

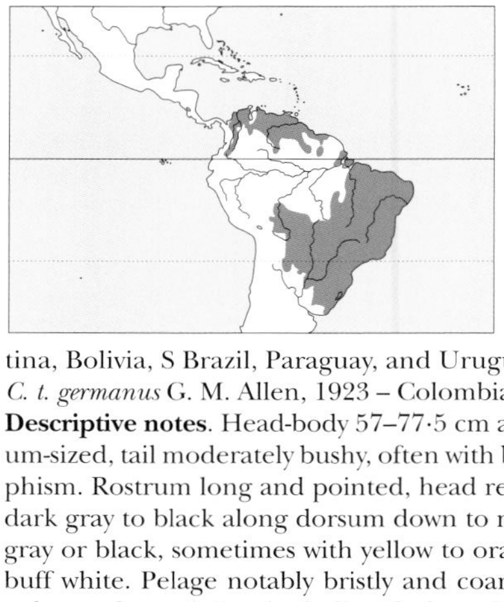

Taxonomy. *Canis thous* Linnaeus, 1766. Suriname.
Five subspecies are recognized.
Subspecies and Distribution.
C. t. thous Linnaeus, 1766 – N Brazil, the Guianas, and SE Venezuela.
C. t. aquilus Bangs, 1898 – N Colombia, N Venezuela.
C. t. azarae Wied-Neuwied, 1824 – NE & C Brazil.
C. t. entrerianus Burmeister, 1861 – Argentina, Bolivia, S Brazil, Paraguay, and Uruguay.
C. t. germanus G. M. Allen, 1923 – Colombia (Bogotá region).
Descriptive notes. Head-body 57–77·5 cm and tail 22–41 cm; weight 4·5–8·5 kg. Medium-sized, tail moderately bushy, often with black tip and dark at base. No sexual dimorphism. Rostrum long and pointed, head relatively short and narrow. Pelage generally dark gray to black along dorsum down to midline; midline to ventrum including legs gray or black, sometimes with yellow to orange flecks; neck and underparts cream to buff white. Pelage notably bristly and coarse. Substantial inter- and intra-population pelage color variation including dark to almost black (e.g. northern Venezuela, Amazonia, central Brazil), silver gray (e.g. Venezuelan Llanos), and pale gray-yellow rufous (e.g. Ceará, Brazil). Continuous black dorsal line from neck to tail tip variably present. The dental formula is I 3/3, C 1/1, PM 4/4, M 1/2 = 44.
Habitat. Occupies most habitats including marshland, savannah, cerrado, caatinga, chaco-cerrado-caatinga transitions, scrubland, woodlands, dry and semi-deciduous forests, gallery forest, Atlantic forest, Araucaria forest, isolated savannah within lowland Amazon forest, and montane forest. Records up to 3000 m. Readily adapts to deforestation, agricultural and horticultural development (e.g. sugarcane, eucalyptus, melon, pineapples), and habitats in regeneration. In the arid Chaco regions of Bolivia, Paraguay, and Argentina, confined to woodland edge. Vegetative habitats generally utilized in proportion to abundance, varying with individual fox's social status and climatic season. Radio-tagged foxes in seasonally flooded savannas of Marajó, Brazil, preferred wooded savannah and regenerating scrub. In the central Llanos of Venezuela, fox home ranges were generally located in open palm savannah (68% of sightings) and closed habitats (shrub, woodlands, deciduous forest, 32% of sightings). The foxes shifted to higher ground in response to seasonal flooding. In Minas Gerais, Brazil, two radio-tagged foxes were observed most often at the interface of livestock pasture and gallery forest "vereidas" and less frequently in eucalyptus/agricultural plantations (8%).
Food and Feeding. Omnivorous: diet includes fruit, vertebrates, insects, amphibians, crustaceans, birds, and carrion. An opportunistic predator; diet at any one location varies according to availability, season, and probably social status. In areas of human disturbance, a large proportion of the diet may comprise foods such as cultivated fruits, domestic fowl, and refuse. In the Venezuelan Llanos, the percent volume of food items from the contents of 104 fox stomachs from four different locations included: small mammals (26%), fruit (24%), amphibians (13%), insects (11%); the dry season diet was predominantly small mammals, reptiles, and amphibians, with insect and fruit becoming more frequent in the wet season. In one Venezuelan location, land crabs (*Dilocarcinus* spp.) were the most frequently occurring dietary item in the rainy season, and in the Iberá Wetlands (Corrientes, Argentina), aquatic birds were identified in 87% of 23 fox scats collected in the vicinity of a bird breeding colony. Vertebrates were the most frequently encountered food item (69%) of 74 prey items identified in 22 scats collected at elevations of above 2600 m in the eastern Colombian Andes, but were the least favored food item (15%) in feces collected from the lowland wooded savannahs of Marajó (Brazil), where cultivated and wild fruit (57%) and insects (86%) were more frequently encountered. Crab-eating Foxes hunt individually, but most commonly as pairs; 1–3 adult-sized offspring may accompany them. Cooperative hunting apparently is rare. They will tolerate close proximity when foraging on concentrated, easily available food items such as turtle eggs, fruit, insects (e.g. termites), and sizeable carrion (e.g. goat carcass). The young start to hunt with the parents at about six weeks of age. Hunting strategies include spring-pouncing to capture vertebrates, ground-level lateral head movements to snatch insects, and directional maneuvers in pursuit of land crabs. The foxes in Marajó deliver a series of shoulder blows, with face up-turned, to some food items (e.g. toads, eggs) prior to comsuming them. In the same region, foxes search for and consume small stones from specific open gravel sites, presumably as a source of minerals. Foxes cache food items but do not regularly urine-mark them. They probably act as seed dispersers of a range of wild and cultivated plant species, as indicated by the presence of germinating seeds in their scats. Examples include *Acacia aroma* and *Celtis tala* (montane Chaco, Argentina), *Butia capitata* (Uruguay), *Hovenia dulcis* (Iguaçú National Park, Brazil), *Ficus* spp. (south-eastern Brazil), *Psidium guineense*, *Humiria balsamifera*, and *Anacardium occidentale* (Amazonian Brazil).
Activity patterns. Primarily nocturnal and crepuscular.
Movements, Home range and Social organization. Social groups comprise a breeding pair and 1–5 offspring (older than one year). Family members usually travel around their home ranges in pairs or, if offspring are present, in loosely knit family groups. Separated foxes maintain contact by long distance, high-pitched, bird-like trill vocalizations. In Marajó, Brazil, territorial breeding pairs were located less than 100 m apart on a mean 54% (n = 7) of occasions during the period of activity, whereas close proximity of breeding adults and their adult-sized offspring varied from 7·2% to 93·3% between given pairings. In Marajó, Brazil adult foxes occupied stable territories of 5·3 km^2 (range 0·5–10·4 km^2), whereas in pasture/eucalyptus habitats in Minas Gerais (Brazil), an adult male's range was 2·2 km^2. In dry forest sites in Santa Cruz, Bolivia an adult female and two adult males occupied mean home ranges of 2·2 km^2 (range 1·1–2·8 km^2). In the central Venezuelan Llanos, three adult foxes and three adult fox pairs showed dry season home ranges (mean 0·7 km^2; range 0·5–1 km^2) to be generally larger than wet season home ranges (mean 0·7 km^2; range 0·3–1 km^2). Shrinkage of fox range sizes in the wet season is thought to be in response to changes in the availability of dry habitats and/or prey density. Dispersing offspring established territories adjoining their natal range. The average distance between range centers was 2·4 km (range 1·9–2·9 km). After dispersal, these foxes interacted amicably with kin members both inside and outside their natal ranges. Four male foxes returned to their natal range 3–13 months after their dispersal, in two cases following the death of their mate and in one case after breeding. Group latrines are not usual features of Crab-eating Fox society; however, a latrine comprising over 72 scats visited by at least four adult-sized individuals was observed in Maraca Ecological Station, Brazil. The use of scat latrines located near resting sites has also been reported.
Breeding. In the wild, litters are produced once per breeding year. Litters were observed in Brazil in the months of June to December. In the Venezuelan Llanos, litters were recorded between December and February and lactating females were seen in June. Elsewhere in Venezuela litters were observed year round (January, May, July, and October), and lactating foxes were recorded in August. On emergence from the natal den at 2–3 months, the mean litter size is 2·6 (range 2–3). It is not known whether the presence of a dominant female inhibits ovulation in subordinate females. In captivity, births have been recorded in January, February, March, June, and October, and foxes may breed twice annually at intervals of 7–8 months. Gestation period is 56 days (range 52–59 days), and neonatal weight is 120–160 g. Cub rearing is the responsibility of both breeding adults. Additional helpers have not been observed directly in the wild. However, the strong social affiliations between adults and dispersed returning offspring during subsequent breeding periods are strongly suggestive of sibling helpers. In captivity, both sexes bring solid food (they do not regurgitate) to the young who consume solids from day 16–20. Pups first leave the den around day 28, but more regularly from day 45, at which time they develop the adult pelage. Lactation lasts for approximately 90 days. Post-weaning dependency lasts for up to five months, until sexual maturity, which occurs at approximately nine months. Offspring disperse when they are 18–24 months old. Crab-eating Foxes do not regularly excavate burrows, but rest aboveground in dense undergrowth (including when rearing pups), and also occasionally adopt abandoned burrows of other animals such as armadillos (Dasypodidae spp.).
Status and Conservation. CITES Appendix II. Classified as Least Concern on *The IUCN Red List*. Crab-eating Foxes are considered common in most range countries, and populations are probably stable. The species is currently listed as "potentially vulnerable" in the Argentine Red Data Book, but not listed as threatened in Bolivia, Brazil, and Colombia. There is little documentation for populations in Suriname, French Guiana, and peripheral areas of lowland Amazon forest. No specific protective legislation exists for this species, though hunting wildlife is officially forbidden in most range countries. Crab-eating Foxes are potentially threatened by pathogens from domestic dogs. The Crab-eating Fox is also perceived as a pest of poultry throughout much of its range (and in Uruguay as a predator of lambs), and consequently is often shot, trapped, and poisoned indiscriminately. In some countries, pest control is limited by specific quotas (without official bounties), although the system is often ignored, abused, or not enforced. Trapping occurred extensively in dry forest regions in Bolivia before the early 1980s, when single pelts were worth US$ 30, but the species currently has little commercial value as a furbearer. Crab-eating Foxes are also often killed by vehicles on roadways in some areas.

Bibliography. Biben (1982, 1983), Bisbal (1988), Bisbal & Ojasti (1980), Brady (1978, 1979), Cabrera (1931, 1958), Cordero-Rodríguez & Nassar (1999), Courtenay (1998), Courtenay & Maffei (2004), Courtenay, Macdonald *et al*. (1994), Courtenay, Quinnell & Chalmers (2001), Courtenay, Quinnell, Garcez & Dye (2002), Courtenay, Santana *et al*. (1996), Cravino, Calvar, Berruti *et al*. (1997), Cravino, Calvar, Poetti *et al*. (2000), Eisenberg *et al*. (1979), Facure & Monteiro-Filho (1996), Hill *et al*. (1997), Macdonald & Courtenay (1996), Maffei & Taber (2003), Montgomery & Lubin (1978), Motta-Junior *et al*. (1994), Parera (1996), Paz *et al*. (1995), Sunquist *et al*. (1989).

Genus *ATELOCYNUS*

Cabrera, 1940

13. Short-eared Dog *Atelocynus microtis*

French: Renard à petites oreilles / **German**: Kurzohrfuchs / **Spanish**: Zorro orejicorto

Other common names: Short-eared Fox

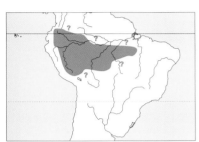

Taxonomy. *Canis microtis* Sclater, 1883, Pará, Brazil.

Phylogenetic analysis showed *A. microtis* to be a distinct taxon most closely related to another monotypic Amazonian canid genus, *Speothos*, and this hypothesis is now widely accepted. Monotypic.

Distribution. W lowland Amazonia. Bolivia, Brazil, Colombia, Ecuador, Peru.

Descriptive notes. Head-body 72–100 cm, tail 25–35 cm; weight 9–10 kg. The head is fox-like, with a long, slender muzzle and rounded, relatively short ears. The pelt color can range from black to brown to rufous gray. Pelage is often darkest in a dorsal line from the head to the tail. However, various color patterns are observed in different individuals, and it is not clear whether color varies with age, habitat, or molt; in Madre de Dios (Peru), both reddish and black individuals have been observed. The tail is bushy, particularly in comparison to the short pelage on the rest of the body, with a dark mid-dorsal band of thick erectile hairs and light-colored underside. The nasal bones are short; the forehead slightly convex; the frontal sinus small; the presphenoid very narrow with lateral wings and large bulla. The dental formula is I 3/3, C 1/1, PM 4/4, M 2/3 = 42. The lower third incisor is short and not caniniform. The upper canines are distinctively long, their tips projecting outside the closed mouth for about 50 mm. The upper molars are narrow for their length.

Habitat. Favors undisturbed rainforest in the Amazonian lowlands. Recorded in a wide variety of lowland habitats, including terra firme forest, swamp forest, stands of bamboo, and primary succession along rivers. Sightings often associated with rivers and creeks, and there are reliable reports of Short-eared Dogs swimming in rivers. Records are very rare in areas with significant human disturbance, such as near towns or in agricultural areas. It is unclear whether the Short-eared Dog is able to utilize habitats outside wet lowland forests, although it has been documented at 1200 m in the Ecuadoran Andes at the edge of cloud forest.

Food and Feeding. A generalist carnivore with fish the most important item in their diet, according to one study at Cocha Cashu, Peru (present in 28% of 21 scat samples). Insects (mainly Coleoptera) were the second most frequently occurring item (17% of samples). Mammal remains, including agouti (*Dasyprocta* spp.), marsupials, and small rodents) were present in 13% of the scats and the remains of fruits were found in 10%. Fruits of the palm *Euterpe precatoria* were found germinating in two scats, suggesting that Short-eared Dogs may facilitate seed dispersal for some species. Short-eared Dogs have been reported to eat fallen *Brosimum* fruits, and the Cofan Indians of Ecuador report that they are attracted to fallen bananas. Close to 4% of droppings contained the remains of frogs, including *Osteocephalus taurinus*, and this dietary habit is supported by independent observations elsewhere. Crabs (10·3% of samples), birds (10·3%), reptiles (3·4%), and vegetable fiber (3·4%) were other components of the diet at Cocha Cashu. The Short-eared Dog has been reported hunting alone and in pairs.

Activity patterns. Mostly diurnal, although it has also been photographed at night walking on trails of Madidi National Park, Bolivia, and one animal was captured in Colombia swimming after a Lowland Paca (*Cuniculus paca*) in a river at 03:00 h.

Movements, Home range and Social organization. Ranging behavior and patterns remain largely unknown. The Short-eared Dog is mainly solitary. Three adult animals were observed to use a 1·6 km stretch of white sandy beach in Peru, infrequently using and sharing latrines with Neotropical Otters. Both wild and captive males have been reported to bear a strong musky odor, which is hardly noticeable in females.

Breeding. Breeding time is not known precisely, but pups have been found throughout the species' range from April to December, suggesting that parturition occurs in the dry season. Three dens have been found inside hollow logs, one of them containing two adults and two pups, and another with the female and two pups. Another den containing three pups was found in a Lowland Paca burrow.

Status and Conservation. Classified as Near Threatened on *The IUCN Red List*. The species is on the Brazilian list of endangered species and on the preliminary list of Colombian endangered species. The Short-eared Dog is notoriously rare, and sightings are uncommon across its range. However, this may not always have been the case; the first biologists to study the species found it relatively easy to trap during mammal surveys in Amazonian Peru in 1969, and specimens were collected around the same time in Peru's Manu Basin (now Manu National Park), suggesting that the species was also relatively common in that area at that time. For unknown reasons, it appears to have temporarily vanished from the region between 1970 and 1987. Over the last decade, it appears that it may be recovering in south Peru and east Ecuador, with increasing numbers of sightings in recent years at both sites. Between 1987 and 1999, biologists working in the Peruvian department of Madre de Dios, mostly in the vicinity of Cocha Cashu Biological Station, reported 15 encounters with Short-eared Dogs. Threats include diseases from domestic dogs and habitat loss. There are no reports of widespread persecution of the species. An ongoing distribution survey suggests that the Short-eared Dog is rare throughout its range and threatened by the large-scale forest conversion underway in Amazonia. There are no known reports of the species being hunted or trapped for its fur. The species avoids developed areas, and there are no known cases of road kills, so the impact of vehicles on population numbers is probably minimal.

Bibliography. Defler & Santacruz (1994), Emmons & Feer (1997), Grimwood (1969), Hershkovitz (1961), Leite & Williams (2004), Nowak (1999), Pacheco *et al*. (1995), Parker & Bailey (1990), Peres (1991), Pitman *et al*. (2002), Rodriguez (1998), Terborgh *et al*. (1984).

ssp *culpaeus*

14

ssp *andinus*

15

PLATE 24

inches | 12
cm | 30

16

17

18

19

20

21

Genus *PSEUDALOPEX*
Burmeister, 1856

14. Culpeo *Pseudalopex culpaeus*

French: Renard des Andes / **German**: Andenfuchs / **Spanish**: Zorro andino

Other common names: Andean Fox

Taxonomy. *Canis culpaeus* Molina, 1782. Santiago Province, Chile.
The taxonomic status of the Culpeo is still unresolved, despite a range of propositions for including it under *Dusicyon*, *Canis*, and *Lycalopex*. Six subspecies are recognized.

Subspecies and Distribution.
P. c. culpaeus Molina, 1782 – W & C Argentina and C Chile.
P. c. andinus Thomas, 1914 – altiplano of Bolivia, N Chile, and Peru.
P. c. lycoides Philippi, 1895 – Tierra del Fuego.
P. c. magellanicus Gray, 1837 – Argentina and S Chile.
P. c. reissii Hilzheimer, 1906 – Ecuadorian Andes and extreme S Colombia (Nariño).
P. c. smithersi Thomas, 1914 – Argentina (Córdoba Mts).

Descriptive notes. Head-body 44·5–92·5 cm for males and 49–89 cm for females, tail 30·5–49·3 cm for males and 31–45 cm for females; weight 3·4–13·8 kg for males and 3·9–10 kg for females. The largest fox in the genus *Pseudalopex*. The broad head and wide muzzle impart a powerful appearance. Males larger and on average 1·5 times heavier than females. White to light tawny chin and body underparts. Dorsal parts of the head, including the ears and neck, as well as legs and flanks are tawny or rufous. The rump is darker, ranging in color from tawny to dark gray, according to the subspecies. The tail is long, bushy, and gray, with a black tip and a dark dorsal patch near its base. Feet and legs are bright tawny with no black. Specimens from northern ranges (i.e. *andinus*) are lighter in color. Compared to the South American Gray Fox, Culpeos have longer canines and shorter second molars. The dental formula is I 3/3, C 1/1, PM 4/4, M 2/3 = 42.

Habitat. The Culpeo ranges from rugged and mountain terrain up to the tree line, to deep valleys and open deserts, scrubby pampas, sclerophyllous matorral, and broad-leaved temperate southern beech forest in the south. The Culpeo uses the entire range of habitat moisture gradients from the dry desert to broad-leaved rainforest. In the Andes of Peru, Chile, Bolivia, and Argentina it reaches elevations of up to 4800 m, where it occupies colder and dryer environments than any other South American canid.

Food and Feeding. Diet includes wild ungulates, domestic sheep (northern Patagonia), European Hares (*Lepus europeus*), European Rabbits, small mammals, lizards, birds, and insects. Although it is an opportunistic predator, the Culpeo is considered more carnivorous and a consumer of larger mammalian prey than the other South American foxes. Most trophic studies found seasonal differences in diet composition, probably in response to prey availability. In Argentine Patagonia, Culpeos showed a preference for hares and selected among rodent species for those that may be more vulnerable. Culpeos in central Chile selected the largest small mammals available. Although the bulk of the diet consists of animal prey, Culpeos are often described as consumers of fruits and berries and are therefore thought to disperse seeds of a variety of plant species. Highest fruit consumption occurs when small mammals are the least abundant. Culpeos tend to forage solitarily. Their foraging activity may be influenced by the nocturnal habits of their main prey, but also by persecution.

Activity patterns. In Argentina, Magallanes, and the Chilean desert, and highland Peru (where it is intensively persecuted) the Culpeo is almost completely nocturnal. This contrasts with the diurnal activity shown in north-central Chile, where it is protected. Culpeos have been recorded moving linear distances of about 7 km in north-western Patagonia, but desert-dwelling foxes in northern Chile have been recorded moving three times as far.

Movements, Home range and Social organization. Culpeos seem to be solitary foxes. Spatial studies throughout their range indicate that they have inter- and intra-sexual non-overlapping home ranges. Small areas of spatial overlap occur at sites of human refuse, but the foxes still segregate temporally. Females are apparently more spatially intolerant than males. In north-central Chile, home ranges of females averaged 8·9 km² and were 2·5 times larger than those of males. In contrast, Culpeo home ranges in Torres del Paine National Park (south Chile) were only 4·5 km² in size and similar for males and females. Desert-dwelling Culpeos show high variability in home range size, ranging from 10 km² for Culpeos living in ravines to 800 km² for foxes associated with highland salt flats and lakes.

Breeding. In the Patagonian steppe of Argentina, male Culpeos produce sperm between June and mid-October (early winter to early spring). Females are monoestrous and mating occurs from the beginning of August through October. Gestation is 58 days. Based on embryo counts, estimated mean litter size is 5·2 (range 3–8). Neonates weigh about 170 g. Juveniles reach adult size within seven months and can reproduce

during the first year. Although the sex ratio of 253 individuals was skewed in favor of males in the Neuquén population, some 30 years later the sex ratio approached parity, as expected for intensively hunted populations.

Status and Conservation. CITES Appendix II. Classified as Least Concern on *The IUCN Red List*. In Chile the species is considered Insufficiently Known and the subspecies *P. c. lycoides* is considered Endangered. Despite being similarly decreed as "endangered" in Argentina, due to the number of Culpeo pelts traded during the 1970s and early 1980s, national trade and export of this product has remained legal. Culpeos appear to withstand intense hunting levels and still maintain viable regional populations. Recent estimates reported densities of 0·2–1·3 individuals/km² in north-western Patagonia, Argentina, and 0·3–1·3 individuals/km² in Chile. Hunting has been banned since 1980, although law enforcement is not strict. Although Culpeo fur exports were banned in Bolivia in 1986, the species is not protected in that country. Culpeos are persecuted to reduce predation on livestock and poultry. They prey on newborn lambs and account for an estimated 60% of the attacks by predators in Patagonia. Predation by feral and domestic dogs may threaten Culpeos in some areas, and road kills occur frequently in Argentina.

Bibliography. Bustamante *et al.* (1992), Cofré & Marquet (1999), Corley *et al.* (1995), Crespo (1975), Crespo & de Carlo (1963), Ebensperger *et al.* (1991), Glade (1993), Iriarte *et al.* (1989), Jaksic & Yáñez (1983), Jaksic, Schlatter & Yáñez (1980), Jaksic, Yáñez & Rau (1983), Jiménez (1993), Jiménez & Novaro (2004), Jiménez, Yáñez & Jaksic (1996), Jiménez, Yáñez, Tabilo & Jaksic (1996), Johnson (1992), Johnson & Franklin (1994a, 1994b), Langguth (1975), Marquet *et al.* (1993), Meserve *et al.* (1987), Novaro (1995, 1997a, 1997b), Novaro, Funes & Walker (2000), Novaro, Funes, Rambeaud & Monsalvo (2000), Romo (1995), Salvatori *et al.* (1999), Simonetti (1986), Travaini, Juste *et al.* (2000), Travaini, Zapata *et al.* (2000), Wayne *et al.* (1989), Yáñez & Jaksic (1978), Yáñez & Rau (1980), Zunino *et al.* (1995).

15. Darwin's Fox *Pseudalopex fulvipes*

French: Renard de Darwin / **German**: Darwin-Fuchs / **Spanish**: Zorro chilote

Taxonomy. *Vulpes fulvipes* Martin, 1837, Chile.
Known until recently only from the Island of Chiloé, Chile. Taxonomic status previously uncertain and confusing; was considered to be an island form of the South American Gray Fox (*P. griseus*). However, the discovery of a mainland population in sympatry with the South American Gray Fox and the analysis of mitochondrial DNA of the three Chilean foxes (including *P. culpaeus*), provides strong evidence for considering the Darwin's Fox as a legitimate species. It is now accepted that current populations of Darwin's Fox are relicts of a former, more widely distributed species. Similarities in pelage coloration between *P. fulvipes* and *P. sechurae* from the coastal desert of Peru (2000 km to the north) support speculations of a phylogenetic relationship between these two species. Monotypic.

Distribution. Endemic to Chile, with a disjunct distribution in the forests of Chiloé Island, and on the mainland coastal mountains in Nahuelbuta National Park. Evidence of a new population was foud recently at Punta Chan Chan, N of Valdivia.

Descriptive notes. Head-body 48·2–56·1 cm for males and 48–59·1 cm for females, tail 19·5–25·5 cm for males and 17·5–25 cm for females; weight 1·9–3·95 kg for males and 1·8–3·7 kg for females. A small, stout fox with an elongated body and short legs. Muzzle short and thin, extending into a rather rounded forehead. The agouti hair on the torso contributes to its dark appearance. Rufous markings on the ears and along the legs below the knees and elbows. White markings under the chin, along the lower mandible, on the underbelly and on the upper and inner part of the legs. The tail is dark gray, relatively short and quite bushy—all useful traits for distinguishing this species from congenerics. The skull is shorter and the auditory bulla smaller than the South American Gray Fox, but the dentition is heavier. Dental formula is I 3/3, C 1/1, PM 4/4, M 2/3 = 42.

Habitat. Generally believed to be a forest obligate species found only in southern temperate rainforests. They inhabit dense Valdivian forest, which is very moist all year round. The forest is dominated by fruit-bearing trees in the family Mirtaceae; there are a few native conifers and several species of broad-leaved evergreens. Radio-tracking along a gradient of disturbance on Chiloé indicated that, in decreasing order, foxes use old-growth Valdivian forest followed by secondary forest followed by pastures and openings; about 70% of home ranges comprised old-growth forest. However, when compared to the availability of each forest gradient, foxes showed preference for secondary forest and avoided old growth. On the Pacific coast of Chiloé, Darwin's Foxes live in a fragmented environment of coastal sand dunes and dense evergreen forest. On the northern part of the island, they use a relatively flat, fragmented landscape of broad-leaf forest and cow pasture. The mainland population uses dense forest; animals are found with decreasing frequency in dense monkey-puzzle tree-southern beech (*Araucaria-Nothofagus* spp.) forest, open *Nothofagus* forest and open pasture, respectively.

Food and Feeding. Omnivorous, with a broad diet, and highly opportunistic. These traits facilitate its survival in a highly fluctuating environment with low prey availability.

On following pages: 16. South American Gray Fox (*Pseudalopex griseus*); 17. Pampas Fox (*Pseudalopex gymnocercus*); 18. Sechuran Fox (*Pseudalopex sechurae*); 19. Hoary Fox (*Pseudalopex vetulus*); 20. Northern Gray Fox (*Urocyon cinereoargenteus*); 21. Island Fox (*Urocyon littoralis*).

Fecal analysis showed that the mainland population ate primarily small mammals, followed, in decreasing levels of importance, by reptiles, insects, birds, and arachnids. The proportions of these prey classes fluctuated strongly according to season. Berries were also included in the diet, occurring in about. 20% of the feces. On the mainland Darwin's Foxes rely heavily on the seeds of monkey-puzzle trees from March to May. On Chiloé, fecal analysis revealed that insects were the most abundant food item in the diet during the warm season, followed by amphibians, mammals, birds, and reptiles; 49% of feces contained seeds. During late summer and fall, the diet was almost entirely fruits of Mirtaceae trees. Foxes may be considered a key species because of their role in dispersing the seeds of forest plants. An experiment indicated that a high percentage of the seeds of one tree species (*Amomyrtus luma*) collected from feces germinated under field conditions. Darwin's Foxes also eat carrion in small amounts, as evidenced by the remains (e.g. hair) of sheep, pigs, cattle, and horses in feces. Local settlers reported that lone foxes also kill Southern Pudu deer (*Pudu puda*; about 10 kg in weight) by biting their ankles and then the throat. In addition, coastal foxes feed on shellfish and shorebirds, and have been observed feeding on large brown algae on the beach.

Activity patterns. Darwin's Foxes seem to concentrate their activity during the daytime in forested areas. In Nahuelbuta, they forage mainly at night, when the sympatric and larger South American Gray Fox is less active. They have also been observed hunting ducks at midday in a coastal marsh.

Movements, Home range and Social organization. In Chiloé, radio-tracking indicated that Darwin's Foxes are solitary when not breeding, but will congregate at food sources, such as carcasses and seaweed stranded on beaches. A pair appears to be the basic social unit during the breeding season. Home ranges average about 1·6 km² for males and 1·5 km² for females. Given the very large range overlaps among neighboring foxes, and that individuals share their home range with an average of 4·7 males and 3·3 females, Darwin's Fox appears to be non-territorial. On the mainland, pairs persist throughout the year, and are often found in close proximity. In contrast with the Chiloé population, mainland pairs have been known to share their home ranges with offspring from previous years. All family members associate closely with each other, showing very little aggressive behavior towards one another. To date, no evidence has been reported of older siblings serving as helpers to new litters. The maintenance of a large family group may be influenced by a paucity of suitable territories for potentially dispersing juveniles. Dispersal appears to be delayed and may be opportunistic.

Breeding. On the mainland, lactating females have been caught in October and pups have been documented leaving the den area and venturing out with both parents in December. Litter size is estimated to be 2–3 pups. Weaning occurs in February. During this period the female spends relatively less time with the pups, and a greater proportion of their interactions are agonistic, whereas the male spends more time playing with and grooming the pups. A den was located in a rock cavity (2 m deep) in *Araucaria–Nothofagus* forest with a bamboo understory, and a small pup was found denning in a hollow rotten log. During mating, males and females are together for a few days. During the first few weeks after parturition, females move little and apparently stay in the den.

Status and Conservation. CITES Appendix II. Classified as Critically Endangered on *The IUCN Red List*. Population size is currently estimated as less than 250 mature individuals with most of the foxes occurring in Chiloé Island. Protected by Chilean law since 1929, but enforcement is not always possible and some poaching occurs. The conservation status is "rare" on the mainland and "vulnerable" on Chiloé Island. More recently, Darwin's Fox has been considered as "critical", becoming the second most urgent Chilean terrestrial mammal conservation priority. The mainland population is reported to be vulnerable and its survival uncertain if current environmental trends continue. Although the species is protected in Nahuelbuta National Park, foxes are exposed to substantial mortality risks when they move to lower, unprotected private areas in search of milder conditions during the winter. Some foxes even breed in these areas. Unleashed dogs are common both on Chiloé and in Nahuelbuta and represent a significant conservation threat. Dogs have been reported to attack and kill foxes and are also vectors of potentially fatal diseases. The island population, being protected in Chiloé National Park, appears to be relatively safe. This 430 km² protected area encompasses most of the pristine rainforest on the island. However, although the park appears to have a sizable fox population, foxes also live in the surrounding areas where substantial forest cover remains. These areas are vulnerable and continuously subjected to logging, forest fragmentation, and poaching by locals.

Bibliography. Armesto *et al.* (1987), Cabrera (1958), Cofré & Marquet (1999), Glade (1993), Iriarte & Jaksic (1986), IUCN (2008), Jaksic *et al.* (1990), Jiménez (2000), Jiménez & McMahon (2004), Jiménez *et al.* (1990), McMahon (2002), McMahon *et al.* (1999), Medel *et al.* (1990), Miller *et al.* (1983), Osgood (1943), Pine *et al.* (1979), Redford & Eisenberg (1992), Spotorno (1995), Yahnke (1995), Yahnke *et al.* (1996).

16. South American Gray Fox *Pseudalopex griseus*

French: Renard d'Argentine / **German**: Argentinischer Kampfuchs / **Spanish**: Zorro de Magallanes

Other common names: Chilla, Small Gray Fox

Taxonomy. *Vulpes griseus* Gray, 1837, Chile.

Formerly believed to include an island form, which since has been recognized as Darwin's Fox. The Pampas Fox has recently been suggested to be conspecific with *P. griseus* on the basis of a craniometric and pelage-characters analysis, leading to the conclusion that *P. gymnocercus* and *P. griseus* are clinal variations of one single species, namely *Lycalopex gymnocercus*. Four subspecies are recognized.

Subspecies and Distribution.

P. g. griseus Gray, 1837 – Argentine and Chilean Patagonia.

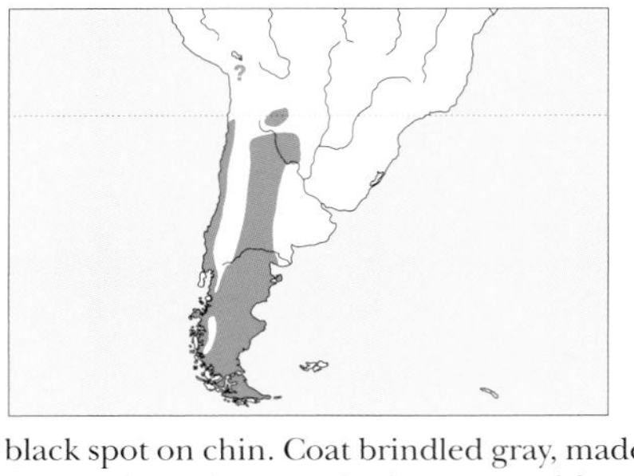

P. g. domeykoanus Philippi, 1901 – N & C Chile, possibly S Peru.

P. g. gracilis Burmeister, 1861 – W Argentina (Monte Desert).

P. g. maullinicus Philippi, 1903 – S Argentine and Chilean temperate forests.

Introduced (*griseus*) in Tierra del Fuego.

Descriptive notes. Head-body 50·1–66 cm, tail 11·5–34·7 cm; weight 2·5–5 kg. A small fox with large ears and a rufescent head flecked with white. Well-marked black spot on chin. Coat brindled gray, made up of agouti guard hairs with pale underfur. Black patch across thighs. Legs and feet pale tawny. Underparts pale gray. Tail long and bushy, with dorsal line and tip black and a mixed pale tawny and black pattern on the underside. The cranium is small, lacking an interparietal crest. Teeth widely separated. The dental formula is I 3/3, C 1/1, PM 4/4, M 2/3 = 42.

Habitat. Steppes, grasslands and scrublands. South American Gray Foxes generally inhabit plains and low mountains, but they have been reported to occur as high as 3500–4000 m. Although they occur in a variety of habitats, they prefer shrubby open areas. In Chile, they hunt more commonly in flat open patches of low scrub. In Chilean Patagonia, their typical habitat consists of shrubby steppe composed of coirón (*Festuca* spp., *Stipa* spp.) and ñires (*Nothofagus antarctica*). Burning and destruction of forests for sheep farming seems to have been advantageous for these foxes. In Torres del Paine National Park, 58% of twelve individuals monitored showed preferential use of matorral shrubland or *Nothofagus* thicket habitat within their home ranges. In the Mendoza desert, Argentina, they prefer the lower levels of shrubby sand dunes rather than higher sections. They tolerate a variety of climates, including hot and dry areas such as the Atacama coastal desert in northern Chile (less than 2 mm average annual rainfall, 22°C mean annual temperature), the humid, temperate Valdivian forest (2000 mm average annual rainfall, 12°C mean annual temperature), and the cold environment of Tierra del Fuego (c. 400 mm average annual rainfall, 7°C mean annual temperature).

Food and Feeding. South American Gray Foxes are omnivorous generalists, feeding on a variety of foods, including mammals, arthropods, birds, reptiles, fruit, and carrion. Fruits ingested include berries of *Cryptocarya alba* and *Lithraea caustica* in Chile, pods of *Prosopis* spp., and the berry-like fruits of *Prosopanche americana* and of several Cactaceae in Argentina. A tendency to carnivory is apparent, however, since vertebrates, especially rodents, are reported to be the most important prey in most studies. Small mammals were the most frequently occurring vertebrate prey in most sites in the Chilean matorral and in the temperate rainforests of southern Chile. In Torres del Paine National Park, the European Hare was the most represented vertebrate prey, followed by carrion and akodontine rodents. In the Argentine Patagonian steppe, carrion was the most important food item in 42 stomachs collected in winter (representing 62% of biomass ingested), followed by hares and cricetine rodents. In Argentina's southern Patagonia, diet also consisted primarily of carrion, followed by birds, rodents, and fruit. Diet included invertebrates, carrion, birds, and rodents in Tierra del Fuego. In the harshest habitats of its range, the foxes' diets include increasingly higher proportions of non-mammal food as small mammal availability decreases. Lizards were the most consumed vertebrate prey in winter, the season of lowest small mammal availability in coastal northern Chile. Small-mammal consumption decreased from autumn to summer, and fruit consumption increased. In central Chile, berries appeared in 52% of the droppings (n = 127) collected in autumn, while in spring, when small mammal availability is highest, berries were present in only 18% of the feces (n = 62). In Mendoza (Monte desert), fruit was represented in 35% of feces (n = 116), followed by small mammals (19% frequency of occurrence). Foraging occurs mostly in open areas. Although hunting groups of up to 4–5 individuals have been reported, South American Gray Foxes mostly hunt solitarily, except perhaps at the end of the breeding season, when juveniles may join the parents in search of food. In Torres del Paine National Park, the most common foraging behavior consisted of slow walking, with abrupt, irregular turns through low vegetation. The same report noted that prey appear to be located by sound, sight, and smell. Mice are captured with a sudden leap or by rapidly digging holes. Scavenging is common, as well as defecation on and around Guanaco (*Lama guanicoe*) and domestic goat carcasses. Caching behavior has also been reported.

Activity patterns. Direct observations and prey activity patterns suggest that South American Gray Foxes are crepuscular, although they are commonly seen during the day. Radio-tracking showed that they were primarily nocturnal in Torres del Paine National Park, whereas they were active during both day and night in Reserva Nacional Las Chinchillas.

Movements, Home range and Social organization. The basic component of social organization in Torres del Paine National Park is the breeding monogamous pair, accompanied by occasional female helpers. Male dispersal and occasional polygyny is also reported. Solitary individuals were seen from March to July, while pairs comprised 42% of sightings during August. The male and female of an observed pair maintained an exclusive home range year-round, which did not overlap with home ranges of neighboring pairs. Intraspecific interactions were few and usually aggressive. Individual home range sizes (n = 23) averaged 2·0 km².

Breeding. Mating occurs in August and September, the gestation period is 53–58 days and 4–6 pups are born in October. Dens are located in a variety of natural and man-made places such as a hole at the base of a shrub or in culverts under a dirt road The pups may be moved to a new location during the nursing period. During the first few days the mother rarely leaves the den and the male provisions her with food. Pups are cared for by both parents on an approximately equal time basis. Young foxes start to emerge from the den when they are about one month old, and start to disperse (8–65 km) at 6–7 months of age. Two interesting phenomena concerning breeding behavior may occur: litters of two females combine (associated with polygyny) and the presence of female helpers. Both seem to be related to food availability and litter size. Female helpers contribute by bringing provisioning food to the den and increasing anti-predator vigilance.

Status and Conservation. CITES Appendix II. Classified as Least Concern on *The IUCN Red List*. Considered "locally common" in Argentina and stable in the southern half of the country where habitat is more favorable. Reported to have expanded their range in Tierra del Fuego since being introduced there: in 1996 their density was estimated at 1 per km². Hunting them and fur trading are legal in Argentine Patagonia and Tierra del Fuego. All Chilean populations are currently protected by law, except for those from Tierra del Fuego. The main threat to South American Gray Fox populations in the past was commercial hunting for fur. Hunting intensity has apparently declined in recent years. Illegal killing still occurs in some regions, as the foxes are perceived to be voracious predators of small livestock, poultry and game. The usual means of hunting are by shooting, dogs, poison, snares, and foothold traps. Around 45% of the mortality documented in Torres del Paine National Park resulted from either poaching or dog attacks. Road kills are frequently observed in Argentina, especially in summer.

Bibliography. Cabrera (1958), Campos & Ojeda (1997), Durán *et al.* (1985), González del Solar & Rau (2004), González del Solar *et al.* (1997), Jaksic, Jiménez *et al.* (1990), Jaksic, Schlatter & Yáñez (1980), Jaksic, Yáñez & Rau (1983), Jayat *et al.* (1999), Jiménez (1993), Jiménez, Yáñez, Tabilo & Jaksic (1996), Johnson & Franklin (1994a, 1994b, 1994c), Mares *et al.* (1996), Marquet *et al.* (1993), Martínez *et al.* (1993), Medel & Jaksic (1988), Novaro, Funes & Walker (2000), Rau *et al.* (1995), Simonetti *et al.* (1984), Yáñez & Jaksic (1978), Zunino *et al.* (1995).

17. Pampas Fox *Pseudalopex gymnocercus*

French: Renard d'Azara / **German**: Pampasfuchs / **Spanish**: Zorro de La Pampa
Other common names: Azara's Fox

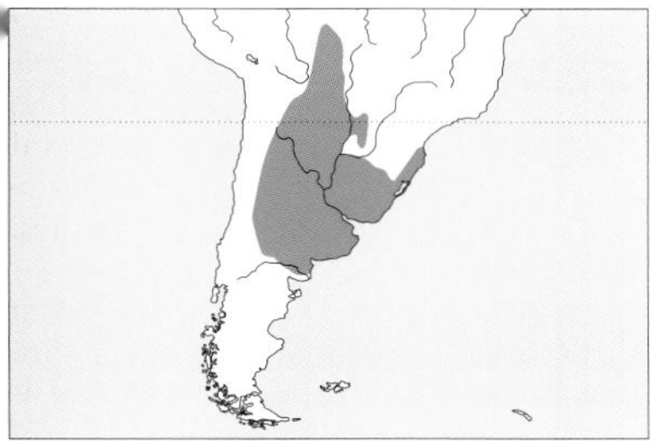

Taxonomy. *Procyon gymnocercus* Fischer, 1814, Paraguay.

Three subspecies have been proposed. Their geographic limits are not precise and it has been suggested that along their borders they could coexist and interbreed.

Subspecies and Distribution.

P. g. gymnocercus Fischer, 1814 – subtropical grasslands of NE Argentina, SE Brazil, Paraguay, and Uruguay.

P. g. antiquus Ameghino, 1889 – Pampas grasslands, monte scrublands, and open woodlands of C Argentina.

P. g. lordi Massoia, 1982 – Chaco-montane tropical forest ecotone in NW Argentina (Salta & Jujuy Provinces).

The subspecific status of the Pampas Fox from Entre Ríos Province in Argentina remains unclear, and there are no data regarding the taxonomic position of Bolivian foxes.

Descriptive notes. Head-body 59·7–74 cm for males and 50·5–72 cm for females, tail 28–38 cm for males and 25–41 cm for females; weight 4–8 kg for males and 3–5·7 kg for females. Medium-sized, smaller than Culpeo. The head, somewhat triangular in shape, is reddish with a pale gray to white ventral surface. Ears triangular, broad and relatively large, reddish on the outer surface and white on the inner surface. The rostrum is narrow, ventrally pale, black in the chin and reddish to black dorsally. The eyes are oblique in appearance. The body, back, and sides are gray, like the outer surface of the hindlimbs, which have a characteristic black spot on the lower rear side. There is a dark, almost black band along the back and tail. The tail is relatively long, bushy, and gray, with a black tip. The outer surface of the front limbs and the distal surface of the hindlimbs are reddish. Smaller size and lack of interparietal crest distinguish its skull from that of the Culpeo. Dental formula is I 3/3, C 1/1, PM 4/4, M 2/3 = 42.

Habitat. The Pampas Fox is a typical inhabitant of the pampas grasslands of South America's Southern Cone. It prefers open habitats, tall grass plains and sub-humid to dry habitats, but is also common in ridges, dry scrublands and open woodlands. In drier habitats in the southerly and easterly parts of its range, the species is replaced by the South American Gray Fox. Where its range overlaps with that of the Crab-eating Fox, the Pampas Fox selects more open areas. Apparently it has been able to adapt to the habitat alterations caused by extensive cattle breeding and agricultural activities.

Food and Feeding. Like most other medium-sized foxes, the Pampas Fox is a generalist and adaptable carnivore. Its diet shows great geographic variation and may include both wild and domestic vertebrates (particularly rodents and birds), fruit, insects, carrion, and garbage. Based on stomach contents, wild mammals and sheep appeared to be the two most common food items in Uruguay, while in La Pampa Province, Argentina, European Hares and rodents were the most common food items, followed by birds and carrion. In Buenos Aires Province, Argentina, there was a high frequency of rodents and birds, but also of insects, fruits, and crabs. Seasonal and local variations in diet are likely connected to variations in food availability. The Pampas Fox is a solitary and opportunistic carnivore. Large, highly concentrated food resources (i.e. large mammal carcasses) may cause several individuals to gather, possibly beyond the borders of normal home ranges. Food caching behavior has been observed, apparently related to an increase in the availability of rodents.

Activity patterns. Forages both day and night, although activity is mainly nocturnal in areas with severe hunting pressure.

Movements, Home range and Social organization. Pampas Foxes are thought to form monogamous pairs, but they are solitary most of the time: 88% of observations in the Paraguayan Chaco and 93% in Argentine La Pampa Province were of single individuals. Pairs are frequently observed from the time of mating until pups leave the natal den. In a Sierra grassland area, the respective home ranges of two adult males were estimated at 0·4 and 0·45 km². Defecation-site features suggest that droppings are used in intraspecific communication. Long-distance calls, which peak in frequency during the breeding period, may serve to maintain contact between pair members, as well as play a role in territorial behavior. When pairs are raising pups, both adult foxes have been observed using a brief and repeated alarm call if they detect a potential threat to the young.

Breeding. In central Argentina, pups are born from October to December. Gestation lasts 55–60 days, and litter sizes range from 3–5. Dens may be located in a variety of shelters, such as a hole at the base of a tree trunk, an armadillo (Dasypodidae spp.) den, or among rocks. Pups are frequently moved to a new location. The young stay at the den for the first three months. Both pair mates have been observed to guard the den, and males provide food to pups and females at the den. Females may breed at 8–12 months of age.

Status and Conservation. CITES Appendix II. Classified as Least Concern on *The IUCN Red List* and the Argentina Red List of Mammals. Abundant or common in most areas. In Argentina trade was prohibited in 1987. However, it continues to be hunted. In Uruguay and Paraguay the species is protected by law. In Argentina and southern Brazil the Pampas Fox was considered an important predator of sheep and goats, and was consequently persecuted by livestock ranchers. The Pampas Fox is currently threatened by the official implementation of control measures (promoted by ranchers) and the use of non-selective methods of capture. Fox control by government agencies involves the use of bounty systems without any thorough studies on population abundance or the real damage that this species may cause. In rural areas, direct persecution is also common, even where hunting is illegal. Most of the species' range in the Pampas region has suffered massive habitat alteration due to extensive cattle ranching and agriculture. Although apparently able to withstand hunting pressure and habitat loss, the sum of these threats may nevertheless eventually cause the depletion of fox populations. Rural residents have traditionally hunted the Pampas Fox for its fur, an important source of income. Hunting pressure has resulted in diminished populations in north-west Argentina. In Uruguay, illegal trade is still widespread. Pampas Foxes are also frequently struck by cars in some areas.

Bibliography. Barquez *et al.* (1991), Branch (1994), Brooks (1992), Cabrera (1958), Cajal (1986), Chebez (1994), Cravino *et al.* (1997), Crespo (1971), Diaz & Ojeda (2000), Farias, A.A. (2000), García, J. (1991), García, V.B. (2001), Lucherini *et al.* (2004), Massoia (1982), Novaro & Funes (1994), Redford & Eisenberg (1992), Vuillermoz & Sapoznikow (1998), Zunino *et al.* (1995).

18. Sechuran Fox *Pseudalopex sechurae*

French: Renard de Sechura / **German**: Sechura-Fuchs / **Spanish**: Zorro del Sechura
Other common names: Sechura Desert Fox, Peruvian Desert Fox

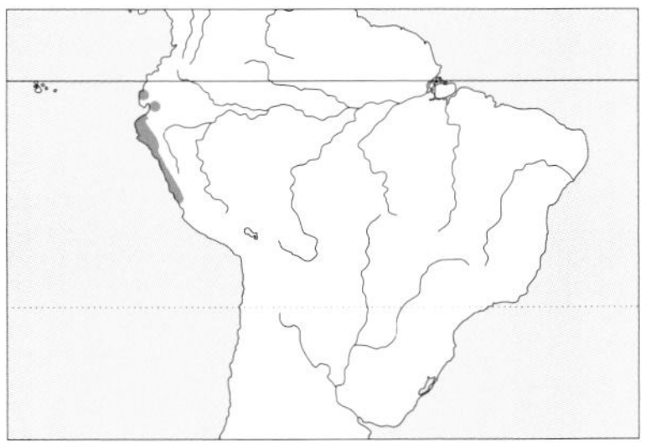

Taxonomy. *Canis sechurae* Thomas, 1900, NW Peru.

Monotypic.

Distribution. Coastal zones of NW Peru and SW Ecuador, between 3° S and 12° S latitude.

Descriptive notes. Head-body 50–78 cm and tail 27–34 cm for males; weight 2·6–4·2 kg for males. The smallest species of the genus *Pseudalopex*. The head is small, with relatively long ears (about two thirds the length of the head) and a short muzzle. Face is gray, and there is a rufous-brown ring around the eyes. The ears may be reddish on the back; the dark muzzle may have paler hairs around the lips. The pelage consists of pale underfur with agouti guard hairs; the underparts are fawn or cream-colored. There is sometimes a dark stripe down the back. The forelimbs (up to the elbows) and the hindlimbs (up to the heels) are usually reddish in color. The tail is relatively long and densely furred, ending in a dark tip. The dental formula is I 3/3, C 1/1, PM 4/4, M 2/3 = 42. The carnassials are slightly smaller, and the grinding teeth larger, than in allied forms; the canines are "fox-like".

Habitat. Occupies a variety of habitats ranging from sandy deserts with low plant density to agricultural lands and dry forests. Few details of habitat preferences are known.

Food and Feeding. The Sechuran Fox is a generalist omnivore that preferentially consumes vertebrate prey or carrion when available, but often depends predominantly on seeds or seed pods. Feces collected during late winter and early spring in the inland Sechuran Desert contained mainly the remnants of undigested seeds or seed pods of algarrobo (*Prosopis juliflora*), zapote (*Capparis scabrida*) and vizcacho (*C. avicennifolia*). The syrupy matrix surrounding the seeds may be the actual source of nourishment. In a germination experiment, seeds recovered from feces sprouted earlier than those gathered from the ground, suggesting that the foxes not only act as seed dispersers, but affect the ability of the seeds to germinate rapidly when sporadic rains occur. Fox droppings along the coast contained crabs and several bird species. Following El Niño rains, fox droppings revealed a dramatic dietary shift to grasshoppers and mice (*Par-*

alomys gerbillus) as these prey became more abundant. In central Peru, the main summer foods were insects, scorpions (*Carica candicans*), fruits, and rodents. The lack of standing water in the inland desert habitat suggests that the foxes can survive without drinking. However, they may lick condensation from vegetation on foggy mornings. No food caching has been recorded.

Activity patterns. Primarily nocturnal. Radio-telemetry tracking indicated that individuals emerged from their rocky daytime sleeping dens before sunset and remained active through most of the night before re-entering the dens at dawn. The phases of the moon did not influence this activity pattern, perhaps because the foxes were consuming seeds and seed pods rather than hunting. Occasionally, they are seen during the day.

Movements, Home range and Social organization. Little known. Groups larger than three individuals are rare, and usually only observed where food sources are concentrated. The home range of a radio-tracked adult male adjoined that of one adult female accompanied by two almost full-grown juveniles. However, they each foraged separately during the night and occupied separate dens during the day.

Breeding. Few details of breeding behavior known. Births are reported to occur primarily in October and November.

Status and Conservation. CITES not listed. Classified as Near Threatened on *The IUCN Red List*. While the species is easily observed in rural areas and disturbed environments from the states of Piura to La Libertad in Peru, large population fluctuations due to disease and persecution are causes for concern. Footprint surveys in Piura, Peru, show an average of 12·6 foxes per km. The Sechuran Fox is uncommon in Ecuador. In Peru, hunting outside established areas and trade has been prohibited since 2000, but it has proven difficult to control trade in rural areas. The most important threats are the market for handicrafts and amulets that are made of Sechuran Fox parts, and persecution because of damage to livestock. In Peru, the attitude of rural inhabitants to the species is antagonistic (68·3% of correspondents) or indifferent (31·7%). The stated reasons for favoring persecution were predation on domestic fowl and guinea pigs (65% of correspondents), the consumption of vegetables or stored goods (13·3%), and belief that goat predation occurs (10%). The Sechuran Fox also faces some pressure in agricultural zones and from urbanization and habitat degradation; habitat loss is considered the principle threat to this species in Ecuador.

Bibliography. Asa & Cossios (2004), Asa & Wallace (1990), Birdseye (1956), Cabrera (1931), Centro de Datos para la Conservación (1989), Huey (1969), Langguth (1975).

19. Hoary Fox *Pseudalopex vetulus*

French: Renard chenu / **German**: Brasilianischer Kampfuchs / **Spanish**: Zorro brasileño

Other common names: Small-toothed Dog

Taxonomy. *Canis vetulus* Lund, 1842, Minas Gerais, Brazil.
Monotypic.

Distribution. Confined to Brazil, associated with the Cerrado habitats of the central Brazilian plateau.

Descriptive notes. Head-body 49–71·5 cm for males and 51–66 cm for females, tail 27–38 cm for males and 25–31 cm for females; weight 2·5–4 kg for males and 3–3·6 kg for females. Slender with a relatively short, pointed muzzle and large ears. Pelage color is variable: the upperparts are pale gray, whereas the underparts are generally buff yellow to chestnut, including the neck, chest and a patch behind the ears. The anterior part of the neck is buff white, but the underside of the lower jaw is dark, almost black, as are both the tail base and tail tip; a dark spot on the dorsal surface of the tail base is variably present. Near melanic forms have been described. Dental formula is I 3/3, C 1/1, PM 4/4, M 2/3 = 42.

Habitat. Occurs in open cerrado habitats, but readily adapts to insect-rich livestock pastures and agricultural fields. Rarely observed in densely wooded cerrado, floodplains, or dry or gallery forests.

Food and Feeding. Omnivorous, though the diet is mainly insects, particularly ground-dwelling harvester termites (*Synthermes* spp. and *Cornitermes* spp.), recorded in 87% of feces across its geographical range. Dung beetles are consumed in great quantities when seasonally abundant. Other prey includes small mammals, grasshoppers, birds, and reptiles. Hoary Foxes tend to hunt as individuals or in loosely-knit pairs, with or without their juvenile offspring. Foraging group sizes of 3–5 were most common during periods of insect swarming. Hoary Foxes consume termites directly from the ground surface, or from the underside of dried cattle dung, which they flip over by pushing the dung along the ground at speed. Fox pups start eating insects at the age of at least two months. During the early rainy season, adult and young foxes catch flying ant and termite elates, as well as dung beetles.

Activity patterns. Predominantly nocturnal.

Movements, Home range and Social organization. Monogamous. One study group living in pasture were an adult breeding pair and their five juvenile offspring. They shared largely overlapping home ranges of 4·6 km² (range 4·5–4·6 km²). Contact rates of a single breeding pair estimated by radio-telemetry indicated that they spent up to 35% of their activity period in close proximity, though this varied substantially when they were rearing offspring (October to May). Spot sightings in different habitats and localities revealed that groups were composed of single animals on 75% of occasions, followed by pairs (30%), and groups larger than two (4%). Vocalizations are most common during the mating season and include a roar and threatening bark. Hoary

Foxes urinate using a raised leg position; frequent urination in small quantities is typical of territory marking behavior.

Breeding. In the wild, females produce litters of 4–5 offspring once a year during July and August. Pups are born in disused armadillo burrows, particularly dens of *Euphractus sexcinctus*. Offspring are cared for by the breeding male and female; there is no evidence that other foxes help. During late lactation, the female may visit the den a couple of times per night to nurse; in her absence, the male babysits, grooms, and guards the pups against potential predators. Post-weaning female contact declines substantially, whereas the male stays with the pups during hunting expeditions to insect patches close to the den. The estimated lactation period in the wild is three months. Juveniles of both sexes disperse when 9–10 months old and may establish home ranges adjacent to their natal territory.

Status and Conservation. CITES not listed. Classified as Least Concern on *The IUCN Red List*. Considered "vulnerable" in individual state faunal status accounts, but not listed in the Brazilian list of threatened mammals. No reliable data on population size, but considered locally abundant in the central highland cerrado biome, although populations appear smaller than those of the sympatric Crab-eating Fox, for which population estimates are similarly lacking. There is no specific hunting legislation for Hoary Foxes. The principal biome where Hoary Foxes occur is the cerrado, which is being destroyed at a rate of 3% each year, largely in the interests of agriculture (livestock and soybean). It appears that Hoary Foxes adapt to livestock pasture rich in termites and dung beetles. Breeding foxes are found in deforested wooded areas; thus it is possible that deforestation may not have a negative impact on the species. Areas of high human population density are unlikely to be suitable. Hoary Foxes are killed indiscriminately as predators of domestic fowl, although Crab-eating Foxes are probably more often the predators. Young foxes are often taken as pets. Some are killed by domestic dogs when dens are located in peri-urban areas. Road kills have been recorded.

Bibliography. Cabrera & Yepes (1960), Coimbra-Filho (1966), Costa & Courtenay (2003), Courtenay & Maffei (2004), Dalponte (1997, 2003), Dalponte & Courtenay (2004), Fonseca *et al.* (1994), Juarez & Marinho (2002), Silveira (1999), Stains (1974).

Genus *UROCYON*
Baird, 1857

20. Northern Gray Fox *Urocyon cinereoargenteus*

French: Renard gris / **German**: Graufuchs / **Spanish**: Chacalillo gris

Other common names: Tree Fox

Taxonomy. *Canis cinereoargenteus* Schreber, 1775, eastern North America.
Sufficiently distinct from vulpine foxes to warrant recognition as a separate genus. The Northern Gray Fox often clusters genetically with two other ancient lineages, the Raccoon Dog and the Bat-eared Fox, but the exact relationship is unclear. *Urocyon* is currently considered a basal genus within the Canidae and has only two surviving members, the Northern Gray Fox and Island Fox (*U. littoralis*). Up to sixteen subspecies are recognized.

Subspecies and Distribution.
U. c. cinereoargenteus Schreber, 1775 – E USA.
U. c. borealis Merriam, 1903 – SE Canada and USA (New England).
U. c. californicus Mearns, 1897 – SW USA (S California).
U. c. costaricensis Goodwin, 1938 – Costa Rica.
U. c. floridanus Rhoads, 1895 – Gulf of Mexico.
U. c. fraterculus Elliot, 1896 – Mexico (Yucatan).
U. c. furvus G. M. Allen & Barbour, 1923 – Panama.
U. c. guatemalae G. S. Miller, 1899 – S Mexico S to Nicaragua.
U. c. madrensis Burt & Hooper, 1941 – Mexico (S Sonora, SW Chihuahua & NW Durango).
U. c. nigrirostris Lichtenstein, 1830 – SW Mexico.
U. c. ocythous Bangs, 1899 – USA (Central Plains) and adjoining S Canada.
U. c. orinomus Goldman, 1938 – S Mexico (Isthmus of Tehuantepec).
U. c. peninsularis Huey, 1928 – NW Mexico (Baja California).
U. c. scottii Mearns, 1891 – N Mexico and SW USA.
U. c. townsendi Merriam, 1899 – W USA (California & Oregon).
U. c. venezuelae J. A. Allen, 1911 – Colombia, Venezuela.

Descriptive notes. Head-body 56–66 cm for males, 54–57·8 cm for females, tail 33·3–44·3 cm for males, 28·0–40·7 cm for females; weight 3·4–5·5 kg for males and 2–3·9 kg for females. Medium-sized with a stocky body, moderately short legs and medium-sized ears. Coat grizzled gray on the back and sides with a dark longitudinal stripe on top of a black-tipped tail. Conspicuous cinnamon-rusty color on its neck, sides and limbs. Face with dark and white markings. There is also white on its ears, throat, chest, belly and hind limbs. The tail is thick and bushy, and the fur has a coarse appearance. The dental formula is I 3/3, C 1/1, PM 4/4, M 2/3 = 42. The posterior ventral border of the dentition has a prominent notch or "step", and on the cranium, the temporal ridges are separated anteriorly but connect posteriorly to form a distinctive "U" shape.

Habitat. Closely associated with deciduous and southern pine forests interspersed with old fields and scrubby woodlands in eastern North America. In the west, commonly found in mixed agricultural, woodland, chaparral, riparian landscapes, and shrub habitats. In Central America, occupies forested areas and thick brush habitats, and in South America forested montane habitats. Northern Gray Foxes occur in semi-arid areas of the south-western USA and northern Mexico where cover is sufficient. They also live at the margins of some urban areas.

Food and Feeding. Omnivorous. During winter, prey consists largely of rabbits (*Sylvilagus* spp.) and rodents. In spring and summer it diversifies to include insects (e.g. grasshoppers), birds, and sometimes carrion. Northern Gray Foxes also feed on natural fruits and nuts, often consuming more of these foods in the fall as their availability increases.

Activity patterns. Mostly nocturnal.

Movements, Home range and Social organization. Monogamy with occasional polygyny is probably most typical. The basic social unit is the mated pair and their offspring of the year; it is not known whether breeding pairs remain together during consecutive years. Offspring typically disperse at 9–10 months of age, and although long-distance dispersal (over 80 km) has been reported, young foxes may also return to and settle down near their natal ranges. Gray Foxes exhibit some territoriality, as home ranges of adjacent family groups may overlap, but core areas appear to be used exclusively by a single family. Home range size varies from 0·8 km² to 27·6 km². Foxes increase their home ranges during late fall and winter, possibly in response to changes in food resource availability. Scent marking consists of urine and feces depositions in conspicuous locations. The foxes communicate vocally with growls, alarm barks, screams, and "coos" and "mewing" sounds during greetings. Northern Gray Foxes engage in allogrooming, adults grooming juveniles and each other.

Breeding. Northern Gray Foxes reach sexual maturity at ten months of age, although not all females breed in their first year. Breeding generally occurs from January to April, with gestation lasting about 60 days. Litter size average is 4, ranging from 1–10. Pups accompany adults on foraging expeditions at three months and forage independently at four months. Pups are fed mainly by females, but males may also participate in parental care. Northern Gray Foxes give birth and rear their pups in earthen dens, which they either dig themselves or modify from other species. They will also den in wood and brush piles, rock crevices, hollow logs, hollows under shrubs, and under abandoned buildings. They may even den in hollows of trees up to nine meters above the ground. In eastern deciduous forests, dens are in brushy or wooded areas, where they are less conspicuous than the dens of sympatric Red Foxes. Use of dens diminishes greatly during non-reproductive seasons, when Northern Gray Foxes typically rest in dense vegetation during the day.

Status and Conservation. CITES not listed. Classified as Least Concern on *The IUCN Red List*. Common where it occurs, but appears to be restricted to locally dense habitats where it is not excluded by Coyotes and Bobcats. Reported densities range from 0·4/km² in California to 1·5/km² in Florida. The Gray Fox is legally protected as a harvested species in Canada and the USA. Trapping is legal throughout much of its range, and is likely to be the most important source of mortality where it occurs and probably limits populations locally.

Bibliography. Chamberlain (2002), Chamberlain & Leopold (2000), Cohen & Fox (1976), Davis & Schmidly (1994), Eisenberg (1989), Farias, V. (2000), Follman (1973, 1978), Fox (1970), Fritzell (1987), Fritzell & Haroldson (1982), Fuller & Cypher (2004), Greenberg & Pelton (1994), Grinnell *et al.* (1937), Hall (1981), Harrison (1997), Nicholson (1982), Nicholson & Hill (1981), Nicholson *et al.* (1985), Sullivan (1956), Trapp & Hallberg (1975), Wayne *et al.* (1997), Wood (1958), Yearsley & Samuel (1982).

21. Island Fox *Urocyon littoralis*

French: Renard insulaire / **German:** Insel-Graufuchs / **Spanish:** Cachalillo isleño

Other common names: Island Gray Fox, Channel Islands Fox

Taxonomy. *Vulpes littoralis* Baird, 1858, San Miguel Island, California, USA.

Urocyon is currently considered a basal genus within the Canidae and has only two surviving members, *U. cinereoargenteus* and *U. littoralis*. The latter is believed to be a direct descendant of the former, having reached the Channel Islands either by chance over-water dispersal or human-assisted dispersal. A series of genetic analyses justifies the current classification of Island Foxes as a separate species and the recognition of six subspecies.

Subspecies and Distribution.

U. l. littoralis Baird, 1858 – SW USA (San Miguel I).
U. l. catalinae Merriam, 1903 – SW USA (Santa Catalina I).
U. l. clementae Merriam, 1903 – SW USA (San Clemente I).
U. l. dickeyi Grinnell & Linsdale 1930 – SW USA (San Nicolas I).
U. l. santacruzae Merriam, 1903 – SW USA (Santa Cruz I).
U. l. santarosae Grinnell & Linsdale 1930 – SW USA (Santa Rosa I).

Descriptive notes. Head-body 47–59 cm for males and 45·6–63·4 cm for females, tail 14·5–31 cm for males and 11·5–29·5 cm for females; weight 1·4–2·5 kg for males an 1·3–2·4 kg for females. The Island Fox is the smallest North American canid. Males are significantly heavier than females. The head is gray with black patches on the sides of the muzzle, and the upper and lower lips are outlined in black. White patches on the muzzle extend behind the lateral black patches, to the cheek, and blend into the ventral surface of the neck, which is mostly white. There are small white patches on the side of the nose. Variable degrees of white and rufous color on the chest and belly. The body and tail are mostly gray, the tail with a conspicuous black stripe on the dorsal surface ending in a black tip. Pelage is relatively short. Eight mammae are present. Dental formula is I 3/3, C 1/1, PM 4/4, M 2/3 = 42. Island Foxes typically have fewer caudal vertebrae (15–22) than the Northern Gray Fox (21–22).

Habitat. Present in all habitats on the islands, including native perennial and exotic European grassland, coastal sage scrub, maritime desert scrub, *Coreopsis* scrub, *Isocoma* scrub, chaparral, oak woodland, pine woodland, riparian, and inland and coastal dune. Generally not found in areas highly degraded by human disturbance or overgrazing. Recently, Foxes have become scarce owing to precipitous population declines. On the northern Channel Islands declines are principally a consequence of hyperpredation by golden eagles (*Aquila chrysaetos*); on those islands the foxes are more numerous in habitats with dense cover.

Food and Feeding. Island Foxes are omnivorous and feed on a wide variety of insects, vertebrates, fruits, terrestrial molluscs, and near-shore invertebrates. The relative abundance of insects, mammals, and plant material in the diet has been found to differ by habitat type, and by island, depending upon availability of food items. For example, North American Deermouse (*Peromyscus maniculatus*) occur at high densities on San Miguel Island, where they constitute a large proportion of Fox diet. On Santa Cruz Island, Jerusalem crickets (*Stenopelmatus fuscus*) are a principal prey. The fruits of the coastal prickly pear cactus (*Opuntia littoralis*) are a principal food on San Clemente Island. Bird remains in droppings are usually occur infrequently (3–6%), except in San Miguel Island where bird remains were found in 22% (n = 208). Island Foxes primarily forage alone, by coursing back and forth through suitable habitat patches and then moving past little-used habitats to other suitable habitat patches.

Activity patterns. Island Foxes forage mostly at night, but also during the day.

Movements, Home range and Social organization. Island Foxes typically form monogamous pairs occupying discrete territories. Full-grown young may remain within their natal range into their second year. The home ranges are among the smallest recorded for any canid, ranging between 0·15 and 0·9 km². On Santa Cruz Island, home ranges expanded when neighboring foxes were killed by golden eagles, suggesting that density of foxes and the spatial distribution of neighbors may influence territory size. Foxes communicate using visual, auditory and olfactory cues. Males have been observed chasing and fighting with other males. Foxes demarcate territory boundaries with latrine sites and have been observed urinating as frequently as every 6–9 m.

Breeding. Foxes breed once a year, mainly in April. Recent research suggests they may have induced ovulation, allowing for plasticity in the timing of reproduction. Litter size varies from one to five, but most litters are smaller, from one to three. Average litter size for 24 dens located on Santa Cruz was 2·2. Weaning is complete by mid- to late June and pups reach adult weight and become independent by September. Although most foxes are typically monogamous, extra-pair fertilization has been recorded: of 16 pups whose paternity was tested genetically, 25% were the result of extra-pair fertilizations. Dens consist of rock piles, dense brush, and natural cavities in the ground or under tree trunks.

Status and Conservation. CITES not listed. Classified as Critically Endangered on *The IUCN Red List*. Listed by the state of California as "threatened". Four of the six subspecies were also listed in 2004 as "USA federally endangered", including *santacruzae, santarosae, littoralis, and catalinae*. In recent years there have been catastrophic population declines. Island Fox numbers fell from approximately 6000 individuals to less than 1500 in 2002. The current primary threats to the species include golden eagle predation on the northern Channel Islands and the introduction of canine diseases, especially canine distemper virus (CDV), to all populations. An outbreak of CDV decimated the Santa Catalina Island Fox population from 1998–2000. All populations are small, several critically, and are thus especially vulnerable to any catastrophic mortality source, be it predation, canine disease, or environmental extremes.

Bibliography. Collins (1991a, 1991b, 1993), Collins & Laughrin (1979), Coonan (2002), Coonan & Rutz (2002), Cooper *et al.* (2001), Crooks & van Vuren (1995, 1996), Elliot & Popper (1999), Fausett (1982), Garcelon, Roemer *et al.* (1999), Garcelon, Wayne & Gonzales (1992), Goeden *et al.* (1967), Hall (1981), Kovach & Dow (1981), Laughrin (1973, 1977), Moore & Collins (1995), Roemer (1999), Roemer & Wayne (2003), Roemer, Coonan, Garcelon *et al.* (2001), Roemer, Coonan, Munson & Wayne (2004), Roemer, Donlan & Courchamp (2002), Roemer, Garcelon *et al.* (1994), Schmidt *et al.* (2002), Suckling & Garcelon (2000), Thompson *et al.* (1998), Timm, Barker *et al.* (2002), Timm, Stokely *et al.* (2000), Wayne, Geffen *et al.* (1997), Wayne, George *et al.* (1991).

PLATE 25

inches 14
cm 35

ssp *procyonoides*

22

ssp *ussuriensis*

winter

23

typical
morph

summer

winter

24

blue morph

25

26

Genus *NYCTEREUTES*
Temminck, 1839

22. Raccoon Dog *Nyctereutes procyonoides*
French: Tanuki / **German**: Marderhund / **Spanish**: Perro mapache
Other common names: Tanuki

Taxonomy. *Canis procyonoides* Gray, 1834, Canton, China.
The Raccoon Dog lineage probably diverged from other canids as early as 7–10 million years ago. Some features of the skull resemble those of South American canids, especially the Crab-eating Fox (*Cerdocyon thous*), but genetic studies have revealed that they are not close relatives. Six subspecies are recognized.
Subspecies and Distribution.
N. p. procyonoides Gray, 1834 – W & SW China and N Indochina.
N. p. albus Hornaday, 1904 – Japan (Hokkaido).
N. p. koreensis Mori, 1922 – Korean Peninsula.
N. p. orestes Thomas, 1923 – C & S China.
N. p. ussuriensis Matschie, 1907 – NE China, E Mongolia, and SE Russia.
N. p. viverrinus Temminck, 1839 – Japan.
Introduced (*ussuriensis*) to the Baltic states, Belarus, Bulgaria, Czech Republic, Finland, Germany, Hungary, Moldova, Poland, Romania, W Russia, Serbia, Slovakia, Sweden, and Ukraine, occasionally seen in Austria, Bosnia, Denmark, France, the Netherlands, Norway, Slovenia, and Switzerland.
Descriptive notes. Head-body 49·2–70·5 cm for males and 50·5–69 cm for females, tail 15–23 cm for males and 15–20·5 cm for females; weight 2·9–12·4 kg for males and 3–12·5 kg for females. In autumn and winter, race *ussuriensis* is very fat and has thick fur, giving an expression of a round animal with short, thin legs. Black facial mask, small rounded ears, and pointed muzzle. Hair is long on cheeks. The body color varies from yellow to gray or reddish, with black hairs on the back and shoulders and also dorsally on the tail. Legs, feet, and chest are dark. Underhair is gray or reddish. The tail is rather short and covered with thick hair. In summer when the fur is thin and fat reserves small, the animal looks much slimmer than in autumn. Dental formula is I 3/3, C 1/1, PM 4/4, M 2/3 = 42; M_3 sometimes missing. Body size of race *albus* is smaller than that of *ussuriensis*. Race *viverrinus* is similar to *albus* but with somewhat shorter fur, shorter hindlegs, and generally darker color. Skull and teeth are smaller than those of *ussuriensis*. Mandible width and jaw height for the skull and the lower and upper molars clearly distinguish the two subspecies.
Habitat. Typically found near water, and during autumn, habitat selection appears to be affected by reliance on fruits and berries. In Japan, Raccoon Dog habitat includes deciduous forests, broad-leaved evergreen forests, mixed forests, farmlands, and urban areas from coastal to sub-alpine zones. In the countryside, the species prefers herbaceous habitats and is less likely to use *Cryptomeria* plantations throughout the year, although riparian areas are often used. In urban environments, Raccoon Dogs inhabit areas with as little as 5% forest cover. In the Russian Far East, they avoid dense forests in favor of open landscapes, especially damp meadows and agricultural land. In the introduced range, Raccoon Dogs favor moist forests and shores of rivers and lakes, especially in early summer. In late summer and autumn they favor moist heaths with abundant berries. In the Finnish archipelago, however, they prefer barren pine forests, where they feed on crowberries (*Empetrum nigrum*).
Food and Feeding. Raccoon Dogs are omnivores and seasonal food habits shift as food availability changes. In most areas small rodents form the bulk of their diet in all seasons. Frogs, lizards, invertebrates, insects (including adults and larvae of *Orthoptera*, *Coleoptera*, *Hemiptera*, *Diptera*, *Lepidoptera*, *Odonata*), and birds and their eggs are also consumed, especially in early summer. Plants are eaten frequently; berries and fruits serve as an important and favored food source in late summer and autumn, when Raccoon Dogs decrease their food intake before entering winter dormancy. Oats, sweet corn, watermelon, and other agriculture products often are found in Raccoon Dog stomachs. Carrion, fish, and crustaceans are consumed when available. As opportunistic generalists, Raccoon Dogs forage by searching close to the ground and may also climb trees for fruits. They mainly forage in pairs, usually wandering some distance from each other.
Activity patterns. Mainly nocturnal, leaving their dens 1–2 hours after sunset. When they have pups, females also forage during the daytime while the male is babysitting. In spring, Raccoon Dogs are also seen during daytime when sunbathing on south-facing slopes of hills. In areas where winters are harsh they enter a form of hibernation (winter lethargy) in November and become active again in March. The Raccoon Dog is the only canid known to hibernate.
Movements, Home range and Social organization. Both males and females defend their home range against individuals of the same sex. Home range size varies according to the abundance of food. The core areas of different pairs are fully exclusive, especially during the breeding season. Peripheral areas of home ranges may overlap to some extent. In autumn there is more overlap than in spring and summer. Different

pairs seem to avoid each other even when their home ranges partially overlap. Resting sites may be shared with related family members, and latrine sites may be shared by several individuals. Home range sizes in Russia vary from 0·4–20 km² (larger ranges in introduced populations in western Russia). In southern Finland, home ranges recorded by radio-tracking ranged from 2·8 to 7 km². In Japan, home range size varies from as little as 0·07 km² in an urban setting to 6·1 km² in a sub-alpine area. Strictly monogamous, the male and female form a permanent pair, sharing a home range and foraging together. Only if one of the pair dies will the remaining member form a new pair bond. Some non-paired adults may stay within the same area and/or share the resting or feeding sites or dens, but usually do not move together. Raccoon Dogs do not bark, but growl when menaced. In Japan their vocalizations are higher in tone than those of a domestic dog and more or less resemble the sounds of a domestic cat.
Breeding. Testosterone levels in males peak in February/March, and progesterone levels in females coincide even with absence of males, suggesting that the species is monoestrous, with seasonal and spontaneous ovulation. Raccoon Dogs reach sexual maturity at 9–11 months and can breed in the first year, but a first-year female will enter estrus more than one month later than older females. Females can reproduce every year. Mating usually occurs in March, and the onset of spring and the length of winter lethargy determine the time of ovulation. Mating occurs in the back-to-back copulatory posture typical of other canids. Gestation period is nine weeks, parturition mostly occurring in May (varies from April to June). The parents settle in a den about a week before the pups are born. Raccoon Dogs will den in old European Badger (*Meles meles*) setts or fox dens, or alternatively dig their own dens in soft sandy soil. They will also use active Badger setts, usually together with Badgers. Winter dens usually are located within their home range, but if suitable dens are not available, they may be several kilometers outside the summer home range. Mean litter size varies between four and five in Japan (birth weight approximately 100 g) to nine in Finland and Poland (birth weight about 120 g), and also in the original distribution area in south-eastern Russia. Litter size in north-western Russia is smaller (6–7) on average because of the harsh winters. Litter size is affected by the abundance of wild berries: when berries are abundant, females are in good condition the following spring, and fetal mortality is low and litter sizes are large. At higher latitudes, the young are born later and remain small and slim in late autumn, and may not reproduce the following spring. Therefore, the productivity of the population is lower in areas with long winters compared to areas with milder climates. Pups start emerging from the den at three to four weeks of age and are weaned at about one week later. Both sexes exhibit parental care, taking turns attending the den during the early nursing period. Because the food items of Raccoon Dogs are small, food is not carried to the den. The pups are fed with milk until they start to forage for themselves. The young usually reach adult body size by the first autumn.
Status and Conservation. CITES not listed. Classified as Least Concern on *The IUCN Red List*. In many countries where the Raccoon Dog is hunted legally, hunting is permitted year round (e.g. Sweden, Hungary and Poland). However, in Finland females with pups are protected in May, June, and July, in Belarus hunting is allowed from October to February, and in Mongolia hunting requires a license and is allowed only from October to February. In Japan, hunting and trapping of the species also requires a license or other form of permission and is restricted to a designated hunting season. Species abundance is unknown in the Far East outside of Japan, where it is considered common. In its European range the species is common to abundant, although rare in Denmark and Sweden. Threats across its range include road kills, persecution, government attitudes, epidemics (scabies, distemper, and rabies), and pollution.

Bibliography. Bannikov (1964), Fukue (1991, 1993), Helle & Kauhala (1995), Ikeda (1982, 1983), Kauhala (1992, 1996), Kauhala & Auniola (2000), Kauhala & Helle (1995), Kauhala & Saeki (2004), Kauhala, Helle & Pietilä (1998), Kauhala, Helle & Taskinen (1993), Kauhala, Kaunisto & Helle (1993), Kauhala, Laukkanen & von Rége (1998), Korhonen (1988), Korhonen *et al.* (1991), Kowalczyk *et al.* (1999, 2000), Kozlov (1952), Nasimovic & Isakov (1985), Saeki (2001), Ward & Wurster-Hill (1990), Wayne (1993), Yachimori (1997), Yamamoto (1984), Yamamoto *et al.* (1994), Yoshioka *et al.* (1990).

Genus *OTOCYON*
Müller, 1836

23. Bat-eared Fox *Otocyon megalotis*
French: Otocyon / **German**: Löffelhund / **Spanish**: Zorro orejudo

Taxonomy. *Canis megalotis* Desmarest, 1822, Cape of Good Hope, South Africa.
Included by some authors in a separate subfamily, the Otocyoninae, on account of its atypical dentition. More recently this species was considered to have affinities with the vulpine line. Occurs in two distinct populations that are geographically separated by about 1000 km. The two populations were probably connected during the Pleistocene. Two subspecies are recognized.

On following pages: 24. Arctic Fox (*Alopex lagopus*); 25. Swift Fox (*Vulpes velox*); 26. Kit Fox (*Vulpes macrotis*).

435

Subspecies and Distribution.
O. m. megalotis Desmarest, 1822 – S Africa.
O. m. virgatus G. S. Miller, 1909 – E Africa.
Descriptive notes. Head-body 46·2–60·7 cm for males and 46·7–60·7 cm for females, tail 23–34 cm for males and 27·8–34 cm for females; weight 3·4–4·9 kg for males and 3·2–5·4 kg for females. A small, slight animal with slender legs, a long bushy tail and conspicuously large ears. Males are often slightly heavier than females. The back of the ears, front part of the snout, face mask, front and lower part of the back legs, and the mid-dorsal part of the tail are black. A whitish band extends from across the forehead up the first three quarters of the frontal rim of the ears. Some animals have a broad dark mid-dorsal band. Beige to honey-colored fur covers the lower jaw, the throat, chest, and underparts. The body and tail fur is thick and soft on the upper parts, with a black base and white tip, giving a grizzled or gray appearance. Bat-eared Foxes have 46–50 teeth, the largest number for any non-marsupial land mammal. They are unique amongst living eutherians (odontocetes excepted) in having four to five functional lower molars, and are the only modern canids with three to four upper molars. The milk dentition is typically canid, with unreduced carnassials. In adults, the carnassial shear is lost and molars become the most bunodont, verging on zalambdodont, of any canid. Supernumerary molars yield a dentition of I 3/3, C 1/1, PM 4/4, M 3-4/4-5 = 46–50.
Habitat. In southern Africa prime habitat is mainly short-grass plains and areas with bare ground, but foxes are also found in open scrub vegetation and arid or semi-arid shrub land and open arid savannah. The range of Bat-eared Foxes overlaps almost completely with that of termites of the *Hodotermes* and *Microhodotermes* genera that prevail in their diet. In East Africa Bat-eared Foxes are common in open grassland and woodland boundaries, but not on short-grass plains. Those areas occupied by Bat-eared Foxes usually contain more harvester termite (*H. mossambicus*) foraging holes and dung from migratory ungulates where beetles are likely to be found.
Food and Feeding. Insects are the primary food sources in open grassland and woodland edge habitats. Harvester termites and beetles are typically the most commonly consumed prey items. Diet is supplemented by orthopterans, beetle larvae, and ants. In open shrub savannahs, arachnids and fruit (consumed seasonally) may be among the more common food items. Small mammals, birds, eggs, and reptiles are eaten sporadically in southern Africa, but rarely in eastern Africa. There is seasonal variation in the proportion of particular taxa consumed: in the Serengeti dung beetles are the main source of food during the rainy season, when termite activity is reduced. When both beetles and termites are scarce, Bat-eared Foxes will dig up beetle larvae from the ground. Harvester termites and dung beetles are more abundant in areas inhabited by clusters of Bat-eared Fox families, and local differences in *H. mossambicus* density are inversely related to territory size. Although Fox water requirements may be met by the high water content of their insect prey or by berries during the summer, water is nevertheless a critical resource during lactation. Groups forage as a unit. Foraging techniques depend on prey type, but food is often located by walking slowly, nose close to the ground and ears cocked forward. Prey is detected mostly by sound and often excavated by digging. Foraging and feeding rates are higher when feeding on termite patches than on more dispersed insects. When feeding on termite patches, group members feed closely together, but when feeding on beetles, beetle larvae or grasshoppers, they can forage up to 200 m apart.
Activity patterns. Changes in daily and seasonal *H. mossambicus* availability directly affect Bat-eared Fox activity patterns. Activity is mostly nocturnal in eastern Africa. In southern Africa, nocturnal foraging during summer gradually changes to an almost exclusively diurnal pattern in winter, in accordance with the activity changes of *H. mossambicus*. Diurnal foraging peaks when insect activity is highest. Bat-eared Fox groups in the Serengeti frequently patrol known *Hodotermes* patches in their territory after leaving the den in the evening.
Movements, Home range and Social organization. In southern Africa Bat-eared Foxes live in monogamous pairs with their pups, while in eastern Africa they live in stable family groups consisting of a male and up to three closely related females with pups. Adult group size varies with the time of year, with a mean of 2·7 for southern Africa and 2·4 for eastern Africa; group size prior to pup dispersal is six. Additional females in extended family groups are usually philopatric daughters, sometimes from several generations, organized in an age-based hierarchy where all females breed. Young pups are taught to forage by the male, and social learning by pups also seems to play a role. In the Serengeti, parents facilitate better access to *H. mossambicus* patches by regularly guiding the smaller and more vulnerable pups from the breeding den to "nocturnal feeding dens". Nuclear family groups persist until cub dispersal. Home ranges vary from less than 1 km² to more than 3 km². Home ranges overlap widely and may be clustered around harvester termite colonies. Territories are patrolled and urine-marked during part of the year. Group size determines the outcome of territorial conflicts. Territory inheritance is not uncommon in the Serengeti and neighboring groups can be closely related, with animals visiting each other from time to time. Foxes engage in frequent and extended allogrooming sessions, which increase markedly during courtship. Vigorous and extended social play is very common, including among adults after the young have dispersed. Communication is primarily visual, and often based on a variety of ear and tail positions. The unique "inverted U" position of the tail, for example, is indicative of various states of arousal including fear, play and alarm. Vocalizations are mostly soft and sparingly used, except when the Foxes are highly alarmed or excited during play.
Breeding. Bat-eared Foxes become sexually mature at 8–9 months of age. Pair-bonding and mating occur from July to September, and involve up to ten copulations per day for several days. Copulatory ties last about four minutes, and are followed by post-copulatory play. Foxes have one litter per year. Births occur between October and December, following a gestation period of 60–75 days. Litter size ranges from 1–6, and neonates weigh 99–142 g. Dens are excavated or adapted from abandoned dens of other mammals, e.g. Spring hare, Aardvark, and even termite mounds and warthog (*Phacochoerus* spp.) holes. Dens can be located in clusters and may have several entrances, chambers, and tunnels. Small pups nurse inside the den and are sometimes moved between dens. They first emerge for brief periods when they are 8–12 days old. Dens are carefully maintained throughout the year and often used for generations. Parental care such as grooming, playing, and guarding against predators is mostly the responsibility of males. Female investment during lactation is high compared to other canids, and their insectivorous diet prevents mothers and/or pups from being provisioned directly. However, the high level of male parental care enables females to maximize their foraging time, compensating for the fact that their nutritional intake is limited to small, dispersed food items. Weaning (at 10–15 weeks) occurs after the first rains and the subsequent flush of insects. In Serengeti, the Bat-eared Fox commonly exhibits polygyny, communal breeding, and indiscriminate allosuckling. The number of pups raised averages 2·6, but in extended family units with more than one breeding female it averages 3·6. Sharing male partners enables additional breeding females to sustain the energetic costs associated with reproduction.
Status and Conservation. CITES not listed. Classified as Least Concern on *The IUCN Red List*. No current legal protection known. The species is common in conservation areas in southern and eastern Africa, becoming uncommon in arid areas and on farmland. Primary threats are hunting for skins, persecution as erroneously perceived predators of young lambs, and road kills. Population numbers can fluctuate from abundant to rare depending on rainfall, food availability, breeding stage and disease. Rabies and canine distemper have been reported to cause drastic population declines in some areas.
Bibliography. Berry (1978), Gittleman (1989), Guilday (1962), Kieser (1995), Koop & Velimirov (1982), Kuntzsch & Nel (1992), Lamprecht (1979), Le Clus (1971), Maas (1993a, 1993b), Maas & Macdonald (2004), Mackie (1988), Mackie & Nel (1989), Malcolm (1986), Nel (1978, 1990, 1993, 1999), Nel & Bester (1983), Nel & Maas (2004), Nel & Mackie (1990), Nel *et al.* (1984), Pauw (2000), Skinner & Smithers (1990), Smithers (1971), Stuart (1981), Waser (1980).

Genus *ALOPEX*

Kaup, 1829

24. Arctic Fox *Alopex lagopus*

French: Renard arctique / **German**: Polarfuchs / **Spanish**: Zorro ártico
Other common names: Polar Fox

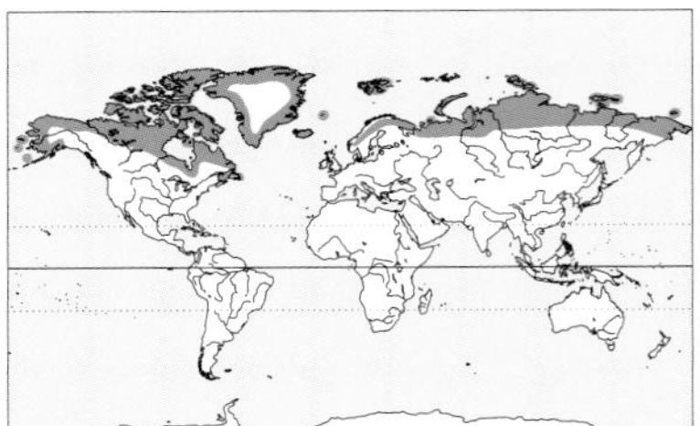

Taxonomy. *Canis lagopus* Linnaeus, 1758, Lapland, Sweden.
Sometimes placed as subgenus of *Vulpes* or *Canis*. The most closely related species are *V. velox* and *V. macrotis*, neither of which occur in the tundra. Four subspecies recognized.
Subspecies and Distribution.
A. l. lagopus Linnaeus, 1758 – most of the circumpolar range, in all Arctic tundra habitats.
A. l. beringensis Merriam, 1902 – Russia (Commander Is).
A. l. fuliginosus Bechstein, 1799 – Iceland, Greenland, Svalbard.
A.l. pribilofensis Merriam, 1902 – Alaska (Pribilof Is).
Descriptive notes. Head-body 55–75 cm (males), 50–65 cm (females), tail 28–42·5 cm for males and 25·5–32 cm females; weight 3·58–4·23 kg for males and 3·14–3·69 kg for females. Males are slightly larger than females. A small fox with rather short legs and a long fluffy tail. Thick and soft winter fur with dense underfur and long guard hairs. Occurs in two distinct color morphs, "blue" and "white". Both morphs change seasonally: "blue" molts from chocolate brown in summer to paler brown tinged with blue sheen in winter. In winter, the "white" morph is almost pure white with a few dark hairs at the tip of the tail and along the spine; in summer, it is brown dorsally and pale gray to white on its underside. Color morphs are determined genetically at a single locus, "white" being recessive. The "blue" morph comprises less than 1% of the population throughout most of its continental range, but comprises 25–30% in Fennoscandia (Norway, Sweden, and Finland) and 65–70% in Iceland. The proportion of "blue" morphs also increases in coastal areas and on islands, where it can reach up to 100% (e.g. Mednyi Island, Russia; St. Paul Island, Alaska). Within each morph there is considerable variation in appearance, which seems to be independent of the genetic locus for color morph. In Sweden, there occasionally are sand-colored foxes in summer, but they appear to be of the "white" morph without brown pigment, and in Iceland, cinnamon colored foxes of both the white and blue color morph occur. The dental formula is I 3/3, C 1/1, PM 4/4, M 2/3 = 42.
Habitat. Arctic and alpine tundra of Eurasia, North America, and the Canadian archipelago, Siberian islands, Greenland, inland Iceland, and Svalbard. Sub-Arctic maritime habitat in the Aleutian island chain, Bering Sea Islands, Commander Islands, and coastal Iceland.
Food and Feeding. The Arctic Fox is an opportunistic predator and scavenger. In most inland areas it is heavily dependent on fluctuating rodent populations. Main prey in-

clude Lemmings, both *Lemmus* spp. and *Dicrostonyx* spp. In Fennoscandia, *L. lemmus* was the main prey in summer (85% frequency of occurrence in feces) followed by birds (Passeriformes, Galliformes, and Caridriiformes, 34%) and Reindeer (*Rangifer tarandus*, 21%). In winter, ptarmigan and grouse (*Lagopus* spp.) are common prey, in addition to rodents and Reindeer. Changes in Fox populations have been observed to follow those of their main prey in three- to five-year cycles. Foxes living near ice-free coasts have access to inland prey and also sea birds, seal carcasses, fish, and invertebrates connected to the marine environment, leading to relatively stable food availability and a more generalist strategy. In late winter and summer, foxes found in coastal Iceland feed on seabirds (*Uria aalge*, *U. lomvia*), seal carcasses, and marine invertebrates. Inland foxes rely more on Ptarmigan in winter, and migrant birds, such as geese and waders, in summer. In certain areas, foxes rely on colonies of arctic geese, which can dominate their diet locally. Arctic Foxes forage singly, presumably the most efficient foraging technique in view of the species' main prey base of rodents and birds. When food is abundant, they cache food for later use. Caches can contain single prey items or a variety of items, and sometimes include lemmings or goose eggs.

Activity patterns. Arctic Foxes remain active year round. They are primarily nocturnal, but exhibit flexible activity patterns, often in accordance with main prey species.

Movements, Home range and Social organization. The basic social unit of the Arctic Fox is the breeding pair. Both parents take an active part in rearing the pups. For the first three weeks after birth, the pups are mostly dependent on milk and the female rarely leaves the natal den. During this time, the male provides food for the female. As meat increasingly forms a larger proportion of the pups' diet, the roles of the parents become more similar and the female takes an active part in hunting and provisioning the pups. Non-breeding foxes, usually yearlings from the previous litter, may help. Supernumerary females generally emigrate before the pups attain independence of the den at 8–10 weeks. However, on Mednyi Island, there are permanent Arctic Fox groups comprising up to six adults, and complex social systems have also been observed on other islands. Temporary groups of non-breeding individuals are also sometimes formed. Arctic Foxes normally are strongly territorial when breeding, with natal dens generally used by only one family group. Breeding pairs remain together in the same territory and use the same natal den for up to five years. Territories may include more than a single breeding pair, and closely related breeding pairs may even share a den. Home ranges in inland areas vary with lemming abundance (15–36 km^2), but generally are smaller in coastal habitats (e.g. 5–21 km^2 in Alaska). On Svalbard, home range sizes range from 10 km^2 to as large as 125 km^2. Home ranges of group members generally overlap widely with each other, but very little with those of neighboring groups. Scent marking of territories with urine is common. Vocalizations and postures such as an erected tail to attract the attention of conspecifics are common during territory disputes. In Alaska, seasonal migrations are reported when individuals leave breeding grounds in autumn, travel to the coast, and return in late winter or early spring. Large-scale emigrations have been recorded in Canada, Fennoscandia, and Russia. These may result from drastic reductions in food supplies, such as a population crash in lemmings.

Breeding. Mating occurs between February and May and births take place from April to July. Gestation lasts 51–54 days and pup weight at birth is 80–85 g, but may be lower in larger litters. Litter size varies with food availability, being larger in areas with rodents. Recorded mean litter sizes at weaning varied from 2·4 (St. Paul Island) to 7·1 (Russia). On Wrangel Island, Russia, in years with high lemming abundance, up to 19 pups per litter have been observed. The ability of Arctic Foxes to produce large litters is facilitated by their access to large and relatively safe dens. Den sites are large, with complex burrow systems, and the largest dens are preferred for breeding. These may have up to 150 entrances and are usually situated on elevated mounds, river banks or ridges. Good denning sites lie above the permafrost layer, accumulate comparatively little winter snow and are sun-exposed, often facing south. The average lifespan of dens in the Canadian tundra has been estimated at 330 years. Some are used repeatedly, year after year, others infrequently. Pup rearing is confined to the snow-free period from June to September, after which the young gradually become independent. Lactation generally lasts 8–10 weeks. Growth rate from weaning in early July to late August has been recorded at 30–34 g/day. Foxes reach sexual maturity at ten months.

Status and Conservation. CITES not listed. Classified as Least Concern on *The IUCN Red List*. The Arctic Fox, however, is regionally threatened in Sweden ("endangered"), Finland ("critical") and mainland Norway ("endangered"). In 1983, following the introduction of mange caused by ear canker mites (*Otodectes cynotis*) transmitted by dogs, the Mednyi Island foxes were listed in the Russian Red Data Book. The world population of Arctic Foxes is on the order of several hundred thousand animals. In most areas, population status is believed to be good. The species is common in the tundra of Russia, Canada, coastal Alaska, Greenland, and Iceland. Exceptions are Fennoscandia, Mednyi Island (Russia), and the Pribilof Islands, where populations are at critically low levels. On the Pribilof Islands, fox populations appear to be declining further. In most of its range, the Arctic Fox is not protected. However, the species and its dens have received total legal protection in Sweden since 1928, in Norway since 1930, and in Finland since 1940. In Europe, the Arctic Fox is a priority species under the Actions by the Community relating to the Environment (ACE) and is therefore given full protection. On St. Paul Island the declining population currently has no legal protection. In Norway (Svalbard), Greenland, Canada, Russia, and Alaska, trapping is limited to licensed trappers operating in a defined trapping season. The enforcement of trapping laws appears to be uniformly good. In Iceland, bounty hunting takes place over most of the country outside nature reserves. Hunting for fur has long been a major mortality factor for the Arctic Fox; however, the decline of the fur industry has reduced the threat of over-exploitation for most populations. In some areas gene swamping by farm-bred Blue Foxes may threaten native populations. There can also be indirect threats such as diseases and organochlorine contaminants, or direct persecution, as occurs on St. Paul Island. Misinformation as to the origin of Arctic Foxes on the Pribilofs continues to foster negative attitudes and the long-term persistence of this endemic subspecies is in jeopardy.

Bibliography. Angerbjörn, Hersteinsson & Tannerfeldt (2004), Angerbjörn, Ströman & Becker (1997), Angerbjörn, Tannerfeldt, Bjärvall *et al.* (1995), Angerbjörn, Tannerfeldt & Erlinge (1999), Audet *et al.* (2002), Chesemore (1975), Dalerum *et al.* (2002), Eberhardt, Garrott & Hanson (1983), Eberhardt, Hanson *et al.* (1982), Elmhagen *et al.* (2000), Frafjord (1994), Frafjord & Kruchenkova (1995), Frafjord & Prestrud (1992), Garrott & Eberhardt (1982, 1987), Hersteinsson (1984), Hersteinsson & Macdonald (1982, 1992, 1996), Hersteinsson *et al.* (1989), Kaikusalo & Angerbjörn (1995), Macpherson (1969), Nasimovic & Isakov (1985), Ovsyanikov (1993), Prestrud (1992a, 1992b, 1992c), Samelius & Lee (1998), Tannerfeldt & Angerbjörn (1998).

Genus *VULPES*

Frisch, 1775

25. Swift Fox *Vulpes velox*

French: Renard véloce / **German**: Prärie-Flinkfuchs / **Spanish**: Zorro veloz

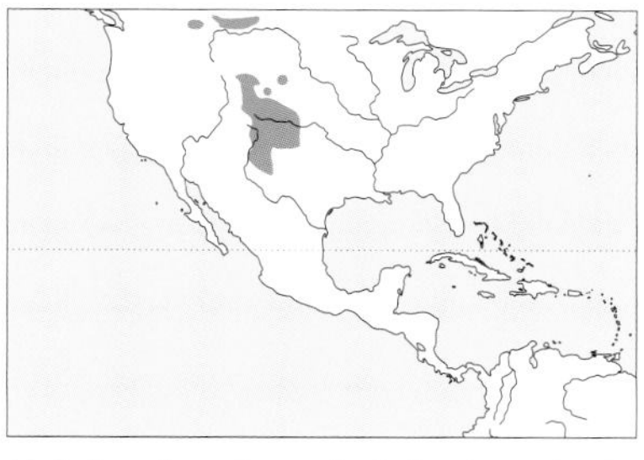

Taxonomy. *Canis velox* Say, 1823, River Platte region, USA.

Phenotypically and ecologically similar to *V. macrotis*; interbreeding occurs in western Texas and eastern New Mexico, and some suggest these foxes are conspecific. Both are closely related to Arctic Foxes, and some authorities place the latter under *Vulpes*. Although significant geographic variation exists among Swift Foxes, their classification into northern (*hebes*) and southern (*velox*) subspecies is probably unjustified. Monotypic.

Distribution. Great Plains in S Canada (Alberta & Saskatchewan) and USA (Montana, and from N Wyoming and SW South Dakota to C New Mexico & NW Texas).

Descriptive notes. Head-body 50–54·5 cm for males and 47·5–54 cm for females, tail 25–34 cm for males and 25–30·2 cm for females; weight 2–2·5 kg for males and 1·6–2·3 kg for females. One of the smallest canids; characteristic black patches on each side of the muzzle. The winter pelage is dark grayish across the back and sides extending to yellow-tan across the lower sides, legs, and the ventral surface of the tail. Black tail tip. The ventral fur is white with some buff on the chest. In summer, the fur is shorter and more rufous. The Swift Fox can be easily confused with the closely related Kit Fox. Dental formula: I 3/3, C 1/1, PM 4/4, M 2/3 = 42.

Habitat. Predominately short-grass and mixed-grass prairies in gently rolling or level terrain. In Kansas, Swift Foxes have been found to den and forage in fallow wheat fields. Survival rates between foxes in grassland and cropland sites were not significantly different, suggesting that Swift Foxes may be able to adapt to such habitat in some cases. The distribution and density of dens are considered important components of Swift Fox habitat requirements, particularly in terms of evading Coyote predation or Red Fox competition.

Food and Feeding. Swift Foxes are opportunistic foragers, feeding on a variety of mammals, but also birds, insects, plants, and carrion. Leporids have been reported as a primary prey item in several studies. In South Dakota, mammals accounted for 49% of prey occurrences, with Black-tailed Prairie Dogs (*Cynomys ludovicianus*) as the primary prey item. In Kansas and Nebraska, murid rodents were the most frequently occurring prey. Insects also present, but likely to constitute only a small portion of biomass. Birds and their eggs are also consumed, as are plant materials, including prickly pear cactus fruit, wild plums, and sunflower seeds, which are consumed relatively frequently but most often in relatively small amounts. Swift Foxes are mostly solitary hunters. Caching of food has been observed.

Activity patterns. Swift Foxes forage throughout the night, and show some crepuscular activity. They will hunt diurnal species such as birds and ground squirrels in the summer.

Movements, Home range and Social organization. The typical social group consists of a mated pair with pups, although occasionally a trio or group of two males and two or three females have been reported, with one breeding female and non-breeding helpers. Home range size averages between 10·4 km^2 and 32·3 km^2. They are territorial: an individual will nearly totally exclude same-sex individuals from its core activity area. Areas used by mated pairs have minimal overlap with areas used by adjacent pairs. Pups remain with the parents until dispersal; in a study only 33% of juveniles had left natal home ranges by 9·5 months of age while all recaptured individuals aged 18 months or older had dispersed. Vocal repertoire in captivity consists of courting/territorial call, agonistic chatter, submissive whine, submissive chatter, precopulatory call, growls, excited yips and barks, and social yips.

Breeding. Primarily monogamous, although additional female helpers are occasionally observed at den sites. Swift Foxes are monoestrous and the timing of breeding (December to March) is dependent upon latitude. The mean gestation period is 51 days and average litter sizes of 2·4–5·7 have been reported. In Colorado, litter sizes were greater for mated pairs with helpers than for those without. Pups open their eyes at 10–15 days, emerge from the natal den after approximately one month, and are weaned at 6–7 weeks of age. Both members of the pair provide for the young, and juveniles remain with the adults for 4–6 months. Swift Foxes are among the most burrow-dependent canids and depend on dens throughout the year. They will excavate their own dens and modify the burrows of other species. Dens serve several functions, such as providing a refuge from predators, protection from extreme climate conditions in both summer and winter, and shelter for raising young.

Status and Conservation. CITES not listed. Classified as Least Concern on *The IUCN Red List*. The Swift Fox has been down-listed from "extirpated" to "endangered" in Canada as a result of reintroduction programs. Following their extirpation by 1938, reintroduction releases since 1983 have established a small Swift Fox population in Alberta, Saskatchewan and Montana, which now constitutes the northern extent of the species' range. In the USA, the species was cited as "warranted, but precluded" from endangered status under the federal Endangered Species Act. Swift Foxes are primarily prairie specialists, and conversion of grassland to cropland threatens to reduce population sizes and further fragment populations. The conversion of native grassland prairies has been implicated as one of the most important factors in the contraction of the Swift Fox range. Landscape alteration likely influences local and seasonal prey availability, increases risk of predation on Swift Foxes, and leads to competition with other predators such as the Coyote and Red Fox. In Canada, expansion of the oil and gas industry and associated road development are impacting previously isolated prairie areas. Greater urbanization coupled with Coyote control may facilitate Red Fox expansion, which could lead to the competitive exclusion of Swift Foxes in established prairie areas. Landowners who are attempting to protect their livestock from Coyote depredation use poisons illegally and Swift Foxes readily consume such baits.

Bibliography. Andersen *et al.* (2003), Asa & Valdespino (2003), Avery (1989), Cameron (1984), Carbyn *et al.* (1994), Covell (1992), Egoscue (1979), Harrison (2003), Herrero *et al.* (1991), Hillman & Sharps (1978), Hines & Case (1991), Jackson & Choate (2000), Kamler, Ballard, Fish *et al.* (2003), Kamler, Ballard, Gese *et al.* (2004), Kamler, Ballard, Gilliland *et al.* (2003), Kilgore (1969), Kitchen *et al.* (1999), Mercure *et al.* (1993), Moehrenschlager (2000), Moehrenschlager & Macdonald (2003), Moehrenschlager & Moehrenschlager (2001), Moehrenschlager & Sovada (2004), Olson *et al.* (1997), Pechacek *et al.* (2000), Pruss (1994), Rohwer & Kilgore (1973), Schauster *et al.* (2002a, 2002b), Sovada & Carbyn (2003), Sovada, Anthony & Batt (2001), Sovada, Roy, Bright & Gillis, (1998), Sovada, Roy & Telesco (2001), Sovada, Slivinski & Woodward (2003), Stromberg & Boyce (1986), Tannerfeldt *et al.* (2003), Uresk & Sharps (1986), Zimmerman (1998), Zimmerman *et al.* (2003), Zumbaugh *et al.* (1985).

26. Kit Fox *Vulpes macrotis*

French: Renard nain / **German**: Wüsten-Flinkfuchs / **Spanish**: Zorro chico

Other common names: Desert Fox

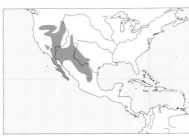

Taxonomy. *Vulpes macrotis* Merriam, 1888, California, USA.

Has been considered conspecific with *V. velox*, based on morphometric similarities and protein-electrophoresis. Others have treated *V. macrotis* as a distinct species based on multivariate morphometric data and more recent mitochondrial DNA analysis. Nominal subspecies *macrotis* (Merriam, 1888) from sout-western California is extinct. Seven extant subspecies are recognized.

Subspecies and Distribution.

V. m. arsipus Elliot, 1904 – NW Mexico (N Sonora) and SW USA (SE California & S Arizona).

V. m. devius Nelson & Goldman, 1909 – NW Mexico (S Baja California).

V. m. muticus Merriam, 1902 – SW USA (San Joaquin Valley of California).

V. m. neomexicanus Merriam, 1902 – N Mexico (NW Chihuahua) and C USA (Colorado, New Mexico & W Texas).

V. m. nevadensis Goldman, 1931 – USA (Great Basin).

V. m. tenuirostris Nelson & Goldman, 1931 – NW Mexico (N Baja California).

V. m. zinseri Benson, 1938 – N-C Mexico.

Descriptive notes. Head-body 48·5–52 cm for males and 45·5–53·5 cm for females, tail 28–34 cm for males and 25–30·5 cm for females; weight 1·7–2·7 kg for males and 1·6–2·2 kg for females. One of the smallest foxes on the American continent. The large ears are its most conspicuous characteristic. The fur is short, with yellowish to grayish head, back and sides; the shoulders and the outside of the legs, are brownish-yellow. The belly and the inner side of legs are yellowish-white and the tip of the tail is black. The neck, legs and belly may have buffy highlights. The hair is dense between the foot-pads. Dental formula: I 3/3, C 1/1, PM 4/4, M 2/3 = 42. Mean cranial measurements from 35 specimens of race *mutica* were: condylobasal length 114·4mm; zygomatic breadth 62·1mm; palatal length 57·8mm; interorbital breadth 23·1mm; postorbital breadth 21·4mm.

Habitat. Arid and semi-arid regions including desert scrub, chaparral, halophytic, and grassland communities. It is found at elevations ranging from 400–1900 m, although Kit Foxes generally avoid rugged terrain. They use agricultural lands to some extent and can successfully inhabit urban environments.

Food and Feeding. Kit Foxes primarily consume rodents, lagomorphs, and insects. Main prey includes kangaroo rats (*Dipodomys* spp.), prairie dogs (*Cynomys* spp.), Black-tailed Jackrabbits (*Lepus californicus*), and cottontails (*Sylvilagus* spp.). Other items consumed include birds, reptiles, and carrion. Plant material is rarely consumed, with the occasional exception of cactus fruits. Kit Foxes mostly forage solitarily.

Activity patterns. Mainly nocturnal and occasionally crepuscular.

Movements, Home range and Social organization. Kit Foxes are primarily monogamous with occasional polygyny (i.e. multiple paternity litters detected) and pairs usually mate for life. Young from previous litters, usually females, may delay dispersal and remain in natal home ranges assisting with raising the current litter. Kit Foxes are not strongly territorial and home ranges of 2·5–11·6 km² may overlap, although core areas generally are used exclusively by one family group. Kit Foxes sometimes bark at approaching predators or to recall pups, and they may emit a loud "chittering" call, during intraspecific encounters. Foxes also emit barking sequences, probably to contact or attract mates or potential mates.

Breeding. Kit Foxes mate from December to January and give birth from February to March after a gestation of 49–55 days. Litter size ranges from 1–7 (mean 4). Reproductive success for yearling females is considerably lower and varies annually with food availability for all age classes. Pups emerge from dens at about four weeks, are weaned at about eight weeks, begin foraging with parents at about 3–4 months, and become independent at about 5–6 months. Mean dispersal age in California was eight months. Kit Foxes use dens all year round and have multiple dens. Although they can excavate their own dens, preferring loose-textured soils, they frequently occupy and modify the burrows of prairie dogs, kangaroo rats, ground squirrels (*Spermophilus* spp.), and American Badgers. Occasionally, they will den in man-made structures (e.g. culverts, pipes), but young are almost always born in earthen dens.

Status and Conservation. CITES not listed (considered a subspecies of *V. velox*). Classified as Least Concern on *The IUCN Red List*. Considered "vulnerable" in Mexico. In the USA, the San Joaquin Kit Fox (*muticus*) is listed federally as "endangered", and as "threatened" in the State of California. In Oregon, Kit Foxes are classified as "endangered". The species is common to rare. In the USA, abundance is largely unknown. Population trends are assumed to be relatively stable where there are no significant threats. The endangered San Joaquin Kit Fox is probably still declining due to continuing habitat loss, fragmentation, and degradation. The main threat to the long-term survival of the Kit Fox is habitat conversion, mainly to agriculture but also to urban and industrial development. Human-induced habitat transformation is probably causing a decline of Kit Fox populations in Mexico, where Prairie Dog towns supporting important populations of Kit Foxes are being converted to agricultural fields. In Mexico, Kit Foxes are sometimes shot opportunistically, but are not actively persecuted.

Bibliography. Cotera (1996), Cypher *et al.* (2000), Dragoo *et al.* (1990), Egoscue (1956, 1962, 1975), Hall (1981), Jiménez-Guzmán & López-Soto (1992), Knapp (1978), Koopman, Cypher & Scrivner (2000), Koopman, Scrivner & Kato (1998), List (1997), List & Cypher (2004), McGrew (1979), Mercure *et al.* (1993), Morrell (1972), O'Farrell (1987), Ralls *et al.* (2001), Spiegel (1996), US Fish & Wildlife Service (1998), Warrick & Cypher (1998), White & Ralls (1993), White *et al.* (1995), Zoellick *et al.* (1987).

Plate 26 ➤

PLATE 26

inches ⎯⎯ 14

cm ⎯⎯ 35

ssp *vulpes*

27

ssp *silacea*

silver gray morph

28

ssp *alascensis*

29

30

32

31

35

33

34

27. Red Fox *Vulpes vulpes*

French: Renard roux / **German**: Rotfuchs / **Spanish**: Zorro rojo

Other common names: Silver Fox, Cross Fox

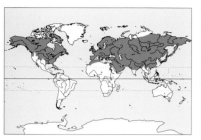

Taxonomy. *Canis vulpes* Linnaeus, 1758, Sweden.
The North American Red Fox, *V. fulva*, previously considered a separate species, is now considered conspecific with the Palaearctic *V. vulpes*. Forty-four subspecies were described on the basis of regional variation, but these have doubtful ecological significance as evidenced by successful introductions and re-introductions around the world.

Subspecies and Distribution.

V. v. vulpes Linnaeus, 1758 – N Europe (Scandinavia).
V. v. abietorum Merriam, 1900 – SW Canada (Alberta & British Columbia).
V. v. aegyptiacus Sonnini, 1816 – Egypt, Israel, and Lybia.
V. v. alascensis Merriam, 1900 – Alaska and NW Canada (NW Territories & Yukon).
V. v. alpherakyi Satunin, 1906 – Kazakhstan.
V. v. anatolica Thomas, 1920 – Turkey.
V. v. arabica Thomas, 1902 – Arabian peninsula.
V. v. atlantica Wagner, 1841 – Algeria (forested Atlas Mts).
V. v. bangsi Merriam, 1900 – NE Canada (Labrador).
V. v. barbara Shaw, 1800 – NW Africa (Barbary Coast).
V. v. beringiana Middendorff, 1875 – NE Siberia (shore of Bering Strait).
V. v. cascadensis Merriam, 1900 – NW USA (Cascade Mountains, Oregon & Washington).
V. v. caucasica Dinnik, 1914 – SW Russia (Caucasus).
V. v. crucigera Bechstein, 1789 – Europe through N & C Russia.
V. v. daurica Ognev, 1931 – E Russia (Amur, Siberia & Transbaikalia).
V. v. deletrix Bangs, 1898 – NE Canada (Newfoundland).
V. v. dolichocrania Ognev, 1926 – SE Siberia (S Ussuri).
V. v. flavescens Gray, 1843 – N Iran.
V. v. fulva Desmarest, 1820 – E USA.
V. v. griffithii Blyth, 1854 – Afghanistan and N Pakistan.
V. v. harrimani Merriam, 1900 – Alaska (Kodiak I).
V. v. hoole Swinhoe, 1870 – S China (Fujian to Sichuan).
V. v. ichnusae G. S. Miller, 1907 – Corsica and Sardinia.
V. v. induta G. S. Miller, 1907 – Cyprus.
V. v. jakutensis Ognev, 1923 – E Siberia (S of Yakutsk).
V. v. japonica Gray, 1868 – Japan.
V. v. karagan Erxleben, 1777 – Mongolia, Kazakhstan, and Kirgizstan.
V. v. kenaiensis Merriam, 1900 – Alaska (Kenai Peninsula).
V. v. kurdistanica Satunin, 1906 – Armenia and NE Turkey.
V. v. macroura Baird, 1852 – USA (Mountain States).
V. v. montana Pearson, 1836 – Himalayas form China (Yunnan) to C Pakistan.
V. v. necator Merriam, 1900 – SW USA (California & Nevada).
V. v. ochroxantha Ognev, 1926 – E Russian Turkestan, Aksai, Kirgizstan, Semirechie.
V. v. palaestina Thomas, 1920 – Jordan and Lebanon.
V. v. peculiosa Kishida, 1924 – Korea.
V. v. pusilla Blyth, 1854 – NW India to Irak.
V. v. regalis Merriam, 1900 – N Great Plains of Canada and USA.
V. v. rubricosa Bangs, 1898 – E Canada.
V. v. schrencki Kishida, 1924 – N Japan (Hokkaido) and NE Russia (Sakhalin).
V. v. silacea G. S. Miller, 1907 – Iberian Peninsula.
V. v. splendidissima Kishida, 1924 – E Russia (N & C Kurile Is).
V. v. stepensis Brauner, 1914 – steppes of S Russia.
V. v. tobolica Ognev, 1926 – Russia (lower basin of Ob River).
V. v. tschiliensis Matschie, 1907 – NE China.

Foxes of European origin were introduced into E USA and Canada in the 17th century, subsequently mixed with local subspecies. Also introduced to Australia in 1800s, and the Falkland Islands (Malvinas).

Descriptive notes. Head-body 59–90 cm for males and 45–68 cm for females, tail 36–44 cm for males and 28–49 cm for females; weight 4–14 kg for males and 3–7 kg for females. The largest fox in the genus *Vulpes*, with an enormous geographical variation in size. Males generally larger than females. The species is substantially smaller in the Middle East deserts than in Europe. Smaller also in North America. Muzzle slender and pointed, white on upper lip. Ears large, pointed, erect and black-backed. Pelage is reddish-brown but may vary from brown to russet red to yellowish-gray. Three main color morphs: red, silver, and cross (grayish-brown with long black guard hairs down back and across shoulders). Throat and/or chest may have white markings. Legs long and slender. Lower legs black. Tail long, thick, and bushy, sometimes with white tip. Red Foxes in North America are comparatively light weight, rather long for their mass, and with considerable sexual dimorphism. British foxes are heavier but relatively short. European foxes are closer to the general average among populations. Body mass and length are positively related to latitude (i.e. Bergmann's Rule), but this is a smaller effect than that related to geographical origin. Dental formula I 3/3, C 1/1, PM 3/4, M 3/3 = 42.

Habitat. Red Foxes recorded in habitats as diverse as tundra, desert, grassland, and forest, as well as in cities. Natural habitat is dry, mixed landscape, with mosaics of scrub, woodland and farmland. They are also abundant on moorlands, mountains, deserts, sand dunes and farmland from sea level to 4500 m. Red Foxes flourish in urban areas, where they are most common in low-density residential suburbs and less common in areas dominated by industry or commerce. In many habitats, foxes appear to be closely associated with humans, even thriving in intensive agricultural areas. Also in large cities, including Washington DC, London, Paris, and Stockholm.

Food and Feeding. Adaptable and opportunistic omnivores, with a diet ranging from invertebrates (e.g. earthworms and beetles) to mammals, birds, fruit, and carrion. As predators, foxes typically kill birds and mammals up to about 3·5 kg. They cache food that is in excess of their requirements and have a highly developed memory for locations of hoards. They scavenge in rural areas (e.g. on deer and sheep carcasses in Europe and Canada, which may be the major food source in upland areas in winter), and in urban areas (on bird-feeding tables, compost heaps, and refuse). They are independent and thus generally solitary foragers, although individuals may forage in close proximity where resources are clumped.

Activity patterns. Foraging is mainly nocturnal and crepuscular, although more diurnal where undisturbed.

Movements, Home range and Social organization. The basic social unit is a pair, but groups with up to six members (usually one adult male and 2–5 probably related females) may share a territory, depending on habitat. Range size is habitat-dependent and can vary from less than 0·4 km² to over 40 km². There are reports of overlapping home ranges in some urban and rural environments, and of drifting territories in other urban settings. Mating behavior is highly variable, either monogamous pairs, a single male with two breeding females that may or may not share a communal den, or a single breeding female with several non-breeding female helpers. There is always only one breeding male in the group, although additional matings do occur outside the group. Territorial males make frequent excursions beyond their territories during the mating season, during which itinerant males also make incursions into territories. There is socially-mediated suppression of reproduction amongst females, with lowest productivity tending to occur where fox density is high or food supply poor. Where food is not limited, social status itself can suppress reproduction, with only the dominant female breeding. Behavioral mechanisms by which this occurs include harassment of subordinates, infanticide and cannibalism of subordinate vixens' pups. A hormonal mechanism whereby stress leads to lowered productivity through fetal reabsorption has also been identified. In populations where productivity is low, reproductive performance is suppressed consistently at all stages of pregnancy from conception to birth. Juveniles may disperse between six and twelve months of age, mostly between October and January. All or most males disperse, but the proportion of each sex dispersing varies among habitats and may depend on extent of mortality (e.g. due to rabies or control). Males typically disperse farther than females. Dispersal distances generally range from less than 5 km to more than 50 km, but distances of up to 394 km have been recorded in the USA. Red Foxes communicate with facial expressions, vocalizations, and scent marking. Scent marking involves urine and feces, anal sac secretions, the violet or supracaudal gland (more active in males during breeding season), and glands around the lips, in the angle of the jaw, and between pads of the feet. Some 28 different categories of vocalization have been described, used to communicate over long distances and at close quarters.

Breeding. Males are seasonally fecund. Mating occurs between December and February (June to October in Australia); the onset of breeding is correlated with day length and so starts earlier at more southerly latitudes. Following a gestation period of 49–55 days, births occur from March to May. Lactation lasts for four weeks, and the pups are fully weaned at 6–8 weeks. Sexual maturity is reached at 9–10 months. The proportion of breeding females in the group, and litter size (3–12 young per litter), varies with food availability. Fox populations that are dense relative to food resources are generally less productive than those that are less dense. A single litter per year is the norm. In high-density populations where interactions with the dominant female are high, subordinate females do not usually breed. The male provides food to the lactating female, who is generally confined to the den prior to weaning. Food is provided for the pups by both parents. Non-breeding females may also feed, groom, and tend pups and have been known to adopt orphaned pups. If two females breed within a group, they may share a den and litters may be communally suckled.

Status and Conservation. CITES not listed. Classified as Least Concern on *The IUCN Red List*. Widely regarded as a pest and unprotected. *V. v. necator* in the Sierra Nevada, California (USA) is rare, possibly declining. The subspecies *griffithi, montana,* and *pusilla* (= *leucopus*) are listed as CITES Appendix III (India). Most countries and/or states where trapping or hunting occurs have regulated closed versus open seasons and restrictions on methods of capture. In the EU, Canada, and the Russian Federation, trapping methods are regulated. Red Fox density is highly variable, ranging within the UK from 0·025 individuals/km² in Scotland to 30/km² in some urban areas where food is superabundant. Density in mountainous rural areas of Switzerland is 3/km². In northern boreal forests and Arctic tundra, the foxes occur at densities of 0·1/km², and in southern Ontario, Canada at 1/km². Threats include habitat degradation and fragmentation, exploitation and persecution, and government policies. Other threats come from local, national, or international socio-economic and political factors, such as increasing human population and thus increasing development. The Red fox's versatility and eclectic diet are likely to ensure its persistence despite changes in landscape

On following pages: 28. Corsac Fox (*Vulpes corsac*); 29. Tibetan Fox (*Vulpes ferrilata*); 30. Indian Fox (*Vulpes bengalensis*); 31. Pale Fox (*Vulpes pallida*); 32. Rüppell's Fox (*Vulpes rueppellii*); 33. Cape Fox (*Vulpes chama*);
34. Blanford's Fox (*Vulpes cana*); 35. Fennec Fox (*Vulpes zerda*).

and prey base. There are currently bounties in Pakistan to protect game birds such as houbara bustards (*Chlamydotis undulata macqueenii*).

Bibliography. Ables (1975), Baker & Harris (2004), Cavallini (1995), Doncaster & Macdonald (1991), Englund (1970), Harris (1977, 1989), Harris & Rayner (1986), Harris & Smith (1987), Hatting (1956), Heydon & Reynolds (2000), Johnson & Hersteinsson (1993), Larivière & Pasitschniak-Arts (1996), Macdonald (1976, 1977a, 1977b, 1979b, 1980a, 1980b, 1987), Macdonald & Bacon (1982), Macdonald & Newdick (1982), Macdonald & Reynolds (2004), Macdonald et al. (1999), McIntosh (1963), Meia (1994), Meia & Weber (1996), Voigt & Macdonald (1984).

28. Corsac Fox *Vulpes corsac*

French: Renard corsac / **German**: Steppenfuchs / **Spanish**: Zorro estepario
Other common names: Corsac

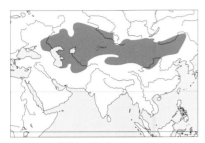

Taxonomy. *Canis corsac* Linnaeus, 1768, northern Kazakhstan.

It has been suggested that *Canis ekloni* from northern Tibet is a subspecies of the Corsac Fox. However, *C. ekloni* is a junior synonym of *V. ferrilata*. Four subspecies are recognized.

Subspecies and Distribution.
V. c. corsac Linnaeus, 1768 – N part of range to pre-Altai steppe.
V. c. kalmykorum Ognev, 1935 – Volgo-Ural steppes and Volga Basin.
V. c. scorodumovi Dorogostaiski, 1935 – N China, Mongolia, and Russia (Transbaikalia).
V. c. turcmenicus Ognev, 1935 – plains of C Asia and N Afghanistan, NE Iran, and Kazakhstan.

Descriptive notes. Head-body 45–59·5 cm for males and 45–50 cm for females, tail 19–30 cm for males and 25–30 cm for females; weight 1·6–3·2 kg for males and 1·9–2·4 kg for females. Typically vulpine in appearance. Males slightly bigger than females, but sexual dimorphism not pronounced. Head grayish-ocher or brown, ears banded brown on front side, back of ears ocher-gray or reddish-brown. Breast, belly, and groin white or yellowish. Front of forelegs light yellow, sides rusty-yellow, hindlegs paler. Summer fur short and sparse, winter fur dense, soft and silky, straw-grayish with ocher. Awn hairs tipped silver-white. Tail about half body length or slightly more, grayish-brown, covered with dense bushy hair, tip dark, often black. Skull similar to that of *V. vulpes*, but smaller, shorter and wider, and with canine teeth more robust. The dental formula is I 3/3, C 1/1, PM 4/4, M 2/3 = 42.

Habitat. Typically inhabits steppes, semi-deserts, and deserts, avoiding mountains, forested areas, and dense bush. In the western part of the range, Corsac Foxes occur in low-grass steppe, avoiding dense and tall-grass steppes. They also occur in sandy habitats and shrubland semi-deserts, and in favorable years, in forested steppes. They avoid areas where depth of snow exceeds c. 15 cm, preferring areas where the snow is either shallow or highly compressed. Corsac Foxes appear to depend on ground squirrels (*Spermophilus* spp.) and marmots (*Marmota* spp.) for food and shelter (the burrows being enlarged and used for daytime refuge).

Food and Feeding. Generally opportunistic, with a highly variable diet throughout its range that probably changes in accordance with availability. The bulk of the diet often includes the most common rodents of an area. Birds, reptiles (lizards, snakes and young tortoises), and insects are also frequently consumed, especially in summer, as well as small amounts of vegetation (including fruit and seeds). During winter and periods of low prey abundance, scavenged Gray Wolf kills and carcasses of wild and domestic ungulates are a major source of food in some areas. Typical prey in western Siberia includes voles (*Microtus gregalis*, *Arvicola terrestris*), lemmings (*Lagurus* spp.), ground squirrels (*Spermophilus* spp.), and jerboas (*Allactaga* spp.) Common winter prey also often includes Arctic Hares (*Lepus timidus*) and birds such as gray partridges (*Perdix perdix*) and snow buntings (*Pleptrophenax nivalis*). In the forest-steppe of Kazakhstan, the diet consists primarily of lemmings and sousliks. On the Ustyurt Plateau and in Turkmenistan the main prey are gerbils (*Meriones* spp., *Rhombomys opimus*); in Transbaikalia and Mongolia, the main prey species are gerbils (*Meriones* spp.), jerboas (*Allactaga* spp. and *Dipus* spp.), hamsters (*Cricetulus* spp. and *Phodopus* spp.), Brandt's Voles (*Lasiopodomys brandtii*), Siberian Marmots (*Marmota sibirica*), and pikas (*Ochotona* spp.). The foxes are solitary foragers, although near carrion or the remains of wolf kills several Corsacs may gather together. The foxes hunt by stalking prey and making sudden short-distance attacks. They locate ground-nesting birds and other small prey by sound and smell. Despite their small size they can kill prey up to the size of young marmots, hares, ducks, pheasants, and geese.

Activity patterns. Corsac Foxes are active mainly at night. Hunting starts in the evening and continues through the first part of the night, with a second peak of activity before dawn. Sometimes they are also active in daytime, especially during the summer months.

Movements, Home range and Social organization. The basic social unit is the breeding pair, and monogamous pairs may persist for life. During winter, several Corsacs may gather in a single den, indicating a relatively high degree of sociality. Polygamous families may occur under favorable feeding conditions. In optimal habitats during years of high prey abundance, the home range of a family pair may be as small as 1 km². In contrast, home ranges are significantly larger in habitats with low food abundance, and may reach 35–40 km². Corsacs occupy dens, often the burrows of marmots, during the day. Dens provide shelter from weather, but may also serve as important refuges from predation by larger canids such as Wolves and Red Foxes. Scent marking is important for maintaining territories, and marking with urine and feces is most

frequent near dens. Barking is the most common vocalization. Barks have many different tonal variations, and are used during courtship, territorial demonstrations, and alarm. They are higher in pitch than the barks of Red Foxes and sound similar to a cat's mew. Close distance vocalizations include high-tone rhythmic sounds, peeping, chirping, and yelping.

Breeding. Across the range of the species, mating takes place from January to early March. There is only one litter per year and gestation varies from 52 to 60 days. The earliest birth time is mid-March, most births occurring in April. Average litter size in Kazakhstan was 5·5 (range = 2–10). Pups usually emerge from dens in mid-May. At 28 days they start eating meat. The male takes an active part in parental care by feeding the young, and in favorable years helpers may assist with feeding and guarding the young. Pups reach adult size at four to five months, and in captivity sexual maturity is reached by nine months. They disperse by the end of summer, but do not venture far from their natal range, and some are likely to return to stay over the autumn-winter season.

Status and Conservation. CITES not listed. Classified as Least Concern on *The IUCN Red List*. Current population status and the nature of major threats is unknown in most regions. Corsac Foxes were once considered ubiquitous across Central Asia, but notable declines have occurred in recent years following the collapse of the former Soviet Union. In Russia the Corsac Fox is rare in most regions, but relatively common in western Siberia and Transbaikalia. The species is common between the Volga and Ural rivers, but probably declining in Turkmenistan, Kazakhstan, Mongolia, and northern China. Corsac Foxes are rare in Tajikistan and Uzbekistan and the south-western portion of their range. In many countries, hunting them is legal during certain seasons, but enforcement of wildlife laws and regulations rarely occurs. Over-hunting and illegal poaching (even in protected areas) remains the most significant threat to the species. In Mongolia, increased hunting for furs in recent years has depleted populations throughout the country and led the species' listing as "near threatened" in 2006.

Bibliography. Allen (1938), Chirkova (1952), Geptner et al. (1967), Heptner & Naumov (1992), Kadyrbaev & Sludskii (1981), Murdoch et al. (2009, In press), Ognev (1962), Poyarkov & Ovsyanikov (2004), Sidorov & Botvinkin (1987), Sidorov & Polischuk (2002), Sludskyi & Lazarev (1966), Wingard & Zahler (2006).

29. Tibetan Fox *Vulpes ferrilata*

French: Renard du Tibet / **German**: Tibet-Fuchs / **Spanish**: Zorro tibetano
Other common names: Sand Fox, Tibetan Sand Fox

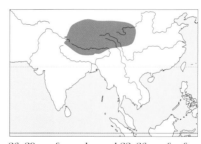

Taxonomy. *Vulpes ferrilatus* Hodgson, 1842, near Lhasa, Tibet.
Monotypic.

Distribution. Widespread in the Tibetan Plateau from Ladakh in India, E across China including parts of the Xinjiang, Gansu, Qinghai, and Sichuan provinces and all of the Xizang. In Nepal, N of the Himalaya, especially in the Mustang area.

Descriptive notes. Head-body 51·5–65 cm for males and 49–61 cm for females, tail 26–29 cm for males and 22–26 cm for females; weight 3·2–4·6 kg for males and 3–4·1 kg for females. Small and compact, with a soft, dense coat, a conspicuously narrow muzzle, and a bushy gray tail with a white tip. Tan to rufous-colored on the muzzle, crown, neck, back, and lower legs. The cheeks, sides, upper legs, and rump are gray. The back of the relatively short ears is tan to grayish tan and the inside is white. The undersides are whitish to pale gray.

Habitat. Upland plains and hills from about 2500–5200 m. Found in treeless alpine meadow, alpine steppe, and desert steppe. Most of the range lies in semi-arid to arid environments with average annual precipitation of 100–500 mm, most of which occurs in summer. The climate is harsh, with temperatures reaching +30 °C in summer and dropping to –40°C in winter.

Food and Feeding. Principal diet consists of pikas (*Ochotona* spp.) and rodents. An analysis of 113 droppings from north-western Tibet revealed 95% Plateau Pika (*Ochotona curzoniae*) and small rodents (*Pitymus*, *Alticola*, and *Cricetulus* spp.). A further 2·7% consisted of Tibetan Antelope (*Pantholops hodgsoni*), probably scavenged, and the remainder was made up of insects, feathers, *Ephedra* berries, and other vegetation. Other reported prey items in the diet include Tibetan Woolly Hare (*Lepus oiostolus*) and a lizard species (*Phrynocephalus* spp.). Himalayan Marmot (*Marmota himalayana*), musk deer (*Moschus* sp.), Bharal (*Pseudois nayaur*), and livestock were present in droppings from eastern Qinghai Province, China. The foxes mainly hunt alone by trotting through or stalking in Pika colonies.

Activity patterns. Often hunts during the day, on account of the diurnal activity patterns of pikas and other main prey species.

Movements, Home range and Social organization. Most aspects of the Tibetan Fox's reproductive and social behavior remain largely unknown. They are usually seen alone or in male-female pairs (of 90 foxes observed, all but six pairs were solitary), although one family of three adults and two juveniles was observed. Burrows are located at the base of boulders, along old beach lines, low on slopes, and other such sites. There may be one to four entrances to a den.

Breeding. Mating is thought to occur in February, with 2–5 young born in May. Main habitat factors associated with the location of 54 summer dens were, in order of importance: distance to water, slope degree, position along the slope, small mammal den numbers, and vegetation type. Most dens were located in grasslands (96%) with moderate slope.

Status and Conservation. CITES not listed. Classified as Least Concern on *The IUCN Red List*. Species legally protected in several large Chinese reserves, but actual protection remains minimal, and there is no special protection outside reserves. Hunting pressure for fur is reported to be high on the entire Tibetan plateau since the 1960s. Over 300 foxes have been killed per year since the 1990s in Shiqu County, Sichuan Province, China. In general, Fox density appears to be low. Population abundance is limited partly by prey availability and partly by human hunting pressure.

Bibliography. Clark *et al.* (2008), Feng *et al.* (1986), Gao *et al.* (1987), Nowak (1999), Piao (1989), Schaller (1998), Schaller & Ginsberg (2004), Wang Zhenghuan *et al.* (2003), Wu Wei *et al.* (2002), Zheng (1985).

30. Indian Fox *Vulpes bengalensis*

French: Renard du Bengale / **German**: Bengalfuchs / **Spanish**: Zorro bengalí

Other common names: Bengal Fox

Taxonomy. *Canis bengalensis* Shaw, 1800, Bengal, India.
Monotypic.
Distribution. Endemic to the Indian subcontinent. Ranges from the foothills of the Himalayas in Nepal to the S tip of the Indian peninsula, also in Bangladesh and Pakistan.
Descriptive notes. Head-body 39–57·5 cm for males and 46–48 cm for females, tail 24·7–32 cm for males and 24·5–31·2 cm for females; weight 2·7–3·2 kg for males and over 1·8 kg for females. Medium-sized, with typical vulpine appearance, though smaller than Red Foxes (*V. vulpes*). The pelage varies from yellowish gray to silver gray, but lacks the rusty red hair that is typical of the Red Fox. The dorsal region is darker than the underparts, which are a pale cream. The ears have darker brown hair on the back. The nose and lips are black, and the eyes have dark tear marks. The muzzle is pointed, with tan to black hair around the upper part. The winter coat can be quite luxuriant. The limbs are slender, with some rufous coloring, and the tail is more than half the body length and has a black tip. The tail is carried trailing during normal travel, kept horizontal when the fox is running, and raised to almost vertical when the fox makes sudden turns. Females have three pairs of mammae. The dental formula is I 3/3, C 1/1, PM 4/4, M 2/3 = 42.
Habitat. Prefers semi-arid plains, open scrub and grassland habitats where it can easily hunt and dig dens. Avoids dense forests, steep terrain, tall grasslands, and true deserts. The species is relatively abundant in areas of India where rainfall is low and the typical vegetation is scrub, thorn, or dry deciduous forests, or short grasslands.
Food and Feeding. Indian Foxes are omnivorous, opportunistic feeders. Their diet consists mainly of insects (e.g. crickets, winged termites, grasshoppers, ants, beetle grubs) and spiders, small rodents, including Soft-furred Field Rats (*Millardia meltada*), field mice (*Mus booduga*), and Indian Gerbils, and birds and their eggs, including indian mynahs (*Acridotheres tristis*), ashy-crowned finch larks (*Eremopterix grisea*) and gray partridges (*Francolinus pondicerianus*). Other prey species include ground lizards, rat snakes (*Ptyas mucuosus*), hedgehogs (*Paraechinus nudiventris*), and Indian Hares (*Lepus nigricollis*). Indian Foxes feed on fruits of ber (*Ziziphus* spp.), neem (*Azadirachta indica*), mango (*Mangifera indica*), jambu (*Syizigium cumini*), banyan (*Ficus bengalensis*), melons, fruits, and the shoots and pods of *Cicer arietum*. They have also been reported eating the freshly voided pellets of sheep. They forage alone.
Activity patterns. In most parts of their range Indian Foxes are crepuscular and nocturnal. However, they may also hunt at midday if the temperature is mild, as on rainy days.
Movements, Home range and Social organization. The basic social unit is the breeding pair, and pair bonds may last for several years. Larger aggregations may exist when grown pups remain in the natal group for longer than normal. Two lactating females have been observed suckling pups in a single den during one year. Four adult-sized foxes were also observed resting together on two occasions. The common vocalization of the Indian Fox is a chattering cry that seems to have a major role in maintaining territoriality and may also be used as an alarm call. Foxes also growl, whimper, whine, and growl-bark. Indian Foxes scent-mark with droppings and urine.
Breeding. December to January. During the breeding season, the male vocalizes intensively, mostly in early evening and early morning. The gestation period is 50–53 days and parturition occurs between January and March. Litter size is usually 2–4. Both parents bring food to the pups and guard the den, and helpers have not been observed. The parents take turns foraging and rarely is the den left unguarded. Post-natal care lasts approximately 4–5 months, after which the young disperse, usually at the onset of the monsoon (June/July in north-west India), when food is plentiful. Dens are used primarily during the pup-rearing period, and are excavated in open habitat, never in dense vegetation. Indian Foxes will usually excavate their own dens but occasionally they will appropriate and enlarge gerbil holes. Dens consist of a mosaic of tunnels in various stages of excavation, leading to a small chamber about 0·5–1 m below the surface where the pups are born. A den complex will usually have from two to seven holes, though as many as 43 have been recorded. The holes and tunnels of a well-used den site in Gujarat covered an area 10 × 8 m. Breeding sites are reused by breeding pairs in consecutive years. Pups are rarely moved between dens during the denning period, though once the pups become more mobile, they may use any of the numerous dens within their parents' territory.
Status and Conservation. CITES not listed. Classified as Least Concern on *The IUCN Red List*. The Indian Wildlife Protection Act (1972) prohibits hunting of all wildlife

and lists the Indian Fox in Schedule II. Although the Indian Fox is widespread, it occurs at low densities throughout its range, and populations can undergo major fluctuations in response to prey availability. Densities of breeding pairs may range from 0·15–0·1/km² during periods of peak rodent abundance to 0·01/km² during periods of low rodent abundance. In more diverse and stable prey systems, Fox densities are more constant (0·04–0·06/km²). In protected grasslands such as in Rollapadu Wildlife Sanctuary, Andhra Pradesh, Fox density was 1·6/km² and in unprotected areas only 0·4/km²; in the latter area, the population declined five-fold due to an epidemic in 1995. The Indian Fox population is decreasing, due to loss of short grassland-scrub habitat to intensive agriculture and development projects, although the rate of decline remains unknown. In certain states like Gujarat, Maharashtra, and Rajasthan, Indian Fox habitat is widespread, with minimal threats, but in other states, like Karnataka and Tamil Nadu, habitats are limited and decreasing. In Tamil Nadu, humans are a major mortality factor, especially nomadic tribal people who kill foxes for their flesh, teeth, claws, and skin. People also often block fox dens with stones, and foxes are hunted using smoke, nets and dogs at dens. Indian Foxes are often killed on roads, and major highways in the semi-arid tracts are likely to become barriers to dispersal.

Bibliography. Acharjyo & Misra (1976), Johnsingh (1978), Johnsingh & Jhala (2004), Manakadan & Rahmani (2000), Mitchell (1977), Mivart (1890a), Prakash (1975), Prater (1980), Rahmani (1989), Roberts (1977), Rodgers *et al.* (2000), Shrestha (1997), Tripathi *et al.* (1992).

31. Pale Fox *Vulpes pallida*

French: Renard pâle / **German**: Blassfuchs / **Spanish**: Zorro pálido

Other common names: Pallid Fox, African Sand Fox

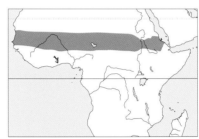

Taxonomy. *Canis pallidus* Cretzschmar, 1826, Sudan.
Has been associated with *V. rueppellii* and *V. zerda*. It also has been suggested that these desert foxes are closely related to *V. bengalensis* and *V. chama*. Five races have been described, four of which are recognized here. Variation may be clinal.
Subspecies and Distribution.
V. p. pallida Cretzschmar, 1827 – Sudan (Kordofan) to Eritrea, and Ethiopia.
V. p. edwardsi Rochebrune, 1883 – Mali, S Mauritania, and Senegal.
V. p. harterti Thomas & Hinton, 1921 – Burkina Faso, Niger, and N Nigeria.
V. p. oertzeni Matschie, 1910 – N Cameroon, Chad, and NE Nigeria to S Libya in the N and Sudan (Darfur province) in the S.
Descriptive notes. Head-body 38–55 cm, tail 23–29 cm; weight 2–3·6 kg. A small, very pale fox with longish legs and large ears. Pale face, elongated muzzle with relatively long whiskers, and a black eye-ring. Large ears, white inside and rufous-brown on the outer surface. Body creamy-white to sandy fawn, relatively thin coat, back sometimes flecked with black or rufous, with darker mid-dorsal line. Flanks paler than dorsal pelage, merging into white or buffy-white undersides, and legs rufous. Long, bushy tail, reddish brown with conspicuous black tip and a dark patch above tail gland. Females have three pairs of mammae. The skull is small, with a relatively short maxillary region, and well-developed upper molars in relation to relatively weak carnassial teeth. Bullae of the Pale Fox are slightly larger and the nasals appreciably longer than in Rüppell's Fox. Dental formula is I 3/3, C 1/1, PM 4/4, M 2/3 = 42.
Habitat. Typically inhabits very dry sandy and stony sub-Saharan desert and semi-desert areas, but its distribution extends southwards into moister Guinean savannahs to some extent. May occur near human habitation and cultivated fields where food is more readily available than in natural habitats.
Food and Feeding. Well-developed molars suggest Pale Foxes are essentially herbivorous, eating mainly berries, wild fruit such as melons, and vegetable matter. They also feed on small rodents, ground-nesting birds, small reptiles, and invertebrates. Foraging habits are unknown.
Activity patterns. Active from dusk till dawn, resting during the day in extensive burrows occupied by several individuals.
Movements, Home range and Social organization. Movements and home ranges unknown. Little is known of their habits, but Pale Foxes are gregarious and have been observed in pairs and small family groups.
Breeding. Gestation period in captivity is 51–53 days. Three to six young are born; weaning takes six to eight weeks. Pale Foxes dig extensive burrows, 2–3 m deep and up to 15 m in length, often under sandy tracks or near villages, and line the inner chambers with dry vegetation.
Status and Conservation. CITES not listed. Classified as Data Deficient on *The IUCN Red List*. Threats are unknown, although occasional persecution due to livestock depredation (i.e. poultry) may take place.

Bibliography. Bueler (1973), Coetzee (1977), Dorst & Dandelot (1970), Haltenorth & Diller (1980), Happold (1987), Kingdon (1997), Rosevear (1974), Sillero-Zubiri (2004).

32. Rüppell's Fox *Vulpes rueppellii*

French: Renard de Rüppell / **German**: Sandfuchs / **Spanish**: Zorro de Rüppell

Other common names: Sand Fox, Rüppell's Sand Fox

Taxonomy. *Canis rüeppelii* Schinz, 1825, Sudan.

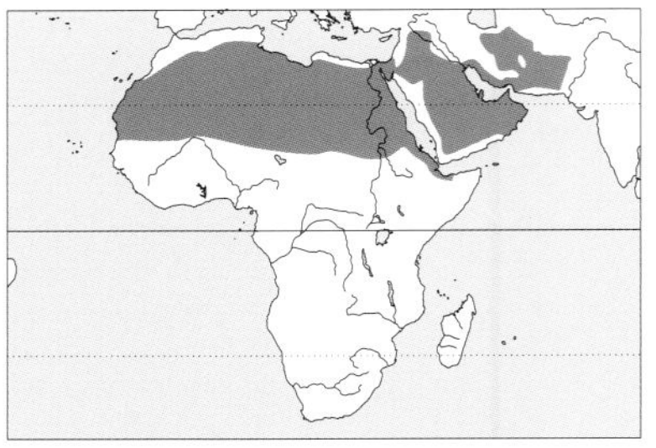

Six subspecies are recognized.

Subspecies and Distribution.

V. r. rueppellii Schinz, 1825 – Egypt and Sudan (Nubian Desert).

V. r. caesia Thomas & Hinton, 1921 – N & W Africa.

V. r. cyrenaica Festa, 1921 – SW Egypt, Lybia, extreme NW Sudan.

V. r. sabaea Pocock, 1934 – Arabian Peninsula and Middle East.

V. r. somaliae Thomas, 1918 – Eritrea, Ethiopia, and Somalia.

V. r. zarudnyi Birula, 1913 – Baluchistan in Afghanistan, Iran, and Pakistan.

Descriptive notes. Head-body 40–55 cm for males and 34·5–55·9 cm for females, tail 25·1–38·7 cm for males and 22–36·3 cm for females; weight 1·1–2·3 kg for males and 1·1–1·8 kg for females. One of the smaller *Vulpes* species, Rüppell's Fox is slighter in build than the Red Fox, and has smaller limbs. The ears are long and large in relation to the head, rather similar to Fennec Fox, but lack darker markings on the back of the ears. Coat color is variable. The head is beige to a pale sand color. The ears and face are usually pale, with most animals having black whisker patches running up to the eye, although this too is variable. Dorsal pelage varies from pale sandy to grayish and even sometimes reddish, with a more or less silvery sheen due to black speckling. Flanks and underbody are usually paler. The legs are beige to fawn, and the plantar and digital pads are almost completely covered by hairs. The black speckling from the back culminates in a dense black patch at the base of the tail, which is bushy and usually tipped white, a useful diagnostic feature. The fur is very fine and soft, thicker and darker in winter and lighter colored in summer. Females have three pairs of mammae. The braincase is rounded, the postorbital processes are blunt and narrow, the zygomatic arches are strong, and the bullae are relatively large (though not so expanded as in Fennec Fox). The dental formula is I 3/3, C 1/1, PM 4/4, M 2/3 = 42.

Habitat. Typical habitat includes sand and stone deserts. In Saudi Arabia, Rüppell's Fox has been found in open and stony habitat, often with sparse vegetation that includes herb and grass species (*Fagonia indica*, *Indigofera spinosa*, *Tribulus* spp., *Stipagrostis* spp., and *Panicum turgidum*). Annual rainfall averages 100 mm per year, with a maximum of 240 mm per year. On the northern fringe of the Sahara, Rüppell's Fox may be found in areas with up to 150 mm annual rainfall. In Morocco the general habitat offers sparse to very sparse vegetation cover, dominated by small brushes (*Hammada scoparia*, *Panicum turgidum*, *Fagonia* spp.) mostly concentrated in wadis (with *Acacia* spp., *Argania spinosa*, *Balanites aegyptiaca*, *Maerua crassifolia*, and *Capparis decidua* trees). Rüppell's Foxes also live in coastal areas with extremely sparse vegetation and no trees. They can survive in areas without any available water, as in central Saudi Arabia on the fringes of the Arabian Empty Quarter, in Algeria, and in the western Sahara.

Food and Feeding. Generalist predators, with a high invertebrate content in their diet, as well as rodents, lizards, snakes, birds, and wild fruits. Some studies have shown that Rüppell's Foxes consume prey relative to availability, suggesting opportunistic feeding habits. Little is known about their feeding behavior except that they forage alone, and may scavenge at camps and permanent human settlements.

Activity patterns. Mainly crepuscular and nocturnal. They tend to remain in dens throughout the day, although active animals have been seen during the daytime in winter. They leave the den in the hour following sunset and alternate periods of activity throughout the night. They are usually inactive in the early hours of the morning.

Movements, Home range and Social organization. Little is known. Adults usually live as monogamous pairs, but the species may be gregarious. Groups of 3–15 individuals, which may represent extended family groups, have been sighted. Grouping may be incidental, however; it could be the result of close aggregation of dens in the few areas where denning sites are available. In Oman, large home ranges covered some 69 km², and social units were spatially separate. Mean annual home range in Mahazat as-Sayd, Saudi Arabia was 16·3 km². Males showed significantly larger seasonal home ranges than females.

Breeding. In Saudi Arabia, mating takes place from December to February, which usually coincides with the first rains after the harsh summer period. Captures of young pups have been made in early March in Saudi Arabia and in March in the western Sahara. Very young animals have been recorded in Algeria in May, and captures of young pups in Saudi Arabia peaked from July to August, following the dependency period. In Mahazat as-Sayd gestation lasts 7–8 weeks and litter size is 2–3. Young pups remain dependent on their parents for an undefined period before they venture out from the den site area. Both sexes reach sexual maturity at around 9–10 months. Dens are commonly located under slabs of rock or dug at the base of trees or bushes. In areas with few shelters the species may use very exposed dens, often in the middle of plains. Some of these burrows are dug by Honey Badgers. In open areas any disturbance induces flight; in Niger, the animals often flee from their dens when threatened. In Oman, study animals changed den sites frequently, probably as an anti-predator strategy or perhaps due to resource availability. Shallow scrapes in a packed silt substrate may offer effective cooling, and midday temperatures may be 12–15°C lower inside these dens than outside.

Status and Conservation. CITES not listed. Classified as Least Concern on *The IUCN Red List*. Classed as "lower risk/near threatened" in Morocco (including W Sahara). In Saudi Arabia, there is currently no effective legislation for the protection of native carnivores. In Israel, the species is fully protected by law. In Morocco, Rüppell's Foxes may be hunted as they are considered pests. Although widespread throughout the Arabian Peninsula, the species is limited by the large desert areas. Population density is usually low, but seems higher in areas where food is more freely available, for example near human settlements. In a fenced protected area of Saudi Arabia, density was 0·7/km². Lower population estimates outside the fenced reserve indicate that the species may be very vulnerable in the over-grazed, human-influenced landscape of central Arabia. Habitat loss, fragmentation and degradation, direct and indirect persecution by hunting, and indiscriminate use of poisons, appear to be the main threats. In Israel, the species is on the verge of extinction due to competitive exclusion by Red Foxes, which are expanding their range following human settlement in the Negev Desert. Competitive pressure from Red Foxes may also be affecting populations in the United Arab Emirates.

Bibliography. Coetzee (1977), Cuzin (1996), Cuzin & Lenain (2004), De Smet (1988), Dragesco-Joffé (1993), Harrison & Bates (1991), Hufnagl (1972), Kingdon (1997), Kowalski (1988), Lenain (2000), Lindsay & Macdonald (1986), Olfermann (1996), Osborn & Helmy (1980), Petter (1952), Rosevear (1974), Valverde (1957), Yom-Tov & Mendelssohn (1988).

33. Cape Fox *Vulpes chama*

French: Renard du Cap / **German**: Kap-Fuchs / **Spanish**: Zorro de El Cabo

Other common names: Silver Fox

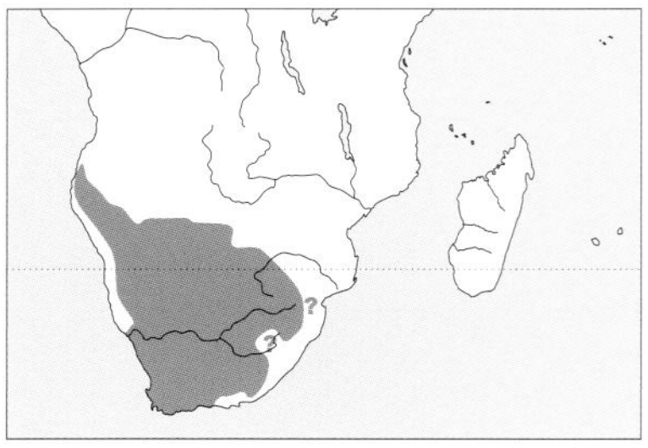

Taxonomy. *Canis chama* A. Smith, 1833, South Africa.

Monotypic.

Distribution. Widespread in the C and W regions of S Africa, reaching to about 15° N in SW Angola. Occupies mainly arid and semi-arid areas, but also occurs in regions with higher precipitation and denser vegetation, such as the fynbos biome of South Africa's Western Cape Province. Cape Foxes have expanded their range over recent decades to the SW, where the species reaches the Atlantic and Indian Ocean coastlines. May occur in SW Swaziland, and possibly also in Lesotho.

Descriptive notes. Head-body 45–61 cm for males and 51–62 cm for females, tail 30–40·6 cm for males and 25–39 cm for females; weight 2–4·2 kg for males and 2–4 kg for females. One of the smallest canids and only vulpine fox occurring in southern Africa has a slender build and a black-tipped tail. The overall coloration of the upperparts is grizzled silver-gray, the lower limbs, head, and back of the long ears being reddish-brown to pale tawny-brown. There is some freckling of white hairs on the face, concentrated mainly on the cheeks; the fronts of the ears are also fringed with white hairs. The upper chest is fawny-red, with the underparts colored off-white to pale fawn. The upper region of the front legs is reddish-yellow, with a dark brown patch on the backs of the thighs of the hindlegs. The body pelage is soft, with a dense underfur of wavy hairs overlaid by a thick guard coat of predominantly black hairs; the guard hairs are light-colored at the base and have silvery bands. During the molting period, from October to December, much of the guard coat is lost, giving the foxes a rather dull and "naked" appearance. The claws of the front feet are long, sharp, and curved and there is pronounced hair growth between the foot-pads. The tail is very bushy and the overall impression is that of a black to very dark-brown tail. Females have one pair of inguinal and two pairs of abdominal mammae. The skull is narrow and elongated, with a narrow rostrum and a rather weak zygomatic arch. The canines are long, slender and strongly curved and the two upper molars are broad as an adaptation to crushing. The dental formula is I 3/3, C 1/1, PM 4/4, M 2/3 = 42.

Habitat. Mainly open country, including grassland with scattered thickets and lightly wooded areas, particularly in the dry Karoo regions of South Africa, the Kalahari Desert, and the fringes of the Namib Desert. Also in lowland fynbos in the Western Cape, as well as agricultural lands, where the foxes lie up in surviving pockets of natural vegetation during the day and forage on arable and cultivated fields at night. Along the eastern flank of the Namib Desert in Namibia, they occupy rock outcroppings and inselbergs, ranging out onto bare gravel plains at night. In Botswana, they have been recorded in *Acacia* scrubland, short grassland, and especially on the edges of shallow seasonal pans, as well as cleared and overgrazed areas. In the central Karoo of South Africa they occupy the plains as well as low, rocky ridges and isolated rock outcroppings. In KwaZulu-Natal, South Africa, they have been recorded at elevations of 1000–1500 m.

Food and Feeding. The Cape Fox consumes a wide range of food items, including small rodents (murids), hares, reptiles, birds, invertebrates, and some wild fruits. An analysis of the contents of 57 stomachs collected across western and central South Africa and Botswana showed that rodents were the most commonly eaten mammal prey; beetles (larvae and adults) and grasshoppers comprised the majority of invertebrate intake. Birds and reptiles are occasionally included in the diet, but are probably less important. The largest wild prey species recorded are hares and spring hares. Cape Foxes will also scavenge and occasionally take young lambs and goats. Foraging is solitary, although foxes may occasionally gather in loose groupings to forage at an abundant food source. They obtain their prey mostly by digging rapidly with their front paws, often preceded by periods of intent listening. Caching of prey is common.

Activity patterns. Cape Foxes forage almost exclusively at night, peaking shortly after sundown and just before dawn.

Movements, Home range and Social organization. Cape Foxes live in monogamous pairs. In the Free State of South Africa, they appear to have overlapping home ranges, that vary from 1–4·6 km² in size. Defended territory is believed to consist of a limited area around the den in which the female has her litter. Vocal communication mainly consists of a high-pitched howl, ending with a sharp bark. Females may bark when a potential predator approaches a den occupied by pups. Facial expressions and tail positions play an important role in visual communication.

Breeding. Breeding appears to be non-seasonal in some areas, and strongly seasonal in others. The majority of births take place in spring and summer (August to October). Juveniles and sub-adults have been recorded in the Western and Northern Cape Provinces during November and December. Gestation lasts about 52 days, and litter size is from one to six pups. Young are born in burrows dug by adults in sandy soil, or in enlarged spring hare or Aardvark burrows. Births have also been known to occur in crevices, cavities amongst boulders, and occasionally, dense vegetation. Although both parents feed the pups, the female is the main provider and no helpers are found at dens. Both parents will defend the pups against potential predators. Their habit of abandoning one den for another could serve to avoid the accumulation of parasites and to confuse potential predators. Pups first begin to hunt at about 16 weeks, and become independent and disperse at the age of about five months. Communal denning has been recorded in the southern Kalahari, and a litter of eight pups found in the Free State perhaps reflects a similar situation.

Status and Conservation. CITES not listed. Classified as Least Concern on *The IUCN Red List*. Although treated as a pest across most of its range, it is partially protected in several South African provinces and is not listed as a problem species; no permit, however, is required to kill this fox in pest control operations, resulting in population reductions in some areas. Generally common to fairly abundant across much of its range, the species is considered to be stable. Population estimates are only available for South Africa's Free State province, where average density was 0·3 foxes per km², yielding a total population estimate of 31,000 individuals. Habitat loss/changes are not a major factor influencing the conservation status of the Cape Fox. In fact, in the Western Cape Province and elsewhere, changing agricultural practices have resulted in range extensions for the species. Expansion of semi-arid karroid vegetation during the process of desertification, especially eastwards, has also resulted in range extensions of this canid. The illegal but widespread and indiscriminate use of agricultural poisons on commercial farms poses the greatest threat.

Bibliography. Bester (1982), Bothma (1966, 1971c), Brand (1963), Coetzee (1977, 1979), Crawford-Cabral (1989), Kok (1996), Le Clus (1971), Lynch (1975, 1994), Meester *et al.* (1986), Monadjem (1998), Roberts (1951), Rowe-Rowe (1992b), Skinner & Smithers (1990), Smithers (1971, 1983), Stuart (1975, 1981), Stuart & Stuart (2001, 2004), Travassos (1968).

34. Blanford's Fox *Vulpes cana*

French: Renard de Blanford / **German**: Afghanfuchs / **Spanish**: Zorro persa
Other common names: Royal Fox, King Fox, Afghan Fox

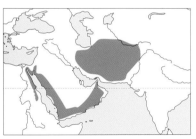

Taxonomy. *Vulpes canus* Blanford, 1877, Pakistan.
Genetic analysis revealed that Blanford's Fox and Fennec Fox (*V. zerda*) are consistently associated as sister taxa, and define a taxonomic grouping that previously had not been recognized. However, the two species diverged as much as 3–4 million years ago, which coincides with the appearance of desert regions in the Middle East and northern Africa. Monotypic.

Distribution. Arid mountainous regions of the Middle East. Known populations in Egypt, Israel, Jordan, Oman, Saudi Arabia, and United Arab Emirates. The species also ranges across much of Afghanistan and Iran, and surrounding regions in Pakistan, Tajikistan, Turkmenistan, and Uzbekistan.

Descriptive notes. Head-body 38·5–80 cm for males and 38·5–76·2 cm for females, tail 26–35·5 cm for males and 29–35 cm for females; weight 0·8–1·4 kg for males and 0·8–1·6 kg for females. A small fox with a long and very bushy tail. Males have 3–6% longer bodies and front legs than females. Head is orange buff, especially in winter. The face is slender with a distinctive dark band extending from the upper part of the sharply pointed muzzle to the internal angle of the eyes. The ears are pale brown on both sides with long white hairs along the antero-medial border. The body is brownish-gray, fading to pale yellow on the belly. The winter coat is soft and woolly with a dense, black under wool. Its dorsal region is sprinkled with white-tipped hair. The summer coat is less dense, the fur is paler, and the white-tipped hairs are less apparent. Specimens from the eastern part of the distribution may be predominantly gray. A distinctive mid-dorsal black band extends from the nape of the neck caudally, becoming a mid-dorsal crest throughout the length of the tail. The tail is similar in color to the body, usually with a black tip, although in some individuals the tip is white. The feet are dorsally pale yellowish-white, while posteriorly they are dark gray. Unlike other fox species in the Middle East deserts, the blackish pads of the feet and digits are hairless and the claws are cat-like, curved, sharp, and semi-retractile. The dental formula is I 3/3, C 1/1, PM 4/4, M 2/3 = 42.

Habitat. Confined to dry, mountainous regions, generally below 2000 m. All the records collected on the Persian Plateau are from foothills and mountains in the vicinity of lower plains and basins, where the species' habitat comprises the slopes of rocky mountains with stony plains and patches of cultivation. Appears to avoid higher mountain ranges and lower, warmer valleys, although the densest known population is found in the Judaean Desert, 100–350 m below sea level. In the Middle East, Blanford's Foxes

are confined to mountainous desert ranges and inhabit steep, rocky slopes, canyons, and cliffs. Blanford's Foxes are not limited by access to water in the Arabian Desert, and in Israel they inhabit the driest and hottest regions.

Food and Feeding. Blanford's Foxes in Israel are primarily insectivorous and frugivorous. Invertebrates are the major food, beetles, grasshoppers, ants, and termites being eaten most often. They eat the fruits of two caperbush species, *Capparis cartilaginea* and *C. spinosa*, fruits and plant material of *Phoenix dactylifera*, *Ochradenus baccatus*, *Fagonia mollis*, and various species of Gramineae. Remains of vertebrates were present in about 10% of fecal samples analysed in one study. Blanford's Foxes in Pakistan are largely frugivorous, feeding on Russian olives (*Eleagnus bortensis*), melons, and grapes. They are almost always solitary foragers, only occasionally foraging in pairs. Foraging behavior includes unhurried movements back and forth between rocky patches in a small area, sniffing and looking under large stones and occasionally digging, standing near a bush prior to circling the bush or pouncing upon prey within, and short, fast sprints after small terrestrial or low-flying prey. Food caching is rare or absent, unlike other fox species.

Activity patterns. Strictly nocturnal, likely an anti-predator response to diurnal raptors. The onset of activity is governed largely by light conditions, and closely follows sunset. Foxes are active about 8–9 hours per night, independent of the duration of darkness. Average distance travelled per night is approximately 9 km. Climatic conditions at night in the desert appear to have little direct effect on the activity of Blanford's Foxes.

Movements, Home range and Social organization. Radio-tracking studies in Israel indicated that Blanford's Foxes were organized as strictly monogamous pairs in territories of about 1·6 km² that overlapped minimally. Three of five territories contained one non-breeding, yearling female during the mating season, but there was no evidence of polygyny.

Breeding. Blanford's Foxes live in monogamous pairs. Females are monoestrous and come into estrus during January and February. Gestation period is about 50–60 days, and litter size is 1–3 pups. Females have 2–6 active teats, and the lactation period is 30–45 days. Neonates are born with soft, black fur. The body mass of a sub-adult is reached in about 3–4 months (700–900 g). Young are entirely dependent upon their mother's milk until they begin to forage for themselves. At two months of age the young start to forage, accompanied by one of the parents, and at three months of age they start to forage alone. Adult foxes have never been observed to carry food to the young. As in other small canids, food appears not to be regurgitated to the young. Males have been observed grooming and accompanying two- to four-month-old juveniles, but have not been seen feeding them or the female. Sexual maturity is reached at 10–12 months of age. Offspring often remain within their natal home range until autumn (October–November). Blanford's Fox dens in Israel were usually on a mountain slope and consisted of large rock and boulder piles or scree. The foxes appeared to use only available natural cavities and never dug burrows. Dens were used for rearing young during spring and for daytime resting throughout the year. During winter and spring, both members of a pair frequently occupied the same den, or adjacent dens at the same site, while during summer and autumn they often denned in separate locations. Frequent changes in den location from day to day were more common in summer and autumn.

Status and Conservation. CITES Appendix II. Classified as Least Concern on *The IUCN Red List*. Fully protected in Israel. There is a ban on hunting in Jordan and Oman, but no legal protection is known for Egypt, Saudi Arabia, United Arab Emirates, Iran, Afghanistan, or Pakistan. Fairly common in south-eastern Israel, where density has been estimated at 2 km² in Ein Gedi, and 0·5 km² in Eilat. The threat from habitat loss in Israel is limited, as most of the area where this species occurs is designated as protected. Political developments may change the status of the northern Judaean Desert. Human development along the Dead Sea coasts may also pose a considerable threat to existing habitat. Similar concerns exist for the populations in the UAE. Military activities may affect populations in Afghanistan.

Bibliography. Al Khalili (1993), Geffen (1994), Geffen & Macdonald (1992, 1993), Geffen, Dagan *et al.* (1992), Geffen, Hefner, Macdonald & Ucko (1992a, 1992b, 1992c, 1993), Geffen, Hefner & Wright (2004), Geffen, Mercure *et al.* (1992), Harrison & Bates (1989, 1991), Hassinger (1973), Ilany (1983), Lay (1967), Mendelssohn *et al.* (1987), Peters & Rödel (1994), Roberts (1977), Smith *et al.* (2003), Wickens (1984).

35. Fennec Fox *Vulpes zerda*

French: Renard fennec / **German**: Fennek / **Spanish**: Fenec

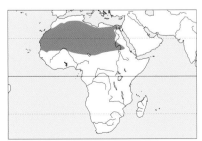

Taxonomy. *Canis zerda* Zimmermann, 1780, Sahara region.
Previously placed in the genus *Fennecus* now included in the genus *Vulpes*. Two previously described races, *saarensis* and *zaarensis* are synonyms. Monotypic.

Distribution. Widespread in the sandy deserts and semi-deserts of N Africa to N Sinai.

Descriptive notes. Head-body 33·3–39·5 cm, tail 12·5–25 cm; weight 0·8–1·87 kg.

The Fennec Fox is the smallest canid, with extremely large ears that give it the greatest ear to body ratio in the family. The muzzle and legs are slender and delicate. Pelage is typically sandy or cream-colored, although it may have a light fawn, red or gray cast; underparts are paler. The ears are darker dorsally and white or whitish inside and on the edges. Eyes are large and dark; dark streaks extend from the inner eye down and outward to either side of the muzzle. Upperparts of limbs reportedly colored reddish-sandy in individuals from North Africa, whereas those from farther south are nearly white in these areas. The coat is very thick and long; dense fur on the feet extends to cover the pads. The tail is also well-furred, with a darker tip and a slightly darker spot covering the caudal gland. Females have three pairs of mammae. It has a vulpine skull, but with very large tympanic bullae. The canines are small and narrow. The dental formula is I 3/3, C 1/1, PM 4/4, M 2/3 = 42.

Habitat. Fennecs subsist in arid desert environments. Stable sand dunes are believed to be ideal habitat, although the foxes also live in very sparsely vegetated sand dunes near the Atlantic coast. Annual rainfall is less than 100 mm per year on the northern fringe of the Fennec's distribution. On the southern fringe, it may be found up to the Sahelian areas that receive as much as 300 mm rainfall per year. In the Sahara, sparse vegetation is usually dominated by *Aristida* spp., and *Ephedra alata* in large sand dunes. On small sand dunes, it is dominated by *Panicum turgidum*, *Zygophyllum* spp., and sometimes by trees like *Acacia* spp. and *Capparis decidua*.

Food and Feeding. Fennecs are omnivorous, consuming insects, small rodents (e.g. *Jaculus jaculus*, *Gerbillus* spp., and *Meriones* spp.), lizards (e.g. *Acanthodactylus* spp.), geckos (e.g. *Stenodactylus* spp.), skinks (e.g. *Scincus albifasciatus*), eggs, small birds (e.g. larks and sandgrouse), and various fruits and tubers. Fennecs hunt alone. They have not been seen using the "mouse jump" hunting strategy typical of most fox species, but reportedly dig to find insects and small vertebrates. Like other foxes they cache food by burying it.

Activity patterns. Primarily nocturnal, although crepuscular activity is also reported. In southern Morocco, animals were commonly active in winter until around mid-morning.

Movements, Home range and Social organization. Movements and home ranges are unknown. Fennecs are thought to be moderately social, with the basic social unit believed to be a mated pair and their offspring. Like some other canids, the young of the previous year may remain in the family even when a new litter is born. Play behavior is common, even among adults, although males show more aggression and urine-mark around the time of estrus. Captive Fennecs engage in high levels of social behavior, and typically rest in contact with each other.

Breeding. First mating is reported to occur at nine months to one year. Fennecs mate in January and February and give birth in March and April. They most commonly give birth once annually, but more than one litter per year is possible under some conditions. The copulatory tie is exceptionally long, lasting as much as two hours and forty-five minutes. Gestation is 50–52 days. Litter size ranges from 1–4, and weaning takes place at 61–70 days. Dens are always dug in sand, in open areas or places sheltered by plants such as *Aristida pungens* and *Calligonum comosum*. Dens may be huge and labyrinthine, especially in the most compacted soils, covering up to 120 m² and with as many as 15 entrances, and may be close together or even interconnected. In soft sand, dens are usually small and simple, with just one entrance and one tunnel leading to a chamber.

Status and Conservation. CITES Appendix II. Classified as Least Concern on *The IUCN Red List*. Listed as "lower risk/least concern" in Morocco, which probably reflects the true status across their range. Legally protected in Morocco (including the Western Sahara). Current population size is unknown but is assumed to be adequate, based on observations that the Fennec Fox is still commonly trapped and sold commercially in northern Africa. In southern Morocco, Fennecs were commonly seen in all sandy areas away from permanent human settlements. The primary threat appears to be trapping for photographic exhibition, sale to the pet trade or tourists, and for fur by the indigenous people of North Africa. Though restricted to marginal areas, new permanent human settlements such as those in southern Morocco have resulted in the disappearance of Fennecs in these areas.

Bibliography. Asa *et al.* (2004), Bauman (2002), Bekoff *et al.* (1981), Bueler (1973), Clutton-Brock *et al.* (1976), Coetzee (1977), Cuzin (1996), Dorst & Dandelot (1970), Dragesco-Joffé (1993), Ewer (1973), Gangloff, L. (1972), Gauthier-Pilters (1962, 1967), Koenig (1970), Nowak (1999), Osborn & Helmy (1980), Petter (1957), Rosevear (1974), Saint Girons (1962), Saleh & Basuony (1998), Stains (1974), Valdespino (2000), Valdespino *et al.* (2002), Volf (1957).

CLASS MAMMALIA

ORDER CARNIVORA

SUBORDER CANIFORMIA

Family URSIDAE (BEARS)

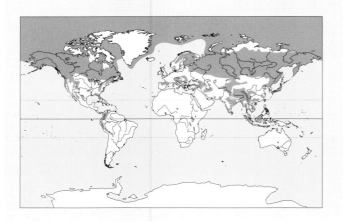

- Large mammals with big head and thick neck, small eyes, rounded ears, no facial vibrissae; muscular bodies with stout legs, large paws, and short tail.
- 100–280 cm.

- Holarctic, Neotropical, and Oriental regions.
- Forested environments (boreal, temperate, and tropical) to tundra and semi-desert; one species in Arctic.
- 5 genera, 8 species, at least 44 extant taxa.
- 1 species Endangered, 5 Vulnerable; 2 subspecies Extinct since 1600.

Systematics

The bear family consists of only eight extant species. Of these, six are sometimes grouped together in the subfamily Ursinae, and some systematists consider all the ursine species within a single genus, *Ursus*. This is quite a change from just a few decades ago, when each species of bear was classified in its own genus, with only the Brown Bear classified as *Ursus*. The closely related Polar Bear was in the genus *Thalarctos*, the American Black Bear in *Euarctos*, and the Asiatic Black Bear in *Selenarctos*. Sun Bears (*Helarctos*) and Sloth Bears (*Melursus*) are still considered distinct, single-species genera by many; others use these generic names as subgenera. As there are no clear rules for what constitutes a genus, this classification changes with general consensus, based on newly-discovered morphological, ecological, zoogeographical, and molecular attributes.

The other two bear species each occupy their own subfamily (although this taxonomic classification is not universally accepted): the Andean Bear (*Tremarctos ornatus*) in Tremarctinae and the Giant Panda (*Ailuropoda melanoleuca*) in Ailuropodinae. These species are distinct both morphologically and genetically. Whereas the ursine bears have 74 chromosomal pairs, the Andean Bear has 52, and the Giant Panda 42. The ursine chromosomes are mainly acrocentric (almost no short arms, because the two chromatids cross very close to the ends), whereas the other two species have primarily biarmed chromosomes (chromatids crossing near the middle). Inter-breeding among captive ursine bears, in a host of combinations, has produced viable and generally fertile offspring, and in at least one case, a *Tremarctos ornatus* × *Ursus thibetanus* cross also produced viable offspring.

Divergence times of the three bear subfamilies are disputed because fossil dates and molecular clocks differ. One of the key taxa at the node of this divergence was *Ursavus*, a widespread and diverse genus, apparently descended from the Canidae, with species ranging in size from foxes to small bears. The first true bear is obviously impossible to identify, due to the incomplete fossil record and a somewhat ambiguous definition as to what a bear is. Renowned paleontologist Bjorn Kurtén pointed to *Ursavus elmensis* (although known only from its teeth and jaws) as a likely candidate, thus attracting the name "dawn bear". More likely, different species of *Ursavus* spawned different branches of the bear family, including some branches that have since become fully extinct (including the once common, large bodied genera *Indarctos* and *Agriotherium*). Miocene fossils of these early bears have been found in localities across North America, southern Europe, Iran, India, China, Libya, and even South Africa (bears no longer exist anywhere in Africa).

The Giant Panda, once a taxonomic enigma, is now classified squarely within the Ursidae. The original taxonomic quandary stemmed from its strong morphological similarities to the Red Panda, which had been discovered earlier—hence the unfortunate common name "panda" and generic name, *Ailuropoda*, meaning panda-like foot (referring to the unusual false thumb of both species, used to manipulate bamboo). Both fossil and genetic evidence indicate that the two pandas

URSIDAE

| AILUROPODINAE | TREMARCTINAE | URSINAE |

Giant Panda	Andean Bear	typical bears
1 species	1 species	6 species
(*Ailuropoda*)	(*Tremarctos*)	(*Helarctos, Melursus, Ursus*)

Subdivision of the Ursidae

Figure: Toni Llobet

FAMILY
SUBFAMILY

are not closely related, and very few authorities recognize the Red Panda as a bear.

Giant Pandas are believed to have descended from the smaller *Ailurarctos*, found in Yunnan Province in southern China (fossil dated at about 7–8 million years ago). This form, similar to and once thought to be a type of *Ursavus*, demonstrates the clear linkage of Giant Pandas with ancestral bears. At least four species of *Ailuropoda* have been named, ranging from the small and medium-sized *microta* and *wulingshanensis*, respectively, of the late-Pliocene to early Pleistocene, to the large *baconi* in the Pleistocene, and finally the Recent (extant) medium-sized *melanoleuca*. All are characterized by teeth adapted for crushing fibrous material, so it seems that bamboo eating in this lineage developed quite early. Because none of these species occur together in fossil localities, they may represent chronospecies—an evolutionary progression where one type slowly transformed into another, corresponding with significant climatic changes that occurred in China during this period. The earliest records of these pandas were from about 2·4 million years ago, so the five million year gap between these and *Ailurarctos* leaves much to the imagination.

The Tremarctine or "short-faced" bears are known from late Miocene fossils of *Plionarctos* in western North America. These bears diverged from the ursine line at least seven (and possibly as much as 12-15) million years ago. There has been considerable debate over the systematics of this group. As many as five genera and twice that number of species have been recognized, although it has been difficult to differentiate taxa from fossil fragments as small as a single tooth. Certainly the most notable species of this group is the giant short-faced bear (*Arctodus simus*), the largest bear that ever lived, with large males weighing upward of 800 kg. Stable isotope analyses of the bones of this species, which show particularly high levels of ^{15}N, indicate that it was highly carnivorous; in fact, it is the largest known carnivorous mammal. It once ranged across North America, from Alaska to southern Mexico. The species mainly disappeared about 20,000 years ago (although persisteing in some relict populations until about 11,500 years ago). Its disappearance was contemporaneous with the advance of Brown Bears (*Ursus arctos*) across the North American continent, at a time when Brown Bears were more carnivorous than they are today.

The Florida Cave Bear (*Tremarctos floridanus*) is the only known congener to the present day Tremarctine bear, the Andean Bear, a South American endemic. *T. floridanus*, which was about 50% larger than today's *ornatus*, lived across the southern USA during the Pleistocene, from the south-eastern seaboard to the west coast. At least one specimen was found in Central America (Belize), evidence of the eventual movement of this genus into South America in the late Pleistocene. Tremarctines may have migrated from North to South America at least

twice; in the early Pleistocene, a group that became two closely-related genera (*Arctotherium* and *Pararctotherium*) spread from Venezuela through Brazil to southern Chile. One now extinct species reached 52° S latitude, the most southern bear.

The first truly identifiable representative of the Ursine bears is *Ursus minimus*, which appears about 5–6 million years ago. Of the present day ursine bears, this species looks (from its skull and dentition) to be most closely related to the Asiatic Black Bear (*Ursus thibetanus*). While both the common and specific names for this modern species reflect its distribution in Asia, it was actually widespread in Europe during the Pliocene (but withdrew to Asia partway through the Pleistocene). It is thus unclear where this species, or the ursine line, originated, or even which of the modern ursine bears is actually the oldest.

Some authorities have posited, based on the fossil record, that present day Brown Bears diverged in Asia, either from a *U. minimus*-like ancestor, or from another line of early ursines called the Etruscan bears (*Ursus etruscus*). Alternatively, Brown Bears may have originated in Europe, diverging from European Cave Bears (*Ursus spelaeus*). This split occurred 1·2

Sloth Bears, mistakenly classified among the sloths more than 200 years ago, have a shaggy coat, small molars, and a gap in their teeth through which they suck termites. They dig for termites and ants with their long, straight claws. They also eat fruits, when available, usually from the ground. Although Sloth Bears and Sun Bears are in separate genera, some data suggest the two species are related.

Melursus ursinus
Ranthambhore National Park,
India.
Photo: Günter Ziesler

million (based on fossils) to 2·8 million years ago (based on genetic analyses). Cave bears tended to be quite large, with males estimated to weigh 400–500 kg. However, sizeable differences in morphology and genetics among various cave "populations" indicate a degree of reproductive isolation that suggests the possible existence of several distinct species, or at least subspecies. These bears died out about 15,000 years ago, commensurate with both changing climate and increased predation pressure by man.

Another possible derivative of the *U. minimus* line is the American Black Bear (*Ursus americanus*). A possible direct ancestor to *americanus* has been found in North America, which may suggest that American and Asiatic Black Bears evolved separately from a similar relative, rather than the American form being derived from the Asiatic form, as previously speculated. Dating to about three million years ago, fossil remains of *U. americanus* are not uncommon, particularly in caves.

The divergence of Sloth Bears (*Melursus ursinus*) and Sun Bears (*Helarctos malayanus*) from the ursine stock is even murkier. Various genetic and morphological studies have produced contradictory results, and their taxonomic affiliation with the other ursine bears has ranged from sister species to distinct genera. Some analyses have suggested that these two species are more closely related to each other than to any of the other living bears; their geographic ranges slightly overlap in eastern India, and cross-matings of captive individuals have produced viable offspring. On the other hand, the paucity of fossil remains of Sun Bears in mainland Asia compared to a greater abundance on the Sundaic Islands (Sumatra, Borneo, and Java, although now extinct on Java) may suggest that their origin was there, rather than the mainland. Compared to other species of bears, fossil records for these two species are sparse, but what exists suggests that both species looked much as they do today well back into the Pleistocene, indicating a rapid radiation, along with the other ursine bears, 2–4 million years ago.

The ursine bear whose evolution is best understood seems to be the Polar Bear (*Ursus maritimus*). Genetic evidence clearly indicates a close association and recent divergence of this species from the Brown Bear. Remarkably, the mitochondrial DNA of one group of Brown Bears living on the islands of Admiralty, Baranof, and Chichagof (ABC) of south-east Alaska more closely matches that of Polar Bears sampled from across a broad region of the Arctic than it does any other Brown Bears, including those living on the mainland immediately across from these islands. This implies that Polar Bears evolved from Brown Bears in North America relatively recently (maybe only 200,000 years ago). A few cases of Brown Bear-Polar Bear hybrids occurring

naturally in the wild (and confirmed by DNA) attest to their close affinity.

The unique genetics of the ABC islands Brown Bears suggests a long separation (about 300,000 years) between this island stock and other Brown Bears, probably related to past periods of glaciation. The degree of distinctiveness of the ABC islands Brown Bear genetic clade, and its close relationship to a sister species, may be unique among mammals. The isolation of this clade, though extreme, is characteristic of many Brown Bear populations across their range, which spans a vast area of North America, Europe, and Asia (and previously North Africa).

Many slight and some major differences in size, shape, and coloration of Brown Bears, distinct to certain geographic areas, previously prompted some extraordinary taxonomic splitting. In the early 1900s, C. Hart Merriam proposed nearly 80 different Brown Bear species (now all *U. arctos*) in North America alone, a taxonomic superfluousness that was largely retained for more than half a century. In contrast, only a half dozen or so full species of Brown Bear were proposed for Eurasia. In fact, most Old World taxonomists recognized only one species, whose scientific name, designated by Linneaus, means bear in both Latin and Greek.

The North American subdivisions of Brown Bears—even if they were just considered to be subspecies—have not been upheld by genetic analysis, whereas a few Asian subspecies have been corroborated as genetically distinct. The Isabelline or red bear (*U. arctos isabellinus*), for example, which ranges from the western Himalayas to the Gobi Desert, is genetically and morphologically distinct. The range of this subspecies is bounded by large expanses of inhospitable desert that have kept it from intermingling with other Brown Bears. Bears in the Gobi Desert are also isolated from other bears, but genetically they fall within *isabellinus*. Some scientists and conservationists had hoped that the Gobi bear could be distinguished as a separate subspecies or even full species (*U. gobiensis*), which would have brought this bear and region more international attention.

In Europe, ancient Brown Bears had a rather uniform phylogeographical pattern, which contrasts sharply with the distinct genetic clades seen in today's European Brown Bears. The continent is genetically divided into Eastern and Western lineages, with the latter also subdivided into two groups. Each of these groups has been genetically dated, their source populations in southern Europe identified, and recolonization pathways surmised. One theory holds that the separate genetic lineages stem from extended isolation of discrete populations during the last major glaciation. In fact, Brown Bears have been

*High, humid cloud forests are
ideal habitat for* **Andean Bears***.
They also live in high altitude
grasslands as well as thorn forest
or scrub desert at much lower
elevations. They occur on both
the eastern and western slopes
of the Andes. Adaptations for
their arboreal lifestyle include a
somewhat shortened nose, which
brings their eyes more forward,
and curved front claws. Their
jaw muscles are adapted for
chewing fibrous plants, especially
bromeliads. They also eat fruit,
insects, and meat. Because food
is available all year long, they do
not hibernate. In one mountain
location they were found to be
completely diurnal, sleeping from
just after sunset until dawn. They
are reported to be primarily diurnal
elsewhere, but too little is known yet
about this species to generalize. The
Andean Bear, with only 52 pairs
of chromosomes rather than the 74
pairs in most other bear species,
is distinct genetically as well as
morphologically and is placed in a
subfamily of its own. The pattern
of pale fur on the face, which can
make these "Spectacled Bears"
look like they are wearing glasses,
is highly individualistic. Some
have only a "monocle"; some have
almost completely white faces; and
some have no markings at all.*

Tremarctos ornatus
Cerro Chaparri, Peru.
Photo: Tui de Roy/
Roving Tortoise Photos

a model species for investigating Quaternary ice age refugia and subsequent expansion (data from some smaller mammals match the patterns seen among bears). However, contrary evidence (DNA from bears that died thousands of years ago) suggests that the current Brown Bear lineages are instead due to population reductions and fragmentation caused by humans, with limited subsequent dispersal of female bears. Notably, despite the genetic distinctiveness of these lineages, none has been designated as a separate subspecies.

Historically, subspecies has been a rather loosely applied and over-used taxonomic unit. Nevertheless, some subspecific designations are clear and meaningful. For example, Sri Lankan Sloth Bears (*Melursus ursinus inornatus*) and Bornean Sun Bears (*H. malayanus euryspilus*) are probably valid subspecies, long separated from their mainland counterparts and showing morphological distinctions that appear not to be artifacts of their environment: geneticists can separate them by their DNA. Likewise, Asiatic Black Bears on Taiwan (*U. thibetanus formosanus*), Japan (*U. t. japonicus*), and in a long-isolated arid thorn forest in the Baluchistan region of southern Pakistan and Iran (*U. t. gedrosianus*) appear to be valid, genetically distinct subspecies. It certainly seems likely, though, that most of the many subspecific names that have been applied to Asiatic and American Black Bears and Brown Bears would not be sustained by genetic analysis. Recent genetics work has shown, though, that while these bears are highly vagile, genetic mixing is constrained by barriers such as mountains, rivers, and salt water channels separating islands, resulting in many distinct lineages.

Although the eight species of bears now seem quite fixed, enough uncertainty about their genetics exists to ponder the possibility of another, unidentified species. As recently as the mid-1980s, an expedition was launched to investigate reports of a new species of bear in the Himalayas of Nepal. While the findings were inconclusive, it appeared that local people had simply distinguished large adult Asiatic Black Bears from sub-adults, owing to the latter's greater use of trees. Indeed, in many remote parts of the world, local people frequently distinguish more species of bears, based on size, behavior, or coloration, than are recognized by science.

Recently, scientists pursued an investigation of a striking "golden" (blond) colored bear in South-east Asia. Genetic analysis of hairs taken from animals held in captivity showed it to be just a rare color phase of the Asiatic Black Bear—even a subspecies designation was deemed unwarranted. Showing again the arbitrariness of subspecies, a similarly rare light color phase of the American Black Bear—white, but not albino—is still formally called the Kermode Bear (*U. americanus kermodei*). These white bears are found only in a few distinct populations (principally on islands) in British Columbia, Canada. A single recessive gene that causes the white color, which is expressed in 10–20% of the individuals, has been identified. Females sometimes produce one white cub and one black cub, the latter where the gene is either not expressed or not present, suggesting, most bizarrely, that litters can be split into subspecies!

Morphological Aspects

Bears have big bodies, thick necks, large heads with small dark eyes and small erect ears, stout legs, a weighty hind end, and a short tail. They are the most massive members of the Carnivora. Record large Brown Bears and Polar Bears weigh in excess of 750 kg. What is the largest species of bear? That is a difficult question, because it depends whether one is comparing the very largest individuals, average individuals from populations where bears tend to be large, or averages from throughout the species range. In overall average size, Polar Bears have the edge, because Brown Bears in some populations are quite small (adult males averaging less than 150 kg), especially where their diet is primarily vegetation. High quantities of salmon in the diet distinguish the notably big Brown Bears of Kodiak Island (often referred to as Kodiak bears), the Alaskan Peninsula, and Kamchatka (eastern Russia), where average adult males exceed 300 kg.

The Sun Bear is the smallest species of bear. Adult females generally weigh less than 45 kg and males less than 65 kg. Sun Bears on the island of Borneo are notably smaller than on Sumatra or mainland South-east Asia.

Sexual dimorphism is present in all bear species, and is noticeable in individuals as young as one year old. In Brown Bears, Polar Bears, and both species of Black Bear, adult males tend to be more than 1·5 times larger than adult females. In populations of these species where both males and females are smaller, sexual dimorphism is often less (as low as 1·1–1·2), and in populations where the bears are large, the difference between males and females is greater (up to 2·2–2·3). Sexual dimorphism among the largest Brown Bears and Polar Bears is, among mammals, exceeded only by some seals and sea lions. Sexual dimorphism seems to be less in the other species of bears, which tend to be smaller.

American Black Bears *use very diverse habitats, from subarctic to tropical, including temperate and boreal forest to dry scrub forest to swamp, ranging from sea level to at least 3000 m elevation. Among the bears, they are the species most comfortable living near humans: they are often more comfortable with human presence than most humans are with their presence. They have a diverse, opportunistic diet. Black bears vary in weight regionally and seasonally. Males are much heavier than females, and northern bears are heavier than those living in the southern part of their range. All are heavier in the fall, before they enter hibernation. This species, although inhabiting only three countries, is more numerous than all the other species of bears combined.*

Ursus americanus
La Mauricie National Park,
Quebec, Canada.
Photo: P. Henry/Arco Digital Images/
CD Gallery

The large size of bears protects them from other predators. It also enables bears in temperate regions to store sufficient fat to survive a long winter fast, and makes them sufficiently mobile to locate rich food sources that may be well outside their normal home range. To carry this weight, they have stout legs and fully plantigrade hindfeet; the front feet on some species are only partially plantigrade, as the carpal pad does not actually touch the ground in a normal gait. All bears have five toes on both front and back feet; the Giant Panda also has an extended wrist bone (radial sesamoid). This bone, although not a sixth digit, functions as an opposable "false thumb", facilitating the manipulation of bamboo while feeding. The claws of all bears are strong, non-retractable, and longer on the front than the hindfeet.

The hairiness of the feet and length and shape of claws vary among species. Polar Bears have the most extensive hair separating the individual digital pads and main plantar foot pad—an obvious adaptation for walking on ice. Brown Bears and American Black Bears have hairier feet than Asiatic Black Bears. Foot pads are nearly naked on the Sun Bear and Sloth Bear, and in the case of the Sloth Bear, the digital pads are all fused and in a much straighter alignment than in the other bears. Sloth Bears and Sun Bears also have especially long claws (6–10 cm) on the front feet. In Sloth Bears, these long straight claws are clearly adapted for digging, as termites and ants are dietary staples. In Sun Bears, the long front claws are more curved. They may aid in tree climbing, as this species is the most arboreally dexterous. However, the Sun Bear's long claws also function well for digging and tearing apart wood for insects, when fruits are lacking. The Andean Bear and both species of Black Bear are also able tree climbers, but they have short, curved claws.

Anatomical studies have indicated that the musculature of the ankles of the more arboreal bears is modified for both strength and flexion. Likewise, the shoulder girdle and forelimbs are similar in many ways to other arboreal mammals in being especially designed to resist pulling forces along the long axis of the limb. However, bears do not hang or swing from tree branches, like primates.

Skulls of bears are massive. The eight species are sometimes divided into two groups, based on whether they have an elongated or shortened rostrum and palate. Included in the latter group are Sun Bears, Andean Bears, and Giant Pandas. A shorter skull positions the eyes more forward-looking, another adaptation for arboreality. Additionally, the shorter, higher-backed skulls provide a large point of attachment for their jaw-closing muscles. Both the Andean Bear and Giant Panda rely on vigorous chewing of very fibrous foods (bromeliads and bamboo, respectively), and the Sun Bear chews into hard trees to obtain stingless bees and other insects. All three of these species, but most notably the panda, have skulls and jaws that exert and withstand high bite forces.

Bears have a maximum of 42 teeth, including six upper and six lower incisors, four canines, sixteen premolars, and four upper and six lower molars. However, there is a great deal of variability in the number of premolars, not only among species, but also among individuals within species, even individuals in the same population. In Brown, Polar, and the two Black Bears, the first three premolars are very small, peglike, and not used for chewing, so they sometimes do not form, do not erupt above the gum, or are lost with age, leaving a diastema (gap) behind the canines. Sloth Bears are missing the inside upper incisors, producing a space through which termites can be sucked in. They have the smallest molars, as much of their insect food is not chewed; however, Sloth Bears have more functional front premolars than the other ursine bears. Giant Pandas have the most massive molars, which are necessary for crushing and grinding bamboo. Although Polar Bears are almost wholly carnivorous, their teeth are much more like the omnivorous Brown Bear than the sharp, slicing teeth of a carnivore, due to their late evolution and small, relatively soft prey (typically young seals).

All eight species have large stout canines, which tend to be larger in males than in females; they are also more often broken in males as a result of fights for mates. Canines are used by both sexes in fights (or mock-fight displays) to gain access to resources, to kill or protect cubs, and for protection from other predators (e.g. Tigers and Gray Wolves). They are also used to acquire food: Polar Bears for killing seals, Brown Bears for catching salmon and burrowing rodents, Brown and Black bears for killing ungulates, Black Bears and Sun Bears for chewing into wood for insects. Relative to skull size, Giant Pandas have the smallest canines.

All bears have an acute sense of smell. In fact, their sense of smell is far better than that of dogs. Recent studies of the bear's entire olfactory system, from the nose to the brain, by former neurosurgeon George Stevenson, indicate that their sense of smell is likely better than that of any mammal—several thousand times better than a human. Because of this, they tend to rely more on their nose than their sight to find foods, and their mental map of resources within their home range may be based more on smells than visual objects. At times, they may appear not to distinguish a person in plain view if they cannot detect the person's scent, thus giving the false impression that their sight is poor. Their sight is, in fact, reasonably good. They rely on color vision (which is not as good as a primate's) to forage on fruits. However, even though bears can travel and forage during the dark, their night vision is not good, and they rely heavily on olfactory and tactile cues. Observers using night-vision goggles to watch wild American Black Bears found the bears to be notably more tolerant of each other and of the human observers in the dark than they were during the day; they were also better able to catch salmon at night (an accomplishment, given that they lack facial vibrissae).

The coloration of bears provides little indication of how much they rely on visual cues in their social interactions. Aside from the Giant Panda's unique and enigmatic black and white blotched coat color, the other bears are mainly uniformly black, brown, or white. There are notable variations and patterns in color, though. Conspicuous white chest patches, common to several species, may enhance their threatening appearance when they stand upright. Asiatic Black Bears have a large white crescent-shaped marking on their chest, prompting the common names "moon bear" or "white-breasted bear". They also generally have a white chin patch. Sloth Bears have a somewhat similar white chest marking, but also have a very pale muzzle. Sun Bears may have a more circular chest patch, which is often more yellowish, hence giving them their name. However, their chest markings are very individualistic, varying from a V or U-shape, to a more irregular V or U or series of small blotches, to a circle with either a light or black center. In some areas, local people distinguish two types of Sun Bears based in part on variation in this color pattern. Andean Bears have even more individualistic light color patterns on their chest, neck, and face. The common name "Spectacled Bear" (not "speckled bear", as it is often incorrectly called) derives from the white rings that broadly encircle their eyes, giving them the appearance of wearing glasses. However, some of these bears have only one white "monocle", some have nearly fully white faces, and some have few or no facial markings.

No one has yet found a geographic relationship to variation in the color patterns of Andean Bears and Sun Bears. However, such a pattern clearly exists with Brown Bears. Some Asian populations have prominent white markings that extend from the chest over the shoulders and connect behind the neck. The overall hue of the coat color of the Brown Bear also varies geographically, from populations of primarily dark brown and even black individuals in parts of eastern Asia, to south Asian populations of so-called "Himalayan red bears" (*U. a. isabellinus*, often with a rufous coat) or "Tibetan blue bears" (*U. a. pruinosus*, with black legs and black shaggy ears), to inland North American Grizzly Bears, where various shades of brown and gray mix to produce a grizzled color. Locals formerly called Grizzly Bears "silvertips", and famed early explorers Lewis and Clark referred to them as "white bears" because of the sheen of their white-tipped guard hairs.

Ironically, the most consistent geographic relationship with coat color occurs in the American Black Bear, which in some areas is rarely black. Non-black variants include various shades of brown, dark gray, and white. Very few brown phase individuals occur in eastern North America, but their occurrence rises steadily moving westward, to 80–90% in portions of the Rocky Mountains, California, and the south-western USA. This distribution appears related in part to more open and arid environments, and also their present or past association with Grizzly Bears. It may have been advantageous for Black Bears living with Grizzly Bears, potential predators on Black Bears, to mimic Grizzly Bear coloration. Coat color is inherited, and litters may contain individuals of different colors. However, coat color can also change after a molt. White chest patches are also inherited. Most cubs begin life with at least some white hairs on their chest, but unlike the Asian species, which all have prominent blazes, most adult American Black Bears have either no chest patch or just a small remnant.

Hair is coarse and its length varies from less than 2 cm in the Sun Bear to up to 20 cm in Sloth Bears. An especially long patch on the backs of some Sloth Bears aids young in clinging and riding on the mother. Sloth Bears, Asiatic Black Bears, and some Brown Bears also have especially long hairs around the neck, forming a ruff or mane. This characteristic does not appear to be sexually dimorphic. For bears in seasonal environments, winter coats are significantly longer and have denser underfur than summer coats.

Brown Bears *are so large that the are virtually immune to predatio except by other Brown Bears. Onl the largest individuals, though, reliant on meat, such as salmon, ungulates, or ground squirrels; mostly they subsist on plant matter. Due to extreme variation in size and coat coloration, early naturalists once thought there we some 80 species in North Americ alone. Among these was the Grizzly Bear, whose fur has pale, "grizzled" tips. Black or partially black-colored Brown Bears occur Eurasia. Now all are classified as* Ursus arctos, *which means "bea bear." This species occupies the largest geographic area and wide range of habitats of any bear, fro deserts to tundra to various kind of forests. The muscular shoulder hump is typical of this species.*

Ursus arctos
Katmai National Park and Preserve, Alaska, USA.
Photo: Art Wolfe

A thick layer of fat and dense fur insulates **Polar Bears** from icy Arctic water. They are able swimmers and considered a marine mammal. They paddle with their huge forepaws and can stay underwater for up to two minutes. Some Polar Bears stay near shore, while others are more pelagic. All are reliant on ice as a platform for hunting seals. Under its thick fur coat, the Polar Bear's skin is black.

Although the fur looks white, it is actually translucent. The long guard hairs are hollow, but they do not, as was once theorized, funnel sunlight to the skin. Polar Bears have much more hair on the bottom of their paws than is seen in other species. The foot pads have small soft bumps that may help give the bears traction on ice; the pads may also contain scent glands.

Polar Bears and Brown Bears are closely related, and occasionally produce wild hybrids. The two species apparently diverged as recently as 200,000 years ago. Some individual Brown Bears are larger than any Polar Bear, but, overall, Polar Bears are the larger species. Although they are almost totally carnivorous, their teeth are more like those of Brown Bears than those of other carnivores such as dogs or cats, which reflects their recent divergence from Brown Bears.

Above: *Ursus maritimus*
Photo: Doc White/Ardea

Below: *Ursus maritimus*
Svalbard.
Photo: Hanne & Jens Eriksen

Here we have two bears inhabiting very different climatic areas, but both obviously enjoying a good sleep. Other bears have thinner fur on their bellies, but **Polar Bears** are thickly furred above and below. Only pregnant females hibernate in a den, but in more southerly parts of their range all Polar Bears are driven onshore when the ice melts, and do not eat for several months. On the sea ice they hunt for seals, which occasionally rest on the ice or poke their head through an air hole to breathe. Their home ranges vary widely in size, and can be enormous: one female was tracked travelling from Alaska to Greenland. It is hard to track males' movements because their necks are bigger than their heads, making it difficult to use radio collars. **Sun Bears** are primarily diurnal, except when living near human activities, such as plantations or gardens near homes. Motion-sensitive cameras set up along forest roads photographed them at night, whereas radio-collared bears in the forest mainly slept through the night. Much of their foraging is done in fruit trees. If disturbed, they slide quickly down the trunk like all bears, they descend tail first. Sun Bears sometimes sleep in trees, but usually only when near humans. Otherwise, they sleep on the ground, often in tree cavities or under fallen trees. Females use similar shelters as birthing dens.

Above: *Ursus maritimus*
Canada.
Photo: Eberhard Hummel

Below: *Helarctos malayanus*
Photo: Mark Newman/FLPA

*About 150 years ago, a French zoologist saw **Brown Bears** swimming off the coast of Russia and suggested they be named* Ursus arctos piscator; piscator *being the Latin word for "fisherman". This subspecies is now known as* Ursus arctos beringianus, *and the bears still swim in the Bering Sea. Brown Bears living along the coasts of western Canada and Alaska readily take to the water as well, in order to catch salmon, their dietary mainstay. They also occasionally find and feast on the beach-cast carcass of a whale, sometimes assembling in great numbers to take advantage of such an enormous food source.*

Ursus arctos
Alaska, USA.
Photo: Stefan Meyers/Ardea

Skin glands of bears have not been well studied, but it is apparent from behavioral studies that such glands function in chemical communication. Bears vigorously rub their backs and necks on trees or the ground, apparently leaving a scent that other bears react to. Scent glands may also exist in the feet, enabling Polar Bears to follow scent trails. Giant Pandas of both sexes have particularly well-developed anogenital scent glands. Relative to their size, they also have longer tails than other bears, which are used to spread this scent.

Habitat

All bear species except the Polar Bear are mainly forest dwellers. However, bears not only use a variety of forest types, but also occupy non-forested habitats, including scrub, tundra, and alpine areas above treeline.

Habitats vary by latitude and elevation, and different bear species range across different spans of this gradient. Brown Bears have by far the most extensive range, latitudinally, longitudinally, and elevationally. They range across Europe, Asia, western North America, and also once occupied North Africa (the only living bear to inhabit that continent). Each of the other species occupies either a single continent, or in the case of the Polar Bear, a single geographic region.

Polar Bears inhabit ice-covered seas of the Northern Hemisphere. They can be found on shorefast ice, the ice edge, or on large chunks of drifting ice. They use the ice as a platform for hunting seals. As such, their distribution and density coincide with availability and access to this prey. Annual ice (ice that melts each year) along shorelines, which has cracks that provide breathing holes for seals, is thus favored over thick, multi-annual ice.

Polar Bears also range onto land if the sea ice melts during summer. During winter, pregnant females use these terrestrial habitats for denning. Brown Bears (barren-ground grizzlies) share portions of this treeless Arctic coastal plain, and in some cases are found near or even together with Polar Bears. In one unique situation in north-eastern Canada, American Black Bears inhabit northern tundra, assuming the niche of the Grizzly Bear, which apparently occupied this area as recently as the early 1900s, but may have disappeared after a dramatic decline in Reindeer (*Rangifer tarandus*), their probable chief prey.

Boreal forests of Alaska and Canada are occupied by both Brown and American Black Bears, whereas only Brown Bears inhabit the vast taiga of Eurasia, stretching from Scandinavia through Siberia. This biome contains mainly coniferous trees, as well as many wetland areas like bogs, fens, and marshes. Soils in these forests tend to be low in nutrients, so fruit-producing trees and shrubs are less abundant than in deciduous forests; thus, bears living in these forests may be more reliant on roots, forbs, pine nuts, ants, or ungulates for food. Along the North Pacific Ocean, this zone becomes a temperate coniferous rainforest, and spawning salmon become a dietary staple for both Brown Bears and American Black Bears.

Temperate deciduous forests in eastern North America are occupied solely by American Black Bears. Considerable dispute exists about whether Grizzly Bears once occurred in this region. Certainly they were not there at the time of European exploration; moreover, even prior to that, no evidence has been uncovered of interactions between Native Americans and Grizzly Bears in this region. Conversely, Native Americans and Grizzly Bears have a long history on the western side of the continent. But some fossil finds indicate that Grizzly Bears once did inhabit eastern deciduous forests. Some scientists have theorized that they may have been extirpated by competition from American Black Bears, which, because of their smaller size, are better able to take advantage of small, ephemeral patches of fruit. Also, because Black Bears live at higher densities and have higher reproductive rates, they could have better survived exploitation by early human inhabitants of this area. Seemingly inconsistent with this argument is the fact that Grizzly Bears also do not occur in the eastern boreal forests, whereas they either outcompete or at least coexist with Black Bears in similar forests in western North America. One explanation may have to do with which species arrived first: Brown Bears may not be able to occupy areas already inhabited by a high density of Black Bears, and since eastern North America was first inhabited by Black Bears, Brown Bears were never able to gain a foothold. This scenario also may explain why many islands in south-east Alaska and British Columbia, which could support Brown Bears, are inhabited only by Black Bears (at very high densities), whereas the nearby mainland supports both species.

In Europe, temperate deciduous forests are occupied exclusively by Brown Bears. These bears exist in a niche much like that of the American Black Bear in eastern North America, in-

Bears communicate using
vocalizations, body language,
and scent. They may bare their
teeth in an aggressive display, as
in this **American Black Bear**. An
aggravated bear will huff and
snort, gnash its teeth, and may
lunge forward and slap the ground
with its forepaws. Scent from other
bears may be sensed by exposing
an organ in the roof of the mouth.
Scientists have long thought bears
to be primarily solitary, but recent
observations have indicated that
they regularly scent mark on trees,
and data from bears wearing GPS
collars indicate that they interact
more than expected.

Ursus americanus
Michigan, USA.
Photo: Dave Maslowski/
Maslowski Productions

dicating that Brown Bears can live, and indeed thrive, in such habitats. Dietary overlap between Brown Bears in many parts of Europe and Black Bears in the eastern USA exceeds 80%. Asiatic Black Bears and Brown Bears once coexisted in Europe, but the Black Bears ultimately retreated to Asia.

In Asia, Asiatic Black Bears dominate the temperate deciduous forests. In parts of China and the Russian Far East, for example, where Brown Bears and Asiatic Black Bears overlap, Black Bears tend to live mainly in broad-leaved forests, whereas Brown Bears live in coniferous forests at higher elevations.

Giant Pandas also live in temperate forests. Presently, they exist only in montane forests with dense stands of bamboo at altitudes of 1200–4100 m (more typically 1500–3000 m). This is not necessarily their preferred habitat. They once occupied lowland areas in eastern China, but were extirpated by human alteration of this habitat. Remnant populations exist only in mountainous areas that could not be farmed.

Moving southward, the mosaic of tropical forests in Southeast Asia are occupied both by Asiatic Black Bears and Sun Bears. These species are sympatric in lowland semi-evergreen, mixed deciduous, and dry dipterocarp forests. Black Bears are far more common than Sun Bears in montane evergreen forests at elevations above 1200 m, possibly due to the paucity of termites—a common food for Sun Bears when fruits are scarce.

Tropical evergreen rainforests of peninsular Malaysia, Borneo, and Sumatra are occupied only by Sun Bears. They use dipterocarp forests, lower montane forests, peat swamps, and limestone/karst hills throughout this area. Asiatic Black Bears do not range south of the Isthmus of Kra on the Malaysian Peninsula, where rainfall increases and the climate becomes aseasonal; the reason for this abrupt limit to their range is as yet unknown.

Sun Bears range as far west as the tropical wet evergreen forests (not true rainforests) of Eastern India. In this region they coexist with both Asiatic Black Bears and Sloth Bears. If there is any place in the world where three species of bears are sympatric, this would be it; however, it is unclear, with present data, whether all three species actually live together within any of the small forest patches of this area, or if small differences in habitat separate them.

The tropical, mainly dry, forests, scrub, and thorn woodlands of peninsular India and Sri Lanka are occupied exclusively by Sloth Bears. In some places within this area, forest cover is so

sparse, due to removal by people, that Sloth Bears seek shelter in crevices in boulder fields, and only come out at night to forage, often in cropfields. Sloth Bears also live in alluvial grasslands on the Indian subcontinent, where termites, a preferred prey, are abundant.

As elevation increases, in the Himalayan Mountain system of northern India, Nepal, Pakistan, and Afghanistan, Sloth Bears drop out, and are replaced by Asiatic Black Bears in the foothills and Brown Bears higher up. The limit for Asiatic Black Bears is near treeline, although this occurs at quite a high elevation (4300 m) in eastern India. Brown Bears replace Black Bears above this, and exist well into the alpine tundra. Indeed, Brown Bear sightings, and tracks in the snow, have been reported at elevations of 5500–5800 m, in dry rocky areas with sparse ground vegetation. They also exist throughout the mainly treeless Tibetan Plateau.

High altitude environments are also home to Andean Bears, on the South American continent. These bears range up to 4700 m, just below the permanent snowline, where they subsist on terrestrial Bromeliads in high-altitude tussock grasslands (called by various names: e.g. puna, páramo, jalca, along different portions of their range). It is unknown, however, whether these bears can survive in this habitat without making seasonal forays to lower, forested areas with more diverse foods. The prime habitat for this species is the humid cloud forest along both eastern and western slopes of the Andes Mountains.

Bears are rare in desert environments. Andean Bears range to low elevation (200–250 m), in very dry areas along the western slopes of the Peruvian Andes. Bears living in this coastal semi-desert congregate in riparian areas and at water holes. American Black Bears exist in similarly arid (semi-desert) conditions in south-western USA and Mexico, and Asiatic Black Bears occupy an arid thorn-brush region of southern Pakistan and Iran called Baluchistan. Brown Bears exist in even more arid conditions. In Biblical times they roamed from Morocco to Egypt, Israel, and Lebanon, although these areas were more heavily vegetated then. Today they still exist in scrubby, arid areas of central Asia. Most notably, an isolated remnant population of Brown Bears inhabits the Gobi Desert of south-western Mongolia, where they cluster around the few scattered oases that are slowly drying up.

Bears are also found in various human-modified habitats. Some human alterations improve, while others diminish the

When **Brown Bears** fight, they rear up and strike with their forepaws and bite at each others' heads and necks. Their large canines and long, slightly curved front claws can inflict considerable damage. Standing upright is a sign of dominance; growling and roaring are threatening vocalizations. When an individual is subordinate, it lowers its head and turns sideways to the dominant bear instead of facing it, and may sit, lie down, or back away to avoid being attacked. All eight bear species have large, stout canine teeth; the canines of male bears are more likely to be broken as a result of fights. Bears of the same age, sex, and social status are most likely to be aggressive toward each other. In approach of the breeding season, males have high testosterone levels and are especially aggressive toward potential rivals. Bears also may act aggressively when defending access to a clumped food source, such as an ungulate kill. At salmon streams, where both food and bears are abundant, females seek out spots away from males to avoid attacks and keep their cubs safe.

Ursus arctos
Alaska, USA.
Photo: Malcolm Schuyl/FLPA

*This may be just an adolescent sparring match; however, serious fights also may occur among **Polar Bears**, especially over food or mates. Large males are aggressive in defending a seal they have killed and also fight for access to receptive females. Bears may have the keenest sense of smell of any mammal. Polar Bears may be able to smell seals beneath the ice. They also use scent to locate females in estrus and follow them for long distances; they are highly aggressive toward other males who are also intent on mating.*

Ursus maritimus
Churchill, Manitoba, Canada.
Photo: Roland Seitre

quality of habitat for bears. Logging operations produce woody debris that fosters production of ants, beetles, and other insects sought by bears. Forest cutting and clearing also enhances light penetration, thus stimulating growth and fruit production of some plants. This tends not to be the case on drier sites, however, where loss of forest canopy desiccates the ground. Similarly, scarification, herbicidal treatments, and planting monocultures reduce habitat suitability for bears. In mid-successional, heavily-managed forests of north-western USA and Japan, American and Asiatic Black Bears strip bark on coniferous trees and eat the cambium because of shortages of food. Sun Bears may use selectively logged areas, and even feed in oil palm plantations near forest edges; however, there is no evidence that Sun Bears can survive solely in plantations or heavily disturbed forests. Sloth Bears seem to be able to survive in degraded forests where termites and other insects may be prevalent, but only if they are able to find shelter (e.g. rocky outcrops) during the heat of the day.

Bears sometimes settle near human dwellings, where they gain access to garbage, bird feeders, cultivated fruit trees, and other human-related foods. American and Asiatic Black Bears are most notable in this regard, but even Polar Bears, when stranded on land by melted sea ice, use human settlements as foraging habitat. However, historically, bears were eliminated from many of the areas that today support the highest human densities and/or have the most severe alterations of the landscape. Giant Pandas, for example, were extirpated from a broad area of eastern China. Likewise, Brown Bears were eliminated from much of Europe and Grizzly Bears from much of western USA; in both these cases, though, the bears were intentionally exterminated while much suitable bear habitat remained.

General Habits

Contrary to popular belief, most bears are not nocturnal. People often assume that they are only because those bears that live near humans and eat human-related foods, and hence are seen by people most frequently, tend to be active at night—hoping to avoid encounters with people. Bears at a garbage dump, bears raiding campgrounds, and bears depredating crops are classic examples. Without humans as a factor, however, bears are most active in early morning and early evening, continue activity through the day with short bouts of rest, and then sleep

most of the night. Accordingly, Brown Bears in North America tend to be diurnally active, whereas Brown Bears in Europe, which have more frequent interactions with people (because of small patches of heavily managed habitat and heavy hunting pressure) are far more nocturnal. In a study on Borneo, Sun Bears tracked in the forest using radio-telemetry were diurnally active, whereas those photographed with remote cameras along roads used by people were nocturnal.

There are exceptions, however, to the general diurnal nature of bears. Sloth Bears are active during the day, but tend to be even more active at night, a behavior that appears related to high daytime temperatures. In areas denuded of forest, these bears are especially nocturnal. However, young Sloth Bears and females with cubs are more diurnally active than other bears apparently in an attempt to avoid intraspecific conflicts as well as encounters with nocturnal predators. American and Asiatic Black Bears become equally active day and night when feeding on abundant hard mast, such as acorns, in fall. This holds for bears preparing for hibernation, as well as those in more southerly areas that do not hibernate. Likewise, Giant Pandas, which have a virtually unlimited supply of food (bamboo) are only slightly more active during the day than at night. They probably eat until satiated and then eat again as soon as there is room in their gut.

Bears generally sleep on the ground. They may crawl into a brushpile, a rock crevice, or even a former winter den, as protection or to stay cool. Sometimes they build a shallow "day bed" from ground vegetation—a misnomer since such beds are more apt to be used at night. Sun Bears and Andean Bears also build nests of leaves and branches in trees for sleeping, but even these two species, the most arboreal of the bears, sleep mainly on the ground. Sun Bears often sleep inside hollow logs, in tree cavities, or under tree roots. They seem to use tree nests most often when near people, probably feeling more secure and better able to detect danger when elevated. Similarly, studies of Andean Bears indicate that they commonly use tree nests as resting sites and possible guard posts when preying on livestock; in this case they may spend several days consuming a carcass, and may even bring parts up into the tree. Asiatic Black Bears also often build tree nests, but these tend to be related more to feeding than sleeping. In order to reach fruit or nuts at the ends of branches, they break the branches inward toward the trunk, and then pile the broken branches into what appears to be a nest; as such, it is not only a result of feeding, but also functions as a secure platform from which to feed. These bears also make large, bowl-shaped ground nests out of grasses or twigs, which they use as sleeping sites, especially when staying in one area for several days.

Overall, bears tend to be active 50–60% of the 24-hour day. Most of their active time is spent foraging. During seasons or years when foods are abundant, they generally attempt to maximize energy consumption by feeding more. When foods are more scarce, they reduce their level of activity. Only Giant Pandas seem to employ the opposite (time-minimizing rather than energy-maximizing) foraging strategy.

In north temperate regions, food for bears entirely disappears over the winter. Brown Bears, American Black Bears, and Asiatic Black Bears have adapted to this situation by entering a long winter fast. This fast is not obligatory, as evidenced by the fact that in each of these species, some or all individuals continue to be active through the winter if food remains available.

During their winter fast, bears remain in dens. They use natural structures like rock caves or crevices, hollows in trees or stumps, cavities under root masses of a fallen tree, or inside a brush pile. They also create dens by excavating a hole into an embankment, under tree roots, into an inactive ant hill, or even into the snow (Polar Bears). Some bears, particularly (but not solely) larger males, may simply weave conifer boughs or other vegetation into an above-ground nest. Bears in open dens may accumulate snow on their back: their thick layer of fat and dense undercoat insulates them so well that the outer hairs are near ambient temperature.

A long-standing debate about whether bears are true hibernators stems from the fact that, unlike smaller hibernators, their core body temperature drops only a few degrees (from 37 °C to 31–35 °C). This is likely an adaptation related to their large size. Even if their winter dens are protected and secluded, they are nevertheless vulnerable to being preyed upon by other bears or predators such as wolves. Their reduced but still relatively warm body temperature enables them to quickly arouse and fend off such potential attacks.

During the denning period, heart rate, respiratory rate, and metabolism are all reduced, and bears live almost solely on their fat reserves. They recycle normally toxic metabolic wastes (urea) and also recycle water. They conserve bone mass, muscle mass, and strength despite not exercising or even standing for the entire winter, a period that may span 3–7.5 months. The most exercise they get is via periodic bouts of shivering (several times a day); this is not a result of the cold, but rather a mechanism for maintaining muscle tone and strength as well as a means of warming internal organs and accelerating and thus maintaining heart function. Bears are the only mammals known to be able to sustain this condition over a prolonged period without eating, drinking, urinating, or defecating. Moreover, while in this state of total food deprivation, pregnant females give birth to cubs. Given this spectacular suite of adaptations, this state is properly called hibernation. Smaller hibernating mammals periodically awake to void or ingest food or water.

Day-length, combined with weather factors, like temperature and snowfall, may prompt hibernation, as bears in northern latitudes den earlier than those in more southerly areas. However, food supply also influences denning dates. Bears generally enter dens either when they have gained sufficient weight or when food supplies are exhausted and it becomes energetically unprofitable to remain active. Occasional years of widespread food failure in parts of Russia have resulted in non-hibernating, malnourished Brown Bears, called "shatuns", wandering about late into the fall (the Russian term derives from a verb meaning to loaf about idly or stagger around). In the Lake Baikal region, where this phenomenon is particularly prevalent, shatuns were recorded 19 times over a span of 44 years. Shatuns have been known to kill and cannibalize hibernating bears.

Bears are likewise stimulated to exit their dens by a combination of day-length and weather. Warm weather may cause snowmelt, and allow water to enter the den. However, bears are not fooled into leaving their dens by unusual warm spells during mid-winter. Throughout their range, varying largely by latitude, hibernating bears become active between late March and mid-May. Females giving birth to cubs enter dens earlier and come out later than other bears, whereas adult males, which have the largest fat reserves, normally den for the shortest period. Depending on the duration of hibernation, sex, age, amount of fat, and whether they give birth, bears lose from less than 10% to more than 40% of their pre-denning weight.

Communication

Bears tend to be solitary: they are considered the most asocial of the Carnivora. Exceptions include females with cubs, generally brief male–female mating associations, and temporary

*A lone Gray Wolf would not present a problem for an active adult **Brown Bear** such as this Grizzly Bear. However, wolves have been known to occasionally kill bears in dens. The sound of noisy young cubs moaning, squealing, and squawking when they are hungry, distressed, nervous, or uncomfortable may attract potential predators, like wolves. Native Americans once used these sounds to locate dens.*

Ursus arctos
Yellowstone National Park, USA.
Photo: Gerard Lemmo

Sun Bears *dig into the ground
and rip into decaying wood with
their long, curved front claws to
find termites, ants, and beetles.
They even claw and chew their wa
into living trees to reach colonies
of stingless bees. They use their
long tongues to reach into crevices
for bees, grubs, and honey. They
eat a great variety of fruits, but
when fruit is scarce they depend
almost entirely on insects, eating
more than 100 species. Sun Bears
also occasionally consume reptiles
small mammals, or bird eggs.
They like palm shoots, too, but
when they eat this new growth, it
unfortunately kills the tree.*

Helarctos malayanus
Malaysia.
Photo: Roland Seitre

congregations of bears at rich food sources. Nevertheless, they have an extensive array of communications, ranging from scent, vocalizations, body postures, physical or chemical markings of objects in the environment, to physical interactions with each other, all suggesting that they are more social than generally supposed. Indeed, recent studies, utilizing bears with Global Positioning System (GPS) collars or bears that can be readily observed, have found that they interact more with each other than previously thought.

Bears view their world largely through their nose. They use their keen sense of smell to locate food sources from great distances. Such food finding may be aided by following trails of other bears. It seems unlikely that bears would purposefully leave a scent trail for other bears to follow, but the scent of a bear's trail probably does confer information about the location of good feeding areas. For example, observations of bears clustered in the same cornfield well outside their home range, and well beyond the distance that they could reasonably smell the corn, suggests that the congregation must have arisen in part by bears following other bears. Similarly, male Polar Bears have been observed to identify and follow sexually-receptive females over long distances, apparently from scent associated with their tracks. Bears are sometimes killed in dens by other bears that apparently followed their scent trail.

Bears also intentionally scent-mark. This is an adaptation to the forested habitats and normal low densities in which they exist. By marking trees or other objects, the scent remains as an active, concentrated signal far longer than it would if just dissipated into the air. In essence, through scent marking, they are able to communicate in absentia.

To scent-mark a tree, bears may stand on their hindlegs and rub their back and head on the trunk. Once explained as back-scratching to relieve an itch, or a way to remove shedding hair (which it does), this behavior is now widely accepted as chemical communication. It is performed by both sexes. Sometimes, bears also bite or claw the tree, thereby mixing their scent with the aromatic scents of the sap, especially that of conifer trees. This also creates a visual mark. Trees (or even telephone and power poles) in prominent places along trails, ridgelines, or forest openings—places where bears are likely to travel—are marked most often, and may be marked repeatedly by different bears, each putting its own scent over previous marks. The extent of such marking varies among species, and also varies geographically within species, which makes explanations for this behavior elusive. Scent marks may identify

individuals present in the area, reduce home range overlap, aid in navigation or memory of nearby food resources, advertise reproductive state or dominance status, arouse and attract mates, or threaten conspecifics. Enigmatically, Sloth Bears have even been observed to rub over the scent of Tigers, a potential predator.

Giant Pandas perform the most elaborate scent-marking rituals of any bear species. This seems almost counter-intuitive given their conspicuous black and white coat pattern, which has a vague role in visual communication. To mark a tree, a panda backs up to the trunk, raises its tail and secretes and

American Black Bears *eat a
variety of fruits and nuts; this
individual is eating acorns, a key
fall food. Plucking nuts or fruit
from a shrub with the lips can
take a lot of time, so bears tend to
"high-grade", foraging in areas
where concentrations are high.
Sometimes several bears congregat
at such feeding spots. American
Black Bears in the eastern USA,
where deciduous forests usually
offer a plentiful supply of acorns
and other nuts, generally reach
sexual maturity earlier than their
conspecifics in the west. Nuts are
particularly important in the fall,
prior to hibernation, because they
are rich in fat.*

Ursus americanus
Coahuila, Mexico.
Photo: Patricio Robles Gil

This **Asiatic Black Bear** has found a jackfruit, a giant relative of the fig that grows on trees in Southeast Asia. Asiatic Black Bears regularly climb trees to get fruits and nuts. They create "feeding platforms" by breaking branches to access food items that are out of reach, and then sit on the broken branches to eat. They also feed on the ground, eating succulent new plant matter in spring and berries on shrubs in regenerating forests, and digging for insects. Several males may gather where food is particularly abundant; females, which are smaller than males, tend to avoid these concentrations. When their natural forest foods are scarce, the bears raid orchards, agricultural fields, and garbage dumps. In the northern parts of their range, where food becomes scarce or entirely disappears during the winter, both sexes hibernate for 5–6 months. Mast crops such as acorns, beechnuts, walnuts, chestnuts, pine nuts, and hazelnuts enable them to store fat prior to hibernation. Like other bears, they are primarily diurnal, but when crops such as acorns are abundant, they may be active day and night, whether or not they will hibernate. In the tropics, only pregnant females hibernate.

Ursus thibetanus
Cambodia.
Photo: Terry Whittaker/FLPA

circular motion. The bushy tail aids in spreading of the scent. Pandas encountering scent marks sniff, lick, and exhibit a brief flehmen, where they curl the upper lip, expose the teeth, and inhale, thereby transferring chemical stimuli to the vomeronasal organ in the roof of the mouth. Flehmen is used especially by males to assess female reproductive state. Pandas continue to respond to anogenital scent marks that are as much as three months old. However, their reactions to scent marks diminish with the age of the mark, indicating that they are cognizant of the freshness of the mark.

Controlled studies on Giant Pandas have shown that they can also differentiate individuals from their glandular secretions. Anecdotal information on other species of bears likewise suggests that at least some scent marks are individually recognizable. Bears routinely sniff each other when they meet, apparently using scent for individual recognition. It is unclear why bears sometimes roll in odorous objects, seeming to cover up their own scent. Especially astounding, given their reliance on scent communication, female bears in a den with young cubs will readily adopt (and seemingly not distinguish) foreign cubs introduced by a person, even cubs from captive situations covered in human scent.

Many, maybe all, species of bears mark with urine and possibly feces. Bears have been observed dripping small amounts of urine at selected locations, particularly near places where other bears have marked or bedded. Females have long vulval hairs that, when approaching estrus, are wet with urine, and rub along vegetation as they walk. Bears also may purposefully step through brush to disperse dripping urine.

A particularly unusual, but not well-understood behavior of some bears is the stiff-legged gait. Early naturalists wrote about deep sunken footprints of Brown and American Black Bears that appeared to be the result of bears walking repeatedly over the same tracks. Later observations revealed that they not only sometimes walk over the same tracks, but also walk with their front knees locked, thrusting and scuffing their feet to create deeper tracks. It is presumed that these are a signal to other bears, and likely contain distinguishable scents. Bears encountering a set of such marks will often strut over the same tracks, apparently displacing the previous scent with their own.

Bears also have a surprisingly large vocal repertoire, used for communication when the animals are close. They have an extended pouch near the pharynx, apparently to resonate sounds. Bears that are distressed by the proximity or behavior of another animal communicate their aggravation by "huffing"

*Bears have color vision, and **Sun Bears** use it when they are foraging for fruit. Figs are a staple food in times of food shortages. At times when fruits are abundant, such as masting years, when many species of trees fruit synchronously, the diets of these bears may include more than 20 families of plants. Where Sun Bears and Asiatic Black Bears coexist, scientists can tell which species has climbed a particular fruiting tree from the claw marks on the trunk: the Sun Bear's claws are closer together.*

Helarctos malayanus
Malaysia.
Photo: Roland Seitre

rubs a dark sticky substance from the anogenital region about 50 cm off the ground. They may also urinate in the process. In fact, female scent marks seem to contain mainly urine. They often select conifer trees, possibly because the scent adheres longer to the soft, textured bark. Most impressively, on occasion a panda will climb the tree backwards with its hindfeet until it is upside-down, in a full handstand, thus enabling higher deposition of the scent. To mark logs or rocks, they squat and rub the surface of the glandular area with a back and forth or

Polar Bears hunt on sea ice, relying almost entirely on marine mammals, especially Ringed Seals, for food. An average Polar Bear may eat 50 seals a year. Most of these are pups caught in lairs under the snow where they were born, or soon after they emerge. Usually larger prey, including Walruses, Belugas, and Bearded Seals, can be taken only by adult male bears. When prey is scarce or foraging is difficult, as it is on pack ice in the winter, Polar Bears can live on stored fat for extended periods of time.

Ursus maritimus
Svalbard.
Photo: Patricio Robles Gil

White-tailed Deer are so numerous in some forests and even suburban areas in the USA that they, and especially their fawns, can be an easy source of protein for the **American Black Bear**. These bears kill opportunistically, and also eat carrion. A single blow by a bear's paw can kill a small ungulate. Livestock can also become prey. American Black Bears do not usually dig for rodents. They do, however, feed heavily on much smaller prey: ants. In some parts of their range, when the bears first emerge from hibernation, before fruits ripen, they may get as much as 80% of their nourishment from ants, ant eggs, and ant pupae. They use their acute sense of smell to find ant colonies in rotten logs and their canine teeth to rip the logs open.

Ursus americanus
USA.
Photo: D. K. Maslowski/FLPA

As spawning salmon struggle upstream, **Brown Bears** pin them to the bottom with their teeth or paws, or snag them in mid-air. At first, the bears are hungry and unselective in their choice of fish. Later they may be choosier, taking parts that offer the most energy, like the brains of male fish and the eggs of females that have not yet spawned. The largest Brown Bears get the best fishing spots, relegating smaller individuals and **American Black Bears** to less rich spawning locations. In spawning areas where the two bear species are not sympatric, American Black Bears have proportionately more fish in their diet than where they have to share spawning areas with Brown bears. Brown Bears that eat a lot of salmon, such as those from Kodiak Island and the Alaskan Peninsula, in Alaska, and Kamchatka, in eastern Russia, are especially large. In addition to the protein, fatty acid, vitamins, and minerals they get from fish, however, the bears need carbohydrates, so they also feed on nearby fruit. Scientists have determined that bears eating a mixed fish and fruit diet gain weight faster than if they eat all one or all the other. Curiously enough, salmon fishing helps the environment, because when the bears defecate away from the stream, they add marine nitrogen to the ecosystem.

Above: **Ursus arctos**
Katmai National Park, Alaska, USA.
Photo: John Shaw/NHPA

Below: **Ursus americanus**
Anan Creek, Tongass National Forest, Alaska, USA.
Photo: Geoff Trinder/Ardea

(forcibly expelling air through pursed lips), "snorting" (like huffing, but expelling air through the nose), and "chomping" (or jaw popping; not actually a vocalization, but a sound made by gnashing their teeth). To humans (and presumably other species) these sounds are threatening—indeed, a bear emitting these sounds hopes to be effective in deterring an intruder. More importantly, these sounds also may serve as a sign of agitation to another bear. Bears often enhance this threat/ nervous display by slapping the ground with their forepaws or slapping and pulling down branches on nearby trees, while lunging forward. They also sometimes make the huffing sound when retreating from a threatening situation.

"Humming" is another unique vocalization produced by all the bears, except the Giant Panda. This sound is closest in form and context to "purring" (which bears do not do). Humming consists of a sustained series of short pulsing sounds of about the same tone and volume, coming from low in the throat and repeated at a rate of about ten per second, interrupted only by quick inhalations. This sound was once thought to be emitted primarily by nursing cubs. However, careful study by Gustav Peters has revealed that cubs do not hum when they are ingesting milk, but rather when they are sucking a nipple but not nursing. Similarly, bears hum when sucking their own paw or the ear of a sibling. Moreover, bears older than cubs may hum as well. It appears to be a vocalization indicative of general contentment. A mother in a den is thus informed by the sound that her cubs are contented. This would be particularly advantageous to mothers that are hibernating and thus not fully aware of their cubs' condition. The acoustic drone and vibration of the humming sound would likely be reassuring to the mother and might also have a soothing effect on the individual emitting the sound.

On the flip side of humming are the "moaning", "squealing", and "squawking" sounds emitted by cubs when they are distressed, nervous, uncomfortable, or hungry. These sounds vary in duration, pitch and volume, rising to a sharp and piercing level when a cub is particularly disturbed. Native people who hunted bears in their dens often keyed in on these distinctive sounds of bear cubs. Similarly, these sounds could attract other predators, which raises the intriguing question of how, evolutionarily, the benefits of these vocalizations outweighed their potentially disastrous consequences.

An array of other vocalizations has been described for bears, including "roars" (aggressive threat), "gulp-grunts" (fe-males calling cubs), and an assortment of "grunts", "moans", "bellows", and "growls" that have not been well catalogued or interpreted. Sun Bears and Giant Pandas are also known for their high intensity "bark", used when startled, excited, or to advertise their presence or sexual receptivity.

Although bears are not primarily visually-oriented animals, some of their communication relies on visual cues. To human observers, they appear to have few facial expressions, making their emotional state difficult (at least for us) to interpret. Their ears do not move much, except when they are very agitated and about to charge, whereupon they are flattened back. Their lips become squared off with huffing and chomping, as a sign of stress and agitation. Eye contact is important, which may be one reason that even American Black Bears, which have a very uniform coloration, generally have light colored markings just above their eyes. A fixed stare signifies dominance or threat, while an averted gaze indicates submission or appeasement.

Posture appears to be an important means of communication. The position of the head, exposure of the teeth, and the angle at which a bear faces another bear are important cues when bears meet. Obviously, the tail is so short that this, unlike other Carnivores, has no function in ursid communication, except in the Giant Panda, where it is used not only in scent marking, but also may be raised when a female is sexually receptive to a nearby male.

All bears have the ability to stand on their hindlegs, and even walk bipedally for short distances. Standing enables them to sniff the air or listen to sounds from a higher vantage point. But standing and especially walking also communicates aggression. Bears will sometimes fight in a standing position. They also stand, raise their front paws, and step or lunge forward to scare off an intruder. In so doing, the white chest marking, prominent on several of the species, becomes suddenly visible, accentuating the threatening display.

Food and Feeding

Despite being a small family, members of the Ursidae exhibit an extraordinary range of diets. The diets of Polar Bears and Giant Pandas are both very narrow, and on opposite ends of the dietary spectrum—the former is a carnivore that eats seals; the latter is an herbivore and obligate consumer of bamboo. The other six species are all omnivores, although one, the

This **Asiatic Black Bear** is making it clear with its fixed stare that it does not intend to share its ungulate meal. The large "Mickey Mouse" ears are characteristic of this species. Most bears are omnivorous, consuming fruit, nuts, leaves, roots, insects, and meat. This is true for Asiatic Black Bears. They prey on a variety of small hoofed mammals, which can be a significant portion of their diet in some places. Unlike American Black Bears, however, they seldom eat fish.

Ursus thibetanus
Dachigam National Park,
Jammu & Kashmir, India.
Photo: Joanna Van Gruysen/Ardea

Brown Bears are both predators and scavengers. They kill ungulates and also find carcasses and eat carrion. Additionally, they frequently dig for living marmots, pikas, and ground squirrels, and sometimes for smaller rodents. They have been known to take muskrats and even eat clams. Members of the deer family are much more important prey, however. Brown Bears seek out newborn fawns and calves, but also prey on adult Reindeer (barren-ground Caribou) in the Arctic, Moose, Red Deer (Elk), and other ungulates. They sometimes chase herds of Elk, bringing down and killing young animals with the swat of a forepaw. They usually kill adults they have brought down by biting the neck or skull. In parts of Alaska where Moose are primary prey, one Brown Bear may kill three or four adult females and five to seven calves a year. They are also capable of turning unguarded livestock into "deadstock". Amazingly, however, some Brown Bears in northern Europe satisfy about a fifth of their annual energy requirement by eating mound-building forest ants. The bears dig into the mounds and eat 4000 or more ants at each sitting. They excavated about a quarter of all the ant mounds in a study area in Scandinavia every year. Similarly, Brown Bears in some places in the Rocky Mountains of North America eat enormous quantities of army cutworm moths. These are rich in energy and highly digestible. In one month a bear eating them can consume as much as half its yearly intake of calories.

Ursus arctos
Dalarna, Sweden.
Photo: Staffan Widstrand

ears

*At first glance, one might think these were Polar Bears diving into a marine mammal feast, but in fact they are **Brown Bears** with pale fur. The ranges of Brown Bears and Polar Bears overlap in the southern part of the Arctic. Although Brown Bears are skillful predators, these juveniles, big though they are, could not have killed this animal themselves. More likely, they were lucky enough to find the carcass. The bears are presumably littermates. Young Brown Bears stay with their mother for two or three years, and littermates sometimes remain together longer than that.*

Ursus arctos
Photo: Steve McCutcheon/FLPA

Sloth Bear, is highly myrmecophagous (eating largely ants and termites). The relative amount of meat, insects, foliage, roots, fruits, and nuts in the diets of the omnivorous bears varies among species and also within species, depending on habitat.

Food habits of bears have been studied in a variety of ways. Like other carnivores, but unlike herbivores, bears have no caecum, so their digestion of plant foods is often incomplete. Whole fruits sometimes pass through completely undigested. This aids biologists in documenting what bears eat, but variation in the digestibility of different food items confounds interpretation of bear diets based on scat (fecal) analysis, as food types that are more completely digested are under-represented or unidentifiable. Correction factors have been developed to convert compositional analysis of scats to biomass of food consumed.

Assessments of food habits have also been obtained by observing bears directly, especially individuals that have become habituated to close human presence. Evidence of feeding provides another means of assessing food habits. For example, Asiatic Black Bears and Sun Bears routinely climb trees to consume various sorts of fruits, and the composition of their diet can be estimated by the number of trees of each type with their claw marks on the bark. One study in Thailand found that these two species of bear, living sympatrically, but differentiated by the width of their claw marks on trees (the spacing of Sun Bear claws being narrower), each consumed over 80 species of fruit, and their diets overlapped by 75–90% (depending on the habitat type).

Fruits are also the dietary mainstay for American Black Bears, for Andean Bears in most of their range, and for Brown Bears and Sloth Bears in large portions of their range. Most fruits consumed by these species are shrub-borne. In places where fruits are abundant, they are a major component of the diet, if only seasonally. However, bears rarely subsist on an exclusively frugivorous diet. Such a diet imposes several constraints. First, fruits are often so scattered among the branches and under the leaves that bears must spend a lot of time just searching for them. Second, it takes time to pick (using their lips) individual fruits. In combination, these factors limit the total amount of biomass that bears can obtain from fruits. Hence, their foraging strategy often involves high-grading: they search out clumps of abundant fruits (often found in forest openings, such as along roads) and concentrate on that patch until the fruit density is so reduced that it is no longer profitable to continue foraging there. They bypass places with low fruit abundance, and

in so doing trade foraging time for travel time to another rich patch. Because of their larger size, Brown (Grizzly) Bears are less able than American Black Bears to subsist on a diet of principally fruit; hence, in areas where these two species overlap, and where foods other than fruits are lacking, Black Bears are far more common (densities about ten times greater than Grizzly Bears).

Another important constraint of frugivory relates to the generally low protein value of fleshy fruits. To meet minimum protein requirements on an all fruit diet, bears must consume far more fruits than they would otherwise need in terms of caloric intake. In one captive study, energy metabolism for maintenance increased about two-fold when dietary protein was reduced from 12% (considered to be fairly low protein) to 4% (a typical fruit diet). Bears fed only apples lost weight, whereas those fed apples with a protein supplement gained weight. Large bears may be particularly constrained by the inability to obtain sufficient protein on a frugivorous diet. This in combination with the above factors may be reasons why Brown Bears, in particular, need mixed diets, and hence seek out habitats with forbs, insects, or preferably meat.

Nuts, technically a fruit, are commonly referred to as "hard mast" because they are harder and drier than fleshy fruits. They also generally have a higher fat composition. Nuts are thus beneficial for bears preparing for hibernation. Clear associations have been observed between hard mast abundance in the fall, and the subsequent condition and reproductive output of bears in their dens that winter.

Available hard mast for bears varies regionally and by habitat within regions. Key types of hard mast include acorns, beechnuts, hazelnuts, walnuts, hickory nuts, chestnuts (European and Asian species were more resistant to the blight than the American chestnut), and pine nuts. Pine nuts are limited in North America, but are a staple for Brown Bears across Siberia. In the Smoky Mountains of eastern USA, acorns accounted for nearly 75% of average annual caloric production among all bear foods; however, acorn availability varies 17-fold from years of good to years of poor production. Bears compete with squirrels and other animals storing nuts for winter, and have been known to seek out and raid squirrel middens (caches of nuts). In one study, an American Black Bear, aided by squirrel middens, ate 3000 hazelnuts in a day. In temperate regions, some nuts may remain intact over-winter, providing bears with a rich food source in spring, after hibernation.

More than 60 species of bamboo grow in the mountain ranges in China where **Giant Pandas** live. Dense stands of it grow as an understory on land so steep and rugged it is not used by humans. The Giant Pandas choose species of bamboo that are comparatively high in protein and low in fiber. They sit or lie back, holding the stalk in one forepaw, and bite off chunks they crush, but barely chew before swallowing. The false thumb they use to hold the bamboo is actually an enlarged wrist bone. Giant Pandas are unique among bears in being almost total vegetarians. They rely on bamboo for more than 99% of their food intake, and spend about twelve hours out of every 24, day and night, collecting it and eating it. A lot of the bamboo they eat passes through undigested, so they must eat 9–18 kg of bamboo a day to satisfy their nutritional needs. Bamboo is subject to occasional mass flowerings, after which the plants die. When this happens, some Giant Pandas starve, while others are prompted to eat whatever they can find, including crops and garbage. Other rare items in the diet include leaves, stems, and roots of various plants other than bamboo, as well as rodents and young hoofed mammals. Fossil teeth from four million years ago indicate their ancestors also ate a highly fibrous diet.

Ailuropoda melanoleuca
Wolong Nature Reserve, China.
Photo: Juan Carlos Muñoz

Herbaceous vegetation, such as grasses, sedges, clover, horsetails, and forbs, is the main spring food for bears in many areas. These foods tend to have higher protein than fruits, but seem to be less preferred by bears, given that they readily abandon them when fruits become available in early summer. However, the timing of this switch coincides with increasing fiber content and hence lower digestibility of the herbaceous plants as they mature. Forbs, which retain more of their nutritional value for bears through the seasons, are included in summer and fall diets more so than graminoids (grasses and sedges). Brown (Grizzly) Bears in particular are known for foraging on the roots or bulbs of forbs; their digging, which can make a field look as though it was ploughed, may have a strong influence on plant community structure. Andean Bears rely heavily on Bromeliads. They eat the succulent hearts of epiphytic species (which grow on trees) as well as terrestrial species (*Puya*, the heart of which is similar to the shape and texture, but not nutritive value, of pineapple). In arid environments Andean Bears eat both the fruit and pulp of cacti, and American Black Bears eat sotol and yucca.

Several species of bears eat bamboo (especially newly-sprouting shoots), but bamboo (a type of grass) is not a major food source for any bear other than the Giant Panda. Pandas eat other plants, and also occasionally eat meat, but over 99% of their diet is bamboo. They eat different types of bamboo by geographic location, and differing parts of the plant during different seasons. They bend and bite off the stem, and then, sitting or lying down and holding the stem with a forepaw, they push the bamboo into the side of their mouth, severing a 2–5 cm piece, which (remarkably, considering its woodiness) is swallowed after less than ten chews. For many months of the year they discard the leafy top of the plant, which has a much higher level of protein, but in other seasons they eat both stems and leaves, or mainly leaves.

It was once thought that bears, other than Giant Pandas, could not maintain weight on a wholly herbaceous diet. Accordingly, the time interval prior to the ripening of fruits has often been called the "negative foraging period". In actuality, this loss of weight is only true for large bears (e.g. adult males), which are constrained in having large energy requirements but a relatively small mouth (limiting their intake) and gut (limiting their capacity before satiation). The largest of the omnivorous bears, adult male Brown Bears, are thus forced to be more carnivorous.

The extent of carnivory varies enormously among bears. Polar Bears are obligate carnivores, feeding principally on Ringed Seals (*Pusa hispida*), and to a lesser extent on Bearded Seal (*Erignathus barbatus*) and Harp Seal (*Pagophilus groenlandicus*). Ringed Seals have adapted to a long history of Polar Bear predation by giving birth in under-the-snow lairs. Nevertheless, Polar Bears are significant predators of Ringed Seal pups. They also hunt adult seals when they come up to breath through holes or cracks in the ice. Polar Bears also scavenge carcasses of larger animals, such as Walruses (*Odobenus rosmarus*) and whales, as do Brown Bears.

Brown Bears also scavenge winter-killed ungulates, and may be significant predators of ungulates (including livestock) in some areas. In the Arctic, a large portion of this species' diet consists of Reindeer (barren-ground Caribou). Elsewhere they prey on Moose (*Alces* sp.), Red Deer (Elk) (*Cervus elaphus*), and other deer, and may be the most significant source of mortality for calves and fawns. They kill bedded neonates by tracking their scent. In some areas they chase herds of Elk, and use their forepaws to drag or swat the rumps of running calves, bringing them down. They also kill adults, generally pulling them down and biting the neck and skull. In several areas in Alaska, Brown Bears are the primary cause of mortality for adult female Moose. Adult male bears may kill 3–4 adult Moose and 5–7 calves per year in some places. In alpine meadows the bears dig for ground squirrels, marmots, pikas, and occasionally smaller rodents, and in some wetter areas have been known to prey on Muskrats (*Ondatra zibethicus*) and even clams.

American Black Bears also commonly prey on neonate ungulates, but typically do not dig for rodents. In Asia, where there is a higher diversity of ungulates, Asiatic Black Bears prey on adult animals of smaller-bodied species, such as muntjac and serow. Andean Bears prey on rodents and wild ungulates, but not commonly, and occasionally are known to take free-ranging domestic livestock (cattle). Sun Bears, Sloth Bears, and Giant Pandas have the lowest proportion of mammalian meat in their diets.

Fish are a large component of the diet in some populations of Brown Bear and American Black Bear, mainly along the Pacific coast, where they prey on spawning salmon. Likewise, in some inland populations bears feed on spawning populations of freshwater trout (which are in the salmon family). Bears catch fish mainly with their mouth, or sometimes with their paws. When the fish are abundant, bears selectively prey on the most energy-rich fish (those that have not yet spawned) and body parts (eggs of females, brains of males). By consuming salmon and defecating some distance from the salmon stream, bears transfer marine nitrogen to terrestrial ecosystems.

Although in some systems, spawning salmon represent a virtually unlimited supply of food, bears feeding at salmon

Whereas bears can obtain much of their dietary water from foods, especially fleshy fruits, they also drink water from ponds, streams, or water holes. The frequency with which they drink varies by the habitat in which they live, the seasonal availability of foods, and the availability of surface water.

Brown Bears *occupy the most diverse habitats of all the species of bears. They inhabit arid areas, like the Gobi Desert, Arctic and high-alpine tundra, and Asian steppe, to moist coniferous taiga, to temperate rainforests. In much of Europe they occupy deciduous forests, where they fill an ecological niche very similar to that of American Black Bears in North America and Asiatic Black Bears in temperate parts of Asia.*

Ursus arctos
Photo: José Luis Gómez de Francisco

streams also feed extensively on fruit. Whereas salmon are rich
sources of protein, fatty acids, vitamins, and minerals, they are
deficient in carbohydrates. Recent captive studies have shown
that bears feeding on an *ad libitum* diet of mixed meat and
fruit gain weight faster than on an all meat or all fruit diet.
Apparently weight gain is regulated by the balance of protein
from meat and carbohydrates from fruit. Notably, in smaller
bears (American Black Bears and young Brown Bears), the
optimal dietary mix is more slanted toward fruit, whereas in
larger Brown Bears the optimum balance contains more meat.
These different nutritional targets also coincide with social
constraints on foraging. Large Brown Bears are able to dominate the best salmon foraging areas, while smaller Brown Bears
and Black Bears are relegated to areas with poorer fishing, so
must seek more fruit. In spawning areas where Brown Bears
are absent or rare, salmon constitute a larger proportion of the
diet of American Black Bears.

Insects, another source of protein, also represent a major
component of bear diets in some seasons or circumstances. All
species except Polar Bears consume insects, although generally
they represent a small portion (lesser than 10%) of the annual
diet. Ants, particularly ant eggs and pupae, are a principal food
and prime source of protein for American Black Bears in some
portions of their range, composing up to 80% of the diet for
the month prior to the ripening of summer fruits. Bears often find ants by locating a rotten log, sniffing it, and then, if a
colony of ants is detected, biting into the log with their canines.
Ants are not a major food for Brown Bears in North America,

except in areas and years when other high-quality foods are in low supply. On the Eurasian taiga, however, abundant mound-building forest ants constitute up to 20% of the annual energy intake of Brown Bears, with 4000–5000 ants consumed per excavated mound (a small proportion of the ants occupying the mound). In one study area in Scandinavia, about one-fourth of ant mounds were excavated annually by bears.

Sloth Bears are specifically adapted to feeding on ants and termites, but even in this species, the proportion of insects in the diet varies geographically and seasonally. In Nepal during the non-fruiting season, ants compose about a quarter and termites make up half to two-thirds of the Sloth Bear diet. Even in the fruiting season, insects compose nearly 60% of the diet. By contrast, during the fruiting season in southern India, insects compose less than 10% of the diet.

Sun Bears subsist primarily on insects during periods of fruit scarcity, which in the Sundaic portion of their range (Borneo and Sumatra) occur immediately after periodic masting events (synchronous massive fruiting). During these periods, Sun Bears spend more than 90% of their time feeding on insects, especially termites and beetles, in logs and in underground colonies.

Moths and caterpillars also play a significant role in the diet of some bears. American Black Bears have been observed to feast on up to 25,000 tent caterpillars a day during infestations of this species (which birds avoid). At several high elevation sites in the Rocky Mountains, Brown (Grizzly) Bears congregate to feed exclusively on dense aggregations of army cutworm moths. The moths migrate to these sites to forage on the nectar of alpine flowers, and seek shelter under the rocks of talus slopes. Bears dig pits to excavate the moths, and may consume half their yearly calories in a month of foraging on these highly-digestible, high-energy insects.

Bees are typically not a principal dietary component, but all bears show a predilection for honey. Hence, they are frequent raiders of apiaries. The generic name of the Sloth Bear suggests a special fondness for honey (*Melursus* means honey bear in Latin), but the common name "honey bear" refers to either this species or the Sun Bear. Sun Bears are noted predators of stingless bees, which live in colonies in tree cavities. These bears use their canines to chew through live tree trunks, and then use their extraordinarily long tongue to extract both the bees and their nest materials.

All bears are opportunistic in seeking alternate foods when their primary foods are in short supply. Polar Bears stranded ashore have been observed eating plants and fledgling sea-birds. Garbage is a ubiquitous attractant for bears, and all except the Polar Bear and Giant Panda feed at times on agricultural crops, especially corn or oats (but typically not wheat). Sloth Bears sometimes feed on groundnuts (peanuts) and Sun Bears will eat the growth stems of coconut and oil palm trees in plantations. Bears utilizing artificial food sources often gain more weight and tend to have better reproduction, although they may also suffer high mortality from people defending their property from raiding bears. Recent technical advances have enabled scientists to quantify the amount of corn and meat (including livestock) in the diet of individual bears from analysis of isotopic ratios of carbon and nitrogen in their hair.

Breeding

The age of sexual maturity in bears varies from two to more than ten years old. Age of maturity corresponds with body condition and hence the food supply. Captive bears tend to mature faster than wild bears, and wild bears that obtain meat (ungulates or fish) or artificial foods (e.g. garbage, crops, livestock) mature faster than those without access to such foods. In a few rare cases, American Black Bears, presumably with access to artificial foods, gave birth at two years old, meaning that they reached maturity and bred as yearlings at about 18 months old.

The average age of maturity is younger in populations with more abundant and more diverse natural food supplies. American Black Bears, for example, generally reach sexual maturity earlier in eastern than in western North America, because food supplies, particularly fall hard mast, is greater in the deciduous forests of the east. In eastern populations, the average age of first birthing is typically three to five years old. In some eastern populations, many females give birth at age three. In western populations, the average age of first birthing is often near five years, and may exceed six years.

In Brown Bears, the average age of first birthing ranges from 4·4 to 9·6 years. In Polar Bears it ranges from 4·6 to 7·2 years. Data are not available for the other species in the wild. Data on age of senescence are available only for Brown Bears and American Black Bears, both of which stop producing cubs in their mid-20s, but may live to their mid-30s.

Less information is available on male reproduction. Based on testosterone levels and observed pairings with females, it appears that males in any given population mature at about the same age as females. Generally, though, males compete for mates, so newly-maturing males may not actually breed, unless

Its hibernating mother's fur is a warm comforter for this tiny **Brown Bear** *cub. It was born while its mother was in the middle of an extended fast. The whole time she is denning, she does not eat, drink, urinate, or defecate. Her heart rate slows dramatically, but her body temperature only drops a few degrees, enabling her cubs to stay warm as they nurse, grow, and develop. Her milk contains more than five times the fat of cow's milk. Because she is hibernating, she conserves muscle and protein, using the fat she put on prior to hibernation to keep her alive and nourish her offspring.*

Ursus arctos
Photo: L. Lee Rue/FLPA

the population has many more females than males (as in some hunted populations). Males often show scars from pre-mating rivalries, and testosterone levels may decline in young males at the losing end of such battles. For an extended period leading up to and including the breeding period, males significantly reduce foraging as they invest their time monitoring the receptivity of females. They seem to be able to judge the order of estrus among multiple potential mates.

All bear species except the Sun Bear have a defined mating season. The Brown Bear, both species of Black Bears and the Sloth Bear generally mate during May–July. This period tends to be extended in more southerly populations of these species. In Polar Bears and Giant Pandas, mating is somewhat earlier, beginning in March and ending in May or June. The mating period for Andean Bears in the wild is unknown. In Northern Hemisphere zoos it coincides with the Brown and Black Bear cycles, but in South American zoos mating occurs more often during the austral summer, with births during May–October. Anecdotal information from the wild suggests that times of mating may be somewhat variable, but little actual data are available. Sun Bears appear to mate and give birth throughout the year, but data from the wild are sparse and limited to small portions of the range.

Males apparently find receptive females using scent cues; in Giant Pandas, vocalizations are also important. In some low-density populations, mating sites may be consistent from year to year, thereby reducing the chance that receptive females will go unbred. Often several males, some ranging well beyond their normal home range, congregate near females as estrus approaches. Mating may not occur for several days. The most dominant male, often the largest, mates first. This male may consort with the female for several days (up to two weeks in some instances), and fend off approaches by other males. Courtship includes urogenital sniffing and licking, posturing, vocalizing, and attempted mountings.

The male mounts from behind, clasping the female around the chest with his forepaws, sometimes mouthing or biting her neck. In Pandas this mating posture is modified, possibly because of the male's shorter penis: the female crouches, muzzle tucked into her chest, while the male squats behind and props his front paws on her back. Duration of successful copulations is highly variable, from less than one minute to more than 20 minutes, and sometimes approaching one hour. Copulation may be interrupted by the challenge of another male. One male mates with a single female multiple times, and after volun-

tarily departing is replaced by a series of other males (typically three or four, but up to 20) in descending dominance order. Estrous periods vary from a few days to over three weeks.

American Black Bears and Asiatic Black Bears both appear to be induced ovulators, meaning that mating activity stimulates ovulation. This may clarify the function of the male's baculum (penis bone) and explain the often prolonged pairing and multiple copulations by the first male to mate. A few enigmatic cases have been observed, however, of pseudopregnancies in females in captivity. These females had no physical contact with males, but probably received some chemical stimulation; they ovulated and underwent a false pregnancy in which their progesterone profiles mimicked those of pregnant females. Sufficient work has not been conducted on the other bear species to know whether they are also induced ovulators, but their frequent copulations suggest that they are.

Induced ovulation benefits females in low-density populations by ensuring fertilization immediately after ovulation. Likewise, it benefits wide-ranging males in promoting fertilization during short pair bonds, thus enabling them to mate with multiple females. It also may provide females more control over paternity, as ovulation may not occur during a brief mating with a non-dominant male.

Whereas females mate with several males and sometimes produce litters of mixed paternity, and males mate with multiple females, a surprisingly small number of males actually sire offspring. In one study of American Black Bears, each breeding female had encounters with an average of 3·3 males during the breeding season, but because of differences in the timing and order of mating, only three of 22 resident males fathered 20 (91%) of 22 cubs (based on genetic analysis) during a three-year period.

Following fertilization, the embryo develops to the blastocyst stage and then becomes dormant. It does not implant for several months. Although it has been reasoned that this period of delayed implantation (or embryonic diapause) provides bears with an easy escape from a pregnancy if they are unable to gain sufficient fat for the winter, empirical evidence indicates that bears in poor physical condition more often consume their cubs at birth. The variable period of diapause, however, may provide bears a means of adjusting the birth date independent of the conception date.

The total gestation period, from conception to birth, ranges among and within species: 3–3·5 months in Sun Bears, 3–6

*If anything can save the **Giant Panda** from extinction, it will be the "ooooh" factor. Bear cubs are adorable, but probably none more so than Giant Pandas. At birth, they are extremely tiny, helpless, pink creatures, much smaller in proportion to the mother than other newborn bears. By about three weeks, they have black and white fur, but their eyes are still closed. The cub stays in the den, a cave or hollow log, for up to six weeks, carried by the mother, in her mouth, from den to den. By about three months, it is mobile. Giant Pandas often have twins, but the female only takes care of the firstborn, if it is healthy, and only it survives. The evolutionary explanation for this enigmatic behavior is still a mystery.*

Ailuropoda melanoleuca
Qinling Mountains, China.
Photo: Adrian Warren/Ardea

months in Giant Pandas, 4–7 months in Sloth Bears, and normally 6–8 months in the other five species. Implantation of the blastocyst apparently occurs about 60 days prior to birth. This period is only 40–50 days in Giant Pandas, explaining their extremely altricial (very small and helpless) cubs at birth. All bears give birth to altricial cubs—the weight being 10% or less what would be expected for a mother of that size. Panda cubs are extreme in this regard, being only 0·1% of the mother's weight at birth, about one-third to one-quarter that of other bears.

For those bears that hibernate during winter, birthing occurs while they are mid-way through an extended fast. This is a seemingly peculiar adaptation. However, if these mothers were

to give birth after hibernation, they would need to nourish their developing cubs through the placenta, which would require them to break down their own body proteins throughout the hibernation period. By cutting the *in utero* period short, the small newborns switch to milk enriched by the mother's fat stores, thus conserving the mother's proteins and muscle mass. Milk from hibernating American Black Bears and Brown Bears averages about 7% protein and 20% fat (more than five times that of cow's milk). For Polar Bears the fat content is about 35%—presumably necessary for the cubs to put on sufficient fat before they emerge from the den, often at ambient temperatures of –30°C to –40°C. Non-hibernating mothers in

tropical regions do not share this same constraint related to placental nourishment, but may have inherited the shortened implantation phase and low cub birth weights from ancestors that hibernated.

As a consequence of producing altricial cubs, all bears give birth in protective dens, and mothers may need to guard their cubs in the den for an extended period. Thus, even bears that would normally not hibernate because food remains available may be forced to fast after birthing. This is certainly true for Sloth Bears and Polar Bears. In the case of Polar Bears, female denning and birthing occur during fall and winter, when males and non-pregnant females are bountifully hunting seals, following a period of summer fasting.

Average litter size ranges from approximately one in pandas and most populations of Sun Bears, to three in some well-fed eastern populations of American Black Bears. Rare litter sizes of six cubs have been observed in both American Black Bears and Brown Bears. Litter sizes of four cubs are not uncommon in these species, and have been recorded as well for Polar Bears and Asiatic Black Bears. Andean Bears also have a maximum of four cubs, whereas Sloth Bears have a maximum of three, but two is the norm for both of these species. Giant Pandas are unusual in producing twins about half the time, but only raising a single cub (the other is abandoned or consumed at birth). As a general rule among bears, litter size is smaller for first-time mothers. Litter size also varies geographically, apparently related to overall abundance and types of food, yet year-to-year differences in food abundance seem to have little effect on number of cubs per litter.

The sex ratio of litters is often said to be 50:50, but in reality tends to favor males in most populations. Statistical evidence of a skewed sex ratio requires sample sizes that are not obtainable in most bear studies. In one odd case, a Canadian population of American Black Bears was reported to produce 71% male cubs; however, the study spanned only three years, so may have been an artifact. Longer-term studies often show biased sex ratios for short periods, but a gradual evening out after many years. Mortality of male cubs generally exceeds that of females, due to their greater boldness and inquisitiveness, resulting in more accidents (like falling out of trees) and predation (because they wander farther from their mother).

All of the bear species can, under favorable circumstances, produce litters every two years. In this case, offspring are weaned from milk at about nine months, and retained under maternal care for about 17 months. For those bears that hibernate, the cubs den with the mother as yearlings (one-year-olds). However, certain individuals, or all individuals within certain populations may retain cubs for longer. For Polar Bears, litter intervals of three years are most common. In Brown Bears, two-year intervals are common in Europe but longer intervals tend to be the norm in North America. In one Brown Bear population in Canada, inter-litter intervals average 4·4 years, and in a population in a harsh environment in northern Pakistan, intervals average nearly six years. Lighter-weight offspring may remain with their mother longer, thereby enhancing their foraging skills and growth rates, and extending the mother's interval between births. Mothers will not produce new cubs when still accompanied by older offspring.

Family break-up is prompted by interactions between the mother and a male. Males may cause the break-up in some cases, but in the few actual instances that have been observed the presence of a male prompted the female to chase away her own young. In one observed case, the young were casually suckling their mother (for comfort, but not obtaining milk) when she was approached by a male; she instantly turned against the cubs and aggressively chased them away. After family break-up, siblings may stay together as a group for several days (or much longer in some cases), or separate and periodically rejoin each other. In rare instances they may reunite with their mother.

Male bears sometimes kill cubs, but they do so at the risk of injury or death from the mother defending them. Presumably males can distinguish cubs that they have sired, based on recognition of mothers with whom they mated. Female mating with multiple males may be a strategy to confuse male paternity and thus reduce infanticidal tendencies. In Scandinavia, it was shown that males who killed cubs were mainly breeding residents; by killing an entire litter they induced the female to return to breeding status, thus providing the male with an additional breeding opportunity. This is called sexually-selected infanticide (SSI). No adequate explanation has been advanced to explain why this behavior is limited to this area. It has not been documented among the several long-term and detailed

*Pregnant **Polar Bears** give birth in maternity dens they dig in snow banks near the coast, farther inland in peat banks, or on drifting sea ice. Females first give birth when they are five or six years old. They mate in the spring. Apparently mating induces ovulation. As with other bears that hibernate, there is a period of delayed implantation before the fertilized eggs attach to the uterus and the fetuses develop. The tiny cubs, which weigh about 0·6 kg, are born in mid-winter. They stay in the den with the female until March or April. By then they weigh 10–12 kg and are ready to follow their mother onto the ice and learn to hunt seals. Litters of two are common. Females have four mammae, so that is the maximum litter size.*

Ursus maritimus
Photo: Silvestris Fotoservice/FLPA

studies of Brown Bears in other places, nor in other species of bears. In other studies, infanticide has been observed (especially in Grizzly Bears, which sometimes kill and cannibalize each other), but the collective data do not support SSI as the most likely explanation.

Movements, Home range and Social organization

After break-up of females from their offspring, the independent young bears initially remain within their mother's home range. As they get older, their home ranges expand, but females generally continue to use part of their mother's range. Female dispersal beyond the natal range is rare, although exceptions have been observed in some rapidly expanding populations, and in Giant Pandas. Almost universally (except possibly Pandas), young males ultimately disperse. Their age of dispersal (one to four years after family break-up) and dispersal distance relates to their size, habitat characteristics, and the density of bears in the surrounding population.

Long-term associations between bears aside from mothers and offspring are unusual. Pairs of young Sloth Bears (some related, some unrelated) may stay together for extended periods, possibly as protection from predators (especially Tigers). Pairs of Sun Bears also have been reported, but these may simply be mothers with nearly-grown offspring, as single-cub litters are common in this species.

Although bears maintain a solitary life, measured in terms of their day-to-day proximity to other bears, they nonetheless appear to communicate regularly with other bears via scent marking. The actual information conveyed is still not well understood. If a bear dies (e.g. killed by a hunter), some time is required for other bears to recognize the vacancy and use the area.

Bears exhibit varying degrees of territoriality. In some areas and some species, adult females maintain exclusive areas within their home ranges—areas that they share only with their independent female offspring, and even then, each individual eventually carves out a core area of its own. In most populations, however, no evidence of territoriality has been found, although neighboring individuals often avoid using overlapping parts of home ranges at the same time. It appears that territoriality can

be sustained only within certain levels and distributional patterns of food and within a limited range of bear densities.

Rich feeding sites often attract congregations of bears, which are formally known as a sleuth or sloth, although these terms are no longer used. Probably most well known are the large groups of Brown or American Black Bears at salmon spawning streams and garbage dumps. These bears also gather at moth aggregations, in rich berry patches, and in cornfields. Polar Bears may congregate at carcasses of whales, or while feeding

Like other bear cubs, **Andean Bear** littermates play, sometimes roughly while learning life skills. Female Andean Bears usually have one or two cubs, but can produce litters of three or four. Like all bears, they give birth to very tiny, altricial cubs. Even though Andean Bears do not hibernate, the female probably has to stay with her cubs in the natal den, fasting and guarding them, for some period of time. Females usually have a litter every two years, after the cubs from her previous litter no longer accompany her. In zoos, Andean Bear cubs are weaned at about nine months and independent at about 17 months, but no data are available in the wild.

Tremarctos ornatus
Photo: Luis Casiano

at seabird colonies when the bears are stranded onshore during the summer. Sloth Bears are known to congregate under Mahwa trees (*Madhuca longifolia*) when the succulent flowers are in bloom. Inexplicably, several (2–4) unrelated Sloth Bears also have been observed feeding on scattered termite colonies near each other. Congregated denning areas have been reported for Sloth Bears (rock outcrops used to escape heat) and Polar Bears (maternity dens). In arid regions, both American Black Bears and Andean Bears have been observed congregating at water holes.

When bears congregate, they generally do so peaceably, although with occasional squabbles over access to food. In general, though, fights are avoided by recognition of a dominance hierarchy. Large, dominant males typically procure the best feeding spots and feeding times. Males have been known to dominate some prime feeding sites to the exclusion of females. Apparent avoidance by females of males at rich feeding sites has so far been documented for five of the species, leading to a situation where the sexes are, in essence, seasonally segregated. For example, female Asiatic Black Bears avoid feeding within a rich oak stand in central Taiwan when high acorn production attracts a large number of males. Likewise, during the monsoon season in Nepal, when Sloth Bear males move to higher, drier feeding areas, females remain in the flooded lowlands, apparently to avoid conflicts within the preferred but limited feeding areas.

Seasonal movements in response to changing food conditions are common among bears. In mountainous areas, bears move as different foods become available at different elevations. In areas with less topography, bears move laterally to different habitats, sometimes 50 or more kilometers away, well outside their normal home range. In some years, large numbers of bears move in basically the same direction toward areas with concentrated foods, giving rise to some historical accounts of bear "migrations". Migrations along well-trodden Brown Bear trails, stretching tens of kilometers, are commonly mentioned in the Russian literature.

Home range sizes of bears, excluding seasonal movements, also are related to food abundance. Across species, home range size varies by more than five orders of magnitude. Polar Bears, living in an environment with the sparsest food, have home ranges that are at least double, and up to 30 times larger than the largest known Brown Bear home ranges; Brown Bear home ranges are, in general, larger than those of the other terrestrial bears. Within each species, great variability exists not only among individuals, but also across populations. In Brown and American Black Bears, the best-studied species, average home ranges in different populations vary by at least two orders of magnitude. As such, home range size provides a useful index of food availability. In Brown Bears, average home range size increases markedly from coastal areas with spawning fish, to deciduous forests with hard mast, to boreal forests, and to Arctic tundra, where one study reported home ranges of 8000 km². Bear density affects home range size as well, either compounding or confounding the effects of food. In coastal areas, for example, bear home range sizes are small both because of the abundant food and the high density of neighboring bears.

Consistent with other polygamous mammals, male bears have significantly (often 2–5 times, but up to nearly 20 times) larger home ranges than females. This occurs in part because males are physically larger and thus require more food. Due to the foraging constraints previously discussed, males are probably more apt than females to move about to find rich food patches than to linger in a patch where their consumption rate is low. Maybe more importantly, males profit reproductively by overlapping the home ranges of multiple potential breeding partners.

Relationship with Humans

Bears have had a long, varied, and complex relationship with people. They are easily tamed, taught to "dance" and even to ride a bicycle, for circuses and street shows. In parts of Asia they are often kept as pets. Yet, somewhat surprisingly, they have never been domesticated.

Bears have been the subject of much lore and mythology. The ancient Greeks and Romans viewed the bear as a symbol of motherhood, given their care of very small cubs born during the harshest winter months. Observations of mother bears, appearing from underground dens with newborn cubs in spring apparently gave rise to the verb "to bear", meaning to give birth or produce (e.g. bearing fruit).

A host of other words in many European languages originate from references to bears. Most notably, the word "arctic" (originating from the Greek word *arktos*, meaning bear), the

This **Brown Bear** cub may be scampering up the tree at its mothers prodding, to escape danger. Although cubs readily climb, in North America adults cannot climb trees, whereas in Europe they can and do. Brown Bear cubs in Europe are often active during the day, but learn to be nocturnal as they get older. The adults are mostly nocturnal, unlike their counterparts in western North America, who live farther from people and tend to be diurnal. Brown Bears were extirpated from large areas of Europe by the beginning of the twentieth century, but are gradually making a comeback, and expanding their range, either naturally or from human reintroductions. Europe now has about 14,000 Brown Bears, excluding European Russia. Gene flow is an issue, though, because today's populations are fragmented, and several are still very small. The largest populations of this species exist in Russia, Canada, and Alaska. Brown Bears and American Black Bears are the only two species not listed on The IUCN Red List as globally threatened.

Ursus arctos
Finland.
Photo: José María Fernández
Díaz-Formentí

northernmost region, points toward the pole star, also called Alpha Ursae Minoris in the constellation Ursa Minor. For centuries, navigation was aided by reference to this star, which is easily found by visually aligning two stars in the very prominent constellation Ursa Major, the great bear. This gave us the term "to take a bearing".

Native people in northern regions (in the range of Brown, Polar, or Black Bears) used bearskins for clothing, rugs, and blankets; meat for food; and fat for cooking, waterproofing, skin conditioning, and medicine. Hibernating bears were particularly vulnerable to human predation, and provided great relief to cold, hungry, and sick northern people. Other bear parts such as teeth, claws, paws, and skulls have been popular for ornamentation and ceremonial use. The latter uses have a clear connection to the strength and intelligence, and hence considerable power, conveyed by the image of the bear. Native people often selected animals as their spiritual guardians, and popularly chose a bear.

In many cultures, the spirits of humans and bears were interchangeable. This belief arises from the physical resemblance of the two when a bear is skinned – a bear with its coat off seems to become a human form, with similarly-proportioned body, ten fingers and toes, forward-looking eyes, and vestigial tail. The sharing of foods between bears and humans (bears eating human foods, humans eating berries from the wild), and bears' ability to stand on two legs on flat feet add to the perceived closeness of the species. Fables of people living with or even becoming bears (temporarily) are common. One of the best known is the North American Indian legend of the bear-mother, where a woman picking berries is led into a den (subtly abducted) by members of a bear clan and eventually gives birth to twin bear-sons, but after the death of her bear-husband, returns to her human life.

Another common legend, prevalent throughout northern regions, is that dead bears acted as emissaries to a spiritual or supernatural underworld. Elaborate, ritualized ceremonies thus became associated with the hunting of bears to ensure that slain animals were properly venerated. Many native people who hunted bears avoided use of the word "bear", but instead substituted an honorific kinship term, such as "cousin" or "brother" to refer to the dead animal. In some areas, bears were held in captivity for extended periods, later to be sacrificed in elaborate ceremonies. Cubs of wild bears were sometimes taken explicitly for this purpose. This practice reached an extreme among the Ainu of northern Japan and the Russian Far East, where bear cubs became favored children, living in homes and even being breast-fed.

The mythical transformability of bears, and their connection to the underworld, probably stems from their seasonal transitions from surface activity to a seemingly comatose state underground. In some places in Europe, primitive or ancestral humans even used the same underground caves as bears. Art inscribed on cave walls, often featuring bears, dates back 30,000 years.

Adding to their mystique, bears readily transform from a four-legged to a bipedal creature. This appears to have given rise to Nepali and Tibetan legends of the Yeti: in these cultures, beings are not necessarily static, so a bear walking on four legs is a bear, but after switching to two legs becomes a Yeti. The fact that a bear's hindfootprints, which look very human-like, often cover its front tracks, strengthened the belief that this creature commonly walked bipedally for long distances (and thus might really be an ape, leaving tracks in the snow—hence becoming the "abominable snowman").

Bears also have been recognized as having special medicinal value. In part this derives from their affinity for honey, and the use of honey in medicine (from which the word "medved", meaning bear in Russian, is derived). The bear's gall bladder has particular medicinal value, which has earned it a prominent role in Oriental pharmacopoeia. For about 3000 years, practitioners of traditional Chinese and Korean medicine have used dried bear bile to remedy conditions involving "heat" (e.g. fever, burns, infection, inflammation, toxicity, liver ailments, high blood pressure). Recent scientific examinations of bear bile indicate that it contains unique components that do indeed have medicinal qualities. Ursodeoxycholic acid, the primary medicinal agent, is now synthesized under the generic name Ursodiol, and various other trade names.

Whereas many benefits have been derived from bears, bears have historically been viewed as a danger, posing risks of attacking people, preying on livestock, and destroying crops and other property. The Grizzly Bear, in particular, gained a reputation for being a potential killer of both people and livestock. As a consequence, when European settlers invaded the Grizzly's

*Churchill, on the shore of Hudson Bay near the center of Canada, calls itself the **Polar Bear** capital of the world, not without reason. Hundreds of hungry Polar Bears gather there every fall waiting for the sea ice to freeze so they can hunt seals. Tourists flock to see them, providing Churchill with an economic boom that helps balance the disruption to normal life caused by the bears' presence. Late freezes and earlier thaws have prolonged the bears' stays near Churchill. "Problem bears" that come into the town itself are caught and held in enclosures until the ice returns. If they are females with cubs, they are airlifted by helicopter to more remote areas.*

Ursus maritimus
Churchill, Manitoba, Canada.
Photo: Gerard Lemmo

range in the western USA during the 19th century, they sought to eliminate these bears. At first, the cattle and sheep brought by these Europeans were a prime source of food for the bears, helping them to thrive, but ultimately, livestock predation catalyzed government-organized predator eradication programs, which in short order purged grizzlies from the entire southern portion of their range. In a period of less than 100 years, a population of about 50,000 Grizzly Bears living south of the Canadian border was reduced to less than 1000, with remnant populations covering less than 2% of their former range.

Europe also lost Brown Bears from a wide area, but over a much longer span of time. They were eliminated from Denmark about 5000 years ago and from Belgium, Netherlands, Luxembourg, and the United Kingdom at least 800 years ago. The long period of extirpation continued through the early 1900s. Bears were eliminated from Germany in 1838, Switzerland in 1904, and nearly eliminated from Norway during the 1920s. Living alongside people for millennia, the more aggressive European bears were gradually eliminated from the gene pool, and others learned to be wary of people, yielding today a much less aggressive Brown Bear than exists in North America.

Attacks by Brown/Grizzly Bears tend to be more common in North America than in Europe or Asia, and have increased. Attacks by American Black Bears are also becoming more common (roughly equal to attacks by grizzlies, with 1–2 fatalities per year), as growing numbers of Black Bears and humans encounter each other more frequently. These rates of attack, however, pall in comparison to those recorded in India for both Sloth Bears and Asiatic Black Bears. These bears have little habitat left that is not encroached upon by humans. In one Indian state, Asiatic Black Bears caused over 170 human casualties, including 20 deaths, over 15 years. More dramatically, attacks by Sloth Bears during a recent five-year period in another Indian state resulted in more than 700 human casualties, of which nearly 50 were fatal.

Humans often inadvertently attract bears by leaving potential foods available to them. Discarded food scraps are a notable bear attractant, and a cause of bears becoming a nuisance. Public garbage dumps where such foods accumulate can draw in many bears. Ironically, such places are often sites of public amusement, as otherwise bears can rarely be seen. A classic example is Yellowstone National Park, USA, where open pit garbage dumps were once a highlight for tourists. "Bear shows" at Yellowstone garbage dumps began in the early 1900s. Bleachers were constructed to accommodate the increasing numbers of tourists, and food waste was left out on concrete platforms to attract bears. This practice was stopped in the 1940s, but bears continued to have access to garbage dumps until they were closed in 1971. Because the bears had insufficient time to adjust to this rapid loss of a once important and reliable food source, many became nuisances in campgrounds and elsewhere, and were killed as a result.

All bears, except Polar Bears, have been known to prey on livestock, raid apiaries, damage crops and fruit trees, and/or strip bark from plantation trees. People whose property is damaged may respond by trying to kill the bears, by shooting, or with traps or poison—the legality and use of these vary regionally. In many poorer regions of the world, people stay out in their cropfields all night in a makeshift shelter with a campfire, lights, and noisemakers, and sometimes a pet dog, hoping to scare off marauding bears. Fruit trees can be protected by tacking cheap metal sheeting around the trunk to prevent bears from climbing. More sophisticated deterrents include trained guard dogs (especially the Finnish Karelian breed) and electric fencing. Provision of supplemental food has been used to reduce bark stripping in plantations, as bears seem to eat cambium only when they are very hungry.

Status and Conservation

Two principal factors have caused a general, prolonged decline in bear populations worldwide: direct human exploitation and habitat destruction. People kill bears in defense of livestock, crops or other property, or simply because they fear being attacked. This explains the purposeful, government-subsidized destruction of Brown Bears across Europe and North America that lasted into the early 1900s. People also kill bears for their products. Most of the illegal hunting of bears in Asia is related to the commercial sale of gall bladders and paws (an expensive dietary delicacy).

On the other hand, legal hunting of bears for sport, subsistence, or personal use tends not to have an adverse impact on bear populations, and may even serve to protect them. This was

*Some **Brown Bears** still live in the Cantabrian Mountains in northern Spain, and there are small populations in Italy, Greece, and France. The problem is that these populations are scattered and there is no natural interbreeding and sharing of genes among them. The areas where they live are like islands separated by vast seas of human habitation. That also imposes a mortality risk for the bears. Although the species* Ursus arctos *is not considered endangered, some of these isolated populations are considered Vulnerable, Endangered, or Critically Endangered by* The IUCN Red List.

Ursus arctos
Cangas del Narcea, Spain.
Photo: José María Fernández
Díaz-Formentí

*Catching **Sloth Bear** cubs and training them to be "dancing bears" is illegal, but it continues to occur. If they are rescued, they cannot be released because they are too habituated to humans an[d] ill-equipped to survive on their own. Instead, they are brought to rescue centers to live out their live[s] in captivity. Although they are classified as Vulnerable on* The IUCN Red List, *laws permit Slo[th] Bears to be killed if they threaten life or property. This species can survive in degraded forests if it ca[n] find shelter. Its main strongholds, though, are within forest reserves established to protect Tigers. There is no accurate information about population sizes, but with increasing human impact on the environment, it is assumed they a[re] in decline.*

Melursus ursinus
Keoladeo Ghana National Park,
Rajasthan, India.
Photo: Roland Seitre

not necessarily true in the past, but improved understanding of bear biology, advances in monitoring techniques, and general concern over past over-exploitation have led to much better management of bear hunting. In North America and Europe, modern-day hunting involves an infrastructure of managers, researchers, and enforcement personnel, as well as an informed public who share ownership in what is perceived as a harvestable resource. The result is a system in which illicit hunting is disdained and thus more readily prevented (ironically) than in places where all hunting is banned.

Loss, degradation, and fragmentation of habitat is as problematic to the viability of bear populations as is direct killing; it also results in more direct killing. Because bears generally rely on forests, the continual loss and degradation of forests worldwide diminishes the number of bears that the landscape can support. Moreover, forest fragmentation exposes bears to greater risk of contact with humans. Bears living in small forest patches are more likely to find gardens and cropfields at the forest edge and hence be killed as nuisances. Bears in small forest fragments are also more exposed to hunters and traps than they would be in large expanses of forest that are less accessible to humans.

As a result of these issues, it is apparent that most bear populations in southern Asia (especially south-eastern Asia) and probably South America are declining. This is surmised mainly from the fact that forest loss and poaching are high; actual population estimates and trend monitoring are virtually nonexistent in these areas. However, poachers have been caught, bear parts have been seized, and traps (wire snares), poison baits, and baited bombs (which explode when bitten by a bear) have been found in great numbers. Bears are also still taken from the wild for street shows (dancing bears) in India and for bear-baiting events (bears fighting with dogs) in Pakistan, even though both are illegal.

In China and Vietnam, several thousand bears are held in small cages and farmed for their bile. The Chinese bear farming industry claims that this practice reduces the poaching pressure on wild bears because it creates a surplus of commercial bear bile. To deal with this surplus, they have marketed products containing bear bile (e.g. soaps and shampoos) that are unrelated to traditional Chinese medicine. The surplus of farmed bile has also caused the price of this commodity to be reduced, thereby possibly attracting more users. Thus, it is unclear whether the increased production of bile has reduced

poaching pressure. Many traditional users prefer wild bile (which has more concentrated bile acids, the active ingredient) and shun manufactured bile or bile substitutes.

In stark contrast to the situation in Asia, in North America, careful harvest management, forest management, and increasing numbers of "bear aware" or "bear smart" programs to reduce bear nuisance activity (through both public education and aversive conditioning of bears) have, over the past two decades, resulted in thriving American Black Bear populations. Across the continent, the number of American Black Bears has been increasing by about 2% per year. This species is now more than twice as numerous, with a total population of about 900,000, as all the other bears combined.

Brown Bears are also generally doing well in North America and Europe. In Europe, successful reintroductions have bolstered populations in Italy, Austria, and France, and some of these translocated bears have subsequently spilled over into other countries, including Andorra and Switzerland. However, the situation in many places in Europe is still precarious, with several isolated populations still having less than 50, or in some cases less than ten bears. Occasionally a single reproductive female is killed, and the population is significantly set back.

Six of the eight bears (all but the American Black and Brown Bear) are listed as globally threatened on *The IUCN Red List*. None are naturally rare, and few are significantly impacted by natural food failures or disease—all are on the list because of continuing human impacts. The Giant Panda is listed as Endangered and the others as Vulnerable. The Brown Bear's non-threatened listing is a bit misleading. Although globally the Brown Bear is quite numerous, many small populations are threatened, and many of these are unique insofar as their genetics or ecology. Some of these are included on national lists of threatened animals. One of the most difficult situations for conservation arises where sparse bear populations are legally protected, yet cause significant damage to livestock and property and even threaten human lives. This is presently the case in Tibet, for example, where conservation strategies have resulted in escalating incidences of bear problems resulting in significant losses for local people.

The CITES treaty (Convention on International Trade in Endangered Species) restricts the trade of all the species of bears across national boundaries. This is true even for the abundant American Black Bear. This species was listed by CITES specifically to prevent gall bladders of illegally taken Asiatic Black

Could **Polar Bears** adapt to a warmer world? Could Ringed Seals? Ringed Seals give birth in lairs under ice and snow. They, and especially their pups, are the mainstay of the Polar Bear's diet. The bears depend on seasonal pack ice to hunt seals. When it melts during the summer, the bears are forced ashore, and must fast until it freezes again. If this fast is prolonged, the impact on pregnant females is especially severe. If they lack sufficient reserves of fat when they den to give birth, they and their cubs, if any are produced, may starve. The United States and Canadian governments have proposed listing both Polar Bears and Ringed Seals as nationally threatened, although the latter are not currently considered threatened by the IUCN. Polar Bears are listed as Vulnerable on The IUCN Red List because their habitat is shrinking and its quality is declining. Computer models of the annual extent, thickness, and duration of marine sea ice are gloomy. It has been declining for the last half century, and if this continues, the number of Polar Bears worldwide could be reduced by more than 30% in the next half century; the species' survival through the next century remains perilous. Climate change and loss of ice could also lead to more exploration for oil and gas, shipping, and toxic contaminants in the environment, further impacting these bears.

Ursus maritimus
Svalbard.
Photo: Bryan & Cherry Alexander/
NHPA

There may be a few as 2000 **Giant Pandas** still living in the mountains in China. This tiny total population is fragmented, with parcels of bamboo forest separated by clearings, agriculture fields, and forested areas with no bamboo. This fragmented range poses a particular problem during years when bamboo flowers and dies, because the pandas are restricted in where they can go. Giant Pandas are considered Endangered on The IUCN Red List, and they receive the highest level of protection the Chinese government can give them. Their habitat in China is patrolled to prevent poaching, and there is no virtually no trade in panda pelts. The number of living pandas that can be exported from China, and the conditions under which it is permitted, are strictly controlled. Zoos and other captive breeding facilities are much more successful at raising Giant Pandas than they were in the past. They have even found ways of keeping a second cub alive when twins are born. However, successful captive breeding brings its own challenges facilities are overcrowded, but there are few or no places to release captive animals into the wild. These animals would need chunks of habitat that were large enough for them to find sufficient food, but with few resident pandas. Efforts are currently underway to try to increase the area of available habitat for this species.

Ailuropoda melanoleuca
Wolong Nature Reserve, China.
Photo: Juan Carlos Muñoz

*Lacking actual **Andean Bear** population estimates, scientists rely on population indices based on signs left by the species, including trails, climbed trees, tree nests, bed sites, feeding remains, and scats to track their status. Andean Bears are listed as Vulnerable on* The IUCN Red List *and are protected in every country where they occur, but as forest habitat shrinks they are brought closer to people; many are killed when they raid crops or attack livestock. Like other bears, they are also hunted for medicinal or ritual uses. Populations in the northern parts of their range are especially isolated, restricting gene flow. Efforts are underway in some areas to create corridors to connect small populations.*

Tremarctos ornatus
Ecuador.
Photo: Pete Oxford/naturepl.com

Bears from being sold under the guise of having been from a legally hunted American Black Bear. While this treaty helps depress bear poaching through confiscations and arrests, enforcement is difficult. In some remote areas of the world, officials admit that illegal animal parts, including bear gall bladders and paws, routinely cross country lines by the truckload.

One of the most effective means of conserving bears is through establishment of protected areas, where human use is monitored and controlled, and the habitat is protected. For example, the Chinese government has set up a system of more than 60 such reserves to protect Giant Pandas; this, combined with habitat improvements outside the reserves, seems to be resulting in geographic expansion of this species. A high percentage of the ranges of Sloth Bears and Andean Bears are also within reserves, even though very few of these were established specifically to protect the bears. In India, a system of reserves established for Tigers has been vital in protecting bears.

Captive breeding is not an effective solution to the conservation issues impacting bears. Bears generally reproduce well in captivity. This is now true even for Giant Pandas: with recent improvements to captive conditions, more knowledge of their biology, and assistance from artificial insemination, captive panda numbers in China are now burgeoning. The problem, though, is that rarely can captive-reared bears of any species be successfully released into the wild. They are often either killed by resident wild bears, or become a nuisance or threat to people because of their non-wary nature. Moreover, if the conditions in the wild that resulted in a decline of the natural population still persist, then introducing more bears is unlikely to help.

A new and significant challenge for bear conservation relates to the effects of global warming. The conspicuous dwindling of Arctic sea ice is projected to have large-scale detrimental effects on Polar Bears (and their prey) over the next 50 years. Already in several areas these bears are forced to stay ashore for longer periods, without access to seals, resulting in lower body weights and reduced survival of some age classes. Effects of climate change on other ecosystems are still too complex to allow definitive predictions. There are noteworthy concerns, though, about flooding in lowland habitats (the prime habitat for Sloth Bears), and significant changes in vegetation due to altered temperature and precipitation. What will happen to the bamboo that pandas rely upon, or the pine nuts that are so important to northern Brown Bears? What will be the effects on spawning salmon or moth aggregations? For a few bear species we at least

know enough about their ecology to pose as yet unanswerable questions such as these—but for the other species, especially in tropical areas, our knowledge of both the bears and their habitat is as yet so limited that even the crucial questions remain elusive.

General Bibliography

Alt (1989), Amstrup (2003), Apps *et al.* (2006), Barnes *et al.* (2002), Belant *et al.* (2006), Bellemain *et al.* (2006), Bininda-Edmonds *et al.* (1999), Boone *et al.* (2004), Bromlei (1965), Christiansen (1999b, 2007), Craighead *et al.* (1995), Dahle & Swenson (2003a), Davis (1955), Derocher, Andersen & Wiig (2005), Derocher, Andriashek & Arnould (1993), Erdbrink (1953), Felicetti *et al.* (2003), Ferguson & McLoughlin (2000), Fredriksson *et al.* (2006), Galbreath, Groves & Waits (2007), Galbreath, Hean & Montgomery (2000), Garshelis (2002, 2004), Garshelis & Hellgren (1994), Gende *et al.* (2001), Goldstein (2002), Goldstein *et al.* (2006), Hallowell (1926), Hamdine *et al.* (1998), Harlow *et al.* (2004), Hellgren (1998), Herrero (2002), Hobson *et al.* (2000), Hofreiter *et al.* (2004), Holm *et al.* (1999), Hwang & Garshelis (2006), Hwang *et al.* (2002), Inman & Pelton (2002), IUCN (2008), Jacoby *et al.* (1999), Japan Bear Network (2006), Jin *et al.* (2007), Jordan (1976), Joshi, Garshelis & Smith (1997), Joshi, Smith & Garshelis (1999), Kaczensky *et al.* (2006), Kilham & Gray (2002), Kleiman (1983), Kovach & Powell (2003), Krause *et al.* (2008), Kurtén (1976), Kurtén & Anderson (1980), Larivière & Ferguson (2003), Laurie & Seidensticker (1977), Linnell *et al.* (2000), Lohuis *et al.* (2007), Loreille *et al.* (2001), Manlius (1998), Mattson (1990, 1998), Mattson & Jonkel (1990), Mattson & Merrill (2002), Mattson *et al.* (2005), Mazza & Rustioni (1994), McLoughlin, Case *et al.* (1999), McLoughlin, Ferguson & Messier (2000), Meijaard (1999a), Miller *et al.* (2006), Mizukami *et al.* (2005), Mowat & Heard (2006), Nielsen, Munro *et al.* (2004), Normua *et al.* (2004), Noyce & Garshelis (1998), Noyce *et al.* (1997), Pagès *et al.* (2008), Paisley & Garshelis (2006), Peacock *et al.* (2007), Peters *et al.* (2007), Peyton (1980), Pocock (1932c, 1932d), Prevosti *et al.* (2003), Ramsay & Dunbrack (1986), Reid, Jiang *et al.* (1991), Reimchen (1998a, 1998b), Ritland *et al.* (2001), Robbins *et al.* (2007), Rode & Robbins (2000), Rode, Farley & Robbins (2006), Rode, Robbins & Shipley (2001), Rogers (1980), Rounds (1987), Sacco & Van Valkenburgh (2004), Salesa *et al.* (2006), Sasaki *et al.* (2005), Schaller *et al.* (1985), Schwartz & Franzmann (1991), Schwartz, Keating *et al.* (2003), Schwartz, Miller & Haroldson (2003), Servheen (1989), Servheen *et al.* (1999), Seryodkin *et al.* (2003), Shepard & Sanders (1985), Sommer & Benecke (2005), Sowerby (1920), Steinmetz & Garshelis (2008), Stenhouse *et al.* (2005), Stirling (1988, 1993), Stirling & Derocher (1990), Stirling & Parkinson (2006), Swaisgood *et al.* (2004), Swenson *et al.* (1999), Talbot & Shields (1996), Tedford & Martin (2001), Vaisfeld & Chestin (1993), Valdiosera *et al.* (2007), Van Gelder (1977), Vaughan (2002), Veitch & Harrington (1996), Waits, Sullivan *et al.* (1999), Waits, Talbot *et al.* (1998), Welch *et al.* (1997), White *et al.* (1998), Wong *et al.* (2004), Wooding & Ward (1997), Zager & Beecham (2006).

1

2

facial variants

3

4

ssp *thibetanus*

5

ssp *gedrosianus*
brown morph

black morph

6

ssp *americanus*

ssp *kermodei*
white morph

brown morph

PLATE 27

inches   40

cm   100

Subfamily AILUROPODINAE

Genus *AILUROPODA*

Milne-Edwards, 1870

1. Giant Panda *Ailuropoda melanoleuca*

French: Ours panda / **German**: Bambusbär / **Spanish**: Panda

Other common names: Da Xiong Mao (meaning large bear cat)

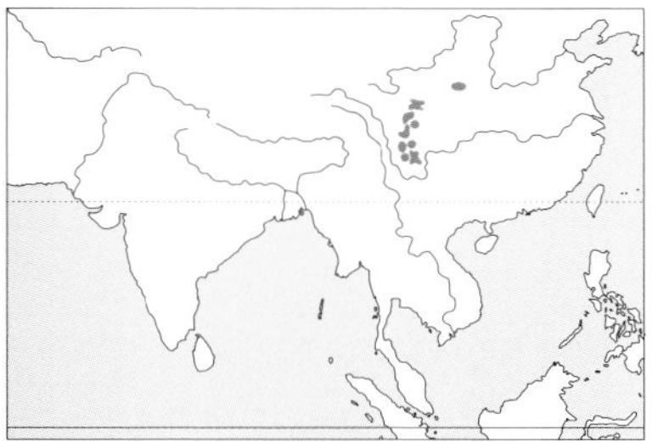

Taxonomy. *Ursus melanoleucus* David, 1869, Sichuan Province, China.

Previously included in genus *Ursus*. Once placed in a separate family, morphological and molecular evidence now strongly supports placement in Ursidae. No subspecies yet recognized, although one population in Qinling Mountains, Shaanxi Province, shows differences in cranial and dental morphology, pelage characteristics, and genetics indicative of isolation for several thousand years, and a subspecies designation (*qinlingensis*) has been proposed.

Distribution. C China (Sichuan, Gansu & Shaanxi Provinces).

Descriptive notes. Head-body 120–180 cm, tail 10–16 cm; males weigh 85–125 kg (sometimes exceeding 150 kg in captivity), about 10–20% more than females, which weigh 70–100 kg. Stocky, barrel-shaped body, large forelimbs, wide massive head with short muzzle and erect ears (10 cm). Hairs are coarse and oily. Specific name *melanoleuca* refers to distinctive black and white color pattern, which is unique among mammals. Face is white with an oblong black patch around each eye, black ears, and a black nose. Forelegs are black, continuing up over shoulders with a narrower band across the back. Hindlegs below the hips are also black. The remainder of the body, including the tail, is white. Occasionally, individuals may have more brown than black coloration. Forepaws are modified with a greatly enlarged radial sesamoid bone, which functions as a sixth digit for grasping bamboo. This "false thumb" is nearly equal in size to the metacarpal bones of the five true digits, and has its own pad that opposes the first digit, although it cannot be moved like an independent thumb. Bamboo is held within the haired furrow between the digits and plantar (palmar) pad, which can be tightly flexed. The Giant Panda's generic name, meaning panda foot, derives from the foot's likeness to the structure and function of the foot of the Red Panda, a bamboo-eater that was discovered and named earlier. Claws are short, both front and rear.

Habitat. Occupy temperate montane forests with dense stands of bamboo at altitudes of 1200–4100m, or more typically 1500–3000m. Bamboo is a dominant understory plant in broad-leaved, broad-leaved mixed with conifer, and subalpine conifer forests in the mountainous regions of central China. However, the type and density of bamboo greatly affect habitat use by Giant Pandas. The growth rate of bamboo, and hence its suitability to Pandas, is also related to the amount of overstory tree canopy. Remaining habitat for Pandas is steep and rugged, being the only land that was not farmed and settled by people in a once-extensive range that extended from Beijing to eastern China and south to present day Vietnam and Myanmar. Within this remaining habitat, Pandas seek areas with relatively gentle slopes and high moisture.

Food and Feeding. Their diet is almost entirely bamboo (over 99%); however, they occasionally feed on leaves, stems or roots of other plants as well as some meat, from rodents and young ungulates, either killed or scavenged. During large-scale flowering and die-off of bamboo, individuals may seek other foods, including crops and human garbage. For unknown reasons, some individuals do this even when bamboo is readily available. Across the six mountain ranges that they inhabit, Giant Pandas utilize over 60 species of bamboo, 35 of which constitute their main food source. They select species higher in protein and lower in fiber, hence more digestible. They use different species of bamboo in different elevational bands, varying with the seasons and coinciding with the germination and growth of the plants. They eat different parts of bamboo at different times of year, alternating between young tender leaves and shoots, versus stems and branches. They prefer shoots and stems of certain lengths and diameters, selecting those that are easier to hold and chew. Pandas sit or recline to eat. Holding a stem in one paw, a Panda inserts it in the side of its mouth and repeatedly and rapidly bites off chunks approximately the width of its palate, chewing very little. Scats of any individual Panda thus have intact fragments of bamboo that are all approximately the same length. This characteristic has been exploited in population surveys, where the size of bamboo fragments in scats is used to differentiate individuals with overlapping home ranges.

Activity patterns. Pandas are active about 50% of the day, mostly collecting or eating bamboo. Activity occurs rather uniformly through the day and night, in bursts of a few hours. Little variation occurs seasonally. Unlike other bears, which exhibit an energy-maximizing strategy, increasing consumption and activity when food is most plentiful, Pandas are least active when feeding on abundant and nutritious leaves. Because food is available throughout the year, Pandas do not hibernate, although during cold and snowy conditions they may take temporary shelter in hollow trees, rock crevices, and caves. They climb trees, although infrequently, to escape danger, to rest, or in courtship—during the mating season males may vocalize from trees to attract females, and estrous females may climb to fend off suitors. However, they spend less time in trees than several other species of bears (Andean Bears, Sun Bears, Asiatic Black Bears) because they do not feed there.

Movements, Home range and Social organization. Individuals have home ranges of 1–60 km², averaging 5–15 km², depending on gender and habitat. Range size changes seasonally, and they make seasonal elevational shifts (sometimes referred to as vertical migrations), which vary by area, corresponding with growth patterns of various kinds of bamboo. Typically they descend to lower elevations during winter, to escape deep snow, and to high elevations in summer. They can move several hundred meters in elevation in just a few days. Home ranges overlap, but pandas may remain in smaller core areas of only about 30 ha for half their time; these core ranges overlap little among animals of the same sex, but adult males overlap the core ranges of several females. Communication and spacing appears to be maintained by extensive scent marking, using secretions from anogenital glands. Secretions are often deposited on stumps, logs or trees along prominent ridges. One study used fecal genetics to investigate relatedness of Pandas living in the same vicinity, and inferred that, unlike all other bears, females rather than males disperse from their natal area. In another study, two radio-collared males settled near their mother, whereas two young females dispersed. As Panda range has expanded, several young, apparently dispersing females have appeared in several new areas, including a large city.

Breeding. Mating occurs from March through May. Vocalizations (bleating, chirping) and scent marking are used to attract mates. Pairs may remain together for days or weeks prior to mating. Both sexes may mate with multiple (3–5) partners. Peak estrus lasts less than one week. Females use rock dens or hollow trees for birthing. Cubs are born in August or September, 3–5·5 months after mating; a variable period of delayed implantation accounts for the variability in total gestation. At 80–200 grams, the infant at birth is only about 0·1% of the mother's weight, one-third to one-quarter that of other bears. Infants are born pink in color, with short, sparse white hair; the typical black and white pelage is achieved by three weeks of age. Litter size at birth is often two, generally born about two hours (but up to 36 hours) apart; however, the mother raises just the first born, if it is healthy. Thus, functional litter size in the wild is only one. In captivity, females can be fooled into raising two cubs by switching them every twelve hours. This is the only species of bear to regularly give birth to more cubs than it can raise—the explanation for this unusual reproductive strategy remains elusive. Also, unusual for bears, Panda mothers change dens multiple times, carrying their cub in their mouth, and also periodically leave the den to feed. During the birthing process they only fast for 2–3 weeks. Pandas are often erroneously believed to be poor breeders. This impression stemmed from the previous low reproductive performance of captive animals, now known to have resulted from inadequate captive conditions. Studies of wild Pandas indicate that their reproductive rates are comparable to some other species of bears, with cub production beginning at 5–7 years and inter-litter intervals of two or three years. Breeding continues into the early-20s, so a female could wean six or more cubs in her lifetime.

Status and Conservation. CITES Appendix I. Listed as Endangered on *The IUCN Red List*. The Giant Panda is considered a threatened and precious species in China. They are also listed as Endangered under the USA Endangered Species Act, thereby regulating import of captive animals into the USA. Their total population in the wild has been estimated at less than 2000, but this may be revised as better methodology is developed for estimating numbers (e.g. using DNA in their feces to identify individuals). They are a Category I species (maximum level of protection) under the Chinese Wildlife Conservation Law. A national conservation plan, adopted by the Chinese government in 1992, guides conservation initiatives for this species. Intentional poaching of Pandas has been largely curtailed by severe penalties and increased patrolling in their remaining habitats. Markets for their skins have virtually disappeared, and other body parts are not used in traditional Chinese medicine. However, they are still sometimes killed in snares set for Musk Deer and other species. Limited and degraded habitat remains their greatest threat. The species only exists in portions of six mountain ranges separated by expanses of agriculture, and within these, inhabitable bamboo forests are separated by a patchwork of clearings and forested areas without bamboo. Conservation measures have included the establishment of a network of more than 60 Panda reserves, a ban on logging, and a policy that compensates farmers who convert agricultural fields on steep slopes to forest. However, small population size and restricted total range remains a threat to the viability of this species. A further threat relates to the panda's reliance on bamboo for food. Bamboo is subject to periodic, synchronous flowering and die-offs at intervals of 15–120 years, and the fragmented habitat restricts where Pandas can move when such die-offs occur. Effects of climate change on bamboo abundance and flowering cycles are as yet very uncertain. Captive breeding in China has now succeeded (with the aid of artificial insemination) to the extent that captive facilities will soon be overpopulated, providing a potential stock for augmenting wild Panda populations. However, the lack of suitable release sites—having adequate habitat but few resident pandas—limits hopes of eventually releasing many of these captive Pandas into the wild.

Bibliography. Endo *et al.* (1999), Garshelis *et al.* (2008), Johnson, K.G. *et al.* (1988b), Lindburg & Baragona (2004), Liu *et al.* (2005), Loucks, Lü, Dinerstein, Wang, Fu & Wang (2003), Loucks, Lü, Dinerstein, Wang, Olson *et al.* (2001), Lü, Johnson *et al.* (2001), Lü, Pan *et al.* (2000), Lü, Wang & Garshelis (2007), Lumpkin & Seidensticker (2002), Pan *et al.* (2001), Reid & Gong (1999), Schaller, Hu *et al.* (1985), Schaller, Teng *et al.* (1989), Wan *et al.* (2005), Xu *et al.* (2007), Zhan, Li *et al.* (2006), Zhan, Zhang *et al.* (2007), Zhu *et al.* (2001).

On following pages: 2. Andean Bear (*Tremarctos ornatus*); 3. Sun Bear (*Helarctos malayanus*); 4. Sloth Bear (*Melursus ursinus*); 5. Asiatic Black Bear (*Ursus thibetanus*); 6. American Black Bear (*Ursus americanus*).

Subfamily TREMARCTINAE

Genus *TREMARCTOS*

Gervais, 1855

2. Andean Bear   *Tremarctos ornatus*

French: Ours à lunettes / **German**: Brillenbär / **Spanish**: Oso de anteojos

Other common names: Spectacled Bear, Ucumari

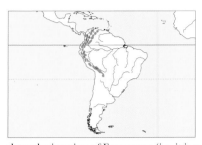

Taxonomy. *Ursus ornatus* Cuvier, 1825, type specimen purportedly from northern Chile, but the species does not occur there.

No subspecies have been designated, but substantial variation exists in color patterns within different portions of the range. Recent genetic examination in the northern part of the range indicates that gene flow is extremely low (populations are isolated), and that this situation predates the invasion of Europeans (i.e. it is not human-caused). Monotypic.

Distribution. Andes Mountains of Venezuela, Colombia, Ecuador, Peru and Boliva, with controversial evidence of existence in N Argentina.

Descriptive notes. Head-body 130–190 cm, tail less than 10 cm; weight of males 100–175 kg (rarely to 200 kg), females 60–80 kg. Coat is black or sometimes dark brown with creamy white biblike marking on chin, neck, and/or chest and typically some white markings around the muzzle and eyes. The extent of white markings is highly variable. Individuals with complete white circles around both eyes gave rise to the common name Spectacled Bear. However, many if not most do not have complete circles around both eyes; some have partial circles, some are highly asymmetrical, and some have virtually no facial markings or, conversely, an almost all buff-white face. The muzzle is variably-colored and short compared to the ursine bears. Claws are short on both front and rear feet. The underside of the feet have hair between the digital and plantar pads, but not between the plantar and carpal front pads (similar to Asiatic Black Bears).

Habitat. Andean Bears range in elevation from 200 to over 4700 m. Preferred habitat includes various sorts of humid and very humid montane cloud forest. They also occupy higher elevation elfin forest, and puna and páramo (high-altitude) grasslands, as well as lower elevation thorn forest and scrub desert (in western Peru).

Food and Feeding. Omnivorous diet includes many kinds of fruits, vegetative material, and meat. Especially important through most parts of the range are the succulent parts of plants in the family Bromeliaceae, both epiphytic and terrestrial bromeliads. In high altitude grasslands, the heart of the terrestrial *Puya* is a dietary mainstay, as this bromeliad is the only abundant food available for much of the year. The bears must strip away the stiff thorny leaves to get to the heart, which looks somewhat like a pineapple but is vegetative and bland. Bears may eat only one in ten of this obiquitous plant, possibly related to differences in nutritional composition. In the forest, they regularly climb trees to obtain *Tillandsia*, an epiphytic bromeliad; they eat the basal meristematic tissue and drop the remaining pieces of leaves to the forest floor, providing a highly visible sign of their feeding activity. Bears select patches (with *Puya*) or trees (with *Tillandsia*) that have a high density of large bromeliads. Bromeliads compose from 90% to less than 15% of their diet, depending on season and geographic area. Fruits compose the other core part of the diet, varying inversely to the bromeliads. Both shrub and tree-borne fruits are consumed (e.g. Lauraceae, Moraceae, Ericaceae, Euphorbiaceae). Fruit abundance varies seasonally with rainfall. Other foods include palm petioles, bamboo shoots, bulbs of orchids, and in drier habitats, fruits and pulp of cacti and, remarkably, the soft cortex of the pasallo tree (*Bombax discolor*). Near human settlements, they routinely raid cornfields. Animal matter is another potentially important food, although never a large dietary component. They eat insects, snails, and small mammals, but more significantly in terms of total nutrition, they occasionally take large mammals such as deer and free-ranging or unguarded pastured cattle. Considerable controversy has surrounded the issue of whether most meat in their diet is from animals that killed or scavenged—there is clear evidence that they sometimes prey on cattle, but they probably also find carrion. A test of their attraction to beef demonstrated this: a small (0·5 kg) chunk of meat placed in an open area attracted two different radio-collared bears from a distance of 1·5 km in 5–15 hours. When feeding on a cattle carcass, which may take several days to consume, they often construct ground and tree nests for resting. Tree nests are made from a collection of bent and broken branches. They also sometimes build nests in fruit trees.

Activity patterns. In one high-elevation site in Bolivia, composed of mixed grassland and cloud forest, Andean Bears were entirely diurnal. They slept 9–12 hours at night, awoke near sunrise, took brief rests during the day, and began their night's rest just after sunset. This pattern did not vary seasonally. In other areas, bears are reported to be somewhat more active at night, but are still principally diurnal. Because food is available year-round throughout their range, Andean Bears do not hibernate.

Movements, Home range and Social organization. Limited information indicates that home ranges may be as small as 10 km² or as large as 150 km². Males have larger ranges than females, and ranges within and between sexes broadly overlap. They are reported to move along an altitudinal gradient among different habitat types, following season-

al changes in available food resources. Andean Bears may gather at rich feeding areas (e.g. cornfields and cactus groves) and at waterholes in arid environments.

Breeding. Presumed mating pairs have been seen between March and October; however, no real information is available on the normal timing of breeding of wild Andean Bears. In captivity in the Northern Hemisphere, births occur from December through February, coinciding with the timing of births in northern species of bears. However, in zoos in South America, Andean Bear births tend to occur more regularly during May–October. Anecdotal information on probable birthing dates in the wild is equivocal. Gestation periods in captivity range from 5·5–8·5 months, indicating a variable period of delayed implantation, and litter size is most commonly two. Litters in the wild are commonly one or two (but up to three or four). Females can produce cubs at two-year intervals, beginning at 4–7 years of age.

Status and Conservation. CITES Appendix I. Listed as Vulnerable on *The IUCN Red List*. Andean Bears are also protected by national legislation in each of the five range countries. However, loopholes in these laws and lack of adequate enforcement result in bears being killed while depredating crops or livestock, or poached for their parts. Andean Bear products are used for medicinal or ritual purposes, and live bears are also sometimes captured and sold. These problems are exacerbated by habitat loss and fragmentation, which not only reduces their natural foraging area, but also puts the bears in closer proximity to people, crops, and livestock. In a few select areas, management plans have been established, with community involvement, to ameliorate bear-human conflicts. A survey in 1998 revealed that less than 20% of the range was legally protected as parks, reserves or sanctuaries. Since then, additional protected areas have been created and others enlarged, but at the same time, more forested land outside the protected areas has been lost to agriculture or fragmented by road development, and mining activities. Some conservation organizations are working to maintain or establish corridors among populations, especially in the northern part of the range, where many Andean Bear populations are isolated in small to medium-sized patches. Habitat patches are larger in the southern part of the range (Peru, Bolivia). Valid rangewide or country-wide population estimates are lacking; guesstimates range from about 13,000–25,000. Efforts are underway to survey various parts of the range to obtain information on presence-absence and relative abundance, based on incidence of sign (bear trails, climbed or rubbed trees, tree nests, bed sites, feeding remains, scats).

Bibliography. Cuesta *et al.* (2003), Garshelis (2004), Goldstein (2002, 2004), Goldstein, Paisley *et al.* (2006), Goldstein, Velez-Liendo *et al.* (2007), Jorgenson & Sandoval (2005), Kattan *et al.* (2004), Mondolfi (1983, 1989), Paisley (2001), Paisley & Garshelis (2006), Peralvo *et al.* (2005), Peyton (1980, 1987), Peyton *et al.* (1998), Rodríguez-Clark & Sánchez-Mercado (2006), Ruiz-Garcia (2003), Troya *et al.* (2004).

Subfamily URSINAE

Genus *HELARCTOS*

Horsfield, 1825

3. Sun Bear   *Helarctos malayanus*

French: Ours malais / **German**: Malaienbär / **Spanish**: Oso malayo

Other common names: Malayan Sun Bear, Dog Bear, Honey Bear

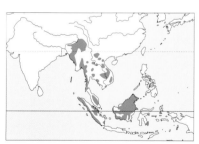

Taxonomy. *Ursus malayanus* Raffles, 1822 [presented orally in 1820, often incorrectly ascribed as 1821], Sumatra, Indonesia. Cranial differences support separation into two subspecies.

Subspecies and Distribution.

H. m. malayanus Raffles, 1822 – Bangladesh, NE India, and S China (Yunnan) through SE Asia to Malaysia, and Sumatra.

H. m. euryspilus Horsfield, 1825 – Borneo.

Descriptive notes. Head-body 100–150 cm, tail 3–7 cm; weight 30–80 kg. Males are heavier than females, but the degree of sexual dimorphism (10–20%) is less than most other bears. The Bornean subspecies is notably smaller, with a maximum weight of 65 kg. The body is stocky, and compared to other bears, the front legs more bowed, front feet turned more inward, muzzle shortened, ears especially small, and hair very short, often with obvious whorls. Coat color is black or less commonly dark brown, typically with a prominent white, yellow, or orange chest marking. The chest marking is highly variable among individuals, usually a U or circular shape, but occasionally more amorphous, and sometimes with dark patches or spots. The bear takes its common name from this marking, which may look like a sun. The muzzle is pale, and the forehead may be wrinkled. The exceptionally long tongue (20–25 cm) is used for feeding on insects and honey. The canine teeth, which are particularly large in relation to the head, and the large front feet with long claws, are used for breaking into wood (e.g. to prey on stingless bees) and termite colonies. Soles of the feet have little hair.

Habitat. In mainland South-east Asia, where there is a prolonged dry season, Sun Bears inhabit semi-evergreen, mixed deciduous, dry dipterocarp, and montane evergreen forest, largely sympatric with Asiatic Black Bears. In Borneo, Sumatra, and peninsular Malaysia, areas with high rainfall throughout the year, they inhabit mainly tropical evergreen dipterocarp rainforest and peat swamps. They also use mangrove forest and oil palm plantations in proximity to other, more favored habitats. They occur from near sea level to over 2100 m elevation, but are most common in lower elevation forests.

Food and Feeding. Omnivorous diet includes insects (over 100 species, mainly termites, ants, beetles and bees), honey, and a wide variety of fruits. In Bornean forests, fruits of the families Moraceae (figs), Burseraceae and Myrtaceae make up more than 50% of the fruit diet, but consumption of fruits from at least 20 other families of trees and lianas were identified in just one small study site (100 km^2) in East Kalimantan. Availability of foods varies markedly from masting years when most species fruit synchronously, to inter-masting years when little fruit is available and the bears turn mainly to insects. Figs (*Ficus*) are a staple food during inter-mast periods. On the mainland, fruiting is more uniform (predictable) from year to year, but varies seasonally. However, there is an enormous diversity of fruits, so some fruit is available at all times of year. In Thailand, about 40 families of trees are climbed by Sun Bears, mostly for food; fruits from Lauraceae (cinnamon) and Fagaceae (oak) are favorites. Sun Bears are especially known for preying on colonies of stingless bees (*Trigona*), including their resinous nesting material. The bees form nests in cavities of live trees, so to prey on them Sun Bears chew and claw through the tree, leaving a conspicuous hole. These bears consume little vegetative matter, although they seem to relish the growth shoots of palm trees (palm hearts), the consumption of which kills the tree. Occasionally they also take reptiles, small mammals, and bird eggs.

Activity patterns. Activity has been described as mainly nocturnal or mainly diurnal. This variability depends on proximity to human activities: in heavily disturbed areas, such as oil palm plantations, Sun Bears are chiefly nocturnal. Camera traps along roads typically obtain photographs of bears mainly at night, whereas signals from radio-collared bears farther from roads indicate that they are active mainly during the day. They spend a large proportion of time feeding in trees when fruit is abundant. They also sometimes build tree nests of branches and leaves for sleeping. This behavior has been attributed to previous predation pressure by Tigers; however, it appears to occur commonly only in heavily-disturbed forests or near people. Sun Bears have been observed to slide rapidly down tree trunks when disturbed by people. Although arboreally adept, they cannot swing or jump from tree to tree. Normally they sleep on the ground, often in cavities of either standing or fallen trees, or under such trees. Females use similar sites for birthing dens. This species does not hibernate.

Movements, Home range and Social organization. Home range information is very limited. Two males radio-tracked for about one year in Borneo during a fruiting failure had minimum known ranges of 15–20 km^2 (but likely ranged beyond this); one of them centered his activity on a garbage dump. Two Bornean females living in a small, isolated forest patch (100 km^2, more than half of which had been burned in a forest fire and was rarely used by Sun Bears) had home ranges of only about 4 km^2. Most sightings have been of solitary bears or mothers with a cub, but gatherings of multiple bears have been witnessed at rich feeding sites.

Breeding. This is the only species of bear without an obvious breeding and birthing season. Cubs are born during all months, both in captivity and in the wild. However, data have not been collected across the range, so it is possible that greater reproductive seasonality occurs in areas with strongly seasonal environments. Females have four teats, but maximum observed litter size is two, and normal litter size is only one. Captive-born cubs have shown an unusual female bias. The gestation period in captivity is much shorter than in other bears: it is normally 3–3·5 months (indicating a shortened or nonexistent period of delayed implantation), but in a few odd cases stretched to 6–8 months, like most other bears. Mating in captivity occurs at 3–6 month intervals if pregnancy does not result. If cubs die, estrus reoccurs in 2–5 weeks, making the interbirth interval as short as 4–4·5 months. No information is available on normal cub dependency or intervals between litters in the wild. The earliest known age of estrus in the wild is three years old. Birthing takes place in a secluded den. In captivity, mothers sometimes carry their cub in their mouth, suggesting that bears in the wild may be able to move dens occasionally after the cub is born.

Status and Conservation. CITES Appendix I. Listed as Vulnerable on *The IUCN Red List*. Although quantitative estimates of population sizes and trends are lacking, rates of habitat loss and degradation, combined with persistent poaching, indicate that the global population of this species has declined by more than 30% during the past three decades. Additionally, it is strictly protected under national wildlife laws throughout its range; however, there is generally insufficient enforcement of these laws. None of the eleven countries where the Sun Bear occurs has implemented any conservation measures specifically for this species. Commercial poaching, especially for gall bladders (used in traditional Chinese medicine) and paws (a delicacy), is a considerable threat, especially in mainland South-east Asia. Local hunters in one area of Thailand estimated that commercial poaching reduced the abundance of Sun Bears by 50% in 20 years. In Malaysia and Indonesia, deforestation is the prime threat. Clear-cutting to expand oil palm (*Elaeis guineenis*) plantations (which is likely to worsen with increased biofuel production) and unsustainable logging (both legal and illegal) are escalating at alarming rates. Prolonged droughts, spurring natural and human-caused fires, are compounding the habitat-loss problem, resulting in diminished availability of food and space for bears, sometimes causing their starvation. Where bears do not die directly from food scarcity, they seek out agricultural crops adjacent to the forest, and are poisoned or trapped and killed by local people. Some headway has been made in establishing buffer zones around protected forested areas, educating local people on nonlethal deterrents, and increasing communication between local people and sanctuary managers, resulting in shared problem solving.

Bibliography. Augeri (2005), Fredriksson (2005), Fredriksson, Danielsen & Swenson (2007), Fredriksson, Steinmetz *et al.* (2007), Fredriksson, Wich & Trisno (2006), Hesterman *et al.* (2005), Japan Bear Network (2006), McCusker (1974), Meijaard (1999a, 1999b, 2001, 2004), Normua *et al.* (2004), Schwarzenberger *et al.* (2004), Steinmetz & Garshelis (2008), Steinmetz *et al.* (2006), Wong, Servheen & Ambu (2002, 2004), Wong, Servheen, Ambu & Norhayati (2005).

Genus *MELURSUS*

Meyer, 1793

4. Sloth Bear *Melursus ursinus*

French: Ours paresseux / **German**: Lippenbär / **Spanish**: Oso bezudo

Other common names: Honey Bear, Lip Bear

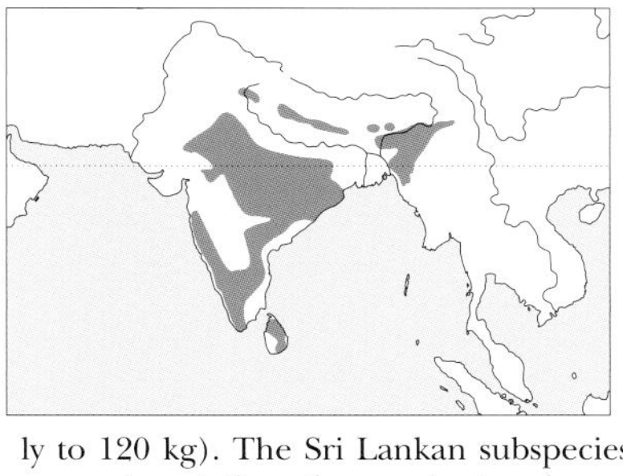

Taxonomy. *Bradypus ursinus* Shaw, 1791, Bihar (earlier Bengal), India.

Previously included in genus *Bradypus* = sloth. Two subspecies recognized.

Subspecies and Distribution.

M. u. ursinus Shaw, 1791 – India, Nepal, Bhutan, and Bangladesh.

M. u. inornatus Pucheran, 1855 – Sri Lanka.

Descriptive notes. Head-body 140–190 cm, tail 8–17 cm; weight of males 70–145 kg (rarely to 190 kg), females 50–95 kg (rarely to 120 kg). The Sri Lankan subspecies is smaller, and with a less-shaggy (shorter, sparser) coat than the nominate subspecies. Coat color is black, with rare brown or reddish-brown individuals. Hair length tends to be longer than in other bears, especially around the neck, shoulders, and back (up to 15–20 cm). The ears are also covered with long hair. Underfur is lacking, and ventral body hair is sparse. The muzzle has very short hair, and is distinctly light-colored up to the eyes. The lips are highly protrusible (hence this bear is sometimes called the Lip Bear), adapted for sucking termites, and the nose can be closed during such sucking, by pushing it against the side of the feeding excavation. The chest is normally marked by a prominent white V or U-shaped band. Sloth Bears have long (6–8 cm) slightly curved, ivory-colored front claws (for digging), and shorter rear claws. The long front claws (along with their coarse, shaggy coat and missing two upper incisors) are what seem to have caused an early taxonomist to call it a sloth. Soles of the feet are naked; unlike other bears, there is no hair between the digital pads and plantar pad on front and hindfeet, and also no hair separating the carpal and plantar (palmar) pad on the front. Unique among the bears, the digital pads are partially fused and are in a nearly straight line.

Habitat. Occupies a wide range of habitats on the Indian subcontinent, including wet and dry tropical forests, savannas, scrublands, and grasslands. Densities are highest in alluvial grasslands, and second-highest in moist or dry deciduous forests. Characteristically a lowland species, mainly limited to habitats below 1500 m, but ranges up to 2000 m in the forests of the Western Ghats, India. In Sri Lanka, it inhabits dry monsoon forests below 300 m. The climate throughout the range is monsoonal, with pronounced wet and dry seasons. This causes some variation in food habits and habitat use: very dry or very wet conditions can hamper feeding on termite colonies.

Food and Feeding. Sloth Bears are both myrmecophagous and frugivorous. Ants, termites, and fruit dominate their diet, with proportions varying seasonally and regionally. Fruits (from at least ten families of trees and shrubs) constitute up to 90% of the diet during the fruiting season in southern India and 70% in Sri Lanka, but less than 40% in Nepal, where fewer fruits are available. Sloth Bears more often eat fallen fruits off the ground than climb to eat fruits in trees. However, they will readily climb to consume honey. During the non-fruiting season, insects make up 95% of the diet in Nepal and 75–80% in S India and Sri Lanka. The relative proportion of termites to ants in the diet also varies considerably by region; in Nepal and Sri Lanka this ratio is more than 2:1, whereas in central India the ratio varies from about 1:1 to 1:5, favoring ants. Sloth Bears feed on termites by digging into their mounds or underground colonies, then alternately sucking up the termites and blowing away debris. These distinctive "vacuuming" sounds can be heard from 200 m away. Although most of their diggings are less than 60 cm deep, they occasionally dig down 1–2 m. Sloth Bears typically eat little vegetative matter other than fruits and some flowers, and they rarely prey on mammals or eat carrion. However, where their habitat is severely degraded by intensive human use and most of their normal foods are not available, they feed heavily on cultivated fruits and agricultural crops such as peanuts, corn, potatoes, and yams.

Activity patterns. These bears are more nocturnal than other bears, likely a response to the heat and sparse cover of their environment. Overall amount of activity varies widely, from 40–70% of the 24-hour day, depending on conditions. In a national park in Nepal, with dense cover and moderate temperatures, most Sloth Bears are active both day and night, but are more active at night; conversely, subadults and females with cubs are diurnal, possibly to avoid being killed by nocturnal predators (Tigers) and other bears. In a park in Sri Lanka, with higher temperatures but dense cover, the bears are similarly more active at night and show lower levels of activity during the day. Where cover is much sparser, Sloth Bears often remain in shelter dens, usually crevices among boulders in rocky hillocks, the whole day, becoming active only near sunset. In central India, average daytime temperatures immediately outside shelter dens under a patchy (less than 25%) tree canopy, average 39°C (up to 44°C) compared to 28°C inside the dens. In winter, pregnant females den to give birth, whereas males and non-pregnant females remain active. It is unclear whether denning females actually undergo physiological hibernation in terms of reduced metabolism, recycling of body wastes, and preservation of muscle mass; they do not have large fat supplies to sustain them, like hibernating bears of other species, but they manage to survive without eating or drinking for 2 months. About 2 weeks before emerging from birthing dens with their cubs, they make nightly excursions from the den to feed.

Movements, Home range and Social organization. Home ranges vary from very small (by ursid standards), averaging only 2 km² for females and under 4 km² for males in Sri Lanka, to moderately small (9 km² for females, 14 km² for males) in Nepal, to over 100 km² for some individuals in India. In an alluvial floodplain in Nepal, adult male bears shift to higher elevation, forested habitat during the monsoon and use areas nearly twice as large as during the dry season. Females and younger males also expand their ranges, but seem to avoid the upland areas dominated by adult males. Significant seasonal range shifts have not been observed in areas that do not seasonally flood. Bears living in protected areas with intact habitat rarely use adjacent degraded forests and agricultural areas. Movement paths are often highly circuitous, and rates of travel for active bears are rather slow (maximum about 1 km/h) compared to other ursids, probably reflective of abundant foods. Home ranges extensively overlap, and bears may occasionally feed very close to other individuals without apparent social interaction; however, even in dense populations, it appears that adult females maintain areas of exclusive use within their range. Unrelated subadults have been observed to join together for several weeks, and sibling subadults to stay together for up to 19 months after leaving their mother, possibly as coalitions against attacks by older bears or other predators. Females ultimately settle near their mothers. Subadult males are presumed to disperse, but empirical data are lacking.

Breeding. Mating generally occurs from May to July. Males congregate near estrous females and fight for mating access. Females mate with multiple (often 3) males in the order of their established dominance, related largely to weight, and males mate with multiple females. Male-female pairs mate multiple times over a period of one hour to 1–2 days; copulations last 2–15 minutes. Females generally remain in estrus for only two days, rarely up to one week. Cubs are born from November through January. The 4–7 month gestation includes a period of delayed implantation. The birthing season may be somewhat lengthened in Sri Lanka, although previous reports of cubs being born throughout the year have not been corroborated by recent studies. Cubs are born in dens, either natural caves or holes excavated by the mother, and emerge with their mother at 2–2·5 months of age. The most common litter size is two cubs, although in some populations litters of one are also common; it is not known whether the latter represents cub mortality shortly after birth or small litters at birth. Litters of three are rare. Females have trouble raising litters of three because they carry their cubs on their back, and the third cub, carried over the hips, may bounce off. The long hair near the mother's shoulders is a preferred riding place because it provides a better grip for the cub. Cubs remain on the back even when the mother vigorously digs for termites in deep holes (more than 1 m). Mothers with cubs on their back travel more slowly than bears without cubs. Cubs ride either head first or crosswise for 6–9 months (by which time they are each about one-third the mass of the mother), increasing their time on the ground as they age. When threatened, they scamper to their mother's back for refuge rather than climbing a tree, probably an adaptation to living in an environment with few trees and formidable predators (Tigers), some predators that can climb trees (Leopards), and large animals that can knock over trees (elephants, rhinoceroses). Cubs nurse for 12–14 months, and remain with their mother for either 1·5 or 2·5 years, so litter intervals are either two or three years.

Status and Conservation. CITES Appendix I. Listed as Vulnerable on *The IUCN Red List*. Sloth Bears are also protected to varying degrees by national laws in all five range countries. However, they can be killed to protect life or property; this is not uncommon, given their aggressive nature and increasing numbers of encounters between bears and people, often resulting in human casualties. Although no reliable large-scale population estimates exist for this species, best guesstimates indicate about 20,000 or fewer animals rangewide. Substantial fragmentation and loss of habitat suggests that their population has declined by more than 30% over the past 30 years. The recent possible extirpation of Sloth Bears in Bangladesh highlights serious concerns over persistence of small, isolated Sloth Bear populations throughout their range. Populations appear to be reasonably secure inside protected areas, but are faced with deteriorating habitat and direct killing outside. About half to two-thirds of the Sloth Bears in India live outside protected areas, and half the occupied range in Sri Lanka is not protected. Habitat has been lost, degraded, and fragmented by overharvest of forest products (timber, fuelwood, fodder, fruits, honey), establishment of monoculture plantations (teak, eucalyptus), settlement of refugees, and expansion of agricultural areas, human settlements, and roads. Commercial trade in bear parts has been reported, but its current extent and impact on Sloth Bears is uncertain. Poaching also occurs for local use (e.g. male reproductive organs used as aphrodisiac; bones, teeth and claws used to ward off evil spirits; bear fat used for native medicine and hair regeneration). Capture of live cubs to raise as "dancing bears" remains a significant threat in some parts of India because laws against this are not adequately enforced. Some non-governmental organizations have been rescuing these bears (although they cannot be released to the wild) and training the people who hunted them in alternate types of work, in exchange for a commitment that they will not resume the practice.

Bibliography. Akhtar *et al.* (2004, 2007), Bargali *et al.* (2004, 2005), Chhangani (2002), Garshelis, Joshi & Smith (1999), Garshelis, Joshi, Smith & Rice (1999), Garshelis, Ratnayeke & Chauhan (2007), Japan Bear Network (2006), Joshi, Garshelis & Smith (1995, 1997), Joshi, Smith & Garshelis (1999), Laurie & Seidensticker (1977), Rajpurohit & Krausman (2000), Ratnayeke, Van Manen & Padmalal (2007), Ratnayeke, Van Manen, Pieris & Pragash (2007), Yoganand *et al.* (2006).

Genus *URSUS*

Linnaeus, 1758

5. Asiatic Black Bear *Ursus thibetanus*

French: Ours à collier / **German**: Kragenbär / **Spanish**: Oso negro asiático

Other common names: Himalayan Black Bear, Moon Bear, White-breasted Bear, Asian Black Bear

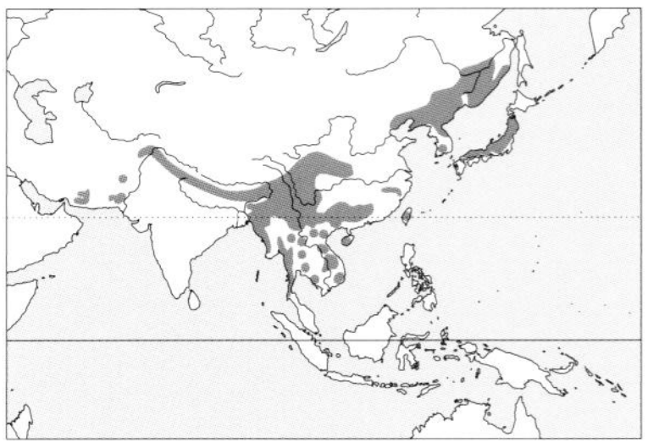

Taxonomy. *Ursus thibetanus* Cuvier, 1823, Sylhet region (presently divided between Assam India and Bangladesh).

Previously included in genus *Selenarctos* = moon bear. Some subspecies have been corroborated as distinct genetic clades (*formosanus, japonicus, ussuricus*). Seven subspecies recognized.

Subspecies and Distribution.

U. t. thibetanus Cuvier, 1823 – Nepal, NE India, Bhutan, Bangladesh, Myanmar, Thailand, Laos, Cambodia, Vietnam.

U. t. formosanus Swinhoe, 1864 – Taiwan.

U. t. gedrosianus Blanford, 1877 – SE Iran, C & S Pakistan.

U. t. japonicus Schlegel, 1857 – Japan.

U. t. laniger Pocock, 1932 – Himalayas from Afghanistan to N India (Jammu and Kashmir, Himachal Pradesh & Uttarakhand).

U. t. mupinensis Heude, 1901 – C & S China.

U. t. ussuricus Heude, 1901 – Russian Far East, NE China, Korean Peninsula.

Descriptive notes. Head-body 110–190 cm, tail less than 12 cm; adult males are heavier (60–200 kg; rarely to 250 kg) than adult females (35–140 kg; rarely to 170 kg). Maximum weights occur in autumn, prior to hibernation. Island populations (Japan, Taiwan) tend to be smaller-bodied than mainland populations. Ears are rounded and relatively large compared to other bears. Coat color black, typically with prominent white marking on the chest, often in the shape of a V or crescent (from which the common name "moon bear" derives), and white chin patch. However, white markings vary in size and color, sometimes being small or absent. Uncommonly the coat color is brown (*gedrosianus*) or blond (rare color phase in South-east Asia). Muzzle color varies from light to dark. Typically there are long, coarse hairs around the neck, sometimes also extending to the cheeks; the extent and frequency of these characteristics varies regionally, as does overall hair length and density of underfur. Some subspecies were differentiated largely by the degree of shagginess of pelts from collected specimens. Proportional length of legs to body also varies considerably, with some individuals being quite short and squat. Both front and rear foot pads have hair separating the toes from the plantar pad, but unlike other *Ursus* species, the front carpal pad (corny protuberance) is connected with the plantar pad by bare skin. Front claws are about 5 cm long, slightly longer than the rear claws, and curved.

Habitat. Occupy both broad-leaved and coniferous forests, from near sea level to just above treeline (4300m in north-eastern India), and spanning from the temperate zone to the tropics. Most of range coincides with forest, especially forests with hard mast (oak or beech), but is also found in regenerating forests with berries and cultivated plantations. This species also occupies arid subtropical thorn-forests (southern Iran and Pakistan) and seasonally uses alpine meadows. In tropical South-east Asia, Asiatic Black Bears inhabit both evergreen and deciduous forests, virtually the same as the Sun Bear, except Sun Bears rarely reach into montane habitats (above 1200 m).

Food and Feeding. Foods often include succulent vegetation (shoots, roots, forbs and leaves) in spring, insects and a variety of tree and shrub-borne fruits in summer, and nuts (hard mast) in autumn. In some areas, mammalian ungulates (especially small-bodied species) may compose a sizeable portion of the diet; however, these bears rarely eat fish. Asiatic Black Bears regularly climb trees to obtain fruits, because most fruits in their range are tree-borne. In tropical regions fruit diversity is especially high. For example, in Thailand their diet includes over 80 species of tree-borne fruits, commonly including those in the cinnamon (Lauraceae), pea-bean (Leguminosae), mahogany (Meliaceae), and oak-beech-chestnut (Fagaceae) families. In temperate regions, where they must store fat for hibernation, hard mast, such as oak acorns, beechnuts, walnuts, chestnuts, hazelnuts, and pine nuts, is a key fall dietary component. When feeding in hard mast trees they often break branches inward toward the trunk and pile them up in the canopy forming a platform or "nest" upon which they sit. When natural forest foods are lacking, they feed in agricultural fields (corn, oats, millet, barley, buckwheat) and fruit orchards. In plantations, when food supplies are short, they strip bark and eat cambium of conifer trees, damaging the trees.

Activity patterns. Active diurnally most of the year, often with peak activity periods in morning and evening. More uniformly active, day and night, during the fall, when foods are clumped and abundant. Overall level of activity may vary seasonally, but is generally in the range of 50–60% over a 24-hour period. In northern latitudes, where food becomes unavailable in winter, both sexes hibernate. They typically den November–April, but some remain in dens until the end of May (which is later than other species of bears). In the tropics, except for females giving birth during the winter, Asiatic Black Bears generally do not hibernate.

Movements, Home range and Social organization. Most reported home ranges based on ground radio-tracking are 20–60 km² for adult females and twice as large for males. However, tracking is often done in remote, mountainous habitats, and bears sometimes wander beyond the tracking area, so true home ranges are likely larger than reported. Home ranges of 100–250 km² have been observed using GPS and satellite radio collars, which obtain locations anywhere the bear goes. Seasonal movements are common, corresponding with changing food conditions, by habitat or elevation. Home range overlap appears to be extensive, but studies of dispersal patterns and relatedness among neighboring bears have not been conducted. Females often avoid areas with clumped, preferred foods, which attract high densities of males.

Breeding. Breeding generally occurs during June–July and birthing during November–March; however, timing of reproduction is not known for all portions of the range, especially in the tropics. The full gestation period of 6–8 months includes 4–6 months of delayed implantation. Age of first reproduction is typically 4–5 years for both sexes. Modal litter size is two cubs (range 1–3, rarely four), but the average is less than two, produced at most every two years.

Status and Conservation. CITES Appendix I. Listed as Vulnerable on *The IUCN Red List*. The so-called Baluchistan Bear (*U. t. gedrosianus*), living in south-eastern Iran, and southern Pakistan, is listed as Endangered under the USA Endangered Species Act. Reliable population estimates do not exist anywhere in the range; however, two of 18 range countries estimate total populations of less than 100 (Iran, South Korea), whereas at the other extreme, three countries estimate populations of 5000–15,000 (India, Japan, Russia) and one (China) estimates more than 20,000 Asiatic Black Bears. Most countries report declining populations due to habitat loss and poaching. Habitat loss from logging, agriculture, human settlements, roadways, and erosion is most severe in southern portions of the range. The species is protected throughout its range by national and international laws. Sport hunting for Asiatic Black Bears is legal only in Japan and Russia, with annual harvests of about 500 and 100 bears, respectively; however, illegal kills and nuisance kills exceed hunting kills by a factor of five or more in both countries. Bear depredations on crops and apiaries, and attacks on people, have increased throughout the range, and have led to more direct killing, using guns, poisons, and bombs that explode when bitten. Poaching also appears to be increasing, spurred by commercial demands for meat, skins, paws, and gall bladders. The demand for these products has fueled a growing network of international trade throughout South-east Asia, and has encouraged many subsistence hunters to turn to commercial hunting. Paws are sold as an expensive delicacy (made into a soup), especially in China. Bile in gall bladders is dried and sold as a traditional Chinese medicine; it has been used as such for nearly 3000 years. To supply an increasing demand, bear farms have been established in China and Vietnam, where bile is drained from over 12,000 Asiatic Black Bears and sold commercially. This technique was originally developed in North Korea in the 1970s, and "perfected" over the years in China. Some officials assert that the increased production of bile from farming reduces poaching of wild bears; conversely, the cheaper and more available farmed bile also may encourage more use, and thus ultimately more demand for wild bile, which is considered more potent. Farmed bile is now produced in such surplus that it is incorporated into many non-traditional Chinese medicine products, such as shampoos, lotions, cosmetics, sports drinks, and toothpaste. Prompted by animal welfare-related concerns, several hundred bears have been removed from farms and taken to rescue facilities run by non-governmental organizations. However, the large total number of captive, non-releasable bears and the opinion of government officials that farming aids in the conservation of wild bears, make the situation rather intractable.

Bibliography. Bromlei (1965), Carr *et al.* (2002), Erdbrink (1953), Fan & Song (1997), Galbreath *et al.* (2000), Garshelis & Steinmetz (2007), Gutleb & Ziaie (1999), Hashimoto (2002), Hashimoto *et al.* (2003), Huygens & Hayashi (2001), Huygens, Goto *et al.* (2001), Huygens, Miyashita *et al.* (2003), Hwang (2003), Hwang & Garshelis (2006), Hwang *et al.* (2002), Izumiyama & Shiraishi (2004), Japan Bear Network (2006), Lekagul & McNeely (1991), Li (2004), Mizukami *et al.* (2005), Ohnishi *et al.* (2007), Oka *et al.* (2004), Pocock (1932d), Reid, Jiang *et al.* (1991), Sathyakumar (2001), Schaller *et al.* (1989), Servheen *et al.* (1999), Seryodkin *et al.* (2003), Shepherd & Nijman (2008), Steinmetz & Garshelis (2008), Stubblefield & Shrestha (2007).

6. American Black Bear *Ursus americanus*

French: Ours noir / **German:** Baribal / **Spanish:** Oso negro americano

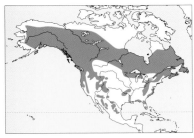

Taxonomy. *Ursus americanus* Pallas, 1780, eastern North America.
Genetic comparisons among the various purported subspecies have not been performed, except in a few cases. Recent genetic evidence indicates that *luteolus*, formerly thought to occur only in Louisiana, extends northward to Arkansas, and also may not be differentiated from *floridanus* in Florida, Alabama, and Mississippi. Sixteen subspecies presently recognized.

Subspecies and Distribution.
U. a. americanus Pallas, 1780 – Alaska to E Canada and E USA.
U. a. altifrontalis Elliot, 1903 – Pacific coast USA and Canada (S British Columbia).
U. a. amblyceps Baird, 1859 – SW USA.
U. a. californiensis J. Miller, 1900 – SW USA (interior California).
U. a. carlottae Osgood, 1901 – W Canada (Queen Charlotte Is).
U. a. cinnamomum Audubon & Bachman, 1854 – Rocky Mts of Canada and USA.
U. a. emmonsii Dall, 1895 – SE Alaska.
U. a. eremicus Merriam, 1904 – E Mexico.
U. a. floridanus Merriam, 1896 – SE USA (Florida).
U. a. hamiltoni Cameron, 1957 – E Canada (Newfoundland).
U. a. kermodei Hornaday, 1905 – W Canada (coastal British Columbia).
U. a. luteolus Griffith, 1821 – S USA (Louisiana).
U. a. machetes Elliot, 1903 – W Mexico.
U. a. perniger J. A. Allen, 1910 – Alaska (Kenai Peninsula).
U. a. pugnax Swarth, 1911 – islands of SE Alaska.
U. a. vancouveri Hall, 1928 – SW Canada (Vancouver I).

Descriptive notes. Head-body 120–190 cm, tail less than 12 cm. Weights vary regionally and seasonally, adult males are heavier (60–225 kg, rarely up to 400 kg) than adult females (40–150 kg, but occasionally more than 180 kg). Straight facial profile, from forehead to nose, distinguishes this species from the partially sympatric Brown (Grizzly) Bear. Muzzle color is usually tan, with short hairs. Sometimes a small tan circular mark occurs slightly above each eye. Eyes are often blue at birth, but turn brown during the first year. Body hairs are rather uniform in length, but much sparser ventrally. A thick underfur is grown in fall, and molted in late spring. Coat color varies from uniformly black to various shades of brown, including cinnamon (reddish-brown) and blond. Brown-phase American Black Bears are common in western USA, less common in western Canadian Provinces, and rare along the west coast of Canada, across Alaska, and in eastern North America and Mexico. Rare white-colored (non-albino) bears occur in coastal British Columbia and gray (often called blue) bears occur in south-east Alaska. White chest markings, from one or more small spots to a large crescent-shaped blaze, occur to varying degrees, but in most populations are uncommon (except in cubs). Claws are short. Hair separates the digital pads from the main foot pad on the front and rear feet. There is also hair between the front (palmar) foot pad and carpal pad, which in normal walking does not touch the ground. Foot pads are shed in winter, when bears are in dens.

Habitat. Found primarily in temperate and boreal forests, but also range into subtropical areas (Florida and Mexico) as well as into the subarctic. They inhabit areas as diverse as dry Mexican scrub forests, Louisiana swamps, Alaskan rainforests, and Labrador tundra (where they occupy the typical niche of the Grizzly Bear). They tend to occupy more forested habitats than the Grizzly Bear, especially where the two species are sympatric. Elevationally they range from sea level to 3000 m, and up to 3500 m for winter denning.

Food and Feeding. American Black Bears are generalist, opportunistic omnivores with diets varying seasonally from herbaceous vegetation (mainly in spring) to roots, buds, numerous kinds of fleshy fruits, nuts, insects in life stages from egg to adult, and vertebrates from fish to mammals, including their own kills as well as carrion. They are also attracted to human-related foods, including garbage, birdseed, corn, oats, apples, honey and brood in apiaries. Feeding increases dramatically in the fall, in preparation for hibernation, and focuses on foods rich in fat. American chestnuts (*Castanea dentata*) were once a key fall food in eastern North America, but after blight destroyed this food source in the early to mid-1900s, oak (*Quercus*) acorns and beechnuts (*Fagus grandifolia*) became the main fall foods. Farther west, hazelnuts (*Corylus*), whitebark pine nuts (*Pinus albicaulis*), madrone (*Arbutus xalapensis*), mansanita (*Arctostaphylos*), huckleberries (*Vaccinium*), and buffalo berries (*Shepherdia canadensis*) are principal fall foods. In arid regions, succulents such as yucca and cacti are important, especially during droughts.

Activity patterns. Mainly diurnal, commonly with an early morning and evening peak in activity and a lull in midday. They tend to sleep through the night, but nocturnal activity may increase during fall, especially in places with clumped, abundant foods. It has been theorized that gut capacity and passage rates of food may limit the length of feeding bouts when intake rates are high, prompting more uniform feeding throughout the day. Alternately, or additionally, large weight gains in fall may pose energetic constraints on feeding. More nocturnal activity also occurs when feeding in areas near human activity. Total time active per day averages 50–60%, but may be less when abundant human-related foods are available. Virtually no activity occurs for the 3–7 months of winter hibernation. In some southern portions of the range, where food is available year-round, only parturient females and those with cubs from the previous year hibernate.

Movements, Home range and Social organization. Home range sizes vary widely, from 3–1100 km² among individuals, and from 5–500 km² among population means. In one unusual case on the tundra of Labrador, Canada, where food supplies were especially sparse, males ranged over 7000 km², much like Brown Bears in similar environments. Home ranges are compressed where and when food is abundant, and where bear density is high. Likewise, overlap among home ranges tends to be greater where food abundance and bear density are high. Male home ranges are 2–10 times larger than those of females. Males thus overlap a number of potential breeding partners. In some areas, females (but not males) appear to be territorial, with portions of their home range not shared by other females. Female offspring remain within their natal range for a few years, gaining continued protection from the presence of their mother, and gradually expand their range to include other areas and less of their mother's range as they age. Males, when 1–4 years old, disperse from the natal range. Dispersal distances vary from less than 10 to more than 200 km; dispersers may travel more than 40 km in a week. Seasonal movements, especially to fall mast areas, are common for both sexes, although again, males move farther. In mountainous areas, shifts occur elevationally in accordance with changing food conditions; in flatter terrain, fall movements of 20 km to more than 50 km are not unusual, with greater movements in years when food supplies are particularly sparse. Single-day movements of more than 20 km have been reported. Such fall excursions are commonly referred to as the "fall shuffle", in reference to the intermixing of individuals from various places (as well as the shuffling gait). Typically, bears that leave their normal home range in the fall return to a more familiar area to den.

Breeding. Mating typically occurs from mid-May to July, but may extend longer, especially in more southerly regions. Copulation induces ovulation. Males locate females by scent. Estrous females actively attract males by scent marking. Both sexes travel widely during the breeding season, and adult males may significantly reduce foraging. Testosterone levels are elevated in breeding males, which increases aggression. Access to females is governed by a male dominance hierarchy and male-male interactions; the extent of fighting among males varies among populations, and is related to density and sex ratios. Male-female breeding pairs may remain together for several days and copulate multiple times. Both sexes breed with multiple partners, but a small proportion of breeding males actually sire offspring. Implantation of the blastocyst occurs in November and birthing in January or February (occasionally December) while the mother is hibernating. Cubs are born highly altricial, weighing 200–450 g, 20 cm in length, eyes closed and nearly hairless. Females give birth beginning at age 3–8 years, depending on food availability and hence their growth rate, and can produce cubs every other year until their mid-to-late 20s. Mothers and cubs leave the birthing den when cubs are 2·5–3·5 months old. They readily climb trees as a refuge when the mother is off feeding, sometimes several kilometers away. They nurse until autumn, but increasingly consume wild foods beginning in late spring. They den with their mother over their first birthday, and remain with her for 16–17 months. Family breakup is usually instigated by the mother's breeding activity. Where food is less abundant, the inter-birth interval may be prolonged to three or more years, enabling a period of recovery without cubs. Litter sizes range from 1–5, averaging 2·5 cubs in eastern North America and 2·0 in western North America, and tend to be slightly male-biased.

Status and Conservation. Not globally threatened, listed as Least Concern by *The IUCN Red List*, but is listed on Appendix II of CITES under the similarity of appearance provision; this mandates tagging of exported parts legally taken by hunters, so they cannot be confused with parts from illegally taken bears of other species. With a total population estimated at about 900,000, American Black Bears are more than twice as abundant as all other species of bears combined, even though they exist in only three countries in North America (Canada, USA, Mexico). Continent-wide, numbers appear to be increasing by about 2% per year, and more than 60% of USA states and Canadian provinces report increasing populations. Approximately 40,000–50,000 are harvested annually by sport hunters in 28 USA states and twelve Canadian provinces and territories. In Mexico, no hunting is allowed, and the species is considered nationally endangered, but appears to be increasing and expanding its range. The Louisiana subspecies (*luteolus*) was listed as threatened under the USA Endangered Species Act because of severe loss and fragmentation of its habitat combined with unsustainable human-caused mortality. *U. a. floridanus* is listed as threatened by the state of Florida. The Kermode Bear (*kermodei*) or "spirit bear", a white-phase American Black Bear, was selected as the official provincial mammal of British Columbia, and provided the inspiration for a large system of protected areas (Great Bear Rainforest Agreement) where logging in coastal temperate rainforest is severely restricted.

Bibliography. Alt (1989), Ayres *et al.* (1986), Barber & Lindzey (1986), Beck (1991), Beckman & Berger (2003), Beecham & Rohlman (1994), Boone *et al.* (2003), Costello *et al.* (2003), Czetwertynski *et al.* (2007), Fair (1990), Garshelis (2004), Garshelis & Hellgren (1994), Garshelis & Hristienko (2006), Garshelis & Noyce (2008), Garshelis & Pelton (1980), Garshelis, Crider & Van Manen (2007), Garshelis, Quigley *et al.* (1983), Hellgren *et al.* (2005), Hewitt & Doan-Crider (2008), Inman & Pelton (2002), Kilham & Gray (2002), Kovach & Powell (2003), Larivière (2001d), Lee & Vaughan (2003), Linnell *et al.* (2000), Mitchell *et al.* (2005), Noyce & Garshelis (1994), Onorato *et al.* (2007), Pelton (2003), Pelton *et al.* (1999), Ritland *et al.* (2001), Rogers (1987), Rounds (1987), Samson & Huot (1995), Vaughan (2002), Veitch & Harrington (1996), Warrillow *et al.* (2001), White *et al.* (2000), Williamson (2002).

Plate 28 ➤

PLATE 28

inches   32

cm   80

ssp *arctos*

ssp *horribilis*

ssp *syriacus*

7

ssp *pruinosus*

ssp *middendorffi*

ssp *lasiotus*

8

7. Brown Bear *Ursus arctos*

French: Ours brun / **German**: Braunbär / **Spanish**: Oso pardo
Other common names: Grizzly Bear, Kodiak Bear

Taxonomy. *Ursus arctos* Linnaeus, 1758, northern Sweden.
Genetic data corroborate the distinctiveness of some subspecies, such as *isabellinus* in Central Asia, but not others. Eight subspecies have been recognized in North America (seven of which are extant), but genetically these group into only three or four discrete clades, none of which match current subspecies designations. Conversely, whereas only one subspecies (*arctos*) has been recognized for Europe, two geographically distinct lineages have been identified. California race *californicus* (Merriam, 1896) and north-western Africa race *crowtheri* (Schinz, 1844) are extinct. Fourteen extant subspecies currently recognized.

Subspecies and Distribution.
U. a. arctos Linnaeus, 1758 – Europe and W Russia.
U. a. alascensis Merriam, 1896 – most of Alaska (excluding Alaska Peninsula, SE panhandle & Kodiak Island group).
U. a. beringianus Middendorff, 1853 – NE Russia (Kamchatka Peninsula & N Kuril Islands northward through the Koryak Autonomous District, and along W coast of the Sea of Okhotsk).
U. a. collaris Cuvier, 1824 – Russia (Siberia, from E of the Yenisey River to the Bering Sea, but excluding Kamchatka and more southern parts of the Russian Far East), N Mongolia.
U. a. dalli Merriam, 1896 – SE Alaska (N of Alexander Archipelago).
U. a. gyas Merriam, 1902 – Alaska peninsula.
U. a. horribilis Ord, 1815 – W Canada (Yukon, North-West Territories, British Columbia & Alberta), inland W USA (extirpated from S Wyoming to Mexico).
U. a. isabellinus Horsfield, 1826 – N India, Pakistan, Afghanistan, N to Kazakhstan and Mongolia (Gobi Desert).
U. a. lasiotus Gray, 1867 – Russia (Southern Kuril Islands, Sakhalin, Ussuri/Amur river region of the Russian Far East), NE China, North Korea, and Japan (Hokkaido).
U. a. middendorffi Merriam, 1896 – Alaska (Kodiak Island & nearby islands).
U. a. pruinosus Blyth, 1853 – Tibetan Plateau, China, N Nepal.
U. a. sitkensis Merriam, 1896 – SE Alaska (Alexander Archipelago & adjacent coastal area).
U. a. stikeenensis Merriam, 1914 – W Canada (W British Columbia), and formerly W USA (W Washington and Oregon).
U. a. syriacus Hemprich & Ehrenberg, 1828 – Middle East, from Turkey to Iran (extirpated in Syria), Caucasus mountains of Russia, Georgia, Armenia and Azerbaijan.

Descriptive notes. Head-body 150–280 cm, shoulder height up to 150 cm, tail 6–21 cm. Weights vary regionally and seasonally, with food availability. Adult males are heavier (130–550 kg; rarely up to 725 kg) than adult females (80–250 kg, but occasionally up to 340 kg). Facial profile from forehead to nose is concave. Body profile includes a distinct muscular shoulder hump with long hairs. Coat color varies from uniform brown to mixed shades of brown, blond, and silver-tipped (grizzled), to partly gray or black, or fully black. The grizzled phase (Grizzly Bear) occurs in interior North America, whereas the black and partially black phases occur in eastern and central Asia. Color can lighten with bleaching from the sun. Prominent markings, from a white or cream-colored chest patch to a solid band that wrap across the chest and around the shoulders to the back, vary regionally and individually. Such markings are often present on cubs, but may be lost with age. Body hairs are sparser ventrally. Underfur is grown in fall, and molted in spring. Long, powerful, slightly curved front claws (4–10 cm) varying from dark brown to yellow to white, are characteristic. Foot pads are like that of the American Black Bear.

Habitat. Brown Bears occupy a wider range of habitats than any other bear, including both coniferous and deciduous forests, meadows, grasslands, Arctic shrublands and tundra, alpine tundra, semi-deserts and deserts. Their range overlaps that of both the American and Asiatic Black Bear, and also slightly that of the Polar Bear. They exist at elevations from sea level (temperate rainforests and Arctic tundra) to well above treeline (dry Asian steppes); highest elevation sightings (tracks in snow) have been at 5500 m (possibly 5800 m) in the Himalayas, and highest latitude sightings at 74° N (Canada), well into Polar Bear range.

Food and Feeding. Food habits vary regionally from principally herbivorous to principally carnivorous, depending on habitat. Plant foods include grasses, sedges, horsetails, forbs, roots, berries, and nuts. Animal foods include insects, rodents, ungulates, and fish. Insects are a significant dietary component in broadleaved forests of Europe, rodents and ungulates are most important in Arctic and alpine areas and some Boreal forests, and fish are paramount along the Pacific Coast, from British Columbia to Alaska to Kamchatka (Russia). Herbaceous vegetation tends to be the chief component of the spring diet. Later the bears switch to roots, berries, pine nuts, acorns, ants, bees, moths, ground squirrels, marmots, pikas, neonate ungulates, or spawning salmon, depending on availability. This species is morphologically and behaviorally well adapted to digging up insects and underground rodents, killing ungulates (including domestic species, like sheep and cattle), and catching salmon. In North America they rarely climb trees, whereas in Europe and parts of Asia they do so more regularly.

Activity patterns. Active diurnally in North America, except where human activity is high. Nocturnally active in most of Europe, possibly due to more frequent contact with humans, both historically and presently. Young bears in Europe are active uniformly through the day, but apparently learn to become more nocturnal through negative experiences with people. Total time active per day (40–80%) varies with local conditions (food, day length). The period of hibernation also varies regionally: at the northern extremes of their range they may hibernate for seven months (October–May); conversely, on Kodiak Island, Alaska, where winters are mild and some food may remain available, about one-quarter of the males do not den all winter, an unusual anomaly among Brown Bears. In Russia, following seasons with very poor food, large numbers of malnourished bears may wander about for much of the winter.

Movements, Home range and Social organization. Individual home range sizes vary by nearly four orders of magnitude (7–30,000 km²), related to food supply and bear density. Home ranges are largest in the barren-ground Arctic tundra, averaging 8000 km² for males. Range sizes are smaller in boreal or montane forests, where large mammals are a main dietary component, and smaller yet in deciduous or mixed forests with hard mast. In coastal areas, with abundant food and high bear density, home ranges are smallest, averaging less than 200 km² for males and less than 100 km² for females. Male home ranges are typically three to four times larger than those of females; both sexes increase their ranges during the mating season to maximize overlap with potential mates. Bear density and home range overlap are high in coastal populations with abundant and predictable food (spawning salmon). In interior populations, with less abundant or more variable food, home ranges overlap less, and bears may be somewhat territorial. In extreme northern populations, where food resources are scarce, home ranges are large and indefensible, so overlap is high. Home range overlap is also positively associated with relatedness, because female offspring often settle near their mother, assuming part of their natal home range. Multigenerational, matrilineal assemblages occur in established populations, whereas females may be more prone to disperse and settle among unrelated individuals in expanding populations. Males disperse in either case, but their dispersal age (1–4 years old) is related to their growth rate, and dispersal distance is inversely related to bear density. In a low density, expanding population in Scandinavia, one-third to half the females dispersed, settling 15 km from the natal range, on average, and 80–90% of males dispersed, generally settling over 100 km and up to nearly 500 km away. Seasonal movements are common for both sexes. In mountainous terrain, regular seasonal altitudinal shifts correspond with changing food conditions at different elevations and habitats. Lateral movements to seasonally abundant food sources may involve large numbers of bears traveling along well-worn routes, akin to a migration. Movements to fall feeding areas, followed by returns to denning sites, are often direct and rapid: travels exceeding 20 km in twelve hours have been recorded. At rich feeding areas, such as salmon streams, females with cubs avoid places with a high density of males, apparently because of threats of infanticide.

Breeding. Mating is promiscuous, and generally occurs from mid-May to mid-July. Within individual populations, the breeding period in any given year is narrower, typically about one month. Estrus can be as brief as one day to as long as a month, and male-female pairings can last from just a few hours to three weeks. Copulation generally lasts 10–40 minutes, and induces ovulation. Implantation of the blastocyst is delayed until six to eight weeks prior to birthing, which usually occurs in January or February, while the mother is hibernating in a secluded den. Food conditions, especially the proportion of meat (particularly salmon) in the diet, largely affect reproductive rates. Average age of first birthing varies among populations from four to ten years, and average litter size varies from 1·3–2·5 cubs. Maximum litter size is five. Inter-birth intervals are as short as two years in some European populations, more typically three years and sometimes more than four years in North America, and averages 5·7 years in a high altitude population in Pakistan. Extended litter intervals result from mothers spending extra time to raise cubs in poorer habitats. Offspring generally remain with the mother until she breeds; however, where inter-birth intervals are greatly extended, mothers may recoup for a year or more without offspring. Females continue to produce cubs until their mid to late 20s, but may live another ten years after that.

Status and Conservation. Only populations in central Asia (Mongolia to the Himalayas, China, Nepal, Bhutan) fall under CITES Appendix I; all others are CITES Appendix II. The species as a whole is not considered threatened by *The IUCN Red List* (Least Concern), but some individual European populations are separately red-listed (Vulnerable–Critically Endangered), and other threatened populations will be added in the near future. These small populations tend to exist in remnant wild areas surrounded by more extensive human development, which act as mortality sinks. Forty-seven countries in North America, Europe, and Asia are inhabited by Brown Bears. During the past 500 years they have been extirpated from 17 other countries, including large parts of Europe, North Africa, the Middle East, and Mexico. In the lower 48 states of the USA, they were exterminated from more than 98% of their original range within 100 years of the arrival of European settlers, and have not since recovered. The total world population is estimated to exceed 200,000. Fairly reliable population estimates exist for several areas in North America (USA 33,000; Canada 25,000) and Europe (14,000, excluding Russia), but for few areas in Asia. Russia has the largest number of Brown Bears, believed to exceed 100,000. The species is relatively abundant in more northern parts of its distribution, but smaller, fragmented populations exist farther south. Populations are sufficiently large to sustain legal hunting in Russia, several former Soviet Republics, Japan (Hokkaido Island), Canada, Alaska (USA), and several European countries. Conversely, populations with fewer than 100 individuals exist along the USA–Canadian border and in southern Europe where several small, isolated populations persist: two in the Pyrenees (France and Spain), one with less than 10 bears and the other with about 20, two populations in the Cantabrian Mountains (Spain) containing 20–30 and 80–100 bears, a population in the Appenine Mountains (Italy) with 40–50 bears, and in the the Alps (Italy, Austria, and Slovenia) with 35–40 bears. Small, disconnected populations are also scattered across southern Asia, and in some areas even the present existence of this species is unknown (Bhutan, Iraq). As wide-ranging omnivores, Brown Bears are attracted to areas with human-related foods, where they may threaten life and damage property (livestock, cropfields) and may be killed as a consequence. Small numbers of mortalities, especially adult females, can threaten the viability of small, isolated populations. Most small populations are legally protected by national laws and international agreements, but with varying degrees of enforcement. Moreover, even where hunting is banned, other sorts of human-caused mortality (management removals, self-defense, malicious killing, poaching, mistaken hunting of Black Bear) dominate the population dynamics of these bears. Reintroductions and population augmentations have helped to restore numbers and expand geographic range in the USA and Western Europe. Numerous protected areas around the world have Brown Bears, but few are large enough to support a self-sustaining population; therefore, Brown Bear conservation must be integrated with many other human land-uses.

Bibliography. Bellemain, Nawaz *et al.* (2007), Bellemain, Swenson & Taberlet (2006), Bromlei (1965), Brown (1985), Ciarniello *et al.* (2007), Clark *et al.* (2002), Craighead, F.C. (1976), Craighead, J.J. *et al.* (1995), Dahle & Swenson (2003a, 2003b, 2003c), Doupé *et al.* (2007), Ferguson & McLoughlin (2000), Fernández-Gil *et al.* (2006), Galbreath *et al.* (2007), Garshelis (2004), Garshelis *et al.* (2005), Groupe National Ours dans les Pyrénées (2008), Hall (1984), Hilderbrand, Jenkins *et al.* (1999), Hilderbrand, Schwartz *et al.* (1999), IUCN (2008), Japan Bear Network (2006), Kaczensky *et al.* (2006), Kasworm *et al.* (2007), LeFranc *et al.* (1987), Linnell *et al.* (2000), MacHutchon & Wellwood (2003), Mattson & Merrill (2002), McLellan & Hovey (1995, 2001), McLellan, Hovey *et al.* (1999), McLellan, Servheen & Huber (2007), McLoughlin, Case *et al.* (1999), McLoughlin, Ferguson & Messier (2000), Miller *et al.* (2006), Mowat & Heard (2006), Munro *et al.* (2006), Nellerman *et al.* (2007), Nielsen, Herrero *et al.* (2004), Nielsen, Stenhouse & Boyce (2006), Pasitschniak-Arts (1993), Proctor *et al.* (2004, 2005), Rode *et al.* (2006), Saarma *et al.* (2007), Schwartz, Haroldson *et al.* (2006), Schwartz, Keating *et al.* (2003), Schwartz, Miller & Haroldson (2003), Servheen *et al.* (1999), Seryodkin *et al.* (2003), Støen, Bellemain *et al.* (2005), Støen, Zedrosser *et al.* (2006), Swenson *et al.* (2000), Talbot & Shields (1996), Vaisfeld & Chestin (1993), Valdiosera, García *et al.* (2007), Valdiosera, García-Garitagoitia *et al.* (2008), Van Daele (2007), Waits *et al.* (1998), Xu *et al.* (2006), Zager & Beecham (2006), Zedrosser *et al.* (2007).

8. Polar Bear *Ursus maritimus*

French: Ours blanc / **German**: Eisbär / **Spanish**: Oso polar
Other common names: White Bear, Nanook

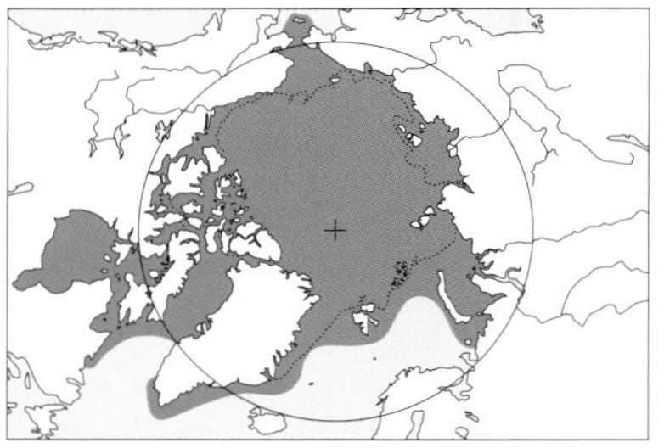

Taxonomy. *Ursus maritimus* Phipps, 1774, Spitsbergen, (Svalbard) Norway.
Considered a sister species to *U. arctos*. Most closely related to Brown Bears on the Admiralty, Baranof, Chichagof islands of south-east Alaska. Although several distinct populations or stocks have been delineated, small genetic differences have been found among these, and no subspecies have been differentiated. Monotypic.
Distribution. Arctic Ocean: Canada, USA (Alaska), Greenland, Norway (Svalbard), Russia. Have been sighted within 0·5° of North Pole.
Descriptive notes. Head-body 180–280 cm, shoulder height up to 170 cm, tail 6–13 cm; adult males are about twice as heavy (300–650 kg, but up to 800 kg) as adult females (150–250 kg, but up to 500 kg when pregnant), making them one of the most sexually-dimorphic mammals. Size varies regionally, being smallest in eastern Greenland, and progressively larger westward to the Bering Sea. Facial profile is straight, the neck is longer than in other bears, and the ears are small in relation to head and body size. Coat color appears white or yellowish, with no other markings, but can accumulate colors from the environment (e.g. blood and oils from killed prey). In reality, both guard hairs and underfur are translucent, and guard hairs are hollow, thus enhancing their insulation properties. However, a previous assertion that they act as fiber optic tubes, funneling sunlight to the skin for warmth, has been disproven. The skin is black, but only the black nose is visible. Summer coats are shorter than winter coats, but unlike other bears, coat thickness is not sparser ventrally. Additionally, the paws are well-furred on the underside, and have small soft papillae and vacuoles that may act as suction cups for traction on ice. The feet are also relatively large, providing more surface area for swimming and walking on thin ice. The claws are shorter and more curved than Brown Bears, and are usually dark-colored.
Habitat. Arctic ice provides a necessary platform for hunting seals. Annual ice adjacent to coastlines (shore fast ice) regularly fractures, providing open leads where seals can breathe. The seasonal fluctuations between freezing and open water also promotes high productivity of fish, the prey of seals. Thus, this habitat is preferred by seals, and is consequently a favored habitat for Polar Bears, which hunt seals along the ice cracks and edges. Polar Bears also hunt from large chunks of drifting ice, and to a lesser extent, multiannual pack ice, where seal density is lower and access to seals more difficult. For this reason, density of Polar Bears is low close to the North Pole. In summer, when the ice retreats, bears either migrate northward or use nearshore terrestrial habitats. Parturient females stay ashore to den and give birth. In Hudson Bay (Canada) they den 10–80 km inland in peat banks; elsewhere maternity dens are typically in snow caves along coastal areas. However, in the Beaufort Sea, half the pregnant females den on drifting sea ice. Non-pregnant bears do not hibernate, but do use shelter dens. At lower latitudes, they use shelters on land during ice-free periods to escape heat and conserve energy when precluded from hunting seals; at high latitudes (above 75° N) they seek shelters on thick sea ice during winter, when foraging is most difficult and weather conditions harshest.
Food and Feeding. Almost strictly carnivorous, preying mainly on young Ringed Seals (*Pusa hispida*), to a lesser extent Bearded Seals (*Erignathus barbatus*), and in some areas, Harp Seals (*Pagophilus groenlandicus*). The principal focus on Ringed Seals is evident in the close association between Polar Bear density and Ringed Seal density, and in the unique behavior of these seals, which give birth in subnivian lairs as an anti-predation strategy. One study found that an average Polar Bear consumes fewer than 50 Ringed Seals a year, 80% being pups caught either in their lairs or shortly after emerging from their lairs. Polar Bears also occasionally prey on other marine mammals, such as Walruses (*Odobenus rosmarus*), and Beluga (*Delphinapterus leucas*) whales. These large prey, including Bearded Seals (which are much larger than Ringed Seals), are taken mainly by adult male bears. When ashore, depending on availability, Polar Bears have been observed to prey on Reindeer (*Rangifer tarandus*), seabirds, or fish; and eat carrion (dead whales), berries, vegetation, and human garbage.
Activity patterns. Appear to be mainly diurnal. Seasonal changes in activity vary regionally with dynamics of sea ice and abundance of prey. Activity, measured by percent of time active and distance moved, is elevated when seal pups are particularly naïve and vulnerable to predation, and when older seals are molting and basking on the ice. In contrast to other predators, Polar Bears are most active when prey is most abundant. They become hyperphagic, and are able to store fat to withstand extended periods when foraging is more difficult, such as during the winter on the pack ice. Periods of rapid annual ice formation and ablation, during summer and fall, also result in greater activity. Parturient females den for about six months (mid-September to mid-March in most areas); non-pregnant Polar Bears do not hibernate.
Movements, Home range and Social organization. Although once thought to wander aimlessly or be carried passively on shifting ice, recent data collected using satellite radio collars have shown that Polar Bears have definite home ranges that are used year to year. However, these ranges can be enormous: one female bear traveled over 5200 km from Alaska to Greenland in four months. Nevertheless, most bears seem to remain within a discrete population, or stock; 19 or 20 such populations have been identified across the geographic range. Home ranges and movements are highly variable by region, habitat, season, and reproductive condition or family association. Around Svalbard, nearshore bears tend to have smaller home ranges than pelagic bears. In the Canadian Arctic, bears that live in areas with highly variable and unpredictable ice conditions (including ice-free periods) have larger ranges than bears living on more stable ice. Individual ranges as large as 600,000 km^2 have been reported, but so have ranges of less than 1000 km^2. Means among different populations range from 20,000–250,000 km^2. Little movement data have been collected on males, because they cannot be radio-collared (their necks are bigger than their heads), but data from implanted transmitters indicate that, unlike terrestrial bears, their ranges are not larger than those of females. With females being so mobile, and having highly overlapping ranges, males can include multiple potential breeding partners within their range, even if their range is not larger than the females'. Female maternity dens are highly congregated in some areas, such as Wrangel Island, parts of Svalbard, Franz Josef Land, Novaya Zemlya, and near Churchill, Manitoba.
Breeding. Breeding occurs from March to June. Mating induces ovulation, and males spar for mating partners. Implantation of the fertilized egg is delayed until autumn, about the time that females enter maternity dens. In some areas this follows a period of on-shore fasting, so by the time these mothers emerge from dens the following spring they may not have eaten for eight months. Birthing occurs mid-November to January, so the total gestation, including the period of delayed implantation, is from 6·5 to more than 8·5 months. Cubs stay in the den until March or early April. Two-cub litters are most common, and average litter size is less than two in virtually all populations; however, litters of three are not uncommon in some areas, and litters of four have been reported. Females have only four mammae (other bears, except Sun Bears and Giant Pandas have six), so this is the maximum litter size. Average age of first birthing ranges among different populations from 4·6–7·2 years. Productivity increases into the teen years, but then declines through the early 20s, and ceases by the late 20s. Intervals between litters average 2·1–3·6 years. Cubs separate from their mother either at 17 months, or more commonly a year later. Cubs may nurse through their second birthday. The fat content of milk is very high initially (more than 30%), but declines through the nursing period.
Status and Conservation. CITES Appendix II. In 2006 *The IUCN Red List* status was upgraded to Vulnerable due to projections of dramatic reductions in habitat (coverage and stability of the ice sheet) over the next 50–100 years. Demographic consequences to Polar Bears are already becoming apparent in some areas, in terms of reduced numbers and reduced survival of juveniles and old adults. Ringed Seals are also suffering increased mortality from Polar Bear predation because of melting of their subnivian dens. Accordingly, the USA listed the species as nationally threatened and Canada listed it as a species of special concern. This would impose further constraints on activities that affect these bears or their habitat, such as hunting, recreational viewing, shipping, and oil and gas exploration and development. The effects of sea ice change will vary

enormously by region, which is difficult to forecast, but overall are likely to be dramatic and permanent. Nineteen fairly discrete populations have been identified, with a total world population estimated at 20,000–25,000; about half this number resides in the Canadian territory of Nunavut. Under an agreement for co-management of Polar Bear populations that was ratified in 1976, the five range countries coordinate and consult with each other on research activities, methods of population estimation and monitoring, and proposals for increased protection. Most importantly, under this treaty, harvest is restricted: the taking of cubs or females with cubs is prohibited, and harvest is limited to native people for subsistence use. This includes consumption of meat, use of hides for clothing, and creation of handicrafts. In some territories of Canada, a portion of the annual harvest is allocated to non-native sport hunters who employ native guides and hunt using dogsleds and other traditional methods. This generates income for the native communities. Harvests are regulated to be sustainable. Recently, pressure has mounted to reduce or prohibit harvests so as not to compound the effects of diminishing sea ice habitat from global warming.

Bibliography. Amstrup (2003), Amstrup & Gardner (1994), Amstrup et al. (2001), Bentzen et al. (2007), Derocher (1999), Derocher, Andersen & Wiig (2005), Derocher, Andriashek & Stirling (1993), Derocher, Wiig & Anderson (2002), Durner & Amstrup (1995), Ferguson, Taylor, Born et al. (1999), Ferguson, Taylor, Rosing-Asvid et al. (2000), Garshelis (2004), Linnell et al. (2000), Mauritzen et al. (2001), Messier et al. (1992, 1994), Paetkau et al. (1999), Parks et al. (2006), Ramsay & Stirling (1990), Regehr et al. (2007), Rosing-Asvid (2006), Schliebe et al. (2006), Shields et al. (2000), Stirling (1988, 2002), Stirling & Øritsland (1995), Stirling & Parkinson (2006), Taylor et al. (2001), Thiemann et al. (2007).

CLASS MAMMALIA
ORDER CARNIVORA
SUBORDER CANIFORMIA

Family AILURIDAE (RED PANDA)

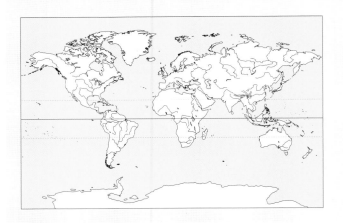

- Small to medium mammals with round head, short muzzle, large and pointed ears, and bushy tail; muzzle, lips, cheeks, and edges of ears white, eyes with small dark patches, and tail with alternate red and buff colored rings.
- 79–122 cm.

- Mountains of Central Asia.
- Forested mountainous areas; typically deciduous and coniferous forests with bamboo-thicket understory.
- 1 genus, 1 species, 2 taxa.
- 1 species Vulnerable; none Extinct since 1600.

Systematics

The Red Panda (*Ailurus fulgens*) is the only living species in the Family Ailuridae, with a restricted distribution extending from Nepal in the west to south-western China in the east. However, fossils imply a much wider distribution for the family. *Parailurus* appears closest to *Ailurus* in general cranial and dental morphology. These have been unearthed from the lower Pliocene of England, Europe, and North America, implying a European-Asian origin for the Ailuridae, followed by a trans-Beringian radiation. Fossil materials of the extant *A. fulgens* from the middle Pleistocene were discovered in Guizhou, Yunnan, and Hubei provinces, China. Although no intermediate forms between *Parailurus* and *Ailurus* are known, the smaller size and diminished range of the latter suggest that it may be a specialized offshoot of the early ailurine lineage, surviving the Pleistocene glaciations in the mountainous refugia of southern China. Notably, a new genus and species of the family, *Pristinailurus bristoli*, the earliest and most primitive form so far known, was discovered in lacustrine sediment deposits of the late Miocene to early Pliocene in the southern Appalachian Mountains, supplying new evidence of immigration events between eastern North America and eastern Asia in the late Tertiary period.

Contrary to the relatively clear evolutionary history, the phylogenetic position of the Red Panda has not yet been resolved, primarily due to its unique morphology and peculiar specialization to herbivory. It was first described as closely resembling a raccoon (procyonid) by Cuvier, although he gave it the name *Ailurus* based on its superficial likeness to the domestic cat. Subsequent morphological and molecular evidence has supported several hypotheses: that it is related to the ursids (or ursids plus pinnipeds); to the procyonids; to the musteloids (including procyonids plus some or all mustelids); that it is a sister taxon to the Giant Panda, with uncertainty about their broader relationships; or, finally, that it is an unresolved monotypic lineage within the arctoids. Recent research confirmed that *Ailuropoda* is the sister group to the true bears, but the position of *Ailurus* is less clear now than at any time in the past.

Two subspecies, the nominate *Ailurus fulgens fulgens* and *A. f. styani*, have been recognized. The Nujiang River in Yunnan Province, China, is considered the natural boundary separating them. Compared with *fulgens*, *styani* is distinguishable by its longer winter coat, darker body color, larger skull, and more robust teeth. However, extensive variation in morphological characteristics has been found among individuals, casting doubts upon this classification. Recent molecular studies also failed to detect significant genetic differentiation between subspecies. Most captive individuals in zoos represent the nominate form.

Morphological Aspects

The head and body length is usually 51–73 cm, the tail length is 28–49 cm, and the weight is usually 3–6 kg. The head is round, with a short muzzle and large, pointed ears. Small, dark-colored eye patches are present. The muzzle, lips, cheeks, and edges of the ears are white. The dorsal pelage is chestnut brown and the ventral pelage and limbs are black, not particularly cryptic in its current habitat. The tail is bushy, with alternate red and buff colored rings. The feet have hairy soles, and the claws are semi-retractile. Females have eight mammae.

The skull is robust, with broad zygomatic arches and a large occipital condyle to support the jaw muscles. The teeth are heavily cusped, and have elaborate crown patterns that help the Red Panda chew bamboo. In addition, the forepaw has an

The **Red Panda** *is not, in spite of its scientific name, a glowing cat, even though* ailurus *means "cat" in ancient Greek and* fulgens *means "glowing" in Latin. Nor are Red Pandas closely related to the Giant Panda, as was once thought, even though they eat bamboo and have an unusual wrist bone like that bear. They climb trees and have short legs and long, ringed tails, but they are no procyonids, either. This species, whose taxonomic position has puzzled scientists since the early 1800s, is now placed in a family all its own.*

Ailurus fulgens
Darjiling, West Bengal, India.
Photo: Roland Seitre

elongated radial sesamoid, adapted for grasping bamboo stems while feeding.

Habitat

The Red Panda is found in temperate forests of the Himalayas and in the mountains of northern Myanmar and western Sichuan, and Yunnan, at elevations of 1500–4800 m, even up to the snowline at 5000 m in summer. In the Meghalaya of India, it has been found in tropical forests at much lower elevations, between 700–1400 m.

Within this distribution, its habitats are closely associated with forests that have a bamboo-thicket understory. In Singhalila National Park in the eastern Himalayas, Red Pandas are relatively more abundant in an altitudinal range of 2800–3600 m. Higher bamboo cover, bamboo height, and canopy cover are important habitat components. In the Xiaoxiangling Mountains, Sichuan Province, China, the Red Pandas prefer habitats with a high density of shrubs, fallen logs, and tree stumps, which can give them easy access to bamboo leaves. A similar habitat preference was found in the Qionglai Mountains, another mountain range in Sichuan Province, where Red Pandas were found to occur more frequently at sites with a high density of fallen logs and tree stumps. Its distribution globally is estimated to be about 69,900 km², of which 37,436 km² is in China, but the animals are not found in every part of this range.

Communication

Although they live apart for most of the year, Red Pandas can exchange information by means of smells, sounds, and visual signals. Chemical signals are deposited in urine, feces or secretions from the anal and circumanal glands. Feces deposited in well-defined latrines can serve to delineate home range or territories. In addition, small pores are found on the furred pads of the male's paws. Colorless fluid secreted by glands in the paws leaves a scent trail, helping an individual delineate its home range and move about at night. Males were observed to mark more frequently and for a longer time than females at all times of the year. Frequency of scent marking is highest during the mating season.

The paired auditory bullae on the base of the Red Panda's skull seem small, implying that hearing is not the animal's most important sense. Even so, seven distinct calls have been recorded, including a "wheee" or "wheeet", "whuufff", and an "unhh". Although the vocal repertoire is small, there is considerable variability within some call types.

Except during the mating season, encounters are infrequent. Red Pandas in the wild can keep their distance through a system of mutual avoidance. Their tear tracks and forehead patterns are said to be unique, helping individuals recognize one another at a distance. Visual displays include "staring", which was reported to occur at a greater distance, and arching of the head and the tail, as well as a deliberate raising and lowering of the head while emitting a low intensity puffing, which occurred when two individuals were in proximity.

Food and Feeding

The Red Panda occupies a highly specialized niche as a bamboo feeder, its diet consisting chiefly of bamboo leaves. This is the primary food item in all seasons, constituting about 90%,

Red Pandas tend to live alone except during the mating season, but they are not usually hostile toward each other. They communicate and maintain spatial separation with scent marks, including urine, feces, and glandular secretions. As the mating season approaches, a pair will spend more and more time together, and both will do more scent marking. When the female is receptive, a period that lasts a maximum of about 36 hours, she lets the male know by bounding around playfully, flicking her tail. Copulation occurs on the ground. Red Pandas may be able to recognize each other at a distance. it has been suggested that each individual has a unique forehead pattern and tear tracks, the streak of dark fur from eye to mouth. Encounters can involve visual displays with individuals trying to "stare" each other down or raising and lowering their heads while making puffing sounds.

Ailurus fulgens
Wolong Giant Panda Reserve,
Sichuan, China.
Photo: Jean-Paul Ferrero/Auscape

Red Panda cubs are born with thick grayish fur. Their eyes and ears are sealed. At first, they do not do anything much except nurse, and their mother spends more than half her time in the nest with them. Their eyes open by day 18. By the time they are two months old, littermates play together in the nest and start to try to peek out at the world. By then, they have the fur pattern of adults, with white faces and dark tear tracks, and the bottoms of their feet are covered with white fur. A month later, they actually leave the nest and begin to eat solid food, although they do not have a full set of teeth until they are six months of age.

Ailurus fulgens
Photo: Roland Seitre

91·4%, and over 80% of its annual diet in the Xiaoxiangling, Liangshan, and Qionglai Mountain ranges, China. New shoots are an important seasonal food item in spring, and fruits are eaten in late summer and autumn.

Red Pandas often walk on fallen logs or stand or sit on tree stumps to reach the leaves on bamboo stems. In contrast to the Giant Panda, which bites off mouthfuls of leaves and branch tips, Red Pandas usually meticulously nip off single leaves from the junction of leaf and branch. In Wolong Reserve, 87·5% of the leaves were eaten at the bottom two nodes as compared to 47·3% at the top two nodes, suggesting that their leaf selectivity is related to access; a small animal feeding on a tall food source.

The Red Panda has evolved a set of optimal feeding strategies to deal with its poor-quality diet of bamboo, which is low in protein and fat and high in fiber. It usually feeds on the most nutritious bamboo species in its habitat. For example, it was found to prefer *Qiongzhuea macrophyla* in the Liangshan Mountains, *Bashania fargesii* in the Qionglai Mountains, and *Himalayacalamus falconeri* in Langtang National Park, Nepal. Bamboo leaves, which are the most nutritious part of the bamboo plant, containing higher crude protein and fat and lower cellulose

and lignin than stems and branches, are the most common items in the diet. The seasonal supplementary food items it consumes, such as new shoots in spring and fruits in autumn, are both abundant in nutrition and easily digestible.

Breeding

Males and females become sexually mature at 18–20 months of age, and their breeding behavior is strictly seasonal. The mating season falls between early January and mid-March. As the mating season comes near, the frequency of anogenital rubbing, sniffing, and licking increases. In captivity, the concentration of estradiol reaches a peak before mating, accompanied by an increased concentration of progesterone. For males, fecal testosterone concentration was found to be obviously higher in the mating season, and closely correlated with the frequent occurrence of reproductive behaviors. Females are considered polyestrous. They remain receptive for approximately 12 to 36 hours, during which copulation may occur two or three times, implying ovulation is induced in this species. Mean gestation

Red Pandas usually have two cubs, although litter size can range from one to four. Females move their cubs frequently, probably in response to disturbances. The cubs are full grown at a year and sexually mature about six months later. They typically stay with their mother until the next breeding season. Red Pandas in captivity in the Northern Hemisphere, and in the wild, mate between early January and mid-March, and most births occur in June. In the Southern Hemisphere, Red Pandas in captivity mate in July and August, the austral winter.

Ailurus fulgens
Photo: Roland Seitre

When it is cold out, a **Red Panda** may curl up in a sheltered spot to snooze, with its nose tucked under a hindleg, using its tail as a warm comforter. Females also select safe, sheltered places such as rock crevices or tree holes to give birth and raise their young. Red Pandas use relatively small home ranges, but they have some specific habitat requirements: they need forests where there is a thick understory of bamboo. The greatest threat to their continued survival as a species is habitat destruction. The Red Panda is currently listed as Vulnerable on The IUCN Red List.

Ailurus fulgens
Photo: Axel Gebauer

length in captivity was found to be 135 days, with a range of 114 to 145 days.

Births occur in June and July. Wild Red Pandas may use hollow trees or rock crevices in a safe and silent environment as nest sites. In captivity, in the days before parturition, a pregnant female begins to carry nest materials such as sticks, grasses, and leaves into a suitable nest site. Litter size ranges from one to four with a mode of two, and with the extreme value of five. Neonates weigh 110 to 130 g in captivity. During the first 7 to 10 days after birth, they remain essentially immobile except when nursing. By the 18th day, their eyes are open and the young begin to orient toward light. Young make their first excursions out of the nest at approximately 90 days. When they are approximately twelve months of age, they have attained adult size.

Movements, Home range and Social organization

A capable climber, the Red Panda is scansorial. The normal mode of progression on the ground is by a cross-extension gait, although faster movements are accomplished by trotting or bounding. They go up trees much as they move on the ground, with a cross-extension gait of fore-and hindlimbs. Movement in trees is facilitated by flexibility of the joints and of the pectoral and pelvic girdles. They always descend from trees head first, gripping the tree trunk bilaterally with the hindfeet, which is faster than backing down. The long and heavy tail is not prehensile, but functions for support and counterbalance when the animal is climbing or moving on or between branches. When they move on the ground, the tail is carried straight out and horizontal to the ground.

Individuals in the wild live in a small area all year round, covering from about 1 km² to less than 4 km². In the Qionglai Mountains, China, the daily distance traveled ranges from 235 to 481 m.

Relationship with Humans

The Red Panda seems a mild and silent animal in the wild, posing almost no threat to human life or property. With its medi-

um-sized body and brilliantly colored pelage F. G. Cuvier, the author of its scientific description in 1825, thought it a "beautiful species, one of the handsomest of known quadrupeds". It is a popular animal for exhibition at zoos, parks, reserves, and other facilities, which represents a potential threat to wild populations because most exhibited individuals are captured from the wild. In south-western China, some local residents used to use its fur to make hats, which newly married couples regarded as a talisman for a happy marriage. Trapping wild Red Pandas for trade was largely stopped after the species was listed on CITES Appendix I. However, the conflict between preserving this animal and meeting the desires of people seems likely to continue. In Langtang Natural Park, Nepal, the Red Panda population faces high rates of mortality among adults (44%) and cubs (86%). Cub mortality was most often attributed to disturbances caused by livestock grazing, which results in habitat destruction.

Status and Conservation

CITES Appendix I species. *The IUCN Red List* categorizes the Red Panda as Vulnerable. The global population of Red Pandas is estimated at about 16,000–20,000, in an estimated habitat area of about 69,900 km². However, the population has probably decreased sharply in the past several decades due to habitat loss and fragmentation, poaching, trade, forest fires, road construction, and other disturbances. In China, it is estimated that the population has decreased by as much as 40% over the last 50 years. Red Pandas are now confined to parts of Sichuan, Yunnan, and Xizang, and are extinct in the rest of their original range, in Guizhou, Gansu, Shaanxi, and Qinghai provinces.

In China, a number of laws and regulations heve been designed to protect the animal. These are encoded in the National Constitution, the criminal laws, the Wild Animal Protection Law (under which the Red Panda is classed as a category II species), the Forestry Law, and the Environmental Protection Law. In India, the Red Panda is protected under Schedule I of the Indian Wild Life (Protection) Act of 1972, which prohibits its killing or capture. It is also legally protected in Bhutan and Nepal. By 2002, no fewer than 43, 20, five, and seven protected areas related to the Red Panda had been established in China, India, Bhutan, and Nepal, respectively.

ssp *fulgens*

ssp *styani*

PLATE 29

| inches | 10 |
| cm | 25 |

FAMILY AILURIDAE
Red Panda

Plate 29
Species Accounts

Genus *AILURUS*
Cuvier, 1825

Red Panda   *Ailurus fulgens*

French: Panda roux / **German**: Kleiner Panda / **Spanish**: Panda rojo
Other common names: Lesser Panda, Fire Fox, Golden Dog, Bear Cat

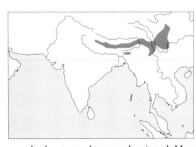

Taxonomy. *Ailurus fulgens* Cuvier, 1825, Nepal. Two subspecies recognized.
Subspecies and Distribution.
A. f. fulgens Cuvier, 1825 – E Himalayas in Bhutan, India, Nepal, Sikkim; China (S & SE Xizang & NW Yunnan), NE India (Meghalaya), and N Myanmar.
A. f. styani Thomas, 1902 – China (W Sichuan & N Yunnan).
Descriptive notes. Head-body 51–73 cm, tail 28–49 cm; weight 3–6 kg. Head round, muzzle short, ears large and pointed. Muzzle, lips, cheeks, and edges of ears white, eyes with small dark patches. Dorsal pelage chestnut brown, ventral pelage and limbs black. Tail bushy, with alternate red and buff colored rings. Feet with hairy soles, and claws semi-retractile. Females have eight mammae. Forepaw with elongated radial sesamoid. Skull robust, with broad zygomatic arches and large occipital condyles. Teeth heavily cusped, with elaborate crown patterns. Compared with *fulgens*, *styani* is distinguishable by its longer winter coat, darker body color, larger skull, and more robust teeth.
Habitat. Temperate forests of mountains at elevations of 1500–4800 m. In Meghalaya of India, in tropical forests at much lower elevations, between 700–1400 m. Typically in forests with bamboo-thicket understory. High bamboo cover, bamboo height, and canopy cover are important; preferred habitats have a high density of shrubs, fallen logs, and tree stumps, yielding easy access to bamboo leaves.
Food and Feeding. Diet largely vegetarian, 80–90% consisting of bamboo leaves, new shoots important in spring, fruits eaten in late summer and autumn. Usually feeds on the most nutritious bamboo species in its habitat. Also eats roots, lichens, small vertebrates, birds eggs, insects and grubs.
Activity patterns. Captive animals are nocturnal and crepuscular, and exhibit a polyphasic activity pattern throughout the night. In the wild, the Red Panda was thought to be most active at dawn, dusk, and at night, but several recent studies have consistently shown it is more active in the daytime than at night. In Wolong Nature Reserve, China, a subadult female, a female, and a male were reported to be active 36·5%, 49%, and 45% of the time, respectively. In Fengtongzhai Nature Reserve, bordering the former reserve on the north, six radio-collared Red Pandas had an average daily activity rate of 48·6%, with two peaks from 7:00 h to 10:00 h and from 17:00 h to 18:00 h. Generally, numerous periods of rest are interspersed with frequent activity periods.
Movements, Home range and Social organization. A subadult female in Wolong Reserve occupied a home range of 3·43 km², with a mean linear daily movement of 481 m. Subsequent research in the same area showed that a female and a male possessed home ranges of 0·94 km² and 1·11 km², with a daily distance moved of 235 m and 325 m, respectively. In Fengtongzhai Reserve, the daily movement distance was 461 m and the home range covered 2·34 km² for six collared individuals. Intrasexual and intersexual overlapping of home ranges occurred extensively. Perhaps due to difference in habitat quality and population density, both the females and males in Langtang Nature Reserve, Nepal, had larger home ranges (1·02 to 9·62 km²) than those in Sichuan, China. Several studies reported that Red Pandas live in groups of three to five individuals with blood relationships. Other studies found the Red Panda solitary outside the breeding season, with territories well posted by scent marking. Olfactory communication is the primary method of conveying social signals, through the secretions from anogenital glands deposited in the environment. Secretions from foreskin glands and glands on the soles of the feet can impart an individual's information, too. Red Pandas leave droppings in groups, and their repeatedly-used defecation sites (latrines) probably facilitate communication among neighbors.
Breeding. Both sexes sexually mature at 18–20 months and breeding behavior is strictly seasonal. Mating season is from early January to mid-March. Females are considered polyestrous, ovulation is induced. Mean gestation length in captivity 135 days, with range of 114 to 145 days. Births occur in June and July in hollow trees or rock crevices. Litter size one to four with a mode of two, extreme value of five. Neonates weigh 110-130 g in captivity. They remain essentially immobile in the first 7-10 days except when nursing. Eyes open by day 18, first excursions out of nest at approximately 90 days. Adult size is reached at twelve months of age.
Status and Conservation. CITES Apendix I. Classified as Vulnerable on *The IUCN Red List*. Global population estimated at 16,000–20,000, in estimated area of 69,900 Km². In China, the population decreased by up to 40% due to habitat loss and fragmentation, poaching, trade, forest fires, road construction, and other disturbances during the past 50 years, and became extinct in Guizhou, Gansu, Shaanxi, and Qinghai provinces. Protected in all countries where it now occurs with 43, 20, 5, and 7 protected areas established in China, India, Bhutan, and Nepal, respectively.

Bibliography. Bininda-Edmonds (2004), Choudhury (2001), Dawkins (1888), Endo *et al*. (1999), Flynn & Nedbal (1998), Flynn *et al*. (2000), Fox *et al*. (1996), Hu (1991), Hu & Wang (1984), IUCN (2008), Johnson, K.G. *et al*. (1988a), Li, C. *et al*. (2003), Li, M. *et al*. (2004), Liu *et al*. (2003, 2004), MacClintock (1988), Nowak (1999), Pen (1962), Pradhan *et al*. (2001), Rabinowitz & Khaing (1998), Reid, Hu & Huang (1991), Roberts & Gittleman (1984), Spanner *et al*. (1997), Tedford & Gustavson (1977), Wei, Feng, Wang & Hu (1999, 2000), Wei, Feng, Wang & Li (1999), Wei, Feng, Wang, Zhou & Hu (1999), Wei, Lü *et al*. (2005), Wei, Wang *et al*. (2000), Yonzon & Hunter (1991a, 1991b), Zhang, Wei, Li & Hu (2006), Zhang, Wei, Li, Zhang. *et al*. (2004).

CLASS MAMMALIA

ORDER CARNIVORA

SUBORDER CANIFORMIA

Family PROCYONIDAE (RACCOONS)

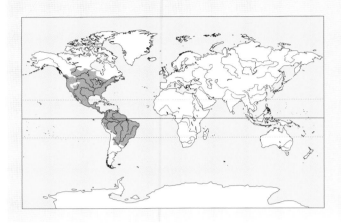

- Medium-sized mammals, many species with facial masks and/or long ringed tails.
- 54–144 cm.

- North, Central, and South America.
- Found in every forest type within their range; some also use urban areas or arid lands with rocky shelters.
- 6 genera, 12 species, 78 extant taxa.
- 1 species Critically Endangered; none Extinct since 1600.

Systematics

Within the Carnivora, the Procyonidae is a medium-sized family of medium-sized mammals. Because the six genera are diverse in their appearance the family was not immediately recognized as a coherent group of species. For example, the Northern Raccoon was first described as a fox (*Vulpi affinis*), and then a bear (*Ursus lotor*), and the Kinkajou as a primate (*Lemur flavus*).

Once the group was recognized, the Procyonidae were clearly categorized as members of the dog side of the order, in the suborder Caniformia. Within this group their position has jostled around over the years with authors suggesting they are closer to the bears, the weasels, or the Asian Red Panda. At some point biologists considered the Red Panda to be a member of the Procyonidae, but modern genetic analysis clearly shows this not to be the case. Recent studies have found a number of nuclear and mitochondrial genes all telling the same story, of a genetic similarity between procyonids and the Mustelidae, forming a clade known as the Musteloidea. Based on genetic, neontological, and paleontological evidence the Red Panda is now recognized as being in its own ancient, monotypic family (Ailuridae), which is the closest living lineage to the Musteloidea.

The time of the procyonid–mustelid split is calibrated as $29 \cdot 02 \pm 1 \cdot 13$ million years ago by genetic clock analysis, which is consistent in being slightly earlier than the first fossil recognized as a procyonid (*Pseudobassaris*), estimated at $27 \cdot 6$ million years ago. These early procyonids originated in Europe and moved through Asia and into North America, presumably across the Bering land bridge, by the middle or late Miocene. Fossils from France and Germany show that the family was diverse in Europe 25–18 million years ago, but these procyonids eventually went extinct without any surviving species in the old world.

The Procyonidae continued to diversify in North America during the Miocene. One prehistoric procyonid, *Cyonasua*, made an early appearance in South America during the Late Miocene, presumably by rafting across the interamerican seaway from North America. It gave rise to a number of descendants, but this group was presumed to have gone extinct by the end of the Pliocene, and was therefore not a progenitor to modern taxa. Based on fossil evidence, all living procyonids were thought to have originated in North America and diversified only after entering South America in a second migration. This second migration has been tied to the "Great American Interchange" that occurred after the Panamanian land bridge was completed (2–3 million years ago).

However, recent genetic data suggest that most splits in the Procyonidae occurred in the Miocene, and that diversifica-

tion well preceded the Great American Interchange. For example, the estimated divergence dates for the two extant coatis (*Nasua*) species is $6 \cdot 5$ million years ago; $5 \cdot 5$ million years ago for the three extant raccoons (*Procyon*) species. These dates make more sense if early raccoons and coatis entered South America at the same time as *Cyonasua*, well before the formation of the Panamanian land bridge. Fossil evidence from the tropical forested habitats used by most procyonids is not common, but this hypothesis might eventually be tested through discovery of older fossils of *Nasua* and *Procyon* in the Neotropics.

The six genera of Procyonidae are all easily recognizable and uncontroversial. However, just above and below this taxonomic level things are less certain and relationships are chang-

*Primates have eyes that face forward, and so do **Kinkajous**. This confused an early naturalist, who thought he had discovered a new kind of lemur. Kinkajous have small ears, short limbs, and woolly coats. They also have muscular, strongly prehensile tails. This is one way to distinguish them from olingos, which weigh much less but are similar in length and also inhabit the forest canopy: only the Kinkajou can hang by its tail, and frequently does. Olingos are also different from Kinkajous in having a more pointed snout, gray fur, and a sharper lateral line separating their darker back and paler belly. Across its distribution, the Kinkajou's fur color can range from yellowish to olive to brown; some individuals in Panama have a tail with a white tip.*

Potos flavus
Estación Chaiul, Chiapas, Mexico.
Photo: Xavier Ferrer & Adolf de Sostoa

Northern Olingos *are found in the forests of Central America, mostly above 1000 m. The Lowland Olingo lives in Central and South American lowland forests. A third species of olingo, the Andean Olingo, was recently discovered in the cloud forests of Ecuador and Colombia. Olingos use their long, fluffy tails for balance rather than for grasping. They are less closely related to Kinkajous than one might suspect. Like Kinkajous, they specialize in eating tree fruits and are highly nocturnal, but the two genera apparently evolved separately, and the olingos' closest relatives are the raccoons.*

Bassaricyon gabbii
Monteverde Forest Reserve,
Costa Rica.
Photo: Michael & Patricia Fogden

ing as the family finally receives additional evolutionary study. Cladistic analyses of morphological data starting in the 1980s consistently placed the genera into two subfamilies, with Kinkajous (*Potos flavus*) and olingos together in the Potosinae and with the other four genera (raccoons, coatis, Mountain Coatis (*Nasuella olivacea*), and Ringtails (*Bassariscus astutus*) all together in the Procyoninae. Within this larger group the coatis and raccoons were placed as sister taxa. However, two recent genetic studies that included both nuclear and mitochondrial genes told a substantially different story, identifying three distinct lineages: coatis and Ringtails, olingos and raccoons, and Kinkajous (Mountain Coatis were not analysed). The Kinkajous were sister to the other two clades, and are estimated to have diverged 21·6–24 million years ago. These results emphasize the

morphological and ecological flexibility of the Procyonidae, with different taxa evolving convergent morphology, confusing evolutionary studies that used only physical characters. The olingos are a prime example in that they have converged on some of the same morphological adaptations for arboreal fruit eating as the Kinkajou, but started from an ancestry shared with raccoons.

The exact number of species within the Procyonidae has likewise been controversial, and has suffered from little taxonomic revision over the last 50 years. Early taxonomists in the late 1800s and early 1900s described many different populations and variations as distinct species, especially for raccoons and olingos. This resulted in the recognition of five species of raccoons living on different oceanic islands and five species of

Raccoons' forepaws are very *sensitive organs of touch. It is easy to see why they are as often called "hands" as "paws". The* Crab-eating Raccoon *has the black mask and banded tail typical of* Procyon, *but its brownish throat and dark legs and feet distinguish it from the Northern Raccoon. This species is somewhat longer, too: the head and body measure 54–76 cm and the tail is 25–38 cm long. The Northern Raccoon's head and body measure 44–62 cm and its tail length is 19–36 cm. Why do raccoons have masks? So far, scientists have not been able to identify any evolutionary advantage. Perhaps it makes a nocturnal predator's face less visible at night.*

Procyon cancrivorus
Pantanal, Mato Grosso, Brazil.
Photo: Eberhard Hummel

This face is familiar throughout much of North America, even in urban areas. There are many more **Northern Raccoons** *today than there were in the 1920s, when college students wore raccoon coats to football games and raccoons were heavily hunted for their fur. These adaptable animals vary in size: the largest are in the north-western USA and the smallest in the south-east. The extent of genetic variation within Northern Raccoons needs to be evaluated. The raccoons living on some islands in the Caribbean were long thought to be three separate, endemic species, but DNA studies showed otherwise: they are introduced Northern Raccoons, and are now viewed as invasive pests, destroyers of native birds and other fauna. However, the Cozumel Raccoon probably lived on Cozumel Island, Mexico, long before humans arrived.*

Procyon lotor
Ontario, Canada.
Photo: Bob Gurr/DRK

olingos, including three from the small country of Costa Rica. For the last 100 or so years, biologists have suspected that many of these species would not hold up to modern evolutionary analyses. Although many field guides reviewing the regional fauna noted this suspicion, no one reviewed the variation within two groups until recently. In both cases the new data supported long-held suspicions, but also turned up surprises.

Reviews of the morphology and genetics of island raccoons supported the often-held view that the three species of raccoons described from Caribbean islands (*Procyon maynardi* from New Providence Island, Bahamas; *P. minor* from Guadeloupe, Lesser Antilles; *P. gloveralleni* from Barbados, Lesser Antilles) and one from a small island off western Mexico (*P. insularis* from Tres Marias Island) were not distinct enough to be considered unique species. The latter was considered a valid subspecies (*P. lotor insularis*), but the Caribbean forms were confirmed to be recent (few hundred years) introductions from the eastern USA.

From a conservation standpoint this was a dramatic switch for the Caribbean raccoons—from cherished endemic species to invasive pest. Raccoons are infamous nest predators that are known to impact bird and reptile populations on the mainland. This effect is likely to be even greater on oceanic islands where nesting oceanic birds and turtles have lived for millennia without encountering mammalian predators, and therefore have few natural defense mechanisms. Also, this revised taxonomy completely flips the interpretation of the extinction of the Barbados Raccoon (last recorded in 1964). Initially viewed as a tragic loss of endemic biodiversity, it is now viewed as a fortunate extirpation of a potentially damaging introduced species.

The status of the Cozumel procyonids is not as clear cut as these other island forms. Cozumel Raccoons are obviously different from mainland forms in being 15% smaller with reduced dentition. Recent genetic evidence suggests that they are relatively new to Cozumel, within the last 50,000 years, but were likely present well before Mayans populated this region. They probably established themselves on Cozumel Island without the assistance of humans, rapidly evolved into a dwarf form,

and are a distinct form of raccoon. From the broader perspective of evolutionary biology 50,000 years is not very long, and the rapid dwarfing isn't surprising in view of the plastic nature of the family. Another endemic Cozumel procyonid, the Cozumel Coati, seems to have followed a parallel evolutionary history with similar dwarfing and genetic differences suggesting about 50,000 years of isolation. However, the most recent taxonomic revision of the family was inconsistent in recognizing the Cozumel Raccoon as a distinct species (*Procyon pygmaeus*) but the Coati as a subspecies (*Nasua narica nelsoni*).

Simplistic comparisons of island and mainland forms, such as has been done in Cozumel, are limited if the variation across mainland forms has not been studied. Unfortunately, this is the case for most procyonids, meaning that proper taxonomic evaluation of the Cozumel forms will have to wait until the mainland forms are better studied. Only after the genetic and morphologic differences between mainland and island forms are compared to those seen across the range of the mainland species can the species-level taxonomy of the Cozumel procyonids be fairly evaluated. The morphological and genetic variation of any procyonid genus has only recently been comprehensively reviewed across its range, resulting in dramatic revision of the olingos.

Over most of the last century five species of olingos were recognized, including three broad-ranging species (Northern Olingo *Bassaricyon gabbii* from Central America and northern South America, Lowland Olingo *B. alleni* from west South America, and Beddard's Olingo *B. beddardi* from north-east South America) and two small-area endemics from Costa Rica (Chiriqui Olingo *B. pauli* and Harris's Olingo *B. lasius*). Although taxonomists reviewing Neotropical mammals have long suspected that all five species would not hold up to modern evolutionary analyses, such analyses were conducted only recently. The genetic and morphological results support the doubters' suspicions by combining the five previously described forms into two olingo species. One, Lowland Olingo, ranges broadly throughout lowland forests of Central and South America. The second, Northern Olingo, has a wide elevational range (near

The **Ringtail** is very closely related to the Cacomistle, but the two are different from head to toe to tail. The Ringtail's most distinctive feature is its very long, bushy, black and white ringed tail. The Cacomistle is larger than the Ringtail, its tail is even longer in proportion to its head and body length, and the rings go all the way around, while the underside of the Ringtail's tail is white. The last third or so of the Cacomistle's tail is almost solid black, whereas the Ringtail's tail is ringed almost to the end. At the other end of the animal, the Ringtail's muzzle is grayer, while the Cacomistle's is blacker, and Ringtails show more contrast in their facial markings. Moving to the toes, the Cacomistle has long, curved claws on its blackish feet, whereas the Ringtail has short, straight claws that it can partially retract and its hindlegs are longer than its forelegs. The long, thin bodies of Ringtails resemble those of weasels, but Ringtails are heavier. The coat color varies: Ringtails tend to have darker coats in forests and at higher elevations and higher latitudes, and paler coats in more arid habitat and in the southern part of their range. The Ringtail's whiskers, which are mostly black, help it navigate through dark, narrow crevices in the dry, rocky outcroppings or talus slopes where it dens and hunts.

Bassariscus astutus
Coronado National Forest,
Arizona, USA.
Photo: Michael Durham/DRK

507

*The white snout of the **White-nose Coati** distinguishes it from the South American Coati, which has a brown or gray muzzle. Coatis have incredibly long toenails, as befits animals that scratch to find food, and extremely long, ringed tails. Not surprisingly, their closest relatives are Ringtails and Cacomistles. Coatis are the only procyonids in which there is significant sexual dimorphism: males are about 20% larger than females. Some scientists classify one subspecies, N. narica nelsoni, known as the Dwarf Coati, as a full species. Genetic studies will eventually settle the debate about the status of this small coati from Cozumel Island, Mexico. It is listed as Endangered on* The IUCN Red List *with a total population estimated at 150.*

Nasua narica
Tucson, Arizona, USA.
Photo: Thomas Dressler/Ardea

sea level to about 2000 m), but is usually found in mountains above 1000 m in the central part of Mesoamerica—throughout central Nicaragua and Costa Rica and extending into western Panama in the Chiriqui Mountains. However, the data held a surprise: an undescribed species from the Andean cloud forests of Ecuador and Colombia. Undiscovered carnivore species are rare in science, and this was the first new American carnivore described in over 20 years. This new species diverged from Lowland Olingos some 4–6 million years ago, coinciding with an active period in the formation of the Andes. The two Olingo species may overlap in some areas, as they were documented only 5 km apart in Ecuador. This new species is of immediate conservation concern because its range is restricted to Andean cloud forest, which is prized for agriculture. Indeed, over 50% of its potential habitat has already been converted to agricultural or other human uses.

The uncertainty of species-level taxonomy of the Procyonidae can be seen from these examples, both of which have enormous conservation implications. If we are to set priorities for conservation of the species in the Procyonidae it is critical that we extend this work into the other genera. For example, genetic variation within White-nosed Coati (*Nasua narica*) and

The generic name Nasua *comes directly from* nasus, *the Latin word for nose, so the **South American Coati**'s scientific name is "nose nose". Its nose is, indeed, very long, and is darker in color than that of the White-nosed Coati. The South American Coati's basic coat color is brown, and can be very dark brown, but can also be orangish or reddish, sometimes highlighted with yellow. Breeding experiments have shown that even in the same litter, the fur color can differ. The tail is the same color as the back, but sometimes the paler rings are almost invisible. Not surprisingly, these variations led early naturalists to describe several species. Twelve subspecies are currently recognized.*

Nasua nasua
Left: Kaa-Iya del Gran Chaco National Park, Bolivia.
Photo: Luiz Claudio Marigo

Right: SE Brazil.
Photo: Greg & Yvonne Dean/
WorldWildlifeImages.com

A band of **South American Coatis** typically includes one dominant male and a number of females and their young. As many as 65 coatis have been seen in a group, although bands of 5–30 are more common. These matrilineal bands spend their nights in trees and do much of their daytime foraging together on the ground. Group members share parental care, groom each other, and combine forces to attack potential predators. Living in groups probably reduces the risk to any individual coati of falling victim to a predator. When they are foraging, group members stop frequently to look around. Individuals at the front of the group are the most watchful, and the ones at the edge of the group are more vigilant than those in the center. In the group hierarchy, after the dominant male, male juveniles and female juveniles rank second and third. This may be because these "young adults" fiercely defend food resources while older females tolerate their aggression. **White-nosed Coatis** are also very gregarious, and equally large groups have been reported. The size of a coati group fluctuates over time with births and deaths and the emigration of young males to other groups. Sometimes groups contain individuals who are not in the matrilineal line. These coatis get less support and are treated with more aggression than related band members. Large groups may split into smaller groups, sometimes just for a few hours or a few days, and sometimes permanently. Groups are usually somewhat antagonistic toward neighboring groups.

Above: **Nasua nasua**
Pantanal, Mato Grosso, Brazil.
Photo: Staffan Widstrand/naturepl.com

Below: **Nasua narica**
Villahermosa, Tabasco, Mexico.
Photo: Roland Seitre

Aggressive and submissive behaviors are amazingly similar across species, making it is easy to tell which **Northern Raccoon** and which **South American Coati** is angry and which is "apologizing" here. The reasons for aggressive behavior are harder to pin down without more information. There can be disputes over territorial or breeding rights or access to food resources. Also, females are typically very protective of their young. The aggressive animal does everything it can to look larger and more ferocious, rearing up with its hair erect and its teeth bared; the submissive one crouches and sometimes rolls on its back to make it clear that it wil not fight. As would be expected of social animals, coatis use a variety of vocalizations with their fellow band members, including sounds linked to aggression and appeasement. Coati bands are likely to treat unrelated individua somewhat aggressively. Northern Raccoons do not live in groups, but are often quite tolerant of each other. Where food is abundant and they can share space without competing, females may forage together and even den together. Where the raccoon population is dense, males cannot defend territories from each other, and the sometimes form male bonds that last for years. Where density is lou males are more likely to try to set u and defend territories. Raccoons are not very vocal, but they, too, have a variety of sounds that are used at close range.

Above: **Procyon lotor**
Photo: Stefan Meyers/Ardea

Below: **Nasua nasua**
near Manaus, Amazonas, Brazil.
Photo: Luiz Claudio Marigo

Procyon cancrivorus
Ecuador.
Photo: David Hosking/FLPA

Northern Raccoon (*Procyon lotor*) needs to be evaluated to offer perspective on the uniqueness of their Cozumel forms. Three other broad-ranging species, Crab-eating Raccoons (*Procyon cancrivorus*), South American Coatis (*Nasua nasua*), and Kinkajous should also be examined for evolutionary patterns throughout their range. As with the olingos, there is the potential to find undescribed species. Finally, the Mountain Coati needs to be sequenced to confirm its place within the family's phylogeny.

Morphological Aspects

Procyonids are mid-sized mammals, ranging roughly from 1–10 kg. Raccoons and coatis are relatively robust in body form, while the more dedicated arboreal forms Kinkajous, olingos, and Ringtails, have a more slender build. coatis have strong sexual dimorphism, with larger males, while other species show little or no dimorphism.

All of the Procyonidae are good climbers, although some are better at it than others. For example, the postures and forepaws of raccoons and coatis are well adapted for terrestrial life but compromise their climbing ability. Although they frequently climb up a tree for food or escape, they rarely move between tree canopies. The Kinkajou, on the other hand, is one of the most specialized tree climbers in the Order Carnivora. Kinkajous regularly move from tree-top to tree-top in the dark, covering 2 km per night. They have fully reversible hindfeet for descending branches and hanging, and display remarkable

Potos flavus
Brazil.
Photo: Nick Gordon/Ardea

Northern Raccoons *have many good reasons for grooming themselves. For one, they molt annually. They have long guard hairs and dense underfur, which they shed each spring and they are wearing a new, glossy coat by fall. Researchers found hair in raccoon scats throughout the year. They found the most hair in their feces during the spring molt, and the least in mid-winter, when the raccoons' coats were in prime condition. Another reason to groom is to try to keep external parasites, such as ticks, under control. Raccoons can be heavily burdened with ectoparasites: researchers identified eleven specie. on raccoons in Alabama, USA.*

Procyon lotor
Photo: Duncan Usher/Ardea

vertebral flexibility. Their most conspicuous climbing adaptation is their long prehensile tail, from which they often hang to reach fruit. This is a trait shared with only one other Carnivore, the unrelated Binturong. The two species have converged in developing muscular tails with more, longer vertebrae at the base of the tail and more robust vertebrae at the tip. These provide enhanced flexion-extension of the proximal part of the tail and increased strength and flexing capacity at the tip.

Raccoons are famous for using their dexterous hands to manipulate food, and their hands have been found to be very sensitive to touch. However, tests suggest that they are not substantially more dexterous than many other mammals. Like most carnivorans, they do not use convergent grasping or digit manipulation, and frequently use bimanual grasping. Kinkajous, on the other hand, do have a fully convergent grasp, allowing

them to hold food with one hand. Coatis are even less dexterous, with few fine control movements, but they are excellent diggers and shredders. Their feet, not to mention their long noses, make them well adapted to scrounging for invertebrates along the forest floor.

Black masks and banded tails are conspicuous characters in many species of Procyonidae. The banded tails are striking in *Procyon*, *Bassariscus*, and *Nasua*, but are barely discernable in *Bassariscus* and completely absent in *Potos*. Raccoons are famous for having a bold black mask, which is also present to a lesser extent in *Bassariscus*. There is no obvious adaptive purpose to the banded tail. Black face masks in other mid-sized carnivorans are thought to function as a warning to potential predators that the species is especially fierce (e.g. Badgers) or stinky (e.g. Skunks). Raccoons obviously don't meet either

South American Coatis *eat a wide variety of foods. A detailed study of 226 coati fecal samples in Brazil found that almost all contained plant parts, and most also contained insect remains. Forty-nine species of fruits were identified. A great many of the coatis had also eaten spiders and millipedes, especially during the rainy season. When these and other arthropods were scare, fruits were most important in their diets. Fewer than 10% of the feces contained the remains of vertebrates. Birds have been seen following bands of foraging coatis, catching invertebrates that the coatis stir up, but miss.*

Nasua nasua
Caiman Ecological Refuge, Pantanal, Mato Grosso, Brazil.
Photo: Tui de Roy/
Roving Tortoise Photos

South American Coatis are primarily diurnal and are omnivorous feeders. The individual in the above photo may have found a snack hidden in the leaves of the plant, or it may be lapping a few drops of water. The one below appears to have caught a satisfying meal: a frog. Coatis climb small trees and vines easily, and can hold onto vines with their feet. However, they do most of their foraging on the forest floor, and if they are disturbed while they are in a tree, they will run to the ground to escape. A coati that wants to descend from a large tree usually climbs out to the end of a branch and makes its way down from branch to branch. It cannot reverse its hindfeet and dash down a trunk headfirst the way a Kinkajou can. On the ground, coatis forage in leaf litter with their noses and dig with their foreclaws. One study found that scent was very important in finding food, and that coatis could smell food items from distances of 20–25 m. South American Coatis are excellent diggers and shredders, but do not have much fine control with their claws. Invertebrates are an important component of their diet. They kill and detoxify spiny or poisonous prey such as scorpions and tarantulas by rolling the prey item on the ground with their paws. Their diet also includes fruit, both plucked from trees and found on the ground.

Nasua nasua
Above: Ecuador.
Photo: Pete Oxford/naturepl.com

Below: Amazonas, Brazil.
Photo: Luiz Claudio Marigo

Northern Olingos, the largest of the three olingo species, eat fruit and nectar in trees in Central American rainforests. They also capture and eat small arboreal animals, but there is very little specific information about their diets. The teeth of the Bassaricyo species suggest that these animals may be predators, and in captivit Lowland Olingos will eat meat. In the field they have only been seen eating fruits and flowers, however, and the extent to which they consume insects or hunt small prey is unknown. Least is known about the food habits of a newly described species, the Andean Olingo, except that it, to is nocturnal and eats tree fruits, especially wild figs. Kinkajous are almost entirely frugivorous and nectivorous and often feed in the same trees as olingos. They are al. more aggressive, and sometimes chase olingos away from fruiting trees. Not much is known about the social behavior of olingos, but Kinkajous are social, and protect their food resources from olingos, which are apparently more solitar Olingos use their long tails for balance when climbing and reaching for fruit, but do not hav prehensile tails, and cannot copy the Kinkajou's trick of hanging b its tail to reach and eat fruit.

Bassaricyon gabbii
Monteverde Forest Reserve,
Costa Rica.
Photos: Michael & Patricia Fogden

of these criteria, so the function of the mask remains a bit of a mystery.

Habitat

Most procyonids are relative generalists when it comes to habitat preferences, although the Andean Olingo and Mountain Coati specialize on high Andean cloud forests. Throughout the Americas, procyonids are usually closely associated with trees. Any healthy American forest will have at least one procyonid species climbing its trees, potentially as many as six in some parts of Panama.

Kinkajous, the most arboreal of the family, are found in virtually all tropical forests from lowland rainforest to high cloud forest to dry forest. White-nosed and South American Coatis likewise use a variety of forest habitats, but also move into drier Chaco, cerrado, and mountainous deserts. Raccoons are tied to the aquatic environments they feed in, and find abundant habitat within wet forests. They will also follow waterways and shorelines into drier areas. More recently, Northern Raccoons have also adapted well to urban habitats, where they reach their highest density. Ringtails are found in many forest types, but have moved further from forests than other procyonids. They do well in rocky deserts where cliffs provide them the shelter and hunting grounds other species seek in trees. Cacomistles (*Bassariscus sumichrasti*) are restricted to rainy tropical areas, but have been found using a variety of habitats, including mature oak cloud forest, secondary forest, and overgrown pastures.

Forest fragmentation and destruction have varying effects on procyonid species. Northern Raccoons are infamous for benefiting from fragmentation and taking advantage of anthropogenic foods in urban areas. Ringtails may also prosper in urban areas, although not as much as raccoons. If not heavily hunted, Cacomistles, South American Coatis, White-nosed Coatis, and Kinkajous all appear to be able to survive moderate levels of forest fragmentation. Although they all suffer from the destruction of forests, they may benefit from the more abundant fruits typical of secondary and edge forests, as well as the reduced large predator populations there. Lowland Olingos appear to be rarer than Kinkajous in any forest, and may be more sensitive to fragmentation and habitat modification. There are no data on the response of Mountain Coatis or Andean Olingos to habitat fragmentation, although presumably we would know more about these species if they commonly occurred in disturbed areas, suggesting that they are sensitive to disturbance.

Communication

All procyonid species studied are reported to make a host of typical mammalian vocalizations including hisses, growls, twitters, squeaks, and screams. These are interpreted to serve a variety of typical functions in close-range communications,

A bird or reptile that lays eggs on
the ground could possibly lose its
next generation to a **White-nosed
Coati**. Coatis also climb, so nests
in vines or trees can be raided, too.
They use their sense of smell to find
most of their food, and youngsters
are often seen sniffing the muzzles
of adults while the adults are
feeding, presumably to learn what
to eat. The young coati watching
so intently here will soon know
that eggs are delicious, and equally
importantly, will learn how to
break the shell. Procyonid predation
on the eggs and hatchlings of
endangered sea turtles is of special
concern. Humans employ many
tricks, such as placing heavy wire
cages over turtle nests, to try to
thwart coatis, raccoons, and other
predators, with less than total
success.

Nasua narica
Villahermosa, Tabasco, Mexico.
Photo: Roland Seitre

including aggression, appeasement, alarm, and sexual solicita-
tion. None are made frequently.

The diurnal and social coatis are more vocal than other species in the family. In addition to the typical sounds described
above, they also use a high-frequency chirp vocalization to
keep in contact with their group as they spread out and forage through the forest understory. Some have suggested that
the unique features of each coati's chirp may allow individual
recognition. The coatis also have an alarm call given in several-second bursts when a danger is detected, resulting in each
member of the band running up the nearest tree to survey the
situation. In Guatemala, breeding males were observed using

a version of this alarm call in a unique manner. A number of
males would each run up a tree near a band of females and repeat a vocalization similar to the alarm call for several minutes
at a time. This was interpreted as a type of lek song, trying to attract a female up the tree to breed with the male. If a male was
not chosen by a mate as the female band moved on, he would
descend the tree and run ahead of the band to repeat the display in another tree, forming a type of "moving lek".

The three most arboreal species, Kinkajous, olingos, and Cacomistles have all been reported making loud calls that probably function to communicate over long distances. This behavior
is unusual in the Carnivora, although it is common in arboreal

Like primates, **Kinkajous** have
what is called a convergent grasp,
meaning that they can hold things
in one hand. This is useful for an
animal that feeds almost entirely
in the tree canopy, mostly on fruit.
Another asset is the Kinkajou's
ability to hang by its tail, freeing
up both hands to pluck fruit. A
study in Panama documented a
diet that was almost entirely fruit,
the rest being nectar and leaves;
the Kinkajous ate the fruits of 78
species of plants. They require a
lot, because fruit moves quickly
through their digestive systems.
When they are foraging, they
generally move from tree to tree
alone, but they also meet and
socialize in large fruiting trees.

Potos flavus
Brazil.
Nick Gordon/Ardea

White-nosed Coatis do most of their foraging on the ground, but also climb to get fresh fruit. An adult male coati will sometimes try to claim a fruiting plant as his own, but groups of females and juveniles have been seen chasing males from trees. Other than that, individuals do not cooperate to find food, nor do adults share food. Coatis spend as much as 90% of the day foraging. While a band is moving, the coatis stay in contact with each other by making short, high frequency chirping calls. Each coati's chirp is unique, which may allow individuals to recognize each other. Groups also use louder contact calls described as squawks. White-nosed Coatis can apparently thrive in fragmented habitats if they are not persecuted.

Nasua narica
Costa Rica.
Photo: Michael & Patricia Fogden

Primates. In the Kinkajou the call is described as a "puff-bark" or "snort-weedle", consisting of one snort call followed by repeated weedle calls and lasting from a few seconds up to 15 minutes. The Lowland Olingo has a shorter call, described from various parts of its range as sounding like "whey-chuck", "wer-toll", and "wake-up". Andean Olingos probably make similar calls, although this has not been recorded. The Cacomistle's call has been described as "uyoo-whaa" or "boyo-baa-wow". The function of these calls is not well studied. Presumably it serves as a warning to animals in neighboring territories to maintain spacing. It may also serve to unite animals from the same social group, as has been observed occasionally for Kinkajous.

Although their vocalizations are more conspicuous to our human senses, olfactory communication is probably more important to their Carnivoran senses. Procyonids have a keen sense of smell. For example, Northern Raccoons are reportedly able to detect acorns buried under 5 cm of sand. In another experiment, South America Coatis found 96% of food sources by scent. They detected 50% of these small food plots that were within 20 m, with some an average detection distance of 9 m. All species have special adaptations to mark objects with scent, including the anal scent glands common to most Carnivores, as well as specialized skin glands in some species. Northern Raccoons and Ringtails will sometimes use fecal latrines, which

Drinking can be dangerous as predators tend to focus on water holes. This **South American Coati** could be a male, since they are often solitary. Females and juveniles are more likely to forage and drink in groups, which helps them escape predation. Large groups can safely stay longer at water holes than small groups or solitary coatis. Predation rates can be high in some coati populations. The non-human predators on South American Coatis include Jaguars, Pumas, Ocelots, and Jaguarundis.

Nasua nasua
Pantanal, Mato Grosso, Brazil.
Photo: Haroldo Palo Jr/NHPA

Northern Raccoons *typically mate in February or March, although some mate as late as June. The cubs are born about two months later, usually in a tree den. Litters of seven have been recorded, but four is the most common number. Where raccoon density is high and males cannot defend territories from other males, females usually copulate with more than one male in the two or three days when they are receptive, and litters often have multiple fathers. Outside of the mating season, males and females live apart, and males do not provide parental care. Newborn raccoons weigh less than 100 g and are completely dependent on their mother. Their eyes open when they are 18–24 days old. Reports about how long they nurse vary, from as little as seven weeks to as long as four months, but there seems to be agreement that the youngsters continue nursing for some period of time after they have started eating solid food. They first emerge from the natal den, following their mother, at as early as six weeks. However, some report cite litters that were not seen out of the nest until they were nine or ten weeks old. The difference could perhaps be explained by the species' very extensive distribution, from habitats with long, cold winters to habitats where winter never comes, and also by whether the female became pregnant early or late in the mating season.*

Procyon lotor
Baton Rouge, Louisiana, USA.
Photos: C. C. Lockwood/DRK

presumably also serve a type of "bulletin board" communication function. Scent marks generally are used to denote territorial boundaries or communicate with potential mates. Cacomistles are unusually smelly; males in particular have a strong overall body odor. In addition, the fluid from their anal gland is stronger smelling than in the Ringtail, and may serve a defensive function akin to that of Skunks.

Food and Feeding

Procyonids are among the least carnivorous families within the Carnivora, and include one species that is in the running as the most frugivorous mammal, and another that might hold the title for the most omnivorous.

Northern Raccoons are incredibly omnivorous, taking advantage of practically any fruit, insect, or anthropogenic food source that is locally abundant. Because of their large geographic range, the species as a whole encounters and eats a huge variety of foods. Nonetheless, there is some focus to their feeding, and they are quite good at foraging for aquatic prey using their hands. The diet of South American raccoons has not been as well studied, although they also appear to be flexible in eating a variety of foods; one study reported primarily aquatic prey while another reported primarily fruit.

Coatis are also omnivorous, and might be said to specialize in foraging for leaf-litter foods with their noses. They move along the ground rooting under leaves and logs with their long snouts, and extracting invertebrate prey with quick shallow excavations using their long foreclaws. Coatis are well noted for dispatching and detoxifying spiny or poisonous prey, such as scorpions and tarantulas, by rolling them on the ground with their paws. Fruit is also an important food item for White-nosed and South American Coatis. They find it by rooting underneath fruiting trees or climbing them to pick fresh fruit. Mountain Coatis have not been found to eat much fruit, getting almost all their food in the form of invertebrates. Prey is primarily extracted from the ground, leaving thousands of small holes in the ground in areas they have intensively foraged.

Ringtails and Cacomistles are omnivores specialized for climbing to find food. Both eat a mixture of fruit and small prey. Cacomistles are chiefly forest residents, and hunt prey in the treetops. Ringtails are at home in the trees, but also pounce on prey as they navigate cliffs and rocky outcrops. Ringtails eat more vertebrate prey than other procyonids, including lizards,

snakes, birds, and mammals up to the size of hares. Less is known about the Cacomistle's diet, although reports suggest a roughly even split between prey and fruit.

Kinkajous are the most specialized feeders in the family, with populations from Panama, Venezuela, and French Guiana eating primarily (up to 99%) fruit. Small amounts of flowers, nectar, and leaves were also eaten by these populations, but no invertebrate foods were recorded. This contrasts with a study in Bolivia that found substantial amounts of ants and ant nest material in the stomachs of six Kinkajous.

We probably know the least about the diet of olingos. The Lowland Olingo diet has been described from only eight feces, which contained fruits and flowers also known from local Kinkajou diets. Andean Olingos were observed eating fig fruits, but no quantitative assessment of their diet has been attempted. In captivity Lowland Olingos eat more animal protein than Kinkajous, and their tooth morphology suggests they should be more predatory than Kinkajous.

Breeding

Across the range of the Procyonidae, seasonality varies between the typical winter/summer of the temperate zone to a variety of wet/dry patterns in the tropics, with some forests having very little seasonality in their ever-present rainfall. In the temperate zones, procyonids follow the typical pattern of breeding in the spring. Elsewhere this seems to vary depending on local conditions, although few details are known about the timing of breeding for most species. Kinkajou populations seem to be only loosely coordinated in the timing of breeding by different females. White-nosed and South American Coatis, on the other hand, are tightly synchronous in their breeding, with all females coming into estrus within a two-week period.

Kinkajous and Lowland Olingos are polyestrous, Ringtails are monestrous, and Northern Raccoons are spontaneous ovulators. Ringtails have the shortest gestation period at 51–54 days. Kinkajous more than double that at 100–120 days. The dedicated arboreal species (Kinkajou, Lowland Olingo, Cacomistle) all typically have only one young per litter. Coati, raccoon, and Ringtail litters typically have 2–4 cubs. Most species are reproductively mature by two years, and breed every year. Some female Kinkajous are suspected to reproduce bi-annually to recover from their extensive gestation and lactation periods. Parental care in all species is exclusively by the mother.

Northern Raccoons *born in tree nests start their education with climbing lessons, the first of which is how to descend: slowly, carefully, and backwards, like bears. Some procyonids can reverse their hindfeet and run down head first, but raccoons cannot. Their education will also include what to eat: almost anything; and where to find it: almost anywhere. They will depend heavily on their sense of smell to find food, and less on their other senses. Lessons about avoiding predators are not a high priority, since raccoons have outlasted their former primary predators, Gray Wolves and Pumas, which have become extinct from many parts. In some areas, Coyotes may prey on raccoons, and domestic dogs are to be avoided. These youngsters may spend most of their first autumn traveling alone, but if they live in a norther climate, they will likely return to den with their mother when winter comes. They may have to spend weeks or months in a den, not hibernating, because their heart rate and body temperature will not decrease, but living on stored body fat. Young born late in the season may not put on enough weight to survive the hardships of their first winter. For example, in one area, densities were as much as one third higher in autumn than in spring, reflecting winter mortalities as well as summer births. Diseases, especially rabies, are another serious problem in raccoon populations, and a problem for the raccoons' human neighbors and their pets, especially where raccoon density is high.*

Procyon lotor
Hamilton County, SW Ohio, USA.
Photo: Dave Maslowski/
Maslowski Productions

*This litter of **White-nosed Coatis** was born in a tree nest, away from the band, after a gestation period of 70–77 days. Coati families rejoin the band when the young are about 40 days old. Females nurse their young for up to four months, and will also nurse and care for the offspring of other females in their band. Breeding in coatis is highly seasonal: a population of coatis in Panama all bred within a month of each other. Males seeking to mate climb higher in trees than the females, vocalizing, and the females choose which male to approach. White-nosed Coati females reach breeding age at 22 months. Males do not breed until they are almost three years old, and often have to wait until they are older to compete successfully. Coatis have a life span of at least nine years in the wild, and have lived as long as 17 years in captivity.*

Nasua narica
Monteverde Forest Reserve,
Costa Rica.
Photo: Michael & Patricia Fogden

Movements, Home range and Social organization

Most procyonids are nocturnal, sleeping the day away in a tree hole or rock den and emerging only after the sun has set. The exceptions are the coatis, which sleep in trees during the night and are active in the day. Nocturnality probably functions, at least in part, to help avoid predation by large diurnal raptors. Coatis counter for this risk by foraging in groups and calling alarms whenever potential predators are sighted. Raccoons and Kinkajous appear to be strictest in their nocturnality, while Lowland Olingos and Cacomistles are sometimes seen during the day. Northern Raccoons living in cold climates may spend long periods resting in dens during winter. They do not hibernate, but use stored fat to maintain their body temperature over long periods of time.

The space use by procyonids generally fits broad-scale predictions of space increasing with body size. Within the family, it also seems that the climbing animals cover less ground. Kinkajous, Lowland Olingos, Cacomistles, and Ringtails all use home range areas between 20–50 ha and cover 2–4 km per night. In contrast, the slightly larger, but much more terrestrial coatis and raccoons typically have home ranges of hundreds or thousands of hectares. Both of these species live in a wide variety of habitats and vary space use according to the amount of available food.

White-nosed Coatis vary in home range size from 0·33 to 13·5 km², with their smallest range in tropical forest and their largest in arid mountains. Northern Raccoons use the smallest areas (5–79 ha) in urban areas, where they exploit abundant anthropogenic foods. Rural animals also exploit agricultural foods and use slightly larger home ranges of 50–300 ha. Truly wild animals, using no anthropogenic foods, have been found using very large home ranges. For example, in North Dakota prairies, Raccoons used home ranges from 800–2500 ha and some individuals traveled as far as 14 km in one night. Dispersal distances for Northern Raccoons have been estimated to average 11 km, but have been recorded as high as 275 km. Dispersal in other species has not been studied.

Coatis are the most social of the Procyonidae, and their behavior has been studied in the most detail. Females and their young travel in matrilineal groups of up to 65 individuals, although smaller (10–30) groups are more common. These groups presumably help reduce predation risk, and members

are especially vigilant along the leading edge of the group. Groups may also help females and juveniles gain access to fruiting trees that would otherwise be defended by the larger males. Coati groups move together throughout the day, and sleep together during the night. Adult males sometimes trail along with a group, but are more likely to forage alone. Male South American Coatis are more likely to travel with groups than White-nosed Coatis. *Nasuella* has not been studied in as much detail, but has been observed forming diurnal groups.

The other procyonid taxa, all nocturnal, have long been presumed to be solitary. However, careful study with radio-te-

***Kinkajous** typically have one pup, although very occasionally a litter of two is born. Females only have two mammae, so no more than two would survive. The pups develop slowly, nursing for almost two months and not climbing skillfully until they are about three months old. Females have been seen carrying their young by mouth. When a female is foraging, she apparently leaves her pup alone in a tree to wait for her. If this young Kinkajou is a male, it will probably stay with or settle near its natal group when it reaches maturity, at about 18 months of age. If it is a female, maturity will come later, when it is more than two years old, and it will disperse, either to a new group or to live alone.*

Potos flavus
Misahuallí, Napo, Ecuador.
Photo: José María Fernández
Díaz-Formentí

Northern Raccoons almost always
live close to water, and forage
in swamps and streams, feeling
with their sensitive hands for
aquatic prey, as these young ones
are learning to do. When they are
finding food on land, their noses
are much more important, and
extremely sensitive: raccoons are
reported to be able to smell acorns
buried about 5 cm deep under
sand. Their noses also lead them
to garbage cans, carrion, fruits,
and nests: few foods are off limits.
Young raccoons stay with their
mother for about eight months,
and sometimes den with her during
their first winter. Usually young
males eventually disperse, but
females stay within their mother's
range.

Procyon lotor
W USA.
Photo: Tom & Pat Leeson/Ardea

lemetry and nocturnal observation has revealed a hidden sociality in two species. Kinkajous were found to live within social
groups of about five animals, although they typically move and
feed alone. Group members meet up to socialize and groom
each other at larger feeding trees. They also sleep together in
tree-holes on at least 70% of days. The social groups were unusual in containing two adult males and one adult female, and
appeared to be patrilineal.

Raccoons show different social organizations depending
on their local density. In low density habitats males have large
home ranges, which they try to defend against other males, and
which overlap with multiple female ranges in a typical polygynous system. However, as densities increase males are unable to
defend territories by themselves, and coalitions of males form.
These typically include 2–3 males who move together and associate on a nightly basis. This sociality is presumably cooperative, although the details of this are not yet known. At these
high densities multiple paternity is common, and the breeding
system has been judged as promiscuous.

Raccoons and coatis have male biased dispersal. Females
typically remain in their mothers' social band (coatis) or set
up their own home range within or adjacent to their mothers'
(raccoons). This leads to a matrilineal social structure. Kinkajous appear to be the opposite, setting up a patrilineal social
structure. Genetic patterns suggest that female Kinkajous disperse further and young males stay closer to home, presumably
to form coalitions with their brothers, fathers, and uncles.

One raccoon population was made up primarily of animals
under the age of two, with very few individuals over seven. The
age structure of other species in the wild is unknown. The maximum ages for captive animals are 16·5 years for Ringtails, 25
for Lowland Olingos, and 40·5 for Kinkajous.

The social organization of the other procyonids has not
been studied in as much detail. Given the intriguing sociality
found in Kinkajous and Northern Raccoons it will be interesting to see what secrets the other species are hiding in their nocturnal ways.

Relationship with Humans

Most procyonids have little interaction with humans. Their nocturnal, and often arboreal, habits keep them hidden from most
people. They do not cause problems by attacking livestock like
some other carnivorans. In the tropics some species raid fruit
from trees in gardens, but they are often viewed as cute, wel-

comed visitors rather than food-stealing pests. The Northern
Raccoon is an exception to all this. The most successful urban
carnivore in the Americas, it is viewed as a cute neighbor or a
big pest by millions of people.

All procyonids are relatively flexible in their choice of foods
and habitat, but Northern Raccoons are remarkable in their
adaptation to urban areas. Starting especially in the 1970s and
80s, Northern Raccoons began populating urban areas at high
densities, enjoying the free food left in garbage cans as well
as the reduced predation pressure from larger carnivorans.
These twin points of more food and fewer predators resulted in increased survival, higher annual recruitment, and increased site fidelity, leading to very high raccoon populations
in urbanized areas. Related to this, Northern Raccoons had
to evolve new tolerances of other raccoons, especially when
feeding at productive garbage dumps where dozens of animals
could meet up.

In addition to the nuisance of raccoons in the garbage,
these high-density, frequently interacting populations have
caused problems for humans (and other beasts) by spreading
disease. Starting in the 1980s, a new strain of raccoon rabies
spread rapidly through high-density raccoon populations
along the east coast of the USA. This served to reduce urban
raccoon populations in some areas (which is probably a good
thing) but also spilled over to other wildlife populations, not
to mention humans.

Nonetheless, raccoons are charismatic, cute animals, with
their black masks and ringed tails, and many people are willing
to forgive their transgressions with the garbage can and retain
a favorable opinion of them. Raccoons are common mascots
for a variety of events, and a popular stuffed animal toy for kids.
Their ringed tails are also popular with fur trappers, with prices
and trapping pressure fluctuating widely over the last century.
For example, the coonskin cap popularized by the Davy Crock-
ett TV show in the 1950s caused a twenty-four-fold increase in
pelt prices, and is considered one of the first television-inspired
fads. Over most of the century annual harvests of raccoons
ranged from 400,000 to two million, reaching an all-time high
of 5·1 million in the winter of 1979/80.

American Indians also hunted raccoons, using their meat,
skin, and bones as food, tools, and ornaments. Raccoon penis bones were used as ceremonial charms, and their furs as
pouches and clothing. The raccoon's charismatic appearance
and behavior also worked their way into native cultures, where
stories represent the raccoon as a trickster, and occasional
corn thief.

Crab-eating Raccoons breed once a year, producing litters of 2–7 pups. Litters of 3–4 are most common. The female locates her natal den in a hollow tree or rock crevice, or may use a den abandoned by another animal. Not much is known about breeding in Crab-eating Raccoons, but as with Cozumel Raccoons their natural history is assumed to be very similar to that of Northern Raccoons. Where Crab-eating Raccoons and Northern Raccoons overlap, scientists have not found evidence of interbreeding. Newborn raccoons are toothless, with their eyes sealed; some time after three weeks their eyes open and their faces begin to have a mask.

Procyon cancrivorus
Llanos, Venezuela.
Photo: M. Watson/Ardea

Status and Conservation

As a family, the Procyonidae are generally common in any habitat. Species like raccoons, coatis, Ringtails, and Kinkajous are all adaptable and relatively abundant. The raccoons and coatis, in particular, have large litters, can breed relatively fast, and therefore can sustain relatively high mortality from harvests or roadkill. This adaptability can cause trouble in areas where Northern Raccoons have been introduced and may harm native species, especially those which nest on or near the ground.

The Cozumel Raccoon and Cozumel Coati are unique and highly endangered taxa that are in need of immediate conservation attention. Recent taxonomic revisions have shown that other Caribbean Raccoon species were not valid taxa, but the result of recent introductions to the islands, and therefore should not be targets of conservation efforts. Similarly, a recent revision of olingo taxonomy has shown two Central American olingos considered Endangered by *The IUCN Red List* (*Bassaricyon lasius* and *B. pauli*) are not valid species. However, one new olingo species was recently described. This new species has a small range in a region with intensive conversion of forest to agriculture, and will likely require conservation. The Mountain Coati, likewise, is known from a small area and may be endangered by the conversion of forest to agriculture.

Ringtail births occur after a short gestation period of only 51–54 days. Litters, usually born in May or June, range from one to four. Newborns have fuzzy hair on their back and their eyes are sealed. At three or four weeks their eyes open and deciduous teeth erupt. They soon begin eating solid food. They walk well at six weeks, climb at eight weeks, and are weaned at about ten weeks. Ringtails reach sexual maturity at about two years, but earlier mating has been reported. Captives live for 12–14 years, but the average lifespan in the wild is shorter.

Bassariscus astutus
Uinta National Forest, Utah, USA.
Photo: Kevin Schafer/NHPA

General Bibliography

Baskin (1982, 2003), Beisiegel & Mantovani (2006), Bisbal (1986), Booth-Binczik *et al.* (2004b), Carbone *et al.* (2005), Compton *et al.* (2001), Cuaron *et al.* (2004), Daily *et al.* (2003), Dalerum (2007), Decker (1991), Decker & Wozencraft (1991), Delisle & Strobeck (2005), Di Blanco & Hirsch (2006), Dos Santos & Hartz (1999), Ford & Hoffmann (1988), Fulton & Strobeck (2006, 2007), Garcia *et al.* (2002), Gatti *et al.* (2006), Gehrt (2003, 2004), Gehrt & Fritzell (1998a, 1998b, 1999a, 1999b), Goldman (1950), Gompper (1995, 1996, 1997), Gompper & Decker (1998), Gompper *et al.* (1997), Hass (2002b), Hass & Valenzuela (2002), Helgen & Wilson (2003, 2005), Helgen, Maldonado *et al.* (2008), Hirsch (2007a, 2007b), Hunt (1996), IUCN (2008), Iwaniuk & Whishaw (1999), Jetz *et al.* (2004), Julien-Laferrière (1999), Kaufmann (1962), Kays (1999a, 2000, 2003), Kays & Gittleman (1995, 2001), Kays *et al.* (2000), Koepfli *et al.* (2006), Kortlucke (1973), Li Yu & Ya-ping Zhang (2006), LoGiudice (2003), Lotze & Anderson (1979), Maffei *et al.* (2002), Marquez & Farina (2003), McClearn (1992), McFadden (2004), McFadden *et al.* (2006), Michalski & Peres (2005), Mugaas *et al.* (1993), Munoz-Garcia & Williams (2005), Naveda (1992), Newman *et al.* (2005), Nielsen & Nielsen (2007), Poglayen-Neuwall (1962, 1976a, 1976b, 1989), Poglayen-Neuwall & Poglayen-Neuwall (1980), Poglayen-Neuwall & Toweill (1988), Pons *et al.* (1999), Prange & Gehrt (2004), Prange *et al.* (2004), Recuenco *et al.* (2007), Redford & Stearman (1993), Redford *et al.* (1989), Riley *et al.* (1988), Rodriguez-Estrella *et al.* (2000), Smith *et al.* (2006), Valenzuela & Ceballos (2000), Valenzuela & Macdonald (2002), Wainwright (2007), Wesley-Hunt & Flynn (2005), Wilson *et al.* (1997), Wright, Carrasco *et al.* (1999), Wright, Zeballos *et al.* (2000), Wurster-Hill & Gray (1975), Yonezawa *et al.* (2007), Youlatos (2003), Yu *et al.* (2004), Zeveloff (2002), Zielinski *et al.* (2005).

1

2

3

4

5

ssp *nelsoni*

7

ssp *narica*

color variant

6

typical
morph

8

9

10

11

12

PLATE 30

inches 12

cm 30

Genus *BASSARICYON*

J. A. Allen, 1876

1. Lowland Olingo *Bassaricyon alleni*

French: Olingo d'Allen / **German**: Makibär / **Spanish**: Olingo de Allen

Taxonomy. *Bassaricyon alleni* Thomas, 1880, Sarayacu, on the Bobonasa river, Upper Pastasa river [Ecuador].
The Lowland Olingo was initially described as five different species but is now recognized as one broadly ranging olingo with three subspecies.
Subspecies and Distribution.
B. a. alleni Thomas, 1880 – South America, E of the Andes.
B. a. medius Thomas, 1909 – Chocó region of W Colombia, Ecuador, and NW Venezuela.
B. a. orinomus Goldman, 1912 – E Panama.
Descriptive notes. Head-body 30–49 cm, tail 35–53 cm; weight 0·9–1·6 kg. Olingos are tawny brown in color with long tails that sometimes appear ringed. They are often mistaken for Kinkajous when glimpsed at night through the canopy vegetation. Kinkajous are approximately twice the weight of olingos, although overall length is similar, making size an unreliable indicator for identifying animals running through the trees. The two species can be distinguished even under field conditions by key characters of the snout, lateral line, and tail. Olingos are different from Kinkajous in having a more pointed snout with gray fur, and a sharper lateral line separating their darker back and lighter-colored belly. Olingo tails are much bushier than the muscular tail of a Kinkajou, and sometimes show faint rings. Finally, the tail of an olingo is not prehensile, so is only used to balance, and can not grab branches as Kinkajous frequently do. Olingos also have a similar body form to Cacomistles, but are differentiated in being browner (not gray) with a slimmer tail that has only faint annulations.
Habitat. The Lowland Olingo is found in moist tropical forests up to 1800 m, but usually below 1500 m.
Food and Feeding. Olingos are primarily frugivorous and the extent to which they also hunt prey is uncertain. Reports from the field only describe olingos consuming fruits and flowers, but information from captivity, and dental morphology, suggest they may also consume insects or other small prey. They have been recorded feeding on the same fruit and flower resources as Kinkajous in Panama and Peru, and were sometimes displaced from feeding trees by aggressive Kinkajous.
Activity patterns. Olingos are completely arboreal and primarily nocturnal, spending daylight hours resting in tree holes or other arboreal den sites.
Movements, Home range and Social organization. Movement data are only available for one male olingo that used a home range of 37 ha and moved 4–5 km per night. Their social organization is not described, but they appear to be more solitary than Kinkajous. Social vocalizations and scent marking have been recorded in captivity. A long-distance call has been described from a variety of field workers variously as a "whey-chuck", "wer-toll", and "wake-up".
Breeding. Olingo reproductive behavior is well described from captive animals. They are polyestrous, with an estrous cycle of 24 days. Matings take place during one to three consecutive nights and copulations can last up to 68 minutes. The gestation period is about 74 days, after which one young is born. Pups can stand up after about three weeks and walk well after ten weeks, but require three to five months to develop climbing skills. Independent feeding starts at about seven weeks.
Status and Conservation. Olingos are classified by *The IUCN Red List* as Least Concern, but seem to occur at lower densities and be more sensitive to disturbance than other procyonids.
Bibliography. Garza *et al.* (2000), Janson & Emmons (1990), Kays (1999b, 2000), Mendes & Chivers (2002), Poglayen-Neuwall (1976a, 1973, 1989), Redford & Stearman (1993).

2. Northern Olingo *Bassaricyon gabbii*

French: Olingo commun / **German**: Mittelamerika-Makibär / **Spanish**: Olingo de Gabb

Taxonomy. *Bassaricyon gabbii* J. A. Allen, 1876, Talamanca, Costa Rica.
Four subspecies recognized.
Subspecies and distribution.
B. g. gabbii J. A. Allen, 1876 – Costa Rica (Talamanca Mts).
B. g. lasius Harris, 1932 – N Costa Rica.
B. g. pauli Enders, 1936 – Panama (Chiriqui Mts).
B. g. richardsoni J. A. Allen, 1908 – Nicaragua, possibly Guatemala and Honduras.
Descriptive notes. Head-body 35–49 cm, tail 40–53 cm; weight 1–1·6 kg. This is the largest olingo, differing from others in the genus by being more yellowish brown and often having a prominently ringed tail. It is also more sexually dimorphic than other olingos, with males having more robust heads.

Habitat. Found in forests within the central part of Mesoamerica. This olingo has a wide elevational range (near sea level to about 2000 m) but is most common in mountainous forests above 1000 m. This is probably the species recently recorded in the lowlands of Guatemala, and perhaps also seen in the mountains of Honduras.
Food and Feeding. Northern Olingos have been seen feeding on fruit and nectar in rainforest trees, but no details have been published on their diet. Anecdotal evidence suggests they may also catch small animal prey in the trees.
Activity patterns. Northern Olingos are arboreal and typically nocturnal. Olingos in Monteverde, Costa Rica, have been recorded active during the day; it is unclear if this is typical for the species or if this is in response to being fed by humans at the tourist lodge.
Movements, Home range and Social organization. Northern Olingos are typically seen as singletons, but other details of their behavior have not been studied.
Breeding. The breeding behavior of the Northern Olingo has not been described but is presumed to be similar to the Lowland olingo.
Status and Conservation. Classified as Least Concern by *The IUCN Red List*, but probably more sensitive to disturbance than other procyonids. In eastern Costa Rica it is considered highly vulnerable to habitat fragmentation and was recorded from the Las Cruces Forest reserve, and from some forest remnants, but not from open habitats. The recent change in the taxonomy of this group, and limited geographic range of this species, will probably require a revision of its conservation status.
Bibliography. Daily *et al.* (2003), Garza *et al.* (2000), Wainwright (2007).

3. Andean Olingo *Bassaricyon* n. sp.

French: Olingo des Andes / **German**: Anden-Makibär / **Spanish**: Olingo andino

Taxonomy. *Bassaricyon* n. sp. Helgen, in prep, Las Máquinas, Ecuador.
Monotypic.
Distribution. The species lives in Andean cloud forest above 1500 m in Colombia, Ecuador, and possibly N Peru.
Descriptive notes. Head-body 32–40 cm, tail 33–43 cm; weight 0·75–1·1 kg. The Andean Olingo is similar in overall form to the Lowland Olingo, although obviously different in being of smaller size with a much longer, denser, and more richly colored pelage. In Ecuador Olingos have black-tipped, tan colored fur. Colombian animals are red-brown. The tail is not conspicuously banded, although when viewed in the right light a banding pattern is sometimes seen.
Habitat. Cloud forest between 1500–2750 m.
Food and Feeding. All records to date describe Olingos eating fruit, especially wild figs.
Activity patterns. Nocturnal and arboreal.
Movements, Home range and Social organization. Nothing is known about their movements or social behaviors, although they are typically seen as singletons.
Breeding. The Olingo has a single pair of mammae and probably raises one young at a time.
Status and Conservation. This newly-described species has not been evaluated by *The IUCN Red List*. It apparently has a small geographic range in the Northern Andes, with a specialization on cloud forest habitats that are threatened by deforestation.
Bibliography. Helgen *et al.* (In prep).

Genus *BASSARISCUS*

Coues, 1887

4. Ringtail *Bassariscus astutus*

French: Bassaris rusé / **German**: Nordamerikanisches katzenfrett / **Spanish**: Cacomixtle

Taxonomy. *Bassaris astuta* Lichtenstein, 1830, Mexico City, Mexico.
Fourteen subspecies recognized.
Subspecies and Distribution.
B. a. astutus Lichtenstein, 1830 – SE Mexico.
B. a. arizonensis Goldman, 1932 – USA (in and near Arizona).
B. a. bolei Goldman, 1945 – Mexico (Guerrero).
B. a. consitus Nelson & Goldman, 1932 – C & W Mexico.

On following pages: 5. Cacomistle (*Bassariscus sumichrasti*); 6. South American Coati (*Nasua nasua*); 7. White-nosed Coati (*Nasua narica*); 8. Mountain Coati (*Nasuella olivacea*); 9. Kinkajou (*Potos flavus*); 10. Crab-eating Raccoon (*Procyon cancrivorus*); 11. Northern Raccoon (*Procyon lotor*); 12. Cozumel Raccoon (*Procyon pygmaeus*).

B. a. flavus Rhoads, 1893 – N Mexico and
S & C USA.

B. a. insulicola Nelson & Goldman, 1909 –
Mexico (San José I).

B. a. macdougalli Goodwin, 1956 – Mexico
(Tehuantepec, Oaxaca).

B. a. nevadensis G. S. Miller, 1913 – USA
(Nevada & Utah).

B. a. octavus Hall, 1926 – USA (S California).

B. a. palmarius Nelson & Goldman, 1909 –
Mexico (Baja California).

B. a. raptor Baird, 1859 – USA (N California & S Washington).

B. a. saxicola Merriam, 1897 – Mexico (Espíritu Santo I).

B. a. willetti Stager, 1950 – USA (SW California & E Arizona).

B. a. yumanensis Huey, 1937 – USA (Gila Mts, Arizona).

Descriptive notes. Head-body 30–37 cm, tail 31–44 cm; weight 0·87–1·1 kg. Ringtails are slimmer than cats but more robust than weasels, with incredibly long, bushy, black and white tails. This combination is unmistakable, and Ringtails are only likely to be confused with their congeners, Cacomistles. The two species are sympatric in part of their range, but can be distinguished by a number of characters. Ringtails are about one fourth smaller, with more contrasting facial and tail markings, and longer hindlimbs, which gives them a downward slanting profile from rump to nose. The body color of Ringtails is grayish above and white or buff below. Cacomistles are browner above and gray or tan below. The feet of the two species are also different, reflecting their different habitats, with Ringtails having short, straight, semi-retractile claws and digital foot pads surrounded by hair except behind the first digits. Finally, the Ringtail tail has black rings of uniform size, which are broken by white on the ventral surface, whereas the Cacomistle tail has unbroken black rings and the distal one third of the tail is nearly uniformly black. Within their range, the Ringtail coat color varies in predictable ways in being darker in forests, higher elevations, and higher latitudes and lighter in drier habitats, lower elevations and in the south of its range.

Habitat. Ringtails use a variety of habitats characterized by rocky outcroppings, canyons, or talus slopes. These include montane conifer forests, riparian areas, dry tropical habitats, chaparral, and deserts, including small urban nature preserves. They are typically found from sea level to 1400 m but are occasionally reported to 2900 m.

Food and Feeding. Ringtails eat small animals and fruit. Their steady, gliding motion allows them to catch a variety of prey the size of hares and smaller including rodents, lizards, snakes, and birds. Ringtails pin prey to the ground with their forefeet and begin their meal by consuming the head. Their diet varies seasonally and regionally as they take advantage of opportunities including raiding bat caves, predating bird nests, and feeding on nectar from agave. Individual meals consumed by wild Ringtails have been estimated at 55–90 g; captive animals can be maintained on 25 g of cat food and raisins per day.

Activity patterns. Ringtails are strongly nocturnal, with an aversion to daylight that begins soon after birth and persists through adulthood. Animals begin activity at or just after dusk and are back in their den sleeping before dawn, or within 45 minutes after daybreak.

Movements, Home range and Social organization. In high quality habitat Ringtails can live in densities of up to 20 ind/km² and use home ranges as small as 5 ha. However, densities are typically an order of magnitude lower, for example, 2·2–4·2 ind/km² in woodland habitat, where home ranges averaged 43 ha for males and 20 ha for females. Ringtails do not appear to be creatures of habit. They change dens frequently, rarely using the same rock crevice, hollow tree, or underground burrow for more than three consecutive days. In some areas their home ranges may also be dynamic, changing with the seasons, to the extent that some individuals use completely different areas from month to month. Ringtails appear to have a typical carnivore social structure with little sociality and males attempting to overlap and mate with one or more females. Telemetry studies suggest a social structure based on land tenure, with no signs of monogamy. Wild animals typically den separately, but can be kept together in captivity. Given their asocial tendencies most Ringtail communication is based on scent marks left in conspicuous places to denote territorial boundaries or communicate with potential mates. These marks include urine rubbed on the ground and on raised objects, and latrine areas with accumulated feces. These marks increase conspicuously just before and during the mating season. When they do encounter another animal, Ringtails may use a variety of generic vocalizations including squeaks, chucking and barks, hisses, grunts, growls, and metallic chirps.

Breeding. Ringtails are monestrous, and females show a vulva tumescence one to two weeks before copulation. Breeding can occur anytime between February and May, but is typically in March or April. The female will become receptive to a male for 24–36 hours. In this time the male chases the female and copulates several times per hour, in a sitting position. Ringtails have the shortest gestation of any procyonid, at 51–54 days, leading to birth of a litter of 1–4 young in May or June. Newborns are altricial, with fuzzy hair on their back and sealed eyelids that open after 3–4 weeks. Deciduous teeth appear at 3–4 weeks, with permanent dentition growing in by 17–20 weeks. They begin to eat solid food at 30–40 days and are weaned at about ten weeks. Cubs can walk well at six weeks and climb by eight weeks. Ringtails typically reach sexual maturity at two years, although mating has been reported after just one year. Captive animals live for 12–14 years, with one animal reaching 16·5 years.

Status and Conservation. Classified as Least Concern by *The IUCN Red List*. Ringtails are relatively common and widespread. In some regions they have adapted to find

food and shelter in rural and urban habitats. They are harvested for their fur, although the fur is rated as poor quality and used only as trim.

Bibliography. Barja & List (2006), Poglayen-Neuwall & Poglayen-Neuwall (1980), Poglayen-Neuwall & Toweill (1988), Rodriguez-Estrella *et al.* (2000), Stake & Cimprich (2003), Suzan & Ceballos (2005), Toweill & Teer (1972, 1977), Winkler & Adams (1972).

5. Cacomistle *Bassariscus sumichrasti*

French: Bassaris de Sumichrast / **German:** Mittelamerikanisches Katzenfrett /
Spanish: Cacomixtle meridional

Taxonomy. *Bassaris sumichrasti* Saussure, 1860, Veracruz, Mexico.
Five subspecies recognized.
Subspecies and Distribution.
B. s. sumichrasti Saussure, 1860 – Mexico (Veracruz, Oaxaca, Quintana Roo & Campeche).
B. s. latrans Davis & Lukens, 1958 – Mexico (Guerrero).
B. s. notinus Thomas, 1903 – Costa Rica and Panama.
B. s. oaxacensis Goodwin, 1956 – Mexico (Oaxaca).
B. s. variabilis Peters, 1874 – S Mexico (Chiapas), Guatemala and Belize to Costa Rica.

Descriptive notes. Head-body 38–50 cm, tail 39–55 cm; weight 0·7–1·2 kg. Cacomistles are very similar to Ringtails in having slender gray bodies with bushy ringed tails. The two are distinguished by the Cacomistle being a bit larger, with less contrasting facial and tail markings, a browner back and tanner belly, and a shorter black muzzle. The rings on the tail of the Cacomistle also differ in being unbroken, and the distal one third of the tail is nearly uniformly black.

Habitat. Tropical lowland wet forest to 2700 m.

Food and Feeding. Cacomistles are generalist feeders, eating roughly equal amounts of fruit and insects. They will opportunistically kill and eat very small vertebrate prey, and captive animals have caught and eaten free-flying birds within their enclosures.

Activity patterns. Cacomistles are active in the mid and upper layers of the forest canopy at night. Their activity begins immediately after sunset and continues at a relatively constant pace (60–75% active) until an hour or two before sunrise. Males are slightly more active than females. Cacomistles may not be strictly nocturnal, as some animals have been recorded vocalizing in the daytime.

Movements, Home range and Social organization. Cacomistles in Costa Rica used an average home range size of 20 ha in a landscape of mixed forest and overgrown pasture. In another Costa Rican study, animals consistently moved approximately 2·5 km per night. Although individuals are typically solitary, there is extensive overlap between males and females, and between different males. Whether this overlap relates to family social groups is unknown. Multiple males can be kept together harmoniously in captivity. Cacomistles frequently vocalize with calls of 2–3 repeated syllables sounding like "uyoo-whaa" or "boyo-baa-wow". These probably play both a territorial and spacing role, as wild animals will approach a playback of the call, but retreat if it is too loud. A variety of other social vocalizations have been described for captive animals. Scent is also an important mode of communication for Cacomistles, and marks are made in four different ways: urine, cheek glands, anal glands, and a strong overall body odor. This strong body odor is present only in males, and is a pungent, sweaty smell detectable by humans from 3–6 m away. Scent marking probably functions to communicate a variety of social messages. The fluid from the anal gland is stronger-smelling than in the Ringtail, and has been hypothesized as serving a defensive function.

Breeding. Estrus in Cacomistles lasts about 44 days and is followed by a gestation period of about 63–65 days leading to a litter size of one. Young are able to walk with a wobbly gait after about one month, hop after about two months, and begin climbing in about their third month. Captive animals begin eating solid food between 48–60 days.

Status and Conservation. Classified as Least Concern by *The IUCN Red List*. Cacomistles are locally common, especially in the northern parts of their range.

Bibliography. Coates-Estrada & Estrada (1986), Garcia *et al.* (2002), Poglayen-Neuwall (1991, 1992a, 1992b), Poglayen-Neuwall & Poglayen-Neuwall (1994), Reid (1997), Vaughan *et al.* (1994).

Genus *NASUA*
Storr, 1780

6. South American Coati *Nasua nasua*

French: Coati brun / **German:** Nasenbär / **Spanish:** Coatí rojo

Taxonomy. *Viverra nasua* Linnaeus, 1766, America, later restricted to Pernambuco Brazil.
Twelve subspecies recognized.
Subspecies and Distribution.
N. n. nasua Linnaeus, 1766 – French Guiana S through NE Brazil to N Bahia.
N. n dorsalis Gray, 1866 – Amazonian Brazil, Peru, and Ecuador.

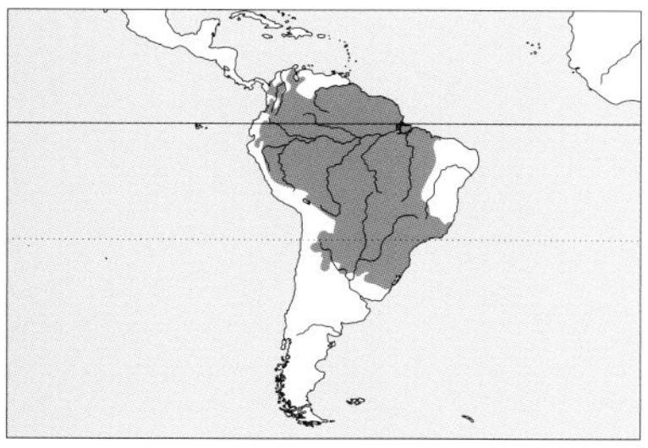

N. n. aricana Vieira, 1945 – Brazil (Mato Grosso), Bolivia (Santa Cruz), Paraguay, and N Argentina.
N. n. boliviensis Cabrera, 1956 – Bolivia (Cochabamba, the Yungas).
N. n. candace Thomas, 1912 – Colombia.
N. n. cinerascens Lönnberg, 1921 – N Argentina (Chaco).
N. n. manium Thomas, 1912 – Ecuador W of the Andes.
N. n. montana Tschudi, 1844 – Peru.
N. n. quichua Thomas, 1901 – S Ecuadorian Andes (Azuay).
N. n. solitaria Schinz, 1821 – SE Brazil (Minas Gerais, S. Bahia), NE Argentina (Misiones).
N. n. spadicea Olfers, 1818 – S Brazil and Uruguay.
N. n. vittata Tschudi, 1844 – Venezuela, the Guianas.

Descriptive notes. Head-body 43–58 cm, tail 42–55 cm; weight 2–7·2 kg. Males larger than females. Coatis are unique in the animal world, with their long pointed snouts and ringed tails, which are typically held vertically. The South American Coati is distinguished from the White-nosed Coati by having a brown or gray (not white) muzzle and in having hair on the neck in a reversed, anterior position. The South American Coati is also much larger than the Mountain Coati. The pelage coloration of South American Coatis is variable across their range, and even within a litter. They are always brownish, but range from orangish or reddish to very dark brown, often with yellow highlights. The rings in the tail may be strongly or weakly evident.

Habitat. Found in a variety of forested habitats including rainforest, riverine gallery forest, cloud forest, and xeric Chaco, cerrado, and dry scrub forests up to 2500 m elevation.

Food and Feeding. Omnivorous feeders, South American Coatis eat a wide variety of invertebrates and fruit including larval beetles, scorpions, spiders, centipedes, and coleopterans. Rodents, fish, crabs, and carrion have also been reported. The most detailed study of South American Coati diet comes from south-eastern Brazil, where 226 fecal samples included plant parts (85·4%), insects (75·7%), millipedes (53·9%), 49 species of fruits (48·7%), spiders (33·6%), organic waste (9·7%), vertebrates (9·3%), and gastropods (2·6%). There was considerable variation over the year, with spider and millipede consumption increasing with rainfall, and fruits being an important food during periods of arthropod scarcity. Coatis are skilled at rolling noxious invertebrates in the leaf litter with their forepaws to remove spines, but will also reject some invertebrate species that emit noxious fluids or smells. A variety of bird species, including hawks, trogons, woodcreepers, and tanagers, have been observed following coati bands. These birds capture prey trying to escape the foraging coatis.

Activity patterns. This diurnal species spends nights in the trees. Most reports suggest that South American Coatis spend most of their days active on the ground. However, a population in the Atlantic forest of Brazil was encountered in the trees 60% of the time, where they were observed hunting small prey from bromeliads.

Movements, Home range and Social organization. The density of coatis across South America varies greatly. In some places it is one of the rarest mammals while in others it is among the most frequently observed. Published estimates range from 6·2–13 animals/km². Little is known about the movement patterns of South American Coatis, although one coati group in the Brazilian Atlantic forest had a home range of about 500ha. Females and their young travel in matrilineal bands of up to 65 individuals, although smaller (10–30) band sizes are typical. South American Coati groups typically have one male, and he is the dominant animal in the group. Dominance is hierarchical according to age and sex, with male juveniles ranking second, followed by female juveniles, then adult females, and finally male and female subadults. The ability of juveniles to outrank larger adults comes from their aggressive defense of food resources and may not reflect "dominance" in the traditional sense as much as being "tolerated aggression". Groups probably reduce the risk of predation to individual coatis through increased vigilance. For example, coatis frequently stop moving and silently look around with their heads raised to scan for predators. Animals at the edge of the group are more vigilant than those at the center, and animals at the front edge of the group were the most watchful. The primary predators of South American Coatis appear to be the larger felids, as coatis have been reported in the diet of the three largest predators in the region, Jaguars, Pumas, and Ocelots.

Breeding. After a 74–77 day gestation period, females leave their social groups to give birth to young in a tree nest, and return to the group after five or six weeks. Litter size ranges from 1–7 and is typically 3–4. Allonursing has been observed in captivity. Pups can walk well by 24 days and begin climbing by about four weeks. Breeding is seasonal, but the timing varies across their range.

Status and Conservation. Classified as species of Least Concern by *The IUCN Red List*. Coatis are hunted and are sometimes an important food source. If not hunted, they can flourish in disturbed habitat.

Bibliography. Alves-Costa & Eterovick (2007), Alves-Costa *et al.* (2004), Beisiegel (2001, 2007), Beisiegel & Mantovani (2006), Bisbal (1986), Di Blanco & Hirsch (2006), Gompper & Decker (1998), Hirsch (2007a), Marquez & Farina (2003), Michalski & Peres (2005), Redford & Stearman (1993), Roldan & Simonetti (2001), Romero & Aureli (2007), Trolle (2003), Yanosky & Mercolli (1992).

7. White-nosed Coati *Nasua narica*

French: Coati à nez blanc / **German**: Weißrüssel-Nasenbär / **Spanish**: Coatí pizote

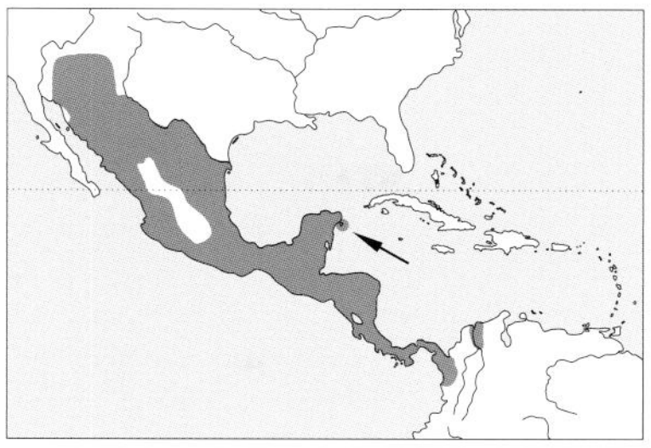

Taxonomy. *Viverra narica* Linnaeus, 1766. "America" subsequently restricted to Achotal, Isthmus of Tehuantepec, Veracruz, Mexico.

Its precise southernmost distribution and potential overlap with *N. nasua* are not well known. The Dwarf Coati, *nelsoni*, is sometimes considered a full species. Four subspecies recognized.

Subspecies and Distribution.
N. n. narica Linnaeus, 1766 – S Mexico, Central America, and N & W Colombia.
N. n. molaris Merriam, 1902 – Mexico and SW USA.
N. n. nelsoni Merriam, 1901 – Mexico (Cozumel I).
N. n. yucatanica J. A. Allen, 1904 – Mexico (Yucatán Peninsula).

Descriptive notes. Head-body 43–68 cm, tail 42–68 cm; weight 3·5–5·6 kg. Males are about 20% larger than females. *N. n. nelsoni*, commonly referred to as the Dwarf Coati, is smaller: head-body 41·6–43·7 cm, tail 32·8–34·8 cm. Coatis are unique in the animal world, with their long pointed snouts and upright, ringed tails. The White-nosed Coati is distinguished from the South American Coati by its white muzzle and in having hair on the neck in a normal posterior position. Pelage coloration is quite variable, ranging from pale to reddish to almost black, often overlaid with some yellow or silver. The rings in the tail may be strongly or weakly evident.

Habitat. White-nosed Coatis occupy a variety of wooded habitats, especially tropical rainforests, ranging up to 2879 m. In the north they concentrate in riparian pinyon-oak-juniper habitats, but occasionally range into deserts and savannas.

Food and Feeding. White-nosed Coatis are omnivorous, eating primarily invertebrates and fruit but also consuming vertebrates and carrion when available. In Panama, 44% of coati foraging was on leaf-litter invertebrates, 56% on fruit, and less than 1% on vertebrates. As they walk along searching for food they use their long snouts to constantly sniff in the leaf litter. Prey is dug up or extracted from debris. Animals with harmful bites or stings are often killed by rolling them between the paws, which also removes hairs or spiny projections. Coatis eat fallen fruit under trees, but also climb to pick fresh fruit. Although they are adept climbers, most (over 90%) of their foraging is done on the ground. At least one species of bird, an understory hawk, is thought to associate with bands of White-nosed Coatis to hunt prey fleeing foraging coatis. White-nosed Coatis have been observed grooming themselves with the resin of *Trattinnickia aspera*, presumably for some pharmaceutical value.

Activity patterns. White-nosed Coatis are primarily diurnal, spending the night hiding in trees or rocky ledges. They spend about 90% of their waking hours foraging, although they may take rests of up to two hours in the high-fruit season.

Movements, Home range and Social organization. The amount of space used by coatis is flexible across their range, with population averages varying from 0·33 to 13·5 km² in different habitats. The high end of this variation is in Arizona, where home range size averaged 13·5 km² for bands, 6·1 km² for solitary males, and did not fluctuate greatly between seasons or years. In Mexican dry forest home range size averaged 3·8 km² and was not different between males and bands in total area. Bands used roughly half as much area in the wet season, although males did not change ranging behavior seasonally. Additionally, range size varied greatly (from 45 and 362 ha) within the dry forest in ways that were not related to food abundance, but to the dispersion of water sources during the dry season. In Panamanian rainforest, home range size averaged about 0·33 km² for both males and females. Coatis are among the most gregarious of the Carnivora. White-nosed Coati groups have been reported as large as 30, although 5–18 animals are more typical. These matrilineal groups, known as bands, are composed primarily of related females and their offspring. Some non-relatives may also be in the band, although they receive more aggression, and less coalition support, from other band members. The size of groups fluctuates over time due to mortality, newly born juveniles, and emigrating subadult males. Large groups often split into subgroups that separate for several hours or days, and sometimes fission permanently into two groups. Fusion of previously separate groups has also been noted, although groups are typically slightly antagonistic to neighboring groups. Most males are solitary, and are usually chased away if they approach female groups. However, some males are tolerated, and groups may have a few adult males associating with them. These are typically older offspring remaining in their natal home range and they do not sire offspring with the group. They may associate with groups to take advantage of grooming or for the safety in numbers. Group members show a variety of cooperative behaviors including shared parental care, grooming, shared vigilance, and cooperative attacks on potential predators. Food is not shared between adults, although juveniles are tolerated by feeding animals. Group members do not cooperate to hunt invertebrates and females are actually more efficient when hunting away from the group. However, grouping may help the smaller females gain access to fruiting trees, as groups cooperate to chase away larger males that would otherwise be dominant in one-on-one interactions. Reducing predation risk seems to be a universal benefit of grouping in coatis. For example, in dry forests larger coati groups can drink more at water holes, a focal point for predators. Predation rates can be high, causing more than 50% of deaths in some populations in Mexico and Arizona. Predation rates are highest on solitary coatis and next-highest on small groups, with larger groups having the lowest predation rate. These lower rates result from a suite of anti-predator behaviors, including foraging with the juveniles in the center of the group, sharing vigilance, and alarm calling, and mobbing and attacking predators. Given their diurnal and social tendencies, it is not surprising that White-nosed Coatis have a rich repertoire of specific vocalizations for aggression, appeasement, alarm, and sexual contact. The two most common calls are chirps and squawks. Squawks are longer-duration, low-maximum frequency, wide-bandwidth calls with six resonances and little frequency modulation. Chirps are tonal calls of shorter duration, with frequency modulations. Chirps are high frequency, extending above the human hearing range into ultrasonic frequencies (30–55 kHz). They seem to function as contact calls, being emitted only while bands of coatis are moving. The short duration and high frequency of the calls may allow for contact with nearby group members while minimizing auditory detection by predators. Unique features of each coati's chirp also may allow individual recognition. Like most Carnivora, coatis are also known to scent-mark. Males mark with a perineal gland throughout the year, while females primarily mark only before the mating season.

Breeding. Breeding is highly seasonal in White-nosed Coatis, typically within a 2–4 week period. This occurs in late January in Panama. Mating has been observed in the trees and on the ground. The mating system for coatis in Tikal National Park, Guatemala has been described as a mobile lek, with aggregations of males following female bands and climbing into the trees above them to display. Male vocalizations were similar to the alarm calls given by coatis in bands, but they were repeated steadily for many minutes at a time, not given in several-second bursts as in alarm situations. Females then selected one of these males to mate, by climbing up into the tree where he was displaying. This unique behavior has not been described for other coati populations, so it is unclear how widespread it is. Females can first breed at 22 months, but often wait another year or two depending on ecological conditions. Males can first mate at 34 months, but because of competition for matings, may not be successful until they are four or five years old; some males are probably never able to breed. Females leave their bands to give birth in a tree after a 70–77 day gestation period. Young coatis begin to walk at eleven days and are able to rejoin the band with their mothers by 40 days. Litter size is 1–6, although some die before rejoining the band. Most females rejoin the band with an average of 3·5 juveniles. Females nurse for up to four months, and will nurse and care for offspring from other band members. Young males leave the band and become solitary after about two years. Animals in captivity have lived to 17 years, and to at least nine in the wild.

Status and Conservation. Most White-nosed Coatis are classified as a species of Least Concern by *The IUCN Red List* as they are widespread and often common in a variety of habitats. Their groups are vulnerable to hunting, but can thrive in fragmented habitats if not persecuted. One subspecies, *nelsoni*, is restricted to Cozumel Island, Mexico, where the total population is estimated at only 150 animals, and is listed as Endangered.

Bibliography. Booth-Binczik *et al.* (2004a, 2004b), Burger & Gochfeld (1992), Chapman (1935), Compton *et al.* (2001), Cuaron *et al.* (2004), Gompper (1995, 1996, 1997), Gompper & Hoylman (1993), Gompper & Krinsley (1992), Gompper *et al.* (1997, 1998), Hass (2002b), Hass & Valenzuela (2002), Kaufmann (1962), Maurello *et al.* (2000), Ratnayeke *et al.* (1994), Valenzuela & Ceballos (2000), Valenzuela & Macdonald (2002), Wright *et al.* (2000).

Genus *NASUELLA*
Hollister, 1915

8. Mountain Coati *Nasuella olivacea*
French: Coati des montagnes / German: Berg-Nasenbär / Spanish: Coatí oliva

Taxonomy. *Nasua olivacea* Gray, 1865; Santa Fé de Bogota, Colombia.
Three subspecies recognized.
Subspecies and Distribution.
N. o. olivacea Gray, 1865 – Colombia.
N. o. meridensis Thomas, 1901 – Venezuela.
N. o. quitensis Lönnberg, 1913 – Ecuador.
Descriptive notes. Head-body 36–39 cm, tail 20–24 cm; weight 1–1·5 kg. Roughly half the size of *Nasua*, the Mountain Coati has a gray-brown back and 6–8 bands on

the tail. Its snout is more elongated and comes to a sharper point than in other coati species, and the tip of its nose is naked.
Habitat. Montane forests above 2000 m.
Food and Feeding. Primarily insectivorous, all 54 scat samples analyzed in Colombia contained insects, especially Coleoptera (41%), Orthoptera, Myriapoda, and Hymenoptera. Vertebrates and fruits were also eaten, each representing about 7% of the diet. Although all coati species find food on the forest floor, Mountain Coatis appear to be unique in leaving behind many small holes as they forage, with as many as 5000 being observed in one heavily foraged 35 m² area. This may be related to their more elongated, sharper snouts.
Activity patterns. From anecdotal reports, Mountain Coatis appear to be primarily diurnal and terrestrial, but this has not been studied in detail.
Movements, Home range and Social organization. Because Mountain Coatis are sometimes seen in groups, and sometimes alone, they are presumed to have a social organization similar to other coatis, but there have been no studies on their behavior or movement patterns.
Breeding. A litter size of four is reported but their breeding biology has not been studied.

Status and Conservation. With only one published study from the field we know very little about Mountain Coatis and *The IUCN Red List* has classified them as Data Deficient. One report from Venezuela suggests that they may be vulnerable to habitat fragmentation.
Bibliography. Bisbal (1993), Linares (1998), Rodríguez-Bolaños *et al.* (2000).

Genus *POTOS*
Geoffroy Saint-Hilaire & Cuvier, 1795

9. Kinkajou *Potos flavus*
French: Kinkajou / German: Wickelbär / Spanish: Kinkajú

Taxonomy. *Lemur flavus* Schreber, 1774, Surinam.
Seven subspecies recognized.
Subspecies and Distribution.
P. f. flavus Schreber, 1774 – the Guianas.
P. f. chapadensis J. A. Allen, 1904 – Amazonia.
P. f. chiriquensis J. A. Allen, 1904 – Central America and S Mexico.
P. f. megalotus Martin, 1837 – Colombia and Panama.

P. f. meridensis Thomas, 1902 – Venezuela.
P. f. modestus Thomas, 1902 – W Ecuador.
P. f. nocturnus Wied-Neuwied, 1826 – E Brazil.
Descriptive notes. Head-body 42–76 cm, tail 39–57 cm; weight 1·4–4·5 kg. Adult males are slightly larger than adult females. At first look, the Kinkajou appears more like a monkey than a carnivore, and indeed, it was first described as a lemur. Kinkajous are honey-colored animals with large forward facing eyes, small forward facing ears, and muscular prehensile tails. They have uniform dark colored flanks that blend to lighter-colored buffy underparts. Although 2–3 times larger than olingos, the two species can be confused as they run through treetops at night. The olingo shows a much sharper transition from dark dorsal fur to light ventral fur, and its non-prehensile tail is fluffy, not muscular like that of the Kinkajou. The Kinkajou's fur is woolly, and, across its range, can be a variety of shades, including tawny olive, yellowish-tawny, clay colored, or wood brown. Many animals have a dark mid-dorsal stripe, and some animals in central Panama have a white-tipped tail. In seasonal forests the weight of individual Kinkajous fluctuates over the course of a year in synchrony with fruit availability.
Habitat. Kinkajous are found in most tropical forest types that can produce fruit year-round. This includes rainforest, cloud forest, dry forest, and gallery forest. They have been found from sea level up to 2500 m. Kinkajous are strongly arboreal and rarely seen on the ground. They use all parts of the forest canopy.
Food and Feeding. Kinkajous are primarily frugivorous and nectivorous, although some consumption of insects has been recorded. Kinkajous select for larger, more productive fruiting trees. Fruit made up 90–99% of the diet of a population of Kinkajous in Panama, with the rest being nectar and leaves. Of the 78 species eaten from 29 families of plants, Moraceae was the most important, especially *Ficus*. Fruit and flowers were also the only food types observed from studies in French Guiana and Venezuela, making the Kinkajou one of the most frugivorous mammals. However, one report from Bolivia noted substantial amounts of ants from nine different species in the stomachs of six Kinkajous. All Kinkajou feeding is arboreal. An animal will sometimes hang by its prehensile tail and use both of its forepaws to handle fruit.
Activity patterns. Kinkajous are among the most nocturnal animals. They typically emerge from their dens about 15 minutes after sunset and retire 15–30 minutes before sunrise. All activity is arboreal, and travelling between trees occupies 50–65% of their time, with the rest of their activity split between eating and resting.
Movements, Home range and Social organization. Kinkajous have a flexible social structure, with individuals typically moving between trees alone, but socializing in groups at large feeding trees and day dens. Home range size varies from 10–50 ha, with males using slightly larger areas than females. Nightly travel distance averages about 2 km. Density of Kinkajous probably relates to the fruit production of local forests, and estimates from different forests range from 12–74 animals/km². Most Kinkajous live in small, patrilineal groups consisting of two adult males, one adult female, a subadult, and a juvenile offspring. Additionally some females apparently live outside of stable groups and consort with males from neighboring social groups. Dispersal is female-biased; young males appear to stay with their natal group, or disperse to a neighboring territory. Group members overlap regularly in home ranges, but separate each night for most foraging, thus reducing competition over food. During the course of the night group members meet up and socialize at large fruiting trees, where feeding competition is not important, with larger feeding groups, on average, in larger fruiting trees. Group members also socialize around day dens, where some group members sleep together at least 55% of the time. Kinkajous prefer to den in tree holes but have also been recorded making nests in palm trees. In Panama one Kinkajou group was observed using 44 different dens over the course of a year, preferentially sleeping in a few near the center of their range. Social behavior typically includes grooming bouts focused on the ears and head, where an animal can not groom itself. Grooming interactions are most frequent between adult and subadult males, and females and ju-

veniles. In addition, males have been observed playing with juveniles from their group, including chases through the canopy and play-boxing while hanging by their tails. Aggressive behavior is less common within social groups, but short fights between males have been observed. Neighboring social groups appear to strictly observe territorial boundaries. Aggression between neighboring females has been recorded, involving tree-top chases, with the subordinate animal eventually jumping to the forest floor to flee. Kinkajous communicate through vocalizations and specialized scent glands. Short-range social interaction calls include brief hisses and screams. The long-range call is a two part "snort-weedle" consisting of one quick snort sound followed by a variable number of weedle vocalizations. This call is sometimes repeated for as long as 15 minutes. The snort-weedle sometimes appears to call-in other social group members, but may have other functions as well. Kinkajous also communicate through scent marks, which are made by three unique glands, one on their abdomen, one on their throat, and a pair of mandibular glands. These glands produce a subtle smell that is slightly fruity and musky. Given the three different types of scent glands, different marks probably have different purposes, which have been hypothesized to include territorial markers, trail markers, and sexual signals. Adult Kinkajous do not face high predation risk because they are generally too nocturnal for eagles, too large for owls, and too arboreal for large cats. Nonetheless, individuals occasionally venture too close to the ground, or are active in daylight, making themselves vulnerable to predation, and have been recorded in the diet of Jaguars, Ocelots and eagles.

Breeding. Kinkajous do not have an obvious breeding season, although this may be masked by the variation in the timing of fruiting seasons across their large range. Kinkajous are polyestrous, with gestation times of 100–120 days, and typically give birth to one pup, although litters of two have been recorded. Pups are dependent on their mothers for an extensive period of time. They do not take solid food until eight weeks and are not fully mobile in the tree branches until they are three months old. Males have not been observed contributing to the care of offspring, and mothers apparently "park" the young pups alone in the trees while they forage. Male Kinkajous reach maturity at 1·5 years and females at 2·25 years. In captivity one Kinkajou lived for 40·5 years, although 20 years is more common.

Status and Conservation. Kinkajous are classified by *The IUCN Red List* as Least Concern. They are common over much of their range and are considered moderately sensitive to habitat fragmentation. They are occasionally hunted for meat but are not a preferred food item, and there is no market for their fur. Some animals are sold into the pet trade.

Bibliography. Bisbal (1986), Daily et al. (2003), Ford & Hoffmann (1988), Hernández & Porras (2005), Julien-Laferrière (1993, 2001), Kays (1999a, 1999b, 2000, 2003), Kays & Gittleman (1995, 2001), Kortlucke (1973), Naveda (1992), Poglayen-Neuwall (1962, 1966, 1976b), Redford & Stearman (1993), Redford et al. (1989), Walker & Cant (1977), Weckel et al. (2006).

Genus *PROCYON*
Storr, 1780

10. Crab-eating Raccoon *Procyon cancrivorus*
French: Raton crabier / **German:** Krabbenwaschbär / **Spanish:** Mayuato

Taxonomy. *Ursus cancrivorus* Cuvier, 1798 Cayenne, French Guiana.
Four subspecies recognized.
Subspecies and Distribution.
P. c. cancrivorus Cuvier, 1798 – Venezuela, Trinidad and Tobago, the Guianas.
P. c. aequatorialis J. A. Allen, 1915 – Ecuador.
P. c. nigripes Mivart, 1886 – Amazonia to Argentina.
P. c. panamensis Goldman, 1913 – Costa Rica, Panama, Colombia.

Descriptive notes. Head-body 54–76 cm, tail 25–38 cm; weight 3·1–7·7 kg. Crab-eating Raccoons are grayish, with the characteristic Raccoon black mask and black banded tail. Their legs and feet are dark brown, distinguishing Crab-eating Racoons from Northern Raccoons, which have white feet. Crab-eating Raccoons also are different in having the hair on the back of the neck slanting forward, appearing reversed, and a brownish throat.

Habitat. Crab-eating Raccoons use a broad range of waterside habitats, including swamps, rivers, and beaches. They appear to be more strongly tied to water and less adapted to urban areas than the Northern Raccoon.

Food and Feeding. In Venezuela Crab-eating Raccoons are recorded eating primarily aquatic prey, including crawfish, fish, and snails. In Brazil fruit was much more important (53% of diet), followed by a mixture of insects and vertebrate prey.

Activity patterns. Nocturnal, these raccoons sleep in tree holes during the day. Their nocturnal foraging is primarily on the ground around waterways. Of 55 raccoon camera trap photos recorded in Bolivia, 85% were nocturnal, 13% crepuscular, and only 2% diurnal.

Movements, Home range and Social organization. Usually solitary but sometimes seen in pairs or groups. No details are known about their social organization.

Breeding. Presumed to be similar to Northern Raccoons.

Status and Conservation. Considered Least Concern by *The IUCN Red List*, Crab-eating

Raccoons are not adapted to urban life like their northern cousins, but are not highly sensitive to habitat fragmentation. They are the third most frequent species to be found as roadkill in southern Brazil.

Bibliography. Bisbal (1986), Carrillo-Jimenez & Vaughan (1993), Cherem et al. (2007), Dos Santos & Hartz (1999), Gatti et al. (2006), Gomez et al. (2005), Lohmer (1976), Maffei et al. (2002), Marquez & Farina (2003), Michalski & Peres (2005), Mugaas et al. (1993), Srbek-Araujo & Chiarello (2005), Yanosky & Mercolli (1993).

11. Northern Raccoon *Procyon lotor*
French: Raton laveur / **German:** Waschbär / **Spanish:** Mapache común

Taxonomy. *Ursus lotor* Linnaeus, 1758, Pennsylvania, USA.
Historically, more than 50 types of Northern Raccoons have been named. However, more recent work has shown this species to have a high degree of morphological plasticity in the face of environmental variation. Caribbean forms were recently shown to be recent introductions from the east USA and are no longer considered unique species. The taxonomy of mainland forms has not yet been revised with modern methods, so the twenty recognized subspecies remain poorly defined.

Subspecies and Distribution.
P. l. lotor Linnaeus, 1758 – NE USA.
P. l. auspicatus Nelson, 1930 – SE USA (Central Florida Keys).
P. l. elucus Bangs, 1898 – SE USA (Florida).
P. l. excelsus Nelson & Goldman, 1930 – NW USA (in and near Idaho).
P. l. fuscipes Mearns, 1914 – S USA (Texas) and NE Mexico (Tamaulipas, Coahuila).
P. l. grinnelli Nelson & Goldman, 1930 – Mexico (S Baja California).
P. l. hernandezii Wagler, 1831 – Mexico.
P. l. hirtus Nelson & Goldman, 1930 – Central Plains of USA and Canada.
P. l. incautus Nelson, 1930 – SE USA (W Florida Keys).
P. l. inesperatus Nelson, 1930 – SE USA (E Florida Keys).
P. l. insularis Merriam, 1898 – W Mexico (Maria Madre I).
P. l. litoreus Nelson & Goldman, 1930 – E USA (coastal Georgia).
P. l. marinus Nelson, 1930 – SE USA (Florida Everglades).
P. l. megalodous Lowery, 1943 – S USA (coastal Louisiana).
P. l. pacificus Merriam, 1899 – NW USA.
P. l. pallidus Merriam, 1900 – SW USA.
P. l. psora Gray, 1842 – SW USA (California).
P. l. pumilus G.S. Miller, 1911 – Central America.
P. l. simus Gidley, 1906 – W USA (N California).
P. l. vancouverensis Nelson & Goldman, 1930 – SW Canada (Vancouver I).

Descriptive notes. Head-body 44–62 cm, tail 19–36 cm; weight 2·7–10·4 kg. Northern Raccoons have relatively short ringed tails and striking black masks. Their body fur is grizzled gray, and often long. There may be some reddish color on the nape of the neck. Animals in arid areas are lighter in color, whereas those in humid forests are darker. The largest raccoons are in the north-west USA and the smallest in the south-east.

Habitat. Raccoons use a variety of habitat types, preferring waterways such as streams, rivers, lake shores, and wetlands. The have adapted well to urban habitats.

Food and Feeding. Northern Raccoons are among the most omnivorous mammals on Earth. They will take advantage of any locally abundant food source they can get their hands on, including fruits, nuts, grains, invertebrates, fish, and small terrestrial vertebrates. A variety of plant products make up a majority of their diet in all seasons. In urban areas raccoons are famous for ingenious ways of procuring garbage, and in rural areas, for raiding crops. In natural settings raccoons are typically tied to aquatic habitats, and aquatic invertebrates such as crabs and crayfish often make up a substantial portion of their diet. They occasionally catch frogs, lizards, snakes, and other terrestrial vertebrates, although these are rare in their diet compared with invertebrate prey. Raccoons are reported to be able to detect a single acorn buried under 5 cm of sand, and much of their animal food comes not after dramatic chases but from using their keen sense of smell to locate nests and predate eggs or nestlings. This can be a problem for the egg-layers in areas where raccoon density is elevated because of human subsidization. Nest predation has been implicated in reducing the population size of turtles, green iguanas, and some low-nesting bird species. The Raccoon's keen nose also makes it a good scavenger, able to detect fresh carcasses. Competition with other omnivores is not obvious. Opossums did not change population parameters, diet, or habitat use in an area where raccoons had been removed. Food passes through the raccoon digestive system in 9–14 hours, long enough to make it probable that they function as important seed dispersers for the fruit plants they feed on. Northern Raccoons received their species name, *lotor*, meaning "the washer", because they are thought to wash their food before eating it. They are fond of dunking their food, although there is no indication this has any washing function, since they submerge both clean and dirty foods. One alternative hypothesis is that getting their hands wet increases the pliability of the skin on their fingers, thus increasing their tactile sensitivity. Indeed, raccoons use their dexterous hands to procure much of their food, prying under rock on stream bottoms or into garbage cans.

Activity patterns. Raccoons are primarily nocturnal, with activity peaking slightly before midnight. However, they will venture out in daylight to take advantage of food sources, for example, to forage at low tide. In cold areas raccoons may enter a dormant period during winter, spending weeks or months in a den. This is not hibernation, as their heart rate and body temperature do not decrease. Instead, they burn through stored body fat to maintain themselves over this period, sometimes losing more than 50% of their mass during winter.

Movements, Home range and Social organization. Raccoon populations have increased and spread substantially over the past century. Their numbers were at an all-time low in the 1920s and 1930s following severe persecution for the fur trade. Game management regulations allowed them to begin their recovery in the 1940s, and by the 1980s their populations were estimated to be twenty times larger than in the 1930s. Their range expanded, too, and they are now found in nearly all of the lower 48 states, including deserts and mountain regions where they had previously been rare or absent. The spread of agriculture and concurrent decline of the Gray Wolf and Puma were probably both important factors in the increase and spread of the raccoon. The raccoon is one of the most successful native species at adapting to urban and rural environments, but raccoons also occur in wilderness. Densities in natural areas have been estimated as 0·5–4 ind/km^2 in northern prairies and 3·5–6 ind/km^2 in hardwood forests. Their populations increase where they can find anthropogenic food sources. These subsidized densities range from 1–27 ind/km^2 for rural areas and 50–100 ind/km^2 in cities. Some estimates from urban parks are as high as 333 ind/km^2, although these calculations do not take into account the area used by raccoons outside of the park. In Chicago, densities were typically one third higher in the autumn than in the spring, reflecting the litters born in the summer and mortalities that occurred during the winter. The higher densities in urban areas are caused by a combination of demographic factors, including increased survival, higher annual recruitment, and increased site fidelity. These factors are all encouraged by the raccoon's ability to learn how to take advantage of abundant anthropogenic food, and apparently also by high levels of intraspecific tolerance. Most individuals in a population are under two years old, and few reach as old as seven years. Some trapping studies found a male-biased sex ratio, but subsequent research suggests that this result may have occurred because the males were more trappable, and females actually outnumber males in most populations. Corresponding with their higher densities, urban raccoons typically use smaller home ranges than rural animals: 5–79 ha compared to 50–300 ha, often focusing their activities around a few select sources of anthropogenic food. Wilderness animals use even larger home ranges, averaging between 800–2500 ha in North Dakota, where individuals were recorded travelling as far as 14 km in one night. Typical nocturnal movements cover less ground and consist of a few periods of rapid movement between den and feeding sites, followed by more lengthy periods of small, localized movements at foraging sites. Patterns of home range overlap and social organization in raccoons vary predictably with density and available resources. Female raccoons appear to space themselves out according to the available food, and sometimes water, resources. Where food is rare or scattered females are more solitary. Where food is more abundant, and many individuals are able to share space without competing for food, related females may overlap more in home range and occasionally interact during nocturnal foraging or in diurnal resting dens. Males adopt strategies that allow them to maximize their individual fitness, given this distribution of females. In low densities, males will set up territories and defend them against other males, attempting to gain exclusive access to the female(s) they spatially overlap. In areas with medium densities of females, males cannot defend a territory alone, and they share space with other males. One study found that 3–4 of these overlapping males formed stable bonds that lasted for several years. These male groups frequently travelled and denned together, overlapping many different females, but no other males. The raccoon mating system appears to vary across these situations, between polygyny in low density areas and promiscuity in higher density areas. In the polygynous systems males compete for access to estrous females within a predictable dominance hierarchy related to body weight and canine width. In promiscuous systems females mate with multiple males, and most litters (88% in one study) have multiple paternities. The primary predators of adult raccoons were probably Gray Wolves and Pumas. The extinction of these large predators from many areas, especially in urban or rural areas, probably freed raccoons from substantial predation risk throughout much of their range. Raccoons and Coyotes are sympatric over much of their ranges, but the nature of interactions appears to be variable. In Kansas, 40% of raccoon mortalities came from Coyote predation, and raccoons make up a substantial portion of the diet of Coyotes in some parts of Ohio and Maine (some of this may be scavenging on roadkill). However, most studies of Coyote diet find little evidence of raccoon predation, and other studies of raccoon mortality have found no Coyote predation. One detailed study of raccoon and Coyote movements in Illinois found no avoidance by raccoons of areas preferred by Coyotes, or of their scent marks. In some areas, humans have replaced other predators as the major cause of death, either through directed hunting, or accidental deaths such as road kills. Disease has also been found to be important in a number of raccoon populations. Diseases spread more easily between individuals living at high density, so it is not surprising that disease can spread rapidly in urban raccoon populations. Raccoon rabies has been one of the most dramatic examples of wildlife disease in North America. From the 1950s to 1970s a strain of raccoon rabies spread slowly northward out of Florida into Georgia. In 1980, an illegal translocation of 3500 raccoons from Florida to Virginia for hunting purposes set off an epidemic. Apparently at least one of these animals was harboring the rabies virus, and an outbreak spread at a rate of 40km/year up the Atlantic coast, north into Ontario and west into Ohio and Pennsylvania. This epidemic has caused high mortality in urban raccoons, noticeably reducing their populations in some areas, and also spilled over to impact other wildlife, pets, and humans. Another species that suffers from parasite spillover from superabundant raccoons has been the Allegheny Woodrat (*Neotoma magister*). Woodrats suffer high mortality from infections of raccoon roundworm parasites, which have little effect on the raccoons themselves. Woodrats pick up the parasites while feeding on seeds from raccoon latrines. Raccoons do not habitually sing or call out, but do have a variety of vocalizations that occur during close-range social interactions, including a twittering used by females to encourage their young to follow them away from the den. Scent marking is probably the most important means of communication. Raccoons have paired anal scent glands for this purpose, but also use feces, urine, and other specialized skin glands. In some areas raccoons defecate in habitual latrines, although it is unclear if these serve a social function or are just a by-product of high raccoon density.

Breeding. Northern Raccoons are spontaneous ovulators. Mating typically occurs in February and March, although being consummate opportunists, litters can also be conceived outside of this period. In Texas many females with litters that failed in the spring came into a second estrus later in the year, resulting in a second, but smaller, breeding pulse in the population. Mating appears to be the only time males and females associate. Males consort with females over a period of 1–3 days, with females serially visiting and copulating with more than one male during this time. Gestation averages 63 days (range 54–70) and most litters have 3–4 cubs, typically from multiple fathers. Newborns eat solid food at nine weeks but nursing continues until 16 weeks. Cubs first leave the nest at 6–7 weeks and often spend much of their first autumn travelling alone. Many juveniles return to mom for winter denning, ultimately dispersing when she comes into estrus the following spring. Males disperse to new areas, covering distances averaging 11 km, although distances up to 275 km have been reported. Females often stick close to home, overlapping in some or all of their home ranges, and sometimes reuniting in winter to form extensive communal dens.

Status and Conservation. Raccoons are considered Least Concern by *The IUCN Red List* since they are among the most abundant medium-sized mammals in their range. Because of their abundance they have been one of the most economically important furbearers in North America, with fur harvests in 1930s and 1940s ranging between 0·4–2 million skins annually and reaching an all-time high of 5·1 million in 1979/80. However, because of their high reproductive potential and ability to exploit human settlements they saw no obvious broad scale population reductions from this harvest. The fur trade has declined in the last two decades and raccoons are now widely viewed as urban pests, potentially dangerous because of rabies. Their subsidized populations near human settlements may cause conservation problems for other species due to disease spillover or nest predation. Through breeding for the fur trade they have become established as an invasive species in Europe, Russia, and Japan. They are also an introduced species on some Caribbean islands, where they endanger native island fauna not adapted to dealing with a mammalian predator with a keen sense of smell.

Bibliography. Chamberlain *et al.* (1999), DeVault *et al.* (2004), Gehrt (2003, 2004), Gehrt & Clark (2003), Gehrt & Fritzell (1996a, 1996b, 1997, 1998a, 1998b, 1999a, 1999b), Gehrt & Prange (2007), Helgen & Wilson (2003), Helgen, Maldonado *et al.* (2008), Ikeda *et al.* (2004), Kamler & Gipson (2004), Kasparian, Hellgren & Ginger (2002), Kasparian, Hellgren, Ginger, Levesque *et al.* (2004), Kennedy & Lindsay (1984), LoGiudice (2006), Nielsen & Nielsen (2007), Prange *et al.* (2004), Ratnayeke *et al.* (2002), Rogers & Caro (1998), Schmidt (2003), Smith *et al.* (2006), Zeveloff (2002).

12. Cozumel Raccoon *Procyon pygmaeus*

French: Raton de Cozumel / **German**: Cozumel-Waschbär / **Spanish**: Mapache de Cozumel

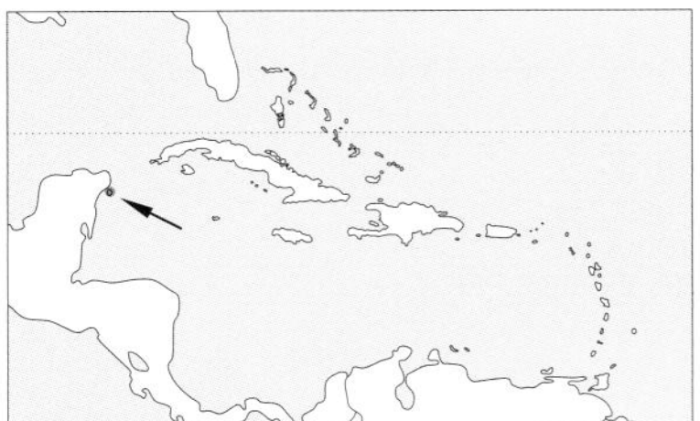

Taxonomy. *Procyon pygmaeus* Merriam, 1901, Cozumel Island, Mexico.

Recent genetic evidence suggests that *P. pygmaeus* is a relatively recent addition to Cozumel, in the last 50,000 years, but was likely present well before Mayans populated this region. It has always been considered a unique species because of its smaller size. Monotypic.

Distribution. Known only from Mexico (Cozumel I).

Descriptive notes. Head-body 35–43 cm, tail 22–25 cm; weight averages 3·7 kg (males), 3·3 kg (females). Cozumel Raccoons look just like Northern Raccoons, but are smaller. Compared with nearby raccoons from the Yucatán area, Cozumel Raccoons are 15% smaller.

Habitat. Use the mangrove and coastal wetlands on Cozumel Island.

Food and Feeding. Both isotopic data and scat analyses suggest an omnivorous diet with crabs being the most important (more than 50%) item followed by fruits and insects. Raccoons living near humans are approximately 0·5 kg heavier, suggesting that they may be using anthropogenic foods.

Activity patterns. No details on Cozumel Raccoon activity have been reported.

Movements, Home range and Social organization. Nothing is known specifically about behavior; it is presumed to be similar to that of Northern Raccoons.

Breeding. Lactating females have been recorded May–July.

Status and Conservation. Classified as Critically Endangered on *The IUCN Red List* due to their restricted range and small population numbers. The population of raccoons on Cozumel Island is estimated to be fewer than 250 adults.

Bibliography. Cuaron *et al.* (2004), McFadden (2004), McFadden, Sambrotto *et al.* (2006), McFadden, Wade *et al.* (2005).

CLASS MAMMALIA
ORDER CARNIVORA
SUBORDER CANIFORMIA

Family MEPHITIDAE (SKUNKS)

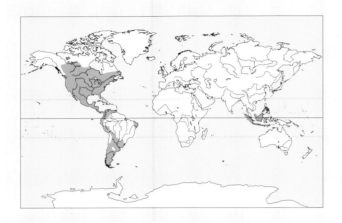

- Small- to medium-sized mammals with striking black and white color pattern and large scent glands at the base of the tail.
- 30–134 cm.

- South-east Asia, North, Central, and South America.
- Found in almost all habitats within their range except for the most arid deserts and the colder alpine and arctic climates.
- 4 genera, 12 species, 60 extant taxa.
- 1 species Vulnerable; none Extinct since 1600.

Systematics

"Les enfants du diable" or children of the devil; the phrase applied by F. Gabriel Sagard-Théodat to describe skunks in his *Histoire du Canada*. Skunks have extremely enlarged scent glands at the base of their tail, and these glands are used to squirt a noxious fluid at potential predators. This unique method of defense and self-preservation has helped sustain their undeserved reputation.

The enlarged anal scent glands of skunks have long been one of the characters that united them with the weasel family. Historically, skunks have been classified as weasels in the family Mustelidae. Characters that have been used to classify skunks as members of the weasel family are based on the loss of the carnassial notch on the upper fourth premolar, the loss of the upper second molar, as well as the enlarged scent glands. The problem with these character states is that they are associated with a high degree of homoplasy (similar traits not derived from a shared common ancestor), such as the loss of the notch on the carnassial, which occurred more than once in independent lineages of carnivores. All carnivores have scent glands and these glands are enlarged in mustelids. Skunks take that enlargement to an extreme. The association of a nipple with the scent gland, rather than a duct as in mustelids, suggests that the scent gland in skunks is autapomorphic, or uniquely derived. Of the characters used to unite skunks and mustelids, two of the shared character states are plesiomorphic (primitive), and the polarity, primitive or derived, of two additional characters is uncertain.

Skunks have been assumed to be more closely related to different subfamilies in the Mustelidae. The relationship to the badgers (subfamily Melinae) was based on shared characteristics between skunks and stink badgers. A comprehensive analysis of the Mustelidae based on cranial, post-cranial, and soft anatomy was performed, and it was shown that the stink badgers grouped with the skunks. The subfamily with the strongest support for a closer relationship between mustelids and skunks is the Lutrinae (otters). Four of the characters that are shared between skunks and otters are based on tooth morphology, which can be variable among taxa, and the fifth character, the auditory bullae, is plesiomorphic. More recent morphological data on fossils indicate a sister group relationship between the otters and the skunks, confirming the previous findings. This conclusion was based only on comparison of several features of the cranium, dentition, and soft anatomy between skunks and otters, rather than a phylogenetic analysis, including other taxa, of those characters. One of the primary difficulties in determining the relationships among subfamilies of mustelids is the diagnosis of monophyletic (derived from a single common ancestor) groups on the basis of shared derived as opposed to shared primitive characteristics. The morphological data uniting the skunks with any particular subfamily or even to the family Mustelidae have been based on primitive character states and convergent similarity.

A skunk by any other name would be as odiferous. Examinations of non-morphological characters have revealed a somewhat different picture of mustelid relationships. For instance, chromosomal data of various carnivores indicated that the

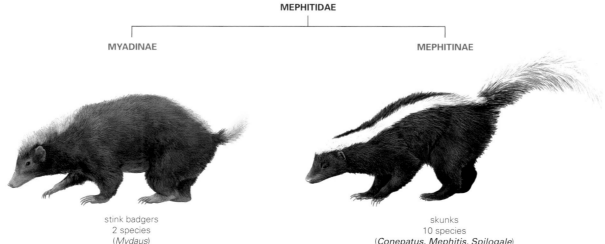

MEPHITIDAE

MYADINAE

stink badgers
2 species
(*Mydaus*)

MEPHITINAE

skunks
10 species
(*Conepatus, Mephitis, Spilogale*)

Subdivision of the Mephitidae

Figure: Toni Llobet

FAMILY
SUBFAMILY

Mydaus marchei
Philippines.
Photo: Daniel Heuclin/NHPA

skunks are remarkably different from the weasel family. Those data suggest that in terms of their chromosomes skunks are autapomorphic relative to mustelids, yet these characters say little about the actual placement of skunks with respect to mustelids. Serum proteins suggest that the weasels, badgers, and otters shared a common ancestry long after the lineage leading to the modern skunks diverged.

Recent molecular studies of carnivore relationships based on DNA hybridization suggested that the Procyonidae (raccoons) and pinnipeds (the three families of marine carnivores: seals, sea lions, and walrus) group more closely than skunks to other mustelids. Studies that have included comprehensive taxonomic sampling, including zorillas and stink badgers, as well as analyses of DNA sequence from both mitochondrial DNA and nuclear genes, have shown that New World skunks and Oriental stink badgers represent a distinct family. Molecular and genetic data collected since the early 1960s all have concluded that skunks are not mustelids. In fact, Red Pandas (Ailuridae) may be more closely related to skunks than are weasels. Furthermore, most of the data have led to the conclusion that raccoons (Procyonidae) are more closely related to weasels than are skunks. Likely, the "mustelids" that appeared in the Oligocene were not actually mustelids, but rather were the ancestor to the superfamily Musteloidea, which includes the four modern families Mephitidae, Ailuridae, Procyonidae, and Mustelidae.

The molecular data may allow us to better understand the evolution of morphological traits in carnivores. Part of the discrepancy between the two types of data, morphological and genetic, may reside with the family (and some of the subfamilies within) Mustelidae not being monophyletic. If, as the molecular data suggest, the family is not monophyletic, then the interpretation of some morphological character changes may need to be reanalyzed.

Part of the answer may be obtained by considering existing information from the fossil record. The earliest true carnivores first appeared during the late Paleocene/early Eocene. These carnivores were small, arboreal, viverrid-like (or weasel-like) forms belonging to the extinct Viverravidae and Miacidae. Throughout the late Eocene and into the Oligocene these early forms gave rise to the Caniformia (Mustelidae, Canidae, Procyonidae, and Ursidae) and the Feliformia (Felidae, Viverridae, and Hyaenidae). During this same time period, open-land communities were becoming prevalent. Many regions in North America were composed of arid-climate biota and there is evidence of widespread tropical savannas during the early Miocene. This period also was marked by the first occurrence of composite flowers, grasses, grazing ungulates, and rodents. The appearance of the first mustelid-like carnivores was coincident with the increase of ground burrowing rodent diversity.

By the Oligocene the families Ursidae, Procyonidae, Canidae, and Mustelidae could be distinguished by characters of the basicranium. Many Oligocene and early Miocene taxa had been identified as Mustelidae, but after careful examination it was later concluded that many of these taxa were actually procyonids or canids. The fossil record for mustelids is incomplete, and many of the early workers named new taxa without sufficient comparative material, resulting in the placement of many taxa into incorrect subfamilies or families.

The early mustelid-like forms that appeared in the late Eocene cannot be traced to the modern mustelid descendants. What is recognized today as modern mustelids first appeared in the Old World during the mid-Miocene. It has been suggested that most of the earliest known mustelid fossils, dating back 20–25 million years ago, have more advanced traits than those of modern skunks and the stink badger in several cranial features.

Based on DNA/DNA hybridization, indications are that the origin of the skunk lineage occurred in the Oligocene about 40 million years ago, which is prior to the musteloid stem group that gave rise to the Procyonidae. Because mephitids and mustelids retain many primitive traits it is difficult to find synapomorphies (shared derived traits) that are diagnostic for a monophyletic Mustelidae or characteristics that distinguish other groups of mustelid-like carnivores. As a result, the Mustelidae has been a catch-all category for many of the early, poorly differentiated taxa as well as divergent genera of doubtful affinity.

One of the earliest known skunks was *Palaeomephitis steinheimensis*, which occurred about 11–12 million years ago. Molecular, morphological, and fossil data suggest that the stink badgers were an early offshoot of the skunk family. The fossil data suggest stink badgers are more closely aligned with the Old World skunks and represent a separate subfamily, Myadinae within the Mephitidae. The New World skunks represent the subfamily Mephitinae.

The close relationship of the North American skunks is well supported, with three living genera recognized including *Mephitis* (Hooded and Striped Skunks), *Spilogale* (spotted skunks), and *Conepatus* (hog-nosed skunks). Though not as controversial as the human, chimpanzee, gorilla trichotomy, the relationships of the three North American genera of skunks is equally exciting. Fossil and morphological data suggest that *Spilogale* is more primitive than the other two genera. Recent chromosomal evidence has shown a relationship between *Conepatus* and *Spilogale*; whereas, the molecular data (DNA sequence) based on mitochondrial DNA and nuclear DNA suggest a close relationship between *Spilogale* and *Mephitis*. It is likely that these three genera diverged in a relatively short time period during their evolution.

Within each genus the number of taxa (species and subspecies) may not be accurate. A revision of this family has not been

American Hog-nosed Skunks
*have one white stripe on the back,
while the Central and South
American species in the genus*
Conepatus *have two. They and
Striped and Hooded Skunks are
all about the size of small house
cats. They are all equipped for
digging, with strong shoulders an
front legs and long, curved front
claws. Hog-nosed Skunks spend
more time and energy digging for
grubs and larvae than do other
mephitids. Their shoulder blades
and humerus resemble those of the
American Badger, a case of two
animals evolving similarly but
separately for fossorial lifestyles.
If threatened, the American Hog-
nosed Skunk can put on quite a
show, standing on its hindlegs
and even taking a few steps
forward, then coming down on at
fours, hissing, and flinging dirt
backwards with its paws. Pushed
to extreme measures, it stomps its
front paws, raises its tail, bares it:
teeth, and sprays and bites.*

Conepatus leuconotus
Colima Volcano, Michoacán, Mexico
Photo: Patricio Robles Gil

performed, but certainly is needed. The two species of *Mydaus* (stink badgers) were at one time considered different genera. The last revision of the genus *Mephitis* was completed in 1901 under the genus name *Chincha*. *Spilogale* was last revised in 1959 based on morphology, at the time only two species were recognized; currently four species are accepted. *Spilogale* is quite variable in chromosome numbers, and likely more species will be recognized after a more thorough examination of molecular techniques in addition to the morphological data. A complete revision of *Conepatus* has never been conducted and is sorely needed.

Morphological Aspects

Striped Skunks (*Mephitis mephitis*) are one of the most recognizable mammals in North America as a result of their black and white color pattern. In addition to the basic color, other colors such as brown and red have been observed in the wild. As a result of domestic breeding in the pet trade colors such as brown, gray, cream, apricot, completely white (non albino), and albino have been selected for in Striped Skunks.

Color patterns are variable among the species, with the Striped Skunk's "V" as the most recognizable pattern. American Hog-nosed Skunks (*Conepatus leuconotus*), stink badgers, and some Hooded Skunks (*Mephitis macroura*) have a single stripe down the mid-back. Central and South American skunks have two stripes. The spotted skunks have a series of six stripes which are broken, giving an appearance of spots. A marking between the eyes also is variable among the skunks. *Mephitis* usually has a white bar between the eyes, and *Spilogale* has a large spot, while in *Conepatus* and *Mydaus,* white markings between the eyes are absent.

Striped, hooded, and hog-nosed skunks are approximately the same size, approaching that of a small house cat. Hog-nosed skunks tend to be the largest and Hooded Skunks the smallest of this group, but there is a large amount of overlap in size. Spotted skunks are the smallest of the skunks and range from barely a handful to about the size of a squirrel. Stink badgers are intermediate in size to the Striped and spotted skunks, about as long as spotted skunks but slightly lighter in weight than Striped Skunks, and have a much shorter tail than the American skunks.

Little is known regarding the skeleton of *Mydaus*, whereas more research has been conducted on the other three genera. There is approximately a 2% difference in size between

the skeletons of *Mephitis* and *Conepatus*. These two genera are about 30% larger than the spotted skunks and about 20% larger than the stink badgers. Based on overall skeletal similarity, *Mephitis* and *Spilogale* are more similar to each other than to *Conepatus*. The spotted skunks also share characteristics with weasels (Family Mustelidae) as a result of parallel evolution.

Sexual dimorphism is more prominent in spotted skunks than in the other genera, but all the skunk species exhibit some degree of sexual dimorphism. Males tend to have a larger sagittal crest, a longer lambdoidal ridge, a larger postorbital process, and a distinct mastoidal process. A baculum is present in males, but is small compared to other carnivores. Females have an *os clitoris*.

The skull of *Spilogale* more closely resembles a weasel, and the structure of the tympanic bullae is proportionally larger than in the other skunks. The skull of *Mephitis* is intermediate between *Spilogale* and *Conepatus*, but shares more similarities with *Spilogale*. The skull is larger and has more curves along the top side than *Spilogale*. The skull of *Conepatus* is more robust than the other genera. This genus lacks the pronounced postorbital process, but the postorbital constriction is prominent due to the inflated brain case and mastoid sinuses. The hard palate of *Conepatus* extends past the first upper molar. In *Mephitis* and *Spilogale* the hard palate does not proceed past the upper first molar; whereas in *Mydaus*, the palate extends well beyond the teeth. Stink badgers share characteristics with the three genera mentioned above. Particularly notable are the relatively larger olfactory bulbs and a less expanded neocortex than other carnivores, particularly in temporal and occipital regions, and the anatomy of the middle ear is similar. There is a foramen connecting the tympanic cavity to the mastoid sinus in skunks. *Mephitis*, *Mydaus*, and *Spilogale* have the same dental formula (I 3/3, C 1/1, P 3/3, M, 1/2) of 34 teeth; whereas *Conepatus* has one fewer upper premolar and thus only 32 teeth. The deciduous teeth in the four genera are absorbed in utero, and the permanent dentition appears at weaning.

The cervical vertebrae are alike in the New World skunks. The foramina transversaria is present throughout all the cervical vertebrae. *Conepatus* has only one pair of foramina in the atlas; whereas *Mephitis* and *Spilogale* have two.

The number of thoracic vertebrae corresponds to the number of ribs. The anticlinal vertebra usually is number twelve in *Mephitis*, 14 in *Conepatus*, and eleven in *Spilogale*. These vertebrae are heaviest in *Conepatus*, especially the centra. The thoracic region is similar in *Mephitis* and *Spilogale*. *Mephitis* and

Conepatus have 16 pairs of ribs; whereas *Spilogale* only has 14. The ribs are more curved in *Conepatus* and long and thin in *Spilogale*. The sternebrae of *Mephitis*, *Spilogale*, and *Conepatus* is similar, but the manubrium is diamond shaped in *Conepatus*, cruciform in *Mephitis*, and has a blunt cranial extremity and no ventral curvature in *Spilogale*.

The vertebrae of the lumbar region have interlocking zygapophyses, wide neural spines, thick laminae and pronounced metapophyses. *Spilogale* has seven lumbar vertebrae, whereas *Mephitis* and *Conepatus* have only five. The processes of the lumbar vertebrae are variable in size and shape among the genera of skunks.

The sacral vertebrae are not fused to each other or to the ilium in skunks. The large transverse processes have roughened articular surfaces and there are two sacral foramina present. The tail of *Mephitis* has 24 or 25 caudal vertebrae. There are 21 caudal vertebrae in *Conepatus*, and *Spilogale* has 23. The caudal vertebrae show gradual reduction in processes and prominences toward the end of the tail.

There is considerable individual variation in the scapula bone, especially within *Mephitis* and *Conepatus*. This bone is roughly rectangular in these two genera, but is more delicate in *Mephitis*. The scapula of *Spilogale* is the least variable and more closely resembles that of *Mephitis*. It is long and has straight axillary and coracoid borders; whereas in *Mephits* and *Spilogale* the borders are not straight and scapula is shortened. There is more sexual dimorphism seen in *Mephitis* and *Conepatus* than in *Spilogale*. In *Conepatus*, the scapula is similar to that seen in the American Badger (*Taxidea*) suggesting more fossorial tendencies. *Conepatus* spends more time and energy digging than the other skunks.

Skunks do not have a supracondyloid foramen on their humeri as seen in weasels. The humerus of *Mephitis* is similar to *Spilogale* only larger. Whereas, other than the smaller size and lack of supracondyloid foramen, the humerus of *Conepatus* is similar in appearance to the American badger (convergent evolution) in that both species are adapted for digging.

The ulna of *Conepatus* has a slight "S" curve caused by a longitudinal torsion. This shape allows for an increased area for muscle attachment. The pronator muscles are enlarged to attach to the ulna. Again, this is an adaptation for digging. There is less variation in the radii of the skunks. However, *Spilogale* has greater concavity of the postaxial border, which aligns the extensor tendons of the forearm, compared to *Mephitis* and *Conepatus*.

The bones of the forepaw in New World skunks are dissimilar. Each has the same seven bones, but they are arranged differently. The carpals of the radial side are reduced or flattened in *Conepatus*, and on the ulnar side they are larger compared to *Mephitis*. Also, the articulation between the zeugopodium and the autopodium is more evenly shared between the ulna and radius. In *Mephitis* and *Spilogale* the articulation is primarily with the radius. The metacarpus and phalanges are longer and less curved in *Conepatus*.

The pelvic girdle is less specialized in the skunks than the pectoral girdle. The pelvis of *Conepatus* is smaller than in *Mephitis*. The obturator foramen is ovoid in *Conepatus*, triangular in *Mephitis*, and egg-shaped in *Spilogale*.

The femur is shorter than the tibia in *Mephitis* and *Spilogale*, whereas they are approximately the same size in *Conepatus*. Given the muscle attachment and length of these bones, *Conepatus* should be able to run faster than *Mephitis* and *Spilogale*. In the New World skunks the morphology of the tibiae and fibulae, and the arrangement of the hindfoot are similar.

Overall, the skeleton of the skunks is similar among the genera. However, *Spilogale* appears to have some adaptations which are comparable to weasels given the similarity of behaviors and habits of these skunks to weasels. *Conepatus* has more derived characters associated with the upper body, which are used for digging.

Skunks are plantigrade in their locomotive state. When foraging they will amble along at a slow pace usually sniffing and digging the ground for potential food items. When not foraging, they will walk with a symmetrical, four-beat gait for stability. When running skunks will use an asymmetrical gallop. The locomotion pattern seen in skunks is considered to be primitive for mammals. Spotted skunks also are quite capable climbers. They can go up and down trees in a "squirrel-like" fashion. They are rather agile and acrobatic.

The typical black and white aposematic coloration of the fur on skunks is used to warn predators of the possible consequences of pursuit. The color pattern in spotted skunks may have a dual purpose in that the broken stripes may make it more difficult for predators to see them, and the skunks can make themselves look larger when performing a front handstand. They have a spot on each hip, which could be misinterpreted as eye spots when in the handstand position. This would make them appear even larger.

Skunks use their five senses to various degrees. They have a well-developed olfactory system (they smell good?), and the olfactory bulb of the brain is large. The sense of smell is used primarily to detect food, and skunks can develop "search images" for food using their sense of smell. Their sense of vision

Molina's Hog-nosed Skunks have two white stripes that may or may not come together on the head. Their fur, which can be black, reddish, or brown, is sometimes used to make blankets. Like other Conepatus *species, they have long claws, a naked nose pad, 32 teeth, and two anal scent glands. They are slightly larger than Humboldt's Hog-nosed Skunks, which occur farther south. Molina's Hog-nosed Skunks eat invertebrates, and seem to have a special preference for beetles, but like other skunks, they are opportunists, also consuming frogs, lizards, rodents, birds, and bird and reptile eggs. Most of their foraging occurs at night. During the day they settle into caves or rock crevices, burrows made by other animals, or dens they've dug themselves. They are seen in grassland, savannas, steppe, canyons, and shrub forests, but not in heavily forested areas.*

Conepatus chinga
Magdalena, Buenos Aires, Argentina.
Photo: Darío Podestá

Striped Hog-nosed Skunks
typically have two narrow white stripes running from the head to the rump, like the individual pictured below, but the color pattern can vary. They have comparatively short tails, less than half the length of the head and body, and no white fur on the forehead. Like all skunks, their ears are small and inconspicuous. Skunks listen for and move quietly away from potential predators. They also use their ears to locate insects and other prey, but probably rely more on their noses when foraging. Their vision is not especially keen, but they can detect movement from a considerable distance. Hog-nosed Skunks use their hairless, flexible snouts to root for small food items such as insects, worms, and grubs. Their diet is omnivorous and includes fruit when it is available. They prefer grasslands, shrub woodlands, clearings, and other fairly open habitats. Most avoid areas that have a very long dry season, although one subspecies occurs in a hot desert environment in Peru. Striped Hog-nosed Skunks are the largest of the Central and South American species of Conepatus. *The largest individuals live in the northern part of their range. Females tend to be slightly smaller than males, but their sizes overlap.*

Conepatus semistriatus
Above: Parque Estadual da Serra de Caldas Novas, Brazil.
Photo: Frederico Gemesio Lemos

Below: Das Emas National Park, Brazil.
Photo: Flávio Rodrigues

The nose of a hog-nosed skunk resembles a pig's, or hog's, in being hairless, flexible, and useful for rooting, but there is a significant difference. Only mammals in the ig family (Suidae) have noses that end in a disc, and only they have a special bone behind the disc that strengthens the snout for serious digging. Like all South American skunks, and like Striped Skunks, **Humboldt's Hog-nosed Skunks** *have a double stripe, but they lack the white stripe between the eyes en in Striped Skunks. Their dark fur is typically black, but can be dark brown or reddish. The tail is short in proportion to the body. hese skunks move from den to den every few days, sometimes circling ack to an old den. They often den in small caves, hollow trees, and the like, but sometimes den under buildings and woodpiles. They ay be somewhat more carnivorous than insectivorous. Both carrion nd garbage can be dietary staples.*

Conepatus humboldtii
Santa Cruz, Argentina.
Photo: Günter Ziesler

is not as good, but they can detect movements from a considerable distance. When they are running away they are very good about not running into obstacles. Their vision is adapted to a nocturnal existence and they have more rods than cones in the retina. They also have a tapetum lucidum which reflects light back to the retina giving them an amber eye shine when light is flashed on them at night. Skunks also have a good sense of hearing. They will use sounds in the environment to escape from a potential predator, by meandering or even running away prior to being detected. Skunks use touch to examine their environment as well. Often they will scratch at different surfaces to investigate. Skunks also will use their forepaws to roll potential food sources, such as tenebrionid beetles or centipedes, to remove any toxins. Finally, skunks often will taste an object by licking it to determine if it is worth eating.

Habitat

Skunks have been reported at elevations from sea level up to 4200 m but are more common at lower elevations, from sea level to 1800 m. Skunks occur primarily in the Western Hemisphere from Canada to Argentina. There is a relict genus with two species, the stink badgers, occurring in the Philippines, Java, Borneo, and Sumatra. Skunks are found in almost all habitats except for the hot arid deserts of the south-western USA and the colder arctic climates of Canada. However, Striped Skunks have recently been seen above the Arctic Circle in the community of Kuujjuaraapik, Nunavik, Canada.

Northern Mexico and the south-western USA have the highest diversity of skunks with three genera and five species. These species occur in sympatry where their ranges overlap. Striped Skunks tend to be dominant in interspecies interactions. However, interactions are not usually aggressive unless the animals are cornered. In fact the individual animals can be quite tolerant of one another. Captive skunks of various species in western Texas were observed denning together during the daylight hours, but were more defensive and aggressive toward one another at night.

Throughout the range of skunks there usually are no more than two species occupying a particular habitat. *Mephitis* and *Spilogale* share the greatest amount of territory. These two genera easily partition resources in their environment. Spotted skunks are more carnivorous and three dimensional; whereas Striped Skunks are more omnivorous and two dimensional.

In North and Central America skunks are found in numerous habitats from temperate to tropical regions including arid lowlands, deciduous or ponderosa forest, forest edges, pastures, rocky canyons, riparian habitats, stream beds, rocky terrain, open desert scrub, and mesquite grasslands. In the south-central part of their range they occur in tropical areas as well as in mountains and coastal plains. They can be found in areas characterized by both thorn woodland varying in density from sparse to thick enough to form a loose canopy and in riparian forests where the understory includes briers, tall grasses, and tall weeds. Skunks can occupy a variety of habitats ranging from pine–oak forest to low scrub and cacti. They also can occur in mesquite brushland and improved pasture habitat with a few areas of semi-open native grassland that has been used exclusively for cattle ranching. Many skunks will utilize cornfields surrounded by brush land or grassy plains to forage and construct dens.

Striped Skunks are commensal with humans and notorious for being found in urban areas throughout their range. Hooded Skunks in the desert south-west also are considered to do well in urban areas, and may actually compete with Striped Skunks for den sites and resources. However, with man's encroachment into the environments currently occupied by skunks, spotted and hog-nosed skunks have been observed in towns. These skunks are not normally considered to occur in urban areas, but recently have been appearing in wildlife rescue centers when they are found in cities.

Skunks will dig holes in the ground or use burrows excavated by other animals. During warmer months skunks will nest above ground under cover, and some skunks (Hooded and Spotted) will even nest in trees. The brushy cover of stream beds not only provides food, but den sites as well. Woodland habitats are used as den sites, and in agricultural areas dens can be found along fencerows, beneath irrigation canals, and in heavily vegetated areas along streams. Spotted skunks tend to prefer den sites protected from predators and the weather. These sites can be found in dark, dry holes including natural crevices in trees, in talus slopes, haystacks, under houses or rocks, and in the walls of houses or barns. Skunks will switch from cool dens in the summer to warm holes in the winter.

The only skunks in South America are the hog-nosed skunks. No more than two species potentially come in contact throughout their range. However, these species tend to occupy very similar habitats. Because they are opportunistic foragers they are able to cope in many habitats varying from the Paraguayan Chaco to the Patagonian steppe and in the dry lowlands to the Altiplano. They prefer open grassland habitats, savannas, steppe, canyons, and arid shrubbery habitats when foraging. They tend to avoid heavily forested areas. In fact, their populations may increase in areas were forests have been cleared. They prefer areas with natural herbaceous vegetation and the open, grassy areas are preferred to the drier shrubby environments. These skunks often will use anything from grasslands with scattered palms to sparse deciduous forests, shrub woodlands, and open grassy areas mixed with sedges and herbaceous plants during the dry season. Hog-nosed skunks choose not to inhabit areas that have prolonged dry seasons. During the wet season they will spend more time on higher ground in open deciduous forests. Clearings and pastures near evergreen forests also are frequented.

Hog-nosed skunks will den in shrub forests and in talus slopes. Den sites in rocky areas are usually found in crevices or shallow caves. Otherwise they burrow into the ground to construct dens, digging burrows at the roots of trees and in hollow trees, and prefer to den in flat or rolling topography. These skunks also will den under man-made structures (under buildings) and woodpiles. Burrows tend to be about 1–2 m in length and approximately 0·3 m below the earth's surface. When available, they will use burrows dug by other animals such as armadillos.

Stink badgers are found in montane regions, but have been seen at lower elevations as low as sea level. They will utilize caves on some islands, and they occur in secondary forests and open grounds adjacent to forests. These skunks, like their North American counterparts, have been detected in mixed agriculture and secondary forest throughout Palawan as well as in residential and cultivated areas. Stink badgers have been found in a variety of habitats including grasslands, grassland/forest mosaics, grassland-shrub, natural damp grassland, and open damp soil along streams. Shrubs are commonly used for shelter. Occasionally, they have been reported in rice fields and freshwater swamp forests where they forage. They also have been seen foraging along roads and paths.

General Habits

Normally, when skunks are foraging they will walk slowly, and their tails will be held slightly above the ground with the tip dragging behind, elevated, in an arc, or held straight up in the air. A skunk that has been mildly disturbed will stand at attention, and the hair of the tail and body will become erect. Depending on the situation the skunk will either run away or start demonstrating threat behaviors. These behaviors can include charging toward the threat, stomping, and/or hissing. Most skunks will get into a "U" position and face the threat with both ends.

Skunks have a unique method of self defense that has allowed them to become bold in their nightly activities. The paired anal scent glands that are found in all carnivores are greatly enlarged in skunks, and there is a papilla associated with each gland that allows the skunks to spray a noxious fluid at potential predators. However, the first response of a skunk to a potential predator is to run away.

The scent glands of skunks are modified sweat glands or apocrine glands. These glands produce odors in most mammals, including humans. Skunk apocrine glands work continuously producing the oily musk, and it only takes a small amount for it to be effective. However, large amounts can be stored within the glands. Sixty cubic centimeters of musk were removed from the glands of one animal. Skunks only release a small quantity at a time, usually less than one cubic centimetre, and they rarely run out of musk. A Hooded Skunk was observed spraying one researcher nine times in eleven seconds. Ninety minutes later he sprayed again three more times.

A skunk that had been rescued and released was filmed spraying for a nature television documentary. It took several camera shots and angles to get the required footage. For the first camera shot the animal sprayed about six or seven times in rapid succession. By the fourth camera shot the number of sprays and the volume had decreased. This animal was both running low and beginning to realize that the camera crew was not a serious threat. Skunks that run out of spray during a predator attack usually are fighting for their lives. They are likely to be killed by the predator before running out of spray.

A skunk's scent glands are at the base of its tail on either side of the rectum. The glands are covered by a smooth muscle layer that is controlled by a direct nerve connection to the brain.

The spotted skunks are the smalle of the skunks, they have more weasel-like bodies than the other genera, and all four species have fur patterns consisting of six stripes. The pattern of the **Wester Spotted Skunk** is similar to that the Eastern Spotted Skunk, with complex design of stripes running along the back and sides, as well as spots. Where the ranges of the two species potentially overlap, the Western Spotted Skunk tends to have a larger spot between the eyes and wider white stripes in comparison to the Eastern Spotte Skunk. On moonless nights, sucl a complex color pattern might break up the outline of the skunk body, keeping it better hidden fron predators.

Spilogale gracilis
Minnesota, USA.
Photo: Thomas Lazar/naturepl.com

*Skunks have 34 teeth, except for the hog-nosed skunks, which have 32, possessing one less upper premolar. Skunks teeth are sharp, as seen in this **Eastern Spotted Skunk**, although they are rarely used in defense, since spraying is more effective and accurate, and can be employed from a distance. Like other skunks, Eastern Spotted Skunks are mostly nocturnal, but seldom risk going out on moonlit nights. Their natural predators, which are also nocturnal, include Coyotes, Bobcats, foxes, and owls. These skunks run with their bodies low to the ground, but when they are moving slowly they stretch their legs and hold their heads up to get higher off the ground. They are good climbers, able to go up and down trees like squirrels, and sometimes den above the ground, in hollow trees.*

Spilogale putorius
Photo: Roland Seitre

The decision to spray is a conscious one. The smooth muscle makes a slight contraction to force the liquid through ducts connected to papillae just inside the anal sphincter which is everted to expose the nipples.

Skunks can spray from the time they are born. The very young animals produce a "poof" of gas that is not very potent, and does not have staying power. The older animals, from about six weeks to adult, spray a liquid that is composed of several sulfur compounds, called thiols, as well as associated esters called thiolacetates. The volatile thiols produce an immediate odor, whereas the esters linger on the surface of whatever was sprayed. When the acetates become wet again either from the rain or even a humid day, they release the volatile thiols. This results in a persistent odor.

When being chased by a predator and not exactly sure where the pursuer is located, the skunk will emit a cloud of spray in an atomized mist while running away. The mist is light, takes awhile to settle to the ground, and can be carried long distances by the wind. A predator will run through this cloud, pick up the scent, and usually stop pursuit. This is the "shotgun" method. When the skunk is cornered or knows exactly where the predator is located, it emits the liquid in a stream that, with precise aim, usually is directed towards the face of the predator. This intense spray will sting and temporarily blind the predator in addition to overwhelming the olfactory. This is the "·357 magnum" method.

Given the opportunity a skunk will usually try to escape from a predator. Depending on the animal it may release an atomized cloud if it perceives a predator is getting too close. The stream is used when the predator is much closer, usually about 50–125 cm. While in the process of capturing a skunk to be relocated, one researcher got within 100 cm of the skunk before it decided to spray. The researcher managed to duck the stream aimed high at his face. Unfortunately, his wife, standing behind him about ten feet away, hit by several small droplets (the stream breaks apart the further it travels) across the front of her blouse, lamented that she didn't know why she thought she was resistant to the spray. Distances of up to 300–350 cm have been recorded.

The skunk does all of this without getting a drop on itself. Skunks are actually clean smelling animals. It is what was hit by the spray that smells like "skunk". If a skunk is in a situation where it would get its own spray on itself, the skunk's chances of survival usually are low. An animal hit by a car will often get the musk on itself, but usually after death. If a skunk is caught by a predator it can get some of the liquid on itself in the midst of a fight. However, in those situations the predator likely has already been sprayed and has not been deterred. The skunk will spray to defend itself even if it gets spray on itself.

The individual personality of the skunk also will determine when and how often it will spray. They usually only spray when they fear for their life; although, some skunks are easier to scare than others.

Communication

Skunks are primarily solitary meaning that much of their communication is with other species. However, at times skunks do interact with one another. Young animals are born with their eyes and ears closed. When they are hungry or if the mother leaves for a short time, they will let out a high pitched crying sound of a single repeated syllable. Once their eyes and ears have opened and they become more mobile, when a litter of young is playing they will wrestle and vocalize with high pitched squealing, screeching, and guttural sounds. When mom needs to get them under control she will utter a deeper pitched, drawn out screech sounding similar to a pig. This usually quiets the young, and they gather close to her.

Skunks also will use vocalizations when interacting with other members of their species, other species as potential competitors, and other species as potential predators. During breeding season or when adults are fighting, they will express a variety of screeching, squealing, and snorting sounds in addition to biting one another. Adult animals will use low pitched guttural sounds when establishing dominance over a resource (usually food). These animals will "butt bump" each other to gain position. They also will screech and attempt to bite one another.

Skunks use forms of threat, or warning communication, when dealing other species. Stink badgers will feign death to ward off a potential predator. They will spray of course if this does not work, as they usually are focused on the threat. Spotted skunks will let out a blood curdling high pitched screech as

Striped Skunks *usually have a white stripe between the eyes, a white stripe across the forehead, and a white "V" down the back. Contrary to myth, the amount of white fur and the width of the "V" have nothing to do with how much snow will fall, nor can you tell the sex of a skunk by its stripes. Skunks are born with a striping pattern on their skin that they keep for life. Some individuals are completely black and some are completely white; occasionally albinos occur. It may be difficult to distinguish between Striped Skunk and Hooded Skunks as both have a white bar between the eyes, and their stripe patterns can vary. Hooded Skunks have longer fur on the head and neck, larger ears, and a longer tail; they are found in a wide variety of temperate and tropical habitats. Striped Skunks have a very wide distribution, occurring almost everywhere in the United States and well into Mexico and Canada, even beyond the Arctic Circle. In cold weather, they may den for days on end, but they do not hibernate. Their habitats vary even more widely than their appearance: they live almost everywhere except very dry deserts. They are found in wetlands, canyon bottoms, gulches, brush along the banks of streams, wooded ravines, and rocky outcrops. In pastures they may find shelter along fencerows or under piles of refuse, and occasionally even burrow into level ground. They are most numerous where there is good cover and ample food. Farms attract small rodents and large insects, and provide skunks with other amenities as well. Suburban and even urban settings also house their share of the Striped Skunk population.*

Mephitis mephitis
Above: Montana, USA.
Photo: Malcolm Schuyl/FLPA

Below: Hamilton County,
SW Ohio, USA.
Photo: Dave Maslowski/
Maslowski Productions

a warning behavior. This is usually done toward a conspecific or a competitor. They also perform a characteristic handstand making them appear larger. This handstand is not usually accompanied by vocalization. Striped and Hooded Skunks have similar threat behaviors. They will take a few steps or charge forward then stomp with their forepaws. Then they will drag the forepaws in toward the body as they move backwards for three to four steps. They will often let out a hissing noise while stomping. The guard hairs on the body are usually fluffed up, and the tail is pointed straight up. Hog-nosed skunks will raise their front paws off the ground almost to a standing position and stomp the ground with force. They too will let out a loud snorting noise to accompany the stomp. These skunks will make a low pitched hissing noise exhaling air through the mouth when they are stressed or concerned, but not yet threatened, as a warning that they are present.

Different species of skunks will use a variety of the above behaviors and vocalizations when they come into contact. Spotted skunks will let out their squeal and rush out to attack a potential competitor or predator, and then usually retreat depending on the nature of the threat. Spotted skunks have also been observed going into a front handstand in the presence of an American Hog-nosed Skunk. Striped and Hooded Skunks will charge and bite one another until the loser leaves the area. Hog-nosed skunks will also bite and wrestle with other species. Throughout most of the range of overlap, Striped Skunks tend to dominate arguments. When skunks come into contact with others from different parts of their home ranges they will use these forms of communication to establish dominance with a minimal amount of damage. Both parties must be willing to fight before a fight will actually occur.

The aposematic coloration of skunks is another form of communication with other species. This pattern serves as a warning color to potential predators that there is a consequence associated with an attack. Striped Skunks have been reported to repel coyotes without firing a shot using only warning coloration and defensive threat behavior. If the behaviors, noises, and coloration do not deter a predator, then the last form of communication is the musk glands. The noxious fluid will temporarily blind and choke any predator determined to attack.

Food and Feeding

Skunks are opportunistic omnivores and will eat a wide variety of food items. Often when injured or orphaned skunks make it to a wildlife rehabilitation center they are fed a high protein cat food diet as they are mistakenly considered to be closely associated with cats. A high protein, strictly carnivorous diet can incapacitate skunks. Longevity in captive skunks can be attributed to a well balanced diet (this is true of many species). Unfortunately, skunks do not survive long in the wild and therefore, diet usually is not a limiting factor.

All of the mephitids, without exception, will eat insects, although Hog-nosed skunks tend to have a more insectivorous diet than the other skunks. These skunks generally find their prey by sniffing and digging, using their flexible noses and long claws to root up arthropods in the soil. The bone and muscle structure of hog-nosed skunks is similar to badgers, so they are quite capable diggers when searching for insects and other invertebrates. Some of the bugs recorded in their diet include ground beetles and their larvae, grasshoppers, crickets, and spiders.

One species of skunk, Molina's Hog-nosed Skunk (*Conepatus chinga*), will actively search for beetles in the environment even when other prey may be more readily available. Like other skunks, hog-nosed skunks will eat other food items they find by chance while foraging, including frogs, lizards, rodents, and birds as well as bird and reptile eggs. More vertebrates are consumed during winter months when arthropods are harder to find.

Humboldt's Hog-nosed Skunk (*Conepatus humboldtii*) will consume more carrion than is expected based on available resources, suggesting that their diet may be one of the more carnivorous of the hog-nosed skunks. The South American skunks also are known to frequent urban garbage dumps as well as fruit and vegetable gardens.

The American Hog-nosed Skunks are known to consume a wider variety of foods including pears, raisins, squash, green beans, radishes, green peppers, and an assortment of other fruits and vegetables when ripe. These skunks are reportedly harder to trap than other North American skunks as they do not take readily to standard baits set out at trap sites. They may actually have to learn what items can be consumed. However, they have been observed devouring pears without any prior exposure and one animal was caught in a trap baited with a peanut butter sandwich. Adult animals have been seen pouncing on and eating mice that happen in their path.

The Striped Skunks are efficient at finding food. Their diets include insects, such as beetles, grasshoppers, crickets, moths, cutworms, caterpillars, bees, and wasps. They also will eat earthworms, snakes, snails, clams, crayfish, fish, frogs, mice, moles, rats, squirrels, wild fruits, grains, corn, nuts, birds' eggs, carrion, and garbage. Striped Skunks use their long foreclaws to dig for insects and grubs. They will search in rotten or fallen logs for mice and insects. Around gardens they will forage for ripe fruits and vegetables, but primarily they are looking for insects, and benefit gardeners by eating insects that can damage garden crops. Striped and Hooded Skunks, as well as spotted skunks, will eat larger birds' eggs by "hiking" the egg with their front paws between their back legs and smashing the shell against a hard surface.

Spotted skunks are the most carnivorous of the skunks and will actively hunt and pursue small prey such as rodents, lizards, and birds. These items are taken more frequently during seasons (dry and/or cold) when other prey items are not abundant. They too will consume a variety of insects including grasshoppers, beetles, caterpillars, millipedes, centipedes, and ants. Spotted skunks also eat easily digestible ripe fruits and some vegetable matter as well. These skunks can tolerate a higher protein diet, but still can not handle a strictly carnivorous diet such as that seen in cats.

Captive stink badgers have been observed eating soft animal matter such as worms, crickets and small beetles, and the entrails of chickens. Stink badgers in the wild also are omnivorous, and consume eggs, carrion, and some vegetable material, in addition to worms and insects. They also consume small freshwater crabs as well as various plant parts. Their mobile snout and long claws are used for rooting insects and freshwater molluscs. While foraging, stink badgers move slowly, root-

Skunks and raccoons seldom have reason to interact, but occasions do arise, like with this **Striped Skunk** and this Northern Raccoon. They are most likely to be in the same place at the same time to take advantage of a plentiful food supply. For example, Striped Skunks have been seen with other predators, including Coyotes, raccoons, and snakes, at Bracken Cave in Texas. Millions of bats leave the cave at dusk, and terrestrial predators gather hoping to snag the occasional bat that falls to the ground. In such a situation, the two carnivores would probably ignore each other. Skunks can fight, but are usually only aggressive if another animal appears suddenly or corners them. However, a pregnant female or one with kits would not tolerate the presence of a male skunk, let alone a raccoon. Usually her three behaviors would persuade the animal violating her space to leave her alone before she had to resort to spraying.

Mephitis mephitis
S Arizona, USA.
Photo: Marty Cordano/DRK

ing around in the upper soil layer using their snout to dig out grubs much the same way hog-nosed skunks forage.

When resources are plentiful some species of skunks will gather with other predators at the "feeding trough". For example, Striped Skunks have been observed at Bracken Cave foraging for bats alongside coyotes, raccoons, rattlesnakes, owls, and hawks. The terrestrial predators will wait for occasional bats to fall to the ground when they start their nightly flights.

There is anecdotal evidence from North and South America to suggest that some skunks may be resistant to rattlesnake venom. Many of the skunk species are known to consume snakes, including rattlesnakes, and the scent of a skunk is known to elicit a defensive posture in snakes. However, resistance does not infer immunity. A young American Hog-nosed Skunk was struck in the face by a western diamondback and was dead within a couple of hours. Whether it was the venom directly or suffocation from the swelling around the face and throat that killed the skunk is unknown. Additionally, a Western Spotted Skunk (*Spilogale gracilis*) was found in the belly of red diamond rattlesnake. Although, not a common prey item for them, snakes do occasionally consume weasels and skunks.

Breeding

Skunks are rather capable breeders, yet little research has gone into the study of reproduction in most skunk species, with the exception of the Striped Skunk and the spotted skunks. Striped Skunks usually breed from February through March and the young are born starting in April, but births can continue until early June. These skunks usually only go into estrus once a year. However, if a litter is lost early a second litter may be produced.

The black and white color pattern of skunks serves as the first line of defense. Most predators recognize the warning colors as something not to be messed with. However, more threatening behaviors may be required in order the get the predator's attention. Spotted skunks, like this **Western Spotted Skunk**, are more acrobatic than the other skunks and to make themselves appear larger and more intimidating they will perform a front handstand. Spotted skunks are capable of spraying in this position, but will usually drop on all four feet to spray. This **Striped Skunk** probably has its tail up just to maintain its balance as it walks across the log, but this sight reminds us of its capabilities. Nerves connect the glands on either side of its rectum to its brain. If it sprays, it has made a conscious decision to do so. A strong muscle surrounding the gland contracts, forcing the liquid musk through ducts just inside the anal sphincter. The sphincter everts, exposing the nipples, and the skunk emits a mist or a stream of spray, depending on its target.

Left: **Spilogale gracilis**
SE Albuquerque, New Mexico, USA.
Photo: Jerry Dragoo

Right: **Mephitis mephitis**
Montana, USA.
Photo: Tom Vezo

Striped Skunks will breed in their first year, and young males will exhibit breeding behavior in mid- to late summer of their first year, although they are not yet in reproductive condition. Females are usually in estrus for about a week and a half. Males will breed with many females given the opportunity and most of the females become pregnant by the end of the breeding season. Striped Skunks can have as many as twelve offspring per litter, but the average is five to seven. Females usually have twelve mammae, but the number can range from 10–15.

Striped Skunks are known to be induced ovulators. The eggs are shed within 40–50 hours of copulation. Sperm of Striped Skunks are long lived. Egg fertilization has been recorded up to 96 hours post-coitus and motile sperm have been found in skunk vaginae as late as 72 hours post-coitus. Because skunks are monestrous (one estrous cycle per year) they cannot afford to shed eggs before copulation. This strategy ensures that the eggs will be fertilized. Induced ovulation is an adaptation that provides a mechanism with which to reduce the risk of unsuccessful mating. Induced ovulation likely evolved through sexual selection as a reproductive strategy beneficial for both sexes. The Striped Skunk is a solitary species that lives in dynamic environments, so induced ovulation ensures that matings will be productive. High levels of luteinizing hormones (LH) are required for ovulation to occur. LH is produced by the anterior pituitary gland which is controlled by the hypothalamus. The hypothalamus requires environmental stimuli before the signal to turn on production of LH can occur. That environmental stimulus is an aggressive male. It is not known if induced ovulation occurs in other species of skunks, except for the Eastern and Western Spotted Skunks, both of which are spontaneous ovulators.

Approximately 36 hours post-coitus, the follicles show pre-ovulatory changes and are much larger than in unmated females. The size of the corpus luteum is at its largest eleven days post-coitus, at which point the onset of embryonic migration and enlargement occur. The first polar body is pushed out at ovulation and the second extruded at fertilization. Pronuclear stages are present at around 42–48 hours and three to eight-cell stages are found between 72–96 hours. The morulae enter the uterus at seven days. Blastocysts are observed during the embryonic enlargement at day eleven. A few days later the mass is implanted in the uterus.

Striped Skunks that breed early in the season have a brief, obligate period of delayed implantation. Mating in Striped Skunks occurs from mid- February to early April, and gestation lasts from 59–77 days. The longer gestation periods occur in the females that bred early in the season. Also, progesterone levels in females that mate early take longer to increase (about 4–7 days) and peak around 27 days post-coitus. Those females that breed later have progesterone levels that increase within 2–4 days and peak at 19 days post-coitus.

Longer periods of delayed implantation are known in the Western Spotted Skunk, and extensive research has been conducted regarding this phenomenon. Development of the embryo becomes arrested at the blastocyst stage of embryogenesis, and pituitary secretion of prolactin hastens renewed development and implantation in the Western Spotted Skunk. The Western Spotted Skunk is unique in that its blastocysts undergo a 180–220-day period of arrested development before implantation. Separating the time between conception and birth, delayed implantation allows females to track environmental conditions more closely. These skunks then can expect an earlier date of parturition. Pineal melatonin secretion facilitates regulation of implantation of blastocysts. The secretion of melatonin is controlled by the pars tuberalis of the pituitary gland, and is determined by the amount of available sunlight during the photoperiod. Epidermal growth factors (EGF) may play an important role in regulating embryonic development in this species, and a change in the number and/or functional status of the EGF-Receptors may be a prerequisite for blastocyst activation and implantation in the spotted skunk.

Most copulations in the Western Spotted Skunk occur in late September and early October. Significant increases in serum testosterone concentration, testis size and ejaculate volume are observed from August to November. These increases are observed from early March through late April in Eastern Spotted Skunks. Testosterone serum levels are low in mid- January and peak in October in the western form, whereas serum levels increase in March through April and are lowest in December for the eastern form. Concentration of testosterone in serum, testis size and ejaculate volume increase seasonally as photoperiod decreases in Western Spotted Skunks; whereas these concentrations increase with increasing photoperiod in Eastern Spotted Skunks, peaking in March and April. Although a second period of breeding is possible in Western Spotted Skunks, the different breeding seasons make them reproductively isolated.

Gestation in the Eastern Spotted Skunk is estimated to be from 50 to 65 days, with only a two-week period of delayed im-

Striped Skunks are crepuscular or nocturnal, and are, thus, usually very active at night. They do not hibernate, but in the northern part of their range they may go into a torpor state during severe winter weather, and females, sometimes with a single male, may den together to conserve body fat and heat. Males are much less likely to den with each other. Striped Skunks may dig their own simple, shallow den or use any protected place, like a hollow log, crevice, rock pile, or under a building. Sometimes dens are "borrowed" from other mammals, such as marmots or badgers. Occasionally the females are clever enough to dig their dens under fences, where they are less likely to be destroyed by farm machinery.

Mephitis mephitis
Arizona, USA.
Photos: Marty Cordano/DRK

plantation. First-season litters are produced in late May and early June. Litter size averages five but ranges from 2–9 kits. Western Spotted Skunks give birth in April or May to a litter of 2–6 young. Gestation lasts for about 210–230 days. Little is known about the reproductive cycles in Southern Spotted Skunks (*Spilogale angustifrons*), and because this species is found at the southern end of the distributions of Eastern and Western Spotted Skunks the breeding season in this species would be an interesting study.

During the breeding season of spotted skunks it has been reported that males sometimes suffer spells of "madness" and run amuck. Throughout these spells the male will travel in a gallop and attack anything in his path. Often these animals were assumed to be rabid, but further investigation showed that hardly any were infected with rabies. It was believed that the violent frenzy was the result of unsatisfied sexual desires or possibly of having been bested by a rival male. During the late summer and early fall months males tend to be captured more than females. This could be due to increased movement of males during the breeding season, which corresponds to these months.

Observations regarding litters and seasons are primarily all that is available regarding the breeding behavior of many of the other skunk species. Anecdotal observational data suggest that some of the other skunk species such as the American Hog-nosed Skunk and the Eastern Spotted Skunk (*Spilogale putorius*) and Pygmy Spotted Skunk (*Spilogale pygmaea*) also have a short period of delayed implantation.

The American Hog-nosed Skunk breeds from late February through early March and can has a gestation period of at least 70 days, which is similar to the longer period seen in Striped Skunks. Parturition occurs in April through May, and females usually have litters of one to three; small litters of one to two half-grown young have been observed in late July through mid-August. American Hog-nosed Skunks have three pairs of mammae.

Breeding season in Pygmy Spotted Skunks occurs from April through August, with most births occurring around July and August. Gestation usually lasts from 43–51 days, and there may be a short period of delayed implantation. More than one litter per year may be produced. The number of young per litter can range from one to six in this species.

The South American hog-nosed skunks have only one breeding season, and the gestation periods are assumed to be around 60 days, although 42 days is the shortest reported. Molina's Hog-nosed Skunk may have a longer breeding season than the other skunks. Whether or not delayed implantation occurs is not known. These hog-nosed skunks usually have litters of two to five young.

The reproductive biology of the Hooded Skunk is poorly known. Breeding likely takes place from mid-February to the end of March. Females have two pairs of inguinal, one pair of abdominal, and two pairs of pectoral mammae. Litter size ranges from three to eight. Females may nurse young through August.

Stink badgers have two inguinal and four pectoral mammae, and females may produce two to three young per litter. Adults can be seen year round whereas young have been seen from November through March.

In all the species of skunks that have been examined, males have a relatively small baculum compared to other carnivores. The exact purpose of this bone is not fully understood. In carnivores the length of the baculum is independent of sexual dimorphism within a species, and also is not an indicator of the duration of coitus, suggesting that it does not serve to provide vaginal friction during prolonged intromission. The baculum also does not simulate ovulation in induced ovulator species. Life history and/or mating systems need to be studied to understand the evolution of the baculum. It has been suggested that multi-male mating systems, long bacula, and long periods of delayed implantation all evolved to accommodate sexual selection in high latitude snowy environments.

Movements, Home range and Social organization

The primary period of activity for skunks is at night. Most species are considered to be crepuscular, but can be active throughout the night depending on available resources and time of the year. For example they may be more active during breeding season. Skunks can be active during the daylight hours as well. Activity during the day is not an indicator of disease in skunks. Young animals in their first summer and early fall can be quite active during the day and continue into the night. Young animals that are not foraging can often be found playing or wrestling with one another during the day.

The hog-nosed skunks of South America are primarily active at night and spend much of their time sniffing out or digging up insects while foraging for food. Those skunks that live in cold weather climates tend to dig less and are not as active during the winter months especially during periods of snow cover. They also may be more active during the day in colder weather. Striped Hog-nosed Skunks (*Conepatus semistriatus*) are not seen during the daylight hours as frequently as the other species.

Humboldt's Hog-nosed Skunks
sniff, scratch, and root around
in search of ground beetles, beetle
larvae, grasshoppers, crickets,
and spiders. They also eat fruit
and small vertebrates such as
lizards and rodents, as well as
garbage, vegetables, and carrion.
Eating carrion presents a special
risk. Sheep farmers trying to
control a predator like the Culpeo
sometimes put poisoned carcasses
out, inadvertently poisoning
skunks. More ranchers now raise
cattle instead of sheep, which has
lessened this hazard.

Conepatus humboldtii
Patagonia, Chile.
Photo: Eberhard Hummel

This species may not be as affected by colder weather as are some of the other species.

Molina's Hog-nosed Skunks reportedly have a much larger home range than the other two species in South America. However, this conclusion is based on an extremely small sample size and may represent only individual variation rather than a taxonomic distinction. Their home range is reported up to 195 ha, whereas the other two species have home ranges from seven to over 50 ha.

Early in their first year *Conepatus* tend to have smaller home ranges that increase in size as they get closer to the time they disperse from their natal dens. These skunks will make little sorties up to about 1·5 km away from their den to explore new areas. Often when the young finally disperse they will move into the areas previously investigated.

At the end of a hard night's work, these skunks will settle at a den site near where they stopped foraging. They have a variety of dens within their home range and do not use the same site more than a few days at a time. However, they will reuse a previous den.

Like other skunks, *Conepatus* are solitary animals. However, in areas where resources are stable and den sites are safe and secure, several animals may bed down together. Usually, these animals are the young of the year and litter mates. Once they become adults they become more solitary in their daily activities. Available resources will often determine the population density of these skunks during any particular year. Population densities have been estimated from 0·4 to 0·16 animals/km² in some areas.

Like their South American counterparts, the American Hog-nosed Skunks are solitary and active primarily at night, although they have been observed foraging in the heat of the day in Texas and New Mexico. Some times individuals will interact and even bed down together. This species will den in hollows in the roots of trees or fallen trunks and in cavities under rocks. They are quite capable of digging their own holes as well. When threatened, these skunks will run for cover and will take refuge in prickly pear cactus or in thick mesquite brush where available.

Hooded and Striped Skunks have similar habits even in areas where their ranges overlap. Hooded Skunks are active after dusk and travel along rock walls, streambeds, and in weedy fields. They tend to be solitary except when females are raising young; although several may feed together at a feeding station, especially in urban areas. Females normally do not den together during the winter months; however Striped Skunks will den together during the winter months in the northern part of their range where it is colder and the snow cover is significant. In the southern parts of their range they may actually be more active during the winter than in summer.

Home ranges of Hooded Skunks can occupy an area from 2·8–5·0 km². Densities of 1·3 up to 25 Hooded Skunks/km² have been reported. Female Hooded Skunks tend to stay at a den site longer than males before moving to a different den within the home range. Males will move greater distances from one den site to the next. Hooded Skunks will sometimes den in trees; whereas Striped Skunks are rarely found above ground level. The skunks' home ranges are smaller in urban areas. Hooded Skunks are more common in urbanized areas than previously thought, and in some places are more numerous than Striped Skunks. Their numbers are often underreported because it can be difficult to distinguish between the two species.

Skunks use plantigrade locomotion
and while foraging they move
along slowly, usually sniffing and
digging the ground for possible
food items. **Eastern Spotted**
Skunks *are more agile and better*
climbers than Striped Skunks
or hog-nosed skunks, making
them better predators on small
mammals and reptiles, although
they are less adept diggers. Like
other skunks, spotted skunks do
most of their foraging at night.
Grasshoppers, beetles, caterpillars,
millipedes, centipedes, and ants are
all important foods. During dry
seasons or cold weather, when fewer
insects are available, they depend
more on small mammals, birds,
and bird eggs. They can tolerate
a higher protein diet than other
skunk genera, but unlike cats, they
cannot stay healthy on an entirely
carnivorous diet.

Spilogale putorius
New Jersey, USA.
Photo: L. Lee Rue/FLPA

Home ranges of Striped Skunks are variable depending on the available resources (food and shelter primarily). Where there is plenty of food, skunks will tend to have smaller ranges. Home ranges are reported as anywhere from 0·5 km² to over 12 km². Although Striped Skunks often are found dead on the road, they tend to avoid crossing roads with heavy traffic, and these roads can set the boundaries for some home ranges. Autumn is a time when numerous skunks will be found dead on the road as a result of juveniles dispersing to find new den sites. During the winter months in the northern part of their range, Striped Skunks become more sedentary and cover less area on their nightly forays. Females may den together to conserve body heat during cold spells. In the southern part of their range, their home ranges remain about the same size year-round.

Home ranges for spotted skunks vary from small (64 ha) to large (4359 ha). Spotted skunks have a patchy distribution throughout their range. In areas where they are common they have been reported in densities of five to 40 individuals per square kilometer. Spotted skunks are less likely than other skunks to be seen during the daylight hours, and often will avoid being out when the moon is bright. These skunks tend to move greater distances in the spring than in the summer and fall.

During the day they usually den alone, but multiple individuals will use the same den on different days. In the colder climates some individuals have been known to share the same den at the same time. These skunks prefer cover where they feel more protected in areas such as under thick brush or even in prickly pear cactus. Spotted skunks are more three dimensional compared to other skunks and often their dens can be found elevated and away from terrestrial predators. Home ranges tend to be larger in the drier months due to more limiting resources. Food is scarcer during the dry season and skunks have to travel greater distances to meet dietary requirements.

Stink badgers are active year-round. They are nocturnal, and during the day they shelter in underground burrows that they dig, or they use burrows dug by other animals. However, they have been observed to be active during the day. Burrows normally are 60 cm deep. Little has been reported about the size of home ranges and the animals' movement within them. However, it has been observed that some stink badgers may live in pairs.

Stink badgers are ungainly and awkward when walking, but when startled can maintain a steady trot for 100 yards. Even at a trot they are no faster than a walking human. Stink badgers in general are not aggressive animals. They walk with left and right feet apart, and hindfeet usually in line with front feet.

Relationship with Humans

Often when people think of skunks they associate the animal with rabies, a bad odor, or both. Often skunks will move into an urban area and set up residence under a house. As a result skunks have attained a not entirely deserved negative reputation. However, skunks can be beneficial to humans as well. Spotted skunks throughout the plains states used to be welcomed by local farmers because of their mousing abilities. These skunks would hunt around wheat and corn silos for rodent pests that were consuming grain. In agricultural areas skunks are more interested in the insects they find rather than the crops that are grown. Farmers recognized that skunks were the only effective predators of the hop grub and their service in combating the grub made them valuable assets. Consider that the next time you drink a "skunky" beer. Some of the other agricultural pests that skunks forage on are army worms (common and wheathead), tobacco worms, white grubs of June bugs (and adults), grasshoppers, cutworms, cicadas, crickets, Sphinx moths, and the Colorado potato beetle. Often when skunks are digging in (and destroying) a lawn, it is because they are after the larvae and grubs of an agricultural pest. So, the skunk is not the problem, but rather the symptom of a problem.

Skunks can be viewed as nuisances, because urban and suburban areas are attractive to them. Skunks generally are looking for three things: food, water, and shelter.

Recreational and residential areas provide ample water as well as numerous den sites. There also are plenty of food resources available from improperly contained garbage and pet food. Vigilance in controlling this food supply can help solve the problem of nuisance skunks, raccoons, rats, and other animals that take advantage of human largesse.

Skunks that take up residence around a home can be persuaded to move on by making the area inhospitable to them. They basically are looking for two things, food and shelter. Removing pet food or not feeding pets outside will force skunks to search elsewhere for food. Garbage also should be contained. This also will stop raccoons, possums, and maybe even bears from digging in the garbage for food. Eliminating den areas also will make it harder for skunks to feel secure. When skunks move in under a house or shed, the opening(s) should be located and fine sand or flour can be sifted to observe tracks to determine which direction the skunks were going last. The entrance can be blocked when the skunk leaves, and then fencing, such as chicken wire buried one foot into ground and attached to the wall in an "L" shape, with the base of the "L" facing away from the house, can be used to ensure the skunks

*In cold winter weather, **Striped Skunks** lower their level of activit, but since they do not hibernate they face the challenge of finding food when insects and fruit are r available and birds are not layin eggs. If they live near farms, they may scavenge in fields for leftove vegetables: this skunk has found an ear of corn. They also hunt fo small vertebrates, especially mice and voles, which remain active all year, even under snow. Being opportunists, they will also feed o carrion, enter barns to find anim feed, and may rely more on garba than they would during warm weather. Their bodies cope with winter food shortages by storing f and metabolizing it over the win In the spring, a Striped Skunk may weigh half what it weighed preceding fall.*

Mephitis mephitis
Denver, Colorado, USA.
Photo: Dave Maslowski/
Maslowski Productions

Striped Skunks may be welcome visitors when they take down and eat a wasp nest, as this one is doing, but they are also notorious for raiding apiaries. Their method of attack is to scratch the ground in front of a beehive and to scratch on the hive itself. This brings the bees out to investigate the disturbance, and the skunk eats them as they swarm out. Skunks are reported to beat at the bees with their forepaws or roll them on the ground, apparently trying to kill the bees and make them safe to eat, but skunks do get stung. In 1935, researchers at the University of California trapped four skunks that were raiding hives. One skunk had 65 stings in its mouth, tongue, and gums. The animal was found to have a stomach full of bees. There were many more in its intestines, and feces near the hive were composed mostly of the remains of bees. A skunk may return to a hive several nights in a row, until the hive is empty. If it scratches its way into the hive, it also eats the wax, pollen, and honey, but the bees themselves are the primary target. Predation on bees may be highest when other insects are scarce. In some parts of the USA, beekeepers have been known to shoot, poison, or trap skunks. Advice about how to protect hives includes fencing them with poultry wire, with the bottom of the fence buried so a skunk cannot dig under it, or elevating the hives 1 m off the ground and putting smooth sheet metal around the base.

Mephitis mephitis
North America.
Photo: Stephen J. Krasemann/DRK

All skunks, including stink badgers, eat eggs. This can be a problem for poultry farmers, but it may be a greater problem for wild birds that nest on the ground. The United States Geological Survey, part of the Department of the Interior, studied predation by **Striped Skunks** on gadwall, tracking skunks wearing radio collars at night and checking on the nests the following day. The skunks visited 13 nests in one night, ate all of the eggs in most of the nests, and returned a night or two later to eat the rest of the eggs. They almost always ate the eggs right at the nest. The exception was a skunk whose den was very close to the nest: eggshells were found along the trail between the nest and its den. There was no evidence that the skunks cached eggs. One skunk visited a nest the night a brood hatched. In the morning, the female and her ducklings were still there, suggesting that she was able to protect them from the skunk. Northern Raccoons are also major predators on gadwall eggs. The researchers concluded that if the predator was a skunk, each eggshell would have a big hole in it or be severely damaged, rather than having puncture holes; most of the nest material would still be there; and the female bird would still be alive. Striped, Hooded, and Eastern Spotted Skunks have all been seen breaking eggs by throwing them between their back legs until the egg hits something hard and cracks, rather than biting them.

Mephitis mephitis
Above: Hamilton County,
SW Ohio, USA.
Photo: Dave Maslowski/
Maslowski Productions

Below: Montana, USA.
Photo: Jeff Foot/Dcom/DRK

do not return. Chicken wire will still allow roots to penetrate the soil so landscaping can be incorporated into the skunk removal process.

If the skunks still are under the house, a one-way door can be constructed with sturdy wire mesh, also folded into an "L" shape. A hinge should be placed on the top side to allow the door to swing out. The door will fall closed behind the skunk when it pushes its way out. The skunk will not be able to return because the opening will be blocked by the wire mesh on which the skunk will be standing when it tries to return through the opening. After the skunk is gone a more secure block (chicken wire) can be applied to seal the opening.

It is not a good idea to do this after the breeding season; if the adult skunk is a female, baby skunks may be under the house as well. Adult females that are pregnant or have just recently given birth will have enlarged nipples and mammary glands, which may be visible if the skunk is seen foraging in the yard. If the gender of the adult animal can not be determined it is best to wait until late summer or early fall to obstruct access.

Encounters with healthy skunks need not be a negative experience. Often if a skunk is met unexpectedly its first response will be to run away. By remaining calm during the encounter the experience can be enjoyable and entertaining. As long as no sudden movements are made the skunk will continue about its activity ignoring anything not directly related to its nightly foraging. Skunks are creatures of habit and their activity patterns are predictable. If the skunk suddenly becomes aware of a threat, again its response will be to run away.

In the event that an encounter does become negative, the sulfur compounds in the musk must be oxidized to reduce the odor. Odor problems in the house can be eliminated or reduced by closing all windows and doors and then boiling apple cider vinegar. After boiling begins the vinegar can be left to simmer for about 20–30 minutes. Then the windows can be opened to ventilate the house. This of course may leave a lingering vinegar smell for a short time. Household bleach or vinegar can be added to a wash or rinse cycle to remove the odor from clothes. The musk that has been sprayed on decks and walls can be removed by using a little household bleach. Finally, if all else fails, time will usually remove the odor.

Paul Krebaum provided a recipe for a solution to oxidize the thiols in skunk spray. In the event that someone (or someone's pet) gets sprayed this remedy usually works: add 1/4 cup baking soda to one quart 3% Hydrogen Peroxide and one teaspoon liquid (pet) shampoo. Mix these ingredients immediately prior to use and apply while foaming. The oxygen released by the foaming neutralizes the thiols (the odor part) and the detergent removes the oily part that holds the odor in

the animal's fur. Let stand for about five minutes then rinse with tap water. Avoid getting this solution in the pet's eyes as it may cause corneal ulcerations. This is an oxidation reaction so it may cause fading of the fur color.

Many skunk species have been managed as nuisance animals in both urban and rural areas primarily through trapping, shooting, and poisoning. Some of these strategies are used as a predator control method to reduce the number of animals that may be feeding on a particular game bird and/or its eggs, or they are used to reduce populations in urban areas where disease and destruction are considered a problem. In the short term, these policies may initially reduce population densities, but a better and longer term solution would be to limit access to the resources that skunks may be using.

Approximately 45,000 to 60,000 people die each year from rabies worldwide. While the actual number of human deaths as a result of rabies exposure is low in the USA, the costs associated with the disease run over US$ 300 million annually. These costs include disease detection (i.e. maintenance of rabies laboratories), prevention (vaccination of pets, and pre-exposure for researchers studying rabies vectors), control (animal control programs), and medical costs, such as those incurred for rabies post exposure prophylaxis (PEP).

Rabies has been recognized for well over 4000 years. Bats are one of the major host of the virus; however the disease also is maintained and transmitted by many terrestrial mammals, especially carnivores. Domestic, privately owned, community owned, and feral dogs are the primary reservoir of the rabies virus worldwide. In the USA, however, because of an aggressive program to vaccinate pets, wildlife species are the predominant reservoirs and vectors of rabies. Rabies has been reported in skunks for at least 180 years and before 1990, Striped Skunks were the primary species responsible for reported cases of rabid animals in the USA. In 1990, raccoons became the species associated with the most cases of rabies reported in wildlife, followed by skunks.

Additionally, skunks suffer from an undeserved reputation as being rabies "carriers" that transmit but do not succumb to the virus. Skunks, like other mammals, die from rabies when symptoms occur. Once the virus begins shedding in the saliva, skunks have been shown to go as long as six days (usually less) before showing any clinical symptoms of the disease. Clinical signs of rabies in skunks can last from 1–18 days before the animal dies. A skunk can be infected and harbor a latent form of the virus for up to 18 months (but usually not longer than 2–6 weeks), but they cannot transmit the virus by biting before the virus reaches the salivary glands. There is no evidence of a true carrier state. Skunks cannot excrete the virus in saliva and remain clinically free of symptoms for long periods of time, nor do skunks recover

Striped Skunks are seldom found more than a few kilometers from water, indicating that they need to drink regularly. They can swim, but seldom do, and they do not dive. A swimming skunk paddles along with its head and tail above the water. Skunks will eat fish and aquatic crustaceans if they chance upon them. Marsh and riparian habitats can be rich in small mammal, insect, and other prey.

Mephitis mephitis
Oak Hammock Marsh, Winnipeg, Manitoba, Canada.
Photo: Mike Read

Striped Hog-nosed Skunks breed in the early spring and have 2–5 kits about two months later. Little is known about their breeding behavior, but like other species, they are mostly solitary outside of the breeding season, and males play no role in caring for the young. The kits are born in dens. Sometimes Hog-nosed Skunks use the burrows of armadillos or other mammals, but they often dig their own, usually among tree roots or under fallen trees. Early in their first year, when the young skunks are getting ready to disperse, they venture farther and farther from their natal den, exploring new areas. When they do disperse, they often settle in a one of the areas they have investigated. Several of them, usually littermates, may bed down together. As adults they become more solitary, although when their food supply is plentiful they may live in closer proximity to each other. No specific information is available about their earliest growth and development, but their first weeks may be very like those of Striped Skunks or American Hog-nosed Skunks. Skunks are born with white and pinkish, wrinkled skin. After the first couple of days, the skin becomes sparsely covered with hair. The skin is pigmented, showing where their stripes will be (the pink skin is later covered with black fur, whereas the white skin is covered with white fur). Their eyes open when they are about three weeks old and they start responding to sounds a few days to a week later. Their anal glands contain musk, although it is not terribly pungent, at birth. They can expel odor when they are only a couple of days old, and can aim as soon as their eyes open.

Conepatus semistriatus
Venezuela.
Photos: Benjamin Busto

This young **Western Spotted Skunk** was born blind and hairless. Its eyes opened when it was about a month old. Chances are it has 1–5 littermates. Its litter was born in the spring. Its mother bred the previous fall and underwent an apparently long gestation period of more than 200 days. This included an extended period of delayed implantation, during which the development of the embryos was suspended. Months later, they implanted in the uterus, finished developing, and she gave birth. Western Spotted Skunks are isolated reproductively from Eastern Spotted Skunks because in the latter species delayed implantation only lasts two weeks.

Spilogale gracilis
S California, USA.
Photo: Kenneth W. Fink

from clinical signs and continue to excrete the virus. If an animal is merely incubating the virus and bites someone, it will not transmit the virus. Unfortunately, at present there is no way to detect the latent form in an animal. Animals can be exposed to and contract the virus at any time. The amount of virus and the body part exposed have some affect on the time of incubation. For an animal to contract rabies, it has to be exposed to another animal that is shedding the virus, usually through a bite.

Presently, there are at least three recognized skunk strains of the rabies virus in the USA. The northern skunk strain found in the north-central mid-western plains and eastern states is similar to the fox and dog strains of Texas and Arizona. The southern skunk strain occurs in the south central states. This strain is more similar to the raccoon strain found on the East Coast. A third strain occurs in California and is similar to the gray fox strain in Texas. Recently, new strains of skunk rabies also have been found in Mexico. Skunks do succumb to rabies in the eastern states as well, but the strain in that area is associated with rabid raccoons. Skunks are not yet known to maintain

that strain in their populations, but issues of spillover and potential establishment are worrisome, because current oral vaccines targeting raccoons do not effectively immunize skunks. Massachusetts and Rhode Island, where only the raccoon strain occurs, had more rabid skunks than raccoons reported in 1999, which suggests that the raccoon strain potentially could become enzootic in skunk populations. Additionally, in 2001 several skunks were diagnosed with a bat strain (Big Brown Bat *Eptesicus fuscus*) of the rabies virus in Flagstaff, Arizona. Skunks are susceptible to the various strains of rabies found in other terrestrial mammals and bats.

Transfer of rabies virus from skunks to humans is a well-recognized health threat in urban areas. Striped Skunks are often attracted to housing areas, due to the presence of pet food, water, garbage, and high populations of invertebrates in urban landscaping, and consequently are more likely to encounter humans and their pets. Striped Skunks are believed to account for a substantial number of animal-to-human exposures (not infections) each year. Most information on prevalence and molecu-

Female **Striped Skunks** usually come into estrus and breed once a year, usually in February or March. Ovulation is induced: the act of copulation causes the ovaries to release the eggs. After fertilization, implantation of the blastocysts in the uterus occurs within two weeks. The litter is born 59–77 days later, in the spring or early summer. A female usually has twelve mammae, so she could theoretically nurse twelve young, but litters of 5–7 are most common. The kits are born toothless, with their eyes and ears sealed. They can see and hear when they are about a month old, and are soon playing with one another. They have teeth and are weaned by eight weeks of age. Young females are sexually mature and can breed by about ten months of age. When a female is pregnant, she becomes aggressive towards males, and after her litter is born, if she is disturbed, she may kill her kits.

Mephitis mephitis
Hamilton County, SW Ohio, USA.
Photo: Dave Maslowski/
Maslowski Productions

Young **Striped Skunks** learn
what to eat and how to find it by
following their mother on foraging
trips. They waddle slowly along,
looking, sniffing, and listening
for insects and other prey while
they are foraging, but often move
rapidly, in easy bounds, to and
from feeding areas. The young
skunks will learn to pounce on
small mammals and catch them
with their front feet. If they are
threatened while they are out and
about, they are able to spray. From
six weeks on, Striped Skunks can
spray a potent mixture that could
stop most predators in their tracks

Mephitis mephitis
Montana, USA.
Photo: Jeff Foot/Dcom/DRK

lar biology of the rabies virus in terrestrial wildlife comes from animals submitted for testing following potential human exposure. Little is known about the prevalence of rabies in natural populations, and how enzootic or epizootic levels of the disease interact with the ecology of various species. Data are needed on the population dynamics and genetics, space use, and mortality patterns of skunks in urban and remote areas to enhance our knowledge of the ecology and disease status of these species.

Much of the data regarding the ecology of Striped Skunks and rabies has been collected in Canada and the northern USA, and in this range it has been demonstrated that rabies occurrences may be seasonal. In the winter female skunks will den together in communal dens thereby making rabies transmission easier. In addition to the increased contact, the stress involved with communal denning may contribute to the onset of rabies. During breeding seasons skunks will interact with each other more frequently and the fierce breeding behavior is ideal for rabies transmission. Rabies in skunks occurs more frequently during the breeding season and females may be predominately more likely to become rabid. During the summer males are more solitary and females can be found with their young, but do not interact much with other conspecifics. The occurrence of rabies at this time of year is less detectable. Fall is the time of year that young skunks disperse. They tend to be solitary, but do encounter other dispersing skunks. Additionally, other ecological factors may influence the spread of rabies and include such variables as population density, age structure, reproductive rate, survival rate, home range size, dispersal distances, and population genetics. The interaction of different species of skunks in the south-western USA and northern Mexico also has not been studied even though each of these species has been reported with rabies. The different species have different tolerances to humans and to one another. An effective rabies program for one species may not reduce the incidence of rabies in general. Rabies in stink badgers is unknown, but not unlikely.

Trap, vaccinate, and release programs currently are being used in many urban areas to manage populations of skunks where rabies is endemic. Population reduction techniques have been used in the past, but generally are not considered to be effective. Oral rabies vaccines are under development at this time, but as of yet a viable oral vaccine has not been found, nor has a bait delivery system been determined.

What is important to remember about skunks and rabies is that not all skunks have rabies. A skunk that is aggressive and "attacks" someone should be tested (not just for rabies but for other diseases such as distemper as well). A skunk that is digging for grubs in the back yard and runs away when approached is acting like a normal skunk. Rabies is a disease that should be respected but not feared. There is a preventative measure that is virtually 100% effective if applied prior to the onset of rabies symptoms. Most people know when they have encountered a skunk, so death from skunk rabies is preventable. It is more likely that an unvaccinated pet will contract the skunk strain of rabies and pass that on to a human than it is to contract the skunk strain directly from a skunk. Vaccinate your pets!

Striped and spotted skunks in North America and hog-nosed skunks in South America historically were important furbearing animals and were trapped for their pelts. These pelts were used to make various items such as coats and blankets. During the turn of the century in North America, skunks became such an important source of fur that fur farms appeared to satisfy the needs of consumers. The use of fur today is not as popular and there are many activist groups trying to ban the use of fur and stop fur farming of all mammals. Although not as popular today, skunks still are trapped, usually as non target animals, and sold in the fur trade. During World War II trappers in the USA were salvaging skunks not only for fur, but for their fat as well. The fat was use to make glycerin which was needed for ammunition used with the Browning ·50 caliber machine gun. Skunks made a significant contribution, albeit involuntarily, to the war effort.

When the price of furs dropped, some of the fur farms converted to the pet industry. In many states in the USA it is legal to own skunks as pets. Many of these are raised on commercial farms and have been bred for various color variations. Some states will only allow pet skunks to be non-black and white to distinguish them from wild skunks. In states where it is illegal to keep skunks as pets or where it is illegal to rehabilitate skunks many citizens will take matters into their own hands when they find orphaned skunks. Often these people will try to raise the animal either to release or to make as a pet (regardless of legal issues). It should be noted that skunks do not make good pets. What makes a good pet is a good pet owner.

Status and Conservation

Only the Pygmy Spotted Skunk currently has any international conservation concern. Humboldt's Hog-nosed Skunk is listed with CITES as Appendix II. However, they are considered Least Concern on *The IUCN Red List*. None of the other species are listed as globally threatened in either CITES or *The IUCN Red List*, although there is some concern regarding some of these species within their respective ranges. Hunting pressure may be one of the primary factors causing a decline in many populations in Patagonia.

Many of the peripheral populations of the American Hog-nosed Skunk also are on the decline. Competition with feral hogs could be a contributing factor to the extirpation of this species in the Big Thicket region of Texas. However, within the past couple of years a number of animals have been found approaching their larger historical range. They currently are near the Colorado border in New Mexico, and have been seen in southern Texas along the Gulf Coast.

The Pygmy Spotted Skunk is locally abundant in some areas, but habitat destruction as a result of the building of tourist resorts and road construction throughout its range may be detrimental to this species. There is concern about the Eastern Spotted Skunk as few observations of this species have been seen in the past few decades in several areas within its range of distribution. Today, the Eastern Spotted Skunk is considered to be threatened in many of the states within its historical range. The Island Spotted Skunk (*Spilogale gracilis amphialus*) in California is listed as a subspecies of special concern.

The Palawan Stink Badger (*Mydaus marchei*) is considered common where it occurs, but it may be vulnerable because its range is so restricted, and in Texas the Hooded Skunk may be on its way out. It has been many years since one has been seen or collected in south-western Texas. However, in other parts of its range they still seem to be common.

Many of these skunks have been hunted or trapped for their fur and even for food, but some have been collected and sold as souvenirs. Nuisance animals often are trapped and killed or poisoned, and automobiles take a toll on several of the species. But skunks also are susceptible to a whole host of internal and external parasites and diseases which can significantly affect certain populations. Numerous birds of prey and larger terrestrial carnivores are known to feast on skunks. Whether this is a result of hunting or feeding on carrion cannot always be determined.

Skunks, one of the most recognized mammals in North America, are often much maligned and misunderstood. They are an integral part of the environment and fascinating component of the earth's biodiversity. Their behavioral idiosyncrasies, made possible by their unique method of defense, make them extremely entertaining to watch in the wild, and their beneficial habits far outweigh any potential negative attributes. The world is a better place with them than without.

General Bibliography

Abramov & Rozhnov (2007), Anderson (1989), Aranda & Lopez-de Buen (1999), Arias *et al.* (2006), Árnason & Widegren (1986), Baer (1994), Baker & Baker (1975), Banks (1931), Baskin (1982), Beasom (1974), Bentler *et al.* (2007), Blanton *et al.* (2006), Bonaparte (1845), Bryant *et al.* (1993), Canevari & Ambro-

sini (1988), Cantú-Salazar (2002), Cantú-Salazar, Fernandez & Hidalgo-Mihart (2004), Cantú-Salazar, Hidalgo-Mihart *et al.* (2005), Carey & Kershner (1996), Carreno *et al.* (2005), Cervantes *et al.* (2002), Charlton *et al.* (1991), Chasen (1940), Chomel (1999), Constantine (1948), Cowles (1938), Crabb (1948), De Mattos *et al.* (1999), Donadio *et al.* (2001, 2004), Doty & Dowler (2006), Dragoo (1993), Dragoo & Honeycutt (1997, 1999a, 1999b, 1999c), Dragoo, Bradley *et al.* (1993), Dragoo, Fagre *et al.* (1989), Dragoo, Honeycutt & Schmidly (2003), Dragoo, Matthes *et al.* (2004), Duhaut-Cilly (1834), Duncan & Mead (1992), Enders & Mead (1996), Engeman *et al.* (2003), Esselstyn *et al.* (2004), Ferguson & Larivière (2004), Ferguson *et al.* (1996), Findley *et al.* (1975), Flynn *et al.* (2005), Forbes (1879), Frey & Conover (2007), Fuller, T.K. *et al.* (1987), Ganley-Leal *et al.* (2007), Gehrt (2005), Gehrt *et al.* (2006), George (2006), Gompper & Hackett (2005), Gray (1825), Greenwood & Sargeant (1994), Greenwood *et al.* (1997), Grimwood (1976), Grinnell *et al.* (1937), Gunson *et al.* (1978), Hall & Dalquest (1950), Hall & Kelson (1952, 1959), Hanlon *et al.* (2002), Hass (2002a, 2003), Hass & Dragoo (2006), Hoffmeister (1986), Hoogstraal (1951), Howell (1901, 1906, 1920), Huet (1887), Hunt (1974), Hwang & Larivière (2003, 2004), Hwang *et al.* (2007), IUCN (2008), Johnson (1921), Kaplan & Mead (1993, 1994), Kaplan *et al.* (1991), Kelker (1937), Kinlaw (1995), Kipp (1965), Klauber (1972), Kloss (1927), Krebs, J.W., Rupprecht & Childs (2000), Krebs, J.W., Wilson & Childs (1995), Kruuk (2000), Kurtén & Anderson (1980), Lantz (1923), Larivière & Ferguson (2002, 2003), Larivière & Messier (1996), Ledje & Árnason (1996a, 1996b), Ledoux & Kenyon (1975), Leopold (1959), Leslie *et al.* (2006), Long (1978, 1981), Long & Killingley (1983), Lopez-Forment & Urbano (1979), Loza-Rubio *et al.* (1999), Manaro (1961), Martin (1989), McCullough & Fritzell (1984), Mead (1968a, 1968b, 1993), Mearns (1897a, 1897b), Medellín *et al.* (1998), Merriam (1890a, 1890b), Meslin (1999), Mitchell (1923), Nams (1991, 1997), Neiswenter & Dowler (2007), Owen *et al.* (1996), Palone (2005), Paria *et al.* (1994), Parker (1975), Patton (1974), Perelman *et al.* (2008), Petter (1971), Pocock (1921), Polder (1968), Prange & Gehrt (2007), Prange *et al.* (2006), Pybus (1988), Rabor (1986), Radinsky (1973), Reed & Kennedy (2000), Reese (1993), Rosatte (1984, 1988), Rosatte & Gunson (1984a, 1984b), Rosatte, Power & MacInnes (1991), Rosatte, Power, MacInnes & Campbell (1992), Rosatte, Pybus & Gunson (1986), Sato, Hosoda *et al.* (2004), Sato, Wolsan *et al.* (2006), Schmidly (1977, 1983, 2002, 2004), Schmidt-Kittler (1981), Schreiber *et al.* (1989), Seton (1926), Simpson (1945), Slaughter *et al.* (1974), Suzan & Ceballos (2005), Teska *et al.* (1981), Theodat (1636), Thom *et al.* (2004), Thomas (1900a, 1900b), Tinline (1988), Tolson *et al.* (1987), Travaini *et al.* (1998), Van De Graaff (1969), Van Gelder (1959), Verts (1967), Verts *et al.* (2001), Vos *et al.* (2002), Wade-Smith & Richmond (1978a, 1978b), Wade-Smith & Verts (1982), Wade-Smith *et al.* (1980), Walker (1930), Walton & Larivière (1994), Wang & Qiu (2004), Wang *et al.* (2005), Wayne *et al.* (1989), Wolsan (1999), Wood (1990), Wood, Fisher & Graham (1993), Wood, Morgan & Miller (1991), Wood, Sollers *et al.* (2002), Wozencraft (1989, 2005), Wurster & Benirschke (1968), Wyss & Flynn (1993), Zapata *et al.* (2001).

PLATE 31

1

2

inches 10

cm 25

3
color variants

4
color variants

5

6
color
variants

7

8
typical morph

color variants

9

10

11

12

Subfamily MYADINAE

Genus *MYDAUS*

Cuvier, 1821

1. Sunda Stink Badger *Mydaus javanensis*

French: Télagon de Java / **German**: Sunda-Stinkdachs / **Spanish**: Melandro indonesio

Other common names: Malayan Stink Badger, Sunda Stink Badger, Teledu

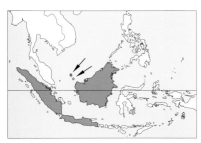

Taxonomy. *Mephitis javanensis* Desmarest, 1820, "l'île de Java". [Indonesia, Java]. Three subspecies are recognized.

Subspecies and Distribution.

M. j. javanensis Desmarest, 1820 – Java, Sumatra.

M. j. lucifer Thomas, 1902 – Borneo.

M. j. ollula Thomas, 1902 – Bunguran I, Natuna I.

Descriptive notes. Head-body 37–52 cm, tail 3·4–7·5 cm; weight 1·4–3·6 kg. Stink badgers are brownish-black in color with a white patch on the head. They have thick, coarse fur that gets thinner on the sides and belly. There is a narrow white stripe along the back down to the tail. This stripe sometimes is only partial, and variable. It can run from head to tail, but also can be interrupted. These stink badgers are small with stout bodies. The nose is long, mobile, and sparsely haired. The legs are short and strong. Sunda Stink Badger has larger ears and a longer tail than Palawan Stink Badger. These stink badgers also have well-developed anal scent glands. The skull shows a long rostrum and is rounded with a large braincase. The coronoid process of the lower jaw is recurved.

Habitat. Sunda Stink Badger is reported to occur in montane regions above 2100 meters, but it has been seen at lower elevations (almost to sea level) as well. On Borneo this species reportedly inhabits caves. However, they also are known to burrow into the ground to den. They occur in secondary forests and open grounds adjacent to forests.

Food and Feeding. Captive stink badgers have been observed to consume worms, insects, and the entrails of chickens. Stink badgers in the wild are omnivorous, and consume eggs, carrion, and some vegetable material, in addition to worms and insects. Sunda Stink Badger, when foraging, uses its snout and claws for rooting in the soil in search of food.

Activity patterns. Stink badgers are active year-round. They are nocturnal. During the day they shelter in underground burrows that they dig, or they use burrows dug by other animals. Burrows normally are 60 cm deep.

Movements, Home range and Social organization. Sunda Stink Badger may "growl" and attempt to bite when handled. If threatened, a stink badger raises its tail and ejects a pale greenish noxious fluid. Natives report that this secretion can blind or even asphyxiate dogs. Some natives reportedly have been rendered unconscious after being sprayed by the musk. The anal scent glands are used primarily for defense. Little has been reported about the size of home ranges and the animals' movement within them. However, it has been reported that these stink badgers may live in pairs.

Breeding. Sunda Stink Badgers have two inguinal and four pectoral mammae. Natives report that stink badgers may produce 2–3 young. Litters are probably reared in a burrow.

Status and Conservation. Not listed with CITES. Classified as Least Concern in *The IUCN Red List*. They have been known to cause damage in plantations by digging up seedlings, and have been killed as pests for this reason. The old Javanese sultans used the musk, in suitable dilution, in the manufacture of perfumes. Some natives eat the flesh of *Mydaus*, removing the scent glands immediately after the animals are killed. Others mix shavings of the skin with water and drink the mixture as a cure for fever or rheumatism.

Bibliography. Chasen (1940), Davis (1962), Forbes (1879), Hwang & Larivière (2003), Jentink (1895), Kloss (1927), Long (1978), Long & Killingley (1983), Lönnberg & Mjöberg (1925), Moulton (1921), Thomas (1902b).

2. Palawan Stink Badger *Mydaus marchei*

French: Télagon de Palawan / **German**: Palawan-Stinkdachs / **Spanish**: Melandro de Palawan

Other common names: Teledu, Skunk Badger

Taxonomy. *Mydaus marchei* Huet, 1887, l'ile Palaouan [Philippine Isles, Palawan]. The species was once considered a separate genus, *Suillotaxus*, due to its smaller size, broader upper second premolar, and a shorter tail than that found in *M. javanensis*. However, this variation was later deemed to be no greater than that found in other species of the family. Monotypic.

Distribution. Philippines (Palawan I, Calamian I).

Descriptive notes. Head–body 32–49 cm, tail 1·5–4·5 cm; weight 844–2490 g. Palawan Stink Badgers have a sharp face with an elongated and mobile muzzle. The body is squat but heavy, their legs are short, and they walk on plantigrade feet. The claws on

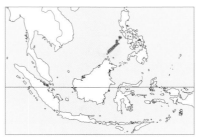

the front feet are elongated, curved, and strong. The inner digits of the forepaws are joined by webbing and a muscle extending towards the tips. Stink badgers have small eyes and essentially vestigial external pinnae. The white stripes down the back can be divided, single and narrow, or absent. Like other members of the family the anal scent glands are well-developed and produce a noxious odor. The cheek teeth are rounded with low cusps rather than sectorial, and the first upper molar is larger than the last upper premolar.

Habitat. Palawan Stink Badgers have been detected in mixed agriculture and secondary forest throughout Palawan as well as in residential and cultivated areas. They have been found in grasslands and grassland/forest mosaics, grassland-shrub, natural damp grassland, and open damp soil along streams. Occasionally, they have been reported in rice fields and freshwater swamp forests where they forage. Shrubs are commonly used for shelter. They also have been seen foraging along roads and paths.

Food and Feeding. Their diet consists of soft animal matter such as worms of every kind, birds' eggs, carrion, insects (including crickets and small beetles), and insect grubs. They also consume small freshwater crabs as well as various plant parts. Their mobile snout and long claws are used for finding insects and freshwater molluscs. While foraging, stink badgers move slowly, rooting around in the upper soil layer using their snout to dig out grubs.

Activity patterns. Palawan Stink Badger is nocturnal, but has been seen active both day and night. While walking they are ungainly and awkward, but when startled can maintain a steady trot for 90 m. Even at a trot they are no faster than a walking human. Stink badgers walk with left and right feet apart, and hindfeet usually in line with front feet.

Movements, Home range and Social organization. These stink badger are not aggressive. When threatened, they exhibit various threat behaviors. Stink badgers snarl, show their teeth, and stamp their forefeet on the ground in a similar way to North American skunks. They also have been observed to feign death (with the anal area directed at the observer). As a last resort they will squirt a yellowish fluid from their anal glands. The musk is reportedly pungent, but not offensive, smelling faintly of almonds and stink ants. The Palawan Stink Badger also leaves a scent behind in its wanderings, suggesting that the discharge from its anal glands may be used for more than just defense. Little has been reported about their home ranges and movement within them. When not active, stink badgers take refuge in underground dens.

Breeding. Little has been recorded regarding the breeding habits of this species. Palawan Stink Badgers have six teats, four pectoral and two inguinal. Likely there are 2–3 young in a litter, which is born in the den. Adults can be seen year round whereas young have been seen from November through March.

Status and Conservation. Not listed on CITES. *The IUCN Red List* considers them as Least Concern. The species has a restricted geographic range, but they are common where they occur, and it has been suggested that the former vulnerable listing is not justified. Humans sometimes eat stink badgers. They also are potential prey for Common Palm Civets, Leopard Cats, and Malay Civets. They have been found infected with the nematode *Blattophila*, and the pentastomid *Waddycephalus teretiusculus*. These stink badgers eat insects that harm tree growth and agriculture.

Bibliography. Esselstyn *et al.* (2004), Grimwood (1976), Hoogstraal (1951), Huet (1887), Hwang & Larivière (2004), Jentink (1895), Kruuk (2000), Lawrence (1939), Long (1978, 1981), Long & Killingley (1983), Rabor (1986), Sanborn (1952), Self & Kuntz (1967), Wozencraft (2005).

Subfamily MEPHITINAE

Genus *CONEPATUS*

Gray, 1837

3. American Hog-nosed Skunk *Conepatus leuconotus*

French: Moufette à dos blanc / **German**: Ferkelskunk / **Spanish**: Zorrino dorsiblanco

Taxonomy. *Mephitis leuconota* Lichtenstein, 1832, "Río Alvarado" [Veracruz]. The white-backed hog-nosed skunks were considered as two distinct species. Genetic, morphometric, and color patterns have been used to relegate them to this single species. Three subspecies are recognized.

Subspecies and Distribution.

C. l. leuconotus Lichtenstein 1832 – S USA (S Arizona, New Mexico & Texas), most of Mexico (except Yucatán Peninsula) and S to Nicaragua.

On following pages: 4. Molina's Hog-nosed Skunk (*Conepatus chinga*); 5. Striped Hog-nosed Skunk (*Conepatus semistriatus*); 6. Humboldt's Hog-nosed Skunk (*Conepatus humboldtii*); 7. Hooded Skunk (*Mephitis macroura*); 8. Striped Skunk (*Mephitis mephitis*); 9. Pygmy Spotted Skunk (*Spilogale pygmaea*); 10. Eastern Spotted Skunk (*Spilogale putorius*); 11. Western Spotted Skunk (*Spilogale gracilis*); 12. Southern Spotted Skunk (*Spilogale angustifrons*).

C. l. figginsi F.W. Miller, 1925 – USA (SE Colorado, NE New Mexico, Oklahoma panhandle).

C. l. telmalestes Bailey 1905 – S USA (Big Thicket region of E Texas).

Descriptive notes. Head–body 34–51 cm (males), 38–50 cm (females), tail, 14–41cm (males), 12·2–34 cm (females), length of hindfoot 2·2–9 cm (males), 3–9 cm (females) and length of ear 0·8–3·6 cm (males), 0·8–3·3 cm (females); weight 2–4 kg. American Hog-nosed Skunk is as large as or larger than the Striped Skunk. They can be distinguished readily from other skunks by the color pattern of the dorsal pelage. These are the only skunks that lack a white dot or medial bar between the eyes and that have primarily black body fur with a single white stripe. The stripe starts as a single wedge-shaped white patch of fur on the head that widens near the shoulders to approximately half the width of the back. The stripe ranges from substantially reduced or absent on the rump to completely covering the entire back. The tail is white along its total length dorsally, but ventrally it can be black or white at the base. Their body generally is larger, and the tail is shorter in proportion to the body, than in other skunks. American Hog-nosed Skunks can be distinguished from the Striped Hog-nosed Skunks of Central and South America by the single dorsal stripe: the latter have two stripes bilateral to the spine. The snout of American Hog-nosed Skunk is relatively long and the nose pad, which is naked, is about 2 cm wide by 2·6 cm long, and resembles the nose of a small hog. This species has small and rounded ears. Its legs are stocky and the feet are plantigrade. The hindfeet are broad and large; the soles are naked about half the length of the foot. The upper body is powerfully built for digging and climbing and the foreclaws are very long. The skull is relatively deep (deepest in the temporal region) and the nares are large and truncated. The auditory bullae are not inflated, and the palate ends behind upper molars. The carnassial teeth are not well-developed, and they as well as the large upper molar provide an increased crushing surface. The dental formula is I 3/3, C 1/1, P 2/3, M 1/2 = 32. *Conepatus* resorb the milk teeth prior to birth. The scent glands are at the base of the tail on either side of the rectum. Two major volatile components [(*E*)-2-butene-1-thiol and (*E*)-*S*-2-butenyl thioacetate] and four minor components (phenylmethanethiol, 2-methylquinoline, 2-quinoline-methanethiol, and bis[(*E*)-2-butenyl] disulfide) are found in the anal sac secretions of American Hog-nosed Skunks.

Habitat. American Hog-nosed Skunk can be found in canyons, stream beds, and rocky terrain. They also are found in open desert-scrub and mesquite-grasslands. In the south-central part of their range they can be found in tropical areas as well as in mountains and coastal plains. They also are known to visit cornfields surrounded by brush or grassy plains, and scattered thickets of bull-horn acacia and other thorny plants. They can be found in both thorn woodland and riparian forest. In thorn woodland, the trees can vary in density from sparse to thick enough to form a loose canopy. Trees associated with the riparian forest habitat include pecan (*Carya illinoensis*), sycamore (*Platanus occidentalis*), Texas persimmon (*Diospyros texana*), and live-oak (*Quercus virginiana*). The understory of the riparian forests where hog-nosed skunks have been found includes briers, tall grasses, and tall weeds. American Hog-nosed Skunks have been found in pine–oak forest in the San Carlos Mountains, and north of these mountains on the Tamaulipan plain, which consists of low scrub and cacti. They also can occur in mesquite-brushland and improved pasture habitat where a few areas of semi-open native grassland have been used exclusively for cattle ranching. Thorny brush and cactus constitute the predominant vegetation in the region of southern Texas where these skunks occur.

Food and Feeding. They have been observed attacking and devouring small rodents. However, this species is more insectivorous by nature and will spend hours digging for grubs and larvae. They also will eat pears, raisins, squash, green beans, radishes, green peppers, and a variety of other fruits and vegetables (with the exception of lima beans). Naturalists have trouble finding bait suitable for trapping these carnivores and have often had to capture individuals by hand. These skunks also may be capable of obtaining their daily water requirements from their food depending on the moisture content of the menu.

Activity patterns. These skunks are solitary and largely nocturnal, but not strictly so. They have been observed feeding during the heat of the day in New Mexico and Texas. They den in hollows in the roots of trees or fallen trunks and in cavities under rocks, and will take refuge in prickly pear cactus when aggravated. When an American Hog-nosed Skunk is threatened by a predator, its first response is to flee to cover. It may then turn to face its pursuer and, depending on the size and threat of the predator, stand on its hindlegs and even take two or three steps forward. Then it will come down hard on its front paws and exhale a burst of air in a loud hiss. Finally, it will draw its paws under its body, flinging dirt backwards. A defensive, frightened individual will crouch, stomp its front paws, raise its tail and hold it flat against its back, and bare its teeth. In this position it can bite and spray a predator, and will do both. American Hog-nosed Skunk can squirt a noxious liquid from anal scent glands, either as a mist when the threat is not specifically located, or as a stream directed toward a specific threat. The mist can be emitted while on the run.

Movements, Home range and Social organization. American Hog-nosed Skunks are solitary by nature, but will tolerate each other as well as other species depending on the situation. Males and females stay together briefly during breeding season. Females stay with their litters until early fall, when the young disperse. Little is known about the home range of this species.

Breeding. These skunks breed from late February through early March. A captive female had a gestation period of at least 70 days. Parturition occurs in April through May, and by late August the young begin to disperse. Females usually have litters of one to three; small litters of one to two half-grown young have been observed in late July through mid- August. American Hog-nosed Skunks have three pairs of mammae.

Status and Conservation. Not listed with CITES. Classified as Least Concern in *The IUCN Red List*, but populations have been declining for many years throughout a major portion of its historical range in the USA. The eastern Texas subspecies, *telmalestes*, is presumed extirpated throughout its range in the Big Thicket region. In his *Biological Survey of Texas*, V. Bailey wrote, "the white-backed skunk is said to be the commonest species, and under a trapper's shed at a ranch on Tarkington Prairie in November, 1904, I saw eight or ten of their skins hanging up to dry with a small number of skins of Striped Skunk." No new specimens of this subspecies have been collected in the Big Thicket area of Texas since Bailey's report in 1905. A telling, albeit fictional, explanation for the skunk's decline is provided by Larry McMurtry, in his novel *Lonesome Dove*: one of his characters meets a couple in NE Texas. "In the dusk it was hard to make out much about her except that she was thin. She was barefoot and had on a dress that looked like it was made from part of a cotton sack. 'I gave twenty-eight skunk hides for her,' the old man said suddenly". A more likely cause for the decline of hog-nosed skunk populations may be found in the increase in the number of trappers or possibly in the increased number of feral hogs that have been introduced into the area. Feral hogs compete, to some degree, with several species of wildlife for certain foods. They eat a variety of items, including fruits, roots, mushrooms, and invertebrates, depending on the season. Their rooting behavior is competitive with the rooting behavior of hog-nosed skunks. Feral hogs can have detectable influences on wildlife and plant communities as well as domestic crops and livestock, extensively disturbing vegetation and soil. In southern Texas, where 95% of the native vegetation in the Rio Grande Valley in Texas has been transformed from subtropical plant communities to cotton, sorghum, sugar cane, vegetable crops, and citrus orchards, several additional hog-nosed skunk populations may now be extirpated. However, a population was found recently in southern Texas and currently is being studied. Because hog-nosed skunks generally are associated with rough rocky areas and brushy habitat, the conversion of native vegetation to row-crop agriculture may be partially responsible for the skunks' decline. However, habitat modification may not be the primary cause of the observed decline, because specimens of this skunk have been collected in cultivated areas near Veracruz, Mexico. A more direct cause may be associated with use of pesticides in agriculture. Hog-nosed skunks are primarily insectivorous, and use of pesticides has increased throughout their range in conjunction with row-crop agriculture. In Colorado, no new specimens of this species have been collected since 1933. However, a road-killed animal was seen just south of the Colorado border in New Mexico in 2003. American Hog-nosed Skunks are taken by many predators, mainly large canids and felids, and by birds of prey. Additionally, the skunks support numerous parasites. External parasites include fleas (*Pulex*) and ticks (*Ixodes texanus*); intestinal parasites are roundworms (*Psyalopteris maxillaris*) and cestodes; and subcutaneous nematodes (*Filaria martis*) and *Skrjabingylus chitwoodorum* –infect the frontal sinuses. In west Texas, American Hog-nosed Skunks have been found infected with several species of helminth parasites, including *Filaroides milksi*, *Filaria taxidaea*, *Gongylonema* sp., *Macracanthorhynchus ingens*, *Mathevotaenia mephitis*, *Oncicola canis*, *Pachysentis canicola*, *Physaloptera maxillaris*, and *P. rara*. In natural habitats, hog-nosed skunks are not known to survive for more than three or four years, but American hog-nosed skunks can live for 16 years or more in captivity.

Bibliography. Bailey (1905), Beasom (1974), Dalquest (1953), Davis (1951), Davis & Schmidly (1994), Dragoo (1993), Dragoo & Honeycutt (1999a, 1999b), Dragoo & Sheffield (In press), Dragoo *et al.* (2003), Hall & Dalquest (1963), Hall & Kelson (1952), Leopold (1959), Lichtenstein (1827-1834), Matson & Baker (1986), McMurtry (1985), Meaney *et al.* (2006), Merriam (1902), Miller (1925), Neiswenter *et al.* (2006), Patton (1974), Reid (1997), Schmidly (1983, 2002, 2004), Schmidly & Hendricks (1984), Slaughter *et al.* (1974), Tewes & Schmidly (1987), Wood *et al.* (1993).

4. Molina's Hog-nosed Skunk *Conepatus chinga*

French: Moufette de Molina / **German**: Anden-Skunk / **Spanish**: Zorrino chileno

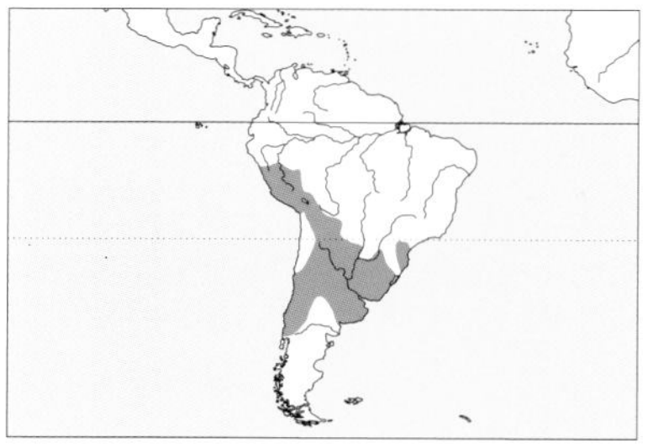

Taxonomy. *Viverra chinga* Molina, 1782, "Chili", restricted to "alrededores de Valparaíso". [Chile].

A taxonomic revision of the species is needed. Seven subspecies are recognized.

Subspecies and Distribution.

C. c. chinga Molina, 1782 – C Chile coastline (from Coquimbo to Concepcion).

C. c. budini Thomas, 1919 – W Argentina (Catamarca, La Rioja, San Juan, San Luis & N Mendoza).

C. c. gibsoni Thomas, 1910 – Argentina (Pampas region).

C. c. inca Thomas, 1900 – Peru.

C. c. mendosus Thomas, 1921 – W Argentina (SW Mendoza) W to C Chile (Los Ríos & Los Lagos regions).

C. c. rex Thomas, 1898 – Bolivia.

C. c. suffocans Illiger, 1815 – SE Brazil, Uruguay, Paraguay and NE Argentina.

Descriptive notes. Head–body 35–49 cm (males), 30–45 cm (females), tail 14·6–29 cm (males), 13·3–28 cm (females); weight 1–3 kg. As in most skunk species, males are larger than females. These skunks are slightly larger than the Humboldt's Hog-nosed Skunks farther south. The pelage color is black, brown, or dark reddish, with two white stripes running down the back slightly to the side. These stripes may or may not join on the head. There is considerable variation in color pattern. The ears are short and the nose pad is thick and naked. The palms of the feet are hairless and have thick swellings on the pads. The digits are short and the claws are long. There are 32 teeth, as in other *Conepatus*. These skunks also have two scent glands at the base of the tail just inside the rectum, which are used to expel noxious fluid as a defense mechanism.

Habitat. Molina's Hog-nosed Skunks occur in a variety of habitats and can be found from the dry lowlands to the Altiplano in Bolivia. They have been found from the Paraguayan Chaco to the precordillerean steppe. They forage in grassland, savannas, steppe, and canyons, and den in shrub forests and in talus slopes. Dens in rocky areas are usually found in crevices. Elsewhere, they burrow into the ground, sometimes at the roots of trees, to construct dens. They will also den in caves and use burrows abandoned by other animals. They tend to avoid heavily forested areas. In fact, their populations may increase in areas where forests have been cleared.

Food and Feeding. Like other skunks, is an omnivorous and opportunistic feeder. Invertebrates constitute the bulk of the diet, but small vertebrates, including frogs, lizards, rodents, and birds as well as bird and reptile eggs are consumed. More vertebrates are consumed during winter months when arthropods are harder to find. Otherwise the diet is similar year round. Arthropod prey items include beetle larvae and spiders. Beetles are found in abundance in skunk faeces even when beetles in the environment are more scarce, suggesting that beetles are a favorite food item.

Activity patterns. These skunks are considered to be crepuscular, but can be active throughout the night with their activity usually starting between 19:00 h and 22:00 h. They are active most of the night and settle early in the morning, before 05:00 h. Much of their time is spent searching for food either by digging up insects or sniffing and searching around brush. They tend to dig less in winter when the ground is frozen.

Movements, Home range and Social organization. Molina's Hog-nosed Skunk is primarily solitary when foraging. Home ranges of this species (based on a small sample size) are from 3·5–12 times larger than home ranges in other *Conepatus* and average about 195 ha.

Breeding. Little is known about the breeding behavior of this species. They have been reported to have a single breeding season, like the other South American skunks. They are similar in ecology and habit to the Humboldt's Hog-nosed Skunk, so presumably they have a similar gestation period (approximately 60 days) and produce a single annual litter of 2–5 offspring. The breeding season may be longer than in other species.

Status and Conservation. Molina's Hog-nosed Skunks are not listed with CITES, and are classified as Least Concern in *The IUCN Red List*. These skunks too have been hunted and trapped for their pelts, which have been used to make blankets. They are susceptible to poisons set out for other animals. They are preyed upon by various birds of prey as well as larger mammalian carnivores. This species also harbors several internal and external parasites.

Bibliography. Anderson (1997), Arias *et al.* (2006), Cabrera (1958), Cabrera & Yepes (1960), Canevari & Ambrosini (1988), Donadio *et al.* (2001), Eisenberg & Redford (1999), Molina (1782), Thomas (1900b, 1910, 1919), Travaini *et al.* (1998), Wozencraft (2005).

5. Striped Hog-nosed Skunk *Conepatus semistriatus*

French: Moufette d'Amazonie / **German**: Amazonas-Skunk / **Spanish**: Zorrino amazónico

Taxonomy. *Viverra semistriatus* Boddaert, 1785, Originally described from "Mexico". Type locality later described as "Minas de Montuosa, cerca de Pamplona, departamento del norte de Santander, Colombia".

Eight subspecies are recognized.

Subspecies and Distribution.

C. s. semistriatus Boddaert, 1785 – Colombia and Venezuela.

C. s. amazonicus Lichtenstein, 1838 – NE & C Brazil.

C. s. conepatl Gmelin, 1788 – SE Mexico (Veracruz and along coast to Campeche).

C. s. quitensis Humboldt, 1812 – Ecuador.

C. s. taxinus Thomas, 1924 – higher elevation in N Peru.

C. s. trichurus Thomas, 1905 – Costa Rica, W Panamá.

C. s. yucatanicus Goldman, 1943 – SE Mexico (Yucatán & Quintana Roo), Belize, Guatemala, Honduras and Nicaragua.

C. s. zorrino Thomas, 1900 – low hot desert regions of N Peru.

Descriptive notes. Head–body 35–50 cm (males) and 33–45 cm (females), tail 14·3–30·9 cm (males) and 13·5–26 cm (females); weight 1·4–3·5 kg. The tail is less than half the total body length. Striped Hog-nosed Skunks in South America tend to get smaller from north to south. The Striped Hog-nosed Skunk is larger than the other South American species, Molina's and Humboldt's Hog-nosed Skunks. The pelage coloration typically is black with two narrow white stripes running from the head to the rump. There is extensive variation in color pattern. Striped hog-nosed Skunks have small, pig-like noses that are used for rooting insects. Like other *Conepatus*, the claws are long and the forelimbs are adapted for digging. These skunks also are able to spray a noxious fluid as a means of defense.

Habitat. Striped Hog-nosed Skunks use grasslands with scattered palms, sparse deciduous forests, shrub woodlands, and open grassy areas mixed with sedges and herbaceous plants during the dry season. They prefer not to hang out in areas that have prolonged dry seasons. During the wet season they spend more time on higher ground in deciduous forests. Clearings and pastures near evergreen forests also are frequented by this species. Den sites are dug among tree roots or fallen trees. Burrows are about 1–2 m in length and about 0·3 m below the surface. When not using the burrows dug for themselves these skunks will use burrows dug by other animals such as armadillos.

Food and Feeding. Like other hog-nosed skunks, this species is an opportunistic omnivore. They feed on many invertebrates, but may not dig as much as the other species. Additionally, they consume small vertebrates, including reptiles, mammals, and birds, as well as fruits when they are available.

Activity patterns. Striped Hog-nosed Skunks are primarily nocturnal. They become active shortly after sunset. One animal was reported to become active between 19:30 h and 24:00 h and stay out for about six hours at a time. The phase of the moon appeared not to affect activity periods. Though it is not outside the realm of possibility, these skunks rarely are seen during daylight hours.

Movements, Home range and Social organization. Like other skunks, these animals are primarily solitary (except for mothers with offspring). Home ranges can cover from 18–53 ha.

Breeding. These skunks breed in the early spring. Gestation lasts about 60 days. Litter sizes can range from 2–5. Otherwise, little is known about the breeding behavior of this species.

Status and Conservation. Not listed with CITES, and classified as Least Concern in *The IUCN Red List*. The status of this skunk is uncertain. Although not abundant, this species appears to do well in disturbed environments.

Bibliography. Ceballos & Oliva (2005), Goldman (1943), Hall (1981), Hall & Dalquest (1963), Lichtenstein (1838), Reid (1997), Sunquist *et al.* (1989), Thomas (1900a, 1905, 1924), Wozencraft (2005).

6. Humboldt's Hog-nosed Skunk *Conepatus humboldtii*

French: Moufette de Humboldt / **German**: Patagonischer Skunk / **Spanish**: Zorrino patagónico

Taxonomy. *Conepatus humboldtii* Gray, 1837, Magellan Straits, Chile.

Two of the subspecies have been regarded as distinct species, but morphology and color pattern have been used to relegate them to subspecies of *C. humboldtii*. Three subspecies are recognized.

Subspecies and Distribution.

C. h. humboldtii Gray, 1837 – Patagonia (Chile and Argentina) to the Strait of Magellan.

C. h. castaneus d'Orbigny & Gervais, 1847 – C Argentina (S provinces of Buenos Aires & La Pampa to N Rio Negro; it also follows along the Colorado and Black Rivers to Neuquen and S Mendoza).

C. h. proteus Thomas, 1902 – subandean C Argentina (Catamarca, La Rioja, San Juan, San Luis & N Mendoza).

Descriptive notes. Head–body 22–32 cm (males), 20–30 cm (females), tail 16·5–20·2 cm (males) and 18–18·5 cm (females); weight 0·5–2·5 kg. Males on average are about 4–6% heavier than females. Humboldt's Hog-nosed Skunks tend to be the smallest of the hog-nosed skunks. These skunks, like all South American skunks, have a double stripe similar to that seen in North American Striped Skunks. Typically, they are black and white, but they can range in color from black to dark brown or reddish brown. It has been suggested that the brownish color appears as the result of age. There is considerable variation in the striping pattern. Humboldt's Hog-nosed Skunks do not have any white markings between the eyes. The tail generally is shorter in proportion to the body than in other skunks. The forelimbs and claws are well adapted for digging. Like other skunks in the genus the nose is long and flexible and used for rooting for burrowing insects. The post carnassial molars have large grinding areas relative to the cutting edge of their carnassial teeth.

Habitat. Humboldt's Hog-nosed Skunks use a variety of habitats. They prefer to den in flat or rolling topography. These skunks will den in shallow caves, below tree roots, in hollow trees, under rocks and cracks between stones, and in abandoned tunnels of other animals. They will use habitat from desert areas to forests. In addition to being found in shrub or forest cover, they use man-made structures, denning under buildings and woodpiles. They use areas with natural herbaceous vegetation, except where poisons are used to control the Culpeo (*Pseudalopex culpaeus*). They are susceptible to poisoning although not targeted. They do however, prefer more open, grassy areas compared to the drier shrubby environments.

Food and Feeding. These skunks are opportunistic feeders and usually capture their prey easily. They generally find their prey by sniffing and digging, using their flexible noses and long claws, primarily in grassy habitats. Like other skunks in the genus they eat a variety of insects, including ground beetles and their larvae, grasshoppers, crickets, and spiders. They will consume fruit when it is available. These skunks also eat a variety of vertebrates, such as lizards and rodents. Carrion is eaten in larger quantities than expected based on relative abundance, when compared with other food items. This would suggest that this species is more carnivorous than insectivorous, but still opportunistic. They also are known to frequent urban garbage sites and vegetable gardens.

Activity patterns. This species is generally nocturnal or crepuscular in nature. Humboldt's Hog-nosed Skunks become more active during the day as winter approaches, and are less active when there is snow cover. They use a variety of den sites during the day and normally do not use the same den site for more than a couple of days at a time. They will however, reuse dens that they occupied previously. They are active for about 50% of the day. Their activity period starts between 20:00–22:00 h and continues until 07:00 h the next morning. Some skunks will remain active until 09:00 h and even until 12:00 h. They rarely are seen between 12:00–19:00 h. During periods of activity they have been observed digging or foraging, walking, and even playing. Young animals will venture as far as 1·3 km from their natal dens to survey new territory before returning home. They may eventually relocate to the areas they investigated.

Movements, Home range and Social organization. Humboldt's Hog-nosed Skunks tend to be solitary for most of their lives. However, in stable areas where shelters are secure, small groups of young individuals may den together. These individuals usually are related and will stay together until they become adults. The home range of juvenile skunks increases in the fall and winter as they explore new areas away from the natal home range. Home range sizes are relatively small and are about 7–16 ha. Home ranges of different individuals can overlap. These skunks usually are not found in high numbers. Density estimates of 0·04 to 0·16 km² have been reported in Chile.

Breeding. Little is known about the reproductive biology of these skunks. The young are born in the spring and disperse in late summer. Gestation has been recorded as short as 42 days, but probably is closer to 60 days. Females generally have only one litter per year and the litters range from 2–5 offspring.

Status and Conservation. Currently, Humboldt's Hog-nosed Skunks is listed with CITES as Appendix II. They are considered Least Concern on *The IUCN Red List*. The pelt of this species has been used for blankets, and as a result they were hunted and over 100,000 skins were exported. In several areas in Chile it has been suggested that hunting pressures be reduced or stopped in order to conserve this species. Humboldt's Hog-nosed Skunks are preyed upon by various raptors as well as Puma. Grazing pressures potentially could decrease populations of this skunk. Additionally, they have been eliminated in some areas as a result of poisoning of other species.

Bibliography. Arias *et al*. (2006), Cabrera (1958), Canevari & Ambrosini (1988), Dragoo *et al*. (2003), Fuller, T.K. *et al*. (1987), Gray (1837), Johnson, W.E. *et al*. (1988), Kipp (1965), Osgood (1943), Thomas (1902a), Wozencraft (2005), Zapata *et al*. (2001).

Genus *MEPHITIS*

Geoffroy Saint-Hilaire & Cuvier, 1795

7. Hooded Skunk *Mephitis macroura*

French: Moufette à capuchon / **German**: Haubenskunk / **Spanish**: Mofeta encapuchada

Taxonomy. *Mephitis macroura* Lichtenstein, 1832, Gebirgs-Gegenden nordwestlich von der Stadt Mexico" (Mexico, mountains north-west of Mexico City).

Four subspecies are recognized.

Subspecies and Distribution.

M. m. macroura Lichtenstein, 1832 – C & W Mexico (Nayarit E to Tamaulipas) and S to Honduras, but not including the Yucatán Peninsula.

M. m. eximius Hall & Dalquest, 1950 – E Mexico (S Veracruz).

M. m. milleri Mearns, 1897 – N Mexico (Sonora and Sinaloa to Coahuila N) to S USA (S Arizona, New Mexico & Texas).

M. m. richardsoni Goodwin, 1957 – Nicaragua and Costa Rica.

Descriptive notes. Head–body averages about 31 cm (males) and 28 cm (females), tail 27–43 cm; weight averages 957 g (males) 882 g (females). Individuals achieve their greatest weight by late summer. Hooded Skunks in the more southern part of their range are smaller than animals in the northern part of the range. Hooded Skunks have three typical color patterns, but there is considerable variation. These patterns are: two thin stripes running down the side of the body from the shoulder to mid-abdomen; a single band running down the back from the forehead to the tail (this single white stripe is interspersed with black hair giving a gray appearance), and a combination of both. These skunks also have a white bar between the eyes. The skull is similar to that of the Striped Skunk, but the auditory bullae are larger. Hooded Skunk can be differentiated externally from Striped Skunk by the long hairs on the back of the neck and head, its relatively longer tail, and larger ears. The anal secretions of the Hooded Skunk have seven major components, which comprise 99% of the volatiles. These components are (E)-2-butene-1-thiol, 3-methyl-1-butanethiol, S-(E)-2-butenyl thioacetate, S-3-methylbutenyl thioacetate, 2-phenylethanethiol, 2-methylquinoline, and 2-quinolinemethanethiol. There are several minor components as well, including phenylmethanethiol, S-phenylmethyl thioacetate, S-2-phenylethyl thioacetate, bis[(E)-2-butenyl] disulfide, (E)-2-butenyl 3-methylbutyl disulfide, bis(3-methylbutyl) disulfide, and S-2-quinolinemethyl thioacetate. The Hooded Skunk's secretion contains four compounds not reported from the Striped Skunk: phenylmethanethiol, S-phenylmethyl thioacetate, 2-phenylethanethiol, and S-2-phenylethyl thioacetate.

Habitat. This skunk occurs in a wide variety of temperate and tropical habitats. It is most common in arid lowlands, but also occurs in deciduous or ponderosa forest, forest edges, pastures, rocky canyons, and riparian habitats. Hooded Skunks use similar habitats to Striped Skunks, but are found more often in scrub and urban habitats. Hooded Skunks occur from sea level to 3110 m, in low elevation desert areas (below 2500 m), in rocky canyons, or in heavily vegetated streamsides and valleys, often in association with mesquite, pine–oak, and other shrubs and grasses. Hooded Skunks appear to prefer intermediate elevations in rocky slopes, at the bases of cliffs, or on the rocky sides of arroyos, but are also encountered in heavy growth of weeds and shrubs

in riparian areas. Dense, brushy cover of stream sides may be important for this species. Hooded Skunks den in holes dug in the ground, rock crevices, and holes in logs. They have even been observed denning more than 1 m above ground in trees, but they are more likely to den on rocky hillsides. They prefer woodland habitats more than do Striped Skunks. In agricultural areas Hooded Skunks den along fencerows, beneath irrigation canals, and in heavily vegetated areas along streams. Hooded Skunks are less likely than Striped Skunks to den around human dwellings. However, radio-collared individuals were frequently located under buildings and sheds and in culverts.

Food and Feeding. The diet of this species consists primarily of insects (including beetles and grasshoppers), fruits, small vertebrates, and birds' eggs. Hooded Skunks break chicken eggs by throwing them between their back legs rather than biting them. Vertebrates are taken opportunistically. When foraging, Hooded Skunk moves slowly, snuffling among leaves and pouncing on grasshoppers and beetles.

Activity patterns. Hooded Skunks remain active all year and have been trapped in the winter. The anal glands are used in self defense. One animal was observed spraying nine times in eleven seconds and again three more times 90 minutes later. The defensive behavior of Hooded Skunk is similar to that of Striped Skunk. Hooded Skunks are active after dusk and travel along rock walls, streambeds, and in weedy fields. They tend to be solitary except when females are raising young, although several may dine together at a feeding station. Females normally do not den together during the winter months.

Movements, Home range and Social organization. Home ranges of Hooded Skunks can occupy from 2·8–5·0 km². Densities of 1·3–3·9 up to 25 Hooded Skunks/km² have been reported. Females, when not nursing, tend to stay at a den site longer than males before moving to a different den within the home range. Males will move greater distances from one den site to the next compared to females. The skunks' home ranges are smaller in urban areas. Urban skunks share mitochondrial DNA (mtDNA) haplotypes with non-urban skunks, which suggests that gene flow occurs between urban and non-urban skunk populations. Genetic data suggest that Hooded Skunks in urban areas represent newer, expanding populations (lower genetic diversity) compared to urban Striped Skunks, which have higher genetic diversity and more stable populations. They are more common in urbanized areas than previously thought, and in some places are more numerous than Striped Skunks. Their numbers are often under-reported because it can be difficult to distinguish the two species.

Skunks can actually be beneficial because they eat insect pests and rodents.

Breeding. The reproductive biology of the Hooded Skunk is poorly known. Breeding likely takes place from mid-February to the end of March. Males have a baculum, and females have two pairs of inguinal, one pair of abdominal, and two pairs of pectoral mammae. Litter size ranges from 3–8. Females may nurse young through August.

Status and Conservation. Classified as Least Concern in *The IUCN Red List*. Little is known about the status of this species, but they may not be uncommon in some parts of their range in the SW USA. However, in Texas, there is concern about population levels and that the species may no longer occur in that state. In Mexico, they are very abundant and survive in human-altered habitats such as cultivated fields, pastures, and suburban areas. There is a need for more research on Hooded Skunks. During a four year study period in Arizona, survival rates of adult skunks were low (24–56%). Predation accounted for most of the mortality, but disease and parasites were contributing factors. Great horned owls (*Bubo virginianus*), mountain lions, bobcats, jaguars, and coyotes may kill Hooded Skunks. Captive Hooded Skunks have lived for at least eight years. Historically, the pelt has not been considered to be of great value, so this skunk has not been hunted to the extent that other species have. Its fur is very long, light and of low economic value. The flesh has been used for food in some areas, and the fat and scent glands have been used for medicinal purposes. Roundworms (*Physaloptera maxillaris*), fleas (Pulicidae), and the nematode *Skrjabingylus chitwoodorum* occur in Hooded Skunks in Trans Pecos, Texas. A new species of *Skrjabingylus* (*S. santacecilliae*) was recently described in this skunk species. Rabies rarely is reported in Hooded Skunks; however, a case of rabies in this species has been documented. There is no reason to suspect that they do not contract the virus; more likely they go unnoticed or are misidentified as Striped Skunks. Hooded Skunks also are susceptible to feline distemper. Hooded Skunks have been found with numerous fleas, ticks, lice, and mites.

Bibliography. Aranda & Lopez-de Buen (1999), Armstrong *et al*. (1972), Bailey (1931), Baker (1956), Carreno *et al*. (2005), Ceballos & Miranda (1986), Dalquest (1953), Davis (1944), Davis & Lukens (1958), Davis & Russell (1954), Dragoo *et al*. (2004), Findley *et al*. (1975), Goodwin (1957), Hall & Dalquest (1950), Hass (2002a, 2003), Hass & Dragoo (2006), Hoffmeister (1986), Hubbard (1972), Janzen & Hallwachs (1982), Lichtenstein (1827–1834), Mearns (1897b), Patton (1974), Reid (1997), Schmidly (1977, 2004), Wood *et al*. (2002).

8. Striped Skunk *Mephitis mephitis*

French: Moufette rayée / **German**: Streifenskunk / **Spanish**: Mofeta rayada

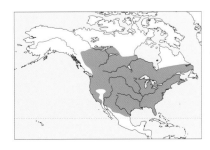

Taxonomy. *Viverra mephitis* Schreber 1776, eastern Canada [Province of Quebec].

A complete taxonomic revision has not been done since 1901. Thirteen subspecies are recognized.

Subspecies and Distribution.

M. m. mephitis Schreber, 1776 – E Canada

M. m. avia Bangs, 1898 – Midwestern USA (Most of Illinois, N half of Missouri & E half of Kansas).

M. m. elongata Bangs, 1895 – E & SE USA (Virginia S to E Georgia, Florida, S Alabama & Mississippi).
M. m. estor Merriam, 1890 – W USA (S Utah through Arizona and W New Mexico) to N Mexico (Sonora & Chihuahua).
M. m. holzerni Mearns, 1897 – SW USA (S California).
M. m. hudsonica Richardson, 1829 – C & W Canada and NC USA (from NE Washington to Wisconsin and S into Colorado).
M. m. major Howell, 1901 – NW USA (N Nevada & Utah to Oregon & Idaho).
M. m. mesomelas Lichtenstein, 1832 – S USA (W Texas & Oklahoma to Arkansas & Louisiana).
M. m. nigra Peale & Palisot de Beauvois, 1796 – SE Canada (New Brunswick & Nova Scotia) and E USA (from New England to Ohio & Indiana and S to Mississippi & Alabama.
M. m. notata Howell, 1901 – NW USA (C Washington).
M. m. occidentalis Baird, 1858 – W USA (N California to SW Oregon).
M. m. spissigrada Bangs, 1898 – NW USA (W Washington).
M. m. varians Gray, 1837 – S Great Plains USA (E New Mexico, Texas, Oklahoma & Kansas) S to NW Mexico (Chihuahua, Coahuila, Nuevo Leon, and Tamaulipas).

Descriptive notes. Head–body 23–40 cm (males), 17–34 cm (females), tail length 20–47 cm (males), 15–36·3 cm (females); weight 0·8–4·1 kg (males), 0·6–3·6 kg (females). Striped Skunks are about the size of house cats, with small triangular-shaped heads. The basic color of skunks is black and white, but other colors, such as brown and red, have been observed in the wild. The typical pattern seen in Striped Skunks is the white "V" down the back and a white bar running between the eyes from the forehead to the middle of the rostrum. Color pattern in Striped Skunks is highly variable and can range from completely black to completely white (non-albino). The striping pattern cannot be used to determine the sex of the animal, nor can it be used to predict how much snow will fall. Skunks are born with their stripes before they have hair. The nose pad is relatively small, and the ears are small and rounded. Striped Skunks have short stocky legs and five toes on each foot. They walk on the soles (plantigrade) of their feet. Occasionally, the heel of the hindfeet will be lifted off the ground when they walk. The claws on the front feet are longer than those of the back feet. The tail is less than half the total body length, with long flowing hairs. The skull is heavy and squarish and widest at the attachment of the zygomata, and the forehead is convex. The dental formula for Striped Skunks is I 3/3, C 1/1, P 3/3, M 1/2, for a total of 34 teeth. The anal secretions of this animal are composed of several major volatile components. These components include: *E*)-2-butene-1-thiol, 3-methyl-1-butanethiol, S-(*E*)-2-butenyl thioacetate, *S*-3-methylbutanyl thioacetate, 2-methylquinoline, 2-quinolinemethanethiol, and *S*-2-quinolinemethyl thioacetate.

Habitat. Striped Skunks use a variety of habitats and tend to be more numerous where good cover and abundant food are available. They can be found in open, exposed areas, but prefer brushy, weedy stream and gulch bottoms or canyons. In open areas they will burrow into banks or even level ground and as a result are able to occupy many habitats. Other habitats where they can be found include a mixture of woodlands, brushy corners, and open fields broken by wooded ravines and rocky outcrops. They will also utilize cultivated areas, pasture, and hay crops. In other parts of their range they use wetlands surrounded by agricultural areas, grasslands, woodlot edges, fencelines, and refuse piles. Striped Skunks may not have a preference for any particular habitat as long as food and shelter are available.

Food and Feeding. Striped Skunks are opportunistic omnivores. With the exception of lima beans, most skunks will eat almost anything. They will feast primarily on insects, such as beetles, grasshoppers, crickets, moths, cutworms, caterpillars, bees, and wasps. They also will eat earthworms, snakes, snails, clams, crayfish, fish, frogs, mice, moles, rats, squirrels, wild fruits, grains, corn, nuts, birds' eggs, carrion, and garbage. Striped Skunks use their long foreclaws to dig for insects and grubs. They will search in rotten or fallen logs for mice and insects. Around gardens they will forage for ripe fruits and vegetables, but they primarily are looking for insects, and benefit gardeners by eating insects that can damage garden crops. They also will take advantage of any pet food left outside.

Activity patterns. Striped Skunks are crepuscular or nocturnal. In the northern part of their range they may go into a torpor (they are not true hibernators) during cold spells or when snow cover is particularly deep. However, in the southern parts of the range, they may actually be more active during the milder winters. When a Striped Skunk perceives a threat, its first response is to run away. If that does not work, it will spray a noxious chemical from the anal scent glands. However, before spraying, skunks use a series of threat behaviors. They will stomp the ground with both front feet. Sometimes they will charge forward a few paces and then stomp or will edge backwards while dragging their front feet, all the while with the tail up in the air. Each scent gland has a nipple associated with it and skunks can aim and direct the spray with highly coordinated muscle control. When a skunk is being chased by a predator, but cannot see the predator, the spray is emitted as an atomized cloud that the predator must run through. This is the "shotgun" method and usually is enough to deter most predators. When the skunk has a target to focus on the spray is emitted as a stream directed at the predator's face. This is the "·357 Magnum" technique. Trapped or cornered skunks will curl into a "U" shape so that both ends face the predator.

Movements, Home range and Social organization. Home ranges of Striped Skunks can be quite variable depending on the available resources (food and shelter primarily). Where there is plenty of food, skunks will tend to have smaller ranges. Home ranges are reported for anywhere from 0·5 km^2 to over 12 km^2. Although Striped Skunks are often found dead on the road, they tend to avoid crossing roads with heavy traffic, and these roads can set the boundaries for some home ranges. During the winter months in the northern part of their range, Striped Skunks become more sedentary and cover less area on their nightly forays. In the southern part of their range, their home ranges remain about the same size year-round. Striped Skunks are solitary most of the time. In the winter females (and occasionally a single male) may den together to conserve heat and body fat. Most males are solitary during the winter. In the southern part of the range communal dens are rarely found during the winter months. During the summer females raise their young, and by early fall the young have left the den.

Breeding. Striped Skunk usually breed from February through March and the young are born starting in April, but births can continue until early June. These skunks usually only go into estrus once a year. However, if a litter is lost early a second litter may be produced. Striped Skunks will breed in their first year, and young males will exhibit breeding behavior in mid- to late summer of their first year, although they are not yet in reproductive condition. Females are usually in estrus for about a week and a half. Striped Skunks are induced ovulators. Ovulation occurs between 40 and 50 hours after first insemination. Males will breed with many females given the opportunity. Most of the females become pregnant by the end of the breeding season. Gestation usually lasts from 59–77 days. Females that breed early in the season may undergo a short period of delayed implantation. Striped Skunks can have as many as twelve offspring per litter, but the average is about 5–7. Females usually have twelve mammae, but the number can range from ten to15. Young skunks are born blind, deaf, and naked. Within a couple of days the black and white hairs cover the pink and white skin. They are born with their scent glands intact and are capable of spraying within the first week of birth. The early scent is more a gas than a liquid. The eyes and ears open after about 28 days (sometimes earlier). After about 6–8 weeks the young are weaned. They begin to forage and explore with mom at this time. By the end of summer or early fall the young begin to disperse.

Status and Conservation. Classified as Least Concern in *The IUCN Red List*. Striped Skunks are not considered for any kind of protection as they appear to be doing well throughout their range. Some of the earliest legislation to protect skunks, in the form of closed trapping seasons, was in New York in 1894. Farmers recognized that skunks were the only effective predators of the hop grub and their service in combating the grub made them valuable assets. Striped Skunks are known to harbor numerous ectoparasites and endoparasites, including fleas, lice, ticks, mites, and various helminth infestations. Intestinal roundworms, nematodes, and lung flukes have been reported. Parasite loads can be a major contributor to mortality. Skunks are a primary vector of rabies in some parts of their range. They also have been found to be infected with canine distemper, histoplasmosis, leptospirosis, listerosis, mycoplasma, pulmonary aspergillosis, sarcocystis, streptococcus, toxoplasma, tularemia, and West Nile Virus. Natural mammalian predators for skunks include humans, domestic dogs, coyotes, red foxes, lynx, bobcats, badgers, mountain lions, and fishers. Various birds of prey including great horned owls, eagles, crows, and vultures also will eat skunks. Turnover in skunk populations is high, so a large percentage of animals in any population consist of young of the year. The average lifespan for wild skunks is about 2–3·5 years. However, Striped Skunks kept in captivity live on average to about 8–12 years of age.

Bibliography. Bailey (1931), Baird (1857), Bangs (1895, 1898a), Bentler *et al.* (2007), Blanton *et al.* (2006), Doty & Dowler (2006), Ganley-Leal *et al.* (2007), Gehrt (2005), Gehrt *et al.* (2006), Gray (1837), Greenwood & Sargeant (1994), Hall (1981), Hass (2003), Hass & Dragoo (2006), Howell (1901), Hwang *et al.* (2007), Kelker (1937), Lantz (1923), Mearns (1897a, 1897b), Merriam (1890b), Neiswenter & Dowler (2007), Neiswenter *et al.* (2006), Rosatte (1988), Verts (1967), Wade-Smith & Richmond (1978a, 1978b), Wade-Smith & Verts (1982), Wood (1990).

Genus *SPILOGALE*

Gray, 1865

9. Pygmy Spotted Skunk *Spilogale pygmaea*

French: Moufette naine / **German**: Zwerg-Fleckenskunk / **Spanish**: Mofeta chica

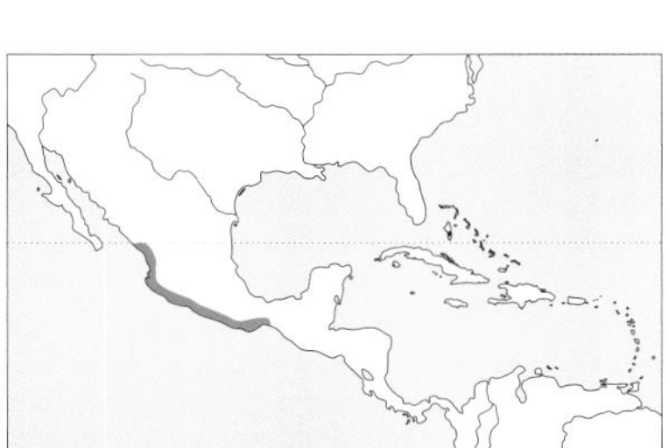

Taxonomy. *Spilogale pygmaea* Thomas, 1898, Rosario, Sinaloa, W. Mexico.
Three subspecies are recognized.

Subspecies and Distribution.
S. p. pygmaea Thomas, 1898 – W Mexico (Pacific coastal regions of Sinaloa & Nayarit).
S. p. australis Hall, 1938 – W Mexico (Pacific coastal region from Michoacán to Guerrero & Oaxaca).
S. p. intermedia López-Forment & Urbano, 1979 – W Mexico (Pacific coastal regions of Jalisco & Colima).

Descriptive notes. Head–body 19–21 cm, tail 6·7–7·3 cm (males) and 5·9–6·7 cm (females), hindfoot 2–3·4 cm, ear 1·8–3·3 cm; weight 150–320 g. Tail length has been used to distinguish the sexes. The Pygmy Spotted Skunk is the smallest of the skunks. The body is elongated and the legs are relatively short. This skunk has six continuous white stripes running down the back and sides; the rest of the fur color is brown to black. There is a white stripe across the forehead above the eyes that continues down the side of the body. Pygmy Spotted Skunks have a short rostrum with a black nose pad, short, rounded ears, short legs, and slender feet with small curved claws. The skull is small and fragile and does not have a sagittal crest. The dental formula is I 3/3, C 1/1, P 3/3, M 1/2 for a total of 34 teeth. These skunks have small canines but relatively large molars.

Habitat. These skunks inhabit deciduous tropical forest, semi-evergreen forest, and desert scrub. They have been observed in coastal sand dunes with only herbaceous vegetation for cover. They have a patchy distribution, but nearly all individuals have been captured in coastal habitats. However, remains have been found in owl pellets about 115 km from the coast at an altitude of 500 m. They are found from sea level up to 1630 m, but are generally found below 350 m. Pygmy Spotted Skunks are scarce, but if enough habitat is preserved, they are believed to be able to survive in disturbed environments.
Food and Feeding. Pygmy Spotted Skunks are opportunistic feeders and consume a variety of invertebrates. Rodents are not taken as frequently as by other spotted skunks, but may be selected as alternative prey when the availability of arthropods is low. Spiny pocket mice are common in the tropical dry forest, and during the dry season, their density is high. During this season rodents also may be easier to detect due to the desiccation of leaf litter. Birds are rarely taken by these skunks and plant material is less likely to be consumed, although, highly digestible fruits may be eaten. Pygmy Spotted Skunks use food sources such as ants, beetles, and spiders in relation to their abundance in the environment. However, some invertebrates, such as insect larvae, millipedes and centipedes, are selected in higher abundance. True bugs (Hemiptera) tend to be avoided as do crickets and grasshoppers (Orthoptera). Pygmy Spotted Skunks will eat cockroaches (*Blattaria*) during the dry season; they may select food items in response to seasonal variation in prey abundance.
Activity patterns. They are nocturnal and den underground or in fallen logs, among rocks, or simply under dense vegetation. They will use dens dug by other animals such as gophers, squirrels, armadillos, and turtles. They use pathways and stream beds to move to and from bodies of water. Much of their activity occurs below the leaf litter or brush, where they search for the burrows of small rodents. Pygmy Spotted Skunks stomp their feet when threatened. They have been observed doing a partial handstand similar to other species of spotted skunks. Anal secretions are usually only released as a last resort.
Movements, Home range and Social organization. These skunks are solitary most of the year except during the breeding season. Males will defend their territory against other males, and only allow females access to their territory.
Breeding. Breeding occurs from April through August, with most births occurring around July and August. Gestation usually lasts from 43–51 days, and there may be a short period of delayed implantation. More than one litter per year may be produced. The number of young per litter can range from one to six in this species. The young are born with fine white hair, but the skin pigmentation pattern is similar to that of adults. Newborn kits weigh about 7 g, and their eyes and ears do not open until they are 29–32 days old. Most of the teeth are present at 47 days.
Status and Conservation. Not listed with CITES. Classified as Vulnerable in *The IUCN Red List*. This skunk is locally abundant in certain areas, but is considered to be vulnerable throughout much of its range in Mexico due to habitat destruction as a result of tourist resort and road construction. These animals also have been stuffed and sold as souvenirs. Skulls have been recovered from barn owl pellets, and snakes and other carnivores probably prey on Pygmy Spotted Skunks. They have been found with various parasites including ticks, cestodes, nematode, and intestinal worms.
Bibliography. Cantú-Salazar (2002), Cantú-Salazar, Fernandez & Hidalgo-Mihart (2004), Cantú-Salazar, Hidalgo-Mihart *et al.* (2005), Ceballos & Miranda (1986), Ceballos & Oliva (2005), Hall (1938), Lopez-Forment & Urbano (1979), Medellín *et al.* (1998), Schreiber *et al.* (1989), Teska *et al.* (1981), Thomas (1898b).

10. Eastern Spotted Skunk *Spilogale putorius*

French: Moufette tachetée / **German**: Östlicher Fleckenskunk / **Spanish**: Mofeta oriental

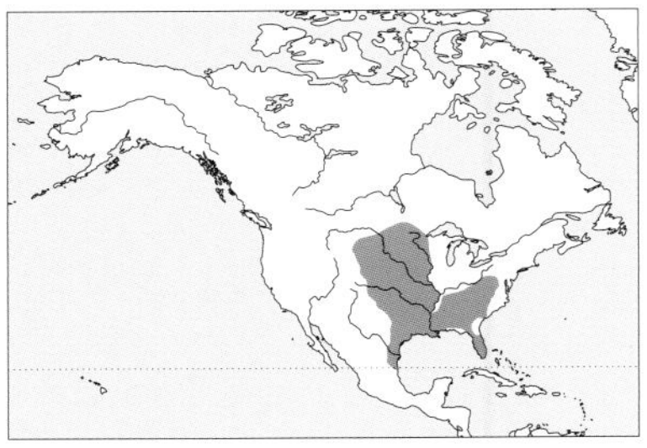

Taxonomy. *Viverra putorius* Linnaeus, 1758, South Carolina.
Three subspecies are recognized.
Subspecies and Distribution.
S. p. putorius Linnaeus, 1758 – E & SE USA (Mississippi, Alabama & N Florida, through Georgia, N to SC Pennsylvania).
S. p. ambarvalis Bangs, 1898 – SE USA (Peninsular Florida).
S. p. interrupta Rafinesque, 1820 – USA (Canadian border in Minnesota, C North Dakota, E Wyoming, E Colorado, W Oklahoma, NW Texas, south to C Texas, and east to the Mississippi River along Louisiana, Arkansas, Missouri & Iowa, up to Wisconsin.
Descriptive notes. There is considerable variation in size of Eastern Spotted Skunks. Head–body 23–33 cm, mean 30 cm (males), and 19–33 cm, mean 29 cm (females), tail 8–28 cm, mean 16·4 cm (males), and 8·5–21 cm, mean 15·4 cm (females); weight 276–885 g (males) and 207–475 g (females). Eastern Spotted Skunks are smaller than Striped Skunks and more weasel-like in body shape. The pelage of Eastern Spotted Skunks is black with a complex striping pattern of six stripes; the stripes can be interrupted, giving a somewhat spotted appearance. There are usually two white spots on the rump, as well as a white spot between the eyes. The dorsal stripes run down the vertebral column from the head toward the tail. Two stripes run below the dorsal stripes over the shoulder and continue across the ears, forming a small white spot in front of the ears. A third set of stripes continues from the front feet past the end of the shoulder stripes. Locomotion in Eastern Spotted Skunks is plantigrade and these skunks run with their bodies low to the ground. While walking more slowly and cautiously, they will extend their limbs and raise their heads to get higher off the ground. Spotted skunks have five toes on each foot. They are not such efficient diggers as *Conepatus* or *Mephitis*, but are much more agile and able to climb. The dental formula for this species is I 3/3, C 1/1, P 3/3, M 1/2, totaling 34 teeth. The P^2 is always small and may be absent.
Habitat. These skunks are rarely found in the open, preferring either forested areas or habitats containing significant vegetative cover. In the Plains States, these skunks inhabit riparian woodlands and areas of vegetation along fences. They also are found in brushy and rocky habitats, but avoid wetlands. They have been observed on sandy soils and beaches in Florida. Eastern Spotted Skunks seem to prefer habitat with extensive vegetative cover, as this cover provides protection from various predators. They den in protected, dark, dry holes including natural crevices in trees, and will den off the ground to an elevation of seven meters in hollow trees. They dig their own burrows, or den in holes previously occupied by other animals, in talus slopes, haystacks, under houses or rocks, and in the walls of houses or barns. They prefer warm holes in the winter and cool dens in the summer, and will change den sites to accommodate these needs.
Food and Feeding. Eastern Spotted Skunks forage primarily at night. They are secretive and not often seen. These skunks are exceptional mousers and do farmers a great service when they forage around barns and buildings. They are omnivores, but tend to be more carnivorous than *Mephitis* or *Conepatus*. The diet consists mainly of insects, small mammals, birds, and birds' eggs. Like a center hiking an American football, the skunk uses its front paws to throw an egg through its back legs in order to crack the shell. These skunks also will eat fruits and vegetables in the summer and fall when they are available.
Activity patterns. They are generally nocturnal. They usually avoid moonlit nights. On nights when the moon is not out they normally have two periods of activity. They will come out soon after sunset and again before sunrise. They will be active throughout the night as well. Eastern Spotted Skunks have been observed during the day on rare occasions. Spotted skunks are quite agile and are capable of climbing. This agility also can be observed in their threat behavior as they are able to perform front handstands. When faced with a potential predator, the skunk rushes forward, then stands on its forepaws with its hind end elevated off the ground. This behavior has been reported to last for up to eight minutes in short, 2–5 second bursts of handstanding. However, a young, captive animal from a wildlife rehabilitation effort was observed crouching under a couch on all fours until a domestic cat came into the room. The skunk rushed out from under the couch toward the cat. As soon as its tail cleared the cushion it went into a handstand/run. The cat began to trot away. The skunk followed on its front feet, bouncing around a table, about 1·5 m and then jumped up on a stand approximately 6 cm off the ground, ran along the stand, hopped off the end and continued to chase the cat to the other end of the room. The cat finally ran off and the skunk dropped down on all fours and went back under the couch. Spotted skunks have been reported to spray from the hand-stand position, but they usually drop down and face the predator with both ends in a "U" shape. The handstand is usually just a threat behavior used to drive off the predator.
Movements, Home range and Social organization. These skunks usually den alone, but in cold winter months several skunks may bed down together. They usually use more than one den site within their home range. Eastern Spotted Skunks move from den to den and more than one individual has been captured at the same den site in capture-recapture studies. They may also share dens, but with only one animal using the den at a time. Captive male animals have been reported to be aggressive toward one another to the point of one animal killing the other. Females tended not to engage in fatal fights, but remained defensive while in the same cage. Young animals will wrestle and screech at one another, but will also sleep together. Young animals will usually separate before reaching full adulthood. Spotted skunks have a patchy distribution throughout their range. Where they occur they can be found at a density of about nine animals per km² to about 20 and even 40 per km². Eastern Spotted Skunks tend to move greater distances in the spring than in the summer and fall. Home ranges can be up to 4359 ha.
Breeding. Reproduction in the Eastern Spotted Skunk is different from that in the Western Spotted Skunk. The main breeding season for this species is during March and April, although some individuals may breed again in July, August, or September to produce a second litter. Gestation is estimated to be from 50 to 65 days, with only a two-week period of delayed implantation. First-season litters are produced in late May and early June. Litter size averages five but ranges from 2–9 kits. Young are born naked or with sparse, fine, black and white pelage. The claws are well- developed at birth. The eyes and ears open at about 30 days and teeth become visible at 32 days. They can make squealing vocalizations at an early age. The young are weaned after about two months.
Status and Conservation. Not listed in CITES. Classified as Least Concern in *The IUCN Red List*. However, there has been concern over the lack of observations of this species throughout its range in the last few decades. Population densities of Eastern Spotted Skunks were believed to be low when settlers first arrived on the Great Plains. When small farm operations flourished there prior to the 1920s, spotted skunks became more numerous as farm buildings provided shelter as well as a supply of mice and rats. When the small farms gave way to larger operations, the density of spotted skunks became lower. Today, the Eastern Spotted Skunk is considered to be threatened in many of the states within its historical range. Natural predators of spotted skunks include larger carnivores such as domestic dogs, coyotes, foxes, feral cats and bobcats, and birds of prey such as owls. Ectoparasites found on Eastern Spotted Skunks include fleas and ticks, and endoparasites include various tapeworms, roundworms, and coccidian protozoans. Humans also are known to be a major cause of mortality because of the

number of skunks hit by cars. Pneumonia and coccidiosis are diseases that have been reported in this species. Rabies has been reported, but rarely. Histoplasmosis has also been found, and microfilaria, listeriosis, mastitis, tularemia, distemper, and Q fever are likely to affect Eastern Spotted Skunks.

Bibliography. Bangs (1898b), Choate *et al*. (1973), Crabb (1948), Dragoo & Honeycutt, (1999b), Gompper & Hackett (2005), Howell (1906), Kinlaw (1995), Manaro (1961), McCullough & Fritzell (1984), Mead (1968a), Mitchell (1923), Pocock (1921), Reed & Kennedy (2000), Seton (1926), Van Gelder (1959).

11. Western Spotted Skunk *Spilogale gracilis*

French: Moufette gracile / **German**: Westlicher Fleckenskunk / **Spanish**: Mofeta occidental

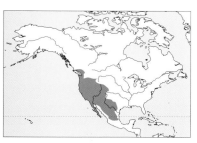

Taxonomy. *Spilogale gracilis* Merriam, 1890, Grand Cañon of the Colorado (altitude 3500 feet), Arizona, north of San Francisco Mountain.
Western Spotted Skunks were once considered the same species as Eastern Spotted Skunks. Chromosomal and reproductive data have been used to elevate these skunks to specific status. Seven subspecies are recognized.

Subspecies and Distribution.
S. g. gracilis Merriam, 1890 – W USA (from E Washington & E Oregon to NE California, and then E to W Montana & E Wyoming to C Colorado, and possibly the Black Hills, South Dakota. Then S to N New Mexico, N Arizona, C Nevada and E & C California).
S. g. amphialus Dickey, 1929 – SW USA (occurs only on Santa Rosa I and Santa Cruz I in Santa Barbara County, California).
S. g. latifrons Merriam, 1890 – SW Canada (SW British Columbia) S and W to NW USA (Washington and Oregon). The distribution follows the crest of the Cascade Mts.
S. g. leucoparia Merriam, 1890 – S USA (found from C Arizona, C New Mexico, and W & C central Texas) S to N Mexico (Coahuila & C Durango).
S. g. lucasana Merriam, 1890 – NW Mexico (S Baja California N to Santo Domingo on the W coast and La Paz on the E coast).
S. g. martirensis Elliot, 1903 – NW Mexico (N & C Baja California).
S. g. phenax Merriam, 1890 – SW USA (From California west to crest of Sierra Nevada).
Descriptive notes. Head–body 25–37 cm (males) and 24–27 cm (females), tail 10–21 cm (males) and 8·5–20·3 cm (females); weight 255–997 g (males) and 269–566 g (females). *Spilogale* is more weasel-like in body plan than any of the other genera (*Mephitis, Conepatus, Mydaus*). Western Spotted Skunks are similar in color pattern to the Eastern Spotted Skunks in that they also have six stripes along the back and sides. One set of stripes runs parallel to the backbone, and beside those stripes is another set that extends past the shoulders and over the ears. The third set of stripes runs from the shoulder to the abdomen and then curves upwards towards the back. There is also a spot on each of the hips. The color pattern may break up the body outline on moonless nights. Where the two species potentially come together the Western Spotted Skunks tends to have wider white stripes and a larger spot between the eyes. The Western Spotted Skunks is reportedly longer and more slender with a longer tail than the Eastern Spotted Skunks. The feet each have five toes and locomotion is plantigrade. Western Spotted Skunks are quite capable climbers. The skull is flatter and wider than that of the Eastern Spotted Skunks, and the front region of the skull is depressed to the level of the cranium. The baculum of the Western Spotted Skunk is shorter than and not as curved as that of the Eastern Spotted Skunk. Western Spotted Skunks also have two muscular musk glands at the base of the tail inside the anal sphincter. These glands are capable of ejecting a noxious yellow fluid that is used in defense to deter a predator. The musk is composed of three major thiols, (E)-2-butene-l-thiol, 3-methyl-1-butanethiol, and 2-phenylethanethiol, and several minor components, including phenylmethanethiol, 2-methyl-quinoline, 2-quinoline methanethiol, bis[(E)-2-butenyl] disulfide, (E)-2-butenyl 3-methylbutyl disulfide, and bis(3-methylbutyl) disulfide. The Western Spotted Skunks does not have the thiol esters associated with the musk as seen in *Mephitis* and *Conepatus*. While the spray is as pungent as in the other skunks it does not have the "staying power" without the thiol esters.
Habitat. These skunks are found along streams in riparian thickets composed of willows and cottonwoods or alder, salmonberry, tan oak and other hardwoods. They also occur in all stages of dry forests and pine–oak forests, and use canyons, cliffs, rock piles, lava fields, and dry valleys. They prefer areas where they can find cover protection from predators. These skunks will use tunnels and holes of other animals such as mountain beavers in Oregon and wood rats and ground squirrels in other parts of their range. Western Spotted Skunks have been found in older buildings in rural settings, but also have been taken in urban houses and apartments. They also will den around other man-made structures such as dams as long as protective cover is available.
Food and Feeding. Western Spotted Skunks eat a variety of food items. They are omnivores, but tend to have a mostly carnivorous diet. They eat small mammals, birds, and lizards. They consume a number of insects including grasshoppers, beetles, caterpillars, and ants. They also will eat fruits and vegetable matter to supplement their diets.
Activity patterns. They are generally nocturnal. They prefer to move under the cover of darkness, but have been observed during daylight hours. When nervous they will walk with heavy deliberate steps. Spotted skunks are quite agile and are capable of climbing. Like other spotted skunks, they can perform handstands and walk on only their front paws. When faced with a potential predator, the skunk rushes forward, then

stands on its forepaws with its hind end elevated off the ground. It can spray in this position, but usually drops to all fours and faces the predator with both ends before spraying.
Movements, Home range and Social organization. Western Spotted Skunks usually den alone, but they use multiple dens. Dens may be used by multiple individuals, but not necessarily at the same time. The skunks usually den in areas that provide protective cover, such as under shrubs or prickly pear cactus. During the late summer and early fall months males tend to be captured more than females. This could be due to increased movement of males during the breeding season, which corresponds to these months. Young animals when playing will let out a loud, ear piercing, high pitched screech when excited. Young males of the same litter will wrestle more aggressively than females. They tend to leave the maternal den sooner in order to look for mates. Western Spotted Skunks have a patchy distribution throughout their range and very little study has been done of home range, density, and dispersal. However, in an island population these skunks have a larger home range (about twice the size) in the drier months than during the wet months.
Breeding. These skunks breed in September and October and undergo a period of delayed implantation. Although a second period of breeding is possible, this breeding season makes them reproductively isolated from Eastern Spotted Skunks. Western Spotted Skunks give birth in April or May to a litter of 2–6 young. Gestation lasts for about 210–230 days. Young are born blind and naked. Their eyes open after about 28 days and they are weaned after two months. Young begin to disperse after about three months.
Status and Conservation. . Not listed in CITES. Classified as Least Concern in *The IUCN Red List*. The island spotted skunk in California is listed as a subspecies of special concern. Several larger carnivores such as domestic dogs, coyotes, foxes, feral cats, bobcats, and birds of prey such as owls are known to prey on spotted skunks. Various intestinal parasites including tapeworms, roundworms, and coccidia have been found in spotted skunks. They also are susceptible to fleas and ticks. Humans have been known to trap and shoot spotted skunks for fur and they have been poisoned as non target animals during predator control efforts. In the USA, rabies has been reported, but it is rare. Western Spotted Skunks have been reported to survive over ten years in captivity.
Bibliography. Bailey (1905, 1931, 1936), Carey & Kershner (1996), Crooks & Van Vuren (1995), Dickey (1929), Doty & Dowler (2006), Genoways & Jones (1968), Grinnell *et al*. (1937), Hall (1926), Hall & Kelson (1952), Howell (1906), Mead (1968b), Merriam (1890a, 1890b), Neiswenter & Dowler (2007), Neiswenter *et al*. (2006), Patton (1974), Seton (1926), Van Gelder (1959), Verts & Carraway (1998), Verts *et al*. (2001), Wood *et al*. (1991).

12. Southern Spotted Skunk *Spilogale angustifrons*

French: Moufette de Howell / **German**: Südlicher Fleckenskunk / **Spanish**: Mofeta meridional

Taxonomy. *Spilogale angustifrons* Howell, 1902, Tlalpan, Distrito Federal, Mexico.
This skunk has been classified as a subspecies of *Spilogale putorius* off and on throughout its taxonomic history. Recent chromosomal data have helped to elevate it back to species status. There are five subspecies recognized.
Subspecies and Distribution.
S. a. angustifrons Howell, 1902 – C Mexico (Distrito Federal & C Michoacan).
S. a. celeris Hall, 1938 – highlands of Nicaragua S towards C Costa Rica.
S. a. elata Howell, 1906 – highlands of SE Mexico (Chiapas), Guatemala, El Salvador, and Honduras.
S. a. tropicalis Howell, 1902 – S Mexico (E Puebla, C Morelos, & C Guerrero, and SE towards Oaxaca and along the Pacific Coast) to E El Salvador.
S. a. yucatanensis Burt, 1938 – Mexico (occurs throughout the Yucatán Peninsula), Belize and N Guatemala.
Descriptive notes. Very few specimens are available for measurements. Head–body 21–25 cm (males) and 20–24 cm (females), tail 10·1–14·5 cm; weight 240–533 g. The color pattern in this species is very similar to other species of spotted skunks. They have a white spot between the eyes and a series of six vertical white stripes along the back and sides. The top set of white stripes runs along the middle of the back towards the rear of the animal where they branch off and become horizontal on the hips. The next pair runs from the ears parallel to the top stripes. The third set runs from the forelegs along the side and sometimes joins the horizontal stripes on the hips. The tip (one third of the tail) is white. There is considerable variation in this color pattern. Southern Spotted Skunks have five toes on each foot and long claws. The skull is small and narrow with a highly arched cranium. The rostrum is also narrow. The dental formula for this skunk is: I 3/3, C 1/1, P 3/3, M 1/2 = 34. This species, like other skunks, is endowed with well- developed scent glands, which can expel a noxious fluid to repel potential predators.
Habitat. These skunks are found in rocky hills with brush and sparse trees, but they also can be found in pine–oak forests at high elevations. They can occur in a variety of habitats such as rainforests, dry thickets, pine forests, and grasslands. They are commonly found in agricultural fields as well. Southern Spotted Skunks have been found from sea level to about 2800 m. They make dens under logs or rocks, in hollow trees, and between the roots of trees and shrubs. They also use dens abandoned by armadillos and other mammals.

Food and Feeding. Like other spotted skunks, Southern Spotted Skunks feed mainly on insects and small mammals. They also will consume amphibians and wild fruit. 50% of their diet consists of invertebrates and the remainder consists of vertebrates and vegetation (including fruits).

Activity patterns. These animals presumably are nocturnal. Like the other skunks they are equipped with anal scent glands that can be used in defense. Southern Spotted Skunks probably have very similar activity patterns to Eastern and Western Spotted Skunks.

Movements, Home range and Social organization. Home ranges for this species have been estimated at about 64 hectares. In areas where they are common they have been reported in densities of 5–8 individuals per square kilometer.

Breeding. The breeding season in this species has not been studied. Because Eastern and Western Spotted Skunks have different periods of delayed implantation, the breeding season in this species would be an interesting study.

Status and Conservation. Not listed in CITES. Classified as Least Concern in *The IUCN Red List*. This species is just recently being recognized by taxonomists and is therefore not likely to have been considered for special conservation status. However, it is reported that where they do occur they are common. This species has been reported with antibodies to rabies, parvovirus, and toxoplasma.

Bibliography. Baker & Baker (1975), Ceballos & Oliva (2005), Cervantes *et al.* (2002), Hall (1938), Hall & Kelson (1952, 1959), Howell (1902, 1906), Kinlaw (1995), Owen *et al.* (1996), Reid (1997), Suzan & Ceballos (2005), Van Gelder (1959), Verts *et al.* (2001).

CLASS MAMMALIA

ORDER CARNIVORA

SUBORDER CANIFORMIA

Family MUSTELIDAE (WEASELS AND RELATIVES)

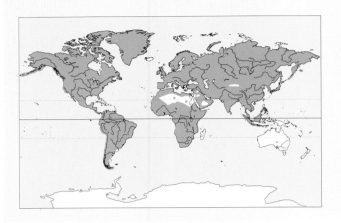

- Small- to medium-sized mammals with long bodies and short limbs.
- 13–195 cm.

- Holarctic, Neotropical, African, and Oriental regions.
- Forests, grasslands, tundras and oceans, from the Arctic to the tropics.
- 22 genera, 57 species, at least 217 extant taxa.
- 7 species Endangered, 5 species Vulnerable; 1 species Extinct since 1600.

Systematics

The Mustelidae is the largest family within the Carnivora, comprising 57 species of weasels, martens, polecats, badgers, and otters. The exact number of species is still debated, but further taxonomic research will help resolve this situation. Mustelids are found on all continents except Antarctica, although within the Australasian region, humans introduced the Ermine (*Mustela erminea*) and Least Weasel (*Mustela nivalis*) to New Zealand.

Resolving relationships within the Mustelidae has been challenging and many taxonomic schemes have been proposed. Pocock (1921) used descriptive analyses of external characters (such as the structure of the rhinarium and feet) to divide the extant mustelids into 15 subfamilies. Simpson (1945), on the other hand, proposed five subfamilies, based on both phylogeny and "similarity in adaptiveness": Lutrinae (otters), Melinae (badgers), Mellivorinae (Honey Badger), Mephitinae (skunks), and Mustelinae (martens and weasels). However, morphological similarity does not necessarily reflect phylogenetic affinity, as has been demonstrated in many other groups that show adaptive radiation. Nonetheless, Simpson's subfamilial classification of the Mustelidae was followed for many years.

During the last decade, the validity of Simpson's five-subfamily classification scheme has been challenged, and even the monophyly of the Mustelidae itself has been reconsidered. DNA phylogenetic studies, using both mitochondrial and nuclear sequences, have consistently demonstrated that skunks (*Conepatus, Mephitis,* and *Spilogale*) and stink badgers (*Mydaus*) descended from a common ancestor and together form a lineage that diverged prior to the split between the Mustelidae and Procyonidae (raccoons, olingos, and coatis). The skunks and stink badgers have now been placed in a separate family, the Mephitidae. Recently, Wozencraft (2005) placed all the mustelids (excluding the skunks and stink badgers) into two subfamilies: the Mustelinae (weasels, polecats, martens, and badgers) and the Lutrinae (otters).

Molecular studies have now confirmed that the Lutrinae is monophyletic, but that the Mustelinae is polyphyletic. Based on these results, some authors have recently proposed dividing the Mustelidae into eight subfamilies: Lutrinae (otters), Mustelinae (weasels and mink), Galictidinae (grisons, striped polecats/weasels, and Marbled Polecat), Helictidinae (ferret-badgers), Martinae (Wolverine, Tayra, and martens), Melinae (Hog Badger and Eurasian badgers), Mellivorinae (Honey Badger), and Taxidiinae (American Badger).

A recent molecular study, using mitochondrial and nuclear DNA data obtained from 22 gene segments, resolved the Mustelidae into seven primary divisions that include four major clades and three monotypic lineages. The otters (*Aonyx, Enhydra, Hydrictis, Lontra, Lutra, Lutrogale,* and *Pteronura*) form a sister clade to one comprising weasels and mink (*Mustela* and *Neovison*). These clades, in turn, are sister to a clade that includes the grisons, striped polecats/weasels, and Marbled Polecat (*Galictis, Ictonyx, Poecilogale,* and *Vormela*). The ferret-badgers (*Melogale*) form a monotypic lineage that is sister to these three combined clades. The fifth major clade comprises two subclades, one containing the Hog Badger (*Arctonyx collaris*) and Eurasian badgers (*Meles*), and another containing the Tayra (*Eira barbara*), Wolverine (*Gulo gulo*), and martens (*Martes*). Finally, the American Badger (*Taxidea taxus*) and Honey Badger (*Mellivora capensis*) each form monotypic lineages that diverged early within the Mustelidae; each of these two lineages form successive sister groups to all the other mustelid genera. The only genus missing from this study was *Lyncodon*, and thus the phylogenetic relationships of the enigmatic Patagonian Weasel (*Lyncodon patagonicus*) remains obscure.

The Mustelidae are small- to medium-sized carnivores, most with long bodies and short limbs, like the **Sable**. *All mustelids have five toes on each foot and many species have strong claws. Dense, stiff hairs cover the soles of the Sable's feet, and although it is mainly terrestrial, it can climb well. Like other mustelid species, the Sable can point its ears forward or swivel them to the side, but cannot fold them back. It prefers mature forests, and is often found in mountainous habitat, especially near streams. The Sable preys on small mammals, but also eats birds, reptiles, amphibians, fish, insects, fruits, honey, nuts, and berries. The Sable's long, silky winter fur, which can range in color from pale brown to almost black, is commercially valuable.*

Martes zibellina
Russia.
Photo: Mikhail Zhilin/FLPA

MUSTELIDAE

TAXIDIINAE

American Badger
1 species
(*Taxidea*)

MELLIVORINAE

Honey Badger
1 species
(*Mellivora*)

MELINAE

Hog Badger and Eurasian badgers
4 species
(*Arctonyx, Meles*)

MARTINAE

Wolverine, Tayra, and martens
10 species
(*Eira, Gulo, Martes*)

HELICTIDINAE

ferret-badgers
4 species
(*Melogale*)

GALICTIDINAE

grisons, striped polecats/weasels, and Marbled Polecat
6 species
(*Galictis, Vormela, Ictonyx, Poecilogale*)

LUTRINAE

otters
12 species
(*Pteronura, Lontra, Enhydra, Hydrictis, Lutra, Aonyx, Lutrogale*)

MUSTELINAE

weasels and mink
19 species
(*Mustela, Neovison, Lyncodon*)

FAMILY
SUBFAMILY

Subdivision of the Mustelidae

Figure: Toni Llobet

These molecular topologies are partly incongruent with some previous cladistic analyses based on morphology. For example, one morphological study did not group *Eira, Gulo,* and *Martes* within a monophyletic clade, and found that the ferret-badgers (*Melogale*) were a sister group to all the remaining mustelids. Also, alternative topologies were recovered when certain morphological characters were weighted differentially. These studies thus highlighted the difficulty of using traditional morphological features to define systematic relationships; some characteristics may either be convergent features or primitive generalized characters in the group.

Within the subfamily Lutrinae, the otters are now resolved into three primary lineages, one containing Old World otters (*Aonyx, Hydrictis, Lutra,* and *Lutrogale*) and the Sea Otter (*En-*

hydra lutris), a second containing New World otters (*Lontra*), and a third containing the monotypic Giant Otter (*Pteronura brasiliensis*). The number of otter species is, however, still debated. The Congo Clawless Otter (*Aonyx congicus*) is considered a separate species by some authors, based on morphological and ecological evidence. However, further research is needed to determine its taxonomic status, and it is here included as a subspecies of the African Clawless Otter (*Aonyx capensis*). The Japanese Otter (*Lutra nippon*) has also been considered a valid species, based on recent morphological and molecular analyses. Again, further research is needed, and it is here considered a subspecies of the Eurasian Otter (*Lutra lutra*).

Within the subfamily Mustelinae (*Mustela* and *Neovison*), the American Mink (*Neovision vison*) and Long-tailed Weasel (*Mus-*

American Badgers *have a body
type that it typical for the badgers,
being stocky with short legs and a
short tail. They also have a skull
that is almost triangular and very
flat. Their eyes have a nictitating
membrane that can close like
an eyelid, and the long, strong
claws on the forefeet have nerve
endings; both of these features
are adaptations for their fossorial
lifestyle. Their feet are partly
webbed, which probably helps them
walk on snow. The fur pattern
varies: for example, the white
stripe on the forehead can stop at
the neck or continue all the way to
the rump. American Badgers are
classified in a genus of their own,*
Taxidea, *and diverged from the
other mustelids about 21 million
years ago, in the early Miocene.
The ancestors of* Taxidea *arrived
in North America before the Bering
Strait first opened, which happen
around 5.5 million years ago.*

Taxidea taxus
Minnesota, USA.
Photo: Art Wolfe

tela frenata) form a sister clade to all the other *Mustela* species. Within the latter clade, the Malay Weasel (*Mustela nudipes*) and the Back-striped Weasel (*Mustela strigidorsa*) are sister to a clade comprising species largely distributed in temperate regions of the Northern Hemisphere. The species of "true" weasels (*Mustela*) and mink have previously been divided into five or nine subgenera, based on morphological criteria. However, recent molecular analyses suggest that only one proposed subgenus (*Putorius*) constitutes a natural group: the Steppe Polecat (*Mustela eversmanni*), European Polecat (*Mustela putorius*), and the Black-footed Ferret (*Mustela nigripes*). The genus *Mustela* is paraphyletic with respect to *Neovison*, which suggests that the recent placement of the American Mink in the separate genus *Neovison* may not be warranted, despite the observed differences in karyotype and morphology between this taxon and other species of *Mustela*. The European Mink (*Mustela lutreola*) inhabits much of Europe and parts of Russia. The American

Mink is found throughout Canada and the United States, and was introduced to Eurasia. Although they have similar morphology and ecology, molecular data reveal that they are distantly related. This is clearly an example of either parallel or convergent evolution within the Mustelidae to fill a similar ecological niche.

In the subfamily Galictidinae, the Lesser Grison (*Galictis cuja*) and Greater Grison (*Galictis vittata*) of Central and South America form a sister group to a clade containing the Marbled Polecat (*Vormela peregusna*) of Eurasia and three African species, the Saharan Striped Polecat (*Ictonyx libycus*), Zorilla (*Ictonyx striatus*), and African Striped Weasel (*Poecilogale albinucha*). The monophyly of this latter group is of interest because they all exhibit an aposematically-colored pelage and defense behaviors that include threat displays and excretion of pungent musk from enlarged anal glands. There is also a north-to-south progression in the branching order of this group, from the Mar-

Like other badger species, the
Honey Badger *is a short, stocky
animal with a short tail. Females
are somewhat larger than males.
The Honey Badger has a massive
skull and 32 robust teeth. The
number of teeth in mustelid
species varies: most have 34, 36,
or 38. The Sea Otter is the only
other mustelid with 32 teeth; the
African Striped Weasel and the
Patagonian Weasel have only 28.
Honey Badgers are strong diggers
with long, strong claws on their
broad forefeet. They also climb and
swim well.*

Mellivora capensis
Okavango Delta, Botswana.
Photo: Richard du Toit/naturepl.com

FAMILY MUSTELIDAE
Weasels and relatives

The long, hairless snout of the **Hog Badger** *explains its common name, and its impressive claws gave rise to the name of its genus,* Arctonyx. Arct *means "bear" in Greek and* onyx *means "claw". Hog Badgers use their snouts and claws to root for earthworms, insects, snails, tubers, and other food items, and also use their claws to excavate burrows. Scientists have recently decided to divide the genus* Arctonyx *into three species:* A. collaris *is large with short fur, and is distributed throughout South-east Asia from eastern India to Myanmar, Thailand, Vietnam, Cambodia, and Laos;* A. albogularis *is medium in size and shaggy, and is found in temperate regions in Asia from Tibet to China; and* A. hoevenii *is the smallest, darkest species, and is endemic to the Indonesian island of Sumatra.*

Arctonyx collaris
Photo: Roland Seitre

bled Polecat to the Zorilla and African Striped Weasel, which renders the genus *Ictonyx* paraphyletic. This suggests that the African Striped Weasel should be placed into the genus *Ictonyx*.

As for the subfamily Martinae, which contains *Eira*, *Gulo*, and *Martes*, the last genus is clearly paraphyletic and it has been proposed that the Fisher (*Martes pennanti*) should now be placed in its own genus, *Pekania*. The two New World species, the Tayra and Fisher, either form a clade or successive monotypic lineages sister to a clade containing the Wolverine and the remaining species of *Martes*. Molecular evidence indicates that the "true" martens (*Martes*, excluding the Fisher) are monophyletic and are a sister group to the Yellow-throated Marten (*Martes flavigula*). Within the "true" *Martes*, various analyses of the molecular data have resulted in different phylogenetic placements of the American Marten (*Martes americana*) and Japanese Marten (*Martes melampus*) relative to the European Pine Marten (*Martes martes*) and Sable (*Martes zibellina*) clade.

One mustelid species, the Sea Mink (*Neovison macrodon*), has been declared extinct. It was said to have resembled the American Mink, but lived among rocks along the ocean, feeding mainly on fish. No complete specimen is known to exist, and descriptions are based only on observations and numerous bone fragments and teeth found along the New England coast. The Sea Mink was intensely hunted for its fur and was apparently exterminated by about 1880.

The Colombian Weasel (*Mustela felipei*) was only discovered in 1978 and its relationship to the rest of the Mustelidae has not yet been determined. Other rare and endangered species, such as the Nilgiri Marten (*Martes gwatkinsii*), have yet to be included in any molecular phylogeny studies. The domestic Ferret, which is often given the subspecific name *Mustela putorius furo*, is commonly kept as a pet in many parts of the world. It is generally thought to be a descendant of the European Polecat, but the Steppe Polecat may also have been involved in its ancestry.

Molecular dating analyses indicate that following the initial divergence of *Taxidea* in the Early Miocene, around 21 million years ago, mustelids underwent two main bursts of diversification. The first burst occurred during a 3–4 million year interval from the Middle to Late Miocene (12·5–8·8 million years ago) and gave rise to most of the extant primary clades and lineages. The second and larger burst occurred during the Pliocene epoch (5·3–1·8 million years ago) in which as many as 20 generic-level or specific-level lineages originated within a 3·5 million

year span of time. The majority of these diversification events occurred in the Old World, largely in Eurasia.

Paleoenvironmental and biotic changes, driven by changes in climate during the latter half of the Neogene (between 23 million years ago and the present), may have promoted these two bursts of diversification within the Mustelidae. There was a marked cooling of the global climate near the end of the Middle Miocene, which continued through to the Holocene. This period of cooling coincided with the formation of a permanent Antarctic ice sheet in the Middle to Late Miocene and an Arctic ice sheet in the Pliocene. In addition, the sea level lowered several times during the Late Miocene and Pliocene. These changes resulted in drier and seasonal climates, which in turn promoted a shift from closed vegetation habitats (tropical and subtropical forests) to more open vegetation habitats (woodlands and grasslands). By the early Late Miocene, the Eurasian continent was a mosaic of vegetation types and was generally more heterogeneous in vegetation structure than it had been in the Early to Middle Miocene. These vegetational changes may have fostered diversification in a variety of faunal lineages, including mustelids, through geographic isolation, divergent selection within different habitats, and ecological opportunities provided by the creation of new niches. The turnover in mustelids in western Eurasia remained high throughout the Late Miocene.

Although the evidence for faunal change in other parts of Eurasia is less clear, changes in habitat and the extinction of early mustelid lineages may have created ecological opportunities that fostered the burst of diversification of modern mustelids. Further cooling and drying events during the Pliocene caused a dramatic expansion of grasslands and steppe at mid-latitudes, and the development of taiga at high latitudes, in both Eurasia and North America. Coupled with these changes was the diversification of prey species, such as rodents and passerine birds, which exploited these new habitats. These changes provided new niches for predators, and may have promoted the Pliocene burst of mustelid diversification. For instance, some *Mustela* species are specialists in hunting small rodent prey and several *Martes* species are closely associated with taiga forest habitat, which expanded across the Holarctic during the Plio-Pleistocene. The fossil evidence indicates that taxa ancestral to these living species primarily evolved in forested habitats.

In Africa, the split between the Saharan Striped Polecat and the clade containing the Zorilla and African Striped Weasel (3–

3·5 million years ago) marginally overlaps with a major increase in the dryness of African climates that occurred 2·9–2·4 million years ago. The Saharan Striped Polecat occurs in North Africa along margins of the Sahara Desert, and the Zorilla and African Striped Weasel both occur south of the Sahara. Their divergence may thus have been caused by this climate shift, especially considering that extensive desert conditions in the Sahara did not occur until the Late Pliocene (around 2·8 million years ago).

It appears that the vast majority of the modern diversification of mustelids occurred in the Old World, specifically in Eurasia, which contains the majority of extant species and where most of the earliest fossils of extant lineages have been found. In contrast to the extensive in situ diversification that took place in Eurasia, mustelid faunas of Africa and the New World are largely composed of Eurasian genera or species that repeatedly colonized these regions.

The fossil record and the divergence times from phylogeny studies both indicate that the mustelid faunas of Africa, North America and South America, were assembled gradually over time. Most of the mustelid diversity in North and South America may have originated from lineages that repeatedly dispersed from Eurasia via the Bering land bridge, during intervals when this land bridge was open. The earliest immigrants to North America arrived in the Early Miocene and included genera that belonged to the extinct subfamily Leptarctinae, and also a group referred to as "paleomustelids" (whose affinities to the "neomustelids" remains ambiguous). There is still uncertainty, however, about the number of intercontinental dispersal events underlying the biogeographic distribution of extant genera and species, and therefore, how much of mustelid continental diversity is a result of in situ versus ex situ evolution. Further-

more, the sequence of dispersal events has been difficult to decipher, due to an incomplete fossil record. However, it appears that nine separate dispersal events from Eurasia and only one in situ speciation event account for the diversity of mustelids that are either endemic to North America (e.g. North American River Otter *Lontra canadensis*, Black-footed Ferret, and Fisher) or have part of their distribution there (e.g. Holarctic species such as the Wolverine, Ermine, and Least Weasel).

Multiple mustelid genera entered North America during the Late Miocene (11·2–5·3 million years ago), prior to the first opening of the Bering Strait around 5·5 million years ago, which severed the route across Beringia. Many genera that colonized North America during the Late Miocene or earliest Pliocene became extinct. Nonetheless, among this wave of dispersal were the earliest representatives of *Lutra* (which may represent *Lontra*, given that New World river otters have been reclassified into *Lontra*) and *Mustela*, both of which are first recorded in North America from the Late Miocene to Early Pliocene (5·9–4·6 million years ago). These taxa may have been the forerunners of modern species of *Lontra* and of *Mustela/Neovison* found in North and South America today.

Meline badgers (*Arctonyx* and *Meles*) are presently found only in the Old World. However, the recent discovery of Late Miocene to Early Pliocene fossils of meline badgers at two different sites in North America indicates that this lineage had also immigrated into North America and was a component of the New World mustelid fauna. Two extinct genera of American badgers are recorded from the Late Miocene, *Chamitataxus* (c. 7·3 million years ago) and *Pliotaxidea*, (c. 6·5 million years ago). Based on morphological evidence, *Pliotaxidea* has been shown to be a sister group to *Taxidea*, suggesting that the lin-

European Badgers *are larger and heavier than American Badgers. They have thick, coarse, grayish dorsal fur, black legs and underparts, and prominent black and white head stripes. All four feet have strong claws. Unlike most mustelids, badgers walk with their feet flat on the ground. As is commonly found in burrowing animals, their eyes and ears are small. European Badgers have 38 teeth; Asian Badgers, although in the same genus, have 34. At dusk, European Badgers leave the elaborate burrow systems, called setts, and travel to their foraging areas. They spend their nights snuffling in leaf litter in search of earthworms and other food items. Before dawn they retrace their path to the sett, which typically is sheltered by shrubs and is in soil that is easy to dig and offers good drainage. They use the same sett year after year. The underground nests are outfitted with dry grass or other bedding material, and are kept clean; dung pits are located outside the burrow system.*

Meles meles
Sussex, England.
Photo: Derek Middleton/FLPA

eage leading to *Taxidea* arrived in North America before the opening of the Bering Strait.

Following these earlier dispersal events, fossil evidence indicates that the Ermine, Black-footed Ferret, Least Weasel, and American Marten entered North America later, during the Pleistocene. The molecular divergence time for the Black-footed Ferret, around 0·6 million years ago, supports a Pleistocene dispersal scenario for this species.

Although there are fewer fossil records of mustelids from Africa and South America than from the northern continents, it appears that these regions were also colonized through successive dispersal events. Among the extinct genera known from Late Miocene deposits in East Africa are the gigantic and cat-like *Ekorus*, the largest known mustelid, and an otter, *Vishnuonyx*. The earliest known remains of the Zorilla are from the Pleistocene, which suggests a later immigration of this species into Africa. Of the nine African species of mustelids, at least four are derived from separate colonizations from Eurasia (African Clawless Otter, Spotted-necked Otter, European Polecat, and Honey Badger) whereas two are derived from in situ speciation events (Zorilla and African Striped Weasel).

The mustelids found in South America today are largely descended from North American immigrants that arrived as part of the Great American Interchange following the rise of the Panamanian isthmus, 3–2·5 million years ago. In the New World otter clade, the North American River Otter is a sister taxon to the Marine Otter (*Lontra felina*) and Neotropical Otter (*Lontra longicaudis*), both of which are found in Central and/or South America. This split is estimated to have occurred 2·8–3·4 million years ago, which is when the Panamanian land bridge formed. The Long-tailed Weasel ranges from North America to northern South America, and two species of weasels (Amazon Weasel *Mustela africana* and Colombian Weasel) are endemic to South America. The fossil evidence indicates that *Mustela* colonized South America from the north, apparently well after the Panamanian isthmus was in place. Molecular data reveal that the Giant Otter, Greater Grison, Lesser Grison, and Tayra originated in Eurasia and dispersed separately into South America, although these species have been allied with extinct taxa from North America. For example, the Giant Otter may be related to the extinct genus *Satherium* from the Pliocene of North America. However, paleontological studies suggest that the ultimate ancestry of these extinct taxa lies in Eurasia.

Morphological Aspects

Mustelids are small to medium-sized carnivores. The smallest member of the group, and also the smallest carnivore in the world, is the 25 g Least Weasel, an inhabitant of Europe and North America. The largest mustelid is the aquatic Sea Otter, which can reach 45 kg. The Wolverine is the largest terrestrial member of the Mustelidae and can weigh up 18 kg; it is a circumpolar species that ranges across Eurasia and North America.

Most mustelids have long slender bodies, short limbs, and long tails. Some species, such as the Wolverine and badgers, have a stockier body shape. Sexual size dimorphism is highly pronounced in this family, with males often reaching twice the size of females. Several hypotheses have been advanced to explain this dimorphism: the size difference might allow males and females to feed on different prey items, thus allowing coexistence where the prey base is limited; smaller females can access prey inside their burrows, even during pregnancy; larger males are able to roam widely and find more females during the mating season, and can compete with other males for access to females.

Most mustelids are digitigrade (the animal stands and moves on its toes), but badgers are plantigrade (the whole foot is placed on the ground) and the more arboreal species (e.g. martens) are semi-digitigrade (moving on their digits and partly on their soles), particularly when moving along branches. In the digitigrade species, the limb bones are elongated and the metapodials in the feet are long and often closely bound together. These adaptations increase the stride length for efficient movement on the ground and help absorb stresses while travelling at speed. In plantigrade species, the metapodials are shorter and the limbs are generally shorter and heavier.

Most mustelids are terrestrial, but the Mustelidae exhibits a wide diversity of lifestyles: fossorial (badgers), semi-fossorial (weasels and polecats), semi-arboreal (martens), semi-aquatic (mink and otters), and aquatic (Sea and Marine Otters). The fossorial badgers spend much of their lives underground and possess a variety of adaptations for this way of life, which include a stocky body, small eyes and ears, a short tail, powerful forelimbs, and long, strong claws. Weasels and polecats have long, tubular bodies that allow them to hunt in the burrows of rodents and lagomorphs (hares, rabbits, and pikas). Arboreal

Wolverines *have typical mustelid short limbs, large feet, strong claws, and rounded ears, and, like many species of the Mustelidae family, are ornamented with pale stripes and patches. Males are significantly larger than females. Wolverines are the largest terrestrial mustelid species. Their closest relatives, the Tayra, the Fisher, and the martens, weigh less than half as much. Their large feet, which are heavily covered with fur, act almost like snowshoes on soft, deep snow. They do not seem to be hindered by such snowy conditions and they are active all year long. They eat a great deal of carrion and prey opportunistically on deer and a variety of small mammals, especially rodents. Humans living in remote areas sometimes view Wolverines as nuisance animals. They are accused of killing sheep and domestic reindeer, and they break into cabins to feast on human food. In addition, these large carnivores follow traplines and eat trapped furbearing animals. Wolverines themselves are hunted for their long, warm fur, which is used to make parkas. The combination of persecution and hunting pressure has led to this species being listed as* Near Threatened *on* The IUCN Red List.

Gulo gulo
Finland.
Photo: Kerstin Hinze/naturepl.com

Small-toothed Ferret-badgers
are small and slender, with long
snouts and thick, strong claws.
They are hunted for their fur
and meat in China and India.
Their fur, which is used for
collars and jackets, can vary from
black to gray. Ferret-badgers use
their snouts and claws to dig for
earthworms and other food, which
they find mainly by smell. They are
active all year, mainly at night.
They shelter in burrows, rock
crevices, or trees. The Large-toothed
and Small-toothed Ferret-badgers
have the widest distributions of
the four species within the genus
Melogale.

Melogale moschata
Photo: Frank W. Lane/FLPA

martens have sharp, well-developed claws and a long tail that acts as counterbalance while they travel along tree branches.

The semi-aquatic otters and mink are skilful swimmers and can dive underwater. They have various morphological adaptations for efficient aquatic propulsion: long bodies, short limbs, long tails (flattened dorsoventrally in some otter species), and partially or fully webbed feet. The two species of mink forage both on land and in water. This generalist lifestyle has resulted in compromises, and mink possess intermediate adaptations that allow them to exploit both habitats. For example, they lack fully webbed feet, but instead have partial webbing for aquatic locomotion. They are considered weak swimmers compared to otters, and their underwater locomotion is much slower.

Sea Otters are almost exclusively aquatic and rarely venture onto land. They even rest and sleep at sea. They have a long body, short limbs, a tail that is slightly flattened dorso-ventrally, and flipper-like feet. They do not use their forelimbs for swimming and they are even less mobile on land than river otters. River otters must actively swim to maintain themselves on the surface, whereas Sea Otters can float passively as they have very dense fur that can trap air and provide extra buoyancy.

Mustelid coat patterns vary considerably between species, from uniform throughout to striped or mottled patterns. Many species have markings on the chin, lips, throat, and neck area. The primary function of coat coloration in a small carnivore is concealment, from both predators and prey; a small carnivore is vulnerable to attack from a larger carnivore and it needs to remain undetected by its potential prey. However, some mustelid species, such as the Marbled Polecat, Saharan Striped Polecat, and African Striped Weasel, have very obvious and contrasting black and white stripes, which warn predators of their ability to eject foul-smelling musk from their anal glands.

Some mustelid species have well-defined facial markings consisting of pale and dark bands or patches. Badgers, for example, have black and white stripes that run from the nose to the back of the head. A number of hypotheses have been suggested to account for these distinctive markings: that they act as an anti-glare device, they help to maintain group cohesiveness, they elicit grooming, they are used in mate choice, they enhance the size of the teeth or the body, or they provide disruptive coloration. The most favored hypothesis is that facial markings function to deter predation by larger carnivores, by acting as a warning coloration of the owner's fighting abilities.

Coat color in mammals is under complex genetic control and color mutations have been reported in mustelids. In domestic species, it has been possible to produce variations in color by selection and crossing. Various color morphs have

been selected in American Mink on fur farms, from natural browns or blacks to white, spotted, and sapphire.

The Ermine, Least Weasel, and Long-tailed Weasel undergo a complete change in coat color from summer to winter. The winter coat is white, making the animal inconspicuous against the background of winter snow. This change to white occurs only in the northern part of their range or at high elevations; in warmer, southerly, or more low-lying areas, the winter coat is dark. The molt from the summer brown pelage to completely white winter fur is gradual; the belly becomes white first, then the back. In northern North America, the winter molt occurs in November and weasels have a fully white coat by December. The reverse molt begins in late winter, so that weasels return to their brown summer coat by late April or May. Interestingly, the black tail tip of the Ermine and Long-tailed Weasel remains black during winter. Experimental tests suggest that the black-tipped tail attracts the attention of predators away from the body, increasing the chances that an attacker (especially a bird of prey) will aim for the tail, giving the weasel a chance to escape. The tail of the Least Weasel is probably too short for such a strategy, and its tail is entirely brown during summer and completely white during winter.

It has been shown in the Ermine that the normal cycle of pigmentation, as well as that of molting, is under the control of the pituitary gland. If individuals are held under a twelve hour dark/twelve hour light regime, they will molt to brown, but if the pituitary gland is removed, they will only grow white hair. If these animals are then injected with corticotropin or a melanocyte-stimulating hormone, the new hair is pigmented. Changes in the levels of these hormones are, therefore, responsible for controlling pigmentation. The involvement of the pituitary gland also suggests that the pigmentation cycle is determined by daylength. However, since a molt can be in either direction – white to brown or brown to white – it is clear that the light requirements for the two cycles are not identical.

Ermine from the south of England do not normally change to white at the winter molt However, if they are kept at low temperatures, the autumn molt is to white. In spring, they molt to brown, even if they are kept cold. In Wisconsin, USA, Ermine normally molt to white during the winter. Some individuals were kept at 21°C, and others at –7°C, under artificially increasing daylength. All molted to brown much earlier than they would have done in natural lighting, but the animals kept at the lower temperature required a longer exposure to the increased lighting before moulting was initiated. It therefore appears that in the English animals, the lighting requirements for pigment inhibition are normally not fulfilled by the time the

Martens, such as this **Yellow-throated Marten**, are often seen in trees. They climb readily and even pursue prey along branches, aided by short, sharp claws on their forefeet. Martens are also good swimmers, so if this **Japanese Marten** missed its landing, it could swim to safety. Both species live in forests. Japanese Martens are mostly nocturnal, while Yellow-throated Martens are more diurnal. Both eat a wide variety of foods, mostly taking small prey, but they also include a little plant matter in their diets. Both Martens are classified as Least Concern on The IUCN Red List. However, one subspecies of the Yellow-throated Marten (Martes flavigula robinsoni) *from Java* is listed as Endangered, and one subspecies of the Japanese Marten (M. melampus tsuensis), which is found only on Japan's Tsushima Islands, is classified as Vulnerable; this subspecies has been protected from trapping since 1971. There are two other Martes species in Asia, the Sable, which has a wide distribution in China, Japan, Mongolia, North Korea, and Russia, and the Nilgiri Marten, from India. The latter is very similar to the Yellow-throated Marten and is sometimes considered a subspecies. Its pelage is mostly brown, and there are distinct yellowish markings on the throat. Very little is known about the Nilgiri Marten, which is classified as Vulnerable on The IUCN Red List.

Above: **Martes flavigula**
Russia.
Photo: Roland Seitre

Below: **Martes melampus**
Tokyo, Japan.
Photo: Nature Production/
naturepl.com

molt occurs, whereas in the American ones they are. Cold temperatures slow down the start of molting, perhaps permitting the processes leading to the inhibition of pigment formation to "catch up", thus causing a white molt instead of a brown one. In the English climate, where winters are usually mild, and prolonged snowy conditions are rare, there is an adaptive value in having the light responses of the molting and pigment cycles so arranged that temperature may swing the balance either way. On the other hand, in northern North America, where snowy winters are the norm, one might expect these responses to be arranged so that by the time the winter molt occurs, pigment formation will already have been inhibited.

Mustelids have a small, flattish head; the muzzle is fairly long in terrestrial species, but is shorter in the otters. The snout is particularly long in the Hog Badger and the ferret-badgers and is used to root through the forest floor for invertebrates. There are vibrissae (whiskers) on the muzzle (mystacial), above the eyes (superciliary), on the cheeks (genal), and below the chin (inter-ramal). These are enlarged hairs whose bases are richly supplied with sensory nerve endings, so that they function as tactile organs. They tend to be somewhat reduced in fossorial species, but they are particularly well-developed in the aquatic otters; their vibrissae are very stiff so that they stand out from the body while in water.

Mustelids generally have small round ears, but they tend to be larger in the martens. The ears can be directed forward or rotated laterally in response to auditory stimuli, but they cannot be folded back. The bursa, a small purse of folded skin on the edge of the ear, is absent in otters, most badgers, and some other mustelids that inhabit burrows. Little is known about the hearing abilities of mustelids, but particularly in those species that prey on small mammals, we might expect them to be sensitive to high frequencies. Hearing underwater presents otters with several problems as the mammalian ear primarily evolved to receive airborne sounds. However, little is known of the importance, sensitivity, and mechanism of hearing in otters, either in water or on land.

The eyes of most mustelids are quite small, but they tend to be proportionally larger in nocturnal species: a larger eye has a wider aperture that allows more light to enter at night. There is also a reflective layer, the tapetum lucidum, outside the receptor layer of the retina. Light that has passed through the retina without being absorbed is reflected back again and so has a second chance of stimulating a receptor. When a bright light is

shone in a mustelid's eye, the "eyeshine" is the reflected light that has not been absorbed on the return journey and which passes back to the observer.

Vision is important in the semi-aquatic otter species because the other sensory systems used by terrestrial mustelids (most notably, olfaction) do not function underwater. For otters, underwater vision presents three fundamental problems: a need to increase light-gathering capacity when foraging in murky water; a need to accommodate for a spectral shift in light quality; and a need to modify the eye's light focusing capacity underwater because of refractive differences. Otter eyes have been modified to some extent to accommodate these problems; for instance, well-developed sphincter and ciliary muscles distort the focusing lens of the eye. However, otters have also retained a high visual acuity on land because of several important activities requiring vision in terrestrial habitats. In fact, there are indications that otter eyes function better in air than in water. In the Asian Small-clawed Otter and Sea Otter, visual acuity in water is somewhat reduced as these species use their tactile forelimbs to locate and capture invertebrate prey. The visual acuity of the semi-aquatic American Mink in air has been found to be comparable to that of the Asian Small-clawed Otter and the terrestrial Ferret, but is much poorer in water than on land.

Olfaction is an important sense in mustelids, and for many species it may be the primary means of detecting predators, locating prey, and communicating with conspecifics (using the strong scents produced from anal and subcaudal glands). Since the olfactory sensory tissues are located in the nasal fossae, mammals can smell only airborne chemicals. We might expect, therefore, that otters would have little need for highly developed olfactory abilities, especially for hunting prey underwater. However, all otter species have large nasal fossae and well-developed turbinates, suggesting a keen sense of olfaction, although the olfactory lobes of otters are small relative to other mustelids. Some observations indicate that otters do have a good sense of smell: they deposit scent in their spraints and Sea Otters can detect males and estrous females by moving to a down-wind position of other otters.

Although the acuity of the different senses (smell, hearing, vision, and touch) within the Mustelidae is not precisely known for most mustelids, their importance appears to vary, depending on the lifestyle and foraging techniques of each species. For instance, some terrestrial mustelids appear to rely heavily on

The patterned coat of the **Marbled Polecat** acts as a warning to potential predators that it can protect itself with a foul spray. It is the only species in the genus Vormela; the grisons, Zorilla, Saharan Striped Polecat, and African Striped Weasel are closely related. Marbled Polecats are generally found in fairly open areas with sparse vegetation, but can occur in forests. They shelter in burrows dug by large rodents, or they excavate their own, aided by their long claws. Marbled Polecats dig lying down, with their chin on the ground, and use their forepaws and teeth to remove obstacles, such as roots. They eat rodents and other small mammals, birds, reptiles, amphibians, snails, insects, and fruits. They can climb well, but usually feed on the ground.

Vormela peregusna
near Moscow, Russia.
Photo: Roland Seitre

smell and hearing while foraging, whereas otters rely mostly on vision or touch to find prey underwater. Martens in particular appear to have good eyesight, and capture prey following short and intense chases on the ground and in trees.

The feet of all mustelids have five digits. The usual structure of the footpads is five digit pads, five plantar pads (one for each digit, but they can be indistinct), and two metapodial pads (metacarpal pads on the forefeet and metatarsal pads on the hindfeet). In river otters, the pads are nearly obliterated and the interdigital webs are enlarged to produce a paddle-like structure. They have muscles in the feet that regulate interdigital web tension, which also assists their propulsion through wa-

ter. These adaptations are taken to an extreme in the aquatic Sea Otter, where the hindfeet resemble the flippers of a seal. However, paddle-like feet are not particularly suited for otter species that feed largely on crustaceans in shallow water and must feel for their prey in crevices and under stones. They do not need to be highly skilled swimmers and instead need thin, mobile fingers not united by a web, and a fine sense of touch. The African Clawless Otter and Asian Small-clawed Otter, both of which specialize in feeding on crabs and shellfish have incomplete webbing on the feet, particularly on the forefeet. The feet of some terrestrial mustelids are partly webbed, possibly enhancing their ability to travel on snow.

Like Marbled Polecats, **Zorillas**, as well as Saharan Striped Polecats, and African Striped Weasels, can squirt a pungent musk from their enlarged anal glands when alarmed or attacked. Similar to skunks, Zorillas have a conspicuous black and white pelage, and their defensive behaviors include threat displays. The ancient Greek words for "marten" (iktis) and "claw" (onyx) were combined to form the generic name (Ictonyx) of the Zorilla and the Saharan Striped Polecat (Ictonyx libycus). Zorillas use a wide variety of habitats, even venturing into urban gardens. They eat invertebrates, small rodents, birds, eggs, reptiles, and amphibians.

Ictonyx striatus
Harnas Wildlife Sanctuary, Namibia.
Photo: Michael & Patricia Fogden

*The **African Striped Weasel** has a long body and short limbs, with a long, bushy, white tail. Its black fur is broken up with white dorsal stripes, which first divide into two stripes, then become four white to yellowish lines above the shoulders, and finish off with white on top of the head. Males can be twice as heavy as females. African Striped Weasels are mostly solitary; if a small group is seen, it is usually a female with her young. Females tolerate males only during the breeding season. African Striped Weasels are found in forests, but are often seen in open areas, such as grassland; 75% of sightings in KwaZulu-Natal, South Africa, were recorded in this habitat. So little is known about the natural history and ecology of the African Striped Weasels that it is listed as Data Deficient on* The IUCN Red List.

Poecilogale albinucha
KwaZulu-Natal, South Africa.
Photo: Nigel J. Dennis/NHPA

Mustelid feet are also equipped with strong, non-retractile claws. The claws are well-developed in mustelid species with highly fossorial habits, such as badgers, and in species that rely heavily on their claws to dig out prey items from the ground, such as grisons. In mustelids that regularly climb trees, such as martens, the claws of the forefeet are short and sharp. In the African Clawless Otter, the feet are clawless except for the three middle toes of each hindfoot, which bear small grooming claws. In the Asian Small-clawed Otter, claws are present but reduced.

The tail of most mustelids is long and thickly furred. A long tail helps provide balance, particularly for the more arboreal species (martens and some weasels). Otters have a long tail, which serves as a rudder in water, facilitating quick changes in direction when pursuing prey. The few mustelid species with a short tail are the badgers: they are fossorial and a long tail would likely be an unnecessary hindrance for an animal living in a tight, underground burrow.

Skin glands in the Mustelidae have an important function in olfactory communication. In certain areas of the body, these glands secrete substances whose function is to exchange information. In a few mustelids, glandular patches are found on the ventral surface: a glandular area marked externally by shorter hair has been found in the American Marten and the Wolverine. In badgers and otters, enlarged skin glands may also be found at the base of the tail.

In the Mustelidae, there are anal sacs that open just within the anus. These sacs are vesicular cutaneous invaginations, one on either side of the anus, which are connected to a short canal or duct. The walls of the vesicles are composed of secretory epithellium; secretory glands may also open into the canals. The whole structure is invested with a muscular coat, which is particularly well-developed in those species capable of expelling the secretion to some distance.

Anal sacs are almost universally present within the Mustelidae, but in the otters they are very reduced and they are said to be completely absent in the Sea Otter. The Honey Badger is unusual in possessing an eversible anal pouch, very much like that of the mongooses (Herpestidae). In the Eurasian badgers, the ducts of the anal sacs open just internal to the anus, which is sunk in a slight depression. Above this, the skin is invaginated to form a pocket that is partly divided at its base into right and left halves. The skin lining the pouch is hairy and highly glandular and secretes copiously. A sub-caudal pocket of this type is also present in the Hog Badger, but is absent in the American Badger. In the American Badger, there is an elongated depression in the skin of the abdomen, just in front of the penis, into which a series of little glandular pockets opens on either side; this gland is said to be present in the male only. The Marbled Polecat, Saharan Striped Polecat, Zorilla, and African Striped Weasel have particularly enlarged anal glands and, like skunks, are able to excrete pungent musk when alarmed or attacked. Also like skunks, they have a conspicuous black and white pelage and defense behaviors that include threat displays.

The skeletal structure of the Mustelidae reflects their shape: in the long, slender species, the ribcage is shallow but very elongated, sometimes extending almost half the length of the body. The skull of most mustelids has a long, low braincase, which extends far back behind the glenoid. Many species also have a strong sagittal crest to support the attachment of the jaw muscles. The zygomatic arches are weak, which indicates that most of the jaw action is done by the temporalis muscles, rather than the masseter muscles. In the Eurasian Otter, for instance, the temporalis constitutes almost 80% of the total mass of the jaw musculature and the masseter less than 20%. In other carnivores, the anterior temporalis and zygomatico-mandibularis muscles are responsible for exerting the main force when the jaws are wide open and the canines are being driven home, whereas the masseter and the posterior part of the temporalis are more important when the carnassial shear is being used and the jaws are nearly closed. The shape of a mustelid skull reflects a modification of this system, in which the posterior part of the temporalis has taken over most of the work normally performed by the masseter, which is correspondingly reduced in size. The pre- and post-glenoid processes are therefore enlarged. In some species, particularly badgers, these processes are so well-developed that the only way to remove the mandible from a skull is to slip it out sideways. This condition of the glenoid is sometimes taken to indicate a powerful bite, but in fact it is a reflection of the unusual arrangement of the jaw muscles rather than of any remarkable strength.

Mustelidae dentition is very diversified and is linked to the wide range of diets. Depending on the species, mustelids have a total of 28 to 38 teeth, with a dental formula on each side of the jaw comprising three upper/three lower incisors, one upper/ one lower canine, two-four upper/two-four lower premolars, and one upper/one-two lower molars (I3/3, C1/1, P2–4/2–4, M1/1–2). The Sea Otter is the only species with two lower incisors. The small incisors are mainly used for nipping food items, such as the flesh from carcasses, and the canines are used to grasp and kill prey by piercing the neck or skull. The characteristic carnassial teeth of the Carnivora (the fourth upper premolar and the first lower molar) are specially adapted to cutting through flesh with a scissor-like action. The premolars, depending on their particular shape, may either aid in holding prey or, like the molars, be used mainly for crushing food items. The incisors of mustelids are not specialized, the canines are elongate, the premolars are small and sometimes reduced in number, and a constriction is usually present between the lateral and medial halves of the upper molar. The second lower molar, if present, is reduced to a simple peg.

Mustelid species with a high carnivorous component in their diet have carnassial teeth with developed sharp blades, while others have developed crushing teeth suitable for eating fruit or hard-shelled prey. In the Honey Badger, the crushing function of the dentition is emphasized: the molars are rather broad and the protocone of P⁴ is large and heavy. In some badgers and otters, the adaptations to crushing are even more marked. The molars are broad, flat and multicusped, and the carnassials have an enlarged protocone and reduced blade. Also, the temporalis and masseter muscles are well- developed and the power of the bite is considerable. The most extreme development of crushing molars is found in the otter species that are specialized feeders of shelled invertebrates, such as the African Clawless Otter and Asian Small-clawed Otter, which live mainly on crustaceans, and the Sea Otter, which feeds extensively on molluscs, crabs, and sea urchins. In these species, the teeth are extremely broad and the carnassials highly molarized.

Male mustelids possess a well-developed penis bone called a baculum or os penis. This baculum may help in penetrating the vaginal orifice and provide vaginal stimulation. In its simplest form, it is a rod-like structure, grooved below for the passage of the urethra and the corpus spongiosum. The shape of this baculum varies between species, with each species showing distinctive characters. The function and the significance of the different shapes and sizes are unknown.

Habitat

Mustelids are found all on continents except Antarctica, from lowlands to montane areas. They are a very diverse group and species occur in practically all habitat types including oceans (e.g. Marine Otter and Sea Otter), rivers (e.g. North American River Otter and Spotted-necked Otter), temperate forests (e.g. European Pine Marten and American Marten), tropical forest (e.g. Tayra and Yellow-throated Marten), dry open woodlands (African Striped Weasel), tundra (e.g. Wolverine), steppe (e.g. Steppe Polecat), and grasslands (e.g. Black-footed Ferret). Some mustelids appear to be very adaptable, for instance, the Ermine and Least Weasel can be found in a wide range of habitats, from grasslands to woodlands, and the Honey Badger occurs in habitats ranging from forests to deserts. For these species, habitats that provide high prey abundance and suitable cover are the prime requisites. A number of mustelid species are also found near or within human settlements. Stone Martens (*Martes foina*) are quite frequently seen in some European towns and cities and are known to use buildings and other human structures as dens.

Although most mustelids are terrestrial, the family Mustelidae includes species that are fossorial (badgers typically hunt and den in underground burrows), semi-arboreal (martens often forage in trees and rest in cavities well above ground level), semi-aquatic (otters and mink forage in rivers), and aquatic (Sea Otters rarely venture out of the ocean).

Several factors determine where an animal lives, including the availability of food, den and rest sites, and the presence of competitors and predators. The type and density of food available is determined to a large degree by habitat type: riparian habitats are associated with aquatic prey, such as crustacea, amphibia, and fish; open habitats often have high invertebrate densities; and scrubby habitats tend to support high densities of small vertebrates. Mustelids coexist with other carnivores, with which they may compete for prey or may be in danger of becoming prey, thus the presence of other carnivore species may well affect the presence, population densities, and habitat use of mustelids.

The spatial use of an area differs among species and is often dependent upon habitat variables. For instance, otters have home ranges that tend to be long and thin, following a stream

*The massive, flattened tail of the **Giant Otter** so impressed British naturalist John Edward Gray, that in 1837 he created a genus for this animal,* Pteronura, *using the Greek words for "wing"* (pteron) *and "tail"* (oura). *The Giant Otter is the largest South American otter, 2–3 times heavier than the Southern River Otter and the Neotropical Otter. The Marine Otter, which inhabits the Pacific Coast of South America, is even smaller, weighing less than 6 kg compared to the Giant Otter's 22–32 kg. The Giant Otter has large eyes, a massive skull, and a flattened head. The white or yellow markings on its chest, throat, and lips sometimes combine to form a bib. All four feet are fully webbed.*

Pteronura brasiliensis
Amana Sustainable Development
Reserve, Amazonas, Brazil.
Photo: Luiz Claudio Marigo

*North American River Otters,
with their elongated bodies,
flattened tails, and fully-webbed
feet, are highly mobile and can
swim long distances, even under
ice during the winter. They are
hunted for their fur, which is short
and very dense. The chest, throat,
and chin are grayish; the body,
legs, and tail are darker, ranging
from brown to black. A group seen
swimming together is most likely
a female and her offspring; large
groups of up to 15 females and
their young are sometimes found
along coastal shorelines. Males
also form groups, but these break
up during the breeding season,
when it's "every otter for himself".*

Lontra canadensis
Grand Teton National Park,
Wyoming, USA.
Photo: Tom & Pat Leeson/Ardea

or river. Habitat use can also vary with seasons. During the winter, some weasels will hunt or rest under the snow, and martens may increase their arboreal activity because of the difficulty of moving through deep snow.

Habitats that provide suitable den/resting sites are very important for mustelids. Resting sites need to provide safe havens from larger predators, and females with young need secure sites to raise their offspring. Most mustelids are small species that can be preyed upon by larger predators, such as snakes, raptors and larger carnivores, and are therefore likely to be highly selective in their choice of den/resting sites, choosing sites that minimize exposure to predation. These may also be chosen to provide protection from the elements: for example, tree-shaded sites are cooler places to sleep on a hot, sunny day and will also provide shelter when it rains. Fossorial species, such as badgers, den in elaborate underground burrows called setts. These have numerous entrances, passages, and chambers, and are used year after year; they increase in complexity over time, and eventually they may cover several hectares. Many terrestrial mustelids choose rest sites in secure places on the ground, such as in dense vegetation, hollow logs, or rock piles. Arboreal species, such as the martens, also use cavities in trees or sleep on branches. Some mustelids seem to regularly change their rest sites, although some sites may be re-used several times.

*The whiskers of the **Sea Otter**
stand out stiffly underwater, and
its hindfeet resemble the flippers
of a seal. All four of its feet are
webbed, but when it swims, it
propels itself only with its hindlegs.
Its tail is thick, from the base to
the tip, and is slightly flattened.
The Sea Otter's extremely dense
underfur traps air bubbles, which
provides insulation and also
makes Sea Otters buoyant enough
to float effortlessly. They can sleep
at sea and are somewhat clumsy
on land. Their lungs are 2–3
times larger than those of terrestrial
mammals of the same size, which
makes long dives possible. Sea
Otters are unusual in lacking anal
glands, but they have an acute
enough sense of smell that a male
can detect an estrous female if he is
downwind of her. Males are about
a third heavier than females, and
can weigh up to 45 kg.*

Enhydra lutris
Prince William Sound, Alaska, USA.
Photo: Gerard Lacz/FLPA

Male **Spotted-necked Otters** *are larger and heavier than females, but even the largest individuals are much smaller than Sea Otters which are more than seven times heavier. Like other otters, they have a long body, short limbs, fully webbed feet, and a long tail. Spotted-necked Otters have creamy-white to white mottled markings on their upper chest an throat, lending to their common name. Spotted-necked Otters are seldom found far from water and live in freshwater rivers, lakes, and swamps, where they prey on fish, crabs, and frogs. They are mainly diurnal and are often see in groups. They are usually most active early and late in the day. They rest in dense vegetation, roc cavities, holes in root systems, or bank dens, sometimes digging the own burrows.*

Hydrictis maculicollis
Photo: David Hosking/FLPA

Mustelids can have an impact on their own environment and may play an important role in maintaining ecosystems. For instance, the Sea Otter can limit the distribution and abundance of its invertebrate prey, and is therefore considered a "keystone species". In areas lacking Sea Otters, herbivorous sea urchins overgraze kelp forests. Kelp is a crucial component in coastal food webs, providing habitat and food for many other species. European Badgers (*Meles meles*) are tremendous dirt movers and their presence is easily recognizable because of the large dirt piles around burrow entrances. In agricultural areas, badgers may be persecuted because of their digging habits, as their holes are deemed dangerous for roaming cattle and a nuisance for the operation of farm machinery.

Forest-dependent mustelid species are heavily impacted by forest loss, fragmentation, and degradation through activities such as selective logging and clearcutting. Fragmentation can affect populations by reducing habitat connectivity, which lowers dispersal success and increases the probability of inbreeding. This may ultimately result in local extinctions or population declines. Forested corridors will have to be preserved in order to combat the effects of global warming and to allow gene flow among disparate populations.

There is a high demand for timber and land throughout the tropics. Forests are fast disappearing and the land is being converted to other uses such as growing crops and expanding urban areas. Lowland forest is particularly vulnerable and little remains in some countries. Studies on tropical rainforest fragmentation have shown that the diversity and abundance of plant and animal species is influenced by the size of the habitat, with larger areas usually containing a greater number of

Eurasian Otters *are much more graceful in water than on land, but they sometimes travel several kilometers overland from one bod of water to another. When travelli over snow or ice, they often run and slide. They are excellent swimmers and can stay submerge for as long as five minutes. They have short, dense fur and claws on all four webbed feet. Males are much larger than females. Eurasian Otters find most of thei food in water, but they sometimes also eat small mammals and birds. They den in burrows, log jams, rock crevices, or among roo systems, always close to water.*

Lutra lutra
Poland.
Photo: Roland Seitre

As its name implies, the **African Clawless Otter** is basically clawless, with only three small grooming claws on each hindfoot. Its long, fingerlike front toes, which it uses to probe for crabs and shellfish, leave this clawless footprint (below). Asian Small-clawed Otters also mainly eat crabs and shellfish. They have claws on all their digits, but these are very reduced. Both species rely on their sense of touch when foraging. Lacking completely webbed feet, these two species are not as skilled swimmers as other otters. African Clawless Otters inhabit rainforests and lowland swamp forests. They also live along saltwater coasts, but as they require fresh water to drink, coastal populations are only found near freshwater tributaries. Their diet is not restricted to crabs and shellfish, and they also eat frogs, fish, and invertebrates. When foraging at night, African Clawless Otters normally walk along in shallow water feeling for prey with their forefeet, but sometimes they plunge their heads into clear water to scan for prey. They can dive and stay underwater for almost a minute. One subspecies of the African Clawless Otter, the Congo Clawless Otter (Aonyx capensis congicus), is considered a separate species by some authors, but further research is needed to determine its taxonomic status.

Aonyx capensis
South Africa.
Photos: Geoff McIlleron

579

species. Mustelid species that are severely impacted by habitat fragmentation and degradation are those with specialist habitat requirements or large home ranges. For example, the current low numbers or absence of American Martens in some areas of North America may be partly attributable to forestry practices. This species is very sensitive to habitat destruction, and clear-cutting can completely eliminate American Martens from an area. The availability of hollow trees for use as resting sites and natal dens is especially critical, and logging procedures that eliminate old stumps or older trees may be detrimental to American Marten populations.

Otters and mink use rivers and lakes and are thus heavily affected by water pollution. Toxic chemicals that enter water can kill them and their prey. If otters and mink consume contaminated food, they are susceptible to bioaccumulation of toxic compounds in the body tissues, which can lead to impaired reproduction or death. Over the last few decades, aquatic habitats have been drastically altered or lost following draining of wetlands, water extraction, siltation, and removal of riparian vegetation.

In some regions, several mustelid species are found in the same community and habitats. For example, seven species of mustelids are sympatric in the British Isles (Ermine, Least Weasel, European Polecat, American Mink, European Pine Marten, European Badger, and Eurasian Otter). Competition for resources is likely to be higher between closely related species than distantly related animals; therefore, the coexistence of several mustelids in some areas is of great interest and suggests some form of resource partitioning. This may occur through several means: temporal (e.g. nocturnal/diurnal), spatial (e.g. terrestrial/arboreal), or dietary. Divergence in these ecological traits should, therefore, be greatest between closely related mustelids, especially sister species occupying the same area. For instance, in Africa, the African Striped Weasel preys almost exclusively on rodents whereas the Zorilla has a more generalized diet that includes invertebrate prey. However, although ecological factors are important in determining the structure of mustelid communities, historical factors should also be considered. Phylogenetic history has been instrumental in structuring mus-

telid assemblages on different continents. Mustelid communities are largely composed of species that belong to different lineages and which differ significantly in their ecomorphology. These fundamental differences may facilitate their coexistence within a community.

Communication

For mustelids to interact with each other and other species, it is not necessary for them to have actual physical contact. Within the Mustelidae, various signaling systems have been developed whereby the actions of a signal sender may, at some distance, influence the responses of a receiver. Communication between animals requires a signal to be sent, a receiver to detect the information, and an ability to process and utilize the information detected. The sensory capabilities of the receiver are therefore an important component. Many mustelids are considered to possess good eyesight, hearing and smell, although how acute these senses are is not well known.

There are three main ways that mustelids can communicate with each other: visual, vocal, and olfactory. Most mustelids are solitary species, so visual and vocal communication will be most prevalent when a male and female come together during the breeding season and when a female has young. The repertoire of mustelid calls and visual signals is unlikely to be extensive or complex as compared to the more sociable carnivore species, but unfortunately we know little about how they communicate with each other in the wild.

Within the Mustelidae, the main means of communication with conspecifics appears to be scent marking, primarily using the secretions from anal and sub-caudal glands. Olfactory signals have the advantage of being persistent, lasting days to weeks, compared to visual or auditory communication, which are instantaneous. Scent marks may attract or repel other individuals and can be responded to when the animal that made them is far away, out of earshot, as well as out of sight; scent also works in the dark. Scent serves to advertize occupancy of an area, and in solitary species, probably also serves to facilitate contact during the breeding season. The scent marks left by mustelids thus play an important role in territory marking and mating, and may carry information about the sex, breeding condition, and other characteristics of the individual.

Individual animals may gain an advantage over others by denying them access to resources such as food and mates. They do so either by being territorial or by gaining high status within a social group. Scent marking is centrally involved in the advertisement of both land tenure and social status. Fights over the possession of a territory are rare because individuals are generally reluctant to enter occupied areas. A resident animal, by virtue of having gained and held a territory, is likely to be an animal of high quality and fighting ability. It is in the resident's interest to be recognized as such, in a completely unambiguous manner, and in a way that precludes any possibility of bluff. Territorial scent marking may be way one way to achieve this; only a long-term resident can have had the opportunity to cover an area with scent marks. If an intruder should meet an individual whose odor matches that of the majority of scent marks in any area, then it can be reasonably sure it has met the resident, and would do well to withdraw as rapidly as possible.

Most mustelids possess well-developed anal glands and each species is capable of producing its own unique, pungent smell; nearly 100 compounds have been found in the scent of the Eurasian Otter, consisting of proteins, mucopolysaccharides, and lipids. Anal gland secretions are released during defecation, at latrines, and sometimes against stationary objects. Also many mustelids, on meeting, sniff each other in the region of their scent organs or the places where secretions have been applied to the body. Some scent compounds are common to all individuals and may function in species-level recognition, whereas others are variable among individuals, and may function in individual-level recognition. Many scent organs support rich populations of bacteria that may, by their metabolism, modify the animal's own secretions.

Many species are able to determine an individual's gender using olfactory clues. In some cases, this may happen because the scent marks are deployed in different ways, or in different

*A long body and neck, and long whiskers, are not unique to **Smooth-coated Otters**, but these features are strikingly illustrated here. These large otters are often seen in groups consisting of an adult pair and their offspring from one or more litters. Smooth-coated Otters often forage in small shallow rivers, irrigation canals, swamps flooded by monsoons. They also inhabit rice fields adjacent to coastal mangroves, and can live in salt water if there is fresh water for drinking nearby. Smooth-coated Otters usually swallow small fish whole while still in the water; they go on land to rest, defecate, or eat large fish. Eurasian Otters, Hairy-nosed Otters, and Asian Small-clawed Otters may also occur with Smooth-coated Otters in numerous locations, including several river systems in Thailand and Malaysia.*

Lutrogale perspicillata
Periyar, India.
Photo: Gertrud & Helmut Denzau

Japanese Weasels have dark brown fur in the summer but molt to a much paler, yellowish pelage in the winter. **Least Weasels** also molt in most parts of their range. This alert individual is seen here in its summer coat; its winter coat will be all white. In these weasels, and other long, thin Mustela species, the ribcage is shallow but very elongated, sometimes extending almost half the length of the body. The Least Weasel is the smallest carnivore in the world. There is great geographic variation in size, but the smallest adults weigh only 25 g. Male Least Weasels are, on average, larger than females; male Japanese Weasels are almost twice the weight of females. Scientists have speculated about such sexual dimorphism: it might allow males and females to feed on different prey items, helping them to share a limited prey base; it might permit females to chase small fossorial prey in burrows; or it might help males be able to roam more widely in search of mates. Male Least Weasels generally take larger prey than females and spend less time hunting in tunnels. The Least Weasel's energy requirements are seemingly endless and it hunts night and day; Japanese Weasels are primarily nocturnal. Both of these animals eat a wide variety of prey, including insects, reptiles, and small mammals. Japanese Weasels have been introduced in parts of Japan and Russia to control reptiles and rats.

Above: *Mustela itatsi*
Nagano, Japan.
Photo: Nature Production/
naturepl.com

Below: *Mustela nivalis*
Sichuan, China.
Photo: Xi Zhi Nong/naturepl.com

In the northern part of their range, or at high elevations, **Ermines**, Least Weasels, and Long-tailed Weasels completely change their coat color from summer to winter. They are brown in the summer (above) and white in the winter (below), which helps camouflage these animals in both seasons. This change happens gradually, the belly becoming white first and then the back (middle). The tip of the tail of the Ermine and Long-tailed Weasel remains black in the winter. Some experiments suggest that the black tail tip may distract the attention of a predator, such as a bird of prey, away from the body, giving the weasel a slightly better chance of escaping. The tail of the Least Weasel, which is completely white in winter, is probably too short to make a difference. Experiments have also been conducted to determine what triggers the color change. For example, Ermines from the south of England, which do not normally have white coats in winter, were kept at low temperatures and they molted to white in the fall. The following spring, they molted to brown even if they were kept cold. In another experiment, in Wisconsin, USA, some individuals with white winter coats were kept at 21°C and others at −7°C, under artificial lights that gradually increased the daylength. Both groups molted to brown much earlier than they would have in the wild, but the animals kept at the lower temperature took longer to start molting.

Mustela erminea
Top and middle: Sabiñánigo, Huesca, Spain.
Photos: Javier Ara Cajal

Bottom: Pamir Mountains, Tajikistan
Photo: Patricio Robles Gil

The **Patagonian Weasel** has a long, slender body and short limbs. Its pelage is grayish-white, with a wide band of white on the top of its head, and dark brown coloring on its nape, cheeks, chin, throat, and limbs. It is one of the few mustelids with only 28 teeth, and its teeth offer a clue to its lifestyle: the molars, or chewing teeth, are reduced and its carnassial teeth, used for shearing meat, are strong and sharp, suggesting a carnivorous diet. It is thought to prey mostly on birds and small mammals, and may rely heavily on a fossorial rodent, the tuco-tuco. The Patagonian Weasel, the only species in the genus Lyncodon, was mentioned in a journal kept by a teenage cabin boy and fiddler on the HMS Beagle with Charles Darwin.

Lyncodon patagonicus
Puerto Madryn, Chubut, Argentina.
Photo: Darío Podestá

quantities, by the two sexes. In other cases, the distinction is based on differences in the chemical composition of the odor. An ability to distinguish between individuals on the basis of odor has been demonstrated in the European Badger, in which the relevant information is encoded in the glandular secretions from the sub-caudal scent gland. The Eurasian Otter can discriminate between the spraints of different individuals, regardless of their sex.

The place chosen for setting a scent mark will obviously affect the likelihood of its being noticed by a conspecific. Scent marks appear not to be randomly distributed and are generally set on much-frequented pathways and other important places, such as territorial boundaries. European Pine Martens leave anal scent marks throughout their ranges, males pausing to do so seven to eight times per kilometer and females three to four times over the same distance. The European Badger places blobs of its anal sac secretion onto feces at latrine pits. In addition, it has a sub-caudal scent gland whose secretions cover the skin and hair of the perianal region; this is mixed with the anal sac secretion, and often with fecal matter. These secretions are used in "squat-marking", a behavior in which the badger briefly presses its nether region onto the substrate. Both sexes squat-mark, but males do so most frequently and dominant females more frequently than subordinate ones. Much of this squat-marking behavior takes place near the sett, at latrine sites, and along the borders of the group's territory. Badgers also frequently pause to squat-mark as they travel the many paths that transverse their home range, the same spots being repeatedly re-marked. Conspicuous objects such as hummocks and tussocks are also repeated marked by all passing badgers, sometimes from a handstand position. Badgers also squat-mark on vegetation before taking it down into their sett to be used as bedding, rejecting any vegetation that has been marked by strange badgers.

Eurasian Otters deposit spraints at nose height on the top of prominent objects, such as large rocks and tussocks of grass, throughout their home range. Repeated sprainting and urination at these sites by successive generation of otters can lead to the formation of distinct mounds and to the lush growth of nitrophilous grasses and algae, all of which make them visually conspicuous. In coastal areas, where Eurasian Otters forage ex-

clusively in the sea, spraint sites are dispersed along the coast in an organized manner, with most of them clumped together at distinct spraint stations. Typically, most spraint stations contain a relatively large pool of fresh water and are connected to one another, and to the sea, by distinct trails through the vegetation. Within stations, nearly half of the spraint sites occur right on the edges of the pools, with the rest dispersed along trails and at junctions, thus ensuring their encounter whatever the direction of approach by another otter. With spraint stations spaced out in this way, at regular and frequent intervals, any otter landing from the sea will never be more than a short distance from the nearest scent mark. Coastal otters require fresh water for drinking and washing salt from their pelage. By placing their spraints on prominent objects, around and on the trails leading to freshwater pools, otters increase yet further the likelihood of their being detected by other individuals. Spraints are also deposited at dens (holts), which are themselves uniformly spaced throughout the otter's home range.

Because scents gradually evaporate, the difference between a fresh mark and an old one may be detectable and give an indication when an animal was last present in an area. Temporal information may be important during foraging, allowing individuals to avoid areas in which other individuals have recently fed, and which will, therefore, be unproductive. European Badgers squat-mark onto the grass as they forage for earthworms and it has been suggested that this informs the badger where it has been in the recent past.

Sometimes the object to be scent-marked is another individual of the same species. Such allomarking is common in mustelids that live in organized groups, such as European Badgers. Allomarking leads to a similarity of odor among members of a group, allowing them to recognize each other, even in the dark. European Badgers engage in social squat-marking, whereby one badger wipes its anal region on the flank of another badger. When two European Badgers meet at night, away from the sett, they often sniff each other's flanks and rumps. Sometimes European Badgers indulge in mutual squat-marking, whereby two individuals back into each other, with their tails raised and their sub-caudal pockets open, and press their anal regions together. This behavior is quite rare but seems to take place when clan members have been sepa-

The soft, luxurious fur of the
American Mink has played a very
important role in the fur trade
and fashion industry. Although it
is still trapped in the wild, today
over 25 million American Mink
are bred on farms in the USA
and Europe, and more recently
in China. Escapees from these
farms have established viable
wild populations in places where
it is not native. American Mink
prefer areas with dense vegetation
and live near waterways or in
wetlands, such as swamps and
marshes, but they are sometimes
found far from water. They also
inhabit some coastal beaches.
American Mink are excellent
swimmers and divers, although
they do not have webbed feet.
They prey on small mammals,
fish, birds, amphibians, reptiles,
crustaceans, molluscs, insects,
and earthworms. The American
Mink and the European Mink
are similar morphologically and
fill similar ecological roles, but
molecular studies suggest that they
are only distantly related. The Sea
Mink was said to have resembled
the American Mink, but to have
lived among rocks along the ocean,
feeding mainly on fish. It was so
heavily hunted for its fur that by
the end of the nineteeth century the
Sea Mink had disappeared. It is
now declared Extinct by the IUCN.

Neovison vison
Adams County, SW Ohio, USA.
Photo: Dave Maslowski/
Maslowski Productions

Sea Otters congregate in social groups, called "rafts", which are generally segregated by sex. These rafts vary in size according to region, but can number up to 2000 individuals. Such large floating groups are usually seen where the water is less than 40 m deep, although Sea Otters often live and forage in much deeper water. Females with young form groups throughout the entire year, but groups of adult males are only seen outside of the breeding season.

Enhydra lutris
Prince William Sound, Alaska, USA.
Photo: Michael Gore/FLPA

American Badgers are not very vocal animals, but this threatened individual may be making growling sounds. Unlike European Badgers, American Badgers are solitary. They den alone, usually using several burrows. In the summer they may dig a new burrow each day. In severe cold weather, American Badgers may enter a torpor state in their dens, but they do not truly hibernate. Their heartbeat slows to about half the normal rate, their body temperature drops, and they live on stored fat. They wake up every few days, so they may be frequently seen outside their burrow when snow covers the ground.

Taxidea taxus
Yellowstone National Park, Wyoming, USA.
Photo: Dave Watts/ Lochman Transparencies

rated for some days. It is always accompanied by intense sniffing of the flanks.

All the badgers in a clan squat-mark each other, but not equally. In one group of six badgers, the dominant male made 66% of the social marks, two other males 19%, and the three females the remaining 15%. Of the marks made by the dominant male, 78% were directed towards the sows. In this way, the flanks and rumps of each badger came to bear a mixture of the secretions of all the clan members, but a mixture dominated by the odor of the top-ranking boar. By marking at high rates, a dominant boar provides a mechanism by which subordinate animals can recognize him in encounters. In a hierarchical social system, there is often intense competition between dominant and subordinate individuals for access to mates during the breeding season. At this time, the correct signaling of social status is important in order to minimize confrontations. By marking females, the dominant male reinforces his status. During courtship, the dominant boar remains close to the sow, continually sniffing her and attempting to mount. Most of his advances are met with a growl and snap of the teeth. Typically, the male responds by squat-marking the female, thereby verifying his high social status and suitability as a mate; this usually results in the sow ceasing her aggression.

Mustelid scent organs are often used when an individual is excited, aggressive, or perhaps frightened. For instance, the air surrounding fighting American Mink is usually redolent with the sickly sweet odor released from their anal sacs. Some mustelids have scent organs that are specialized for the release of relatively large quantities of odor into the air and are used in self-defense or as a deterrent against attackers. The Zorrilla, Saharan Striped Polecat, African Striped Weasel, and Marbled Polecat, have enlarged anal sacs that produce particularly disgusting secretions, which can be ejected in the direction of attackers.

Urine and feces can be used as scent marking substances and can also be used as visual signals. In many species, the frequency of scent marking increases markedly in the breeding season, and particularly during courtship as the female approaches estrus. As sex hormones are excreted in urine, it may carry information about the reproductive condition of an individual. There is some evidence that vaginal secretions may be involved in the recognition of the estrous state of a female. In female mammals, blood titers of estradiol increase during the follicular phase of the estrous cycle and drop abruptly at ovulation. Estrogen levels are therefore an accurate indication of changes in female receptivity. Although males cannot follow changes in blood levels, they can monitor steroids in urine.

The renal handling of steroids is very efficient, and urine levels reflect accurately the production by the ovaries. In an unmated female Eurasian Otter (which is continually polyestrous if unmated) estradiol levels peaked on 16 occasions over two years, with a mean periodicity of 36 days.

Feces are normally coated with mucus secreted by the cells of the large intestine, but the secretions of the anal sacs can be added as well. The type of food eaten can also give feces a distinctive odor. In a solitary species that ranges over a large area, the value of feces in information transfer may be greater if they are concentrated in one particular spot than if they are widely distributed. Mustelids are known to deposit their feces in spe-

cific latrine sites. These are often found in conspicuous places, and thus seem to play an important role in marking territories. In many river otters, such as the Eurasian Otter, spraints are deposited by males at territory boundaries and by females around den sites. However, the significance of sprainting and scent production by the Sea Otter is unclear. Sea Otter spraints have a distinctly mustelid odor, but there is no evidence that Sea Otters deposit spraints strategically; they seem simply to deposit spraints whenever the need to defecate arises, which usually occurs in the water, where the spraints either sink or rapidly degrade. Male Sea Otters often sniff the anogenital region of females, presumably to determine reproductive condition. Olfaction in the Sea Otter thus appears to function briefly, over short distances, whereas other otter species use sprainting to extend olfactory clues, both spatially and temporally.

Visual signals are non-persistent and stop when an individual finishes making them or moves out of visual range. They only carry over short distances and their main use is in face-to-face encounters, not only between individuals of the same species, but also between different species (when mustelids encounter larger predators, for example). Many carnivore species are capable of a wide range of expressive movements and displays using erectile hairs, mobile ears and tails, and different postures (such as standing with an arched back or crouching). Special markings on the pelage also help accentuate parts of the body. Depending on the species, these features may be used in different combinations and to various degrees to express an animal's mood and make threat and appeasement displays.

Within the Mustelidae, some species have well-marked facial masks or stripes on the head, and these markings may play an important role in visual communication. Small mustelids, though predators themselves, coexist with larger carnivores that could potentially kill them. However, many mustelid species can be formidable opponents to larger predators, especially if they are close in size. These facial marks could, therefore, warn others of their ability to counterattack. Distinctive colorations in mustelids could also warn larger predators of the obnoxious smells that can be produced from their anal glands. Some mustelids are prone to emit their anal gland secretion if

startled, and in many species the odor produced is sufficiently unpleasant that it is likely to deter an attacker. This behavior is quite well known within the Mephitidae: skunks have a nauseous spray that can be projected to a considerable distance. In association with this, skunks have a black and white warning coloration and a special threat display. Three mustelids, the Zorrilla, Saharan Striped Polecat, and African Striped Weasel also have a very conspicuous black and white pelage that warns attackers of their ability to eject foul smelling scents.

Vocal signals can be received over considerable distances and may be particularly useful when thick cover and darkness limit visibility. Many mustelids, however, are small and vulnerable to attacks from larger predators, so advertising their presence using loud sounds would increase their predation risk. Moving silently while foraging also helps to minimize detection by their prey. Thus, mustelids are usually quiet when active, and vocal communication appears to be important only over a short range, in face-to-face encounters between individuals. Their vocalizations appear to be quite limited, and most auditory signals are emitted under stress or attack. Common vocalizations include contact and threat calls, and sounds made when an animal is stressed or in pain. For example, the vocal repertoire of adult Least Weasels includes three agonistic sounds: a harsh chirp, a hiss, and a squeal, which are all used in threatened or stressful situations, sometimes separately or in different combinations. They also use a trilling call, which is given by both sexes when mating, and by a female when she wishes to summon her young.

The most vocal mustelids tend to be those that form social groups, such as some otter species. They emit various sounds, although the purpose of each vocalization is sometimes unclear. The African Clawless Otter emits powerful, high-pitched shrieks when disturbed or trying to attract attention. The Asian Small-clawed Otter lives in family groups and has over twelve different calls. The Giant Otter has been observed to vocalize frequently and nine basic vocalizations have been recognized including "hah" (indicates a low level of alarm or interest), "snort" (given when suddenly alarmed or facing a source of danger), "wavering scream" (given during a bluff-charge),

*Squabbles can break out in **European Badger** communities over hierarchical disputes within the group or territorial issues. Individuals mark the borders of their territories and latrine pits near setts with anal sac secretions and scent from glands under the tail. Males scent-mark more than females, and dominant females more frequently than subordinate ones. Some spots along paths that badgers use for traveling are marked repeatedly; they sometimes even do handstands to place their marks higher. Badgers use vegetation as bedding in the sett and scent-mark it as their own. European Badgers even mark each other (allomarking), which enables group members to recognize other individuals of the same sett, even in the dark. Dominant males do more allomarking than the other badgers in the group, with a majority of the marking directed towards females. This reinforces their status and helps minimize confrontations that can occur for access to mates during the breeding season.*

Meles meles
Hessen, Germany.
Photo: M. Delpho/CD-Gallery

"growl" (offensive threat), "hum" (reassurance contact call), "coo" (given in a close contact situation), "whistle" (intergroup contact call), and squeaks, whines, and wails made by the young.

Food and Feeding

Although mustelids have a wide diversity of diets, most species are carnivorous, relying on animal prey to sustain their daily energy needs. However, some species are omnivorous and will also consume plant material such as fruits and nuts. The range and type of prey consumed varies according to the size and lifestyle (aquatic or terrestrial) of the species. Most mustelids are predatory, but some species will consume carrion opportunistically.

Most of our information on the food eaten by mustelids comes from identifying the remains in scats and in the stomach contents of dead animals. These results are often expressed as frequency of occurrence or percentage volume, or a combination of both. Dietary studies are fraught with biases and other complications, so unless correction factors are applied to give more accurate estimates, interpretations of these findings can give misleading conclusions as to which food items are the most important in the diet of an animal. Different recording methods also complicate comparisons between studies.

Members of the genera *Mustela* and *Neovision* (weasels, polecats, and mink) are mainly carnivorous. They are specialist predators of small mammals and birds, but may also include some invertebrates and plant food (fruit, berries, and nuts) in their diet. The smaller species are able to hunt rodents (voles, rats, and mice) and lagomorphs (rabbits, hares, and pikas) inside their burrows. Lagomorphs, rodents (mainly voles), and birds are about equally important in the diet of the Ermine, whereas the larger Long-tailed Weasel may take a higher proportion of lagomorphs and rats, and the smaller Least Weasel usually eats a higher proportion of small rodents. These small weasels are formidable predators and are capable of killing prey much larger than themselves, such as adult hares. Mink forage both on land and in water, so in addition to small mammals and birds, they eat aquatic prey, including fish, crayfish, frogs, and aquatic invertebrates.

The martens (*Martes*) are more omnivorous than the weasels, and both insects and fruit are significant food items in their diets. They take advantage of locally and seasonally abundant food, so their diets show more seasonal variations: small mammals are important throughout the year, insects are consumed during the summer months, fruit and berries are eaten during late summer/autumn, and small birds are often taken in the winter. Martens are agile tree climbers and are able to hunt arboreal prey, such as squirrels. The Fisher is a renowned predator of North American Porcupines (*Erethizon dorsata*), but also eats hares and carrion, especially Moose (*Alces alces*) and White-tailed Deer (*Odocoileus virginianus*) carcasses.

The largest terrestrial mustelid, the Wolverine, has a varied diet that shows seasonal changes. Although Wolverines will occasionally kill ungulates, they often scavenge on large carcasses of Reindeer (*Rangifer tarandus*), Moose, and other ungulates that were killed by other predators, such as Gray Wolves, or died from natural causes.

Very little is known about the diets of the Asian ferret-badgers, but they are reported to eat small vertebrates, invertebrates (including insects and earthworms), and fruits. They appear to find food mainly by smell and sound, and use their claws and probing snouts to dig for roots and earthworms.

Badgers are powerful diggers and have a varied diet. In some parts of the European Badger's range, invertebrates (particularly earthworms) are a major food component. However, small mammals (especially rodents) are also frequently eaten and plant foods are always major food items: fruit and nuts in late summer/autumn, and roots and grass in winter and spring. However, American Badgers are mainly carnivorous and plant food is not a major part of their diet. They obtain most of their food by excavating the burrows of fossorial animals; small mammals including marmots, ground squirrels, and voles are major prey items. There are reports of American Badgers forming "hunting partnerships" with Coyotes. The Coyote apparently uses its keen sense of smell to locate burrowing rodents and the

This Coyote apparently poked its nose into the wrong den and got more than it bargained for. American Badgers can be ferocious if they are cornered or threatened and will defend themselves from other predators. Although Coyotes may occasionally prey on American Badgers, their relationship is complex and not always antagonistic. There are reports of these two predators hunting together, apparently cooperatively. Coyotes, with their keen sense of smell, are able to locate burrowing rodents, and American Badgers can dig down to reach these rodents with amazing speed. The Coyote catches the rodents that flee from the burrow and the badger feasts on the ones trapped underground.

Taxidea taxus
Arizona, USA.
Photo: W. L. Miller/FLPA

Crocodilians and **Giant Otters** are natural enemies. Crocodiles may attack a litter of young otters, and Giant Otters would willingly eat a clutch of caiman eggs, although their normal diet is almost entirely fish. This was probably a noisy encounter. Like other carnivores that live in groups, Giant Otters are very vocal. They may have made a "hah" sound when they first saw the caiman, indicating a low level of alarm or interest, or they may have snorted. Snorts are alarm vocalizations given in the face of danger. If the Giant Otters had charged, trying to bluff the caiman into departing, they might have uttered "wavering screams" and threatening growls. If there were young otters present, they may have chimed in with squeaks, whines, and wails. After an encounter like this, the adults would probably have soothed them with reassuring "hums". Two other calls have been observed in Giant Otter groups: a "coo" that is used in a close contacts and a "whistle" that is an intergroup contact call. Very few animals prey on adult Giant Otters, but the young are vulnerable to predation by large felids and anacondas, as well as caimans. Large numbers of caimans live in the vast South American wetland that is the Pantanal, so encounters between Giant Otters and crocodilians may occur with some regularity. Interestingly, there are reports of Giant Otters eating large prey like anacondas and black caimans.

Pteronura brasiliensis
Pantanal, Mato Grosso, Brazil.
Photos: Günter Ziesler

Taxidea taxus
Minnesota, USA.
Photo: Roland Seitre

American Badger digs them up with its powerful claws. Both predators then share the proceeds.

Honey Badgers eat mostly small vertebrates and insects, but they also consume roots, berries, and fruit. They are strong diggers, and do not hesitate to dig after rodents or other prey hiding underground. Their favorite foods are the larvae of honeybees and honey, although this may be seasonal, as honey is more widely available in the drier months of the year. The supposed relationship between the Honey Badger and a bird, the greater honeyguide (*Indicator indicator*), may be mythical. Although these two animals may occur together at the nests of bees, no one has observed and recorded all of the stages of this symbiotic relationship, from the initial attraction by a greater honeyguide of a Honey Badger, through guiding to a nest by the honeyguide, to the breaking open of the nest by the Honey Badger.

The main food of most otter species is fish and the species selected appear to be related to their ease of capture. Crayfish and amphibia are also important and show marked seasonal fluctuations. Crayfish are inaccessible in their winter refuges and are preyed upon during their active period, when the water is warm. Amphibia, on the other hand, are often easily caught in their winter retreats as they are not hidden away under stones, but simply sit on the mud at the bottom of ponds and ditches. There may also be a peak of frog catching during the spring spawning period. Small mammals and birds (waterfowl) appear quite regularly in otter diets but are usually minor components. Reptiles and molluscs are also taken only occasionally, and aquatic insects are eaten in varying amounts. Crustaceans are important food items for some otter species: the African Clawless Otter and Asian Small-clawed Otter both specialize in feeding on crabs and shellfish.

Mustela and *Martes* mustelids hunt alone, possibly using their senses of smell and hearing as the main means of locating prey, although movement may also be an important factor that triggers an attack. Once within striking distance, it leaps on top, clutches the prey's body with the forelimbs, and kills with a bite to the neck or occipital region (which usually crushes the back of the skull). When a weasel attacks prey that is too large to handle in this way, it will pull the prey off its feet by clasping it; the weasel then throws itself on its side, raking backwards vigorously with the hind feet as it does so. A few preliminary bites may then be delivered on the prey's body before making a definitive killing bite.

The Wolverine, when it attacks large animals such as reindeer, leaps upon the back of the prey and rides it, clutching with its forelimbs, and kills by bites to the neck. Small rodents are sometimes killed with a blow with the paw, but a bite to the neck normally follows even if the prey is already dead.

The Fisher is a major predator of the North American Porcupine. To accomplish the task of killing these heavily quill-laden animals, Fishers have developed a highly specialized method of attack. When a Fisher encounters a Porcupine, it forces the rodent to the ground and circles it repeatedly, directing rapid bites at the Porcupine's unprotected face. The Porcupine turns constantly, trying to present its quill-protected back to the attacker, or to swipe the Fisher with its quilled tail. Through repeated bites to the face, the Fisher eventually subdues and kills the Porcupine, which it eats starting from the underbelly.

Most river otters hunt mainly by sight. When searching for prey, an otter will swim along at the surface in a leisurely manner with the head pointed downwards, so that the eyes are under water. Every now and then, a sudden dive is made. A pursuit might take two to three minutes, with the otter surfacing briefly for a breath about every thirty seconds; the prey is finally seized with a quick, snatching bite. In some otter species that forage in groups, such as the Giant Otter, cooperative hunting is observed; the group drives fish into shallow backwaters, where they are easy to catch. The African Clawless Otter and Asian Small-clawed Otter have particularly dexterous forefeet that they use to catch crabs and crayfish in crevices.

The Sea Otter eats sedentary molluscs and sea urchins, and sluggish bottom-living fish. Since this type of prey does not require long pursuits it is not necessary for Sea Otters to make very prolonged dives. When foraging at depths of 10–25 m, they only stay down for about a minute and a half. Although sight is usually used in prey capture, molluscs and echinoderms hidden in crevices are mainly located by touch. Sea urchins, a prey species with short spines, are simply turned about in the paws, the spines are brushed off, and they are then bitten open. To break open hard-shelled prey, such as molluscs, Sea Otters are unique amongst mustelids in using a stone tool as an anvil. The Sea Otter brings up a suitable flat stone along with its prey,

Wolverines *are mainly nocturnal, but they can occasionally be found active during the day. They do not appear hindered by deep snow, and they live in regions with short summers and long winters. They tend to prefer tundra in the summer and taiga habitat in the winter. These solitary mustelids can travel 30 km or more in a day, often at a loping gallop. Wolverine homes ranges are so large that they do not try to mark the entire boundaries, but they leave urine and feces on prominent objects such as rocks or trees. Scent gland on their hindfeet may also leave a trail. Gray Wolves are their main predators and there is some evidence that if wolf scent is present in an area, a Wolverine will move on.*

Gulo gulo
Photo: Konrad Wothe/FLPA

turns upon its back, places the stone on its chest, then clutching the mollusc in both paws, it bangs the shell down upon the anvil until it breaks. In getting an abalone off a rock, the stone is used as a hammer and the mollusc is pounded until the shell is smashed. If food is abundant, Sea Otters will gather several urchins or mussels on a single dive and carry them to the surface, held in a fold of loose skin under the armpit. Interestingly, they do not use right or left sides at random, but show a degree of handedness by always using the same paw to put the food under the arm.

Scavengers, such as the Fisher or Wolverine, will remain near a large carcass for several days, abandoning it only after all the edible parts have been consumed or the carcass has

been lost to larger scavengers, such as bears. Mustelids are known to cache surplus food, particularly when prey is abundant. These reserves are important for their survival during periods when food is scarce. For instance, American Mink will often use rock crevices or seldom-used burrows to cache prey such as live frogs, which they paralyze by a bite at the back of the neck. Surplus killing sometimes occurs when some mustelids encounter large groups of domestic animals, such as rabbits or poultry.

The long bodies of small mustelids enable them to navigate narrow passages and small cavities, but this body shape incurs an energetic cost. Their tubular shape has a high body surface area/volume ratio, which results in a greater lost of body heat.

Tayras *can move headfirst up and down vertical tree trunks, alternately grasping the trunk with their forefeet and their hindfeet as they bound up or down. They occasionally rest in the forks of trees, and captive individuals have been found to prefer elevated nest boxes. Tayras often travel long distances in the course of a day, usually moving in a more or less straight line rather than back and forth. They are often seen in the forest canopy. Although Tayras are primarily diurnal, they still rest at times during the day, and because many of the rodents that they prey on are nocturnal, they may also hunt at dawn and dusk.*

Eira barbara
Brazil.
Photo: Jany Sauvanet/NHPA

Sea Otters rest by floating belly-up in the water with their feet sticking out above the surface. They are generally diurnal, and at night they may entangle their body in long strands of kelp to keep themselves from drifting away while they are sleeping. Kelp "forests" are an essential part of the coastal ecosystem, providing habitat and food for many species. Sea Otters prey on sea urchins—herbivorous invertebrates that eat kelp. Where there are too few Sea Otters, sea urchins become overabundant and overgraze, destroying the kelp habitat. Sea Otters are thus a "keystone species" that help keep this complex coastal ecosystem in balance.

Enhydra lutris
Monterey Bay, California, USA.
Photo: Jeff Foot/Dcom/DRK

Hence, many mustelids must consume a greater amount food to sustain themselves than a similar-sized animal. It is estimated that weasels must eat one third of their body mass in food daily, and that pregnant females must eat about two thirds of their mass each day. Not surprisingly, mustelids, particularly the smaller species, are constantly hunting for food, especially during the colder months of winter.

The activity patterns of mustelids are influenced by a number of factors including daily temperatures, interference from competitors, limitations of the visual system, risk of predation, and social behavior. Their foraging activity is often related to food availability, and most species time their hunting to coincide with the movements of their prey. For instance, weasels are active primarily at night because their small mammal prey are usually nocturnal. However, their demanding metabolism and limited gut capacity make frequent meals a necessity, and some diurnal foraging is necessary, thus many species are active both day and night.

Most mustelids are active throughout the year, but badgers may become inactive during winter. This period of inactivity or hibernation is an adaptation to the temporary decrease in availability of their main prey. American Badgers prey on ground squirrels and pocket gophers, which hibernate during winter. Also, because American Badgers capture these rodents through digging, hunting is difficult in frozen ground. European Badgers in some areas primarily eat earthworms, which in

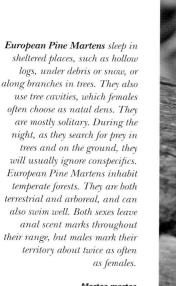

European Pine Martens sleep in sheltered places, such as hollow logs, under debris or snow, or along branches in trees. They also use tree cavities, which females often choose as natal dens. They are mostly solitary. During the night, as they search for prey in trees and on the ground, they will usually ignore conspecifics. European Pine Martens inhabit temperate forests. They are both terrestrial and arboreal, and can also swim well. Both sexes leave anal scent marks throughout their range, but males mark their territory about twice as often as females.

Martes martes
Photo: C. Wermter/CD-Gallery

Although mustelids have a wide diversity of diets, most species are carnivorous, relying on animal prey to sustain their daily energy needs. The **Greater Grison** eats small mammals such as agoutis, cavies and opossums, birds, reptiles and amphibians, and occasionally fish. Its skull is powerful and massive, with well-developed carnassial shearing teeth. It has strong claws for digging out prey, such as Rock Cavies, which the grison attacks in their burrows. The Greater Grison is an excellent swimmer, and climbs readily. Although primarily diurnal and solitary, it is occasionally active at night. A female and a young grison have been observed 2 m up in a palm tree, knocking down debris, which was examined by an adult male on the ground.

Galictis vittata
Venezuela.
Photo: Benjamín Busto

cold weather are deep underground and inaccessible. To survive these food shortages, badgers decrease their metabolism and body temperature, and undergo long periods of sleep. In North America, this period of hibernation can be as long as five months, from November to March.

Breeding

Since most mustelids are solitary and range over a large area, males and females must locate each other and come together in order to mate. Scent marking by both sexes, using secre-

tions from the anal glands, urine and feces, may thus play an important role during the breeding season. When members of the opposite sex meet, pair bonds are short, and soon after mating they part company. Both sexes may then continue to seek other partners, but females soon start to prepare for parturition. Male mustelids usually do not take part in raising the young and the responsibility for parental care is left solely to the female.

Mustelids are difficult to study in the wild and most of our observations of their mating behavior come from captive animals. In the European Pine Marten and Stone Marten, the approach of the mating period is announced by a large increase

Although some studies have shown that **European Pine Martens** spend much of their foraging time on the ground, hunting voles, mice, and beetles, they are also good climbers, and will spend considerable time in trees, exploring hollows and cavities in search of prey such as squirrels and birds. While European Pine Martens seem to favor small mammals, a study in Finland showed that they also preyed on Mountain Hares. Other food sources include amphibians, earthworms, wasps and bees, honey, carrion, and fruit. In Central Poland, where the closely related European Pine Marten and Stone Marten are found together, there is a large overlap in diet, but European Pine Martens feed more on rodents and birds, and Stone Martens on fruit and insects.

Martes martes
near Lake Constance, on Germany.
Photo: Manfred Danegger/NHPA

In much of North America, the **American Mink** is a major predator of Muskrats, as shown by this kill. Fluctuations in Muskrat populations have a direct effect on American Mink abundance. American Mink are very successful generalist predators, eating rodents, birds, fish, and amphibians in varying proportions in different habitats. They spend most of their time hunting near water, but can hunt underwater as well. They are also agile climbers and occasionally forage in trees. Given the opportunity, like other mustelids, American Mink will kill more than their immediate needs and store the surplus, using rock crevices or burrows to cache prey.

Neovison vison
Canada.
Photo: T. Kitchin & V. Hurst/NHPA

in scenting behavior and vocalizations. Both sexes make a special piping call at this time and the female also makes a "clucking" sound, which is not heard at other seasons. Presumably, in the wild, these signals serve both to indicate readiness for social contact and to facilitate meetings between the sexes; they may also have physiologically stimulating effects. In martens, the female normally has two or three periods of heat, separated by quiescent intervals of a few days, so a breeding pair may remain together for a short time. During this period, they remain in contact, sleep together, groom each other, and may indulge in play behavior that sometimes goes over into fighting. Although mating is often interspersed with fighting, this is commonly initiated by the female and does not apparently lead to injury. A lasting bond is not formed; a male marten will try to mate with several females and a female will accept a different male for successive periods of heat. During copulation, the male grips the female by the neck and holds her sides with his forepaws; if she does not at once assume the mating posture, with her hindquarters raised and the tail turned aside, he will drag her around until she does. Mating usually takes place on the ground, but since martens are arboreal, it may also take place on the branch of a tree. Copulations are often quite long in some mustelid species; in American Martens and Least Weasels, it may last around 90 minutes.

In captive weasels, the course of events is very similar. Male and female weasels are hostile outside of the mating season. They show a readiness to mate by giving a trilling call and as soon as they are brought together, the female starts to leap playfully around the male. He responds very promptly by seizing her by the scruff of the neck and then mounts, clasping the female in the lumbar region. She may struggle, and will sometimes break loose from his clasp, but by maintaining the neck grip, the male is able to drag her around until she adopts the right position; a prolonged copulation then follows. Alternating bouts of fighting and mating then continue for some hours, but the fighting is semi-playful and no injuries are inflicted.

In the North American River Otter, males tend to become very aggressive during the breeding season and will range over a wider area than usual at this time. Although otters sometimes mate on land, they commonly do so in the water. The male grips the female by the scruff of the neck and contrives to bend his body round the base of her tail so as to reach her vulva. Captive Smooth-coated Otters have been reported to use a ventroventral orientation for copulating. A female Sea Otter floats on the surface of the water with her back extended so as to be slightly concave, thus lowering her vulva towards the male, who lies besides her or slightly to one side, his belly against her back. The male clasps the female round the chest with his paws and also grips her with his teeth on whatever part of her face he can reach. This grip is often strong enough to produce wounds on the female's nose.

Many species of mustelids appear to be induced ovulators: eggs are shed from the ovary only in response to the stimulus provided by copulation. Since eggs and sperm do not remain viable for very long, the correct timing of ovulation in relation to mating is essential, and triggering ovulation by copulation may be the simplest solution. The large baculum in the penis of many male mustelids may ensure that the stimulation during copulation is sufficient to cause ovulation. The nerve impulses produced by the mechanical stimulation of the cervix result in the liberation of a hormone "releasing factor", which activates the pituitary gland. A luteinising hormone is then released that causes ovulation.

In some mustelids, there is a delay in the implantation of the fertilized egg into the uterus. Normally, once an egg has been fertilized, it starts its development as it travels down the oviduct, and very shortly after reaching the uterus implantation takes place; the formation of the placenta is initiated and gestation proceeds without interruption. In delayed implantation, the initial stages of cell division occur and the egg reaches the uterus in the blastocyst stage. It then becomes inactive, cell division ceases, and implantation does not take place. The free blastocyst remains quiescent for a period that may be as long as several months (for example, at least eight months in the North American River Otter). It then resumes activity, implantation, and formation of the placenta take place, and gestation proceeds in the normal way. The physiological basis of delayed implantation is not yet fully understood in any species; it is not clear what causes the blastocyst to become inactive or what triggers it to resume its development at the end of the period of delay.

Several hypotheses have been advanced to explain the adaptive value of delayed implantation. One hypothesis is that delayed implantation is strongly linked to seasonal fluctuations in environmental conditions. Mammals living in high latitude seasonal environments must give birth and raise young during the short summer season when conditions are favorable. Early parturition allows for maximum offspring growth, thus most births occur in spring. However, in mammalian species with a

Several mustelids, such as weasels and this **European Polecat**, are capable of tackling prey much larger and heavier than themselves. However, dietary studies of European Polecats have shown that the most important prey items in parts of its range are frogs and toads. They will also eat birds and eggs, fish, carrion, invertebrates, and fruit. Juveniles eat more fruits and invertebrates, and fewer mammals, than adults. European Polecats constantly move as they search for prey, exploring burrows, hollow logs, trees, and rock crevices. They sometimes raid farms, killing rabbits and poultry, and are considered a pest species by gamekeepers. The European Polecat is possibly the ancestor of the domestic Ferret (Mustela putorius furo), which is used to hunt rabbits in parts of Europe and North Africa.

Mustela putorius
Derbyshire, UK.
Photo: Paul Hobson/naturepl.com

relatively fixed gestation length, the time of mating determines the time of parturition, so for births to occur in spring a male and female must mate during the winter. Species with delayed implantation are able to shift their mating season away from the snow season to a time when males are more mobile and can better find receptive females. The evolution of delayed implantation thus decouples the timing of parturition and mating, allowing both to occur during the same optimal spring/summer season.

Adaptations to more southern latitude environments may have led to the loss of delayed implantation in some mustelid species. Interestingly, the Ermine and the Long-tailed Weasel both have a long implantation delay, but the Least Weasel breeds successfully without a delay, even though its range extends as far north as the Arctic Circle. Also, some species, such as the American Mink, have a short and variable delay. Why this should be so is still not clear.

In general, female mustelids only have one litter per year, except for the Least Weasel, which can produce two or three litters annually. If a litter is lost, a female will come into heat again almost at once, presumably in response to the sudden cessation of the suckling stimulus.

Most females give birth to their young in a secure place, such as a burrow or a cavity in a tree. Since the young are well

In many areas, **Wolverines** are dependent on larger predators, especially Gray Wolves, to provide kills. Their diet includes the carcasses of large ungulates, such as Moose and Reindeer. They will cover long distances in search of carcasses. Deep snow, which hampers large ungulates like Reindeer, enables Wolverines to get close to them. They kill larger prey by a bite to the neck or throat. Wolverines also prey opportunistically on deer, sheep, small mammals, birds, and eggs. Rodents may be dug out of the ground. Wolverines tend to avoid humans, so winter ski resorts may affect the choice of habitat and pre available to them.

Gulo gulo
Kuhmo, Finland.
Photo: Staffan Widstrand

*Martens, such as the **European Pine Marten**, are more omnivorous than weasels, and take advantage of what is seasonally abundant, including birds. While small mammals are taken all year long, in some places, insects are consumed during the summer months, fruits and berries are important in late summer and autumn, and birds are often taken in the winter. These patterns may vary according to what is available locally. For instance, in Minorca, birds are the second most important prey item in the European Pine Marten's diet in March and April, and the main food in May and June. In the Scottish Highlands, by contrast, birds are eaten all the year round, but are never an important component of the diet. Although opportunistic, European Pine Martens in Scotland have a very strong preference for Field Voles over other small mammals.*

Martes martes
Álava, Spain.
Photo: José Luis Gómez de Francisco

protected, they are born at an early stage of development. Most mustelids are born naked, with their eyes closed, and only capable of crawling. However, the Sea Otter has unusually precocial young; they are born with their eyes open and are much more developed than other mustelids. The single youngster does not need to be able to swim long distances, as the mother carries it on her chest most of the time, but it must be able to look after itself when she dives for food.

After the young are born, the mother licks them free of their embryonic membranes, licks their fur dry, and eats the membranes and the afterbirth. When litters are large, the food value of the placentas is considerable and the female may not need to leave her young to hunt during the period immediately following parturition. Licking the young dry has the obvious function of preventing them from becoming chilled, as drying the hair out permits it to take up its normal insulating air layer. In the Sea Otter pup, this process is of particular importance. Unlike seals, Sea Otters do not have a layer of blubber, and depend entirely on the properties of their fur for insulation; the trapped air layer also provides extra buoyancy. A pup that is not properly dried out will therefore very soon die. A mother Sea Otter thus gives her youngster an unusually prolonged initial grooming: one female was recorded spending nearly four hours grooming her newborn pup, interrupting the process only once to groom herself.

Although the development of the young is a continuous process, three stages can be recognized: the early nestling period, when the only nourishment the young receive is their mother's milk; the mixed nutrition period, during which the young begin to eat solid food, but still continue to take milk as well; and a period of post-weaning dependence on the parent, before the young finally become fully independent.

During the first few days and weeks, the mother nurses her offspring, cleans them, and keeps them warm. The newborn are barely able to crawl, but they are capable of searching for a teat on which to suckle. Many of them show the "milk tread"—a series of alternating movements of the forepaws pushing against the mother's body as they suck—which has the effect of simulating milk flow. Should the mother need to move the young to a new den, the usual method of transport is to pick the youngster up by the scruff of the neck. The youngster responds by remaining limp and passive until it is set down again. The hair on the back of a young Ermine's neck grows very rapidly and by the age of two to three weeks, they have

developed a distinctive mane; it is possible that this precocious growth of neck hair serves as a protection when being carried by the mother. The neck-carrying method is seen in otters, but in the African Clawless Otter and Asian Small-clawed Otter, the mother usually holds a youngster clasped against her chest or chin and hobbles along on three legs. The Sea Otter uses the same method of clutching the young to her chest, the difference being that she swims on her back as she does so.

During the nestling period, the locomotor abilities of the young improve, their eyes open, and they begin to emerge from the maternal den and play together. The role of play is not fully understood, but it often comprises behavior similar to that exhibited by adults during mating. Playing with food items may help improve foraging and hunting abilities.

The mother soon starts to provide the young with solid food and the period of mixed nutrition begins. In a few species, around this time, the young lick at the mother's mouth and apparently drink her saliva. This behavior has been recorded in the Long-tailed Weasel. The significance of this "mouth suckling" is not fully understood; it is not known whether the saliva contains something of physiological importance, whether it is merely a source of fluid, or a whether the smell of food the mother has just recently eaten plays some role in encouraging the young to start eating solid food.

Once the young emerge from the safety of the maternal den, they are very vulnerable to getting lost or to attack by predators. However, there are two types of behavior patterns that serve to minimize these dangers. The first is "alarm behavior", whereby the young respond to a parental alarm call by either fleeing, taking cover, or turning to face the danger with bristled hair and hissing/spitting vocalizations. The second type of protective behavior is "contact-keeping", in which the young show a strong tendency to remain together, often using contact calls. For example, the cubs of the Asian Small-clawed Otter give a "lost" call; if one youngster becomes separated, he gives this special call and the rest of the litter respond at once by running to him. As the young mature, contact calling is used less frequently. Whether the mother uses a similar call to summon her offspring is not clear.

Weaning is a gradual process: the proportion of solid food in the diet increases, and suckling becomes less frequent and finally ceases altogether. There is often a significant time interval between weaning and independence, during which the parent kills for the young until they are strong enough and

experienced enough to fend for themselves. Weasels and martens start carrying killed prey to their young in the den when they are around five or six weeks old. As most mustelids are highly skilled predators, in many species there is a further period of "apprenticeship" during which the young learn to make their own kills. During this time, the young are provided, under maternal supervision, with the opportunity to make their own kills, and discover how to perfect their hunting and killing techniques. At first, the mother may carry home prey she has killed and which she leaves for the young to eat. A little later, she brings home live prey, sets it down before the young, and allows them to kill it.

Some young mustelids may learn foraging skills by watching their mother. Sea Otter juveniles are seen diving after the mother, and although they are not able to stay under as long

as she can, it seems likely that they learn the sorts of places in which food is to be found. They may also, by watching her, learn something of the methods of collecting and opening the different types of prey. It appears, however, that the Sea Otters' anvil tool using behavior is innate.

Once the young are independent they leave their mother and disperse to establish their own place to live. In general, post-weaning males tend to disperse widely and females remain near the area of their birth. The age at which mustelids reach adult size and sexual maturity varies between species; many can breed during the first year following their birth. Least Weasels, the smallest mustelid species, are sexually mature at three months and, if small rodents are abundant, may produce young in their first summer; larger species, such as Sea Otters, Giant Otters, and Wolverines, reach sexual maturity after two years. Longevity in the Mustelidae ranges from one to two years in the small weasels to up to 20 years in the larger species.

Movements, Home range and Social organization

Mustelid movements are mainly concerned with finding food, patrolling and scent-marking territorial boundaries, and searching for mates during the breeding season. Mustelids can cover long distances; Wolverines, for instance, can move up to 30 km in one day.

Mustelids move on land using various gaits, including walking, bounding, and running. The larger, stockier mustelids often use a slow, rolling, bearlike shuffle. Most mustelids can trot or gallop at speed and often sit on their haunches to look around. The bound is a very typical mustelid gait and is best described as a jump forward, with the two front feet touching the ground simultaneously and the back feet landing an instant later in the same position as the forefeet. This leaves a very distinct trail pattern of two side-by-side tracks, with each set of prints separated by the mustelid's stride length.

Otters can bound and run on land, but when an otter travels on snow it will get down on its belly and slide, pushing itself along with its short legs. Mink will also sometimes slide for short distances on snow, but otter slides can be very long. On flat snow, an otter will tuck its forefeet under its belly and slide forward, occasionally pushing with its back feet to maintain momentum. On a slope, it will simply glide, with hardly any foot movements, leaving a narrow groove in the snow as a track. It is also common for otters to slide down muddy or snowy banks and splash into water. This play behavior can continue

Despite the animal's name, examination of stomach contents indicates that honey, while a favorite food, is only a secondary item in the diet of the **Honey Badger**. *These badgers open beehives by tearing away the wood of trees, or they scoop out combs from the cracks in rocks using the claws of their forefeet. They can extract the grubs from the comb with their incisors. The often-described symbiotic relationship between the Honey Badger and the greater honeyguide may be a myth. Although the Honey Badger and this bird species are found together at bees' nests, no one has observed and recorded all of the stages of this supposed relationship, from the greater honeyguide attracting the Honey Badger's attention and guiding it to the site, to the breaking open of the nest by the Honey Badger.*

Mellivora capensis
Photo: Terry Whittaker/FLPA

Honey Badgers *occur in a diverse range of habitats, and exploit a wide range of food that is to be found there. In arid parts of the badger's range, scorpions are a common prey item. With their massive skulls and powerful limbs, Honey Badgers are able break open the clay capsules of estivating lungfish, and even the carapaces of turtles. They are good swimmers and can chase turtles underwater. They are also strong diggers, and do not hesitate to dig after rodents, large spiders, or other prey hiding underground. Six Honey Badger stomachs that were examined contained an abundance of such subterranean prey.*

Mellivora capensis
Stone Hills Game Sanctuary, Zimbabwe.
Photos: Richard Peek

There are reports of **Honey Badgers** hunting and eating large snakes, including pythons and cobras. When Honey Badgers eat, they hold the food with their front claws while resting their forelegs on the ground—a position that can be seen both here and in the previous photo involving a scorpion. Another mustelid species capable of tackling snakes is the Zorilla, which has been recorded killing cobras. The Zorilla approaches the snake cautiously, and bites it on the back several times, before retreating rapidly. Each bite is directed to the rear half of the snake, and is accompanied by vigorous shaking. After 4–5 such attacks, the Zorilla pins the snake to the ground with its forefeet, and repeatedly bites it 10–15 cm from its head. Most snakes are eaten head first, but occasionally the tail or even flanks may be consumed first. Male Honey Badgers cover large distances while foraging, around 27 km/day. Female Honey Badgers forage in a relatively small area, covering just 10 km/day. Females zig-zag short distances from bush to bush, digging on average 10·2 holes for every kilometer of distance covered; males dig only 1·3 holes for every kilometer. Honey Badgers are mostly solitary, but are sometimes seen in pairs. Gatherings may occur at feeding sites, and males have been seen after a night's foraging traveling some distance to meet up with a group of other Honey Badgers. One such group showed no aggression, but continuously uttered a wide range of grunts, hisses, squeaks, and whines, while rolling in the sand, sniffing each other, and scent-marking.

Mellivora capensis
Stone Hills Game Sanctuary,
Zimbabwe.
Photos: Richard Peek

Despite its name, the **Fisher** rarely
eats fish. The name may originate
from the French word "fichet",
referring to the pelt of the European
Polecat. The Fisher is a solitary
hunter and its hunting strategies
vary with prey type. For example,
it is a major predator of the North
American Porcupine, and it uses
its tree climbing abilities to force
the porcupine down to the ground
where it then circles the heavily
quilled but slow moving rodent,
subduing and eventually killing
it with bites to its unprotected face.
Avoiding open areas, Fishers are
usually found in dense, closed
canopy forests. For example, in
south-central Maine, USA, during
the winter they hunt intensively
in dense patches of coniferous
undergrowth, where Snowshoe
Hare tracks are common. These
hares are caught after rapid zig-
zagging chases. Small mammals,
insects, reptiles, birds, fruit, and
fungi, are also major components
of the Fisher's diet, especially in the
absence of porcupines and hares.

Martes pennanti
Minnesota, USA.
Photo: Roland Seitre

for hours, with groups of otters repeatedly climbing the bank
and sliding back down. Otters can also hunt and travel long
distances under ice during the winter, by breathing air that is
trapped in small pockets. However, when ice is present, otters
often stay close to areas of open water created by fast currents.

Many mustelids have long, tubular bodies that allow them to
hunt in the burrows of their prey, to forage within nooks and
crevices on the ground, and to live and hunt under the snow
during the winter. Some species are also agile tree climbers, particularly the martens, the Fisher, and some weasels. Martens can
climb with great dexterity and speed, descend head first, and
jump from tree to tree. They are fast predators, able to move
swiftly in trees and on the ground in pursuit of their prey. Martens often hunt and chase squirrels in trees, and will use tree
cavities in which to give birth and raise their young. For weasels,
tree climbing is mostly used to access food, such as birds' eggs
and nestlings, or to escape from terrestrial predators.

Otters and mink are good swimmers and can dive underwater. River otters use a combination of their forefeet, hindfeet,
and tail for swimming; mink use their forefeet, occasionally
using a hindfoot for turning or diving. Although river otters
spend a considerable amount of their time foraging for prey
in water, they rest and den on land, and sometimes travel long
distances overland from one water body to another. Because of
their shortened limbs and webbed feet, they are generally less
mobile on land than terrestrial mustelids. Mink are considered
weaker swimmers than otters, and their underwater locomotion is much slower. Otters typically remain underwater for
60–120 seconds, with a maximum of around four minutes. Sea
Otters can obtain food by diving to depths that can exceed 100
m, but most foraging dives are to 25–80 m.

Badgers are powerful diggers. Digging in badgers first involves soil cutting, whereby the forefeet and claws are used to
break the hard soil. Once the soil has been sufficiently loos-
ened, it is then shifted back. After a hole has been started, the
badger may rest its head on the opposite side of the hole to
support its forequarters, while using both feet to excavate; the
hindfeet are less specialized and are only used in helping to
move the soil backward.

Information on home ranges and spatial organization can
be provided by radio-telemetry studies, in which individuals are
captured and fitted with radio collars and then tracked over

many months, with their position recorded on a regular basis.
A number of factors affect home range sizes, including body
size, sex, age, habitat quality, diet, the availability of food resources and den sites, and climate (rainfall, temperatures, and
seasonal patterns). Even within a species, home range sizes can
be highly variable, depending on the prevalence of these factors in different areas. For example, in Wisconsin, the mean
home range of American Marten males was 4·3 km² whereas, in
Labrador, the mean home range for males was 45 km².

Generally, the larger mustelids have higher energy demands
and thus require larger home ranges than smaller individuals,
although other factors, such as the type of diet (e.g. carnivorous or omnivorous), can mitigate this general body-size/home
range relationship. The largest terrestrial mustelid, the Wolverine, can weigh as much as 18 kg and have a home range of up
to 917 km², whereas ranges as small as 0·002 km² have been
recorded in the smallest mustelid, the 25 g Least Weasel. Male
mustelids are usually larger than females, so based on body size
we might expect males to have larger home range sizes, and in
general, male mustelids do occupy much larger home ranges
than females. When females are with young, they may concentrate their foraging within small core areas of their normal
home range, returning to the maternal den at the end of each
foraging trip. In contrast, during this same period, males may
roam freely throughout their home range.

All mustelids, except the European Badger and some otter
species, are solitary. For most of the time, an individual mustelid has very little contact with conspecifics, except during the
breeding season and when a female has young. Solitary living
indicates both an absence of strong selection pressures for
cooperation (such as increased foraging efficiency, improved
young production, and more successful predator defense) and
the presence of factors promoting solitariness (such as prey
characteristics and hunting methods). Mustelids generally take
animal prey that is much smaller than themselves and which
can be subdued alone. In this situation, the presence of conspecifics in their immediate surroundings would have a negative
effect on foraging efficiency, through disturbance of prey or
through depletion of local food resources.

In general, food resources determine the distribution and
size of female home ranges, whereas male ranges are determined by the resulting female ranges. Female mustelids are

Although less agile in water than otters, **American Mink** can swim well, diving to depths of 5–6 m and swimming underwater for up to 30 m. In Eurasia, where the American Mink has been introduced, the staple food items on rivers and streams are fish, mammals, and amphibians, whereas on lakes and ponds they are predominantly fish and birds, such as the common coot. Female American Mink have been found to favor small streams, whereas males prefer large streams. **North American River Otters** can remain underwater for up to four minutes, and can swim at speeds of 11 km/h. They hunt by swimming along at the surface in a leisurely manner, with their head pointed downwards and eyes underwater. Every now and then they make a sudden dive. A pursuit might take 2–3 minutes, with the otter surfacing briefly for a breath about every 30 seconds, before the prey is seized with a quick, snatching bite. Fish are consumed in inverse proportion to their swimming abilities, meaning that slow-moving species are captured and eaten more often. In shallow or murky water, North American River Otters hunt and detect prey with their vibrissae, or by feeling with their forefeet. They inspect log jams, pools of deeper water in shallow streams, areas below waterfalls, natural eddies, or any other areas likely to hold fish and other prey, such as crayfish or amphibians. There are seasonal fluctuations in the North American River Otter's diet. For instance, crayfish, which hide away in the winter, are only preyed upon when the water is warm, but amphibians, which simply sit in the mud during cold weather, are easier to catch in the winter. The proportion of amphibians in the otter's diet may also increase at spawning time. They will take rodents, birds, molluscs, and even fruit as well, but, generally, the abundance and availability of fish is the primary determinant of North American River Otter abundance.

Above: **Neovison vison**
Photo: Brian Bevan/Ardea

Below: **Lontra canadensis**
Photo: Wayne Lankinen/DRK

Salmon spawning runs provide a glut of food for fish eaters like the **North American River Otter**. Generally, otters do little damage to "game" fish stocks, such as salmon and trout, because of their preference for hunting slower moving fish. They can, however, cause considerable damage in fish farms, and may make return visit North American River Otters have a complex social system. At different times of the year and in different parts of their range, they may be found alone, in families, or in larger groups. The benefits of group-living could include cooperative foraging, whereby the members of a group work together to contain a school of fish, driving it to shore or to one another. Through cooperative foraging, each otter in the group is able to consume a higher proportion of schooling fish than a solitary otter. In coastal areas, most female and some male North American River Otters remain solitary year round. But at the end of the breeding season, when males become less aggressive towards one another, they may form large social groups. This coincides with the arrival, near the shore, of large shoals of normally pelagic (deep sea) fish. Males have been observed to leave social groups for the duration of the mating season, and rejoin the groups before the arrival of the schooling fish. Females are likely to have fewer opportunities to take advantage of cooperative foraging because they are nursing offspring, but non-reproductive females do join male groups.

Lontra canadensis
Wyoming, USA.
Photo: John Cancalosi/DRK

*Adult **Giant Otters** consume an estimated 3 kg of fish daily. The main fish species eaten are trahiras, piranhas, and catfish, from 10 cm to 60 cm in length. The fish are caught with the mouth and held in the otter's forepaws while being eaten. Small fish may be eaten in the water, but larger prey is taken to shore. Other prey items are rare, but may include crabs, small mammals, amphibians, birds, molluscs, snakes, caimans, and turtles. Up to 20 otters may live in a group, which may hunt cooperatively to drive fish into the shallows. Some fishermen believe that Giant Otters are competitors for their fish stocks, although dietary studies have shown little overlap between otter prey and fish of commercial interest.*

Pteronura brasiliensis
Pantanal, Mato Grosso, Brazil.
Photo: Günter Ziesler

principally concerned with defending a home range that provides enough food in which to rear offspring, whereas males maximize their reproductive success by encompassing as many females in their range as possible; consequently, male ranges are only indirectly affected by food resources. This spacing pattern typically results in intra-sexual territoriality, whereby male home ranges have little or no overlap with those of other males, but greatly overlap the smaller female home ranges. Females are often more tolerant of each other than are males, but their home ranges overlap only slightly as well. However, for home ranges to be exclusive and non-overlapping, a mustelid's food resources must be evenly distributed and stable. If these resources vary in space and time, home ranges must be larger to provide sufficient food at all times. A larger home range, may contain a surplus of food for most of the year, which may allow several individuals to utilize the same area; in this situation, a system of overlapping ranges may develop.

There are some variations to this intra-sexual territoriality pattern in solitary mustelids. For example, male Ermine home ranges are either enlarged or abandoned altogether during the breeding season. This has been attributed to a change in the critical resource, from food to mates, which results in two different "social structures" for males, depending on the time of year.

Several field studies have now reported extensive variation in social spacing patterns between and within mustelid species. These variations may be caused by factors such as intra- and inter-specific competition or phylogenetic inertia. Unfortunately, some mustelid species are so poorly known that any within-species variation has not yet been identified.

Social groups have been recorded in the European Badger and in some otter species, such as the Giant Otter, which live in family groups consisting of a mated adult pair, one or more subadults, and one or more young of the year. The North American River Otter also exhibits a high intra-specific variation in social systems, between as well as within different habitats. In the Sea Otter, social groups are generally segregated by sex. These groups, called "rafts", vary in size according to the region; they are small in California (2–12 animals), but can be large in Alaska, where hundreds of males may congregate in groups. Females with young form groups during the entire year, whereas groups of adult males only occur outside of the breeding season; during the breeding season, males become intolerant of each other and will travel extensively to mate with available females.

European Badgers in Britain form mixed-sex groups of up to 23 individuals that share a territory and setts. However, elsewhere in continental Europe, they may be non-social and often live alone or in pairs, with either intra- or inter-sexual territories. European Badgers do not appear to obtain any direct benefits from group living, as do other social carnivores, such as alloparental care in African Wild Dogs or defense of kills and cooperative hunting in Spotted Hyaenas. One possible explanation for why badger social groups exist in the British Isles is that the mild, damp climate and the high prevalence of pasture provide ideal conditions for earthworms (*Lumbricus terrestris*), which are their principal prey in this region. Such super-abundant food could account for the inflated densities of European Badgers, which then find themselves sharing den sites in an unusually crowded social environment. In continental Europe, European Badgers may feed on different foods, such as European Rabbits (*Oryctolagus cuniculus*) in Spain, and insects and fruits in Italy. Another (non-exclusive) explanation for why some European Badgers occupy territories in groups is the Resource Dispersion Hypothesis. Groups may form where prey is unpredictably dispersed but locally abundant. Thus, conspecifics can share surpluses, but all have an individual stake in maintaining access to several patches, thereby leading to overlapping home ranges. They defend a similar space, thus creating a spatial group, but may not gain any behavioral benefits from group living. If a social group is a result of individuals sharing dispersed resources, then this itself may be considered an explanation for their sociality, and no behavioral explanations need to be invoked.

The benefits of group-living in river otters could include cooperative foraging, whereby a group of otters work together to contain a school of fish. Social otters, through cooperative foraging, can each consume a higher proportion of schooling fish than solitary individuals. In coastal areas, most female and some male North American River Otters remain solitary year-round, but large groups of males can also be found, and a few females may briefly form mixed-sex groups. In these areas, schooling pelagic fishes usually arrive in the nearshore environment at the end of the otters' mating season. Males leave social groups for the duration of the mating season, but later rejoin a group before the arrival of the schooling fish. Females are likely to have fewer opportunities to take advantage of cooperative foraging because they are nursing offspring. However,

*The primary diet of the **Eurasian Otter** consists of aquatic prey: fish, including eels, as seen here, frogs, and invertebrates, such as crabs and crayfish. In general, the mean proportion of fish in the diet declines from 94% on seashores, to 71% on lakes and fish ponds, to 64% on rivers and streams. Seasonal variations in fish consumption can be related to changes in fish activity and to environmental conditions. For instance, the proportion of fish may drop in winter, when flooding increases water speeds and stirs up silt, reducing visibility and making hunting more difficult. At such times, hibernating amphibians may be a primary alternative food source, although Eurasian Otters may hunt birds and small mammals when out of water as well.*

Lutra lutra
Scotland, UK.
Photo: Nick Gordon/Ardea

some non-reproductive females do join male groups during this time.

Social groups can form through the retention of offspring, but only if conspecifics can tolerate each other; for example, Red Foxes can form social groups in urban areas. This tolerance does not occur in mustelids, except for the European Badger and some otter species. Like Red Foxes, Stone Martens can also inhabit urban areas, yet they have maintained a rigid, intra-sexual territoriality. They have evolved to display increased aggression towards offspring of dispersing age, which has overridden any cost-benefit trade-offs for tolerating conspecifics in an urban environment. Similarly, European Pine Martens occupy suitable environments for groups to form, but this does not happen because of an evolved intolerance of con-

specifics: immature animals are ousted by their mother when they become independent. In urban areas, Red Foxes form social groups. Stone Martens may also inhabit urban areas and eat similar foods, yet they have maintained a rigid intra-sexual territoriality. They have evolved to display increased aggression towards offspring of dispersing age, which has overridden any cost-benefit trade-offs for tolerating conspecifics in an urban environment.

Relationship with Humans

Mustelids have played a fairly prominent role in human economies and culture since early times. Characteristics such as cour-

*Although **Eurasian Otters** catch their prey with their mouths, they use their forepaws to control it while eating. Vigorous, agile prey like eels (previous photo), and potentially dangerous prey, such as this large crab, may be brought ashore to be dealt with. Unlike Sea Otters, which can float passively while they handle their prey, Eurasian Otters and other river otters have to swim actively to stay on the surface. They swim using movements of the hindlegs and tail. Usually foraging dives last 1–2 minutes, five at the most.*

Lutra lutra
Scotland, UK.
Photo: Solvin Zankl/naturepl.com

Sea Otters are unique amongst mustelids in using a stone tool as an anvil to break open hard-shelled prey like clams. The otter brings up a suitable flat stone along with its prey, turns upon its back, places the stone on its chest, then clutching the mollusc in both paws, it bangs the shell down upon the stone until it breaks. During the dive, the Sea Otter may also use the stone as a hammer to dislodge bivalve molluscs, such as abalones, free from rocks. Clams, mussels, and other bivalve molluscs are the main items in the diet. Other prey items include sea urchins, crabs, squid, octopus, chitons, tubeworms, and scallops. Very occasionally, Sea Otters will also eat fish, although they prefer dealing with prey that cannot swim away. However, they are capable of swimming at up to 9 km/h underwater. When foraging, at depths of 10–25 m, they rarely stay down for more than a minute and a half, and usually for less than a minute. In one study off coastal Washington, USA, an average of 77% of all dives were successful in capturing prey; adults were slightly more successful than sub-adults. Sea Otters forage in both rocky and soft-sediment communities on or near the ocean floor. They have good underwater vision, and most prey is captured by sight, although molluscs and sea urchins hidden in crevices are mainly located by touch. To deal with the spines on sea urchins, the Sea Otter turns the sea urchin around in its paws, brushing the spines off before biting it open. In order to maintain their body temperature in a life lived constantly in the sea, the Sea Otter's metabolic heat production is 2–3 times greater than that of similar-sized terrestrial mammals, which in turn requires it to consume between one-fifth and one-third of its body mass in food every day.

Enhydra lutris
California, USA.
Photo: Tom & Pat Leeson/Ardea

Across much of their range, **European Badgers** rely predominantly on earthworms, which can make up nearly two thirds of their diet. But at certain times of year and in certain places fruit can make up the bulk of what they eat. European Badgers will kill and eat small mammals, amphibians, and invertebrates, but they also consume a large proportion of vegetable matter, such as acorns, cereals (particularly maize), tubers and roots, and grass. During bouts of cold weather or deep snow, European Badgers may sleep in their sett for days or weeks. In northern Europe, this winter sleep may last several months, and up to seven months in Siberia. Throughout this period, they live off fat reserves accumulated in the summer and autumn. The activity pattern of the **Least Weasel** is at the opposite extreme. Their tubular body shape and small size means that they have a high surface area to volume ratio, which results in a greater lost of body heat. Least Weasels need to eat far more food than other mammals of similar size. Estimates suggest that they must eat one third of their body mass in food daily, and that pregnant females must eat about two thirds. These high energy requirements mean that the Least Weasel has to be constantly active in search of prey, so activity and rest periods occur in rapid succession. Small mustelids, such as weasels, are primarily active at night because their small mammal prey is usually nocturnal. However, their demanding metabolism and limited gut capacity mean that Least Weasels need to consume 5–10 meals per day, so some diurnal foraging is necessary. They are also active throughout the cold months of winter. Least Weasels are carnivorous and mainly eat small mammals, but as this picture shows, they may very occasionally take fruit

Above: *Meles meles*
Berwickshire, UK.
Photo: Laurie Campbell/NHPA

Below: *Mustela nivalis*
near Lake Constance, Germany.
Photo: Manfred Danegger/NHPA

European Polecats are generally found in close proximity to rivers, streams, or lakes, so access to fresh water for drinking is not a problem. Other mustelids have behavioral or physiological adaptations to cope with a scarcity or absence of fresh water. Most otter species require fresh water for drinking and to wash the salt from their fur. Smooth-coated Otters can live in saltwater areas, but only if they have access to fresh water nearby. The Sea Otter, which lives entirely at sea, can drink seawater. Sea Otter kidneys also produce very concentrated urine to avoid unnecessary water loss.

Mustela putorius
near Lake Constance, Germany.
Photo: Manfred Danegger/NHPA

age, cunning, strength and ferocity have been attributed to mustelids and they often appear in local folklore, legends, and stories. Because of these perceived traits of mustelids, magical powers have sometimes been attributed to the body parts of a number of species, which are sometimes used in traditional medicine.

Otters are well known by the general public and are popular exhibits in zoos. They are very charismatic, active and playful animals and people enjoy watching them. They also feature in popular fiction and films such as *Ring of Bright Water* and *Tarkar the Otter*. European Badgers are also well-recognized, well-liked animals, and badger watching is popular in some parts of Europe. They have been depicted as "handsome and kind" in various cultures: for instance, in Japan as *Tamuki*, in Germany as *Meister Grimbart*, and in English literature as *Mr Badger* in Kenneth Grahame's charming novel *The Wind in the Willows*. Badgers also serve as emblems: the American Badger is the state animal of Wisconsin and the mascot of the University of Wisconsin. However, our relationship with badgers is somewhat ambivalent: a few people in Europe participate in the cruel practise of "badger baiting", where a European Badger is caught in the wild, enclosed in a pit with dogs, and forced to fight for its life, simply for amusement.

European Badgers play a role in the transmission of bovine tuberculosis (bovine TB) in Britain and Ireland. Tuberculosis in cattle is caused by the bacterium *Mycobacterium bovis*. When tubercle bacilli invade cattle, they typically cause a chronic disease that is usually characterized by lesions in the lungs. This bacterium can infect a variety of mammals, including European Badgers. Is not known how long bovine TB has been present in European Badgers; the development of the pastoral system in Britain and the practice of keeping domestic cattle have taken place over hundred of years. Cattle may have passed *M. bovis* infections to badgers, by excreting live bacilli in their dung, which badgers root through when searching for dung beetles and their larvae. Badgers may also have picked up the infection from sputum that cattle coughed onto pasture as they grazed.

The principal sites of *M. bovis* infection in the European Badger are the respiratory and urinary systems. In advanced cases, lesions may be found throughout the lung tissue, and when these lesions rupture, large numbers of bacilli are expelled and may be excreted in the sputum. An animal in this condition is highly infectious and capable of passing on the disease through coughing and sneezing.

Since the discovery of this disease in badgers in the early 1970s, a number of control actions have been implemented. Cattle owners were advised on methods of killing badgers in infected areas, legislation permitting the use of hydrogen cyanide gas to kill badgers in their setts was passed, and experimental eradication programs were set up in south-west England. However, there is still no scientific proof that badgers can infect cattle with bovine TB, although the circumstantial evidence is substantial.

Right from the beginning this issue attracted fierce public debate. On one side were farmers who saw the badger as a threat to their livelihood, and on the other were people to whom killing a popular native mammal was repugnant. There is now some evidence that badger control may actually exacerbate the spread of this disease by causing social disruption in badger populations, leading to increased movements and dispersal.

Resolving this situation is very difficult. The two extreme options of doing nothing and eliminating badgers in infected areas are clearly unacceptable. Radical solutions, such as not keeping cattle in problem regions, do not seem realistic at the present time. The development of a safe, effective vaccine could help in controlling outbreaks of the disease, but may not be the panacea that everyone would wish for. Certainly, this extremely contentious issue will continue as long as bovine TB persists in badgers and cattle.

Other mustelid species are sometimes found in close proximity to humans, exploiting food resources and using buildings as den sites. Due to their small size and secretive habits, mustelids often live near people without raising any awareness or concern. However, their predatory habits have made some mustelid species undesirable. Wolverines have been severely persecuted as they sometimes prey on large domestic species and have long been perceived by hunters as competitors for game animals. Moreover, they are reported to raid camps and traplines. Otters foraging in fish farms are a problem for aquaculturists, which often results in otters being persecuted. Some

Most mustelids are solitary and
range over a large area, so males
and females must locate each other
in order to mate. Sex hormones an
vaginal secretions in the female's
urine may indicate her estrous
state. Female **Tayras** enter estrus
several times each year for periods
of 3–20 days, while male Tayras
appear ready to mate year round.
Vocalizations may also be used to
indicate readiness to mate. In som
martens, both sexes make a piping
call, and the female also makes a
"clucking" sound, which are not
heard at other seasons. Male and
female weasels, which are hostile
to each other outside the mating
season, show a readiness to mate b
trilling to each other.

Eira barbara
Tambopata-Candamo Reserved Zone
Peru.
Photo: Günter Ziesler

mustelids, in particular polecats and mink, will raid farms and kill rabbits and poultry. In Europe, Stone Martens sometimes den in attics, where they damage roofing insulation material, and they are known to damage automobile hoses and wires. However, these problems are usually local and ephemeral in nature, and many of them can be solved without resorting to broad-scale exterminations. For example, predator-proof fencing can be installed around poultry farms and raiding individuals can be selectively removed to another area. Unfortunately, some mustelid species are still viewed as pests: for instance, hunters often consider mustelids as competitors for game animals. The Least Weasel, European Polecat, and the Stone Marten, were listed as pest species in some regions of France and can be legally trapped and killed. Trapping mustelids that are considered as pests often results in the accidental trapping of other species, such as the endangered European Mink.

Small mustelids can in fact be beneficial to humans because they prey on mice, voles, and rats, which are pests in agricultural areas and around garbage dumps. In the past, local hunters in various countries exploited the predatory abilities of several mustelid species. In South America, grisons were trained to catch chinchillas, and in some regions of tropical America, the Tayra was kept to protect houses and belongings from rodents. The European Polecat was domesticated to produce the Ferret, which is still often used for hunting rabbits in some parts of Europe and north-west Africa. In Asia, Asian Small-clawed Otters and Smooth-coated Otters are trained to catch fish and bring them back to their trainers.

The major economic value of mustelids is derived from their fur; in 2003, the global value of retail sales of fur garments, trims and accessories was US$ 11·3 billion. People have always hunted animals for their fur, to clothe themselves or for

Mating in the **European Mink**
occurs from February to March.
The male grips the female by the
neck with his jaws, and holds her
sides with his forepaws. If she does
not at once assume the mating
posture, with her hindquarters
raised and the tail turned aside,
he will drag her around until
she does. In some mustelids, the
female normally has 2–3 periods
of heat, separated by intervals
of a few days, so a breeding pair
may remain together for a short
time, sleeping together, grooming
each other, and indulging in play
behavior that sometimes goes over
into fighting, though usually
without injury. Soon after mating
they part company. Both sexes
may then continue to seek other
partners.

Mustela lutreola
Estonia.
Photo: Roland Seitre

Mating in the **American Badger** occurs in late July or August, but implantation of the fertilized eggs into the uterus is delayed until December–February, and births take place in late March or early April. Although the total gestation period is about seven months, the actual embryonic development is just six weeks. A female American Badger has a wide range of dens to choose from in which to give birth. One radio-tracked female in Minnesota used 50 different dens during the summer, and was never found in the same den on two consecutive days. American Badgers either excavate their own dens, or take over and modify those of other burrowing animals. The entrances are marked by mounds of earth. The burrow can be as long as 10 m, and can extend 3 m below the surface. The young are born in a bulky nest of dry grass in an enlarged chamber. The site of the natal den must offer safety from predators, since the female will need to leave the young unattended while foraging. It must be sheltered from the weather, and be in an area relatively rich in prey, since the female will need to concentrate her foraging within a small core area of her normal range while she has dependent young. European Badgers select den sites that have high surrounding shrub density, large shrubs covering the burrow, and are close to the center of the territory. Their communal setts are extended year after year, and may eventually cover several hectares.

In Britain, these setts may be home to clans of up to 20 or more badgers. Female otters may use natal den sites that are outside of their normal areas of activity, and they are careful to choose places that are beyond the reach of floods. Female Marine Otters give birth in rocky caves; these dens are spaces between boulders that remain above water even at high tide, and may have underwater entrances.

Taxidea taxus
Minnesota, USA.
Photo: Roland Seitre

The lack of suitable den sites can be detrimental to some mustelids. **American Martens** need hollow trees as resting sites and natal dens, and forestry practices that eliminate old trees and stumps can reduce their numbers, while clear cutting can completely eliminate them from an area. They may also give birth in rock crevices, burrows, and old squirrel nests. The natal den is lined with dry vegetation. Mating takes place from July to August, but as in some other mustelids, implantation of the fertilized eggs in the uterus is delayed, for between 190 and 250 days. The young are born in late March or April. Although the total gestation period is from seven to nine months, actual embryonic development takes just four weeks. Without this delay, American Martens would have to mate in late winter in order for the young to be born in spring, when prey abundance and other environmental conditions are most favorable for raising offspring. One theory for delayed implantation is that it enables these species to shift their mating season away from the snow season, to a time when males are more mobile and can better find receptive females. The evolution of delayed implantation thus decouples the timing of mating and parturition, allowing both to occur during the same optimal spring/summer season. Some mustelid species in more southerly latitudes may have lost the ability to delay implantation. Interestingly, the Least Weasel, which is found as far north as the Arctic Circle, breeds successfully without an implantation delay. Least Weasels are also unusual among mustelids in being able to produce 2–3 litters annually. In general, mustelids only have one litter per year, although if a female loses a litter, she will come into heat again almost at once.

Martes americana
Butler County, SW Ohio, USA.
Photo: Dave Maslowski/Maslowski Productions

*Litter size can vary considerably within species. In the **American Mink**, numbers range from two to ten, with an average of five. Ermine litters may contain as many as 18, but 4–8 is more usual. Most mustelids are born at an early stage of development: naked, eyes closed, and just capable of crawling to find the mother's nipples. Some perform the "milk tread"—alternate movements of the forepaws against the mother's body—which stimulates the flow of milk. After the young are born, the mother licks them free of their embryonic membranes, licks their fur dry, and eats the membranes and the afterbirth. The female may gain enough food from the afterbirths to not need to hunt in the period immediately following birth.*

Neovison vison
Hamilton County, SW Ohio, USA.
Photo: Dave Maslowski/
Maslowski Productions

trade, but nowadays, there are many practical substitutes and fur has become more of a luxury item. Mustelid species from northern regions with cold climates have been the most heavily exploited including American Mink, North American River Otters, American Martens, and Fishers in North America, and Sables in Russia. In other parts of the world, fur from mustelids is only used locally, generally for clothing, but sometimes as good-luck charms or to make sacred ornaments. For instance, skins of the African Striped Weasel are used in traditional African ceremonies.

The colonization of North America was largely driven by the search for good trapping grounds. Trappers and traders penetrated all parts of the continent, and there were frequent conflicts as fur companies from various European nations attempted to gain control of territories with good populations of fur-bearers. Wild mustelids constituted a substantial proportion of the furs traded from North America in the 18th and 19th centuries, and pelts of mink and otter were particularly important to the economy of the northern lands. Ermine pelts were commonly used in England for ceremonial clothing, to trim coats, and make stoles. However, this rich resource of fur-bearers was soon over-exploited and trappers often had to move to even more remote places.

The Sea Mink, once common along the coasts of Maine, Massachusetts, New Brunswick, Newfoundland, and Nova Scotia, was intensely hunted for fur and was exterminated by

*Female mustelids that need to transfer their young to a new den employ a variety of grips. They may, like this **American Badger**, hold the cub around the body. The more usual method of transport is to pick the youngster up by the scruff of the neck. The youngster responds by remaining limp until it is set down again. The hair on the back of a young Ermine's neck grows very rapidly; this may give the female something to hold on to, or protect the young Ermine's neck from her jaws. Some otters use the neck-carrying method, but the African Clawless Otter and Asian Small-clawed Otter mother clasps the youngster against her chest or chin, and hobbles along on three legs.*

Taxidea taxus
Yellowstone National Park,
Wyoming, USA.
Photo: Leo Keeler/Auscape

The **Sea Otter** has unusually
precocial (well-developed) young.
The single youngster is born with
its eyes open, and may take some
solid food shortly after birth. The
mother gives her youngster an
initial grooming that may last
several hours. Sea Otters lack
blubber and depend on their fur
for insulation, so a pup that is not
licked completely dry will soon die.
At first, the youngster does not need
to be able to swim long distances,
as the mother carries it on her chest
most of the time, but it must be able
to look after itself when she dives
for food. Young Sea Otters start
diving after two months, but suckle
until almost adult size, remaining
dependent on their mother until
they are 5–8 months old.

Enhydra lutris
Prince William Sound, Alaska, USA.
Photo: Kevin Schafer

about 1880. By the early 20th century, excessive trapping had severely depleted the American Marten and Fisher in many areas of North America. Protective measures, such as closed hunting seasons and legislation, subsequently allowed these two species to make a comeback in some areas, and reintroduction programs have been carried out in several states. The trapping of fur-bearers is still a very important economic activity in several areas, such as North America and Russia, but nowadays, many places regulate trapping on a sustainable basis.

Uncontrolled over-hunting not only has dramatic impacts on mustelid populations but can also have cascading effects on ecosystems. During the 18th and 19th centuries, Sea Otters were heavily hunted for their high quality fur. Because of their conspicuous and gregarious habits, they were easy to hunt and over-hunting resulted in a drastic reduction in their populations. This had a profound effect on local sea communities. Sea Otters prey on sea urchins, which in turn graze on algal stands, such as the biodiversity-rich forests of underwater kelp. Where Sea Otters were eliminated, sea urchins became abundant and overgrazed kelp beds, which became rare. Sea Otters are thus a "keystone species" essential to the structural stability of their marine ecosystem.

To meet the high demand for fur, captive breeding has been attempted with a number of mustelids, particularly the American Mink and Sable. Intensive mink farming for fur began in Canada during the early 1900s and was expanded to include the USA, Europe, and more recently, China. At first, ranch-raised mink fur was used to substitute and augment the harvest from the wild, but later, by selection and breeding of various races, furs of desired qualities, densities and colors were produced, from natural browns or blacks to white, spotted, and sapphire, with the popularity of colors following fashion trends. Because of special care and feeding, farm-raised mink are often 2–3 times larger than wild individuals, adding to the value of their skins. Today, the majority of American Mink pelts come from captive stock and over 25 million mink fur skins are sold annually.

Escapes from fur farms resulted in the establishment of wild populations of American Mink throughout Europe and parts of Asia. These accidental introductions have often had undesirable consequences for native species. In continental Europe, the American Mink now competes with the European Mink and may have contributed to its decline. In Britain, American Mink have played a role in the decline of Water Vole populations, although habitat alterations along rivers and in wetland areas may have been a more important factor.

Some mustelid species have been deliberately introduced to some areas. The Ermine and Least Weasel were introduced to New Zealand in the 1880s to control European Rabbits. The consequences of this introduction were devastating to the local fauna, especially flightless birds. Today, Ermine are present in virtually all forested areas, whereas the Least Weasel is now quite rare. Although European Rabbits and rats are abundant in New Zealand, smaller prey are scarce; there are no voles, and feral house mice are the only rodents under 50 g. Because Least Weasels are specialized predators of small rodents, es-

The natal dens of **Fishers** are
situated high up in hollow trees.
The eyes of the young Fishers
open at around seven weeks,
and weaning begins after two
to three months. Although the
development of young mustelids
is a continuous process, three
stages can be recognized. During
the early nestling period, the only
nourishment the young receive is
their mother's milk. Then a period
of mixed nutrition begins, during
which the mother starts to provide
the young with solid food, but still
suckles them. Finally there is a
period of post-weaning dependence
on the parent, before the young
finally become fully independent.

Martes pennanti
Photo: Konrad Wothe/
Arco Digital/CD-Gallery

European Polecats are weaned when they are about a month old and are independent at around three months. Adult males are much larger than females, are more likely to be active nocturnally, and have much larger home ranges. European Polecats mate from March to June and give birth about 42 days later. Litter size is typically 3–7, but can be as large as twelve. The neonates weigh only 9–10 g. Newborn Steppe Polecats are even smaller, only 4–6 g, and are born in larger litters of 8–10. They open their eyes in 4–5 weeks and are weaned and start hunting with their mother at 6–7 weeks. They also disperse at about three months.

Mustela putorius
Photo: Konrad Wothe/CD-Gallery

pecially voles, they are greatly handicapped by the absence of voles in New Zealand.

Some mustelid species are hunted for food, particularly in Africa and Asia. In some regions of Africa, bushmeat is an important source of protein for village communities. In Ghana, a study showed that 75% of the population depended on wild animal protein, and that wild fauna made up 62% of the animal protein eaten by the rural population. In Guinea, the amount of bushmeat sold in a town of 30,000 inhabitants was about 131 tons a year, involving 21 species of mammals, including the Honey Badger and Spotted-necked Otter. Antelopes, deer, pigs, and primates are the most sought-after prey, but the

usual methods of hunting are not very selective and most animals are caught according to their frequency. Local hunters use dogs, spears, traps, and snares. Blowpipes and poisoned darts are also used to catch arboreal animals. Meat from small carnivores can be up to 15% of the bushmeat consumed in some communities.

Over the last few decades, a colossal trade in live animals and animal parts had developed throughout South-east and Central Asia. China, in particular, has long been a major market for wildlife products, and Oriental communities throughout the rest of the world provide additional markets. Numerous species are now targeted for the huge illegal trade in wildlife for food,

There's a big world waiting for this **Wolverine** cub. It was probably born in a remote northern area where there are few humans. Wolverines are born fully furred, but with their eyes closed, between January and April. Natal dens are in alpine, subalpine, taiga, or tundra habitat, and are often covered with snow. Litters of 1–5 have been reported, but 2–4 is more usual. The cubs nurse for about two months. They are the size of adults and ready to strike out on their own when they are around a year old. Wolverines are sexually mature after 2–3 years. Females give birth every two years, often partnering with the same male in successive years; males may have more than one partner in the same year.

Gulo gulo
Finland.
Photo: Roland Seitre

*These playful young **Ermines** could be part of a litter of 18, although the typical litter size is 4–8. Ermines are born blind and naked. They open their eyes at 4–6 weeks and eat solid food at about the same age. However, they continue to nurse for as long as twelve weeks. At 2–3 months, they have a full set of 34 permanent teeth and are learning to hunt. Females reach sexual maturity very early and sometimes mate during their first summer. Males attain full size and sexual maturity after a year. As adults, both sexes are solitary. Females maintain exclusive territories, while a male's territory may overlap with more than one female's, but not with another male's. Territorial borders are patrolled and marked with scent. Neighboring individuals tend to avoid each other, but during the mating season, males searching for mates will ignore territorial boundaries.*

Mustela erminea
Vall d'Aran, Pyrenees, Spain.
Photo: Oriol Alamany

traditional medicines, skins and bones, and pets. The increased use of guns has made it easier to hunt wary animals, particularly at night, when electric torches are also used. Wire-snares and other traps are effective in catching animals, but are unselective in what they catch, and non-targeted animals are also taken and killed. Wildlife traders have penetrated into the remotest areas and actively encourage the hunting of animal species for which there is a demand. In some countries, professional hunters from outside are a major threat, such as Vietnamese hunters in Laos.

A few mustelid species are kept as pets. The Ferret, a domesticated form of the European Polecat, is bred and raised in captivity and exported worldwide. The American Mink has been bred in captivity on fur farms for around a hundred years and is now considered a domesticated animal. Although farm-raised mink are not bred to be tame, they can be tamed and kept as pets. This is a difficult process and mink usually do not make good pets because they have strong jaws, sharp teeth, and can be highly aggressive. In South-east Asia, there is a particularly large demand for animals as pets, and this includes some mustelid species. In Medan, North Sumatra, one of the region's major centers for domestic and international wildlife trade, a five-year study of the pet trade industry recorded 300 bird species, 34 species of mammals (including otter species), and 15 reptile species. Many of these animals are exported by sea and air to Malaysia, Singapore, Thailand, and other global destinations. Also, many animals are imported to Indonesia from other Asian countries, including China. Local hunters may specifically target animals that are in high demand, and plantation and forest workers may supplement their income by opportunistically catching mammals to sell as pets and for other uses. Most of this wildlife trade is illegal, violating national laws; CITES regulations and international laws are also often ignored and not enforced.

Status and Conservation

One mustelid species disappeared during the 19th century. The Sea Mink that formerly occurred along the coasts of eastern Canada and north-eastern USA has not been seen since 1894 and has thus been declared Extinct. Seven mustelid species are listed as Endangered (Giant Otter, Marine Otter, Southern River Otter *Lontra provocax*, Sea Otter, Hairy-nosed Otter *Lutra sumatrana*, European Mink, and Black-footed Ferret), five are classified as Vulnerable (Nilgiri Marten, Marbled Polecat, Asian Small-clawed Otter, Smooth-coated Otter, and Colombian Weasel), and four are listed as Near-Threatened (Hog Badger, Wolverine, Eurasian Otter, and Mountain Weasel *Mustela altaica*). It is interesting to note that most of the otter species are of conservation concern. The remaining mustelid species are classified as either Least Concern (35 species), or Data Deficient (six species). The reality is, however, that there is so little information about most mustelids that it is difficult to accurately assess their extinction risks.

The Black-footed Ferret was classified as Extinct in the Wild in 1996 by *The IUCN Red List*, but has recently made a small comeback due to concentrated conservation efforts. This species may once have been common on the Great Plains of North America, where they thrived on prairie dogs. The destruction of prairie dog colonies for the sake of agriculture led to a decline in Black-footed Ferret numbers and eventually they became so rare that many people considered them to be extinct. However, unconfirmed sightings continued from several states, and in 1981 a small population of Black-footed Ferrets was discovered in Wyoming. Intensive field studies were initiated, and by July 1984, the population was estimated to contain 129 individuals. But then, the number of ferrets began to fall, apparently due to a decline in their prairie dog prey; also, canine distemper was somehow introduced into the wild population. By 1987, the remaining 18 individuals were brought into captivity to start a breeding program. By 1991, there were 180 individuals in captivity and 49 ferrets were released into south-eastern Wyoming; 91 more were released in 1992, and another 48 in 1993. Most of these animals are thought to have died, but some are known to have survived and reproduced; at least six litters were born in the wild in 1993. Additional reintroductions have been carried out in Montana, South Dakota, and Arizona, but the current status of this species is still extremely precarious.

The most important reason for the decline of many other mustelid species appears to be habitat destruction. Otters and mink are dependent on waterbodies, which limits their distri-

Young mustelids may learn foraging and hunting skills by accompanying and watching their mother. In many predatory species there is also an "apprenticeship" period, during which the young learn to make their own kills. **Eurasian Otter** cubs emerge from the den and begin to swim at two months, and have learned to hunt and are independent at about a year. **European Badger** littermates are ready to separate from their mother at a younger age, when they are about 6–7 months old. European Badgers are sexually mature after a year, whereas Eurasian Otters take 2–3 years to reach reproductive age. Female European Badgers have six mammae, and there can be as many as six in a litter, but 3–4 is more common. They can breed in any season, but most mate from late winter to mid-summer. The fertilized eggs can implant in the uterus and develop immediately, or implantation can be delayed. Most births occur in February or March. Eurasian Otters typically mate in late winter or early spring and give birth about two months later, usually to 2–3 young. The natal den is often located in the bank of a stream, with the main entrance opening underwater and sloping upward into the bank to the nest chamber.

Above: *Lutra lutra*
Bavaria, Germany.
Photo: José Luis Gómez de Francisco

Below: *Meles meles*
UK.
Photo: Jack Bailey/Ardea

613

The **Altai Mountain Weasel**, *which takes its common name from the Altai Mountains in China, is classified as Near Threatened on* The IUCN Red List. *These small, slim weasels live in mountain meadows, steppes, and forests, and their numbers may be in decline because of habitat conversion due to livestock over-grazing. They are also affected by the agricultural control of pikas, one of their main food sources. Very little is known about this weasel and field studies are needed to learn more about its natural history, ecology, and conservation status.*

Mustela altaica
Tso-Kar, Ladakh, India.
Photo: Otto Pfister

bution and makes them very vulnerable to habitat alterations and pollution. Across the world, increasing human populations have generated an ever-increasing demand for fresh water and food, which has had several consequences for otter and mink species. Wetlands have been drained and rivers modified through channelization and by hydroelectric developments. Shoreline habitats have been destroyed or altered through deforestation, bush clearance, and overgrazing.

Humans catch fish, crabs, and other freshwater and marine food that are consumed by otters, and view otters as competitors for these resources, which has often led to their persecution. Boating and fishing on lakes and along rivers may disturb otters and force them away from these areas. Human activities near water often produce pollution: pesticide and fertilizer run-offs from agricultural land, toxic chemicals from industrial processes, and sewage from urban areas. Pollution either affects otters and mink directly through toxic poisoning or indirectly from eating contaminated prey. Their position at the top of the aquatic food chain makes them susceptible to bioaccumulated toxins and chemicals in their tissue following the consumption of contaminated fish. The most harmful biocontaminants are mercury, polychlorinated biphenyls, and organochlorine compounds. These chemicals have negative effects on normal body functions and may lead to impaired reproduction and even death.

Water pollution is also a great threat to marine mustelid species; oil spills, in particular, have had devastating effects on Sea Otter populations. The best known and well-publicized

Not enough is known about the **Large-toothed Ferret-badger**, *the Bornean Ferret-badger, and the Javan Ferret-badger to determine their conservation status. All three species are listed as Data Deficient on* The IUCN Red List. *The ecology and natural history of the fourth ferret-badger species, the Small-toothed Ferret-badger, are a little better known, and its current survival in the wild does not seem to be threatened. The Javan Ferret-badger, which used to be classified as a subspecies of the Large-toothed Ferret-badger, occurs only on the Indonesian island of Java; the Bornean Ferret-badger has only been recorded from one mountain region of Borneo.*

Melogale personata
Thailand.
Photo: Roland Seitre

Lontra longicaudis
Iguazú National Park,
Misiones, Argentina.
Photo: José Calo

event was the 1989 catastrophic 11-million-gallon spill by the oil tanker *Exxon Valdez*, in Prince William Sound, Alaska, one of the best habitat areas for Sea Otters. It is estimated that 2800 to 5000 Sea Otters died shortly after this spill, and deaths of Sea Otters continued because of oil residues in their prey. In coastal areas that were exposed to oil spills, North America River Otters have been found with elevated levels of blood haptogloblin, interleukin-6 immunoreactive protein, and low body weights. Their home ranges are larger in oiled areas, compared to non-oiled places, and individuals also change their habitat use, possibly due to declines in the richness and diversity of prey species.

Forest loss, fragmentation, and degradation, are the primary threats to forest-dependent mustelids. Fragmentation of forests results in a sub-division of populations into smaller units, and smaller populations have a higher extinction risk from intrinsic and extrinsic factors (disease, climate changes, fire, etc.). Fragmentation may also restrict dispersal and gene flow between isolated groups, resulting in a higher occurrence of inbreeding. Inbreeding can result in the loss of important alleles that confer resistance to infectious diseases, and also allows harmful recessive genes to be expressed. Logging roads allow greater access for hunters, which can lead to increases in hunting pressure. Forest degradation, such as selective logging, can also have serious consequences for forest species. Although not as destructive as clear cutting, it can dramatically alter the structure of a forest, affecting the availability of food resources and suitable den sites. For example, the availability of hollow

Vormela peregusna
Hadzhi Dimitar, Dobrich, Bulgaria.
Photo: Boris Nikolov

Asian Small-clawed Otters, *the world's smallest otters, are threatened by habitat destruction and water pollution, and listed as Vulnerable on* The IUCN Red List. *Organochlorines in water affect the entire food chain, not just otter species. In addition, in parts of their range they are seen as competitors for fish. They are also hunted for their organs, which are used in traditional medicine.* **Smooth-coated Otters** *are also listed as Vulnerable. In the past, they were common and their populations were stable, but this is changing rapidly as the human population expands and impacts the otters and their habitat. Smooth-coated Otters are legally protected throughout their range, but these laws are difficult to enforce. Threats include habitat destruction and pollution, deliberate hunting for their fur (especially in India, Nepal, and Bangladesh), and persecution— otters eat fish and crustaceans, so fish and shrimp farmers kill them as pests. Compounding these problems, the movements of Smooth-coated Otters are restricted because they cannot cross arid areas, so their populations are fragmented. Both Asian Small-clawed and Smooth-coated Otters may soon need intensive conservation measures. Field studies are also required to learn more about the ecology of these two otter species.*

Above: **Aonyx cinereus**
Borneo.
Photo: Tim Laman

Below: **Lutrogale perspicillata**
Kaziranga National Park,
Assam, India.
Photo: James Warwick/NHPA

The **Giant Otter** *is listed as* Endangered *on* The IUCN Red List. *Its total wild population is estimated at between 1000 and 5000 individuals, and these animals are protected throughout their range. They once lived in Argentina and Uruguay, but they may now be extinct in those two countries. As with many endangered otter species, Giant Otters are threatened by human encroachment on their habitat, water pollution and habitat degradation, and diseases (such as canine parvovirus that is transferred by domestic livestock). Giant Otters are also killed for their pelts, for meat, or because fishermen see them as competition. They are caught and sold to zoos, and cubs are stolen from dens and kept as pets.*

Pteronura brasiliensis
San Martín River, Beni, Bolivia.
Photo: Ángel M. Sánchez

trees for use as resting sites and natal dens is especially critical for American Martens, and logging procedures that eliminate old stumps or older trees may be detrimental to local populations. For the conservation of forest-dependent mustelids, remaining forests need to be legally protected and appropriately managed, in ways that take into account the needs of mustelids as well as more charismatic animal species, which are often given priority. Habitat corridors connecting these forest patches should also be maintained.

A number of mustelid species are trapped in the wild, either on purpose or accidentally. During the last two centuries, over-hunting of several species in North America and Eurasia led to dramatic declines in local populations and range contractions. The implementation of protective measures, such as closed hunting seasons and legislation, have allowed many species to make a comeback, and the trapping of fur-bearers in

these countries is now regulated at sustainable levels. However, hunting pressures in some African and Asian countries appear to be increasing and may be unsustainable, particularly if habitats are also being destroyed or altered. The demand for mustelid meat, skins, and other body parts in these regions must be eliminated or considerably reduced. Existing protection laws need to be enforced and new ones enacted.

Some mustelids are threatened by foreign species, one example being the threat to the European Mink by the accidental introduction of the American Mink into Europe. The European Mink has disappeared over much of its former range and competition with the American Mink has been hypothesized as a contributing factor. For instance, non-fertile crossings between male American Mink and female European Mink prevent European Mink from successfully reproducing. In Spain and France, programmes have been started to control

Some fishermen believe that **Marine Otters** *compete with them for fish and shrimp, which may lead to their persecution. Other humans hunt them for their pelts. In addition to poaching and excessive hunting, habitat destruction and water pollution are also major threats. Marine Otters are listed as Endangered on* The IUCN Red List. *They are protected in Argentina, Chile, and Peru, so killing them is illegal, but enforcement is difficult. It is estimated that fewer than 1000 of these small otters remain along the rocky coasts of the Pacific, including a population of 300 or fewer animals in Peruvian waters. Marine Otters stay within 150 m of the coast, and sometimes venture into freshwater tributaries.*

Lontra felina
Arica, Chile.
Photo: Gonzalo González Cifuentes

American Mink *were accidentally introduced to many countries in Europe, Russia, China, and Japan as a result of individuals escaping from fur farms and establishing wild populations. Interspecific competition with the American Mink may be one of the reasons why the* **European Mink** *is listed as Endangered on* The IUCN Red List. *However, many other factors also impact the conservation status of this species. Once hunted for its fur, the European Mink has disappeared from nine countries where it once lived, and is now legally protected throughout its range. Many freshwater habitats have become uninhabitable because of water pollution and other changes caused by humans, including the construction of hydroelectric dams. Efforts to control Coypu and other pest species in France have resulted in the accidental poisoning and trapping of European Mink. European Mink may also interbreed with European Polecats. Studies are underway to evaluate the genetic viability of some European Mink populations. The European Zoo Association is undertaking a captive breeding program and reintroduction efforts are underway in Germany and Russia. In Spain and France, programs have been started to control the invasive American Mink population.*

Above: **Neovison vison**
Álava, Spain.

Below: **Mustela lutreola**
La Rioja, Spain.

Photos: José Luis Gómez de Francisco

Denizens of the Great Plains in the western USA, **Black-footed Ferrets** *specialize in feeding on prairie dogs, hunting these large rodents in their burrow systems and even using the burrows as den sites. When settlers took the land for farming and ranching, and destroyed prairie dog colonies, the ferrets disappeared. Fortunately, in 1981, a small population of Black-footed Ferrets was discovered in Wyoming, which was estimated at 129 individuals in 1984. Unfortunately, by 1987, there were only 18 individuals left. This remnant population was brought into captivity and breeding efforts began. Captive breeding has been successful and several reintroduction efforts have been attempted. Three of the reintroduced populations are doing well enough that the status of the Black-footed Ferret, although still precarious, has been downgraded on* The IUCN Red List *from Extinct in the Wild to Endangered.*

Mustela nigripes
Colorado, USA.
Photo: Shattil & Rozinski/
naturepl.com

the American Mink population. The European Mink is also severely threatened by the loss and degradation of freshwater river systems. It was widely trapped for commercial purposes, but it is now legally protected in all range states. However, accidental trapping still poses a threat. In France, secondary poisoning of European Mink has occurred as a result of efforts to control Coypu (*Myocastor coypus*). Accidental mortality from vehicle collisions is a problem in some areas. The European Mink has recently colonized and spread into northern Spain. However, recent genetic studies indicate that there is very low genetic variability within this species, which could pose an additional threat.

Many mustelids have never been studied by scientists in the wild. Considering the lack of data on the distribution and conservation status of several mustelid species, field surveys investigating these aspects are important for identifying the sites and the problems on which conservation activities should concentrate. Ascertaining the exact geographic range of a species is especially important to determine if its distribution includes well-managed areas of sufficient size. However, even when a reserve is known to be within the range of an endangered species, it must be verified that the species actually occurs within the protected area, and that the area contains a viable population.

Field studies are also vital for determining the ecological requirements of a species for long-term conservation measures. To formulate population viability models and predict extinction risks for mustelids, we need to know a great deal about their ecology and natural history. A better understanding of the social structure of a species and its dispersal patterns is essential for estimating the minimum population sizes needed for preserving genetic variability. The reasons for peculiar distribution patterns, and the factors that impact population sizes, also require investigation. Field research into feeding ecology and breeding behavior can also help captive management programs.

Taxonomic revisions are necessary in order to provide a systematic framework and to define important units for conservation purposes, and for answering scientific questions. Animal protection laws are usually applied to defined entities, such as recognized species or subspecies, so identifying these entities is very important. Subspecies may have particular adaptations to the local climate or to different competitors, predators, parasites or strains of pathogens, so recognizing them is crucial. Recent molecular and morphological studies have clearly shown

the value of taxonomic research in establishing valid species and subspecies, but further work is needed to resolve certain issues, such as the status of the Congo Clawless Otter and Japanese Otter. Molecular studies also provide a tool for identifying the geographic origin of mustelid species that are taken for the wildlife trade and sold in markets. Captive breeding programs can also benefit from molecular studies, which may help define conservation units (i.e. species, subspecies, and populations) and help evaluate the genetic diversity of captive populations for breeding purposes.

Captive breeding can be a powerful tool in ensuring the survival of an endangered species, particularly where short-term protection of the animal and its natural habitats is not likely to be successful. A captive breeding programme of the European Mink was launched in 1992 under the European Zoo Association and reintroduction efforts are underway in Germany and Russia. However, captive breeding raises many ethical and welfare issues. There is also considerable debate about how great a role it should play in conservation strategies and many conservationists argue that captive breeding should only be used as a last resort. There are several potential difficulties with captive breeding programs. The conditions in captivity are different from those that a species has to live with in the wild, and there is a risk that captive breeding over several generations may select animals that would not be able to reproduce if subject to natural selection. The management of captive populations could also lead to changes in a species' genetic structure, and we do not know the consequences of such changes and their impact on long-term fitness. Finally, to maintain sufficiently large captive populations requires large amounts of money, which might be better spent on in situ conservation programs.

General Bibliography
Anderson (1970), Aulerich & Ringer (1979), Aulerich *et al.* (1974), Brown & Lasiewski (1972), Colyn *et al.* (2004), Deanesley (1943, 1944), Dunstone (1993), Erlinge (1979), Estes (1989), Ewer (1973), Ferguson & Larivière (2002), Ferguson *et al.* (1996), Gorman & Trowbridge (1989), Hall (1981), IUCN (2008), Johnson *et al.* (2000), King (1990), Koepfli *et al.* (2008), Larivière & Ferguson (2002), Long & Killingley (1983), McDonald & Larivière (2001, 2002), Moors (1977, 1980), Neal & Cheeseman (1996), Pocock (1921), Powell (1979, 1982, 1985, 1993), Ralls & Harvey (1985), Sato *et al.* (2003), Schreiber *et al.* (1989), Simpson (1945), Taylor (1989b), Van Zyll de Jong (1972), Wozencraft (2005).

1

2

3

ssp *albogularis*

ssp *collaris*

ssp *hoevenii*

4

5

6

PLATE 32

inches   10

cm   25

Subfamily TAXIDIINAE

Genus *TAXIDEA*

Waterhouse, 1839

1. American Badger *Taxidea taxus*

French: Blaireau d'Amérique / **German**: Amerikanischer Dachs / **Spanish**: Tejón americano

Taxonomy. *Ursus taxus* Schreber, 1778, Canada.
Four subspecies are recognized.
Subspecies and Distribution.
T. t. taxus Schreber, 1778 – S Canada (Alberta, British Columbia, Manitoba, Ontario & Saskatschewan) and NC USA.
T. t. berlandieri Baird, 1858 – N & C Mexico and SC USA (W of the Mississippi River).
T. t. jacksoni Schantz, 1946 – NE USA (Great Lakes Region).
T. t. jeffersonii Harlan, 1825 – W USA (NW to California).

Descriptive notes. Head-body 42–72 cm, tail 10–15·5 cm; weight 7·6–8·7 kg (males), 6·3–7·1 kg (females), adult males weigh on average 25% more than females. The American Badger's body appears flat dorso-ventrally, with a flat head, and short tail and limbs. The upperparts are grayish-white to yellowish-brown or silvery black; the underparts are buffy. The feet are dark brown to black. Black patches are present on the face, cheeks, chin, and throat. A dorsal white stripe runs from the nose to the neck, and in some populations, to the rump. The claws on the forefeet are long and strong. There are four pairs of mammae. The skull is wedge-shaped, almost triangular. Dental formula: I 3/3, C 1/1, P 3/3, M 1/2 = 34.

Habitat. American Badgers are found in grasslands, prairie habitats, shrubs and steppes, and open woodlands. In British Columbia, they prefer open range and agricultural habitats that have fine sandy-loam and well-drained soils.

Food and Feeding. The diet includes small mammals (especially marmots, ground squirrels, prairie dogs, pocket gophers, cottontail rabbits, mice, voles, chipmunks, and squirrels), birds, eggs, reptiles, amphibians, and invertebrates (insects and molluscs). Carrion is also eaten. In British Columbia, the six main prey species are the Columbian Ground Squirrel (*Spermophilus columbianus*), Yellow-bellied Marmot (*Marmota flaviventris*), Northern Pocket Gopher (*Thomomys talpoides*), Muskrat (*Ondatra zibethicus*), Southern Red-backed Vole (*Myodes gapperi*), and Meadow Vole (*Microtus pennsylvanicus*). In south-eastern Wyoming, prairie dogs were found in 57% of stomach and fecal samples from female American Badgers. The most common food item in the diet in west-central Minnesota and south-eastern North Dakota is small mammals (98%, primarily Muridae and Geomyidae). Other prey includes insects (40%), and birds and eggs (32%, mostly ducks Anatidae). Reptiles, amphibians and molluscs are also eaten, but are less common than other foods. Insects and birds' eggs are more common in the diet during spring (April–May) than summer (June–July). Birds are more frequent in the diets of adults than juveniles. In South Dakota, 40% of stomach contents were mammals, 35% were of plant origin, 10% were birds, 10% were insects, and the remainder was mostly inorganic materials. American Badgers obtain most of their food by excavating the burrows of fossorial animals. If large prey is taken, such as a rabbit, the badger may dig a hole, carry in the prey, and remain below ground with it for several days. There are reports of American Badgers forming a "hunting partnership" with Coyotes. The Coyote apparently uses its keen sense of smell to locate burrowing rodents and the American Badger digs them up with its powerful claws. Both predators then share the proceeds. The techniques used by American Badgers when hunting Richardson's Ground Squirrels (*Spermophilus richardsonii*) have been observed. They frequently hunted hibernating squirrels in the autumn, sometimes hunted infants in the spring, but rarely hunted active squirrels in the summer. They always captured hibernating and active squirrels underground, but sometimes intercepted fleeing squirrels aboveground. The most common hunting technique used was excavation of the burrow, but plugging of openings accounted for 5–23% of hunting actions. Plugging occurred predominantly in mid-June to late July, before most ground squirrels hibernated, and in late August to late October when juvenile males were active, but other squirrels were in hibernation. American Badgers usually used soil from around the tunnel opening or soil dragged 30–270 cm from a nearby mound to plug tunnels. They kill ground squirrels with a single grasping bite directed dorsally or laterally to the thorax. The canines and third upper incisors generally only bruise the skin, without puncturing it, but cause extensive hemorrhaging in the thoracic cavity. Food items are sometimes buried and eaten later.

Activity patterns. Mainly nocturnal, but can be active at any hour. American Badgers rest underground in burrows; these are either self-excavated or are modified burrows that were initially made by another animal. The burrow can be as long as 10 m and can extend 3 m below the surface. A bulky nest of grass is located in an enlarged chamber; the entrances are marked by mounds of earth. American Badgers are active all year, but during severe winter weather they may sleep in the den for several days or weeks. During this period of inactivity, heart rates are reduced by 50% and the body temperature decreases by 9 °C.

Movements, Home range and Social organization. Daily movement may exceed 10 km and dispersal movements may be greater than 100 km. Mean home range size is up to 12·3 km² for males and up to 3·4 km² for females. Home ranges overlap, but adults are solitary except during the breeding season. In Utah, mean home range size was 5·83 km²; the mean size of female home ranges (2·37 km²) was less than half that of the males. In Idaho, mean home range size was 2·4 km² for males and 1·6 km² for females. In south-eastern Wyoming, the mean home range size of females (3·4 km²) was smaller than that of males (12·3 km²); mean overlap was less for females than for males, and the mean home range size of males was larger during the breeding season than during the non-breeding season (breeding = 11·1 km², non-breeding = 5·4 km²). A radio-tracked female in Minnesota used an area of 752 ha during the summer. She had 50 dens within this area and was never found in the same den on two consecutive days. In the autumn, she shifted to an adjacent area of 52 ha and often reused dens. In the winter, she used a single den and traveled infrequently within an area of 2 ha. Population density may be as high as 5/km². In south-eastern Wyoming, the density varies between 0·8–1·1/km².

Breeding. Mating occurs in late July or August. Implantation of the fertilized eggs into the uterus is delayed until December–February, and births take place in late March or early April. The total gestation period is about seven months; actual embryonic development is about six weeks. Litter size is one to five, usually two. The young are born underground in a nest of dry grass. They are weaned at about six weeks and disperse soon after. Some young females may mate in the first breeding season following birth, when they are about four months old; males wait until the following year.

Status and Conservation. Classified as Least Concern in *The IUCN Red List*. American Badgers are considered common. Although this species has little importance in the fur trade, it is harvested for its fur in many parts of its range. American Badgers are also persecuted because of the damage they do to pasture and agricultural land.

Bibliography. Anderson & Johns (1977), Armitage (2004), Azevedo et al. (2006), Eldridge (2004), Goodrich & Buskirk (1998), Harlow (1981), Hart & Trumbo (1983), Hoodicoff (2006), Lampe (1982), Lindzey (1978, 2003), Long (1973), Long & Killingley (1983), Messick & Hornocker (1981), Michener (2004), Michener & Iwaniuk (2001), Minta (1993), Minta et al. (1992), Murie (1992), Sargeant & Warner (1972), Sovada et al. (1999), Van Vuren (2001), Wozencraft (2005).

Subfamily MELLIVORINAE

Genus *MELLIVORA*

Storr, 1780

2. Honey Badger *Mellivora capensis*

French: Ratel / **German**: Honigdachs / **Spanish**: Ratel
Other common names: Ratel

Taxonomy. *Viverra capensis* Schreber, 1776, Cape of Good Hope, South Africa.
Ten subspecies are recognized.
Subspecies and Distribution.
M. c. capensis Schreber, 1776 – S Africa N to Angola, Mozambique, and Zambia.
M. c. buechneri Baryshnikov, 2000 – C Asia including Afghanistan, Kazakhstan, Turkmenistan, and Uzbekistan.
M. c. concisa Thomas & Wroughton, 1907 – Algeria, Morocco, and Subsaharan Africa from Mauritania to Ethiopia.
M. c. cottoni Lydekker, 1906 – C Africa from Gabon to Tanzania.
M. c. inaurita Hodgson, 1836 – Nepal.
M. c. indica Kerr, 1792 – India and Pakistan.
M. c. maxwelli Thomas, 1923 – Kenya and Somalia.
M. c. pumilio Pocock, 1946 – S Arabian Peninsula and Yemen.
M. c. signata Pocock, 1909 – Guinea and Sierra Leone.
M. c. wilsoni Cheesman, 1920 – Iran, Iraq, Israel, Jordan, Kuwait, Lebanon, Saudi Arabia, and Syria.

Descriptive notes. Head-body 73·3–95 cm (males), 81·2–96 cm (females), tail 14·3–23 cm (males), 15·2–22·5 cm (females); weight 7·7–10·5 kg (males), 6·2–13·6 kg (females). The Honey Badger is a short, stocky animal, with strong limbs and a short tail. The upperparts, from the top of the head to the base of the tail, are gray to pale yellow or whitish, and contrast sharply with the dark brown or black of the underparts. Completely black individuals have been reported from some parts of Africa. The tail is black, with a gray or white tip. The front feet are broad, with strong, long claws (> 25 mm), whereas the hindfeet have small claws (15 mm). There are two pairs of mammae. The skull is massive, with short orbital processes and robust teeth. Dental formula: I 3/3, C 1/1, P 3/3, M 1/1 = 32.

Habitat. Honey Badgers are found in diverse habitats including deep forests, subtropical dry evergreen forests, tropical thorn forests, open *Acacia*, *Combretum* and *Terminalia* woodlands, open riparian woodland (dominated by *Acacia albida*), Tarai or marshes,

On following pages: 3. Hog Badger (*Arctonyx collaris*); 4. Japanese Badger (*Meles anakuma*); 5. Asian Badger (*Meles leucurus*); 6. European Badger (*Meles meles*).

floodplain grasslands (dominated by *Vetivaria nigritana*), bushveld, afro-alpine steppes, rocky hills and kopjes, *Rhigozum* scrub sandveld, savannah, dry swamps, waterless sandplains, coastal sandveld, and deserts. They tolerate habitats with a rainfall of over 2000 mm (annually) as well as arid areas with less than 100 mm annual rainfall. Honey Badgers are found from sea level up to 4050 m.

Food and Feeding. The diet is mostly mammals, insects, amphibians, reptiles and birds, but also includes roots, berries, and fruit (such as ber *Zizyphus jubata*). Favorite foods are honey and the larvae of honeybees (Hymenoptera). However, their adaptation to burrowing, together with the abundance of subterranean animals found in six stomachs, suggests that honey is only a secondary food item. Consumption of honey may also be seasonal because it is more widely available in the drier months of the year. In October and November, Honey Badgers in the Kalahari Gemsbok National Park, South Africa, were found to eat mainly rodents, which occurred in 60% of scats and made up c. 30% of the volume of food. Ostrich (*Struthio camelus*) chicks, Spring Hares (*Pedetes capensis*), Meerkats, as well as domestic sheep and goats, were also eaten. They are strong diggers, and do not hesitate to dig after rodents or other prey hiding underground. Food items are detected mostly by smell or sound. Excess food may be cached in a den. When Honey Badgers eat, the food is held between the front claws while the forelegs rest on the ground. Beehives are opened by tearing away the wood of trees; honey combs are also scooped out from the cracks of rocks with the claws of the forefeet. Grubs are removed from the comb with their incisors. The clay capsules of estivating lungfish (*Protopterus aethiopicus*), cases of insect pupae, carapaces of turtles, or skins of animals are peeled away to expose the softer inner parts to be eaten. Honey Badgers dig large spiders out of holes 15–25 cm deep in the ground. Fish are caught with the claws at the edge of streams or from drying pans. They may raid campgrounds or dumpsters at night and are widely blamed for breaking into poultry houses and apiaries. The anecdotal relationship between the Honey Badger and a bird, the greater honeyguide (*Indicator indicator*), may be mythical. Although these two animals may occur together at the nests of bees, a complete observation of this supposed symbiotic relationship, from the initial attraction by a greater honeyguide of a Honey Badger, through guiding to a nest by the honeyguide, to the breaking open of the nest by the Honey Badger does not exist.

Activity patterns. Primarily nocturnal, although diurnal observations are numerous. Honey Badgers shelter in burrows, thick brush, caves, clumps of fallen bamboo, hollow trees, old ruins, rock shelters, dens excavated by themselves, or abandoned burrows. Hollow trees are entered from the top.

Movements, Home range and Social organization. Honey Badgers are good swimmers and can chase turtles underwater. They can also climb trees. Daily movements average 10–30 km, with males covering longer distances than females. Female Honey Badgers forage in a relatively small area, covering c. 10 km/day. They zig-zag short distances from bush to bush, digging on average 10·2 holes/km. Males engage in long-distance foraging, covering c. 27 km/day; only c. 1·3 holes/km are dug. Mean straight-line distance between dens from one day to the next is c. 2·5 km for short-distance foragers and c. 10·1 km for long-distance foragers. Males and females differ significantly in their rate of travel (3·8 km/h and 2·7 km/h, respectively), straight line (6·2 km and 2·4 km) and actual distance (13·8 km and 7·7 km) moved during an active period, but do not differ in the percentage of their home range area traversed in a single day (3%). Honey Badgers are mostly solitary, but pairs may be seen and aggregations may occur at feeding sites. Occasionally, after foraging in a particular area for most of the night, a male may suddenly move off to a location less than 9 km away, where it may meet up with other adults. On one occasion in Zimbabwe, six animals met up; they showed no aggression but continuously uttered a wide range of grunts, hisses, squeaks, and whines while rolling in the sand, sniffing each other, and scent marking. Such gatherings may last more than 18 min, and the Honey Badgers may retreat to the same den during the day. Radio-telemetry in the southern Kalahari revealed that the mean home range size of adult males (541 km²) was significantly larger than the mean home range size of adult females (126 km²). While mean home range overlap in females was moderate (13%) and home range centres were regularly spaced, females did not appear to actively defend a territory and no direct interactions between females were observed. Scent marking appears to mediate spatial-temporal separation and females show a loosely territorial spacing pattern. In contrast, the home ranges of males encompassed the overlapping home ranges of up to 13 females. Young males tended to have smaller home ranges (151 km²) than adult males and showed a spacing pattern more similar to adult females than adult males.

Breeding. Mating occurs throughout the year and there appears to be no distinct breeding season. The gestation period is 50–70 days. Litter size is commonly one to two. Only the mother raises the young. The young are born blind and helpless inside a burrow. At two days of age, one captive Honey Badger weighed c. 0·23 kg and was hairless except for a few hairs on the face; the head and body length was 19·7 cm, and the tail was 3·8 cm. It uttered squeaks and low guttural sounds during the first weeks, usually at feeding time; vocalization changed to deep, drawn-out, ominous growls at ten weeks. Within three months, the young have a fully developed adult pelage. The claws are fully formed on each foot at four weeks of age. The eyes open after 33 days and teeth begin erupting at 36 days and are fully developed at around three months. Adult size is reached after six months. Attempts at walking progress from a swimming motion (using all four legs) at age two to three weeks, to a forward dragging movement by the front legs at age five weeks, to a trot, similar to that of an adult, at eight weeks. Climbing starts at ten weeks. The young reach independence after 12–16 months.

Status and Conservation. Classified as Least Concern in *The IUCN Red List*. Honey Badgers do not occur at high densities and are considered uncommon throughout their range. Persecution by beekeepers and livestock farmers is probably the greatest threat to this species.

Bibliography. Begg, C. *et al.* (2005a, 2005b), Begg, K. (1995), Dean *et al.* (1990), Kruuk & Mills (1983), Smithers & Chimimba (2005), Stuart (1981), Vanderhaar & Hwang (2003), Wozencraft (2005).

Subfamily MELINAE

Genus *ARCTONYX*
Cuvier, 1825

3. Hog Badger *Arctonyx collaris*
French: Balisaur / **German:** Schweinsdachs / **Spanish:** Tejón porcino

Taxonomy. *Arctonyx collaris* Cuvier, 1825, Indonesia.

Arctonyx was regarded as monotypic until late 2008, when this volume was in proof. Based on a review of the most available specimens in world museums, three distinctive species are now recognized within this genus. *A. albogularis* (Blyth, 1853) is a shaggy-coated, medium-sized badger widely distributed in temperate Asia, from Tibet and the Himalayan region to eastern and southern China. *A. collaris* (Cuvier, 1825), is an extremely large, shorter-haired badger, distributed throughout South-east Asia, from eastern India to Myanmar, Thailand, Vietnam, Cambodia and Laos. The disjunctly distributed species *A. hoevenii* (Hubrecht, 1891) is the smallest and darkest member of the genus and is endemic to the Barisan mountain chain of Sumatra.

Distribution. C, E & S China and E Mongolia to Sub-Himalayan zone in Bhutan and NE India; also, Bangladesh, Indochina, and Sumatra.

Descriptive notes. Head-body 55–70 cm, tail 12–17 cm; weight 7–14 kg. The Hog Badger is stocky and sparsely furred, with a flat head, a long nose that extends to form a small "trunk", conspicuous ears, small eyes, and long claws. The elongated snout is hairless and resembles the nose of a pig: hence the name Hog Badger. The pelage is yellowish or grayish with black and white hairs mixed throughout. There are alternating black and white stripes on the top of the head; the white stripes meet behind the ears and merge with the pale throat. The tail is short and sparsely covered with white hairs. The claws are well-developed on the forefeet and are pale in color. The skull is narrow and high with a long rostrum. Dental formula: I 3/3, C 1/1, P 4/3, M 1/2 = 36.

Habitat. Forests, grasslands and plantations adjacent to forests, at elevations up to 3500 m.

Food and Feeding. The diet includes earthworms, insects, small mammals, snails, reptiles, tubers, and roots. In China, Hog Badgers were found to eat more mammals and gastropods than other sympatric small carnivore species. They use their hoglike nose to root through the forest floor.

Activity patterns. Nocturnal. Activity peaks occur between 03:00 h and 05:00 h and between 19:00 h and 21:00 h. Hog Badgers spend the day resting in underground burrows or in rock crevices; they can dig their own burrows. They undergo a period of inactivity during winter months and in central China, they may hibernate from November to February or March.

Movements, Home range and Social organization. Solitary and terrestrial.

Breeding. Mating occurs from May to September, depending on the locality. Births typically occur the following February or March. The long delay between mating and parturition suggests that this species undergoes delayed implantation of the fertilized eggs into the uterus. Litter size is three to five. The young are weaned after four months and become independent soon after.

Status and Conservation. Classified as Near Threatened in *The IUCN Red List*. The Hog Badger is thought to be common throughout its range. However, hunting by dogs is a threat to this species and it is also susceptible to snaring. Hog Badgers are hunted and farmed for food in China. They are also eaten in India, and hunted in Vietnam and some areas of Laos.

Bibliography. Francis (2008), Helgen, Lim & Helgen (2008), Lekagul & McNeely (1991), Parker (1979), Pocock (1941a), Wang & Fuller (2003a), Wozencraft (2005, 2008).

Genus *MELES*
Brisson, 1762

4. Japanese Badger *Meles anakuma*
French: Blaireau du Japon / **German:** Japanischer Dachs / **Spanish:** Tejón japonés

Taxonomy. *Meles anakuma* Temminck, 1844. Japan.
Some authors consider *M. anakuma* as a subspecies of the Asian Badger.
Monotypic.

Distribution. Japan (Honshu, Kyushu & Shikoku Is).

Descriptive notes. Head-body 50–80 cm, tail 14–20 cm; weight 6–17 kg. The Japanese Badger has a stocky body, short legs, grayish pelage, and contrasting black and white

stripes on the head and upper neck. The foreclaws are well-developed for digging; the hindclaws are much smaller.

Habitat. Japanese Badgers are found in fields and forests, often in close proximity to humans in suburban habitats.

Food and Feeding. In Hinode, a suburb of Tokyo, scat analysis revealed that during spring and summer, earthworms (Megaseolocidae) occur at high frequency in the diet, with berries (*Rubus* sp.), beetles, and persimmon (*Dymopyrus kaki*) also eaten during summer months. Scavenged food is eaten in early spring when earthworm availability is low, and in the autumn, Japanese Badgers switch from eating worms when Persimmon is abundant.

Activity patterns. Primarily nocturnal, although sometimes active in the daytime. Breeding females, in particular, often forage during the day and in the spring. Between July and October, Japanese Badgers usually emerge from their setts around sunset and return around sunrise. After November, the time between emergence and return becomes shorter. From January to February, most activity ceases, and Japanese Badgers stay in their setts most of the time. The total hibernation period varies from 42–80 days, during which the body temperature is reduced. Den/resting sites are in underground burrows called setts or in couches. In Japan, the resting sites in each badger's home range were found to be within 630 m of each other. Setts were sited within the core areas of home ranges and were mostly on a sub-ridge. Couches were mainly in deciduous forest, and along the forest edge, and were generally sited towards the periphery of home ranges.

Movements, Home range and Social organization. Japanese Badgers form family groups consisting of a mother and her offspring. Mature adult males seldom visit the family except in early spring, and they are found to have large home ranges that encompass the home ranges of two to three adult females. The home ranges of each sex do not overlap, suggesting intra-sexual territoriality. Japanese Badgers use an average of 13·5 setts in a year; adult males and females seldom stay in the same sett together. Male offspring share a sett with their mother for up to 26 months, whereas female offspring remain with the mother for only 14 months. The average time male offspring spend with their mothers decreases when young are between 15 and 19 months old. In Hinode, Tokyo, the mean home range size of males (40 ha) was found to be larger than that of females (11 ha).

Breeding. Mating occurs from April to August. Implantation of the fertilized eggs into the uterus is delayed until February. Litter size varies from one to three. Male offspring continue growing for 24 months, but females reach adult size in a year. Sexual maturity is reached after two years.

Status and Conservation. Classified as Least Concern in *The IUCN Red List*. Field studies are needed are learn more about the natural history, ecology, and conservation status of the Japanese Badger.

Bibliography. Abramov & Puzachenko (2006), Kaneko (2001, 2005), Kaneko *et al.* (2006), Sato *et al.* (2003), Tanaka (2005, 2006), Wozencraft (2005).

5. Asian Badger *Meles leucurus*

French: Blaireau d'Asie / **German**: Asiatischer Dachs / **Spanish**: Tejón asiático

Taxonomy. *Taxidea leucurus* Hodgson, 1847, China.
The Asian Badger has been considered conspecific with the European Badger by some authors, but is listed here as a distinct species. Two subspecies are recognized.

Subspecies and Distribution.
M. l. leucurus Hodgson, 1847 – C, E & S China.
M. l. amurensis Schrenck, 1859 – NE China (Manchuria), Kazakhstan, Mongolia, North and South Korea, and Russia (E of Volga River).

Descriptive notes. Head-body 49·5–70 cm, tail 13–20·5 cm; weight 3·5–9 kg. The Asian Badger bears a great resemblance to the European Badger. The body is stocky, with short legs and a short tail. The coarse and dense pelage is grayish-silver throughout. The face is white with two narrow blackish-brown stripes running over the eye and above the ear. The nose is long with a large rhinarium. The soles of the feet are naked. The front claws are well-developed for digging, whereas the hindclaws are much smaller. There are three pairs of mammae. The skull is narrow with an elongated rostrum. Dental formula: I 3/3, C 1/1, P 3/3, M 1/2 = 34.

Habitat. Forests and fields, and in close proximity to humans.

Food and Feeding. The diet is mainly invertebrates (earthworms and insects), small mammals, and plant material.

Activity patterns. Nocturnal.

Movements, Home range and Social organization. Asian Badgers are gregarious and live in communal setts with multiple tunnels and den entrances.

Breeding. Nothing known.

Status and Conservation. Classified as Least Concern in *The IUCN Red List*. Although the European Badger has been well studied in Europe, little is known specifically

about the Asian Badger, although it is presumed that there are few differences in basic natural history between these two species. Field studies are needed to learn more about the natural history, ecology, and conservation status of the Asian Badger. This species is legally hunted in China, Russia, and Mongolia.

Bibliography. Abramov & Puzachenko (2006), Neal & Cheeseman (1996), Wozencraft (2005, 2008).

6. European Badger *Meles meles*

French: Blaireau d'Europe / **German**: Europäischer Dachs / **Spanish**: Tejón europeo
Other common names: Eurasian Badger

Taxonomy. *Ursus meles* Linnaeus, 1758, Sweden.
Up to twenty-three subspecies have been proposed, but a taxonomic revision is needed.

Distribution. Europe, E up to Volga River, Russia; also Caucasus and Middle East from Turkey, Israel, Lebanon, and Syria, to N Afghanistan.

Descriptive notes. Head-body 56–90 cm, tail 11·5–20·2 cm; weight 10–16 kg, adult males are larger than females. The European Badger has a stocky body, with short legs and a short tail. The coarse and dense pelage is grayish, with black underparts and limbs. On each side of the face is a dark stripe that extends from the nose to the ear and encloses the eye; white stripes border the dark stripe. The tip of the ears is white. The nose is long with a large rhinarium. All the feet have strong claws. There are three pairs of mammae. Dental formula: I 3/3, C 1/1, P 4/4, M 1/2 = 38. The first premolars are vestigial and sometimes absent.

Habitat. European Badgers are mainly found in deciduous, mixed, and coniferous woodland, hedges, scrub, riverine habitat, agricultural land, grassland, steppes, and semi-deserts. They prefer densely forested areas adjacent to open fields, up to 1700 m. Occasionally, they are found in suburban areas. In central Spain, European Badgers prefer mid-elevation mountain areas, where both dehesas (open woods with pastures) and pine forests prevail; lower elevation areas are avoided. They are associated with watercourses and prefer trees and rock covered areas. In the Swiss Jura Mountains, European Badgers use forests and wooded pastures in the winter and spring and grain fields in the summer and autumn.

Food and Feeding. The diet includes earthworms (*Lumbricus terrestris*) and other invertebrates (such as insects and molluscs), small mammals (mice, rabbits, rats, voles, shrews, moles, hedgehogs), birds, reptiles, amphibians, carrion, nuts, acorns, berries, fruits, tubers, and mushrooms. In forests, European Badgers rely predominantly on earthworms (on average, 62% in diets). In farmlands and pastures, earthworms and plant material (usually garden fruit and cereals) play equally important roles (34% each). In England, the main foods are earthworms, insects, fruit, and wheat; grass is also ingested in substantial quantities. Earthworms are the most frequent food items, but wheat is almost as important in terms of percentage volume. In Poland, earthworms constitute 82–89% of the biomass consumed in spring. In summer and autumn, the proportion declines to 56% in pristine forest, and to 24% in a mosaic of forests, fields, and orchards. Supplementary food items during this time are amphibians (in forests) and garden fruits (in a rural landscape). In Denmark, earthworms, small mammals, cereals, and arthropods dominate the diet. In central Switzerland, the diet comprises 55% faunal material and 45% vegetal material. Earthworms have the highest frequency of occurrence. Voles, insects, and maize are eaten during most of the year, but never in large volumes, while wasps, cherries, plums, and oats are eaten seasonally and in large volumes. In Italy, earthworms and maize are the staple foods and together account for 57% of the mean estimated volume. Earthworm consumption varies seasonally, with a marked decrease in summer; this decline is compensated by a significant increase in fruits eaten. Maize is consumed all year round with no significant seasonal variation (from 21% in summer to 44·6% in winter). Prey items include amphibians (9%) and mammals (7·2%, primarily rodents and lagomorphs). In a dry Mediterranean coastal habitat in central Italy, European Badgers feed primarily on fruits and insects (90% of the total amount of food eaten each year). Other less important food items include myriapods, molluscs, birds, and mammals; earthworms do not play an important role in the diet in any period of the year.

Activity patterns. European Badgers show crepuscular or nocturnal activity, generally starting after sunset and ending before sunrise, and are active on average for about eight hours per day. The highest level of activity is between 20:00 h and 03:00 h. During the day, they mainly rest in elaborate, communal burrow systems (setts) with numerous entrances, passages, and chambers, but other types of rest sites may be used. Setts may cover an area of 0·25 ha; they are used year after year and increase in complexity over time, and may eventually cover several hectares. There are two types of burrows: "main" setts (with many entrances) and small "outliers" (with usually only one entrance). Nests may be located 10 m from an entrance, 2–3 m below the surface, and have a diameter of 1·5 m. Within a burrow system, European Badgers may utilize one nest for several months and then move to another part of the burrow. The living quarters are kept quite clean. Bedding material (dry grass, bracken, moss, or leaves) is dragged backwards into the den. Around setts, there are several dung pits, sunning grounds, and play areas. Well-defined paths, up to 2–3 km, extend from the sett to foraging areas. In south-western Spain, setts are located almost everywhere, but European Badgers prefer easily dug, well-drained soils, with good vegetation cover within foraging habitats. They select sites with high surrounding shrub density, large shrubs covering the burrow, and close to the centre of the territory. During bouts of cold weather or deep snow, European Badgers may sleep in the sett for days or weeks. In northern Europe, this winter sleep may last several months. During this period, there is a substantial drop in body temperature and the badger lives off fat reserves accumulated in the summer and autumn. In south-west Portugal, main setts are the most frequently used rest sites (62·3%); however, an average of 14 other resting sites are used in each territory. Females use more than twice as many occasional resting sites as do males. Generally burrows (predominantly main setts) are most frequently used during winter and autumn, whilst non-burrow shelters are preferred during spring and summer, when the weather is hot, dry and not windy. In northern Italy, ten setts (mean number of entrances = 2·1) were detected in the study area. Each radio-collared badger used 2–3 setts, occupying one sett from one to eight months before moving to another one. All badgers shared (although in different periods) one main sett located in the inner part of their ranges.

Movements, Home range and Social organization. Mean daily movement ranges from 1·2 km in England to 7 km in Poland. Average speed of movement varies from 0·3 km/h in Spain to 1·1 km/h in Switzerland. European Badgers in Britain form clans of mutli-male and multi-female groups, of up to 23 animals (average = six). Elsewhere in their range they commonly live alone, or in pairs with either intra- or inter-sexual territories. Clans are led by a dominant male and female, and usually have more females than males. Individuals move around alone within a clan range. These ranges are marked using latrine sites and secretions from the sub-caudal glands; sometimes fights may occur at territorial boundaries. In England, many clans have ranges of 50–150 ha, with little overlap; the minimum distance between the main burrows of clans is 300 m. In the Bialowieza Primeval Forest, Poland, the daily home range was 2·1 km² (19% of their total home range size). The size of territories varied from 8·4 to 25·5 km² (mean 12·8 km²). The mean individual home range was 9·3 km² and varied seasonally and among animals of different age and sex classes (from 4–24·4 km²). Home ranges of adult badgers were significantly larger than those of subadults. European Badgers occupied larger home ranges in summer, when earthworm availability was low. They moved with an average speed of 0·9 km/hour (maximum 7·1 km/hour). Adults of both sexes visited territory boundaries significantly more often than subadult individuals. In Denmark, home range size varied between 2·96 km² and 3·94 km²; individuals

from a social group had similar home ranges (95% overlap), whereas home ranges of individuals from neighboring social groups had little overlap (1–2%). In the Swiss Jura Mountains, radio-collared European Badgers travelled up to 9460 m each night; they avoided pastures and the vicinity of houses during their night trips. The average home range size was 320 ha, but the ranging behavior varied between seasons. Den-watching, night-lighting, and radio-tracking data suggested that European Badgers live in pairs in this wet and cold region. In an area of agricultural lowland in northern Italy, radio-tracked animals showed considerable home range overlap, with an overall mean size of 3·83 km². Population density estimates range from 0·4 to 1·5 individuals per 100 ha.

Breeding. Mating can occur year-round, but typically occurs in late winter to midsummer. Implantation of the fertilized eggs into the uterus can either be immediate or delayed for about ten months; the time of implantation seems to be controlled by light and temperature conditions. Embryonic development lasts six to eight weeks. The total gestation may thus be up to 9–12 months. Births occur mainly from February to March. Litter size is usually three or four, but can be as many as six. The young weigh 75 g at birth; their eyes open after one month. They nurse for 2·5 months and usually separate from the mother in the autumn. Both sexes reach sexual maturity after one year.

Status and Conservation. Classified as Least Concern in *The IUCN Red List*. European Badgers are generally considered common and of no special conservation concern, although declines in numbers have occurred in some areas. They sometimes damage property or consume crops, and thus are often regarded as pests and persecuted. The hair is used to make various kinds of brushes, and badger skin has been used to make rugs. European Badgers are commonly killed on roads; as many as 50,000 may be killed each year in Great Britain. They are vectors of bovine tuberculosis, which has led to controversial efforts to reduce European Badger numbers in parts of Britain.

Bibliography. Balestrieri et al. (2004), Elmeros et al. (2005), Fischer & Weber (2003), Goszczynski et al. (2000), Kowalczyk, Jedrzejewska & Zalewski (2003), Kowalczyk, Zalewski & Jedrzejewska (2004, 2006), Kowalczyk, Zalewski, Jedrzejewska & Jedrzejewski (2003), Kruuk & Parish (1987), Long & Killingley (1983), Loureiro et al. (2007), Madsen et al. (2002), Marassi & Biancardi (2002), Melis et al. (2002), Neal & Cheeseman (1996), Page et al. (1994), Palphramand et al. (2007), Pigozzi (1991), Remonti et al. (2006), Revilla & Palomares (2002), Revilla et al. (2001), Rodríguez et al. (1996), Roper (1994), Roper & Lups (1995), Roper et al. (2001), Rosalino et al. (2002), San et al. (2007), Shepherdson et al. (1990), Virgos & Casanovas (1999), Weber & Ferrari (2005), Wozencraft (2005, 2008).

Plate 33 ➤

color variants
7

PLATE 33

inches   12
cm   30

8

9

ssp *peninsularis*
10

11

ssp *flavigula*

12

13

14

15

16

Subfamily MARTINAE

Genus *EIRA*

C. E. H. Smith, 1842

7. Tayra *Eira barbara*

French: Tayra / **German**: Tayra / **Spanish**: Taira

Taxonomy. *Mustela barbara* Linnaeus, 1758, "Pernambuco", Brazil.
Seven subspecies are recognized.
Subspecies and Distribution.
E. b. barbara Linnaeus, 1758 – Argentina, Brazil, and Paraguay.
E. b. inserta J. A. Allen, 1908 – El Salvador and Honduras to Costa Rica.
E. b. madeirensis Lönnberg, 1913 – W Brazil, E Ecuador, and NE Peru.
E. b. peruana Tschudi, 1844 – Amazonian Bolivia and SE Peru.
E. b. poliocephala Traill, 1821 – the Guianas, E Venezuela, and lower Amazon Basin.
E. b. senex Thomas, 1900 – Mexico to Guatemala.
E. b. sinuensis Humboldt, 1812 – Panama to Colombia, W Ecuador, W Venezuela, and Trinidad.

Descriptive notes. Head-body 55·9–71·2 cm, tail 36·5–46 cm; weight 2·7–7 kg, adult males are 30% larger than females. The Tayra is large and slender, with elongated limbs and a long brushy tail. The pelage is dark, but the head and neck are grayish or grizzled tan. In Guyana, a yellow morph also occurs. The feet have naked soles and strong claws. Dental formula: I 3/3, C 1/1, P 3/3–4, M 1/1–2 = 34. The first premolars are missing, although the upper first premolar is sometimes retained.

Habitat. Tayras are found in tropical and subtropical forests, including secondary rainforests, gallery forests, cloud forests, and dry scrub forests. They sometimes occur in gardens, plantations, and in agricultural fields. Tayras may hunt in grasslands, although much of their time is spent in forested areas. In the Ilanos of Venezuela, Tayras are usually found along gallery forests; at night, they may cross extensive grasslands, presumably moving from one forest to another. In Veracruz, Mexico, Tayras generally are restricted to forested habitats. They are found in the Atlantic rainforest of Brazil, in deciduous and scrub forest of the Pantanal in Paraguay and Bolivia, and in gallery and scrub forest and tall grass savannas in Argentina, Bolivia, and Paraguay. In Belize, no significant habitat preference was found for the Tayra.

Food and Feeding. The diet includes fruits, small vertebrates, insects, and carrion. In Venezuela, three species of vertebrate (*Echimys semivillous, Rhipidomys* sp., and *Iguana iguana*) and four species of fruit (*Genipa americana, Zanthozylum culantrillo, Guazuma tomentosa*, and *Psychotria anceps*) were recorded from 18 scats; both *E. semivillous* and *G. americana* were found in 50% of the scats. In Belize, four species of small mammals were found in 31 scats: *Didelphis marsupialis* (9·6%), *Oryzomys palustris* (22·5%), *Sigmodon hispidus* (32·3%), and *Rattus rattus* (29·0%). In addition, 19·4% small birds, 58·0% arthropods, and 67·7% fruit were found. The primary fruit eaten was *Calocarpum mammosum*. Additional fruits consumed included *Cecropia mexicana, Astrocaryum standleyanum*, and *Spondias mombin*. Prey and other foods are detected primarily by smell, as its eyesight is relatively poor. Prey are captured after persistent chases; the Tayra does not stalk or ambush prey.

Activity patterns. Primarily diurnal, with peaks of activity in the early morning and late afternoon. On occasion, some nocturnal activity may occur, especially near human habitations. Rest sites are in hollow trees or underground burrows.

Movements, Home range and Social organization. Tayras spend a large proportion of their time foraging or resting in trees. They are normally solitary, but adult pairs and small groups, consisting of a female with her young, are sometimes seen. In the Ilanos of Venezuela, a female with two young maintained a home range of 2·25 km² around a den until the pups were about three months old, after which her range expanded to almost 9 km². Upon expansion of her home range and weaning of the young, the female used new dens daily that were an average of 867 m apart. In Belize, Tayras traveled an average of 6·89 km per day. A female had a home range of 16·03 km² over a 13-month period, one male had a home range of 24·44 km² over a 10-month period, and another male had a home range of only 2·11 km² over a 3-month period; the short duration of radio-tracking for the last animal may have accounted for the small size of the observed home range. The home ranges of all three animals overlapped greatly. In south-eastern Brazil, a female had a home range of 5·3 km²; she did not show a preference for any particular habitat type within her home range, but her use of secondary forest and grassland agreed with previous studies.

Breeding. In captivity, breeding activity of adult Tayras occurs during the day. However, on Barro Colorado Island, Panama, two males and one female may have engaged in nocturnal sexual behavior. Males appear ready to mate year round and can reproduce by 18 months of age. Female Tayras have their first estrus at about 22 months of age; the estrous cycle is c. 52 days in young females and c. 94 days in older females. Females enter estrus several times each year for periods of 3–20 days. Gestation lasts 63–67 days. Delayed implantation does not occur. Tayras give birth to one to three young, but two are most common. In the wild, males do not remain with females, who raise the young alone. The young are born blind, covered in fur, and weigh about 100 g. The ears open at 27–34 days and the eyes open at 35–47 days. Deciduous teeth begin emerging at day 36 and are completely erupted by day 99. Permanent teeth appear at day 115 and are completely emerged by day 224. The young consume solid food by day 70 and are weaned by day 100. Five stages of development have been defined. First is the infant stage, days 1–50, during which the young suckle and do not leave the den. During days 50–75, the fledgling stage, the young leave the den for short periods, and solid food is provided by the mother, in addition to milk. The weaning stage, days 75–100, includes exploratory excursions, with independent feeding on fruits and insects. During the transition stage, days 100–200, the birth den is abandoned, the young are weaned, and they begin to hunt with their mother and kill prey on their own. During dispersal, days 200–300, family bonds break down and the young go their separate ways. The young reach adult size at six months. When outside the den, the young and mother use a clicking call to maintain contact if they are not within sight of one another. Mothers are protective of their young and will carry them by the middle of the body when a threat is perceived. This protective behavior persists as the young grow and mothers may also carry or drag them back to the den by their necks or ears. Prey-catching ability develops slowly and is learned. When only three months old, the young will follow and bite rodents and small birds on the rump or limbs. Through experience, bite placement is improved, resulting in killing bites to the base of the skull. The mother will bring wounded prey to her young and release it for them to catch and kill.

Status and Conservation. Classified as Least Concern in *The IUCN Red List*. The Tayra is considered common throughout most of its range. However, the range of *E. b. senex* has been greatly reduced in Mexico because of the destruction of tropical forests and the spread of agriculture. Remaining populations are small and threatened by habitat loss and hunting. The Tayra is a popular species for zoo exhibits and is frequently kept in captivity.

Bibliography. Galef *et al.* (1976), Michalski *et al.* (2006), Poglayen-Neuwall (1975, 1978), Presley (2000), Ramirez-Pulido *et al.* (2005), Wozencraft (2005).

Genus *GULO*

Pallas, 1780

8. Wolverine *Gulo gulo*

French: Carcajou / **German**: Vielfraß / **Spanish**: Gotón

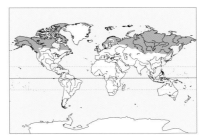

Taxonomy. *Mustela gulo* Linnaeus, 1758, Lapland.
Two subspecies are recognized.
Subspecies and Distribution.
G. g. gulo Linnaeus, 1758 – NE & NW China, Mongolia, Russia, and Scandinavia.
G. g. luscus Linnaeus, 1758 – Canada and W USA (Alaska, California, Idaho, Oregon, Montana, Washington & Wyoming).

Descriptive notes. Head-body 65–105 cm, tail 21–26 cm; weight 11–18 kg (males), 6–12 kg (females), adult males are larger and heavier than females. The Wolverine is heavily built and stocky, and is the largest terrestrial member of the Mustelidae. The pelage is long and varies in color from almost blond to dark brown, with two distinctive yellowish stripes that run from the top of the neck to the rump. White patches on the throat, belly or limbs are common. The head is large, with a broad forehead, broad nose, and rounded ears. The limbs are relatively short and the tail is bushy. The feet are large, with well-developed claws. The skull is exceptionally robust and broad, with a well-developed sagittal crest. Dental formula: I 3/3, C 1/1, P 4/4, M 1/2 = 38. The teeth are big and strong; the carnassials are very large.

Habitat. Wolverines are found in mature conifer forests in the taiga and in the treeless tundra. They are inhabitants of remote northern areas where there are few humans. Wolverines make greater use of forested areas during winter, and greater use of tundra during summer. Altitudinal movements may also occur seasonally, with higher elevations being occupied during the summer and lower altitudes during the winter, probably because of snow accumulation and prey abundance. In central Idaho, USA, radio-tracked Wolverines used higher elevations in summer versus winter, and they shifted use of cover types from whitebark pine (*Pinus albicaulis*) in summer to lower elevation Douglas-fir (*Pseudotsuga menziezii*) and lodgepole pine (*Pinus contorta*) communities in winter. Wolverines also preferred northerly aspects, but avoided roads and ungulate winter range. In British Columbia, Canada, radio-telemetry revealed that Wolverines negatively responded to human disturbance within occupied habitat; males tended to avoid helicopter skiing areas. Habitat associations of females were more complex, but in the summer they avoided roads and recently logged areas. In the Columbia Mountains, where winter recreation is widespread, females prefer alpine and avalanche en-

On following pages: 9. American Marten (*Martes americana*); 10. Yellow-throated Marten (*Martes flavigula*); 11. Stone Marten (*Martes foina*); 12. Nilgiri Marten (*Martes gwatkinsii*); 13. European Pine Marten (*Martes martes*); 14. Japanese Marten (*Martes melampus*); 15. Fisher (*Martes pennanti*); 16. Sable (*Martes zibellina*).

vironments where Hoary Marmot (*Marmota caligata*) and Columbia Ground Squirrel prey are found in the summer. During the winter, females tend to avoid areas with helicopter and backcountry skiing, and prefer areas where Moose (*Alces alces*) can be found.

Food and Feeding. The diet includes the carcasses of large ungulates, such as Moose and Reindeer (*Rangifer tarandus*). In many areas, Wolverines are dependent on the ability of larger predators, especially Gray Wolves, to provide kills. In coastal areas, they also feed on the carcasses of whales and seals that wash ashore. Wolverines also prey opportunistically on deer, sheep, small mammals (rodents such as *Marmota* and *Myodes*, lagomorphs, and ground squirrels), birds, and eggs. Berries, nuts and fungus are occasionally eaten. Within two study areas in British Columbia, scat analysis revealed a diet that varied regionally and seasonally: Moose, Reindeer, and Hoary Marmots were abundant and common prey items within both study areas. Mountain Goats (*Oreamnos americanus*) and North American Porcupine (*Erithizon dorsata*) were more frequent prey items in the Columbia Mountains, while Snowshoe Hare (*Lepus americanus*) and American Beaver (*Castor canadensis*) were more frequent prey items in the Omineca Mountains. Reindeer, Hoary Marmots, and North American Porcupines were found in significantly higher frequencies in the diet of reproductive females. Predation on ungulates (such as Reindeer) is facilitated when there is deep snow. Wolverines kill larger prey by a bite at the neck or throat. Small rodents may be chased, pounced upon, or dug out of the ground. Excess food is cached for later use and is covered with earth or snow, or sometimes wedged in the forks of trees. In Alberta and British Columbia, cache sites were in stands of black spruce (*Picea mariana*) or mixed-wood of high complexity, dominated by conifers, and in which the trembling aspen (*Populus tremuloides*) and balsam poplar (*Populus balsamifera*) component consisted of mostly dead or dying trees. These sites offered relatively good visibility of the surrounding area; caches were never located in the very dense homogenous spruce stands. Cache sites were classified as "simple caches", composed of a single feeding site and/or excavation, and "cache complexes", involving one or more feeding "stations", latrines, resting sites, and climbing trees that may have been used as avenues of escape from competitors or predators. The better used cache complexes were accessed by numerous well-used trails made by the Wolverines themselves. Caches contained the remains of Moose that were believed to have been killed by Wolves.

Activity patterns. Mainly nocturnal, but occasionally active during the day. Rest sites may be a rough bed of grass or leaves in a cave or rock crevice, in a burrow made by another animal, or under a fallen tree. In Alberta and British Columbia, resting sites were located on top of the snow in relatively open locations that offered good visibility of the surroundings. Wolverines do not appear to be hindered by deep snow and are active year round.

Movements, Home range and Social organization. Wolverines are solitary and mainly terrestrial, but are also strong swimmers and agile tree climbers. Their scavenging habits dictate covering long distances. Daily movements in excess of 30 km are common; males travel more widely than females. They are capable of reaching speeds of 45 km/h. In north-western Alaska, the home ranges of males were 488–917 km^2 and 53–232 km^2 for females. In south-central Alaska, home ranges averaged 535 km^2 for males and 105 km^2 for females. In Yukon, home ranges were 209–269 km^2 for males and 76–269 km^2 for females. The home range of each male overlaps three or four females. However, in Montana, there was extensive overlap between the ranges of both the same and opposite sexes, and no territorial defense was observed. Population densities vary from one animal per 50 km^2 in Siberia to one per 500 km^2 in Scandinavia. North American densities vary from one per 65 km^2 to one per 200 km^2.

Breeding. Wolverines exhibit a polygamous mating system, as some males produce offspring with more than one female in a single year. Females often reproduce with the same male in subsequent breeding years, but sometimes change their partner, possibly as a consequence of a change in the territory-holding male in the area. Females are monoestrous and apparently give birth about every two years. Mating occurs from May to August. Ovulation is induced; implantation of the fertilized eggs into the uterus is delayed until the following November to March. Births occur from January to April, after a total gestation period of 215–270 days. Maternal dens are located in alpine, subalpine, taiga, or tundra habitat; reports of dens in low elevation, densely forested habitats are rare. Dens in Alaska are usually long, complex snow tunnels with no associated trees or boulders. In Idaho, dens are associated with fallen trees or boulders. In both areas, all dens are covered with at least 1 m of snow. Litter size is one to five; usually two to four. The young weigh about 84 g at birth and are born fully furred, but with their eyes closed. Weaning occurs after seven to eight weeks, and adult size is reached by November, when the young separate from the mother. Females raise the young alone. Sexual maturity is attained after two or three years.

Status and Conservation. Classified as Near Threatened in *The IUCN Red List*t. Wolverines are harvested for their pelt; although their fur is not used widely in commerce it is valued for parkas. Fur trapping has contributed to a decline in numbers and distribution of the Wolverine. Wolverines are also intensely hunted because they are considered a nuisance animal: they follow traplines and devour trapped furbearers, they break into cabins and food caches, they allegedly prey on domestic reindeer, and they attack sheep. Protection and recovery measures are needed to restore populations across its previously known range.

Bibliography. Aubry *et al.* (2007), Banci & Harestad (1988), Copeland & Whitman (2003), Copeland *et al.* (2007), Hedmark *et al.* (2007), Hornocker & Hash (1981), Krebs *et al.* (2007), Krott (1960), Landa, Linden & Kojola (2000), Landa, Strand, Linnell & Skogland (1998), Landa, Strand, Swenson & Skogland (1997), Lofroth *et al.* (2007), Magoun & Copeland (1998), Mead *et al.* (1991), Pasitschniak-Arts & Larivière (1995), Stroganov (1969), Whitman *et al.* (1986), Wozencraft (2005, 2008), Wright & Ernst (2004a, 2004b).

Genus *MARTES*

Pinel, 1792

9. American Marten *Martes americana*

French: Martre d'Amérique / **German**: Fichtenmarder / **Spanish**: Marta norteamericana

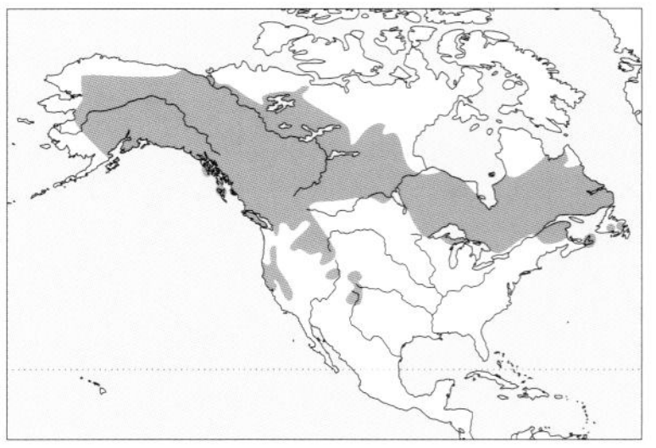

Taxonomy. *Mustela americanus* Turton, 1806, North America.

The number of subspecies is debated and here we recognize eight.

Subspecies and Distribution.

M. a. americana Turton, 1806 – E Canada (Ontario & Quebec) anf NE USA.

M. a. abietinoides Gray, 1865 – SW Canada (C British Columbia & SW Alberta) and NW USA (N Montana & Idaho).

M. a. actuosa Osgood, 1900 – Alaska and NW Canada (N Alberta, N British Columbia, Northwest Territories & Yukon).

M. a. atrata Bangs, 1897 – NE Canada (Newfoundland and Labrador).

M. a. caurina Merriam, 1890 – W Canada (W British Columbia) and USA (S Alaska & W Washington).

M. a. humboldtensis Grinnell & Dixon, 1926 – SW USA (NW California).

M. a. kenaiensis Elliot, 1903 – Alaska (Kenai Peninsula).

M. a. nesophila Osgood, 1901 – SW Alaska and W Canada (islands off British Columbia, and perhaps along nearby mainland).

Descriptive notes. Head-body 36–45 cm (males), 32–40 cm (females), tail 20–23 cm (males), 18–20 cm (females); weight 470–1250 g (males), 280–850 g (females), adult males are about 65% heavier than females. The American Marten has a long, slender body, with short limbs, bushy tail, and large rounded ears. The pelage ranges from light beige to dark brown, and often shows shades of orange. Many individuals have yellow to bright orange throat and upper chest patches. The head is pale gray and the legs and tail are almost black. The feet are fully furred, each digit has a strong claw. There are four pairs of mammae. The skull is long and narrow, with elongated auditory bullae. Dental formula: I 3/3, C 1/1, P 4/4, M 1/2 = 38.

Habitat. American Martens are found predominantly in mature conifer or conifer-dominated mixed forests. Preferred habitats are mature old-growth spruce-fir communities, with greater than 30% canopy cover, a well-established understory of fallen logs and stumps, and lush shrub and forb vegetation. They avoid large open spaces such as clearcuttings, but may use riparian areas, meadows, forest edges, and rocky alpine areas above the timberline. In the coastal forests of California, American Martens select the largest available patches of old-growth, old-growth and late-mature, or serpentine habitat; dense, spatially extensive shrub cover is a key habitat element. In Alberta, during the winter, American Martens use young forests, and mature/old coniferous and deciduous stands, according to their availability. In the Selkirk and Purcell Mountains of south-west Canada, American Martens were detected in all habitats sampled including recently logged areas, regenerating stands, dry Douglas-fir (*Pseudosuga menziesii*) forest and subalpine parkland. They selected for greater crown closure and older stands at the finer resolution; no selection for forest structure was detected at the larger resolution except that American Martens selected against increased overstory heterogeneity. They preferred coniferous stands over deciduous-dominated stands and were more abundant in wetter than in dryer areas. In a clearcut boreal landscape in western Quebec, in which black spruce (*Picea mariana*) is the predominant forest type, American Martens avoid open regenerating stands composed mostly of recent clearcuts with sparse regeneration. They do not select coniferous stands, even those that are mature or overmature, but prefer deciduous and mixed stands, a large proportion of which has a dense coniferous shrub layer. Winter home ranges usually contain less than 30–35% open or closed regenerating stands and more than 40–50% uncut forest. In south-eastern Labrador, American Martens avoid areas with low productivity and low canopy cover (< 20%), but show no selection for tree species composition or cover among more productive forests. In eastern Newfoundland, mature coniferous forest is the dominant cover type in most American Marten home ranges and is the only forest type used proportionately more than its availability by resident individuals. Other forest types used in proportion to their availability include coniferous scrub and insect-defoliated stands; open areas and sites recently disturbed by fire are avoided at this scale. In northern Maine, in an area where trapping and timber harvesting had been excluded for more than 35 years, American Martens were found to use nearly all the available habitat, although during the summer, they preferred stands that had substantial mortality caused by spruce budworm (*Choristoneura fumiferana*). Mature, well-stocked coniferous forest was the least abundant forest type in the home ranges of both sexes, in both seasons, whereas mature, well-stocked deciduous forest was the most abundant.

Food and Feeding. The diet consists mostly of rodents and other small mammals, including voles, mice, chipmunks, squirrels (*Tamiasciurus* and *Glaucomys* sp.), and lagomorphs, especially the Snowshoe Hare. Other food items include birds, eggs, reptiles, amphibians, invertebrates (insects, earthworms), fruits, and berries. In Newfoundland, Meadow Voles were the most prevalent food item found in scats (80% in summer and 47·5% in winter); Snowshoe Hares occurred in 28% of winter samples, and 16% other food types were found in scats during each season. In the mixed-conifer forests of southern Sierra Nevada, where the American Marten and Fisher are sympatric, the diet of Fishers appeared to include more remains of birds, lizards, hypogeous fungi, and insects than that of American Martens. However, the dietary overlap between these two species was high. The diets of both species were more diverse than previously reported in North America, perhaps due to the absence or rarity of large prey (Snowshoe Hares and North American Porcupines) or to a greater diversity of available prey types in the southern Sierra Nevada. American Martens hunt and find food by constant searching, sometimes in trees, and often tunnel under snow during winter to search for microtines.

Activity patterns. Primarily nocturnal and crepuscular, but can be active during the day. Den/rest sites are in hollow logs or trees, in rock crevices, or in burrows. Large logs, large snags, and large, live spruce and fir trees are important characteristics for den sites in the central Rocky Mountains. Squirrels provide important denning structures as well as prey for American Martens.

Movements, Home range and Social organization. American Martens are solitary and partly arboreal, but spend a considerable amount of time on the ground. They can also swim and dive well. The home ranges of males are 2–3 times larger than those of females: up to 45 km² for males (overall average c. 9 km²) and up to 28 km² for females (overall average c. 3 km²). The degree of overlap of home ranges varies, but generally male home ranges overlap those of several females, and individuals are intolerant of conspecifics of the same sex. In Minnesota, the home ranges of three males were 10·5, 16·6 and 19·9 km², and 4·3 km² for one female; there was considerable overlap between the ranges of two of the males. In Wisconsin, mean winter home range size was 3·29 km², with the home ranges of males (mean = 4·25 km²) significantly larger than females (mean = 2·32 km²). In Newfoundland, home range estimates were 29·54 km² for males and 15·19 km² for females. In Labrador, the mean home range for males was 45 km² and 27·6 km² for females. In a forest preserve that was closed to trapping, the proportion of males maintaining residency throughout the study period was found to be higher than that of females, indicating that the home ranges of females were more dynamic than the home ranges of males. Neither males nor females adjusted the size of their home ranges among seasons; however, males tended to shift location of their home ranges in response to increases in available space. Females either maintained a high degree of fidelity among seasons or completely abandoned previously established home ranges. Abandonment of existing home ranges by some females may have resulted from stresses associated with a high density in an untrapped population. Population densities vary from 0·5 to 1·7 per km².

Breeding. Mating occurs from July to August. Implantation of the fertilized eggs into the uterus is delayed for 190–250 days; embryonic development is about 28 days. Total gestation period is thus 220–275 days. The young are born in late March or April, usually in a hollow tree or arboreal cavity; the natal nest is lined with dry vegetation. In the Sierra Madre Range, Wyoming, natal and maternal dens included rock crevices (28%), snags (25%), Red Squirrel (*Tamasciurus hudsonicus*) middens (19%), and logs (16%). Litter size is one to five, usually two to three. Neonates weigh c. 28 g, open their eyes after 39 days, are weaned after six weeks, and reach adult size after three months. Sexual maturity is attained at 15–24 months.

Status and Conservation. Classified as Least Concern in *The IUCN Red List*. American Martens are considered common in some parts of their range, and are legally harvested for the fur trade. However, by the early 20th century, excessive trapping had severely depleted the American Marten in many areas, particularly in Alaska, Canada, and western United States. Protective regulations subsequently allowed the species to make a comeback in some areas and reintroduction programs have been carried out in Michigan, Wisconsin, and parts of north-eastern USA and south-eastern Canada. Current low numbers or absences in some areas seem attributable to forestry practices; this species is very sensitive to habitat destruction, and clear-cutting can completely eliminate American Martens from an area. The availability of hollow trees for use as resting sites and natal dens is especially critical, and logging procedures that eliminate old stumps or older trees may be detrimental to American Marten populations.

Bibliography. Buskirk (1984), Buskirk & MacDonald (1984), Clark *et al.* (1987), Dumyahn & Zollner (2007), Gosse & Hearn (2005), Hagmeier (1961), Mowat (2006), Poole & Graf (1996), Potvin *et al.* (2000), Powell *et al.* (2003), Proulx (2006), Raine (1983), Ruggiero *et al.* (1998), Simon *et al.* (1999), Slauson *et al.* (2007), Smith & Schaefer (2002), Soutiere (1979), Wozencraft (2005).

10. Yellow-throated Marten *Martes flavigula*

French: Martre à gorge jaune / **German**: Buntmarder / **Spanish**: Marta papigualda

Taxonomy *Mustela flavigula* Boddaert, 1785, Nepal.
Six subspecies are recognized.
Subspecies and Distribution.
M. f. flavigula Boddaert, 1785 – Bangladesh, Bhutan, C, E & S China, India, Nepal, and Pakistan.
M. f. borealis Radde, 1862 – NE China, North and South Korea, and Russia.
M. f. chrysospila Swinhoe, 1866 – Taiwan.
M. f. indochinensis Kloss, 1916 – Cambodia, Laos, Myanmar, Thailand, and Vietnam.
M. f. peninsularis Bonhote, 1901 – Borneo, Malay Peninsula, and Sumatra.
M. f. robinsoni Pocock, 1936 – Java.
Descriptive notes. Head-body 45–65 cm, tail 37–45 cm; weight 1·3–3 kg. The Yellow-throated Marten has a long, slender body and a long, dark tail; the tail is 60–70% of head and body length. The ears are large and round. The pelage varies geographically

and with season. The top of the head and neck, the tail, the lower limbs, and parts of the back are dark brown to black; the rest of the body is pale brown. There are bright orange-yellow markings from the chin to the chest. There are two pairs of mammae. The skull is strong; the temporal ridges do not approach to form a sagittal crest. Dental formula: I 3/3, C 1/1, P 4/4, M 1/2 = 38. Males have larger canines than females.

Habitat. Forests, including dry and hill evergreen, mixed and moist deciduous, and dry dipterocarp forest, at elevations of 200–3000 m. In Thailand, radio-collared Yellow-throated Martens generally used the different types of habitat in proportion to their availability; however, one male was observed to use open forest-grassland less than it was available.

Activity patterns. Primarily diurnal; activity peaks occur during the morning (06:00–08:00 h) and late afternoon (16:00–18:00 h). Reduced activity periods are scattered during the night (20:00–04:00 h) and are greater during lunar nights than other nights. The highest average monthly activity is during October, whereas the lowest is during March. Wet season activity is significantly greater than dry season activity. Den/rest sites are in holes, rocks crevices, or hollow trees.

Food and Feeding. The diet includes small rodents, pikas, snakes, lizards, frogs, insects, birds, eggs, fruit, honey, berries, and nectar. It has been reported that Yellow-throated Martens prey on musk deer (*Moschus* sp.) and the young of Wild Boar (*Sus scrofa*), deer, and gorals.

Movements, Home range and Social organization. Yellow-throated Martens climb trees with great agility, but often come to the ground to hunt. They are seen in pairs or small family groups. In Phu Khieo Wildlife Sanctuary, Thailand, five adult Yellow-throated Martens were radio-tracked for 4–16 months. The mean daily movement was 770 m for four males and 1349 m for one female. The cumulative home range sizes for four males were 1·7, 3·5, 10·1 and 11·8 km², and 8·8 km² for one female. Home ranges generally increased during the wet season; however, the range of one male increased marginally during the dry season. Mean range overlap was 34%.

Breeding. Believed to breed in August, and give birth in April to litters of two to five young. Gestation is 220–290 days.

Status and Conservation. Classified as Least Concern in *The IUCN Red List*. The subspecies *M. f. robinsoni* is classified as Endangered. Little is known about Yellow-throated Martens and further field studies are needed to learn more about their natural history, ecology, and conservation status.

Bibliography. Francis (2008), Grassman, Tewes & Silvy (2005), Lekagul & McNeely (1991), Nandini & Karthik (2007), Pocock (1941a), Wozencraft (2005, 2008).

11. Stone Marten *Martes foina*

French: Fouine / **German**: Steinmarder / **Spanish**: Garduña
Other common names: Beech Marten

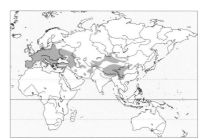

Taxonomy. *Mustela foina* Erxleben, 1777, Germany.
Up to fifteen subspecies have been proposed, but a taxonomic revision is needed.
Distribution. Mainland C & S Europe, Caucasus, Middle East, C Asia to Mongolia, C & SW China, and N Myanmar. Introduced to Ibiza I (Spain), but now extirpated, and to USA (Wisconsin).
Descriptive notes. Head-body 40–54 cm, tail 22–30 cm; weight 1·1–2·3 kg. The Stone Marten has a long body, short limbs, and a bushy tail about half of the head and body length. The pelage ranges from grayish brown to dark brown, with a conspicuous white or pale yellow neck and throat patch, which often splits into two parts that extend to the anterior part of the legs. The tail and legs are darker than the back. The upper lip has a medial rhinarial groove. There are two pairs of mammae. Dental formula: I 3/3, C 1/1, P 4/4, M 1/2 = 38. The third upper premolar has slightly convex outer edges (they are concave in the European Pine Marten.

Habitat. Stone Martens are found in forests and open and rocky areas, at elevations up to 4000 m. They also occur in fragmented forests, hedgerows, and cultivated areas, and in close proximity to humans. They are generally found in more open environments than other marten species and appear to avoid conifer forests. In a fragmented agricultural landscape, Stone Martens were found to prefer areas with wood and scrub vegetation and watercourses with continuous vegetation along their verges; they tended to avoid arable land.

Food and Feeding. The diet consists of rodents, birds, eggs, reptiles, amphibians, insects, fruits, and berries. In France, voles (*Microtus* sp.) make up to 30–55% of the total diet; there is strong seasonality, with microtines eaten more often in winter and spring. In the Swiss Jura, mammals are the main prey, representing 37·9% of all food items; Water Voles (*Arvicola terrestris*) were found in 90·4% of scats during peak vole numbers. In central Italy, fruit and berries are the staple diet, but mammals and birds are also important; the diet varies seasonally in relation to resource availability, with a predominance of fruit in autumn and insects in summer. In east-central Italy, the winter diet is almost completely frugivorous; fruit represents 84% of the total volume in the diet, with a 55% occurrence. Berries from juniperus (42·2%, *Juniperus* sp.) and from sloe (29·7%, *Prunus spinosa*) are the most common food items. In south-eastern Romania, birds (45·2% of the biomass) and mammals (36·1%) predominate in the diet; reptiles, amphibians, insects, and fruits are supplementary food. In the Caucasus, the diet is 85% murine rodents during the summer; vegetable matter forms a major part of the late summer and early fall food in some areas.

Activity patterns. Primarily nocturnal and crepuscular. Den/rest sites are inside rock crevices, stone heaps, hollow trees, abandoned burrows, and in buildings.

Movements, Home range and Social organization. Stone Martens are solitary. They are good climbers, but rarely go high into trees. Home ranges vary between 12–211 ha, being larger in summer and smaller during winter. The home ranges of males are generally larger than those of females, and adult ranges are larger than immature animals. In central Italy, radio-telemetry revealed intra-sexual territoriality; males travelled longer distances than females, although home range sizes did not differ significantly between the sexes.

Breeding. Mating occurs in summer, but because of delayed implantation of the fertilized eggs into the uterus, births do not occur until the following spring. The overall gestation lasts 230–275 days, although true gestation is c. 30 days. Litter size typically is three to four, but may reach up to eight. Sexual maturity may be attained at 15–27 months.

Status and Conservation. Classified as Least Concern in *The IUCN Red List*. The Stone Marten is considered common throughout most of Europe and Asia. It is hunted for its pelt, but this does not have the same quality of the European Pine Marten.

Bibliography. Baghli *et al.* (2002), Canivenc *et al.* (1981), Feller (1993a, 1993b), Francis (2008), Genovesi & Boitani (1997), Genovesi, Secchi & Boitani (1996), Genovesi, Sinibaldi & Boitani (1997), Lodé (1994), Lopez-Martin *et al.* (1992), Michelat *et al.* (2001), Padial *et al.* (2002), Pandolfi *et al.* (1996), Posluszny *et al.* (2007), Roberts (1977), Romanowski & Lesinski (1991), Rondinini & Boitani (2002), Sacchi & Meriggi (1995), Stone & Cook (2002), Stroganov (1969), Virgos *et al.* (2000), Wozencraft (2005, 2008).

12. Nilgiri Marten *Martes gwatkinsii*

French: Martre des Nilgiri / **German**: Südindischer Buntmarder / **Spanish**: Marta india

Taxonomy. *Martes gwatkinsii* Horsfield, 1851, Madras, India.

The Nilgiri Marten has been considered a subspecies of the Yellow-throated Marten by some authors. Monotypic.

Distribution. India (Western Ghats).

Descriptive notes. Head-body 50–70 cm (male), tail 35–50 cm (male); weight 1–3 kg (male). The Nilgiri Marten is very similar to the Yellow-throated Marten. The pelage is mostly dark brown; the shoulders and torso are rufous-brown. There are distinct rusty-yellow to lemon-yellow markings on the throat. The skull is low and flat.

Habitat. Forests, between 120 and 2383 m elevation.

Food and Feeding. Very little known, but there are reports of Nilgiri Martens preying on crows, Indian Giant Squirrels (*Ratufa indica*), Indian Spotted Chevrotains (*Tragulus meminna*), and Bengal monitor lizards (*Varanus bengalensis*), and feeding on honey and nectar.

Activity patterns. Appear to be diurnal. Nilgiri Martens are seen on the ground, but they at least partly arboreal as several recent sightings were of individuals in the canopy or in the hollows of trees (*Elaeocarpus* sp.).

Movements, Home range and Social organization. Solitary individuals and pairs have been seen.

Breeding. Nothing known.

Status and Conservation. CITES Appendix III (India). Classified as Vulnerable in IUCN Red List. Very little is known about this species; it is a high priority for field studies to learn more about its natural history, ecology, and conservation status.

Bibliography. Balakrishnan (2005), Christopher & Jayson (1996), Kurup & Joseph (2001), Madhusudan (1995), Pocock (1941a), Wirth & Van Rompaey (1991), Wozencraft (2005).

13. European Pine Marten *Martes martes*

French: Martre des pins / **German**: Baummarder / **Spanish**: Marta europea

Other common names: Pine Marten

Taxonomy. *Mustela martes* Linnaeus, 1758, Sweden.

At least thirteen subspecies have been proposed, but a taxonomic revision is needed.

Distribution. Most of Europe up to Russia (W Siberia) and major Mediterranean islands (Mallorca, Minorca, Corsica, Sardinia, and Sicily); also Middle East in Turkey, Caucasus, Iraq, and Iran.

Descriptive notes. Head-body 45–58 cm, tail 16–28 cm; weight 0·8–1·8 kg, adult males are larger than females. The European Pine Marten has a long body, short limbs, and a bushy tail about half of the head and body length. The pelage is yellowish-brown to dark brown, with a light yellow patch on the throat and chest. The underfur is dark on the sides (it is lighter in the Stone Marten). The rhinarium is black. The plantar soles are hairy. There are two pairs of mammae. Dental formula: I 3/3, C 1/1, P 4/4, M 1/2 = 38. The third upper premolar has outer edges that are slightly concave (they are convex in the Stone Marten).

Habitat. European Pine Martens are found in mature deciduous and coniferous forests. In Norway, they prefer spruce-dominated forests with large trees, and avoid clearcuts and open habitats. In north-east Belarus, the higher food abundance in woodlands on clay soil results in a higher population density and a more even distribution of European Pine Martens than in woodlands on sandy soil, where they mainly live in valley habitats.

Food and Feeding. The diet consists of small mammals (including mice, voles, and squirrels), birds, amphibians, invertebrates, honey, fruits, and berries. In western Scotland, European Pine Martens prey extensively on small mammals (particularly Field Voles *Microtus agrestis*) and birds. Invertebrates are also important dietary items, with a high intake of beetles (particularly *Geotrupes* sp.) from March to September. Predation on birds and the intake of earthworms is highest during the winter; fruits (bramble and rowan berries) are also important in autumn and late winter. In the Scottish Highlands, the diet is very varied and includes small mammals, large mammal carrion, birds, insects, and fruits. Small mammals are consistently important, whereas large mammal carrion, fruits and insects, are seasonal; birds are eaten at all times of the year, but are not a major part of the diet. Although appearing to be opportunist feeders, European Pine Martens did have strong food preferences: of the small mammals eaten, 94% were Field Voles. Insect species were also selectively eaten. Beetles (*Geotrupes stercorosus*, *Carabus* sp., and *Serica brunnea*) and Hymenoptera (*Vespula vulgaris* and *Bonibus* spp.) were consumed in large numbers when encountered. The diet indicated that European Pine Martens foraged on the ground, in glade areas within the forest, around night-time. In northern boreal Finland, the analysis of 5677 scats revealed that the European Pine Marten is an opportunistic generalist; its most favored food being small rodents (especially *Clethrionomys* sp.). Snow cover decreased the consumption of *Microtus* sp., but not *Clethrionomys* sp. or the Wood Lemming (*Myopus schisticolor*). Other food items were: Eurasian Red Squirrel (*Sciurus vulgaris*), Mountain Hare (*Lepus timidus*), carcasses of Reindeer, eggs, birds, common frog (*Rana temporaria*), berries, and mushrooms. In north-east Belarus, the diet includes rodents, birds, fruits, and carrion. In woodlands on sandy soil, European Pine Martens specialize in feeding on carrion in the cold season and on berries in the warm season. In winter, Bank Vole densities and the biomass of carrion are crucial food factors. In central Poland, where the European Pine Marten and Stone Marten are sympatric, both species feed mainly on small rodents, birds, and fruits. Although there is a high overlap in the trophic niches of both species, European Pine Martens feed more frequently on rodents and birds and Stone Martens on fruits and insects. In north-west Spain, mammals constitute the main prey all year round (50% ingested biomass), followed by fruit (28·1%), birds (20·9%), insects (0·8%) and reptiles (0·2%). Small mammals are the major prey species (41·6% ingested biomass), mainly *Apodemus* sp. (19·1%). Mammals are the most consumed prey in spring (65·8%) and winter (79·5%). However, in summer and autumn, European Pine Martens feed mainly on rowanberries (*Sorbus aucuparia*) (summer: 49·7%, autumn: 59·9%), followed by mammals (summer: 27·2%, autumn: 30·9%). On the island of Minorca, a total of 28 different food items were identified in 723 scats. Small mammals were the most important food overall, constituting 34% of the volume. During March to April, small mammals were the principal food consumed (63% of volume), followed by birds (19%). From May to June, birds were the main food (40%), followed by small mammals. Plant material and insects were the most important foods from July to August, when they made up 68% of the diet. Excess food may be cached for later use.

Activity patterns. Mainly nocturnal. On the island of Minorca, radio-collared European Pine Martens were primarily nocturnal, being active at night 53% of the time in autumn/winter and 59% in spring; daytime activity levels were 19% and 14%, respectively. In Poland, radio-telemetry revealed that 69% of the martens' active time was during the night. The activity rhythms of European Pine Martens vary between sexes and seasons. In spring, male activity peaks at 20:00–00:00 h, whereas in summer and autumn/winter, activity is bimodal, peaking at 18:00–22:00 h and 02:00–04:00 h. Female activity in spring is more evenly distributed than that of males, but in summer their activity peaks at 20:00–00:00 h. In autumn/winter, females have a bimodal rhythm, with peaks at 18:00–20:00 h and 02:00–06:00 h. In breeding females, activity rhythms change in the course of pregnancy and nursing. On average, European Pine Martens start their activity 73 min before sunset and finish 87 min after sunrise. Females became active earlier than males, but both sexes terminate their activity at the same time. On average, both sexes are active for around nine hours per day; they decrease their activity from 13 hours per day on warm days to 2·5 hours per day on cooler days. The number of activity bouts per day varies from one to six (mean 2·6); the activity bouts of males are significantly longer (4 hours, on average) than those of females (3 hours). In the cold season, the duration of short inactive bouts increases and inactivity lasts longer in females than in males. Den/rest sites are in hollow trees or logs, under debris, or under snow. In Great Britain, most dens are associated with trees (44·3%), rocks (27·6%) and buildings (13·8%); 69·6% of all dens are elevated, although only 9·8% are in elevated tree cavities, perhaps indicating a scarcity of arboreal cavities.

Movements, Home range and Social organization. European Pine Martens are terrestrial, but are also good climbers and will spend considerable time in trees exploring hollows and cavities in search of prey. Nightly movements may be up to 20–30 km. European Pine Martens are mostly solitary. Average home range size is 23 km² for males and 6·5 km² for females. There is little or no overlap between the ranges of individuals of the same sex, but male home ranges greatly overlap those of one or more females. Independent subadults are tolerated within the exclusive ranges of adults of the same sex. In Bialowieza National Park, Poland, the mean annual home range of males (2·58 km²) was larger than that of females (1·41 km²). Daily ranges averaged 49 ha in females and 54 ha in males and constituted 0·3% to 88% of annual home ranges. Seasonal home ranges also differed significantly between males and females. Both sexes held the smallest ranges in December to January; female ranges increased in April to May, whereas those of males increased in June to September when they were mating. There was very little home range overlap between neighboring males (mean 4–6%) or females (mean 6%). Year-round, neighboring individuals of the same sex neither avoided nor attracted each other and females attracted males only during the spring/summer mating season. Daily movement distance averaged 5·1 km and the mean speed was 0·6 km/h. With increasing temperature, European Pine Martens moved faster, covered longer distances, and used larger daily ranges. Mobility and home range use were affected by breeding activity. In spring, females rearing cubs had longer daily movement distances and moved faster than non-breeding females. In summer, males covered larger daily ranges during the mating period than outside it. On the island of Minorca, female home ranges were non-overlapping and averaged 0·47 km² (range = 0·31–0·66 km²); two male home ranges were partially exclusive, measuring 4·92 km² and 9·19 km²; male home ranges averaged 16 times greater than those of females. In Poland, population densities ranged from 3·6 to 7·6 individuals per 10 km².

Breeding. Mating occurs in mid-summer, but because of delayed implantation of the fertilized eggs into the uterus, births do not take place until March or April of the following year. Total gestation is 230–275 days. During the breeding season, captive females exhibited one to four periods of sexual receptivity, which usually lasted one to four days and recurred at intervals of 6–17 days. Litter size is two to eight, usually three to five. In Great Britain, natal dens comprise buildings (44·3%), trees (22·8%), other man-made structures (17·1%), and rocks (14·3%). At birth, the young weigh about 30 g. Their eyes open after 32–38 days, weaning occurs after six or seven weeks, and the young separate from the mother in the autumn. Sexual maturity is attained in the second year.

Status and Conservation. Classified as Least Concern in *The IUCN Red List*. The European Pine Marten was greatly hunted for its fur, leading to a serious decline of populations in the 1970s, but since then it has recovered in many areas.

Bibliography. Bermejo & Guitian (2000), Birks *et al.* (2005), Brainerd & Rolstad (2002), Clevenger (1993a, 1993b, 1993c), Coope (2007), Goszczynski *et al.* (2007), Posluszny *et al.* (2007), Pulliainen & Ollinmaki (1996), Putman (2000), Rosellini *et al.* (2007), Russell & Storch (2004), Selas (1991), Sidorovich *et al.* (2005), Stroganov (1969), Wozencraft (2005, 2008), Zalewski (2000, 2001), Zalewski *et al.* (1995, 2004).

14. Japanese Marten *Martes melampus*

French: Martre du Japon / **German**: Japanischer Marder / **Spanish**: Marta japonesa

Taxonomy. *Mustela melampus* Wagner, 1841, Japan.
Three subspecies are recognized.
Subspecies and Distribution.
M. m. melampus Wagner, 1841 – Japan (Honshu, Kyushu, Shikoku Is).
M. m. coreensis Kuroda & Mori, 1923 – North and South Korea.
M. m. tsuensis Thomas, 1897 – Japan (Tsushima I).
Introduced on Sado and Hokkaido Is.

Descriptive notes. Head-body 47–54·5 cm, tail 17–22·3 cm; average weight is 1·5 kg for males and 1 kg for females. The Japanese Marten has a long body, short limbs, and a bushy tail. The pelage is yellowish-brown to dark brown, with a conspicuous white patch on the throat and upper chest.

Habitat. Broadleaf forests.

Food and Feeding. The diet includes small mammals, birds, amphibians, invertebrates (insects, centipedes, spiders, crustaceans, earthworms), fruits, and seeds. In the Kuju Highland on Kyushu, the mean frequencies of occurrence of food items in scats were 79·7% animals and 51·1% plants. The diet comprised mainly insects, mammals, crustaceans, and 36 plant species. There were high frequencies of insects from June to October, mammals in February, April and December, crustaceans in August and October, and plants in October and December. Scats collected from the Tsushima Islands revealed that small mammals comprised a relatively stable proportion of the diet throughout the year (range 8·2 to 16·8%), whereas birds showed a peak from January (11·3%) to March (14·6%). Amphibians, mostly small adult frogs (*Rana tsushimensis*), were most common in the diet in February (9·7%). Insects were the most common animal prey, but their proportions in the diet varied greatly from 10·5% in May to 27·8% in August, and they were consistently least common throughout the winter. Centipedes (mostly *Scolopendra subspinipes*) were frequently eaten during May and June (16·9–17·4%). Plant materials were the most common of all foods throughout the year (28·8–53·9%). Berries and seeds occurred at the highest frequency in April (41%, especially *Rubus hirsutus* and *Elaeagnus pungens*) and in September (47·3%, especially *Vitis ficifolia* and *Ficus electa*).

Activity patterns. Primarily nocturnal. Resting sites are in trees and in ground burrows.

Movements, Home range and Social organization. On the Tsushima Islands, the mean home range size was 0·7 km² for eight males and 0·63 km² for three females; home ranges were not significantly different between the sexes and ranged from 0·5–1 km². There was little overlap of home ranges.

Breeding. Nothing known.

Status and Conservation. Classified as Least Concern in *The IUCN Red List*. The subspecies *M. m. tsuensis* is classified as Vulnerable. The Japanese Marten is trapped for its fur

during the hunting season (1 December to 31 January), except on Hokkaido Island. The subspecies *M. m. tsuensis*, found only on the Tsushima Islands, has been protected from trapping since 1971. Predation by feral dogs and highway mortality appear to be major threats.

Bibliography. Arai *et al.* (2003), Kuroda & Mori (1923), Otani (2002), Shusei *et al.* (2003), Tatara (1994), Tatara & Doi (1994), Wozencraft (2005).

15. Fisher *Martes pennanti*

French: Pékan / **German**: Fischermarder / **Spanish**: Marta pekan

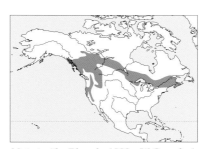

Taxonomy. *Mustela pennanti* Erxleben, 1777, Eastern Canada.
Recent molecular studies have suggested that the Fisher should be placed in its own genus, *Pekania*. Three subspecies are recognized.
Subspecies and Distribution.
M. p. pennanti Erxleben, 1777 – E Canada and NE USA.
M. p. columbiana Goldman, 1935 – W Canada and and USA (Rocky Mts).
M. p. pacifica Rhoads, 1898 – W Canada (coastal British Columbia) and W USA.

Descriptive notes. Head-body 55–65 cm (males), 45–55 cm (females); tail 30–50 cm (males), 30–40 cm (females); weight 3·5–5·5 kg (males), 2–2·5 kg (females), adult males are roughly twice the weight of females. The Fisher has a long body, short limbs, a bushy tail, and large feet with strong claws. It is the largest member of the genus *Martes*. The pelage is silvery-brown to black; the back of the neck and head are often grayish or silver. White markings on the throat and upper chest are common. The skull has a strong sagittal crest, which is particularly well-developed in older males. Dental formula: I 3/3, C 1/1, P 4/4, M 1/2 = 38.

Habitat. Fishers are found in dense forests with a closed canopy; they avoid open areas. In north-eastern Canada and United States, they also occur in fragmented, mixed woodlots interspersed with agricultural land. In California, mid-seral Douglas-fir (*Pseudotsuga menziesii*) and white fir (*Abies concolor*) forest types compose the greatest proportion of Fisher home ranges in the Coastal Mountains; the greatest proportion of home ranges in the Sierra Nevadas are in the intermediate tree size class with dense canopy closure, and in mixed conifer forests. In south-central Maine, Fishers use a variety of forest types, especially during summer. During winter, they hunt intensively in dense patches of coniferous undergrowth (where Snowshoe Hare tracks are common) and use deciduous stands less than expected by availability.

Food and Feeding. The diet includes lagomorphs (especially the Snowshoe Hare), North American Porcupines, ungulate carrion, small mammals, birds, reptiles, invertebrates, and fruit. During the winter in British Columbia, 18 types of mammalian and avian prey were found in 256 stomachs. The most commonly occurring prey species were Snowshoe Hares, Red Squirrels, and Southern Red-backed Voles. The diet varied between sexes: female fishers consumed small prey more frequently than did males. In the mountains of California's Sierra Nevada, where the Snowshoe Hare and North American Porcupine are absent, other mammals are the most frequent food item; however, reptiles (20·4%) and insects (55·7%) are major components of the diet, and at least six fungal species are also eaten. In the mixed-conifer forests of the southern Sierra Nevada, where Fishers and American Martens occur together, the diets of both species are more diverse than reported elsewhere in North America. Although the diet of Fishers includes more birds, lizards, hypogeous fungi, and insects than that of American Martens, the dietary overlap is high. The great diversity of the diet in these two species may be due to the absence or rarity of large prey (such as Snowshoe Hares and North American Porcupines) or to a greater diversity of available prey types in the southern Sierra Nevada compared to other areas. In south-eastern Manitoba, Fishers prey heavily on Snowshoe Hares (84·3% frequency occurrence). In Vermont, most of the diet is mammalian (72%), with avian prey (15%) and fruit (10%) of secondary importance. In south-central Maine, winter foods include apples, porcupines, hares, Eastern Gray Squirrels (*Sciurus carolinensis*), Red Squirrels, Northern Flying Squirrels (*Glaucomys sabrinus*), mice (*Peromyscus*), voles (*Clethrionomys gapperi* and *Microtus*), and shrews (*Sorex* and *Blarina*). The fall and winter diet in West Virginia and Maryland includes ten mammal species, four bird species, one gastropod species, and two types of vegetation. White-tailed Deer (*Odocoileus virginianus*) is the most frequent dietary component. Medium-sized mammals such as Northern Raccoon and small mammals such as *Peromyscus* sp. are also major dietary components, although small mammals occur less frequently than reported elsewhere. Diet overlap between the sexes was found to be considerable and differences between the sexes in the occurrence of major food groups (small mammals, medium-sized mammals, large mammals, birds, and fruit) were not significant. Hunting strategies vary with prey type. Snowshoe Hares are caught after rapid zig-zagging chases. Fishers hunt porcupines by searching for their dens. The arboreal skills of Fishers enable them to chase porcupines down trees to the ground, where they kill them after lengthy attacks, during which the Fisher repeatedly bites the porcupine's face (which is unprotected by quills).

Activity patterns. Active during the day and night; most activity occurs shortly before sunrise and after sunset. Males and females show similar amounts of activity, and both sexes are active more frequently in summer than winter. Den/rest sites are in hollow logs or trees, brush piles, or in rock crevices. Fishers in California select rest sites in forested areas that have dense canopies, large trees, and steep slopes. In the Coastal

Mountains and Sierra Nevada in California, standing trees (live and dead) are the most common resting structures, with California black oak (*Quercus kelloggii*) and Douglas-fir the most frequent species in the Sierra and Coastal areas, respectively. Resting structures are within the largest diameter trees available, averaging 117·3 cm for live conifers, 119·8 cm for conifer snags, and 69 cm for hardwoods. Females use cavity structures more often than males, while males use platform structures significantly more than females. The diversity of types and sizes of rest structures used by males suggests that males are less selective than females. In the Sierra Nevada study area, where surface water is less common, Fishers prefer rest sites within 100 m of water. In a central hardwood forest, Fishers were found to rest in hardwood, softwood, and mixedwood forest types in proportion to their availability in the summer, but tended to avoid hardwood areas in winter. They used nests, cavities, and burrows in proportion to their availability in winter, but in the summer, Fishers preferred nests to cavities, and burrows were not used. Males tended to use larger cavity trees and mixed forest stands more often than females. During spring, summer, and fall in south-central Maine, Fishers prefer using rest sites in the branches of conifers, within coniferous stands.

Movements, Home range and Social organization. Fishers are primarily terrestrial, but are also good tree climbers. They are capable of long movements in short time spans; individuals have been reported to move 90 km in three days, 45 km in two days, and 10–11 km in only a few hours. Usual daily movements are 1·5–3 km. Movements of males are greatest during the spring breeding season; non-reproductive females move similar distances during all seasons. Adult Fishers are solitary outside of the breeding season. Mean home range sizes are up to 40 km² for males and up to 20 km² for females. There is little overlap between the ranges of individuals of the same sex, but there is extensive overlap between the ranges of opposite sexes. In the Coastal Mountains and Sierra Nevada in California, the mean home range size of males (39·4 km²) was significantly greater than that of females (9·8 km²); the home ranges of females were significantly greater in the Coastal area than in the Sierras. In eastern Ontario, the mean adult home range size was 4·4 km², with up to 71% overlap of adjacent intrasexual home ranges. In Quebec, in an area where trapping had been prohibited for more than 20 years, mean home range size was 9·2 km² for adult males and 5·4 km² for adult females. In south-central Maine, the home ranges of females were stable between seasons and years, but males moved extensively from February through April, and their ranges shifted between years. Home ranges averaged 30·9 km² for males (range = 10·6–78·2 km²) and 16·3 km² for females (range = 8·1–39·1 km²). The ranges of adults usually did not overlap with others of the same sex, except for males during spring. Fishers of both sexes shifted or enlarged their ranges to include areas left vacant when others of the same sex were removed. Population density in preferred habitat is one per 2·6–7·5 km², but in other areas it may be as low as one per 200 km². The adult population density was calculated as 32·7/100 km² in eastern Ontario, 2·7/10 km² in Quebec, and 1/2·8–10·5 km² (summer) and 1/8·3–20 km² (winter) in south-central Maine.

Breeding. Mating occurs from March to May. Implantation of the fertilized eggs into the uterus is delayed and births occur from January to early April. Litter size is up to six, but averages two to three. Natal and maternal dens are located high up in hollow trees. The young weigh less than 50 g and are born with their eyes and ears closed. The eyes open around seven weeks, weaning begins after two to three months, and separation occurs in the fifth month. Females reach adult weight after six months and males after one year.

Status and Conservation. Classified as Least Concern in *The IUCN Red List*. Fishers are considered common throughout most of their range, particularly in Canada, but they may be threatened in the western USA. They are trapped for their fur. In the 19th and early 20th centuries, excessive fur trapping and habitat destruction through logging led to a decline in Fisher populations over most of its range. Closed hunting seasons, protective regulations, and reintroductions were then initiated in many areas. The Fisher has made a comeback in parts of the eastern United States, but it is still vulnerable in the western states, where it seems to be dependent on old-growth forests.

Bibliography. Arthur & Krohn (1991), Arthur *et al.* (1989a, 1989b), Dzialak *et al.* (2005), Garant & Crete (1997), Kilpatrick & Rego (1994), Koen *et al.* (2007), Koepfli *et al.* (2008), Paragi *et al.* (1994), Powell (1979, 1981, 1993), Powell *et al.* (2003), Raine (1983, 1987), Van Why & Giuliano (2001), Weir & Corbould (2007), Wozencraft (2005), Zielinski, Duncan *et al.* (1999), Zielinski, Truex *et al.* (2004a, 2004b).

16. Sable *Martes zibellina*

French: Martre zibeline / **German**: Zobel / **Spanish**: Marta cibelina

Taxonomy. *Mustela zibellina* Linnaeus, 1758, Russia.
Thirty subspecies have been proposed, but a taxonomic revision is needed.
Distribution. China, Japan (Hokkaido), Mongolia, North Korea, and Russia.
Descriptive notes. Head-body 38–56 cm (males), 35–51 cm (females); tail 12–19 cm (males), 11·5–17·2 cm (females); weight 800–1800 g (males), 700–1560 g (females), adult males are slightly larger than females. The Sable has a long body and short legs,

and a short bushy tail around a third of the head and body length. The pelage is long and silky, and varies from pale grayish-brown to dark brown, almost black. The summer pelage is shorter and darker. The top of the head is lighter than the body, and the white neck patch is vestigial. The soles are covered with extremely dense, stiff hairs. The skull is long and narrow. Dental formula: I 3/3, C 1/1, P 4/4, M 1/2 = 38.

Habitat. Sables are found in deciduous and coniferous forests, and often occur in mountain regions and near streams. They typically prefer mature forests of large trees with a dense canopy. In the Daxinganling Mountains, China, Sables prefer late succession mixed forests, with large trees and coarse woody debris, intermediate to dense tree canopy cover, and high densities and diameters of larch tree holes. They avoid open areas, but use the middle of slopes and slope bottoms, and rest on ridge tops with abundant logs, boles, or roots.

Food and Feeding. The diet consists mostly of small mammals (rodents, pikas, hares), but also includes birds, reptiles, amphibians, fish, insects, fruits, honey, nuts, and berries. The summer diet in the Middle Yenisei taiga, Siberia, comprises microtine rodents, mainly Northern Red-backed Voles *Clethrionomys rutilus* (52·3% of the biomass). Plant food (seeds of Siberian pine *Pinus sibirica* and berries of *Vaccinium* sp.) is also frequently eaten (79·4% of scats and 19·9% of biomass). Shrews, birds, and insects are supplementary food (25% of biomass). In the Daxinganling Mountains, China, the winter diet is mainly small mammals (54·1%), berries and pine nuts (32·4%), birds (12·5%), eggs (2·2%), and ants (1%). The main small mammal prey is Gray Red-backed Voles (*Clethrionomys rufocanus*) and Northern Red-backed Voles (*Myodes rutilus*), followed by Mountain Hares (*Lepus timidus*) and Siberian Chipmunks (*Eutamias sibiricus*). Birds include hazel grouses *Tetrastes bonasia* (8·1%), Eurasian jays *Garrulus glandarius* (0·7%), and great tits *Parus major* (0·5%). Plant items include berries of *Vaccinium vitisideae* (20·9%) and pine nuts of *Pinus pumila* (8·8%). In north-eastern China, remains of mammals were found in 89% of scats, followed in frequency by soft and hard mast, and birds. Sables selected for *C. rufocanus* more than shrews (*Sorex caecutiens*), but ate *C. rutilus* in proportion to its availability. In eastern Hokkaido, Japan, the diet includes mammals, insects, plants, birds, reptiles, amphibians, fish, and crustaceans. Mammals are the commonest food items throughout the year, with voles *Clethrionomys* sp. (frequency of occurrence 56·5%), Siberian Chipmunks (19·3%) and mice *Apodemus* sp. (14·6%), most often found in scats. Insects are eaten mainly in the summer (48·8%) and less often in other seasons (9·3% on average). Plant materials, chiefly fruits, are consumed mainly in autumn (45·7%) and winter (68·4%), but are rare in the diet during spring (5·1%) and summer (1·3%).

Activity patterns. Active both during the day and at night. In the Daxinganling Mountains, China, radio-collared Sables were found to be nocturnal in spring and winter, and diurnal in summer and autumn. Den/rest sites are in holes among or under rocks, in hollow logs, under tree roots, or in burrows (which may be several meters long and lead to an enlarged nest chamber lined with dry vegetation and fur). In Japan, Sables prefer resting in dense tree forests that have many tree species and woody debris.

Movements, Home range and Social organization. Sables are mainly terrestrial, but are also good tree climbers. They are solitary outside of the breeding season. Home ranges may be up to 30 km², especially in the desolate forests of Siberia. In the Daxinganling Mountains, China, the average home range size of males was 13·03 km² and 7·18 km² for females. There was considerable overlap of home ranges between males and females (average 62%), but virtually no overlap between male individuals. In a cool-temperate mixed forest in Japan, home ranges were 0·50–1·78 km² (mean 1·12 km²); the home ranges of some individuals overlapped extensively. Reported population densities vary from one per 1·5 km² in pine forests to one per 25 km² in larch forests.

Breeding. Mating occurs from June to August. Implantation of the fertilized eggs into the uterus is delayed and births occur the following spring, in April or May. Total gestation is 250–300 days; actual embryonic development is 25–40 days. Litter size is one to five, usually three or four. The young weigh 30–35 g at birth, open their eyes after 30–36 days, emerge from the den at 38 days, and are weaned after seven weeks. Sexual maturity is reached at 15–16 months.

Status and Conservation. Classified as Least Concern in *The IUCN Red List*. The Sable is considered common throughout most of its distribution. It is hunted for its fur, which is one of the most valuable furs produced in Europe and Asia. Sables are also raised on fur farms to help sustain the fur trade; over 25,000 are harvested annually. This species was once common in China, but is now considered rare.

Bibliography. Brzezinski (1994), Buskirk *et al.* (1996a, 1996b), Ma *et al.* (1999), Miyoshi & Higashi (2005), Murakami (2003), Stroganov (1969), Wozencraft (2005, 2008), Xu, Jiang, Ma, Jin *et al.* (1996), Xu, Jiang, Ma, Li & Buskirk (1997), Zhang & Ma (2000).

Plate 34 ➤

PLATE 34

inches 8

cm 20

17

18

19

20

21

22

23

24

25

26

Subfamily HELICTIDINAE

Genus *MELOGALE*

Geoffroy Saint-Hilaire, 1831

17. Bornean Ferret-badger *Melogale everetti*

French: Mélogale d'Everett / **German:** Borneo-Sonnendachs / **Spanish:** Melandro de Borneo

Taxonomy. *Helictis everetti* Thomas, 1895, Borneo.
Some authors consider *M. everetii* and/or *orientalis* as conspecific with *M. personata*. Monotypic.
Distribution. N Borneo.
Descriptive notes. Head-body 35–40 cm, tail 16–17 cm; weight 1–2 kg. The Bornean Ferret-badger has a small, slender body and a long snout. The dorsal pelage is dark brown throughout, including the tail. The undersides are paler. The head is black with a facial mask that consists of white or yellow patches, which are variable in size and shape. The claws on the forefeet are well-developed for digging. The skull and teeth are small.
Habitat. Forests and grasslands, from 900 to 3000 m.
Food and Feeding. The diet is said to include insects and other invertebrates, small vertebrates, and fruits.
Activity patterns. Reported to be nocturnal. Rest sites are in holes or rock crevices.
Movements, Home range and Social organization. Appears to be solitary. Mainly terrestrial, but also reported to be an agile tree climber.
Breeding. A litter of three is said to be common.
Status and Conservation. Classified as Data Deficient in *The IUCN Red List*. The only recorded sightings of Bornean Ferret-badgers have occurred on the Kinabalu massif, near and within the National Park. There is no information on its susceptibility to habitat change or what hunting levels occur in its range. Very little is known about this species and field studies are needed to learn more about its natural history, ecology, and conservation status.
Bibliography. Dinets (2003), IUCN (2008), Lekagul & McNeely (1991), Long & Killingley (1983), Neal & Cheeseman (1996), Payne *et al.* (1985), Wozencraft (2005).

18. Small-toothed Ferret-badger *Melogale moschata*

French: Mélogale de Chine / **German:** China-Sonnendachs / **Spanish:** Melandro chino
Other common names: Chinese Ferret-badger

Taxonomy. *Helictis moschata* Gray, 1831, S China.
Six subspecies are recognized.
Subspecies and Distribution.
M. m. moschata Gray, 1831 – SE China (Guangdong, Guangxi, Guizhou, Yunnan & Hainan I) and N Laos.
M. m. ferreogrisea Hilzheimer, 1905 – C China.
M. m. millsi Thomas, 1922 – S China (NW Yunnan) through N Myanmar to NE India.
M. m. sorella G. M. Allen, 1929 – E China (Fujian).
M. m. subaurantiaca Swinhoe, 1862 – Taiwan.
M. m. taxilla Thomas, 1925 – Vietnam.
Descriptive notes. Head-body 30–40 cm, tail 10–15 cm; weight 0·8–1·6 kg. The tail is less than half of the head and body length. The Small-toothed Ferret-badger has a small, slender body and a long snout. The pelage varies from gray to black, with the darker fur contrasting with the light patches on the neck and head. The head has a distinct black-and-white pattern, generally with more black than the Large-toothed Ferret-badger but this is quite variable. The white stripe on the top of the head is narrow and incomplete and rarely extends past the shoulders. The tail is bushy, pale brown in color, and with a white tip. The limbs are short, and the feet have strong, thick, fairly straight claws. There are two pairs of mammae. The skull is long, high, and smooth, with widely separated temporal ridges. Dental formula: I 3/3, C 1/1, P 4/4, M 1/2 = 38. The teeth are relatively small, compared to Large-toothed Ferret-badger, with distinct gaps between the premolars. In the upper jaw: labial edge of P⁴ is slightly concave; P⁴ length over 6 mm; P¹ is slightly smaller than P². In the lower jaw: M₁ talonid is without distinct cusps.
Habitat. Tropical and subtropical forests, wooded hillsides, grasslands, and cultivated areas. Often occurs in close proximity to humans.
Food and Feeding. The diet is said to include invertebrates (insects, earthworms), small mammals, birds, frogs, lizards, eggs, and fruits. In Taiwan, invertebrates had a relative importance index of 89%. In China, 163 scats contained 33% seeds and at least eight plant species. Small-toothed Ferret-badgers find food mainly by smell and sound and use their digging claws and probing snouts to dig for roots and earthworms.
Activity patterns. Nocturnal and crepuscular. Active year-round, but less active during the winter months. During the spring, both sexes are active outside their burrows for around eight hours; during the winter this decreases to less than six-and-a-half hours. Rest sites are in burrows, rock crevices, or in trees. In south-east China, radio-collared Small-toothed Ferret-badgers used a variety of shelters as daybeds including rodent dens (47%), firewood stacks (20%), open fields (17%), and rock piles around houses (5%). The distance between daily resting sites averaged 101 m and they often (51% of occasions) returned to rest sites used the previous day.
Movements, Home range and Social organization. Small-toothed Ferret-badgers are solitary and mainly terrestrial, but they may climb trees. In south-east China, the size of resting home ranges (daybed locations only) of six radio-collared individuals averaged 11 ha (range 1–25 ha); no sex-specific differences in home range size were detected.
Breeding. Mating occurs in March. In south-east China, capture data suggests that Small-toothed Ferret-badgers give birth in May. Gestation is from 60 to 80 days. Litter size is usually one to four. The young are born blind and well-furred; the eyes remain closed for at least two weeks. There is one record of a female still nursing two nearly full-grown young in June.
Status and Conservation. Classified as Least Concern in *The IUCN Red List*. Very little is known about Small-toothed Ferret-badgers and more field studies are needed to learn more about their natural history, ecology, and conservation status. In Laos and Vietnam, there is often some confusion between Small-toothed and Large-toothed Ferret Badgers, so careful distinction between these two species needs to be made in these two countries. Small-toothed Ferret-badgers are hunted for their fur and meat in China and north-east India; in China, their fur is used for collars and jackets.
Bibliography. Allen (1929), Francis (2008), Lekagul & McNeely (1991), Neal (1986), Storz & Wozencraft (1999), Wang & Fuller (2003a), Wozencraft (2005, 2008), Zhou *et al.* (2008).

19. Javan Ferret-badger *Melogale orientalis*

French: Mélogale de Java / **German:** Java-Sonnendachs / **Spanish:** Melandro javanés

Taxonomy. *Gulo orientalis* Horsfield, 1821, Java.
The Javan Ferret-badger was previously considered a subspecies of the Large-toothed Ferret-badger. Two subspecies are recognized.
Subspecies and Distribution.
M. o. orientalis Horsfield, 1821 – E Java and Bali.
M. o. sundaicus Sody, 1937 – W Java.
Descriptive notes. Head-body 35–40 cm, tail 16–17 cm; weight about 2 kg. The Javan Ferret-badger has a small, slender body, and a long snout. The pelage is dark brown, with paler undersides. The head is black with a facial mask consisting of white or yellow patches. The skull is small.
Habitat. Forests and grasslands.
Food and Feeding. Said to be omnivorous.
Activity patterns. Reported to be nocturnal.
Movements, Home range and Social organization. Terrestrial, but also said to be an agile tree climber.
Breeding. Litter size is said to vary from one to three.
Status and Conservation. Classified as Data Deficient in *The IUCN Red List*. Recorded recently in Central Java (perhaps Dieng Plateau), Gunung Halimun Nature Reserve, and Gunung Gede. Very little is known about this species and field studies are needed to learn more about its natural history, ecology, and conservation status.
Bibliography. IUCN (2008), Lekagul & McNeeley (1991), Long (1992), Long & Killingley (1983), Neal & Cheeseman (1996), Pocock (1941a), Riffel (1991), Wozencraft (2005).

20. Large-toothed Ferret-badger *Melogale personata*

French: Mélogale indien / **German:** Burma-Sonnendachs / **Spanish:** Melandro birmano
Other common names: Burmese Ferret-badger

Taxonomy. *Melogale personata* Geoffroy Saint-Hilaire, 1831, Southern Burma.
Three subspecies are recognized.
Subspecies and Distribution.
M. p. personata Geoffroy Saint-Hilaire, 1831 – NE India to S Myanmar and Thailand.
M. p. nipalensis Hodgson, 1836 – Nepal.
M. p. pierrei Bonhote, 1903 – Cambodia, China, Laos, and Vietnam.
Descriptive notes. Head-body 35–40 cm, tail 15–21 cm; weight 1·5–3 kg. The tail is

On following pages: 21. Lesser Grison (*Galictis cuja*); 22. Greater Grison (*Galictis vittata*); 23. Marbled Polecat (*Vormela peregusna*); 24. Saharan Striped Polecat (*Ictonyx libycus*); 25. Zorilla (*Ictonyx striatus*); 26. African Striped Weasel (*Poecilogale albinucha*).

over half the head and body length. The Large-toothed Ferret-badger has a small, slender body and a long snout. The pelage is coarse, thick and short, and varies from fawn brown to dark brown. The sides of the body are heavily frosted white, contrasting slightly with the darker back. The white stripe on the back of the neck extends at least to the middle of the back, and often as far as the base of the tail. The head has a distinct pattern of black (or dark brown) and white patches, which varies among individuals. The bushy tail is pale and usually white on the distal half. The sagittal crest on the skull is large and low. Dental formula: I 3/3, C 1/1, P 4/4, M 1/2 = 38. The teeth are larger than Small-toothed Ferret-badger, especially P⁴. In the upper jaw: P⁴ length over 8 mm; P¹ is significantly smaller than P².

Habitat. Reported to live in forests, grasslands, and agricultural areas.

Food and Feeding. The diet is said to include insects, earthworms, snails, small vertebrates (lizards, frogs, rodents, small birds), fruit, nuts, and eggs.

Activity patterns. Reported to be nocturnal. Rests in underground burrows or under rocks during the day.

Movements, Home range and Social organization. Believed to be solitary. Mainly terrestrial, but also said to be an agile tree climber.

Breeding. Litter size is reported to be up to three, with the young usually born in May and June.

Status and Conservation. Classified as Data Deficient in *The IUCN Red List*. Very little is known about this species and field studies are needed to learn more about its natural history, ecology, and conservation status. In Laos and Vietnam, there is often some confusion between Small-toothed and Large-toothed Ferret Badgers, so careful distinction between these two species needs to be made in these two countries.

Bibliography. Francis (2008), Lekagul & McNeely (1991), Long & Killingley (1983), Neal & Cheeseman (1996), Pocock (1941a), Wozencraft (2005, 2008).

Subfamily GALICTIDINAE

Genus *GALICTIS*

Bell, 1826

21. Lesser Grison *Galictis cuja*

French: Petit Grison / **German**: Kleingrison / **Spanish**: Grisón chico

Taxonomy. *Mustela cuja* Molina, 1782, Chile.

Four subspecies are recognized.

Subspecies and Distribution.

G. c. cuja Molina, 1782 – W Argentina and Chile.

G. c. furax Thomas, 1907 – NE Argentina, C & E Brazil, Paraguay, and Uruguay.

G. c. huronax Thomas, 1921 – C and S Argentina.

G. c. luteola Thomas, 1907 – W Bolivia and SE Peru.

Descriptive notes. Head-body 28–50·8 cm, tail 12–19·3 cm; weight 1–2·5 kg. The Lesser Grison has a long body and short limbs. The pelage is yellowish-gray to brown; the face, throat, upper chest, and limbs are black. A white stripe extends across the forehead and down the sides of the neck, separating the black of the face from the gray or brown of the back. The claws are strong and curved. Dental formula: I 3/3, C 1/1, P 3/3, M 1/2 = 34.

Habitat. Lesser Grisons are found in a wide variety of habitats, from sea level to 4200 m, including seashore, arid scrub, chaco desert, Gran Chaco, Chiquitano woodland, open thorn woodland, cerrado, caatinga, savannah, steppes, evergreen shrublands, semi-deciduous lower montane forest, brushy areas below the timberline, Tucuman-Bolivian woodlands, wet forest, Brazilian Atlantic forest, high Andean shrublands, *Polylepis* woodlands, puna grasslands, marshes, high elevation wet meadows "bofedales", *Equisetum*-dominated scrub, overgrazed pastures, and agricultural areas of the Pampas. Most localities in Bolivia are between 2000 and 4200 m. Lesser Grisons frequently occur near water.

Food and Feeding. The diet includes small mammals (especially rodents and lagomorphs), birds, eggs, amphibians, reptiles, invertebrates, and fruit. In central Chile, the diet was found to consist of 35·2% rodents, 26·5% introduced European Rabbits (*Oryctolagus cuniculus*), 20·7% unidentified mammals, 14·7% reptiles (*Liolaemus chiliensis* and *Philodryas chamissonis*), and 2·9% unidentified passeriform birds. Average prey weight was 350 g. In Patagonia, Argentina, the diet is 46·3% rodents, 18·9% lagomorphs, 17·9% lizards, and 16·8% birds; as lagomorph density increases, its percentage in the diet increases up to 96·8%. In coastal south-eastern Argentine, mammals, including rodents (79·1%, at least eight species) and European Hare *Lepus europaeus* (20·9%), are the main prey items year-round; birds (7·8%) and invertebrates (5·2%) are also eaten. Lesser Grisons frequently prey on guinea pigs and are capable of running down and killing Dwarf Cavies (*Microcavia australis*).

Activity patterns. Active mainly during the day, with occasional activity at night. Rest sites are in hollow trees, crevices, boulder piles, burrows of other animals, at the base of *Polylepis* trees, amongst tree roots and rocks, or in banks adjacent to wet meadows at high elevations. Four or five individuals may occupy a burrow system, which may reach

4 m in depth. One burrow system occupied by five individuals in Chile was on a slope among rocks and roots of a *Guevina avellana* tree in *Nothofagus obliqua* woods; leaves of *Greiga* obscured the entrances.

Movements, Home range and Social organization. Mostly solitary, although pairs or small groups are occasionally seen.

Breeding. Gestation is around 39 days. Litter size is two to five. Offspring have been observed in March, August, September, and October.

Status and Conservation. Classified as Least Concern in *The IUCN Red List*. Lesser Grisons are generally considered not to be threatened, but field studies are needed to learn more about their natural history, ecology, and conservation status.

Bibliography. Wozencraft (2005), Yensen & Tarifa (2003b), Zapata *et al.* (2005).

22. Greater Grison *Galictis vittata*

French: Grand Grison / **German**: Großer Grison / **Spanish**: Grisón

Taxonomy. *Viverra vittata* Schreber, 1776, Surinam.

Four subspecies are recognized.

Subspecies and Distribution.

G. v. vittata Schreber, 1776 – the Guianas and Venezuela.

G. v. andina Thomas, 1903 – Bolivia and Peru.

G. v. brasiliensis Thunberg, 1820 – Brazil.

G. v. canaster Nelson, 1901 – Mexico to Colombia and Ecuador.

Descriptive notes. Head-body 47·5–55 cm, tail 16 cm; weight 1·4–3·3 kg. The Greater Grison has a long body and short limbs. The pelage is smoky gray on the upper sides; the face, throat, undersides, and all four limbs are black. A white stripe extends across the forehead and down the sides of the neck, separating the black of the face from the gray or brown of the back. The skull is strong and massive. Dental formula: I 3/3, C 1/1, P 3/3, M 1/2 = 34.

Habitat. Greater Grisons are found in virgin and secondary low-elevation rainforests, lower montane forests, upland monte alto forests, tropical dry forests, closed deciduous forests, cerrado, yungas woodlands, shrub woodlands, chaco, palm savannah, secondary growth, open fields, plantations, and partially flooded rice fields adjacent to ranches. They are often found near rivers, streams, and wetlands, from sea level to 1500 m elevation, but mostly below 500 m. However, on the east slopes of the Andes Mountains in Bolivia they range up to 2000 m. A radio-collared female spent 27·8% of her time in open habitats (69·2% of her prey came from there); the remaining 72·2% was spent in closed woodlands and forests (where she obtained 27·8% of her prey).

Food and Feeding. The diet includes small mammals, birds, eggs, amphibians, reptiles, invertebrates, and fruit. In Venezuela, seven stomachs contained remains of diurnal rodents (*Sigmodon alstoni*), a lizard (*Ameiva ameiva*), a dove (*Zenaida auriculata*), and an eel-like fish. Two other stomachs contained an opossum (*Didelphis marsupialis*), an unidentified rodent, a lizard (*Ameiva ameiva*), and an amphibian (*Colestethus auriculata*). In Para, Brazil, a Greater Grison was observed carrying a large toad (*Bufo marinus*) in its mouth, apparently unaffected by the toad's toxic skin glands. In Panama, a Greater Grison was seen pursuing an Agouti (*Dasyprocta punctata*) at 08:15 h; another Agouti was attacked in a river at midday. In Peru, a Greater Grison was observed eating a piranha-like characin fish. In north-eastern Brazil, Greater Grisons are major predators of Rock Cavies or Mocos (*Kerodon rupestris*), which they attack in their burrows. The stomachs of two males and two females contained Moco remains and another species of cavy (*Galea spixii*). Greater Grisons hunt alone, in pairs, or in small family groups. An adult female was seen travelling in association with a nearly grown male and a three-fourths grown female.

Activity patterns. Primarily diurnal, but occasionally active at night. A captive male from Ecuador was nearly 100% diurnal, with a rest period of several hours at midday. Three captive Greater Grisons in Panama were very active in the early morning and late afternoon and rested for four to five hours around midday. Greater Grisons forage during the day at Cocha Cashu, Peru. However, in Venezuela, a radio-collared individual was active for 10–12 h per day, mostly at night (77·1% of the time); all sightings were in the daytime (06:00–11:25 h). Rest sites are under tree roots or in hollow logs, underground burrows, or rock cavities.

Movements, Home range and Social organization. Primarily terrestrial, but also excellent swimmers and able to climb trees. In Venezuela, two individuals were observed climbing into a tree, and on another occasion, a female and a young climbed 2 m into a palm tree, while an adult male waited below looking upward. The two grisons scratched around in the tree, knocking down wood and debris, which were examined by the male. Greater Grisons are mostly solitary, but occasionally travel in pairs or small groups. One female in Venezuela had a home range of 4·2 km². She traveled 1 km (straight line) between consecutive daily rest sites and moved 2–3 km per 24-h period. Population densities have been estimated at 1–2·4 individuals/km², but radio-tracking data suggests much lower densities.

Breeding. Gestation is around 39 days. Litter size is one to four. Offspring have been observed in March, August, September, and October. A neonate female, with umbilical cord still attached, weighed less than 50 g. She was covered in short fur and her eyes were closed. The eyes opened after two weeks, and by three weeks she could eat meat. Full growth was reached by four months. The testes of three captive males descended at c. four months of age.

Status and Conservation. Classified as Least Concern in *The IUCN Red List*. Greater Grisons are considered endangered in some parts of their range, such as Mexico and Costa Rica. In Venezuela, they are threatened by hunting and habitat destruction. Greater Grisons occur in medium (860 ha) and large (36,000 ha) fragments in Brazilian Atlantic forests, but are absent from small (60–80 ha) patches of forest. Their fur has no commercial value, but skins and live animals are sold as decorations or pets.
Bibliography. Wozencraft (2005), Yensen & Tarifa (2003a).

Genus *VORMELA*
Blasius, 1884

23. Marbled Polecat *Vormela peregusna*
French: Zorille marbrée / **German**: Tigeriltis / **Spanish**: Turón jaspeado

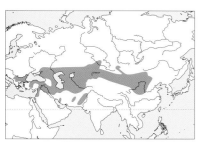

Taxonomy. *Mustela peregusna* Güldenstädt, 1770, Russia.
Six subspecies are recognized.
Subspecies and Distribution.
V. p. peregusna Güldenstädt, 1770 – Russia.
V. p. alpherakii Birula, 1910 – Afghanistan, Iran, Pakistan, Tajikistan, Turkmenistan, and Uzbekistan.
V. p. euxina Pocock, 1936 – Bulgaria, Greece, Macedonia, Montenegro, Romania, Serbia, Turkey, and Ukraine.
V. p. negans G. S. Miller, 1910 – NC & W China and S Mongolia.
V. p. pallidior Stroganov, 1948 – Kazakhstan.
V. p. syriaca Pocock, 1936 – Armenia, Azerbaidjan, Egypt, Georgia, Iraq, Israel, Lebanon, and Syria.
Descriptive notes. Head-body 31–32·6 cm (males), 28·8–47·7 cm (females), tail 16·5–17·5 cm (males), 15·5–17·8 cm (females); weight 330–715 g (males), 295–600 g (females), adult males are slightly larger than females. The Marbled Polecat has a long body and short limbs. The pelage is yellowish and is mottled with reddish or brown markings. The ears are large and white, the muzzle is short, and there is a conspicuous white stripe across the head. The area around the mouth is white. The fur is black around the eyes, giving a masked appearance. The tail is bushy and covered with black and white hairs. The limbs are short and the feet have long claws. There are five pairs of mammae. The skull is short and broad. Dental formula: I 3/3, C 1/1, P 3/3, M 1/2 = 34.
Habitat. The Marbled Polecat is found in open desert, semi-desert, semi-arid rocky areas in upland valleys, steppe country, arid subtropical scrub forest, and low hill ranges. It is generally not found on higher mountain ranges, but has been recorded up to 2100 m. In Europe, the Marbled Polecat inhabits steppes with sparse hawthorn bush and sloe trees, and old fields. In western Yugoslavia, they occur in montane-steppe and woodland-steppe areas. In eastern Yugoslavia, Marbled Polecats are found from river terraces and low hills to mountainous meadows. In western Serbia, they inhabit the outskirts of settlements. On the Sinai Peninsula in Egypt, one adult male was captured in a sparsely vegetated sandy area. In Lebanon, Marbled Polecats are restricted to cultivated areas in close association with humans. In Israel, they live in the steppes and hills. In Central Asia, the Marbled Polecat is found in oases, tugai (river-valley complexes of forest, scrub, and meadow), dunes with sparse bush vegetation, clay steppes, and salt marshes; it is also found in irrigated country, melon patches, and vegetable fields, and sometimes enters buildings to forage. In Kazakhstan, Marbled Polecats are found in shifting dune country containing saxaul (*Haloxylon*), winter fat (*Eurotia ceratoides*), and pea trees, and in salt marshes overgrown in saxaul. Marbled Polecats are also found in wormwood deserts, semi-deserts, and occasionally fescue and needle-grass steppes of the foothills. In north-western China and the Ordos Desert, the Marbled Polecat occurs in forested areas, and in Siberia, it inhabits the western foothills of the Altai and the Cuya steppe.
Food and Feeding. The diet includes small mammals (ground squirrels *Spermophilus* sp., Gray Dwarf Hamsters *Cricetulus migratorius*, Libyan Jirds *Meriones libycus*, mice, voles, and rabbits), birds, reptiles, amphibians, snails, insects, and fruits. In Quetta and Kandahar, rodents, small birds, lizards, snails, and beetles are eaten. In Israel, Marbled Polecats show a high seasonal variability in the diet. During summer, mole crickets (*Gryllotalpa gryllotalpa*) make up 66% of the diet, whereas in winter, 62% of the diet is rodents, such as voles (*Microtus guentheri*), House Mice (*Mus musculus*), Lesser Blind Mole Rats (*Spalax leococon ehrenbergi*), and *Meriones* sp. Marbled Polecats may take small poultry. Excess food may be cached for later use. The eyesight of Marbled Polecats is quite weak and they rely principally on a well-developed sense of smell. They have two kinds of killing bites: the first is the penetration of the prey's body by the canines, the second is crushing the prey without canine penetration. To kill small vertebrate prey, Marbled Polecats crush the thorax. If the prey struggles, they may pin the prey down with the forepaws and deliver headshakes or follow up by a bite to head or neck. On large prey, such as Guinea Pigs (*Cavia porcellus*), a Marbled Polecat bites the nape of the neck and eventually severs the spinal column at the base of the skull. With rats, it bites the throat. Fleeing prey are bitten dorsally, but defending prey are bitten on the head and neck.
Activity patterns. Mainly nocturnal and crepuscular, but sometimes active during the day. Den/rest sites are in burrows of large ground squirrels or other rodents, or they

dig their own dens. Marbled Polecats in Central Asia live in tunnel systems dug by the Great Gerbil (*Rhombomys opinus*). In Baluchistan, they live in burrows dug by the rodents or they may use underground irrigation tunnels. Sleeping chambers are 60–100 cm from the den entrance. In winter, they line the den with grass. When a Marbled Polecat digs, it presses its chin and hindpaws firmly to the ground and removes earth with its forelegs. Obstacles such as roots are pulled out with the teeth.
Movements, Home range and Social organization. Marbled Polecats are good climbers, but feed mainly on the ground. Nightly movements may be up to 1 km. They are solitary except during the breeding season. In Israel, home ranges were 0·5–0·6 km²; there were some overlaps of ranges and some encounters between individuals, but each animal foraged and rested alone.
Breeding. Mating occurs from March to early June. Pregnant females have been observed in January, February, and May. In Israel, it is estimated that births occur from early February to early March. In Kazakhstan and Central Asia, Marbled Polecats give birth in February or March. Delayed implantation of the fertilized eggs into the uterus occurs and the total gestation length is from 243 to 327 days. Litter size is four to eight. Only the mother cares for the young, which are reared in a nest of grass and leaves within a burrow. The eyes do not open until 40 days, but the young begin eating solid food at 30 days. Weaning occurs at 50–54 days and dispersal occurs at 61–68 days. Females attain adult size and sexual maturity at three months; males reach adult size at five months and sexual maturity at one year.
Status and Conservation. Classified as Vulnerable in *The IUCN Red List*. The subspecies *V. p. peregusna* is classified as Vulnerable. The major threat to this species is the loss of natural steppe and desert habitats. Steppe habitats are declining in Europe as they are converted to farmland. Secondary poisoning by rodenticides and population declines in key prey species may also be threats. Small numbers of Marbled Polecats are harvested for fur in Pakistan and Lebanon.
Bibliography. Ben-David (1998), Ben-David et al. (1991), Gorsuch & Larivière (2005), Qumsiyeh (1996), Wozencraft (2005, 2008).

Genus *ICTONYX*
Kaup, 1835

24. Saharan Striped Polecat *Ictonyx libycus*
French: Zorille de Libye / **German**: Streifenwiesel / **Spanish**: Hurón del Sahara
Other common names: Saharan Striped Weasel

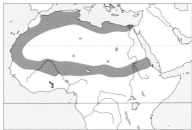

Taxonomy. *Mustela libyca* Hemprich & Ehrenberg, 1833, Libya.
Four subspecies are recognized.
Subspecies and Distribution.
I. l. libycus Hemprich & Ehrenberg, 1833 – Algeria, Morocco, Libya, and Tunisia.
I. l. multivittata Wagner, 1841 – E Chad and C Sudan.
I. l. oralis Thomas & Hinton, 1920 – Egypt, Eritrea, and N Sudan.
I. l. rothschildi Thomas & Hinton, 1920 – Burkina Faso, Mali, Mauritania, Niger, Nigeria, and Senegal.
Descriptive notes. Head-body 20·7–26 cm, tail 11·4–18 cm; weight 200–600 g, adult males are slightly larger than females. The Saharan Striped Polecat has a black and white pelage, with poorly defined black and white stripes along the sides of the body. The head is black with a white patch on the upper lip; there is a large white mark on the forehead. The limbs are short. The tail is short and bushy, and mostly white except for the black tip. There are four pairs of mammae. The skull is small, with a short rostrum. Dental formula: I 3/3, C 1/1, P 3/3, M 1/2 = 34.
Habitat. Sub-desert habitats, especially stony areas, steppes, and areas of sparse brush. Also found in cultivated areas and coastal sand dunes.
Food and Feeding. The diet apparently consists of rodents, small birds, eggs, lizards, and insects. Food is located by smell and by sound, and the front claws are used to dig up food items.
Activity pattern. Nocturnal. Rest sites are in burrows or rock crevices.
Movements, Home range and Social organization. Mostly solitary.
Breeding. Gestation is 37 to 77 days. Litter size is one to three. The young are born from January to March. They are born blind and covered with short hair. In captivity, neonates were 5 g at birth; they took some solid food after five weeks, and weighed 250 g at two months.
Status and Conservation. Classified as Least Concern in *The IUCN Red List*. A poorly known species and field studies are needed to learn more about its natural history, ecology, and conservation status.
Bibliography. Hufnagl (1972), Niethammer (1987), Rosevear (1974), Setzer (1957), Sitek (1995), Wozencraft (2005).

25. Zorilla *Ictonyx striatus*
French: Zorille commune / **German**: Zorilla / **Spanish**: Hurón estriado
Other common names: Striped Polecat

Taxonomy. *Bradypus striatus* Perry, 1810, South Africa.

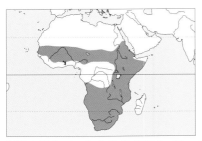

As many as twenty-two subspecies have been proposed, but a taxonomic revision is needed.

Distribution. Sub-Saharan Africa from Mauritania and Senegal in the W to Sudan, Ethiopia and Djibouti in the E and S to South Africa. Absent from W & C African rainforests.

Descriptive notes. Head-body 28–38 cm (males), 28–34 cm (females), tail 16·5–28 cm (males), 17·5–28 cm (females); weight 0·80–1·20 kg (males), 0·42–0·75 kg (females), adult males are 50% heavier than females. The Zorilla has a black pelage with four white dorsal stripes that unite on the top of the neck. There are three white patches on the head. The undersides and limbs are black, and the tail is a mixture of black and white hairs. The soles of the feet are naked; there are claws on all the feet, but they are longer and straighter on the forefeet. There are three pairs of mammae. The skull is heavily built, the rostrum is short and blunt, and the sagittal crest is poorly defined or absent. Dental formula: I 3/3, C 1/1, P 3/3, M 1/2 = 34.

Habitat. Zorillas are found in a wide variety of habitats, including mountains, sand plains, forest, swamps, riverine woodlands, floodplains, grasslands, coastal hummocks, and town gardens.

Food and Feeding. The diet is mainly insects and small rodents, but birds, eggs, reptiles, amphibians, and invertebrates are also eaten. In South Africa, the percentage occurrence of food items in 21 stomachs was 62% insects, 38% mammals, 10% birds, 10% arachnids, 5% frogs, and 5% myriapods. In the Cape Province, stomachs contained birds, mammals, reptiles, and insects (Coleoptera, Coleoptera larvae, Orthoptera, Lepidoptera, and Diptera). One stomach from Kalahari National Park, South Africa, contained mostly reptile remains. In Botswana, twelve stomachs contained insects, reptiles, and small mammals. Most prey are detected by sight or smell, and captured after stalking or short chases. Larger mammals, such as ground squirrels (*Xerus*) and spring hares, are followed to their burrows and killed. Zorillas often hunt for invertebrates in loose soil, plant debris, and at the base of grass tufts. Typically, a Zorilla pushes its nose into loose soil and sniffs audibly. When food is detected, it is excavated with the forefeet. Slow prey are bitten directly, whereas faster-moving prey, such as moths, mantids, or beetles, may either be bitten or pinned to the ground with a forefoot and eaten head first. All parts of insects are eaten. Rats (*Rattus*) are located mainly by sight. On occasion, rats are stalked and quickly captured or are chased. They are captured either by direct biting or by being pinned to the ground with the forefeet and then bitten. Most killing bites are directed at the back of the neck, head, or chest. Rats larger than 140 g usually require more bites and pinning with the forefeet. Occasionally, Zorillas roll while biting. Large rats are eaten by biting at the flesh and holding the skin with the forefeet. Birds presented to captive Zorillas are quickly and easily killed by a bite at the head, and then eaten head first. Zorillas will consume young birds completely, but they leave most of the feathers, feet, and tibia of mature birds. The contents of broken eggs are readily consumed, but captive Zorillas experience initial difficulty with unbroken eggs. Eventually, they learn to open them by biting or rolling the egg against a hard object such as a rock. Once cracked, the egg is easily opened and consumed. Zorillas will kill snakes and can attack large cobras. Snakes are approached cautiously and bitten on the back several times, after which the Zorilla retreats rapidly. Each bite is directed to the posterior half of the snake and is accompanied by vigorous shaking. After four or five such attacks, the Zorilla pins the snake to the ground with the forefeet, and repeatedly bites 10–15 cm from the head. Some of the bites involve vigorous shaking. Most snakes are eaten head first, but occasionally the tail or even flanks may be consumed first. Lizards are captured following short chases, pinned to the ground with the forefeet, and killed by a bite at the head. Lizards are entirely consumed and eaten head first. Amphibians are pinned to the ground with the forefeet and killed by biting the head and neck region; all parts of amphibians are eaten.

Activity pattern. Nocturnal. Rest sites are in holes, crevices, hollow logs, or under buildings. Zorillas can dig their own burrows, but often use those dug by other animals.

Movements, Home range and Social organization. Terrestrial, but can climb and swim well. Zorillas generally are solitary, but pairs may be seen. Larger groups are rare, and usually comprise a female and her young. Adult males and females are together only during mating, and adult males are intolerant of other males.

Breeding. Mating occurs in the spring. The young are born in late spring or summer, after a short gestation of 36 days. Litter size is two to three. Females have one litter per year, but may breed again if the first litter is lost early. The young are born blind and hairless; color patterns appear after one week. The eyes open after 40 days and the young start to eat solid food at c. 33 days, when their canine teeth erupt; they can kill mice at 60 days. Adult size is reached at 20 weeks.

Status and Conservation. Classified as Least Concern in *The IUCN Red List*. Zorillas are considered common throughout their range. They are not protected outside of national parks, where the most common threat is free-roaming domestic dogs.

Bibliography. Larivière (2002a), Rowe-Rowe (1978a, 1978b, 1978c), Smithers & Chimimba (2005), Stuart (1981), Wozencraft (2005).

Genus *POECILOGALE*
Thomas, 1883

26. African Striped Weasel *Poecilogale albinucha*
French: Zorille à nuque blanche / **German**: Weißnackenwiesel / **Spanish**: Hurón de nuca blanca

Taxonomy. *Zorilla albinucha* Gray, 1865, South Africa.
Monotypic.

Distribution. C & S Africa from Angola, PR Congo, DR Congo, Uganda, and Kenya to Eastern Cape

Descriptive notes. Head-body 27–33 cm (males), 24–32 cm (females), tail 13·8–20 cm (males), 14–15·8 cm (females); weight 283–380 g (males), 210–290 g (females), adult males are 35–50% heavier than females. The African Striped Weasel has a long body and short limbs. The pelage is black with contrasting dorsal white stripes; the white fur first divides into two lines, then into four distinct white to yellowish lines above the shoulders. The top of the head is white. The tail is long, brushy, and white. The feet are small, with sharp claws. There are two to three pairs of mammae. The skull is long and narrow, and the rostrum is short and broad. Dental formula: I 3/3, C 1/1, P 2/2, M 1/1 = 28.

Habitat. African Striped Weasels are found in forests, savannahs, grasslands, pine plantations, and cultivated land. They can be found up to 2200 m, but are more common below 1500 m. In KwaZulu-Natal, South Africa, questionnaire surveys revealed that 75% of sightings occurred in grasslands, 19% in young pine plantations, and 6% in cultivated land.

Food and Feeding. The diet mainly consists of small mammals, particularly rodents, but also includes reptiles, insects, and birds' eggs. Out of twelve stomachs obtained in KwaZulu-Natal, six contained small mammals (*Mastomys natalensis*, *Rhabdomys pumilio*, and *Mus minutoides*). African Striped Weasels hunt by scent, with vision being used only in the last 50 cm. Their shape enables them to hunt inside the burrows of rodents. When prey is sighted, the weasel stops and then lunges at the prey; short chases may occur. In captivity, all prey were killed within seven minutes. Prey are seized by the back of the neck. African Striped Weasels do not shake the prey when attempting to kill; instead, they roll around and vigorously kick at the back of their victim, possibly dislocating the neck and immobilizing the prey. Although most killing bites are directed at the back of the head and the neck, females may use throat bites when killing large prey. In captivity, African Striped Weasels were unsuccessful in killing rats (*Rattus*) that were more than 108% the mass of the weasel. One weasel can consume 3–4 mice in a night, but surplus killing may occur. Prey may be cached for future consumption. Small mammals are eaten head first and are usually entirely consumed. Occasionally, the prey's stomach and its contents are not eaten. The head, tail, legs, and dorsal skin of large rodents are typically not consumed.

Activity patterns. Mostly nocturnal, but activity may occur during the day. Rest sites are in holes, hollow logs, or within rock crevices. African Striped Weasels are powerful diggers and may dig their own dens.

Movements, Home range and Social organization. African Striped Weasels are mostly solitary, but pairs or small groups are observed (typically a female with young). Females tolerate the proximity of males only during the mating season.

Breeding. Mating occurs in spring or summer. Females give birth to a litter of two or three, after a gestation of 30 days. The young are born in a burrow and weigh around 4 g at birth. The eyes open after seven weeks and the canines erupt at 35 days. The young are fully mobile and weaned after eleven weeks; they start killing prey at 13 weeks. Adult size is reached at 20 weeks, and sexual maturity is attained after eight months. Females rear their young without the assistance of males.

Status and Conservation. Classified as Least Concern in *The IUCN Red List*. The African Striped Weasel is considered uncommon. Little is known about this species and field studies are needed to learn more about its natural history, ecology, and conservation status.

Bibliography. Ansell (1960a), Larivière (2001c), Rowe-Rowe (1972, 1978a, 1978b, 1978c), Smithers & Chimimba (2005), Stuart (1981), Wozencraft (2005).

Plate 35 ➤

27

28

PLATE 35

inches ————————— 16
cm ————————— 40

29

30

31

32

33

34

35

36

ssp *capensis*

ssp *congicus*

37

38

Subfamily LUTRINAE

Genus *PTERONURA*

Gray, 1837

27. Giant Otter *Pteronura brasiliensis*

French: Loutre géante / **German:** Riesenotter / **Spanish:** Nutria gigante

Taxonomy. *Mustela brasiliensis* Gmelin, 1788, Brazil.
Monotypic.
Distribution. Amazon and Orinoco basins from Venezuela to Paraguay and S Brazil. Formerly also Argentina and Uruguay, but now may be extinct there.
Descriptive notes. Head-body 100–130 cm (males), 100–120 cm (females), tail 45–65 cm; weight 26–32 kg (males), 22–26 kg (females), adult males are slightly larger than females. The Giant Otter is the largest South American otter. It has a broad and flattened head and large eyes. The pelage is reddish to dark brown or almost black. There are large and distinctive white to yellow markings on the upper chest, neck, throat, and lips that contrast sharply with the darker body; these patches may unite to form a large "bib". The rhinarium is fully haired. The tail is large and flattened dorso-ventrally. All the feet are fully webbed. The skull is massive and flat.
Habitat. Giant Otters are found in slow-moving rivers and creeks within forests, swamps, and marshes. They also occur in lakes, reservoirs, and agricultural canals. Although Giant Otters may inhabit dark or murky water, they prefer clear water and waterways with gently sloping banks and good cover.
Food and Feeding. Primarily fish eaters; adults consume an estimated 3 kg of fish daily. The main fish species eaten are from the suborder Characoidei and are 10–60 cm in length. Other prey items are rare, but may include crabs, small mammals, amphibians, birds, and molluscs. There are records of Giant Otters eating large prey such as anacondas and other snakes, black caimans, and turtles. On the Jauaperi River in the central Brazilian Amazon, remains of fish were found in all spraints. The main fish groups were Perciformes (Cichlidae, 97·3%), Characiformes (86·5%) and Siluriformes (5·4%). The Characiformes were represented mainly by Erythrinidae (*Hoplias* sp. 90·6%), followed by Serrasalmidae (28%). The Anostomidae occurred with a frequency of 18·7%. On the Aquidauana River, the Characiformes were the most frequent fish group, represented in 100% of all samples, followed by Siluriformes (66·6%) and Perciformes (33·3%). Prey is caught with the mouth and held in the forepaws while being consumed. Small fish may be eaten in the water, but larger prey are taken to shore.
Activity patterns. Diurnal. Giant Otters frequently go ashore to groom, play or defecate. Rest sites are in burrows, under root systems, or under fallen trees. At certain points along a stream, areas of about 50 m² are cleared and used for resting and grooming. Dens may consist of one or more short tunnels that lead to a chamber about 1·2–1·8 m wide. Nine vocalizations have been distinguished including screams of excitement and coos, given upon close intra-specific contact.
Movements, Home range and Social organization. Giant Otters are excellent swimmers and seem clumsy on land; however, they are capable of moving considerable distances between waterways. Daily travel may reach 17 km. During the dry season, when the young are being reared, activity is generally restricted to one portion of a waterway. In the wet season, movements are far more extensive. Giant Otters live in family groups that consist of a mated adult pair, one or more subadults, and one or more young of the year. These groups may reach 20 individuals, but are usually four to eight. Solitary animals also occur as transients. Home ranges are 12–32 linear km of creeks or rivers, or 20 km² of lakes or reservoirs. The core area of the home range is defended actively by family members; this core area encompasses 2–10 km of creek or 5 km² of lake. Both sexes regularly patrol and mark their territory; groups tend to avoid each other and fighting appears to be rare.
Breeding. The young are apparently born at the start of the dry season, from August to early October, although births may also occur from December to April. Gestation is 65–70 days, although evidence of delayed implantation of the fertilized eggs into the uterus has been observed in captivity. Litter size is up to five, usually one to three. Neonates weigh c. 200 g and measure c. 33 cm. They are able to eat solid food by three to four months and weaning occurs after nine months. The young remain with the parents until the birth of the next litter and probably for some time afterward. Adult size is reached after ten months and sexual maturity is attained at about two years.
Status and Conservation. CITES Appendix I. Classified as Endangered in *The IUCN Red List*. The Giant Otter is protected throughout its distribution. The current total wild population is estimated at between 1000 and 5000 individuals. Major threats are habitat degradation, water pollution, and the ever-increasing encroachment of humans on their habitats, which may lead to a potential future reduction in population size of around 50% over the next 20 years. Other threats for this species are the continued illegal killing for their skins or meat, captures for the zoo trade, or robbing of

dens for cubs to be sold as pets. There are also conflicts with fishermen as otters are perceived to reduce available fish stock, although studies have shown little overlap in otter prey species and those of commercial interest. Canine diseases that are transferred through domestic livestock, such as parvovirus and distemper, are also a threat.
Bibliography. Autuori & Deutsch (1977), Brecht-Munn & Munn (1988), Carter & Rosas (1997), Chebez (2008), Corredor & Tigreros (2006), Defler (1986b), Duplaix (1980), IUCN (2008), Laidler & Laidler (1983), Parera (1992), Rosas *et al.* (1999), Van Zyll de Jong (1972), Wozencraft (2005).

Genus *LONTRA*

Gray, 1843

28. North American River Otter *Lontra canadensis*

French: Loutre du Canada / **German:** Nordamerikanischer Fischotter / **Spanish:** Nutria neártica
Other common names: River Otter

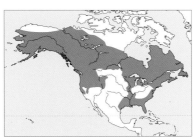

Taxonomy. *Lutra canadensis* Schreber, 1776, Eastern Canada.
Seven subspecies are recognized.
Subspecies and Distribution.
L. c. canadensis Schreber, 1776 – E Canada (Maritime Provinces, Ontario & Quebec), NE USA (Maine through New York) and Great Lakes of USA (Michigan and Wisconsin).
L. c. kodiacensis Goldman, 1935 – Alaska (Kodiak and Shuyak Is).
L. c. lataxina Cuvier, 1823 – E & SE USA.
L. c. mira Goldman, 1935 – S Alaska (Prince of Wales I), SW Canada (Vancouver I).
L. c. pacifica Rhoads, 1898 – W USA and W Canada.
L. c. periclyzomae Elliot, 1905 – W Canada (Queen Charlotte Is).
L. c. sonora Rhoads, 1898 – SW USA (Arizona, California, Colorado, Nevada, New Mexico & Utah).
Descriptive notes. Head-body 70–73 cm (males), 58·3–71·3 cm (females), tail 42–47 cm (males), 31·7–40 cm (females); weight 7·7–9·4 kg (males), 7·3–8·4 kg (females), adult males are approximately 5% larger than females. The North American River Otter has an elongated body, short limbs, and a tail that is flattened dorso-ventrally. The pelage is short and very dense, varying in color from brown to black, with a grayish upper chest, throat, and chin. The rhinarium is bare and there are long vibrissae on each side of the face. All four feet are fully webbed and equipped with small claws. The skull is flat, with a broad rostrum and large braincase. Dental formula: I 3/3, C 1/1, P 4/3, M 1/2 = 36.
Habitat. North American River Otters are found along streams, rivers, ponds, lakes, reservoirs, and in saltwater marshes. Generally, they prefer waterways with well-vegetated shorelines, and avoid areas with no shoreline vegetation. They inhabit the murky waters of southern alluvial valleys as well as the crystal-clear waters of rocky mountain streams. In many areas, they occur in close association with American Beavers; Beaver ponds provide prey and dens/rest sites.
Food and Feeding. The diet is mainly fish, but also includes amphibians, crustaceans (especially crayfish), rodents, molluscs, reptiles, birds, and fruits. In many areas, the abundance and availability of fish is the primary determinant of North American River Otter abundance. Typically, fish are consumed in inverse proportion to their swimming abilities: slow-moving species are captured and eaten more often. In coastal areas, the fish eaten are those that are abundant, intermediate in size, and found close to shore. North American River Otters hunt by sight and by touch. They inspect log jams, pools of deeper water in shallow streams, areas below waterfalls, natural eddies, or any other areas likely to hold fish and other prey. Upon detection, prey are pursued until captured. In shallow or murky water, North American River Otters hunt and detect prey with their vibrissae or by feeling with their forefeet. They can remain underwater for up to four minutes, and can swim at speeds of 11 km/h. They may hunt in small family groups, herding fish to shore or to each other to facilitate capture.
Activity patterns. Mainly nocturnal, with some crepuscular activity; diurnal activity increases during colder months. Active year round, even when water freezes in winter. Rest sites are in dry bank dens, Beaver lodges, or other natural cavities accessible from underwater.
Movements, Home range and Social organization. North American River Otters are highly mobile, aquatic animals and can travel more than 40 km in a single day. Daily movements average 4–5 km for males and 2–3 km for females. They typically travel in water and are able to swim long distances under ice during the winter. North American River Otters may travel long distances over land from one watershed to another. When traveling on land, they often slide instead of bounding, especially if snow is present or when going downhill on slippery ground. When sliding, they push forward with their back legs, while the front feet are tucked under the belly. They will also play on steep banks next to water, repeatedly climbing up the bank and sliding back down into the water. North American River Otters have a complex social system, which varies across

On following pages: 29. Marine Otter (*Lontra felina*); 30. Neotropical Otter (*Lontra longicaudis*); 31. Southern River Otter (*Lontra provocax*); 32. Sea Otter (*Enhydra lutris*); 33. Spotted-necked Otter (*Hydrictis maculicollis*); 34. Eurasian Otter (*Lutra lutra*); 35. Hairy-nosed Otter (*Lutra sumatrana*); 36. African Clawless Otter (*Aonyx capensis*); 37. Asian Small-clawed Otter (*Aonyx cinereus*); 38. Smooth-coated Otter (*Lutrogale perspicillata*).

their range. They often occur in groups of up to 15 individuals; the largest groups are found along coastal shorelines. These groups mainly consist of a female with young. In coastal areas, groups consist either of adult females with young, or male groups. The cohesiveness of male groups disappears during breeding, when each male attempts to find and mate with numerous females. Home ranges may reach 275 km² for males and 135 km² for females. In south-eastern Minnesota, annual home ranges of males were 3·2 times greater than those of females, and annual core areas of males were 2·9 times greater than those of females; 69% of the individuals exhibited core-area overlap. In general, conspecifics were not excluded from home ranges or core areas and signs of cooperation were evident, suggesting that they were social rather than territorial. Population densities range from one per 4 km of water in Idaho to one per 1·25 km of coastal water in Alaska.

Breeding. North American River Otters are polygynous. Mating occurs from December in the south to April in the north. Implantation of the fertilized eggs into the uterus is delayed for eight months; embryonic development lasts 61–63 days. Births occur from February to April, usually in a bank den or an abandoned Beaver lodge. In south-eastern Minnesota, two females used man-made brush piles as maternal dens, four used small limestone caves, one used a cavity in the roots of a big-toothed aspen (*Populus grandidentata*) and one used a American Beaver bank den. Dens were located a mean of 316 m from the nearest body of water. Seven of eight females placed dens outside of their normal activity areas, and all females appeared to select den sites that were protected from flood events. Litter size is one to five. The young are born furred, blind, and toothless. The eyes open after 30–38 days, and weaning occurs after twelve weeks. Sexual maturity is reached after two years. Males do not provide parental care.

Status and Conservation. CITES Appendix II. Classified as Least Concern in *The IUCN Red List*. North American River Otters are considered to be fairly common throughout their range. However, one subspecies, *L. c. sonora*, may be of concern in Mexico. One threat is water pollution, which not only reduces the availability of prey, but also affects reproduction due to bioaccumulation of toxic pollutants. In coastal areas, oil spills are the most severe threats. Throughout their range, they are harvested for their fur, but this controlled harvest does not constitute a major threat when habitat conditions are suitable. Reintroductions have been successful in areas where North American River Otters were once common.

Bibliography. Gorman, Erb, McMillan & Martin (2006), Gorman, Erb, McMillan, Martin & Homyack (2006), Green (1932), Hall (1981), Larivière & Walton (1998), LeBlanc et al. (2007), Melquist & Hornocker (1983), Reid et al. (1994), Serfass (1995), Serfass & Rymon (1985), Shannon (1989), Van Zyll de Jong (1972), Wozencraft (2005).

29. Marine Otter *Lontra felina*

French: Loutre chungungo / **German**: Südamerikanischer Meerotter / **Spanish**: Chungungo

Taxonomy. *Mustela felina* Molina, 1782, Chile.
The Marine Otter was previously included in the genus *Lutra*. Monotypic.
Distribution. Pacific coast from N Peru to S Chile, and extreme S of Argentine Patagonia.
Descriptive notes. Head-body 53·3–78·7 cm, tail 30–36·2 cm; weight 3·2–5·8 kg. The smallest of the South American otters. The pelage is dark brown throughout except for a grayish neck and throat. Large vibrissae occur on each upper lip. All the feet are fully webbed. The skull is small and flat, with a broad rostrum.

Habitat. Marine Otters are found in marine environments, along rocky coasts that harbor a high diversity of prey. They spend most of their time within 150 m of shore, but occasionally may venture into freshwater tributaries flowing into the sea.
Food and Feeding. The diet is primarily crustaceans, molluscs, and fish, but also includes birds, small mammals, and fruit. Along the Chilean coast, the diet consists of crabs (69·8%), fish (19·9%), shrimp (6·4%), and molluscs (3·9%). On the Valdivian coast in the south of Chile, spraints contained 25 species: 52% crustaceans, 40% fish, and 8% molluscs. Marine Otters showed opportunistic feeding behavior, selecting prey seasonally according to their availability. Marine Otters fish by first swimming to a hunting area, where they then dive underwater for 6–64 seconds. Captured prey are consumed in the water if they are small enough to be handled easily, or taken ashore if larger. Crabs are almost always taken ashore. Prey can be carried in the mouth, or carried on the belly while swimming dorsally. Unlike Sea Otters, Marine Otters do not use rocks as anvils to crack open bivalves or shellfish. At Isla Choros, northern Chile, Marine Otters spent more time foraging in a wave-protected site compared with a wave-exposed habitat. Successful dives reached 26·9% in the wave-exposed habitat and 38·2% in the wave-protected habitat. Foraging dives were 18% shorter in wave-exposed as compared with wave-protected habitat.
Activity patterns. Mainly diurnal. Marine Otters spend about 40% of their time hunting and 60% resting or grooming. They make extensive use of caves, rock crevices, and natural cavities for resting sites. Many areas used for resting at low tide are underwater during high tides.
Movements, Home range and Social organization. Marine Otters are strong swimmers, but their daily movements occur within 150 m of the coast. Long coastal movements are not documented. Marine Otters are solitary and seldom hunt in groups; observed groups are likely to consist of a female with her young. Among adults, home

ranges overlap. Six Marine Otters were radio-tracked in central Chile. Females exhibited intra-sexual territoriality, but there was no territoriality between males or between sexes. Home ranges were less than 4134 m long and less than 110 m wide; range size did not differ between sexes. Marine Otters concentrated their activity in the littoral zone and spent 81% of their time on land, mostly resting. Core areas were associated with resting places and dens. Population density varies from 0·04–10 otters per km of coastline.
Breeding. Mating occurs in December or January. Gestation lasts 60–65 days and births take place in January, February, or March. Females give birth in rocky caves; these dens are spaces between boulders that remain above water even at high tide, and many have underwater entrances. Litter size is two to four. The young remain with their mother for up to ten months.
Status and Conservation. CITES Appendix I. Classified as Endangered in *The IUCN Red List*. It is estimated that fewer than 1000 Marine Otters remain, including a Peruvian population of 200–300. This species is protected in Argentina, Chile, and Peru. Major threats include human occupation of the coast, water pollution, and illegal killing for their pelts or by fisherman who blame Marine Otters for the reduction of local fish or shrimp populations.

Bibliography. Castilla (1981), Eisenberg (1989), Larivière (1998), Medina (1995), Medina, Boher et al. (2007), Medina, Rodriguez et al. (2004), Ostfeld et al. (1989), Sielfeld (1983), Van Zyll de Jong (1972), Wozencraft (2005).

30. Neotropical Otter *Lontra longicaudis*

French: Loutre néotropicale / **German**: Südamerikanischer Fischotter / **Spanish**: Nutria neotropical

Taxonomy. *Lutra longicaudis* Olfers, 1818, Brazil.
Three subspecies are recognized.
Subspecies and Distribution.
L. l. longicaudis Olfers, 1818 – Argentina, Bolivia, Ecuador, S Brazil, Paraguay, Peru, and Uruguay.
L. l. annectens Major, 1897 – Belize, Colombia, Costa Rica, Ecuador, El Salvador, Guatemala, Honduras, Mexico, Panama, Nicaragua, and Venezuela.
L. l. enudris Cuvier, 1823 – NE Brazil, the Guyanas, and Trinidad.
Descriptive notes. Head-body 36–66 cm, tail 37–84 cm; weight 5–15 kg, adult males are 20–25% larger than females. The Neotropical Otter is heavily built, with a long body, short limbs, and fully webbed feet. The pelage is dark brown, with a gray neck and throat. The muzzle is broad, with a yellowish white tip and long vibrissae on each side. The skull is heavy, long, and flat.
Habitat. Neotropical Otters are found in fast flowing, clear rivers and streams, in both deciduous and evergreen forests, at elevations up to 3000 m. They prefer waterways with clear water, abundant waterside vegetation, and high availability of potential den sites; they are rare or absent from sluggish, murky, lowland waters. In Northern Mexico, along a 30 km stretch of river, the habitat preferred by a Neotropical Otter included pools that averaged more than 0·8 m deep, more than 14·6 m wide, with over 64% under-story vegetation cover, and rock talus/vegetation cover within 4·8 m of the water's edge.
Food and Feeding. The diet is mainly fish, but also includes crustaceans, molluscs, small mammals, birds, reptiles, and insects. In southern Brazil, spraint analysis revealed a diet comprising mainly fish (including Loricariidae, Callichthyidae, Cichlidae, Pimelodidae, Auchenipteridae, and Erythrinidae), and also mammals and insects. In the coastal plain of Santa Catarina State, southern Brazil, spraints contained fish (mainly *Hoplias malabaricus* and *Geophagus brasiliensis*) and crustaceans (mainly the river crab *Trichodactylus fluviatilis*). The presence of fruits, reptiles, birds, and mammals in the diet was occasional and opportunistic. On Ibera Lake, Argentina, 205 spraints contained mainly fish (Cichlidae, Characidae, Synbranchidae, Loricariidae, and Erythrinidae), but also crustaceans and molluscs. Seasonal variation was observed in the diet: in the summer, crustaceans and vertebrates (other than fish) increased. A higher percentage of benthic fish species was also observed in the summer, while pelagic and benthopelagic species increased in the winter. Such dietary changes may have resulted from the different habitat used in different seasons, from the lake coast in winter towards a more internal marshy area in summer. Foraging dives last 20–30 seconds. Small prey are eaten while in an upright position at the water's surface; large prey are taken ashore.
Activity patterns. Mainly diurnal, with activity peaks in the middle or late afternoon. May become nocturnal in areas of high human activity. Rest sites are in natural cavities along riverbanks, in excavated burrows, or in dense grass. In Brazil, two large caves were also used as shelters and to raise young. Neotropical Otters mainly use rest sites located high on riverbanks, probably because they are less vulnerable to flooding. Sprainting sites are usually on solid, high and dry areas, in close proximity to deep water; these sites include logs, root systems, rocks, sand bars, and planks under bridges.
Movements, Home range and Social organization. Neotropical Otters are graceful swimmers and divers, and are seldom seen out of the water. On land, they move with a humping gait, with the head and tail carried low. Neotropical Otters are solitary, but breeding pairs and females with young are seen occasionally. Population densities vary from 0·8 to 2·8 otters per km of shoreline.

Breeding. Mating occurs mostly in spring, but may occur throughout the year in certain localities. Gestation lasts 56–86 days. Litter size may be up to five, but is typically two or three. Births occur in nests of grass and leaves located on the banks of streams, in hollow logs or trees, among root systems, or in cavities excavated by the female. The young are born blind but fully furred. Their eyes open after 44 days, and they start to venture outside the natal den when c. 52 days old. Aquatic activity starts at c. 74 days. Before they are old enough to follow the female, the young spend most of the day playing near the natal den. Females raise the young alone as males do not provide parental care.

Status and Conservation. CITES Appendix I. Classified as Data Deficient in *The IUCN Red List*. Because the Neotropical Otter is secretive and lives in remote areas, the status of populations is unknown in many regions. The major threat for this species is hunting for its pelt. Another threat is water pollution caused by mining and ranching. Neoptropical Otters are sometimes kept in captivity and trained to catch fish. Conservation goals should aim at reducing hunting pressure, protecting areas, and enacting stricter regulations to prevent water pollution.

Bibliography. Arcila & Ramirez (2004), Gallo (1991), Helder & Ker De Andrade (1997), Kasper *et al.* (2004), Larivière (1999b), Mondolfi (1970), Pardini & Trajano (1999), Parera (1993), Passamani & Camargo (1995), Quadros & Monteiro-Filho (2001), Van Zyll de Jong (1972), Wozencraft (2005).

31. Southern River Otter *Lontra provocax*

French: Loutre du Chili / **German**: Patagonischer Fischotter / **Spanish**: Huillin

Other common names: Huillin

Taxonomy. *Lutra provocax* Thomas, 1908, Patagonia.
Monotypic.
Distribution. Argentina and Chile.
Descriptive notes. Head-body 57–61 cm, tail 35–40 cm; weight 5–10 kg, males are about 10% larger than females. This medium-sized otter is dark-brown with pale undersides and a grayish neck and throat. All four feet are fully webbed. The skull is flat, but strongly built. The dentition is broad and adapted for crushing.

Habitat. Southern River Otters are found in lakes, rivers, and some coastal marshes. In Argentina, they are associated with dense mature forests that have thick undergrowth extending close to the shore of water bodies. In southern Chile, radio-tracked Southern River Otters used rivers more frequently than expected, whereas they avoided small streams. Temperate evergreen swamp forests and river and stream banks with a high density of riparian vegetation, woody debris and exposed roots, were found to be the preferred habitats; canalized rivers and streams lacking these characteristics were avoided.

Food and Feeding. The diet is mostly fish (under 10 cm in length) and crustaceans, but also includes molluscs and birds. The relative importance of each food type may vary seasonally or geographically. In central Chile, the diet comprises 75% fish and 63% crustaceans; the highest occurrence of fish occurs in the spring and summer. In the southern marine habitats of Chile, Southern River Otters feed mainly on fish. In Argentina, crustaceans largely dominate the diet (99%) and fish occur rarely (less than 2%). Differences in the proportion of fish and crustaceans in the diet may reflect the differential availability of prey types in different habitats: fish productivity is low in freshwater lakes compared to the oceans, which may explain the high proportion of crustaceans in freshwater lakes.

Activity patterns. Primarily nocturnal, with occasional activity during the day. Den/rest sites are rock crevices, hollow trees or logs, earth banks, or under root systems; Southern River Otters may excavate their own dens. Dens occur from 0·7 to 50 m from the shoreline; most are within 3–8 m of the water's edge. They often have multiple terrestrial but no underwater entrances. The density of dens along the southern coast of Chile was 2·8 per km of coastline. Latrines are common near den entrances or inside dens; they are 50–80 m from one another and 3–6 m from water.

Movements, Home range and Social organization. Southern River Otters may move up to 5 km per night. They are mostly solitary; females with young and breeding pairs are the only social groups recorded. In the Queule River, southern Chile, the observed behavior of radio-tracked otters suggested intra-sexual territoriality; no home range overlap among males existed, while there was an average of 33% overlap of home ranges among females, and 87% between sexes. In core areas, only one case of overlapping between an adult male and an adult female was observed. Average home range and core area lengths were 11·3 km and 0·9 km, respectively. The population density in Chile ranges from 0·25 to 0·73 individuals per km of coastline.

Breeding. In central Chile, mating occurs in July and August, and young are born in September or October. Litter size averages one or two, but may reach up to four.

Status and Conservation. CITES Appendix I. Classified as Endangered in *The IUCN Red List*. The major threats to this species are the destruction of its habitat and hunting, especially in Chile. The high price of otter skins in Chile, combined with low wages for unskilled workers, generates much uncontrolled and illegal harvest.

Bibliography. Aued *et al.* (2003), Chéhébar (1986), Chéhébar *et al.* (1986), Larivière (1999c), Medina (1996), Medina *et al.* (2003), Sielfeld (1983), Van Zyll de Jong (1972), Wozencraft (2005).

Genus *ENHYDRA*

Fleming, 1822

32. Sea Otter *Enhydra lutris*

French: Loutre de mer / **German**: Meerotter / **Spanish**: Nutria marina

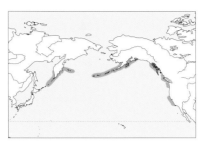

Taxonomy. *Mustela lutris* Linnaeus, 1758, Kamchatka, Russia.
Three subspecies are recognized.
Subspecies and Distribution.
E. l. lutris Linnaeus, 1758 – NE Russia (Commander Is, Kamchatka, Kurile Is & Sakhalin I).
E. l. kenyoni Wilson, 1991 – Aleutian Is through Alaska and W Canada (Vancouver I) to W USA (Washington).
E. l. nereis Merriam, 1904 – USA (California).

Descriptive notes. Head-body 100–120 cm, tail 25–37 cm; weight 21–45 kg (males), 14–33 kg (females). The Sea Otter is one of the largest species within the Mustelidae. Sea Otters have long bodies and short limbs. The pelage is reddish-brown to dark brown, with a gray or creamy-colored head, throat, and chest. The underfur is very dense, averaging 100,000 hairs per cm². The head is wide and blunt, with long and thick vibrissae on the upper lips. The ears are small and set low to the sides, and capable of closing when the otter dives. The tail is slightly flattened dorso-ventrally, but uniform in thickness from the base to tip. All four feet are webbed and clawed. There is one pair of mammae. A fold of skin in the armpits enables the Sea Otter to transport prey at sea while foraging. The Sea Otter lacks anal glands. The skull is flat, broad and strong. Dental formula: I 3/2, C 1/1, P 3/3, M 1/2 = 32. The molars are broad and flat, with rounded crowns. This is the only carnivore species with four (instead of six) lower incisors.

Habitat. Sea Otters are found in coastal marine habitats from sheltered and sandy bays to rocky shorelines exposed to rough seas. Although marine mammals, they rarely venture more than one km from shore. Typically, they live and forage in waters at depths of up to 100 m, but the highest densities of Sea Otters occur in waters less than 40 m deep.

Food and Feeding. The diet is mostly marine invertebrates such as abalones, sea urchins, crabs, and molluscs. Other prey include squid, octopus, chitons, tubeworms, scallops, and, very occasionally, fish. In the northern Kodiak Archipelago, clams were the most frequently identified prey (57–67%, mostly *Saxidomus giganteus*); mussels (*Mytilus* sp.), crabs (primarily *Telmessus* sp.), and green sea urchins (*Strongylocentrotus droebachiensis*) contributed 25% to the diet. On the north side of the Alaska Peninsula, the dominant prey species in 50 spraints were mussels (*Mytilus edulis*), followed by three species of clams (*Siliqua* sp., *Spisula polynyma*, and *Tellina lutea*), sand dollars (*Echinarachnius parma*), and helmet crabs (*Telmessus cheiragonus*). In south-east Alaska, butter clams (*S. giganteus*) are the major prey items. Sea Otters on the outer coast of Washington feed heavily on bivalves (63%) and have a diverse diet consisting of several prey groups. In contrast, Sea Otters in the Strait of Juan de Fuca have a restricted diet dominated by more than 60% red urchins (*Strongylocentrotus franciscanus*), with only two other prey species comprising more than 10% of their diet. Sea Otters forage in both rocky and soft-sediment areas on or near the ocean floor. They have good underwater vision and most prey is captured by sight. Prey hiding under rocks or in crevices may also be captured by feeling with the forefeet. Underwater dives are sustained by lungs that are 2–3 times larger than those of similar-sized terrestrial mammals. Most hunting dives last 50–90 seconds. In coastal Washington, the average dive time was 55 seconds and average surface time was 45 seconds, irrespective of dive success. At least 77% of all dives were successful in capturing prey. Prey capture success was significantly lower for subadults (63%) than adults (82%). Sea Otters break the exoskeleton of large or hard-shelled prey by hitting the prey item on a rock carried by the otter on its belly. Sea Otters face a tremendous thermoregulatory challenge because of their constant life at sea. When in water, buoyancy and insulation are provided by their fur and the air bubbles trapped within it. The integrity of their pelage is thus essential to thermoregulation. Their metabolic heat production is 2–3 times greater than that of similar-sized terrestrial mammals. To sustain such heat production requires that Sea Otters consume 20–33% of their body mass in food daily. Sea Otters can drink seawater, and their kidneys produce very concentrated urine to avoid unnecessary water loss.

Activity patterns. Generally diurnal, with peaks in activity at dawn and dusk. Daytime foraging increases when females care for young. In Prince William Sound, Alaska, more time was spent foraging (30%) than on any other activity, and foraging bouts were longer than all other activities. Sea Otters rest by floating belly-up in the water with their feet out of the water. They sometimes rest on rocks near the water and often spend the night in a kelp bed, lying under strands of kelp to avoid drifting while sleeping. Ten vocalizations have been described for Sea Otters including screams of distress (heard especially when mothers and young are separated) and coos (heard mostly when individuals are content or in familiar company).

Movements, Home range and Social organization. Sea Otters can spend their entire life at sea, and their movements on land are awkward. In the water, they are graceful and can move at speeds of 1–1·5 km/h at the surface and up to 9 km/h underwater. Annual total movements of both sexes frequently cover 50–100 km. Sea Otters are basically solitary, but they sometimes rest in concentrations of up to 2000 individuals, and groups may occur at feeding areas. They aggregate by sex and age, with males and females occupying separate sections of coastline. During the breeding season, some males move into the areas occupied by females and establish territories. Male territories are usually about 20–50 ha; female home ranges may be twice as large. These territories typically are located in prime feeding or resting areas, locations that are attractive to breeding females. The boundaries are vigorously patrolled and intruding males are repulsed, but serious fighting is rare. The owner of a territory seeks to mate with any female that enters, though sometimes a pair bond is formed for a few days or weeks.

Breeding. Sea Otters are polygynous: males may mate with more than one female during the season. Mating and births occur throughout the year, but parturition peaks are in May and June in the Aleutians and from January to March off the coast of California. Implantation of the fertilized eggs into the uterus is delayed, and total gestation lasts from 4–12 months. Births occur in water. Litter size is one, very rarely two. At birth, neonates weigh 1·4–2·3 kg. The female swims on her back and nurses with the young on her chest. Young Sea Otters may take some solid food shortly after birth, but may nurse until they are almost adult size. The period of dependency on the mother is thought to be about five to eight months. Offspring start diving after two months. Sexual maturity is reached at four years of age. Most females do not have young every year, although some females are capable of annual reproduction. Males may begin mating at five or six years, but usually do not become active breeders until several more years have passed.

Status and Conservation. CITES Appendix I and II. Classified as Endangered in *The IUCN Red List*. Sea Otters are hunted for their fur, which has led to a large reduction in local populations and their distribution. Extirpated in Japan (coastal Hokkaido) and Mexico (Baja California), but now translocations have now reestablised Sea Otters in south-east Alaska, south-west Canada (Vancouver I), and north-west USA (Washington and Oregon). They are legally harvested in Alaska, with the annual harvest slightly exceeding 1000 animals. Sea Otters are also persecuted as perceived competitors for shellfish. In the last few decades, massive oil spills, such as that of the Exxon Valdez in 1989, have also decimated Sea Otter populations.

Bibliography. Bodkin (2003), Doroff & DeGange (1994), Estes (1980), Estes & Palmisano (1974), Gentry & Peterson (1967), Green & Brueggeman (1991), Hall & Schaller (1964), Hattori *et al.* (2005), IUCN (2008), Kenyon (1969), Pearson & Davis (2005), Pearson *et al.* (2006), Sandegren *et al.* (1973), Shimek & Monk (1977), Wilson *et al.* (1991), Wozencraft (2005).

Genus *HYDRICTIS*
Pocock, 1921

33. Spotted-necked Otter *Hydrictis maculicollis*
French: Loutre à cou tacheté / **German**: Fleckenhals-Otter / **Spanish**: Nutria moteada

Taxonomy. *Lutra maculicollis* Lichtenstein, 1835, Cape Province, South Africa.

The Spotted-necked Otter was previously included in the genus *Lutra* by some authors, but recent molecular studies have shown that its inclusion in *Lutra* would make this genus paraphyletic. Monotypic.

Distribution. Sub-Saharan Africa from Guinea Bissau in the W to SW Ethiopia, E Kenya, and Tanzania in the E, and S to N Namibia, Botswana, and NW Zimbabwe; also Malawi, Mozambique, and E South Africa.

Descriptive notes. Head-body 71–76 cm (males), 57–60·5 cm (females), tail 38·5–44 cm (males), 41–44 cm (females); weight 5·7–6 kg (males), 3·8–4·7 kg (females), adult males are larger and heavier than females. The Spotted-necked Otter has a long body, short limbs, and a long tail. The pelage varies from reddish to dark brown. There are creamy-white to white mottled markings on the upper chest and throat. All the feet are fully webbed and there are claws on all the digits. The skull is long and narrow and lightly built, but with a well-developed sagittal crest. Dental formula: I 3/3, C 1/1, P 4/3, M 1/2 = 36.

Habitat. Spotted-necked Otters are found in freshwater rivers, lakes, and swamps with large areas of open water; they are absent from coastal or estuarine areas. They seldom venture more than 10 m away from water and prefer shallow, freshwater areas, where there is continuity of lakeside vegetation, low pollution, and no crocodiles. In KwaZulu-Natal, South Africa, Spotted-necked Otters were most often located in rivers (40% of 706 locations) and near dams (45%), with only occasional use of swamps (3%) and oxbow lakes (2%).

Food and Feeding. The diet includes fish (*Barbus, Clarias, Haplochromis, Micropterus salmoides, Salmo trutta*, and *Tilapia*), crabs (*Potomonautes*), and frogs (mostly *Xenopus laevis* and *Rana*). Insects and birds are also occasionally eaten. Crabs are the major dietary item during spring, summer, and autumn, whereas fish dominate in winter. Most fish consumed are less than 20 cm in length. In the fish-rich waters of east and central Africa, the diet consists almost entirely of fish, whereas in the fish-poor waters of South Africa, crabs and frogs are consumed in addition to fish. On Lake Victoria, Tanzania, 61% of spraints collected contained 46% *Haplochromis*, 14% *Tilapia*, catfish (*Bagrus* or *Clarias*), and 1% crab (*Potamon niloticus*). Direct observations of feeding Spotted-necked Otters also revealed a diet dominated by *Haplochromis*. On Lake Muhazi, Rwan-

da, 154 spraints contained 80% fish, 10% insects, 3% molluscs, 2% birds and frogs. In Eastern Cape Province, South Africa, the diet is mostly fish (47%), crabs (38%), and frogs (8%). In KwaZulu-Natal, the frequency of occurrence of food items in 516 spraints was 64% fish, 43% crabs, 43% amphibians, and 18% insects. In contrast, 228 spraints collected near a trout river contained 39% crabs, 38% fish, 20% frogs, 2% insects (mostly dragonfly larvae, Odonata), and unidentified birds. In a non-trout area, 66 spraints contained 30% crabs, 27% frogs, 25% fish, 10% birds (mostly Anatidae and little grebe *Tachybaptus ruficollis*), and 5% insects. In three stomachs from the Cape Province, South Africa, one contained crabs, one contained frogs and fish, and one contained frogs, fish, a beetle (Coleoptera), and a caterpillar. Spotted-necked Otters generally fish alone and almost all fishing is done within 10 m from the shore. When fishing in groups, cooperation among individuals may help facilitate prey capture by herding fish toward each other. Fishing in groups probably occurs when females are training their young. Fish are captured during short dives of less than 20 seconds. Once underwater, a Spotted-necked Otter scans for prey, turning its head from side to side. Prey are detected visually and pursued until captured. Crabs, fish, and frogs are captured with the mouth; the forefeet are not used in prey capture. Fish smaller than 10 cm are consumed in the water, but larger fish are taken to shore for consumption. Fishing forays typically last 10–20 minutes, but may last up to 3 h.

Activity patterns. Mostly diurnal, with activity peaks during early morning and late afternoon. In KwaZulu-Natal, Spotted-necked Otters were most active from 06:00–09:00 h and 15:00–21:00 h. Nocturnal activity usually only occurs during periods of full moon. Rest sites are in rock cavities, bank dens, holes in root systems, or dense vegetation. Spotted-necked Otters can dig their own burrows. In KwaZulu-Natal, resting sites were among trees and shrub roots (29%), reeds (21%), small islands near dams (23%), tall grass (14%), swamps (11%), and sheltered places among rocks (2%). A 4·2-km section of river contained ten resting sites, with a mean distance of 467 m between dens.

Movements, Home range and Social organization. Spotted-necked Otters travel mostly in water, swimming underwater and surfacing briefly to breathe. Swimming speed reaches 3–4 km/h. Spotted-necked Otters may be found in small family groups of up to five individuals, although groups of up to 20 animals have been reported. Group size varies according to locality. Of 14 sightings in KwaZulu-Natal, six were singles, three were pairs, three were trios, one was of four, and one of five. In Rwanda, 75% of observations were of solitary Spotted-necked Otters; pairs or trios occurred on occasion and usually consisted of a female with young. In Rwanda, maximum group size was eleven and most animals foraged alone. In Lake Victoria, Tanzania, Spotted-necked Otters were most often seen in groups of three and solitary animals were observed on only five occasions; these groups often travelled together, but fed individually. The home ranges of males are larger than those of females. In KwaZulu-Natal, the mean home range size for three males was 16·2 km², and 5·8 km² for three females. Spotted-necked Otters appeared to be non-territorial as there was large intra- and inter-sexual overlap of home ranges. Population density on Lake Muhazi (3·4 km² in size), Rwanda, was two otters per km of shoreline. In KwaZulu-Natal, density was 0·4–0·6 otters per km of shoreline. Near Kageye, Tanzania, 9–10 otters occupied a 10-km section of the coast of Lake Victoria. In KwaZulu-Natal, the density of otters was estimated at one otter per 6–11 km of river and at one otter per 1·6–2·4 km of river.

Breeding. In Tanzania, mating occurs in July and the young are born in September, after a gestation of c. 60 days. In Zambia, three two-week-old cubs from one litter were captured in December. Delayed implantation probably does not occur. Litter size is one to three. Neonates are blind and helpless. The young remain with the mother for up to one year. Males do not provide parental care.

Status and Conservation. CITES Appendix II. Classified as Least Concern in *The IUCN Red List*. Although this is a widespread species, there are local population declines occurring. Spotted-necked Otters are sensitive to habitat alterations and pollution, and because they consume fish, they are susceptible to bioaccumulation of pesticides and other toxic chemical compounds. Throughout Africa, otters are killed for their skins and meat or because they are regarded as competitors for food, particularly in rural areas where fishing is an important source of income. During the last few years, their habitats have been drastically changed or lost following bush clearance, deforestation, overgrazing, siltation, draining of wetlands, water extraction, or denudation of riparian vegetation.

Bibliography. Angelici *et al.* (2005), Koepfli & Wayne (1998), Kruuk & Goudswaard (1990), Larivière (2002b), Lejeune (1989), Mortimer (1963), Perrin & Carugati (2000), Perrin & D'Inzillo (2000), Procter (1963), Roberts (1951), Rowe-Rowe (1977a, 1977b, 1995), Rowe-Rowe & Somers (1998), Skinner & Smithers (1990), Smithers & Chimimba (2005), Somers & Purves (1996), Stuart (1985), Wozencraft (2005).

Genus *LUTRA*
Brisson, 1762

34. Eurasian Otter *Lutra lutra*
French: Loutre d'Europe / **German**: Eurasischer Fischotter / **Spanish**: Nutria paleártica
Other common names: European Otter

Taxonomy. *Mustela lutra* Linnaeus, 1758, Sweden.

The Japanese Otter (*L. nippon*) is considered by some authors to be a valid species, based on recent morphological and molecular analyses. However, further research is needed to determine its taxonomic status; it is here considered a subspecies of *L. lutra*. Up to twenty-eight subspecies have been proposed, but a taxonomic revision is needed.

Distribution. Wide distribution in the Palearctic: from Europe to Russian Far East, North and South Korea, and Japan; also N Africa, Middle East, C Asia, Sub-Himalayan zone, S India, Sri Lanka, C, E & S China, Taiwan, Indochina, and Sumatra.

Descriptive notes. Head-body 50–82 cm, tail 33–50 cm; weight 5–14 kg, adult males are typically 50% larger than females. The Eurasian Otter has a long body and a conical tail. The short, dense pelage is brown to almost black throughout, with slightly paler undersides. The legs are short; the feet are fully webbed and have well-developed claws. There are two to three pairs of mammae. The cranium is large and flat. Dental formula: I 3/3, C 1/1, P 4/3, M 1/2 = 36.

Habitat. Eurasian Otters are found along lakes, ponds, rivers, and streams, and in marshes, swamps, and coastal and estuarine wetlands, from sea level up to 4120 m. They avoid areas of deep water.

Food and Feeding. The diet is mainly fish, frogs, and aquatic invertebrates (including crustaceans and crabs). Birds and small mammals (such as rodents and lagomorphs) may be consumed on occasion. In general, the mean proportion of fish declines from 94% on seashores, to 71% on lakes and fish ponds, to 64% on rivers and streams. On inland waters, the abundance of crayfish is an essential food item. In Northern Ireland, over 50% of spraints were composed of sticklebacks (*Gasterosteus aculeatus*), salmonids and cyprinids, with Sticklebacks constituting the most frequently occurring prey category. The frequency of occurrence of eels (*Anguilla anguilla*) was found to be consistently higher in spraints collected from smaller streams. In eastern Poland, fish constitutes 51% of the food biomass consumed in spring-summer and 40% in autumn-winter, with perch (*Perca fluviatilis*), pike (*Esox lucius*), and roach (*Rutilus rutilus*) being captured most frequently. Amphibians (mainly *Rana temporaria*) make up 34% of the food biomass in spring-summer and 58% in autumn-winter. The cold season diet depends on river size. On small rivers with forested valleys, Eurasian Otters feed nearly exclusively on amphibians (72–90% of food biomass). As the size of the river increases, and riverside habitat becomes more open (sedge and reed marshes instead of forests), Eurasian Otters shift to catching predominantly fish (up to 76%). In southern Poland, the main component of the diet is fish (47·9%, including brown trout *Salmo trutta* and rainbow trout *Oncorhynchus mykiss*). Other important food items are 21·4% frogs (*R. temporaria*) and 30% birds, small mammals, aquatic and terrestrial invertebrates, and plant debris. In southern Italy, spraint analysis revealed that fish represented the dominant food (57·3% mean volume), followed by amphibians (18·9%) and crayfish (15·6%). Seasonal variations in fish consumption were related to changes in fish activity and to environmental conditions; the importance of fish decreased in winter, when flooding increased water speeds and turbidity, and thus reduced the hunting efficiency of the otters. Hibernating amphibians represented a primary alternative resource. Insects and reptiles were eaten more frequently in summer, while birds predominated during their breeding season. In Hungary, the primary food is fish (89·8% for riverine and 87·5% for backwater habitats); Eurasian Otters living in riverine habitats, compared to backwaters, consume more birds (3·9% and 0·7%, respectively), less mammals (0·5% and 0·9%, respectively), less reptiles and amphibians (5·6% and 10·2%, respectively) and less invertebrates (0·1% and 0·6%, respectively); most fish eaten are small-sized (below 100 g), and the most frequently taken species is *Carassius* sp. In Iran, the major food items are 38·1% chub (*Alburnoides bipunctatus*) and 34·8% carp (*Cyprinus carpio*). Prey are captured with the mouth, but the forepaws are used to handle the prey for consumption.

Activity patterns. Mainly nocturnal and crepuscular, but can also be active during the day. Den/rest sites are in burrows, among root systems, log jams, or in rock crevices, in close proximity to water.

Movements, Home range and Social organization. Eurasian Otters are excellent swimmers and divers. They are usually found no more than a few hundred meters from water, but they may travel several kilometers overland between wetlands. They swim using movements of the hindlegs and tail; usually dives last one or two minutes, five at the most. When traveling on the ground, snow, or ice they may use a combination of running and sliding. Males typically are solitary, whereas females may occur in groups, either with their own young or with unrelated, reproductive females and their young. The straight-line length of a home range may reach an average of 15 km for males and 7 km for females. Males and females typically defend their range against members of the same sex, but the home ranges of males may overlap those of several females. Population densities may be one otter per 2–3 km of lakeshore or 5 km of river.

Breeding. Females are polyestrous, with the cycle lasting four to six weeks; estrus lasts about two weeks. Mating typically occurs in late winter or early spring. The gestation period is 60–63 days and births peak in April or May. The main entrance of bank burrows may open underwater and then slope upward into the bank to a nest chamber that is above the high-water level. Litter size is one to five, usually two to three. The young are born blind and weigh about 130 g at birth. They open their eyes after one month and emerge from the den and begin to swim at two months. They nurse for three to four months and separate from the mother at about one year. Sexual maturity is attained after two or three years.

Status and Conservation. CITES Appendix I. Classified as Near Threatened in *The IUCN Red List*. The Japanese Otter, once common, has no recent confirmed sightings and may be extinct. Eurasian Otters are vulnerable to water pollution because their bodies accumulate contaminants and heavy metals, which affect reproduction. They also are killed accidentally on roads and deliberately for their fur.

Bibliography. Chruszcz *et al.* (2007), Conroy *et al.* (1998), Francis (2008), Imaizumi & Yoshiyuki (1989), Kruuk & Conroy (1991), Kruuk *et al.* (1989), Lanszki & Sallai (2006), Lanszki & Szeles (2006), Philcox *et al.* (1999), Preston *et al.* (2006), Prigioni *et al.* (2006), Rasooli *et al.* (2007), Stroganov (1969), Suzuki *et al.* (1996), Wozencraft (2005, 2008).

35. Hairy-nosed Otter *Lutra sumatrana*

French: Loutre de Sumatra / **German**: Haarnasen-Otter / **Spanish**: Nutria indonesia

Taxonomy. *Barangia sumatrana* Gray, 1865, Sumatra.
Monotypic.

Distribution. Mainland SE Asia in Myanmar, Cambodia, Vietnam, and Peninsular Malaysia; also Borneo and Sumatra.

Descriptive notes. Head-body 50–82 cm, tail 37·5–50 cm; weight 3·5–6 kg, adult males are larger than females. The Hairy-nosed Otter is small, with a dark brown pelage and paler undersides. The upper lip, sides of the face, chin, and throat are white. The rhinarium is covered with hair, with only the upper edge and margins of the nostrils naked. The limbs are short and strong, the feet are fully webbed and clawed, and the tail is flat dorso-ventrally. The skull is flat but strongly built.

Habitat. Coastal wetlands, peat swamps, swamps, large rivers, lakes, and mountain streams.

Food and Feeding. The diet is said to be primarily fish, but also includes snakes, frogs, small mammals, crabs, and insects.

Activity patterns. Reported to be nocturnal.

Movements, Home range and Social organization. Nothing known.

Breeding. Nothing known.

Status and Conservation. CITES Appendix II. Classified as Endangered in *The IUCN Red List*. The Hairy-nosed Otter is the rarest and least known among the five species of otters occurring in Asia. Once believed to be extinct, it has been rediscovered in different parts of South-east Asia such as Cambodia (Tonle Sap wetlands), Malaysia (Terengganu and Maur), Sumatra, Thailand (Phru Toa Daeng Peat Swamp Forest), and Viet Nam (U Minh Thuong Nature Reserve in Mekong Delta). Historically it has also been reported from Brunei, Myanmar, and Penang Island. Very little is known about the Hairy-nosed Otter, but it is likely that it is threatened by destruction of peat swamp forests for logging and agriculture. Research is critically needed on all aspects of this species' ecology and biology.

Bibliography. Banks (1949), Francis (2008), IUCN (2008), Lekagul & McNeely (1991), Medway (1969), Nguyen *et al.* (2001), Poole (2003), Sivasothi & Burhanuddin (1994), Tate (1947), Van Zyll de Jong (1972), Wozencraft (2005).

Genus *AONYX*

Lesson, 1827

36. African Clawless Otter *Aonyx capensis*

French: Loutre à joues blanches / **German**: Fingerotter / **Spanish**: Nutria africana
Other common names: Cape Clawless Otter, Congo Clawless Otter

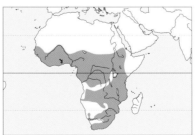

Taxonomy. *Lutra capensis* Schinz, 1821, Cape of Good Hope.
The Congo Clawless Otter (*Aonyx congicus*) is considered a separate species by some authors, based on morphological and ecological evidence; however, further research is needed to determine its taxonomic status. It is here included as a subspecies of *A. capensis*. Two subspecies are recognized.

Subspecies and Distribution.
A. c. capensis Schinz, 1821 – Sub-Saharan Africa from Senegal in the W to E Ethiopia, and E Africa to Western Cape. Absent from Congo Basin and the most arid zones of Namibia, Botswana, and South Africa.
A. c. congicus Lönnberg, 1910 – Congo Basin in WC Africa.

Descriptive notes. Head-body 76·2–88 cm (males), 73–73·6 cm (females), tail 46·5–51·5 cm (males), 49·5–51·5 cm (females); weight 10–21 kg (males), 10·6–16·3 kg (females), adult males are larger and heavier than females. The African Clawless Otter is large and heavily built. The pelage is dark brown to black throughout, but the sides of the face, neck and throat are white or pale gray. There is a quadrangular dark brown patch between the eye and the nose; the cheeks are white. The hindfeet are partially webbed, but the front feet are not. The toes are clawless except for the three middle toes of each hindfoot, which bear small grooming claws. The cheek teeth are smaller in *congicus* than in *capensis*. Dental formula: I 3/3, C 1/1, P 4/3, M 1/2 = 36.

Habitat. African Clawless Otters are mainly found in rainforests and lowland swamp forests, but may also inhabit forested rivers and streams in open coastal plains and semi-arid country. They occur mostly in fresh water; some populations inhabit saltwater coasts, but because they require fresh water to drink, even coastal populations occur near freshwater tributaries. They also occupy many natural or man-made lakes and reservoirs, but prefer areas of shallow water. In South Africa, African Clawless Otters prefer riverine habitats covered with dense vegetation, while areas of short grass are avoided. They also select areas with boulders and/or reed beds, which provide high crab density and shelter. In southern Nigeria, African Clawless Otters are mainly restricted to brackish streams (with mangrove vegetation along the banks) and, more occasionally, transitional habitats between freshwater and brackish-water environments.

Food and Feeding. African Clawless Otters are primarily crab eaters, but other foods such as frogs, fish, and insects are consumed. Fish increases in importance in the diet during winter, when they are lethargic and easier to capture. Lobsters, octopus, and shellfish are eaten along the seacoast. In two reserves in the Eastern Cape Province, South Africa, the diet was more varied at Mkambati (15 prey species) than Dwessa (seven species). In terms of relative percentage frequency of occurrence, the spiny lobster (*Panulirus homarus*) was found to be the most common prey item at both Mkambati (37·9%) and at Dwessa (35·2%), followed by fish (31% and 36·6%, respectively), crabs (22·4% and 19·7%) and molluscs (3·1% and 4·2%). Lobster and fish are relatively abundant within these reserves, suggesting prey availability rather than selective feeding influenced diet. At another site in the Eastern Cape Province, the three most common prey categories found in otter spraints were the crab *Potamonautes perlatus* (51%), insects (19%), and the fish *Tilapia sparrmanii* (18%). At Betty's Bay, South Africa, fish are the most important prey category (59% of the biomass), followed by octopus (15%), red rock crab *Plagusia chabrus* (13%), cape lobster *Jasus lalandii* (10%), and the brown rock crab *Cyclograpsus punctatus* (0·8%). In eastern Zimbabwe, the diet is mainly the river crab *Potamon perlatus* (42%). African Clawless Otters use various hunting methods. In shallow or murky water, they detect crabs with their forefeet as they feel around underwater rock crevices. Prey is grabbed with the forefeet and then bitten and eaten. In shallow but clear water, African Clawless Otters may immerse their heads and scan for prey visually while feeling under rocks with the forefeet. In deeper water, they dive straight down and can remain underwater for up to 50 seconds. African Clawless Otters eat small prey while they swim upright at the surface, whereas larger prey are taken to shore for consumption. In South Africa, African Clawless Otters were observed to select open water within 8 m of the shore. Foraging involved moving into shallow water (c. 0·2 m deep) and walking along the substrate feeling for prey with the forefeet. African Clawless Otters prefer hunting at depths of 0·5–1·5 m.

Activity patterns. Mainly nocturnal, but may be active during the day in areas remote from human disturbance. Rest sites are in burrows (holts), under large rocks or root systems, or in dense vegetation near water; they may dig their own burrows. In South Africa, the occurrence of spraints, couches and resting places is closely tied to freshwater sources; holts are located adjacent to river banks, oxbow lakes, or dam shores, and spraint sites are found in dense, tall grass cover beside water less than 1 m deep. In the Tsitsikama Coastal National Park, South Africa, the activity at several holts indicated about 32% utilization, with an estimated one otter to every three holts.

Movements, Home range and Social organization. African Clawless Otters are highly mobile and nightly movements may reach 13 km. Although mostly solitary, family groups comprising one female with her young, or groups of males, may occur. Home ranges are estimated at 14–20 km². In South Africa, a radio-tracked adult male had a minimum home range of 19·5 km of coast, with a core area of 12 km; an adult female had a 14·3 km-long home range, with a 7·5 km core area. Apparently, there was a clan-type social organization, with groups of related animals defending joint territories. In another area in South Africa, total range length varied from 4·9 to 54·1 km and core length from 0·2 to 9·8 km; the total area of water used varied between 4·9 and 1062·5 ha, and core areas from 1·1 to 138·9 ha. The pattern of home range use by females was suggestive of territoriality, whereas male otters had overlapping home ranges, both with other males and females. Population densities vary with food abundance (especially crabs) and range from 2–7 otters per 10 km of coastline or stream. Along the coast of South Africa, the mean population density was one per 1·9 km and dens were spaced at intervals of 470 m.

Breeding. Mating may occur anytime during the year, but most births occur during the start of the rainy season. Births have been recorded in July and August in Zambia, and young have been found in March and April in Uganda. There appears to be no set breeding season in West Africa. Most births in a coastal area of South Africa occurred in December and January. Gestation lasts 63 days. The litter size is one to three. The young are born blind, but with some fur. Their eyes open after 16–30 days, and weaning occurs after 60 days. Sexual maturity is reached during the first year.

Status and Conservation. CITES Appendix I and II. Classified as Least Concern in *The IUCN Red List*; the Congo Clawless Otter (*congicus*) is also listed as Least Concern. Habitat alteration and water pollution are the main threats to this species, as it affects the abundance of crabs and other prey. Additionally, the African Clawless Otter is hunted for its pelt and medicinal purposes in some areas and killed in others as a perceived competitor for fish, particularly where the Rainbow Trout has been introduced.

Bibliography. Angelici *et al.* (2005), Arden-Clark (1986), Baranga (1995), Carugati *et al.* (1995), Emmerson & Philip (2004), Kingdon (1971-1982), Ligthart *et al.* (1994), Nel & Somers (2007), Perrin & Carugati (2000), Purves *et al.* (1994), Reuther *et al.* (2003), Roberts (1951), Rosevear (1974), Rowe-Rowe (1977a, 1977b, 1992a, 1995), Rowe-Rowe & Somers (1998), Somers (2000), Somers & Nel (2004), Somers & Purves (1996), Stuart (1981), Van der Zee (1981, 1982), Van Niekerk *et al.* (1998), Verwoerd (1987), Watson & Lang (2003), Wozencraft (2005).

37. Asian Small-clawed Otter *Aonyx cinereus*

French: Loutre cendrée / **German**: Zwergotter / **Spanish**: Nutria chica
Other common names: Oriental Small-clawed Otter

Taxonomy. *Lutra cinerea* Illiger, 1815, Batavia, Indonesia.
Three subspecies are recognized.

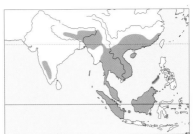

Subspecies and Distribution.
A. c. cinereus Illiger, 1815 – S & SE China (including Hainan), Mainland SE Asia, Philippines (Palawan), Borneo, Sumatra, and Java.
A. c. concolor Rafinesque, 1832 – Sub-Himalan zone in Nepal, Bhutan, NE India, N Myanmar, and SW China.
A. c. nirnai Pocock, 1940 – SW India.

Descriptive notes. Head-body 36–44 cm (males), 43·2–46·8 cm (females), tail 22·5–27 cm (males), 26–27·5 cm (females); weight 2·40–3·80 kg. Asian Small-clawed Otters are the smallest of the world's otter species. They have long bodies and short legs, and dorso-ventrally flattened tails. The pelage is uniformly brown except for the neck, throat and chin, which are grayish-silver, sometimes almost white. The head is quite small, with eyes that are proportionally larger than in other otters. There are two pairs of mammae. Claws are present but reduced on all the feet; the webbing on all the feet is incomplete. The skull is small, short and wide. Dental formula: I 3/3, C 1/1, P 3/3, M 1/2 = 34. The first premolars are usually absent. The upper and lower carnassials and the upper molar are very large.

Habitat. Asian Small-clawed Otters are found along lakes and rivers, in coastal wetlands, marshes, mangroves, and rice fields. They sometimes occur close to human settlements.

Food and Feeding. The diet is primarily crabs and shellfish. Fish, amphibians, snakes, small mammals, and insects are also eaten. In Thailand, 95% of spraints contained the crab *Potamon smithianus*, 40% contained amphibians and fish, 15% contained small mammals, and 5% contained arthropods. The size of crabs consumed by Asian Small-clawed Otters reflects what is available in the watershed they inhabit. Asian Small-clawed Otters coexist with Eurasian, Hairy-nosed, and Smooth-coated Otters in numerous locations, including several river systems in Thailand and Malaysia. Although all three species consume the same prey, the Asian Small-clawed Otter is predominantly a crab eater, whereas the other species consume mostly fish. Prey are captured mostly by sight, but also by touch, using their dextrous forefeet. Shellfish are dug up and left in the sun so that the heat causes them to open, allowing Asian Small-clawed Otters to consume them without having to crush the shells.

Activity pattern. Primarily diurnal, although reported to be nocturnal or crepuscular when found close to humans. During the day, Asian Small-clawed Otters often rest and groom on grassy or sandy banks near water. In marshes, they use mostly islands. Resting sites often show signs of spraint smearing, a behavior also observed in captivity. Defecation sites used by the Asian Small-clawed Otter occasionally are shared with Eurasian and Smooth-coated Otters and thus cannot be differentiated with certainty. Asian Small-clawed Otters have a diverse vocal repertoire that includes at least twelve different sounds, such as alarm, greeting, and mating calls.

Movements, Home range and Social organization. Asian Small-clawed Otters are playful and sociable animals, and often travel and forage in groups of up to 12–13 individuals. In captivity, they can swim underwater at speeds of 0·7–1·2 m/s.

Breeding. Asian Small-clawed Otters are monogamous and both parents help in raising the offspring. In captivity, females come into estrus every 28–30 days and estrus lasts three days. Gestation is c. 60 days. Females in captivity build a nest of grass two weeks before parturition. One pair may produce up to two litters per year. Litter size can be up to seven, but averages four. Neonates weigh about 50 g and measure around 14 cm in length, and are covered in silver gray fur. The eyes are closed until the fifth week. The young learn to swim at seven weeks of age, and attain sexual maturity during their first year. In captivity, males spend more time maintaining the nest, whereas females spend more time grooming and training young. In the wild and in captivity, older siblings may help raise offspring.

Status and Conservation. CITES Appendix II. Classified as Vulnerable in the Asian Small-clawed Otters are threatened by habitat destruction and pollution from organochlorines. Local persecution may also affect populations where they are perceived as competitors for fish resources. In parts of Asia, their organs have traditional medicinal value. Very little is known about the ecology of this species and field studies are needed.

Bibliography. Foster-Turley & Engfer (1988), Francis (2008), Kruuk *et al.* (1994), Larivière (2003a), Leslie (1970), Medway (1969), Nor (1990), Shariff (1985), Wozencraft (2005, 2008), Yoshiyuki (1971).

Genus *LUTROGALE*

Gray, 1865

38. Smooth-coated Otter *Lutrogale perspicillata*

French: Loutre indienne / **German**: Indischer Fischotter / **Spanish**: Nutria lisa

Taxonomy. *Lutra perspicillata* Geoffroy Saint-Hilaire, 1826, Sumatra.
Three subspecies are recognized.

Subspecies and Distribution.
L. p. perspicillata Geoffroy Saint-Hilaire, 1826 – SE Asia from India, S China, and Mainland SE Asia to Borneo, Sumatra, and E Java.
L. p. maxwelli Hayman, 1957 – Iraq and possibly bordering Iran.
L. p. sindica Pocock, 1940 – Afghanistan and Pakistan.

Descriptive notes. Head-body 59–75 cm, tail 37–45 cm; weight 7–11 kg. A large otter, with a very smooth pelage, naked rhinarium, and fully clawed and webbed feet. The pelage ranges from reddish-brown to dark brown, with paler undersides. The upper lip, sides of face, throat, and upper chest are gray. The upper margin of the rhinarium is flat. The vibrissae are well-developed and the tail is flat dorso-ventrally. The large feet have webbing that extends to the second joint of each digit. There are two pairs of mammae. The skull is high and wide, with a broad rostrum. Dental formula: I 3/3, C 1/1, P 4/3, M 1/2 = 36.

Habitat. Smooth-coated Otters are found in inland and coastal wetlands, seasonally flooded swamps, mangroves, and along rivers and irrigation canals. They prefer waterways with banks that are rocky and well vegetated. Smooth-coated Otters are not restricted to deep water and often forage in small, shallow rivers and seasonally flooded swamps during the monsoons (July–September) and early winter (October–February) in India and Nepal. They commonly inhabit rice fields adjacent to mangroves along coastal areas. In Malaysia, Smooth-coated Otters were found to be more abundant in mangroves. On Java, they are restricted to coastal wetlands. When occupying saltwater areas, Smooth-coated Otters require freshwater nearby.

Food and Feeding. The diet is mainly fish, but may also include small mammals, invertebrates (insects, crabs, and crustaceans), frogs, snakes, and birds. Most fish consumed are 5–30 cm in length. In Rajasthan, India, spraints contained fish (96%), insects (7%), birds (5%), molluscs (3%), frogs (1%), and worms (1%). At Periyar Lake in Kerala, India, fish were found to be the major prey: 32% tilapia (*Tilapia mossambica*), 26% catfish (*Heteropneustes fossilis*), 16% curmuca barb (*Gonoproktopterus curmuca*), 15% European carp (*Cyprinus caprio*), 3% Deccan mahsheer (*Tor khudree*), and 1% Periyar barb (*Barbus micropogon*); a higher intake of bottom-dwelling catfish was observed during periods of low water. Other food items were 4% frogs, 2% crabs, 0·7% birds, and 0·02% insects. In Nepal, spraints contained mainly fish; minor food items were frogs, crabs, shrimp, snakes, and insects. In Perak, Malaysia, Smooth-coated Otters eat mostly fish (82% of spraints, mainly *Trichogaster pectoralis*), followed by molluscs, mammals, and insects (Coleoptera). In Thailand, 70% of spraints contained fish, 13% amphibians, 11% crabs, 4% snakes, and 2% arthropods. Smooth-coated Otters forage in the less rocky areas of lake shallows. Most foraging activity occurs in water; they go on land to rest and defecate. Small fish are swallowed whole, but large fish are taken to shore.

Activity patterns. Mainly diurnal, with a rest period around midday. Den/rest sites occur under tree roots, in openings created by piles of boulders, or in dense vegetation. Smooth-coated Otters often dig their own dens and they sometimes rest on bare sand and grassy areas along river banks. In Nepal, eight dens were in exposed tree roots and one was a tunnel in the sand. In India and Nepal, dens are found in swamps; these are sometimes used as natal den sites and nurseries. Spraint sites often smell of rotten fish. In Thailand, spraint sites occur on small rocks, sand banks, and large boulders, 1–3 m above water level. The mean number of spraints on each site was 2·2. Smooth-coated Otters often roll and rub on grassy areas, especially after defecation.

Movements, Home range and Social organization. Smooth-coated Otters are excellent swimmers and are able to swim underwater for long distances. They are social and are often seen in groups of up to eleven individuals; groups typically consist of a mated pair with young from previous litters. It is estimated that a group of Smooth-coated Otters requires 7–12 km of river to sustain their needs. Population density is 1–1·3 otters per km of water.

Breeding. In India and Nepal, mating occurs in the winter (October–February). Gestation lasts 60–63 days. Litter size is one to five. The young are born blind; the eyes open after ten days. Weaning occurs after three to five months. Adult size is reached after one year and sexual maturity after two to three years.

Status and Conservation. CITES Appendix II. Classified as Vulnerable in *The IUCN Red List*. Although the Smooth-coated Otter may have been quite common in the past and populations stable, it is now likely this is changing rapidly and that this species will soon be in need of urgent help. Increasing human population across its range is putting the Smooth-coated Otter under pressure through habitat destruction and pollution. There is widespread conflict with aquaculturalists and fishermen, who kill them as pests and competitors. There is also deliberate trapping for fur in India, Nepal, and Bangladesh, mainly for export to China. Although legally protected throughout its range, this is weakly enforced. Movements of Smooth-coated Otters are limited due to arid regions, leading to poor dispersal and population fragmentation. Several authorities have recommended that *ex situ* as well as *in situ* conservation efforts should be made. Field studies are needed to learn more about its natural history, ecology, and conservation status.

Bibliography. Anoop & Hussain (2004, 2005), Biswas (1973), Corbet & Hill (1992), Francis (2008), Hussain (1996), Hwang & Larivière (2005), Kruuk *et al.* (1994), Lekagul & McNeely (1991), Medway (1969), Shariff (1985), Tate (1947), Wozencraft (2005, 2008), Yadav (1967).

39

40

41
winter
summer

42

43

44
northern
variant
summer
winter
ssp *frenata*

45

46

47

48

49

50
summer
winter
white variant

51

52

53

PLATE 36

inches
cm

54

55

56

57

Subfamily MUSTELINAE

Genus *MUSTELA*

Linnaeus, 1758

39. Amazon Weasel *Mustela africana*

French: Belette des tropiques / **German**: Amazonas-Wiesel / **Spanish**: Comadreja amazónica

Other common names: Tropical Weasel

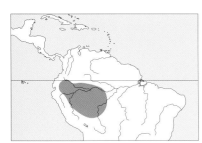

Taxonomy. *Mustela africana* Desmarest, 1818, Brazil.
Monotypic.
Distribution. Amazon Basin in Bolivia, Brazil, Colombia, Ecuador, and Peru.
Descriptive notes. Head-body 24–38 cm, tail 16–21 cm. The Amazon Weasel has a long, slender body and short limbs. The pelage is reddish to dark brown, with paler undersides. The underparts have a longitudinal median stripe of the same color as the upper parts. The tail is uniformly brown. The plantar surfaces on the feet are nearly naked.
Habitat. Has been reported from primary forest and humid riparian habitats.
Food and Feeding. Nothing known.
Activity pattern. Possibly diurnal: a group of four were seen around 10:00 h. Has been found denning in a hollow tree stump.
Movements, Home range and Social organization. Said to be primarily terrestrial, but also reported to be a good swimmer and climber. Has been seen in a group of four.
Breeding. Nothing known.
Status and Conservation. Classified as Least Concern in *The IUCN Red List*. One of the least known species within the Mustelidae. Amazon Weasels are a high priority for field studies to learn more about their natural history, ecology, and conservation status.
Bibliography. Ferrari & Lopes (1992), Izor & de la Torre (1978), Wozencraft (2005).

40. Altai Mountain Weasel *Mustela altaica*

French: Belette des montagnes / **German**: Altai-Wiesel / **Spanish**: Comadreja de montaña

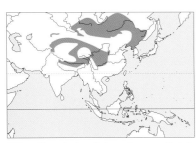

Taxonomy. *Mustela altaica* Pallas, 1811, Altai Mountains, China.
Monotypic.
Distribution. Altai, Tien Shan, Pamir, and Himalayan ranges; also C, W, SW & NE China, Mongolia, and Russia (S & SE Siberia) to North Korea.
Descriptive notes. Head-body 22·4–28·7 cm (males), 21·7–24·9 cm (females); tail 10·8–14·5 cm (males), 9–11·7 cm (females); weight 217–350 g (males), 122–220 g (females), adult males are slightly larger than females; the tail is more than 40% of the head and body length. The Altai Mountain Weasel has a long, slender body and short limbs. The summer pelage is grayish-brown; in winter, the dorsal pelage is yellowish-brown, with pale undersides. The tail is the same color as the upperparts. The feet are white. The skull has a short rostrum and a long cerebral cranium.
Habitat. Alpine meadows, steppes and forests, from 1500 to 4000 m.
Food and Feeding. The diet includes small mammals (rodents, pikas, and rabbits), small birds, lizards, frogs, fish, insects, and berries. Altai Mountain Weasels search for prey around rock crevices, brushy areas, and uprooted trees, often investigating prey burrows.
Activity pattern. Mainly nocturnal or crepuscular. Den/rest sites are in rock crevices, among tree roots, or in rodent burrows.
Movements, Home range and Social organization. Mainly terrestrial, but also climbs and swim well.
Breeding. In Kazakh, mating occurs in February or March. Gestation is 35–50 days. Litter size is two to eight; lactation last two months.
Status and Conservation. Classified as Near Threatened in *The IUCN Red List*. Very little is known about the Altai Mountain Weasel and field studies are needed to learn more about its natural history, ecology, and conservation status. It is of little importance in the fur trade, but is occasionally hunted and may be susceptible to habitat conversion.
Bibliography. Lunde & Musser (2003), Meiri *et al.* (2007), Pocock (1941a), Stroganov (1969), Van Bree & Boeadi (1978), Wozencraft (2005, 2008).

41. Ermine *Mustela erminea*

French: Belette hermine / **German**: Hermelin / **Spanish**: Armiño

Other common names: Stoat, Short-tailed Weasel

Taxonomy. *Mustela erminea* Linnaeus, 1758, Sweden.
Thirty-four subspecies are recognized.
Subspecies and Distribution.
M. e. erminea Linnaeus, 1758 – Finland, Norway, NW Russia, and Sweden.
M. e. aestiva Kerr, 1792 – most of mainland N & C Europe to C Asia in Kazakhstan, Kyrgyzstan, and Tajikistan.
M. e. alascensis Merriam, 1896 – S Alaska.
M. e. anguinae Hall, 1932 – SW Canada (Vancouver I, British Columbia).
M. e. arctica Merriam, 1896 – Alaska and NW Canada.
M. e. bangsi Hall, 1945 – C Canada and NC USA.
M. e. celenda Hall, 1944 – Alaska (Prince of Wales I).
M. e. cicognanii Bonaparte, 1838 – SE Canada and NE USA.
M. e. fallenda Hall, 1945 – W Canada (British Columbia) and NW USA (N Washington).
M. e. ferghanae Thomas, 1895 – Afghanistan, N India, and Pakistan.
M. e. gulosa Hall, 1945 – NW USA (E Washington).
M. e. haidarum Preble, 1898 – W Canada (Queen Charlotte Is, British Columbia).
M. e. hibernica Thomas & Barrett-Hamilton, 1895 – Ireland.
M. e. initis Hall, 1944 – Alaska (Baranof I).
M. e. invicta Hall, 1945 – SW Canada (Alberta) and NW USA (Idaho & Montana).
M. e. kadiacensis Merriam, 1896 – Alaska (Kodiak I).
M. e. kaneii Baird, 1857 – NE China, Russia (E Siberia).
M. e. karaginensis Jurgenson, 1936 – NE Russia (Karaginsky I).
M. e. lymani Hollister, 1912 – E Russia (Altai Mts, Siberia).
M. e. minima Cavazza, 1912 – Switzerland.
M. e. mongolica Ognev, 1928 – NW China and Mongolian Altai.
M. e. muricus Bangs, 1899 – USA (N California, Colorado, Idaho, New Mexico, Nevada, Oregon, South Dakota, Utah & Wyoming).
M. e. nippon Cabrera, 1913 – Japan.
M. e. olympica Hall, 1945 – NW USA (Olympic Peninsula, Washington).
M. e. polaris Barrett-Hamilton, 1904 – Greenland.
M. e. richardsonii Bonaparte, 1838 – N Canada.
M. e. ricinae G. S. Miller, 1907 – Scotland (Islay I).
M. e. salva Hall, 1944 – SE Alaska (Admiralty I).
M. e. seclusa Hall, 1944 – SE Alaska (Suemez I).
M. e. semplei Sutton & Hamilton, 1932 – Canada (Franklin & Keewatin Districts).
M. e. stabilis Barrett-Hamilton, 1904 – Great Britain.
M. e. streatori Merriam, 1896 – W USA (NE California, Oregon & coastal Washington).
M. e. teberdina Kornejv, 1941 – Russian Caucasus.
M. e. tobolica Ognev, 1923 – W Siberia.
Introduced to New Zealand.
Descriptive notes. Head-body 22·5–34 cm (males), 19–29 cm (females); tail 4·2–12 cm; weight of males is 208–283 g in Europe, 320 g in Britain, 285–356 g in New Zealand (introduced population), 233–365 g in Ireland, 134–191 g in Russia, 56–206 g in North America, adult males are 40–80% larger than females. The Ermine has a long, slender body and short limbs. Except in certain southern parts of their range, Ermines change color in April–May and October–November. In the summer, the back, flanks, and outer sides of the limbs are reddish or chocolate brown; the underparts are white and the tip of the tail is black. During winter, the pelage becomes white throughout except for the black tip of the tail. There are four pairs of mammae. The skull has a long braincase, inflated tympanic bullae, and is relatively flat. Dental formula: I 3/3, C 1/1, P 3/3, M 1/2 = 34.
Habitat. Ermines are found in a wide range of habitats, including tundra, alpine meadows, woodlands, marshes, mountains, riparian habitats, farmland, and hedgerows, from sea level up to 3000 m. They prefer areas with vegetative or rocky cover. In the mountains of south-east British Columbia, Ermines were detected in all forests surveyed; these covered the range from open dry Douglas-fir forests to dense wet western red cedar (*Thuja plicata*) and western hemlock (*Tsuga heterophylla*) forests, and from very recent clear-cuts to mature stands over 300 years in age. In a subarctic area in Finland, adult females were found to live in areas where the abundance of their preferred *Microtus* prey was the highest; dominant males lived in less productive habitats than females, but in more productive areas than non-dominant mature males.
Food and Feeding. The diet consists mainly of small mammals, such as voles, mice, rats, lemmings, squirrels, and lagomorphs, but also includes birds, eggs, lizards, frogs, snakes, insects, earthworms, and fruit. In Great Britain, the percentage frequency of occurrence in the diet consists of 65% lagomorphs, 16% small rodents, and 17% birds and birds' eggs; males eat a greater proportion of lagomorphs than

On following pages: 42. Steppe Polecat (*Mustela eversmanii*); 43. Colombian Weasel (*Mustela felipei*); 44. Long-tailed Weasel (*Mustela frenata*); 45. Japanese Weasel (*Mustela itatsi*); 46. Yellow-bellied Weasel (*Mustela kathiah*); 47. European Mink (*Mustela lutreola*); 48. Indonesian Mountain Weasel (*Mustela lutreolina*); 49. Black-footed Ferret (*Mustela nigripes*); 50. Least Weasel (*Mustela nivalis*); 51. Malay Weasel (*Mustela nudipes*); 52. European Polecat (*Mustela putorius*); 53. Siberian Weasel (*Mustela sibirica*); 54. Back-striped Weasel (*Mustela strigidorsa*); 55. Egyptian Weasel (*Mustela subpalmata*); 56. American Mink (*Neovison vison*); 57. Patagonian Weasel (*Lyncodon patagonicus*).

females, which eat more small rodents. In Denmark (where European Rabbits are absent), a dietary study showed that rodents are the most important prey group, constituting 84% of their diet (frequency of occurrence). Ermines ate birds and birds' eggs more often than sympatric Least Weasels, while Least Weasels ate more insectivores. Ermines ate more *Microtus* voles and Water Voles than Least Weasels, while Least Weasels ate more Bank Voles (*Clethrionomys glareolus*) and Moles (*Talpa europaea*). In the Italian Alps, 60% of scats contained small rodents, indicating that they were the main prey. However, the frequency of occurrence of fruits in the diet increased significantly in August, after rodent biomass had dropped by more than 50% in July. In the forests of New Brunswick, Canada, the frequency of occurrence of prey is 28·0% soricids, 24·6% arvicolines, and 17·3% cricetines; the Deer Mouse (*Peromyscus maniculatus*, 17·3%) and shrews (*Sorex* sp., 28·0%) have the highest percent occurrence, whereas the Red Squirrel and the Eastern Chipmunk (*Tamius striatus*) comprise 11·2% of the diet. Ermines generally hunt in a zig-zag pattern, progressing by a series of leaps that are up to 50 cm long. Prey are located mostly by smell or sound, and are often pursued into underground burrows or under snow. Ermines usually kill prey by biting the base of the skull. They sometimes attack animals considerably larger than themselves, such as adult hares. Ermines may cache excess food underground for later use during the winter.

Activity patterns. Primarily nocturnal, but can be active at any time during the day. Their long shape makes them sensitive to cold temperatures and this, combined with a high metabolic rate, requires that Ermines hunt constantly to fulfill their energetic demands. Short periods of activity and rest alternate every three to five hours. Dens/rest sites are in crevices, among tree roots, in hollow logs, or in burrows taken over from a rodent. Several nests are maintained within an individual's home range; these are lined with dry vegetation or the fur and feathers of its prey. Ermines can easily run over or tunnel in snow to escape predators and search for food.

Movements, Home range and Social organization. Ermines are solitary and primarily terrestrial, but they are also agile tree climbers and strong swimmers. Daily movements may reach 15 km, but usually average c. 1 km. Movements increase when prey are rare or dispersed. Home ranges may reach 200 ha, but are typically 10–40 ha; male ranges are generally larger than female ranges. Both sexes maintain exclusive territories, but a male home range may overlap one or more female ranges. Males show a marked seasonal shift in their social organization from a pattern of intra-sexual territories during the non-breeding season (autumn and winter) to a non-territorial pattern with extensive and overlapping ranges during the mating season (spring and summer). Boundaries are regularly patrolled and scent-marked, and neighbors usually avoid each other. Population density fluctuates with prey abundance and may range from 2–6 individuals per km².

Breeding. Females are polyestrous, but produce only one litter per year; the estrous cycle is four weeks. Mating occurs in late spring or early summer, but implantation of the fertilized eggs into the uterus is delayed for 9–10 months. Embryonic development is just over one month. Births occur in April or May in the Northern Hemisphere and around October in New Zealand. Litter size may reach 18, but typically is four to eight. Neonates are born blind, naked, and weigh 2·7–4·2 g. Their eyes open after four to six weeks. Solid food is taken after four or five weeks, though lactation may continue until weeks seven to twelve. They grow rapidly and by eight weeks are able to hunt with their mother. At two to three months, their permanent detention is complete. Females reach adult size at six months. They attain sexual maturity at two to three months and sometimes mate during their first summer. Males attain full size and sexual maturity after one year.

Status and Conservation. Classified as Least Concern in *The IUCN Red List*. Ermines are considered common throughout their distribution. They rarely molest poultry and are valuable to humans because they prey on mice and rats. However, Ermines are considered pests in New Zealand, where they were introduced to control rabbits but subsequently decimated populations of native birds. On the Iberian Peninsula, the Ermine is dependent on two *Arvicola* species, which are declining in numbers. Ermines are trapped in North America and Russia for their fur; the white winter fur has long been used in trimming coats and making stoles.

Bibliography. Edwards & Forbes (2003), Elmeros (2006), Erlinge & Sandell (1986), Hellstedt & Henttonen (2006), Hellstedt *et al.* (2006), King (1983, 1990), Martinoli *et al.* (2001), McDonald *et al.* (2000), Mowat & Poole (2005), Robitaille & Raymond (1995), Samson & Raymond (1998), Svendsen (2003), Wozencraft (2005, 2008).

42. Steppe Polecat *Mustela eversmanii*

French: Putois d'Eversmann / German: Steppeniltis / Spanish: Turón estepario

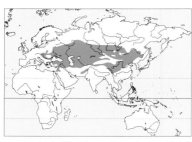

Taxonomy. *Mustela eversmanii* Lesson, 1827, Russia.
The Steppe Polecat was considered conspecific with either *M. putorius* or *M. nigripes* by some authors. Up to nineteen subspecies have been proposed, but a taxonomic revision is needed.
Distribution. SE Europe, Caucasus, and Middle East through C Asia to NE China, Mongolia, and Russian Far East.
Descriptive notes. Head-body 37–56·2 cm (males), 29–52 cm (females); tail 8–18·3 cm (males), 7–18 cm (females); weight 2·05 kg (males), 1·35 kg (females), adult males are larger than females. The Steppe Polecat closely resembles the European Polecat. The pelage is highly variable in color, but generally is yellowish-white to brown, with the upperparts darker than the undersides. The fur on the chest, limbs, and tail is darker in color, and there is a dark mask on the whitish face.

Habitat. Steppe, open grasslands, and semi-desert.
Food and Feeding. The diet includes rodents (voles, hamsters, marmots), other small mammals (pikas, ground squirrels), birds, eggs, reptiles, and insects. In Hungary, the principle food consists of small mammals; their frequency fluctuates between 54% and 93%, reaching a maximum in summer. In all seasons, the most important prey is the Common Vole (*Microtus arvalis*) and the Common Hamster (*Cricetus cricetus*); in addition, the European Souslik (*Spermophilus citellus*) is occasionally consumed in spring and autumn, and Brown Rats (*Rattus norvegicus*) may be eaten in autumn. The European Hare is eaten only in winter (5%). The consumption of birds (mainly Passerines) is considerable in spring (38%) and autumn (29%). A stable isotope study revealed a diet that comprised 27% small mammals (Plateau Pika, Root Vole, and Plateau Zokor) and 47·7% adult passerine birds, with hatchlings contributing 25·6%. Steppe Polecats hunt by exploring the burrows of their mammalian prey and thus they may spend much time underground.
Activity patterns. Primarily nocturnal. Den/rest sites are in burrows expropriated from other animals.
Movements, Home range and Social organization. Steppe Polecats are solitary. They move rapidly, constantly exploring new ground and searching for food, and may cover up to 18 km during the night. Local migrations may occur to areas with greater food abundance or less snow.
Breeding. Mating occurs from February to March, with births from April to May. Gestation lasts 38–41 days. Litters are large, usually from eight to ten. The young weigh 4–6 g at birth, open their eyes after one month, and are weaned and start hunting with the mother at 1·5 months. They disperse at three months. Sexual maturity is reached during the first breeding season, when the young are nine months old.
Status and Conservation. Classified as Least Concern in *The IUCN Red List*; the subspecies *M. e. amurensis*, of south-eastern Siberia and Manchuria, is classified as Vulnerable. Little is known about this species and field studies are needed to learn more about its natural history, ecology, and conservation status. It is not intentionally hunted except in Russia, but is heavily impacted by persecution in the western parts of its range.
Bibliography. Lanszki & Heltai (2007), Stroganov (1969), Wozencraft (2005, 2008).

43. Colombian Weasel *Mustela felipei*

French: Belette de Colombie / German: Kolumbien-Wiesel / Spanish: Comadreja de Don Felipe

Taxonomy. *Mustela felipei* Izor & de la Torre, 1978, Colombia.
Monotypic.
Distribution. Colombia and Ecuador.
Descriptive notes. Head-body 21·7–22·5 cm, tail 11·1–12·2 cm; weight c. 138 g. The Columbian Weasel has a long body and short limbs. The pelage is long and soft, almost entirely dark brown on the back, with pale orange undersides. All the feet have extensive webbing, with naked plantar surfaces.
Habitat. Most specimens were collected near riparian areas, at elevations between 1700–2700 m.
Food and Feeding. Nothing known.
Activity patterns. Nothing known.
Movements, Home range and Social organization. Nothing known.
Breeding. Nothing known.
Status and Conservation. Classified as Vulnerable in *The IUCN Red List*. A very poorly known species, only recently described. Possibly the rarest carnivore in South America, it occurs in a limited area of less than 10,000 km² where deforestation is rampant. Since its discovery, only five specimens have been obtained from western Colombia (provinces of Huila and Cauca) and northern Ecuador. The Columbian Weasel is a high priority for field research to learn more about its natural history, ecology, and conservation status.
Bibliography. Alberico (1994), Fawcett *et al.* (1996), IUCN (2008), Izor & de la Torre (1978), Wozencraft (2005).

44. Long-tailed Weasel *Mustela frenata*

French: Belette à longue queue / German: Langschwanzwiesel / Spanish: Comadreja colilarga

Taxonomy. *Mustela frenata* Lichtenstein, 1831, Ciudad Mexico, Mexico.
Forty-two subspecies are recognized.
Subspecies and Distribution.
M. f. frenata Lichtenstein, 1831 – NE Mexico and S USA (S Texas).
M. f. affinis Gray, 1874 – Colombia.
M. f. agilis Tschudi, 1844 – W Peru.
M. f. alleni Merriam, 1896 – C USA (South Dakota & Wyoming).
M. f. altifrontalis Hall, 1936 – SW Canada (British Columbia) and NW USA (coastal Oregon & Washington).
M. f. arizonensis Mearns, 1891 – SW USA (Arizona).

M. f. arthuri Hall, 1927 – S USA (Louisiana).
M. f. aureoventris Gray, 1865 – Ecuador.
M. f. boliviensis Hall, 1938 – Bolivia.
M. f. costaricensis Goldman, 1912 – Costa Rica.
M. f. effera Hall, 1936 – NW USA (NE Oregon & SE Washington).
M. f. goldmani Merriam, 1896 – El Salvador, Guatemala, and Mexico (Chiapas).
M. f. helleri Hall, 1935 – E Peru.
M. f. inyoensis Hall, 1936 – SW USA (Inyo County, California).
M. f. latirostra Hall, 1936 – NW Mexico (Baja California) and SW USA (S California).
M. f. leucoparia Merriam, 1896 – SW Mexico.
M. f. longicauda Bonaparte, 1838 – Great Plains of Canada and USA.
M. f. macrophonius Elliot, 1905 – S Mexico (Oaxaca & Veracruz).
M. f. macrura Taczanowski, 1874 – Peru (Cajamarca).
M. f. meridana Hollister, 1914 – Venezuela.
M. f. munda Bangs, 1899 – SW USA (NC coastal California).
M. f. neomexicana Barber & Cockerell, 1898 – C & N Mexico and SW USA (New Mexico).
M. f. nevadensis Hall, 1936 – W USA (Great Basin & Rocky Mts).
M. f. nicaraguae J. A. Allen, 1916 – Honduras and Nicaragua.
M. f. nigriauris Hall, 1936 – SW USA (SC coastal California).
M. f. noveboracensis Emmons, 1840 – SE Canada and E USA.
M. f. occisor Bangs, 1899 – NE USA (Maine).
M. f. olivacea Howell, 1913 – SE USA.
M. f. oregonensis Merriam, 1896 – W USA (Cascade Mts of Oregon).
M. f. oribasus Bangs, 1899 – SW Canada (British Columbia) and NW USA (Montana).
M. f. panamensis Hall, 1932 – Panama.
M. f. peninsulae Rhoads, 1894 – SE USA (S Florida).
M. f. perda Merriam, 1902 – Yucatan Peninsula, Belize and Mexico.
M. f. perotae Hall, 1936 – C Mexico.
M. f. primulina Jackson, 1913 – Midwestern USA.
M. f. pulchra Hall, 1936 – SW USA (Kern County, California).
M. f. saturata Merriam, 1896 – W USA (NC California & S Oregon).
M. f. spadix Bangs, 1896 – N USA (Minnesota).
M. f. texensis Hall, 1936 – S USA (C Texas).
M. f. tropicalis Merriam, 1896 – E Mexico (Tamaulipas & Veracruz).
M. f. washingtoni Merriam, 1896 – W USA (NC Oregon & SC Washington).
M. f. xanthogenys Gray, 1843 – SW USA (C California).

Descriptive notes. Head-body length, 22·8–26 cm (males), 20·3–22·8 cm (females); tail 10·2–15·2 cm (males), 7·6–12·7 cm (females); weight 160–450 g (males), 80–250 g (females), adult males are almost twice the size of females. The Long-tailed Weasel has a long body and short limbs. In Canada and the northern United States, the pelage changes from early October to early December and from late February to late April. During the summer, the upperparts are brown, the underparts are buff, and the tip of the tail is black. In winter, the pelage is white except for the black-tipped tail. Subspecies from the southern USA, Mexico and Central America, have distinctive white or yellow facial markings. The plantar surfaces on the feet are furred. There are four pairs of mammae. The skull is long, with large tympanic bullae. Dental formula: I 3/3, C 1/1, P 3/3, M 1/2 = 34.
Habitat. Long-tailed Weasels are found in a wide range of habitats from forested areas to agricultural fields. They show a preference for open, brushy or grassy areas near water.
Food and Feeding. The diet consists mainly of rodents (voles, mice, and rats) and other small mammals (such as lagomorphs and squirrels), but birds, eggs, snakes, grasshoppers, and poultry are also occasionally eaten. Because of their larger size, males generally consume larger prey than females. In North America, Long-tailed Weasels feed upon a wide variety of small vertebrates, but concentrate on rodents and rabbits of small to medium size. The diet of tropical Long-tailed Weasels, although not well known, is thought to consist mainly of small mammals, rabbits, and birds and their eggs. Small-sized prey, such as mice and voles, usually are subdued when the weasel throws its body into a tight coil around the prey; these are then killed by a bite to the nape of the neck. Long-tailed Weasels can kill animals larger than themselves, such as rabbits. Large prey is initially grabbed by the most convenient part of the animal before a killing bite is administered. Underground medium-sized prey is subdued by a ventral attack and killed by grasping the throat, which results in suffocation.
Activity patterns. Primarily nocturnal, but frequently active during the day. Den/rest sites are in hollow logs or stumps, among rocks, or in a burrow taken over from a rodent. Long-tailed Weasels spend large amounts of time exploring holes, crevices, root systems, brush piles, thick vegetation, and under the snow in winter, in search of prey.
Movements, Home range and Social organization. Long-tailed Weasels are solitary and mainly terrestrial, but are also good swimmers and tree climbers. The home ranges of males average larger than those of females, and may include the home ranges of more than one female. During the breeding season, the home ranges of males increase in size, allowing more frequent contact with females. There is little overlap of the home ranges of males. In Kentucky, home ranges vary from 0·16 to 0·24 km² during summer, and 0·10 to 0·18 km² during winter. In Indiana, the

mean home range for males was 1·80 km² and for females 0·52 km². The hourly rate of movement for males (130·5 m) was greater than that of females (79·2 m). Estimates of densities vary widely by habitat and prey availability. Reported population densities are: 0·004–0·008/ha in western Colorado, 0·02–0·18/ha in Kentucky, 0·19–0·38/ha in chestnut–oak forest and 0·07–0·09/ha in scrub oak–pitch pine forest in Pennsylvania, and 0·2–0·3/ha in cattail marsh in Ontario.
Breeding. Females are monoestrous. Mating occurs in July and August. Implantation of the fertilized eggs into the uterus is delayed until the following March; embryonic development is approximately 27 days. Births occur in April or May. Litter size is up to nine, but is usually around six. The young are born blind and weigh about 3 g at birth. They open their eyes after 35–37 days and are weaned at around 3½ weeks. Females attain sexual maturity at three to four months, but males do not mate until the year following their birth.
Status and Conservation. Classified as Least Concern in *The IUCN Red List*. The Long-tailed Weasel is considered to be common throughout most of its distribution; however, several subspecies are considered uncommon. It is able to occupy a wide variety of habitats and can live in close proximity to humans. Long-tailed Weasels are more prone to raid henhouses that other species of *Mustela*, but they are generally beneficial because they prey on rats and mice. They are trapped in North America for their white winter fur.
Bibliography. Gehring & Swihart (2004), King (1990), Sheffield & Thomas (1997), Svendsen (2003), Wozencraft (2005).

45. Japanese Weasel *Mustela itatsi*
French: Putois du Japon / **German**: Japan-Wiesel / **Spanish**: Comadreja japonesa

Taxonomy. *Mustela itatsi* Temminck, 1844, Japan.
The Japanese Weasel was previously considered a subspecies of the Siberian Weasel. Monotypic.
Distribution. Japan. Introduced to Hokkaido and Russia (S Sakhalin).
Descriptive notes. Head-body 28–39 cm (males), 25–30·5 cm (females); tail 15·5–21 cm (males), 13·3–16·4 cm (females); weight 650–820 g (males), 360–430 g (females), adult males are almost twice the weight of females. The Japanese Weasel has a long, slender body and short limbs. The pelage is dark brown in summer, and becomes paler, almost yellowish brown in winter. The upper lips and chin are white.
Habitat. Forests. Often found in close proximity to water and sometimes near human dwellings.
Food and Feeding. The diet includes insects, reptiles, and small mammals. In Hamura, Japanese Weasels eat rodents, fish, arthropods, and crustaceans throughout the year; seasonal changes in the diet are small. In Tachikawa, the main food items are rodents and fruits in winter and spring, and arthropods and crustaceans in summer and autumn. On Zamami Island, where Japanese Weasels were introduced in 1957 and 1958, they eat a wide variety of prey, mainly insects, followed by reptiles and small mammals.
Activity patterns. Nocturnal.
Movements, Home range and Social organization. Solitary.
Breeding. Mating occurs in late winter and births occur in the spring.
Status and Conservation. Classified as Least Concern in *The IUCN Red List*. The Japanese Weasel is considered common throughout its range. This species has been introduced to certain areas to control reptiles and rats. Very little is known about Japanese Weasels and field studies are needed to learn more about their natural history, ecology, and conservation status.
Bibliography. Fujii *et al.* (1998), Keishi *et al.* (2002), Okada *et al.* (2007), Sekiguchi *et al.* (2002), Wozencraft (2005).

46. Yellow-bellied Weasel *Mustela kathiah*
French: Belette à ventre jaune / **German**: Gelbbauchwiesel / **Spanish**: Comadreja china

Taxonomy. *Mustela kathiah* Hodgson, 1835, Nepal.
Monotypic.
Distribution. Bhutan, S & E China, N & NE India, Laos, Myanmar, Nepal, N Thailand, and Vietnam.
Descriptive notes. Head-body 20–29 cm, tail 13–18 cm; weight 150–260 g. The Yellow-bellied Weasel has a long, slender body and short limbs. The upperparts are dark chocolate to rusty brown; the underparts are pale yellow or light orange-brown. The chin and upper lip are whitish. The tail is bushy and the same color as the upperparts. Some white patches may occur on the feet.
Habitat. Pine forests, up to 4000 m (above the timber line). In Western Himalaya from 3000-5200 m in the cold deserts, but in Hong Kong found in much lower altitudes, from close to sea-level to over 200 m.

Food and Feeding. Diet is said to include rodents, birds, eggs, lizards, frogs, insects, and fruit.
Activity patterns. Nothing known.
Movements, Home range and Social organization. Nothing known.
Breeding. Nothing known.
Status and Conservation. Classified as Least Concern in *The IUCN Red List*. This is a poorly known species and field studies are needed to learn more about its natural history, ecology, and conservation status.
Bibliography. Duckworth & Robichaud (2005), Francis (2008), IUCN (2008), Lekagul & McNeely (1991), Pocock (1941a), Wozencraft (2005, 2008).

47. European Mink *Mustela lutreola*
French: Vison d'Europe / **German**: Europäischer Nerz / **Spanish**: Visón europeo

Taxonomy. *Viverra lutreola* Linnaeus, 1761, Finland.
Monotypic.
Distribution. Belarus, Estonia, France, Latvia, Romania, Russia (W of Urals), and N Spain.
Descriptive notes. Head-body 20–36 cm, tail 12–17·5 cm; weight 650–1000 g (males), 500–600 g (females), adult males are slightly larger than females. The European Mink has a long, slender body and short limbs. The pelage is dense and short, and reddish-brown in color; the underparts are paler than the back. A margin of white occurs around the mouth and sometimes on the chest and throat. The skull is flat and narrow. Dental formula: I 3/3, C 1/1, P 3/3, M 1/2 = 34.
Habitat. European Mink are found along streams, rivers, and lakes. They are rarely found more than 100 m from fresh water and prefer waterways with densely vegetated banks. In south-Western Europe, radio-collared European Mink used areas that had low forest cover and bramble or shrub cover along the riverbank; they avoided areas with dense forest cover. In south-western France, radio-collared European Mink had a strong preference for flooded habitats, particularly open marshes, flooded woodlands, and moorlands; they seldom left riparian forest corridors.
Food and Feeding. The diet includes small mammals, birds, amphibians, fish, molluscs, crabs, and insects. The chief prey is often the Water Vole. In northern Spain, scat analysis revealed a diet based on small mammals (relative frequency of occurrence 36·9%), fish (30·6%), and birds (17·8%). The Wood Mouse (*Apodemus sylvaticus*) was the most consumed small mammal and cyprinids (mainly *Barbus* sp.) were the most frequently eaten fish. The average size of consumed fish was 13·5 cm, and the average weight was 31·5 g; males ate larger and heavier fish than females. In north-east Belarus, three out of nine individuals studied were specialists on frogs (77–97%, mainly the common frog *Rana temporaria*). One individual fed mostly on crayfish (*Astacus astacus*, 62%), and the other five were generalist predators. Excess food may be cached for later use.
Activity patterns. Mainly nocturnal and crepuscular. Den/rest sites are in crevices, amongst tree roots and dense bramble patches, or in burrows, either self-excavated or taken from a Water Vole. In south-western France, rest sites were mainly found above ground in flooded areas, under bushes or in cavities between tree roots.
Movements, Home range and Social organization. European Mink are terrestrial, but swim and dive well. Home ranges average 32 ha for males and 26 ha for females. In south-Western Europe, the length of home ranges varied between 11–17 km along watercourses for five males, and was 0·6 and 3·6 km for two females. The home ranges of males were larger than those found in previous studies and most females captured were found within the home range of a male. Males occupied adjoining river sections with minimal range overlap, suggesting an intra-sexual exclusive spacing pattern for males. In autumn and winter, there may be extensive movements to locate swift, non-frozen streams. Population densities may reach 12 animals/10 km of shoreline.
Breeding. Mating occurs from February to March. Gestation is 35–72 days. Births occur in April and May in rock piles, under roots, in hollow trees, or in abandoned buildings. Litter size is two to seven, usually four or five. The young are born blind, and at birth average 8·4 g for males and 7·6 g for females. The eyes open after 30–36 days. They are weaned at ten weeks and attain sexual maturity after 9–10 months.
Status and Conservation. Classified as Endangered in *The IUCN Red List*. The European Mink has declined over much of its former range and has been extirpated from Austria, Bulgaria, Czech Republic, Germany, Hungary, Montenegro, Poland, Serbia, and Slovakia. Habitat loss and degradation is a serious threat in many parts of Europe. Ongoing destruction and degradation of freshwater and associated terrestrial habitats has been caused by hydroelectric development, river channelization, and water pollution. Although its fur is not as valuable as that of the American Mink, the European Mink was widely trapped for commercial purposes. It is now legally protected in all range states and at least part of the population occurs within protected areas. However, accidental trapping still poses a threat. In France, secondary poisoning and trapping of European Mink has occurred as a result of efforts to control Coypu (*Myocastor coypus*) and small carnivore species. Accidental mortality through vehicle collisions is a problem in some areas. Competition with the American Mink (an alien invasive species) has been hypothesized as a contributing factor. In Spain and France, hybridization with the European Polecat may also be a threat. Field studies have been undertaken

to determine its ecological requirements, to analyse the causes of its decline, and to assess the genetic variability of western populations. In Spain and France, programmes have been started to control the American Mink population. A captive breeding programme was launched in 1992 under the European Zoo Association. Reintroduction efforts are underway in Germany and Russia. The European Mink has recently colonized and spread into northern Spain; it was absent from this country before 1950. Recent genetic studies have shown there is very low genetic variability within this species, which could pose an additional threat.
Bibliography. Dunstone (1993), Fournier *et al.* (2007), Garin, Aihartza *et al.* (2002), Garin, Zuberogoitia, *et al.* (2002), Michaux, Hardy *et al.* (2005), Michaux, Libois *et al.* (2004), Palazon *et al.* (2004), Sidorovich *et al.* (2001), Wozencraft (2005), Youngman (1990), Zabala, Zuberogoitia, Garin & Aihartza (2003), Zabala, Zuberogoitia & Martinez-Climent (2006).

48. Indonesian Mountain Weasel *Mustela lutreolina*
French: Putois d'Indonésie / **German**: Indonesisches Bergwiesel / **Spanish**: Comadreja javanesa

Taxonomy. *Mustela lutreolina* Robinson & Thomas, 1917, west Java.
Monotypic.
Distribution. Java and S Sumatra.
Descriptive notes. Head-body 29·7–32·1 cm, tail 13·6–17 cm; weight 295–340 g. Indonesian Mountain Weasels resemble European Mink in both size and color. The pelage is brown throughout, with no facial markings.
Habitat. Specimens have been collected at elevations from 1000–2200 m.
Food and Feeding. Nothing known.
Activity patterns. Nothing known.
Movements, Home range and Social organization. Nothing known.
Breeding. Nothing known.
Status and Conservation. Classified as Data Deficient in *The IUCN Red List*. Virtually nothing is known about this species. This species is known only from the highlands of Sumatra and Java. On Java it occurs as far east as the Ijang plateau. On Sumatra, it is known from Bengkulu Province (Mount Dempo) and recently was recorded north to Kerinci. The Indonesian Mountain Weasel is a high priority for field studies to learn more about its natural history, ecology, and conservation status.
Bibliography. IUCN (2008), Lekagul & McNeely (1991), Lunde & Musser (2003), Meiri *et al.* (2007), Van Bree & Boeadi (1978), Wozencraft (2005).

49. Black-footed Ferret *Mustela nigripes*
French: Putois d'Amérique / **German**: Schwarzfußiltis / **Spanish**: Turón patinegro

Taxonomy. *Putorius nigripes* Audubon & Bachman, 1851, Wyoming, USA.
Monotypic.
Distribution. Great Plains of USA (Arizona, Colorado, Kansas, Montana, New Mexico, South Dakota, Utah & Wyoming) and N Mexico.
Descriptive notes. Head-body 40–50 cm, tail 11·4–15 cm; weight 964–1078 g (males), 764–854 g (females), adult males are larger than females. The Black-footed Ferret has a long body and short limbs. The pelage is yellowish-buff or beige with black hairs throughout; the underparts are paler. The forehead, muzzle, and throat are nearly white. The top of the head and middle of the back are brown. There is a distinctive, broad, horizontal black stripe across the face. The feet and terminal fourth of the tail are black. There are three pairs of mammae. Dental formula: I 3/3, C 1/1, P 3/3, M 1/2 = 34.
Habitat. Black-footed Ferrets are found on short/mid-grass prairies and semi-arid grasslands, in close association with prairie dogs.
Food and Feeding. Black-footed Ferrets specialize in preying on prairie dogs (*Cynomys*), which they hunt by pursuing them inside their burrow systems. Occasionally, they may also eat other small mammals, such as microtine rodents and ground squirrels. One scat study revealed a diet that comprised 87% White-tailed Prairie Dogs (*Cynomys gunnisoni*), 6% mice, and 3% lagomorphs.
Activity pattern. Primarily nocturnal, although daytime activity is not uncommon. Black-footed Ferrets are active throughout the year and continue to hunt prairie dogs during the winter, even though they are in hibernation. Prairie dog burrows are used as den/rest sites and may be modified for their own use.
Movements, Home range and Social organization. Black-footed Ferrets are solitary, except during the breeding season. They seldom move from one prairie dog colony to another. The average nightly movement during winter is 1406 m. The average prairie dog town size occupied by a Black-footed Ferret is 8 ha, but the average size occupied by females with young is 36 ha (range = 10–120 ha). The mean distance between two towns occupied by Black-footed Ferrets is 5·4 km. Population density in Wyoming is estimated to be one ferret per 50 ha of prairie dog colonies.

Breeding. Mating occurs in March and April. Gestation lasts 42–45 days and births occur in May and June. Litter size can range from one to six; the average is three. The young emerge from the burrow in early July and separate from the mother in September or early October. Young males disperse a considerable distance, but young females often remain in the vicinity of their mother's territory. Sexual maturity is attained by one year.

Status and Conservation. Listed as Extinct in the Wild in 1996, but the success of conservation measures has changed their status to Endangered in *The IUCN Red List*. The Black-footed Ferret may once have been common in southern Canada (Alberta, and Saskatchewan), west-central USA (Montana, North Dakota, South Dakota, Nebraska, Wyoming, Arizona, and Texas), and northern Mexico. Destruction of prairie dog colonies for the sake of agriculture led to a decline in Black-footed Ferret numbers and eventually they became so rare that many people considered them to be extinct. However, unconfirmed sigh things continued from several states, and in 1981 a small population of Black-footed Ferrets was discovered in Wyoming. Intensive field studies were initiated, and by July 1984, the population was estimated to contain 129 individuals. However, the number of ferrets then began to fall, apparently due to a decline in their prairie dog prey; also, canine distemper was somehow introduced into the wild population. By 1987, the remaining 18 individuals were brought into captivity to start a breeding program. By 1991, there were 180 individuals in captivity and 49 ferrets were released into south-eastern Wyoming; 91 more were released in 1992, and another 48 in 1993. Most of these animals are thought to have died, but some are known to have survived and reproduced; at least six litters were born in the wild in 1993. Additional reintroductions were carried out in Montana, South Dakota, and Arizona. Today, they are known from 18 reintroduction efforts, only three of which are self sustaining. These self-sustaining populations are in South Dakota and Wyoming; four populations of limited success are in Arizona, Colorado, South Dakota, and Utah; eight populations recently introduced are in Arizona, Kansas, Montana, New Mexico, South Dakota, and Mexico; and three other declining or extirpated populations are in Montana. The current status of this species is still extremely precarious.

Bibliography. Biggins *et al*. (1986), Campbell *et al*. (1987), Hillman & Clark (1980), IUCN (2008), Svendsen (2003), Vargas & Anderson (1998), Wozencraft (2005), Young *et al*. (2001).

50. Least Weasel *Mustela nivalis*

French: Belette pygmée / **German**: Mauswiesel / **Spanish**: Comadreja común

Other common names: Weasel

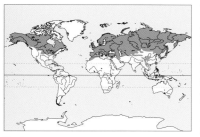

Taxonomy. *Mustela nivalis* Linnaeus, 1766, Sweden.
Nine subspecies are recognized.
Subspecies and Distribution.
M. n. nivalis Linnaeus, 1766 – China, North and South Korea, Mongolia, Russia, Taiwan, and Scandinavia.
M. n. allegheniensis Rhoads, 1900 – NE USA (Allegheny Mts W to Wisconsin).
M. n. boccamela Bechstein, 1800 – Corsica, Italy, Portugal, Sardinia, Sicily, and Spain.
M. n. campestris Jackson, 1913 – C Great Plains, USA.
M. n. eskimo Stone, 1900 – Alaska and NW Canada (Yukon).
M. n. namiyei Kuroda, 1921 – Japan and the Kurile Is.
M. n. numidica Pucheran, 1855 – N Africa.
M. n. rixosa Bangs, 1896 – Canada and N Great Plains of USA.
M. n. vulgaris Erxleben, 1777 – W & C Europe and most of C Eurasia.
Introduced to New Zealand, Malta, Crete, the Azores Is, and apparently also Sao Tome I.

Descriptive notes. Head-body 11·4–26 cm, tail 7–9 cm; weight 25–250 g, males are on average larger than females. There is much geographic variation in size. The tail is only slightly longer than the length of the hindfoot, and is less than 35% of head and body length. The Least Weasel is the smallest species within the Carnivora. It has a long and slender body, with short limbs and tail. Except in certain southern parts of its range, the Least Weasel changes color during the spring and autumn. In summer, the upperparts are brown and the underparts are white. In winter, the entire coat is white, but unlike other weasels that turn white during the winter, the Least Weasel does not posses a black-tipped tail. There are three to four pairs of mammae. The skull has a short rostrum, and a large and long cerebral cranium. Dental formula: I 3/3, C 1/1, P 3/3, M 1/2 = 34.

Habitat. The Least Weasel is found in a wide range of habitats that provide good cover and prey abundance, including agricultural fields, grasslands, forests, prairies, riparian woodlands, hedgerows, mountains (up to 4000 m), alpine meadows, steppes, semi-deserts, and coastal dunes. They are also found near human habitations.

Food and Feeding. The diet is mainly small rodents, but other small mammals (such as lagomorphs, moles, and squirrels), birds, eggs, lizards, frogs, salamanders, insects (mostly beetles), fish, worms, and carrion are also occasionally eaten. The proportions of different small rodent species in the diet roughly reflects their relative abundances throughout the year. In Europe and Russia, *Microtus agrestis*, *M. arvalis*, *M. oeconomus*, *M. brandti*, *Arvicola terrestris*, *Clethrionomys glareolus*, *C. rutilus*, *Apodemus sylvaticus*, *Lemmus lemmus*, and *L. sibiricus* are preyed upon. In North America, *M. pennsylvanicus*, *M. ochrogastere*, *C. rutilus*, *C. gapperi*, *Peromyscus leucopus*, *P. maniculatus*, *Reithrodontomys megalotis*, *Sigmodon hispidus*, *Dicrostonyx rubricatus*, *D. hudsonicus*, and *L. sibiricus* are eaten. In Great Britain, one study showed that the diet consists of 68% rodents (mainly *Microtus agrestis*), 25% lagomorphs, and 5% birds and birds' eggs. The small size of Least Weasels enables them to pursue prey into their burrows, so much of their hunting is underground or under snow. Males readily shift to larger prey such as birds, lagomorphs, and Water Voles, while females continue to search for Field Voles. Thus, males generally take larger prey than females and spend less time hunting in tunnels. Least Weasels take five to ten meals per day. Excess food may be stored, especially in the winter; the cache site may be within the home burrow or near a kill. Killing behavior is innate. Least Weasels respond to movements of prey as a stimulus for attack. The killing bite is delivered at the nape of the neck and penetrates the base of the skull or throat area.

Activity patterns. Active day and night. The high-energy requirements of Least Weasels mean that they have to be constantly active, so active and rest periods occur in rapid succession. However, the timing and extent of their daily activity is related to the activity patterns of their prey. Least Weasels may spend the whole winter under snow. Den/rest sites are in prey burrows, in rock piles, or in other well-concealed sites. Vocalizations in captive animals consist of a repertoire of five different sounds, including a chirp, a hiss, a trill, a squeal, and a squeak.

Movements, Home range and Social organization. Least Weasels constantly move in search of prey. They are mainly terrestrial, but are also agile tree climbers and fairly good swimmers. Movements may reach 1·5 km/h. Least Weasels are solitary outside of the breeding season. Home ranges are 0·6–26/ha for males and 0·2–7/ha for females. Male home ranges overlap with one or more females, but do not overlap with other males. Population densities range from 0·2–1/ha.

Breeding. Breeding may continue throughout the year, even during the winter, but is concentrated in spring and late summer. Delayed implantation does not occur and the gestation period is 34–37 days. Litter size may reach ten, but usually is four to five. Females can have more than one litter annually; second and third litters within a single year may occur during peaks of rodent abundance. Births occur in a burrow or rock crevice; the nest is lined with grass and other material. Females raise the young alone. Newborns are blind, naked, and weigh 1–2 g. The eyes open at 26–30 days, and the young are weaned after 42–56 days. They leave their mother at 9–12 weeks. Adult size is reached after 12–15 weeks. Females reach sexual maturity at three months and may produce a litter in their first summer.

Status and Conservation. Classified as Least Concern in *The IUCN Red List*. The Least Weasel is considered relatively common in Eurasia, but appears to be rare in North America. They are not known to prey on domestic animals and are beneficial to people through its destruction of mice and rats. However, Least Weasels have been introduced to some areas, such as New Zealand, with sometimes devastating effects on the local fauna. Threats include incidental poisoning with rodenticides and persecution. The Least Weasel prefers open agricultural habitats, which are declining in some parts of Europe owing to changes in agricultural practices (rural abandonment).

Bibliography. Brandt & Lambin (2007), Francis (2008), IUCN (2008), Jedrzejewski, Jedrzejewska & Szymura (1995), Jedrzejewski, Jedrzejewska, Zub & Nowakowski (2000), King (1990), Sheffield & King (1994), Svendsen (2003), Wozencraft (2005, 2008).

51. Malay Weasel *Mustela nudipes*

French: Putois à pieds nus / **German**: Nacktfußwiesel / **Spanish**: Comadreja descalza

Taxonomy. *Mustela nudipes* Desmarest, 1822, Indonesia.
Monotypic.
Distribution. Borneo, Peninsular Malaysia, Sumatra, and S Thailand.

Descriptive notes. Head-body 30–36 cm, tail 24–26 cm; weight 1000 g. The Malay Weasel has a long, slender body and short limbs. The pelage is reddish-brown, almost orange throughout, with the head much paler than the rest of the body, often appearing white. The tail is long and bushy; the basal half is the same color as the back, but the distal half is typically all white. The soles of the feet are naked around the pads. There are two pairs of mammae.

Habitat. Rainforests, with records from 400 to 1700 m. Often found in close proximity to water.

Food and Feeding. Diet includes small mammals, birds, amphibians, and reptiles.

Activity patterns. Apparently active both day and night. Rests in holes underground.

Movements, Home range and Social organization. Said to be solitary and terrestrial.

Breeding. Litter size reported to be up to four.

Status and Conservation. Classified as Least Concern in *The IUCN Red List*. This is a poorly known species and field studies are needed to learn more about its natural history, ecology, and conservation status. It is eaten in parts of Sarawak and there is some evidence of medicinal use.

Bibliography. Banks (1949), Duckworth *et al*. (2006), Francis (2008), Franklin & Wells (2005), IUCN (2008), Lekagul & McNeely (1991), Payne *et al*. (1985), Wozencraft (2005).

52. European Polecat *Mustela putorius*

French: Putois d'Europe / **German**: Waldiltis / **Spanish**: Túron europeo

Taxonomy. *Mustela putorius* Linnaeus, 1758, Sweden.
The European Polecat is possibly the ancestor of the domestic Ferret *M. p. furo*. Up to twenty-two subspecies have been proposed, but a taxonomic revision is needed.

Distribution. Most of Europe W of Urals, and Morocco.

Descriptive notes. Head-body 29·5–46 cm (males), 20·5–38·5 cm (females), tail 10·5–19 cm (males), 7–14 cm (females); weight 500–1710 g (males), 400–915 g (females), adult males are larger than females. The European Polecat has a long, slender body and short limbs. The pelage is dark brown to black, with paler, yellowish undersides. The areas between the eye and ear and around the mouth, are silvery white. There are up to five pairs of mammae. Dental formula: I 3/3, C 1/1, P 3/3, M 1/2 = 34.

Habitat. The European Polecat is found in forests, meadows, abandoned fields, and agricultural areas, often in close proximity to water. They sometimes occur near humans, but avoid dense urban areas.

Food and Feeding. The diet consists of amphibians, small mammals, birds, fish, and invertebrates. In Switzerland, the diet of European Polecats is almost exclusively carnivorous, but some fruits are also eaten, mainly by juveniles. Anurans (frogs and toads; mainly *Rana temporaria* and *Bufo bufo*) are the staple food. Other foods of importance are small mammals (mainly Muridae, but also Microtidae and Soricidae), carrion, and eggs. The anuran proportion of the diet is higher in summer than in winter and higher in the mountains than in the lowlands. In mountainous regions, anurans are also the most important food in winter. Juveniles eat more fruits and invertebrates and fewer mammals than adults. Sex-related differences in the importance of the main food categories have not been detected. In Denmark, the stomach contents of 47 European Polecats revealed that they preyed mostly on amphibians (87%) and mammals (34%), and only occasionally on birds (9%) and fish (6%). In Poland, the analysis of 222 scats revealed that anurans (mainly *R. temporaria*) comprised 70 to 98% of the biomass consumed and were found in 60 to 95% of scats. Forest rodents (*Apodemus flavicollis* and *Clethrionomys glareolus*) constituted from 1–29% of the biomass eaten. The consumption of rodents grew with decreasing winter temperature and increasing numbers of rodents. Snow-tracking of individual European Polecats has shown that in wet forests, they move in close proximity to watercourses to search for anurans, whereas in the drier forests, they hunt rodents, mainly by digging. European Polecats constantly move as they search for prey, exploring burrows, hollow logs, trees, tree cavities, rock crevices, and farm buildings.

Activity patterns. Mainly nocturnal, but can be crepuscular and active during the day. In Luxembourg, radio-collared European Polecats were 62% active during the night. Males were more active than females, and activity increased from winter to summer. In central Italy, ten males and six females were monitored using radio-telemetry. Males exhibited a regular and constant nocturnal pattern in every season, preferring the time between 20:00–06:00 h; activity was lower at dawn and dusk, and scarce during daylight hours. Females were significantly diurnal and crepuscular, but individuals revealed a flexibility in their activity pattern, including arrhythmic patterns without apparent temporal organization. Den/rest sites include crevices, hollow logs, burrows made by other animals, and sometimes buildings. In Luxembourg, European Polecats were located in 53 different resting sites, during the day. Aboveground shelters were used more often than underground shelters. Piles of branches, barns and stables, garden sheds and rat dens, were the most used sites, without specific preference for any one type of shelter. However, buildings seem to be of prime importance during severe weather conditions.

Movements, Home range and Social organization. European Polecats are solitary and terrestrial, but also capable of climbing. Daily movements average 1·1 km. In some forest areas, home ranges are 100–150 ha. In Poland, European Polecats occupied stretches of 0·65 to 3·05 km along a stream. The home range of females were exclusive, but they could be completely overlapped by male home ranges. In Luxembourg, the home range size of European Polecats ranged from 42 to 428 ha, with an average of 181 ha. The mean home range size of males (246 ha) was significantly larger than that of females (84 ha). European Polecats concentrated 50% of their space use in only 15% of their home range, possibly indicating that suitable habitat was patchy. Average distance traveled per night by males was 3·6 times greater than that of females. Also, seasonal variation in movements was observed in males, but not in females. Population density is one per km².

Breeding. Mating occurs from March to June. The gestation period is about 42 days. Litter size is typically three to seven, but may be up to twelve. Neonates are blind and weigh 9–10 g. They open their eyes and are weaned after about one month, and become independent at around three months. Sexual maturity may be reached during the first year.

Status and Conservation. Classified as Least Concern in *The IUCN Red List*. In Western Europe, the European Polecat was widely hunted for sport and fur and persecuted as a pest. However, these threats have become less serious as this species is now protected in a number of range states, and rates of hunting have greatly reduced. Accidental mortality from car collisions and secondary rodenticide poisoning are threats. In Rus-

sia and Morocco, this species is commonly hunted. Hybridization with the Ferret is a possible threat in the United Kingdom. Possible competition with the introduced American Mink may also be a problem.

Bibliography. Baghli & Verhagen (2004, 2005), Baghli, Engel & Verhagen (2002), Baghli, Walzberg & Verhagen (2005), Blandford (1987), Brzezinski *et al.* (1992), Fournier *et al.* (2007), Hammershoj *et al.* (2004), Jedrzejewski *et al.* (1993), Lanszki & Heltai (2007), Lodé (1997, 2003), Marcelli *et al.* (2003), Rondinini *et al.* (2006), Stroganov (1969), Virgos (2003), Weber (1989), Wozencraft (2005), Zabala *et al.* (2005).

53. Siberian Weasel *Mustela sibirica*

French: Putois de Sibérie / **German**: Sibirisches Feuerwiesel / **Spanish**: Comadreja siberiana

Taxonomy. *Mustela sibirica* Pallas, 1773, Russia.
Up to twenty-two subspecies have been proposed, but a taxonomic revision is needed.

Distribution. Bhutan, China, India, Japan (Hokkaido), North and South Korea, Nepal, Laos, Mongolia, N Myanmar, Russia, Taiwan, and N Thailand. Introduced to several Japanese islands (Honshu, Kyushu & Shikoku Is).

Descriptive notes. Head-body 28–39 cm (males), 25–30·5 cm (females), tail 15·5–21 cm (males), 13·3–16·4 cm (females); weight 650–820 g (males), 360–430 g (females), adult males are almost twice the size of females. The Siberian Weasel has a long, slender body and short limbs. The pelage is dark brown in summer and becomes paler, almost yellowish-brown in winter. The upper lips and chin are white. There is usually a dark mask around and in front of the eyes. The tail is about 50% of the head and body length, and may have a dark tip. There are four pairs of mammae. The skull is long and narrow. Dental formula: I 3/3, C 1/1, P 3/3, M 1/2 = 34.

Habitat. Siberian Weasels are found in forests, forest steppe, and mountains, from 1500 to 5000 m. They are often found in river valleys, near swamps, and in areas with dense ground vegetation, around villages, and in cultivated areas.

Food and Feeding. The diet is mainly small mammals (rodents, pikas), but may also include amphibians, birds, eggs, fish, invertebrates, berries, and nuts. Siberian Weasels search for prey by exploring hollow trees, logs, cavities, brush piles, and other enclosed spaces.

Activity patterns. Mainly nocturnal and crepuscular. Den/rest sites are under roots, in logs or tree hollows, modified rodent burrows, rock crevices, or buildings.

Movements, Home range and Social organization. Siberian Weasels are solitary and terrestrial, but can climb and swim well. Nightly movements may reach 8 km. There are reports of Siberian Weasels relocating to new areas if food becomes scarce locally.

Breeding. Mating occurs in late winter and early spring. The gestation period is 33–37 days. The young are born in April to June, inside hollow trees, cavities among rocks or stumps, inside buildings, or in a modified rodent burrow; the nest is lined with fur and feathers from prey killed by the mother. The litter size is 2–12, usually five or six. The young open their eyes after one month, and lactation lasts two months. They leave their mother by the end of August.

Status and Conservation. Classified as Least Concern in *The IUCN Red List*. The Siberian Weasel is important in the fur trade. It occasionally attacks domestic fowl, but is generally considered beneficial because it preys on rodents. Little is known about Siberian Weasels and field studies are needed to learn more about their natural history, ecology, and conservation status.

Bibliography. Francis (2008), Lekagul & McNeely (1991), Pocock (1941a), Rhim & Lee (2007), Sasaki & Ono (1994), Stroganov (1969), Wozencraft (2005, 2008), Wu (1999).

54. Back-striped Weasel *Mustela strigidorsa*

French: Putois à dos rayé / **German**: Rückenstreifenwiesel / **Spanish**: Comadreja estriada
Other common names: Stripe-backed Weasel

Taxonomy. *Mustela strigodorsa* Gray, 1853, India.
Monotypic.

Distribution. S China (Guangxi, Guizhou & Yunnan), NE India, N & C Laos, N & C Myanmar, N Thailand, and N & C Vietnam.

Descriptive notes. Head-body 25–32·5 cm, tail 10·3–20·5 cm; weight 700–2000 g. The Back-striped Weasel has a long, slender body and short limbs. The pelage is dark brown with yellowish-white upper lips, cheeks, chin, and throat. A narrow, whitish stripe runs along the back from the head to the base of the tail. Another narrow pale stripe runs along the abdomen. The bushy tail is less than half the head and body length. The tympanic bullae are flattened. Dental formula: I 3/3, C 1/1, P 3/3, M 1/2 = 34.

Habitat. Found mainly in evergreen forests in hills and mountains, but has also been recorded from plains forest, dense scrub, secondary forest, grassland, and farmland. Altitudinal range 90–2500 m.

Food and Feeding. The diet is said to include small rodents.
Activity patterns. Nothing known.
Movements, Home range and Social organization. Has been seen on the ground and in trees.
Breeding. Nothing known.
Status and Conservation. Classified as Least Concern in *The IUCN Red List*. Populations in the wild are suspected to be declining. Back-striped Weasels are sold for traditional medicine in Laos. About 3000 to 4000 pelts were harvested annually in China in the 1970s. Outside China, this species is sold occasionally in Laos and Vietnam. Even though the Back-striped Weasel is not known to have high economic value, hunting or harvesting for trade could be causing major declines because many hunting methods (notably snares) are non-selective. This is a poorly known species and field studies are needed to learn more about its natural history, ecology, and conservation status.
Bibliography. Davies (2006), Evans *et al.* (1994), Francis (2008), Hansel & Tizard (2006), IUCN (2008), Lekagul & McNeely (1991), Pocock (1941a), Ratajszczak & Cox (1991), Schreiber *et al.* (1989), Wozencraft (2005, 2008).

55. Egyptian Weasel *Mustela subpalmata*

French: Belette d'Égypte / **German**: Ägyptisches Wiesel / **Spanish**: Comadreja egipcia

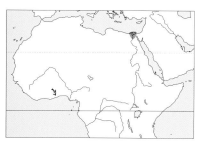

Taxonomy. *Mustela subpalmata* Hemprich & Ehrenberg, 1833, Egypt.
The Egyptian Weasel has often been considered conspecific with the Least Weasel, but is now recognized as a separate species. Monotypic.
Distribution. Egypt.
Descriptive notes. Head-body 27–30 cm, tail 10·7–12·9 cm; weight 45–130 g, but females are smaller than males. The morphology is very similar to that of the Least Weasel.
Habitat. Fields and along irrigation canals. Also found in towns and villages.
Food and Feeding. Diet is said to include small mammals and insects.
Activity patterns. Nothing known.
Movements, Home range and Social organization. Nothing known.
Breeding. Nothing known.
Status and Conservation. Classified as Least Concern in *The IUCN Red List*. Virtually nothing is known about this species; it is a high priority for field studies to learn more about its natural history, ecology, and conservation status.
Bibliography. Setzer (1958), Van Zyll de Jong (1992), Wozencraft (2005).

Genus *NEOVISON*

Baryshnikov & Abramov, 1997

56. American Mink *Neovison vison*

French: Vison d'Amérique / **German**: Amerikanischer Nerz / **Spanish**: Visón americano

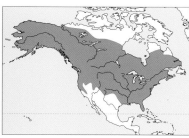

Taxonomy. *Mustela vison* Schreber, 1776, Eastern Canada.
Fifteen subspecies are recognized.
Subspecies and Distribution.
N. v. vison Schreber, 1776 – E Canada and NE USA (Allegheny Mts).
N. v. aestuarina Grinnell, 1916 – SW USA (California & W Nevada).
N. v. aniakensis Burns, 1964 – W Alaska.
N. v. energumenos Bangs, 1896 – W Canada and NW USA.
N. v. evagor Hall, 1932 – SW Canada (Vancouver I.).
N. v. evergladensis Hamilton, 1948 – SE USA (SW Florida).
N. v. ingens Osgood, 1900 – most of Alaska and NW Canada (N Mackenzie & Yukon).
N. v. lacustris Preble, 1902 – C Canada (Keewatin Region, Manitoba & Ontario).
N. v. letifera Hollister, 1913 – Great Plains of USA.
N. v. lowii Anderson, 1945 – E Canada (Labrador & Quebec).
N. v. lutensis Bangs, 1898 – USA (S Carolina to Florida).
N. v. melampeplus Elliot, 1903 – Alaska (Kenai Peninsula).
N. v. mink Peale & Palisot de Beauvois, 1796 – SE USA.
N. v. nesolestes Heller, 1909 – SW Alaska.
N. v. vulgivaga Bangs, 1895 – USA (Arkansas & Louisiana).
Introduced to Belarus, Belgium, China, Czech Republic, Denmark, Estonia, Finland, France, Germany, Great Britian, Iceland, Ireland, Italy, Japan (Hokkaido), Latvia, Lithuania, Netherlands, Norway, Poland, Portugal, Russia, Spain, and Sweden.
Descriptive notes. Head-body 33–43 cm (males), 30–40 cm (females); tail 16·7–20 cm (males), 15·2–18·5 cm (females); weight 850–1805 g (males), 450–840 g (females); adult males are generally 10% longer and 100% heavier than females. The American Mink has a long body and short limbs. The pelage is soft and luxurious; it is brown throughout, but white markings on the chest, throat and chin are common. The feet are fully furred and the claws are short and sharp. There are three pairs of mammae. The skull is long and flat, with a small sagittal crest. Dental formula: I 3/3, C 1/1, P 3/3, M 1/2 = 34.
Habitat. American Mink are found along the edges of small creeks, streams, rivers, lakes, and in wetlands, swamps, marshes, and along coastal beaches. They prefer densely vegetated areas and are sometimes found far from water. Females have been found to prefer small streams, whereas males prefer large streams.
Food and Feeding. The diet includes small mammals, fish, birds, eggs, amphibians, reptiles, and invertebrates, such as crustaceans, molluscs, insects, and earthworms. In much of North America, the American Mink is a major predator of Muskrats; fluctuations in Muskrat populations have a direct effect on American Mink abundance. In Eurasia, where the American Mink has been introduced, the staple food items on rivers and streams are fish (average, 27%), mammals (30%), and amphibians (17%), whereas on lakes and ponds, it is predominantly birds (33%) and fish (28%). On the upper reaches of the Lovat river, north-east Belarus, three out of ten American Mink were found to be small mammal specialists; 86–92% of their scats contained remains of small rodents (mostly the Water Vole and microtines), and small mammals constituted 83–88% of the food biomass consumed; the other seven were generalist predators. In western Poland, the diet of American Mink consists mainly of mammals, birds, and fish. In autumn-winter, mammals constitute up to 56%, fish up to 62%, and birds 4–16%, of the biomass consumed. In spring and summer, however, birds form 45–60% of the biomass eaten; the common coot (*Fulica atra*) is the most frequently consumed prey. Scat analysis in eastern Poland revealed that American Mink relied on three prey groups: fish (40% in spring-summer and 10% in autumn-winter), frogs (32% and 51%, respectively), and small mammals (21% and 36%). Of the available small mammal species, American Mink strongly selected the Root Vole (*Microtus oeconomus*). The cold season diet depended on river size. On small rivers with forested valleys, American Mink fed nearly exclusively on amphibians (72–90% of food biomass). As the size of a river increases and riverside habitat becomes more open (sedge and reed marshes instead of forest), American Mink shift to preying on small mammals (up to 65% in the diet). The stomach contents of 211 individuals in Thy, Denmark, revealed that the diet was mostly mammals (55% occurrence), followed by amphibians (36%), birds (33%), and fish (30%). In Bornholm, Denmark, American Mink prey mostly on birds (50%), followed by mammals (42%), fish (25%) and amphibians (4%). In Italy, the diet is mainly fish, followed by small mammals and birds. American Mink spend most of their time hunting near water, but can also hunt underwater. In a coastal environment of Scotland, radio-tracked American Mink were found to forage selectively at low or mid-tide and within the core areas of their home range; they showed no preference for areas rich in prey when foraging at high tide and between core areas. They also avoided areas with freshwater streams and preferred foraging in the mid-tide zone. Prey on land are detected by sight or sound. Surplus food is sometimes cached.
Activity patterns. Mainly nocturnal, but with frequent periods of daytime activity, especially in areas away from humans. Den/rest sites are in burrows, hollow logs, hollow trees, rock crevices, old buildings, or abandoned dwellings of Muskrats, American Beavers, or Woodchucks (*Marmota* sp.). Burrows may be about 3 m long and 1 m beneath the surface, and have one or more entrances just above the water level. On the northern Iberian Peninsula, radio-collared American Mink selected resting places within dense scrub, close to deep water. Both sexes also used underground dens, but during cold days females rested in buildings much more often than males. Active females used areas of dense scrub, and males used large scrub patches.
Movements, Home range and Social organization. American Mink are good swimmers. They can dive to depths of 5–6 m and swim underwater for about 30 m. They are also agile climbers and occasionally forage in trees. Movements are either short foraging excursions or long travel movements between areas. Daily movements may reach up to 25 km, but usually are less than 5 km. American Mink are solitary outside of the breeding season. Females have home ranges of about 8–20 ha; the ranges of males are larger, sometimes up to 800 ha. Home ranges include 1·8–7·5 km of shoreline for males and 1–4·2 km for females. In the prairies, the average home range of males was 7·7 km². The home ranges of males overlap with those of females, but there is little overlap with other males. Population densities of 1–8 per km² have been recorded.
Breeding. Females are polyestrous but only have one litter per year. Mating occurs from February to April. Implantation of the fertilized eggs into the uterus undergoes a short and variable delay, and gestation may last from 39 to 78 days (average 51 days). Actual embryonic development takes 30–32 days. Births occur in April to June. Litter size ranges from two to ten, with an average of five. The young are born blind; their eyes open after five weeks and weaning occurs at five to six weeks. They leave the nest and begin to hunt at seven to eight weeks, and separate from the mother in the autumn. Females reach adult weight at four months and sexual maturity at twelve months; males reach adult weight at 9–11 months and sexual maturity at 18 months.
Status and Conservation. Classified as Least Concern in *The IUCN Red List*. The American Mink is considered common throughout its range. It is harvested in the wild for its fur, particularly in North America; however, most of the mink fur used in commerce is produced on farms and American Mink are intensively raised in captivity. Most of the conservation issues with this species relate to its introduction to countries outside its natural distribution and the impacts on native fauna. Major threats to American Mink are linked with water pollution.

Bibliography. Aulerich & Ringer (1979), Aulerich *et al.* (1974), Bartoszewicz & Zalewski (2003), Birks & Linn (1982), Bonesi *et al.* (2000), Dunstone (1979, 1983, 1993), Enders (1952), Errington (1954), Hammershoj *et al.* (2004), Larivière (1999a, 2003b), Sidorovich *et al.* (2001), Wozencraft (2005), Zabala *et al.* (2007a, 2007b), Zuberogoitia *et al.* (2006).

Genus *LYNCODON*
Gervais, 1845

57. Patagonian Weasel *Lyncodon patagonicus*

French: Belette de Patagonie / **German**: Patagonisches Wiesel / **Spanish**: Hurón patagónico

Taxonomy. *Mustela patagonica* de Blainville, 1842, Argentina.
Monotypic.
Distribution. Argentina and C & S Chile.
Descriptive notes. Head-body 30–35 cm, tail 6–9 cm; weight 200–250 g. The Patagonian Weasel has a long, slender body and short limbs. The pelage is grayish-white

throughout, with a wide band of white fur on the top of head. The nape, cheeks, chin, throat and limbs are dark brown. Dental formula: I 3/3, C 1/1, P 2/2, M 1/1 = 28.
Habitat. Herbaceous and shrub steppes, and xerophytic woodlands.
Food and Feeding. Reported to enter burrows and prey on fossorial rodents and birds. May be associated with tuco-tuco (*Ctenomys* spp.) communities.
Activity patterns. Reported to be nocturnal and crepuscular.
Movements, Home range and Social organization. Nothing known.
Breeding. Nothing known.
Status and Conservation. Classified as Data Deficient in *The IUCN Red List*. Very little is known about the Patagonian Weasel as it is rarely seen in the wild or collected. No information has been published on its current population status or major threats. Field studies are needed to learn more about its ecology and conservation status.
Bibliography. Ewer (1973), IUCN (2008), Miller *et al.* (1983), Pocock (1926), Wozencraft (2005).

References

References of Scientific Descriptions

Afanas'ev & Zolotarev (1935). *Bull. Acad. Sci. USSR.* **7**: 427 [*Cuon alpinus hesperius*].
Albignac (1971). *Mammalia* **35**: 108 [*Galidia elegans occidentalis*].
Allen, G.M. (1914). *Bull. Mus. Comp. Zool.* **58**: 337 [*Leptailurus serval phillipsi*].
Allen, G.M. (1923). *Proc. Biol. Soc. Washington* **36**: 55 [*Cerdocyon thous germanus*].
Allen, G.M. (1929). *Amer. Mus. Novit.* **358**: 8 [*Melogale moschata sorella*].
Allen, G.M. & Barbour (1923). *Bull. Mus. Comp. Zool.* **65**: 266 [*Urocyon cinereoargenteus furvus*].
Allen, J.A. (1876). *Proc. Acad. Nat. Sci. Philadelphia* **28**: 20 [*Bassaricyon*], 21 [*Bassaricyon gabbii*].
Allen, J.A. (1895). *Bull. Amer. Mus. Nat. Hist.* **7**: 188 [*Lynx rufus texensis*].
Allen, J.A. (1903). *Bull. Amer. Mus. Nat. Hist.* **19**: 609 [*Canis latrans impavidus*], 614 [*Lynx rufus escuinapae*].
Allen, J.A. (1904). *Bull. Amer. Mus. Nat. Hist.* **20**: 52 [*Nasua nasua yucatanica*], 71 [*Puma yagouaroundi panamensis*], 72 [*Potos flavus chiriquensis*], 76 [*Potos flavus chapadensis*], 331 [*Leopardus pardalis maripensis*].
Allen, J.A. (1908). *Bull. Amer. Mus. Nat. Hist.* **24**: 662 [*Eira barbara inserta, Bassaricyon gabbii richardsoni*].
Allen, J.A. (1910). *Bull. Amer. Mus. Nat. Hist.* **28**: 17 [*Herpestes brachyurus palawanus*], 115 [*Ursus americanus perniger*].
Allen, J.A. (1911). *Bull. Amer. Mus. Nat. Hist.* **30**: 259 [*Urocyon cinereoargenteus venezuelae*].
Allen, J.A. (1915). *Bull. Amer. Mus. Nat. Hist.* **34**: 630 [*Procyon cancrivorus aequatorialis*].
Allen, J.A. (1915). *J. Mammal.* **1**: 26 [*Xenogale*].
Allen, J.A. (1916). *Bull. Amer. Mus. Nat. Hist.* **35**: 100 [*Mustela frenata nicaraguae*].
Allen, J.A. (1919). *J. Mammal.* **1**: 25[*Genetta piscivora*].
Allen, J.A. (1919). *Bull. Amer. Mus. Nat. Hist.* **41**: 357 [*Leopardus wiedii nicaraguae*].
Allen, J.A. (1924). *Bull. Amer. Mus. Nat. Hist.* **47**: 205 [*Atilax paludinosus macrodon*], 224 [*Panthera leo azandica*].
Ameghino (1888). *Ráp. Diagn. Mamif. Fós.* 6 [*Panthera onca palustris*].
Ameghino (1889). *Actas Acad. Nac. Cienc. Córdoba* **5**: 298 [*Pseudalopex gymnocercus antiquus*].
Anderson (1945). *Ann. Rept. Provancher Soc. Nat. Hist. Canada, Quebec* 57 [*Neovison vison lowii*].
Audubon & Bachman (1851). *The Viviparous Quadrupeds of North America* **2**: 240 [*Canis rufus*], 267 [*Mustela nigripes*].
Audubon & Bachman (1854). *The Viviparous Quadrupeds of North America* **3**: 125 [*Ursus americanus cinnamomum*].
Bailey (1905). *N. Amer. Fauna* **25**: 175 [*Canis latrans texensis*], 203 [*Conepatus leuconotus telmalestes*].
Baird (1852). In: *Stansbury, Spec. Sess. US Senate, Exec.* No. 3, App. C. 309 [*Vulpes vulpes macroura*].
Baird (1857). *Mammals.* In: *Repts. US Expl. Surv.* **8(1)**: 121 [*Urocyon*].
Baird (1857). *Mammals North. Amer.* 172 [*Mustela erminea kaneii*].
Baird (1858). In: *Repts. US Expl. Surv.* **8(1)**: 143 [*Urocyon littoralis*], 194 [*Mephitis mephitis occidentalis*], 205 [*Taxidea taxus berlandieri*].
Baird (1859). In: *Emory, Rept. US Mexican Bound. Surv.* **2(2)**: 19 [*Bassariscus astutus raptor*], 29 [*Ursus americanus amblyceps*].
Ball (1844). *Proc. Zool. Soc. London* **1844**: 128 [*Leopardus pardalis melanurus*].
Bangs (1895). *Proc. Boston Soc. Nat. Hist.* **26**: 531 [*Mephitis mephitis elongata*], 539 [*Neovison vison vulgivaga*].
Bangs (1896). *Proc. Boston Soc. Nat. Hist.* **27**: 5 [*Neovison vison energumenos*].
Bangs (1896). *Proc. Biol. Soc. Washington* **10**: 8 [*Mustela frenata spadix*], 21 [*Mustela nivalis rixosa*].
Bangs (1897). *Proc. Biol. Soc. Washington* **11**: 49 [*Lynx canadensis subsolanus*], 50 [*Lynx rufus gigas*].
Bangs (1897). *Amer. Nat.* **31**: 162 [*Martes americana atrata*].
Bangs (1898). *Proc. Biol. Soc. Washington* **12**: 31 [*Mephitis mephitis spissigrada*], 32 [*Mephitis mephitis avia*], 36 [*Vulpes vulpes deletrix*], 92 [*Procyon lotor maynardi*], 93 [*Cerdocyon thous aquilus*].

Bangs (1898). *Science, n.s.* **7**: 272 [*Vulpes vulpes rubricosa*].
Bangs (1898). *Proc. Boston Soc. Nat. Hist.* **28**: 219 [*Procyon lotor elucus*], 222 [*Spilogale putorius ambarvalis*], 229 [*Neovison vison lutensis*].
Bangs (1899). *Proc. New England Zool. Club* **1**: 43 [*Urocyon cinereoargenteus ocythous*], 54 [*Mustela frenata occisor*], 56 [*Mustela frenata munda*], 71 [*Mustela erminea muricus*], 81 [*Mustela frenata oribasus*].
Bangs (1899). *Proc. Biol. Soc. Washington* **13**: 15 [*Puma concolor coryi*].
Barber & Cockerell (1898). *Proc. Acad. Nat. Sci. Philadelphia* **50**: 188 [*Mustela frenata neomexicana*].
Barrett-Hamilton (1904). *Ann. Mag. Nat. Hist. 7th Ser.* **13**: 393 [*Mustela erminea polaris*], 394 [*Mustela erminea stabilis*].
Baryshnikov (2000). *Acta Theriologica* **45**: 45 [*Mellivora capensis buechneri*].
Baryshnikov & Abramov (1997). *Zool. Zhurnal* **76(12)**: 1408 [*Neovison*].
de Beaux (1922). *Atti Soc. Ital. Sci. Nat. Milano* **61**: 25 [*Canis simensis citernii*].
Bechstein (1789). *Gemeinn. Nat. Deutschlands* **1**: 250 [*Vulpes vulpes crucigera*].
Bechstein (1799). *Thomas Pennants allgem. bersicht d. vierf. Thiere* **1**: 270 [*Alopex lagopus fuliginosus*].
Bechstein (1800). *Thomas Pennants allgem. bersicht d. vierf. Thiere* **2**: 395 [*Mustela nivalis boccamela*].
Bechtold (1936). *Zeitsch. Säugetierk.* **11**: 149 [*Herpestes edwardsii montanus*], 150 [*Herpestes urva annamensis*], 151 [*Herpestes urva formosanus*], 152 [*Herpestes urva sinensis*].
Bell (1826). *Zool. J.* **2**: 552 [*Galictis*].
Bennett (1833). *Proc. Zool. Soc. London* **1833**: 46 [*Cryptoprocta, Cryptoprocta ferox*], 68 [*Prionailurus viverrinus*].
Bennett (1835). *Proc. Zool. Soc. London* **1835**: 67 [*Herpestes vitticollis*], 118 [*Paguma larvata grayi*].
Benson (1938). *Proc. Biol. Soc. Washington* **51**: 21 [*Vulpes macrotis zinseri*].
Berlandier (1859). In: Baird *US & Mexican Boundary Survey* **2(2)**: 12 [*Puma yagouaroundi cacomitli*].
Birula (1910). *Ann. Mus. Zool. Sci. St. Petersburg* **15**: 333 [*Vormela peregusna alpherakii*].
Birula (1913). *Ann. Mus. Zool. Sci. St. Petersburg* **17**: 270 [*Vulpes rueppellii zarudnyi*].
Birula (1916). *Ann. Mus. Zool. Sci. St. Petersburg* **21**: suppl. i-ii [*Felis silvestris nesterovi*].
de Blainville (1842). *Osteo. Mamm.* **2(10)**: pl. 13 [*Lyncodon patagonicus*].
de Blainville (1843). *Osteo. Mamm.* **2(12)**: pl. 6 [*Panthera leo nubica*], pl. 8 [*Panthera onca peruviana*].
de Blainville (1844). *Osteo. Mamm.* **2**: 6 [*Hyaena hyaena barbara*].
Blanford (1877). *J. Asiat. Soc. Bengal* **46(2)**: 321 [*Vulpes cana*].
Blanford (1877). *Proc. Asiat. Soc. Bengal* 204 [*Ursus thibetanus gedrosianus*].
Blanford (1885). *Proc. Zool. Soc. London* **1885**: 802 [*Paradoxurus jerdoni*].
Blasius (1884). *Ber. Naturforsch Ges. Bemberg* **13**: 9 [*Vormela*].
Blyth (1847). *J. Asiat. Soc. Bengal* **16**: 1178 [*Lynx lynx isabellinus*].
Blyth (1853). *J. Asiat. Soc. Bengal* **23**: 589 [*Ursus arctos pruinosus*], 590 [*Arctonyx albogularis*].
Blyth (1854). *J. Asiat. Soc. Bengal* **23**: 729 [*Vulpes vulpes pusilla*], 730 [*Vulpes vulpes griffithii*].
Blyth (1862). *J. Asiat. Soc. Bengal* **31**: 331 [*Viverra megaspila*], 332 [*Viverra civettina*].
Bocage (1882). *J. Sci. Math. Phys. Nat. Lisboa, ser. 1* **9**: 29 [*Genetta angolensis*].
Bocage (1889). *J. Sci. Math. Phys. Nat. Lisboa, ser. 2* **3**: 179 [*Galerella flavescens*].
Boddaert (1785). *Elench. Anim.* **1**: 84 [*Conepatus semistriatus*], 88 [*Martes flavigula*].
Boitard (1842). *Jard. Plant.* 142 [*Leopardus pardalis pseudopardalis*].
Bonaparte (1838). *Charlesworth's Mag. Nat. Hist.* **2**: 37 [*Mustela erminea cicognanii*], 38 [*Mustela erminea richardsonii, Mustela frenata longicauda*].
Bonhote (1898). *Ann. Mag. Nat. Hist. 7th Ser.* **1**: 120 [*Viverricula indica deserti*].
Bonhote (1901). *Ann. Mag. Nat. Hist. 7th Ser.* **7**: 346 [*Martes flavigula peninsularis*].

Bonhote (1903). *Ann. Mag. Nat. Hist. 7th Ser.* **12**: 592 [*Melogale personata pierrei*].
Bradfield (1936). *Auk* **53(1935)**: 131 [*Suricata suricatta marjoriae*].
Brandt (1842). *Bull. Acad. Sci. St. Petersb.* **9**: 38 [*Otocolobus*].
Brauner (1914). *Sapiski Novoros ob Estest.* **11**: 15 [*Vulpes vulpes stepensis*].
Brisson (1762). *Regnum Animale* **2**: 13 [*Meles*], 168 [*Hyaena*], 201 [*Lutra*].
Brongersma (1935). *Zool. Meded. Leiden* **18**: 26 [*Prionailurus bengalensis borneoensis*].
Brookes (1827). In: Griffith *et al.*, *Anim. Kingdom* **5**: 151 [*Lycaon*].
Brookes (1828). *Cat. Anat. Zool. Mus. J.* **16**: 33 [*Acinonyx*].
Burchell (1824). *Travels*. In: *Interior of Southern Africa* **2**: 592 [*Felis nigripes*].
Burmeister (1854). *Systematische Uebersicht der Thiere Brasiliens* 99 [*Lycalopex*].
Burmeister (1856). *Erläut. Fau. Brasil* 24 [*Pseudalopex*].
Burmeister (1861). *Reis. La Plata-St.* **2**: 400 [*Cerdocyon thous entrerianus*], 406 [*Pseudalopex griseus gracilis*].
Burns (1964). *Can. J. Zool.* **42**: 1073 [*Neovison vison aniakensis*].
Burt (1938). *Occas. Pap. Mus. Zool. Univ. Michigan* **384**: 2 [*Spilogale angustifrons yucatanensis*].
Burt & Hooper (1941). *Occas. Pap. Mus. Zool. Univ. Michigan* **430**: 4 [*Urocyon cinereoargenteus madrensis*].
Cabral (1971). *Bol. Inst. Invest. Cient. Angola* **8**: 65 [*Suricata suricatta iona*].
Cabrera (1913). *Bol. Real Soc. Española Hist. Nat. Madrid* **13**: 392 [*Mustela erminea nippon*].
Cabrera (1917). *Trab. Mus. Nac. Cienc. Nat. Zool.* **31**: 28 [*Leopardus wiedii amazonicus*].
Cabrera (1918). *Bol. Real Soc. Española Hist. Nat. Madrid* **18**: 481 [*Panthera pardus reichenowi*].
Cabrera (1921). *Bol. Real Soc. Española Hist. Nat. Madrid* **21**: 262 [*Atilax paludinosus spadiceus*].
Cabrera (1929). *Mem. Real Soc. Española Hist. Nat. Madrid* **16**: 36 [*Civettictis civetta schwarzi*, *Civettictis civetta congica*].
Cabrera (1940). *Notas Mus. La Plata* **5(29)**: 14 [*Atelocynus*], 16 [*Oreailurus*].
Cabrera (1956). *Neotropica* **2(7)**: 2 [*Nasua nasua boliviensis*].
Cabrera (1957). *Neotropica* **3**: 71 [*Leopardus colocolo crespoi*].
Cabrera & Ruxton (1926). *Ann. Mag. Nat. Hist. 9th Ser.* **17**: 596 [*Nandinia binotata intensa*].
Camerano (1906). *Boll. Mus. Zool. Ed. Anat. Comp. Univ. Torino* **21(545)**: 1 [*Panthera pardus ruwenzorii*].
Cameron (1957). *J. Mammal* **37**: 538 [*Ursus americanus hamiltoni*].
Cavazza (1912). *Ann. Mus. Civ. Stor. Nat. Genova 3a* **5(45)**: 194 [*Mustela erminea minima*].
Chasen & Kloss (1928). *Proc. Zool. Soc. London* **1927**: 817 [*Hemigalus derbyanus sipora*].
Cheesman (1920). *J. Bombay Nat. Hist. Soc.* **27**: 331 [*Felis silvestris iraki*], 335 [*Mellivora capensis wilsoni*].
Colbert & Hooijer (1953). *Bull. Amer. Mus. Nat. Hist.* **102**: 56 [*Viverra zibetha expectata*].
Colyn & Van Rompaey (1990). *Zeitsch. Säugetierk.* **55**: 95 [*Crossarchus ansorgei nigricolor*].
Cope (1889). *Amer. Nat.* **23**: 144. [*Leopardus colocolo braccatus*].
Cornalia (1865). *Mem. Soc. Ital. Sci. Nat.* **1**: 3 [*Leopardus jacobitus*].
Coues (1887). *Science* **9**: 516 [*Bassariscus*].
Crawford-Cabral (1970). *Bol. Inst. Invest. Cient. Angola* **134**: 10 [*Genetta servalina schwarzi*].
Cretzschmar (1826). In: Rüppell, *Atlas Reise Nordl. Afr., Zool. Säugeth.* **1(2)**: 33 [*Vulpes pallida*].
Cuvier (1798). *Tabl. Elem. Hist. Nat. Anim.* 113 [*Procyon cancrivorous*].
Cuvier (1809). *Annales Mus. Hist. Nat. Paris* **14**: 152 [*Panthera pardus melas*].
Cuvier (1816). *Règne Anim.* **1**: 156 [*Genetta*].
Cuvier (1820). *Hist. Nat. Mammif.* **2(18)**: 137 [*Leopardus pardalis mitis*].
Cuvier (1821). *Hist. Nat. Mammif.* **3(24)**: 15 [*Paradoxurus*]; **3(27)**: 2 unnumbered [*Mydaus*].
Cuvier (1823). *Rech. Assemens fossile* **4**: 325 [*Ursus thibetanus*], 437 [*Neofelis nebulosa diardi*].
Cuvier (1823). *Dict. Sci. Natur.* **27**: 242 [*Lontra canadensis lataxina, Lontra longicaudis enudris*].
Cuvier (1824). In: E. Geoffroy Saint-Hilaire & F.G. Cuvier, *Hist. Nat. Mammif.*, pt. 3, **5(42)**: pl. 212 [*Ursus arctos collaris*].
Cuvier (1825). In: E. Geoffroy Saint-Hilaire & F.G. Cuvier, *Hist. Nat. Mammif.*, pt. 3, **5(47)**: 3 [*Crossarchus, Crossarchus obscurus*]; **5(50)**: 3 [*Ailurus, Ailurus fulgens*]; **5(51)**: "Bali-saur", 2 pp. [*Arctonyx, Arctonyx collaris*], 218 [*Tremarctos ornatus*].
Cuvier (1826). In: E. Geoffroy Saint-Hilaire & F.G. Cuvier, *Hist. Nat. Mammif.*, pt. 3, **5(54)**: "Vansire," 2 pp., 1 pl. [*Atilax*].
Cuvier (1829). *Regn. Anim. 2nd ed.* **1**: 158 [*Atilax paludinosus, Cynictis penicillata, Ichneumia albicauda*].
Dall (1895). *Science, n.s.* **2**: 87 [*Ursus americanus emmonsii*].
David (1869). *Nouv. Arch. Mus. Hist. Nat. Paris* **5**: 13 [*Ailuropoda melanoleuca*].
Davis & Lukens (1958). *J. Mammal* **39**: 353 [*Bassariscus sumichrasti latrans*].
de Winton (1896). *Ann. Mag. Nat. Hist. 6th Ser.* **18**: 469 [*Paracynictis selousi*].
de Winton (1898). *Ann. Mag. Nat. Hist. 7th Ser.* **2**: 292 [*Felis chaus nilotica*].
de Winton (1901). *Bull. Lpool. Mus.* **3**: 35 [*Xenogale naso*].
Deraniyagala (1949). *Nat. Mus. Ceylon Pict. Ser.* **1**: 103 [*Panthera pardus kotiya*].
Deraniyagala (1956). *Spolia Zeylan.* **28**: 113 [*Prionailurus rubiginosus koladivinus*].
Desmarest (1804). *Nouv. Dict. Hist. Nat.* **24**: 15 [*Suricata*].
Desmarest (1816). *Nouv. Dict. Hist. Nat.* (2) **6**: 114 [*Leopardus colocolo pajeros*], 115 [*Prionailurus bengalensis javanensis*].
Desmarest (1818). *Nouv. Dict. Hist. Nat.* (2) **19**: 376. [*Mustela africana*].
Desmarest (1820). *Mamm. Ou Descr. Des Espèce de Mamm.* In: *Encycl. Methodique* **1**: 187 [*Mydaus javanensis*], 198 [*Cuon alpinus javanicus*], 203 [*Vulpes vulpes fulva*].
Desmarest (1822). *Encycl. Methodique Mamm. Suppl.* 520 [*Felis silvestris cafra*], 537 [*Mustela nudipes*], **2**(Suppl.): 538 [*Otocyon megalotis*].
Dickey (1929). *Proc. Biol. Soc. Washington* **42**: 158 [*Spilogale gracilis amphialus*].
Dinnik (1914). *Sverikankasa* **2**: 449 [*Vulpes vulpes caucasica*].
Dorogostaiski (1935). *Izv. Irkutsk. gos. Protivochumn. Inst. Sibirii I, D.V. kraya.* **1**: 47 [*Vulpes corsac skorodumovi*].
Doyère (1835). *Bull. Soc. Sci. Nat.* **3**: 45 [*Eupleres, Eupleres goudotii*].
Dwigubski (1804). *Prod. Faun. Ross.* 10 [*Canis lupus communis*].
Elliot (1871). *Proc. Zool. Soc. London* **1871**: 761 [*Prionailurus bengalensis euptilurus*].
Elliot (1896). *Field Columb. Mus. Publ. 11 Zool. Ser.* **1(3)**: 80 [*Urocyon cinereoargenteus fraterculus*].
Elliot (1903). *Field Columb. Mus. Publ. 74 Zool. Ser.* **3**: 170 [*Spilogale gracilis martirensis, Neovison vison melampeplus*].
Elliot (1903). *Field Columb. Mus. Publ. 79 Zool. Ser.* **3**: 151 [*Martes americana kenaiensis*], 225 [*Canis latrans clepticus*].
Elliot (1903). *Field Columb. Mus. Publ. 80 Zool. Ser.* **3**: 234 [*Ursus americanus altifrontalis*], 235 [*Ursus americanus machetes*].
Elliot (1904). *Field Columb. Mus. Publ. 87 Zool. Ser.* **3**: 256 [*Vulpes macrotis arsipus*].
Elliot (1905). *Proc. Biol. Soc. Washington* **18**: 80 [*Lontra canadensis periclyzomae*], 235 [*Mustela frenata macrophonius*].
Emmons (1840). A report on the quadrupeds of Massachusetts 45 [*Mustela frenata noveboracensis*].
Enders (1936). *Proc. Acad. Nat. Sci. Philadelphia* **88**: 365 [*Bassaricyon gabbii pauli*].
Erxleben (1777). *Syst. Regn. Anim. Mammalia* 458 [*Martes foina*], 470 [*Martes pennanti*], 471 [*Mustela nivalis vulgaris*], 566 [*Vulpes vulpes karagan*], 578 [*Crocuta crocuta*].
Eschscholtz (1829). *Zoologischer Atlas* **3**: 1 [*Canis latrans ochropus*].
Festa (1921). *Boll. Mus. Zool. Ed. Anat. Comp. Univ. Torino* **36(740)**: 3 [*Vulpes rueppellii cyrenaica*].
Fetisov (1950). *Izv. Biol.-Geogr. Nauchno-Issl. In-ta Irkutsk, Univ.* **12(1)**: 21 [*Lynx lynx kozlovi*].
Fischer (1814). *Zoognosia* **3**: 178 [*Pseudalopex gymnocercus*], 228 [*Puma yagouaroundi eyra*].
Fischer (1829). *Synopsis Mamm.* 170 [*Genetta genetta senegalensis*], 210 [*Caracal caracal nubica*].
Fitzinger (1855). *Sitz-ber. Math.-nat. Cl. D. K. Acad. Wiss.* **17(2)**: 245 [*Acinonyx jubatus soemmeringii*].
Fleming (1822). *Philos. Zool.* **2**: 187 [*Enhydra*].
Forster (1780). In: Buffon's *Naturgesch. D. Vierfuss.* **6**: 313 [*Felis silvestris lybica, Leptailurus serval constantinus*].
Frisch (1775). *Das Natur-System der Vierfüssigen Thiere* 15 [*Vulpes*].
Gaubert (2003). *Mammalia* **67(1)**: 95 [*Genetta bourloni*].
Geoffroy Saint-Hilaire (1803). *Catal. Mam. Mus. Hist. Nat.* 113 [*Viverricula indica*], 124 [*Puma yagouaroundi*].
Geoffroy Saint-Hilaire (1818). *Descrip. de L'Egypte* **2**: 138 [*Herpestes javanicus*], 139 [*Herpestes edwardsii*].
Geoffroy Saint-Hilaire (1824). *Bull. Sci. Soc. Philom. Paris* **1824**: 139 [*Proteles*].
Geoffroy Saint-Hilaire (1826). *Dictionnaire Classique d'Histoire Naturelle* **9**: 519 [*Lutrogale perspicillata*]; **10**: 214 [*Galidictis fasciata striata*].
Geoffroy Saint-Hilaire (1831). In: Bélanger ed. *Voy. Indes Orient., Mamm., 3 (Zoologie)*: 129 [*Melogale*], 137 [*Melogale personata*], 140 [*Prionailurus rubiginosus*].
Geoffroy Saint-Hilaire (1832). *Mag. Zool.* **2(1)**: pl. 8 [*Genetta pardina*].
Geoffroy Saint-Hilaire (1837). *C. R. Acad. Sci. Paris* **5**: 580 [*Galidia*], 581 [*Galidia elegans, Salanoia concolor*].
Geoffroy Saint-Hilaire (1837). *Ann. Sci. Nat. Zool. (Paris)* **8(2)**: 251 [*Ichneumia*].
Geoffroy Saint-Hilaire (1839). *Mag. Zool., Mamm Art.* **5**: 33 [*Galidictis*].
Geoffroy Saint-Hilaire & Cuvier (1795). *Mag. Encyclop.* **2**: 184 [*Mungos*], 187 [*Mephitis, Potos*].
Gervais (1845). In: d'Orbigny, *Dict. Univ. Hist. Nat.* **4**: 685 [*Lyncodon*].
Gervais (1855). *Hist. Nat. Mammif.* **2**: 20 [*Tremarctos*].
Gidley (1906). *Proc. US Natl. Mus.* **24**: 553 [*Procyon lotor simus*].
Gmelin (1788). In: *Linnaeus, Syst. Nat., 13th ed.* **1**: 84 [*Mungos mungo*], 88 [*Conepatus semistriatus conepatl*], 92 [*Galidictis fasciata*], 93 [*Pteroneura brasiliensis*].
Gmelin (1791). *Anhang Bruce, J., Reisen Africa,* **2**: 27 [*Felis silvestris ocreata*].
Goldman (1912). *Smithsonian Misc. Coll.* **60(2)**: 14 [*Speothos venaticus panamensis*], 16 [*Bassaricyon alleni orinomus*].
Goldman (1912). *Proc. Biol. Soc. Washington* **25**: 9 [*Mustela frenata costaricensis*].
Goldman (1913). *Smithsonian Misc. Coll.* **60(22)**: 15 [*Procyon cancrivorous panamensis*].
Goldman (1925). *J. Mammal* **6**: 122 [*Leopardus pardalis nelsoni*], 123 [*Leopardus pardalis sonoriensis*].
Goldman (1931). *Jour. Washington Acad. Sci.* **21**: 250 [*Vulpes macrotis nevadensis*].
Goldman (1932). *Proc. Biol. Soc. Washington* **45**: 87 [*Bassariscus astutus arizonensis*], 144 [*Panthera onca arizonensis*].
Goldman (1935). *Proc. Biol. Soc. Washington* **48**: 176 [*Martes pennanti columbiana*], 180 [*Lontra canadensis kodiacensis*], 185 [*Lontra canadensis mira*].
Goldman (1936). *Jour. Washington Acad. Sci.* **26**: 33 [*Canis latrans hondurensis*].
Goldman (1936). *Proc. Biol. Soc. Washington* **49**: 137 [*Puma concolor stanleyana*].
Goldman (1937). *J. Mammal* **18**: 44 [*Canis rufus gregoryi*].
Goldman (1938). *Jour. Washington Acad. Sci.* **28**: 497 [*Urocyon cinereoargenteus orinomus*].
Goldman (1943). *J. Mammal* **24**: 229 [*Puma concolor missoulensis*], 230 [*Puma concolor acrocodia*], 384 [*Leopardus wiedii cooperi*].
Goldman (1943). *Proc. Biol. Soc. Washington* **56**: 89 [*Conepatus semistriatus yucatanicus*].
Goldman (1945). *Proc. Biol. Soc. Washington* **58**: 105 [*Bassariscus astutus bolei*].
Goldman (1946). In: Young & Goldman *The Puma* 260 [*Puma concolor capricornensis*].
Goldman (1984). *Can. J. Zool.* **62(8)**: 1624 [*Crossarchus platycephalus*].
Goodwin (1938). *Amer. Mus. Novit.* **987**: 2 [*Urocyon cinereoargenteus costaricensis*].
Goodwin (1956). *Amer. Mus. Novit.* **1757**: 10 [*Bassariscus astutus macdougalli*], 11 [*Bassariscus sumichrasti oaxacensis*].
Goodwin (1957). *Amer. Mus. Novit.* **1830**: 3 [*Mephitis macroura richardsoni*].
Goodwin (1963). *Amer. Mus. Novit.* **2139**: 1 [*Lynx rufus oaxacensis*].
Grandidier (1867). *Rev. Mag. Zool. Paris* (2) **19**: 85 [*Mungotictis decemlineata*].
Gray (1830). *Spicil. Zool.* **2**: 9 [*Nandinia binotata, Genetta maculata*].
Gray (1830). *Illustr. Indian Zool* **1**: pl. 2 [*Felis silvestris ornata*], pl. 3 [*Felis chaus affinis*].
Gray (1831). *Proc. Zool. Soc. London* **1831**: 94 [*Melogale moschata*], 95 [*Paguma*].
Gray (1832). *Proc. Zool. Soc. London* **1832**: 63 [*Viverra tangalunga*], 68 [*Arctogalidia trivirgata*].
Gray (1834). *Illustr. Indian Zool.* **2**: pl. 1 [*Nyctereutes procyonoides*].
Gray (1837). *Proc. Zool. Soc. London* **1836**: 88 [*Herpestes brachyurus, Cynogale, Cynogale bennettii, Paguma larvata leucomystax*].
Gray (1837). *Mag. Nat. Hist. [Charlesworth's]* **1**: 577 [*Prionailurus bengalensis chinensis*], 578 [*Pseudalopex griseus, Pseudalopex culpaeus magellanicus, Herpestes smithii*], 579 [*Hemigalus derbyanus*], 580 [*Pteronura*], 581 [*Conepatus, Conepatus humboldtii, Mephitis mephitis varians*].
Gray (1842). *Ann. Mag. Hist. Nat., 1st Ser.* **10**: 260 [*Leopardus, Prionailurus bengalensis horsfieldi*], 261 [*Procyon lotor psora*].

Gray (1843). *Ann. Mag. Hist. Nat., 1st Ser.* **11**: 118 [*Lontra, Mustela frenata xanthogenys, Vulpes vulpes flavescens*].
Gray (1843). *List. Specimens Mamm. Coll. Brit. Mus.* 46 [*Caracal*], 54 [*Nandinia*].
Gray (1846). *Ann. Mag. Hist. Nat., 1st Ser.* **18**: 211 [*Pardofelis marmorata charltoni, Herpestes semitorquatus*].
Gray (1848). *Proc. Zool. Soc. London* **1848**: 138 [*Galerella ochracea*].
Gray (1853). *Proc. Zool. Soc. London* **1853**: 191 [*Mustela strigidorsa*].
Gray (1857). *Proc. Zool. Soc. London* **1857**: 278 [*Panthera onca hernandesii*].
Gray (1862). *Proc. Zool. Soc. London* **1861**: 308 [*Helogale*].
Gray (1862). *Proc. Zool. Soc. London* **1862**: 262 [*Panthera pardus japonensis*].
Gray (1863). *Cat. Hodgson's Coll. B.M. 2nd ed.* 3 [*Panthera pardus pernigra*].
Gray (1865). *Proc. Zool. Soc. London* **1864**: 55 [*Mustela frenata aureoventris*], 69 [*Poecilogale albinucha*], 703 [*Nasuella olivacea*].
Gray (1865). *Proc. Zool. Soc. London* **1865**: 106 [*Martes americana abietinoides*], 123 [*Lutra sumatrana*], 127 [*Lutrogale*], 150 [*Spilogale*], 518 [*Fossa*], 520 [*Poiana*], 523 [*Salanoia*], 541 [*Paguma larvata leucocephala*], 558 [*Atilax paludinosus robustus*], 564 [*Galerella*], 575 [*Rhynchogale melleri*].
Gray (1866). *Proc. Zool. Soc. London* **1866**: 169 [*Nasua nasua dorsalis*].
Gray (1867). *Proc. Zool. Soc. London* **1867**: 100 [*Leopardus tigrinus pardinoides*], 265 [*Neofelis*].
Gray (1867). *Ann. Mag. Hist. Nat., 3rd Ser.* **20**: 301 [*Ursus arctos lasiotus*].
Gray (1868). *Proc. Zool. Soc. London* **1868**: 517 [*Vulpes vulpes japonica*].
Gray (1874). *Proc. Zool. Soc. London* **1874**: 31 [*Felis silvestris caudata*], 322 [*Catopuma badia*].
Gray (1874). *Ann. Mag. Hist. Nat., 4th Ser.* **14**: 375 [*Mustela frenata affinis*].
Griffith (1821). *Gen. Particular Descrip. Vert. Anim. (Carn.)* 37 [*Neofelis nebulosa*], 93 [*Acinonyx jubatus venaticus*], 236 [*Ursus americanus luteolus*].
Grinnell (1916). *Proc. Biol. Soc. Washington* **29**: 213 [*Neovison vison aestuarina*].
Grinnell & Dixon (1926). *Univ. California Publ. Zool.* **21**: 411 [*Martes americana humboldtensis*].
Grinnell & Linsdale (1930). *Proc. Biol. Soc. Washington* **43**: 154 [*Urocyon littoralis dickeyi, Urocyon littoralis santarosae*].
Groves (1997). *Zeitsch. Säugetierk.* **62**: 336 [*Prionailurus bengalensis rabori*], 337 [*Prionailurus bengalensis heaneyi*].
Güldenstädt (1770). *Nova Comm. Imp. Acad. Sci. Petropoli* **14(1)**: 441 [*Vormela peregusna*].
Günther (1775). *Proc. Zool. Soc. London* **1775**: 243 [*Panthera pardus melanotica*].
Hall (1926). *Univ. California Publ. Zool.* **30**: 39 [*Bassariscus astutus octavus*].
Hall (1927). *Proc. Biol. Soc. Washington* **40**: 193 [*Mustela frenata arthuri*].
Hall (1928). *Univ. California Publ. Zool.* **30**: 231 [*Ursus americanus vancouveri*].
Hall (1932). *Proc. Biol. Soc. Washington* **45**: 139 [*Mustela frenata panamensis*].
Hall (1932). *Univ. California Publ. Zool.* **38**: 417 [*Mustela erminea anguinae, Neovison vison evagor*].
Hall (1934). *Univ. California Publ. Zool.* **40**: 369 [*Canis latrans incolatus*].
Hall (1935). *Proc. Biol. Soc. Washington* **48**: 143 [*Mustela frenata helleri*].
Hall (1936). *Carnegie Inst. Washington* **473**: 91 [*Mustela frenata nevadensis*], 93 [*Mustela frenata effera*], 94 [*Mustela frenata altifrontalis*], 95 [*Mustela frenata nigriauris*], 96 [*Mustela frenata latirostra*], 98 [*Mustela frenata pulchra*], 99 [*Mustela frenata inyoensis, Mustela frenata texensis*], 100 [*Mustela frenata perotae*].
Hall (1938). *Ann. Mag. Nat. Hist. 11th Ser.* **1**: 511 [*Spilogale angustifrons celeris*], 514 [*Spilogale pygmaea australis*].
Hall (1938). *Proc. Biol. Soc. Washington* **51**: 67 [*Mustela frenata boliviensis*].
Hall (1944). *Proc. Biol. Soc. Washington* **57**: 35 [*Mustela erminea salva*], 37 [*Mustela erminea initis*], 38 [*Mustela erminea celenda*], 39 [*Mustela erminea seclusa*].
Hall (1945). *J. Mammal* **26**: 75 [*Mustela erminea invicta*], 79 [*Mustela erminea fallenda*], 81 [*Mustela erminea olympica*], 84 [*Mustela erminea gulosa*], 176 [*Mustela erminea bangsi*].
Hall & Dalquest (1950). *Univ. Kansas Publ. Mus. Nat. Hist.* **1**: 579 [*Mephitis macroura eximius*].
Hamilton (1948). *Proc. Biol. Soc. Washington* **61**: 139 [*Neovison vison evergladensis*].
Hamilton-Smith (1839). In: Jardine's *Nat. Lib.* **9**: 242 [*Chrysocyon*], 250 [*Cerdocyon*]; **25**: 164 [*Canis latrans cagottis*].
Hardwicke (1821). *Trans. Linn. Soc. London* **13**: 225 [*Cuon alpinus sumatrensis*], 236 [*Prionodon linsang*].
Harlan (1825). *Fauna Americana* 309 [*Taxidea taxus jeffersonii*].
Harris (1932). *Occas. Pap. Mus. Zool., Univ. Michigan* **248**: 3 [*Bassaricyon gabbii lasius*].
Harrison (1968). *Mammals of Arabia* **2**: 283 [*Felis silvestris gordoni*].
Hayman (1940). *Trans. Zool. Soc. London* **24**: 687 [*Genetta cristata*].
Hayman (1957). *Ann. Mag. Nat. Hist. 12th Ser.* **9**: 710 [*Lutrogale perspicillata maxwelli*].
Hayman (1958). *Ann. Mag. Nat. Hist. 13th Ser.* **1**: 449 [*Liberiictis, Liberiictis kuhni*].
Heller (1909). *Univ. California Publ. Zool.* **5**: 259 [*Neovison vison nesolestes*].
Heller (1913). *Smithsonian Misc. Coll.* **61(13)**: 9 [*Nandinia binotata arborea*], 12 [*Bdeogale crassicauda omnivore*].
Hemmer (1974). *Zschr. Kölner Zoo* **17**: 14 [*Felis margarita scheffeli*].
Hemmer, Grubb & Groves (1976). *Zeitsch. Säugetierk.* **41**: 301 [*Felis margarita harrisoni*].
Hemprich & Ehrenberg (1828). *Symbolae Physicae Mammalian* **1(sig. a)**: pl. 1 [*Ursus arctos syriacus*].
Hemprich & Ehrenberg (1833). *Symbolae Physicae Mammalian* **2**: pl. 17 [*Panthera pardus nimr*]; **folio k**: 2 [*Ictonyx lybicus, Mustela subpalmata, Genetta genetta dongolana*].
Hendey (1974). *Ann. South Afr. Mus.* **63**: 149 [*Parahyaena*].
Hensel (1872). *Abhandl. Preuss. Akad. Wiss.* **1872**: 73 [*Leopardus tigrinus guttulus*].
Heptner (1945). *C.R. Acad. Sci. Moscow* **49(3)**: 230 [*Caracal caracal michaelis*].
Heude (1892). *Mém. H.N. Emp. Chin.* **2**: 2 (footnote) 102 [*Cuon alpinus lepturus*].
Heude (1901). *Mém. H.N. Emp. Chin.* **5(1)**: 2 [*Ursus thibetanus mupinensis, Ursus thibetanus ussuricus*].
Hilzheimer (1905). *Zool. Anseig.* **28**: 598 [*Panthera tigris amoyensis*].
Hilzheimer (1905). *Zool. Anseig.* **29**: 298 [*Melogale moschata ferreogrisea*].
Hilzheimer (1906). *Zool. Anseig.* **30**: 114 [*Pseudalopex clupaeus reissii*].
Hilzheimer (1913). *Sitz. Ber. Geselsch. Natur. Freunde, Berlin* **5**: 288 [*Acinonyx jubatus hecki*].
Hodgson (1833). *Asiatic Res. 18* **2**: 221 [*Cuon alpinus primaevus*].
Hodgson (1835). *J. Asiat. Soc. Bengal* **4**: 702 [*Mustela kathiah*].
Hodgson (1836). *J. Asiat. Soc. Bengal* **5**: 235 [*Herpestes auropunctatus*], 237 [*Melogale personata nipalensis*], 238 [*Herpestes urva*].
Hodgson (1836). *Asiatic Res. 19* **1**: 61 [*Mellivora capensis inaurita*].
Hodgson (1838). *Ann. Mag. Nat. Hist., Ser. 1* **1**: 152 [*Cuon, Viverricula*].
Hodgson (1842). *J. Asiat. Soc. Bengal* **11**: 276 [*Otocolobus manul nigripectus*], 278 [*Vulpes ferrilata*].
Hodgson (1842). *Calcutta Jour. Nat. Hist.* **2**: 57 [*Prionodon pardicolor*].
Hodgson (1847). *J. Asiat. Soc. Bengal* **16**: 763 [*Meles leucurus*].
Hodgson (1853). *Proc. Zool. Soc. London* **1853**: 192 [*Neofelis nebulosa macrosceloides*].
Hollister (1912). *Proc. Biol. Soc. Washington* **25**: 1 [*Atilax paludinosus rubescens*].
Hollister (1912). *Smithsonian Misc. Coll. 60* **14**: 5 [*Mustela erminea lymani*].
Hollister (1913). *Proc. US Natl. Mus.* **44**: 475 [*Neovison vison letifera*].
Hollister (1914). *Proc. US Natl. Mus.* **48**: 169 [*Panthera onca paraguensis*].
Hollister (1914). *Proc. Biol. Soc. Washington* **28**: 143 [*Mustela frenata meridana*].
Hollister (1915). *Proc. US Natl. Mus.* **49**: 148 [*Nasuella*].
Hollister (1916). *Smithsonian Misc. Coll.* **66(1)**: 6 [*Ichneumia albicauda dialeucos*].
Holmberg (1898). *Seg. Censo Nac. Rep. Argentina* 485 [*Puma yagouaroundi ameghinoi*].
Hornaday (1904). *Ann. Rept. N.Y. Zool. Soc.* **VIII**: 71 [*Nyctereutes procyonoides albus*].
Hornaday (1905). *Ann. Rept. N.Y. Zool. Soc.* **IX**: 82 [*Ursus americanus kermodei*].
Horsfield (1821). *Zool. Res. Java* **1**: plate + 4pp [*Melogale orientalis, Prionailurus bengalensis sumatranus*].
Horsfield (1822). *Zool. Res. Java* **5**: unnumbered last page under *Mungusta javanica* [*Prionodon, Prionodon linsang gracilis*].
Horsfield (1825). *Zool. Jour. London* **2**: 221 [*Helarctos, Helarctos malayanus euryspilus*].
Horsfield (1826). *Trans. Linn. Soc.* **15**: 334 [*Ursus arctos isabellinus*].
Horsfield (1851). *Cat. Mamm. Mus. E. India Co.* 66 [*Arctogalidia trivirgata leucotis*], 90 [*Martes gwatkinsii*].
Horsfield (1855). *Ann. Mag. Hist. Nat., 2nd Ser.* **16**: 105 [*Panthera uncia uncioides*].
Howell (1901). *N. Amer. Fauna* **20**: 36 [*Mephitis mephitis notata*], 37 [*Mephitis mephitis major*].
Howell (1902). *Proc. Biol. Soc. Washington* **15**: 242 [*Spilogale angustifrons, Spilogale angustifrons tropicalis*].
Howell (1906). *N. Amer. Fauna* **26**: 27 [*Spilogale angustifrons elata*].
Howell (1913). *Proc. Biol. Soc. Washington* **26**: 139 [*Mustela frenata olivacea*].
Hubrecht (1891). *Notes Leyden Mus.* **13**: 242 [*Arctonyx hoevenii*].
Huet (1887). *Le Naturaliste*, Ser. 2, **9(13)**: 147 [*Mydaus marchei*].
Huey (1928). *Trans. San Diego Soc. Nat. Hist.* **5**: 203 [*Urocyon cinereoargenteus peninsularis*].
Huey (1937). *Trans. San Diego Soc. Nat. Hist.* **8**: 357 [*Bassariscus astutus yumanensis*].
Humboldt (1812). *Rec. Observ. Zool.* **1**: 246 [*Conepatus semistriatus quitensis*], 348 [*Eira barbara sinuensis*].
Ihering (1911). *Rev. Mus. Paulista* **8**: 224 [*Speothos venaticus wingei*].
Illiger (1811). *Prodr. Syst. Mamm. Avium.* 135 [*Herpestes*].
Illiger (1815). *Abh. Phys. Klasse K. Pruess. Akad. Wiss.* **1804-1811**: 90 [*Aonyx cinereus*], 98 [*Panthera tigris virgata*], 109 [*Conepatus chinga suffocans*], 121 [*Chrysocyon brachyurus*].
Imaizumi (1967). *J. Mamm. Soc. Japan* **3**: 75 [*Prionailurus bengalensis iriomotensis*].
Izor & de la Torre (1978). *J. Mammal.* **59**: 92 [*Mustela felipei*].
Jackson (1913). *Proc. Biol. Soc. Washington* **26**: 123 [*Mustela frenata primulina*], 124 [*Mustela nivalis campestris*].
Jackson (1949). *Proc. Biol. Soc. Washington* **62**: 31 [*Canis latrans thamnos, Canis latrans umpquensis*].
Jackson (1955). *Proc. Biol. Soc. Washington* **68**: 149 [*Puma concolor schorgeri*].
Jardine (1834). *Nat. Lib.* **2**: 266 [*Puma*].
Jourdan (1837). *C. R. Acad. Sci. Paris* **5**: 442 [*Hemigalus*].
Jurgenson (1936). *Bull. So. Nat. Moscow, Sec. Biol.* **45**: 240 [*Mustela erminea karaginensis*].
Kaup (1828). *Oken's Isis. Encyclop. Zeit* **21(11)**: column 1145 [*Crocuta*].
Kaup (1829). *Skizz. Europ. Thierw.* **I**: 83 [*Alopex*].
Kaup (1835). *Das Thierreich In: Seinen Hauptformen* **1**: 352 [*Ictonyx*].
Kerr (1792). In: Linnaeus, *Anim. Kingdom* **1**: 137 [*Canis lupus albus*], 151 [*Prionailurus bengalensis, Puma concolor cougar*], 155 [*Lynx*], 157 [*Lynx canadensis*], 181 [*Mustela erminea aestiva*], 188 [*Mellivora capensis indica*].
Kershaw (1922). *Ann. Mag. Nat. Hist. 9th Ser.* **10**: 103 [*Helogale parvula ruficeps*].
Kingdon (1977). *E. African Mamm.* **IIIA**: 154 [*Genetta servalina lowei*].
Kishida (1924). *Chôsen. Hantô san no Kitsuna* 4 [*Vulpes vulpes peculiosa*].
Kishida (1924). *Mon. Jap. Mamm.* 47 [*Vulpes vulpes schrenckii, Vulpes vulpes splendidissima*].
Kishida (1931). *Lansania* **3** **25**: 73 [*Canis lupus hattai*].
Kloss (1916). *Proc. Zool. Soc. London* **1916**: 35 [*Martes flavigula indochinensis*].
Kloss (1919). *Jour. Nat. Hist. Soc. Siam* **3**: 352 [*Viverricula indica thai*].
Kock, Künzel & Rayaleh (2000). *Senckenbergiana Biologica* **80**: 243 [*Civettictis civetta pauli*].
Kornejev (1941). *Acta Mus. Zool. Kijev.* **1**: 174 [*Mustela erminea teberdina*].
Kratochvíl & Stollmann (1963). *Folia Zoologica* **12(4)**: 315 [*Lynx lynx carpathicus*].
Kuroda (1921). *J. Mammal* **2**: 209 [*Mustela nivalis namiyei*].
Kuroda & Mori (1923). *J. Mammal* **4**: 27 [*Martes melampus coreensis*].
Lataste (1885). *Actes Soc. Linn. Bordeaux* **39**: 231 [*Felis silvestris sarda*].
Lavauden (1929). *C.R. Acad. Sci. Paris* **189**: 197 [*Eupleres goudotii major*].
Lesson (1827). *Manuel de Mammalogie* 144 [*Mustela eversmanii*], 157 [*Aonyx*].
Lichtenstein (1830). *Abh. K. Akad. Wiss. Berlin* **1827**: 106 [*Urocyon cinereoargenteus nigrirostris*], 119 [*Bassariscus astutus*].
Lichtenstein (1831). *Darstellung neuer oder wenig bekannter Säugethiere* pl. 42 [*Mustela frenata*].
Lichtenstein (1832). *Darstellung neuer oder wenig bekannter Säugethiere* pl. 44 [*Conepatus leuconotus*], pl. 45 [*Mephitis mephitis mesomelas*], pl. 46 [*Mephitis macroura*].
Lichtenstein (1835). *Arch. Naturgesch.* **1**: 89 [*Hydrictis maculicollis*].
Lichtenstein (1838). *Abh. Preuss. Akad. Wiss.* **1836**: 275 [*Conepatus semistriatus amazonicus*].
Linnaeus (1758). *Syst. Nat.* **10**: 38 [*Canis, Canis familiaris*], 39 [*Canis lupus*], 39 [*Canis aureus, Alopex lagopus*], 40 [*Vulpes vulpes, Hyaena hyaena*], 41 [*Felis, Panthera leo, Panthera pardus, Panthera tigris*], 42 [*Leopardus pardalis, Panthera onca*], 43 [*Lynx lynx, Herpestes ichneumon, Viverra*], 44 [*Spilogale putorius, Viverra zibetha*], 45 [*Enhydra lutris, Genetta genetta, Gulo gulo,*

Lutra lutra, Mustela], 46 [*Eira barbara, Martes martes, Martes zibellina, Mustela erminea, Mustela putorius*], 47 [*Gulo gulo luscus, Ursus, Ursus arctos*], 48 [*Meles meles, Procyon lotor*].
Linnaeus (1761). *Faun. Suec.* 5 [*Mustela lutreola*].
Linnaeus (1766). *Syst. Nat., 12th ed.* **1**: 60 [*Cerdocyon thous*], 64 [*Nasua nasua, Nasua narica*], 69 [*Mustela nivalis*].
Linnaeus (1768). *Syst. Nat., 12th ed.* **3**: appendix 223 [*Vulpes corsac*].
Linnaeus (1771). *Mantissa Plantarum* **2**: 522 [*Puma concolor*].
Loche (1858). *Rev. Mag. Zool. Paris, Ser. 2* **10**: 49 [*Felis margarita*].
Lönnberg (1910). *Ark. Zool.* **7(9)**: 1 [*Aonyx capensis congicus*].
Lönnberg (1913). *Ark. Zool.* **8(16)**: 2 [*Puma concolor soderstromii*], 7 [*Leopardus colocolo thomasi*], 19 [*Eira barbara madeirensis*], 23 [*Nasuella olivacea quitensis*].
Lönnberg (1914). *Rev. Zool. Africaine* **3**: 273 [*Panthera leo bleyenberghi*].
Lönnberg (1921). *Ark. Zool.* **14(4)**: 103 [*Nasua nasua cinerascens*].
López-Forment & Urbano (1979). *Anales Inst. Biol. UNAM Mexico Ser. Zool.* **1(50)**: 726 [*Spilogale pygmaea intermedia*].
Lowery (1943). *Occas. Pap. Mus. Zool. Louisiana St. Univ.* **13**: 255 [*Procyon lotor megalodous*].
Lund (1839). *Ann. Sci. Nat. Zool. (Paris) (2)* **11**: 224 [*Speothos*].
Lund (1842). *K. Dansk. Vid. Selsk. Naturv. Math. Afhandl.* **9**: 4 [*Pseudalopex vetulus*], 67 [*Speothos venaticus*].
Lundholm (1955). *Ann. Transvaal Mus.* **22**: 290 [*Civettictis civetta australis, Civettictis civetta volkmanni*].
Lydekker (1906). *Proc. Zool. Soc. London* **1906**: 112 [*Mellivora capensis cottoni*].
Major (1897). *Zool. Anzeiger* **20**: 142 [*Lontra longicaudis annectens*].
Martin (1837). *Proc. Zool. Soc. London* **1836**: 11 [*Pseudalopex fulvipes*], 83 [*Potos flavus megalotus*], 108 [*Pardofelis marmorata*].
Massoia (1982). *Neotropica* **28(80)**: 147 [*Pseudalopex gymnocercus lordi*].
Matschie (1900). *Sber. Ges. Naturf. Freunde Berlin* **1**: 54 [*Hyaena hyaena syriaca*].
Matschie (1902). *Verh. V Internat. Zool. Cong. Berlin* **1901**: 1138 [*Genetta maculata mossambica*], 1139 [*Genetta genetta pulchra*], 1141 [*Genetta maculata zambesiana*], 1142 [*Genetta thierryi*].
Matschie (1907). *Wiss. Ergebn. Filchners Exped. to China, 10* **1**: 169 [*Vulpes vulpes tschiliensis*], 178 [*Nyctereutes procyonoides ussuriensis*].
Matschie (1910). *Sber. Ges. Naturf. Freunde Berlin* **8**: 370 [*Vulpes pallida oertzeni*].
Matschie (1912). *Sber. Ges. Naturf. Freunde Berlin* **10**: 64 [*Caracal caracal schmitzi*], 259 [*Leopardus colocolo garleppi*].
May (1896). *California Game Marked Down* 22 [*Puma concolor californica*].
Mazak (1968). *Mammalia* **32**: 105 [*Panthera tigris corbetti*].
Mearns (1891). *Bull. Amer. Mus. Nat. Hist.* **3**: 234 [*Mustela frenata arizonensis*], 236 [*Urocyon cinereoargenteus scottii*].
Mearns (1897). *Proc. US Natl. Mus.* **20**: 458 [*Lynx rufus californicus*], 459 [*Urocyon cinereoargenteus californicus*], 461 [*Mephitis mephitis holzerni*], 467 [*Mephitis macroura milleri*].
Mearns (1901). *Proc. Biol. Soc. Washington* **14**: 139 [*Panthera onca centralis*], 144 [*Panthera onca goldmani*], 150 [*Puma yagouaroundi fossata*].
Mearns (1902). *Proc. US Natl. Mus.* **25**: 245 [*Leopardus pardalis aequatorialis*].
Mearns (1914). *Proc. Biol. Soc. Washington* **27**: 63 [*Procyon lotor fuscipes*].
Merriam (1888). *Proc. Biol. Soc. Washington* **4**: 136 [*Vulpes macrotis*].
Merriam (1890). *N. Amer. Fauna* **3**: 79 [*Lynx rufus baileyi*], 81 [*Mephitis mephitis estor*], 83 [*Spilogale gracilis*].
Merriam (1890). *N. Amer. Fauna* **4**: 11 [*Spilogale gracilis leucoparia, Spilogale gracilis lucasana*], 13 [*Spilogale gracilis phenax*], 15 [*Spilogale gracilis latifrons*], 27 [*Martes americana caurina*].
Merriam (1896). *N. Amer. Fauna* **11**: 12 [*Mustela erminea alascensis*], 13 [*Mustela erminea streatori*], 15 [*Mustela erminea arctica*], 16 [*Mustela erminea kadiacensis*], 18 [*Mustela frenata washingtoni*], 21 [*Mustela frenata saturata*], 24 [*Mustela frenata alleni*], 25 [*Mustela frenata oregonensis*], 28 [*Mustela frenata goldmani*], 29 [*Mustela frenata leucoparia*], 30 [*Mustela frenata tropicalis*].
Merriam (1896). *Proc. Biol. Soc. Washington* **10**: 69 [*Ursus arctos middendorffi*], 71 [*Ursus arctos dalli*], 73 [*Ursus arctos sitkensis*], 74 [*Ursus arctos californicus*], 76 [*Ursus arctos alascensis*], 81 [*Ursus americanus floridanus*].
Merriam (1897). *Proc. Biol. Soc. Washington* **11**: 25 [*Canis latrans lestes*], 28 [*Canis latrans peninsulae*], 29 [*Canis latrans microdon*], 30 [*Canis latrans mearnsi*], 33 [*Canis latrans vigilis*], 185 [*Bassariscus astutus saxicola*], 219 [*Puma concolor hippolestes*].
Merriam (1897). *Science* **5**: 302 [*Arctogalidia*].
Merriam (1898). *Proc. Biol. Soc. Washington* **12**: 17 [*Procyon lotor insularis*].
Merriam (1899). *N. Amer. Fauna* **16**: 103 [*Urocyon cinereoargenteus townsendi*], 104 [*Lynx rufus pallescens*], 107 [*Procyon lotor pacificus*].
Merriam (1900). *Proc. Washington Acad. Sci.* **2**: 14 [*Vulpes vulpes harrimani*], 664 [*Vulpes vulpes necator*], 665 [*Vulpes vulpes cascadensis*], 667 [*Vulpes vulpes bangsi*], 668 [*Vulpes vulpes alascensis*], 669 [*Vulpes vulpes abietorum*], 670 [*Vulpes vulpes kenaiensis*], 672 [*Vulpes vulpes regalis*].
Merriam (1900). *Proc. Biol. Soc. Washington* **13**: 151 [*Procyon lotor pallidus*].
Merriam (1901). *Proc. Washington Acad. Sci.* **3**: 502 [*Puma concolor azteca*], 595 [*Puma concolor bangsi*], 596 [*Puma concolor costaricensis*], 598 [*Puma concolor patagonica*].
Merriam (1901). *Proc. Biol. Soc. Washington* **14**: 100 [*Nasua narica nelsoni*], 101 [*Procyon pygmaeus*].
Merriam (1902). *Proc. Biol. Soc. Washington* **15**: 67 [*Mustela frenata perda*], 68 [*Nasua narica molaris*], 74 [*Vulpes macrotis muticus, Vulpes macrotis neomexicanus*], 78 [*Ursus arctos gyas*], 171 [*Alopex lagopus beringensis, Alopex lagopus pribilofensis*].
Merriam (1903). *Proc. Biol. Soc. Washington* **16**: 73 [*Puma concolor browni*], 74 [*Urocyon cinereoargenteus borealis, Urocyon littoralis catalinae*], 75 [*Urocyon littoralis clementae, Urocyon littoralis santacruzae*].
Merriam (1904). *Proc. Biol. Soc. Washington* **17**: 154 [*Ursus americanus eremicus*], 157 [*Canis latrans goldmani*], 159 [*Enhydra lutris nereis*].
Merriam (1914). *Proc. Biol. Soc. Washington* **27**: 178 [*Ursus arctos stikeenensis*].
Meyer (1793). *Zool. Entdeck* 33 [*Canis lupus dingo*], 155-160. [*Melursus*].
Meyer (1794). *Zool. Ann.* **1**: 394 [*Panthera pardus fusca*].
Meyer (1826). *Beytr. Anat. Des Tiegers* 6 [*Panthera leo persica, Panthera leo senegalensis*].
Middendorff (1853). *Reise äussersten Norden Osten Dibiriens* **2(2)**: pl. 1 [*Ursus arctos beringianus*].
Middendorff (1875). *Uber. Nat. Nord. Ost. Sibiria 4* **2**: 990 [*Vulpes vulpes beringiana*].
Miller, F.W. (1925). *J. Mammal* **6**: 50 [*Conepatus leuconotus figginsi*].
Miller, G.S. (1899). *Proc. Acad. Nat. Sci. Philadelphia* **51**: 278 [*Urocyon cinereoargenteus guatemalae*].
Miller, G.S. (1903). *Smithsonian Misc. Coll.* **45**: 43 [*Hemigalus derbyanus minor*].
Miller, G.S. (1907). *Ann. Mag. Nat. Hist. 7th Ser.* **20**: 391 [*Vulpes vulpes ichnusae*], 392 [*Vulpes vulpes induta*], 393 [*Vulpes vulpes silacea*], 395 [*Mustela erminea ricinae*], 396 [*Felis silvestris grampia*].
Miller, G.S. (1909). *Smithsonian Misc. Coll.* **52**: 485 [*Otocyon megalotis virgatus*].
Miller, G.S. (1910). *Proc. US Natl. Mus.* **38**: 385 [*Vormela peregusna negans*].
Miller, G.S. (1911). *Proc. Biol. Soc. Washington* **24**: 3 [*Procyon lotor pumilus*].
Miller, G.S. (1913). *Proc. Biol. Soc. Washington* **26**: 159 [*Bassariscus astutus nevadensis*].
Miller, J. (1900). *True Bear Stories* 250 [*Ursus americanus californiensis*].
Milne-Edwards (1870). *Ann. Sci. Nat. Zool. (Paris), ser. 5* **13(10)**: 1 [*Ailuropoda*].
Milne-Edwards (1872). *Rech. Mamm.* 223 [*Catopuma temminckii tristis*].
Milne-Edwards (1892). *Rev. Gen. Sci. Pures Appl.* **3**: 671 [*Felis bieti*].
Mivart (1886). *Proc. Zool. Soc. London* **1886**: 347 [*Procyon cancrivorous nigripes*].
Molina (1782). *Sagg. Stor. Nat. Chile* 284 [*Lontra felina*], 288 [*Conepatus chinga*], 291 [*Galictis cuja*], 293 [*Pseudalopex culpaeus*], 295 [*Leopardus colocolo, Leopardus guigna, Puma concolor puma*].
Mori (1922). *Ann. Mag. Nat. Hist. 9th Ser.* **10**: 607 [*Nyctereutes procyonoides koreensis*].
Müller (1776). Linné's *Vollstand, Natursyst. Suppl.* 32 [*Fossa fossana*].
Müller (1836). *Arch. Anat. Physiol., Jahresber. Fortschr. Wiss.* **1835**: 1 [*Otocyon*].
Nelson (1901). *Proc. Biol. Soc. Washington* **14**: 129 [*Galictis vittata canaster*].
Nelson (1930). *Smithsonian Misc. Coll.* **82(8)**: 7 [*Procyon lotor marinus*], 8 [*Procyon lotor inesperatus*], 9 [*Procyon lotor auspicatus*], 10 [*Procyon lotor incautus*].
Nelson (1932). *Proc. Biol. Soc. Washington* **45**: 224 [*Canis latrans dickeyi*].
Nelson & Goldman (1909). *Proc. Biol. Soc. Washington* **22**: 25 [*Vulpes macrotis devius*], 26 [*Bassariscus astutus insulicola, Bassariscus astutus palmarius*].
Nelson & Goldman (1929). *J. Mammal* **10**: 165 [*Canis lupus baileyi*], 347 [*Puma concolor incarum*], 348 [*Puma concolor osgoodi*], 350 [*Puma concolor mayensis*].
Nelson & Goldman (1930). *J. Mammal* **11**: 453 [*Procyon lotor gloveralleni*], 455 [*Procyon lotor hirtus*], 457 [*Procyon lotor litoreus*], 458 [*Procyon lotor excelsus, Procyon lotor vancouverensis*].
Nelson & Goldman (1930). *Jour. Washington Acad. Sci.* **20**: 82 [*Procyon lotor grinnelli*].
Nelson & Goldman (1931). *J. Mammal* **12**: 302 [*Vulpes macrotis tenuirostris*], 304 [*Leopardus wiedii yucatanicus*].
Nelson & Goldman (1931). *Jour. Washington Acad. Sci.* **21**: 209 [*Puma concolor kaibabensis*], 210 [*Puma concolor anthonyi*], 211 [*Puma concolor greeni*].
Nelson & Goldman (1932). *Proc. Biol. Soc. Washington* **45**: 105. [*Puma concolor vancouverensis*].
Nelson & Goldman (1932). *Jour. Washington Acad. Sci.* **22**: 497 [*Bassariscus astutus consitus*].
Nelson & Goldman (1933). *Jour. Washington Acad. Sci.* **23**: 524 [*Puma concolor borbensis*].
Nelson & Goldman (1933). *J. Mammal* **14**: 236 [*Panthera onca veraecrucis*].
Neumann (1900). *Zool. Jahrb. Syst.* **13**: 551 [*Panthera pardus suahelicus*].
Noack (1897). *Zool. Anzeiger* **20**: 517 [*Canis mesomelas schmidti*].
Ogilby (1833). *Proc. Zool. Soc. London* **1833**: 48 [*Cynictis*].
Ogilby (1835). *Proc. Zool. Soc. London* **1835**: 102 [*Mungos gambianus*].
Ognev (1923). *Biol. Mitt. Timiriazeff* **1**: 112 [*Mustela erminea tobolica*], 114 [*Canis lupus cubanensis*], 116 [*Vulpes vulpes jakutensis*].
Ognev (1926). *Ann. Mus. Budapest* **23**: 225 [*Vulpes vulpes ochroxantha*], 227 [*Vulpes vulpes tobolica*], 232 [*Vulpes vulpes dolichocrania*].
Ognev (1926). *Ann. Mus. Zool. Leningrad* **27**: 356 [*Felis margarita thinobia*].
Ognev (1928). *C.R. Acad. Sci. URSS.* 308 [*Otocolobus manul ferrugineus*].
Ognev (1928). *Zh. Okhotnik* **5-6**: 22 [*Lynx lynx wrangeli*].
Ognev (1928). *Mem. Sect. Zool. Amis. Sci. Nat. Moscow* **2**: 18 [*Mustela erminea mongolica*].
Ognev (1931). *Mamm. East Europe* **2**: 331 [*Vulpes vulpes daurica*].
Ognev (1935). *Mamm. USSR.* **3**: 634 [*Vulpes corsac kalmykorum*], 635 [*Vulpes corsac turkmenicus*].
Oken (1816). *Lehrb. Naturgesch., Ser. 3* **2**: 1052 [*Panthera*].
Olfers (1818). In: Eschwege, *J. Brasilien, Neue Bibliothek Reisenb.* **15(2)**: 227 [*Nasua nasua spadicea*], 233 [*Lontra longicaudis*].
d'Orbigny & Gervais (1844). *Bull. Sci. Soc. Philom. Paris* **1844**: 40 [*Leopardus geoffroyi*].
d'Orbigny & Gervais (1847). *Voy. Amer. Merid.* **4**: 19 [*Conepatus humboldtii castaneus*].
Ord (1815). *New Geog. Hist. Coml. Grammar, Philadelphia 2nd ed.* 291 [*Ursus arctos horribilis*].
Osgood (1900). *N. Amer. Fauna* **19**: 42 [*Neovison vison ingens*], 43 [*Martes americana actuosa*].
Osgood (1901). *N. Amer. Fauna* **21**: 30 [*Ursus americanus carlottae*], 33 [*Martes americana nesophila*].
Osgood (1943). *Field Mus. Nat. Hist. Zool. Ser.* **30(548)**: 77 [*Puma concolor araucanus*].
Pallas (1773). *Reise Prov. Russ. Reichs.* **2**: 701 [*Mustela sibirica*].
Pallas (1776). *Reise Prov. Russ. Reichs.* **3**: 692 [*Otocolobus manul*].
Pallas (1777). In: Schreber, *Die Säugethiere* **3(25)**: 426 [*Paradoxurus hermaphroditus*], 451 [*Paradoxurus zeylonensis*].
Pallas (1780). *Spicilegia Zoologica* **14**: 5 [*Ursus americanus*], 25 [*Gulo*].
Pallas (1811). *Zoogr. Rosso-Asiat.* **1**: 34 [*Cuon alpinus*], 98 [*Mustela altaica*].
Peale & Palisot de Beauvois (1796). *A Scientific and Descriptive Catalogue of Peale's Museum*: 37 [*Mephitis mephitis nigra*], 39 [*Neovison vison mink*].
Pearson (1832). *J. Asiat. Soc. Bengal* **1**: 75 [*Felis chaus kutas*].
Pearson (1836). *J. Asiatic Soc. Bengal* **5**: 313 [*Vulpes vulpes montana*].
Perry (1810). *Arcana, Mus. Nat. Hist.* pt. **11**: pl. 41 [*Ictonyx striatus*].
Peters (1850). *Spenersche Z.* **25 June, 1850** (unpaginated) [*Bdeogale*].
Peters (1852). *Monatsb. K. Preuss. Akad. Wiss. Berlin* **1852**: 81 [*Bdeogale crassicauda, Helogale parvula undulata*], 82 [*Bdeogale crassicauda puisa*].
Peters (1874). *Monatsb. K. Preuss. Akad. Wiss. Berlin* **1874**: 704 [*Bassariscus sumichrasti variabilis*].
Peterson & Downing (1952). *Contrib. Royal Ontario Mus. Zool. & Paleont.* **33**: 1 [*Lynx rufus superiorensis*].

Philippi (1895). *Anal. Univers. Chile* **54**: 542 [*Pseudalopex culpaeus lycoides*].
Philippi (1901). *Anal. Univers. Chile* **108**: 168 [*Pseudalopex griseus domeykoanus*].
Philippi (1903). *Arch. Naturg.* **69**: 158 [*Pseudalopex griseus maullinicus*].
Phillips (1912). *Proc. Biol. Soc. Washington* **25**: 85 [*Puma concolor improcera*].
Phipps (1774). *Voyage toward North Pole* 185 [*Ursus maritimus*].
Pinel (1792). *Actes Soc. Hist. Nat. Paris* **1**: 55 [*Martes*].
Pocock (1907). *Proc. Zool. Soc. London* **1907**: 666 [*Leptailurus serval liptostictus*].
Pocock (1908). *Proc. Zool. Soc. London* **1907**: 1041 [*Genetta johnstoni*], 1045 [*Poiana leightoni*].
Pocock (1909). *Proc. Zool. Soc. London* **1909**: 394 [*Mellivora capensis signata*].
Pocock (1915). *Ann. Mag. Nat. Hist. 8th Ser.* **16**: 120 [*Mungotictis*], 506 [*Mungotictis decemlineata lineata*].
Pocock (1915). *Proc. Zool. Soc. London* **1915**: 134 [*Civettictis*].
Pocock (1916). *Ann. Mag. Nat. Hist. 8th Ser.* **17**: 177 [*Paracynictis*].
Pocock (1921). *Proc. Zool. Soc. London* **1921**: 543 [*Hydrictis*].
Pocock (1927). *Ann. Mag. Nat. Hist. 9th Ser.* **20**: 213 [*Panthera pardus saxicolor*], 214 [*Panthera pardus adusta*].
Pocock (1929). *J. Bombay Nat. Hist. Soc.* **33**: 535 [*Panthera tigris sumatrae*].
Pocock (1930). *J. Bombay Nat. Hist. Soc.* **34**: 80 [*Panthera pardus sindica*], 325 [*Panthera pardus delacouri*].
Pocock (1932). *Proc. Zool. Soc. London* **1932**: 33 [*Panthera pardus adersi, Panthera pardus jarvisi*].
Pocock (1932). *J. Bombay Nat. Hist. Soc.* **36**: 115 [*Ursus thibetanus laniger*].
Pocock (1933). *J. Bombay Nat. Hist. Soc.* **36**: 632 [*Viverricula indica mayori*], 640 [*Viverricula indica wellsi*], 643 [*Viverricula indica baptistae*], 654 [*Viverricula indica klossi*], 865 [*Paradoxurus jerdoni caniscus*].
Pocock (1934). *Ann. Mag. Nat. Hist. 10th Ser.* **14**: 636 [*Vulpes rueppellii sabaea, Hyaena hyaena sulatana*].
Pocock (1935). *Proc. Zool. Soc. London* **1935**: 682 [*Canis lupus arctos*].
Pocock (1936). *Proc. Zool. Soc. London* **1936**: 38 [*Cuon alpinus infuscus*], 49 [*Cuon alpinus fumosus*], 50 [*Cuon alpinus laniger*], 718 [*Vormela peregusna euxina*], 720 [*Vormela peregusna syriaca*].
Pocock (1936). *Ann. Mag. Nat. Hist. 10th Ser.* **17**: 403 [*Martes flavigula robinsoni*].
Pocock (1937). *J. Bombay Nat. Hist. Soc.* **39**: 233 [*Herpestes fuscus rubidior*].
Pocock (1939). *Fauna Brit. India* **1**: 273 [*Prionailurus bengalensis trevelyani*], 278 [*Prionailurus rubiginosus phillipsi*], 300 [*Felis chaus kelaarti*].
Pocock (1940). *Ann. Mag. Nat. Hist. 11th Ser.* **6**: 308 [*Puma concolor cabrerae*], 351 [*Leopardus geoffroyi paraguae*], 352 [*Leopardus geoffroyi euxanthus*].
Pocock (1940). *J. Bombay Nat. Hist. Soc.* **41**: 515 [*Aonyx cinereus nirnai*], 517 [*Lutrogale perspicillata sindica*].
Pocock (1941). *Fauna Brit. India* **2**: 49 [*Herpestes vitticollis inornatus*], 156 [*Cuon alpinus adustus*].
Pocock (1941). *Ann. Mag. Nat. Hist. 7th Ser.* 11 **8**: 237 [*Leopardus wiedii boliviae*].
Pocock (1941). *Ann. Mag. Nat. Hist. 11th Ser.* **7**: 263 [*Leopardus colocolo budini*].
Pocock (1941). *Ann. Mag. Nat. Hist. 11th Ser.* **8**: 235 [*Leopardus pardalis steinbachi*].
Pocock (1944). *Proc. Zool. Soc. London* **114**: 71 [*Felis silvestris foxi*], 72 [*Felis silvestris brockmani*].
Pocock (1944). *Ann. Mag. Nat. Hist. 11th Ser.* **11**: 125 [*Felis silvestris tristrami*], 131 [*Felis silvestris pyrrhus*], 694 [*Leptailurus serval tanae*].
Pocock (1946). *Proc. Zool. Soc. London* **115**: 314 [*Mellivora capensis pumilio*].
Pousargues (1893). *Bull. Soc. Zool. Fr.* **18**: 51 [*Dologale dybowskii*].
Preble (1898). *Proc. Biol. Soc. Washington* **12**: 169 [*Mustela erminea haidarum*].
Preble (1902). *N. Amer. Fauna* **22**: 66 [*Neovison vison lacustris*].
Pucheran (1855). In: I. Geoffroy Saint-Hilaire, *Mammiferes*, in: Petit-Thouars, *Voyage Autour du Monde Sur la Frégate Venus...Zoologie* 149 [*Leopardus pardalis albescens*].
Pucheran (1855). *Rev. Mag. Zool Paris* **7(2)**: 111 [*Bdeogale nigripes*], 154 [*Genetta servalina*], 392 [*Melursus ursinus inornatus*], 393 [*Mustela nivalis numidica*].
Radde (1862). *Reise Ost. Sib.* **1**: 19 [*Martes flavigula borealis*].
Raffles (1822). *Trans. Linnaean Soc. Zool. London* **13**: 253 [*Arctictis binturong*], 254 [*Helarctos malayanus*].
Rafinesque (1817). *Amer. Month. Mag.* **2(1)**: 46 [*Lynx rufus fasciatus, Lynx rufus floridanus*].
Rafinesque (1820). *Ann. Nat.* **1**: 3 [*Spilogale putorius interrupta*].
Rafinesque (1832). *Atlantic Jour.* **1**: 62 [*Puma concolor oregonensis, Aonyx cinereus concolor*].
Rhoads (1893). *Proc. Acad. Nat. Sci. Philadelphia* **45**: 417 [*Bassariscus astutus flavus*].
Rhoads (1894). *Proc. Acad. Nat. Sci. Philadelphia* **46**: 152 [*Mustela frenata peninsulae*].
Rhoads (1895). *Proc. Acad. Nat. Sci. Philadelphia* **47**: 42 [*Urocyon cinereoargenteus floridanus*].
Rhoads (1898). *Trans. Amer. Philos. Soc. n. s.* **19**: 429 [*Lontra canadensis pacifica*], 431 [*Lontra canadensis sonora*], 435 [*Martes pennanti pacifica*].
Rhoads (1900). *Proc. Acad. Nat. Sci. Philadelphia* **52**: 751 [*Mustela nivalis allegheniensis*].
Richardson (1829). *Fauna Boreali-Americana* **1**: 55 [*Mephitis mephitis hudsonica*], 60 [*Canis lupus occidentalis*].
Roberts (1924). *Ann. Transvaal Mus.* **10**: 69 [*Cynictis penicillata bradfieldi*].
Roberts (1926). *Ann. Transvaal Mus.* **11**: 248 [*Caracal caracal damarensis, Caracal caracal limpopoensis*].
Roberts (1929). *Ann. Transvaal Mus.* **13**: 90 [*Cynictis penicillata coombsi*], 91 [*Panthera leo krugeri*].
Roberts (1931). *Ann. Transvaal Mus.* **14**: 227 [*Paracynictis selousi sengaani*].
Roberts (1932). *Ann. Transvaal Mus.* **15**: 5 [*Paracynictis selousi bechuanae, Paracynictis selousi ngamiensis*].
Roberts (1933). *Ann. Transvaal Mus.* **15**: 266 [*Atilax paludinosus transvaalensis*].
Roberts (1936). *Ann. Transvaal Mus.* **18**: 253 [*Galerella pulverulenta basutica*].
Roberts (1938). *Ann. Transvaal Mus.* **19**: 243 [*Rhynchogale melleri langi*].
Roberts (1948). *Ann. Transvaal Mus.* **21**: 63 [*Genetta tigrina methi*].
Robinson & Kloss (1917). *Jour. Fed. St. Malaya Mus.* **7**: 243 [*Paguma larvata annectens*].
Robinson & Kloss (1920). *Rec. Indian Mus.* **19(4)**: 176 [*Viverra zibetha sigillata*], 177 [*Viverra tangalunga lankavensis*].
Robinson & Thomas (1917). *Ann. Mag. Nat. Hist. 8th Ser.* **20**: 261 [*Mustela lutreolina*].
Rochebrune (1883). *Bull. Soc. Philom. Paris (7)* **7**: 8 [*Vulpes pallida edwardsi*].
Rochebrune (1885). *Bull. Soc. Philom. Paris. Ser. 9* **17**: 181 [*Caracal caracal lucani*].
Rothschild (1902). *Novit. Zool.* **9**: 443 [*Proteles cristata septentrionalis*].
Rüppell (1835). *Neue Wirbelt. Fauna Abyssin. Gehörig. Säugeth.* **1**: 27 [*Galerella sanguinea*], 33 [*Genetta abyssinica*], 39 [*Canis simensis*].
Ryley (1914). *J. Bombay Nat. Hist. Soc.* **22**: 660 [*Herpestes edwardsii pallens*].
Sale & Taylor (1970). *Journal of East Africa Natural History Society and National Museum* **28**: 11 [*Bdeogale crassicauda nigrescens*].
Satunin (1905). *Mitt. Kauk. Mus.* **2**: 154 [*Felis silvestris caucasica*].
Satunin (1906). *Isv. Kauk. Mus.* **2**: 46 [*Vulpes vulpes alpherakyi*], 48 [*Vulpes vulpes kurdistanica*].
Satunin (1914). *Conspectus Mamm.* **1**: 159 [*Panthera pardus ciscaucasicus*].
Satunin (1915). *Mem. Cauc. Mus. Ser. A* **1**: 391 [*Lynx lynx dinniki*].
Saussure (1860). *Rev. Mag. Zool. Paris 2nd Ser.* **12**: 7 [*Bassariscus sumichrasti*].
Say (1823). In: Long, *Account of an Exped. to the Rocky Mts.* **1**: 168 [*Canis latrans*], 169 [*Canis lupus nubilus*], 487 [*Vulpes velox*].
Schantz (1946). *J. Mammal* **26**: 431 [*Taxidea taxus jacksoni*].
Schinz (1821). In: G. Cuvier, *Das Thierreich* **1**: 199 [*Nasua nasua solitaria*], 214 [*Aonyx capensis*], 235 [*Leopardus wiedii*].
Schinz (1825). In: G. Cuvier, *Das Thierreich* **4**: 508 [*Vulpes rueppellii*].
Schinz (1844). *Synops. Mammalium* **1**: 302 [*Ursus arctos crowtheri*].
Schinz (1844). *Syst. Verz. Säugeth.* **1**: 470 [*Leopardus guigna tigrillo*].
Schlegel (1857). *Handl. Der Dierkunde* **1**: 23 [*Panthera pardus orientalis*], 42 [*Ursus thibetanus japonicus*].
Schlegel (1879). *Notes Leyden Mus.* **1**: 43 [*Macrogalidia musschenbroekii*].
Schreber (1774). *Die Säugethiere* **1**: index [*Potos flavus*].
Schreber (1775). *Die Säugethiere* **2(13)**: pl. 89 [*Canis lupus lycaon*], pl. 92 [*Urocyon cinereoargenteus*]; **2(14)**: pl. 95 [*Canis mesomelas*], pl. 100 [*Panthera uncia*]; **2(15)**: pl. 105 [*Acinonyx jubatus*], pl. 106 [*Leopardus tigrinus*].
Schreber (1776). *Die Säugethiere* **3(16)**: pl. 108 [*Leptailurus serval*], pl. 110 [*Caracal caracal*], pl. 111 [*Civettictis civetta*], pl. 115 [*Genetta tigrina*], pl. 117 [*Suricata suricatta*], pl. 121 [*Mephitis mephitis, Galictis vittata*], pl. 125 [*Mellivora capensis*], pl. 126b [*Lontra canadensis*], pl. 127b [*Neovison vison*].
Schreber (1777). *Die Säugethiere* **3(23)**: 384 [*Panthera pardus panthera*], 387 [*Panthera pardus leopardus*], 397 [*Felis silvestris*]; **3(24)**: 412 [*Lynx rufus*], 414 [*Felis chaus*].
Schreber (1778). *Die Säugethiere* **3(25)**: 520 [*Taxidea taxus*].
Schrenck (1859). *Reisen Amur-Lande* 17 [*Meles leucurus amurensis*].
Schwann (1904). *Ann. Mag. Nat. Hist. 7th Ser.* **13**: 423 [*Felis silvestris mellandi*], 424 [*Felis silvestris ugandae*].
Schwarz (1910). *Ann. Mag. Nat. Hist. 5th Ser.* **8**: 423 [*Macrogalidia*].
Schwarz (1911). *Ann. Mag. Nat. Hist. 8th Ser.* **7**: 637 [*Viverricula indica taivana*].
Schwarz (1912). *Ann. Mag. Nat. Hist. 8th Ser.* **10**: 325 [*Panthera tigris balica*].
Sclater (1883). *Proc. Zool. Soc. London* **1882**: 631 [*Atelocynus microtis*].
Sclater (1898). *Proc. Zool. Soc. London* **1898**: 2 [*Catopuma temminckii dominicanorum*].
Severtzov (1858). *Rev. Mag. Zool. Paris, Ser. 2* **10**: 386 [*Profelis*], 387 [*Pardofelis, Prionailurus, Catopuma*], 389 [*Leptailurus*].
Shaw (1791). *Nat. Misc.* **2**: pl. 58 [*Melursus ursinus*].
Shaw (1800). *Gen. Zool. Syst. Nat. Hist.* **1(2)**: 311 [*Vulpes vulpes barbara*], 330 [*Vulpes bengalensis*].
Shortridge (1931). *Rec. Albany Mus. Grahamstown* **4**: 110 [*Felis nigripes thomasi*].
Smith, A. (1833). *South African Quart. Jour.* **2**: 89 [*Vulpes chama*].
Smith, A. (1834). *South African Quart. Jour.* **2**: 245 [*Acinonyx jubatus fearonii*].
Smith, C.E.H. (1827). In: Griffith *et al.*, *Anim. Kingdom* **2**: 281 [*Paguma larvata*].
Smith, C.E.H. (1839). *Jardine's Nat. Lib.* **9**: 242 [*Chrysocyon*], 259 [*Cerdocyon*].
Smith, C.E.H. (1842). *Jardine's Nat. Lib. 2 Mam.* **35**: 201 [*Eira*].
Smith, C.E.H. (1858). *Jardine's Nat. Lib. 2 Mam.* **15**: 177 [*Panthera leo melanochaita*].
Sody (1931). *Natuurkundig Tijdschr Ned.-Indië* **91**: 351 [*Viverricula indica atchinensis*], 353 [*Viverricula indica muriavensis, Viverricula indica baliensis*].
Sody (1936). *Natuurkundig Tijdschr Ned.-Indië* **96**: 45 [*Prionailurus viviverrinus rizophoreus*].
Sody (1937). *Temminckia* **2**: 211 [*Melogale orientalis sundaicus*].
Sody (1949). *Treubia* **20**: 181 [*Prionailurus bengalensis alleni*].
Sonnini (1816). *Nouv. Dict. Sci. Nat.* **6**: 524 [*Vulpes vulpes aegyptiacus*].
Sparrman (1783). *Resa Goda-Hopps-Udden.*, I. **1**: 581 [*Proteles cristata*].
Stager (1950). *Proc. Biol. Soc. Washington* **63**: 203 [*Bassariscus astutus willetti*].
Stone (1900). *Proc. Acad. Nat. Sci. Philadelphia* **52**: 44 [*Mustela nivalis eskimo*].
Storr (1780). *Prodr. Meth. Mamm.* 34 [*Mellivora*], 35 [*Nasua, Procyon*].
Stroganov (1948). *Trans. Zool. Inst. AN USSR.* **7**: 129 [*Vormela peregusna pallidior*].
Stroganov (1962). *Zveri Sibiri* **2**: 408 [*Lynx lynx neglectus*].
Sundevall (1847). *Ofv. K. Svenska Vet.-Akad. Forhandl. Stockholm* **3**: 121 [*Canis adustus, Helogale parvula*].
Sutton & Hamilton (1932). *Ann. Carnegie Mus.* **21**: 79 [*Mustela erminea semplei*].
Swarth (1911). *Univ. California Publ. Zool.* **7**: 141 [*Ursus americanus pugnax*].
Swinhoe (1862). *Proc. Zool. Soc. London* **1862**: 352 [*Neofelis nebulosa brachyura*], 355 [*Melogale moschata subaurantiaca*].
Swinhoe (1864). *Proc. Zool. Soc. London* **1864**: 380 [*Ursus thibetanus formosanus*].
Swinhoe (1866). *Ann. Mag. Nat. Hist. 3rd Ser.* **18**: 286 [*Martes flavigula chrysospila*].
Swinhoe (1870). *Proc. Zool. Soc. London* **1870**: 517 [*Vulpes vulpes hoole*].
Sykes (1831). *Proc. Zool. Soc. London* **1831**: 100 [*Cuon alpinus dukhunensis*].
Sykes (1831). *Proc. Zool. Soc. London* **1831**: 101 [*Canis lupus pallipes*].
Taczanowski (1874). *Proc. Zool. Soc. London* **1874**: 311 [*Mustela frenata macrura*].
Tate & Rand (1941). *Amer. Mus. Novit.* **1112**: 1 [*Galidia elegans dambrensis*].
Temminck (1820). *Ann. Gen. Sci. Phys.* **3**: 54 [*Lycaon pictus*].
Temminck (1824). *Prospectus de Monographies de Mammifères* xxi [*Arctictis*].
Temminck (1827). *Monogr. Mamm.* **1**: 116 [*Lynx pardinus*], 120 [*Profelis aurata*], 140 [*Profelis aurata celidogaster*].
Temminck (1839). *Tijdschr. Natuurl. Geschied. Physiol.* **5**: 284 [*Canis lupus hodophilax*], 285 [*Nyctereutes, Nyctereutes procyonoides viverrinus*].

Temminck (1844). *Fauna Japonica, Mammalia* 30 [*Meles anakuma*], 34 [*Mustela itatsi*], 43 [*Panthera tigris altaica, Panthera tigris sondaica*].

Temminck (1853). *Esquisses Zool. Sur la Côte de Guiné* 93 [*Ichneumia albicauda loempo*], 95 [*Atilax paludinosus pluto*].

Thomas (1880). *Proc. Zool. Soc. London* **1880**: 397 [*Bassaricyon alleni*].

Thomas (1883). *Ann. Mag. Nat. Hist., 5th Ser.* **11**: 370 [*Poecilogale*].

Thomas (1890). *Proc. Zool. Soc. London* **1890**: 622 [*Ichneumia albicauda grandis*].

Thomas (1892). *Ann. Mag. Nat. Hist., 6th Ser.* **9**: 250 [*Diplogale hosei*].

Thomas (1893). *Ann. Mag. Nat. Hist., 6th Ser.* **12**: 205 [*Nandinia binotata gerrardi*].

Thomas (1894). *Ann. Mag. Nat. Hist., 6th Ser.* **13**: 522 [*Bdeogale jacksoni*].

Thomas (1894). *Proc. Zool. Soc. London* **1894**: 139 [*Rhynchogale*].

Thomas (1895). *Ann. Mag. Nat. Hist., 6th Ser.* **15**: 331 [*Melogale everettii*], 452 [*Mustela erminea ferghanae*].

Thomas (1897). *Ann. Mag. Nat. Hist., 6th Ser.* **19**: 161 [*Martes melampus tsuensis*].

Thomas (1898). *Ann. Mag. Nat. Hist., 7th Ser.* **1**: 41 [*Puma yagouaroundi tolteca*], 42 [*Lynx rufus peninsularis*], 278 [*Conepatus chinga rex*].

Thomas (1898). *Proc. Zool. Soc. London* **1898**: 898 [*Spilogale pygmaea*].

Thomas (1900). *Ann. Mag. Nat. Hist., 7th Ser.* **5**: 146 [*Eira barbara senex*], 148 [*Pseudalopex sechurae*], 217 [*Conepatus semistriatus zorrino*], 499 [*Conepatus chinga inca*].

Thomas (1901). *Ann. Mag. Nat. Hist., 7th Ser.* **8**: 69 [*Nasuella olivacea meridensis*], 188 [*Puma concolor pearsoni*], 248 [*Nasua nasua quichua*].

Thomas (1901). *Proc. Zool. Soc. London* **1901**: 87 [*Genetta victoriae*].

Thomas (1902). *Ann. Mag. Nat. Hist. 7th Ser.* **9**: 239 [*Conepatus humboldtii proteus*], 267 [*Genetta servalina bettoni*], 365 [*Potos flavus meridensis, Potos flavus modestus*], 442 [*Mydaus javanensis lucifer*], 443 [*Mydaus javanensis ollula*].

Thomas (1902). *Ann. Mag. Nat. Hist. 7th Ser.* **10**: 251 [*Ailurus fulgens styani*], 487 [*Genetta genetta grantii*], 489 [*Vulpes vulpes arabica*].

Thomas (1902). *Proc. Zool. Soc. London* **1902**: 119 [*Helogale parvula varia*], 309 [*Atilax paludinosus mitis*].

Thomas (1903). *Ann. Mag. Nat. Hist. 7th Ser.* **11**: 379 [*Bassariscus sumichrasti notinus*].

Thomas (1903). *Ann. Mag. Nat. Hist. 7th Ser.* **12**: 235 [*Leopardus wiedii glauculus*], 237 [*Leopardus tigrinus oncilla*], 239 [*Leopardus geoffroyi salinarum*], 462 [*Galictis vittata andina*], 465 [*Galerella pulverulenta ruddi*].

Thomas (1903). *Proc. Zool. Soc. London* **1903**: 309 [*Atilax paludinosus mitis*].

Thomas (1904). *Ann. Mag. Nat. Hist. 7th Ser.* **13**: 11 [*Ichneumia albicauda ibeana*], 408 [*Ichneumia albicauda loandae*].

Thomas (1904). *Ann. Mag. Nat. Hist. 7th Ser.* **14**: 94 [*Panthera pardus nanopardus*], 97 [*Helogale hirtula*], 198 [*Leopardus wiedii vigens*].

Thomas (1905). *Ann. Mag. Nat. Hist. 7th Ser.* **15**: 585 [*Conepatus semistriatus trichurus*].

Thomas (1907). *Ann. Mag. Nat. Hist. 7th Ser.* **20**: 162 [*Galictis cuja furax*], 163 [*Galictis cuja luteola*].

Thomas (1908). *Ann. Mag. Nat. Hist. 8th Ser.* **1**: 391 [*Lontra provocax*].

Thomas (1909). *Ann. Mag. Nat. Hist. 8th Ser.* **4**: 232 [*Bassaricyon alleni medius*].

Thomas (1910). *Ann. Mag. Nat. Hist. 8th Ser.* **5**: 195 [*Crossarchus ansorgei*], 241 [*Conepatus chinga gibsoni*].

Thomas (1912). *Ann. Mag. Nat. Hist 8th Ser.* **10**: 228 [*Nasua nasua candace*], 229 [*Nasua nasua manium*], 588 [*Atilax paludinosus mordax*].

Thomas (1912). *Proc. Zool. Soc. London* **1912**: 17 [*Chrotogale, Chrotogale owstoni*], 18 [*Diplogale*].

Thomas (1914). *Ann. Mag. Nat. Hist 8th Ser.* **13**: 347 [*Leopardus pardalis pusaeus*], 350 [*Puma yagouaroundi melantho*], 357 [*Pseudalopex culpaeus andinus*], 573 [*Pseudalopex culpaeus smithersi*].

Thomas (1918). *Ann. Mag. Nat. Hist. 9th Ser.* **1**: 244 [*Vulpes rueppellii somaliae*].

Thomas (1919). *Ann. Mag. Nat. Hist. 9th Ser.* **3**: 490 [*Conepatus chinga budini*].

Thomas (1919). *Ann. Mag. Nat. Hist. 9th Ser.* **4**: 31 [*Helogale parvula ivori*].

Thomas (1920). *Ann. Mag. Nat. Hist. 9th Ser.* **5**: 121 [*Vulpes vulpes anatolica*], 122 [*Vulpes vulpes palaestina*].

Thomas (1921). *Ann. Mag. Nat. Hist. 9th Ser.* **8**: 134 [*Herpestes brachyurus sumatrius*], 135 [*Herpestes brachyurus rajah*], 163 [*Galictis cuja huronax*], 222 [*Conepatus chinga mendosus*].

Thomas (1921). *J. Bombay Nat. Hist. Soc.* **28**: 24 [*Herpestes smithii zeylanius*].

Thomas (1922). *J. Bombay Nat. Hist. Soc.* **28**: 432 [*Melogale moschata millsi*].

Thomas (1923). *Ann. Mag. Nat. Hist. 9th Ser.* **11**: 657 [*Nyctereutes procyonoides orestes*].

Thomas (1923). *Ann. Mag. Nat. Hist. 9th Ser.* **12**: 340 [*Mellivora capensis maxwelli*].

Thomas (1924). *Ann. Mag. Nat. Hist. 9th Ser.* **13**: 240 [*Herpestes fuscus phillipsi, Herpestes fuscus siccatus*].

Thomas (1924). *Ann. Mag. Nat. Hist. 9th Ser.* **14**: 286 [*Conepatus semistriatus taxinus*].

Thomas (1925). *Proc. Zool. Soc. London* **1925**: 499 [*Prionodon pardicolor presina*], 500 [*Melogale moschata taxilla*].

Thomas (1926). *Ann. Mag. Nat. Hist. 9th Ser.* **17**: 180 [*Felis silvestris griselda*], 183 [*Dologale, Helogale parvula mimetra*].

Thomas (1927). *Proc. Zool. Soc. London* **1927**: 46 [*Viverra zibetha surdaster*].

Thomas (1928). *Ann. Mag. Nat. Hist. 10th Ser.* **2**: 408 [*Helogale parvula nero*].

Thomas (1929). *Proc. Zool. Soc. London* **1928**: 834 [*Felis chaus fulvidina*].

Thomas & Barrett-Hamilton (1895). *Ann. Mag. Nat. Hist. 6th Ser.* **15**: 374 [*Mustela erminea hibernica*].

Thomas & Hinton (1920). *Ann. Mag. Nat. Hist. 9th Ser.* **5**: 368 [*Ictonyx lybicus oralis*].

Thomas & Hinton (1920). *Novit. Zool.* **27**: 316 [*Ictonyx lybicus rothschildi*].

Thomas & Hinton (1921). *Novit. Zool.* **28**: 3 [*Caracal caracal poecilotis*], 4 [*Vulpes pallida harterti*], 5 [*Vulpes rueppellii caesia*].

Thomas & Schwann (1906). *Proc. Zool. Soc. London* **1906**: 578 [*Genetta maculate letabae*].

Thomas & Wroughton (1907). *Ann. Mag. Nat. Hist. 7th Ser.* **19**: 372 [*Poiana richardsonii ochracea*], 373 [*Crossarchus alexandri*], 376 [*Mellivora capensis concisa*].

Thomas & Wroughton (1908). *Proc. Zool. Soc. London* **1908**: 166 [*Atilax paludinosus rubellus*], [*Bdeogale crassicauda tenuis*].

Thomson (1842). *Ann. Mag. Nat. Hist. 1st Ser.* **10**: 204 [*Poiana richardsonii*].

Thunberg (1811). *K. Svenska Vet.-Acad. Handl. Stockholm* **32**: 165 [*Genetta felina*].

Thunberg (1820). *K. Svenska Vet.-Acad. Handl. Stockholm* 59 [*Parahyaena brunnea*].

Thunberg (1820). *Mem. Acad. Scienc. S. Petersb.* **6**: 401 [*Galictis vittata brasiliensis*].

Townsend (1912). *Bull. Amer. Mus. Nat. Hist.* **31**: 130 [*Canis latrans jamesi*].

Traill (1821). *Mem. Werner. Soc.* **3**: 440 [*Eira barbara poliocephala*].

Tschudi (1844). *Fauna Peruviana* 101 [*Nasua nasua vittata*], 102 [*Nasua nasua montana*], 107 [*Eira barbara peruana*], 110 [*Mustela frenata agilis*].

Turton (1806). In: Linnaeus, *Gen. Syst. Nat.* **1**: 60 [*Martes americana*].

Tytler (1864). *J. Bombay Nat. Hist. Soc.* **33**: 188 [*Paguma larvata tytlerii*].

Valenciennes (1856). *C.R. Acad. Sci.* **42**: 1039 [*Panthera pardus tulliana*].

Van Rompaey & Colyn (1998). *South African Journal of Zoology* **33**: 43 [*Genetta servalina archeri*].

Vieira (1945). *Arq. Zool. Sao Paulo* **4**: 404 [*Nasua nasua aricana*].

Vigors & Horsfield (1827). *Zool. J.* **3**: 449 [*Prionailurus planiceps*], 451 [*Catopuma temminckii*].

Wagler (1831). In: *Isis von Oken* **24**: 514 [*Procyon lotor hernandezii*].

Wagner (1839). *Gelehrte. Anz. I. K. Bayer. Akad. Wiss. München* **9**: 426 [*Galerella pulverulenta*].

Wagner (1841). *Reisen* in: *d. Regenschaft Algier* **3**: 31 [*Vulpes vulpes atlantica*], 76 [*Caracal caracal algira*].

Wagner (1841). *Schreber's Säugethiere, Suppl.* **2**: 221 [*Ictonyx lybicus multivittata*], 229 [*Martes melampus*], 346 [*Arctogalidia trivirgata trilineata*], 547 [*Leptailurus serval brachyurus*].

Wang & Xu (1983). *Acta Zootaxon Sinica* 133 [*Viverra zibetha hainana*].

Waterhouse (1838). *Proc. Zool. Soc. London* **1838**: 55 [*Herpestes fuscus*], 59 [*Genetta poensis*].

Waterhouse (1839). *Proc. Zool. Soc. London* **1838**: 159 [*Taxidea*].

Wied-Neuwied (1824). *Abbild. Naturg. Brasil* 23 [*Cerdocyon thous azarae*].

Wied-Neuwied (1826). *Beitr. Naturg. Brasil* 23 [*Potos flavus nocturnus*].

Wilson (1991). In: Wilson et al. (1991). *J. Mammal.* **72**: 33 [*Enhydra lutris kenyoni*].

Woodhouse (1850). *Proc. Acad. Nat. Sci. Philadelphia* **5**: 147 [*Canis latrans frustror*].

Wozencraft (1986). *J. Mammal.* **67**: 561 [*Galidictis grandidieri*].

Wroughton (1910). *Ann. Mag. Nat. Hist. 8th Ser.* **5**: 205 [*Leptailurus serval hindei*].

Wroughton (1915). *J. Bombay Nat. Hist. Soc.* **24**: 52 [*Herpestes edwardsii moerens*], 64 [*Viverra zibetha pruinosus*].

Wroughton (1921). *J. Bombay Nat. Hist. Soc.* **28**: 23 [*Herpestes edwardsii carnaticus*].

Ximénez (1961). *Com. Zool. Mus. Hist. Nat. Montevideo* **5(88)**: 1 [*Leopardus colocolo munoai*].

Zimmermann (1780). *Geogr. Gesch. Mensch. Vierf. Thiere* **2**: 247 [*Vulpes zerda*].

Zukowsky (1959). *Der Zool. Garten* **24(5-6)**: 343 [*Panthera pardus dathei*].

General List of References

Abbadi, M. (1993). The sand cat in Israel. *Cat News* **18**: 15-16.
Abegg, C. (2003). Encounter with a Siberut palm civet, Mentawai Island, West Sumatra, Indonesia. *Small Carniv. Conserv.* **29**: 20-21.
Ables, E.D. (1975). Ecology of the red fox in North America. Pp. 216-236 in: Fox, M. ed. (1975). *The Wild Canids.* Van Nostrand Reinhold Company, New York.
Abramov, A.V. & Puzachenko, A.Y. (2006). Geographical variability of skull and taxonomy of Eurasian badgers (Mustelidae: *Meles*). *Zool. Zhurnal* **85**: 641-655.
Abramov, A.V. & Rozhnov, V.V. (2007). On the position of the genus *Mydaus* (Mammalia: Carnivora) in the order Carnivora. *Zool. Zhurnal* **86**: 763-765.
Abramov, A.V., Duckworth, J.W., Wang, Y.X. & Roberton, S.I. (2008). The stripe-backed weasel *Mustela strigidorsa*: taxonomy, ecology, distribution and status. *Mammal Rev.* **38(4)**: 247-266.
Acharjyo, L.M. & Misra, R. (1976). A note on the breeding of the Indian fox *Vulpes bengalensis* in captivity. *J. Bombay Nat. Hist. Soc.* **73**: 208.
Acharjyo, L.N. & Mishra, C.G. (1980). Some notes on age of sexual maturity of seven species of Indian wild mammals in captivity. *J. Bombay Nat. Hist. Soc.* **77**: 504-507.
Acharjyo, L.N. & Mishra, C.G. (1983). Further notes on the birth and growth of the leopard cat (*Felis bengalensis*) in captivity. *J. Bombay Nat. Hist. Soc.* **80**: 207-208.
Acharjyo, L.N. & Mohapatra, S. (1977). Some observations on the breeding habits and growth of jungle cat (*Felis chaus*) in captivity. *J. Bombay Nat. Hist. Soc.* **74**: 158-159.
Ackerman, B.B., Lindzey, F.G. & Hemker, T.P. (1984). Cougar food habits in southern Utah. *J. Wildl. Management* **48**: 147-155.
Ackerman, B.B., Lindzey, F.G. & Hemker, T.P. (1986). Predictive energetics model for cougars. Pp. 333-352 in: Miller, S.D. & Everett, D.D. eds. (1986). *Cats of the World: Biology, Conservation and Management.* National Wildlife Federation, Washington, D.C.
Adams, D.B. (1979). The cheetah: native American. *Science* **205**: 1155-1158.
Adelman, G. ed. (1987). *Encyclopedia of Neurosciences.* Birkhauser, Boston, Massachusetts.
Adler, H.J. (1991). Conservation program of *Chrotogale owstoni*, Thomas, 1912: some first results. *Mustel. Viverr. Conserv.* **4**: 8.
Admasu, E., Thirgood, S.J., Bekele, A. & Laurenson, M.K. (2004a). Spatial ecology of white-tailed mongoose in farmland in the Ethiopian highlands. *Afr. J. Eco.* **42**: 153-159.
Admasu, E., Thirgood, S.J., Bekele, A. & Laurenson, M.K. (2004b). A note on the spatial ecology of African civet *Civettictis civetta* and common genet *Genetta genetta* in farmland in the Ethiopian Highlands. *Afr. J. Ecol.* **42**: 160-162.
Adolph, E.F. (1967). The heart's pacemaker. *Scientific American* **216(3)**: 32-37.
Aerts, P. (1990). Mathematical biomechanics and the what, how and why in functional morphology. *Netherlands J. Zool.* **40**: 153-172.
Aerts, P. (1998). Vertical jumping in *Galago senegalensis*. The quest for an obligate mechanical power amplifier. *Phil. Trans. Roy. Soc. London (Ser. B)* **353**: 1607-1620.
Aeschlimann, A. (1965). Notes on the mammals of the Ivory Coast II. *Afr. Wildl.* **19**: 37-55.
Agrawal, V.C., Chakraborty, S. & Chakraborty, R. (1992). Taxonomic study on the large Indian civet, *Viverra zibetha* (Linnaeus) from the Indo-Burmese subregion (Mammalia: Viverridae). *Rec. Zool. Survey India* **91**: 1-7.
Ahlborn, G. & Jackson, R.M. (1988). Marking in free-ranging snow leopards in west Nepal: a preliminary assessment. Pp. 25-49 in: Freeman, H. ed. (1988). *Proceedings of the Fifth International Snow Leopard Symposium.* International Snow Leopard Trust & Wildlife Institute of India, Bombay.
Akhtar, N., Bargali, H.S. & Chauhan, N.P.S. (2004). Sloth bear habitat use in disturbed and unprotected areas of Madhya Pradesh, India. *Ursus* **15**: 203-211.
Akhtar, N., Bargali, H.S. & Chauhan, N.P.S. (2007). Characteristics of sloth bear day dens and use in disturbed and unprotected habitat of North Bilaspur Forest Division, Chhattisgarh, central India. *Ursus* **18**: 203-208.

Alberico, M.S. (1994). New locality record for the Columbian weasel (*Mustela felipei*). *Small Carniv. Conserv.* **10**: 16-17.
Albignac, R. (1969). Notes éthologiques sur quelques carnivores malgaches: le *Galidia elegans* I. Geoffroy. *Terre Vie* **23**: 202-215.
Albignac, R. (1970). Notes éthologiques sur quelques carnivores malgaches: le *Cryptoprocta ferox* (Bennett). *Terre Vie* **24**: 395-402.
Albignac, R. (1971a). Notes éthologiques sur quelques carnivores malgaches: Le *Fossa fossa* (Schreber). *Rev. Ecol. Appl.* **24**: 383-394.
Albignac, R. (1971b). Notes éthologiques sur quelques carnivores malgaches: le *Mungotictis lineata* Pocock. *Terre Vie* **25**: 328-343.
Albignac, R. (1972). The carnivora of Madagascar. Pp. 667-682 in: Battistini, R. & Richard-Vindard, G. eds. (1972). *Biogeography and Ecology in Madagascar.* W. Junk, The Hague.
Albignac, R. (1973). *Mammifères Carnivores. Faune de Madagascar* **36**. ORSTOM/CNRS, Paris.
Albignac, R. (1974). Observations éco-éthologiques sur le genre *Eupleres*, Viverridae de Madagascar. *Terre Vie* **28**: 321-351.
Albignac, R. (1975). Breeding the fossa (*Cryptoprocta ferox*) at Montpellier Zoo. *Int. Zoo Yb.* **15**: 147-150.
Albignac, R. (1976). L'écologie de *Mungotictis decemlineata* dans les forêts décidues de l'ouest de Madagascar. *Terre Vie* **30**: 347-376.
Albignac, R. (1984). The carnivores. Pp. 167-181 in: Jolly, A., Oberlé, P. & Albignac, R. eds. (1984). *Key Environments: Madagascar.* Pergamon Press, Oxford.
Alcover, J.A. (1982). On the differential diet of Carnivora in islands: a method for analysing it and a particular case. *Acta Vertebrata* **9**: 321-339.
Aldama, J.J. & Delibes, M. (1991). Observations of feeding groups in the Spanish lynx (*Felis pardina*) in the Doñana National Park, SW Spain. *Mammalia* **55**: 143-147.
Aldama, J.J., Beltrán, J.F. & Delibes, M. (1991). Energy expenditure and prey requirements of free-ranging Iberian lynx in southwest Spain. *J. Wildl. Management* **55**: 635-641.
Aliag-Rossel, E., Moreno, R.S., Kays, R.W. & Giacalone, J. (2006). Ocelot (*Leopardus pardalis*) predation on agouti (*Daysprocta punctata*). *Biotropica* **38**: 691-694.
Al-Khalili, A.D. (1984). Further notes on the mongoose of Arabia. *Bahrain Nat. Hist. Soc. Newslett. Mars*: 2-4.
Al-Khalili, A.D. (1990). Mongooses of Arabia. *Mustel. Viverr. Conserv.* **3**: 17-18.
Al-Khalili, A.D. (1993). Ecological review and the distribution of Blanford's fox, *Vulpes cana*. Pp. 390-396 in: Bÿttiker, W. & Krupp, F. eds. (1993). *Fauna of Saudi Arabia.* Natural History Museum, Basel, Switzerland.
Allen, G.M. (1911). Mammals of the West Indies. *Bull. Mus. Comp. Zool.* **54**: 175-263.
Allen, G.M. (1929). Mustelids from Asiatic expeditions. *Amer. Mus. Novit.* **358**: 1-12.
Allen, G.M. (1938). The mammals of China and Mongolia. Natural history of central Asia. Pp. 1-620 in: Granger, W. ed. (1938). *Central Asiatic Expeditions of the American Museum of Natural History.* Vol. 11. American Museum of Natural History, New York.
Allen, G.M. (1939). A checklist of African mammals. *Bull. Mus. Comp. Zool.* **83**: 3-763.
Allen, G.M. & Loveridge, A. (1927). Mammals from the Uluguru and Usambara Mountains, Tanganyika Territory. *Proc. Boston Soc. Nat. Hist.* **38**: 413-441.
Allen, J.A. (1924). Carnivora collected by the American Museum Congo Expedition. *Bull. Amer. Mus. Nat. Hist.* **47**: 73-281.
Allin, E.F. (1975). Evolution of the mammalian middle ear. *J. Morph.* **147**: 403-437.
de Almeida, A.E. (1976). *Jaguar Hunting in the Mato Grosso.* Stanwill Press, London.
Al-Safadi, M.M. (1995). On the biology and ecology of the white-tailed and bushy-tailed mongoose (*Ichneumia albicauda* and *Bdeogale crassicauda*) in Yemen. *Zool. Middle East* **11**: 5-13.
Alt, G.L. (1989). *Reproductive Biology of Female Black Bears and Early Growth and Development of Cubs in Northeastern Pennsylvania.* PhD thesis, West Virginia University, Morgantown, West Virginia.

Altman, P.L. & Dittmer, D.S. eds. (1971). *Respiration and Circulation.* Biological Handbooks, Bethesda, Maryland.

Altringham, J.D. (1996). *Bats: Biology and Behaviour.* Oxford University Press, Oxford, England.

Alvarez, W. (1998). T. rex *and the Crater of Doom.* Vintage Press, New York.

Alves-Costa, C.P. & Eterovick, P.C. (2007). Seed dispersal services by coatis (*Nasua nasua*, Procyonidae) and their redundancy with other frugivores in southeastern Brazil. *Acta Oecol.* **32**: 77-92.

Alves-Costa, C.P., Da Fonseca, G.A.B. & Christofaro, C. (2004). Variation in the diet of the brown-nosed coati (*Nasua nasua*) in southeastern Brazil. *J. Mammal.* **85**: 478-482.

de Alwis, W.L.E. (1973). Status of southeast Asia's small cats. Pp. 198-208 in: Eaton, R.L. ed. (1973). *The World's Cats.* Vol. 1. World Wildlife Safari, Winston, Oregon.

Amori, G., Bodganowicz, W., Kryštufek, B., Reijnders, P.J.H., Spitzenberger, F., Stubbe, M., Thissen, J.B.M., Vohralík, V. & Zima, J. eds. (1999). *The Atlas of European Mammals.* Poyser, London.

Amstrup, S.C. (2003). Polar Bear *Ursus maritimus.* Pp. 587-610 in: Feldhamer, G.A., Thompson, B.C. & Chapman, J.A. eds. (2003). *Wild Mammals of North America: Biology, Management and Conservation.* 2nd edition. Johns Hopkins University Press, Baltimore, Maryland.

Amstrup, S.C. & Gardner, C. (1994). Polar bear maternity denning in the Beaufort Sea. *J. Wildl. Management* **58**: 1-10.

Amstrup, S.C., Durner, G.M., McDonald, T.L., Mulcahy, D.M. & Garner, G.W. (2001). Comparing movement patterns of satellite-tagged male and female polar bears. *Can. J. Zool.* **79**: 2147-2158.

Andama, E. (2000). *The Status and Distribution of Carnivores in Bwindi Impenetrable National Park, South-western Uganda.* MSc dissertation, Makerere University, Kampala, Uganda.

Andelt, W.F. (1985). Behavioral ecology of coyotes *Canis latrans* in south Texas, USA. *Wildl. Monogr.* **94**: 5-45.

Andelt, W.F. (1987). Coyote predation. Pp. 128-140 in: Novak, M.J., Baker, A., Obbard, M.E. & Malloch, B. eds. (1987). *Wild Furbearer Management and Conservation in North America.* Ontario Ministry of Natural Resources and the Ontario Trappers Association, Ontario.

Andersen, D.E., Laurion, T.R., Cary, J.R., Sikes, R.S., McLeod, M.A. & Gese, E.M. (2003). Aspects of swift fox ecology in southeastern Colorado. Pp. 139-148 in: Sovada, M. & Carbyn, L. eds. (2003). *Swift Fox Conservation in a Changing World.* Canadian Plains Research Center, University of Regina, Saskatchewan.

Andersen, R., Linnell, J., Odden, J., Gagas, L., Ness, E., Karlsen, J., Wannag, A. & Rena, J.T. (1998). Sosial orgnisering, spredning, reporduksjon og predasjonsatferd hos guape i Hedmark, Framdriftsrapport 1995–1997. *NINA Oppdragsmelding* **519**: 25.

Anderson, A.E. (1983). *A Critical Review of Literature on the Puma* Felis concolor. Colorado Division of Wildlife Special Report **54**. Colorado Division of Wildlife, Fort Collins, Colorado. 91 pp.

Anderson, A.E., Bowden, D.C. & Kattner, D.M. (1992). *The Puma on the Uncompahgre Plateau, Colorado.* Colorado Division of Wildlife Technical Publication **40**. Colorado Division of Wildlife, Fort Collins, Colorado. 126 pp.

Anderson, D. (1977). Gestation period of Geoffroy's cat bred at Memphis Zoo. *Int. Zoo Yb.* **17**: 164-166.

Anderson, D.C. & Johns, D.W. (1977). Predation by badger on yellow-bellied marmot in Colorado. *Southwest. Nat.* **22**: 283-284.

Anderson, E. (1970). Quarternary evolution of the genus *Martes* (Carnivora, Mustelidae). *Ann. Zool. Fennici* **130**: 1-132.

Anderson, E. (1989). The phylogeny of mustelids and the systematics of ferrets. Page 209 in: Seal, U.S., Thorne, E.T., Bogan, M.A. & Anderson, S.A. eds. (1989). *Conservation Biology and the Biology of the Black-footed Ferret.* Yale University Press, New Haven & London.

Anderson, E.M. (1987). *A Critical Review and Annotated Bibliography of Literature on the Bobcat.* Colorado Division of Wildlife Special Report **62**. Colorado Division of Wildlife, Fort Collins, Colorado.

Anderson, M.D. & Richardson, P.R.K. (2005). The physical and thermal characteristics of aardwolf dens. *South Afr. J. Wildl. Res.* **35**: 147-153.

Anderson, M.D., Richardson, P.R.K. & Woodall, P.F. (1992). Functional analysis of the feeding apparatus and digestive tract anatomy of the aardwolf *Proteles cristatus. J. Zool., London* **228**: 423-434.

Anderson, S. (1997). Mammals of Bolivia, taxonomy and distribution. *Bull. Amer. Mus. Nat. Hist.* **231**: 1-652.

Andrén, H., Ahlquist, P., Andersen, R., Kvam, T., Liberg, O., Lindén, M., Odden, J., Overskaug, K., Linnell, J. & Segerström, P. (1998). The Scandinavian lynx projects - Annual report 1997. *NINA Oppdragsmelding* **518**: 11.

Angelici, F.M. (2000). Food habits and resource partitioning of carnivores (Herpestidae, Viverridae) in the rainforests of southeastern Nigeria: preliminary results. *Rev. Écol. (Terre Vie)* **55**: 67-76.

Angelici, F.M. & Gaubert, P. (In press). *Genetta maculata.* In: Kingdon, J.S. & Hoffmann, M. eds. (In press). *The Mammals of Africa.* Vol. 5. Carnivores, Pangolins, Rhinos and Equids. Academic Press, Amsterdam.

Angelici, F.M. & Luiselli, L. (2005). Habitat associations and dietary relationships between two genets, *Genetta maculata* and *Genetta cristata. Rev. Écol. (Terre Vie)* **60**: 341-354.

Angelici, F.M., Luiselli, L. & Politano, E. (1999). Distribution and habitat of selected carnivores (Herpestidae, Mustelidae, Viverridae) in the rainforests of southeastern Nigeria. *Zeitschrift für Säugetierkunde* **64**: 116-120.

Angelici, F.M., Luiselli, L., Politano, E. & Akani, G.C. (1999). Bushmen and mammal fauna: a survey of the mammals traded in bush-meat markets of local people in the rainforests of southeastern Nigeria. *Anthropozoologica* **30**: 51-58.

Angelici, F.M., Politano, E., Bogudue, A.J. & Luiselli, L. (2005). Distribution and habitat of otters (*Aonyx capensis* and *Lutra maculicollis*) in southern Nigeria. *Ital. J. Zool.* **72**: 223-227.

Angerbjörn, A., Hersteinsson, P. & Tannerfeldt, M. (2004). Consequences of resource predictability in the Arctic fox – two life history strategies. Pp. 163-172 in: Macdonald, D.W. & Sillero-Zubiri, C. eds. (2004). *The Biology and Conservation of Wild Canids.* Oxford University Press, Oxford.

Angerbjörn, A., Ströman, J. & Becker, D. (1997). Home range pattern in Arctic foxes. *J. Wildl. Res.* **2**: 9-14.

Angerbjörn, A., Tannerfeldt, M., Bjärvall, A., Ericson, M., From, J. & Norén, E. (1995). Dynamics of the Arctic fox population in Sweden. *Ann. Zool. Fennici* **32**: 55-68.

Angerbjörn, A., Tannerfeldt, M. & Erlinge, S. (1999). Predator-prey relationship: Arctic foxes and lemmings. *J. Anim. Ecol.* **68**: 34-49.

Anon. (1960). Longevity survey. Length of life of mammals in captivity at the London Zoo and Whipsnade Park. *Int. Zoo Yb.* **2**: 288-299.

Anon. (1986). Some notes for the record. *Cat News* **5**: 11.

Anoop, K.R. & Hussain, S.A. (2004). Factors affecting habitat selection by smooth-coated otters (*Lutra perspicillata*) in Kerala, India. *J. Zool., London* **263**: 417-423.

Anoop, K.R. & Hussain, S.A. (2005). Food and feeding habits of smooth-coated otters (*Lutra perspicillata*) and their significance to the fish population of Kerala, India. *J. Zool., London* **266**: 15-23.

Ansell, W.F.H. (1960a). The African striped weasel, *Poecilogale albinucha* (Gray). *Proc. Zool. Soc. London* **134**: 59-64.

Ansell, W.F.H. (1960b). *Mammals of Northern Rhodesia.* Government printer, Lusaka.

Ansell, W.F.H. (1960c). Contributions to the mammalogy of Northern Rhodesia. *Occas. Pap. Natl. Mus. S. Rhod., Nat. Sci.* **24B**: 351-398.

Ansell, W.F.H. (1969). Addenda and corrigenda to "Mammals of Northern Rhodesia" N°3. *Puku* **5**: 1-48.

Ansell, W.F.H. (1974). Some mammals from Zambia and adjacent areas. *Puku, Suppl.* **1**: 1-49.

Ansell, W.F.H. (1978). *The Mammals of Zambia.* The National Parks & Wildlife Service, Chilanga, Zambia.

Anstey, S. (1991). *Large Mammal Distribution in Liberia.* WWF/FDA Wildlife Survey Report. 81 pp. + 32 unnumbered.

Anwaruddin, C. (2001). An overview of the status and conservation of the red panda *Ailurus fulgens* in India, with reference to its global status. *Oryx* **35**: 250-259.

Apps, C.D., McLellan, B.N. & Woods, J.G. (2006). Landscape partitioning and spatial inferences of competition between black and grizzly bears. *Ecography* **29**: 561-572.

Aquino, R. & Puertas, P. (1997). Observations of *Speothos venaticus* (Canidae: Carnivora) in its natural habitat in Peruvian Amazonia. *Zeitschrift für Säugetierkunde* **62**: 117-118.

Arai, S., Adachi, T., Kuwahara, Y. & Yoshida, K. (2003). Food habit of the Japanese marten (*Martes melampus*) at Kuju Highland in Kyushu, Japan. *Mammal. Sci.* **43**: 19-28.

Aranda, M. & Lopez-de Buen, L. (1999). Rabies in skunks from Mexico. *J. Wildl. Diseases* **35**: 574-577.

Aranda, M. & Sánchez-Cordero, V. (1996). Prey spectra of jaguar (*Panthera onca*) and puma (*Puma concolor*) in tropical forests of Mexico. *Stud. Neotrop. Fauna Environm.* **31**: 65-67.

Arcila, D.A. & Ramirez, M. (2004). Captive reproduction of the Neotropical otter in the Santa Fe Zoological Park in Medellin, Colombia. *IUCN Otter Special. Group Bull.* **21**: 1-3.

Arden-Clarke, C.H.G. (1986). Population density, home range size, and spatial organisation of the Cape clawless otter, *Aonyx capensis*, in a marine habitat. *J. Zool., London* **209**: 201-211.

Arias, S.M., Corriale, M.J., Porini, G. & Bo, R.F. (2006). *Proyecto de Investigación y Manejo del Zorrino* (Conepatus humboldtii *y* C. chinga*) en la Provincia de Río Negro, Argentina. Final Report.* Secretaría de Ambiente y Desarrollo Sustentable, Buenos Aires, Argentina.

Aristotle (350 B.C.E.). *The History of Animals.* Translated by D.W. Thompson. URL: http://classics.mit.edu/Aristotle/history_anim.1.i.html

Arivazhagan, C. & Thiyagesan, K. (2001). Studies on the binturongs (*Arctictis binturong*) in captivity at the Arignar Anna Zoological Park, Vandalur. *Zoo Print* **16**: 395-402.

Arivazhagan, C., Arumugam, R. & Thiyagesan, K. (2007). Food habits of leopard (*Panthera pardus fusca*), dhole (*Cuon alpinus*) and striped hyena (*Hyaena hyaena*) in a tropical dry thorn forest of southern India. *J. Bombay Nat. Hist. Soc.* **104**: 178-187.

Armesto, J.J., Rozzi, R., Miranda, P. & Sabag, C. (1987). Plant/frugivore interaction in South American temperate forests. *Rev. Chil. Hist. Nat.* **60**: 321-336.

Armitage, K.B. (2004). Badger predation on yellow bellied marmots. *Amer. Midl. Nat.* **151**: 378-387.

Armstrong, D.M., Jones, J.K. & Birney, E.C. (1972). Mammals from the Mexican state of Sinaloa. Part III. Carnivora and Artiodactyla. *J. Mammal.* **53**: 48-61.

Armstrong, R.B. & Phelps, R.O. (1984). Muscle fiber type composition of the rat hind limb. *Amer. J. Anat.* **171**: 259-272.

Árnason, U. & Widegren, B. (1986). Pinniped phylogeny enlightened by molecular hybridizations using highly repetitive DNA. *Mol. Biol. Evol.* **3**: 356-365.

Arthur, S.M. & Krohn, W.B. (1991). Activity patterns, movements and reproductive ecology of fishers in southcentral Maine. *J. Mammal.* **72**: 379-385.

Arthur, S.M., Krohn, W.B. & Gilbert, J.R. (1989a). Habitat use and diet of fishers. *J. Wildl. Management* **53**: 680-688.

Arthur, S.M., Krohn, W.B. & Gilbert, J.R. (1989b). Home range characteristics of adult fishers. *J. Wildl. Management* **53**: 674-679.

Asa, C.S. (1993). Relative contributions of urine and anal-sac secretions in scent marks of large felids. *Amer. Zool.* **33**: 167-172.

Asa, C.S. & Cossíos, E.D. (2004). Sechuran fox *Pseudalopex sechurae.* Pp. 69-72 in: Sillero-Zubiri, C., Hoffmann, M. & Macdonald, D.W. eds. (2004). *Canids: Foxes, Wolves, Jackals and Dogs. Status Survey and Conservation Action Plan.* IUCN/SSC Canid Specialist Group, Gland & Cambridge.

Asa, C.S. & Valdespino, C. (2003). A review of small canid reproduction. Pp. 117-123 in: Sovada, M.A. & Carbyn, L.N. eds. (2003). *Ecology and Conservation of Swift Foxes in a Changing World.* Canadian Plains Research Center, University of Regina, Saskatchewan.

Asa, C.S. & Wallace, M.P. (1990). Diet and activity pattern of the Sechuran Desert fox (*Dusicyon sechurae*). *J. Mammal.* **71**: 69-72.

Asa, C.S., Valdespino, C. & Cuzin, F. (2004). Fennec fox *Vulpes zerda.* Pp. 205-209 in: Sillero-Zubiri, C., Hoffmann, M. & Macdonald, D.W. eds. (2004). *Canids: Foxes, Wolves, Jackals and Dogs. Status Survey and Conservation Action Plan.* IUCN/SSC Canid Specialist Group, Gland & Cambridge.

Ashenafi, Z.T., Coulson, T., Sillero-Zubiri, C. & Leader-Williams, N. (2005). Behaviour and ecology of the Ethiopian wolf (*Canis simensis*) in a human-dominated landscape outside protected areas. *Anim. Conserv.* **8**: 113-121.

Asher, O., Lupu-Meiri, M., Jensen, B.S., Paperna, T., Fuchs, S. & Oron, Y. (1998). Functional characterization of mongoose nicotinic acetylcholine receptor alpha-subunit: resistance to alpha-bungarotoxin and high sensitivity. *Febs Letters* **431**: 411-414.

Ashman, D., Christensen, G.C., Hess, M.L., Tsukamoto, G.K. & Wickersham, M.S. (1983). *The Mountain Lion in Nevada. Final Report.* PR Project **W-48-15**. Nevada Fish and Game Department, Carson City, Nevada.

Ashraf, N.K.V. (1990). Preliminary survey of the Malabar civet and the brown palm civet. *Small Carniv. Conserv.* **3**: 19-20.

Ashraf, N.K.V., Kumar, A. & Johnsingh, A.J.T. (1993). A survey of two endemic civets of the Western Ghats: the Malabar civet (*Viverra civettina*) and the brown palm civet (*Paradoxurus jerdoni*). *Oryx* **27**: 109-114.

Atkinson, R.P.D. (1997a). Side-striped jackal *Canis adustus*. Page 197 in: Mills, G. & Hes, L. eds. (1997). *The Complete Book of Southern African Mammals.* Struik Publishers, Cape Town.

Atkinson, R.P.D. (1997b). *The Ecology of the Side-striped Jackal (*Canis adustus *Sundevall), a Vector of Rabies in Zimbabwe.* PhD thesis, Wildlife Conservation Research Unit, University of Oxford, Oxford.

Atkinson, R.P.D. & Loveridge, A.J. (2004). Side-striped jackal *Canis adustus*. Pp. 152-155 in: Sillero-Zubiri, C., Hoffmann, M. & Macdonald, D.W. eds. (2004). *Canids: Foxes, Wolves, Jackals and Dogs. Status Survey and Conservation Action Plan.* IUCN/SSC Canid Specialist Group, Gland & Cambridge.

Atkinson, R.P.D., Macdonald, D.W. & Kamizola, R. (2002). Dietary opportunism in side-striped jackals *Canis adustus. J. Zool., London* **257**: 129-139.

Atkinson, R.P.D., Rhodes, C.J., Macdonald, D.W. & Anderson, R.M. (2002). Scale-free dynamics in the movement patterns of jackals. *Oikos* **98**: 134-140.

Aubry, K.B., McKelvey, K.S. & Copeland, J.P. (2007). Distribution and broadscale habitat relations of the wolverine in the contiguous United States. *J. Wildl. Management* **71**: 2147-2158.

Audet, A.M., Robbins, C.B. & Larivière, S. (2002). *Alopex lagopus. Mammal. Species* **713**: 1-10.

Aued, M.B., Chehebar, C., Porro, G., Macdonald, D.W. & Cassini, M.H. (2003). Environmental correlates of the distribution of southern river otters *Lontra provocax* at different ecological scales. *Oryx* **37**: 413-421.

Augeri, D.M. (2005). *On the Biogeographic Ecology of the Malayan Sun Bear.* PhD thesis, University of Cambridge, Cambridge.

Aulerich, R.J. & Ringer, R.K. (1979). Toxic effects of dietary polybrominated biphenyls on mink. *Arch. Environ. Contam. Toxicol.* **8**: 487-498.

Aulerich, R.J., Ringer, R.K. & Iwamoto, S. (1974). Effects of dietary mercury on mink. *Arch. Environ. Contam. Toxicol.* **2**: 43-51.

Austin, S.C. (2002). *Ecology of Sympatric Carnivores in Khao Yai National Park, Thailand.* PhD dissertation, Texas A & M University Kingsville & Texas A & M University, College Station, Texas.

Austin, S.C. & Tewes, M.E. (1999a). Ecology of the clouded leopard in Khao Yai National Park, Thailand. *Cat News* **31**: 17-18.

Austin, S.C. & Tewes, M.E. (1999b). Observations of viverrid, mustelid and herpestid in Khao Yai NP, Thailand. *Small Carniv. Conserv.* **21**: 13-15.

Autuori, M.P. & Deutsch, L.A. (1977). Contribution to the knowledge of the giant Brazilian otter, *Pteronura brasiliensis* (Gmelin 1788), Carnivora, Mustelidae. *Zool. Garten* **47**: 1-8.

Avenant, N.L. & Nel, J.A.J. (1992). Comparison of the diet of the yellow mongoose in a coastal and a karoo area. *South Afr. J. Wildl. Res.* **22**: 89-93.

Avenant, N.L. & Nel, J.A.J. (1997). Prey use by four syntopic carnivores in a strandveld ecosystem. *South Afr. J. Wildl. Res.* **27**: 86-93.

Avery, G., Avery, D.M., Braine, S. & Loutit, R. (1987). Prey of coastal black-backed jackal *Canis mesomelas* (Mammalia, Canidae) in the Skeleton Coast Park, Namibia. *J. Zool., London* **213**: 81-94.

Avery, S.R. (1989). *Vocalization and Behaviour of the Swift Fox (*Vulpes velox*).* MSc thesis, University of Northern Colorado, Greeley, Colorado.

Aymerich, M. (1982a). Biology of the genet (*Genetta genetta*) in Spain. *Mammalia* **46**: 389-394.

Aymerich, M. (1982b). Étude comparative des regimes du lynx pardelle (*Lynx pardina* Temminck, 1824) et du chat sauvage (*Felis silvestris* Screber, 1777) au centre de la Peninsule Iberique. *Mammalia* **46**: 515-521.

Aymerich, M. (1992). Management of a lynx population in the Doñana National Park. Pp. 33-35 in: *The Situation, Conservation Needs and Reintroduction of Lynx in Europe.* Encounters **11**. Convention on the Conservation of European Wildlife and Natural Habitats. Council of Europe Press, Strasbourg.

Ayres, L.A., Chow, L.S. & Graber, D.M. (1986). Black bear activity and human induced modifications in Sequoia National Park. *Int. Conf. Bear Res. Management* **6**: 151-154.

Ayyadurai, M., Natarajan, V., Balasubramanian, P. & Rajan, S.A. (1987). A note on the food of the small Indian civet (*Viverricula indica*) at Point Calimere Wildlife Sanctuary, Tamil Nadu. *J. Bombay Nat. Hist. Soc.* **84**: 203.

Azevedo, F.C.C. (1996). Notes on the behavior of the margay *Felis wiedii* (Schinz, 1821), (Carnivora, Felidae), in the Brazilian Atlantic Forest. *Mammalia* **60**: 325-328.

Azevedo, F.C.C. (2008). Food habits and livestock depredation of sympatric jaguars and pumas in Iguaçu National Park area, south Brazil. *Biotropica* **40**: 494-500.

Azevedo, F.C.C. & Gastal, M.L.A. (1997). Hábito alimentar do lobo-guará *Chrysocyon brachyurus* na APA Gama/Cabeça do Veado. Pp. 238-240 in: Leite, L.L. & Saito, C.H. eds. (1997). *Contribuição ao Conhecimento Ecológico do Cerrado.* Dept. Ecologia, Universidade de Brasília, Brasília.

Azevedo, F.C.C., Lester, V., Gorsuch, W., Larivière, S., Wirsing, A.J. & Murray, D.L. (2006). Dietary breadth and overlap among five sympatric prairie carnivores. *J. Zool., London* **269**: 127-135.

Azlan, J.M. (2003). The diversity and conservation of mustelids, viverrids and herpestids in a disturbed forest in Peninsular Malaysia. *Small Carniv. Conserv.* **29**: 8-9.

Azlan, J.M. (2005). A short note on the activity patterns of *Viverra tangalunga* and *Paradoxurus hermaphroditus* in a secondary forest in Peninsular Malaysia. *Small Carniv. Conserv.* **33**: 27-28.

Azlan, J.M. & Sanderson, J. (2007). Geographic distribution and conservation status of the bay cat *Catopuma badia*, a Bornean endemic. *Oryx* **41**: 394-397.

Azzaroli, L. & Simonetta, A.M. (1966). Carnivori della Somalia ex-Italiana. *Monitore Zool. Ital. Suppl.* **74**: 102-195.

Baer, G.M. (1994). Rabies: an historical-perspective. *Infect. Agents Dis.-Rev. Issues Comment.* **3**: 168-180.

Bagchi, S., Goyal, S.P. & Sankar, K. (2003). Prey abundance and prey selection by tigers (*Panthera tigris*) in a semi-arid, dry deciduous forest in western India. *J. Zool., London* **260**: 285-290.

Baghli, A. & Verhagen, R. (2004). Home ranges and movement patterns in a vulnerable polecat *Mustela putorius* population. *Acta Theriol.* **49**: 247-258.

Baghli, A. & Verhagen, R. (2005). Activity patterns and use of resting sites by polecats in an endangered population. *Mammalia* **69**: 211-222.

Baghli, A., Engel, E. & Verhagen, R. (2002). Feeding habits and trophic niche overlap of two sympatric Mustelidae, the polecat *Mustela putorius* and the beech marten *Martes foina. Z. Jagdwiss.* **48**: 217-225.

Baghli, A., Walzberg, C. & Verhagen, R. (2005). Habitat use by the European polecat *Mustela putorius* at low density in a fragmented landscape. *Wildl. Biol.* **11**: 331-339.

Bahn, P.G. & Vertut, J. (1997). *Journey Through the Ice Age.* Seven Dials, London.

Bailey, T.N. (1974). Social organization in a bobcat population. *J. Wildl. Management* **38**: 435-446.

Bailey, T.N. (1993). *The African Leopard: a Study of the Ecology and Behavior of a Solitary Felid.* Columbia University Press, New York.

Bailey, T.N., Bangs, E.E., Portner, M.F., Malloy, J.C. & McAvinchey, R.J. (1986). An apparent overexploited lynx population on the Kenai Peninsula, Alaska. *J. Wildl. Management* **50**: 279-290.

Bailey, V. (1905). Biological survey of Texas. *North Amer. Fauna* **25**: 1-222.

Bailey, V. (1931). Mammals of New Mexico. *North Amer. Fauna* **53**: 412.

Bailey, V. (1936). The mammals and life zones of Oregon. *North Amer. Fauna* **55**: 1-416.

Baird, S.F. (1857). Part 1, Mammals - General report upon the zoology of the several Pacific railroad routes. Pp. xxxii+757 in: *Reports of Explorations and Surveys to Ascertain the Most Practicable and Economical Route for a Railroad from the Mississippi River to the Pacific Ocean. Made Under The direction of the Secretary of War, in 1853-6, According to Acts of Congress of March 3, 1953, May 31, 1954, and August 5, 1954.* Senate Executive Document No. 78, 33 Congress 2nd session, House Executive Document No. 91, Washington, D.C.

Baker, C.M. (1988a). Scent marking behavior in captive water mongooses (*Atilax paludinosus*). *Zeitschrift für Säugetierkunde* **53**: 358-364.

Baker, C.M. (1988b). Vocalizations of captive water mongooses, *Atilax paludinosus. Zeitschrift für Säugetierkunde* **53**: 83-91.

Baker, C.M. (1988c). *Biology of the Water Mongoose (*Atilax paludinosus*).* PhD thesis, University of Natal, Durban, South Africa.

Baker, C.M. (1989). Feeding habits of the water mongoose (*Atilax paludinosus*). *Zeitschrift für Säugetierkunde* **54**: 31-39.

Baker, C.M. (1992a). *Atilax paludinosus. Mammal. Species* **408**: 1-6.

Baker, C.M. (1992b). Observations on the postnatal behavioral development in the marsh mongoose (*Atilax paludinosus*). *Zeitschrift für Säugetierkunde* **57**: 335-342.

Baker, C.M. (1998). Communication in marsh mongooses (*Atilax paludinosus*): anal gland secretion and scat discrimination in adults and individual variation in vocalisations of juveniles. *South Afr. J. Zool.* **33**: 49-51.

Baker, C.M. & Meester, J. (1986). Postnatal physical development of the water mongoose (*Atilax paludinosus*). *Zeitschrift für Säugetierkunde* **51**: 236-243.

Baker, C.M. & Ray, J.C. (In press). *Atilax paludinosus.* In: Kingdon, J.S. & Hoffmann, M. eds. (In press). *The Mammals of Africa.* Vol. 5. Carnivores, Pangolins, Rhinos and Equids. Academic Press, Amsterdam.

Baker, M.A. (1979). A brain cooling system in mammals. *Scientific American* **240(5)**: 130-139.

Baker, P.J. & Harris, S. (2004). The behavioural ecology of red foxes in urban Bristol. Pp. 207-216 in: Macdonald, D.W. & Sillero-Zubiri, C. eds. (2004). *The Biology and Conservation of Wild Canids.* Oxford University Press, Oxford.

Baker, R.H. (1956). Mammals of Coahuila, Mexico. *Univ. Kansas Publ. Mus. Nat. Hist.* **9**: 125-335.

Baker, R.H. & Baker, M.W. (1975). Montane habitat used by the spotted skunk (*Spilogale putorius*) in Mexico. *J. Mammal.* **56**: 671-673.

Balakrishnan, M. & Sreedevi, M.B. (2007a). Captive breeding of the small Indian civet *Viverricula indica* (E. Geoffroy Saint-Hilaire, 1803). *Small Carniv. Conserv.* **36**: 5-8.

Balakrishnan, M. & Sreedevi, M.B. (2007b). Husbandry and management of the small Indian civet *Viverricula indica* (E. Geoffroy Saint-Hilaire, 1803) in Kerala, India. *Small Carniv. Conserv.* **36**: 9-13.

Balakrishnan, P. (2005). Recent sightings and habitat characteristics of the endemic Nilgiri marten *Martes gwatkinsii* in Western Ghats, India. *Small Carniv. Conserv.* **33**: 14-16.

Baldwin, P. (1954). Thermal tolerance of the mongoose *Herpestes auropunctatus. J. Mammal.* **55**: 645-647.

Baldwin, P., Schwartz, C.W. & Schwartz, E.R. (1952). Life history and economic status of the mongoose of Hawaii. *J. Mammal.* **33**: 335-356.

Balestrieri, A., Remonti, L. & Prigioni, C. (2004). Diet of the Eurasian badger (*Meles meles*) in an agricultural riverine habitat (NW Italy). *Hystrix* **15**: 3-12.

Banci, V. & Harestad, A. (1988). Reproduction and natality of wolverine (*Gulo gulo*) in Yukon. *Ann. Zool. Fennici* **25**: 265-270.

Banfield, A.F.W. (1974). *The Mammals of Canada.* University of Toronto Press, Toronto.

Bangs, O. (1895). Notes on North American mammals. The synonymy of the eastern skunk, *Mephitis mephitica* (Shaw), with the description of a new subspecies from Florida. *Proc. Boston Soc. Nat. Hist.* **26**: 529-536.

Bangs, O. (1898a). Descriptions of two new skunks of the genus *Mephitis. Proc. Biol. Soc. Washington* **12**: 31-33.

Bangs, O. (1898b). The land mammals of peninsular Florida and the coast region of Georgia. *Proc. Boston Soc. Nat. Hist.* **28**: 157-235.

Banks, E. (1931). A popular account of the mammals of Borneo. *J. Malay Branch R. Asiatic Soc.* **9(2)**: 1-139.

Banks, E. (1949). *Bornean Mammals.* Kuching press, Kuching, Malaysia.

Banks, G.R., Buglass, A.J. & Waterhouse, J.S. (1992). Amines in the marking fluid and anal sac secretions of the tiger, *Panthera tigris. Z. Naturforsch.* **47**: 618-620.

Bannikov, A.G. (1964). Biologie du chien viverrin en URSS. *Mammalia* **28**: 1-39.

Baranga, J. (1995). The distribution and conservation status of otters in Uganda. *Habitat* **11**: 29-32.

Barash, D.P. (1971). Cooperative hunting in the lynx. *J. Mammal.* **52**: 480.

Barber, K.R. & Lindzey, F.G. (1986). Breeding behavior of black bears. *Int. Conf. Bear Res. Management* **6**: 129-136.

Barchan, D., Kachalsky, S., Neumann, D., Vogel, Z., Ovadia, M., Kochva, E. & Fuchs, S. (1992). How the mongoose can fight the snake - the binding site of the mongoose acetylcholine receptor. *Proc. Natl. Acad. Sci. USA* **89**: 7717-7721.

Barden, T.L., Evans, M.I., Raxworthy, C.J., Razafimahaimodison, J.C. & Wilson, A. (1991). The mammals of Ambatovaky Special Reserve. Pp. 5-1 to 5-22 in: Thompson, P.M. & Evans, M.I. eds. (1991). *A Survey of Ambatovaky Special Reserve, Madagascar.* Madagascar Environmental Research Group, London.

Bargali, H.S., Akhtar, N. & Chauhan, N.P.S. (2004). Feeding ecology of sloth bears in a disturbed area in central India. *Ursus* **15**: 212-217.

Bargali, H.S., Akhtar, N. & Chauhan, N.P.S. (2005). Characteristics of sloth bear attacks and human casualties in North Bilaspur Forest Division, Chhattisgarh, India. *Ursus* **16**: 263-267.

Barja, I. & List, R. (2006). Faecal marking behaviour in ringtails (*Bassariscus astutus*) during the non-breeding period: spatial characteristics of latrines and single faeces. *Chemoecology* **16**: 219-222.

Barnes, I., Matheus, P., Shapiro, B., Jensen, D. & Cooper, A. (2002). Dynamics of Pleistocene population extinctions in Beringian brown bears. *Science* **295**: 2267-2270.

Barnes, R.G. (1976). Breeding and hand-rearing of the marbled cat *Felis marmorata* at the Los Angeles Zoo. *Int. Zoo Yb.* **16**: 205-208.

Barnett, R., Yamaguchi, N., Barnes, I. & Cooper, A. (2006). The origin, current diversity and future conservation of the modern lion (*Panthera leo*). *Proc. Royal Soc. London (Ser. B Biol. Sci.),* doi: 10.1098/rspb.2006.3555

Barone, M.A., Roelke, M.E., Howard, J., Brown, J.L., Anderson, A.E. & Wildt, D.E. (1994). Reproductive characteristics of male Florida panthers: comparative studies from Florida, Texas, Colorado, Latin America and North American zoos. *J. Mammal.* **75**: 150-162.

Barquez, R., Mares, M. & Ojeda, R. (1991). *Mamíferos de Tucumán.* Oklahoma Museum of Natural History. University of Oklahoma Foundation, Norman, Oklahoma.

Bartels, E. (1964). On *Paradoxurus hermaphroditus javanicus* (Horsfield, 1824) the common palm civet or toddy cat in western Java. Notes on its food and feeding habits. Its economical importance for wood and rural biotopes. *Beaufortia* **10**: 193-201.

Bartmann, W. & Nordhoff, L. (1984). Paarbindung und elternfamilie beim mähnenwolf *Chrysocyon brachyurus* Illiger, 1811. *Z. Köln. Zoo* **27**: 63-71.

Bartoszewicz, M. & Zalewski, A. (2003). American mink, *Mustela vison* diet and predation on waterfowl in the Slonsk Reserve, western Poland. *Folia Zool.* **52**: 225-238.

Basilio, A. (1962). *La Vida Animal en la Guinea Española.* Instituto de Estudios Africanos, Madrid.

Baskin, J.A. (1982). Tertiary Procyoninae (Mammalia: Carnivora) of North America. *J. Vert. Paleo.* **2**: 71-93.

Baskin, J.A. (2003). New Procyonines from the Hemingfordian and Barstovian of the Gulf Coast and Nevada, including the first fossil record of the Potosini. *Bull. Amer. Mus. Nat. Hist.* **279**: 125-146.

Bates, G.L. (1905). Notes on mammals of southern Cameroons and the Benito. *Proc. Zool. Soc. London* **1(5)**: 65-85.

Baudy, R.E. (1971). Notes on breeding felids at the Rare Feline Breeding Center. *Int. Zoo Yb.* **11**: 121-123.

Bauer, H. & Van der Merwe, S. (2004). Inventory of free-ranging lions *Panthera leo* in Africa. *Oryx* **38(1)**: 26-31.

Bauer, H., De Iongh, H.H., Princee, F.P.G. & Ngantou, D. (2001). *Status and Needs for Conservation of Lions in West and Central Africa.* Workshop report. Captive Breeding Specialist Group & African Lion Working Group.

Bauman, K.L. (2002). *Fennec Fox Vulpes zerda.* North American Regional Studbook. 2nd edition. Saint Louis Zoological Park. Saint Louis, Missouri.

Bdolah, A., Kochva, E., Ovadia, M., Kinamon, S. & Wollberg, Z. (1997). Resistance of the Egyptian mongoose to sarafotoxins. *Toxicon* **35**: 1251-1261.

Bearder, S.K. (1977). Feeding habits of spotted hyaenas in a woodland habitat. *East Afr. Wildl. J.* **15**: 263-280.

Bearder, S.K. & Randall, R.M. (1978). The use of fecal marking sites by spotted hyaenas and civets. *Carnivore* **1**: 32-48.

Beasom, S.L. (1974). Selectivity of predator control techniques in south Texas. *J. Wildl. Management* **38**: 166-175.

Beaumont, G.D. (1964). Remarques sur la classification des Félidae. *Eclogae Geol. Helv.* **57**: 837-845.

Beaumont, M., Barratt, E.M., Gottelli, D., Kitchener, A.C., Daniels, M.J., Pritchard, J.K. & Bruford, M.W. (2001). Genetic diversity and introgression in the Scottish wildcat. *Mol. Ecol.* **10**: 319-336.

Beccaceci, M.D. (1992). The maned wolf *Chrysocyon brachyurus* in Argentina. Pp. 50-56 in: Matern, B. ed. (1992). *1991 International Studbook for the Maned Wolf Chrysocyon brachyurus Illiger, 1811.* Frankfurt Zoological Garden, Frankfurt.

Beccaceci, M.D. (1994). Bush dogs in Paraguay. *Canid News* **2**: 17.

Bechthold, G. (1939). Die asiatischen Formen der gattung *Herpestes*, ihre Systematik, Okologie, Verbreitung und ihre Zusammenhange mit den afrianischen Arten. *Zeitschrift für Säugetierkunde* **14**: 113-219.

Beck, T.D.I. (1991). *Black Bears of West-central Colorado.* Technical Publication No. **39**. Colorado Division of Wildlife, Fort Collins, Colorado, USA.

Beckman, J.P. & Berger, J. (2003). Rapid ecological and behavioral changes in carnivores: the responses of black bears (*Ursus americanus*) to altered food. *J. Zool., London* **261**: 207-212.

Beecham, J.J. & Rohlman, J. (1994). *A Shadow in the Forest: Idaho's Black Bear.* University of Idaho Press, Moscow, Idaho.

Begg, C., Begg, K., Du Toit, J. & Mills, M. (2005a). Life-history variables of an atypical mustelid, the honey badger *Mellivora capensis. J. Zool., London* **265**: 17-22.

Begg, C., Begg, K., Du Toit, J. & Mills, M. (2005b). Spatial organization of the honey badger *Mellivora capensis* in the southern Kalahari: home-range size and movement patterns. *J. Zool., London* **265**: 23-35.

Begg, K. (1995). The honey badgers of the Mana Pools National Park. *Endangered Wildl.* **20**: 20-23.

Beier, P. (1993). Determining minimum habitat areas and habitat corridors for mountain lions. *Conserv. Biol.* **7**: 94-108.

Beier, P. (1995). Dispersal of juvenile cougars in fragmented habitats. *J. Wildl. Management* **59**: 228-237.

Beier, P., Choate, D. & Barrett, R.H. (1995). Movement patterns of mountain lions during different behaviors. *J. Mammal.* **76**: 1056-1070.

Beisiegel, B.M. (2001). Notes on the coati, *Nasua nasua* (Carnivora: Procyonidae) in an Atlantic forest area. *Braz. J. Biol.* **61**: 689-692.

Beisiegel, B.M. (2007). Foraging association between coatis (*Nasua nasua*) and birds of the Atlantic Forest, Brazil. *Biotropica* **39**: 283-285.

Beisiegel, B.M. & Mantovani, W. (2006). Habitat use, home range and foraging preferences of the coati, *Nasua nasua*, in a pluvial tropical Atlantic forest area. *J. Zool., London* **269**: 77-87.

Bekoff, M. (1978a). Scent-marking by free-ranging domestic dogs. *Biol. Behav.* **4**: 123-139.

Bekoff, M. ed. (1978b). *Coyotes: Biology, Behavior and Management.* Academic Press, New York.

Bekoff, M. & Diamond, J. (1976). Precopulatory and copulatory behavior in coyotes. *J. Mammal.* **57**: 372-375.

Bekoff, M. & Gese, E.M. (2003). Coyote *Canis latrans.* Pp. 467-481 in: Feldhamer, G.A., Thompson, B.C. & Chapman, J.A. eds. (2003). *Wild Mammals of North America: Biology, Management and Conservation.* 2nd edition. Johns Hopkins University Press, Baltimore, Maryland.

Bekoff, M. & Wells, M.C. (1986). Social ecology and behaviour of coyotes. *Advances Study Behav.* **16**: 251-336.

Bekoff, M., Tyrrell, M., Lipetz, V.E. & Jamieson, R.A. (1981). Fighting patterns in young coyotes: initiation, escalation and assessment. *Aggressive Behavior* **7**: 225-244.

Belant, J.L., Kielland, K., Follmann, E.H. & Adams, L.G. (2006). Interspecific resource partitioning in sympatric ursids. *Ecol. Appl.* **16**: 2333-2343.

Belden, R.C. & Hagedorn, B.W. (1993). Feasibility of translocating panthers into northern Florida. *J. Wildl. Management* **57**: 388-397.

Bell, D., Robertson, S. & Hunter, P.R. (2004). Animal origin of SARS coronavirus: possible links with the international trade in small carnivores. *Phil. Trans. Roy. Soc. London (Ser. B)* **359**: 1107-1114.

Bell, M.B.V. (2007). Cooperative begging in banded mongoose pups. *Curr. Biol.* **17**: 717-721.

Bellemain, E., Nawaz, M.A., Valentini, A., Swenson, J.E. & Taberlet, P. (2007). Genetic tracking of the brown bear in northern Pakistan and implications for conservation. *Biol. Conserv.* **134**: 537-547.

Bellemain, E., Swenson, J.E. & Taberlet, P. (2006). Mating strategies in relation to sexually selected infanticide in a non-social carnivore: the brown bear. *Ethology* **112**: 238-246.

Beltrán, J.F. (1991). Temporal abundance pattern of the wild rabbit in Doñana, SW Spain. *Mammalia* **55**: 591-599.

Beltrán, J.F. & Delibes, M. (1993). Physical characteristics of Iberian lynxes (*Lynx pardinus*) from Doñana, southwestern Spain. *J. Mammal.* **74**: 852-862.

Beltrán, J.F. & Delibes, M. (1994). Environmental determinants of circadian activity of free-ranging Iberian lynxes. *J. Mammal.* **75**: 382-393.

Beltrán, J.F., Aldama, J.J. & Delibes, M. (1992). Ecology of the Iberian lynx in Doñana, southwestern Spain. Pp. 331-334 in: Bobek, B., Perzanowski, K. & Regelin, W. eds. (1992). *Global Trends in Wildlife Management.* Swiat Press, Krakow-Warszawa.

Beltrán, J.F., Rice, J.E. & Honeycutt, R.L. (1996). Taxonomy of the Iberian lynx. *Nature (London)* **379**: 407-408.

Beltrán, J.F., San José, C., Delibes, M. & Braza, F. (1985). An analysis of the Iberian lynx predation upon fallow deer in the Coto Doñana, SW Spain. Pp. 961-967 in: de Crombrugghe, S.A. ed. (1985). *Transactions XVIIth Congress of International Union Game Biologists.* Brussels.

Ben-David, M. (1998). Delayed implantation in the marbled polecat, *Vormela peregusna syriaca* (Carnivora, Mustelidae): evidence from mating, parturition and post-natal growth. *Mammalia* **62**: 269-283.

Ben-David, M., Pellis, S.M. & Pellis, V.C. (1991). Feeding habits and predatory behaviour in the marbled polecat (*Vormela peregusna syriaca*): I. Killing methods in relation to prey size and prey behaviour. *Behaviour* **118**: 127-143.

Bennett, E.T. (1833). Notice of a new genus of *Viverridous Mammalia* from Madagascar. *Proc. Zool. Soc. London* **1833**: 46.

Bennett, E.T. (1835). Notice of a mammiferous animal from Madagascar, constituting a new form among the *Viverridous Carnivora. Trans. Zool. Soc. London* **1**: 137-140.

Bentler, K.T., Hall, J.S., Root, J.J., Klenk, K., Schmit, B., Blackwell, B.F., Ramey, P. C. & Clark, L. (2007). Serologic evidence of west nile virus exposure in North American predators. *Amer. J. Trop. Med. Hyg.* **76**: 173-179.

Bentley, P.J. (1998). *Comparative Vertebrate Endocrinology.* 3rd edition. Cambridge University Press, New York.

Benton, M.J. (1990). *Vertebrate Paleontology.* Unwin Hyman, London.

Bentzen, T.W., Follman, E.H., Amstrup, S.C., York, G.S., Wooller, M.J. & O'Hara, T.M. (2007). Variation in winter diet of southern Beaufort Sea polar bears inferred from stable isotope analysis. *Can. J. Zool.* **85**: 596-608.

Ben Yaacov, R. & Yom Tov, Y. (1983). On the biology of the Egyptian mongoose, *Herpestes ichneumon*, in Israel. *Zeitschrift für Säugetierkunde* **48**: 34-45.

Bequaert, J. (1922). The predaceous enemies of ants. *Bull. Amer. Mus. Nat. Hist.* **45**: 271-331.

Bergerud, A.T. (1983). Prey switching in a simple ecosystem. *Scientific American* **249**: 130-141.

Bermejo, T. & Guitian, J. (2000). Fruit consumption by foxes and martens in NW Spain in autumn: A comparison of natural and agricultural areas. *Folia Zool.* **49**: 89-92.

Bernard, R.T.F. & Stuart, C.T. (1987). Reproduction of the caracal *Felis caracal* from the Cape Province of South Africa. *South Afr. J. Zool.* **22**: 177-182.

Bernard, R.T.F. & Stuart, C.T. (1992). Correlates of diet and reproduction in the black-backed jackal. *South Afr. J. Sci.* **88**: 292-294.

Bernardes, A.T., Machado, A.B.M. & Rylands, A.B. eds. (1990). *Fauna Brasileira Ameaçada de Extinção.* Fundação Biodiversitas, Belo Horizonte, Brasil.

Berrie, P.M. (1973). Ecology and status of the lynx in interior Alaska. Pp. 4-41 in: Eaton, R.L. ed. (1973). *The World's Cats.* Vol. 1. World Wildlife Safari, Winston, Oregon.

Berry, H.H. (1981). Abnormal levels of disease and predation as limiting factors for wildebeest in Etosha National Park. *Madoqua* **12**: 242-253.

Berry, M.P.S. (1978). *Aspects of the Ecology and Behaviour of the Bat-eared Fox,* Otocyon megalotis *(Desmarest, 1822) in the Upper Limpopo Valley.* MSc thesis, University of Pretoria, Pretoria, South Africa.

Berta, A. (1984). The Pleistocene bush dog *Speothos pacivorus* (Canidae) from the Lagoa Santa Caves, Brazil. *J. Mammal.* **65**: 549-559.

Bertram, B.C.R. (1975a). The social system of lions. *Scientific American* **232**: 54-65.

Bertram, B.C.R. (1975b). Social factors influencing reproduction in wild lions. *J. Zool., London* **177**: 463-482.

Bertram, B.C.R. (1979). Serengeti predators and their social system. Pp. 221-248 in: Sinclair, A.R.E. & Norton-Griffiths, M. eds. (1979). *Serengeti, Dynamics of an Ecosystem.* University of Chicago Press, Chicago, Illinois.

Bertram, B.C.R. (1982). Leopard ecology as studied by radio tracking. *Symp. Zool. Soc. London* **49**: 341-352.

Bestelmeyer, S.V. (2000). *Solitary, Reproductive and Parental Behavior of Maned Wolves* Chrysocyon brachyurus. PhD dissertation, Colorado State University, Fort Collins, Colorado.

Bestelmeyer, S.V. & Westbrook, C. (1998). Maned wolf *Chrysocyon brachyurus* predation on Pampas deer *Ozotoceros bezoarticus* in central Brazil. *Mammalia* **62**: 591-595.

Bester, J.L. (1982). *Die Gedragsekologie en Bestuur van die Silwervos* Vulpes chama *(A. Smith, 1833) Met Spesiale Verwysing na die Oranje-Vrystaat.* MSc thesis, University of Pretoria, Pretoria, South Africa.

Beynon, P. & Rasa, O.A.E. (1989). Do dwarf mongooses have a language - warning vocalizations transmit complex information. *South Afr. J. Sci.* **85**: 447-450.

Bezuijen, R.R. (2000). The occurrence of the flat-headed cat *Prionailurus planiceps* in southeast Sumatra. *Oryx* **34**: 222-226.

Bhattacharyya, T. (1992). A brief note on some observations on the breeding biology of the fishing cat (*Felis viverrina*). *Tigerpaper* **14(2)**: 20-21.

Bianchi, R. de C. & Mendes, S.L. (2007). Ocelot (*Leopardus pardalis*) predation on primates in Caratinga Biological Station, southeast Brazil. *Amer. J. Primatology* **69**: 1173-1178.

Biben, M. (1982). Ontogeny of social behaviour related to feeding in the crab-eating fox *Cerdocyon thous* and the bush dog *Speothos venaticus*. *J. Zool., London* **196**: 207-216.

Biben, M. (1983). Comparative ontonogeny of social behaviour in three South-American canids, the maned wolf, crab-eating fox and bush dog - implications for sociality. *Anim. Behav.* **31**: 814-826.

Biewener, A.A. (1990). Biomechanics of mammalian terrestrial locomotion. *Science* **250**: 1097-1103.

Biggins, D.E., Schroeder, M.H., Forrest, S.C. & Richardson, L. (1986). Activity of radio-tagged black-footed ferrets. *Great Basin Nat. Mem.* **8**: 135-140.

Binder, W.J. & Van Valkenburgh, B. (2000). Development of bite strength and feeding behaviour in juvenile spotted hyaenas (*Crocuta crocuta*). *J. Zool., London* **252**: 273-283.

Binford, L.R., Mills, M.G.L. & Stone, N.M. (1988). Hyaena scavenging behaviour and its implications for the interpretation of faunal assemblages from FLK 22 (the Zinj floor) at Olduvai Gorge. *J. Anthropol. Archaeol.* **7**: 99-135.

Bininda-Edmonds, O.R.P. (2004). Phylogenetic position of the giant panda. Pp. 11-35 in: Lindburg, D.G. & Baragona, K. eds. (2004). *Giant Pandas: Biology and Conservation.* University of California Press, Berkeley & London.

Bininda-Edmonds, O.R.P., Decker-Flum, D.M. & Gittleman, J.L. (2001). The utility of chemical signals: an example from the Felidae. *Biol. J. Linn. Soc.* **72**: 1-15.

Bininda-Edmonds, O.R.P., Gittleman, J.L. & Purvis, A. (1999). Building large trees by combining phylogenetic information: a complete phylogeny of the extant Carnivora (Mammalia). *Biol. Rev.* **74**: 143-175.

Birdseye, C. (1956). Observations on a domesticated Peruvian Desert fox *Dusicyon*. *J. Mammal.* **37**: 284-287.

Birks, J.D.S. & Linn, I.J. (1982). Studies of home range of the feral mink, *Mustela vison*. *Symp. Zool. Soc. London* **49**: 231-257.

Birks, J.D.S., Messenger, J.E. & Halliwell, E.C. (2005). Diversity of den sites used by pine martens *Martes martes*: a response to the scarcity of arboreal cavities? *Mammal Rev.* **35**: 313-320.

Bisbal, F.J. (1986). Food habits of some Neotropical carnivores in Venezuela (Mammalia, Carnivora). *Mammalia* **50(3)**: 329-339.

Bisbal, F.J. (1988). A taxonomic study of the crab-eating fox, *Cerdocyon thous*, in Venezuela. *Mammalia* **52**: 181-186.

Bisbal, F.J. (1989). Distribution and habitat association of the carnivores in Venezuela. Pp. 339-362 in: Redford, K.H. & Eisenberg, J.F. eds. (1989). *Advances in Neotropical Mammalogy.* Sandhill Crane Press, Gainesville, Florida.

Bisbal, F.J. (1993). Human impact on the carnivores of Venezuela. *Stud. Neotrop. Fauna Environm.* **28**: 145-156.

Bisbal, F.J. & Ojasti, J. (1980). Nicho trófico del zorro *Cerdocyon thous* (Mammalia, Carnivora). *Acta Biol. Venez.* **10**: 469-496.

Biswas, R.N. (1973). On the domestication of the otter by fishermen in Bangladesh. *J. Bombay Nat. Hist. Soc.* **47**: 379-383.

Biswas, S. & Sankar, K. (2002). Prey abundance and food habits of tigers (*Panthera tigris tigris*) in Pench National Park, Madhya Pradesh, India. *J. Zool., London* **256**: 411-420.

Bittner, S.L. & Rongstad, O.J. (1982). Snowshoe hares and allies. Pp. 146-163 in: Chapman, J.A. & Feldhamer, G.A. eds. (1982). *Wild Mammals of North America.* Johns Hopkins University Press, Baltimore, Maryland.

Blackburn, D.G. (1991). Evolutionary origins of the mammary gland. *Mammal Rev.* **21**: 81-96.

Blancou, J.M. (1968). Note clinique: cas de charbon bactéridien chez les carnivores sauvages de Madagascar. *Rev. Élev. Méd. Vét. Pays Trop.* **21**: 339-340.

Blandford, P.R.S. (1987). Biology of the polecat *Mustela putorius*: a literature review. *Mammal Rev.* **17**: 155-198.

Blanford, W.T. (1885a). Exhibition and description of a skull of an apparently new species of *Paradoxurus* (*P. jerdoni*). *Proc. Zool. Soc. London* **1885**: 612-613.

Blanford, W.T. (1885b). A monograph of the genus *Paradoxurus*, F. Cuvier. *Proc. Zool. Soc. London* **1885**: 780-808.

Blanford, W.T. (1886). Exhibition of and remarks upon a stuffed skin of *Paradoxurus jerdoni*. *Proc. Zool. Soc. London* **1886**: 420.

Blanton, J.D., Krebs, J.W., Hanlon, C.A. & Rupprecht, C.E. (2006). Rabies surveillance in the United States during 2005. *J. Amer. Vet. Med. Assoc.* **229**: 1897-1911.

Blaum, N., Rossmanith, E., Fleissner, G. & Jeltsch, F. (2007). The conflicting importance of shrubby landscape structures for the reproductive success of the yellow mongoose (*Cynictis penicillata*). *J. Mammal.* **88**: 194-200.

Blaum, N., Rossmanith, E., Popp, A. & Jeltsch, F. (2007). Shrub encroachment affects mammalian carnivore abundance and species richness in semiarid rangelands. *Acta Oecol.* **31**: 86-92.

Blomqvist, L. & Nystrom, V. (1980). On identifying snow leopards, *Panthera uncia*, by their facial markings. *Int. Ped. Book Snow Leopards* **2**: 159-167.

Blomqvist, L. & Sten, I. (1982). Reproductive biology of the snow leopard *Panthera uncia*. *Int. Ped. Book Snow Leopards* **3**: 71-79.

Blundell, G.M., Ben-David, M., Groves, P., Bowyer, R.T. & Geffen, E. (2004). Kinship and sociality in coastal river otters: are they related? *Behav. Ecol.* **15**: 705-714.

Bodkin, J.L. (2003). Sea otter. Pp. 735-743 in: Feldhamer, G.A., Thompson, B.C. & Chapman, J.A. eds. (2003). *Wild Mammals of North America: Biology, Management and Conservation.* 2nd edition. Johns Hopkins University Press, Baltimore, Maryland.

Boitani, L. (1995). Ecological and cultural diversities in the evolution of wolf-human relationships. Pp. 3-11 in: Carbyn, L.N., Fritts, S.H. & Seip, D.R. eds. (1995). *Ecology and Conservation of Wolves in a Changing World.* Canadian Circumpolar Institute, Edmonton, Alberta.

Boitani, L., Catullo, G., Marzetti, I., Masi, M., Rulli, M. & Savini, S. (2006). *The Southeast Asian Mammal Databank. A Tool for Conservation and Monitoring of Mammal Diversity in Southeast Asia.* Istituto di Ecologia Applicata, Roma, Italy.

Boitani, L., Corsi, F., De Biase, A., D'inzillo, I., Ravagli, M., Reggiania, G., Sinnibaldi, I. & Trapanese, P. (1999). *A Databank for the Conservation and Management of the African Mammals.* Instituto d'Ecologia Applicata, Roma.

Boland, J.M. (1990). Servals: wetland cats. *Endangered Wildl.* **1**: 4-5.

Boland, J.M. & Perrin, M.R. (1993). Diet of serval *Felis serval* in a highland region of Natal. *South Afr. J. Zool.* **28**: 132-135.

Bonaparte, C.L.J.L. (1845). *Catalogo Methodico dei Mammiferi Europei.* Luigi di Giacomo Pirola, Milano.

Bonesi, L., Dunstone, N. & O'Connell, M. (2000). Winter selection of habitats within intertidal foraging areas by mink (*Mustela vison*). *J. Zool., London* **250**: 419-424.

Boone, W.R., Keck, B.B., Catlin, J.C., Casey, K.J., Boone, E.T., Dye, P.S., Schuett, R.J., Tsubota, T. & Bahr, J.C. (2004). Evidence that bears are induced ovulators. *Theriogenology* **61**: 1163-1169.

Boone, W.R., Richardson, M.E. & Greer, J.A. (2003). Breeding behavior of the American black bear (*Ursus americanus*). *Theriogenology* **60**: 289-297.

Booth-Binczik, S.D., Binczik, G.A. & Labiski, R.F. (2004a). A possible foraging association between white hawks and white-nosed coatis. *Wilson Bull.* **116**: 101-103.

Booth-Binczik, S.D., Binczik, G.A. & Labisky, R.F. (2004b). Lek-like mating in white-nosed coatis (*Nasua narica*): socio-ecological correlates of intraspecific variability in mating systems. *J. Zool., London* **262**: 179-185.

Borissenko, A.V., Ivanova, N.V. & Polet, G. (2004). First recent record of the small-toothed palm civet *Arctogalidia trivirgata* from Vietnam. *Small Carniv. Conserv.* **30**: 5-6.

Bosman, P. & Hall-Martin, A. (1997). *Cats of Africa.* Fernwood, Vlaeberg, South Africa.

Bothma, J. du P. (1966). Food of the silver fox *Vulpes chama*. *Zool. Afr.* **2**: 205-221.

Bothma, J. du P. (1971a). Food of *Canis mesomelas* in South Africa. *Zool. Afr.* **6**: 195-203.

Bothma, J. du P. (1971b). Notes on the movements by the black-backed jackal and the aardwolf in the western Transvaal. *Zool. Afr.* **6**: 205-207.

Bothma, J. du P. (1971c). Food habits of some Carnivora (Mammalia) from southern Africa. *Ann. Transvaal Mus.* **27**: 15-26.

Bothma, J. du P. (1998). *Carnivore Ecology in Arid Lands.* Springer, Berlin.

Bothma, J. du P. & Le Riche, E.A.N. (1984). Aspects of the ecology and behaviour of the leopard *Panthera pardus* in the Kalahari Desert. *Koedoe* **27**(Suppl.): 259-279.

Bothma, J. du P. & Le Riche, E.A.N. (1986). Prey preference and hunting efficiency of Kalahari Desert leopards. Pp. 389-414 in: Miller, S.D. & Everett, D.D. (1986). *Cats of the World: Biology, Conservation and Management.* National Wildlife Federation, Washington, D.C.

Bothma, J. du P. & Le Riche, E.A.N. (1989). Evidence of a flexible hunting technique in Kalahari leopards. *South Afr. J. Wildl. Res.* **19**: 57-60.

Bothma, J. du P. & Le Riche, E.A.N. (1990). The influence of increasing hunger on the hunting behaviour of southern Kalahari leopards. *J. Arid Environm.* **18**: 79-84.

Bothma, J. du P. & Walker, C. (1999). *Larger Carnivores of the African Savannas.* Van Schaik Publishers, Pretoria.

Bothma, J. du P., Nel, J.A.J. & Macdonald, A. (1984). Food niche separation between four sympatric Namib Desert carnivores. *J. Zool., London* **202**: 327-340.

Bottriel, L.G. (1987). *King Cheetah: the Story of the Quest.* E.J. Brill, Leiden, The Netherlands.

Bourlière, F., Minner, E. & Vuattoux, R. (1974). Les grands mammifères de la région de Lamto, Côte d'Ivoire. *Mammalia* **38**: 433-447.

Bourne, G.H. ed. (1972). *The Structure and Function of Muscle.* Academic Press, New York.

Bourne, G.H. ed. (1980). *Hearts and Heart-like Organs.* Academic Press, New York.

Bouskila, Y. (1984). The foraging groups of the striped hyaena (*Hyaena hyaena syriaca*). *Carnivore* **7**: 2-12.

Boydston, E.E., Kapheim, K.M. & Holekamp, K.E. (2006). Patterns of den occupation by the spotted hyena (*Crocuta crocuta*). *Afr. J. Ecol.* **44**: 77-86.

Boydston, E.E., Kapheim, K.M., Van Horn, R.C., Smale, L. & Holekamp, K.E. (2005). Sexually dimorphic patterns of space use throughout ontogeny in the spotted hyaena (*Crocuta crocuta*). *J. Zool., London* **267**: 271-281.

Boydston, E.E., Morelli, T.L. & Holekamp, K.E. (2001). Sex differences in territorial behavior exhibited by the spotted hyena (*Crocuta crocuta*). *Ethology* **107**: 369-385.

Bradshaw, J. & Cameron-Beaumont, C. (2000). The signalling repertoire of the domestic cat and its undomesticated relatives. Pp. 67-93 in: Turner, D. & Bateson, P. eds. (2000). *The Domestic Cat: the Biology of its Behaviour.* Cambridge University Press, Cambridge.

Brady, C.A. (1978). Reproduction, growth and parental care in crab-eating foxes *Cerdocyon thous* at the National Zoological Park, Washington. *Int. Zoo Yb.* **18**: 130-134.

Brady, C.A. (1979). Observations on the behaviour and ecology of the crab-eating fox *Cerdocyon thous*. Pp. 161-171 in: Eisenberg, J.F. ed. (1979). *Vertebrate Ecology in the Northern Neotropics.* Smithsonian Institution Press, Washington, D.C.

Brady, C.A. (1981). The vocal repertoires of the bush dog *Speothos venaticus*, crab-eating fox *Cerdocyon thous* and maned wolf *Chrysocyon brachyurus*. *Anim. Behav.* **29**: 649-669.

Brady, C.A. & Ditton, M.K. (1979). Management and breeding of maned wolves at the National Zoological Park, Washington. *Int. Zoo Yb.* **19**: 171-176.

Brahmachary, R.L. & Dutta, J. (1987). Chemical communication in the tiger and leopard. Pp. 296-302 in: Tilson, R.L. & Seal, U.S. eds. (1987). *Tigers of the World: the Biology, Biopolitics, Management and Conservation of an Endangered Species.* Noyes Publications, Park Ridge, New Jersey.

Brahmachary, R.L, Dutta, J. & Poddar-Sarkar, M. (1991). The marking fluid of the tiger. *Mammalia* **55**: 150-152.

Brainerd, S.M. & Rolstad, J. (2002). Habitat selection by Eurasian pine martens *Martes martes* in managed forests of southern boreal Scandinavia. *Wildl. Biol.* **8**: 289-297.

Bramble, D.M. (1978). Origin of the mammalian feeding complex, models and mechanisms. *Paleobiology* **4**: 271-301.

Bramble, D.M. & Carrier, D.R. (1983). Running and breathing in mammals. *Science* **291**: 251-256.

Bramble, D.M. & Jenkins, F.A. (1993). Mammalian locomotor-respiratory integration: implications for diaphragmatic and pulmonary design. *Science* **262**: 235-240.

Branch, L.C. (1994). Seasonal patterns in long-distance vocalizations of the Pampas fox. *Vida Silvestre Neotrop.* **3**: 108-111.

Brand, C.J. & Keith, L.B. (1979). Lynx demography during a snowshoe hare decline in Alberta. *J. Wildl. Management* **43**: 827-849.

Brand, C.J., Keith, L.B. & Fischer, C.A. (1976). Lynx responses to changing snowshoe hare densities in central Alberta. *J. Wildl. Management* **40**: 416-428.

Brand, D.J. (1963). Records of mammals bred in the National Zoological Gardens of South Africa during the period 1908-1960. *Proc. Zool. Soc. London* **140**: 617-659.

Brandt, M.J. & Lambin, X. (2007). Movement patterns of a specialist predator, the weasel *Mustela nivalis* exploiting asynchronous cyclic field vole *Microtus agrestis* populations. *Acta Theriol.* **52**: 13-25.

Brannon, P.M. (1990). Adaptation of the exocrine pancreas to diet. *Ann. Rev. Nutr.* **10**: 85-105.

Brecht-Munn, M. & Munn, C.A. (1988). The Amazon's gregarious giant otters. *Anim. Kingdom* **91**: 34-41.

Breckwoldt, R. (1988). *A Very Elegant Animal: the Dingo.* Angus & Robertson, Australia.

Breitenmoser, U. & Haller, H. (1993). Patterns of predation by reintroduced European lynx in the Swiss Alps. *J. Wildl. Management* **57**: 135-144.

Breitenmoser, U., Breitenmoser-Würsten, C., Okarma, H., Kaphegyi, T., Kaphegyi-Wallman, U. & Muller, U.M. (2000). *Action Plan for the Conservation of the Eurasian Lynx (*Lynx lynx*) in Europe.* Convention on the Conservation of European Wildlife and Natural Habitats.

Breitenmoser, U., Kaczensky, P., Dötterer, M., Breitenmoser-Würsten, C., Capt, S., Bernhart, F. & Liberek, M. (1993). Spatial organisation and recruitement of lynx (*Lynx lynx*) in a re-introduced population in the Swiss Jura Mountains. *J. Zool., London* **231**: 449-464.

Breitenmoser, U., Slough, B.G. & Breitenmoser-Würsten, C. (1993). Predators of cyclic prey: is the Canada lynx victim or profiteer of the snowshoe hare cycle? *Oikos* **66**: 551-554.

Breitenmoser-Würsten, C., Zimmermann, F., Ryser, A., Capt, S., Laass, J., Siegenthaler, A. & Breitenmoser, U. (2001). *Untersuchungen zur Luchspopulation in den Nordwestalpen der Schweiz 1997-2000.* KORA Bericht **9**. KORA, Bern.

Bridgeford, P.A. (1985). Unusual diet of the lion *Panthera leo* in the Skeleton Coast Park. *Madoqua* **14**: 187-188.

Brink, H., Topp-Jørgensen, J.E. & Marshall, A.R. (2002). First record in 68 years of Lowe's servaline genet. *Oryx* **36**: 323-327.

Brisbin, I.L., Coppinger, R.P., Feinstein, M.H., Austad, S.N. & Mayer, J.J. (1994). The New Guinea singing dog: taxonomy, captive studies and conservation priorities. *Sci. New Guinea* **20**: 27-38.

Britt, A. (1999). Observations on two sympatric, diurnal herpestids in the Betampona NR, eastern Madagascar. *Small Carniv. Conserv.* **20**: 14.

Britt, A. & Virkaitis, V. (2003). Brown-tailed mongoose *Salanoia concolor* in the Betampona Reserve, eastern Madagascar: photographs and an ecological comparison with ring-tailed mongoose *Galidia elegans*. *Small Carniv. Conserv.* **28**: 1-3.

Broad, S. (1987). *The Harvest of and Trade in Latin American Spotted Cats (Felidae) and Otters (Lutrinae).* Wildlife Trade Monitoring Unit, IUCN Conservation Monitoring Centre, Cambridge.

Brocke, R.H., Gustafson, K.A. & Fox, L.B. (1991). Restoration of large predators: potentials and problems. Pp. 303-315 in: Decker, D.J., Krasny, M.E., Goff, G.R., Smith, C.R. & Gross,

D.W. eds. (1991). *Challenges in the Conservation of Biological Resources.* Westview Press, San Francisco, California.

Brocke, R.H., Gustafson, K.A. & Major, A.R. (1990). Restoration of lynx in New York: biopolitical lessons. *Trans. North Amer. Wildl. Nat. Resour. Conf.* **55**: 590-598.

Bromlei, F.G. (1965). *Bears of the South Far-eastern USSR* (translated from Russian in 1973). Indian National Scientific Documentation Center, New Delhi.

Brooks, D. (1992). Notes on group size, density and habitat association of the Pampas fox *Dusicyon gymnocercus* in the Paraguayan Chaco. *Mammalia* **56**: 314-316.

Brooks, T.M. & Dutson, G.C.L. (1994). A sighting of a masked palm civet (*Paguma larvata*) on Java. *Small Carniv. Conserv.* **11**: 19.

Broomhall, L.S., Mills, M.G.L. & duToit, J.T. (2003). Home range and habitat use by cheetahs (*Acinonyx jubatus*) in the Kruger National Park. *J. Zoology, London* **261**: 119-128.

Brotherton, P.N.M., Clutton-Brock, T.H., O'Riain, M.J., Gaynor, D., Sharpe, L., Kansky, R. & McIlrath, G.M. (2001). Offspring food allocation by parents and helpers in a cooperative mammal. *Behav. Ecol.* **12**: 590-599.

Brown, D.E. (1985). *The Grizzly in the Southwest. Documentary of an Extinction.* University of Oklahoma Press, Norman, Oklahoma.

Brown, J.H. & Lasiewski, R.C. (1972). Metabolism of weasels: the cost of being long and thin. *Ecology* **53**: 939-943.

Brown, M. & Munkhtsog, B. (2000). Ecology and behaviour of Pallas cat in Mongolia. *Cat News* **33**: 22.

Bryant, H.N., Russell, A.P. & Fitch, W.D. (1993). Phylogenetic relationships within the extant Mustelidae (Carnivora): appraisal of the cladistic status of the Simpsonian subfamilies. *Zool. J. Linn. Soc.* **108**: 301-334.

Bryden, B.R. (1978). *The Biology of the African Lion (*Panthera leo*) (Linn. 1758) in the Kruger National Park.* MSc thesis, University of Pretoria, Pretoria.

Brzezinski, M. (1994). Summer diet of the sable *Martes zibellina* in the Middle Yenisei taiga, Siberia. *Acta Theriol.* **39**: 103-107.

Brzezinski, M., Jedrzejewski, W. & Jedrzejewska, B. (1992). Winter home ranges and movements of polecats *Mustela putorius* in Bialowieza primeval forest, Poland. *Acta Theriol.* **37**: 181-191.

Bubenik, G.A. & Bubenik, A.B. eds. (1990). *Horns, Pronghorns and Antlers: Evolution, Morphology, Physiology and Social Significance.* Springer, New York.

Buckland-Wright, J. (1969). Craniological observations on *Hyaena* and *Crocuta* (Mammalia). *J. Zool., London* **159**: 17-29.

Buckley-Beason, V.A., Johnson, W.E., Nash, W.G., Stanyon, R., Menninger, J.C., Driscoll, C.A., Howard, J.G., Bush, M., Page, J.E., Roelke, M.E., Stone, G., Martelli, P.P., Wen, C., Ling, L., Duraisingam, R.K., Lam, P.V. & O'Brien, S.J. (2006). Molecular evidence for species-level distinction in modern clouded leopards (*Neofelis nebulosa*). *Curr. Biol.* **16**: 2371-2376.

Bueler, L.E. (1973). *Wild Dogs of the World.* Stein & Day, New York.

Buglass, A.J., Darling, F.M.C. & Waterhouse, J.S. (1990). Analysis of the anal sac secretion of the hyaenidae. Pp. 65-69 in: Macdonald, D.W., Müller-Schwarze, D. & Natynczuk, S.E. eds. (1990). *Chemical Signals in Vertebrates.* Vol 5 Oxford University Press, Oxford.

Buie, D.E., Fendley, T.T. & McNab, J. (1979). Fall and winter home ranges of adult bobcats on the Savannah River Plant, South Carolina. Pp. 42-46 in: *Proceedings of the Bobcat Research Conference.* National Wildlife Federation Science Technical Series **6**.

Burchell, W.J. (1824). *Travels to the Interior of Southern Africa.* Vol. 2. Longman, Hurst, Rees, Orme, Brown & Green, London.

Burger, J. & Gochfeld, M. (1992). Effect of group size on vigilance while drinking in the coati *Nasua narica* in Costa Rica. *Anim. Behav.* **44**: 1053-1057.

Burney, D.A., Burney, L.P., Godfrey, L.R., Jungers, W.L., Goodman, S.M., Wright, H.T. & Jull, A.J.T. (2004). A chronology for late Prehistoric Madagascar. *J. Hum. Evol.* **47**: 25–63.

Burnie, D. & Wilson, D.E. (2001). *Animal.* Dorling Kindersley, New York.

Buskirk, S.W. (1984). Seasonal use of resting sites by marten in south-central Alaska. *J. Wildl. Management* **48**: 950-953.

Buskirk, S.W. & MacDonald, S.O. (1984). Seasonal food habits of marten in southcentral Alaska. *Can. J. Zool.* **62**: 944-950.

Buskirk, S.W., Ma, Y., Xu, L. & Jiang, Z. (1996a). Winter habitat ecology of sables (*Martes zibellina*) in relation to forest management in China. *Ecol. Appl.* **6**: 318-325.

Buskirk, S.W., Ma, Y., Xu, L. & Jiang, Z. (1996b). Diets of, and prey selection by, sables (*Martes zibellina*) in northern China. *J. Mammal.* **77**: 725-730.

Buskirk, S.W., Wu, D. & Cleveland, A. (1990). Diet activity patterns of two female small Indian mongoose (*Herpestes auropunctatus*) in relation to weather. *Zool. Res.* **11**: 355-357.

Bustamante, R.O., Simonetti, J.A. & Mella, J.E. (1992). Are foxes legitimate and efficient seed dispersers? A field test. *Acta Oecol.* **13**: 203-208.

Butler, J.R.A. (1994). Cape clawless otter conservation in a trout river in Zimbabwe: a case study. *Oryx* **28**: 276-282.

Butler, P.J. & Jones, D.R. (1982). The comparative physiology of diving in vertebrates. *Adv. Comp. Physiol. Biochem.* **8**: 179-364.

Butler, T.H. & Hodos, W. (1996). *Comparative Vertebrate Neuroanatomy: Evolution and Anatomy.* Wiley-Liss, New York.

Buttrey, G.W. (1974). *Food Habits and Distribution of the Bobcat,* Lynx rufus rufus, *on the Catoosa Wildlife Management Area.* MSc thesis, Tennessee Technological University, Cookeville, Tennessee.

Cabrera, A. (1931). On some South American canine genera. *J. Mammal.* **12**: 54-66.

Cabrera, A. (1958). Catálogo de los mamíferos de América del Sur. *Rev. Mus. Arg. Cienc. Nat. Bernadino Rivadavia* **4**: 1-307.

Cabrera, A. (1961a). Catálogo de los mamíferos de América del Sur 2. *Rev. Mus. Arg. Cienc. Nat. Bernardino Rivadavia* **4**: 309-732.

Cabrera, A. (1961b). Los félidos vivientes de la República Argentina. *Rev. Mus. Arg. Cienc. Nat. Bernardino Rivadavia* **6(5)**: 161-247.

Cabrera, A. & Yepes, J. (1960). *Mamíferos Sud Americanos (Vida, Costumbres y Descripción).* 2nd edition. Historia Natural Ediar, Compañía Argentina de Editores, Buenos Aires.

Cajal, J.L. (1986). *El Recurso Fauna en Argentina. Antecedentes y Cuadro de Situación Actual.* Ministerio de Educación y Justicia, Secretaría de Ciencia y Técnica, Buenos Aires.

Caldwell, J.R. (1984). South American cats in trade: the German connection. *TRAFFIC Bull.* **6**: 31-32.

Camenzind, F.J. (1978). Behavioral ecology of coyotes on the National Elk Refuge, Jackson, Wyoming. Pp. 267-294 in: Bekoff, M. ed. (1978). *Coyotes: Biology, Behaviour and Management.* Academic Press, New York.

Cameron, M.W. (1984). *The Swift Fox (Vulpes velox) on the Pawnee National Grassland: its Food Habits, Population Dynamics and Ecology.* MSc thesis, University of Northern Colorado, Greeley, Colorado.

Campbell, T.M., Clark, T.W., Richardson, L., Forrest, S.C. & Houston, B.R. (1987). Food habits of Wyoming black-footed ferrets. *Amer. Midl. Nat.* **117**: 208-210.

Campos, C.M. & Ojeda, R.A. (1997). Dispersal and germination of *Prosopis flexuosa* (Fabaceae) seeds by desert mammals in Argentina. *J. Arid Environm.* **35**: 707-714.

Camps-Munuera, D. & Llober, L. (2004). Space use of common genets *Genetta genetta* in a Mediterranean habitat of northeastern Spain: differences between sexes and seasons. *Acta Theriol.* **49**: 491-502.

Canepuccia, A.D., Martinez, M.M. & Vassallo, A.I. (2007). Selection of waterbirds by Geoffroy's cat: effects of prey abundance, size and distance. *Mammal. Biol.* **72**: 163-173.

Canevari, M. & Ambrosini, L. (1988). *Los Zorrinos. Mamíferos Fauna Argentina.* Centro Editor de America Latina, Buenos Aires, Argentina.

Canivenc, R., Mauget, C., Bonnin, M. & Aitken, R.J. (1981). Delayed implantation in the beech marten (*Martes foiana*). *J. Zool., London* **193**: 325-332.

Cant, M.A. (1998). *Communal Breeding in Banded Mongooses and the Theory of Reproductive Skew.* PhD thesis, University of Cambridge, Cambridge, UK.

Cant, M.A. (2000). Social control of reproduction in banded mongooses. *Anim. Behav.* **59**: 147-158.

Cant, M.A. (2003). Patterns of helping effort in co-operatively breeding banded mongooses (*Mungos mungo*). *J. Zool., London* **259**: 115-121.

Cant, M.A. & Gilchrist, J.S. (In press). *Mungos mungo.* In: Kingdon, J.S. & Hoffmann, M. eds. (In press). *The Mammals of Africa.* Vol. 5. Carnivora, Pholidota, Perissodactyla. Academic Press, Amsterdam.

Cant, M.A., Otali, E. & Mwanguhya, F. (2001). Eviction and dispersal in co-operatively breeding banded mongooses (*Mungos mungo*). *J. Zool., London* **254**: 155-162.

Cant, M.A., Otali, E. & Mwanguhya, F. (2002). Fighting and mating between groups in a cooperatively breeding mammal, the banded mongoose. *Ethology* **108**: 541-555.

Cantú-Salazar, L. (2002). *Historia Natural y Uso de Recursos Espaciales y Alimentarios por el Zorrillo Pigmeo, Spilogale pygmaea, en un Bosque Tropical Caducifolio de Jalisco, México.* MSc thesis, Instituto de Ecología, A. C., Xalapa, Veracruz.

Cantú-Salazar, L., Fernandez, E.C. & Hidalgo-Mihart, M.G. (2004). Observation of threat behaviour by a pygmy skunk (*Spilogale pygmaea*) in Jalisco, Mexico. *Mammalia,* **68**: 57-59.

Cantú-Salazar, L., Hidalgo-Mihart, M.G., Lopez-Gonzalez, C.A. & Gonzalez-Romero, A. (2005). Diet and food resource use by the pygmy skunk (*Spilogale pygmaea*) in the tropical dry forest of Chamela, Mexico. *J. Zool., London* **267**: 283-289.

Caraco, T. & Wolf, L.L. (1975). Ecological determinants of group sizes of foraging lions. *Amer. Nat.* **109**: 343-352.

Carbone, C., Christie, S., Conforti, K., Coulson, T., Franklin, N., Ginsberg, J., Griffiths, M., Holden, J., Kawanishi, K., Kinnarid, M., Laidlaw, R., Lynam, A., Macdonald, D.W., Martyr, D., McDougal, C., Nath, L., O'Brien, T., Seidensticker, J., Smith, J.L.D., Sunquist, M., Tilson, R. & Wan Shahruddin, W. (2001). The use of photographic rates to estimate densities of tigers and other cryptic mammals. *Anim. Conserv.* **4**: 75-79.

Carbone, C., Cowlishaw, G., Isaac, N.J.B. & Rowcliffe, J.M. (2005). How far do animals go? Determinants of day range in mammals. *Amer. Naturalist* **165**: 290-297.

Carbyn, L.N. & Patriquin, D. (1983). Observations on home range sizes, movements and social organization of lynx, *Lynx canadensis,* in Riding Mountain National Park, Manitoba. *Can. Field-Nat.* **97**: 262-267.

Carbyn, L.N., Armbruster, H. & Mamo, C. (1994). The swift fox reintroduction program in Canada from 1983 to 1992. Pp. 247-271 in: Bowles, M. & Whelan, C.J. eds. (1994). *Restoration of Endangered Species: Conceptual Issues, Planning and Implementation.* Cambridge University Press, Cambridge.

Carbyn, L.N., Fritts, S.H. & Seip, D.R. eds. (1995). *Ecology and Conservation of Wolves in a Changing World.* Canadian Circumpolar Institute, Edmonton, Alberta.

Cardillo, M., Purvis, A., Sechrest, W., Gittleman, J., Bielby, J. & Mace, G. (2004). Human population density and extinction risk in the world's carnivores. *PLOS Biology* **2**: 909-914.

Carey, A.B. & Kershner, J.E. (1996). *Spilogale gracilis* in upland forests of western Washington and Oregon. *Northwestern Naturalist* **77**: 29-34.

Carley, C.J. (1975). *Activities and Findings of the Red Wolf Recovery Program from Late 1973 to July 1, 1975.* U.S. Fish and Wildlife Service, Albuquerque.

Carlson, A.A., Manser, M.B., Young, A.J., Russell, A.F., Jordan, N.R., McNeilly, A.S. & Clutton-Brock, T. (2006). Cortisol levels are positively associated with pup-feeding rates in male meerkats. *Proc. Royal Soc. London (Ser. B Biol. Sci.)* **273**: 571-577.

Carlson, A.A., Nicol, L., Young, A.J., Parlow, A.F. & McNeilly, A.S. (2003). Radioimmunoassay of prolactin for the meerkat (*Suricata suricatta*), a cooperatively breeding carnivore. *Gen. Comp. Endocrin.* **130**: 148-156.

Carlson, A.A., Russell, A.F., Young, A.J., Jordan, N.R., McNeilly, A.S., Parlow, A.F. & Clutton-Brock, T. (2006). Elevated prolactin levels immediately precede decisions to babysit by male meerkat helpers. *Horm. Behav.* **50**: 94-100.

Carlson, A.A., Young, A.J., Russell, A.F., Bennett, N.C., McNeilly, A.S. & Clutton-Brock, T. (2004). Hormonal correlates of dominance in meerkats (*Suricata suricatta*). *Horm. Behav.* **46**: 141-150.

Carlsson, A. (1910). Die genetischen Beziehungen der madagassischen Raubtiergattung Galidia. *Zool. Jahrb.* **28**: 559-601.

Caro, T.M. (1982). A record of cheetahs scavenging in the Serengeti. *Afr. J. Ecol.* **20**: 213-214.

Caro, T.M. (1994). *Cheetahs of the Serengeti Plains.* University of Chicago Press, Chicago, Illinois.

Caro, T.M. & Collins, D.A. (1986). Male cheetahs of the Serengeti. *Natl. Geogr. Res.* **2**: 75-86.

Caro, T.M. & Collins, D.A. (1987a). Male cheetah social organization and territoriality. *Ethology* **74**: 52-64.

Caro, T.M. & Collins, D.A. (1987b). Ecological characteristics of the territories of male cheetah (*Acinonyx jubatus*). *J. Zool., London* **211**: 89-105.

Caro, T.M. & Fitzgibbon, C.D. (1992). Large carnivores and their prey: the quick and the dead. Pp. 117-142 in: Crawley, M.J. ed. (1992). *Natural Enemies: the Population Biology of Predators, Parasites and Diseases.* Blackwell Scientific, Oxford.

Caro, T.M. & Laurenson, M.K. (1994). Ecological and genetic factors in conservation: a cautionary tale. *Science* **263**: 485-486.

Caro, T.M. & Stoner, C. (2003). The potential for interspecific competition among African carnivores. *Biol. Conserv.* **110**: 67-75.

Caro, T.M., Fitzgibbon, C.D. & Holt, M.E. (1989). Physiological cost of behavioural strategies for male cheetahs. *Anim. Behav.* **38**: 309-317.

Caro, T.M., Holt, M.E., Fitzgibbon, C.D., Bush, M., Hawkey, C.M. & Kock, R.A. (1987). Health of adult free-living cheetahs. *J. Zool., London* **212**: 573-584.

Carpaneto, G.M. & Germi, F.P. (1989a). The mammals in the zoological culture of the Mbuti pygmies in north-eastern Zaire. *Hystrix (n.s.)* **1**: 1-83.

Carpaneto, G.M. & Germi, F.P. (1989b). Mustelidae and Viverridae from north-eastern Zaire: ethnozoological research and conservation. *Small Carniv. Conserv.* **1**: 2-4.

Carpenter, G.P. (1970). Some observations on the rusty-spotted genet (*Genetta rubiginosa zuluensis*). *Lammergeyer* **11**: 60-63.

Carr, M., Yoshizaki, J., van Manen, F.T., Pelton, M.R., Huygens, O.C., Hayashi, H. & Maekawa, M. (2002). A multiscale assessment of habitat use by Asiatic black bears in central Japan. *Ursus* **13**: 1-9.

Carreno, R.A., Reif, K.E. & Nadler, S.A. (2005). A new species of *Skrjabingylus* Petrov, 1927 (Nematoda: Metastrongyloidea) from the frontal sinuses of the hooded skunk, *Mephitis macroura* (Mustelidae). *J. Parasitol.* **91**: 102-107.

Carrillo-Jimenez, E. & Vaughan, C. (1993). Behavioral change in *Procyon* spp. (Carnivora: Procyonidae) caused by tourist visitation in a Costa Rican wildlife area. *Rev. Biol. Trop.* **41**: 843-848.

Carrillo-Rubio, E. & Lafon, A. (2004). Neotropical river otter micro-habitat preference in west-central Chihuahua, Mexico. *IUCN Otter Special. Group Bull.* **21**: 7-11.

Carroll, R.I. (1988). *Vertebrate Paleontology and Evolution.* Freeman, New York.

Carroll, R.I. (1997). *Patterns and Processes of Vertebrate Evolution.* Cambridge University Press, New York.

Carter, S.K. & Rosas, F.C.W. (1997). Biology and conservation of the giant otter *Pteronura brasiliensis. Mammal Rev.* **27**: 1-26.

Carugati, C., Rowe-Rowe, D.T. & Perrin, M.R. (1995). Habitat use by two species of otters in the Natal Drakensberg (South Africa) - preliminary results. *Habitat* **11**: 25-26.

Carvalho, C.T. & Vasconcellos, L.E.M. (1995). Disease, food and reproduction of the maned wolf - *Chrysocyon brachyurus* (Illiger) (Carnivora, Canidae) in southeast Brazil. *Rev. Bras. Zool.* **12**: 627-640.

Carvalho, J.C. & Gomes, P. (2004). Feeding resources partitioning among four sympatric carnivores in the Peneda-Geres National Park (Portugal). *J. Zool.* **263**: 275-283.

Castilla, J.C. (1981). La nutria de mar chilena, especie en extinción. *Creces* **2**: 31-34.

Cat News (2006). Status and conservation of the leopard on the Arabian Peninsula. *Special Issue* **1**: 4-47.

Catania, K.C. (1999). A nose that looks like a hand and acts like an eye: the unusual mechanosensory system of the star-nosed mole. *J. Comp. Physiol.* **185**: 367-372.

Catesby, M. (1731-1743). *The Natural History of Carolina, Florida and the Bahama Islands.* B. White, London.

Catling, P.C., Corbett, L.K. & Newsome, A.E. (1992). Reproduction in captive and wild dingoes *Canis familiaris dingo* in temperate and arid environments of Australia. *Wildl. Res.* **19**: 195-205.

Cavallini, P. (1992a). *Herpestes pulverulentus. Mammal. Species* **409**: 1-4.

Cavallini, P. (1992b). Spatial organization of the yellow mongoose *Cynictis penicillata* in a coastal area. *Ethology, Ecology & Evolution* **5**: 501-509.

Cavallini, P. (1993). Activity of the yellow mongoose *Cynictis penicillata* in a coastal area. *Zeitschrift für Säugetierkunde* **58**: 281-285.

Cavallini, P. (1995). Variation in the body size of the red fox. *Ann. Zool. Fennici* **32**: 421-427.

Cavallini, P. & Nel, J.A.J. (1990a). The feeding ecology of the Cape grey mongoose, *Galerella pulverulenta* (Wagner 1839) in a coastal area. *Afr. J. Ecol.* **28**: 123-130.

Cavallini, P. & Nel, J.A.J. (1990b). Ranging behaviour of the Cape grey mongoose (*Galerella pulverulenta*) in a coastal area. *J. Zool., London* **222**: 353-362.

Cavallini, P. & Nel, J.A.J. (1995). Comparative behavior and ecology of two sympatric mongoose species (*Cynictis penicillata* and *Galerella pulverulenta*). *South Afr. J. Zool.* **30**: 46-49.

Cavallini, P. & Serafini, P. (1995). Winter diet of the small Indian mongoose, *Herpestes auropunctatus,* on an Adriatic island. *J. Mammal.* **76**: 569-574.

Ceballos, G. & Miranda, A. (1986). *Los Mamíferos de Chamela, Jalisco: Manual de Campo.* Universidad Nacional Autónoma de México, México City.

Ceballos, G. & Oliva, G. eds. (2005). *Los Mamíferos Silvestres de México.* 1st edition. Fondo de Cultura Económica, México, D.F.

Centro de Datos para la Conservación (1989). *Lista de Mamíferos del Coto de Caza "El Angolo".* CDC, Lima, Peru.

Cervantes, F., Loredo, J. & Vargas, J. (2002). Abundance of sympatric skunks (Mustelidae: carnivora) in Oaxaca, Mexico. *J. Trop. Ecol.* **18**: 463-469.

Chakraborty, S. (1978). The rusty-spotted cat, *Felis rubiginosa* I. Geoffroy, in Jammu and Kashmir. *J. Bombay Nat. Hist. Soc.* **75**: 478-479.

Chamberlain, M.J. (2002). Movements and space use of gray foxes *Urocyon cinereoargenteus* following mate loss. *Amer. Midl. Nat.* **147**: 409-412.

Chamberlain, M.J. & Leopold, B.D. (2000). Spatial use patterns, seasonal habitat selection, and interactions among adult gray foxes in Mississippi. *J. Wildl. Management* **64**: 742-751.

Chamberlain, M.J., Hodges, K.M., Leopold, B.D. & Wilson, T.S. (1999). Survival and cause-specific mortality of adult raccoons in central Mississippi. *J. Wildl. Management* **63**: 880-888.

Chan, S., Au, J. & Young, L. (1992). A new species of mammals for Hong Kong: the javan mongoose (*Herpestes javanicus*). *Mem. Hong Kong Nat. Hist. Soc.* **19**: 137-138.

Chapin, T.G., Harrison, D.J. & Phillips, D.M. (1997). Seasonal habitat selection by marten in an untrapped forest preserve. *J. Wildl. Management* **61**: 707-717.

Chapman, F.M. (1935). José: two Months from the life of a Barro Colorado coati. *Nat. Hist.* **35**: 299-309.

Chapron, G., Veron, G. & Jennings, A.P. (2006). New carnivore species in Borneo may not be new. Conservation News. *Oryx* **40**: 134.

Chapuis, G. (1966). Contribution à l'étude de l'artère carotide interne des Carnivores. *Mammalia* **30**: 88-96.

Charles-Dominique, P. (1977). *Ecology and Behaviour of Nocturnal Primates. Prosimians of Equatorial West Africa.* Columbia University Press, New York.

Charles-Dominique, P. (1978). Ecologie et vie sociale de *Nandinia binotata* (Carnivores, Viverridés): comparaison avec les prosimiens sympatriques du Gabon. *Terre Vie* **32**: 477-528.

Charlton, K.M., Webster, W.A. & Casey, G.A. (1991). Skunk rabies. Pp. 307-324 in: Baer, G.M. ed. (1991). *The Natural History of Rabies.* 2nd edition. CRC Press, Boca Raton, Florida.

Chasen, F.N. (1940). A handlist of Malaysian mammals: A systematic list of the mammals of the Malay Peninsula, Sumatra, Borneo, and Java, including the adjacent small islands. *Bull. Raffles Mus.* **15**: 1-209.

Chauvet, J.M., Deschamps, E.B. & Hillaire, C. (1996). *Chauvet Cave. The Discovery of the World's Oldest Paintings.* Thames & Hudson, London.

Chavan, S.A. (1987). Status of wild cats in Gujarat. *Tigerpaper* **14**: 21-24.

Chavan, S.A., Patel, C.D., Pawar, S.V., Gogate, N.S. & Pandya, N.P. (1991). Sighting of the rusty spotted cat *Felis rubiginosa* (Geoffroy) in Shoolpaneshwar Sanctuary, Gujarat. *J. Bombay Nat. Hist. Soc.* **88**: 107-108.

Chebez, J.C. (1994). *Los que se Van. Especies Argentinas en Peligro.* Editorial Albatros, Buenos Aires.

Chebez, J.C. (2008). *Los que se Van. Fauna Argentina Amenazada.* Tomo 3. Editorial Albatros, Buenos Aires.

Chéhébar, C. (1986). The huillin in Argentina. *IUCN Otter Special. Group Bull.* **1**: 17-18.

Chéhébar, C., Gallur, A., Giannico, G., Gottelli, M.D. & Yorio, P. (1986). A survey of the southern river otter *Lutra provocax* in Lanin, Puelo and Los Alerces National Parks, Argentina, and evaluation of its conservation status. *Biol. Conserv.* **38**: 293-304.

Chellam, R. (1987). Asiatic lion study. *Cat News* **6**: 31.

Chellam, R. (1993). *Ecology of the Asiatic Lion (*Panthera leo persica*).* PhD thesis, Saurasthra University, Rajkot, India.

Chellam, R. & Johnsingh, A.J.T. (1993). Management of Asiatic lions in the Gir Forest, India. Page 65 in: Dunstone, N. & Gorman, M.L. eds. (1993). *Mammals as Predators. Proceedings of the Symposium of the Zoological Society of London.* Clarendon, Oxford.

Chen, H. (1988). Update on otter-civet. *Malay. Naturalist* **41**: 67.

Chen, N., Li, L., Shan, S., Yugeng, Y. & Sanderson, J. (2005). Status of the Chinese mountain cat in Sichuan Province (China). *Cat News* **43**: 25-27.

Cherem, J.J., Kammers, M., Ghizoni, I.R. & Martins, A. (2007). Running over of mammals on roads of Santa Catarina state, southern Brazil. *Biotemas* **20**: 81-96.

Chesemore, D.L. (1975). Ecology of the Arctic fox *Alopex lagopus* in North America - a review. Pp. 143-163 in: Fox, M.W. ed. (1975). *The Wild Canids. Their Systematics, Behavioral Ecology and Evolution.* Van Nostrand Rheinhold Co., New York.

Chhangani, A.K. (2002). Food and feeding of sloth bear (*Melursus ursinus*) in Aravalli Hills of Rajasthan, India. *Tigerpaper* **29**: 1-6.

Chirkova, A.F. (1952). [Method and some results of accounts of red fox and corsac fox. Pp. 179-203 in: *Methods of Accounts Numbering and Geographical Distribution of Land Vertebrates*]. Nauka, Moscow, USSR. In Russian.

Chivers, D.J. & Hladik, C.M. (1980). Morphology of the gastrointestinal tract in primates: Comparisons with other mammals in relation to diet. *J. Morphol.* **166**: 337-386.

Chivers, D.J. & Langer, P. eds. (1994). *The Digestive System in Mammals: Food, Form and Function.* Cambridge University Press, Cambridge.

Choate, J.R., Fleharty, E.D. & Little, R.J. (1973). Status of the spotted skunk, *Spilogale putorius*, in Kansas. *Trans. Kansas Acad. Sci.* **76**: 226-233.

Chomel, B.B. (1999). Rabies exposure and clinical disease in animals. Pp. 20-26 in: *Rabies Guidelines for Medical Professionals.* Veterinary Learning Systems, Trenton, New Jersey.

Choudhury, A. (1997a). The distribution and status of small carnivores (mustelids, viverrids and herpestids) in Assam, India. *Small Carniv. Conserv.* **16**: 25-26.

Choudhury, A. (1997b). Small carnivores (mustelids, viverrids, herpestids and one ailurid) in Arunachal Pradesh, India. *Small Carniv. Conserv.* **17**: 7-9.

Choudhury, A. (2000). Some small carnivore records from Nagaland, India. *Small Carniv. Conserv.* **23**: 7-9.

Choudhury, A. (2001). An overview of the status and conservation of the red panda *Ailurus fulgens* in India, with reference to its global status. *Oryx* **35**: 250-259.

Choudhury, A. (2002). Some recent records of the spotted linsang *Prionodon pardicolor* from India. *Small Carniv. Conserv.* **27**: 12.

Christiansen, P. (1999a). Scaling of the long bones to body mass in terrestrial mammals. *J. Morph.* **239**: 167-190.

Christiansen, P. (1999b). What size were *Arctodus simus* and *Ursus spelaeus* (Carnivora: Ursidae)? *Ann. Zool. Fennici* **36**: 93-102.

Christiansen, P. (2007). Evolutionary implications of bite mechanics and feeding ecology in bears. *J. Zool., London* **272**: 423-443.

Christiansen, P. (2008). Species distinction and evolutionary differences in the clouded leopard (*Neofelis nebulosa*) and Diard's clouded leopard (*Neofelis diardi*). *J. Mammal.* **89**: 1435-1446.

Christopher, G. & Jayson, E.A. (1996). Sightings of Nilgiri marten (*Martes gwatkinski* Horsfield) at Peppara Wildlife Sanctuary and silent Valley National Park, Kerala, India. *Small Carniv. Conserv.* **15**: 3-4.

Chruszcz, K., Wierzbowska, I., Klasa, A., Snigorska, K. & Amirowicz, A. (2007). Occurrence and diet of Eurasian otter *Lutra lutra* (L.) in the Ojcow National Park (S Poland). *Chronmy Przyrode Ojczysta* **63**: 3-14.

Chuang, S.A. & Lee, L.L. (1997). Food habits of three carnivore species (*Viverricula indica*, *Herpestes urva* and *Melogale moschata*) in Fushan Forest, northern Taiwan. *J. Zool., London* **243**: 71-79.

Chundawat, R.S. & Rawat, G.S. (1994). Food habits of snow leopard in Ladakh, India. Pp. 127-132 in: Fox, J.L. & Du Jizeng eds. (1994). *Proceedings of the Seventh International Snow Leopard Symposium.* International Snow Leopard Trust & Chicago Zoological Society, Seattle, Washington.

Ciarniello, L.M., Boyce, M.S., Heard, D.C. & Seip, D.R. (2007). Components of grizzly bear habitat selection: density, habitats, roads, and mortality risk. *J. Wildl. Management* **71**: 1446-1457.

Clark, H.O., Newman, D.P., Murdoch, J.D., Tseng, J., Wang, Z.H. & Harris, R.B. (2008). *Vulpes ferrilata* (Carnivora: Canidae). *Mammal. Species* **821**: 1-6.

Clark, J.D., Huber, D. & Servheen, C. (2002). Bear reintroductions: lessons and challenges. *Ursus* **13**: 335-345.

Clark, T.W., Anderson, E., Douglas, C. & Strickland, M. (1987). *Martes americana. Mammal. Species* **289**: 1-8.

Clevenger, A.P. (1993a). Pine marten (*Martes martes* L.) home ranges and activity patterns on the island of Minorca, Spain. *Zeitschrift für Säugetierkunde* **58**: 137-143.

Clevenger, A.P. (1993b). Pine marten (*Martes martes* Linne, 1758) comparative feeding ecology in an island and mainland population of Spain. *Zeitschrift für Säugetierkunde* **58**: 212-224.

Clevenger, A.P. (1993c). Spring and summer food habits and habitat use of the European pine marten (*Martes martes*) on the island of Minorca, Spain. *J. Zool., London* **229**: 153-161.

Clevenger, A.P. (1995). Seasonality and relationships of food resource use of *Martes martes*, *Genetta genetta* and *Felis catus* in the Balearic islands. *Rev. Écol. (Terre Vie)* **50**: 109-131.

Clevenger, A.P. (1996). Frugivory of *Martes martes* and *Genetta genetta* in an insular Mediterranean habitat. *Rev. Écol. (Terre Vie)* **51**: 19-28.

Clutton-Brock, J. (1988). *The British Museum Book of Cats.* British Museum Publications, London.

Clutton-Brock, J. (1999). *The Natural History of Domestic Mammals.* 2nd edition. Cambridge University Press & The Natural History Museum, Cambridge & London.

Clutton-Brock, J. & Wilson, D.E. (2002). *Mammals.* Smithsonian Handbooks, Dorling Kindersley, New York.

Clutton-Brock, J. & Wilson, D.E. (2003). *Mammal.* Dorling-Kindersley Limited, New York.

Clutton-Brock, J., Corbet, G.B. & Hill, M. (1976). A review of the family Canidae with a classification by numerical methods. *Bull. Brit. Mus. (Nat. Hist.) Zool.* **29**: 119-199.

Clutton-Brock, T.H., Brotherton, P.N.M., O'Riain, M.J., Griffin, A.S., Gaynor, D., Kansky, R., Sharpe, L. & McIlrath, G.M. (2001). Contributions to cooperative rearing in meerkats. *Anim. Behav.* **61**: 705-710.

Clutton-Brock, T.H., Brotherton, P.N.M., O'Riain, M.J., Griffin, A.S., Gaynor, D., Sharpe, L., Kansky, R., Manser, M.B. & McIlrath, G.M. (2000). Individual contributions to babysitting in a cooperative mongoose, *Suricata suricatta*. *Proc. Royal Soc. London (Ser. B Biol. Sci.)* **267**: 301-305.

Clutton-Brock, T.H., Brotherton, P.N.M., Russell, A.F., O'Riain, M.J., Gaynor, D., Kansky, R., Griffin, A., Manser, M., Sharpe, L., McIlrath, G.M., Small, T., Moss, A. & Monfort, S. (2001). Cooperation, control, and concession in meerkat groups. *Science* **291**: 478-481.

Clutton-Brock, T.H., Brotherton, P.N.M., Smith, R., McIlrath, G.M., Kansky, R., Gaynor, D., O'Riain, M.J. & Skinner, J.D. (1998). Infanticide and expulsion of females in a cooperative mammal. *Proc. Royal Soc. London (Ser. B Biol. Sci.)* **265**: 2291-2295.

Clutton-Brock, T.H., Gaynor, D., Kansky, R., MacColl, A.D.C., McIlrath, G., Chadwick, P., Brotherton, P.N.M., O'Riain, J.M., Manser, M. & Skinner, J.D. (1998). Costs of cooperative behaviour in suricates (*Suricata suricatta*). *Proc. Royal Soc. London (Ser. B Biol. Sci.)* **265**: 185-190.

Clutton-Brock, T.H., Gaynor, D., McIlrath, G.M., Maccoll, A.D.C., Kansky, R., Chadwick, P., Manser, M., Skinner, J.D. & Brotherton, P.N.M. (1999). Predation, group size and mortality in a cooperative mongoose, *Suricata suricatta*. *J. Anim. Ecol.* **68**: 672-683.

Clutton-Brock, T.H., Hodge, S.J., Spong, G., Russell, A.F., Jordan, N.R., Bennett, N.C., Sharpe, L.L. & Manser, M.B. (2006). Intrasexual competition and sexual selection in cooperative mammals. *Nature* **444**: 1065-1068.

Clutton-Brock, T.H., Maccoll, A., Chadwick, P., Gaynor, D., Kansky, R. & Skinner, J.D. (1999). Reproduction and survival of suricates (*Suricata suricatta*) in the southern Kalahari. *Afr. J. Ecol.* **37**: 69-80.

Clutton-Brock, T.H., O'Riain, M.J., Brotherton, P.N.M., Gaynor, D., Kansky, R., Griffin, A.S. & Manser, M. (1999). Selfish sentinels in cooperative mammals. *Science* **284**: 1640-1644.

Clutton-Brock, T.H., Russell, A.F. & Sharpe, L.L. (2003). Meerkat helpers do not specialize in particular activities. *Anim. Behav.* **66**: 531-540.

Clutton-Brock, T.H., Russell, A.F. & Sharpe, L.L. (2004). Behavioural tactics of breeders in cooperative meerkats. *Anim. Behav.* **68**: 1029-1040.

Clutton-Brock, T.H., Russell, A.F., Sharpe, L.L., Brotherton, P.N.M., McIlrath, G.M., White, S. & Cameron, E.Z. (2001). Effects of helpers on juvenile development and survival in meerkats. *Science* **293**: 2446-2449.

Clutton-Brock, T.H., Russell, A.F., Sharpe, L.L. & Jordan, N.R. (2005). 'False feeding' and aggression in meerkat societies. *Anim. Behav.* **69**: 1273-1284.

Clutton-Brock, T.H., Russell, A.F., Sharpe, L.L., Young, A.J., Balmforth, Z. & McIlrath, G.M. (2002). Evolution and development of sex differences in cooperative behavior in meerkats. *Science* **297**: 253-256.

Coates-Estrada, R. & Estrada, A. (1986). Fruiting and frugivores at a strangler fig in the tropical rain forest of Los Tuxtlas, Mexico. *J. Trop. Ecol.* **2**: 349-357.

Coblentz, B.E. & Coblentz, B.A. (1985). Reproduction and the annual fat cycle of the mongoose on St John, United States Virgin-Islands. *J. Mammal.* **66**: 560-563.

Cochrane, J.C., Kirby, J.D., Jones, I.G., Conner, L.M. & Warren, R.J. (2006). Spatial organization of adult bobcats in a longleaf pine-wiregrass ecosystem in southwestern Georgia. *Southeast. Nat.* **5**: 711-724.

Coe, M. (1975). Mammalian ecological studies on Mt. Nimba, Liberia. *Mammalia* **39**: 523-582.

Coetzee, C.G. (1977). Order Carnivora. Part 8. Pp. 1-42 in: Meester, J. & Setzer, H.W. eds. (1977). *The Mammals of Africa: an Identification Manual.* Smithsonian Institution Press, Washington, D.C.

Coetzee, P.W. (1979). *Present Distribution and Status of Some of the Mammals of Albany.* Albany Divisional Council and Grahamstown Municipality, South Africa.

Cofré, H. & Marquet, P.A. (1999). Conservation status, rarity, and geographic priorities for conservation of Chilean mammals: an assessment. *Biol. Conserv.* **88**: 53-68.

Cohen, J.A. (1977). A review of the biology of the dhole or Asiatic wild dog *Cuon alpinus* Pallas. *Anim. Regul. Stud.* **1**: 141-158.

Cohen, J.A. (1978). *Cuon alpinus. Mammal. Species* **100**: 1-3.

Cohen, J.A. & Fox, M.W. (1976). Vocalizations in wild canids and possible effects of domestication. *Behav. Proceedings* **1**: 77-92.

Coimbra-Filho, A.F. (1966). Notes on the reproduction and diet of Azaras fox *Cerdocyon thous azarae* and the hoary fox *Dusicyon vetulus* at Río de Janeiro Zoo. *Int. Zoo Yb.* **6**: 168-169.

Collier, G.E. & O'Brien, S.J. (1985). A molecular phylogeny of the Felidae: immunological distance. *Evolution* **39(3)**: 473-487.

Collins, P.W. (1991a). Interaction between island foxes *Urocyon littoralis* and Indians on islands off the coast of Southern California: I. Morphologic and archaeological evidence of human assisted dispersal. *J. Ethnobiol.* **11(1)**: 51-81.

Collins, P.W. (1991b). Interaction between island foxes *Urocyon littoralis* and native Americans on islands off the coast of Southern California: II. Ethnographic, archaeological and historical evidence. *J. Ethnobiol.* **11(2)**: 205-229.

Collins, P.W. (1993). Taxonomic and biogeographic relationships of the island fox *Urocyon littoralis* and gray fox *U. cinereoargenteus* from Western North America. Pp. 351-390+ in: Hochberg, F.G. ed. (1993). *Third California Islands Symposium: Recent Advances in Research on the California Islands.* Santa Barbara Museum of Natural History, Santa Barbara, California.

Collins, P.W. & Laughrin, L.L. (1979). Vertebrate zoology: the island fox on San Miguel Island. Pp. 12.1-12.47 in: Power, D.M. ed. (1979). *Natural Resources Study of the Channel Islands National Monument, California.* Prepared for the National Park Service, Denver Service Center by the Santa Barbara Museum of Natural History, Santa Barbara, California.

Colon, C.P. (1996). Ecology of the Malay civet (*Viverra tangalunga*) in logged and unlogged forests. *Small Carniv. Conserv.* **15**: 17.

Colon, C.P. (1999). *Ecology of the Malay Civet (*Viverra tangalunga*) in a Logged and an Unlogged Forest in Sabah, East Malaysia.* PhD thesis, Fordham University, New York.

Colon, C.P. (2002). Ranging behaviour and activity of the Malay civet (*Viverra tangalunga*) in a logged and an unlogged forest in Danum Valley, East Malaysia. *J. Zool., London* **257**: 473-485.

Colyn, M. (1984). *Crossarchus ansorgei* Thomas 1910 (Carnivora, Viverridae), seconde recolte en Republique du Zaire. *Ann. Fac. Sci., Kisangani* **2**: 79-86.

Colyn, M. & Van Rompaey, H. (1990). *Crossarchus ansorgei nigricolor,* a new subspecies of Ansorges Cusimanse (Carnivora, Viverridae) from South-Central Zaire. *Zeitschrift fur Säugetierkunde* **55**: 94-98.

Colyn, M. & Van Rompaey, H. (1994a). A biogeographic study of cusimanses (*Crossarchus*) (Carnivora, Herpestidae) in the Zaire Basin. *J. Biogeogr.* **21**: 479-489.

Colyn, M. & Van Rompaey, H. (1994b). Morphometric evidence of the monotypic status of the African long-nosed mongoose *Xenogale naso* (Carnivora, Herpestidae). *Belg. J. Zool.* **124**: 175-192.

Colyn, M., Dudu, A. & Mankoto Ma Mbaelele, M. (1987). Exploitation du petit et moyen gibier des forets ombrophiles du Zaire. 1. Consomation qualitative dans le milieu rural. 2. Analyse de l'effet relatif de la commercialization du gibier à Kisangani (Haut-Zaire). *Nature Faune* **3**: 22-39.

Colyn, M., Dufour, S., Conde, P.C. & Van Rompaey, H. (2004). The importance of small carnivores in forest bushmeat hunting in the Classified Forest of Diecke, Guinea. *Small Carniv. Conserv.* **31**: 15-18.

Colyn, M., Dufour, S. & Van Rompaey, H. (2000). First observation of the Gambian mongoose, *Mungos gambianus,* in Guinea (Conakry). *Small Carniv. Conserv.* **23**: 10.

Compton, L.A., Clarke, J.A., Seidensticker, J. & Ingrisano, D.R. (2001). Acoustic characteristics of white-nosed coati vocalizations: a test of motivation-structural rules. *J. Mammal.* **82**: 1054-1058.

Conroy, J., Melisch, R. & Chanin, P. (1998). The distribution and status of the Eurasian otter (*Lutra lutra*) in Asia - a preliminary review. *IUCN Otter Special. Group Bull.* **15(1)**: 15-30.

Conservation Breeding Specialist Group (SSC/IUCN) (2002). *Evaluation et Plans de Gestion pour la Conservation (CAMP) de la Faune de Madagascar.* CBSG, Apple Valley, Minnesota.

Constantine, D.G. (1948). Great bat colonies attract predators. *Natl. Speleol. Soc. Bull.* **10**: 100.

Coonan, T. (2002). Findings of the Island Fox Conservation Working Group. Unpublished report. National Parks Service, Ventura, California.

Coonan, T. & Rutz, K. (2002). *Island Fox Captive Breeding Program.* Technical report **02-01**. Channel Islands National Park, Ventura, California.

Coope, R. (2007). A preliminary investigation of the food and feeding behaviour of pine martens *Martes martes* in productive forestry from an analysis of the contents of their scats collected in Inchnacardoch Forest, Fort Augustus. *Scottish Forestry* **61**: 3-14.

Cooper, D.M., Kershmer, E.L., Schmidt, G.A. & Garcelon, D.K. (2001). *San Clemente Loggerhead Shrike Predator Research and Management Program - 2000.* Final Report, US Navy, Natural Resources Management Branch, Southwest Division, Naval Facilities Engineering Command, San Diego. Institute for Wildlife Studies, Arcata, California.

Cooper, J. (1942). An exploratory study on African lions. *Comp. Psychol. Monogr.* **17**: 1-48.

Cooper, R.L. & Skinner, J.D. (1979). Importance of termites in the diet of the aardwolf *Proteles cristatus* in South Africa. *South Afr. J. Zool.* **14**: 5-8.

Cooper, S.M. (1989). Clan sizes of spotted hyaenas in the Savuti Region of the Chobe National Park, Botswana. *Botsw. Notes Rec.* **21**: 121-133.

Cooper, S.M. (1990). The hunting behavior of spotted hyaenas (*Crocuta crocuta*) in a region containing both sedentary and migratory populations of herbivores. *Afr. J. Ecol.* **28**: 131-141.

Cooper, S.M. (1991). Optimal hunting group size: the need for lions to defend their kills against loss to spotted hyaenas. *Afr. J. Ecol.* **29**: 130-136.

Cooper, S.M. (1993). Denning behavior of spotted hyaenas (*Crocuta crocuta*) in Botswana. *Afr. J. Ecol.* **31**: 178-180.

Cooper, S.M., Holekamp, K.E. & Smale, L. (1999). A seasonal feast: long-term analysis of feeding behavior in the spotted hyaena *Crocuta crocuta* (Erxleben). *Afr. J. Ecol.* **37**: 149-160.

Copeland, J.P. & Whitman, J.S. (2003). Wolverine. Pp. 672-682 in: Feldhamer, G.A., Thompson, B.C. & Chapman, J.A. eds. (2003). *Wild Mammals of North America: Biology, Management and Conservation.* 2nd edition. Johns Hopkins University Press, Baltimore, Maryland.

Copeland, J.P., Peek, J.M., Groves, C.R., Melquist, N.E., McKelvey, K.S., McDaniel, G.W., Long, C.D. & Harris, C.E. (2007). Seasonal habitat associations of the wolverine in central Idaho. *J. Wildl. Management* **71**: 2201-2212.

Corbet, G.B. (1978). *The Mammals of the Palaearctic Region: a Taxonomic Review.* Cornell University Press, Ithaca, New York.

Corbet, G.B. & Hill, J.E. (1992). *The Mammals of the Indomalayan Region: A Systematic Review.* Oxford University Press, Oxford.

Corbett, L.K. (1979). *Feeding Ecology and Social Organization of Wildcats (*Felis silvestris*) and Domestic Cats (*Felis catus*) in Scotland.* PhD thesis, University of Aberdeen, Aberdeen, Scotland.

Corbett, L.K. (1985). Morphological comparisons of Australian and Thai dingoes: a reappraisal of dingo status, distribution and ancestry. *Proc. Ecol. Soc. Austr.* **13**: 277-291.

Corbett, L.K. (1988). Social dynamics of a captive dingo pack: population by dominant female infanticide. *Ethology* **78**: 177-178.

Corbett, L.K. (1989). Assessing the diet of dingoes from feces: a comparison of 3 methods. *J. Wildl. Management* **53**: 343-346.

Corbett, L.K. (1995). *The Dingo in Australia and Asia.* University of New South Wales Press Ltd, Sydney.

Corbett, L.K. (2001). The conservation status of the dingo *Canis lupus dingo* in Australia, with particular reference to New South Wales: threats to pure dingoes and potential solutions. Pp. 10-19 in: Dickman, C.R. & Lunney, D. eds. (2001). *A Symposium on the Dingo.* Royal Zoological Society of New South Wales, Mosman.

Corbett, L.K. (2003). The Australian dingo. Pp. 639-647 in: Merrick, J.R., Archer, M., Hickey, G. & Lee, M. eds. (2003). *Evolution and Zoogeography of Australasian Vertebrates.* Australian Scientific Publishing Pty, Ltd. Sydney.

Corbett, L.K. (2004). Dingo *Canis lupus dingo.* Pp. 223-230 in: Sillero-Zubiri, C., Hoffmann, M. & Macdonald, D.W. eds. (2004). *Canids: Foxes, Wolves, Jackals and Dogs. Status Survey and Conservation Action Plan.* IUCN/SSC Canid Specialist Group, Gland & Cambridge.

Corbett, L.K. & Newsome, A.E. (1987). The feeding ecology of the dingo III. Dietary relationships with widely fluctuating prey populations in arid Australia: an hypothesis of alternation of predation. *Oecologia* **74**: 215-227.

Cordero-Rodríguez, G.A. & Nassar, J.M. (1999). Ecological data on *Cerdocyon thous* in Barlovento region, State of Miranda, Venezuela. *Acta Biol. Venez.* **19**: 21-26.

Corley, J.C., Fernandez, G.F., Capurro, A.F., Novaro, A.J., Funes, M.C. & Travaini, A. (1995). Selection of cricetine prey by the culpeo fox in Patagonia: a differential prey vulnerability hypothesis. *Mammalia* **59**: 315-325.

Corn, J.L. & Conroy, M.J. (1998). Estimation of density of mongooses with capture-recapture and distance sampling. *J. Mammal.* **79**: 1009-1015.

Corredor, G. & Tigreros, N. (2006). Reproduction, behaviour and biology of the giant river otter *Pteronura brasiliensis* at Cali Zoo. *Int. Zoo Yb.* **40**: 360-371.

Cosson, L., Grassman, L.L., Zubaid, A., Vellayan, S., Tillier, A. & Veron, G. (2007). Genetic diversity of captive binturongs (*Arctictis binturong,* Viverridae, Carnivora): implications for conservation. *J. Zool., London* **271**: 386-395.

Costa, C.H.N. & Courtenay, O. (2003). A new record of the hoary fox *Pseudalopex vetulus* in north Brazil. *Mammalia* **67**: 593-594.

Costello, C.M., Jones, D.E., Inman, R.M., Inman, K.H., Thompson, B.C. & Quigley, H.B. (2003). Relationship of variable mast production to American black bear reproductive parameters in New Mexico. *Ursus* **14**: 1-16.

Cotera, M. (1996). *Untersuchungen zur Ökologischen Anpassung des Wüstenfuchses Vulpes macrotis zinseri B. in Nuevo León, Mexiko.* PhD dissertation, Ludwig-Maximilians-Universität München, Munich, Germany.

Courtenay, O. (1998). *The Epidemiology and Control of Canine Visceral Leishmaniasis in Amazon Brazil.* PhD dissertation, University of London, London, UK.

Courtenay, O. & Maffei, L. (2004). Crab-eating fox *Cerdocyon thous.* Pp. 32-38 in: Sillero-Zubiri, C., Hoffmann, M. & Macdonald, D.W. eds. (2004). *Canids: Foxes, Wolves, Jackals and Dogs. Status Survey and Conservation Action Plan.* IUCN/SSC Canid Specialist Group, Gland & Cambridge.

Courtenay, O., Macdonald, D.W., Lainson, R., Shaw, J.J. & Dye, C. (1994). Epidemiology of canine leishmaniasis: a comparative serological study of dogs and foxes in Amazon Brazil. *Parasitology* **109**: 273-279.

Courtenay, O., Quinnell, R.J. & Chalmers, W.S.K. (2001). Contact rates between wild and domestic canids: no evidence of parvovirus or canine distemper virus in crab-eating foxes. *Vet. Microbiol.* **81**: 9-19.

Courtenay, O., Quinnell, R.J., Garcez, L.M. & Dye, C. (2002). Low infectiousness of a wildlife host of *Leishmania infantum*: the crab-eating fox is not important for transmission. *Parasitology* **125**: 407-414.

Courtenay, O., Santana, E.W., Johnson, P., Vasconcelos, I.A.B. & Vasconcelos, A.W. (1996). Visceral leishmaniasis in the hoary zorro *Dusicyon vetulus*: a case of mistaken identity. *Trans. Royal Soc. Trop. Med. Hyg.* **90**: 498-502.

Couturier, J. & Dutrillaux, B. (1985). Evolution chromosomique chez les carnivores. *Mammalia* **50**: 124-162.

Couturier, J., Razafimahatratra, E., Dutrillaux, B., Warter, S. & Rumpler, Y. (1986). Chromosomal evolution in the Malagasy Carnivora. I. R-banding studies of *Cryptoprocta ferox, Fossa fossana, Galidia elegans,* and *Mungotictis decemlineata. Cytogenet. Cell Genet.* **41**: 1-8.

Covell, D.F. (1992). *Ecology of the Swift Fox (*Vulpes velox*) in Southeastern Colorado.* MSc thesis, University of Wisconsin-Madison, Madison, Wisconsin.

Cowie, M. (1966). *The African Lion.* Golden, New York.

Cowles, R.B. (1938). Unusual defense postures assumed by rattlesnakes. *Copeia* **1938**: 13-16.

Crabb, W.D. (1948). The ecology and management of the prairie spotted skunk in Iowa. *Ecol. Monogr.* **18**: 201-232.

Craighead, F.C. (1976). Grizzly bear ranges and movement as determined by radiotracking. *Int. Conf. Bear Res. Management* **3**: 97-109.

Craighead, J.J., Summer, J.S. & Mitchell, J.A. (1995). *The Grizzly Bears of Yellowstone: their Ecology in the Yellowstone Ecosystem, 1959-1992*. Island Press, Washington, D.C.

Cravino, J.L., Calvar, M.E., Berruti, M.A., Fontana, N.A. & Poetti, J.C. (1997). American southern cone foxes: predators or prey? An Uruguayan study case. *J. Wildl. Res.* **2**: 107-114.

Cravino, J.L., Calvar, M.E., Poetti, J.C., Berrutti, M.A., Fontana, N.A., Brando, M.E. & Fernández, J.A. (2000). Análisis holístico de la predación en corderos: un estudio de caso, con énfasis en la acción de "zorros" (Mammalia: Canidae). *Veterinaria* **35**: 24-41.

Crawford-Cabral, J. (1970). As genetas da Africa Central. *Separata Boll. Inst. Invest. Cientifica Angola* **6**: 3-33.

Crawford-Cabral, J. (1973). As genetas da Guiné Portuguesa e de Moçambique. Pp. 134-155 in: "*Livro de Homenagem" ao Professor Fernando Frade Viegas da Costa 70° Aniversario*. Lisboa.

Crawford-Cabral, J. (1981). The classification of the genets (Carnivora, Viverridae, genus *Genetta*). *Bol. Soc. Portuguesa Ciênc. Nat.* **20**: 97-114.

Crawford-Cabral, J. (1989). Distributional data and notes on Angolan carnivores (Mammalia: Carnivora). 1. Small and median-sizes species. *Garcia de Orta, Sér. Zool., Lisboa* **14**: 3-27.

Crawford-Cabral, J. (1993). A comment on the systematic position of *Poiana*. *Small Carniv. Conserv.* **9**: 8.

Crawford-Cabral, J. (1996). The species of *Galerella* (Mammalia: Carnivora: Herpestinae) occurring in the southwestern corner of Angola. *Garcia de Orta, Sér. Zool., Lisboa* **21**(1): 7-17.

Crawford-Cabral, J. (In press). *Genetta angolensis*. In: Kingdon, J.S. & Hoffmann, M. eds. (In press). *The Mammals of Africa*. Vol. 5. Carnivores, Pangolins, Rhinos and Equids. Academic Press, Amsterdam.

Crawford-Cabral, J. & Fernandes, C. (1999). A comment on the nomenclature of the rusty-spotted genet. *Small Carniv. Conserv.* **21**: 12.

Crawford-Cabral, J. & Fernandes, C. (2001). *The Rusty-spotted Genets as a Group with Three Species in Southern Africa (Carnivora: Viverridae)*. Proceedings of the 8th African Small Mammal Symposium, IRD ed., Paris.

Crawford-Cabral, J. & Pacheco, A.P. (1992). Are the large-spotted and the rusty-spotted genets separate species (Carnivora, Viverridae, genus *Genetta*). *Garcia de Orta, Sér. Zool., Lisboa* **16**: 7-17.

Crawshaw, P.G. (1995). *Comparative Ecology of Ocelot (Felis pardalis) and Jaguar (Panthera onca) in a Protected Subtropical Forest in Brazil and Argentina*. PhD dissertation, University of Florida, Gainesville, Florida.

Crawshaw, P.G. & Quigley, H.B. (1989). Notes on ocelot movement and activity in the Pantanal region, Brazil. *Biotropica* **21**: 377-379.

Crawshaw, P.G. & Quigley, H.B. (1991). Jaguar spacing, activity, and habitat use in a seasonally flooded environment in Brazil. *J. Zool., London* **223**: 357-370.

Creel, S.R. (1996). Behavioural endocrinology and social organisation in dwarf mongooses. Pp. 46-77 in: Gittleman, J. ed. (1996). *Carnivore Behaviour, Ecology and Evolution*. Cornell University Press, Ithaca, New York.

Creel, S.R. (2001). Tough at the top. Pp. 138-139 in: Macdonald, D. ed. (2001). *The New Encyclopedia of Mammals*. Oxford University Press, Oxford.

Creel, S.R. (2005). Dominance, aggression and glucocorticoid levels in social carnivores. *J. Mammal.* **86**: 255-264.

Creel, S.R. (2006). Recovery of the Florida panther – genetic rescues, demographic rescue, or both? Response to Pimm *et al.* (2006). *Anim. Conserv.* **9**: 125-126.

Creel, S.R. (In press). *Helogale parvula*. In: Kingdon, J.S. & Hoffmann, M. eds. (In press). *The Mammals of Africa*. Vol. 5. Carnivores, Pangolins, Rhinos and Equids. Academic Press, Amsterdam.

Creel, S.R. & Creel, N.M. (1991). Energetics, reproductive suppression and obligate communal breeding in carnivores. *Behav. Ecol. Sociobiol.* **28**: 263-270.

Creel, S.R. & Creel, N.M. (1995). Communal hunting and pack size in African wild dogs, *Lycaon pictus*. *Anim. Behav.* **63**: 1325-1339.

Creel, S.R. & Creel, N.M. (2002). *The African Wild Dog: Behavior, Ecology and Conservation*. Princeton University Press, Princeton, New Jersey.

Creel, S.R. & Waser, P.M. (1991). Failures of reproductive suppression in dwarf mongooses (*Helogale parvula*): accident or adaptation? *Behav. Ecol.* **2**: 7-15.

Creel, S.R. & Waser, P.M. (1994). Inclusive fitness and reproductive strategies in dwarf mongooses. *Behav. Ecol. Sociobiol.* **5**: 339-348.

Creel, S.R. & Waser, P.M. (1997). Variation in reproductive suppression among dwarf mongooses: interplay between mechanisms and evolution. Pp. 150-170 in: Solomon, N.G. & French, J.A. eds. (1997). *Cooperative Breeding in Mammals*. University Press, Cambridge.

Creel, S.R., Creel, N.M., Mills, M.G.L. & Monfort, S.L. (1997). Rank and reproduction in cooperatively breeding African wild dogs: behavioral and endocrine correlates. *Behav. Ecol.* **8**: 298-306.

Creel, S.R., Creel, N.M., Munson, L., Sanderlin, D. & Appel, M.J.G. (1997). Serosurvey for selected viral diseases and demography of African wild dogs in Tanzania. *J. Wildl. Diseases* **33**: 823-832.

Creel, S.R., Creel, N.M., Wildt, D.E. & Monfort, S.L. (1992). Behavioral and endocrine mechanisms of reproductive suppression in Serengeti dwarf mongooses. *Anim. Behav.* **43**: 231-245.

Creel, S.R., Monfort, S.L., Creel, N.M., Wildt, D.E. & Waser, P.M. (1995). Pregnancy, estrogens and future reproductive success in Serengeti dwarf mongooses. *Anim. Behav.* **50**: 1132-1135.

Creel, S.R., Monfort, S.L., Wildt, D.E. & Waser, P.M. (1991). Spontaneous lactation is an adaptive result of pseudopregnancy. *Nature (London)* **351**: 660-662.

Creel, S.R., Wildt, D.E. & Monfort, S.L. (1993). Aggression, reproduction, and androgens in wild dwarf mongooses - a test of the Challenge Hypothesis. *Amer. Nat.* **141**: 816-825.

Crespo, J.A. (1971). Ecología del zorro gris *Dusicyon gymnocercus antiquus* (Ameghino) en la provincia de La Pampa. *Rev. Mus. Arg. Cien. Nat. Bernardino Rivadavia, Ecologia* **5**: 147-205.

Crespo, J.A. (1975). Ecology of the Pampas grey fox and the large fox (culpeo). Pp. 179-190 in: Fox, M.W. ed. (1975). *The Wild Canids*. Van Norstrand Reinhold Company, New York.

Crespo, J.A. & de Carlo, J.M. (1963). Estudio ecológico de una población de zorros colorados, *Dusicyon culpaeus culpaeus* (Molina) en el oeste de la provincia de Neuquén. *Rev. Mus. Arg. Cien. Nat. Bernardino Rivadavia, Ecologia* **1**: 1-55.

Crompton, A.W. & Hiiemae, K.M. (1969). How mammalian molar teeth work. *Discovery* **5**: 23-34.

Crompton, A.W. & Parker, P. (1978). Evolution of the mammalian masticatory apparatus. *Amer. Sci.* **66**: 192-201.

Crooks, K.R. & Van Vuren, D. (1995). Resource utilization by two insular endemic mammalian carnivores, the island fox and island spotted skunk. *Oecologia* **104**: 301-307.

Crooks, K.R. & Van Vuren, D. (1996). Spatial organization of the island fox (*Urocyon littoralis*) on Santa Cruz Island, California. *J. Mammal.* **77**: 801-806.

Crowe, D.M. (1975). Aspects of aging, growth, and reproduction of bobcats from Wyoming. *J. Mammal.* **56**: 177-198.

Cuaron, A.D., Martinez-Morales, M.A., McFadden, K.W., Valenzuela, D. & Gompper, M.E. (2004). The status of dwarf carnivores on Cozumel Island, Mexico. *Biodiversity & Conservation* **13**: 317-331.

Cuesta, F., Peralvo, M.F. & van Manen, F.T. (2003). Andean bear habitat use in the Oyacachi River Basin, Ecuador. *Ursus* **14**: 198-209.

Cugnasse, J.M. & Riols, C. (1984). Contribution à la connaissance de l'écologie de la genette (*Genetta genetta* L.) dans quelques départements du sud de la France. *Gibier Faune Sauvage* **1**: 25-55.

Culver, M., Hedrick, P.W., Murphy, K., O'Brien, S. & Hornocker, M.G. (2008). Estimation of the bottleneck size in Florida panthers. *Anim. Conserv.* doi:10.1111/j.1469-1795.2007.00154.x

Culver, M., Johnson, W.E., Pecon-Slattery, J. & O'Brien, S.J. (2000). Genomic ancestry of the American puma (*Puma concolor*). *J. Heredity* **91**: 186-197.

Cunha, G.R., Place, N.J., Baskin, L., Conley, A., Weldele, M., Cunha, T.J., Wang, Y.Z., Cao, M. & Glickman, S.E. (2005). The ontogeny of the urogenital system of the spotted hyena (*Crocuta crocuta* Erxleben). *Biol. Reprod.* **73**: 554-564.

Cunningham, M.W., Dunbar, M.R., Buergelt, C.D., Homer, B.C., Roelke-Parker, M.E., Taylor, S.K., King, R., Citino, S.B. & Glass, C. (1999). Atrial septal defects in Florida Panthers. *J. Wildl. Diseases* **35**: 519-530.

Cuzin, F. (1996). Répartition actuelle et statut des grands mammifères sauvages du Maroc (Primates, Carnivores, Artiodactyles). *Mammalia* **60**: 101-124.

Cuzin, F. & Lenain, D.M. (2004). Rüppell's fox *Vulpes rueppellii*. Pp. 201-205 in: Sillero-Zubiri, C., Hoffmann, M. & Macdonald, D.W. eds. (2004). *Canids: Foxes, Wolves, Jackals and Dogs. Status Survey and Conservation Action Plan*. IUCN/SSC Canid Specialist Group, Gland & Cambridge.

Cypher, B.L. & Spencer, K.A. (1998). Competitive interactions between coyotes and San Joaquin kit foxes. *J. Mammal.* **79**: 204-214.

Cypher, B.L., Warrick, G.D., Otten, M.R.M., O'Farrell, T.P., Berry, W.H., Harris, C.E., Kato, T.T., McCue, P.M., Scrivner, J.H. & Zoellick, B.W. (2000). Population dynamics of San Joaquin kit foxes at the Naval Petroleum Reserves in California. *Wildl. Monogr.* **145**: 1-43.

Czetwertynski, S.M., Boyce, M.S. & Schmiegelow, F.K. (2007). Effects of hunting on demographic parameters of American black bears. *Ursus* **18**: 1-18.

Daciuk, J. (1974). Notas faunísticas y bioecológicas de Península Valdés y Patagonia. XII. Mamíferos colectados y observados en la Península Valdés y zona litoral de los golfos San José y Nuevo (Provincia de Chubut, República Argentina). *Physis (Secc. C.)* **33**: 23-39.

Dahle, B. & Swenson, J.E. (2003a). Home ranges in adult Scandinavian brown bears (*Ursus arctos*): effect of mass, sex, reproductive category, population density and habitat type. *J. Zool., London* **260**: 329-335.

Dahle, B. & Swenson, J.E. (2003b). Factors influencing length of maternal care in brown bears (*Ursus arctos*) and its effect on offspring. *Behav. Ecol. Sociobiol.* **54**: 352-358.

Dahle, B. & Swenson, J.E. (2003c). Seasonal range size in relation to reproductive strategies in brown bears *Ursus arctos*. *J. Anim. Ecol.* **72**: 660-667.

Daily, G.C., Ceballos, G., Pacheco, J., Suzan, G. & Sanchez-Azofeifa, A. (2003). Countryside biogeography of neotropical mammals: conservation opportunities in agricultural landscapes of Costa Rica. *Conserv. Biol.* **17**: 1814-1826.

Dalerum, F. (2007). Phylogenetic reconstruction of carnivore social organizations. *J. Zool.* **273**: 90-97.

Dalerum, F., Tannerfeldt, M., Elmhagen, B., Becker, D. & Angerbjörn, A. (2002). Distribution, morphology and use of Arctic fox dens in Sweden. *Wildl. Biol.* **8**: 187-194.

Dalponte, J.C. (1997). Diet of the hoary fox *Lycalopex vetulus* in Mato Grosso, Brazil. *Mammalia* **61**: 537-546.

Dalponte, J.C. (2003). *História Natural, Comportamento e Conservação de Raposa-do-Campo Pseudalopex vetulus (Canidae)*. PhD dissertation, Universidade de Brasília, DF, Brazil.

Dalponte, J.C. & Courtenay, O. (2004). Hoary fox *Pseudalopex vetulus*. Pp. 72-76 in: Sillero-Zubiri, C., Hoffmann, M. & Macdonald, D.W. eds. (2004). *Canids: Foxes, Wolves, Jackals and Dogs. Status Survey and Conservation Action Plan*. IUCN/SSC Canid Specialist Group, Gland & Cambridge.

Dalquest, W.W. (1953). *Mammals of the Mexican State of San Luis Potosi*. Louisiana State University Press, Baton Rouge, Louisiana.

Dalrymple, G.H. & Bass, O.L. (1996). The diet of the Florida panther in Everglades National Park, Florida. *Bull. Florida Mus. Nat. Hist.* **39**: 173-193.

Dammerman, K.W. (1939). On prehistoric mammals from South Celebes. *Treubia* **17**: 63-72.

Dang, N.X. & Anh, P.T. (1997). New information on the reproduction of Owston's palm civet, *Chrotogale owstoni*, Thomas 1912. *Small Carniv. Conserv.* **16**: 28-29.

Dang, N.X. & Evghenjeva, T.P. (1990). Morphology of scent glands of viverrids in Vietnam. Pp. 29-34 in: Anon. (1990). *Selected Collection of Scientific Reports on Ecology and Biological Resources (1986-1990)*. National Center for Scientific Research of Vietnam, Institute of Ecology and Biological Resources, Hanoi.

Dang, N.X., Anh, P.T. & Huynh, D.H. (1992). The biology and status of Owston's palm civet in Vietnam. *Small Carniv. Conserv.* **6**: 5-6.

Dang, N.X., Anh, P.T., Nhu, N.B. & Chan, L. (1991). Owston's palm civet, *Chrotogale owstoni* in captivity. *Small Carniv. Conserv.* **4**: 7.

Daniels, M.J. & Corbett, L. (2003). Redefining introgressed protected mammals - when is a wildcat a wild cat and a dingo a wild dog? *Wildl. Res.* **30**: 213-218.

Daniels, M.J., Balharry, D., Hirst, D., Kitchener, A.C. & Aspinall, R.J. (1998). Morphological and pelage characteristics of wild living cats in Scotland: implications for defining the "wildcat". *J. Zool., London* **244**: 231-247.

Daniels, M.J., Golder, M.C., Jarrett, O. & Macdonald, D.W. (1999). Feline viruses in wildcats from Scotland. *J. Wildl. Diseases* **35(1)**: 121-124.

Dantzler, W.H. (1989). *Comparative Physiology of the Vertebrate Kidney*. Springer, New York.

Dathe, H. (1968). Breeding the Indian leopard cat at East Berlin Zoo. *Int. Zoo Yb.* **8**: 42-44.

Davidar, E.R.C. (1973). Dhole or Indian wild dog *Cuon alpinus* mating. *J. Bombay Nat. Hist. Soc.* **70**: 373-374.

Davidar, E.R.C. (1975). Observations at the dens of the dhole or Indian wild dog (*Cuon alpinus* Pallas). *J. Bombay Nat. Hist. Soc.* **71**: 373-374.

Davidar, E.R.C. (1990). Observations at a hyena *Hyaena hyaena* Linn. den. *J. Bombay Nat. Hist. Soc.* **87**: 445-447.

Davies, C. (2006). A record of stripe-backed weasel *Mustela strigidorsa* from Mae Wong National Park, Thailand. *Small Carniv. Conserv.* **34-35**: 32.

Davies, G. & Payne, J. (1982). *A Faunal Survey of Sabah*. IUCN/WWF Project n°1692. WWF Malaysia, Kuala Lumpur.

Davis, D.D. (1955). Masticatory apparatus in the spectacled bear *Tremarctos ornatus*. *Fieldiana Zool.* **37**: 25-46.

Davis, D.D. (1958). Mammals of the Kelabit Plateau, northern Sarawak. *Fieldiana Zool.* **39**: 119-147.

Davis, D.D. (1962). Mammals of the lowland rain-forest of north Borneo. *Bull. Natl. Mus.* **31**: 5-129 + 123 plates.

Davis, S.J.M. (1987). *The Archaeology of Animals*. Batsford, London.

Davis, W.B. (1944). Notes on Mexican mammals. *J. Mammal.* **25**: 370-403.

Davis, W.B. (1951). Texas skunks. *Texas Game and Fish* **March**: 19-21, 31.

Davis, W.B. & Lukens, P.W.J. (1958). Mammals of the Mexican state of Guerrero, exclusive of Chiroptera and Rodentia. *J. Mammal.* **39**: 347-367.

Davis, W.B. & Russell, R.J. (1954). Mammals of the Mexican state of Morelos. *J. Mammal.* **35**: 63-80.

Davis, W.B. & Schmidly, D.J. (1994). *The Mammals of Texas*. Texas Parks and Wildlife Press, Austin, Texas.

Dawkins, W.B. (1888). On *Ailurus anglicus*, a new carnivore from the red crag. *Quart. J. Geol. Soc. London* **44**: 228-231.

Dawson, T.J. (1983). *Monotremes and Marsupials: The Other Mammals*. Edward Arnold, Southampton, UK.

De Luca, D.W. & Ginsberg, J.R. (2001). Dominance, reproduction and survival in banded mongooses: towards an egalitarian social system? *Anim. Behav.* **61**: 17-30.

De Luca, D.W. & Mpunga, N. (2002). Preliminary observation of Lowe's servaline genet (*Genetta servalina lowei*) from Udzungwa Mountains National Park, Tanzania. *Small Carniv. Conserv.* **27**: 17-18.

De Luca, D.W. & Mpunga, N. (2005). Small carnivores of the Udzungwa Mountains: presence, distributions and threats. *Small Carniv. Conserv.* **32**: 1-7.

De Luca, D.W. & Rovero, F. (2006). First records in Tanzania for Jackson's mongoose *Bdeogale jacksoni* (Herpestidae). *Oryx* **40**: 468-471.

De Mattos, C.C., De Mattos, C.A., Loza-Rubio, E., Aguilar-Setien, A., Orciari, L.A. & Smith, J.S. (1999). Molecular characterization of rabies virus isolates from Mexico: implications for transmission dynamics and human risk. *Amer. J. Trop. Med. Trop. Hyg.* **61**: 587-597.

De Smet, K.J.M. (1988). *Studie van de Verspreiding en Biotoopkeuze van de Grote Mammalia in Algerije in het Kader van het Natuurbehoud*. PhD dissertation, Rijksuniversiteit Gent, Gent, Belgium.

De Smet, K.J.M. (1989). [*Distribution and Habitat Choice of Larger Mammals in Algeria*]. PhD thesis, Ghent State University, Belgium. In Dutch.

De Vos, A. & Matel, S.E. (1952). The status of the lynx in Canada, 1920-1952. *J. Forestry* **50**: 742-745.

De Vos, A., Manville, R.H. & Van Gelder, R. (1956). Introduced mammals and their influence on native biota. *Zoologica* **41**: 163-194.

Dean, W.R.J., Siegfried, W.R. & Macdonald, I.A.W. (1990). The fallacy, fact and fate of guiding behavior in the greater honeyguide. *Conserv. Biol.* **4**: 99-101.

Deanesley, R. (1943). Delayed implantation in the stoat (*Mustela mustela*). *Nature (London)* **151**: 365-366.

Deanesley, R. (1944). The reproductive cycle of the female weasel (*Mustela nivalis*). *Proc. Zool. Soc. London* **114**: 339-349.

DeBoer, J. (1977). The age of olfactory cues functioning in chemocommunication among male domestic cats. *Behav. Proceedings* **2**: 209-225.

Decary, R. (1950). *La Faune Malgache, son Rôle dans les Croyances et les Usages Indigènes*. Payot, Paris.

Decker, D.M. (1991). Systematics of the coatis, genus *Nasua* (Mammalia: Procyonidae). *Proc. Biol. Soc. Washington* **104**: 370-386.

Decker, D.M. & Wozencraft, C. (1991). Phylogenetic analysis of recent procyonid genera. *J. Mamma.* **72**: 42-45.

Decker, D.M., Ringelberg, D. & White, D.C. (1992). Lipid components in anal scent sacs of 3 mongoose species (*Helogale parvula, Crossarchus obscurus, Suricata suricatta*). *J. Chem. Ecol.* **18**: 1511-1524.

Defler, T.R. (1986a). A bush dog *Speothos venaticus* pack in the eastern llanos of Colombia. *J. Mammal.* **67**: 421-422.

Defler, T.R. (1986b). The giant otter in El Tuparro National Park, Columbia. *Oryx* **20**: 87-88.

Defler, T.R. & Santacruz, A. (1994). A capture of and some notes on *Atelocynus microtis* Sclater, 1883 (Carnivora: Canidae) in the Colombian Amazon. *Trianea* **5**: 417-419.

Dehghani, R., Wanntorp, L., Pagani, P., Kallersjo, M., Werdelin, L. & Veron, G. (2008). Phylogeography of the white-tailed mongoose (Herpestidae, Carnivora, Mammalia) based on partial sequences of the mtDNA control region. *J. Zool., London* **276**: 385-393.

Delgado, E., Villalba, L., Sanderson, J., Napolitano, C., Berna, M. & Esquivel, J. (2004). Capture of an Andean cat in Bolivia. *Cat News* **40**: 2.

Delibes, M. (1980). Feeding ecology of the Spanish lynx in the Coto Doñana. *Acta Theriol.* **25**: 309-324.

Delibes, M. & Gaubert, P. (In press). *Genetta genetta*. In: Kingdon, J. & Hoffmann, M. eds. (In press). *The Mammals of Africa*. Vol. 5. Carnivores, Pangolins, Rhinos and Equids. Academic Press, Amsterdam.

Delibes, M., Blázquez, M.C., Rodríguez-Estrella, R. & Zapata, S.C. (1997). Seasonal food habits of bobcats (*Lynx rufus*) in subtropical Baja California Sur, Mexico. *Can. J. Zool.* **75**: 478-483.

Delibes, M., Palacios, F., Garzon, J. & Castroviejo, J. (1975). Notes sur l'alimentation et la biologie du lynx pardelle, *Lynx pardina* (Temminck, 1824), en Espagne. *Mammalia* **39**: 387-393.

Delibes, M., Rodríguez, A. & Ferreras, P. (2000). *Action Plan for the Conservation of the Iberian Lynx (*Lynx pardinus*) in Europe*. Nature and Environment Series **111**, Council of Europe.

Delibes, M., Rodríguez, A. & Parreño, F. (1989). Food of the common genets (*Genetta genetta*) in Northern Africa. *J. Zool.* **218**: 321-326.

Delisle, I. & Strobeck, C. (2005). A phylogeny of the Caniformia (order Carnivora) based on 12 complete protein-coding mitochondrial genes. *Mol. Phylogen.Evol.* **37**: 192-201.

Derocher, A.E. (1999). Latitudinal variation in litter size of polar bears: ecology or methodology? *Polar Biol.* **22**: 350-356.

Derocher, A.E., Andersen, M. & Wiig, Ø. (2005). Sexual dimorphism of polar bears. *J. Mammal.* **86**: 895-901.

Derocher, A.E., Andriashek, D. & Arnould, J.P. (1993). Aspects of milk composition and lactation in polar bears. *Can. J. Zool.* **71**: 561-567.

Derocher, A.E., Andriashek, D. & Stirling, I. (1993). Terrestrial foraging by polar bears during the ice-free period in western Hudson Bay. *Arctic* **46**: 251-254.

Derocher, A.E., Wiig, Ø. & Anderson, M. (2002). Diet composition of polar bears in Svalbard and the western Barents Sea. *Polar Biol.* **25**: 448-452.

Desai, J.H. (1975). Observations on the reproductive biology and early postnatal development of the panther, *Panthera pardus* L., in captivity. *J. Bombay Nat. Hist. Soc.* **72**: 293-304.

Deutsch, L.A. (1983). An encounter between bush dog *Speothos venaticus* and paca *Agouti paca*. *J. Mammal.* **64**: 532-533.

DeVault, T.L., Brisbin, I. & Rhodes, O.E. (2004). Factors influencing the acquisition of rodent carrion by vertebrate scavengers and decomposers. *Can. J. Zool.* **82**: 502-509.

Dhungle, S.K. & Edge, W.D. (1985). Notes on the natural history of *Paradoxurus hermaphroditus*. *Mammalia* **49**: 302-303.

Di Blanco, Y. & Hirsch, B. (2006). Determinants of vigilance behavior in the ring-tailed coati (*Nasua nasua*): the importance of within-group spatial position. *Behav. Ecol. Sociobiol.* **61**: 173-182.

Di Silvestre, I., Novelli, O. & Bogliani, G. (2000). Feeding habits of the spotted hyaena in the Niokolo Koba National Park, Senegal. *Afr. J. Ecol.* **38**: 102-107.

Diaz, G. & Ojeda, R. eds. (2000). *Libro Rojo de Mamíferos Amenazados de la Argentina*. SAREM, Sociedad Argentina para el Estudio de los Mamíferos, Mendoza.

Diaz, G. & Van Rompaey, H. (2002). The Ethiopian genet, *Genetta abyssinica* (Rüppell 1836) (Carnivora, Viverridae): ecology and phenotypic aspects. *Small Carniv. Conserv.* **27**: 23-28.

Dibello, F.J., Arthur, S.M. & Krohn, W.B. (1990). Food habits of sympatric coyotes, *Canis latrans*, red foxes, *Vulpes vulpes*, and bobcats, *Lynx rufus*, in Maine. *Can. Field-Nat.* **104**: 403-408.

Dickey, D.R. (1929). The spotted skunk of the Channel Islands of southern California. *Proc. Biol. Soc. Washington* **42**: 157-159.

Diefenbach, D.R., Hansen, L.A., Warren, R.J. & Conroy, M.J. (2006). Spatial organization of a reintroduced population of bobcats. *J. Mammal.* **87**: 394-401.

Dietz, J.M. (1984). Ecology and social organization of the maned wolf *Chrysocyon brachyurus*. *Smithsonian Contrib. Zool.* **392**: 1-51.

Dietz, J.M. (1985). *Chrysocyon brachyurus*. *Mammal. Species* **234**: 1-4.

Dinerstein, E. & Mehta, J.N. (1989). The clouded leopard in Nepal. *Oryx* **23**: 199-201.

Dinerstein, E., Loucks, C., Heydlauff, A., Wikramanayake, E., Bryja, G., Forrest, J., Ginsberg, J., Klenzendorf, S., Leimgruber, P., O'Brien, T., Sanderson, E., Seidensticker, J. & Songer, M. (2006). *Setting Priorities for the Conservation and Recovery of Wild Tigers: 2005-2015. A User's Guide*. WWF, WCS, Smithsonian and NFWF-STF, Washington, D.C. & New York.

Dinerstein, E., Wikramanayake, E., Robinson, J., Karanth, U., Rabinowitz, A., Olson, D., Mathew, T., Hedao, P. & Connor, M. (1997). *A Framework for Identifying High Priority Areas for the Conservation of Free-ranging Tigers*. Part I. World Wildlife Fund, US Wildlife Conservation Society & National Fish and Wildlife Foundation's Save the Tiger Fund, Washington, D.C.

Dinets, V. (2003). Records of small carnivores from Mount Kinabalu, Sabah, Borneo. *Small Carniv. Conserv.* **28**: 9.

Divyabhanusinh (1995). *The End of a Trail. The Cheetah in India*. Banyan Books, New Dehli.

Dobroruka, L.J. (1971). Individual variation of the Amur leopard cat, *Prionailurus bengalensis euptilurus* (Elliot, 1871), from Korea. *Vestn. Cesk. Spol. Zool.* **35**: 9-10.

Dobson, M. (1998). Mammal distributions in the western Mediterranean: the role of human intervention. *Mammal Rev.* **28**: 77-88.

Dolbeer, R.A. & Clark, W.R. (1975). Population ecology of snowshoe hares in the central Rocky Mountains. *J. Wildl. Management* **39**: 535-549.

Dollar, L.J. (1999a). Preliminary report on the status, activity cycle and ranging of *Cryptoprocta ferox* in the Malagasy rainforest, implications for conservation. *Small Carniv. Conserv.* **20**: 7-10.

Dollar, L.J. (1999b). Notes on *Eupleres goudotii* in the rainforest of southeastern Madagascar. *Small Carniv. Conserv.* **20**: 30-31.

Dollar, L.J. (2006). Morphometrics, diet and conservation of *Cryptoprocta ferox*. Unpublished PhD thesis, Duke University, Durham, North Carolina.

Dollar, L.J., Ganzhorn, J.U. & Goodman, S.M. (2006). Primates and other prey in the seasonally variable diet of *Cryptoprocta ferox* in the dry deciduous forest of western Madagascar. Pp. 63-76 in: Gursky, S.L. & Nekaris, K.A.I. eds. (2006). *Primate Anti-predator Strategies*. Springer Press, New York.

Donadio, E., Di Martino, S., Aubone, M. & Novaro, A.J. (2001). Activity patterns, home-range and habitat selection of the common hog-nosed skunk, *Conepatus chinga* (Mammalia: Mustelidae), in northwestern Patagonia. *Mammalia* **65**: 49-53.

Donadio, E., Di Martino, S., Aubone, M. & Novaro, A.J. (2004). Feeding ecology of the Andean hog-nosed skunk (*Conepatus chinga*) in areas under different land use in north-western Patagonia. *J. Arid Environm.* **56**: 709-718.

Doncaster, C.P. & Macdonald, D.W. (1991). Drifting territoriality in the red fox *Vulpes vulpes*. *J. Anim. Ecol.* **60**: 423-440.

Doolan, S.P. & Macdonald, D.W. (1996a). Dispersal and extra-territorial prospecting by slender-tailed meerkats (*Suricata suricatta*) in the south-western Kalahari. *J. Zool., London* **240**: 59-73.

Doolan, S.P. & Macdonald, D.W. (1996b). Diet and foraging behaviour of group-living meerkats, *Suricata suricatta*, in the southern Kalahari. *J. Zool., London* **239**: 697-716.

Doolan, S.P. & Macdonald, D.W. (1997). Breeding and juvenile survival among slender-tailed meerkats (*Suricata suricatta*) in the south-western Kalahari: ecological and social influences. *J. Zool., London* **242**: 309-327.

Doolan, S.P. & Macdonald, D.W. (1999). Co-operative rearing by slender-tailed meerkats (*Suricata suricatta*) in the southern Kalahari. *Ethology* **105**: 851-866.

Dorji, D.P. & Santiapillai, C. (1989). The status, distribution and conservation of the tiger *Panthera tigris* in Bhutan. *Biol. Conserv.* **48**: 311-319.

Doroff, A.M. & DeGange, A.R. (1994). Sea otter, *Enhydra lutris*, prey composition and foraging success in the northern Kodiak Archipelago. *US National Marine Fisheries Service Fishery Bulletin* **92**: 704-710.

Dorst, J. & Dandelot, P. (1970). *A Field Guide to the Larger Mammals of Africa*. Collins, London.

Dos Santos, M.D.F.M. & Hartz, S.M. (1999). The food habits of *Procyon cancrivorus* (Carnivora, Procyonidae) in the Lami Biological Reserve, Porto Alegre, Southern Brazil. *Mammalia* **63**: 525-530.

Doty, J.B. & Dowler, R.C. (2006). Denning ecology in sympatric populations of skunks (*Spilogale gracilis* and *Mephitis mephitis*) in west-central Texas. *J. Mammal.* **87**: 131-138.

Doupé, J.P., Furze, M. & Paetkau, D. (2007). Most northerly observation of a grizzly bear (*Ursus arctos*) in Canada: photographic and DNA evidence from Melville Island, Northwest Territories. *Arctic* **60**: 271-276.

Doyère, M. (1835). Notice sur un mammifère de Madagascar formant le type d'un nouveau genre de la famille des Carnassiers insectivores de M. Cuvier. *Ann. Sci. Nat.* **4**: 270-283.

Dragesco-Joffé, A. (1993). *Le Chat des Sables, une Redoutable Chasseur de Serpents. La Vie Sauvage au Sahara*. Delachaux & Niestlé, Lausanne & Paris.

Dragoo, J.W. (1993). The evolutionary relationships of the skunks to each other and the rest of the weasels; with a note on behavioral idiosyncrasies. Pp. 54-67 in: *Eleventh Great Plains Wildlife Damage Control Workshop Proceedings*. Kansas City, Missouri.

Dragoo, J.W. & Honeycutt, R.L. (1997). Systematics of mustelid-like carnivores. *J. Mammal.* **78**: 426-443.

Dragoo, J.W. & Honeycutt, R.L. (1999a). Eastern hog-nosed skunk / *Conepatus leuconotus*. Pp. 190-191 in: Wilson, D.E. & Ruff, S. eds. (1999). *The Smithsonian Book of North American Mammals*. Smithsonian Institution Press, Washington, D.C.

Dragoo, J.W. & Honeycutt, R.L. (1999b). Eastern spotted skunk / *Spilogale putorius*. Pp. 185-186 in: Wilson, D.E. & Ruff, S. eds. (1999). *The Smithsonian Book of North American Mammals*. Smithsonian Institution Press, Washington, D.C.

Dragoo, J.W. & Honeycutt, R.L. (1999c). Western hog-nosed skunk / *Conepatus mesoleucus*. Pp. 191-192 in: Wilson, D.E. & Ruff, S. eds. (1999). *The Smithsonian Book of North American Mammals*. Smithsonian Institution Press, Washington, D.C.

Dragoo, J.W. & Sheffield, S.R. (In press). *Conepatus leuconotus* (Carnivora; Mephitidae). *Mammal. Species*.

Dragoo, J.W., Bradley, R.D., Honeycutt, R.L. & Templeton, J.W. (1993). Phylogenetic relationships among the skunks: A molecular perspective. *J. Mammal. Evol.* **1**: 255-267.

Dragoo, J.W., Choate, J.R., Yates, T.L. & O'Farrell, T.P. (1990). Evolutionary and taxonomic relationships among North American arid land foxes. *J. Mammal.* **71**: 318-332.

Dragoo, J.W., Fagre, D.B., Schmidly, D.J. & Penry, L.B. (1989). First specimen of a hog-nosed skunk (*Conepatus mesoleucus*) from Bexar County, Texas. *Texas J. Sci.* **41**: 331-333.

Dragoo, J.W., Honeycutt, R.L. & Schmidly, D.J. (2003). Taxonomic status of white-backed hog-nosed skunks, genus *Conepatus* (Carnivora: Mephitidae). *J. Mammal.* **84**: 159-176.

Dragoo, J.W., Matthes, D.K., Aragon, A., Hass, C.C. & Yates, T.L. (2004). Identification of skunk species submitted for rabies testing in the desert southwest. *J. Wildl. Diseases* **40**: 371-376.

Drea, C.M. & Frank, L.G. (2003). The social complexity of spotted hyenas. Pp. 121-148 in: de Waal, F.B.M. & Tyack, P.L. eds. (2003). *Animal Social Complexity: Intelligence, Culture and Individualized Societies*. Harvard University Press, Cambridge, Massachusetts.

Drea, C.M., Coscia, E.M. & Glickman, S.E. (1999). Hyenas. Pp. 718-725 in: Knobil, E., Neill, J. & Licht, P. eds. (1999). *Encyclopedia of Reproduction*. Vol. 2. Academic Press, San Diego, California.

Drea, C.M., Place, N.J., Weldele, M.L., Coscia, E.M., Licht, P. & Glickman, S.E. (2002). Exposure to naturally circulating androgens during foetal life incurs direct reproductive costs in female spotted hyenas, but is prerequisite for male mating. *Proc. Royal Soc. London (Ser. B Biol. Sci.)* **269**: 1981-1987.

Drea, C.M., Vignieri, S.N., Cunningham, S.B. & Glickman, S.E. (2002). Responses to olfactory stimuli in spotted hyenas (*Crocuta crocuta*): I. Investigation of environmental odors and the function of rolling. *J. Comp. Psychol.* **116**: 331-341.

Drea, C.M., Vignieri, S.N., Kim, H.S., Weldele, M.L. & Glickman, S.E. (2002). Responses to olfactory stimuli in spotted hyenas (*Crocuta crocuta*): II. Discrimination of conspecific scent. *J. Comp. Psychol.* **116**: 342-349.

Drea, C.M., Weldele, M.L., Forger, N.G., Coscia, E.M., Frank, L.G., Licht, P. & Glickman, S.E. (1998). Androgens and masculinization of genitalia in the spotted hyaena (*Crocuta crocuta*). 2. Effects of prenatal anti-androgens. *J. Reprod. Fertil.* **113**: 117-127.

Dreyer, H. Van A. & Nel, J.A.J. (1990). Feeding site selection by black-backed jackals on the Namib Desert coast. *J. Arid Environm.* **19**: 217-224.

Drüwa, P. (1983). The social behavior of the bush dog (*Speothos*). *Carnivore* **6**: 46-71.

Duckworth, J.W. (1994). Field observation of large-spotted civet *Viverra megaspila* in Laos with notes on the identification of the species. *Small Carniv. Conserv.* **11**: 1-3.

Duckworth, J.W. (1995). Viverrids in an Ethiopian Rift Valley national park. *Small Carniv. Conserv.* **12**: 5-8.

Duckworth, J.W. (1997). Small carnivores in Laos: a status review with notes on ecology behaviour and conservation. *Small Carniv. Conserv.* **16**: 1-21.

Duckworth, J.W. & Nettelbeck, A.R. (2007). Observations of small-toothed palm civets *Arctogalidia trivirgata* in Khao Yai National Park, Thailand, with notes on feeding techniques. *Nat. Hist. Bull. Siam Soc.* **55(1)**: 187-192.

Duckworth, J.W. & Rakotondraparany, F. (1990). The mammals of Marojejy. Pp. 54-60 in Safford, R. & Duckworth, W. eds. (1990). *A Wildlife Survey of the Marojejy Nature Reserve Madagascar*. International Council for Bird Preservation, Study Report **40**. Cambridge.

Duckworth, J.W. & Robichaud, W. (2005). Yellow-bellied weasel *Mustela kathiah*, sightings in Phongsaly province, Laos, with notes on the species' range in south-east Asia, and recen records of other small carnivores in the province. *Small Carniv. Conserv.* **33**: 17-20.

Duckworth, J.W., Lee, B., Meijaard, E. & Meiri, S. (2006). The Malay weasel *Mustela nudipes* distribution, natural history and a global conservation status review. *Small Carniv. Conserv.* **34-35**: 2-21.

Duckworth, J.W., Poole, C.M., Tizard, R.J., Walston, J.L. & Timmins, R.J. (2005). The jungle cat *Felis chaus* in Indochina: a threatened population of a widespread and adaptable species. *Biodiversity & Conservation* **14**: 1263-1280.

Duckworth, J.W., Salter, R.E. & Khounboline, K. (1999). *Wildlife in Lao PDR: 1999 Status Report*. IUCN, Wildlife Conservation Society and Centre for Protected Areas and Watershed Management, Vientiane, Laos.

Duhaut-Cilly, A.B. (1834). *Voyage Autour du Monde: Principalement à la Californie et aux Iles Sandwich, Pendant les Années 1826, 1827, 1828 et 1829*. A. Bertrand, Paris.

Dumyahn, J.B. & Zollner, P.A. (2007). Winter home-range characteristics of American marten (*Martes americana*) in northern Wisconsin. *Amer. Midl. Nat.* **158**: 382-394.

Duncan, M.J. & Mead, R.A. (1992). Autoradiographic localization of binding-sites for 2-[125] Iodomelatonin in the pars tuberalis of the western spotted skunk (Spilogale-Putorius-Latifrons). *Brain Res.* **569**: 152-155.

Dunham, A.E. (1998). Notes on the behavior of the ring-tailed mongoose, *Galidia elegans*, at Ranomafana National Park, Madagascar. *Small Carniv. Conserv.* **19**: 21-24.

Dunham, A.E. & Gaubert, P. (In press). *Genetta johnstoni*. In: Kingdon, J. & Hoffmann, M. eds. (In press). *The Mammals of Africa*. Vol. 5. Carnivores, Pangolins, Rhinos and Equids. Academic Press, Amsterdam.

Dunstone, N. (1979). Swimming and diving behavior of the mink. *Carnivore* **2**: 56-61.

Dunstone, N. (1983). Underwater hunting behaviour of the mink (*Mustela vison* Schreber): an analysis of constraints on foraging. *Acta Zool. Fennica* **174**: 201-203.

Dunstone, N. (1993). *The Mink*. T. & A.D. Poyser Natural History, London.

Dunstone, N., Durbin, L., Wyllie, I., Freer, R., Jamett, G.A., Mazzolli, M. & Rose, S. (2002). Spatial organization, ranging behaviour and habitat use of the kodkod (*Oncifelis guigna*) in southern Chile. *J. Zool., London* **257**: 1-11.

Dunstone, N., Durbin, L., Wyllie, I., Rose, S. & Acosta, G. (1998). Ecology of the kodkod in Laguna San Rafael National Park, Chile. *Cat News* **29**: 18-20.

Duplaix, N. (1980). Observations on the ecology and behaviour of the giant river otter *Pteronura brasiliensis* in Suriname. *Rev. Écol. (Terre Vie)* **34**: 495-620.

Durán, J., Cattan, P. & Yañez, J. (1985). The gray fox *Canis griseus* (Gray) in Chilean Patagonia (Southern Chile). *Biol. Conserv.* **34**: 141-148.

Durant, S. (1998). Is bush country the key to the cheetah's survival in Africa? *Cat News* **28**: 14-15.

Durbin, L.S. (1998). Individuality in the whistle call of the Asiatic wild dog *Cuon alpinus*. *Bioacoustics* **9**: 197-206.

Durbin, L.S., Venkataraman, A.B., Hedges, S. & Duckworth, W. (2004). Dhole *Cuon alpinus*. Pp. 210-219 in: Sillero-Zubiri, C., Hoffmann, M. & Macdonald, D.W. eds. (2004). *Canids: Foxes, Wolves, Jackals and Dogs. Status Survey and Conservation Action Plan*. IUCN/SSC Canid Specialist Group, Gland & Cambridge.

Durner, G.M. & Amstrup, S.C. (1995). Movements of a polar bear from northern Alaska to northern Greenland. *Arctic* **48**: 338-341.

Dzialak, M.R., Serfass, T.L., Brown, C.L. & Krupa, J.J. (2005). Fall and winter diet of the fisher (*Martes pennanti*) in West Virginia and Maryland. *Proc. West Virginia Acad. Sci.* **77**: 7-13.

Earle, R.A. (1981). Aspects of the social and feeding behaviour of the yellow mongoose *Cynictis penicillata* (G. Cuvier). *Mammalia* **45**: 143-152.

East, M.L. & Hofer, H. (1991a). Loud-calling in a female-dominated mammalian society: I. Structure and composition of whooping bouts of spotted hyaenas, *Crocuta crocuta*. *Anim. Behav.* **42**: 637-649.

East, M.L. & Hofer, H. (1991b). Loud-calling in a female-dominated mammalian society: II. Behavioural contexts and functions of whooping of spotted hyaenas, *Crocuta crocuta*. *Anim. Behav.* **42**: 651-669.

East, M.L. & Hofer, H. (2001). Male spotted hyenas (*Crocuta crocuta*) queue for status in social groups dominated by females. *Behav. Ecol.* **12**: 558-568.

East, M.L. & Hofer, H. (2002). Conflict and co-operation in a female-dominated society: a re-assessment of the "hyper-aggressive" image of spotted hyenas (*Crocuta crocuta*). *Advances Study Behav.* **31**: 1-30.

East, M.L., Burke, T., Wilhelm, K., Greig, C. & Hofer, H. (2003). Sexual conflicts in spotted hyenas: male and female mating tactics and their reproductive outcome with respect to age, social status and tenure. *Proc. Royal Soc. London. (Ser. B Biol. Sci.)* **270**: 1247-1254.

East, M.L., Hofer, H. & Wickler, W. (1993). The erect 'penis' is a flag of submission in a female-dominated society: greetings in Serengeti spotted hyenas. *Behav. Ecol. Sociobiol.* **33**: 355-370.

Easterbee, N., Hepburn, L.V. & Jefferies, D.J. (1991). *Survey of the Status and Distribution of the Wildcat in Scotland 1983-1987*. Nature Conservancy Council for Scotland, Edinburgh.

Eaton, R.L. (1970a). Group interaction, spacing and territoriality in cheetahs. *Zeitschr. Tierpsychol.* **27**: 461-491.

Eaton, R.L. (1970b). The predatory sequence, with emphasis on the killing behavior and its ontogeny, in the cheetah *Acinonyx jubatus* (Schreber). *Zeitschr. Tierpsychol.* **27**: 492-504.

Eaton, R.L. (1974). *The Cheetah*. Van Nostrand Reinhold Company, New York.

Eaton, R.L. (1976). The brown hyena: A review of biology, status and conservation. *Mammalia* **40**: 377-399.

Eaton, R.L. (1977). Reproductive biology of the leopard. *Zool. Garten* **47**: 329-351.

Eaton, R.L. (1984). Survey of smaller felid breeding. *Zool. Garten* **54**: 101-120.

Ebensperger, L.A., Mella, J.E. & Simonetti, J.A. (1991). Trophic-niche relationships among *Galictis cuja, Dusicyon culpaeus* and *Tyto alba* in central Chile. *J. Mammal.* **72**: 820-823.

Eberhardt, L.E., Garrott, R.A. & Hanson, W.C. (1983). Winter movements of Arctic foxes *Alopex lagopus* in a petroleum development area. *Can. Field-Nat.* **97**: 66-70.

Eberhardt, L.E., Hanson, W.C., Bengtson, J.L., Garrott, R.A. & Hanson, E.E. (1982). Arctic fox home range characteristics in an oil-development area. *J. Wildl. Management* **46**: 183-190.

Edwards, M.A. & Forbes, G.J. (2003). Food habits of ermine, *Mustela erminea*, in a forested landscape. *Can. Field-Nat.* **117**: 245-248.

Egoscue, H.J. (1956). Preliminary studies of the kit fox in Utah. *J. Mammal.* **37**: 351-357.

Egoscue, H.J. (1962). Ecology and life history of the kit fox in Tooele County, Utah. *Ecology* **43**: 481-497.

Egoscue, H.J. (1975). Population dynamics of the kit fox in western Utah. *Bull. South. Calif. Acad. Sci.* **74**: 122-177.

Egoscue, H.J. (1979). *Vulpes velox. Mammal. Species* **122**: 1-5.

Eisenberg, J.F. (1989). *Mammals of the Neotropics: the Northern Neotropics.* Vol. 1. University of Chicago Press, Chicago, Illinois.

Eisenberg, J.F. & Lockhart, M. (1972). *An Ecological Reconnaissance of Wilpattu National Park, Ceylon.* Smithsonian Contributions to Zoology **101**. 118 pp.

Eisenberg, J.F. & Redford, K.H. (1999). *Mammals of the Neotropics: the Central Neotropics.* Vol. 3. University of Chicago Press, Chicago, Illinois.

Eisenberg, J.F. & Seidensticker, J. (1976). Ungulates in southern Asia: a consideration of biomass estimates for selected habitats. *Biol. Conserv.* **10**: 293-308.

Eisenberg, J.F., O'Conell, M.A. & August, P.V. (1979). Density, productivity and distribution of mammals in two Venezuelan habitats. Pp. 187-207 in: Eisenberg, J.F. ed. (1979). *Vertebrate Ecology in the Northern Neotropics.* Smithsonian Institution Press, Washington, D.C.

Eisentraut, M. (1973). Die Wirbeltierfauna von Fernando Poo und Westkamerun. *Bonn. Zool. Monogr.* **3**: 1-428.

Eisner, T. (1968). Mongoose and millipede. *Science* **160**: 1367.

Eisner, T. & Davis, J.A. (1967). Mongoose throwing and smashing millipedes. *Science* **155**: 577-579.

Eizirik, E., Bonatto, S.L., Johnson, W.E., Crawshaw, P.G., Vié, J.C., Brousset, D.M., O'Brien, S.J. & Salzano, F.M. (1998). Phylogeographic patterns and evolution of the mitochondrial DNA control region in two Neotropical cats (Mammalia, Felidae). *J. Mol. Evol.* **47**: 613-624.

Eizirik, E., Kim, J.H., Menotti-Raymond, M., Crawshaw, P.G., O'Brien, S.J. & Johnson, W.E. (2001). Phylogeography, population history and conservation genetics of jaguars (*Panthera onca*, Mammalia, Felidae). *Mol. Ecol.* **10**: 65-79.

Eldridge, D.J. (2004). Mounds of the American badger (*Taxidea taxus*): significant features of North American shrub-steppe ecosystems. *J. Mammal.* **85**: 1060-1067.

Elliot, T. & Popper, B. (1999). *Predator Management Report for the Protection of the San Clemente Loggerhead Shrike.* US Navy, Natural Resources Management Branch, Southwest Division Naval Facilities Engineering Command, San Diego, California.

Elmeros, M. (2006). Food habits of stoats *Mustela erminea* and weasels *Mustela nivalis* in Denmark. *Acta Theriol.* **51**: 179-186.

Elmeros, M., Madsen, A.B. & Prang, A. (2005). Home range of the badger (*Meles meles*) in a heterogeneous landscape in Denmark. *Lutra* **48**: 35-44.

Elmhagen, B., Tannerfeldt, M., Verucci, P. & Angerbjorn, A. (2000). The Arctic fox *Alopex lagopus*: an opportunistic specialist. *J. Zool., London* **251**: 139-149.

Eloff, F.C. (1964). On the predatory habits of lions and hyaenas. *Koedoe* **7**: 105-112.

Eloff, F.C. (1973a). Ecology and behavior of the Kalahari lion *Panthera leo vernayi* (Roberts). Pp. 90-126 in: Eaton, R.L. ed. (1973). *The World's Cats.* Vol 1. World Wildlife Safari, Winston, Oregon.

Eloff, F.C. (1973b). Water use by the Kalahari lion *Panthera leo vernayi. Koedoe* **16**: 149-154.

Eloff, F.C. (1975). The spotted hyaena *Crocuta crocuta* (Erxleben) in arid regions of southern Africa. *Publ. Univ. Pretoria Nuwe Reeks* **97**: 35-39.

Elton, C. & Nicholson, M. (1942). The ten-year cycle in numbers of the lynx in Canada. *J. Anim. Ecol.* **11**: 215-244.

Emmerson, W. & Philip, S. (2004). Diets of Cape clawless otters at two South African coastal localities. *Afr. Zool.* **39**: 201-210.

Emmons, L.H. (1987). Comparative feeding ecology of felids in a Neotropical rainforest. *Behav. Ecol. Sociobiol.* **20**: 271-283.

Emmons, L.H. (1988). A field study of ocelots (*Felis pardalis*) in Peru. *Rev. Écol. (Terre Vie)* **43**: 133-157.

Emmons, L.H. (1989). Jaguar predation on chelonians. *J. Herpetol.* **23(3)**: 311-314.

Emmons, L.H. (1998). Mammal fauna of Parque Nacional Noel Kempff Mercado. Pp. 129-135 in: Killeen, T. & Schulenberg, T. eds. (1998). *A Biological Assesment of Parque Nacional Noel Kempff Mercado, Bolivia.* RAP Working Papers 10, Conservation International, Washington, D.C.

Emmons, L.H. & Feer, F. (1997). *Neotropical Rainforest Mammals - a Field Guide.* 2nd edition. University of Chicago Press, Chicago, Illinois.

Enders, A.C. & Mead, R.A. (1996). Progression of trophoblast into the endometrium during implantation in the western spotted skunk. *Anat. Rec.* **244**: 297-315.

Enders, R.K. (1952). Reproduction in the mink (*Mustela vison*). *Proc. Amer. Phil. Soc.* **96**: 691-755.

Endo, H., Yamagiwa, D., Hayashi, Y., Koie, H., Yamaya, Y. & Kimura, J. (1999). Role of the panda's `pseudo-thumb'. *Nature (London)* **397**: 399-310.

Engel, T.R. (1998a). Long-term latrine use by rusty-spotted genet *Genetta rubiginosa* in Kenya. *Small Carniv. Conserv.* **18**: 5-8.

Engel, T.R. (1998b). Seeds on the roundabout – tropical forest regeneration by *Genetta rubiginosa. Small Carniv. Conserv.* **19**: 13-20.

Engel, T.R. (2000). *Seed Dispersal and Forest Regeneration in a Tropical Lowland Biocoenosis (Shimba Hills, Kenya).* PhD thesis, University of Bayreuth, Germany.

Engel, T.R. & Van Rompaey, H. (1995). New records of the rare Sokoke bushy-tailed mongoose, *Bdeogale crassicauda omnivora* in the coastal Shimba Hills National reserve and at Diani Beach, Kenya. *Small Carniv. Conserv.* **12**: 12-13.

Engeman, R., Christensen, K.L., Pipas, M.J. & Bergman, D.L. (2003). Population monitoring in support of a rabies vaccination program for skunks in Arizona. *J. Wildl. Diseases* **39**: 746-750.

Engeman, R., Whisson, D., Quinn, J., Cano, F., Quinones, P. & White, T.H. (2006). Monitoring invasive mammalian predator populations sharing habitat with the Critically Endangered Puerto Rican parrot *Amazona vittata. Oryx* **40**: 95-102.

Engh, A.L., Esch, K., Smale, L. & Holekamp, K.E. (2000). Mechanisms of maternal rank 'inheritance' in the spotted hyaena. *Anim. Behav.* **60**: 323-332.

Engh, A.L., Funk, S.M., Van Horn, R.C., Scribner, K.T., Bruford, M.W., Szykman, M., Smale, L. & Holekamp, K.E. (2002). Reproductive skew among males in a female-dominated society. *Behav. Ecol.* **13**: 193-200.

Englund, J. (1970). Some aspects of reproduction and mortality rates in Swedish foxes *Vulpes vulpes*, 1961-63 and 1966-69. *Viltrevy [Swedish Wildlife]* **8**: 1-82.

Erdbrink, D.P. (1953). *A Review of Fossil and Recent Bears of the Old World with Remarks on their Phylogeny Based upon their Dentition.* 2 Vols. Drukkerij Jan de Lange, Deventer, The Netherlands.

Erlinge, S. (1979). Adaptive significance of sexual dimorphism in weasels. *Oikos* **33**: 233-245.

Erlinge, S. & Sandell, M. (1986). Seasonal changes in the social organization of male stoats, *Mustela erminea*: an effect of shifts between two decisive resources. *Oikos* **47**: 57-62.

Errington, P.L. (1954). The special responsiveness of minks to epizootics in muskrat populations. *Ecol. Monogr.* **24**: 377-393.

Espirito-Santo, C., Rosalino, L. & Santos-Reis, M. (2007). Factors affecting the placement of common genet latrine sites in a mediterranean landscape in Portugal. *J. Mammal.* **88**: 201-207.

Esselstyn, J.A., Widmann, P. & Heaney, L.R. (2004). The mammals of Palawan Island, Philippines. *Proc. Biol. Soc. Washington* **117**: 271-302.

Estes, J.A. (1980). *Enhydra lutris. Mammal. Species* **133**: 1-8.

Estes, J.A. (1989). Adaptations for aquatic living by carnivores. Pp. 242-282 in: Gittleman, J.L. ed. (1989). *Carnivore Behavior, Ecology and Evolution.* Cornell University Press, Ithaca, New York.

Estes, J.A. & Palmisano, J.F. (1974). Sea otters: their role in structuring nearshore communities. *Science* **185**: 1058-1060.

Estes, R.D. (1972). The role of the vomeronasal organ in mammalian reproduction. *Mammalia* **36**: 315-341.

Estes, R.D. (1991). *The Behaviour Guide to African Mammals: Including Hoofed Mammals, Carnivores, Primates.* University of California Press, Berkeley, California.

Etling, K. (2001). *Cougar Attacks.* The Lyons Press, Guilford, Connecticut.

Evans, T., Bleisch, W. & Timmins, R. (1994). Sightings of spotted linsang *Prionodon pardicolor* and black-striped weasel *Mustela strigidorsa* in Lao PDR. *Small Carniv. Conserv.* **11**: 22.

Ewer, R.F. (1963). The behaviour of the meerkat *Suricata suricatta* (Schreiber). *Zeitschr. Tierpsychol.* **20**: 570-607.

Ewer, R.F. (1973). *The Carnivores.* Comstock Publishing Associates, Cornell University Press, Ithaca & London.

Ewer, R.F. & Wemmer, C. (1974). The behaviour in captivity of the African civet, *Civettictis civetta* (Schreber). *Zeitschr. Tierpsychol.* **34**: 359-394.

Facure, K.G. & Monteiro-Filho, E.L.A. (1996). Feeding habits of the crab-eating fox, *Cerdocyon thous* (Carnivora: Canidae), in a suburban area of southeastern Brazil. *Mammalia* **60**: 147-149.

Fagen, R.M. & Wiley, K.S. (1978). Felid paedomorphosis, with special reference to *Leopardus. Carnivore* 1(2): 72-81.

Fagotto, F. (1985). The lion in Somalia. *Mammalia* **49**: 587-588.

Fair, J. (1990). *The Great American Bear.* Northwood Press, Minocqua, Wisconsin.

Fan, Z. & Song, Y. (1997). Bears present status and conservation and bear farms of China. Pp. 5-19 in: Williamson, D.F. & Gaski, A.L. eds. (1997). *Proceedings of the Second International Symposium on the Trade of Bear Parts.* TRAFFIC USA/World Wildlife Fund, Washington, D.C.

Fanshawe, J.H. & Fitzgibbon, C.D. (1993). Factors influencing the hunting success of an African wild dog pack. *Anim. Behav.* **45**: 479-490.

Fanshawe, J.H., Ginsberg, J.R., Sillero-Zubiri, C. & Woodroffe, R. (1997). The status and distribution of remaining wild dog populations. Pp. 11-57 in: Woodroffe, R., Ginsberg, J.R. & Macdonald, D.W. eds. (1997). *The African Wild Dog - Status Survey and Conservation Action Plan.* IUCN Canid Specialist Group. IUCN, Gland, Switzerland.

Farias, A.A. (2000). *Composición y Variación Estacional de la Dieta del Zorro Gris Pampeano (*Pseudalopex gymnocercus*) en la Laguna Mar Chiquita (Provincia de Buenos Aires, Argentina).* BSc thesis, UNMdP, Mar del Plata, Argentina.

Farias, V. (2000). *Gray Fox Distribution in Southern California: Detecting the Effects of Intraguild Predation.* MSc thesis, University of Massachusetts, Amherst, Massachusetts.

Farmer, C. (1997). Did lungs and the intracardiac shunt evolve to oxygenate the heart in vertebrates? *Paleobiology* **23**: 358-372.

Fausett, L.L. (1982). *Activity and Movement Patterns of the Island Fox,* Urocyon littoralis *Baird 1857 (Carnivora: Canidae).* PhD dissertation, University of California, Los Angeles, California.

Fawcett, D., Rojas Dias, V. & Montero, H. (1996). Columbian weasel. *Small Carniv. Conserv.* **14**: 7-10.

Feldhamer, G.A., Drickamer, L.C., Vessey, S.H., Merritt, J.F. & Krajewski, C. (2007). *Mammalogy.* 3rd Edition. McGraw Hill, New York.

Feldhamer, G.A., Thompson, B.C. & Chapman, J.A. (2003). *Wild Mammals of North America.* Johns Hopkins University Press, Baltimore, Maryland.

Felicetti, L.A., Robbins, C.T. & Shipley, L.A. (2003). Dietary protein content alters energy expenditure and composition of the mass gain in grizzly bears (*Ursus arctos horribilis*). *Physiol. Biochem. Zool.* **76**: 256-261.
Feller, N.L. (1993a). Diet of the stone marten (*Martes foina*) during a population peak of the water vole (*Arvicola terrestris*, Scherman) in the Swiss-Jura. *Zeitschrift für Säugetierkunde* **58**: 275-280.
Feller, N.L. (1993b). Use of resting sites by stone martens (*Martes foina*) in the Swiss Jura Mountains. *Zeitschrift für Säugetierkunde* **58**: 330-336.
Fellner, K. (1965). Natural rearing of clouded leopards *Neofelis nebulosa* at Frankfurt Zoo. *Int. Zoo Yb.* **5**: 111-113.
Feng Zuojian, Cai Guiguan & Zheng Changlin (1986). [*The Mammals of Xizang*]. Science Press, Beijing. In Chinese.
Ferguson, J.W.H. (1980). *Die Ecologie van die Rooijakkals,* Canis mesomelas *Schreber 1778 met Spesiale Verwysing na Bewegings en Sociale Organisaise.* MSc thesis, University of Pretoria, Pretoria, South Africa.
Ferguson, J.W.H., Nel, J.A.J. & De Wet, M.J. (1983). Social organization and movement patterns of black-backed jackals *Canis mesomelas* in South Africa. *J. Zool., London* **199**: 487-502.
Ferguson, S.H. & Larivière, S. (2002). Can comparing life histories help conserve carnivores? *Anim. Conserv.* **5**: 1-12.
Ferguson, S.H. & Larivière, S. (2004). Are long penis bones an adaption to high latitude snowy environments? *Oikos* **105**: 255-267.
Ferguson, S.H. & McLoughlin, P.D. (2000). Effect of energy availability, seasonality and geographic range on brown bear life history. *Ecography* **23**: 193-200.
Ferguson, S.H., Taylor, M.K., Born, E.W., Rosing-Asvid, A. & Messier, F. (1999). Determinants of home range size for polar bears (*Ursus maritimus*). *Ecol. Letters* **2**: 311-318.
Ferguson, S.H., Taylor, M.K., Rosing-Asvid, A., Born, E.W. & Messier, F. (2000). Relationships between denning of polar bears and conditions of sea ice. *J. Mammal.* **8**: 1118-1127.
Ferguson, S.H., Virgl, J.A. & Larivière, S. (1996). Evolution of delayed implantation and associated grade shifts in life history traits of North American carnivores. *Ecoscience* **3**: 7-17.
Fernandes, C.A. & Crawford-Cabral, J. (2004). Comment on the proposed conservation of *Viverra maculata* Gray, 1830 (currently *Genetta maculata*; Mammalia, Carnivora). *Bull. Zool. Nomencl.* **61**: 257-260.
Fernández-Gil, A., Naves, J. & Delibes, M. (2006). Courtship of brown bears *Ursus arctos* in northern Spain: phenology, weather, habitat and durable mating areas. *Wildl. Biol.* **12**: 367-373.
Ferrari, S.F. & Lopes, M.A. (1992). A note on the behaviour of the weasel *Mustela* cf. *africana* (Carnivora, Mustelidae), from Amazonas, Brazil. *Mammalia* **56**: 482-483.
Ferreras, P., Aldama, J.J., Beltrán, J.F. & Delibes, M. (1992). Rates and causes of mortality in a fragmented population of Iberian lynx *Felis pardina* Temminck, 1824. *Biol. Conserv.* **61**: 197-202.
Ferreras, P., Beltrán, J.F., Aldama, J.J. & Delibes, M. (1997). Spatial organization and land tenure system of the endangered Iberian lynx (*Lynx pardinus*). *J. Zool., London* **243**: 163-189.
Fickett, S.B. (1971). *Food Habits Data for the Bobcat in Florida.* Florida Game and Fresh Water Fish Commission **W-41-R18**.
Findley, J.S., Harris, A.H., Wilson, D.E. & Jones, C. (1975). *Mammals of New Mexico.* University of New Mexico Press, Albuquerque, New Mexico.
Fischer, C. & Weber, J.M. (2003). Distribution of badger setts and latrines in an intensively cultivated landscape. *Rev. Suisse Zool.* **110**: 661-668.
Fish, F.E., Innes, S. & Ronald, K. (1988). Kinematics and estimated thrust propulsion of swimming harp and ringed seals. *J. Exper. Biol.* **137**: 157-173.
Fitzgibbon, C.D. & Fanshawe, J.H. (1989). The condition and age of Thomson's gazelles killed by cheetahs and wild dogs. *J. Zool., London* **218**: 99-107.
Fleming, P., Corbett, L., Harden, R. & Thomson, P. (2001). *Managing the Impacts of Dingoes and Other Wild Dogs.* Bureau of Rural Sciences, Canberra.
Floria, P. & Spinelli, L. (1967). Successful breeding of a cheetah in a private zoo. *Int. Zoo Yb.* **7**: 150-152.
Flower, W.H. (1869). On the value of the characters of the base of the cranium in the classification of the order Carnivora and on the systematic position of *Bassaris* and other disputed forms. *Proc. Royal Soc. London (Ser. B Biol. Sci.)* **1869**: 4-37.
Flynn, J.J. (1996). Carnivoran phylogeny and rates of evolution: morphological, taxic and molecular. Pp. 542-581 in: Gittleman, J.L. ed. (1996). *Carnivore Behavior, Ecology and Evolution.* Cornell University Press, Ithaca & London.
Flynn, J.J. (1998). Early Cenozoic Carnivora ("Miacoidea"). Pp. 110-123 in: Janis, C.M., Scott, K.M. & Jacons, L.L. eds. (1998). *Evolution of Tertiary Mammals of North America.* Cambridge University Press, Cambridge.
Flynn, J.J. & Nedbal, M.A. (1998). Phylogeny of the Carnivora (Mammalia): congruence vs incompatibility among multiple data sets. *Mol. Phylogen. Evol.* **9**: 414-426.
Flynn, J.J., Finarelli, J.A., Zehr, S., Hsu, J. & Nedbal, M.A. (2005). Molecular phylogeny of the Carnivora (Mammalia): assessing the impact of increased sampling on resolving enigmatic relationships. *Syst. Biol.* **54**: 317-337.
Flynn, J.J., Nedbal, M.A., Dragoo, J.W. & Honeycutt, R.L. (2000). Whence the red panda? *Mol. Phylogen. Evol.* **17**: 190-199.
Follman, E.H. (1973). *Comparative Ecology and Behavior of Red and Gray Foxes.* PhD dissertation, Southern Illinois University, Carbondale, Illinois.
Follman, E.H. (1978). Annual reproductive cycle of the male gray fox. *Trans. Illinois State Acad. Sci.* **71**: 304-311.
Fonseca, G.A.B., Rylands, A.B., Costa, C.M.R., Machado, R.B. & Leite, Y.R. (1994). Mamíferos brasileiros sob ameaça. Pp. 1-10 in: Fonseca, G.A.B., Rylands, A.B., Costa, C.M.R., Machado, R.B. & Leite, Y.R. eds. (1994). *Livro Vermelho dos Mamíferos Ameaçados de Extinção.* Fundação Biodiversitas, Belo Horizonte, Brasil.
Fontaine, P.A. (1965). Breeding clouded leopards (*Neofelis nebulosa*) at Dallas Zoo. *Int. Zoo Yb.* **5**: 113-114.
Forbes, H.O. (1879). [Distribution of *Mydaus*]. *J. Zool., London* **1879**: 664-665.
Ford, L.S. & Hoffmann, R.S. (1988). *Potos flavus. Mammal. Species* **321**: 1-9.
Foreman, G.E. (1988). *Behavioral and Genetic Analysis of Geoffroy's Cat (*Felis geoffroyi*) in Captivity.* PhD dissertation, Ohio State University, Columbus, Ohio.
Foster, M.L. & Humphrey, S.R. (1995). Use of highway underpasses by panthers and other wildlife. *Wildl. Soc. Bull.* **232**: 92-94.
Foster-Turley, P. & Engfer, S. (1988). The species survival plan for the Asian small-clawed otter (*Aonyx cinerea*). *Int. Zoo Yb.* **27**: 79-84.
Fournier, P., Maizeret, C., Jimenez, D., Chusseau, J.P., Aulagnier, S. & Spitz, F. (2007). Habitat utilization by sympatric European mink *Mustela lutreola* and polecats *Mustela putorius* in south-western France. *Acta Theriol.* **52**: 1-12.
Fox, J.L. (1994). Snow leopard conservation in the wild - a comprehensive perspective on a low density and highly fragmented population. Pp. 3-15 in: Fox, J.L. & Du Jizeng eds. (1994). *Proceedings of the Seventh International Snow Leopard Symposium.* International Snow Leopard Trust & Chicago Zoological Society, Seattle, Washington.
Fox, J.L. & Chundawat, R.S. (1988). Observations of snow leopard stalking, killing and feeding behavior. *Mammalia* **52**: 137-140.
Fox, J.L., Yonzon, P. & Podger, N. (1996). Mapping conflicts between biodiversity and human needs in Langtang National Park, Nepal. *Conserv. Biol.* **10**: 562-569.
Fox, M.W. (1970). A comparative study of the development of facial expressions in canids; wolf, coyote and foxes. *Behaviour* **36**: 49-73.
Fox, M.W. (1984). *The Whistling Hunters. Field Studies of the Asiatic Wild Dog* Cuon alpinus. State University of New York Press, Albany, New York.
Frafjord, K. (1994). Growth rates and energy demands in captive juvenile Arctic foxes *Alopex lagopus* in Svalbard. *Polar Biol.* **14**: 355-358.
Frafjord, K. & Kruchenkova, E. (1995). Kommandorøyene: Berings tragedie og Stellers fjellrever. *Fauna* **48**: 190-203.
Frafjord, K. & Prestrud, P. (1992). Home ranges and movements of Arctic foxes *Alopex lagopus* in Svalbard. *Polar Biol.* **12**: 519-526.
Frame, G.W. (1975-1976). Cheetah ecology and behaviour. Pp. 74-87 in: *1975-76 Annual Report.* Serengeti Research Institute, Arusha, Tanzania.
Frame, G.W. (1980). *Cheetah Social Organization in the Serengeti Ecosystem of Tanzania.* Paper at the Animal Behavior Society, 9-13 June 1980, Colorado State University, Fort Collins, Colorado.
Frame, G.W. (1992). First record of a king cheetah outside southern Africa. *Cat News* **16**: 3.
Frame, G.W. & Frame, L.H. (1981). *Swift and Enduring: Cheetahs and Wild Dogs of the Serengeti.* Dutton, New York.
Frame, L.H., Malcolm, J.R., Frame, G.W. & van Lawick, H. (1979). Social organization of African wild dogs *Lycaon pictus* on the Serengeti Plains. *Zeitschr. für Tierpsychol.* **50**: 225-249.
Francis, C.M. (2002). An observation of Hose's civet in Brunei. *Small Carniv. Conserv.* **26**: 16.
Francis, C.M. (2008). *A Field Guide to the Mammals of South-east Asia.* New Holland, London.
Frank, L.G. (1986a). Social organization of the spotted hyaena (*Crocuta crocuta*). I. Demography. *Anim. Behav.* **35**: 1500-1509.
Frank, L.G. (1986b). Social organization of the spotted hyaena (*Crocuta crocuta*). II. Dominance and reproduction. *Anim. Behav.* **35**: 1510-1527.
Frank, L.G. (1994). When hyenas kill their own. *New Scientist* **141**: 38-41.
Frank, L.G. (1997). Evolution of genital masculinization: why do female hyaenas have such a large 'penis'? *Trends Ecol. Evol.* **12**: 58-62.
Frank, L.G. & Glickman, S.E. (1991). Neonatal siblicide in the spotted hyena (*Crocuta crocuta*). *Aggressive Behavior* **17**: 67-68.
Frank, L.G. & Glickman, S.E. (1994). Giving birth through a penile clitoris - parturition and dystocia in the spotted hyaena (*Crocuta crocuta*). *J. Zool., London* **234**: 659-665.
Frank, L.G., Davidson, J.M. & Smith, E.R. (1985). Androgen levels in the spotted hyaena *Crocuta crocuta*: the influence of social factors. *J. Zool., London* **206**: 525-531.
Frank, L.G., Glickman, S.E. & Licht, P. (1991). Fatal sibling aggression, precocial development and androgens in neonatal spotted hyaenas. *Science* **252**: 702-705.
Frank, L.G., Glickman, S.E. & Powch, I. (1990). Sexual dimorphism in the spotted hyena (*Crocuta crocuta*). *J. Zool., London* **221**: 308-313.
Frank, L.G., Glickman, S.E. & Zabel, C.J. (1989). Ontogeny of female dominance in the spotted hyaena: perspectives from nature and captivity. *Symp. Zool. Soc. London* **61**: 127-146.
Frank, L.G., Holekamp, K.E. & Smale, L. (1995). Dominance, demography and reproductive success of female spotted hyenas. Pp. 364-384 in: Sinclair, A.R.E. & Arcese, P. eds. (1995). *Serengeti II - Dynamics, Conservation and Management of an Ecosystem.* University of Chicago Press, Chicago, Illinois.
Frank, L.G., Weldele, M.L. & Glickman, S.E. (1995). Masculinization costs in hyaenas. *Nature (London)* **377**: 584-585.
Franklin, C.E. & Axelsson, M. (2000). An actively controlled heart valve. *Nature (London)* **406**: 847-848.
Franklin, N. & Wells, P. (2005). Observation of a Malay weasel in Sumatra. *Small Carniv. Conserv.* **32**: 15.
Franklin, N., Bastoni, Sriyanto, Siswomartono, D., Manansang, J. & Tilson, R. (1999). Last of the Indonesian tigers: a cause for optimism. Pp. 130-147 in: Seidensticker, J., Christie, S. & Jackson, P. eds. (1999). *Riding the Tiger: Tiger Conservation in Human-dominated Landscapes.* Cambridge University Press, Cambridge.
Franklin, W.L., Johnson, W.E., Sarno, R.J. & Iriarte, J.A. (1999). Ecology of the Patagonia Puma *Felis concolor patagonica* in southern Chile. *Biol. Conserv.* **90**: 33-40.
Frazer Sissom, D.E., Rice, D.A. & Peters, G. (1991). How cats purr. *J. Zool., London* **223**: 67-78.
Fredga, K. (1972). Comparative chromosome studies in mongooses (Carnivora, Viverridae). I. Idiograms of 12 species and karyotype evolution in Herpestinae. *Hereditas* **71**: 1-74.
Fredriksson, G.M. (2005). Human-sun bear conflicts in East Kalimantan, Indonesian Borneo. *Ursus* **16**: 130-137.
Fredriksson, G.M., Danielsen, L.S. & Swenson, J.E. (2007). Impacts of El Niño related drought and forest fires on sun bear fruit resources in lowland dipterocarp forest of east Borneo. *Biodiversity & Conservation* **16**: 1823-1838.
Fredriksson, G.M., Steinmetz, R., Wong, S.T. & Garshelis, D.L. (2007). *Helarctos malayanus* sun bear. In: *2007 IUCN Red List of Threatened Species.* URL: http://www.iucnredlist.org.html

Fredriksson, G.M., Wich, S.A. & Trisno (2006). Frugivory in sun bears (*Helarctos malayanus*) is linked to El Niño-related fluctuations in fruiting phenology, East Kalimantan, Indonesia. *Biol. J. Linn. Soc.* **89**: 489-508.

Freeman, H. (1980). The snow leopard, today and yesterday. *Int. Ped. Book Snow Leopards* **2**: 37-43.

Freeman, H. (1983). Behaviour in adult pairs of captive snow leopards (*Panthera uncia*). *Zoo Biology* **2**: 1-22.

Freeman, H., Jackson, R., Hillard, D. & Hunter, D.O. (1994). Project Snow Leopard: a multinational program spearheaded by the International Snow Leopard Trust. Pp. 241-252 in: Fox, J.L. & Du Jizeng eds. (1994). *Proceedings of the Seventh International Snow Leopard Symposium.* International Snow Leopard Trust & Chicago Zoological Society, Seattle, Washington.

Freeman, S. (1990). The evolution of the scrotum: a new hypothesis. *J. Theor. Biol.* **145**: 429-445.

Frese, R. (1980). Some notes on breeding the leopard cat (*Felis bengalensis*) at West Berlin Zoo. *Int. Zoo Yb.* **20**: 220-223.

Frey, S.N. & Conover, M.R. (2007). Influence of population reduction on predator home range size and spatial overlap. *J. Wildl. Management* **71**: 303-309.

Friscia, A.R., Van Valkenburgh, B. & Biknevicius, A.R. (2007). An ecomorphological analysis of extant small carnivorans. *J. Zool., London* **272**: 82-100.

Fritts, S.H. & Sealander, J.A. (1978a). Diets of bobcats in Arkansas with special reference to age and sex differences. *J. Wildl. Management* **42**: 533-539.

Fritts, S.H. & Sealander, J.A. (1978b). Reproductive biology and population characteristics of bobcats in Arkansas. *J. Mammal.* **59**: 347-353.

Fritzell, E.K. (1987). Gray fox and island gray fox. Pp. 408-420 in: Novak, M., Baker, J.A., Obbard, M.E. & Malloch, B. eds. (1987). *Wild Furbearer Management and Conservation in North America.* Ministry of Natural Resources, Ontario.

Fritzell, E.K. & Haroldson, K.J. (1982). *Urocyon cinereoargenteus. Mammal. Species* **189**: 1-8.

Fujii, T., Maruyama, N. & Kanzaki, N. (1998). Seasonal changes in food habits of Japanese weasel in a middle stream of the Tamagawa River. *Mammal. Sci.* **38**: 1-8.

Fukue, Y. (1991). [*Utilisation Pattern of Home Range and Parental Care of the Raccoon Dogs at the Kanazawa University Campus*]. MSc thesis, Kanazawa University, Kanazawa, Japan. In Japanese.

Fukue, Y. (1993). [Study of raccoon dog, *Nyctereutes procyonoides*, in Marunouchi, Kanazawa: morphometric variation]. *Ann. Rep. Botanic Garden, Fac. Sci., Kanazawa Univ.* **16**: 33-36. In Japanese.

Fuller, K.S., Swift, B., Jorgensen, A. & Bräutigam, A. (1987). *Latin American Wildlife Trade Laws.* 2nd edition. World Wildlife Fund, Washington, D.C.

Fuller, T.K. (1989). Population dynamics of wolves in north-central Minnesota. *Wildl. Monogr.* **105**: 1-41.

Fuller, T.K. & Cypher, B.L. (2004). Gray fox *Urocyon cinereoargenteus*. Pp. 92-97 in: Sillero-Zubiri, C., Hoffmann, M. & Macdonald, D.W. eds. (2004). *Canids: Foxes, Wolves, Jackals and Dogs. Status Survey and Conservation Action Plan.* IUCN/SSC Canid Specialist Group, Gland & Cambridge.

Fuller, T.K. & Sievert, P.R. (2001). Carnivore demography and the consequences of changes in prey availability. Pp. 163-178 in: Gittleman, J.L., Funk, S.M., Macdonald, D. & Wayne, R.K. eds. (2001). *Carnivore Conservation.* Cambridge University Press, Cambridge.

Fuller, T.K., Biknevicius, A.R. & Kat, P.W. (1988). Home range of an African wildcat, *Felis silvestris* (Schreber), near Elmenteita, Kenya. *Zeitschrift für Säugetierkunde* **53**: 380-381.

Fuller, T.K., Biknevicius, A.R. & Kat, P.W. (1990). Movements and behavior of large-spotted genets (*Genetta maculata* Gray 1830) near Elmenteita, Kenya (Mammalia, Viverridae). *Tropical Zool.* **3**: 13-19.

Fuller, T.K., Biknevicius, A.R., Kat, P.W., Van Valkenburgh, B. & Wayne, R.K. (1989). The ecology of three sympatric jackal species in the Rift Valley of Kenya. *Afr. J. Ecol.* **27**: 313-324.

Fuller, T.K., Johnson, W.E., Franklin, W.L. & Johnson, K.A. (1987). Notes on the Patagonian hog-nosed skunk (*Conepatus humboldti*) in southern Chile. *J. Mammal.* **68**: 864-867.

Fuller, T.K., Kat, P.W., Bulger, J.B., Maddock, A.H., Ginsberg, J.R., Burrows, R., McNutt, J.W. & Mills, M.G.L. (1992). Population dynamics of African wild dogs. Pp. 1125-1139 in: McCullough, D.R. & Barrett, H. eds. (1992). *Wildlife 2001: Populations.* Elsevier Science Publishers, London.

Fuller, T.K., Mills, M.G.L., Borner, M., Laurenson, K. & Kat, P.W. (1992). Long distance dispersal by African wild dogs in east and south Africa. *J. Afr. Zool.* **106**: 535-537.

Fulton, T.L. & Strobeck, C. (2006). Molecular phylogeny of the Arctoidea (Carnivora): Effect of missing data on supertree and supermatrix analyses of multiple gene data sets. *Mol. Phylogen. Evol.* **41**: 165-181.

Fulton, T.L. & Strobeck, C. (2007). Novel phylogeny of the raccoon family (Procyonidae, Carnivora) based on nuclear and mitochondrial DNA evidence. *Mol. Phylogen. Evol.* **43**: 1171-1177.

Funston, P.J. & Mills, M.G.L. (1997). Aspects of sociality in Kruger Park lions: the role of males. Pp. 18-26 in: Van Heerden, J. ed. (1997). *Lions and Leopards as Game Ranch Animals.* The Wildlife Group, South African Veterinary Association, Onderstepoort, South Africa.

Funston, P.J., Mills, M.G.L. & Biggs, H.C. (2001). Factors affecting the hunting success of male and female lions in the Kruger National Park. *J. Zool., London* **253**: 419-431.

Galbreath, G.J., Groves, C.P. & Waits, L.P. (2007). Genetic resolution of composition and phylogenetic placement of the Isabelline bear. *Ursus* **18**: 129-131.

Galbreath, G.J., Hean, S. & Montgomery, S.M. (2000). A new color phase of *Ursus thibetanus* (Mammalia: Ursidae) from southeast Asia. *Nat. Hist. Bull. Siam Soc.* **49**: 107-111.

Galef, B.G., Mittermeier, R.A. & Bailey, R.C. (1976). Predation by the tayra (*Eira barbara*). *J. Mammal.* **57**: 760-761.

Galis, F. (1999). Why do most mammals have seven cervical vertebrae? Developmental constraints, *Hox* genes and cancer. *J. Exper. Zool.* **285**: 19-26.

Gallo, J.P. (1991). The status and distribution of river otters (*Lutra longicaudis annectens* Major, 1897), in Mexico. *Habitat* **6**: 57-62.

Gambaryan, P.P. (1974). *How Mammals Run.* John Wiley & Sons, New York.

Ganesh, T. (1997). Occurrence of the brown palm civet in the west forest of Kalakad Mundanthurai Tiger Reserve. *J. Bombay Nat. Hist. Soc.* **94**: 556.

Ganesh, T., Ganesan, R. & Soubadra, M. (1998). Diet of the brown palm civet (*Paradoxurus jerdoni*) in Kalakad-Mundanthurai Tiger Reserve, Tamil Nadu. *J. Bombay Nat. Hist. Soc.* **95**: 108-109.

Gangloff, B. (1972). *Contribution à l'Éthologie Comparée des Viverridés.* PhD dissertation, Université de Strasbourg, Strasbourg.

Gangloff, B. (1975). Beitrag zur Ethologie der Schleichkatzen (Bänderlinsang, *Prionodon linsang* (Hardw.), und Bänderpalmenroller, *Hemigalus derbyanus* (Gray)). *Zool. Garten* **45**: 329-376.

Gangloff, B. & Ropartz, P. (1972). Le répertoire comportemental de la genette (*Genetta genetta* L.). *Rev. Écol. (Terre Vie)* **26**: 489-560.

Gangloff, L. (1972). Breeding fennec foxes *Fennecus zerda* at Strasbourg Zoo. *Int. Zoo Yb.* **12**: 115-116.

Ganley-Leal, L.M., Brown, C., Tulman, E.R., Bergman, L., Hinckley, L., Johnson, K.H., Liu, X., Van Kruiningen, H.J. & Frasca, S. (2007). Suppurative polyarthritis in striped skunks (*Mephitis mephitis*) from Cape Cod, Massachusetts: detection of mycoplasma DNA. *J. Zoo Wildl. Med.* **38**: 388-399.

Gao, Y.T., Wang, S., Zhang, M.L., Ye, Z.Y. & Zhou, J.D. eds. (1987). [*Fauna Sinica, Mammalia*]. Vol. 8. Carnivora. Science Press, Beijing, China. In Chinese.

Garant, Y. & Crete, M. (1997). Fisher, *Martes pennanti*, home range characteristics in a high density untrapped population in southern Quebec. *Can. Field-Nat.* **111**: 359-364.

Garbutt, N. (2007). *Mammals of Madagascar: a Complete Guide.* A&C Black Publishers, London.

Garcelon, D.K., Roemer, G.W., Phillips, R.B. & Coonan, T.J. (1999). Food provisioning by island foxes *Urocyon littoralis* to conspecifics caught in traps. *Southwest. Nat.* **44**: 83-86.

Garcelon, D.K., Wayne, R.K. & Gonzales, B.J. (1992). A serological survey of the island fox *Urocyon littoralis* on the Channel Islands, California. *J. Wildl. Diseases* **28**: 223-229.

Garcia, G.G. & Goodman, S.M. (2003). Hunting of protected animals in the Parc National d'Ankarafantsika, north-western Madagascar. *Oryx* **37**: 115-118.

García, J. (1991). Administrando para conservar: el caso de los zorros autóctonos de la Argentina. Pp. 25-36 in: Funes, M.C. & Novaro, A.J. eds. (1991). *Actas Tercera Reunión Patagónica sobre el Manejo de Poblaciones de Zorros.* Junín de Los Andes, Argentina.

Garcia, N.E., Vaughan, C.S. & McCoy, M.B. (2002). Ecology of Central American cacomistles in Costa Rican cloud forest. *Vida Silvestre Neotrop.* **11**: 52-59.

García, V.B. (2001). *Dieta, Uso de Ambiente y Abundancia Relativa del Zorro Gris Pampeano,* Pseudalopex gymnocercus, *en la Reserva de Uso Múltiple Bahía San Blas e Isla Gama, Provincia de Buenos Aires.* BSc thesis, UNMdP, Mar del Plata, Argentina.

García-Perea, R. (1994). The Pampas cat group (genus *Lynchailurus* Severtzov, 1858) (Carnivora: Felidae), a systematic and biogeographic review. *Amer. Mus. Novit.* **3096**: 1-36.

García-Perea, R. (1999). *A Morphological Key to Distinguish Andean Mountain Cats from Pampas Cats (Genus* Lynchailurus*).* Final report to Cat Action Treasury.

García-Perea, R. (2002). Andean mountain cat, *Oreailurus jacobita*: morphological description and comparison with other felines from the altiplano. *J. Mammal.* **83**: 110-124.

García-Perea, R., Gisbert, J. & Palacios, F. (1985). Review of the biometrical and morphological features of the skull of the Iberian lynx, *Lynx pardina* (Temminck, 1824). *Säugetierkunde Mitt.* **32**: 249-259.

Gardner, A.L. (1971). Notes on the little spotted cat, *Felis tigrina oncilla* Thomas, in Costa Rica. *J. Mammal.* **52**: 464-465.

Garin, I., Aihartza, J., Zuberogoitia, I. & Zabala, J. (2002). Activity pattern of European mink (*Mustela lutreola*) in southwestern Europe. *Z. Jagdwiss.* **48**: 102-106.

Garin, I., Zuberogoitia, I., Zabala, J., Aihartza, J., Clevenger, A. & Rallo, A. (2002). Home ranges of European mink *Mustela lutreola* in southwestern Europe. *Acta Theriol.* **47**: 55-62.

Garrott, R.A. & Eberhardt, L.E. (1982). Mortality of Arctic fox pups in northern Alaska. *J. Mammal.* **63**: 173-174.

Garrott, R.A. & Eberhardt, L.E. (1987). Arctic fox. Pp. 395-406 in: Novak, M., Baker, J.A., Obbard, M.E. & Malloch, B. eds. (1987). *Wild Furbearer Management and Conservation in North America.* Ministry of Natural Resources, Ontario.

Garshelis, D.L. (2002). Misconceptions, ironies and uncertainties regarding trends in bear populations. *Ursus* **13**: 321-334.

Garshelis, D.L. (2004). Variation in ursid life histories: is there an outlier? Pp. 53-73 in: Lindburg, D. & Baragona, K. eds. (2004). *Giant Pandas. Biology and Conservation.* University of California Press, Berkeley, California.

Garshelis, D.L. & Hellgren, E.C. (1994). Variation in reproductive biology of male black bears. *J. Mammal.* **75**: 175-188.

Garshelis, D.L. & Hristienko, H. (2006). State and provincial estimates of American black bear numbers versus assessments of population trend. *Ursus* **17**: 1-7.

Garshelis, D.L. & Noyce, K.V. (2008). Seeing the world through the nose of a bear – diversity of foods fosters behavioral and demographic stability. Pp. 139-163 in: Fulbright, T.E. & Hewitt, D.G. eds. (2008). *Wildlife Science: Linking Ecological Theory and Management Applications.* CRC Press, Boca Raton, Florida.

Garshelis, D.L. & Pelton, M.R. (1980). Activity of black bears in the Great Smoky Mountains National Park. *J. Mammal.* **61**: 8-19.

Garshelis, D.L. & Steinmetz, R. (2007). *Ursus thibetanus* Asiatic black bear. In: *2007 IUCN Red List of Threatened Species.* URL: http://www.iucnredlist.org.html

Garshelis, D.L., Crider, D. & Van Manen, F.T. (2007). *Ursus americanus* American black bear. In: *2007 IUCN Red List of Threatened Species.* URL: http://www.iucnredlist.org.html

Garshelis, D.L., Gibeau, M.L. & Herrero, S. (2005). Grizzly bear demographics in and around Banff National Park and Kananaskis Country, Alberta. *J. Wildl. Management* **69**: 277-297.

Garshelis, D.L., Joshi, A.R. & Smith, J.L.D. (1999). Estimating density and relative abundance of sloth bears. *Ursus* **11**: 87-98.

Garshelis, D.L., Joshi, A.R., Smith, J.L.D. & Rice, C.G. (1999). Sloth bear conservation action plan. Pp. 225-240 in: Servheen, C., Herrero, S. & Peyton, B. eds. (1999). *Bears: Status Survey and Conservation Action Plan.* IUCN/SSC Bear and Polar Bear Specialist Groups, Gland & Cambridge.

Garshelis, D.L., Quigley, H.B., Villarrubia, C.R. & Pelton, M.R. (1983). Diel movements of black bears in the Southern Appalachians. *Int. Conf. Bear Res. Management* **5**: 11-19.

Garshelis, D.L., Ratnayeke, S. & Chauhan, N.S. (2007). *Melursus ursinus* sloth bear. In: *2007 IUCN Red List of Threatened Species*. URL: http://www.iucnredlist.org.html

Garshelis, D.L., Wang, H., Wang, D., Zhu, X. & McShea, W.J. (2008). Do revised giant panda population estimates aid in their conservation? *Ursus* **19**: 168-176.

Garza, N.O., McCarthy, T.J., Sierra, J.M., Matson, J.O. & Eckerlin, R.P. (2000). Ampliación del área de distribución de *Bassaricyon baggiii* J.A. Allen, 1876 (Carnivora: Procyonidae) en el norte de America Central. *Rev. Mex. Mastozool.* **4**: 114-116.

Gasaway, W.C., Mossestad, K.T. & Stander, P.E. (1989). Demography of spotted hyaenas in an arid savanna, Etosha National Park, South West Africa/Namibia. *Madoqua* **16**: 121-127.

Gasaway, W.C., Mossestad, K.T. & Stander, P.E. (1991). Food acquisition by spotted hyaenas in Etosha National Park, Namibia: predation versus scavenging. *Afr. J. Ecol.* **29**: 64-75.

Gashwiler, J.S., Robinette, W.L. & Morris, O.W. (1960). Foods of bobcats of Utah and eastern Nevada. *J. Wildl. Management* **24**: 226-229.

Gasperetti, J., Harrison, D.L. & Büttiker, W. (1985). The Carnivora of Arabia. *Fauna Saudi Arabia* **7**: 397-461.

Gatti, A., Bianchi, R., Rosa, C.R.X. & Mendes, S.L. (2006). Diet of two sympatric carnivores, *Cerdocyon thous* and *Procyon cancrivorus*, in a resting area of Espirito Santo State, Brazil. *J. Trop. Ecol.* **22**: 227-230.

Gaubert, P. (2003a). Description of a new species of genet (Carnivora; Viverridae; genus *Genetta*) and taxonomic revision of forest forms related to the large-spotted genet complex. *Mammalia* **67**: 85-108.

Gaubert, P. (2003b). *Systématique et Phylogénie du Genre* Genetta *et des Énigmatiques "Genet-like taxa"* Prionodon, Poiana *et* Osbornictis *(Carnivora, Viverridae): Caractérisation de la Sous-famille des Viverrinae et Étude des Patrons de Diversification au Sein du Continent Africain.* PhD dissertation, Muséum National d'Histoire Naturelle, Paris.

Gaubert, P. (In press a). Nandiniidae (Pocock). In: Kingdon, J.S. & Hoffmann, M. eds. (In press). *The Mammals of Africa.* Vol. 5. Carnivora, Pholidota, Perissodactyla. Academic Press, Amsterdam.

Gaubert, P. (In press b). *Genetta abyssinica*. In: Kingdon, J.S. & Hoffmann, M. eds. (In press). *The Mammals of Africa.* Vol. 5. Carnivores, Pangolins, Rhinos and Equids. Academic Press, Amsterdam.

Gaubert, P. (In press c). *Genetta bourloni*. In: Kingdon, J.S. & Hoffmann, M. eds. (In press). *The Mammals of Africa.* Vol. 5. Carnivores, Pangolins, Rhinos and Equids. Academic Press, Amsterdam.

Gaubert, P. (In press d). *Genetta tigrina*. In: Kingdon, J.S. & Hoffmann, M. eds. (In press). *The Mammals of Africa.* Vol. 5. Carnivores, Pangolins, Rhinos and Equids. Academic Press, Amsterdam.

Gaubert, P. & Begg, C.M. (2007). Re-assessed molecular phylogeny and evolutionary scenario within genets (Carnivora, Viverridae, Genettinae). *Mol. Phylogen. Evol.* **44(2)**: 920-927.

Gaubert, P. & Cordeiro-Estrela, P. (2006). Phylogenetic systematics and tempo of evolution of the Viverrinae (Mammalia, Carnivora, Viverridae) within feliformians: implications for faunal exchanges between Asia and Africa. *Mol. Phylogen. Evol.* **41**: 266-278.

Gaubert, P. & Dunham, A.E. (In press a). *Genetta pardina*. In: Kingdon, J.S. & Hoffmann, M. eds. (In press). *The Mammals of Africa.* Vol. 5. Carnivores, Pangolins, Rhinos and Equids. Academic Press, Amsterdam.

Gaubert, P. & Dunham, A.E. (In press b). *Genetta thierryi*. In: Kingdon, J.S. & Hoffmann, M. eds. (In press). *The Mammals of Africa.* Vol. 5. Carnivores, Pangolins, Rhinos and Equids. Academic Press, Amsterdam.

Gaubert, P. & Veron, G. (2003). Exhaustive sample set among Viverridae reveals the sister-group of felids: the linsangs as a case of extreme morphological convergence within Feliformia. *Proc. Royal Soc. London (Ser. B Biol. Sci.)* **270**: 2523-2530.

Gaubert, P. & Wozencraft, W.C. (2005). Comment on the proposed conservation of *Viverra maculata* Gray, 1830 (currently *Genetta maculata*; Mammalia, Carnivora). *Bull. Zool. Nomencl.* **62**: 242-244.

Gaubert, P., Fernandes, C.A., Bruford, M.W. & Veron, G. (2004). Genets in Africa: an evolutionary synthesis based on cytochrome *b* sequences and morphological characters. *Biol. J. Linn. Soc.* **81**: 589-610.

Gaubert, P., Papes, M. & Peterson, A.T. (2006). Natural history collections and the conservation of poorly known taxa: ecological niche modelling in central African rainforest genets (*Genetta spp.*). *Biol. Conserv.* **130**: 106-117.

Gaubert, P., Taylor, P.J., Fernandes, C.A., Bruford, M.W. & Veron, G. (2005). Detection of cryptic hybrid zones using a multidimensional approach: a case study on genets (*Genetta spp.*) from the southern African subregion. *Biol. J. Linn. Soc.* **86**: 11-33.

Gaubert, P., Taylor, P.J. & Veron, G. (2005). Integrative taxonomy and phylogenetic systematics of the genets (Carnivora, Viverridae, genus *Genetta*): a new classification of the most speciose carnivoran genus in Africa. Pp. 371-383 in: Huber, B.A., Sinclair, B.J. & Lampe, K.H. eds. (2005). *African Biodiversity: Molecules, Organisms, Ecosystems. Proceedings of the 5th International Symposium on Tropical Biology, Museum Koenig, Bonn.* Springer Verlag, Bonn.

Gaubert, P., Tranier, M., Delmas, A.S., Colyn, M. & Veron, G. (2004). First molecular evidence for reassessing phylogenetic affinities between genets (*Genetta*) and the enigmatic genet-like taxa *Osbornictis, Poiana* and *Prionodon* (Carnivora, Viverridae). *Zool. Scr.* **33**: 117-129.

Gaubert, P., Tranier, M., Veron, G., Kock, D., Dunham, A.E., Taylor, P.J., Stuart, C., Stuart, T. & Wozencraft, W.C. (2003). Nomenclatural comments on the rusty-spotted genet (Carnivora, Viverridae) and designation of a neotype. *Zootaxa* **160**: 1-14.

Gaubert, P., Veron, G., Colyn, M., Dunham, A., Shultz, S. & Tranier, M. (2002). A reassessment of the distribution of the rare *Genetta johnstoni* (Viverridae, Carnivora) with some newly discovered specimens. *Mammal Rev.* **32**: 132-144.

Gaubert, P., Veron, G. & Tranier, M. (2001). An investigation of morpho-anatomical characters within the genus *Genetta* (Carnivora, Viverridae), with a remark on *Osbornictis*, the aquatic genet. Pp. 81-89 in: Denys, C., Granjon, L. & Poulet, A. eds. (2001). *African Small Mammals.* IRD ed., Collection Colloques et Séminaires, Paris.

Gaubert, P., Veron, G. & Tranier, M. (2002). Genets and "genet-like" taxa (Carnivora, Viverrinae): phylogenetic analysis, systematics and biogeographic implications. *Zool. J. Linn. Soc.* **134**: 317-334.

Gaubert, P., Volobouev, V.T., Aniskin, V.M., Dunham, A.E. & Cremiere, C. (2004). Karyotype of the rare Johnston's genet *Genetta johnstoni* (Viverridae) and a reassessment of chromosomal characterization among congeneric species. *Acta Theriol.* **49**: 457-464.

Gaubert, P., Wozencraft, W.C., Cordeiro-Estrela, P. & Veron, G. (2005). Mosaics of convergences and noise in morphological phylogenies: what's in a viverrid-like carnivoran? *Syst. Biol.* **54**: 865-894.

Gauthier-Pilters, H. (1962). Beobachtungen en feneks (*Fennecus zerda* Zimm.). *Zietschr. Tierpsychol.* **19**: 440-464.

Gauthier-Pilters, H. (1967). The fennec. *Afr. Wildl.* **21**: 117-125.

Gautier, L. & Goodman, S.M. (2003). Introduction to the flora of Madagascar. Pp. 229-250 in: Goodman, S.M. & Benstead, J.P. eds. (2003). *The Natural History of Madagascar.* The University of Chicago Press, Chicago, Illinois.

Gay, S.W. & Best, T.L. (1995). Geographic variation in sexual dimorphism of the puma (*Puma concolor*) in North and South America. *Southwest. Nat.* **40**: 148-159.

Geertsema, A.A. (1976). Impressions and observations of serval behaviour in Tanzania, east Africa. *Mammalia* **40**: 13-19.

Geertsema, A.A. (1981). The servals of Gorigor. *Wildl. News* **16(3)**: 4-8.

Geertsema, A.A. (1985). Aspects of the ecology of the serval *Leptailurus serval* in the Ngorongoro Crater, Tanzania. *Netherlands J. Zool.* **35(4)**: 527-610.

Geffen, E. (1994). Blanford's fox *Vulpes cana. Mammal. Species* **462**: 1-4.

Geffen, E. & Macdonald, D.W. (1992). Small size and monogamy: spatial organization of the Blanford's fox *Vulpes cana. Anim. Behav.* **44**: 1123-1130.

Geffen, E. & Macdonald, D.W. (1993). Activity and movement patterns of Blandford's foxes. *J. Mammal.* **74(2)**: 455-463.

Geffen, E., Dagan, A.A., Kam, M., Hefner, R. & Nagy, K.A. (1992). Daily energy expenditure and water flux of free-living Blanford's foxes *Vulpes cana*: a small desert carnivore. *J. Anim. Ecol.* **61**: 611-617.

Geffen, E., Hefner, R., Macdonald, D.W. & Ucko, M. (1992a). Diet and foraging behavior of the Blanford's fox *Vulpes cana* in Israel. *J. Mammal.* **73**: 395-402.

Geffen, E., Hefner, R., Macdonald, D.W. & Ucko, M. (1992b). Habitat selection and home range in the Blanford's fox, *Vulpes cana*: compatibility with the Resource Dispersion Hypothesis. *Oecologia* **91**: 75-81.

Geffen, E., Hefner, R., Macdonald, D.W. & Ucko, M. (1992c). Morphological adaptations and seasonal weight changes in the Blanford's fox *Vulpes cana. J. Arid Environm.* **23**: 287-292.

Geffen, E., Hefner, R., Macdonald, D.W. & Ucko, M. (1993). Biotope and distribution of the Blanford's fox. *Oryx* **27**: 104-108.

Geffen, E., Hefner, R. & Wright, P. (2004). Blanford's fox *Vulpes cana*. Pp. 194-198 in: Sillero-Zubiri, C., Hoffmann, M. & Macdonald, D.W. eds. (2004). *Canids: Foxes, Wolves, Jackals and Dogs. Status Survey and Conservation Action Plan.* IUCN/SSC Canid Specialist Group, Gland & Cambridge.

Geffen, E., Mercure, A., Girman, D.J., Macdonald, D.W. & Wayne, R.K. (1992). Phylogeny of the fox-like canids: analysis of mtDNA restriction fragment, site and cytochrome b sequence data. *J. Zool., London* **228**: 27-39.

Gehring, T.M. & Swihart, R.K. (2004). Home range and movements of long-tailed weasels in a landscape fragmented by agriculture. *J. Mammal.* **85**: 79-86.

Gehrt, S.D. (2003). Raccoons (*Procyon lotor* and allies). Pp. 611-634 in: Feldhammer, G.A., Thompson, B.C. & Chapman, J.A. eds. (2003). *Wild Mammals of North America: Biology, Management and Conservation.* 2nd edition. Johns Hopkins University Press, Baltimore, Maryland.

Gehrt, S.D. (2004). Ecology and management of striped skunks, raccoons and coyotes in urban landscapes. Pp. 81-104 in: Fascione, N., Delach, A. & Smith, M. eds. (2004). *People and Predators: from Conflict to Conservation.* Island Press, New York.

Gehrt, S.D. (2005). Seasonal survival and cause-specific mortality of urban and rural striped skunks in the absence of rabies. *J. Mammal.* **86**: 1164-1170.

Gehrt, S.D. & Clark, W.R. (2003). Raccoons, coyotes and reflections on the mesopredator release hypothesis. *Wildl. Soc. Bull.* **31**: 836-842.

Gehrt, S.D. & Fritzell, E.K. (1996a). Second estrus and late litters in raccoons. *J. Mammal.* **77**: 388-393.

Gehrt, S.D. & Fritzell, E.K. (1996b). Sex-biased response of raccoons (*Procyon lotor*) to live traps. *Amer. Midl. Nat.* **135**: 23-32.

Gehrt, S.D. & Fritzell, E.K. (1997). Sexual differences in home ranges of raccoons. *J. Mammal.* **78**: 921-931.

Gehrt, S.D. & Fritzell, E.K. (1998a). Duration of familial bonds and dispersal patterns for raccoons in south Texas. *J. Mammal.* **79**: 859-872.

Gehrt, S.D. & Fritzell, E.K. (1998b). Resource distribution, female home range dispersion and male spatial interactions: group structure in a solitary carnivore. *Anim. Behav.* **55**: 1211-1227.

Gehrt, S.D. & Fritzell, E.K. (1999a). Behavioural aspects of the raccoon mating system: determinants of consortship success. *Anim. Behav.* **57**: 593-601.

Gehrt, S.D. & Fritzell, E.K. (1999b). Survivorship of a nonharvested raccoon population in south Texas. *J. Wildl. Management* **63**: 889-894.

Gehrt, S.D. & Prange, S. (2007). Interference competition between coyotes and raccoons: a test of the mesopredator release hypothesis. *Behav. Ecol.* **18**: 204-214.

Gehrt, S.D., Hubert, G.F. & Ellis, J.A. (2006). Extrinsic effects on long-term population trends of Virginia opossums and striped skunks at a large spatial scale. *Amer. Midl. Nat.* **155**: 168-180.

Geidel, B. & Gensch, W. (1976). The rearing of clouded leopards in the presence of the male. *Int. Zoo Yb.* **16**: 124-126.

Gende, S.M., Quinn, T.P. & Willson, M.F. (2001). Consumption choice by bears feeding on salmon. *Oecologia* **127**: 372-382.

Genov, P. & Wassiley, S. (1989). Der schakal (*Canis aureus* L.) in Bulgarian. Ein beitrag zu seiner verbreitung und biologie. *Zeitschr. Jagdwiss.* **35**: 145-150.

Genovesi, P. & Boitani, L. (1997). Day resting sites of the stone marten. *Hystrix* **9**: 75-78.

Genovesi, P., Secchi, M. & Boitani, L. (1996). Diet of stone martens: an example of ecological flexibility. *J. Zool., London* **238**: 545-555.

Genovesi, P., Sinibaldi, I. & Boitani, L. (1997). Spacing patterns and territoriality of the stone marten. *Can. J. Zool.* **75**: 1966-1971.

Genoways, H.H. & Jones, J.K. (1968). Notes on spotted skunks (genus *Spilogale*) from western Mexico. *An. Inst. Biol. Univ. Nac. Aut. Mex. (Ser. Zool.)* **39**: 123-132.

Gentry, R.L. & Peterson, R.S. (1967). Underwater vision of the sea otter. *Nature (London)* **216**: 435-436.

George, J. (2006). Climate change lures skunks, moose to the Arctic. In: *Nunatsiaq News.* Iqaluit, Nunavik, Quebec.

Geptner, V.G., Naumov, N.P., Urgenson, M.B., Sludskiy, A.A., Chirkova, A.F. & Bannikov, A.G. (1967). [*The Mammals of Soviet Union*]. Vol. 2, Part 1. Vischay shkola, Moscow. In Russian.

Gese, E.M. & Bekoff, M. (2004). Coyote *Canis latrans*. Pp. 81-87 in: Sillero-Zubiri, C., Hoffmann, M. & Macdonald, D.W. eds. (2004). *Canids: Foxes, Wolves, Jackals and Dogs. Status Survey and Conservation Action Plan.* IUCN/SSC Canid Specialist Group, Gland & Cambridge.

Gese, E.M. & Grothe, S. (1995). Analysis of coyote predation on deer and elk during winter in Yellowstone National Park, Wyoming. *Amer. Midl. Nat.* **133**: 36-43.

Gese, E.M., Ruff, R.L. & Crabtree, R.L. (1996a). Foraging ecology of coyotes *Canis latrans*: the influence of extrinsic factors and a dominance hierarchy. *Can. J. Zool.* **74**: 769-783.

Gese, E.M., Ruff, R.L. & Crabtree, R.L. (1996b). Intrinsic and extrinsic factors influencing coyote predation of small mammals in Yellowstone National Park. *Can. J. Zool., London* **74**: 784-797.

Gese, E.M., Ruff, R.L. & Crabtree, R.L. (1996c). Social and nutritional factors influencing the dispersal of resident coyotes. *Anim. Behav.* **52**: 1025-1043.

Gettings, F. (1989). *The Secret Lore of the Cat.* Grafton, London.

Gier, H.T. (1968). *Coyotes in Kansas.* Kansas Agricultural Experiment Station, Kansas State University, Manhattan, Kansas.

Gilchrist, J.S. (2001). *Reproduction and Pup Care in the Communal Breeding Banded Mongoose.* PhD thesis, University of Cambridge, Cambridge.

Gilchrist, J.S. (2004). Pup escorting in the communal breeding banded mongoose: behavior, benefits and maintenance. *Behav. Ecol.* **15**: 952-960.

Gilchrist, J.S. (2006a). Female eviction, abortion and infanticide in banded mongooses (*Mungos mungo*): implications for social control of reproduction and synchronized parturition. *Behav. Ecol.* **17**: 664-669.

Gilchrist, J.S. (2006b). Reproductive success in a low skew, communal breeding mammal: the banded mongoose, *Mungos mungo. Behav. Ecol. Sociobiol.* **60**: 854-863.

Gilchrist, J.S. (2008). Aggressive monopolization of mobile carers by young of a cooperative breeder. *Proc. Royal Soc. London (Ser. B. Biol. Sci.)* **275**: 2491-2498. doi:10.1098/rspb.2008.0597

Gilchrist, J.S. & Otali, E. (2002). The effects of refuse-feeding on home-range use, group size and intergroup encounters in the banded mongoose. *Can. J. Zool.* **80**: 1795-1802.

Gilchrist, J.S. & Russell, A.F. (2007). Who cares? Individual contributions to pup care by breeders vs non-breeders in the cooperatively breeding banded mongoose (*Mungos mungo*). *Behav. Ecol. Sociobiol.* **61**: 1053-1060.

Gilchrist, J.S., Otali, E. & Mwanguhya, F. (2004). Why breed communally? Factors affecting fecundity in a communal breeding mammal: the banded mongoose (*Mungos mungo*). *Behav. Ecol. Sociobiol.* **57**: 119-131.

Gilchrist, J.S., Otali, E. & Mwanguhya, F. (2008). Caregivers recognise and bias response towards individual young in a cooperative breeding mammal, the banded mongoose. *J. Zool., London* **275(1)**: 41-46. doi: 10.1111/j.1469-7998.2007.00405.x

Gingerich, P.D. (1994). The whales of Tethys. *Nat. Hist.* **103(4)**: 86-89.

Ginsberg, J.R. & Woodroffe, R. (1997). Extinction risks faced by remaining wild dog populations. Pp. 75-87 in: Woodroffe, R., Ginsberg, J.R. & Macdonald, D.W. eds. (1997). *The African Wild Dog: Status Survey and Conservation Action Plan.* IUCN/SSC Canid Specialist Group, Gland & Cambridge.

Girman, D.J., Miles, G., Geffen, E. & Wayne, R. (1997). A molecular genetic analysis of social structure, dispersal and pack interactions in the African wild dog *Lycaon pictus*. *Behav. Ecol. Sociobiol.* **40**: 187-198.

Gittleman, J.L. (1989). *Carnivore Behavior, Ecology and Evolution.* Chapman & Hall, London.

Gittleman, J.L. (1996). *Carnivore, Behavior, Ecology and Evolution.* Vol. 2. Comstock Publishing Associates. Cornell University Press, Ithaca, New York.

Gittleman, J.L. & Harvey, P.J. (1982). Carnivore home range size, metabolic needs and ecology. *Behav. Ecol. Sociobiol.* **10**: 57-63.

Glade, A. ed. (1993). *Proceedings of the Conservation Status of Chilean Terrestrial Vertebrate Fauna.* Corporación Nacional Forestal, Santiago, Chile.

Glickman, S.E. (1995). The spotted hyaena from Aristotle to the Lion King: reputation is everything. *Soc. Res.* **62**: 501-537.

Glickman, S.E., Cunha, G.R., Drea, C.M., Conley, A.J. & Place, N.J. (2006). Mammalian sexual differentiation: lessons from the spotted hyena. *Trends Endocrinol. Metabol.* **17**: 349-356.

Glickman, S.E., Frank, L.G., Holekamp, K.E., Smale, L. & Licht, P. (1993). Costs and benefits of "androgenization" in the female spotted hyena: the natural selection of physiological mechanisms. Pp. 87-117 in: Bateson, P.P.G., Klopfer, P.H. & Thompson, N.S. eds. (1993). *Perspectives in Ethology: Behaviour and Evolution.* Vol. 10. Plenum Press, New York.

Goeden, R., Fleschner, C. & Ricker, D. (1967). Biological control of prickly pear cacti on Santa Cruz Island, California. *Hilgardia* **38**: 579-606.

Golani, I. & Keller, A.A. (1975). A longitudinal field study of the behavior of a pair of golden jackals. Pp. 303-335 in: Fox, M.W. ed. (1975). *The Wild Canids: their Systematics, Behavioral Ecology and Evolution.* Van Nostrand, Reinhold, New York.

Golani, I. & Mendelssohn, H. (1971). Sequences of precopulatory behaviour of the jackal *Canis aureus* L. *Behaviour* **38**: 169-192.

Golden, C.D. (2005). *Eaten to Endangerment: Mammal Hunting and the Bushmeat Trade in Madagascar's Makira Forest.* Bachelor of Arts thesis, Harvard College.

Golden, C.D. (In press). An assessment of bushmeat hunting and use in the Makira Forest, NE Madagascar. *Oryx.*

Goldman, C.A. (1982). Management of the civets, genets and their allies (Mammalia: Viverridae) in captivity: part. 1. Paradoxurinae, Hemigalinae and Crytoproctinae. *Amer. Assoc. Zool. Parks Aquariums Reg. Conf. Proc.*: 14-34.

Goldman, C.A. (1984). Systematic revision of the African mongoose genus *Crossarchus* (Mammalia, Viverridae). *Can. J. Zool.* **62**: 1618-1630.

Goldman, C.A. (1987). *Crossarchus obscurus. Mammal. Species* **290**: 1-5.

Goldman, C.A. (In press). *Crossarchus platycephalus.* In: Kingdon, J.S. & Hoffmann, M. eds. (In press). *The Mammals of Africa.* Vol. 5. Carnivores, Pangolins, Rhinos and Equids. Academic Press, Amsterdam.

Goldman, C.A. & Dunham, A.E. (In press). *Crossarchus obscurus.* In: Kingdon, J.S. & Hoffmann, M. eds. (In press). *The Mammals of Africa.* Vol. 5. Carnivores, Pangolins, Rhinos and Equids. Academic Press, Amsterdam.

Goldman, E.A. (1937). The wolves of North America. *J. Mammal.* **18**: 37-45.

Goldman, E.A. (1943). A new skunk of the genus *Conepatus* from Mexico. *Proc. Biol. Soc. Washington* **56**: 89-90.

Goldman, E.A. (1950). Raccoons of North and Middle America. *North Amer. Fauna* **60**: 1-153.

Goldman, H. & Winther-Hansen, J. (2003). First photographs of the Zanzibar servaline genet *Genetta servalina archeri* and other endemic subspecies on the island of Unguja, Tanzania. *Small Carniv. Conserv.* **29**: 1-4.

Goldstein, I. (2002). Andean bear-cattle interactions and tree nest use in Bolivia and Venezuela. *Ursus* **13**: 369-372.

Goldstein, I. (2004). Andean bear use of the epiphytic bromeliad *Tillandsia fendleri* at Quebrada el Molino, Venezuela. *Ursus* **15**: 54-56.

Goldstein, I., Paisley, S., Wallace, R., Jorgenson, J., Cuesta, F. & Castellanos, A. (2006). Andean bear-livestock conflicts: a review. *Ursus* **17**: 8-15.

Goldstein, I., Velez-Liendo, X., Paisley, S. & Garshelis, D.L. (2007). *Tremarctos ornatus* Andean bear. In: *2007 IUCN Red List of Threatened Species.* URL: http://www.iucnredlist.org.html

Golla, W., Hofer, H. & East, M.L. (1999). Within-litter sibling aggression in spotted hyaenas: effect of maternal nursing, sex and age. *Anim. Behav.* **58**: 715-726.

Gomez, H., Wallace, R.B., Ayala, G. & Tejada, R. (2005). Dry season activity periods of some Amazonian mammals. *Stud. Neotrop. Fauna Environm.* **40**: 91-95.

Gompper, M.E. (1995). *Nasua narica. Mammal. Species* **487**: 1-10.

Gompper, M.E. (1996). Sociality and asociality in white-nosed coatis (*Nasua narica*): foraging costs and benefits. *Behav. Ecol.* **7**: 254-263.

Gompper, M.E. (1997). Population ecology of the white-nosed coati, (*Nasua narica*) on Barro Colorado Island, Panama. *J. Zool., London* **241**: 441-455.

Gompper, M.E. & Decker, D.M. (1998). *Nasua nasua. Mammal. Species* **580**: 1-9.

Gompper, M.E. & Hackett, H.M. (2005). The long-term, range-wide decline of a once common carnivore: the eastern spotted skunk (*Spilogale putorius*). *Anim. Conserv.* **8**: 195-201.

Gompper, M.E. & Hoylman, A.M. (1993). Grooming with *Trattinnickia* resin: possible pharmaceutical plant use by coatis in Panama. *J. Trop. Ecol.* **9**: 533-540.

Gompper, M.E. & Krinsley, J.S. (1992). Variation in social behavior of adult male coatis (*Nasua narica*) in Panama. *Biotropica* **24**: 216-219.

Gompper, M.E., Gittleman, J.L. & Wayne, R.K. (1997). Genetic relatedness, coalitions and social behaviour of white-nosed coatis, *Nasua narica. Anim. Behav.* **53**: 781-797.

Gompper, M.E., Gittleman, J.L. & Wayne, R.K. (1998). Dispersal, philopatry and genetic relatedness in a social carnivore: comparing males and females. *Mol. Ecol.* **7**: 157-163.

Gonyea, W.J. (1976). Adaptive differences in the body proportions of large felids. *Acta Anat.* **96**: 81-96.

González del Solar, R. & Rau, J. (2004). Chilla *Pseudalopex griseus.* Pp. 56-63 in: Sillero-Zubiri, C., Hoffmann, M. & Macdonald, D.W. eds. (2004). *Canids: Foxes, Wolves, Jackals and Dogs. Status Survey and Conservation Action Plan.* IUCN/SSC Canid Specialist Group, Gland & Cambridge.

González del Solar, R., Puig, S., Videla, F. & Roig, V. (1997). Diet composition of the South American grey fox *Pseudalopex griseus* Gray, 1836 in northeastern Mendoza. *Mammalia* **61**: 617-621.

Goodman, S.M. (1996a). The carnivores of the Réserve Naturelle Intégrale d'Andringitra, Madagascar. Pp. 289-292 in: Goodman, S.M. ed. (1996). *A Floral and Faunal Inventory of the Eastern Slopes of the Réserve Naturelle Intégrale d'Andringitra, Madagascar: with Reference to Elevational Variation.* Fieldiana Zoology (New Series) **85**.

Goodman, S.M. (1996b). A subfossil record of *Galidictis grandidieri* (Herpestidae: Galidiinae) from southwestern Madagascar. *Mammalia* **60**: 150-151.

Goodman, S.M. (2003a). Predation on lemurs. Pp. 1221-1228 in: Goodman, S.M. & Benstead, J.P. eds. (2003). *The Natural History of Madagascar.* The University of Chicago Press, Chicago, Illinois.

Goodman, S.M. (2003b). *Galidia elegans*, ring-tailed mongoose. Pp. 1354-1357 in: Goodman, S.M. & Benstead, J.P. eds. (2003). *The Natural History of Madagascar.* The University of Chicago Press, Chicago, Illinois.

Goodman, S.M. (2003c). *Galidictis*, broad-striped mongoose. Pp. 1351-1354 in: Goodman, S.M. & Benstead, J.P. eds. (2003). *The Natural History of Madagascar.* The University of Chicago Press, Chicago, Illinois.

Goodman, S.M. & Helmy, I. (1986). The sand cat *Felis margarita* Loche, 1958 in Egypt. *Mammalia* **50**: 120-123.

Goodman, S.M. & Pidgeon, M. (1999). Carnivora of the Réserve Naturelle Intégrale d'Andohahela, Madagascar. Pp. 256-268 in: Goodman, S.M. ed. (1999). A floral and faunal inventory of the Réserve Naturelle Intégrale d'Andohahela, Madagascar: with reference to elevational variation. *Fieldiana Zoology (New Series)* **94**.

Goodman, S.M. & Ramanamanjato, J.B. (2007). A perspective on the paleo-ecology and biogeography of extreme southeastern Madagascar, with special reference to animals. Pp. 25-48 in: Ganzhorn, J.U., Goodman, S.M. & Vincelette, M. eds. (2007). *Biodiversity, Ecology and Conservation of the Littoral Ecosystems in Southeastern Madagascar, Tolagnaro (Fort Dauphin).* Smithsonian Institution/ Monitoring and Assessment of Biodiversity Program Series #**11**. Smithsonian Institution, Washington, D.C.

Goodman, S.M. & Raselimanana, A. (2003). Hunting of wild animals by Sakalava of the Menabe region: a field report from Kirindy-Mite. *Lemur News* **8**: 4-5.

Goodman, S.M. & Rasolonandrasana, B.P.N. (2001). Elevational zonation of birds, insectivores, rodents and primates on the slopes of the Andringitra Massif, Madagascar. *J. Nat. Hist.* **35**: 285-305.

Goodman, S.M. & Soarimalala, V. (2002). Les mammifères de la Réserve Spéciale de Manongarivo. Pp. 382-401 in: Gautier, L. & Goodman, S.M. eds. (2002). Inventaire floristique et faunistique de la Réserve Spéciale de Manongarivo, Madagascar. *Boissiera* **59**.

Goodman, S.M., Ganzhorn, J.U. & Rakotondravony, D. (2003). Introduction to the mammals. Pp. 1159-1186 in: Goodman, S.M. & Benstead, J.P. eds. (2003). *The Natural History of Madagascar*. The University of Chicago Press, Chicago, Illinois.

Goodman, S.M., Kerridge, F.J. & Ralisoamalala, R.C. (2003). A note on the diet of *Fossa fossana* (Carnivora) in the central eastern humid forests of Madagascar. *Mammalia* **67**: 595-598.

Goodman, S.M., Langrand, O. & Rasolonandrasana, B.P.N. (1997). The food habits of *Cryptoprocta ferox* in the high mountain zone of the Andringitra Massif, Madagascar (Carnivore, Viverridae). *Mammalia* **61**: 185-192.

Goodman, S.M., O'Connor, S. & Langrand, O. (1993). A review of predation on lemurs: implications for the evolution of social behavior in small, nocturnal primates. Pp. 51-66 in: Kappeler, P.M. & Ganzhorn, J.U. eds. (1993). *Lemur Social Systems and their Ecological Basis*. Plenum Press, New York.

Goodman, S.M., Raherilalao, M.J., Rakotomalala, D., Rakotondravony, D., Raselimanana, A.P., Razakarivony, H.V. & Soarimalala, V. (2002). Inventaire des vertébrés du Parc National de Tsimanampetsotsa (Toliara). *Akon'ny Ala* **28**: 1-36.

Goodman, S.M., Rasoloarison, R. & Ganzhorn, J.U. (2004). On the specific identification of subfossil *Cryptoprocta* (Mammalia, Carnivora) from Madagascar. *Zoosystema* **26**: 129-143.

Goodman, S.M., Soarimalala, V. & Ratsirarson, J. (2005). Aperçu historique de la population des mammifères des forêts littorales de la province de Toamasina. Pp. 61-68 in: Ratsirarson, J. & Goodman, S.M. eds. (2005). *Suivi de la Biodiversité de la Foret Littorale de Tampolo*. Recherches pour le Développement, Série Sciences Biologiques **22**. Centre d'Information et de Documentation Scientifique et Technique, Antananarivo.

Goodman, S.M., Thomas, H. & Kidney, D. (2005). The rediscovery of *Mungotictis decemlineata lineata* Pocock, 1915 (Carnivora: Eupleridae) in southwestern Madagascar: insights into its taxonomic status and distribution. *Small Carniv. Conserv.* **33**: 1-5.

Goodrich, E.S. (1986). *Studies on the Structure and Development of Vertebrates*. University Press, Chicago, Illinois.

Goodrich, J.M. & Buskirk, S.W. (1998). Spacing and ecology of North American badgers (*Taxidea taxus*) in a prairie-dog (*Cynomys leucurus*) complex. *J. Mammal.* **79**: 171-179.

Goodwin, G.G. (1957). A new kinkajou from Mexico and a new hooded skunk from Central America. *Amer. Mus. Novit.* **1830**: 1-4.

Gordon, C.H., Stewart, A.E. & Meijaard, E. (2007). Correspondence regarding 'Clouded leopards, the secretive top-carnivore of South-East Asian rainforests: their distribution, status and conservation needs in Sabah, Malaysia.' *BMC Ecol.* **7**: 5 doi: 10.1186/1472-6785-7-5.

Gorman, M.L. (1975). The diet of feral *H. auropunctatus* in Fijian Islands. *J. Zool., London* **175**: 273-278.

Gorman, M.L. (1976a). A mechanism for individual recognition by odour in *Herpestes auropunctatus*. *Anim. Behav.* **24**: 141-145.

Gorman, M.L. (1976b). Seasonal changes in reproductive pattern in feral *H. auropunctatus* (Carnivora: Viverridae) in the Fijian islands. *J. Zool., London* **178**: 237-246.

Gorman, M.L. (1979). Dispersion and foraging of the small Indian mongoose *Herpestes auropunctatus* (Carnivora: Viverridae) relative to the evolution of social viverrids. *J. Zool., London* **187**: 65-73.

Gorman, M.L. & Mills, M.G.L. (1984). Scent marking strategies in hyaenas (Mammalia). *J. Zool., London* **202**: 535-547.

Gorman, M.L. & Trowbridge, B.J. (1989). The role of odor in the social lives of carnivores. Pp. 57-88 in: Gittleman, J.L. ed. (1989). *Carnivore Behavior, Ecology and Evolution*. Cornell University Press, Ithaca, New York.

Gorman, M.L., Nedwell, D.B. & Smith, R.M. (1974). An analysis of the contents of the anal scent pockets of *Herpestes auropunctatus* (Carnivora: Viverridae). *J. Zool., London* **172**: 389-399.

Gorman, T.A., Erb, J.D., McMillan, B.R. & Martin, D.J. (2006). Space use and sociality of river otters (*Lontra canadensis*) in Minnesota. *J. Mammal.* **87**: 740-747.

Gorman, T.A., Erb, J.D., McMillan, B.R., Martin, D.J. & Homyack, J.A. (2006). Site characteristics of river otter (*Lontra canadensis*) natal dens in Minnesota. *Amer. Midl. Nat.* **156**: 109-117.

Gorniak, G.C. (1985). Trends in actions of mammalian masticatory muscles. *Amer. Zool.* **25**: 331-337.

Gorsuch, W.A. & Larivière, S. (2005). *Vormela peregusna*. *Mammal. Species* **779**: 1-5.

Gosling, L.M. (1982). A reassessment of the function of scent marking in territories. *Zeitschr. Tierpsychol.* **60**: 89-118.

Gosse, J.W. & Hearn, B.J. (2005). Seasonal diets of Newfoundland martens, *Martes americana atrata*. *Can. Field-Nat.* **119**: 43-47.

Goszczynski, J. (1986). Locomotor activity of terrestrial predators and its consequences. *Acta Theriol.* **31**: 79-95.

Goszczynski, J., Jedrzejewska, B. & Jedrzejewski, W. (2000). Diet composition of badgers (*Meles meles*) in a pristine forest and rural habitats of Poland compared to other European populations. *J. Zool., London* **250**: 495-505.

Goszczynski, J., Posluszny, M., Pilot, M. & Gralak, B. (2007). Patterns of winter locomotion and foraging in two sympatric marten species: *Martes martes* and *Martes foina*. *Can. J. Zool.* **85**: 239-249.

Gottelli, D. & Sillero-Zubiri, C. (1992). The Ethiopian wolf - an endangered endemic canid. *Oryx* **26**: 205-214.

Gottelli, D., Marino, J., Sillero-Zubiri, C. & Funk, S.M. (2004). The effect of the last glacial age on speciation and population genetic structure of the endangered Ethiopian wolf *Canis simensis*. *Mol. Ecol.* **13**: 2275-2286.

Gottelli, D., Sillero-Zubiri, C., Applebaum, G.D., Roy, M.S., Girman, D.J., Garcia-Moreno, J., Osrander, E.A. & Wayne, R.K. (1994). Molecular genetics of the most endangered canid: the Ethiopian wolf *Canis simensis*. *Mol. Ecol.* **3**: 301-312.

Gould, E. & Mckay, G. eds. (1998). *Encyclopedia of Mammals*. 2nd edition. Academic Press, San Diego, California.

Gould, S.J. (1977). *Ontogeny and Phylogeny*. Harvard University Press, Cambridge, Maryland.

Gould, S.J. (1990). An earful of jaw. *Nat. Hist.* **99(3)**: 12-23.

Gould, S.J. (1991). Eight (or fewer) little piggies. *Nat. Hist.* **100(1)**: 22-29.

Grandidier, G. & Petit, G. (1932). *Zoologie de Madagascar*. Société d'Editions Géographiques, Maritimes et Coloniales, Paris.

Grant, J., Hopcraft, C., Sinclair, A.R.E. & Packer, C. (2005). Planning for success: Serengeti lions seek prey accessibility rather than abundance. *J. Anim. Ecol.* **74**: 559-566.

Grassman, L.I. (1998a). Movements and prey selection of the leopard cat (*Prionailurus bengalensis*) in a subtropical evergreen forest in southern Thailand. *Soc. Zool. "La Torbiera" Sci. Rep.* **4**: 9-21.

Grassman, L.I. (1998b). Ecology and behavior of the Indochinese leopard (*Panthera pardus delacouri*) in a subtropical evergreen forest in southern Thailand. *Soc. Zool. "La Torbiera" Sci. Rep.* **4**: 41-57.

Grassman, L.I. (1998c). Movements and fruit selection of two Paradoxurinae species in a dry evergreen forest in Southern Thailand. *Small Carniv. Conserv.* **19**: 25-29.

Grassman, L.I. (2000). Movements and prey selection of the leopard cat (*Prionailurus bengalensis*) in a dry evergreen forest in Thailand. *Acta Theriol.* **45**: 421-426.

Grassman, L.I. (2001). *Spatial Ecology and Conservation of the Felid Community in Phu Khieo Wildlife Sanctuary, Thailand*. Report to Cat Action Treasury.

Grassman, L.I. & Tewes, M.E. (2000). Marbled cat in northeastern Thailand. *Cat News* **33**: 24.

Grassman, L.I. & Tewes, M.E. (2002). Marbled cat pair in northeastern Thailand. *Cat News* **36**: 19-20.

Grassman, L.I., Tewes, M.E. & Silvy, N.J. (2005). Ranging, habitat use and activity patterns of binturong *Arctictis binturong* and yellow-throated marten *Martes flavigula* in north-central Thailand. *Wildl. Biol.* **11**: 49-57.

Grassman, L.I., Tewes, M.E., Silvy, N.J. & Kreetiyutanont, K. (2005). Spatial organization and diet of the leopard cat (*Prionailurus bengalensis*) in north-central Thailand. *J. Zool., London* **266**: 45-53.

Gray, J.E. (1825). Outline of an attempt at the disposition of the Mammalia into tribes and families with a list of the genera apparently appertaining to each tribe. *Ann. Phil., New Ser.* **10**: 337-344.

Gray, J.E. (1837). Description of some new or little known Mammalia, principally in the British Museum collection. *Mag. Nat. Hist., New Ser.* **1**: 577-587.

Gray, J.E. (1864). A revision of the genera and species of Viverrinae animals (Viverridae), founded on the collection in the British Museum. *Proc. Zool. Soc. London* **1864**: 502-579.

Gray, J.E. (1874). Description of a new species of cat (*Felis badia*) from Sarawak. *Proc. Zool. Soc. London* **1874**: 322-323.

Greaves, W.S. (1980). The mammalian jaw mechanism - the high glenoid cavity. *Amer. Nat.* **116**: 432-440.

Green, G.A. & Brueggeman, J.J. (1991). Sea otter diets in a declining population in Alaska. *Marine Mammal Sci.* **7**: 395-401.

Green, H.U. (1932). Observations on the occurrence of the otter in Manitoba in relation to beaver life. *Can. Field-Nat.* **46**: 204-206.

Greenberg, C.H. & Pelton, M.R. (1994). Home range and activity patterns by gray foxes *Urocyon cinereoargenteus* (Carnivora, Canidae), in east Tennessee. *Brimleyana* **21**: 131-140.

Greenwood, R.J. & Sargeant, A.B. (1994). Age related reproduction in striped skunks (*Mephitis mephitis*) in the upper midwest. *J. Mammal.* **75**: 657-662.

Greenwood, R.J., Newton, W.E., Pearson, G.L. & Schamber, G.J. (1997). Population and movement characteristics of radio collared striped skunks in North Dakota during an epizootic of rabies. *J. Wildl. Diseases* **33**: 226-241.

Greer, J.K. (1965). Mammals of Malleco Province, Chile. *Publ. Mus. Michigan State Univ. Biol. Series* **3**: 49-152.

Gregory, E. (1991). Tuned in, turned-on platypus. *Nat. Hist.* **100(1)**: 30-36.

Gregory, W.K. & Hellman, M. (1939). On the evolution and major classification of the civets (Viverridae) and allied fossil and recent Carnivora: a phylogenetic study of the skull and dentition. *Proc. Amer. Phil. Soc.* **81**: 309-392.

Griffin, A.S., Pemberton, J.M., Brotherton, P.N.M., McIlrath, G., Gaynor, D., Kansky, R., O'Riain, J. & Clutton-Brock, T.H. (2003). A genetic analysis of breeding success in the cooperative meerkat (*Suricata suricatta*). *Behav. Ecol.* **14**: 472-480.

Griffiths, M. (1978). *The Biology of Monotremes*. Academic Press, New York.

Grimshaw, J.M., Cordeiro, N.J. & Foley, C.A.H. (1995). The mammals of Kilimanjaro. *J. East Afr. Nat. Hist. Soc.* **84**: 105-139.

Grimwood, I.R. (1969). *Notes on the Distribution and Status of some Peruvian Mammals*. Special Publication Number 21, American Committee for International Wild Life Protection and New York Society, Bronx, New York.

Grimwood, I.R. (1976). The Palawan stink badger. *Oryx* **13**: 297.

Grinnell, J. & McComb, K. (2001). Roaring and social communication in African lions: the limitations imposed by listeners. *Anim. Behav.* **62**: 93-98.

Grinnell, J.D., Dixon, D.S. & Linsdale, J.M. (1937). *Fur-bearing Mammals of California*. Vol. 2. University of California Press, Berkeley, California.

Grobler, J.H. (1981). Feeding behaviour of the caracal *Felis caracal* Schreber 1776 in the Mountain Zebra National Park. *South Afr. J. Zool.* **16**: 259-262.

Grobler, J.H. (1982). Growth of a male caracal kitten *Felis caracal* in the Mountain Zebra National Park. *Koedoe* **25**: 117-119.

Grobler, J.H. & Wilson, V.J. (1972). Food of the leopard *Panthera pardus* (Linn.) in the Rhodes Matopos National Park, Rhodesia, as determined by faecal analysis. *Arnoldia, Rhodesia* **5**: 1-9.

Gros, P.M. (1990). Global Cheetah Project phase I: cheetah status in southern Africa. Unpublished Report for the University of California, Davis, California.

Gros, P.M. (2002). The status and conservation of the cheetah *Acinonyx jubatus* in Tanzania. *Biol. Conserv.* **106**: 177-185.

Groupe National Ours dans les Pyrénées (2008). L'ours - Programme ours brun Pyrénées. URL: http://www.ours.ecologie.gouv.fr.html

Groves, C.P. (1976). The origin of the mammalian fauna of Sulawasi (Celebes). *Zeitschrift für Säugetierkunde* **41**: 201-216.

Groves, C.P. (1980). The Chinese mountain cat. *Carnivore* **3**: 35-41.

Groves, C.P. (1984). Of mice and men and pigs in the Indo-Australian Archipelago. *Canberra Anthropol.* **7**: 1-19.

Groves, C.P. (2001). *Primate Taxonomy.* Smithsonian Institution Press, Washington, D.C.

Grubb, P. (2004). Comment on the proposed conservation of *Viverra maculata* Gray, 1830 (currently *Genetta maculata*; Mammalia, Carnivora). *Bull. Zool. Nomencl.* **61**: 120-122.

Grubb, P., Jones, T.S., Davies, A.G., Edberg, E., Starin, E.D. & Hill, J.E. (1998). *Mammals of Ghana, Sierra Leone and The Gambia.* Trendrine Press, Zennor, St. Ives, Cornwall, UK.

Grzimek, B. (1972). *Grzimek's Animal Life Encyclopedia, Mammals III.* Van Nostrand Reinhold, London.

Guan, Y., Zheng, B.J., He, Y.Q., Liu, X.L., Zhuang, Z.X., Cheung, C.L., Luo, S.W., Li, P.H., Zhang, L.J., Guan, Y.J., Butt, K.M., Wong, K.L., Chan, K.W., Lim, W., Shortridge, K.F., Yuen, K.Y., Peiris, J.S.M. & Poon, L.L.M. (2003). Isolation and characterization of viruses related to the SARS coronavirus from animals in Southern China. *Science* **302**: 276-278.

Guggisberg, C.A.W. (1975). *Wild Cats of the World.* Taplinger, New York.

Guilday, J.E. (1962). Supernumerary molars of *Otocyon. J. Mammal.* **43**: 455-462.

Gunderson, H.L. (1978). A mid-continent irruption of Canada lynx, 1962-63. *Prairie Nat.* **10**: 71-80.

Gunson, J.R., Dorward, W.J. & Schowalter, D.B. (1978). Evaluation of rabies control in skunks in Alberta. *Can. Vet. J.* **19**: 214-220.

Gupta, B.K. (1997). Brown palm civet, *Paradoxurus jerdoni*, in Periyar Tiger Reserve, Western Ghats, India. *Small Carniv. Conserv.* **16**: 30.

Gupta, B.K. (2004). Killing civets for meat and scent in India. *Small Carniv. Conserv.* **31**: 21.

Gutleb, B. & Ziaie, H. (1999). On the distribution and status of the brown bear, *Ursus arctos*, and the Asiatic black bear, *U. thibetanus*, in Iran. *Zool. Middle East* **18**: 5-8.

Guy, P. (1977). A note on the food of the civet *Viverra civetta* (Schreber) in the Engwa Wildlife Research Area, Rhodesia. *South Afr. J. Wildl. Res.* **7**: 87-88.

Hadley, M.E. (1995). *Endocrinology.* 4th edition. Prentice-Hall, Englewood Cliffs, New Jersey.

Haglund, B. (1966). [Winter habits of the lynx (*Lynx lynx* L.) and wolverine (*Gulo gulo* L.) as revealed by tracking in the snow]. *Viltrevy* **4**: 81-299. In Sweddish with English summary.

Hagmeier, E.M. (1961). Variation and relationships in North American marten. *Can. Field-Nat.* **75**: 122-138.

Hahn, D. (2002). *Predicting Wolf Habitat in Eastern North Carolina Using Landscape-scale Habitat Variables.* MSc thesis, Nicholas School of the Environment, Duke University, Durham, North Carolina.

Hall, E.R. (1926). A new subspecies of the California spotted skunk (*Spilogale phenax* Merriam). *J. Mammal.* **7**: 53-56.

Hall, E.R. (1938). Notes on the spotted skunks (genus *Spilogale*), with accounts of new subspecies from Mexico and Costa Rica. *Ann. Mag. Nat. Hist., ser. 11* **1**: 510-515.

Hall, E.R. (1981). *The Mammals of North America.* 2nd edition. John Wiley & Sons, New York.

Hall, E.R. (1984). *Geographic Variation among Brown and Grizzly Bears (Ursus arctos) in North America.* University of Kansas, Special publication **13**, Lawrence, Kansas.

Hall, E.R. & Dalquest, W.W. (1950). Geographic range of the hooded skunk, *Mephitis macroura*, with description of a new subspecies from Mexico. *Univ. Kansas Publ. Mus. Nat. Hist.* **1**: 575-580.

Hall, E.R. & Dalquest, W.W. (1963). The mammals of Veracruz. *Univ. Kansas Publ. Mus. Nat. Hist.* **14**: 165-362.

Hall, E.R. & Kelson, K.R. (1952). Comments on the taxonomy and geographic distribution of some North American marsupials, insectivores and carnivores. *Univ. Kansas Publ. Mus. Nat. Hist.* **5**: 319-341.

Hall, E.R. & Kelson, K.R. (1959). *The Mammals of North America.* Ronald Press Company, New York.

Hall, H.T. & Newsom, J.D. (1976). *Summer Home Ranges and Movements of Bobcats in Bottomland Hardwoods of Southern Louisiana.* Proceedings of the Annual Conference of Southeastern Fish and Wildlife Agencies **30**.

Hall, K.R.L. & Schaller, G.B. (1964). Tool-using behavior of the California sea otter. *J. Mammal.* **45**: 287-298.

Haller, H. (1992). Zur Ökologie des Luchses *Lynx lynx* im Verlaufe seiner Wiederansiedlung in den Walliser Alpen. *Mammal. Depicta* **15**: 65.

Hallowell, A.I. (1926). Bear ceremonialism in the northern hemisphere. *Amer. Anthropol. (New Ser.)* **28**: 1-175.

Haltenorth, T. (1953). *Die Wildkatzen der Alten Welt.* Academische Verlagsgesellschaft, Leipzig.

Haltenorth, T. & Diller, H. (1980). *A Field Guide to the Mammals of Africa Including Madagascar.* William Collins & Sons, London.

Halternorth, T. & Diller, H. (1985). *Mammifères d'Afrique et de Madagascar.* Delachaux et Niestlé, Neuchâtel, Switzerland.

Hamdine, W., Thévenot, M. & Michaux, J. (1998). [Recent history of the brown bear in the Maghreb]. *Compt. Rend. Séances Acad. Sci Paris* **321**: 565-570. In French with English summary.

Hamdine, W., Thévenot, M., Sellami, M. & De Smet, K. (1993). Régime alimentaire de la genette (*Genetta genetta*, Linné 1758) dans le Parc National du Djurdjura, Algérie. *Mammalia* **57**: 9-18.

Hamerton, A.E. (1941). Report on the deaths occurring in the Society's gardens during the years 1939-1940. *Proc. Zool. Soc. London* (1B) **III**: 151-185.

Hamerton, A.E. (1945). Report on the deaths occurring in the Society's gardens during 1944. *Proc. Zool. Soc. London* **115**: 371-386.

Hamilton, P.H. (1976). *The Movements of Leopards in Tsavo National Park, Kenya, as Determined by Radio-tracking.* MSc thesis, University of Nairobi, Nairobi.

Hamilton, W.J. & Hunter, R.P. (1939). Fall and winter food habits of Vermont bobcats. *J. Wildl. Management* **3**: 99-103.

Hamilton, W.J., Tilson, R.L. & Frank, L.G. (1986). Sexual monomorphism in spotted hyaenas, *Crocuta crocuta. Ethology* **71**: 63-73.

Hammershoj, M., Thomsen, E.A. & Madsen, A.B. (2004). Diet of free-ranging American mink and European polecat in Denmark. *Acta Theriol.* **49**: 337-347.

Hanby, J.P., Bygott, J.D. & Packer, C. (1995). Ecology, demography and behavior in lions in two contrasting habitats: Ngorongoro Crater and the Serengeti Plains. Pp. 315-331 in: Sinclair, A.R.E. & Arcese, P. eds. (1995). *Serengeti II: Dynamics, Conservation and Management of an Ecosystem.* University of Chicago Press, Chicago, Illinois.

Hanken, J. & Hall, B. eds. (1993). *The Vertebrate Skull.* University of Chicago Press, Chicago, Illinois.

Hanlon, C.A., Niezgoda, M., Morrill, P. & Rupprecht, C.E. (2002). Oral efficacy of an attenuated rabies virus vaccine in skunks and raccoons. *J. Wildl. Diseases* **38**: 420-427.

Hansel, T. & Tizard, R. (2006). Stripe-backed weasel *Mustela strigidorsa* for sale as traditional medicine in Lao PDR. *Small Carniv. Conserv.* **34-35**: 38.

Happold, D.C.D. (1987). *The Mammals of Nigeria.* Oxford University Press, Oxford.

Haque, M.N. (1989). Small mongoose *Herpestes auropunctatus* feeding on droppings of nilgai *Boselaphus tragocamelus. J. Bombay Nat. Hist. Soc.* **86**: 435.

Harden, R.H. (1985). The ecology of the dingo *Canis familiaris dingo* in northeastern New South Wales Australia. 1. Movements and home range. *Austr. Wildl. Res.* **12**: 25-38.

Hardwicke, T. (1821). Description of the wild dog of Sumatra, a new species of *Viverra*, and a new species of pheasant. *Trans. Linn. Soc. London* **13**: 235-238.

Harlow, H.J. (1981). Torpor and other physiological adaptations of the badger (*Taxidea taxus*) to cold environments. *Physiol. Zool.* **54**: 267-275.

Harlow, H.J., Lohuis, T., Anderson-Sprecher, R.C. & Beck, T.D.I. (2004). Body surface temperature of hibernating black bears may be related to periodic muscle activity. *J. Mammal.* **85**: 414-419.

Harper, G.J., Steininger, M.K., Tucker, C.J., Juhn, D. & Hawkins, F. (2007). Fifty years of deforestation and forest fragmentation in Madagascar. *Environm. Conserv.* **34**: 1-9.

Harrington, F.H. & Paquet, P.C. (1982). *Wolves of the World.* Noyes Publications, Park Ridge, New Jersey.

Harrington, R., Berghaier, R.W. & Hearn, G.W. (2002). The status of carnivores on Bioko Island, Equatorial Guinea. *Small Carniv. Conserv.* **27**: 19-22.

Harris, S. (1977). Distribution, habitat utilization and age structure of a suburban fox *Vulpes vulpes* population. *Mammal Rev.* **7**: 25-39.

Harris, S. (1989). British mammals: past, present and future. *Biol. J. Linn. Soc.* **38**: 1-118.

Harris, S. & Rayner, J.M.V. (1986). Urban fox *Vulpes vulpes* population estimates and habitat requirements in several British cities. *J. Anim. Ecol.* **55**: 575-591.

Harris, S. & Smith, G.C. (1987). Demography of two urban fox *Vulpes vulpes* populations. *J. Appl. Ecol.* **24**: 75-86.

Harrison, D.L. & Bates, P.J.J. (1989). Observations on two mammal species new to the Sultanate of Oman, *Vulpes cana* new record Blanford, 1877 (Carnivora: Canidae) and *Nycteris thebaica* new record Geoffroy, 1818 (Chiroptera: Nycteridae). *Bonn. Zool. Beitr.* **40**: 73-77.

Harrison, D.L. & Bates, P.J.J. (1991). *The Mammals of Arabia.* 2nd edition. Harrison Zoological Museum, Sevenoaks, UK.

Harrison, J. (1974). *An Introduction to the Mammals of Singapore and Malaysia.* 2nd edition. Singapore Branch, Malayan Nature Society.

Harrison, R.J. ed. (1972). *Functional Anatomy of Marine Mammals.* Academic Press, New York.

Harrison, R.L. (1997). A comparison of gray fox ecology between residential and undeveloped rural landscapes. *J. Wildl. Management* **61**: 112-122.

Harrison, R.L. (1998). Bobcats in residential areas. Distribution and homeowner attitudes. *Southwest. Nat.* **43**: 469-475.

Harrison, R.L. (2003). Swift fox demography, movements, denning and diet in New Mexico. *Southwest. Nat.* **48**: 261-273.

Hart, E.B. & Trumbo, M. (1983). Winter stomach contents of South Dakota badgers. *Great Basin Nat.* **43**: 492-493.

Hart, J.A. & Timm, R.M. (1978). Observations on the aquatic genet in Zaire. *Carnivore* **1**: 130-132.

Hart, J.A., Katembo, M. & Punga, K. (1996). Diet, prey selection and ecological relations of leopard and golden cat in the Ituri Forest, Zaire. *Afr. J. Ecol.* **34**: 364-379.

Harveson, P.M., Tewes, M.E., Anderson, G.L. & Laack, L.L. (2004). Habitat use by ocelots in south Texas, implications for restoration. *Wildl. Soc. Bull.* **32**: 948-954.

Harvey, M. (1992). Sociological aspects of spotted hyaena predation on farm livestock in areas adjoining the Hluhluwe/Umfolozi Game Reserve, Natal and solutions to the problem. *IUCN SSC Hyaena Special. Group Newslett.* **5**: 15-19.

Hashimoto, Y. (2002). Seasonal food habits of the Asiatic black bear (*Ursus thibetanus*) in the Chichibu Mountains, Japan. *Mammal Study* **27**: 65-72.

Hashimoto, Y., Kaji, M., Sawada, H. & Takatsuki, S. (2003). Five-year study on the autumn food habits of the Asiatic black bear in relation to nut production. *Ecol. Res.* **18**: 485-492.

Hass, C.C. (2002a). *Reduction of Nuisance Skunks in an Urbanized Area.* Final Report to Arizona Game and Fish Department, Phoenix, Arizona.

Hass, C.C. (2002b). Home-range dynamics of white-nosed coatis in southeastern Arizona. *J. Mammal.* **83**: 934-946.

Hass, C.C. (2003). *Ecology of Hooded and Striped Skunks in Southeastern Arizona.* Final Report to Arizona Game and Fish Department, Phoenix, Arizona.

Hass, C.C. & Dragoo, J.W. (2006). Rabies in hooded and striped skunks in Arizona. *J. Wildl. Diseases* **42**: 825-829.

Hass, C.C. & Valenzuela, D. (2002). Anti-predator benefits of group living in white-nosed coatis (*Nasua narica*). *Behav. Ecol. Sociobiol.* **51**: 570-578.

Hassinger, J.D. (1973). A survey of the mammals of Afghanistan. *Fieldiana Zool.* **60**: 1-195.

Hast, M.H. (1989). The larynx of roaring and non-roaring cats. *J. Anat.* **163**: 117-121.

Hattingh, I. (1956). Measurements of foxes from Scotland and England. *Proc. Zool. Soc. London* **127**: 191-199.

Hattori, K., Kawabe, I., Mizuno, A.W. & Ohtaishi, N. (2005). History and status of sea otters, *Enhydra lutris* along the coast of Hokkaido, Japan. *Mammal Study* **30**: 41-51.

Hawkins, A.F.A. (1994). *Eupleres goudotii* in west Malagasy deciduous forest. *Small Carniv. Conserv.* **11**: 20.
Hawkins, A.F.A., Hawkins, C.E. & Jenkins, P.D. (2000). *Mungotictis decemlineata lineata* (Carnivora: Herpestidae), a mysterious Malagasy mongoose. *J. Nat. Hist.* **34**: 305-310.
Hawkins, C.E. (1998). The behaviour and ecology of the fossa, *Cryptoprocta ferox* (Carnivora: Viverridae) in a dry deciduous forest in western Madagascar. Unpublished PhD thesis, University of Aberdeen.
Hawkins, C.E. (2003). *Cryptoprocta ferox*, fossa. Pp. 1360-1363 in: Goodman, S.M. & Benstead, J.P. eds. (2003). *The Natural History of Madagascar.* The University of Chicago Press, Chicago, Illinois.
Hawkins, C.E. & Racey, P.A. (2005). Low population density of a tropical forest carnivore, *Cryptoprocta ferox*: implications for protected area management. *Oryx* **39**: 35-43.
Hawkins, C.E. & Racey, P.A. (2007). Food habits of an endangered carnivore, *Cryptoprocta ferox*, in the dry deciduous forests of western Madagascar. *J. Mammal.* **89**: 64-74.
Hawkins, C.E., Dallas, J.F., Fowler, P.A., Woodroffe, R. & Racey, P.A. (2002). Transient masculinization in the fossa, *Cryptoprocta ferox* (Carnivora, Viverridae). *Biol. Reprod.* **66**: 610-615.
Haydon, D.T., Laurenson, M.K. & Sillero-Zubiri, C. (2002). Integrating epidemiology into population viability analysis: managing the risk posed by rabies and canine distemper to the Ethiopian wolf. *Conserv. Biol.* **16**: 1372-1385.
Haydon, D.T., Randall, D.A., Matthews, L., Knobel, D.L., Tallents, L.A., Gravenor, M.B., Williams, S.D., Pollinger, J.P., Cleaveland, S., Woolhouse, M.E.J., Sillero-Zubiri, C., Marino, J. & Laurenson, M.K. (2006). Low-coverage vaccination strategies for the conservation of endangered species. *Nature (London)* **443**: 692-695.
Hays, W.S.T. (1999). Annual dispersal cycle of the small Indian mongoose (*Herpestes auropunctatus*) (Carnivora: Herpestidae) in Hawaii. *Pacific Sci.* **53**: 252-256.
Hays, W.S.T. & Conant, S. (2003). Male social activity in the small Indian mongoose *Herpestes javanicus*. *Acta Theriol.* **48**: 485-494.
Hays, W.S.T. & Conant, S. (2007). Biology and impacts of Pacific Island invasive species. 1. A worldwide review of effects of the small Indian mongoose, *Herpestes javanicus* (Carnivora: Herpestidae). *Pacific Sci.* **61**: 3-16.
Hays, W.S.T. & Simberloff, D. (2006). A morphometric trend linked to male sociality in the small Indian mongoose *Herpestes javanicus* in Hawaii. *Acta Theriol.* **51**: 303-310.
Hayssen, V., van Tienhoven, A. & van Tienhoven, A. eds. (1993). *Asdell's Patterns of Mammalian Reproduction.* 2nd edition. Cornell University Press, Ithaca, New York.
Hayward, M.W. (2006). Prey preferences of the spotted hyaena (*Crocuta crocuta*) and degree of dietary overlap with the lion (*Panthera leo*). *J. Zool., London* **270**: 606-614.
Hayward, M.W., Henschel, P., O'Brien, J., Hofmeyr, M., Balme, G. & Kerley, G.I.H. (2006). Prey preferences of the leopard (*Panthera pardus*). *J. Zool., London* **270**: 298-313.
Hayward, M.W., Kerley, G.I.H., Adendorff, J., Moolman, L.C., O'Brien, J., Sholto-Douglas, A., Bissett, C., Bean, P., Fogarty, A., Howarth, D. & Slater, R. (2007). The reintroduction of large carnivores to the Eastern Cape, South Africa. *Oryx* **41**: 205-214.
He, L., Garcia-Perea, R., Li, M. & Wei, F. (2004). Distribution and conservation status of the endemic Chinese mountain cat *Felis bieti*. *Oryx* **38**: 55-61.
Heard, S. (1999). Owston's Palm Civet Conservation Breeding Project Cuc Phuong National Park, Vietnam. *Small Carniv. Conserv.* **20**: 1-6.
Heard, S. & Van Rompaey, H. (1990). Rediscovery of the crested genet. *Mustel. Viverr. Conserv.* **3**: 1-4.
Hedges, S. (1997). Mongoose's secret is to copy its prey. *New Scientist* **153**: 16.
Hedmark, E., Persson, J., Segerstrom, P., Landa, A. & Ellegren, H. (2007). Paternity and mating system in wolverines *Gulo gulo*. *Wildl. Biol.* **13**: 13-30.
Hefetz, A., Ben Yaacov, R. & Yom Tov, Y. (1984). Sex specificity in the anal gland secretion of the Egyptian mongoose *Herpestes ichneumon*. *J. Zool., London* **203**: 205-209.
Helder, J. & Ker De Andrade, H. (1997). Food and feeding habits of the neotropical river otter *Lontra longicaudis* (Carnivora, Mustelidae). *Mammalia* **61**: 193-203.
Helgen, K.M. & Wilson, D.E. (2003). Taxonomic status and conservation relevance of the raccoons (*Procyon* spp.) of the West Indies. *J. Zool., London* **259**: 69-76.
Helgen, K.M. & Wilson, D.E. (2005). A systematic and zoogeographic overview of the raccoons of Mexico and Central America. Pp. 219-234 in: Sanchez-Cordero V. & Medillin R.A. eds. (2005). *Contribuciones Mastozoológicas en Homenaje a Bernardo Villa.* Instituto de Biología e Instituto de Ecología, UNAM, Mexico.
Helgen, K.M. *et al.* (In prep.).
Helgen, K.M., Lim, N.T.L. & Helgen, L.E. (2008). The hog-badger is not an edentate: systematics and evolution of the genus *Arctonyx* (Mammalia: Mustelidae). *Zool. J. Linn. Soc.* **154**: 353-385.
Helgen, K.M., Maldonado, J.E., Wilson, D.E. & Buckner, S.D. (2008). Molecular confirmation of the origin and invasive status of West Indian raccoons. *J. Mammal.* **89**: 282-291.
Helle, E. & Kauhala, K. (1995). Reproduction in the raccoon dog in Finland. *J. Mammal.* **76**: 1036-1046.
Hellgren, E.C. (1998). Physiology of hibernation in bears. *Ursus* **10**: 467-477.
Hellgren, E.C., Onorato, D.P. & Skiles, J.R. (2005). Dynamics of a black bear population within a desert metapopulation. *Biol. Conserv.* **122**: 131-140.
Hellstedt, P. & Henttonen, H. (2006). Home range, habitat choice and activity of stoats (*Mustela erminea*) in a subarctic area. *J. Zool., London* **269**: 205-212.
Hellstedt, P., Sundell, J., Helle, P. & Henttonen, H. (2006). Large-scale spatial and temporal patterns in population dynamics of the stoat, *Mustela erminea*, and the least weasel, *M. nivalis*, in Finland. *Oikos* **115**: 286-298.
Hemmer, H. (1966). Untersuchungen zur Stammesgeschichte der Pantherkatzen (Pantherinae) Teil I. *Veröff. Zool. Staatssammlung München* **11**: 1-121.
Hemmer, H. (1968). Untersuchungen zur Stammesgeschichte der Pantherkatzen (Pantherinae). Tiel II. Studien zur Ethologie des *Neofelis nebulosa* (Griffith 1821) und des Irbis *Uncia uncia* (Schreber 1775). *Veröff. Zool. Staatssammlung München* **12**: 155-247.
Hemmer, H. (1972). *Uncia uncia. Mammal. Species* **20**: 1-5.
Hemmer, H. (1974a). *Felis margarita scheffeli*, eine neue Sandkatzen-Unterart aus der Nushki-Wüste Pakistan. *Senckenbergiana Biol.* **55**: 29-34.
Hemmer, H. (1974b). Studien zur Systematik und Biologie der Sandkatze (*Felis margarita* Loche, 1858). *Z. Köln. Zoo* **17**: 1-20.
Hemmer, H. (1977). Biology and breeding of the sand cat. In: Eaton, R.L. ed. (1977). *The World's Cats 3: Contributions to the Breeding, Biology, Behavior and Husbandry.* Carnivore Research Institute, Univ. Washington, Seattle, Washington.
Hemmer, H. (1978). The evolutionary systematics of living Felidae: present status and current problems. *Carnivore* **1**: 71-79.
Hemmer, H. (1979). Gestation period and postnatal development in felids. *Carnivore* **2(1)**: 90-100.
Hemmer, H. (1999). *Felis silvestris* Schreber, 1775. Pp. 358-359 in: Mitchell-Jones, A.J., Amori, G., Bodganowicz, W., Kryštufek, B., Reijnders, P.J.H., Spitzenberger, F., Stubbe, M., Thissen, J.B.M., Vohralík, V. & Zima, J. eds. (1999). *The Atlas of European Mammals.* Poyser, London.
Hemmer, H., Grubb, P. & Groves, C.P. (1976). Notes on the sand cat, *Felis margarita* Loche, 1858. *Zeitschrift für Säugetierkunde* **41(5)**: 286-303.
Hendey, Q.B. (1974). The late Cenozoic carnivora of the south-western Cape province. *Ann. S. Afr. Mus.* **63**: 1-369.
Henry, V.G. (1997). 90-day finding for a petition to delist the red wolf. *Federal Register* **62**: 64799-64800.
Henschel, J.R. & Skinner, J.D. (1987). Social relationships and dispersal patterns in a clan of spotted hyaenas, *Crocuta crocuta* in the Kruger National Park. *South Afr. J. Zool.* **22**: 18-24.
Henschel, J.R. & Skinner, J.D. (1990a). The diet of the spotted hyaenas *Crocuta crocuta* in Kruger National Park. *Afr. J. Ecol.* **28**: 69-82.
Henschel, J.R. & Skinner, J.D. (1990b). Parturition and early maternal care of spotted hyenas *Crocuta crocuta*: a case report. *J. Zool., London* **222**: 702-704.
Henschel, J.R. & Skinner, J.D. (1991). Territorial behaviour by a clan of spotted hyaenas *Crocuta crocuta*. *Ethology* **88**: 223-235.
Henschel, J.R. & Tilson, R.L. (1988). How much does a spotted hyaena eat? Perspective from the Namib Desert. *Afr. J. Ecol.* **26**: 247-255.
Henschel, P. (2001). *Untersuchung der Ernährungsweise und der Populationsdichte des Leoparden (*Panthera pardus*) im Lopé Reservat, Gabun, Zentralafrika.* Diplomarbeit. Georg-August-Universität zu Göttingen. 45 pp.
Heptner, V.G. & Naumov, N.P. (1992). *Mammals of the Soviet Union.* E.J. Brill, New York.
Heptner, V.G. & Sludskii, A.A. (1992a). [*Mammals of the Soviet Union.* Vol. 2. Carnivora (hyaenas and cats)]. Smithsonian Institution Libraries and the National Science Foundation, Washington, D.C. In Russian.
Heptner, V.G. & Sludskii, A.A. (1992b). [*Mammals of the Soviet Union.* Vol. 3. Carnivores (Feloidea)]. Smithsonian Institution Libraries and the National Science Foundation, Washington, D.C. In Russian.
Heptner, W.G. (1970). Die turkestanische Sicheldünenkatze (Barchankatze), *Felis margarita thinobia* Ognev, 1926. *Zool. Garten* **39**: 116-128.
Herder, S., Simo, G., Nkinin, S. & Njiokou, F. (2002). Identification of trypanosomes in wild animals from southern Cameroon using the polymerase chain reaction (PCR). *Parasite* **9**: 345-349.
Herfindal, I., Linnell, J.D.C., Odden, J., Nilsen, E.B. & Andersen, R. (2005). Prey density, environmental productivity and home-range size in the Eurasian lynx (*Lynx lynx*). *J. Zool., London* **265**: 63-71.
Hermanson, J.W. & Macfadden, B.J. (1996). Evolutionary and functional morphology of the knee in fossil and extant horses (Equidae). *J. Vert. Paleo.* **16**: 349-357.
Hernández, C. & Porras, C. (2005). Posible depredación de *Potos flavus* (Carnivora: Procyonide) por *Leopardus wiedii* (Carnivora: Felidae). *Brenesia* **63/64**: 133.
Herrero, S. (2002). *Bear Attacks: their Causes and Avoidance.* Revised edition. Lyons Press, Guilford, Connecticut.
Herrero, S., Mamo, C., Carbyn, L.N. & Scott-Brown, J.M. (1991). Swift fox reintroduction into Canada. Pp. 246-252 in: Holroyd, G.L., Burns, G. & Smith, H.C. eds. (1991). *Proceedings of the Second Endangered Species and Prairie Conservation Workshop.* Provincial Museum of Alberta, Natural History Section, Occasional Paper No. **15**, Edmonton, Alberta.
Hershkovitz, P. (1961). On the South American small-eared zorro *Atelocynus microtis* Sclater (Canidae). *Fieldiana Zool.* **39**: 505-523.
Hersteinsson, P. (1984). *The Behavioural Ecology of the Arctic Fox* Alopex lagopus *in Iceland.* PhD dissertation, Wildlife Conservation Research Unit, University of Oxford, Oxford.
Hersteinsson, P. & Macdonald, D.W. (1982). Some comparisons between red and Arctic foxes, *Vulpes vulpes* and *Alopex lagopus*, as revealed by radiotracking. *Symp. Zool. Soc. London* **49**: 259-289.
Hersteinsson, P. & Macdonald, D.W. (1992). Interspecific competition and the geographical distribution of red and Arctic foxes *Vulpes vulpes* and *Alopex lagopus*. *Oikos* **64**: 505-515.
Hersteinsson, P. & Macdonald, D.W. (1996). Diet of Arctic foxes *Alopex lagopus* in Iceland. *J. Zool., London* **240**: 457-474.
Hersteinsson, P., Angerbjörn, A., Frafjord, K. & Kaikusalo, A. (1989). The Arctic fox in Fennoscandia and Iceland: management problems. *Biol. Conserv.* **49**: 67-81.
Hes, L. (1991). *The Leopards of Londolozi.* New Holland, London.
Hesterman, H., Wasser, S.K. & Cockrem, J.F. (2005). Longitudinal monitoring of fecal testosterone in male Malayan sun bears (*U. malayanus*). *Zoo Biol.* **24**: 403-417.
Hewitt, D.G. & Doan-Crider, D. (2008). Metapopulations, food and people: bear management in northern Mexico. Pp. 165-181 in: Fulbright, T.E. & Hewitt, D.G. eds. (2008). *Wildlife Science: Linking Ecological Theory and Management Applications.* CRC Press, Boca Raton, Florida.
Heydon, M.J. & Bulloh, P. (1996). The impact of selective logging on sympatric civet species in Borneo. *Oryx* **30**: 31-36.
Heydon, M.J. & Ghaffar, N. (1997). Records of otter civet (*Cynogale bennettii*) from northern Borneo. *Small Carniv. Conserv.* **16**: 27.
Heydon, M.J. & Reynolds, J.C. (2000). Demography of rural foxes *Vulpes vulpes* in relation to cull intensity in three contrasting regions of Britain. *J. Zool., London* **251**: 265-276.
Hildebrand, M. & Goslow, G.E. (2001). *Analysis of Vertebrate Structure.* John Wiley & Sons, New York.

Hilderbrand, G.V., Jenkins, S.G., Schwartz, C.C., Hanley, T.A. & Robbins, C.T. (1999). Effect of seasonal differences in dietary meat intake on changes in body mass and composition in wild and captive brown bears. *Can. J. Zool.* **77**: 1623-1630.

Hilderbrand, G.V., Schwartz, C.C., Robbins, C.T., Jacoby, M.E., Hanley, T.A., Arthur, S.M. & Servheen, C. (1999). The importance of meat, particularly salmon, to body size, population productivity and conservation of North American brown bears. *Can. J. Zool.* **77**: 132-138.

Hill, K., Padwe, J., Bejyvagi, C., Bepurangi, A., Jakugi, F., Tykuarangi, R. & Tykuarangi, T. (1997). Impact of hunting on large vertebrates in the Mbaracayu Reserve, Paraguay. *Conserv. Biol.* **11**: 1339-1353.

Hillard, D. (1989). *Vanishing Tracks.* Arbor House, New York.

Hillman, C.N. & Clark, T.W. (1980). *Mustela nigripes. Mammal. Species* **126**: 1-3.

Hillman, C.N. & Sharps, J.C. (1978). Return of the swift fox to the northern Great Plains. *Proc. South Dakota Acad. Sci.* **57**: 154-162.

Hills, D.M. & Smithers, R.H.N. (1980). The "King Cheetah". *Arnoldia* **9**: 1-23.

Hines, T.D. & Case, R.M. (1991). Diet, home range, movements and activity periods of swift fox in Nebraska. *Prairie Nat.* **23**: 131-138.

Hinton, H.E. & Dunn, A.M.S. (1967). *Mongooses, their Natural History and Behaviour.* Oliver & Boyd, London.

Hirsch, B.T. (2007a). Spoiled brats: is extreme juvenile agonism in ring-tailed coatis (*Nasua nasua*) dominance or tolerated aggression? *Ethology* **113**: 446-456.

Hirsch, B.T. (2007b). *Within-group Spatial Position in Ring-tailed Coatis (*Nasua nasua*): Balancing Predation, Feeding Success, and Social Competition.* PhD thesis, Stony Brook University, New York.

Hiscocks, K. & Perrin, M.R. (1988). Home range and movements of black-backed jackals at Cape Cross Seal Reserve, Namibia. *South Afr. J. Wildl. Res.* **18**: 97-100.

Hiscocks, K. & Perrin, M.R. (1991a). A dietary comparison between two sympatric viverrids, *Helogale parvula* (Sundevall 1846) and *Mungos mungo* (Gmelin 1788). *J. Afr. Zool.* **105**: 307-312.

Hiscocks, K. & Perrin, M.R. (1991b). Den selection and use by dwarf mongooses and banded mongooses in South-Africa. *South Afr. J. Wildl. Res.* **21**: 119-122.

Hoage, R.J., Roskell, A. & Mansour, J. (1996). Menageries and zoos to 1900. Pp. 8-18 in: Hoage, R.J. & Deiss, W.A. eds. (1996). *New Worlds, New Animals. From Menagerie to Zoological Park in the Nineteenth Century.* Johns Hopkins University Press, London & Baltimore.

Hoagland, D.B. & Kilpatrick, C.W. (1999). Genetic variation and differentiation among insular populations of the small Indian mongoose (*Herpestes javanicus*). *J. Mammal.* **80**: 169-179.

Hoagland, D.B., Horst, G.R. & Kilpatrick, C.W. (1989). Biogeography and population biology of the mongoose in the West Indies. *Biogeogr. West Indies* **1989**: 6111-6134.

Hobson, K.A., McLellan, B.N. & Woods, J.G. (2000). Using stable carbon (13C) and nitrogen (15N) isotopes to infer trophic relationships among black and grizzly bears in the upper Columbia River basin, British Columbia. *Can. J. Zool.* **78**: 1332-1339.

Hoctor, T.S., Zwick, P.D. & Carr, M.H. (2000). Identifying a linked reserve system using a regional landscape approach: the Florida ecological network. *Conserv. Biol.* **14**: 984-1000.

Hodge, S.J. (2003). *The Evolution of Cooperation in the Communal Breeding Banded Mongoose.* PhD thesis, University of Cambridge, Cambridge.

Hodge, S.J. (2005). Helpers benefit offspring in both the short and long-term in the cooperatively breeding banded mongoose. *Proc. Royal Soc. London (Ser. B Biol. Sci.)* **272**: 2479-2484.

Hodge, S.J., Flower, T.P. & Clutton-Brock, T.H. (2007). Offspring competition and helper associations in cooperative meerkats. *Anim. Behav.* **74**: 957-964.

Hodgson, B.H. (1842). On a new species of *Prionodon. P. pardicolor nobis. Calcutta J. Nat. Hist.* **2**: 57-60.

Hodgson, B.H. (1847). Observations on the manners and structure of *Prionodon pardicolor. Calcutta J. Nat. Hist.* **8**: 40-45.

Hodos, W. & Butler, A.B. (1997). Evolution of sensory pathways in vertebrates. *Brain Behav. Evol.* **50**: 189-197.

Hofer, H. (1998). Striped hyaena *Hyaena (Hyaena) hyaena* (Linnaeus, 1758). Pp. 21-26 in: Mills, M.G.L. & Hofer, H. eds. (1998). *Hyaenas: Status Survey and Conservation Action Plan.* IUCN/SSC Hyaena Specialist Group, Gland & Cambridge.

Hofer, H. & East, M.L. (1993a). The commuting system of Serengeti spotted hyaenas: how a predator copes with migratory prey. I. Social organization. *Anim. Behav.* **46**: 547-557.

Hofer, H. & East, M.L. (1993b). The commuting system of Serengeti spotted hyaenas: how a predator copes with migratory prey. II. Intrusion pressure and commuters' space use. *Anim. Behav.* **46**: 559-574.

Hofer, H. & East, M.L. (1993c). The commuting system of Serengeti spotted hyaenas - how a predator copes with migratory prey. III. Attendance and maternal care. *Anim. Behav.* **46**: 575-589.

Hofer, H. & East, M.L. (1995). Population dynamics, population size and the commuting system of Serengeti spotted hyaenas. Pp. 332-363 in: Sinclair, A.R.E. & Arcese, P. eds. (1995). *Serengeti II: Dynamics, Conservation and Management of an Ecosystem.* University of Chicago Press, Chicago, Illinois.

Hofer, H. & East, M.L. (1996). The components of parental care and their fitness consequences: a life history perspective. *Verh. Deutschen Gesell. Zool.* **89(2)**: 149-164.

Hofer, H. & East, M.L. (1997). Skewed offspring sex ratios and sex composition of twin litters in Serengeti spotted hyaenas (*Crocuta crocuta*) are a consequence of siblicide. *Appl. Anim. Behav. Sci.* **51**: 307-316.

Hofer, H. & East, M.L. (2003). Behavioural processes and costs of co-existence in female spotted hyenas: a life history perspective. *Evol. Ecol.* **17**: 315-331.

Hofer, H. & East, M.L. (2008). Siblicide in Serengeti spotted hyenas: a long-term study of maternal input and cub survival. *Behav. Ecol. Sociobiol.* **62**: 341-351.

Hofer, H., Campbell, K.L.I., East, M.L. & Huish, S.A. (1996). The impact of game meat hunting on target and non-target species in the Serengeti. Pp. 117-146 in: Taylor, V.J. & Dunstone, N. eds. (1996). *The Exploitation of Mammal Populations.* Chapman & Hall, London.

Hofer, H., East, M.L. & Campbell, K.L.I. (1993). Snares, commuting hyaenas and migratory herbivores: humans as predators in the Serengeti. *Symp. Zool. Soc. London* **65**: 347-366.

Hoffman, T.W. (1990). News. *Mustel. Viverr. Conserv.* **3**: 13.

Hoffmann, J.C., Soares, M.J., Nelson, M.L. & Cullin, A.M. (1984). Seasonal reproduction in the mongoose, *Herpestes auropunctatus.* 4. Organ weight and hormone changes in the female. *Gen. Comp. Endocrin.* **55**: 306-314.

Hoffmann, M.H. & Taylor, M.E. (In press). *Herpestes sanguineus.* In: Kingdon, J.S. & Hoffmann, M. eds. (In press). *The Mammals of Africa.* Vol. 5. Carnivores, Pangolins, Rhinos and Equids. Academic Press, Amsterdam.

Hoffmeister, D.F. (1986). *Mammals of Arizona.* The University of Arizona Press, Tucson, Arizona.

Hofreiter, M., Serre, D., Rohland, N., Rabeder, G., Nagel, D., Conard, N., Münzel, S. & Pääbo, S. (2004). Lack of phylogeography in European mammals before the last glaciation. *Proc. Natl. Acad. Sci. USA* **101**: 12963-12968.

Holden, J. (2006). Small carnivores in Central Sumatra. *Small Carniv. Conserv.* **34&35**: 35-38.

Holekamp, K.E. & Smale, L. (1990). Provisioning and food sharing by lactating spotted hyenas, *Crocuta crocuta* (Mammalia, Hyaenidae). *Ethology* **86**: 191-202.

Holekamp, K.E. & Smale, L. (1993). Ontogeny of dominance in free-living spotted hyaenas: juvenile rank relations with other immature individuals. *Anim. Behav.* **46**: 451-466.

Holekamp, K.E. & Smale, L. (2000). Feisty females and meek males: reproductive strategies in the spotted hyena. Pp. 257-285 in: Wallen, K. & Schneider, J. eds. (2000). *Reproduction in Context.* MIT Press, Cambridge, Maryland.

Holekamp, K.E., Boydston, E.E. & Smale, L. (2000). Group travel in social carnivores. Pp. 587-627 in: Boinski, S. & Garber, P. eds. (2000). *On the Move: Group Travel in Primates and Other Animals.* University of Chicago Press, Chicago, Illinois.

Holekamp, K.E., Boydston, E.E., Szykman, M., Graham, I., Nutt, K., Birch, S., Piskiel, A. & Singh, M. (1999). Vocal recognition in the spotted hyaena and its possible implications regarding the evolution of intelligence. *Anim. Behav.* **58**: 383-395.

Holekamp, K.E., Sakai, S.T. & Lundrigan, B.L. (2007). Social intelligence in the spotted hyena (*Crocuta crocuta*). *Phil. Trans. Roy. Soc. London (Ser. B)* **362**: 523-538.

Holekamp, K.E., Smale, L., Berg, R. & Cooper, S.M. (1997). Hunting rates and hunting success in the spotted hyena (*Crocuta crocuta*). *J. Zool., London* **241**: 1-15.

Holekamp, K.E., Smale, L. & Szykman, M. (1996). Rank and reproduction in the female spotted hyaena. *J. Reprod. Fertil.* **108**: 229-237.

Holekamp, K.E., Szykman, M., Boydston, E.E. & Smale, L. (1999). Association of seasonal reproductive patterns with changing food availability in an equatorial carnivore. *J. Reprod. Fertil.* **116**: 87-93.

Holland, L.Z. & Holland, N.D. (1999). Chordate origins of the vertebrate central nervous system. *Curr. Opin. Neurobiol.* **9**: 596-602.

Hollen, L.I. & Manser, M.B. (2006). Ontogeny of alarm call responses in meerkats, *Suricata suricatta*: the roles of age, sex and nearby conspecifics. *Anim. Behav.* **72**: 1345-1353.

Hollen, L.I. & Manser, M.B. (2007). Motivation before meaning: motivational information encoded in meerkat alarm calls develops earlier than referential information. *Amer. Nat.* **169**: 758-767.

Holm, G.W., Lindzey, F.G. & Moody, D. (1999). Interactions of sympatric black and grizzly bears in northwest Wyoming. *Ursus* **11**: 99-108.

Holt, D.W. (1994). Larder hoarding in the cougar, *Felis concolor. Can. Field-Nat.* **108**: 240-241.

Höner, O.P., Wachter, B., East, M.L. & Hofer, H. (2002). The response of spotted hyenas to long-term changes in prey populations: functional response and interspecific kleptoparasitism. *J. Anim. Ecol.* **71**: 236-246.

Höner, O.P., Wachter, B., East, M.L., Runyoro, V.A. & Hofer, H. (2005). The effect of prey abundance and foraging tactics on the population dynamics of a social carnivore, the spotted hyena. *Oikos* **108**: 544-554.

Höner, O.P., Wachter, B., East, M.L., Streich, W.J., Wilhelm, K., Burke, T. & Hofer, H. (2007). Female mate-choice drives the evolution of male-biased dispersal in a social mammal. *Nature (London)* **448**: 798-801.

Hoodicoff, C. (2006). Badger of prey ecology: the ecology of six small mammals found in British Columbia. *Wildlife Working Report* **WR-109**: i-vi, 1-31.

Hoogerwerf, A. (1970). *Udjung Kulon: the Land of the Last Javan Rhinoceros.* E.J. Brill, Leiden, The Netherlands.

Hoogesteijn, R. & Mondolfi, E. (1992). *The Jaguar.* Armitano Publishers, Caracas, Venezuela.

Hoogesteijn, R. & Mondolfi, E. (1996). Body mass and skull measurements in four jaguar populations and observations on their prey base. *Bull. Florida Mus. Nat. Hist., Biol. Ser.* **39(6)**: 195-219.

Hoogesteijn, R., Hoogesteijn, A. & Mondolfi, E. (1993). Jaguar predation and conservation: cattle mortality caused by felines on three ranches in the Venezuelan llanos. *Symp. Zool. Soc. London* **65**: 391-407.

Hoogstraal, H. (1951). Philippine zoological expedition, 1946-1947. Narrative and itinerary. *Fieldiana Zool.* **33**: 1-86.

Hoppe-Dominik, B. (1984). Étude du spectre des proises de la panthere, *Panthera pardus*, dans le Parc National de Taï en Côte d'Ivore. *Mammalia* **48**: 477-487.

Hoppe-Dominik, B. (1990). On the occurrence of the honey badger (*Mellivora capensis*) and the viverrids in the Ivory Coast. *Small Carniv. Conserv.* **3**: 9-13.

Hornocker, M.G. & Hash, H.S. (1981). Ecology of the wolverine in northwestern Montana. *Can. J. Zool.* **59**: 1286-1301.

Horwitz, L.K. & Smith, P. (1988). The effects of striped hyena activity on human remains. *J. Archaeol. Sci.* **15**: 471-482.

Hose, C. (1893). *A Descriptive Account of the Mammals of Borneo.* Edward Abbott, London.

Howell, A.B. (1930). *Aquatic Mammals: their Adaptations to Life in the Water.* Charles C. Thomas, Springfield, Illinois.

Howell, A.H. (1901). Revision of the skunks of the genus *Chincha. North Amer. Fauna* **20**: 1-47 + viii plates.

Howell, A.H. (1902). Three new skunks of the genus *Spilogale. Proc. Biol. Soc. Washington* **XV**: 241-242.

Howell, A.H. (1906). Revision of the skunks of the genus *Spilogale*. *North Amer. Fauna* **26**: 1-55 + x plates.

Howell, A.H. (1920). The Florida spotted skunk as an acrobat. *J. Mammal.* **1**: 88.

Hu, J. (1991). [Research on reproductive biology of the red panda]. *J. Sichuan Teachers College* **12**: 1-5. In Chinese.

Hu, J. & Wang, Y. (1984). [*Sichuan Fauna Economica-Mammals*]. Sichuan Science and Technology Press, Chengdu, China. In Chinese.

Huang, G.T., Rosowski, J.J., Ravicz, M.E. & Peake, W.T. (2002). Mammalian ear specializations in arid habitats: structural and functional evidence from sand cat (*Felis margarita*). *J. Comp. Physiol. A* **188**: 663-681.

Hubbard, J.P. (1972). Hooded skunk on the Mogollon Plateau, New Mexico. *The Southwest. Nat.* **16**: 458.

Huet, J. (1887). Note sur une espèce nouvelle des mammifère du genre *Mydaus* provenant de l'ile Palaouan. *Le Naturaliste, Ser. 2* **13**: 149-151.

Huey, R. (1969). Winter diet of the Peruvian Desert fox. *Ecology* **50**: 1089-1091.

Hufnagl, E. ed. (1972). *Libyan Mammals*. Oleander Press, Cambridge.

Hugh-Jones, M.E. & de Vos, V. (2002). Antrax and wildlife. *Scientific Tech. Rev. Office Int. Epizooties* **21**: 359-383.

Hulley, J.T. (1976). Maintenance and breeding of captive jaguarundis at Chester Zoo and Toronto. *Int. Zoo Yb.* **16**: 120-122.

Hunt, R.M. (1974). The auditory bulla in Carnivora: an anatomical basis for reappraisal of carnivore evolution. *J. Morphol.* **143**: 21-76.

Hunt, R.M. (1987). Evolution of the Aeluroid Carnivora: significance of auditory structure in the Nimravid cat *Dinictis*. *Amer. Mus. Novit.* **2886**: 1-74.

Hunt, R.M. (1989). Evolution of the Aeluroid Carnivora: significance of the ventral promontorial process of the petrosal and the origin of basicranial patterns in the living families. *Amer. Mus. Novit.* **2930**: 1-32.

Hunt, R.M. (1996). Biogeography of the order Carnivora. Pp. 485-541 in: Gittleman, J.L. ed. (1996). *Carnivore Behavior, Ecology and Evolution*. Comstock Publishing Associates, Cornell University Press, Ithaca & London.

Hunt, R.M. (1998). Evolution of the Aeluroid Carnivora: diversity of the earliest Aeluroids from Eurasia (Quercy, Hsanda-Gol) and the origin of felids. *Amer. Mus. Novit.* **3252**: 1-65.

Hunt, R.M. (2001). Basicranial anatomy of the living linsangs *Prionodon* and *Poiana* (Mammalia, Carnivora, Viverridae), with comments on the early evolution of Aeluroid Carnivora. *Amer. Mus. Novit.* **3330**: 1-24.

Hunter, D.O., Jackson, R., Freeman, H. & Hillard, D. (1994). Project Snow Leopard: a model for conserving Asian biodiversity. Pp. 247-252 in: Fox, J.L. & Du Jizeng eds. (1994). *Proceedings of the Seventh International Snow Leopard Symposium*. International Snow Leopard Trust & Chicago Zoological Society, Seattle, Washington.

Hunter, L.T.B. (1999). Large felid restoration: lessons from Phinda Resource Reserve, South Africa, 1992-1999. *Cat News* **31**: 20-21.

Hunter, L.T.B. & Skinner, J.D. (1995). Cannibalism in male cheetah. *Cat News* **23**: 13-14.

Hunter, L.T.B., Pretorius, K., Carlisle, L.C., Rickelton, M., Walker, C., Slotow, R. & Skinner, J.D. (2007). Restoring lions *Panthera leo* to northern KwaZulu-Natal, South Africa: short-term biological and technical success but equivocal long-term conservation. *Oryx* **41**: 196-204.

Husain, T. (2001). *Survey for the Asiatic Cheetah in Baluchistan Province, Pakistan*. Final report to CAT and the Barbara Delano Foundation, Lahore, Pakistan.

Hussain, S.A. (1996). Group size, group structure and breeding in smooth-coated otter *Lutrogale perspicillata* Geoffroy in National Chambal Sanctuary. *Mammalia* **60**: 289-297.

Hutchinson, J.T. & Hutchinson, T. (1998). Observation of a melanistic bobcat in the Ocala National Forest. *Florida Field Nat.* **28**: 25-26.

Hutton, A.F. (1949). Mammals of the High Wavy Mountains, Madurai district, southern India. *J. Bombay Nat. Hist. Soc.* **48**: 681-694.

Huygens, O.C. & Hayashi, H. (2001). Use of stone pine seeds and oak acorns by Asiatic black bears in central Japan. *Ursus* **12**: 47-50.

Huygens, O.C., Goto, M., Izumiyama, S., Hayashi, H. & Yoshida, T. (2001). Denning ecology of two populations of Asiatic black bears in Nagano Prefecture, Japan. *Mammalia* **65**: 417-428.

Huygens, O.C., Miyashita, T., Dahle, B., Carr, M., Izumiyama, S., Sugawara, T. & Hayashi, H. (2003). Diet and feeding habits of Asiatic black bears in the Northern Japanese Alps. *Ursus* **14**: 236-245.

Hwang, M.H. (2003). *Ecology of Asiatic Black Bears and People-bear Interactions in Yushan National Park, Taiwan*. PhD thesis, University of Minnesota, Minneapolis.

Hwang, M.H. & Garshelis, D.L. (2006). Activity patterns of Asiatic black bears (*Ursus thibetanus*) in the Central Mountains of Taiwan. *J. Zool., London* **271**: 203-209.

Hwang, M.H., Garshelis, D.L. & Wang, Y. (2002). Diets of Asiatic black bears in Taiwan, with methodological and geographical comparisons. *Ursus* **13**: 111-125.

Hwang, Y.T. & Larivière, S. (2003). *Mydaus javanensis*. *Mammal. Species* **723**: 1-3.

Hwang, Y.T. & Larivière, S. (2004). *Mydaus marchei*. *Mammal. Species* **757**: 1-3.

Hwang, Y.T. & Larivière, S. (2005). *Lutrogale perspicillata*. *Mammal. Species* **786**: 1-4.

Hwang, Y.T., Larivière, S. & Messier, F. (2007). Energetic consequences and ecological significance of heterothermy and social thermoregulation in striped skunks (*Mephitis mephitis*). *Physiol. Biochem. Zool.* **80**: 138-145.

Ikeda, H. (1982). *Socio-ecological Study on the Raccoon Dog* Nyctereutes procyonoides viverrinus *with Reference to the Habitat Utilisation Pattern*. PhD dissertation, Kyushu University, Japan.

Ikeda, H. (1983). Development of young and parental care of raccoon dog *Nyctereutes procyonoides viverrinus* Temminck, in captivity. *J. Mammal. Soc. Japan* **9**: 229-236.

Ikeda, H., Ono, Y., Baba, M., Doi, T. & Iwamoto, T. (1982). Ranging and activity patterns of 3 nocturnal viverrids in Omo National Park, Ethiopia. *Afr. J. Ecol.* **20**: 179-186.

Ikeda, M., Izawa, M., Baba, M., Takeishi, M., Doi, T. & Ono, Y. (1983). Range size and activity pattern of three nocturnal carnivores in Ethiopia by radio-telemetry. *J. Ethol.* **1**: 109-111.

Ikeda, T., Asano, M., Matoba, Y. & Abe, G. (2004). Present status of invasive alien raccoon and its impact in Japan. *Global Environm. Res.* **8(2)**: 125-131.

Ilany, G. (1981). The leopard of the Judean Desert. *Israel Land & Nature* **6**: 59-71.

Ilany, G. (1983). Blanford's fox *Vulpes cana* Blanford, 1877, a new species to Israel. *Israel J. Zool., London* **32**: 150.

Ilany, G. (1990). The leopard (*Panthera pardus*) in Israel. *Cat News* **12**: 4-5.

Imaizumi, Y. & Yoshiyuki, M. (1989). Taxonomic status of the Japanese otter (Carnivora, Mustelidae), with a description of a new species. *Bull. Nat. Sci. Mus. (Ser. A, Zool.)* **15**: 177-188.

Inman, R.M. & Pelton, M.R. (2002). Energetic production by soft and hard mast foods of American black bears in the Smoky Mountains. *Ursus* **13**: 57-68.

Inoue, T. (1972). The food habit of Tsushima leopard cat, *Felis bengalensis* ssp., analysed from their scats. *J. Mammal. Soc. Japan* **5**: 155-169.

Iriarte, A.W. (1998). [*Distribution and Status of the Andean Mountain Cat in Chile*]. Final project report to Cat Action Treasury. In Spanish.

Iriarte, A.W. & Sanderson, J. (1999). Home-range and activity patterns of kodkod *Oncifelis guigna* on Isla Grande de Chiloe, Chile. *Cat News* **30**: 27.

Iriarte, J.A. & Jaksic, F.M. (1986). The fur trade in Chile: an overview of seventy-five years of export data (1910-1984). *Biol. Conserv.* **38**: 243-253.

Iriarte, J.A., Franklin, W.L., Johnson, W.E. & Redford, K.H. (1990). Biogeographic variation of food habits and body size of the American puma (*Felis concolor*). *Oecologica* **85**: 185-190.

Iriarte, J.A., Jiménez, J.E., Contreras, L.C. & Jaksic, F.M. (1989). Small mammal availability and consumption by the fox, *Dusicyon culpaeus*, in central Chilean scrublands. *J. Mammal.* **70**: 641-645.

IUCN (2007). *2007 IUCN Red List of Threatened Species*. URL: http://www.iucnredlist.org.html (download 19 September 2007).

IUCN (2008). *2008 IUCN Red List of Threatened Species*. URL: http://www.iucnredlist.org.html (download 30 October 2008).

Iwaniuk, A.N. & Whishaw, I.Q. (1999). How skilled are the skilled limb movements of the raccoon (*Procyon lotor*)? *Behav. Brain Res.* **99**: 35-44.

Izor, R.J. & de la Torre, L. (1978). A new species of weasel (*Mustela*) from the highlands of Colombia, with comments on the evolution and distribution of South American weasels. *J. Mammal.* **59**: 92-102.

Izumiyama, S. & Shiraishi, T. (2004). Seasonal changes in elevation and habitat use of the Asiatic black bear (*Ursus thibetanus*) in the Northern Japan Alps. *Mammal Study* **29**: 1-8.

Jackson, D.L. & Jacobson, H.A. (1987). *Population Ecology of the Bobcat (*Felis rufus*) in Managed Southern Forest Ecosystems*. Federal Aid in Wildlife Restoration Funds, Project **W-48-30-34**.

Jackson, P. (1991). Man versus man-eaters. Pp. 212-213 in: Seidensticker, J. & Lumpkin, S. eds. (1991). *Great Cats. Majestic Creatures of the Wild*. Merehurst, London.

Jackson, P. (1995). Asiatic lion census. *Cat News* **23**: 10.

Jackson, R.M. & Ahlborn, G.G. (1988). Observations on the ecology of snow leopard in West Nepal. Pp. 65-87 in: Freeman, H. ed. (1988). *Proceedings of the Fifth International Snow Leopard Symposium*. International Snow Leopard Trust & Wildlife Institute of India, Bombay.

Jackson, R.M. & Ahlborn, G.G. (1989). Snow leopards (*Panthera uncia*) in Nepal - home range and movements. *Nat. Geogr. Res.* **5**: 161-175.

Jackson, R.M. & Ahlborn, G.G. (1990). The role of protected areas in Nepal in maintaining viable populations of snow leopards. *Int. Ped. Book Snow Leopards* **6**: 51-69.

Jackson, R.M., Hunter, D.O. & Emmerich, C. (1997). SLIMS: an information management system for promoting the conservation of snow leopards and biodiversity in the mountains of central Asia. Pp. 75-91 in: Jackson, R. & Ashiq, A. eds. (1997). *Proceedings of the Fifth International Snow Leopard Symposium*. International Snow Leopard Trust, Lahore, Pakistan.

Jackson, V.L. & Choate, J.R. (2000). Dens and den sites of the swift fox *Vulpes velox*. *Southwest. Nat.* **45**: 212-220.

Jacob, J. & Schliemann, H. (1983). Chemical composition of the secretion from the anal sacs of *Civettictis civetta* (Schreber, 1776). *Zeitschrift für Naturforschung* **38**: 497-500.

Jacoby, M.E., Hilderbrand, G.V., Servheen, C., Schwartz, C.C., Arthur, S.M., Hanley, T.A., Robbins, C.T. & Michener, R. (1999). Trophic relations of brown and black bears in several western North American ecosystems. *J. Wildl. Management* **63**: 921-929.

Jácomo, A.T.A. (1999). *Nicho Alimentar do Lobo Guará* Chrysocyon brachyurus *Illiger, 1811 no Parque Nacional das Emas*. MSc thesis, Universidade federal de Goiás, Goiás, Brazil.

Jaeger, M.M., Pandit, R.K. & Haque, E. (1996). Seasonal differences in territorial behavior by golden jackals in Bangladesh: howling versus confrontation. *J. Mammal.* **77**: 768-775.

Jaksic, F.M. & Yáñez, J.L. (1983). Rabbit and fox introductions in Tierra del Fuego: history and assessment of the attempts at biological control of the rabbit infestation. *Biol. Conserv.* **26**: 367-374.

Jaksic, F.M., Jiménez, J.E., Medel, R.G. & Marquet, P.A. (1990). Habitat and diet of Darwin´s fox *Pseudalopex fulvipes* on the Chilean mainland. *J. Mammal.* **71**: 246-248.

Jaksic, F.M., Schlatter, P. & Yáñez, J.L. (1980). Feeding ecology of central Chilean foxes *Dusicyon culpaeus* and *D. griseus*. *J. Mammal.* **61**: 254-260.

Jaksic, F.M., Yáñez, J.L. & Rau, J.R. (1983). Trophic relations of the southernmost populations of *Dusicyon* in Chile. *J. Mammal.* **64**: 693-697.

Janczewski, D.N., Yuhki, N., Gilbert, D.A., Jefferson, G.T. & O'Brien, S.J. (1992). Molecular phylogenetic inference from saber-toothed cat fossils of Rancho La Brea. *Proc. Natl. Acad. Sci. USA* **89**: 9769-9773.

Janson, C.H. & Emmons, L.H. (1990). Ecological strutucture of the nonflying mammal community at Cocha Cashu Biological Station, Manu National Park, Peru. Pp. 314-338 in: Gentry, A.H. ed. (1990). *Four Neotropical Forests*. Yale University Press, New Haven, Connecticut.

Janzen, D.H. & Hallwachs, W. (1982). The hooded skunk, *Mephitis macroura*, in lowland northwestern Costa Rica. *Brenesia* **19/20**: 549-552.

Japan Bear Network ed. (2006). *Understanding Asian Bears to Secure their Future*. Japan Bear Network, Ibaraki, Japan.

Jayasekara, P., Takatsuki, S., Weerasinghe, U.R. & Wijesundara, S. (2003). Arboreal fruit visitors in a tropical forest in Sri Lanka. *Mammal Study* **28**: 161-165.

Jayat, J.P., Bárquez, R.M., Díaz, M.M. & Martínez, P.J. (1999). Aportes al conocimiento de la distribución de los carnívoros del Noroeste de Argentina. *Mastozool. Neotrop.* **6**: 15-30.

Jayewardene, E.D.W. (1975). Breeding the fishing cat in captivity. *Int. Zoo Yb.* **8**: 150-152.

Jedrzejewska, B., Jedrzejewski, W. & Syzmura, L. (1998). *Predation in Vertebrate Communities: the Bialowieza Primeval Forest as a Case Study.* Springer-Verlag, Berlin.

Jedrzejewski, W., Jedrzejewska, B., Okarma, H., Schmidt, K., Bunevich, A.N. & Milkowski, L. (1996). Population dynamics (1869-1994), demography, and home ranges of the lynx in Bialowieza Primeval Forest (Poland and Belarus). *Ecography* **19**: 122-138.

Jedrzejewski, W., Jedrzejewska, B. & Szymura, L. (1995). Weasel population response, home range and predation on rodents in a deciduous forest in Poland. *Ecology* **76**: 179-195.

Jedrzejewski, W., Jedrzejewska, B., Zub, K. & Nowakowski, W.K. (2000). Activity patterns of radio-tracked weasels *Mustela nivalis* in Bialowieza National Park (E Poland). *Ann. Zool. Fennici* **37**: 161-168.

Jedrzejewski, W., Schmidt, K., Milkowski, L., Jedrzejewska, B. & Okarma, H. (1993). Foraging by lynx and its role in ungulate mortality: the local (Bialowieza Forest) and the Palaearctic viewpoints. *Acta Theriol.* **38**: 385-403.

Jeffrey, S.M. (1977). How Liberia uses wildlife. *Oryx* **14**: 168-173.

Jenkins, D., Watson, A. & Miller, G.R. (1964). Predation and red grouse populations. *J. Appl. Ecol.* **1**: 183-195.

Jenkins, F. & McClearn, D. (1984). Mechanisms of hind foot reversal in climbing mammals. *J. Morphol.* **182**: 197-219.

Jenkins, P.D. & Carleton, M.D. (2005). Charles Immanuel Forsyth Major's expedition to Madagascar, 1894 to 1896: beginnings of modern systematic study of the island's mammalian fauna. *J. Nat. Hist.* **39**: 1779-1818.

Jennings, A.P., Seymour, A.S. & Dunstone, N. (2006). Ranging behaviour, spatial organization and activity of the Malay civet (*Viverra tangalunga*) on Buton Island, Sulawesi. *J. Zool., London* **268**: 63-71.

Jenny, D. (1996). Spatial organization of leopards *Panthera pardus* in Taï National Park, Ivory Coast: is rainforest habitat a "tropical haven"? *J. Zool., London* **240**: 427-440.

Jentink, F.A. (1895). On two mammals from the Calamianes Islands. *Notes Mus. Leyden* **17**: 41-48.

Jerdon, T.C. (1874). *The Mammals of India: a Natural History of all the Animals Known to Inhabit Continental India.* John Wheldon, London.

Jetz, W., Carbone, C., Fulford, J. & Brown, J.H. (2004). The scaling of animal space use. *Science* **306**: 266-268.

Jha, A. (1999). A preliminary survey on the status of civets in Namdapha Biosphere Reserve in Arunachal Pradesh. *Tigerpaper* **26**: 1-5.

Jhala, Y.V. & Moehlman, P.D. (2004). Golden jackal *Canis aureus*. Pp. 156-161 in: Sillero-Zubiri, C., Hoffmann, M. & Macdonald, D.W. eds. (2004). *Canids: Foxes, Wolves, Jackals and Dogs. Status Survey and Conservation Action Plan.* IUCN/SSC Canid Specialist Group, Gland & Cambridge.

Jhala, Y.V., Gopal, R. & Qureshi, Q. eds. (2008). *Status of Tigers, Co-predators and Prey in India.* National Tiger Conservation Authority and Wildlife Institute of India. TR08/001 pp. 164. Dehradun, India.

Jia, Z., Jiang, Z. & Wang, Z. (2000). Observation on the behaviors of masked palm civet in reproductive season. *Acta Theriol. Sinica* **20**: 108-115.

Jia, Z., Jiang, Z. & Wang, Z. (2001). Copulatory behavior in captive masked palm civets, *Paguma larvata*. *Folia Zool.* **50**: 271-279.

Jiang, Z.G., Li, C.W. & Zeng, Y. (2003). Status of the research on masked palm civets. *Chinese J. Zool.* **38**: 120-122.

Jiménez, J.E. (1993). *Comparative Ecology of* Dusicyon *Foxes at the Chinchilla National Reserve in Northeastern Chile.* MSc thesis, University of Florida, Gainesville, Florida.

Jiménez, J.E. (2000). *Viability of the Endangered Darwin´s Fox* Pseudalopex fulvipes: *Assessing Ecological Factors in the Last Mainland Population.* Progress report for the Lincoln Park Zoo Neotropic Fund, Chicago, Illinois.

Jiménez, J.E. & McMahon, E. (2004). Darwin's fox *Pseudalopex fulvipes*. Pp. 50-55 in: Sillero-Zubiri, C., Hoffmann, M. & Macdonald, D.W. eds. (2004). *Canids: Foxes, Wolves, Jackals and Dogs. Status Survey and Conservation Action Plan.* IUCN/SSC Canid Specialist Group, Gland & Cambridge.

Jiménez, J.E. & Novaro, A.J. (2004). Culpeo *Pseudalopex culpaeus*. Pp. 44-49 in: Sillero-Zubiri, C., Hoffmann, M. & Macdonald, D.W. eds. (2004). *Canids: Foxes, Wolves, Jackals and Dogs. Status Survey and Conservation Action Plan.* IUCN/SSC Canid Specialist Group, Gland & Cambridge.

Jiménez, J.E., Marquet, P.A., Medel, R.G. & Jaksic, F.M. (1990). Comparative ecology of Darwin's fox *Pseudalopex fulvipes* in mainland and inland settings of southern Chile. *Rev. Chil. Hist. Nat.* **63**: 177-186.

Jiménez, J.E., Yáñez, J.L. & Jaksic, F.M. (1996). Inability of thin-layer-chromatography to distinguish feces from congeneric foxes by their bile acid contents. *Acta Theriol.* **41**: 211-215.

Jiménez, J.E., Yáñez, J.L., Tabilo, E.L. & Jaksic, F.M. (1996). Niche complementarity of South American foxes: reanalysis and test of a hypothesis. *Rev. Chil. Hist. Nat.* **69**: 113-123.

Jiménez-Guzmán, A. & López-Soto, J.H. (1992). Estado actual de la zorra del desierto, *Vulpes velox zinseri*, en el Ejido El Tokio, Galeana, Nuevo León, México. *Publ. Biol. (FCB/UANL)* **6**: 53-60.

Jin, C., Ciochon, R., Dong, W., Hunt, R.M., Liu, J., Jaeger, M. & Zhu, Q. (2007). The first skull of the earliest giant panda. *Proc. Natl. Acad. Sci. USA* **104**: 10932-10937.

Jobin, A., Molinari, P. & Breitenmoser, U. (2000). Prey spectrum, prey preference and consumption rates of Eurasian lynx in the Swiss Jura Mountains. *Acta Theriol.* **45**: 243-252.

Joeckel, R.M. (1998). Unique frontal sinuses in fossil and living Hyaenidae (Mammalia, Carnivora): description and interpretation. *J. Vert. Paleo.* **18**: 627-639.

Johnsingh, A.J.T. (1978). Some aspects of the ecology and behaviour of the Indian fox - *Vulpes bengalensis* Shaw. *J. Bombay Nat. Hist. Soc.* **75**: 397-405.

Johnsingh, A.J.T. (1979). *Ecology and Behaviour of the Dhole or Indian Wild Dog (*Cuon alpinus*), with Special Reference to Predator Prey Relationships at Bandipur.* PhD dissertation, Madurai Kamraj University, Madurai, India.

Johnsingh, A.J.T. (1982). Reproductive and social behaviour of the dhole *Cuon alpinus* Canidae. *J. Zool., London* **198**: 443-463.

Johnsingh, A.J.T. (1983). Large mammal prey-predators in Bandipur. *J. Bombay Nat. Hist. Soc.* **80**: 1-57.

Johnsingh, A.J.T. & Chellam, R. (1991). India's last lions. *Zoogoer Mag.* **Sept/Oct**: 16-20.

Johnsingh, A.J.T. & Jhala, Y.V. (2004). Indian fox *Vulpes bengalensis*. Pp. 219-222 in: Sillero-Zubiri, C., Hoffmann, M. & Macdonald, D.W. eds. (2004). *Canids: Foxes, Wolves, Jackals and Dogs. Status Survey and Conservation Action Plan.* IUCN/SSC Canid Specialist Group, Gland & Cambridge.

Johnson, A., Vongkhamheng, C., Hedemark, M. & Sithongdam, T. (2006). Effects of human-carnivore conflict on tiger (*Panthera tigris*) and prey populations in Lao PDR. *Anim. Conserv.* **9**: 421-430.

Johnson, C.E. (1921). The "hand-stand" habit of the spotted skunk. *J. Mammal.* **2**: 87-89.

Johnson, D.D., Macdonald, D.W. & Dickman, J.A. (2000). An analysis and review of models of the sociobiology of the Mustelidae. *Mammal Rev.* **30(3-4)**: 171-196.

Johnson, D.R. & Hersteinsson, P. (1993). Inheritance models of North American red fox coat color. *Can. J. Zool.* **71**: 1364-1366.

Johnson, K.G., Schaller, G.B. & Hu, J. (1988a). Comparative behavior of red and giant pandas in the Wolong Reserve, China. *J. Mammal.* **69**: 552-564.

Johnson, K.G., Schaller, G.B. & Hu, J. (1988b). Responses of giant pandas to a bamboo die-off. *Nat. Geogr. Res.* **4**: 161-177.

Johnson, K.G., Wang Wei, Reid, D.G. & Hu Jinchu (1993). Food habits of Asiatic leopards (*Panthera pardus fusea*) in Wolong Reserve, Sichuan, China. *J. Mammal.* **74**: 646-650.

Johnson, W.E. (1992). *Comparative Ecology of Two Sympatric South American Foxes* Dusicyon griseus *and* D. culpaeus. PhD dissertation, Iowa State University, Ames, Iowa.

Johnson, W.E. & Franklin, W.L. (1991). Feeding and spatial ecology of *Felis geoffroyi* in southern Patagonia. *J. Mammal.* **72**: 815-820.

Johnson, W.E. & Franklin, W.L. (1994a). Role of body size in the diets of sympatric gray and culpeo foxes. *J. Mammal.* **75**: 163-174.

Johnson, W.E. & Franklin, W.L. (1994b). Spatial resource partitioning by sympatric grey fox *Dusicyon griseus* and culpeo fox *Dusicyon culpaeus* in southern Chile. *Can. J. Zool.* **72**: 1788-1793.

Johnson, W.E. & Franklin, W.L. (1994c). Conservation implications of the South American grey fox *Dusicyon griseus* socioecology in the Patagonia of southern Chile. *Vida Silvestre Neotrop.* **3**: 16-23.

Johnson, W.E. & O'Brien, S.J. (1997). Phylogenetic reconstruction of the Felidae using 16S rRNA and NADH-5 mitochondrial genes. *J. Mol. Evol.* **44**(Suppl.): 98-116.

Johnson, W.E., Culver, M., Iriarte, J.A., Eizirik, E., Seymour, K.L. & O'Brien, S.J. (1998). Tracking the evolution of the elusive Andean mountain cat (*Oreailurus jacobita*) from mitochondrial DNA. *J. Heredity* **89(3)**: 227-232.

Johnson, W.E., Eizirik, E., Pecon-Slattery, J., Murphy, W.J., Antunes, A., Teeling, E. & O'Brien, S.J. (2006). The late Miocene radiation of modern Felidae: a genetic assessment. *Science* **311**: 73-77.

Johnson, W.E., Fuller, T.K., Arribillaga, G., Franklin, W.L. & Johnson, K.A. (1988). Seasonal changes in activity patterns of the Patagonian hog-nosed skunk (*Conepatus humboldti*) in Torres del Paine National Park, Chile. *Rev. Chil. Hist. Nat.* **61**: 217-221.

Johnson, W.E., Pecon-Slattery, J., Eizirik, E., Kim, J.H., Menotti-Raymond, M., Bonacic, C., Cambre, R., Crawshaw, P., Nunes, A., Seuánez, H.N., Moreira, M.A.M., Seymour, K.L., Simon, F., Swanson, W. & O'Brien, S.J. (1999). Disparate phylogeographic patterns of molecular genetic variation in four closely related South American small cats. *Mol. Ecol.* **8**: 79-94.

Johnson, W.E., Shinyashiki, F., Menotti-Raymond, M., Driscoll, C., Leh, C., Sunquist, M., Johnston, L., Bush, M., Wildt, D., Yuhki, N. & O'Brien, S.J. (1999). Molecular genetic characterization of two insular Asian cat species, Bornean bay cat and Iriomote cat. Pp. 223-248 in: Wasser, S.P. ed. (1999). *Evolutionary Theory and Processes: Modern Perspectives, Essays in Honour of Eviator Nevo.* Kulver Academic Publishing.

Jones, M.L. (1982). Longevity of captive mammals. *Zool. Garten (N.F.)* **52**: 113-128.

Jones, T.S. (1966). Notes on the commoner Sierra Leone mammals. *Nigerian Field* **31**: 4-17.

Jordan, N.R., Cherry, M.I. & Manser, M.B. (2007). Latrine distribution and patterns of use by wild meerkats: implications for territory and mate defence. *Anim. Behav.* **73**: 613-622.

Jordan, R.H. (1976). Threat behavior of the black bear (*Ursus americanus*). *Int. Conf. Bear Res. Management* **3**: 57-63.

Jorgenson, J.P. & Redford, K.H. (1993). Humans and big cats as predators in the Neotropics. *Symp. Zool. Soc. London* **65**: 367-390.

Jorgenson, J.P. & Sandoval, S. (2005). Andean bear management needs and interactions with humans in Columbia. *Ursus* **16**: 108-116.

Joshi, A.R., Garshelis, D.L. & Smith, J.L.D. (1995). Home ranges of sloth bears in Nepal: implications for conservation. *J. Wildl. Management* **59**: 204-214.

Joshi, A.R., Garshelis, D.L. & Smith, J.L.D. (1997). Seasonal and habitat-related diets of sloth bears in Nepal. *J. Mammal.* **78**: 584-597.

Joshi, A.R., Smith, J.L.D. & Cuthbert, F.J. (1995). Influence of food distribution and predation pressure on spacing behavior in palm civets. *J. Mammal.* **76**: 1205-1212.

Joshi, A.R., Smith, J.L.D. & Garshelis, D.L. (1999). Sociobiology of the myrmecophagous sloth bear in Nepal. *Can. J. Zool.* **77**: 1690-1704.

Joslin, P. (1973). *The Asiatic Lion: a Study of Ecology and Behaviour.* PhD thesis, University of Edinburgh, Edinburgh.

Juarez, K.M. & Marinho, J. (2002). Diet, habitat use, and home ranges of sympatric canids in central Brazil. *J. Mammal.* **83**: 925-933.

Julien-Laferrière, D. (1993). Radio-tracking observations on ranging and foraging patterns by kinkajous (*Potos flavus*) in French Guiana. *J. Trop. Ecol.* **9**: 19-32.

Julien-Laferrière, D. (1999). Foraging strategies and food partitioning in the neotropical frugivorous mammals *Caluromys philander* and *Potos flavus*. *J. Zool., London* **247**: 71-80.

Julien-Laferrière, D. (2001). Frugivory and seed dispersal by kinkajous. Pp. 217-226 in: Bongers, F., Charles-Dominique, P., Forget, P.M. & Théry, M. eds. (2001). *Nouragues. Dynamics and Plant-Animal Interactions in a Neotropical Rainforest.* Kluwer Academic Publishers, Dordrecht, The Netherlands.

Juste, J., Fa, J.E., Pérez del Val, J. & Castroviejo, J. (1995). Market dynamics of bushmeat species in Equatorial Guinea. *J. Appl. Ecol.* **32**: 454-467.

Kachuba, M. (1977). Sexual behavior and reproduction in captive Geoffroy's cats (*Leopardus geoffroyi* d'Orbigny and Gervais 1844). *Zool. Garten* **47**: 54-56.

Kaczensky, P., Huber, D., Knauer, F., Roth, H., Wagner, A. & Kusak, J. (2006). Activity patterns of brown bears (*Ursus arctos*) in Slovenia and Croatia. *J. Zool., London* **269**: 474-485.

Kadyrbaev, C.K. & Sludskii, A.A. (1981). [Corsac fox. Pp. 104-132 in: Gvozdev, E.V. & Strautman, E.I. eds. (1981). *Mammals of Kazakhstan*]. Nauka Kazahskoy SSR, Alma-Ata, URSS. In Russian.

Kaikusalo, A. & Angerbjörn, A. (1995). The Arctic fox population in Finnish Lapland during 30 years, 1964-1993. *Ann. Zool. Fennici* **32**: 69-77.

Kamler, J.F. & Ballard, W.B. (2002). A review of native and nonnative red foxes in North America. *Wildl. Soc. Bull.* **30**: 370-379.

Kamler, J.F. & Gipson, P.S. (2000). Home range, habitat selection and survival of bobcats, *Lynx rufus*, in a prairie ecosystem in Kansas. *Can. Field-Nat.* **114**: 388-394.

Kamler, J.F. & Gipson, P.S. (2004). Survival and cause-specific mortality among furbearers in a protected area. *Amer. Midl. Nat.* **151**: 27-34.

Kamler, J.F., Ballard, W.B., Fish, E.B., Lemons, P.R., Mote, K. & Perchellet, C.C. (2003). Habitat use, home ranges, and survival of swift foxes in a fragmented landscape: conservation implications. *J. Mammal.* **84**: 989-995.

Kamler, J.F., Ballard, W.B., Gese, E.M., Harrison, R.L., Karki, S. & Mote, K. (2004). Adult male emigration and a female-based social organization in swift foxes, *Vulpes velox*. *Anim. Behav.* **67**: 699-702.

Kamler, J.F., Ballard, W.B., Gilliland, R.L., Lemons, P.R. & Mote, K. (2003). Impacts of coyotes on swift foxes in northwestern Texas. *J. Wildl. Management* **67**: 317-323.

Kanchanasaka, B. (1998). Ecology of otters in the Upper Khwae Yai River, Thung Yai Naresuan Wildlife Sanctuary, Thailand. *Nat. Hist. Bull. Siam Soc.* **46**: 79-92.

Kaneko, Y. (2001). [Life cycle of the Japanese badger (*Meles meles anakuma*) in Hinode Town, Japan]. *Mammal. Sci.* **82**: 53-64. In Japanese.

Kaneko, Y. (2005). [Changes in Japanese badger (*Meles meles anakuma*) body weight and condition caused by addition of food by local people in a Tokyo suburb]. *Mammal. Sci.* **91**: 157-164. In Japanese.

Kaneko, Y., Maruyama, N. & Macdonald, D.W. (2006). Food habits and habitat selection of suburban badgers (*Meles meles*) in Japan. *J. Zool., London* **270**: 78-89.

Kaplan, J.B. & Mead, R.A. (1993). Influence of season on seminal characteristics, testis size and serum testosterone in the western spotted skunk (*Spilogale gracilis*). *J. Reprod. Fertil.* **98**: 321-326.

Kaplan, J.B. & Mead, R.A. (1994). Seasonal changes in testicular function and seminal characteristics of the male eastern spotted skunk (*Spilogale putorius ambarvilus*). *J. Mammal.* **75**: 1013-1020.

Kaplan, J.B., Berria, M. & Mead, R.A. (1991). Prolactin levels in the western spotted skunk: changes during pre- and periimplantation and effects of melatonin and lesions to the anterior hypothalamus. *Biol. Reprod.* **44**: 991-997.

Kappeler, P.M. (2000). Lemur origins: rafting by groups of hibernators? *Folia Primatol.* **71**: 422-425.

Karanth, K.U. (1986). A possible sighting record of Malabar civet (*Viverra megaspila* Blyth) from Karnataka. *J. Bombay Nat. Hist. Soc.* **83**: 192-193.

Karanth, K.U. (1987). Tigers in India: a critical review of field censuses. Pp. 118-132 in: Tilson, R.L. & Seal, U.S. eds. (1987). *Tigers of the World: the Biology, Biopolitics, Management and Conservation of an Endangered Species.* Noyes Publications, Park Ridge, New Jersey.

Karanth, K.U. (2001). *The Way of the Tiger.* Voyageur Press, Stillwater, Minnesota.

Karanth, K.U. & Sunquist, M.E. (1992). Population structure, density and biomass of large herbivores in the tropical forests of Nagarahole, India. *J. Trop. Ecol.* **8**: 21-35.

Karanth, K.U. & Sunquist, M.E. (1995). Prey selection by tiger, leopard, and dhole in tropical forests. *J. Anim. Ecol.* **64**: 439-450.

Karanth, K.U. & Sunquist, M.E. (2000). Behavioural correlates of predation by tiger (*Panthera tigris*), leopard (*Panthera pardus*), and dhole (*Cuon alpinus*) in Nagarahole, India. *J. Zool., London* **250**: 255-265.

Karanth, K.U., Nichols, J.D., Kumar, N.S., Link, W.A. & Hines, E. (2004). Tigers and their prey: predicting carnivore densities from prey abundance. *Proc. Natl. Acad. Sci. USA* **101(14)**: 4854-4858.

Karpanty, S.M. & Wright, P.C. (2006). Predation on lemurs in the rainforest of Madagascar by multiple predator species: observations and experiments. Pp. 77-99 in: Gursky, S.L. & Nekaris, K.A.I. eds. (2006). *Primate Anti-predator Strategies.* Springer Press, New York.

Kasparian, M.A., Hellgren, E.C. & Ginger, S.M. (2002). Food habits of the Virginia opossum during raccoon removal in the Cross Timbers ecoregion, Oklahoma. *Proc. Okla. Acad. Sci.* **82**: 73-78.

Kasparian, M.A., Hellgren, E.C., Ginger, S.M., Levesque, L.P., Clark, J.E., Winkelman, D.L. & Engle, D.M. (2004). Population characteristics of Virginia opossum in the Cross Timbers during raccoon reduction. *Amer. Midl. Nat.* **151**: 154-163.

Kasper, C.B., Feldens, M.J., Salvi, J. & Grillo, H.C.Z. (2004). Preliminary study by the ecology of *Lontra longicaudis* (Olfers) (Carnivora, Mustelidae) in Taquari Valley, South Brazil. *Rev. Bras. Zool.* **21**: 65-72.

Kasworm, W.F., Proctor, M.F., Servheen, C. & Paetkau, D. (2007). Success of grizzly bear population augmentation in northwest Montana. *J. Wildl. Management* **71**: 1261-1266.

Kattan, G., Hernández, O.L., Goldstein, I., Rojas, V., Murillo, O., Gómez, C., Restrepo, H. & Cuesta, F. (2004). Range fragmentation in the spectacled bear *Tremarctos ornatus* in the northern Andes. *Oryx* **38**: 155-163.

Kaudern, W. (1915). Saugethiere aus Madagaskar. *Ark. Zool.* **18**: 1-101.

Kaufmann, J.H. (1962). The ecology and social behavior of the coati, *Nasua narica*, on Barro Colorado Island, Panama. *Univ. Calif. Publ. Zool.* **60**: 95-222.

Kauhala, K. (1992). *Ecological Characteristics of the Raccoon Dog in Finland.* PhD dissertation, University of Helsinki, Helsinki, Finland.

Kauhala, K. (1996). Habitat use of raccoon dogs *Nyctereutes procyonoides* in southern Finland. *Zeitschrift für Säugetierkunde* **61**: 269-275.

Kauhala, K. & Auniola, M. (2000). Diet of raccoon dogs in summer in the Finnish archipelago. *Ecography* **24**: 151-156.

Kauhala, K. & Helle, E. (1995). Population ecology of the raccoon dog in Finland - a synthesis. *Wildl. Biol.* **1**: 3-9.

Kauhala, K. & Saeki, M. (2004). Raccon dog *Nyctereutes procyonoides*. Pp. 136-142 in: Sillero-Zubiri, C., Hoffmann, M. & Macdonald, D.W. eds. (2004). *Canids: Foxes, Wolves, Jackals and Dogs. Status Survey and Conservation Action Plan.* IUCN/SSC Canid Specialist Group, Gland & Cambridge.

Kauhala, K., Helle, E. & Pietilä, H. (1998). Time allocation of male and female raccoon dogs to pup rearing at the den. *Acta Theriol.* **43**: 301-310.

Kauhala, K., Helle, E. & Taskinen, K. (1993). Home range of the raccoon dog *Nyctereutes procyonoides* in southern Finland. *J. Zool., London* **231**: 95-106.

Kauhala, K., Kaunisto, M. & Helle, E. (1993). Diet of the raccoon dog, *Nyctereutes procyonoides*, in Finland. *Zeitschrift für Säugetierkunde* **58**: 129-136.

Kauhala, K., Laukkanen, P. & von Rége, I. (1998). Summer food composition and food niche overlap of the raccoon dog, red fox and badger in Finland. *Ecography* **21**: 457-463.

Kaunda, S.K.K. (2000). Activity patterns of black-backed jackals at Mokolodi Nature Reserve, Botswana. *South Afr. J. Wildl. Res.* **30**: 157-162.

Kaunda, S.K.K. & Skinner, J.D. (2003). Black-backed jackal diet at Mokolodi Nature Reserve, Botswana. *Afr. J. Ecol.* **41**: 39-46.

Kawanishi, K. & Sunquist, M.E. (2004). Conservation status of tigers in a primary rainforest of Peninsular Malaysia. *Biol. Conserv.* **120**: 329-344.

Kawanishi, K. & Sunquist, M.E. (2008). Food habits and activity patterns of the Asiatic golden cat (*Catopuma temminckii*) and dhole (*Cuon alpinus*) in a primary rainforest of Peninsular Malaysia. *Mammal Study* **33**: 173-177.

Kays, R.W. (1999a). Food preferences of kinkajous (*Potos flavus*): a frugivorous carnivore. *J. Mammal.* **80**: 589-599.

Kays, R.W. (1999b). A hoistable arboreal mammal trap. *Wildl. Soc. Bull.* **27**: 298-300.

Kays, R.W. (2000). The behavior of olingos (*Bassaricyon gabii*) and their competition with kinkajous (*Potos flavus*) in central Panama. *Mammalia* **64**: 1-10.

Kays, R.W. (2003). Social polyandry and promiscuous mating in a primate-like carnivore: the kinkajou (*Potos flavus*). Pp. 125-137 in: Reichard, U.H. & Boesch, C. eds. (2003). *Monogamy: Mating Strategies and Partnerships in Birds, Humans and Other Mammals.* Cambridge University Press, Cambridge.

Kays, R.W. & Gittleman, J.L. (1995). Home range size and social behavior of kinkajous (*Potos flavus*) in the Republic of Panama. *Biotropica* **27**: 530-534.

Kays, R.W. & Gittleman, J.L. (2001). The social organization of the kinkajou *Potos flavus* (Procyonidae). *J. Zool., London* **253**: 491-504.

Kays, R.W. & Wilson, D.E. (2002). *Mammals of North America.* Princeton Field Guides. Princeton University Press, Princeton & Oxford.

Kays, R.W., Gittleman, J.G. & Wayne, R.K. (2000). Microsatellite analysis of kinkajou social organization. *Mol. Ecol.* **9**: 743-751.

Keane, B., Creel, S.R. & Waser, P.M. (1996). No evidence of inbreeding avoidance or inbreeding depression in a social carnivore. *Behav. Ecol.* **7**: 480-489.

Keane, B., Waser, P.M., Creel, S.R., Creel, N.M., Elliott, L.F. & Minchella, D.J. (1994). Subordinate reproduction in dwarf mongooses. *Anim. Behav.* **47**: 65-75.

Keiji, O. (1998). Distribution and invading process of the masked palm civet, *Paguma larvata*, in Chiba Prefecture, Central Japan. *J. Nat. Hist. Mus. Inst., Chiba* **5**: 51-54.

Keishi, S., Go, O., Takeshi, S., Yasuhiko, N., Kojun, T. & Yoshitsugu, K. (2002). Food habits of introduced Japanese weasels (*Mustela itatsi*) and impacts on native species on Zamami Island. *Mammal. Sci.* **85**: 153-160.

Keith, L.B. (1963). *Wildlife's Ten-year Cycle.* University of Wisconsin Press, Madison, Wisconsin.

Keith, L.B. (1990). Dynamics of snowshoe hare populations. Pp. 119-195 in: Genoways, H.H. ed. (1990). *Current Mammalogy.* Plenum Press, New York.

Kelker, G.H. (1937). Insect food of skunks. *J. Mammal.* **18**: 164-170.

Kelly, B.T. (2000). *Red Wolf Recovery Program Adaptive Work Plan FY00-02.* US Fish and Wildlife Service, Alligator River National Wildlife Refuge, Manteo, North Carolina.

Kelly, B.T., Beyer, A. & Phillips, M.K. (2004). Red wolf *Canis rufus*. Pp. 87-92 in: Sillero-Zubiri, C., Hoffmann, M. & Macdonald, D.W. eds. (2004). *Canids: Foxes, Wolves, Jackals and Dogs. Status Survey and Conservation Action Plan.* IUCN/SSC Canid Specialist Group, Gland & Cambridge.

Kelly, B.T., Miller, P.S. & Seal, U.S. eds. (1999). *Population and Habitat Viability Assessment Workshop for the Red Wolf* Canis rufus. SSC/IUCN Conservation Breeding Specialist Group, Apple Valley, Minnesota.

Kelly, M.J., Noss, A.J., Di Bitetti, M.S., Maffei, L., Arispe, R.L., Paviolo, A., De Angelo, C.D. & Di Blanco, Y.E. (2008). Estimating puma densities from camera trapping across three study sites: Bolivia, Argentina and Belize. *J. Mammal.* **89**: 408-418.

Kemp, T.S. (1982). *Mammal-like Reptiles and the Origin of Mammals.* Academic Press, London.

Kennedy, M.L. & Lindsay, S.L. (1984). Morphologic variation in the raccoon, *Procyon lotor*, and its relationship to genic and environmental variation. *J. Mammal.* **65**: 195-205.

Kent, G.C. & Carr, R.K. (2001). *Comparative Anatomy of the Vertebrates.* McGraw Hill, New York.

Kenyon, K.W. (1969). The sea otter in the eastern Pacific Ocean. *North Amer. Fauna* **68**: 1-352.

Kerbis-Peterhans, J.C. & Horwitz, L.K. (1992). A bone assemblage from a striped hyaena (*Hyaena hyaena*) den in the Negev Desert, Israel. *Israel J. Zool.* **37**: 225-245.

Kerridge, F.J., Ralisoamalala, R.C., Goodman, S.M. & Pasnick, S.D. (2003). *Fossa fossana*, Malagasy striped civet. Pp. 1363-1365 in: Goodman, S.M. & Benstead, J.P. eds. (2003). *The Natural History of Madagascar.* The University of Chicago Press, Chicago, Illinois.

Khorozkyan, I. & Malkhasyan, A. (2002). *Ecology of the Leopard (*Panthera pardus*) in Khosrov Reserve, Armenia: Implications for Conservation.* Scientific Report n. **6** – Publisher Societa Zoologica "La Torbiera", Italy.

Khounboline, K. (2005). A large-spotted civet *Viverra megaspila* record from a mid-altitude plateau, Lao PDR. *Small Carniv. Conserv.* **33**: 26.

Kieser, J.A. (1995). Gnathomandibular morphology and character displacement in the bat-eared fox. *J. Mammal.* **76**: 542-550.

Kilgo, J.C., Labisky, R.F. & Fritzen, D.E. (1998). Influences of hunting on the behavior of white-tailed deer: implications for conservation of the Florida panther. *Conserv. Biol.* **12**: 1359-1364.

Kilgore, D.L. (1969). An ecological study of the swift fox *Vulpes velox* in the Oklahoma Panhandle. *Amer. Midl. Nat.* **81**: 512-534.

Kilham, B. & Gray, E. (2002). *Among the Bears. Raising Orphan Cubs in the Wild.* Henry Holt & Co., New York.

Kilpatrick, H.J. & Rego, P.W. (1994). Influence of season, sex, and site availability on fisher (*Martes pennanti*) rest-site selection in the central hardwood forest. *Can. J. Zool.* **72**: 1416-1419.

King, C.M. (1983). *Mustela erminea. Mammal. Species* **195**: 1-8.

King, C.M. (1990). *The Natural History of Weasels and Stoats.* Comstock Publishing Associates, Ithaca, New York.

Kingdon, J. (1971-1982). *East African Mammals.* University of Chicago Press, Chicago, Illinois.

Kingdon, J. (1990). *Arabian Mammals – a Natural History.* Academic Press, San Diego, California.

Kingdon, J. (1997). *The Kingdon Field Guide to African Mammals.* Academic Press, London.

Kingdon, J. & Van Rompaey, H. (In press). *Helogale hirtula.* In: Kingdon, J.S. & Hoffmann, M. eds. (In press). *The Mammals of Africa.* Vol. 5. Carnivores, Pangolins, Rhinos and Equids. Academic Press, Amsterdam.

Kinlaw, A. (1995). *Spilogale putorius. Mammal. Species* **511**: 1-7.

Kipp, H. (1965). Beitrag zur kenntnis der gattung *Conepatus* Molina, 1782. *Zeitschrift für Säugetierkunde* **30**: 193-232.

Kitchen, A.M., Gese, E.M. & Schauster, E.R. (1999). Resource partitioning between coyotes and swift foxes: space, time and diet. *Can. J. Zool.* **77**: 1645-1656.

Kitchen, A.M., Gese, E.M. & Schauster, E.R. (2000a). Changes in coyote activity patterns due to reduced exposure to human persecution. *Can. J. Zool.* **78**: 853-857.

Kitchen, A.M., Gese, E.M. & Schauster, E.R. (2000b). Long-term spatial stability of coyote *Canis latrans* home ranges in southeastern Colorado. *Can. J. Zool.* **78**: 458-464.

Kitchener, A.C. (1991). *The Natural History of the Wild Cats.* Christopher Helm, London.

Kitchener, A.C. (1998). The Scottish wildcat: a cat with an identity crisis? *British Wildlife* **9(4)**: 232-242.

Kitchener, A.C. (1999). Tiger distribution, phenotypic variation and conservation issues. Pp. 19-39 in: Seidensticker, J., Christie, S. & Jackson, P. eds. (1999). *Riding the Tiger. Tiger Conservation in Human-dominated Landscapes.* Cambridge University Press, Cambridge.

Kitchener, A.C. & Daniels, M.J. (2008). Wildcat *Felis silvestris.* Pp. 397-406 in: Harris, S. & Yalden, D.W. eds. (2008). *Mammals of the British Isles: Handbook.* 4th edition. The Mammal Society, Southhampton.

Kitchener, A.C. & Dugmore, A.J. (2000). Biogeographical change in the tiger, *Panthera tigris. Anim. Conserv.* **2**: 113-124.

Kitchener, A.C., Beaumont, M.A. & Richardson, D. (2006). Geographical variation in the clouded leopard, *Neofelis nebulosa,* reveals two species. *Curr. Biol.* **16**: 2377-2383.

Kitchener, A.C., Clegg, T., Thompson, N.M., Wiik, H. & Macdonald, A.A. (1993). First records of the Malay civet, *Viverra tangalunga* Gray, 1832 from Seram with notes on the seram bandicoot *Rhynchomeles prattorum* Thomas, 1920. *Zeitschrift für Säugetierkunde* **58**: 378-380.

Kitchener, A.C., Daniels, M.J., Scott, R. & Balharry, D. (In press). Wildcat *Felis silvestris.* In: Harris, S. ed. (In press). *The Handbook of British Mammals.* 4th edition. Poyser, London.

Klauber, L.M. (1972). *Rattlesnakes: their Habits, Life Histories and Influence on Mankind.* 2nd edition. University of California Press, Berkeley, California.

Kleiman, D.G. (1966). Scent marking in the Canidae. *Symp. Zool. Soc. London* **18**: 167-177.

Kleiman, D.G. (1972). Social behaviour of the maned wolf *Chrysocyon brachyurus* and bush dog *Speothos venaticus*: a study in contrast. *J. Mammal.* **53**: 791-806.

Kleiman, D.G. (1974). The estrous cycle of the tiger (*Panthera tigris*). Pp. 60-75 in: Eaton, R.L. ed. (1974). *The World's Cats.* Vol. 2. World Wildlife Safari, Winston, Oregon.

Kleiman, D.G. (1983). Ethology and reproduction of captive giant pandas (*Ailuropoda melanoleuca*). *Zeitschr. Tierpsychol.* **62**: 1-46.

Kloss, C.B. (1927). A note on Bornean badgers (*Mydaus*). *J. Malay Branch R. Asiatic Soc.* **5**: 348-349.

Knapp, D.K. (1978). *Effects of Agricultural Development in Kern County, California, on the San Joaquin Kit Fox in 1977.* California Department of Fish and Game, Non-game Wildlife Investigations Final Report, Project **E-1-1, Job V-1.21**.

Knick, S.T. (1990). Ecology of bobcats relative to exploitation and prey decline in southeastern Idaho. *Wildl. Monogr.* **108**: 1-42.

Knick, S.T., Sweeney, S.J., Alldredge, J.R. & Brittell, J.D. (1984). Autumn and winter food habits of bobcats in Washington State. *Great Basin Nat.* **44**: 70-73.

Knowlton, F.F., Gese, E.M. & Jaeger, M.M. (1999). Coyote depredation control: an interface between biology and management. *J. Range Manage.* **52**: 398-412.

Kock, D., Künzel, T. & Rayaleh, H.A. (2000). The African civet, *Civettictis civetta* (Schreber 1776), of Djibouti representing a new subspecies. *Senckenbergiana Biol.* **80**: 241-246.

Koehler, G.M. (1990). Population and habitat characteristics of lynx and snowshoe hares in north central Washington. *Can. J. Zool.* **68**: 845-851.

Koehler, G.M. & Hornocker, M.G. (1991). Seasonal resource use among mountain lion, bobcats and coyotes. *J. Mammal.* **72**: 391-396.

Koehler, G.M., Hornocker, M.G. & Hash, H.S. (1979). Lynx movement and habitat use in Montana. *Can. Field-Nat.* **93**: 441-442.

Koehler, K.E. & Richardson, P.R.K. (1990). *Proteles cristatus. Mammal. Species* **363**: 1-6.

Koen, E.L., Bowman, J., Findlay, C.S. & Zheng, L. (2007). Home range and population density of fishers in eastern Ontario. *J. Wildl. Management* **71**: 1484-1493.

Koenig, V.L. (1970). Zur fortpflanzung und jungendentwicklung des wüstenfuchses *Fennecus zerda* Zimm, 1780. *Zeitschr. Tierpsychol.* **27**: 205-246.

Koepfli, K.P. & Wayne, R.K. (1998). Phylogenetic relationships of otters (Carnivora: Mustelidae) based on mitochondrial cytochrome b sequences. *J. Zool.* **246**: 401-416.

Koepfli, K.P., Deere, K.A., Slater, G.J., Begg, C., Begg, K., Grassman, L., Lucherini, M., Veron, G. & Wayne, R.K. (2008). Multigene phylogeny of the Mustelidae: resolving relationships, tempo and biogeographic history of a mammalian adaptive radiation. *BMC Biol.* **6**: 10.

Koepfli, K.P., Jenks, S.M., Eizirik, E., Zahirpour, T., Van Valkenburgh, B. & Wayne, R.K. (2006). Molecular systematics of the Hyaenidae: relationships of a relictual lineage resolved by a molecular supermatrix. *Mol. Phylogen. Evol.* **38**: 603-620.

Köhncke, M. & Leonhardt, K. (1986). *Cryptoprocta ferox. Mammal. Species* **254**: 1-4.

Köhncke, M. & Schliemann, H. (1977). Über zwei foeten von *Cryptoprocta ferox* Bennett, 1833. *Mitt. Hamb. Zool. Mus. Inst.* **74**: 171-175.

Kok, O.B. (1996). Dieetsamestelling van enkele karnivoorsoorte in die Vrystaat, Suid-Afrika. *South Afr. J. Sci.* **92**: 393-398. In Afrikaans with English summary.

Koler-Matznick, J., Brisbin, I.L. & McIntyre, J. (2000). The New Guinea singing dog. Pp. 239-247 in: Crockford, S.J. ed. (2000). *Dogs Through Time: an Archaeological Perspective.* British Archaeological Press, Oxford.

Kolowski, J.M. & Holekamp, K.E. (2006). Spatial and temporal variation in livestock depredation by large carnivores along a Kenyan reserve border. *Biol. Conserv.* **128**: 529-541.

Kolowski, J.M. & Woolf, A. (2002). Microhabitat use by bobcats in southern Illinois. *J. Wildl. Management* **66**: 822-832.

Kolowski, J.M., Katan, D., Theis, K.R. & Holekamp, K.E. (2007). Daily patterns of activity in the spotted hyena. *J. Mammal.* **88**: 1017-1028.

Kolska, L. (1991). Scavenging activities of striped hyaenas *Hyaena hyaena* in Israel. *Israel J. Zool.* **37**: 189.

Konecny, M.J. (1989). Movement patterns and food habits of four sympatric carnivore species in Belize, Central America. Pp. 243-264 in: Redford, K.H. & Eisenberg, J.F. eds. (1989). *Advances in Neotropical Mammalogy.* Sandhill Crane Press, Gainesville, Florida.

Koop, K. & Velimirov, B. (1982). Field observations on activity and feeding of bat-eared foxes *Otocyon megalotis* at Nxai Pan, Botswana. *Afr. J. Ecol.* **20**: 23-27.

Koopman, M.E., Cypher, B.L. & Scrivner, J.H. (2000). Dispersal patterns of San Joaquin kit foxes *Vulpes macrotis mutica. J. Mammal.* **81**: 213-222.

Koopman, M.E., Scrivner, J.H. & Kato, T.T. (1998). Patterns of den use by San Joaquin kit foxes. *J. Wildl. Management* **62**: 373-379.

Korhonen, H. (1988). Voluntary regulation of energy balance in farmed raccoon dogs. *Comp. Biochem. Physiol. Part A: Comp. Physiol.* **89**: 219-222.

Korhonen, H., Mononen, J. & Harri, M. (1991). Evolutionary comparison of energy economy between Finnish and Japanese raccoon dogs. *Comp. Biochem. Physiol. Part A: Comp. Physiol.* **100**: 293-295.

Kortlucke, S.M. (1973). Morphological variation in the kinkajou, *Potos flavus* (Mammalia: Procyonidae), in Middle America. *Occas. Pap. Mus. Nat. Hist. Univ. Kansas* **17**: 1-36.

Koshkarev, E.P. (1984). Characteristics of snow leopard (*Unica uncia*) movements in the Tien Shan. *Int. Ped. Book Snow Leopards* **4**: 15-21.

Kovach, A.I. & Powell, R.A. (2003). Effects of body size on male mating tactics and paternity in black bears, *Ursus americanus. Can. J. Zool.* **81**: 1257-1268.

Kovach, S.D. & Dow, R.J. (1981). *Status and Ecology of the Island Fox on San Nicolas Island, 1980.* Technical Memorandum **TM-81-28**. Pacific Missile Defense Center, Pt. Mugu, California.

Kowalczyk, C. (1989). Behavioral observations of the banded palm civet (*Hemigalus derbyanus* [Gray]) in captivity. *Zool. Garten* **59**: 264-274.

Kowalczyk, R., Jedrzejewska, B. & Zalewski, A. (2003). Annual and circadian activity patterns of badgers (*Meles meles*) in Bialowieza Primeval Forest (eastern Poland) compared with other Palaearctic populations. *J. Biogeogr.* **30**: 463-472.

Kowalczyk, R., Zalewski, A. & Jedrzejewska, B. (2004). Seasonal and spatial pattern of shelter use by badgers *Meles meles* in Bialowieza Primeval Forest (Poland). *Acta Theriol.* **49**: 75-92.

Kowalczyk, R., Zalewski, A. & Jedrzejewska, B. (2006). Daily movement and territory use by badgers *Meles meles* in Bialowieza Primeval Forest, Poland. *Wildl. Biol.* **12**: 385-391.

Kowalczyk, R., Zalewski, A., Jedrzejewska, B. & Jedrzejewski, W. (1999). Strategy of resting site utilisation by coexisting Eurasian badgers, red foxes and raccoon dogs in Bialowieza Primeval Forest (Poland). Page 148 in: *3rd European Congress of Mammalogy, Jyväskylä, Finland May 29- June 3 1999.*

Kowalczyk, R., Zalewski, A., Jedrzejewska, B. & Jedrzejewski, W. (2000). Jenot - ni pies, ni borsuk. *Lowiec Polski* **11**: 1-20. In Polish.

Kowalczyk, R., Zalewski, A., Jedrzejewska, B. & Jedrzejewski, W. (2003). Spatial organization and demography of badgers (*Meles meles*) in Bialowieza Primeval Forest, Poland, and the influence of earthworms on badger densities in Europe. *Can. J. Zool.* **81**: 74-87.

Kowalski, K. (1988). The food of the sand fox *Vulpes rueppellii* Schinz, 1825 in the Egyptian Sahara. *Folia Biol. Cracow* **36**: 89-94.

Kowalski, K. & Rzebik-Kowalska, M. (1991). *Mammals of Algeria.* Zaklad Narodowy Imienia Ossolinskkick Wydawnictwo polskiej Akamemii Nauk Wroclaw, Poland.

Kozlov, V.I. (1952). [Material of the study of the biology of the raccoon dog (*Nyctereutes procyonoides* Gray) in the province of Gorki]. *Zool. Zhurnal* **31**: 761-768. In Russian.

Kram, R. & Taylor, C.R. (1990). Energetics of running: a new perspective. *Nature (London)* **346**: 265-267.

Krause, J., Unger, T., Noçon, A., Malaspinas, A.S., Kolokotronis, S.O., Stiller, M., Soibelzon, L., Spriggs, H., Dear, P.H., Briggs, A.W., Bray, S.C.E., O'Brien, S.J., Rabeder, G., Matheus, P., Cooper, A., Slatkin, M., Pääbo, S. & Hofreiter, M. (2008). Mitochondrial genomes reveal an explosive radiation of extinct and extant bears near the Miocene-Pliocene boundary. *BMC Evol. Biol.* **8**: 220.

Krebs, C.J., Boonstra, R., Boutin, S. & Sinclair, A.R.E. (2001). What drives the 10-year cycle of snowshoe hares? *Bioscience* **51**: 25-35.

Krebs, C.J., Boutin, S., Boonstra, R., Sinclair, A.R.E., Smith, J.N.M., Dale, M.R.T., Martin, K. & Turkington, R. (1995). Impact of food and predation on the snowshoe hare cycle. *Science* **269**: 1112-1115.

Krebs, J., Lofroth, E.C. & Parfitt, I. (2007). Multiscale habitat use by wolverines in British Columbia, Canada. *J. Wildl. Management* **71**: 2180-2192.

Krebs, J.W., Rupprecht, C.E. & Childs, J.E. (2000). Rabies surveillance in the United States during 1999. *J. Amer. Vet. Med. Assoc.* **217**: 1799-1811.

Krebs, J.W., Wilson, M.L. & Childs, J.E. (1995). Rabies, epidemiology, prevention, and future research. *J. Mammal.* **76**: 681-694.

Krishnakumar, H. & Balakrishnan, M. (2003). Feeding ecology of the common palm civet *Paradoxurus hermaphroditus* (Pallas) in semi-urban habitats in Trivandrum, India. *Small Carniv. Conserv.* **28**: 10-11.

Krishnakumar, H., Balasubramanian, N.K. & Balakrishnan, M. (2002). Sequential pattern of behavior in the common palm civet, *Paradoxurus hermaphroditus* (Pallas). *Int. J. Comp. Psychol.* **15**: 303-311.

Krott, P. (1960). Ways of the wolverine. *Nat. Hist.* **69**: 16-29.

Krsti , R.V. (1984). *General Histology of the Mammal: an Atlas for Students of Medicine and Biology.* Springer, New York.

Krubitzer, L. (1995). The organization of neocortex in mammals: are species differences really so different? *Trends Neurosci.* **18**: 408-417.

Kruuk, H. (1972). *The Spotted Hyena. A Study of Predation and Social Behavior.* The University of Chicago Press, Chicago, Illinois.

Kruuk, H. (1976). Feeding and social behaviour of the striped hyaena (*Hyaena vulgaris* Desmarest). *East Afr. Wildl. J.* **14**: 91-111.

Kruuk, H. (1977). Interactions between the spotted hyaena and potential prey species in the Aberdare mountains of Kenya. *East Afr. Wildl. J.* **15**: 165-166.

Kruuk, H. (2000). Note on status and foraging of the pantot or Palawan stink badger, *Mydaus marchei. Small Carniv. Conserv.* **22**: 11-12.

Kruuk, H. & Conroy, J.W.H. (1991). Mortality of otters (*Lutra lutra*) in Shetland. *J. Appl. Ecol.* **28**: 83-94.

Kruuk, H. & Goudswaard, P.C. (1990). Effects of changes in fish populations in Lake Victoria on the food of otters (*Lutra maculicollis* Schinz and *Aonyx capensis* Lichtenstein). *Afr. J. Ecol.* **28**: 322-329.

Kruuk, H. & Mills, M.G.L. (1983). Notes on food and foraging of the honey badger *Mellivora capensis* in the Kalahari Gemsbok National Park. *Koedoe* **26**: 153-157.

Kruuk, H. & Parish, T. (1987). Changes in the size of groups and ranges of the European badger (*Meles meles* L.) in an area in Scotland. *J. Anim. Ecol.* **56**: 351-364.

Kruuk, H. & Sands, W.A. (1972). The aardwolf (*Proteles cristatus* Sparrman 1783) as a predator on termites. *East Afr. Wildl. J.* **10**: 211-227.

Kruuk, H. & Turner, M. (1967). Comparative notes on predation by lion, leopard, cheetah and wild dog in the Serengeti area, East Africa. *Mammalia* **31**: 1-27.

Kruuk, H., Kanchanasaka, B., O'Sullivan, S. & Wanghongsa, S. (1994). Niche separation in three sympatric otters *Lutra perspicillata, L. Lutra* and *Aonyx cinerea* in Huai Kha Khaeng, Thailand. *Biol. Conserv.* **69**: 115-120.

Kruuk, H., Moorhouse, A., Conroy, J.W.H., Durbin, L. & Frears, S. (1989). An estimate of numbers and habitat preferences of otters *Lutra lutra* in Shetland, UK. *Biol. Conserv.* **49**: 241-254.

Krystufek, B. & Tvrtkovic, N. (1992). New information on the introduction into Europe of the small Indian mongoose *Herpestes auropunctatus. Small Carniv. Conserv.* **7**: 16.

Kuhn, H.J. (1960). *Genetta (paragenetta) lehmanni,* eine neue Schleichkatze aus Liberia. *Säugetierkundliche Mitt.* **8**: 154-160.

Kuhn, H.J. & Zeller, U. (1987). *Morphogenesis of the Mammalian Skull.* Paul Parey Scientific Publishers, New York.

Kumar, A. & Rai, N. (1991). Pilot study on the conservation of the Malabar civet. *Small Carniv. Conserv.* **5**: 16.

Kumar, A. & Umapathy, G. (2000). Home range and habitat use by Indian grey mongoose and small Indian civets in Nilgiri Biosphere Reserve, India. Pp. 87-91 in: Hussain, S.A. ed. (2000). *ENVIS Bulletin: Wildlife and Protected Areas, Mustelids, Viverrids and Herpestids of India.* Vol. 2(2). Wildlife Institute of India, Dehra Dun, India.

Kuntzsch, V. & Nel, J.A.J. (1992). Diet of bat-eared foxes *Otocyon megalotis* in the Karoo. *Koedoe* **35**: 37-48.

Kuroda, N. & Mori, T. (1923). Two new and rare mammals from Korea. *J. Mammal.* **4**: 27-28.

Kurtén, B. (1973). Geographic variation in size in the puma (*Felis concolor*). *Commentationes Biologicae* **63**: 1-8.

Kurtén, B. (1976). *The Cave Bear Story, Life and Death of a Vanished Animal.* Columbia University Press, New York.

Kurtén, B. (1982). *Teeth: Form, Function and Evolution.* Columbia University Press, New York.

Kurtén, B. & Anderson, E. (1980). *Pleistocene Mammals of North America.* Columbia University Press, New York.

Kurtén, B. & Granqvist, E. (1987). Fossil pardel lynx (*Lynx pardina spelaea* Boule) from a cave in southern France. *Ann. Zool. Fennici* **24**: 39-43.

Kurtén, B. & Werdelin, L. (1988). A review of the genus *Chasmaporthestes* Hay, 1921 (Carnivora, Hyaenidae). *J. Vert. Paleontol.* **8**: 46-66.

Kurup, D.N. & Joseph, G.K. (2001). Certain observations on the behaviour of Nilgiri marten (*Martes gwatkinsi*) in Periyar Tiger Reserve, Kerala, India. *Small Carniv. Conserv.* **25**: 1-2.

Kurup, G.U. (1987). The rediscovery of the Malabar civet, *Viverra megaspila civettina* Blyth in India. *Cheetal* **28**: 1-4.

Kurup, G.U. (1989). The rediscovery of Malabar civet (*Viverra megaspila civettina*) Blyth in India. *Tigerpaper* **16**: 13-14.

Kutsukake, N. & Clutton-Brock, T.H. (2006a). Aggression and submission reflect reproductive conflict between females in cooperatively breeding meerkats *Suricata suricatta. Behav. Ecol. Sociobiol.* **59**: 541-548.

Kutsukake, N. & Clutton-Brock, T.H. (2006b). Social functions of allogrooming in cooperatively breeding meerkats. *Anim. Behav.* **72**: 1059-1068.

Kuznetzov, G.V. & Baranauskas, K. (1993). Notes on the behaviour, activity, and feeding of the spotted linsang (*Prionodon pardicolor*) in captivity. *Small Carniv. Conserv.* **8**: 5.

Kvam, T. (1991). Reproduction in the European lynx, *Lynx lynx. Zeitschrift für Säugetierkunde* **56**: 146-158.

Laack, L.L., Tewes, M.E., Haines, A.M. & Rappole, J.H. (2005). Reproductive life history of ocelots *Leopardus pardalis* in southern Texas. *Acta Theriol.* **50**: 505-514.

Labisky, R.F. & Boulay, M.C. (1998). Behaviors of bobcats preying on white-tailed deer in the Everglades. *Amer. Midl. Nat.* **139**: 275-281.

Laborde, C. (1986). Description de la locomotion arboricole de *Cryptoprocta ferox* (Carnivore Viverridé Malgache). *Mammalia* **50**: 369-378.

Labuschagne, W. (1979). [*A Bio-ecological and Behavioural Study of Cheetah,* Acinonyx jubatus jubatus *(Schreber, 1776)*]. MSc thesis, University of Pretoria, Pretoria. In Afrikaans.

Labuschagne, W. (1981). *Aspects of Cheetah Ecology in the Kalahari Gemsbok National Park.* 36th Annual Conference of the International Association of Zoo Directors, Washington D.C.

Laidler, K. & Laidler, L. (1983). *The River Wolf.* George Allen & Unwin, London.

Laing, S.P. & Lindzey, F.G. (1993). Patterns of replacement of resident cougars in southern Utah. *J. Mammal.* **74**: 1056-1058.

Lamberton, C. (1930). Contribution à la connaissance de la fauna subfossile de Madagascar. Notes IV-VII. Lémuriens et Cryptoproctes. *Mém. Acad. Malgache* **27**: 1-203.

Lamotte, M. & Tranier, M. (1983). Un spécimen de *Genetta* (*Paragenetta*) *johnstoni* collecté dans la région du Nimba (Côte d'Ivoire). *Mammalia* **47**: 430-432.

Lampe, R.P. (1982). Food habits of badgers in east central Minnesota. *J. Wildl. Management* **46**: 790-795.

Lamprecht, J. (1978). On diet, foraging behaviour and interspecific food competition of jackals in the Serengeti National Park, East Africa. *Zeitschrift für Säugetierkunde* **43**: 210-223.

Lamprecht, J. (1979). Field observations on the behaviour and social system of the bat-eared fox *Otocyon megalotis* Desmarest. *Zeitschr. Tierpsychol.* **49**: 260-284.

Landa, A., Linden, M. & Kojola, I. (2000). Action plan for the conservation of wolverines in Europe (*Gulo gulo*). *Council Europe Nat. Environm. Ser.* **115**: 1-45.

Landa, A., Strand, O., Linnell, J.D.C. & Skogland, T. (1998). Home-range sizes and altitude selection for Arctic foxes and wolverines in an alpine environment. *Can. J. Zool.* **76**: 448-457.

Landa, A., Strand, O., Swenson, J.E. & Skogland, T. (1997). Wolverines and their prey in southern Norway. *Can. J. Zool.* **75**: 1292-1299.

Landholt, L.M. & Genoways, H.H. (2000). Population trends in furbearers in Nebraska. *Trans. Nebr. Acad. Sci.* **26**: 97-110.

Langguth, A. (1975). Ecology and evolution in the South American canids. Pp. 192-206 in: Fox, M.W. ed. (1975). *The Wild Canids.* Van Nostrand Reinhold Company, New York.

Lanier, D.L. & Dewsbury, D.A. (1976). A quantitative study of copulatory behaviour of large Felidae. *Behav. Processes* **1**: 327-333.

Lanszki, J. & Heltai, M. (2007). Diet of the European polecat and the steppe polecat in Hungary. *Mammal. Biol.* **72**: 49-53.

Lanszki, J. & Sallai, Z. (2006). Comparison of the feeding habits of Eurasian otters on a fast flowing river and its backwater habitats. *Mammal. Biol.* **71**: 336-346.

Lanszki, J. & Szeles, G.L. (2006). Feeding habits of otters living on three moors in the Pannonian ecoregion (Hungary). *Folia Zool.* **55**: 358-366.

Lantz, D.E. (1923). Economic value of North American skunks. *Farmer's Bull.* **587**: 1-24.

La Rivers, I. (1948). Some Hawaiian ecological notes. *Wasmann Collector* **7**: 85-110.

Larivière, S. (1998). *Lontra felina. Mammal. Species* **575**: 1-5.

Larivière, S. (1999a). *Mustela vison. Mammal. Species* **608**: 1-9.

Larivière, S. (1999b). *Lontra longicaudis. Mammal. Species* **609**: 1-5.

Larivière, S. (1999c). *Lontra provocax. Mammal. Species* **610**: 1-4.

Larivière, S. (2001a). *Aonyx congicus. Mammal. Species* **650**: 1-3.

Larivière, S. (2001b). *Aonyx capensis. Mammal. Species* **671**: 1-6.

Larivière, S. (2001c). *Poecilogale albinucha. Mammal. Species* **681**: 1-4.

Lariviére, S. (2001d). *Ursus americanus. Mammal. Spec.* **647**: 1-11.

Larivière, S. (2002a). *Ictonyx striatus. Mammal. Species* **698**: 1-5.

Larivière, S. (2002b). *Lutra maculicollis. Mammal. Species* **712**: 1-6.

Larivière, S. (2003a). *Amblonyx cinereus. Mammal. Species* **720**: 1-5.

Larivière, S. (2003b). Mink. Pp. 662-671 in: Feldhamer, G.A., Thompson, B.C. & Chapman, J.A. eds. (2003). *Wild Mammals of North America: Biology, Management and Conservation.* 2nd edition. Johns Hopkins University Press, Baltimore, Maryland.

Larivière, S. & Calzada, J. (2001). *Genetta genetta. Mammal. Species* **680**: 1-6.

Larivière, S. & Ferguson, S.H. (2002). On the evolution of the mammalian baculum: vaginal friction, prolonged intromission or induced ovulation? *Mammal Rev.* **32**: 283-294.

Larivière, S. & Ferguson, S.H. (2003). Evolution of induced ovulation in North American carnivores. *J. Mammal.* **84**: 937-947.

Larivière, S. & Messier, F. (1996). Aposematic behavior in the striped skunk, *Mephitis mephitis. Ethology* **102**: 986-992.

Larivière, S. & Pasitschniak-Arts, M. (1996). *Vulpes vulpes. Mammal. Species* **537**: 1-11.

Larivière, S. & Walton, L.R. (1997). *Lynx rufus. Mammal. Species* **563**: 1-8.

Larivière, S. & Walton, L.R. (1998). *Lontra canadensis. Mammal. Species* **587**: 1-8.

Larkin, P. & Roberts, M. (1979). Reproduction in the ring-tailed mongoose *Galidia elegans* at the National Zoological Park, Washington. *Int. Zoo Yb.* **19**: 188-193.

Larson, S.E. (1997). Taxonomic re-evaluation of the jaguar. *Zoo Biology* **16**: 107-120.

Laughrin, L.L. (1973). *California Island Fox Survey.* State of California Department of Fish and Game, Wildlife Management Branch Administrative Report **73-3**.

Laughrin, L.L. (1977). *The Island Fox: a Field Study of its Behavior and Ecology.* PhD dissertation, University of California, Santa Barbara, California.

Laundré, J.W. & Keller, B.L. (1984). Home-range size of coyotes: a critical review. *J. Wildl. Management* **48**: 127-139.

Lauren, M., Girondot, M. & de Ricqlés, A. (2000). Early tetrapod evolution. *Trends Ecol. Evol.* **15**: 118-123.

Laurenson, M.K. (1995). Implications of high offspring mortality for cheetah population dynamics. Pp. 385-399 in: Sinclair, A.R.E. & Arcese, P. eds. (1995). *Serengeti II: Dynamics, Conservation and Management of an Ecosystem.* University of Chicago Press, Chicago, Illinois.

Laurenson, M.K., Caro, T.M. & Borner, M. (1992). Female cheetah reproduction. *Natl. Geogr. Res.* **8**: 64-75.

Laurie, A. & Seidensticker, J. (1977). Behavioural ecology of the sloth bear (*Melursus ursinus*). *J. Zool., London* **182**: 187-204.

Law, G. & Boyle, H. (1984). Breeding the Geoffroy's cat at Glasgow Zoo. *Int. Zoo Yb.* **23**: 191-195.

van Lawick, H. & van Lawick-Goodall, J. (1970). *Innocent Killers.* Houghton Mifflin, Boston, Massachusetts.

awrence, B. (1939). Mammals. Pp. 28-73 in: Barbour, T., Lawrence, B. & Peters, J.L. eds. (1939). *Collections from the Phillippine Islands*. Bulletin of the Museum of Comparative Zoology at Harvard College, Cambridge.

ay, D.M. (1967). A study of the mammals of Iran. *Fieldiana Zool.* **54**: 1-282.

eakey, L.N., Milledge, S.A.H., Leakey, S.M., Edung, J., Haynes, P., Kiptoo, D.K. & Mc-George, A. (1999). Diet of striped hyaena in northern Kenya. *Afr. J. Ecol.* **37**: 314-326.

eBlanc, F.A., Gallant, D., Vasseur, L. & Leger, L. (2007). Unequal summer use of beaver ponds by river otters: influence of beaver activity, pond size, and vegetation cover. *Can. J. Zool.* **85**: 774-782.

e Clus, F. (1971). *A Preliminary, Comparative Investigation of Feeding, Communication and Reproductive Behaviour in* Vulpes chama *(A.Smith) and* Otocyon megalotis *(Desmarest).* BSc thesis, Rhodes University, Grahamstown, South Africa.

edje, C. & Árnason, U. (1996a). Phylogenetic analyses of complete cytochrome *b* genes of the order Carnivora with particular emphasis on the Caniformia. *J. Mol. Evol.* **42**: 135-144.

edje, C. & Árnason, U. (1996b). Phylogenetic relationships within caniform carnivores based on analyses of the mitochondrial 12s ribosomal RNA gene. *J. Mol. Evol.* **43**: 641-649.

edoux, R.G. & Kenyon, A.J. (1975). Protides of the Mustelidae-II. Immunologic relatedness. *Comp. Biochem. Physiol.* **51A**: 213-217.

ee, D.J. & Vaughan, M.R. (2003). Dispersal movements by subadult American black bears in Virginia. *Ursus* **14**: 162-170.

ee, R.J., Riley, J., Hunowu, I. & Maneasa, E. (2003). The Sulawesi palm civet: expanded distribution of a little known endemic viverrid. *Oryx* **37**: 378-381.

eFranc, M.N., Moss, M.B., Patnode, K.A. & Sugg, W.C. eds. (1987). *Grizzly Bear Compendium.* Interagency Grizzly Bear Committee, Washington, D.C.

eite, M.R.P. & Williams, R.S.R. (2004). Short-eared dog *Atelocynus microtis.* Pp. 26-31 in: Sillero-Zubiri, C., Hoffmann, M. & Macdonald, D.W. eds. (2004). *Canids: Foxes, Wolves, Jackals and Dogs. Status Survey and Conservation Action Plan.* IUCN/SSC Canid Specialist Group, Gland & Cambridge.

ejeune, A. (1989). Éthologie des loutres (*Hydrictis maculicollis*) au lac Muhazi, Rwanda. *Mammalia* **53**: 191-202.

ekagul, B. & McNeely, J.A. (1991). *Mammals of Thailand.* 2nd edition. Kurusapha Ladprao Press, Bangkok, Thailand.

enain, D.M. (2000). *Fox Populations of a Protected Area in Saudi Arabia.* MPh dissertation, University of Herefordshire, Hereford, UK.

eopold, A.S. (1959). *Wildlife of Mexico, the Game Birds and Mammals.* University of California Press, Berkeley & Los Angeles, California.

e Roux, P.G. & Skinner, J.D. (1989). A note on the ecology of the leopard (*Panthera pardus* Linnaeus) in the Londolozi Game Reserve, South Africa. *Afr. J. Ecol.* **27**: 167-171.

eslie, G. (1970). Observations on the oriental short-clawed otter, *Aonyx cinerea*, at Aberdeen Zoo. *Int. Zoo Yb.* **10**: 79-81.

eslie, M.J., Messenger, S., Rohde, R.E., Smith, J., Cheshier, R., Hanlon, C. & Rupprecht, C.E. (2006). Bat-associated rabies virus in skunks. *Emerging Infect. Diseases* **12**: 1274-1277.

ewis, M.E. & Werdelin, L. (2000). The evolution of spotted hyenas (*Crocuta*). *IUCN SSC Hyaena Special. Group Newslett.* **7**: 34-36.

eyhausen, P. (1965). Über die funktion der relativen stimmungshierarchie (Dargestellt am Beispiel der phylogenetischen und ontogenetischen Entwicklung des Beutefangs von Raubtieren). *Zeitschr. Tierpsychol.* **22**: 412-494.

eyhausen, P. (1979). *Cat Behavior: the Predatory and Social Behavior of Domestic and Wild Cats.* Garland STPM Press, New York.

eyhausen, P. & Falkena, M. (1966). Breeding the Brazilian ocelot-cat *Leopardus tigrinus* in captivity. *Int. Zoo Yb.* **6**: 176-182.

eyhausen, P. & Tonkin, B. (1966). Breeding the black-footed cat (*Felis nigripes*). *Int. Zoo Yb.* **6**: 178-182.

, C., Wei, F., Li, M., Liu, X., Yang, Z. & Hu, J. (2003). [Fecal testosterone levels and reproduction cycle in male red panda (*Ailurus fulgens*)]. *Acta Theriol. Sinica* **23**: 115-119. In Chinese.

, M., Wei, F., Goossens, B., Feng, Z., Tamate, H.B., Bruford, M.W. & Funk, S.M. (2004). Mitochondrial phylogeography and subspecific variation in the red panda (*Ailurus fulgens*): implications for conservation. *Mol. Phylogen. Evol.* **36**: 78-89.

, P.J. (2004). China's bear farming and long-term solutions. *J. Appl. Anim. Welfare Sci.* **7**: 71-80.

Yu & Ya-ping Zhang (2006). Phylogeny of the caniform Carnivora: evidence from multiple genes. *Genetica* **127**: 65-79.

ao, Y. (1988). Some biological informations of Desert cat in Qinghai. *Acta Theriol. Sinica* **8**: 128-131.

cht, P., Frank, L.G., Pavgi, S., Yalcinkaya, T.M., Siiteri, P.K. & Glickman, S.E. (1992). Hormonal correlates of masculinization in female spotted hyaenas (*Crocuta crocuta*). 2. Maternal and fetal steroids. *J. Reprod. Fertil.* **95**: 463-474.

chtenstein, H. (1827-1834). *Darstellung neuer oder wenig Bekannter Säugethiere in Abbildungen und Beschreibungen von Fünf und Sechzig Arten auf Fünfzig Colorirten Steindrucktafeln nach den Originalen des Zoologischen Museums der Universität zu Berlin.* C.G. Lüderitz, Berlin.

chtenstein, H. (1838). *Uber die Gattung Mephitis: Abhandlungen Preussische.* Akademie der Wissenschaften Abhandlunger der Königlichen Akademie der Wissenschaften zu Berlin. [no volume]: 249-312.

em, K.F. (1982). Form and function of lungs: the evolution of air breathing mechanisms. *Amer. Zool.* **22**: 739-759.

em, K.F. & Summers, A.P. (2000). Integration of versatile functional design, population ecology, ontogeny and phylogeny. *Netherlands J. Zool.* **50**: 245-259.

em, K.F., Bemis, W.E., Walker, W.F. & Grande, L. (2001). *Functional Anatomy of the Vertebrates.* Harcourt College Publishers, New York.

gthart, M.F., Nel, J.A.J. & Avenant, N.L. (1994). Diet of Cape clawless otters in part of the Breede River system. *South Afr. J. Wildl. Res.* **24**: 38-39.

llegraven, J.A. (1985). Use of the term "trophoblast" for tissues in therian mammals. *J. Morphol.* **183**: 293-299.

Lim, B.L. (1973). The banded linsang and the banded musang of West Malaysia. *Malay Nat. J.* **26**: 105-111.

Lim, B.L. (1976). *Gnathostoma spinigerum* Owen, 1836 (Nematoda: Gnatostomidae) from a civet cat, *Prionodon linsang* Hardwicke, with reference to its dietary habits. *Southeast Asian J. Trop. Med. Public Health* **7**: 530-533.

Lim, B.L. (1991). Civets of Malaysia. *Nat. Malaysiana* **16**: 62-67.

Lim, B.L. (1992). Mongooses of Malaysia. *Nat. Malaysiana* **16**: 4-7.

Lim, B.L. (1999). The distribution, food habits and parasite patterns of the leopard cat (*Prionailurus bengalensis*) in Peninsular Malaysia. *J. Wildl. & Parks* **17**: 17-27.

Lim, B.L. & Rahman bin Omar, I.A. (1961). Observations on the habits in captivity of two species of wild cats, the leopard cat and the flat-headed cat. *Malay. Nat. J.* **15**: 48-51.

Linares, O.J. (1998). *Mamíferos de Venezuela.* Sociedad Conservacionista de Venezuela, Caracas, Venezuela.

Lindburg, D.G. (1989). When cheetahs are kings. *Zoonoz* **62**: 5-10.

Lindburg, D.G. & Baragona, K. eds. (2004). *Giant Pandas. Biology and Conservation.* University of California Press, Berkeley, California.

Lindeque, M. & Skinner, J.D. (1982). A seasonal breeding in the spotted hyaena (*Crocuta crocuta*, Erxleben), in southern Africa. *Afr. J. Ecol.* **20**: 271-278.

Lindsay, I.M. & Macdonald, D.W. (1986). Behaviour and ecology of the Ruppell's fox *Vulpes ruppellii* in Oman. *Mammalia* **50**: 461-474.

Lindzey, F.G. (1978). Movement patterns of badgers in northwestern Utah. *J. Wildl. Management* **42**: 418-422.

Lindzey, F.G. (2003). Badger. Pp. 683-691 in: Feldhamer, G.A., Thompson, B.C. & Chapman, J.A. eds. (2003). *Wild Mammals of North America: Biology, Management and Conservation.* 2nd edition. Johns Hopkins University Press, Baltimore, Maryland.

Linnaeus, C. (1758). *Systema Naturae per Regna Tria Naturae, Secundum Classes, Ordines, Genera, Species, cum Characteribus, Differentiis, Synonymis, Locis.* Editio decima, reformata. Holmiae: Laurentii Salvii **1**: 1-824.

Linnell, J.D.C., Stoen, O.G., Odden, J., Ness, E., Gangas, L., Karlsen, J., Eide, N. & Andersen, R. (1996). *Lynx and Roe Deer in Eastern Hedmark.* NINA Oppdragsmelding **414**. NINA, Trondheim, Norway.

Linnell, J.D.C., Swenson, J.E., Andersen, R. & Barnes, B. (2000). How vulnerable are denning bears to disturbance? *Wildl. Soc. Bull.* **28**: 400-413.

List, R. (1997). *Ecology of the Kit Fox (*Vulpes macrotis*) and Coyote (*Canis latrans*) and the Conservation of the Prairie Dog Ecosystem in Northern Mexico.* PhD dissertation, Wildlife Conservation Research Unit, University of Oxford, Oxford.

List, R. & Cypher, B.L. (2004). Kit fox *Vulpes macrotis.* Pp. 105-109 in: Sillero-Zubiri, C., Hoffmann, M. & Macdonald, D.W. eds. (2004). *Canids: Foxes, Wolves, Jackals and Dogs. Status Survey and Conservation Action Plan.* IUCN/SSC Canid Specialist Group, Gland & Cambridge.

Litvaitis, J.A. & Harrison, D.J. (1989). Bobcat-coyote niche relationships during a period of coyote population increase. *Can. J. Zool.* **67**: 1180-1188.

Litvaitis, J.A., Sherburne, J.A. & Bissonette, J.A. (1986). Bobcat habitat use and home range size in relation to prey density. *J. Wildl. Management* **50**: 110-117.

Liu, X., Toxopeus, A.G., Skidmore, A.K., Shao, X., Dang, G., Wang, T. & Prins, H.H.T. (2005). Giant panda habitat selection in Foping Nature Reserve, China. *J. Wildl. Management* **69**: 1623-1632.

Liu, X., Zhang, Z., Wei, F., Li, M., Li, C., Yang, Z. & Hu, J. (2003). [Nursing behaviors of the captive red panda (*Ailurus fulgens*)]. *Acta Theriol. Sinica* **23**: 366-394. In Chinese.

Liu, X., Zhang, Z., Wei, F., Li, M., Li, C., Yang, Z. & Hu, J. (2004). [Reproductive behavior variations and reproductive strategy in the captive red panda]. *Acta Theriol. Sinica* **24**: 173-176. In Chinese.

Livet, F. & Roeder, J.J. (1987). *La Genette (*Genetta genetta, *Linnaeus 1758).* Encyclopédie des Carnivores de France, SFEPM, Paris.

Ljungquist, B. (1930). Madagaskars rovdjur. *Fauna och Flora* **1930**: 255-262.

Locke, A. (1954). *The Tigers of Terengganu.* Museum Press, London.

Lodé, T. (1994). Feeding-habits of the stone marten *Martes foina* and environmental-factors in western France. *Zeitschrift für Säugetierkunde* **59**: 189-191.

Lodé, T. (1997). Trophic status and feeding habits of the European polecat *Mustela putorius* L., 1758. *Mammal Rev.* **27(4)**: 177-184.

Lodé, T. (2003). Sexual dimorphism and trophic constraints: prey selection in the European polecat (*Mustela putorius*). *Ecoscience* **10**: 17-23.

Lodé, T., Lechat, I. & Le Jacques, D. (1991). Le régime alimentaire de la genette en limite nord-ouest de son aire de répartition. *Rev. Écol. (Terre Vie)* **46**: 339-348.

Lofroth, E.C., Krebs, J.A., Harrower, W.L. & Lewis, D. (2007). Food habits of wolverine *Gulo gulo* in montane ecosystems of British Columbia, Canada. *Wildl. Biol.* **13**: 31-37.

Logan, K.A. & Irwin, L.L. (1985). Mountain lion habitats in the Bighorn Mountains, Wyoming. *Wildl. Soc. Bull.* **13**: 257-262.

Logan, K.A. & Sweanor, L.L. (2001). *Desert Puma: Evolutionary Ecology and Conservation of an Enduring Carnivore.* Island Press, Washington, D.C.

Logan, K.A., Irwin, L.L. & Skinner, R. (1986). Characteristics of a hunted mountain lion population in Wyoming. *J. Wildl. Management* **50**: 648-654.

LoGiudice, K. (2003). Trophically transmitted parasites and the conservation of small populations: raccoon roundworm and the imperiled Allegheny Woodrat. *Conserv. Biol.* **17**: 258-266.

LoGiudice, K. (2006). Toward a synthetic view of extinction: a history lesson from a North American rodent. *Bioscience* **56**: 687-693.

Lohmer, R. (1976). Zur verhaltensontogenese bei *Procyon cancrivorus cancrivorus* (Procyonidae). *Zeitschrift für Säugetierkunde* **41**: 42-58.

Lohuis, T.D., Harlow, H.J., Beck, T.D.I. & Iaizzo, P.A. (2007). Hibernating bears conserve muscle strength and maintain fatigue resistance. *Physiol. Biochem. Zool.* **80**: 257-269.

Long, B. & Hoang, M. (2006). Recent records and notes on the conservation of small carnivores in Quang Nam province, central Vietnam. *Small Carniv. Conserv.* **34/35**: 39-46.

Long, C.A. (1973). *Taxidea taxus. Mammal. Species* **26**: 1-4.

Long, C.A. (1978). A listing of recent badgers of the world, with remarks on taxonomic problems in *Mydaus* and *Melogale*. Pp. 1-6 in: *Reports on the Fauna and Flora of Wisconsin, The Museum of Natural History, Stevens Point, Wisconsin* **14**.

Long, C.A. (1981). Provisional classification and evolution of the badgers. Pp. 55-85 in: Chapman, J.A. & Pursley, D. eds. (1981). *Worldwide Furbearer Conference Proceedings*. Frostburg, Maryland.

Long, C.A. (1992). Is the Javan ferret-badger a subspecies or a species? *Small Carniv. Conserv.* **6**: 17.

Long, C.A. & Killingley, C.A. (1983). *The Badgers of the World*. Charles C. Thomas, Springfield, Illinois.

Lönnberg, E. & Mjöberg, E. (1925). Mammalia from Mount Murud and the Kelabit Country. *Ann. Mag. Nat. Hist.* **16**: 508-513.

Lopez-Forment, W.C. & Urbano, G.V. (1979). Historia natural del zorrillo manchado pigmeo, *Spilogale pygmea*, con la descripción de una nueva subespecie. *An. Inst. Biol. Univ. Nac. Aut. Mex. (Ser. Zool.)*. **1**: 721-728.

López-González, C.A., González-Romero, A. & Laundre, J.W. (1998). Range extension of the bobcat (*Lynx rufus*) in Jalisco, Mexico. *Southwest. Nat.* **43**: 103-105.

Lopez-Martin, J.M., Ruiz, J. & Cahill, S. (1992). Autumn home range and activity of a stone marten (*Martes foina* Erxleben, 1777) in northeastern Spain. *Misc. Zool.* **16**: 258-260.

Loreille, O., Orlando, L., Patou-Mathis, M., Philipp, M., Taberlet, P. & Hänni, C. (2001). Ancient DNA analysis reveals divergence of the cave bear, *Ursus spelaeus*, and brown bear, *Ursus arctos*, lineages. *Curr. Biol.* **11**: 200-203.

Lotze, J.H. & Anderson, S. (1979). *Procyon lotor*. *Mammal. Species* **119**: 1-8.

Loucks, C.J., Lü, Z., Dinerstein, E., Wang, D., Fu, D. & Wang, H. (2003). The giant pandas of the Qinling Mountains, China: a case study in designing conservation landscapes for elevational migrants. *Conserv. Biol.* **17**: 558-565.

Loucks, C.J., Lü, Z., Dinerstein, E., Wang, H., Olson, D.M., Zhu, C. & Wang, D. (2001). Giant pandas in a changing landscape. *Science* **294**: 1465.

Loureiro, F., Rosalino, L.M., Macdonald, D.W. & Santos-Reis, M. (2007). Use of multiple den sites by Eurasian badgers, *Meles meles*, in a Mediterranean habitat. *Zool. Science (Tokyo)* **24**: 978-985.

Louvel, M. (1954). Quelques observations sur le "fosa". *Bull. Acad. Malgache* **31**: 45-46.

Louw, C.J. & Nel, J.A.J. (1986). Diets of coastal and inland dwelling water mongoose. *South Afr. J. Wildl. Res.* **16**: 153-156.

Louwman, J.W.W. (1970). Breeding the banded palm civet and the banded linsang at the Wassenaar Zoo. *Int. Zoo Yb.* **10**: 81-82.

Louwman, J.W.W. & Van Oyen, W.G. (1968). A note on breeding Temminck's golden cat at Wassenaar Zoo. *Int. Zoo Yb.* **8**: 47-49.

Lovallo, M.J. & Anderson, E.M. (1995). Range shift by a female bobcat (*Lynx rufus*) after removal of a neighboring female. *Amer. Midl. Nat.* **134**: 49-412.

Lovallo, M.J. & Anderson, E.M. (1996). Bobcat (*Lynx rufus*) home range size and habitat use in northwest Wisconsin. *Amer. Midl. Nat.* **135**: 241-252.

Lovell, C.D., Leopold, B.D. & Shropshire, C.C. (1998). Trends in Mississippi predator populations, 1980-1995. *Wildl. Soc. Bull.* **26**: 552-556.

Loveridge, A.J. (1999). *Behavioural Ecology and Rabies Transmission in Sympatric Southern African Jackals*. PhD dissertation, Wildlife Conservation Research Unit, University of Oxford, Oxford.

Loveridge, A.J. & Macdonald, D.W. (2001). Seasonality in spatial organization and dispersal of sympatric jackals (*Canis mesomelas* and *C. adustus*): implications for rabies management. *J. Zool., London* **253**: 101-111.

Loveridge, A.J. & Macdonald, D.W. (2002). Habitat ecology of two sympatric species of jackals in Zimbabwe. *J. Mammal.* **83**: 599-607.

Loveridge, A.J. & Macdonald, D.W. (2003). Niche separation in sympatric jackals (*Canis mesomelas* and *C. adustus*). *J. Zool., London* **259**: 143-153.

Loveridge, A.J. & Nel, J.A.J. (2004). Black-backed jackal *Canis mesomelas*. Pp. 161-166 in: Sillero-Zubiri, C., Hoffmann, M. & Macdonald, D.W. eds. (2004). *Canids: Foxes, Wolves, Jackals and Dogs. Status Survey and Conservation Action Plan*. IUCN/SSC Canid Specialist Group, Gland & Cambridge.

Loza-Rubio, E., Aguilar-Setien, A., Bahloul, C., Brochier, B., Pastoret, P.P. & Tordo, N. (1999). Discrimination between epidemiological cycles of rabies in Mexico. *Arch. Med. Res.* **30**: 144-149.

Lü, Z., Johnson, W.E., Menotti-Raymond, M., Yuhki, N., Martenson, J.S., Mainka, S., Huang, S.Q., Zheng, Z., Li, G., Pan, W., Mao, X. & O'Brien, S.J. (2001). Patterns of genetic diversity in remaining giant panda populations. *Conserv. Biol.* **15**: 1596-1607.

Lü, Z., Pan, W., Zhu, X., Wang, D. & Wang, H. (2000). What has the panda taught us? Pp. 325-334 in: Entwistle, A. & Dunstone, N. eds. (2000). *Priorities for the Conservation of Mammalian Diversity. Has the Panda Had its Day?* Cambridge University Press, Cambridge.

Lü, Z., Wang, D. & Garshelis, D.L. (2007). *Ailuropoda melanoleuca* giant panda. In: *2007 IUCN Red List of Threatened Species*. URL: http://www.iucnredlist.org.html

Lucherini, M., Birochio, D. & Sana, D. (1998). The Andean cat in the proposed Aconquija National Park, Argentina. *Cat News* **29**: 17-18.

Lucherini, M., Manfredi, C., Luengos, E., Mazim, F.D., Soler, L. & Casanave, E.B. (2006). Body mass variation in the Geoffroy's cat (*Oncifelis geoffroyi*). *Rev. Chil. Hist. Nat.* **79**: 169-174.

Lucherini, M., Pessino, M. & Farias, A.A. (2004). Pampas fox *Pseudalopex gymnocercus*. Pp. 63-68 in: Sillero-Zubiri, C., Hoffmann, M. & Macdonald, D.W. eds. (2004). *Canids: Foxes, Wolves, Jackals and Dogs. Status Survey and Conservation Action Plan*. IUCN/SSC Canid Specialist Group, Gland & Cambridge.

Lucherini, M., Sana, D. & Birochio, D. (1999). *The Andean Mountain Cat* (Oreailurus jacobita) *and other Wild Carnivores in the Proposed Anconquija National Park, Argentina*. Scientific Report **5**. Società Zoologica "La Torbiera", Novara, Italy.

Lucherini, M., Soler, L., Manfredi, C., Desbiez, A. & Marull, C. (2000). Geoffroy's cat in the Pampas grasslands. *Cat News* **33**: 22-24.

Ludlow, M.E. & Sunquist, M.E. (1987). Ecology and behavior of ocelots in Venezuela. *Natl. Geogr. Res.* **3(4)**: 447-461.

Lu Houji & Sheng Helin (1986). The status and population fluctuation of the leopard ca in China. Pp. 59-62 in: Miller, S.D. & Everett, D.D. eds. (1986). *Cats of the World: Biology Conservation and Management*. National Wildlife Federation, Washington, D.C.

Lumpkin, S. (1991). Cats and culture. Pp. 190-197 in: Seidensticker, J. & Lumpkin, S. eds (1991). *Great Cats. Majestic Creatures of the Wild*. Merehurst, London.

Lumpkin, S. & Seidensticker, J. (2002). *Smithsonian Book of Giant Pandas*. Smithsonian Institution Press, Washington, D.C.

Lunde, D. & Musser, G. (2003). A recently discovered specimen of Indonesian mountai weasel (*Mustela lutreolina* Robinson & Thomas 1917) from Sumatra. *Small Carniv. Conser* **28**: 22.

Luo, S.J., Kim, J.H., Johnson, W.E., van der Walt, J., Martenson, J., Yuhki, N., Miquelle D.G., Uphyrkina, O., Goodrich, J.M., Quigley, H.B., Tilson, R., Brady, G., Martelli, P. Subramaniam, V., McDougal, C., Hean, S., Huang, S.Q., Pan, W., Karanth, K.U., Sun quist, M., Smith, J.L.D. & O'Brien, S.J. (2004). Phylogeography and genetic ancestry o tigers (*Panthera tigris*). *PLOS Biol.* **2(12)**: 2275-2293.

Lynam, A.J., Maung, M., Po, S.H.T. & Duckworth, J.W. (2005). Recent records of large-spo ted civet *Viverra megaspila* from Thailand and Myanmar. *Small Carniv. Conserv.* **32**: 8-11.

Lynch, C.D. (1975). The distribution of mammals in the Orange Free State, South Africa *Navors. Nas. Mus. Bloemfontein* **3**: 109-139.

Lynch, C.D. (1980). Ecology of the suricate, *Suricata suricatta* and yellow mongoose, *Cynict penicillata* with special reference to their reproduction. *Mem. Nasionale Mus.* Pp 145.

Lynch, C.D. (1981). The status of the Cape grey mongoose (*Herpestes pulverulentus* Wagne 1839 (Mammalia: Viverridae). *Navors. Nas. Mus. Bloemfontein* **4**: 121-168.

Lynch, C.D. (1983). The mammals of the Orange Free State. *Mem. Nasionale Mus.* **18** 1-218.

Lynch, C.D. (1994). The mammals of Lesotho. *Navors. Nas. Mus. Bloemfontein* **10**: 177-241.

Ma, J., Xu, L., Zhang, H. & Bao, X. (1999). Activity patterns of sables (*Martes zibellina*) i Daxinganling Mountains, China. *Acta Theriol. Sinica* **19**: 95-100.

Maas, B. (1993a). *Behavioural Ecology and Social Organisation of the Bat-eared Fox in the Serenge National Park, Tanzania*. PhD dissertation, University of Cambridge, Cambridge.

Maas, B. (1993b). Bat-eared fox behavioural ecology and the incidence of rabies in the Se engeti National Park. *Onderstepoort J. Vet. Res.* **60**: 389-393.

Maas, B. & Macdonald, D.W. (2004). Bat-eared foxes, insectivory and luck: lessons from a extreme canid. Pp. 227-242 in: Macdonald, D.W. & Sillero-Zubiri, C. eds. (2004). *Th Biology and Conservation of Wild Canids*. Oxford University Press, Oxford.

MacClintock, D. (1988). *Red Pandas: a Natural History*. Charles Scribner's Sons, New York.

Macdonald, D.W. (1976). Food caching by red foxes and some other carnivores. *Zeitsch Tierpsychol.* **42**: 170-185.

Macdonald, D.W. (1977a). On food preference in the red fox. *Mammal Rev.* **7**: 7-23.

Macdonald, D.W. (1977b). *The Behavioural Ecology of the Red Fox*. PhD dissertation, Universi of Oxford, Oxford.

Macdonald, D.W. (1978). Observations on the behaviour and ecology of the striped hyaen *Hyaena hyaena*, in Israel. *Israel J. Zool.* **27**: 189-198.

Macdonald, D.W. (1979a). The flexible social system of the golden jackal *Canis aureus*. *Beha Ecol. Sociobiol.* **5**: 17-38.

Macdonald, D.W. (1979b). "Helpers" in fox society. *Nature (London)* **282**: 69-71.

Macdonald, D.W. (1980a). The red fox *Vulpes vulpes* as a predator upon earthworms, *Lumb cus terrestris*. *Zeitschr. Tierpsychol.* **52**: 171-200.

Macdonald, D.W. (1980b). Social factors affecting reproduction amongst red foxes (*Vulp vulpes* L. 1758). *Biogeographica* **18**: 123-175.

Macdonald, D.W. (1985). The carnivores: order Carnivora. Pp. 619-722 in: Brown, R.E. Macdonald, D.W. eds. (1985). *Social Odours in Mammals*. Clarendon Press, Oxford.

Macdonald, D.W. (1987). *Running with the Fox*. Unwin Hymen, London.

Macdonald, D.W. (1996a). Dangerous liaisons and disease. *Nature (London)* **379**: 400-401.

Macdonald, D.W. (1996b). Social behaviour of captive bush dogs (*Speothos venaticus*). *J. Zoo London* **239**: 525-543.

Macdonald, D.W. (2001). *The Encyclopedia of Mammals*. Barnes & Noble, New York.

Macdonald, D.W. & Bacon, P.J. (1982). Fox society, contact rate and rabies epizootiolog *Comp. Immunol. Microbiol. Infect. Diseases* **5**: 247-256.

Macdonald, D.W. & Courtenay, O. (1996). Enduring social relationships in a population crab-eating zorros, *Cerdocyon thous*, in Amazonian Brazil (Carnivora, Canidae). *J. Zoo London* **239**: 329-355.

Macdonald, D.W. & Newdick, M.T. (1982). The distribution and ecology of foxes, *Vulp vulpes* (L.), in urban areas. Pp. 123-135 in: Bornkamm, R., Lee, J.A. & Seaward, M.R. eds. (1982). *Urban Ecology*. Blackwell Scientific Publications, Oxford.

Macdonald, D.W. & Reynolds, J.C. (2004). Red fox *Vulpes vulpes*. Pp. 129-136 in: Siller Zubiri, C., Hoffmann, M. & Macdonald, D.W. eds. (2004). *Canids: Foxes, Wolves, Jacke and Dogs. Status Survey and Conservation Action Plan*. IUCN/SSC Canid Specialist Grou Gland & Cambridge.

Macdonald, D.W. & Wise, M.J. (1979). Notes on the behavior of the Malay civet *Viverra ta galunga* Gray. *Sarawak Mus. J.* **48**: 295-299.

Macdonald, D.W., Courtenay, O., Forbes, S. & Mathews, F. (1999). The red fox *Vulpes vulp* in Saudi Arabia: loose-knit groupings in the absence of territoriality. *J. Zool., London* **24** 383-391.

MacHutchon, A.G. & Wellwood, D.W. (2003). Grizzly bear food habits in the northern Y kon, Canada. *Ursus* **14**: 225-235.

Mackie, A.J. (1988). *Bat-eared Foxes* Otocyon megalotis *as Predators on Termites* Hodoterm mossambicus *in the Orange Free State*. MSc thesis, University of Stellenbosch, Stellenbosc South Africa.

Mackie, A.J. & Nel, J.A.J. (1989). Habitat selection, home range use and group size of ba eared foxes in the Orange Free State. *South Afr. J. Wildl. Res.* **19**: 135-139.

Macpherson, A. (1969). The dynamics of Canadian Arctic fox populations. *Can. Wildl. Se Rep. Ser.* **8**: 1-49.

Maddock, A.H. (1993). Analysis of brown hyaena (*Hyaena brunnea*) scats from the Centu Karoo, South Africa. *J. Zool., London* **231**: 679-683.

Maddock, A.H. & Perrin, M.R. (1993). Spatial and temporal ecology of an assemblage of viverrids in Natal, South Africa. *J. Zool., London* **229**: 277-287.

Madhusudan, M.D. (1995). Sightings of the Nigiri marten (*Martes gwatkinsi*) at Eravikulam National Park. *Small Carniv. Conserv.* **13**: 6-7.

Madsen, S.A., Madsen, A.B. & Elmeros, M. (2002). Seasonal food of badgers (*Meles meles*) in Denmark. *Mammalia* **66(3)**: 341-352.

Maehr, D.S. (1990). The Florida panther and private lands. *Conserv. Biol.* **4**: 167-170.

Maehr, D.S. (1997). *The Comparative Ecology of Bobcat, Black Bear and Florida Panther in South Florida.* Bulletin of the Florida Museum of Natural History **40**.

Maehr, D.S. & Brady, J.R. (1986). Food habits of bobcats in Florida. *J. Mammal.* **67**: 133-138.

Maehr, D.S. & Caddick, G.B. (1995). Demographics and genetic introgression in the Florida panther. *Conserv. Biol.* **9**: 1295-1298.

Maehr, D.S. & Cox, J.A. (1995). Landscape features and panthers in Florida. *Conserv. Biol.* **9**: 1009-1019.

Maehr, D.S. & Moore, C.T. (1992). Models of mass growth for 3 North American cougar populations. *J. Wildl. Management* **56**: 700-707.

Maehr, D.S., Belden, R.C., Land, E.D. & Wilkins, L. (1990). Food habits of panthers in southwest Florida. *J. Wildl. Management* **54**: 420-423.

Maehr, D.S., Land, E.D. & Roof, J.C. (1991). Social ecology of Florida panthers. *Natl. Geogr. Res. Explor.* **7**: 414-431.

Maehr, D.S., Land, E.D., Roof, J.C. & McCown, J.W. (1989). Early maternal behavior in the Florida panther (*Felis concolor coryi*). *Amer. Midl. Nat.* **122**: 34-43.

Maehr, D.S., Land, E.D., Shindle, D.B., Bass, O.L. & Hoctor, T.S. (2002). Florida panther dispersal and conservation. *Biol. Conserv.* **106**: 187-197.

Maehr, D.S., Roof, J.C., Land, E.D. & McCown, J.W. (1989). First reproduction of a panther (*Felis concolor coryi*) in southwestern Florida. *Mammalia* **53**: 129-131.

Maffei, L. & Noss, A.J. (2008). How small is too small? Camera trap survey areas and density estimates for ocelots in the Bolivian Chaco. *Biotropica* **40**: 71-75.

Maffei, L. & Taber, A.B. (2003). Área de acción, actividad y uso de hábitat del zorro patas negras *Cerdocyon thous* Linnaeus, 1776 (Carnivora: Canidae) en un bosque seco. *Mastozool. Neotrop.* **10**: 154-160.

Maffei, L., Cuéllar, E. & Noss, A.J. (2002). Uso de trampas-cámara para la evaluación de mamíferos en el ecotono Chaco-Chiquitanía. *Rev. Boliv. Ecol. Conserv. Ambiental* **11**: 55-65.

Maffei, L., Cuéllar, E. & Noss, A.J. (2004). One thousand jaguars (*Panthera onca*) in Bolivia's Chaco? Camera trapping in the Kaa-Iya National Park. *J. Zool., London* **262**: 295-304.

Maffei, L., Noss, A.J., Cuéllar, E. & Rumiz, D.I. (2005). Ocelot (*Felis pardalis*) population densities, activity and ranging behaviour on the dry forest of eastern Bolivia: data from camera trapping. *J. Trop. Ecol.* **21**: 1-6.

Magoun, A.J. & Copeland, J.P. (1998). Characteristics of wolverine reproductive den sites. *J. Wildl. Management* **62**: 1313-1320.

Mahazotahy, S., Goodman, S.M. & Andriamanalina, A. (2006). Notes on the distribution and habitat preferences of *Galidictis grandidieri* Wozencraft, 1986 (Carnivora: Eupleridae), a poorly known endemic species of south-western Madagascar. *Mammalia* **70**: 328-330.

Major, J.T. & Sherburne, J.A. (1987). Interspecific relationships of coyotes, bobcats, and red foxes in western Maine. *J. Wildl. Management* **51**: 606-616.

Makacha, S. & Schaller, G.B. (1969). Observations on lions in the Lake Manyara National Park, Tanzania. *East Afr. Wildl. J.* **7**: 99-103.

Malbrant, R. & Maclatchy, A. (1949). *Faune de l'Equateur Africain Français.* Tome 2. Mammifères. Paul Lechevalier, Paris.

Malcolm, J.R. (1986). Socio-ecology of bat-eared foxes *Otocyon megalotis*. *J. Zool., London* **208**: 457-467.

Malcom, J.R. & Marten, K. (1982). Natural selection and the communal rearing of pups in African wild dogs *Lycaon pictus*. *Behav. Ecol. Sociobiol.* **10**: 1-13.

Malcolm, J.R. & Sillero-Zubiri, C. (2001). Recent records of African wild dogs *Lycaon pictus* from Ethiopia. *Canid News* **4**: 2.

Malek, J. (1993). *The Cat in Ancient Egypt.* British Museum Press, London.

Mallinson, J.J.C. (1969). Notes on breeding the African civet *Viverra civetta* at Jersey Zoo. *Int. Zoo Yb.* **9**: 92-93.

Mallon, D.P. (1988). A further report on the snow leopard in Ladakh. Pp. 89-97 in: Freeman, H. ed. (1988). *Proceedings of the Fifth International Snow Leopard Symposium.* International Snow Leopard Trust & Wildlife Institute of India, Bombay.

Manakadan, R. & Rahmani, A.R. (2000). Population and ecology of the Indian fox *Vulpus bengalensis* at Rollapadu Wildlife Sanctuary, Andhra Pradesh, India. *J. Bombay Nat. Hist. Soc.* **97**: 3-14.

Manaro, A.J. (1961). Observations on the behanor of the spotted skunk in Florida. *Quart. J. Florida Acad. Sci.* **24**: 59-63.

Manlius, N. (1998). L'ours brun en Égypt. The brown bear in Egypt. *Écologie* **29**: 565-581. In French with English summary.

Manser, M.B. (1998). *The Evolution of Auditory Communication in Suricates* Suricata suricatta. PhD thesis, University of Cambridge.

Manser, M.B. (1999). Response of foraging group members to sentinel calls in suricates, *Suricata suricatta*. *Proc. Royal Soc. London (Ser. B Biol. Sci.)* **266**: 1013-1019.

Manser, M.B. (2001). The acoustic structure of suricates' alarm calls varies with predator type and the level of response urgency. *Proc. Royal Soc. London (Ser. B Biol. Sci.)* **268**: 2315-2324.

Manser, M.B. & Avey, G. (2000). The effect of pup vocalisations on food allocation in a cooperative mammal, the meerkat (*Suricata suricatta*). *Behav. Ecol. Sociobiol.* **48**: 429-437.

Manser, M.B. & Bell, M.B. (2004). Spatial representation of shelter locations in meerkats, *Suricata suricatta*. *Anim. Behav.* **68**: 151-157.

Manser, M.B., Bell, M.B. & Fletcher, L.B. (2001). The information that receivers extract from alarm calls in suricates. *Proc. Royal Soc. London (Ser. B Biol. Sci.)* **268**: 2485-2491.

Manser, M.B., Seyfarth, R.M. & Cheney, D.L. (2002). Suricate alarm calls signal predator class and urgency. *Trends Cognitive Sci.* **6**: 55-57.

Manzani, P.R. & Monteiro, E.L.A. (1989). Notes on the food habits of the jaguarundi, *Felis yagouaroundi* (Mammalia: Carnivora). *Mammalia* **53**: 659-660.

Marassi, M. & Biancardi, C.M. (2002). Diet of the Eurasian badger (*Meles meles*) in an area of the Italian Prealps. *Hystrix* **13**: 19-28.

Marcelli, M., Fusillo, R. & Boitani, L. (2003). Sexual segregation in the activity patterns of European polecats (*Mustela putorius*). *J. Zool., London* **261**: 249-255.

Mares, M.A., Bárquez, R.M., Braun, J.K. & Ojeda, R.A. (1996). Observations on the mammals of Tucumán Province, Argentina. I. Systematics, distribution and ecology of the Didelphiomorphia, Xenarthra, Chiroptera, Primates, Carnivora, Perissodactyla, Artiodactyla and Lagomorpha. *Ann. Carnegie Mus.* **65**: 89-152.

Marino, J. (2003). Threathened Ethiopian wolves persist in small isolated afroalpine enclaves. *Oryx* **37**: 62-71.

Marino, J. (2004). *Spatial Ecology of the Ethiopian Wolf* Canis simensis. PhD dissertation, Wildlife Conservation Research Unit, Oxford University, Oxford.

Marino, J., Sillero-Zubiri, C. & Macdonald, D.W. (2006). Trends, dynamics and resilience of an Ethiopian wolf population. *Anim. Conserv.* **9**: 49-58.

Marker-Kraus, L. (1992). *International Cheetah Studbook 1991.* NOAHS Centre, National Zoological Park, Washington, D.C.

Marker-Kraus, L. & Grisham, J. (1993). Captive breeding of cheetahs in North American zoos. *Zoo Biology* **12**: 5-18.

Marker-Kraus, L. & Kraus, D. (1991). Annual report. Unpublished report to the Cheetah Conservation Fund, Windhoek.

Markotter, W., Kuzmin, I., Rupprecht, C.E., Randles, J., Sabeta, C.T., Wandeler, A.I. & Nel, L.H. (2006). Isolation of Lagos bat virus from water mongoose. *Emerging Infect. Diseases* **12**: 1913-1918.

Marquet, P.A., Contreras, L.C., Torres-Murua, J.C., Silva, S.I. & Jaksic, F.M. (1993). Food habits of *Pseudalopex* foxes in the Atacama Desert, pre-Andean ranges and the high-Andean Plateau of northernmost Chile. *Mammalia* **57**: 130-135.

Marquez, A. & Farina, R.A. (2003). Dental morphology and diet in canids and procyonids from Uruguay. *Mammalia* **67**: 567-573.

Marsack, P. & Campbell, G. (1990). Feeding behaviour and diet of dingoes in the Nullarbor region, Western Australia. *Austr. Wildl. Res.* **17**: 349-357.

Marston, M.A. (1942). Winter relations of bobcats to white-tailed deer in Maine. *J. Wildl. Management* **6**: 328-337.

Martin, L.D. (1989). Fossil history of the terrestrial Carnivora. Pp. 536-568 in: Gittleman, J.L. ed. (1989). *Carnivore Behavior, Ecology and Evolution.* Comstock Publishing Associates, Ithaca, New York.

Martin, R.B. & de Meulenar, T. (1988). *Survey of the Status of the Leopard* Panthera pardus *in Sub-Saharan Africa.* Secretariat of the Convention on International Trade in Endangered Species of Wild Fauna and Flora, Lausanne, Switzerland.

Martin, R.B., Burr, D.B. & Sharkey, N.A. (1998). *Skeletal Tissue Mechanics.* Springer-Verlag, New York.

Martínez, D.R., Rau, J.R., Murúa, R.E. & Tillería, M.S. (1993). Depredación selectiva de roedores por zorros chillas (*Pseudalopex griseus*) en la pluviselva valdiviana, Chile. *Rev. Chil. Hist. Nat.* **66**: 419-426.

Martino, S.D., Monteverde, M., Novaro, A. & Walker, S. (2008). New records of the Andean cat (*Leopardus jacobita*) in Neuquén Province, Patagonia, Argentina. Wildlife Conservation Society, September-October.

Martinoli, A., Preatoni, D.G., Chiarenzi, B., Wauters, L.A. & Tosi, G. (2001). Diet of stoats (*Mustela erminea*) in an Alpine habitat: the importance of fruit consumption in summer. *Acta Oecol.* **22**: 45-53.

Maruska, E.J. (1987). White tiger: phantom or freak? Pp. 372-379 in: Tilson, R.L. & Seal, U.S. eds. (1987). *Tigers of the World: the Biology, Biopolitics, Management and Conservation of an Endangered Species.* Noyes Publications, Park Ridge, New Jersey.

Masi, E., Dessì-Fulgheri, F., Messeri, P. & Piazza, R. (1987). Some aspects of the vocal repertoire of the banded mongoose, *Mungos mungo* (Gmelin). *Ital. J. Zool.* **21**: 193-194.

Mason, C.F. & Rowe-Rowe, D.T. (1992). Organochlorine pesticide residues and PCBs in otter scats from Natal. *South Afr. J. Wildl. Res.* **22**: 29-31.

Massoia, E. (1982). *Dusicyon gymnocercus lordi.* Una nueva subespecie del "zorro gris grande" (Mammalia Carnívora Canidae). *Neotropica* **28**: 147-152.

Masters, J.C., de Wit, M.J. & Asher, R.J. (2006). Reconciling the origins of Africa, India and Madagascar with vertebrate dispersal scenarios. *Folia Primatol.* **77**: 399-418.

Masuda, R., Lopez, J.V., Pecon-Slattery, J., Yuhki, N. & O'Brien, S.J. (1996). Molecular phylogeny of mitochondrial cytochrome b and 12S rRNA sequences in the Felidae: ocelot and domestic cat lineages. *Mol. Phylogen. Evol.* **6(3)**: 351-365.

Matjuschkin, E.N. (1978). *Der Luchs. Die Neue Brehm-Bücherei.* A Ziemsen Verlag, Wittenberg Lutherstadt, Germany.

Matson, J.O. & Baker, R.H. (1986). Mammals of Zacatecas. *Spec. Publ. Mus. Texas Tech Univ.* **24**: 1-88.

Matthews, L.H. (1939). Reproduction in the spotted hyaena, *Crocuta crocuta* (Erxleben). *Phil. Trans. Roy. Soc. London* **230**: 1-78.

Mattson, D.J. (1990). Human impacts on bear habitat use. *Int. Conf. Bear Res. Management* **8**: 33-56.

Mattson, D.J. (1998). Diet and morphology of extant and recently extinct northern bears. *Ursus* **10**: 479-496.

Mattson, D.J. & Jonkel, C. (1990). Stone pines and bears. Pp. 223-236 in: Schmidt, W.C. & McDonald, K.J. eds. (1990). *Symposium on Whitebark Pine Ecosystems: Ecology and Management of a High-mountain Resource.* US Forest Service General Technical Report INT-270.

Mattson, D.J. & Merrill, T. (2002). Extirpations of grizzly bears in the contiguous United States, 1850-2000. *Conserv. Biol.* **16(4)**: 1123-1136.

Mattson, D.J., Herrero, S. & Merrill, T. (2005). Are black bears a factor in the restoration of North American grizzly bear populations? *Ursus* **16**: 11-30.

Maurello, M.A., Clarke, J.A. & Ackley, R.S. (2000). Signature characteristics in contact calls of the white-nosed coati. *J. Mammal.* **81**: 415-421.

Mauritzen, M., Derocher, A.E. & Wiig, Ø. (2001). Space-use strategies of female polar bears in a dynamic sea ice habitat. *Can. J. Zool.* **79**: 1704-1713.

Mazak, J.H. (2004). On the sexual dimorphism in the skull of the tiger (*Panthera tigris*). *Mammal. Biol.* **69**: 392-400.

Mazak, J.H. & Groves, C.P. (2006). A taxonomic revision of the tigers (*Panthera tigris*) of southeast Asia. *Mammal. Biol.* **71**: 268-287.

Mazák, V. (1981). *Panthera tigris. Mammal. Species* **152**: 1-8.

Mazza, P. & Rustioni, M. (1994). On the phylogeny of Eurasian bears. *Palaeontographica (Abt. A)* **230**: 1-38.

McBride, C. (1990). *Liontide.* Jonathan Ball, Johannesburg.

McCain, E.B. & Childs, J.L. (2008). Evidence of resident jaguars (*Panthera onca*) in the southwestern United States and the implications for conservation. *J. Mammal.* **89**: 1-10.

McCarthy, T.J. (1992). Notes concerning the jaguarundi cat (*Herpailurus jagouaroundi*) in the Caribbean lowlands of Belize and Guatemala. *Mammalia* **56**: 302-306.

McCarthy, T.M. (2000). *Ecology and Conservation of Snow Leopards, Gobi Brown Bears and Wild Bactrian Camels in Mongolia.* PhD dissertation, University of Massachusetts, Amherst, Massachusetts.

McClearn, D. (1992). Locomotion, posture, and feeding behavior of kinkajous, coatis, and raccoons. *J. Mammal.* **73**: 245-261.

McCord, C.M. (1974). Selection of winter habitat by bobcats (*Lynx rufus*) on the Quabbin Reservation, Massachusetts. *J. Mammal.* **55**: 428-437.

McCord, C.M. & Cardoza, J.E. (1982). Bobcat and lynx. Pp. 728-766 in: Chapman, J.A. & Feldhammer, G.A. eds. (1982). *Wild Mammals of North America.* The Johns Hopkins University Press, Baltimore, Maryland.

McCreery, E.K. & Robbins, R.L. (2001). Proximate explanations for failed pack formation in *Lycaon pictus. Behaviour* **138**: 1467-1479.

McCullough, C.R. & Fritzell, E.K. (1984). Ecological observations of eastern spotted skunks on the Ozark Plateau. *Trans. Missouri Acad. Sci.* **18**: 25-32.

McCusker, J.S. (1974). Breeding Malayan sun bears *Helarctos malayanus* at Fort Worth Zoo. *Int. Zoo Yb.* **15**: 118-119.

McDonald, R.A. & Larivière, S. (2001). Diseases and pathogens of *Mustela* spp., with special reference to the biological control of introduced stoat *Mustela erminea* populations in New Zealand. *J. Roy. Soc. New Zealand* **31**: 721-744.

McDonald, R.A. & Larivière, S. (2002). Captive husbandry of stoats *Mustela erminea. New Zealand J. Zool.* **29**: 177-186.

McDonald, R.A., Webbon, C. & Harris, S. (2000). The diet of stoats (*Mustela erminea*) and weasels (*Mustela nivalis*) in Great Britain. *J. Zool., London* **252**: 363-371.

McDougal, C. (1977). *The Face of the Tiger.* Rivington Books & Andre Deutsch, London.

McDougal, C. (1981). Some observations on tiger behaviour in the context of baiting. *J. Bombay Nat. Hist. Soc.* **77**: 476-485.

McDougal, C. (1987). The man-eating tiger in geographical and historical perspective. Pp. 435-448 in: Tilson, R.L. & Seal, U.S. eds. (1987). *Tigers of the World: the Biology, Biopolitics, Management and Conservation of an Endangered Species.* Noyes Publications, Park Ridge, New Jersey.

McDougal, C. (1988). Leopard and tiger interactions at Royal Chitwan National Park, Nepal. *J. Bombay Nat. Hist. Soc.* **85**: 609-610.

McDougal, C. (1991). Man-eaters. Pp. 204-211 in: Seidensticker, J. & Lumpkin, S. eds. (1991). *Great Cats.* Rodale Press, Emmaus, Pennsylvania.

McDougal, C. (1995). Tiger count in Nepal's Chitwan National Park. *Cat News* **23**: 3-5.

McFadden, K.W. (2004). *The Ecology, Evolution and Natural History of the Endangered Carnivores of Cozumel Island, Mexico.* Columbia University Press, New York.

McFadden, K.W., Sambrotto, R.N., Medellin, R.A. & Gompper, M.E. (2006). Feeding habits of endangered pygmy raccoons (*Procyon pygmaeus*) based on stable isotope and fecal analyses. *J. Mammal.* **87**: 501-509.

McFadden, K.W., Wade, S.E., Dubovi, E.J. & Gompper, M.E. (2005). A serological and fecal parasitologic survey of the critically endangered pygmy raccoon (*Procyon pygmaeus*). *J. Wildl. Diseases* **41**: 615-617.

McGrew, J.C. (1979). *Vulpes macrotis. Mammal. Species* **123**: 1-6.

McIlroy, J.C., Cooper, R.J., Gifford, E.J., Green, B.F. & Newgrain, K.W. (1986). The effect on wild dogs *Canis f. familiaris* of 1080 poisoning campaigns in Kosciusko National Park, New South Wales. *Austr. Wildl. Res.* **13**: 535-544.

McIntosh, D.L. (1963). Reproduction and growth of the red fox in the Canberra district. *CSIRO Wildl. Res.* **8**: 132-141.

McIvor, D.E., Bissonette, J.A. & Drew, G.S. (1995). Taxonomic and conservation status of the Yuma mountain lion. *Conserv. Biol.* **9**: 1033-1040.

McKenna, M.C. & Bell, S.K. (1997). *Classification of Mammals above the Species Level.* Columbia University Press, New York.

McKenzie, A.A. (1990). *Co-operative Hunting in the Black-backed Jackal (*Canis mesomelas*) Schreber.* PhD dissertation, University of Pretoria, Pretoria, South Africa.

McKeown, S. (1992). Joint management of species cheetah breeding programme. Pp. 77-88 in: Mansard, P. ed. (1992). *Cats: Proceedings of the Conference/Workshop Held at Chester Zoo, October 10, 1992 by the Ridgeway Trust for Endangered Cats and the Association of British Wild Animal Keepers.* Ridgeway Trust for Endangered Cats, Hastings, UK.

McLellan, B.N. & Hovey, F.W. (1995). The diet of grizzly bears in the Flathead River drainage of southeastern British Columbia. *Can. J. Zool.* **73**: 704-712.

McLellan, B.N. & Hovey, F.W. (2001). Natal dispersal of grizzly bears. *Can. J. Zool.* **79**: 838-844.

McLellan, B.N., Hovey, F.W., Mace, R.D., Woods, J.G., Carney, D.W., Gibeau, M., Wakkinen, W.F. & Kasworm, W. (1999). Rates and causes of mortality in the interior mountains of British Columbia, Alberta, Montana, Washington, and Idaho. *J. Wildl. Management* **63**: 911-920.

McLellan, B.N., Servheen, C. & Huber, D. (2007). *Ursus arctos* brown bear. In: *2007 IUCN Red List of Threatened Species.* URL: http://www.iucnredlist.org.html

McLoughlin, P.D., Case, R.L., Gau, R.J., Ferguson, S.H. & Messier, F. (1999). Annual and seasonal movement patterns of barren-ground grizzly bears in the Central Northwest Territories. *Ursus* **11**: 79-86.

McLoughlin, P.D., Ferguson, S.H. & Messier, F. (2000). Intraspecific variation in home range overlap with habitat quality: a comparison among brown bear populations. *Evol. Ecol.* **14**: 39-60.

McMahan, L.R. (1986). The international cat trade. Pp. 461-488 in: Miller, S.D. & Everett D.D. eds. (1986). *Cats of the World: Biology, Conservation and Management.* National Wildlife Federation, Washington, D.C.

McMahon, E. (2002). *Status and Conservation of the Zorro Chilote on Mainland Chile.* Progress report for SAG & CONAF, Temuco, Chile.

McMahon, E., Fuller, T.K. & Johnson, W.E. (1999). *Ecología y Conservación en los Zorros Simpátricos de Chile.* Progress report for SAG & CONAF, Temuco, Chile.

McMahon, T.A. (1984). *Muscles, Reflexes and Locomotion.* Princeton University Press, Princeton, New Jersey.

McMurtry, L. (1985). *Lonesome Dove.* Simon & Schuster, New York.

McNeely, J. (1979). Status of tiger in Indonesia. *Tigerpaper* **6**: 21-22.

McNutt, J.W. (1996a). Adoption in African wild dogs, *Lycaon pictus. J. Zool., London* **240**: 163-173.

McNutt, J.W. (1996b). Sex-biased dispersal in African wild dogs *Lycaon pictus. Anim. Behav.* **52**: 1067-1077.

McOrist, S. & Kitchener, A.C. (1994). Current threats to the European wildcat, *Felis silvestris* in Scotland. *Ambio* **23**: 243-245.

Mead, R.A. (1968a). Reproduction in eastern forms of the spotted skunk (genus *Spilogale*). *J. Zool., London* **156**: 119-136.

Mead, R.A. (1968b). Reproduction in western forms of the spotted skunk (genus *Spilogale*). *J. Mammal.* **49**: 373-390.

Mead, R.A. (1993). Embryonic diapause in vertebrates. *J. Exper. Zool.* **266**: 629-641.

Mead, R.A., Rector, M., Starypan, G., Neirinckz, S., Jones, M. & Don-Carlos, M.N. (1991). Reproductive biology of captive wolverine. *J. Mammal.* **72**: 807-814.

Meaney, C.A., Ruggles, A.K. & Beauvais, G.P. (2006). *American Hog-nosed Skunk (*Conepatus leuconotus*): a Technical Conservation Assessment.* USDA Forest Service, Rocky Mountain Region, Golden, Colorado.

Mearns, E.A. (1897a). Preliminary diagnoses of new mammals of the genera *Lynx, Urocyon, Spilogale* and *Mephitis*, from the Mexican boundary line. *Proc. US Natl. Mus.* **20**: 457-461.

Mearns, E.A. (1897b). Preliminary diagnoses of new mammals of the genus *Mephitis, Dorcelaphus* and *Dicotyles*, from the Mexican border of the United States. *Proc. US Natl. Mu* **20**: 467-471.

Mech, L.D. (1970). *The Wolf: the Ecology and Behavior of an Endangered Species.* Natural Histor Press, Doubleday, New York.

Mech, L.D. (1973). Canadian lynx invasion of Minnesota. *Biol. Conserv.* **5**: 151-152.

Mech, L.D. (1974). *Canis lupus. Mammal. Species* **37**: 1-6.

Mech, L.D. (1980). Age, sex, reproduction and spatial organization of lynxes colonizin northeastern Minnesota. *J. Mammal.* **61**: 261-267.

Mech, L.D. (2002). Breeding season of wolves *Canis lupus* in relation to latitude. *Can. Field Nat.* **116**: 139-140.

Mech, L.D. & Boitani, L. eds. (2003). *Wolves: Behavior, Ecology and Conservation.* University of Chicago Press, Chicago, Illinois.

Mech, L.D. & Boitani, L. (2004). Grey wolf *Canis lupus.* Pp. 124-129 in: Sillero-Zubiri, C Hoffmann, M. & Macdonald, D.W. eds. (2004). *Canids: Foxes, Wolves, Jackals and Dog Status Survey and Conservation Action Plan.* IUCN/SSC Canid Specialist Group, Gland & Cambridge.

Mech, L.D., Adams, L.G., Meier, T.J., Burch, J.W. & Dale, B.W. (1998). *The Wolves of Denal* University of Minnesota Press, Minneapolis.

Medel, R.G. & Jaksic, F.M. (1988). Ecología de los cánidos sudamericanos: una revisió *Rev. Chil. Hist. Nat.* **61**: 67-79.

Medel, R.G., Jimenez, J.E., Jaksic, F.M., Yanez, J.L. & Armesto, J.J. (1990). Discovery of continental population of the rare Darwin's fox *Dusicyon fulvipes* (Martin, 1837) in Chile *Biol. Conserv.* **51**: 71-77.

Medellín, R.A., Ceballos, G. & Zarza, H. (1998). *Spilogale pygmaea. Mammal. Species* **600**: 1-3

Medellín, R.A., Chetkiewicz, C., Rabinowitz, A., Redford, K.H., Robinson, J.G., Sanderson E. & Taber, A. (2001). *Jaguars in the New Millennium. A Status Assessment, Priority Detectio and Recommendations for the Conservation of Jaguars in the Americas.* Universidad Naciona Autónoma de México & Wildlife Conservation Society, México, D.F.

Medina, G. (1995). Feeding habits of marine otter (*Lutra felina*) in southern Chile. *Proc. In Otter Colloquium* **6**: 65-68.

Medina, G. (1996). Conservation and status of *Lutra provocax* in Chile. *Pacific Conserv. Bio* **2**: 414-419.

Medina, G., Boher, F., Flores, G., Santibanez, A. & Soto-Azat, C. (2007). Spacing behavio of marine otters (*Lontra felina*) in relation to land refuges and fishery waste in centra Chile. *J. Mammal.* **88**: 487-494.

Medina, G., Kaufman, V.S., Monsalve, R. & Gomez, V. (2003). The influence of riparia vegetation, woody debris, stream morphology and human activity on the use of rivers b southern river otters in *Lontra provocax* in Chile. *Oryx* **37**: 422-430.

Medina, G., Rodriguez, C.D., Alvarez, R.E. & Bartheld, J.L. (2004). Feeding ecology of th marine otter (*Lutra felina*) in a rocky seashore of the south of Chile. *Marine Mammal Sc* **20**: 134-144.

Medway, L. (1969). *The Wild Mammals of Malaya and Offshore Islands Including Singapore.* Oxford University Press, London.

Meester, J.A.J., Rautenbach, I.L., Dippenaar, N.J. & Baker, C.M. (1986). Classification of southern African mammals. *Transvaal Mus. Monogr.* **5**: 1-359.

Meia, J.S. (1994). *Social Organisation of a Red Fox (*Vulpes vulpes*) Population in a Mountainou Habitat.* PhD dissertation, University of Neuchâtel, Neuchâtel, Switzerland.

Meia, J.S. & Weber, J.M. (1996). Social organization of red foxes *Vulpes vulpes* in the Swis Jura Mountains. *Zeitschrift für Saugetierkunde* **61**: 257-268.

Meijaard, E. (1999a). Ursus (Helarctos) malayanus, *the Neglected Malayan Sun Bear.* Netherlands Commission for International Nature Protection, Leiden, The Netherlands.

Meijaard, E. (1999b). Human-imposed threats to sun bears in Borneo. *Ursus* **11**: 185-192.

Meijaard, E. (2001). Conservation and trade of sun bears in Kalimantan. Pp. 26-37 in: Williamson, D.F. & Phipps, M.J. eds. (2001). *Proceedings of the Third International Symposium on the Trade in Bear Parts.* TRAFFIC East Asia, Hong Kong.

Meijaard, E. (2003). Mammals of south-east Asian islands and their late Pleistocene environments. *J. Biogeogr.* **30**: 1245-1257.

Meijaard, E. (2004). Craniometric differences among Malayan sun bears (*Ursus malayanus*); evolutionary and taxonomic implications. *Raffles Bull. Zool.* **52**: 665-672.

Meiri, S. (2005). Small carnivores on small Islands. New data based on old skulls. *Small Carniv. Conserv.* **33**: 21-23.

Meiri, S., Duckworth, J.W. & Meijaard, E. (2007). Biogeography of Indonesian mountain weasel *Mustela lutreolina* and a newly discovered specimen. *Small Carniv. Conserv.* **37**: 1-5.

Melis, C., Cagnacci, F. & Bargagli, L. (2002). Food habits of the Eurasian badger in a rural Mediterranean area. *Z. Jagdwiss.* **48**: 236-246.

Mellen, J.D. (1989). *Reproductive Behavior of Small Captive Cats (*Felis *spp.).* PhD thesis, University of California, Davis, Caifornia.

Mellen, J.D. (1993). A comparative analysis of scent marking, social and reproductive behavior in 20 species of small cats (*Felis*). *Amer. Zool.* **33**: 151-166.

Melquist, W.E. & Hornocker, M.G. (1983). Ecology of river otters in west central Idaho. *Wildl. Monogr.* **83**: 1-60.

Mendelssohn, H. (1985). The striped hyaena in Israel. *IUCN/SSC Hyaena Special. Group Newslett.* **2**: 7-14.

Mendelssohn, H. (1989). Felids in Israel. *Cat News* **10**: 2-4.

Mendelssohn, H., Yom-Tov, Y., Ilany, G. & Meninger, D. (1987). On the occurrence of Blanford's fox *Vulpes cana* Blanford, 1877 in Israel and Sinai. *Mammalia* **51**: 459-462.

Mendes, A.R. & Chivers, D.J. (2002). Abundance, habitat use and conservation of the olingo *Bassaricyon* spp. in Maracá Ecological Station, Roraima, Brazilian Amazonia. *Stud. Neotrop. Fauna Environm.* **37**: 105-109.

van Mensch, P.J.A. & van Bree, P.J.H. (1969). On the African golden cat, *Profelis aurata* (Temminck, 1827). *Biologica Gabonica* **5**: 235-269.

Mercure, A., Ralls, K., Koepfli, K.P. & Wayne, R.K. (1993). Genetic subdivisions among small canids: mitochondrial DNA differentiation of swift, kit and Arctic foxes. *Evolution* **47**: 1313-1328.

Merriam, C.H. (1886). Description of a newly born lynx. *Bull. Nat. Hist. Soc. New Brunswick* **5**: 10-13.

Merriam, C.H. (1890a). Descriptions of twenty-six new species of North American mammals. *North Amer. Fauna* **4**: 1-55.

Merriam, C.H. (1890b). Results of a biological survey of the San Francisco mountain region and desert of the Little Colorado, Arizona. *North Amer. Fauna* **3**: 1-101.

Merriam, C.H. (1902). Six new skunks of the genus *Conepatus. Proc. Biol. Soc. Washington* **15**: 161-165.

Mertens, R. (1925). Insectivoren und carnivoren aus west- und zentral- Afrika. *Senckenbergiana* **7**: 65-74.

Meserve, P.L., Shadrick, E.J. & Kelt, D.A. (1987). Diets and selectivity of two Chilean predators in the northern semi-arid zone. *Rev. Chil. Hist. Nat.* **60**: 93-99.

Meslin, F.X. (1999). Global review of human and animal rabies. Pp. 9-11 in: *Rabies: Guidelines for Medical Professional.* Veterinary Learning Systems, Trenton, New Jersey.

Messeri, P. (1983). A preliminary comparison between social behaviors of 2 viverrids, the dwarf mongoose and the banded mongoose, in Somalia. *Ital. J. Zool.* **17**: 200.

Messick, J.P. & Hornocker, M.G. (1981). Ecology of the badger in southwestern Idaho. *Wildl. Monogr.* **76**: 1-53.

Messier, F., Taylor, M.K. & Ramsay, M.A. (1992). Seasonal activity patterns of female polar bears (*Ursus maritimus*) in the Canadian Arctic as revealed by satellite telemetry. *J. Zool., London* **226**: 219-229.

Messier, F., Taylor, M.K. & Ramsay, M.A. (1994). Denning ecology of polar bears in the Canadian Artic Archipelago. *J. Mammal.* **75**: 420-430.

Meyer-Holzapfel, M. (1968). Breeding the European wild cat *Felis s. silvestris* at Berne Zoo. *Int. Zoo Yb.* **8**: 31-38.

Meza, A.de V., Meyer, E.M. & Gonzalez, C.A.L. (2002). Ocelot (*Leopardus pardalis*) food habits in a tropical deciduous forest of Jalisco, Mexico. *Amer. Midl. Nat.* **148**: 146-154.

Michalski, F. & Peres, C.A. (2005). Anthropogenic determinants of primate and carnivore local extinctions in a fragmented forest landscape of southern Amazonia. *Biol. Conserv.* **124**: 383-396.

Michalski, F., Crawshaw, P.G., de Oliveira, T.G. & Fabian, M.E. (2006). Notes on home range and habitat use of three small carnivore species in a disturbed vegetation mosaic of southeastern Brazil. *Mammalia* **70**: 52-57.

Michaux, J.R., Hardy, O.J., Justy, F., Fournier, P., Kranz, A., Cabria, M., Davison, A., Rosoux, R. & Libois, R. (2005). Conservation genetics and population history of the threatened European mink *Mustela lutreola*, with an emphasis on the west European population. *Mol. Ecol.* **14**: 2373-2388.

Michaux, J.R., Libois, R., Davison, A., Chevret, P. & Rosoux, R. (2004). Is the western population of the European mink, (*Mustela lutreola*), a distinct Management Unit for conservation? *Biol. Conserv.* **115**: 357-367.

Michelat, D., Quere, J.P. & Giraudoux, P. (2001). Characteristics of dens used by stone marten (*Martes foina*, Erxleben, 1777) in the Haut-Doubs. *Rev. Suisse Zool.* **108**: 263-274.

Michener, G.R. (2004). Hunting techniques and tool use by North American badgers preying on Richardson's ground squirrels. *J. Mammal.* **85**: 1019-1027.

Michener, G.R. & Iwaniuk, A.N. (2001). Killing technique of North American badgers preying on Richardson's ground squirrels. *Can. J. Zool.* **79**: 2109-2113.

Miller, C.R., Waits, L.P. & Joyce, P. (2006). Phylogeography and mitochondrial diversity of extirpated brown bear (*Ursus arctos*) populations in the contiguous United States and Mexico. *Mol. Ecol.* **15**: 4477-4485.

Miller, D.J. & Jackson, R. (1994). Livestock and snow leopards: making room for competing users on the Tibetan Plateau. Pp. 315-333 in: Fox, J.L. & Du Jizeng eds. (1994). *Proceedings of the Seventh International Snow Leopard Symposium.* International Snow Leopard Trust & Chicago Zoological Society, Seattle, Washington.

Miller, F.W. (1925). A new hog-nosed skunk. *J. Mammal.* **6**: 50-52.

Miller, F.W. (1930). Notes on some mammals of southern Matto Grosso, Brazil. *J. Mammal.* **11**: 10-23.

Miller, S.D. & Speake, D.W. (1978). Prey utilization by bobcats on quail plantations in south Alabama. *Proc. Ann. Conf. Southeastern Assoc. Fish & Wildl. Agencies* **32**: 100-111.

Miller, S.D. & Speake, D.W. (1979). Progress report: demography and home range of the bobcat in south Alabama. Pp. 123-124 in: *Proceedings of the Bobcat Research Conference.* National Wildlife Federation Science Technical Series **6**.

Miller, S.D., Rottmann, J., Raedecke, K.J. & Taber, R.D. (1983). Endangered mammals of Chile: status and conservation. *Biol. Conserv.* **25**: 335-352.

Mills, M.G.L. (1982a). The mating system of the brown hyaena, *Hyaena brunnea* in the southern Kalahari. *Behav. Ecol. Sociobiol.* **10**: 131-136.

Mills, M.G.L. (1982b). Factors affecting group size and territory size of the brown hyena, *Hyaena brunnea*, in the southern Kalahari. *J. Zool., London* **198**: 39-51.

Mills, M.G.L. (1982c). Notes on age determination, growth and measurements of brown hyaenas *Hyaena brunnea* from the Kalahari Gemsbok National Park. *Koedoe* **25**: 55-61.

Mills, M.G.L. (1983a). Mating and denning behaviour of the brown hyaena *Hyaena brunnea* and comparisons with other Hyaenidae. *Zietschr. Tierpsychol.* **63**: 331-342.

Mills, M.G.L. (1983b). Behavioural mechanisms in territory and group maintenance of the brown hyena, *Hyaena brunnea*, in the southern Kalahari. *Anim. Behav.* **31**: 503-510.

Mills, M.G.L. (1984a). The comparative behavioural ecology of the brown hyaena *Hyaena brunnea* and the spotted hyaena *Crocuta crocuta* in the southern Kalahari. *Koedoe* **27**(Suppl.): 237-247.

Mills, M.G.L. (1984b). Prey selection and feeding habits of the larger carnivores in the southern Kalahari. *Koedoe* **27**(Suppl.): 281-294.

Mills, M.G.L. (1985). Related spotted hyaenas forage together but do not cooperate in rearing young. *Nature (London)* **316**: 61-62.

Mills, M.G.L. (1989). The comparative behavioral ecology of hyenas: the importance of diet and food dispersion. Pp. 125-142 in: Gittleman, J.L. ed. (1989). *Carnivore Behaviour, Ecology and Evolution.* Cornell University Press, Ithaca, New York.

Mills, M.G.L. (1990). *Kalahari Hyaenas: the Comparative Behavioural Ecology of Two Species.* Unwin Hyman, London.

Mills, M.G.L. & Biggs, H.C. (1993). Prey apportionment and related ecological relationships between large carnivores in Kruger National Park. In: Dunstone, N. & Gorman, M.L. eds. (1993). *Mammals as Predators.* Proceedings of the Symposium of the Zoological Society of London **65**. Clarendon, Oxford.

Mills, M.G.L. & Gorman, M.L. (1987). The scent-marking behaviour of the spotted hyaena *Crocuta crocuta* in the southern Kalahari. *J. Zool., London* **212**: 483-497.

Mills, M.G.L. & Hofer, H. (1998). *Hyaenas. Status Survey and Conservation Action Plan.* IUCN/SSC Hyaena Specialist Group, Gland & Cambridge.

Mills, M.G.L. & Mills, M.E.J. (1978). Diet of the brown hyaena *Hyaena brunnea* in the southern Kalahari, South Africa. *Koedoe* **21**: 125-150.

Mills, M.G.L. & Mills, M.E.J. (1982). Factors affecting the movement patterns of brown hyenas, *Hyaena brunnea*, in the southern Kalahari. *South Afr. J. Wildl. Res.* **12**: 11-117.

Mills, M.G.L. & Schenk, T.M. (1992). Predator-prey relationships: the impact of lion predation on wildebeest and zebra populations. *J. Anim. Ecol.* **61**: 693-702.

Mills, M.G.L., Gorman, M.L. & Mills, M.E.J. (1980). The scent marking behaviour of the brown hyaena *Hyaena brunnea. South Afr. J. Zool.* **15**: 240-248.

Mills, M.G.L., Wolff, P. & Le Riche, E.A.N. (1989). Some population characteristics of the lion *Panthera leo* in the Kalahari Gemsbok National Park. *Koedoe* **21**: 163-171.

Minta, S.C. (1993). Sexual differences in spatio-temporal interaction among badgers. *Oecologia* **96**: 402-409.

Minta, S.C., Minta, K.A. & Lott, D.F. (1992). Hunting associations between badgers (*Taxidea taxus*) and coyotes (*Canis latrans*). *J. Mammal.* **73(4)**: 814-820.

Miquelle, D.G. (1998). Tigers and leopards in Jilin Province, China. *Cat News* **28**: 5-6.

Miquelle, D.G., Merrill, T.W., Dunishenko, Y., Smirnov, E.N., Quigley, H.B., Pikunov, D.G. & Hornocker, M. (1999). A habitat protection plan for the Amur tiger: developing political and ecological criteria for a viable land-use plan. Pp. 273-295 in: Seidensticker, J., Christie, S. & Jackson, P. eds. (1999). *Riding the Tiger: Tiger Conservation in Human-dominated Landscapes.* Cambridge University Press, Cambridge.

Miquelle, D.G., Quigley, H., Hornocker, M., Smirnov, E., Nikalaev, I., Pikunov, D. & Quigley, K. (1993). Present status of the Siberian tiger and some threats to its conservation. Pp. 274-278 in: Thompson, I.D. ed. (1993). *Proceedings of the International Union of Game Biologists XXI Congress.* Halifax, Nova Scotia.

Miquelle, D.G., Smirnov, E.N., Quigley, H.G., Hornocker, M.G., Nikolaev, I.G. & Matyushkin, E.N. (1996). Food habits of Amur tigers in Sikhote-Alin Zapovednik and the Russian far east, and implications for conservation. *J. Wildl. Res.* **1**: 138-147.

Mitchell, B., Shenton, J. & Uys, J. (1965). Predation on large mammals in the Kafue National Park, Zambia. *Zool. Afr.* **1**: 297-318.

Mitchell, F.S., Onorato, D.P., Hellgren, E.C., Skiles, J.R. & Harveson, L.A. (2005). Winter ecology of American black bears in a desert montane island. *Wildl. Soc. Bull.* **33**: 164-171.

Mitchell, J.D. (1923). "Mexican polecat", "hydrophobia cat", *Spilogale indianola*, of southern Texas. *J. Mammal.* **4**: 49-51.

Mitchell, R.M. (1977). *Accounts of Nepalese Mammals and Analysis of the Host-Ectoparasite Data by Compute Techniques.* PhD dissertation, Iowa State University, Ames, Iowa.

Mitchell-Jones, A.J., Amori, G., Bogdanowicz, W., Krystufek, B., Reijnders, P.J.H., Spitzenberger, F., Stubbe, M., Thissen, J.B.M., Vohralík, V. & Zima, J. (1999). *Atlas of European Mammals.* The Academic Press, London.

Miththapala, S., Seidensticker, J. & O'Brien, S.J. (1996). Phylogeograhic subspecies recognition in leopards (*Panthera pardus*): molecular genetic variation. *Conserv. Biol.* **10**: 1115-1132.

Miththapala, S., Seidensticker, J., Phillips, L.G., Fernando, S.B.U. & Smallwood, J.A. (1989). Identification of individual leopards (*Panthera pardus kotiya*) using spot pattern variation. *J. Zool., London* **218**: 527-536.

Mivart, S.G. (1890a). *Dogs, Jackals, Wolves and Foxes: a Monograph of the Canidae.* London.

Mivart, S.G. (1890b). Notes on the South-American Canidae. *Proc. Zool. Soc. London* **1890**: 98-113.

Miyoshi, K. & Higashi, S. (2005). Home range and habitat use by the sable *Martes zibellina brachyura* in a Japanese cool-temperate mixed forest. *Ecol. Res.* **20**: 95-101.

Mizukami, R.N., Goto, M., Izumiyama, S., Hayashi, H. & Yoh, M. (2005). Estimation of feeding history by measuring carbon and nitrogen stable isotope ratios in hair of Asiatic black bears. *Ursus* **16**: 85-92.

Mizutani, F. & Jewell, P.A. (1998). Home-range and movements of leopards (*Panthera pardus*) on a livestock ranch in Kenya. *J. Zool., London* **244**: 269-286.

Moehlman, P.D. (1978). *Socioecology of Silver-backed and Golden Jackals.* Serengeti Research Institute report no. **241**. National Geographic Society, Washington, D.C.

Moehlman, P.D. (1979). Jackal helpers and pup survival. *Nature (London)* **277**: 382-383.

Moehlman, P.D. (1983). Socioecology of silver-backed and golden jackals *Canis mesomelas* and *Canis aureus.* Pp. 423-453 in: Eisenberg, J.F. & Kleiman, D.G. eds. (1983). *Recent Advances in the Study of Mammalian Behavior.* American Society of Mammalogists, Lawrence, Illinois.

Moehlman, P.D. (1986). Ecology of cooperation in canids. Pp. 64-86 in: Rubenstein, D.I. & Wrangham, R.W. eds. (1986). *Ecological Aspects of Social Evolution: Birds and Mammals.* Princeton University Press, Princeton, New Jersey.

Moehlman, P.D. (1987). Social organization in jackals. *Amer. Sci.* **75**: 366-375.

Moehlman, P.D. (1989). Intraspecific variation in canid social systems. Pp. 164-182 in: Gittleman, J.L. ed. (1989). *Carnivore Behavior, Ecology and Evolution.* Cornell University Press, Ithaca, New York.

Moehlman, P.D. & Hofer, H. (1997). Cooperative breeding, reproductive suppression and body mass in canids. Pp. 76-128 in: Solomon, N.G. & French, J.A. eds. (1997). *Cooperative Breeding in Mammals.* Cambridge University Press, Cambridge.

Moehrenschlager, A. (2000). *Effects of Ecological and Human Factors on the Behaviour and Population Dynamics of Reintroduced Canadian Swift Foxes (*Vulpes velox*).* PhD dissertation, Wildlife Conservation Research Unit, University of Oxford, Oxford.

Moehrenschlager, A. & Macdonald, D.W. (2003). Movement and survival parameters of translocated and resident swift foxes. *Anim. Conserv.* **6**: 199-206.

Moehrenschlager, A. & Moehrenschlager, C.A.J. (2001). *Census of Swift Fox* Vulpes velox *in Canada and Northern Montana: 2000 - 2001.* Report to Alberta Environmental Protection, Edmonton, Alberta.

Moehrenschlager, A. & Sovada, M. (2004). Swift fox *Vulpes velox.* Pp. 109-116 in: Sillero-Zubiri, C., Hoffmann, M. & Macdonald, D.W. eds. (2004). *Canids: Foxes, Wolves, Jackals and Dogs. Status Survey and Conservation Action Plan.* IUCN/SSC Canid Specialist Group, Gland & Cambridge.

Moffat, D.B. (1975). *The Mammalian Kidney.* Cambridge University Press, New York.

Mohan, R.S.L. (1994). Trade in civetone from the Indian small civet (*Viverricula indica*) from Malabar, India. *Small Carniv. Conserv.* **10**: 13.

Molina, G.I. (1782). *Saggio sulla Storia Naturale del Chili, del Signor Abate Giovani Ignazio Molina.* Stamperia di S. Tommaso d'Aquino, Bologna.

Molteno, A.J., Sliwa, A. & Richardson, P.R.K. (1998). The role of scent marking in a free-ranging, female black-footed cat (*Felis nigripes*). *J. Zool., London* **245**: 35-41.

Monadjem, A. (1998). *Mammals of Swaziland.* The Conservation Trust of Swaziland & Big Game Parks, Swaziland.

Mondolfi, E. (1970). Las nutrias o perros de agua. *Defensa Naturaleza* **1**: 24-26, 47.

Mondolfi, E. (1983). The feet and baculum of the spectacled bear, with comments on Ursid phylogeny. *J. Mammal.* **64**: 307-310.

Mondolfi, E. (1986). Notes on the biology and status of the small wild cats in Venezuela. Pp. 125-146 in: Miller, S.D. & Everett, D.D. eds. (1986). *Cats of the World: Biology, Conservation and Management.* National Wildlife Federation, Washington, D.C.

Mondolfi, E. (1989). Notes on the distribution, habitat, food habits, status and conservation of the spectacled bear (*Tremarctos ornatus* Cuvier) in Venezuela. *Mammalia* **53**: 525-544.

Mondolfi, E. & Hoogesteijn, R. (1986). Notes on the biology and status of the jaguar in Venezuela. Pp. 85-123 in: Miller, S.D. & Everett, D.D. eds. (1986). *Cats of the World: Biology, Conservation and Management.* National Wildlife Federation, Washington, D.C.

Mones, A. & Olazarri, J. (1990). Confirmación de la existencia de *Chrysocyon brachyurus* (Illiger) en el Uruguay (Mammalia: Carnivora: Canidae). *Com. Zool. Mus. Hist. Nat. Montevideo* **12**: 1-5.

Montgomery, G.G. & Lubin, D. (1978). Social structure and food habits of crab-eating fox *Cerdocyon thous* in Venezuelan llanos. *Acta Científica Venez.* **29**: 382-383.

Moore, C.M. & Collins, P.W. (1995). *Urocyon littoralis* Baird, 1858. *Mammal. Species* **489**: 1-7.

Moors, P.J. (1977). Studies of the metabolism, food consumption and assimilation efficiency of a small carnivore, the weasel (*Mustela nivalis* L.). *Oecologia* **27**: 185-202.

Moors, P.J. (1980). Sexual dimorphism in the body size of mustelids (Carnivora): the roles of food habits and breeding systems. *Oikos* **34**: 147-158.

Morales, J., Pickford, M. & Soria, D. (2005). Carnivores from the late Miocene and basal Pliocene of the Tugen Hills, Kenya. *Rev. Soc. Geol. España* **18**: 39-61.

Moran, G. (1984). Vigilance behaviour and alarm calls in a captive group of meerkats *Suricata suricatta. Zeitschr. Tierpsychol.* **65**: 228-240.

Moran, G. & Sorensen, L. (1986). Scent marking behavior in a captive group of meerkats (*Suricata suricatta*). *J. Mammal.* **67**: 120-132.

Moran, G., Timney, B., Sorensen, L. & Desrochers, B. (1983). Binocular depth perception in the meerkat (*Suricata suricatta*). *Vision Res.* **23**: 965.

Moreno, R.S., Kays, R.W. & Samudio, R. (2006). Competitive release in diets of ocelot (*Leopardus pardalis*) and puma (*Puma concolor*) after jaguar (*Panthera onca*) decline. *J. Mammal.* **87**: 808-816.

Moreno, S. & Villafuerte, R. (1995). Traditional management of scrubland for the conservation of rabbits *Oryctolagus cuniculus* and their predators in Doñana National Park, Spain. *Biol. Conserv.* **73**: 81-85.

Morley, C. (2004). Has the invasive mongoose *Herpestes javanicus* yet reached the island of Taveuni, Fiji? *Oryx* **38**: 457-460.

Morrell, S. (1972). Life history of the San Joaquin kit fox. *California Fish and Game.* **58**: 162-174.

Morsbach, D. (1987). Cheetah in Namibia. *Cat News* **6**: 25-26.

Mortimer, M.A.E. (1963). Notes on the biology and behaviour of the spotted-necked otter (*Lutra maculicollis*). *Puku* **1**: 192-206.

Moser, A.A. (2008). *Group Territoriality of the African Lion: Behavioral Adaptation in a Heterogeneous Landscape.* PhD dissertation, University of Minnesota, Minneapolis.

Moss, A.M., Clutton-Brock, T.H. & Monfort, S.L. (2001). Longitudinal gonadal steroid excretion in free-living male and female meerkats (*Suricata suricatta*). *Gen. Comp. Endocrin.* **122**: 158-171.

Mossman, H.W. & Duke, K.L. (1973). *Comparative Morphology of the Mammalian Ovary.* University of Wisconsin Press, Madison, Wisconsin.

Motta-Júnior, J.C. (1997). Ecologia alimentar do lobo-guará, *Chrysocyon brachyurus* (Mammalia: Canidae). Pp. 197-209 in: Ades, C. ed. (1997). *Anais de XV Encontro Anual de Etologia, Brazil.*

Motta-Júnior, J.C., Lombardi, J.A. & Talamoni, S.A. (1994). Notes on crab-eating fox *Dusicyon thous* seed dispersal and food habits in southeastern Brazil. *Mammalia* **58**: 156-159.

Motta-Júnior, J.C., Talamoni, S.A., Lombardi, J.A. & Simokomaki, K. (1996). Diet of the maned wolf *Chrysocyon brachyurus* in central Brazil. *J. Zool., London* **240**: 277-284.

Moulton, J.C. (1921). Occurrence of the Malayan badger or teledu in Borneo. *J. Straits Branch Roy. Asiat. Soc.* **83**: 142-146.

Moutou, F. (2004). The possible role of oriental civets in the recent SARS epidemic. *Small Carniv. Conserv.* **31**: 10-12.

Movchan, V.N. & Opahova, V.R. (1981). [Acoustic signals of cats (Felidae) living in the zoo]. *Zool. Zhurnal* **60**: 601-608. In Russian with English summary.

Mowat, G. (2006). Winter habitat associations of American martens *Martes americana* in interior wet-belt forests. *Wildl. Biol.* **12**: 51-61.

Mowat, G. & Heard, D.C. (2006). Major components of grizzly bear diet across North America. *Can. J. Zool.* **84**: 473-489.

Mowat, G. & Poole, K.G. (2005). Habitat associations of short-tailed weasels in winter. *Northwest Science* **79**: 28-36.

Mowat, G., Slough, B.G. & Boutin, S. (1996). Lynx recruitment during a snowshoe hare population peak and decline in southwest Yukon. *J. Wildl. Management* **60**: 441-452.

Muckenhirn, N.A. & Eisenberg, J.F. (1973). Home ranges and predation of the Ceylon leopard. Pp. 142-175 in: Eaton, R.L. ed. (1973). *The World's Cats.* Vol. 1. World Wildlife Safari, Winston, Oregon.

Mudappa, D. (1998). Use of camera-traps to survey small carnivores in the tropical rain forest of Kalakad-Mundanthurai Tiger Reserve, India. *Small Carniv. Conserv.* **18**: 9-11.

Mudappa, D. (2001). *Ecology of the Brown Palm Civet* Paradoxurus jerdoni *in the Tropical Rainforests of the Western Ghats, India.* PhD thesis, Bharathiar University, Coimbatore, India.

Mudappa, D. (2002). Observations of small carnivores in the Kalakad-Mundanthurai Tiger Reserve, Western Ghats, India. *Small Carniv. Conserv.* **27**: 4-5.

Mudappa, D. (2006). Day-bed choice by the brown palm civet (*Paradoxurus jerdoni*) in the Western Ghats, India. *Mammal. Biol.* **71**: 238-243.

Mudappa, D., Noon, B.R., Kumar, A. & Chellam, R. (2007). Responses of small carnivores to rainforest fragmentation in the southern Western Ghats, India. *Small Carniv. Conserv.* **36**: 18-26.

Mugaas, J.N., Seidensticker, J. & Mahlke, J.K.P. (1993). Metabolic adaptation to climate and distribution of the raccoon *Procyon lotor* and other Procyonidae. *Smithsonian Contrib. Zool.* **542**: 1-34.

Mukherjee, S.K. (1989). *Ecological Separation of Four Sympatric Carnivores in Keoladeo Ghana National Park, Bharatpur, Rajasthan, India.* MSc thesis, Wildlife Institute of India, Dehra Dun, India. 83 pp.

Mukherjee, S.K. ed. (1998a). *Small Cats of India.* Envis Bulletin **1(2)**. Wildlife Institute of India, Dehra Dun, India.

Mukherjee, S.K. (1998b). *Habitat Use by Sympatric Small Carnivores in Sariska Tiger Reserve, Rajasthan, India.* PhD dissertation, Wildlife Institute of India, Dehradun, India.

Mukherjee, S.K., Goyal, S.P., Johnsingh, A.J.T. & Pitman, M.R.P.L. (2004). The importance of rodents in the diet of jungle cat (*Felis chaus*), caracal (*Caracal caracal*) and golden jackal (*Canis aureus*) in Sariska Tiger Reserve, Rajasthan, India. *J. Zool., London* **262**: 405-411.

Muller, C.A. (2007). *Environmental Knowledge in the Banded Mongoose (*Mungos mungo*).* PhD thesis, University of Zurich, Zurich, Switzerland.

Muller, C.A. & Manser, M.B. (2007). 'Nasty neighbours' rather than 'dear enemies' in a social carnivore. *Proc. Royal Soc. London (Ser. B Biol. Sci.)* **274**: 959-965.

Muller, E.F. & Lojewski, U. (1986). Thermoregulation in the meerkat (*Suricata suricatta* - Schreber, 1776). *Comp. Biochem. Physiol Part A Physiol* **83**: 217-224.

Mulligan, B.E. & Nellis, D.W. (1975). Vocal repertoire of the mongoose *Herpestes auropunctatus. Behaviour* **55**: 237-267.

Munoz-Garcia, A. & Williams, J.B. (2005). Basal metabolic rate in carnivores is associated with diet after controlling for phylogeny. *Physiol.Biochem. Zool.* **78**: 1039-1056.

Munro, R.H.M., Nielsen, S.E., Price, M.H., Stenhouse, G.B. & Boyce, M.S. (2006). Seasonal and diel patterns of grizzly bear diet and activity in west-central Alberta. *J. Mammal.* **87**: 1112-1121.

Munson, L., Appel, M.J.G., Carpenter, M.A. & Roelke-Parker, M. (1995). Canine distemper in wild felids. Pp. 135-136 in: *Proceedings of the Joint Conference AAZV / WDA / AAWV 1995.*

Murakami, T. (2003). Food habits of the Japanese sable *Martes zibellina brachyura* in eastern Hokkaido, Japan. *Mammal Study* **28**: 129-134.

Murdoch, J.D. (2003). *Scent Marking Behavior of San Joaquin Kit Foxes.* MSc thesis, University of Denver, Colorado.

Murdoch, J.D., Munkhzul, T., Buyandelger, S., Reading, R.P. & Sillero-Zubiri, C. (2009). Seasonal food habits of corsac and red foxes in Mongolia and the potential for competition. *Mammal. Biol.* doi:10.1016/j.mambio.2008.12.003

Murdoch, J.D., Munkhzul, T., Buyandelger, S., Reading, R.P. & Sillero-Zubiri, C. (In press). The Siberian marmot as a keystone species? Observations and implications of burrow use by corsac foxes in Mongolia. *Oryx.*

Murdoch, J.D., Munkhzul, T. & Reading, R.P. (2006). Pallas' cat ecology and conservation in the semi-desert steppes of Mongolia. *Cat News* **45**: 18-19.

Murie, J.O. (1992). Predation by badgers on Columbian ground squirrels. *J. Mammal.* **73**: 385-394.

Murphy, E.T. (1976). Breeding the clouded leopard at Dublin Zoo. *Int. Zoo Yb.* **16**: 122-124.

Murphy, K.M., Ross, P.I. & Hornocker, M. (1999). The ecology of anthropogenic influences on cougars. Pp. 77-101 in: Clark, T.W., Curlee, A.P., Minta, S.C. & Karieva, P.M. eds. (1999). *Carnivores in Ecosystems: the Yellowstone Experience.* Yale University Press, New Haven, Connecticut.

Murray, D.L. & Boutin, S. (1991). The influence of snow on lynx and coyote movements: does morphology affect behavior? *Oecologia* **88**: 463-469.

Murray, D.L., Boutin, S. & O'Donoghue, M. (1994). Winter habitat selection by lynx and coyotes in relation to snowshoe hare abundance. *Can. J. Zool.* **72**: 1444-1451.

Muul, I. & Lim, B.L. (1970). Ecological and morphological observations of *Felis planiceps*. *J. Mammal.* **51**: 806-808.

Nader, I.A. & Al-Safadi, M.M. (1991). The bushy-tailed mongoose, *Bdeogale crassicauda* Peters, 1850, a new record for the Arabian Peninsula (Mammalia: Carnivora: Herpestidae). *Zool. Anzeiger* **226**: 202-204.

Nagayama, Y., Ogura, G. & Kawashima, Y. (2001). Morphometry of skulls and statistical verification of mongoose (*Herpestes javanicus*) on Okinawa and Amami Ohshima Islands. *Mammal. Sci.* **41**: 159-169.

Nams, V.O. (1991). Olfactory search images in striped skunks. *Behaviour* **119**: 267-284.

Nams, V.O. (1997). Density dependent predation by skunks using olfactory search images. *Oecologia* **110**: 440-448.

Nandini, R. & Karthik, T. (2007). Field observations of yellow-throated martens *Martes flavigula* feeding on flowers in Meghalaya, north-east India. *Small Carniv. Conserv.* **37**: 26-27.

Napolitano, C., Bennett, M., Johnson, W.E., O'Brien, S.J., Marquet, P.A., Barria, I., Poulin, E. & Iriarte, A. (2008). Ecological and biogeographical inferences on two sympatric and enigmatic Andean cat species using genetic identification of faecal samples. *Mol. Ecol.* **17**: 678-690.

Nasimovich, A. & Isakov, Y. eds. (1985). [*Arctic Fox, Red Fox and Racoon Dog: Distribution of Resources, Ecology, Use and Conservation*]. Janka, Moscow. In Russian.

Naughton-Treves, L. (1998). Predicting patterns of crop damage by wildlife around Kibale National Park, Uganda. *Conserv. Biol.* **12**: 156-168.

Naveda, J.A.S. (1992). *Historia Natural y Ecología del Cuchicuchi (*Potos flavus*: Carnivora), en Barlovento, Estado Miranda, Venezuela. 1992.* Thesis, Universidad Central de Venezuela, Caracas.

Nayerul, M.D. & Vijayan, V.S. (1993). Food habits of the fishing cat *Felis viverrina* in Keoladeo National Park, Bharatpur, Rajasthan. *J. Bombay Nat. Hist. Soc.* **90**: 498-500.

Neal, E. (1970a). The banded mongoose, *Mungos mungo* Gmelin. *East Afr. Wildl. J.* **8**: 63-71.

Neal, E. (1970b). The banded mongoose: a little known carnivore. *Behaviour* **60**: 29-31.

Neal, E. (1971). *Uganda Quest.* Collins, London.

Neal, E. (1986). *The Natural History of the Badgers.* Facts on File Publications, New York.

Neal, E. & Cheeseman, C. (1996). *Badgers.* Poyser Books, London.

Neaves, W.B., Griffin, J.E. & Wilson, J.D. (1980). Sexual dimorphism of the phallus in spotted hyaena (*Crocuta crocuta*). *J. Reprod. Fertil.* **59**: 509-513.

Neiswenter, S.A. & Dowler, R.C. (2007). Habitat use of western spotted skunks and striped skunks in Texas. *J. Wildl. Management* **71**: 583-586.

Neiswenter, S.A., Pence, D.B. & Dowler, R.C. (2006). Helminths of sympatric striped, hog-nosed, and spotted skunks in west-central Texas. *J. Wildl. Diseases* **42**: 511-517.

Nel, J.A.J. (1978). Notes on the food and foraging behavior of the bat-eared fox *Otocyon megalotis*. *Bull. Carnegie Mus. Nat. Hist.* **6**: 132-137.

Nel, J.A.J. (1990). Foraging and feeding by bat-eared foxes *Otocyon megalotis* in the southwestern Kalahari. *Koedoe* **33**: 9-16.

Nel, J.A.J. (1993). The bat-eared fox: a prime candidate for rabies vector? *Onderstepoort J. Vet. Res.* **60**: 395-397.

Nel, J.A.J. (1999). Social learning in canids: an ecological perspective. Pp. 259-278 in: Box, H.O. & Gibson, K.R. eds. (1999). *Mammalian Social Learning: Comparative and Ecological Perspectives.* Cambridge University Press, Cambridge.

Nel, J.A.J. & Bester, M.H. (1983). Communication in the southern bat-eared fox *Otocyon m. megalotis* Desmarest, 1822. *Zeitschrift für Säugetierkunde* **48**: 277-290.

Nel, J.A.J. & Loutit, R. (1986). The diet of the black-backed jackals, *Canis mesomelas*, on the Namib Desert coast. *Cimbebasia (Ser. A)* **11**: 91-96.

Nel, J.A.J. & Maas, B. (2004). Bat-eared fox *Otocyon megalotis*. Pp. 183-189 in: Sillero-Zubiri, C., Hoffmann, M. & Macdonald, D.W. eds. (2004). *Canids: Foxes, Wolves, Jackals and Dogs. Status Survey and Conservation Action Plan.* IUCN/SSC Canid Specialist Group, Gland & Cambridge.

Nel, J.A.J. & Mackie, A.J. (1990). Food and foraging behaviour of bat-eared foxes in the south-eastern Orange Free State. *South Afr. J. Wildl. Res.* **20**: 162-166.

Nel, J.A.J. & Somers, M.J. (2007). Distribution and habitat choice of Cape clawless otters, *Aonyx capensis*, in South Africa. *South Afr. J. Wildl. Res.* **37**: 61-70.

Nel, J.A.J., Mills, M.G.L. & Van Aarde, R.J. (1984). Fluctuating group size in bat-eared foxes *Otocyon m. megalotis* in the south-western Kalahari. *J. Zool., London* **203**: 294-298.

Nellerman, C., Støen, O.G., Kindberg, J., Swenson, J.E., Vistnes, I., Ericsson, G., Katajisto, J., Kalterborn, B.P., Martin, J. & Ordiz, A. (2007). Terrain use by an expanding brown bear population in relation to age, recreational resorts and human settlements. *Biol. Conserv.* **138**: 157-165.

Nellis, C.H. & Keith, L.B. (1968). Hunting activities and success of lynxes in Alberta. *J. Wildl. Management* **32**: 718-722.

Nellis, C.H., Wetmore, S.P. & Keith, L.B. (1972). Lynx-prey interactions in central Alberta. *J. Wildl. Management* **36**: 320-329.

Nellis, D.W. (1989). *Herpestes auropunctatus. Mammal. Species* **342**: 1-6.

Nellis, D.W. & Everard, C.O.R. (1983). The biology of the mongoose in the Caribbean. *Stud. Fauna Curaçao Caribbean Islands* **64**: 1-162.

Nellis, D.W. & Small, V. (1983). Mongoose predation on sea turtle eggs and nests. *Biotropica* **15**: 159-160.

Nellis, D.W., Sivak, J.G., McFarland, W.N. & Howland, H.C. (1989). Characteristics of the eye of the Indian mongoose (*Herpestes auropunctatus*). *Can. J. Zool.* **67**: 2814-2820.

Nettelbeck, A.R. (1997). Sightings of binturongs *Arctictis binturong* in the Khao National Park, Thailand. *Small Carniv. Conserv.* **16**: 22-24.

Nevo, E. (1979). Adaptive convergence and divergence of subterranean mammals. *Ann. Rev. Ecol. Syst.* **10**: 269-308.

Newman, C., Buesching, C.D. & Wolff, J.O. (2005). The function of facial masks in "midguild" carnivores. *Oikos* **108**: 623-633.

Newsome, A.E. & Corbett, L.K. (1985). The identity of the dingo *Canis familiaris dingo*. 3. The incidence of dingoes, dogs and hybrids and their coat colors in remote and settled regions of Australia. *Austr. J. Zool.* **33**: 363-376.

Newsome, A.E., Corbett, L.K. & Carpenter, S.M. (1980). The identity of the dingo I. Morphological discriminants of dog and dingo skulls. *Austr. J. Zool.* **28**: 615-626.

Newsome, A.E., Corbett, L.K., Catling, P.C. & Burt, R.J. (1983). The feeding ecology of the dingo. I. Stomach contents from trapping in south-eastern Australia and non-target wildlife also caught in dingo traps. *Austr. Wildl. Res.* **10**: 477-486.

Newton, P.N. (1985). A note on golden jackals *Canis aureus* and their relationship with langurs *Presbytis entellus* in Khana Tiger Reserve. *J. Bombay Nat. Hist. Soc.* **82**: 633-635.

Ngandjui, G. (1998). Etude de la chasse en vue de sa gestion durable: cas du site de la composante sud-est du Programme GEF-Biodiversité, Cameroun. Unpublished report to GTZ/WWF. 70 pp.

Nguyen, X.D., Anh, P.T. & Tuyen, L.H. (2001). New information about the hairy-nosed otter (*Lutra sumatrana*) in Vietnam. *IUCN Otter Special. Group Bull.* **18**: 64-75.

Nicholson, W.S. (1982). *An Ecological Study of the Gray Fox in East Central Alabama.* MSc thesis, Auburn University, Auburn, Alabama.

Nicholson, W.S. & Hill, E.P. (1981). A comparison of tooth wear, lens weights and cementum annuli as indices of age in the gray fox. Pp. 355-367 in: Chapman, J.A. & Pursley, D. eds. (1981). *Proceedings of the Worldwide Furbearer Conference, Frostburg, Maryland.*

Nicholson, W.S., Hill, E.P. & Briggs, D. (1985). Denning, pup-rearing and dispersal in the gray fox in east-central Alabama. *J. Wildl. Management* **49**: 33-37.

Nicoll, M.E. (2008). Notes on *Galidictis fasciata*. Unpublished report.

Nicoll, M.E. & Langrand, O. (1989). *Madagascar: Revue de la Conservation et des Aires Protégées.* Fonds Mondial pour la Nature, Gland, Switzerland.

Nielsen, C.K. & Woolf, A. (2002). Survival of unexploited bobcats in southern Illinois. *J. Wildl. Management* **66**: 833-838.

Nielsen, C.L.R. & Nielsen, C.K. (2007). Multiple paternity and relatedness in southern Illinois raccoons (*Procyon lotor*). *J. Mammal.* **88**: 441-447.

Nielsen, S.E., Herrero, S., Boyce, M.S., Mace, R.D., Benn, B., Gibeau, M. & Jevons, S. (2004b). Modelling the spatial distribution of human-caused grizzly bear mortalities in the Central Rockies ecosystem of Canada. *Biol. Conserv.* **120**: 101-113.

Nielsen, S.E., Munro, R.H.M., Bainbridge, E.L., Stenhouse, G.B. & Boyce, M.S. (2004). Grizzly bears and forestry. II. Distribution of grizzly bear foods in clearcuts of west-central Alberta, Canada. *For. Ecol. Manage.* **199**: 67-82.

Nielsen, S.E., Stenhouse, G.B. & Boyce, M.S. (2006). A habitat-based framework for grizzly bear conservation. *Biol. Conserv.* **130**: 217-229.

Nielsen-Clayton, K. & Woolf, A. (2001). Spatial organization of bobcats (*Lynx rufus*) in southern Illinois. *Amer. Midl. Nat.* **146**: 43-52.

Niethammer, J. (1966). Zur ernährung des sumpfluchses, (*Felis chaus* Guldenstaedt, 1776) in Afghanistan. *Zeitschrift für Säugetierkunde* **31**: 393-394.

Niethammer, J. (1987). Das streifenwiesel (*Poecilictis libyca*) im Sudam und seine Gesamtverbreitung. *Bonn. Zool. Beitr.* **38**: 173-182.

Niethammer, J. & Krapp, F. (1978-2005). *Handbuch der Säugetiere Europas.* Akademische Verlagsgesellschaft, Wiesbaden, Germany.

Nieuwenhuys, R. & Donjelaar, H.J. (1997). *The Central Nervous System of Vertebrates.* Springer, New York.

Nor, B.H.M. (1990). Observation on the parental investment by small-clawed otter in captivity. *J. Wildl. & Parks* **9**: 47-52.

Norberg, U.M. (1990). *Vertebrate Flight: Mechanics, Physiology, Morphology, Ecology and Evolution.* Springer, New York.

Normua, F., Higashi, S., Ambu, L. & Mohamed, M. (2004). Notes on oil palm plantation use and seasonal spatial relationships of sun bears in Sabah, Malaysia. *Ursus* **15**: 227-231.

Norris, D.O. (1996). *Vertebrate Endocrinology.* 3rd edition. Academic Press, San Diego, California.

Norton, P.M. & Henley, S.R. (1987). Home range and movements of male leopards in the Cedarberg Wilderness area, Cape Province. *South Afr. J. Wildl. Res.* **17**: 41-48.

Norton, P.M. & Lawson, A.B. (1985). Radio tracking of leopards and caracals in the Stellenbosch area, Cape Province. *South Afr. J. Wildl. Res.* **15**: 17-24.

Novacek, M.J. (1992). Mammalian phylogeny: shaking the tree. *Nature (London)* **356**: 121-125.

Novaro, A.J. (1995). Sustainability of harvest of culpeo foxes in Patagonia. *Oryx* **29**: 18-22.

Novaro, A.J. (1997a). *Pseudalopex culpaeus. Mammal. Species* **558**: 1-8.

Novaro, A.J. (1997b). *Source-sink Dynamics Induced by Hunting: Case Study of Culpeo Foxes on Rangelands in Patagonia, Argentina.* PhD dissertation, University of Florida, Gainesville, Florida.

Novaro, A.J. & Funes, M.C. (1994). Impact of hunting on Argentinean foxes. *Canid News* **2**: 19-20.

Novaro, A.J., Funes, M.C. & Walker, R.S. (2000). Ecological extinction of native prey of a carnivore assemblage in Argentine Patagonia. *Biol. Conserv.* **92**: 25-33.

Novaro, A.J., Funes, M.C., Rambeaud, C. & Monsalvo, O. (2000). Calibración del índice de estaciones odoríferas para estimar tendencias poblacionales del zorro colorado *Pseudalopex culpaeus* en Patagonia. *Mastozool. Neotrop.* **7**: 81-88.

Nowak, R.M. (1979). North American Quaternary Canis. *Univ. Kansas Mus. Nat. Hist. Monogr.* **6**: 1-154.

Nowak, R.M. (1995). Another look at wolf taxonomy. Pp. 375-397 in: Carbyn, L.N., Fritts, S.H. & Seip, D.R. eds. (1995). *Ecology and Conservation of Wolves in a Changing World: Proceedings of the Second North American Symposium on Wolves.* Canadian Circumpolar Institute, University of Alberta, Edmonton, Alberta.

Nowak, R.M. (1999). *Walker's Mammals of the World*. 6th edition. Johns Hopkins University Press, Baltimore, Maryland.

Nowak, R.M. (2002). The original status of wolves in eastern North America. *Southeast. Nat.* **1**: 95-130.

Nowell, K. (2000). *Far from a Cure: the Tiger Trade Revisited*. TRAFFIC International, Cambridge.

Nowell, K. & Jackson, P. (1996). *Wild Cats: Status Survey and Conservation Action Plan*. IUCN, Gland, Switzerland.

Noyce, K.V. & Garshelis, D.L. (1994). Body size and blood characteristics as indicators of condition and reproductive performance in black bears. *Int. Conf. Bear Res. Management* **9(1)**: 481-496.

Noyce, K.V. & Garshelis, D.L. (1998). Spring weight changes in black bears in northcentral Minnesota: the negative foraging period revisited. *Ursus* **10**: 521-531.

Noyce, K.V., Kannowski, P.B. & Riggs, M.R. (1997). Black bears as ant-eaters: seasonal associations between bear myrmecophagy and ant ecology in north-central Minnesota. *Can. J. Zool.* **75**: 1671-1686.

Nozaki, E., Azuma, S., Sasaki, H. & Torii, H. (1994). Home range of the Malay civet (*Viverra tangalunga*) in Teluk Kaba area, Kutai National Park, East Kalimantan, Indonesia. *Kyoto Univ. Overseas Res. Rep. Stud. Asian Non-human Primates* **spec. number**: 85-94.

Nuñez, R., Miller, B. & Lindzey, F. (2000). Food habits of jaguars and pumas in Jalisco, Mexico. *J. Zool., London* **252**: 373-379.

O'Brien, S.J. (1994). The cheetah's conservation controversy. *Conserv. Biol.* **8**: 1153-1155.

O'Brien, S.J., Wildt, D.E., Goldman, D., Merril, C.R. & Bush, M. (1983). The cheetah is depauperate in genetic variation. *Science* **221**: 459-462.

O'Brien, T.G., Kinnaird, M.F. & Wibisono, H.T. (2003). Crouching tigers, hidden prey: Sumatran tiger and prey populations in a tropical forest landscape. *Anim. Conserv.* **6**: 131-139.

O'Connor, R.M. (1986). Reproduction and age distribution of female lynx in Alaska, 1961-1971 — preliminary results. Pp. 311-325 in: Miller, S.D. & Everett, D.D. eds. (1986). *Cats of the World: Biology, Conservation and Management*. National Wildlife Federation, Washington, D.C.

Odden, J., Linnell, J.D.C., Fossland, P., Herfindal, I., Kvam, T. & Andersen, R. (2002). Lynx predation on domestic sheep in Norway. *J. Wildl. Management* **66**: 98-105.

Odden, M. & Wegge, P. (2005). Spacing and activity patterns of leopards *Panthera pardus* in the Royal Bardia National Park, Nepal. *Wildl. Biol.* **11**: 145-152.

Odden, M. & Wegge, P. (In press). Kill rates and food consumption of leopards in Bardia National Park, Nepal. *Acta Theriol.*: in press.

O'Donoghue, M., Boutin, S., Krebs, C.J. & Hofer, E.J. (1997). Numerical responses of coyotes and lynx to the snowshoe hare cycle. *Oikos* **80**: 150-162.

O'Donoghue, M., Boutin, S., Krebs, C.J., Murrary, D.L. & Hofer, E.J. (1998). Behavioural responses of coyotes and lynx to the snowshoe hare cycle. *Oikos* **82**: 169-183.

O'Donoghue, M., Boutin, S., Krebs, C.J., Zuleta, G., Murray, D.L. & Hofer, E.J. (1998). Functional responses of coyotes and lynx to the snowshoe hare cycle. *Ecology* **79(4)**: 1193-1208.

O'Farrell, T.P. (1987). Kit fox. Pp. 423-431 in: Novak, M., Baker, J.A., Obbard, M.E. & Malloch, B. eds. (1987). *Wild Furbearer Management and Conservation in North America*. Ontario Trappers Association, North Bay, Ontario.

Ognev, S.I. (1962). *Mammals of Eastern Europe and Northern Asia*. Vol. 2. Israel Program for Scientific Translations, Jerusalem, Israel.

Ogura, G., Kawashima, Y., Nakamoto, M. & Oda, S.I. (2000). Postnatal growth in the small Asian mongoose, *Herpestes javanicus auropuctatus*, raised in captivity on Okinawa. *Jap. J. Zoo Wildl. Med.* **5**: 77-85.

Ogura, G., Nonaka, Y., Kawashima, Y., Sakashita, M., Nakachi, M. & Oda, S.I. (2000). Relationship between body length and sexual maturity, and annual reproductive cycle in male mongoose (*Herpestes javanicus*) on Okinawa Island. *Jap. J. Zoo Wildl. Med.* **5**: 141-148.

Ogura, G., Nonaka, Y., Kawashima, Y., Sakashita, M., Nakachi, M. & Oda, S.I. (2001). Relationship between body size and sexual maturation, and seasonal change of reproductive activities in the female feral small Asian mongoose on Okinawa Island. *Jap. J. Zoo Wildl. Med.* **6**: 7-14.

Ogura, G., Otsuka, A., Kawashima, Y., Hongo, F., Uechi, S. & Oda, S.I. (2000). Structure of the anal sac and analysis of the contents of the anal scent pockets in small Asian mongoose (*Herpestes javanicus*) on Okinawa Island. *Jap. J. Zoo Wildl. Med.* **5**: 149-155.

Ogura, G., Sakashita, M. & Kawashima, Y. (1998). External morphology and classification of mongoose on Okinawa Island. *Mammal. Sci.* **38**: 259-270.

Ogutu, J.O. & Dublin, H.T. (2002). Demography of lions in relation to prey and habitat in the Masai Mara National Reserve, Kenya. *Afr. J. Ecol.* **40**: 120-129.

Ogutu, J.O. & Dublin, H.T. (2004). Spatial dynamics of lions and their prey along an environmental gradient. *Afr. J. Ecol.* **42**: 8-22.

Ohnishi, N., Saitoh, S. & Ishibashi, Y. (2007). Low genetic diversities in isolated populations of the Asiatic black bear (*Ursus thibetanus*) in Japan, in comparison with large stable populations. *Conserv. Genetics* **8**: 1331-1337.

Oka, T., Miura, S., Masaki, T., Suzuki, W., Osumi, K. & Saitoh, S. (2004). Relationship between changes in beechnut production and Asiatic black bears in northern Japan. *J. Wildl. Management* **68**: 979-986.

Okada, M., Kuroda, T. & Katsuno, T. (2007). Distribution and habitat of the Japanese weasel (*Mustela itatsi*) at several watersheds in Kanagawa Prefecture. *Nat. Hist. Rep. Kanagawa* **28**: 55-58.

Okarma, H., Jedrzejewski, W., Schmidt, K., Kowalczyk, R. & Jedrzejewska, B. (1997). Predation of Eurasian lynx on roe deer and red deer in Bialowieza Primeval Forest, Poland. *Acta Theriol.* **42**: 203-224.

Olbricht, G. & Sliwa, A. (1995). Analyse der Jugendentwicklung von Schwarzfußkatzen (*Felis nigripes*) im Zoologischen Garten Wuppertal im Vergleich zur Literatur. *Zool. Garten* **65(4)**: 224-236.

Olbricht, G. & Sliwa, A. (1997). In situ and ex situ observations and management of black-footed cats (*Felis nigripes*). *Int. Zoo Yb.* **35**: 81-89.

Olfermann, E. (1996). *Population Ecology of the Rüppell's Fox and the Red Fox in a Semi-desert Environment of Saudi Arabia*. PhD dissertation, University of Bielefeld, Bielefeld, Germany.

Oli, M.K. (1994). Snow leopards and blue sheep in Nepal: densities and predator: prey ratio. *J. Mammal.* **75**: 998-1004.

Oli, M.K., Taylor, I.R. & Rogers, M.E. (1993). Diet of the snow leopard (*Panthera uncia*) in the Annapurna Conservation Area, Nepal. *J. Zool.* **231**: 365-370.

Oliveira, T.G. (1994). *Neotropical Cats: Ecology and Conservation*. EDUFMA, São Luis, Brazil.

Oliveira, T.G. (1998). *Leopardus wiedii*. Mammal. Species **579**: 1-6.

Oliveira, T.G., Tortato, M.A., Silveira, L., Kasper, C.B., Mazim, F.D., Lucherini, M., Jácomo, A.T., Soares, J.B.G., Marques, R.V. & Sunquist, M. (In Press). Ocelot ecology and its effect on the small-felid guild in the lowland Neotropical. In: Macdonald, D. & Loveridge, A. eds. (In press). *Felid Biology and Conservation*. Oxford University Press, Oxford.

Olmos, F. (1993). Notes on the food habits of Brazilian "Caatinga" carnivores. *Mammalia* **57**: 126-130.

Olson, T.L., Dieni, J.S. & Lindzey, F.G. (1997). *Swift Fox Survey Evaluation, Productivity and Survivorship in Southeast Wyoming*. Wyoming Cooperative Fish and Wildlife Research Unit.

Onorato, D.P., Hellgren, E.C., Van Den Bussche, R.A., Doan-Crider, D.L. & Skiles, J.R. (2007). Genetic structure of American black bears in the desert southwest of North America: conservation implications for recolonization. *Conserv. Genetics* **8**: 565-576.

Oosthuizen, W.H., Meyer, M.A., David, J.H.M., Summers, N.M., Kotze, P.G.H., Swanson, S.W. & Shaughnessy, P.D. (1997). Variation in jackal numbers at the Van Reenen Bay seal colony with comments on likely importance of jackals as predators. *South Afr. J. Wildl. Res.* **27**: 26-29.

Orford, H.J.L., Perrin, M.R. & Berry, H.H. (1988). Contraception, reproduction and demography of free-ranging Etosha lions. *J. Zool., London* **216**: 717-733.

O'Riain, M.J., Bennett, N.C., Brotherton, P.N.M., McIlrath, G. & Clutton-Brock, T.H. (2000). Reproductive suppression and inbreeding avoidance in wild populations of cooperatively breeding meerkats (*Suricata suricatta*). *Behav. Ecol. Sociobiol.* **48**: 471-477.

Ortolani, A. (1990). *Howling Vocalizations of Wild and Domestic Dogs: a Comparative Behavioural and Anatomical Study*. BA thesis, Hampshire College, Amherst, Massachusetts.

Osborn, D.J. & Helmy, I. (1980). The contemporary land mammals of Egypt (including Sinaï). *Fieldiana Zool. (New Ser.)* **5, XIX**: 1-579.

Osgood, W.H. (1943). The mammals of Chile. *Field Mus. Nat. Hist. (Zool. Ser.)* **30**: 1-268.

Ososky, J.J. (1998). *Diet of Leopards and Golden Cats in Ndoki Park, Republic of Congo*. MSc thesis, Northern Illinois University, DeKalb, Illinois.

Ostfeld, R.S., Ebensperger, L., Klosterman, L.L., Castilla, J.C. (1989). Foraging, activity budget and social behavior of the South American marine otter *Lutra felina* (Molina 1782). *Natl. Geogr. Res.* **5**: 422-438.

Otali, E. & Gilchrist, J.S. (2004). Effects of refuse feeding on body condition, reproduction and survival of banded mongooses. *J. Mammal.* **85**: 491-497.

Otani, T. (2002). Seed dispersal by Japanese marten *Martes melampus* in the subalpine shrubland of northern Japan. *Ecol. Res.* **17**: 29-38.

Ovsyanikov, N.G. (1993). [*Behaviour and Social Organization of the Arctic Fox*]. Isd-vo TSNIL Glavochoti RF, Moscow. In Russian.

Owen, J.G., Baker, R.J. & Williams, S.L. (1996). Karyotypic variation in spotted skunks (Carnivora: Mustelidae: *Spilogale*) from Texas, Mexico and El Salvador. *Texas J. Sci.* **48**: 119-122.

Owens, D.D. & Owens, M.J. (1979a). Communal denning and clan associations in brown hyenas (*Hyaena brunnea*, Thunberg) of the central Kalahari Desert. *Afr. J. Ecol.* **17**: 35-44.

Owens, D.D. & Owens, M.J. (1979b). Notes on social organization and behavior in brown hyaenas (*Hyaena brunnea*). *J. Mammal.* **60**: 405-408.

Owens, D.D. & Owens, M.J. (1984). Helping behaviour in brown hyenas. *Nature (London)* **308**: 843-845.

Owens, D.D. & Owens, M.J. (1996). Social dominance and reproductive patterns in brown hyaenas, *Hyaena brunnea*, of the central Kalahari Desert. *Animal Behav.* **51**: 535-551.

Owens, M.J. & Owens, D.D. (1978). Feeding ecology and its influence on social organization in brown hyenas (*Hyaena brunnea*, Thunberg) of the central Kalahari Desert. *East Afr. Wildl. J.* **16**: 113-135.

Owens, M.J. & Owens, D.D. (1984). Kalahari lions break the rules. *Int. Wildl.* **14**: 4-13.

Pabst, D.A. (2000). To bend a dolphin: convergence of force transmission designs in cetaceans and scombrid fishes. *Amer. Zool.* **40**: 146-155.

Pacheco, V., de Macedo, H., Vivar, E., Ascorra, C.F., Arana-Cardó, R. & Solari, S. (1995). Lista anotada de los mamíferos peruanos. *Occas. Pap. Conserv. Biol.* **2**: 1-35.

Packer, C. & Kock, R. (1995). Serengeti lions recovering from canine distemper epidemic. *Cat News* **23**: 9.

Packer, C. & Pusey, A.E. (1983). Adaptations of female lions to infanticide by incoming males. *Amer. Naturalist* **121**: 716-728.

Packer, C. & Pusey, A.E. (1987). Intrasexual cooperation and the sex ratio in African lions. *Amer. Naturalist* **130**: 636-642.

Packer, C. & Pusey, A.E. (1997). Divided we fall: cooperation among lions. *Scientific American* **May**: 32-39.

Packer, C., Herbst, L., Pusey, A.E., Bygott, J.D., Hanb, J.P., Cairns, S.J. & Borgerhoff-Mulder, M. (1988). Reproductive success in lions. Pp. 363-383 in: Clutton-Brock, T.H. ed. (1988). *Reproductive Success: Studies of Individual Variation in Contrasting Breeding Systems*. University of Chicago Press, Chicago, Illinois.

Packer, C., Ikanda, D., Kissui, B. & Kushnir, H. (2006). The ecology of man-eating lions in Tanzania. *Nature Faune* **21**: 10-15.

Packer, C., Scheel, D. & Pusey, A.E. (1990). Why lions form groups: food is not enough. *Amer. Naturalist* **136**: 1-19.

Padial, J.M., Avila, E. & Gil-Sanchez, J.M. (2002). Feeding habits and overlap among red fox (*Vulpes vulpes*) and stone marten (*Martes foina*) in two Mediterranean mountain habitats. *Mammal. Biol.* **67**: 137-146.

Paetkau, D., Amstrup, S.C., Born, E.W., Calvert, W., Derocher, A.E., Garner, G.W., Messier, F., Stirling, I., Taylor, M.K., Wiig, Ø. & Strobeck, C. (1999). Genetic structure of the world's polar bear populations. *Mol. Ecol.* **8**: 1571-1584.

Page, R.J.C., Ross, J. & Langton, S.D. (1994). Seasonality of reproduction in the European badger *Meles meles* in south-west England. *J. Zool., London* **233**: 69-91.

Pagés, M., Calvignac, S., Klein, C., Paris, M., Hughes, S. & Hänni, C. (2008). Combined analysis of fourteen nuclear genes refines the Ursidae phylogeny. *Mol. Phylogen. Evol.* **47**: 73-83.

Paintiff, J.A. & Anderson, D.E. (1980). Breeding the margay at the New Orleans Zoo. *Int. Zoo Yb.* **20**: 223-224.

Paisley, S. (2001). *Andean Bears and People in Apolobamba, Bolivia: Culture, Conflict and Conservation.* PhD thesis, University of Kent, Durrell Institute of Conservation and Ecology, Canterbury, UK.

Paisley, S. & Garshelis, D.L. (2006). Activity patterns and time budgets of Andean bears (*Tremarctos ornatus*) in the Apolobamba Range of Bolivia. *J. Zool., London* **268**: 25-34.

Palazon, S., Ruiz-Olmo, J. & Gosalbez, J. (2004). Diet of European mink (*Mustela lutreola*) in Northern Spain. *Mammalia* **68**: 159-165.

Palmer, R. & Fairall, N. (1988). Caracal and African wild cat diet in the Karoo National Park and the implications thereof for hyrax. *South Afr. J. Wildl. Res.* **18**: 30-34.

Palomares, F. (1991). Vocalizations emitted by the Egyptian mongoose, *Herpestes ichneumon*, living in the wild. *Mammalia* **55**: 148-150.

Palomares, F. (1993a). Faecal marking behavior by free-ranging common genets *Genetta genetta* and Egyptian mongooses *Herpestes ichneumon* in southwestern Spain. *Zeitschrift für Säugetierkunde* **58**: 225-231.

Palomares, F. (1993b). Opportunistic feeding of the Egyptian mongoose, *Herpestes ichneumon*, (L) in southwestern Spain. *Rev. Écol. (Terre Vie)* **48**: 295-304.

Palomares, F. (1994). Site fidelity and effects of body-mass on home-range size of Egyptian mongooses. *Can. J. Zool.* **72**: 465-469.

Palomares, F. & Delibes, M. (1988). Time and space use by two common genets (*Genetta genetta*) in Doñana National Park, Spain. *J. Mammal.* **69**: 635-637.

Palomares, F. & Delibes, M. (1992). Some physical and population characteristics of Egyptian mongooses (*Herpestes ichneumon* L, 1758) in Southwestern Spain. *Zeitschrift fur Säugetierkunde* **57**: 94-99.

Palomares, F. & Delibes, M. (1993). Social organization in the Egyptian mongoose - group size, spatial behavior and inter-individual contacts in adults. *Animal Behaviour* **45**: 917-925.

Palomares, F. & Delibes, M. (1994). Spatio-temporal ecology and behaviour of European genets in southwestern Spain. *J. Mammal.* **75**: 714-724.

Palomares, F. & Delibes, M. (2000). Mongooses, civets and genets. Carnivores in southern latitudes. Pp. 119-130 in: Halle, S. & Stenseth, N.C. eds. (2000). *Activity Patterns in Small Mammals.* Springer-Verlag, Berlin.

Palomares, F., Delibes, M., Revilla, E., Calzada, J. & Fedriani, J.M. (2001). Spatial ecology of Iberian lynx and abundance of European rabbits in southwestern Spain. *Wildl. Monogr.* **148**: 1-36.

Palomares, F., Rodríguez, A., Laffitte, R. & Delibes, M. (1991). The status and distribution of the Iberian lynx *Felis pardina* (Temminck) in Coto Doñana area, SW Spain. *Biol. Conserv.* **57**: 159-169.

Palone, R.S. (2005). *Hunters & Trappers Contribute to the War Effort.* In Game News. Pennsylvania Game Commission, Harrisburg, Pennsylvania.

Palphramand, K.L., Newton-Cross, G. & White, P.C.L. (2007). Spatial organization and behaviour of badgers (*Meles meles*) in a moderate-density population. *Behav. Ecol. Sociobiol.* **61**: 401-413.

Pan, W., Lu, Z., Zhu, X., Wang, D., Wang, H., Fu, D. & Zhou, X. (2001). [*A Chance for Lasting Survival*]. Peking University Press, Beijing. In Chinese.

Panaman, R. (1981). Behaviour and ecology of free-ranging farm cats (*Felis catus* L.). *Zeitschr. Tierpsychol.* **56**: 59-73.

Pandolfi, M., DeMarinis, A.M. & Petrov, I. (1996). Fruit as a winter feeding resource in the diet of stone marten (*Martes foina*) in east-central Italy. *Zeitschrift Fur Saugetierkunde* **61**: 215-220.

Panwar, H.S. (1987). Project Tiger: the reserves, the tigers and their future. Pp. 110-117 in: Tilson, R.L. & Seal, U.S. eds. (1987). *Tigers of the World: the Biology, Biopolitics, Management and Conservation of an Endangered Species.* Noyes Publications, Park Ridge, New Jersey.

Paradiso, J.L. & Nowak, R.M. (1971). A report on the taxonomic status and distribution of the red wolf. *US Fish Wildl. Serv., Spec. Sci. Rep.* **145**: 1-36.

Paradiso, J.L. & Nowak, R.M. (1972). *Canis rufus. Mammal. Species* **22**: 1-4.

Paragi, T.F., Arthur, S.M. & Krohn, W.B. (1994). Seasonal and circadian activity patterns of female fishers, *Martes pennanti*, with kits. *Can. Field-Nat.* **108**: 52-57.

Pardini, R. & Trajano, E. (1999). Use of shelters by the neotropical river otter (*Lontra longicaudis*) in an Atlantic Forest stream, southeastern Brazil. *J. Mammal.* **80**: 600-610.

Parera, A.F. (1992). Present knowledge of the giant otter in Argentina. *IUCN Otter Special. Group Bull.* **7**: 19-22.

Parera, A.F. (1993). The neotropical river otter *Lutra longicaudis* in Iberá lagoon, Argentina. *IUCN Otter Special. Group Bull.* **8**: 13-16.

Parera, A.F. (1996). Estimación de la dieta de verano del zorro de monte, *Cerdocyon thous* (Mammalia: Carnivora) en la laguna Iberá, provincia de Corrientes, Argentina. *Rev. Mus. Arg. Cienc. Nat. Bernardino Rivadavia* **136**: 1-5.

Paria, B.C., Das, S.K., Mead, R.A. & Dey, S.K. (1994). Expression of epidermal growth factor receptor in the preimplantation uterus and blastocyst of the western spotted skunk. *Biol. Reprod.* **51**: 205-213.

Parker, C. (1979). Birth, care and development of Chinese hog badgers *Arctonyx collaris albogularis* at Metro Toronto Zoo. *Int. Zoo Yb.* **19**: 182-185.

Parker, G.R. (1981). Winter habitat use and hunting activities of lynx (*Lynx canadensis*) on Cape Breton Island, Nova Scotia. Pp. 221-248 in: Chapman, J.A. & Pursley, D. (1981). *Worldwide Furbearer Conference Proceedings.* R.R. Donnelley & Sons, Falls Church, Virginia.

Parker, G.R., Maxwell, J.W., Morton, L.D. & Smith, G.E.J. (1983). The ecology of the lynx (*Lynx canadensis*) on Cape Breton Island. *Can. J. Zool.* **61**: 770-786.

Parker, R.L. (1975). Rabies in skunks. Pp. 41-51 in: Baer, G.M. ed. (1975). *The Natural History of Rabies.* Academic Press, New York.

Parker, T.A. & Bailey, B. eds. (1990). *A Biological Assessment of the Alto Madidi Region and Adjacent Areas of Northwest Bolivia, May 18-June 15, 1990.* Conservation International, Washington, D.C.

Parker, W.T. (1986). *A Technical Proposal to Re-establish the Red Wolf on the Alligator River National Wildlife Refuge, NC.* US Fish and Wildlife Service, Atlanta.

Parks, E.K., Derocher, A.E. & Lunn, N.J. (2006). Seasonal and annual movement patterns of polar bears on the sea ice of Hudson Bay. *Can. J. Zool.* **84**: 1281-1294.

Pasitschniak-Arts, M. (1993). *Ursus arctos. Mammal. Species* **439**: 1-10.

Pasitschniak-Arts, M. & Larivière, S. (1995). *Gulo gulo. Mammal. Species* **499**: 1-10.

Passamani, M. & Camargo, S.L. (1995). Diet of the river otter *Lutra longicaudis* in Furnas reservoir, south-eastern Brazil. *IUCN Otter Specialist Group Bulletin* **12**: 32-33.

Patel, K. (2006). Observations of rusty-spotted cat in eastern Gujarat, India. *Cat News* **45**: 27-28.

Pathak, B.J. (1990). Rusty-spotted cat *Felis rubiginosa* Geoffroy: a new record for Gir Wildlife Sanctuary and National Park. *J. Bombay Nat. Hist. Soc.* **87**: 8.

Patou, M.L., Debruyne, R., Jennings, A.P., Zubaid, A., Rovie-Ryan, J.J. & Veron, G. (2008). Phylogenetic relationships of the Asian palm civets (Hemigalinae & Paradoxurinae, Viverridae, Carnivora). *Mol. Phylogen. Evol.* **47**: 883-892.

Patterson, B.D., Kasiki, S.M., Selempo, E. & Kays, R.W. (2004). Livestock predation by lions (*Panthera leo*) and other carnivores on ranches neighboring Tsavo National Park, Kenya. *Biol. Conserv.* **119**: 507-516.

Patterson, B.D., Kays, R.W., Kasiki, S.M. & Sebestyen, V.M. (2006). Developmental effects of climate on the lion's mane (*Panthera leo*). *J. Mammal.* **87**: 193-200.

Patterson, G. (1988). *Cry for the Lions.* Frandson Publishers, Sandton, South Africa.

Patton, R.F. (1974). *Ecological and Behavioral Relationships of the Skunks of Trans Pecos Texas.* PhD dissertation, Texas A&M University, College Station, Texas.

Paulraj, S., Sundarajan, N., Manimozhi, A. & Walker, S. (1992). Reproduction of the Indian wild dog *Cuon alpinus* in captivity. *Zoo Biology* **11**: 235-241.

Pauw, A. (2000). Parental care in a polygenous group of bat-eared foxes *Otocyon megalotis* (Carnivora: Canidae). *Afr. Zool.* **35**: 139-145.

Payne, J., Francis, C.M. & Phillips, K. (1985). *A Field Guide to the Mammals of Borneo.* The Sabah Society, Kuala Lumpur.

Paz, E.A., Rodríguez-Mazzini, R. & Clara, M. (1995). Dispersión de la palma butiá (*Butia capitata*) por el zorro de monte (*Cerdocyon thous*) en montes nativos de la Reserva de la Biosfera Bañados del Este, Uruguay. *Comun. Bot. Mus. Hist. Nat. Montevideo* **104**: 1-4.

Peacock, E., Peacock, M.M. & Titus, K. (2007). Black bears in Southeast Alaska: the fate of two ancient lineages in the face of contemporary movement. *J. Zool., London* **271**: 445-454.

Pearson, H.C. & Davis, R.W. (2005). Behavior of territorial male sea otters (*Enhydra lutris*) in Prince William Sound, Alaska. *Aquatic Mammals* **31**: 226-233.

Pearson, H.C., Packard, J.M. & Davis, R.W. (2006). Territory quality of male sea otters in Prince William Sound, Alaska: relation to body and territory maintenance behaviors. *Can. J. Zool.* **84**: 939-946.

Pearson, O.P. (1951). Mammals in the highlands of southern Peru. *Bull. Mus. Comp. Zool.* **106**: 117-174.

Pearson, O.P. & Baldwin, P.H. (1953). Reproduction and age structure in a mongoose population in Hawaii. *J. Mammal.* **34**: 436-447.

Pechacek, P., Lindzey, F.G. & Anderson, S.H. (2000). Home range size and spatial organization of swift fox *Vulpes velox* Say, 1823 in southeastern Wyoming. *Zeitschrift für Saügetierkunde* **65**: 209-215.

Peigné, S., de Bonis, L., Likius, A., Taisso, H., Vignaud, P. & Brunet, M. (2005). The earliest modern mongoose (Carnivora, Herpestidae) from Africa (late Miocene of Chad). *Naturwissenschaften* **92**: 287-292.

Pelton, M.R. (2003). Black bear *Ursus americanus.* Pp. 547-555 in: Feldhamer, G.A., Thompson, B.C. & Chapman, J.A. eds. (2003). *Wild Mammals of North America: Biology, Management and Conservation.* 2nd edition. Johns Hopkins University Press, Baltimore, Maryland.

Pelton, M.R., Coley, A.B., Eason, T.H., Doan, D.L., Pederson, J.A., van Manen, F.T. & Weaver, K.M. (1999). American black bear conservation action plan. Pp. 144-156 in: Servheen, C., Herrero, S. & Peyton, B. eds. (1999). *Bears. Status Survey and Conservation Action Plan.* IUCN/SSC Bear and Polar Bear Specialist Groups. IUCN, Gland & Cambridge.

Pen, M. (1962). Animals of western Szechuan. *Nature (London)* **196**: 14-16.

Pendje, G. (1994). La frugivorie de *Civettictis civetta* (Schreiber) et son rôle dans la dispersion des graines au Mayombe. *Rev. Écol. (Terre Vie)* **49**: 107-116.

Peralvo, M.F., Cuesta, F. & Van Manen, F.T. (2005). Delineating priority habitat areas for the conservation of Andean bears in northern Ecuador. *Ursus* **16**: 222-233.

Pereira, J.A., Fracassi, N.G. & Uhart, M.M. (2006). Numerical and spatial responses of Geoffroy's cat (*Oncifelis geoffroyi*) to prey decline in Argentina. *J. Mammal.* **87**: 1132-1139.

Perelman, P.L., Graphodatsky, A.S., Dragoo, J.W., Serdyukova, N.A., Stone, G., Cavagna, P., Menotti, A., Nie, W., O'Brien, P.C.M., Wang, J., Burkett, S., Yuki, K., Roelke, M.E., O'Brien, S.J., Yang, F. & Stanyon, R. (2008). Chromosome painting shows that skunks (Mephitidae, Carnivora) have highly rearranged karyotypes. *Chromosome Res.* **16**: 1215-1231.

Peres, C.A. (1991). Observations on hunting by small-eared zorro (*Atelocynus microtis*) and bush dogs (*Speothos venaticus*) in central-western Amazonia. *Mammalia* **55**: 635-639.

Perez, M., Li, B., Tillier, A., Cruaud, A. & Veron, G. (2006). Systematic relationships of the bushy-tailed and black-footed mongooses (genus *Bdeogale*, Herpestidae, Carnivora) based on molecular, chromosomal and morphological evidence. *J. Zool. Syst. Evol. Res.* **44**: 251-259.

Perkin, A. (2004). A new range record for the African palm civet *Nandinia binotata* (Carnivora, Viverridae) from Unguja Island, Zanzibar. *Afr. J. Ecol.* **42**: 232-234.

Perkin, A. (2005). Distributional notes on the African palm civet *Nandinia binotata* in Tanzania. *Small Carniv. Conserv.* **32**: 17-20.

Perovic, P.G., Walker, R.S. & Novaro, A.J. (1999). Estudio preliminar del gato andino (*Oreailurus jacobita*) en el noreste de Argentina. Unpublished report.

Perrin, M.R. & Carugati, C. (2000). Habitat use by the Cape clawless otter and the spotted-necked otter in the KwaZulu-Natal Drakensberg, South Africa. *South Afr. J. Wildl. Res.* **30**: 103-113.

Perrin, M.R. & D'Inzillo, I. (2000). Activity patterns of the spotted-necked otters in the Natal Drakensberg, South Africa. *South Afr. J. Wildl. Res.* **30**: 1-7.
Perry, R. (1965). *The World of the Tiger.* Atheneum, New York.
Perry, R. (1970). A conservation plan for the jaguar (*Panthera onca*) in the Pantanal region of Brazil. *Biol. Conserv.* **61**: 149-157.
Peters, G. (1978). *Vergleichende Untersuchung zur Lautgebung einiger Feliden (Mammalia, Felidae).* Spixiana **1** (Suppl.).
Peters, G. (1980). The vocal repertoire of the snow leopard (*Uncia uncia*, Schreber 1775). *Int. Ped. Book Snow Leopards* **2**: 137-158.
Peters, G. (1981). Das Schnurren der Katzen (Felidae). *Säugetierkunde Mitt.* **29**: 30.
Peters, G. (1983). Beobachtungen zum Lautgebungsverhalten des Karakal, *Caracal caracal* (Schreber, 1776) (Mammalia, Carnivora, Felidae). *Bonn. Zool. Beitr.* **34**: 107-127.
Peters, G. (1984a). A special type of vocalization in the Felidae. *Acta Zool. Fennica* **171**: 89-92.
Peters, G. (1984b). On the structure of friendly close range vocalizations in terrestrial carnivores (Mammalia: Carnivora: Fissipedia). *Zeitschrift für Säugetierkunde* **49**: 157-182.
Peters, G. (1987). Acoustic communication in the genus *Lynx* (Mammalia: Felidae) - comparative survey and phylogenetic interpretation. *Bonn. Zool. Beitr.* **38**: 315-330.
Peters, G. (1991). Vocal communication in cats. Pp. 76-77 in: Seidensticker, J. & Lumpkin, S. eds. (1991). *Great Cats. Majestic Creatures of the Wild.* Merehurst, London.
Peters, G. & Hast, M. (1994). Hyoid structure, laryngeal anatomy and vocalization in felids (Mammalia: Carnivora: Felidae). *Zeitschrift für Säugetierkunde* **59**: 87-104.
Peters, G. & Rödel, R. (1994). Blanford's fox in Africa. *Bonn. Zool. Beitr.* **45**: 99-111.
Peters, G. & Sliwa, A. (1997). Acoustic communication in the aardwolf, *Proteles cristatus* (Carnivora: Hyaenidae). *Mammal. Biol.* **62**: 219-238.
Peters, G. & Tonkin-Leyhausen, B. (1999). Evolution of acoustic communication signals of mammals: friendly close-range vocalizations in Felidae (Carnivora). *J. Mammal. Evol.* **6**: 129-159.
Peters, G. & Wozencraft, C. (1989). Acoustic communication by fissiped carnivores. Pp. 14-56 in: Gittleman, J. ed. (1989). *Carnivore Behavior, Ecology and Evolution.* Cornell University Press, Ithaca, New York.
Peters, G., Owen, M. & Rogers, L.L. (2007). Humming in bears: a peculiar sustained mammalian vocalization. *Acta Theriol.* **52**: 379-389.
Peters, R.P. & Mech, L.D. (1975). Scent-marking in wolves. *Amer. Sci.* **63**: 628-637.
Petersen, M.K. (1977). Courtship and mating patterns of margay. Pp. 22-35 in: Eaton, R.L. (1977). *The World's Cats.* Vol. 3(2). Carnivore Research Institute, Burke Museum, University of Washington, Seattle, Washington.
Petersen, M.K. (1979). Behavior of the margay. *Carnivore* **2(1)**: 69-76.
Petersen, M.K. & Peterson, M.K. (1978). Growth rates and other post-natal developmental changes in margays. *Carnivore* **1(1)**: 87-92.
Petit, G. (1935). Description d'un crâne de *Cryptoprocte* subfossile, suivie de remarques sur les affinités de genre *Cryptoprocta*. *Arch. Mus. Natl. Hist. Nat.* **12**: 621-636.
Petter, F. (1952). Le renard famelique. *Terre Vie* **6**: 191-193.
Petter, F. (1957). La reproduction du fennec. *Mammalia* **21**: 307-309.
Petter, G. (1969). Interprétation évolutive des caractères de la denture des Viverridae Africains. *Mammalia* **33**: 607-625.
Petter, G. (1971). Origine, phylogenie et systematique des blaireaux. *Mammalia* **35**: 567-597.
Petter, G. (1974). Rapports phyletiques des viverrides (Carnivores Fissipedes). Les formes de Madagascar. *Mammalia* **38**: 605-636.
Peyton, B. (1980). Ecology, distribution and food habits of spectacled bears, *Tremarctos ornatus*, in Peru. *J. Mammal.* **61**: 639-652.
Peyton, B. (1987). Habitat components of the spectacled bear in Machu Picchu, Peru. *Int. Conf. Bear Res. Management* **7**: 127-133.
Peyton, B., Yerena, E., Rumiz, D.I., Jorgenson, J. & Orejuela, J. (1998). Status of wild Andean bears and policies for their management. *Ursus* **10**: 87-100.
Pham-chong-Ahn (1980). [Morphology and ecology of Viverridae in Vietnam]. *Zool. Zhurnal* **59**: 905-914. In Russian.
Philcox, C.K., Grogan, A.L. & Macdonald, D.W. (1999). Patterns of otter *Lutra lutra* road mortality in Britain. *J. Appl. Ecol.* **36**: 748-761.
Philips, J.A. (1993). Bone consumption by cheetahs at undisturbed kills: evidence for a lack of focal-pallatine erosion. *J. Mammal.* **74**: 487-492.
Phillips, M.K. & Henry, V.G. (1992). Comments on red wolf taxonomy. *Conserv. Biol.* **6**: 596-599.
Phillips, M.K., Henry, V.G. & Kelly, B.T. (2003). Restoration of the red wolf. Pp. 272-288 in: Mech, L.D. & Boitani, L. eds. (2003). *Wolves: Behavior, Ecology and Conservation.* University of Chicago Press, Chicago, Illinois.
Phillips, M.K., Smith, R., Henry, V.G. & Lucas, C. (1995). Red wolf reintroduction program. Pp. 157-168 in: Carbyn, L.N., Fritts, S.H. & Seip, D.R. eds. (1995). *Ecology and Conservation of Wolves in a Changing World.* Occasional Publication **35**. Canadian Circumpolar Institute, University of Alberta, Edmonton, Alberta.
Phillips, W.W.A. (1984). *Manual of the Mammals of Sri Lanka.* 2nd edition. Aitken Spence, Colombo.
Piao, R. (1989). [Surveying the abundance of Tibetan sand fox in Tibet]. *Chinese Wildl.* **6**: 22-26. In Chinese.
Piechocki, R. (1990). *Die Wildkatze.* Die Neue Brehm-Bücherei **189**. A. Ziemsen Verlag, Wittenberg-Lutherstadt, Germany.
Pienaar, U. de V. (1964). The small mammals of the Kruger National Park - a systematic list and zoogeography. *Koedoe* **7**: 1-26.
Pienaar, U. de V. (1969). Predator-prey relationships amongst the larger mammals of Kruger National Park. *Koedoe* **12**: 108-176.
Pierce, B.M., Bleich, V.C. & Bowyer, R.T. (2000). Selection of mule deer by mountain lions and coyotes: effects of hunting style, body size and reproductive status. *J. Mammal.* **81**: 462-472.
Piertney, S.B., Dallas, J.F., Hawkins, C.E. & Racey, P.A. (2000). Microsatellite markers for the fossa (*Cryptoprocta ferox*). *Mol. Ecol.* **9**: 489-504.
Pigozzi, G. (1991). The diet of the European badger in a Mediterranean coastal area. *Acta Theriol.* **36**: 293-306.
Pilsworth, H. (1977). Altruistic mongooses tend their sick friend. *New Scientist* **73**: 517.
Pimentel, D. (1955). Biology of the Indian mongoose in Puerto Rico. *J. Mammal.* **36**: 62-68.
Pimley, L. (1999). Potto's luck. *BBC Wildlife* **12**: 98.
Pimm, S.L., Dollar, L. & Bass, O.L. (2006). The genetic rescue of the Florida panther. *Anim. Conserv.* doi: 10.1111/j.1469-1795.2005.00010.x
Pine, R.H., Miller, S.D. & Schamberger, M.L. (1979). Contributions to the mammalogy of Chile. *Mammalia* **43**: 339-376.
Pitman, N., Moskovits, D.K., Alverson, W.S. & Borman, A. eds. (2002). *Ecuador: Serranías Cofán-Bermejo, Sinangoe. Rapid Biological Inventories.* Report **3**. The Field Museum, Chicago, Illinois.
Pivorunas, A. (1979). The feeding mechanisms of baleen whales. *Amer. Sci.* **67**: 432-440.
Plowden, C. & Bowles, D. (1997). The illegal market in tiger parts in northern Sumatra, Indonesia. *Oryx* **31**: 59-66.
Poche, R.M., Evans, S.J., Sultana, P., Haque, M.E., Sterner, R. & Siddique, M.A. (1987). Notes on the golden jackal *Canis aureus* in Bangladesh. *Mammalia* **51**: 259-270.
Pocock, R.I. (1915a). On the external characters of *Galidia, Galidictis* and related genera. *Ann. Mag. Nat. Hist. (Ser. 8)* **16**: 351-356.
Pocock, R.I. (1915b). The name of the species described by Gray as *Galidictis vittatus*. *Ann. Mag. Nat. Hist. (Ser. 8)* **16**: 505-506.
Pocock, R.I. (1915c). On the species of the Mascarene viverrid *Galidictis*, with the description of a new genus and a note on *Galidia elegans*. *Ann. Mag. Nat. Hist. (Ser. 8)* **16**: 113-124.
Pocock, R.I. (1915d). On some of the external characters of the genus *Linsang* with notes upon the genera *Poiana* and *Eupleres*. *Ann. Mag. Nat. Hist. (Ser. 8)* **16**: 341-351.
Pocock, R.I. (1915e). On the feet and glands and other external characters of the Viverrinae, with the description of a new genus. *Proc. Zool. Soc. London* **1915**: 131-149.
Pocock, R.I. (1915f). On the feet and glands and other external characters of the Paradoxurinae genera *Paradoxurus, Arctictis, Arctogalidia* and *Nandinia*. *Proc. Zool. Soc. London* **1915**: 387-412.
Pocock, R.I. (1915g). On some of the external characters of *Cynogale bennetti*, Gray. *Ann. Mag. Nat. Hist.* **15**: 351-360.
Pocock, R.I. (1915h). On some of the external characters of the banded palm civet (*Hemigalus derbyanus* Gray) and its allies. *Ann. Mag. Nat. Hist.* **93**: 153-162.
Pocock, R.I. (1916a). On the course of the internal carotid artery and the foramina connected therewith in the skulls of the Felidae and Viverridae (Carnivores Fissipedes). *Ann. Mag. Nat. Hist. (Ser. 8)* **17**: 261-269.
Pocock, R.I. (1916b). On the external characters of the mongooses (Mungotidae). *Proc. Zool. Soc. London* **1**: 349-374.
Pocock, R.I. (1916c). On some of the external characters of *Cryptoprocta*. *Ann. Mag. Nat. Hist. (Ser. 8)* **17**: 413-425.
Pocock, R.I. (1916d). A new genus of African mongoose, with a note on *Galeriscus*. *Ann. Mag. Nat. Hist. (Ser. 8)* **17**: 176-179.
Pocock, R.I. (1916e). On some of the cranial and external characters of the hunting leopard or cheetah. *Ann. Mag. Nat. Hist.* **8**: 419-429.
Pocock, R.I. (1917). The classification of existing Felidae. *Ann. Mag. Nat. Hist. (Ser. 9)* **1**: 375-384.
Pocock, R.I. (1919). The classification of the mongooses (Mungotidae). *Ann. Nat. Hist.* **23**: 515-524.
Pocock, R.I. (1921). On the external characters and classification of the Mustelidae. *Proc. Zool. Soc. London* **1921**: 803-837.
Pocock, R.I. (1926). The external characters of the Patagonian weasel (*Lyncodon patagonicus*). *Proc. Zool. Soc. London* **1926**: 1085-1094.
Pocock, R.I. (1927). Description of a new species of cheetah. *Proc. Zool. Soc. London* **1927**: 245-251.
Pocock, R.I. (1929). *Carnivora.* Pp. 896-900 in: *Encyclopaedia Britannica.* Vol. 4. 14th edition.
Pocock, R.I. (1932a). The leopards of Africa. *Proc. Zool. Soc. London* **1932**: 543-591.
Pocock, R.I. (1932b). The marbled cat (*Pardofelis marmorata*) and some other oriental species, with the definition of a new genus of the Felidae. *Proc. Zool. Soc. London* **1932**: 741-766.
Pocock, R.I. (1932c). The black and brown bears of Europe and Asia. Part I. *J. Bombay Nat. Hist. Soc.* **35**: 772-823.
Pocock, R.I. (1932d). The black and brown bears of Europe and Asia. Part II. *J. Bombay Nat. Hist. Soc.* **36**: 101-138.
Pocock, R.I. (1933a). The civet-cats of Asia. *J. Bombay Nat. Hist. Soc.* **36**: 423-449.
Pocock, R.I. (1933b). The civet-cats of Asia. Part II. *J. Bombay Nat. Hist. Soc.* **36**: 629-656.
Pocock, R.I. (1933c). The rarer genera of oriental Viverridae. *Proc. Zool. Soc. London* **1933**: 969-1035.
Pocock, R.I. (1933d). The palm civets or 'toddy cats' of the genera *Paradoxurus* and *Paguma* inhabiting British India. Part I. *J. Bombay Nat. Hist. Soc.* **36**: 855-877.
Pocock, R.I. (1934a). The palm civet or 'toddy cats' and the genera *Paradoxurus* and *Paguma* inhabiting British India. Part II. *J. Bombay Nat. Hist. Soc.* **37**: 172-192.
Pocock, R.I. (1934b). The palm civets or 'toddy cats' of the genera *Paradoxurus* and *Paguma* inhabiting British India. Part III. *J. Bombay Nat. Hist. Soc.* **37**: 314-346.
Pocock, R.I. (1934c). The geographical races of *Paradoxurus* and *Paguma* found to the east of the bay of Bengal. *Proc. Zool. Soc. London* **1934**: 613-683.
Pocock, R.I. (1934d). The races of the striped and brown hyaenas. *Proc. Zool. Soc. London* **1934**: 799-825.
Pocock, R.I. (1935). *The Fauna of British India Including Ceylon & Burma - Mammalia.* Today & Tomorrow's printers & publishers, New Delhi, India.
Pocock, R.I. (1937). The mongooses of British India, including Ceylon and Burma. *J. Bombay Nat. Hist. Soc.* **39**: 211-245.
Pocock, R.I. (1939). *The Fauna of British India, Including Ceylon and Burma.* Mammalia. Vol. 1. Taylor & Francis, London.
Pocock, R.I. (1941a). *The Fauna of British India, Including Ceylon and Burma. Mammalia.* Vol. 2. Taylor & Francis, London.

Pocock, R.I. (1941b). The races of the ocelot and the margay. *Publ. Field Mus. Nat. Hist. (Zool. Ser.)* **27**: 319-369.

Pocock, R.I. (1944). The races of the North African wild cat (*Felis lybica*). *Proc. Zool. Soc. London* **114**: 65-73.

Pocock, R.I. (1945). The perfume-gland of the binturong. *J. Mammal.* **26**: 443.

Pocock, R.I. (1951). *Catalogue of the Genus* Felis. British Museum of Natural History, London.

Poglayen-Neuwall, I. (1962). Beiträge zu einem ethogram des wickelbären (*Potos flavus* Schreber). *Zeitschrift für Säugetierkunde* **27**: 1-44.

Poglayen-Neuwall, I. (1966). On the marking behavior of the kinkajou (*Potos flavus* Schreber). *Zoologica* **51**: 137-141.

Poglayen-Neuwall, I. (1973). The odorous olingo. *Anim. Kingdom* **76**: 10-14.

Poglayen-Neuwall, I. (1975). Copulatory behavior, gestation and parturition of the tayra (*Eira barbara* L., 1758). *Zeitschrift für Säugetierkunde* **40**: 176-189.

Poglayen-Neuwall, I. (1976a). Fortpflanzung, Geburt und Aufzucht, nebst anderen Beobachtungen von Makibaren (*Bassaricyon* Allen, 1876). *Zool. Beitr.* **22**: 179-233.

Poglayen-Neuwall, I. (1976b). Zur Fortpflanzungsbiologie und Jugendentwicklung von *Potos flavus* (Schreber 1774). *Zool. Garten* **46**: 237-283.

Poglayen-Neuwall, I. (1978). Breeding, rearing and notes on the behaviour of tayras (*Eira barbara*) in captivity. *Int. Zoo Yb.* **18**: 134-140.

Poglayen-Neuwall, I. (1989). Notes on reproduction, aging and longevity of *Bassaricyon* spp. (Procyonidae). *Zool. Garten (N.F.)* **59**.

Poglayen-Neuwall, I. (1991). Notes on reproduction of captive *Bassariscus sumichrasti* (Procyonidae). *Zeitschrift für Säugetierkunde* **56**: 193-199.

Poglayen-Neuwall, I. (1992a). Additional observations on reproduction of the Central American cacomixtle, *Bassariscus sumichrasti* (Procyonidae). *Zool. Garten* **6**: 388-398.

Poglayen-Neuwall, I. (1992b). Report on a little-known procyonid, *Bassariscus* (Jentinkia) *sumichrasti* (de Saussure, 1860). *Small Carniv. Conserv.* **7**: 1-3.

Poglayen-Neuwall, I. & Poglayen-Neuwall, I. (1980). Gestation period and parturition of the ringtail, *Bassariscus astutus* (Lichtenstein, 1830). *Zeitschrift für Säugetierkunde* **45**: 73-81.

Poglayen-Neuwall, I. & Poglayen-Neuwall, I. (1994). Observations on the ethology and biology of the Central American cacomixtle, *Bassariscus sumichrasti* (Saussure, 1860) in captivity, with notes on its ecology. *Zool. Garten* **65**: 11-49.

Poglayen-Neuwall, I. & Toweill, D.E. (1988). *Bassariscus astutus. Mammal. Species* **327**: 1-8.

Polder, E. (1968). Spotted skunk and weasel populations den and cover usage in northeast Iowa. *Iowa Acad. Sci.* **75**: 142-146.

Pollack, E.M. (1951a). Observations on New England bobcats. *J. Mammal.* **32**: 356-358.

Pollack, E.M. (1951b). Food habits of the bobcat in the New England states. *J. Wildl. Management* **15**: 209-213.

Pons, J.M., Volobouev, V., Ducroz, J.F., Tillier, A. & Reudet, D. (1999). Is the Guadeloupean racoon [sic] (*Procyon minor*) really an endemic species? New insights from molecular and chromosomal analyses. *J. Zool. Syst. Evol. Res.* **37**: 101-108.

Poole, C.M. (2003). The first records of hairy-nosed otter *Lutra sumatrana* from Cambodia with notes on the national status of three other otter species. *Nat. Hist. Bull. Siam Soc.* **51**: 273-280.

Poole, K.G. (1994). Characteristics of an unharvested lynx population during a snowshoe hare decline. *J. Wildl. Management* **58**: 608-618.

Poole, K.G. (1995). Spatial organization of a lynx population. *Can. J. Zool.* **73**: 632-641.

Poole, K.G. (1997). Dispersal patterns of lynx in the Northwest Territories. *J. Wildl. Management* **61(2)**: 497-505.

Poole, K.G. & Graf, R.P. (1996). Winter diet of marten during a snowshoe hare decline. *Can. J. Zool.* **74**: 456-466.

Porton, I. (1983). Bush dog urine-marking: its role in pair formation and maintenance. *Anim. Behav.* **31**: 1061-1069.

Porton, I., Kleiman, D.G. & Rodden, M. (1987). Aseasonality of bush dog reproduction and the influence of social factors on the estrous cycle. *J. Mammal.* **68**: 867-871.

Posluszny, M., Pilot, M., Goszczynski, J. & Gralak, B. (2007). Diet of sympatric pine marten (*Martes martes*) and stone marten (*Martes foina*) identified by genotyping of DNA from faeces. *Ann. Zool. Fennici* **44**: 269-284.

Potvin, F., Belanger, L. & Lowell, K. (2000). Marten habitat selection in a clearcut boreal landscape. *Conserv. Biol.* **14**: 844-857.

Pough, F.H., Heiser, J.B. & McFarland, W.N. (1996). *Vertebrate Life.* 4th edition. Prentice-Hall, Upper Saddle River, New Jersey.

Pournelle, G. (1965). Observations on birth and early development of the spotted hyaena. *J. Mammal.* **46**: 503.

Poux, C., Madsen, O., Marquard, E., Vieites, D.R., De Jong, W.W. & Vences, M. (2005). Asynchronous colonization of Madagascar by the four endemic clades of primates, tenrecs, carnivores and rodents as inferred from nuclear genes. *Syst. Biol.* **54**: 719-730.

Powell, R.A. (1979). Mustelid spacing patterns: variations on a theme by *Mustela. Zeitschr. Tierpsychol.* **50**: 153-165.

Powell, R.A. (1981). *Martes pennanti. Mammal. Species* **156**: 1-6.

Powell, R.A. (1982). Evolution of black-tipped tails in weasels: predator confusion. *Amer. Naturalist* **119**: 126-131.

Powell, R.A. (1985). Possible pathways for the evolution of reproductive strategies in weasels and stoats. *Oikos* **44**: 506-508.

Powell, R.A. (1993). *The Fisher: Life History, Ecology and Behavior.* 2nd edition. University of Minnesota Press, Minneapolis, Minnesota.

Powell, R.A., Buskirk, S.W. & Zielinski, W.J. (2003). Fisher and marten. Pp. 635-649 in: Feldhamer, G.A., Thompson, B.C. & Chapman, J.A. eds. (2003). *Wild Mammals of North America: Biology, Management and Conservation.* 2nd edition. Johns Hopkins University Press, Baltimore, Maryland.

Power, R.J. (2000). A new distribution range record for the small spotted cat *Felis nigripes* in the Northern Province bushveld. *South Afr. J. Wildl. Res.* **30**: 165-168.

Powzyk, J. (1997). *The Socio-Ecology of Two Sympatric Indrids,* Propithecus diadema diadema *and* Indri indri: *a Comparison of Feeding Strategies and their Possible Repercussions on Species-Specific Behaviors.* PhD thesis, Duke University, Durham, North Carolina.

Poyarkov, A. & Ovsyanikov, N. (2004). Corsac *Vulpes corsac.* Pp. 142-148 in: Sillero-Zubiri, C., Hoffmann, M. & Macdonald, D.W. eds. (2004). *Canids: Foxes, Wolves, Jackals and Dogs. Status Survey and Conservation Action Plan.* IUCN/SSC Canid Specialist Group, Gland & Cambridge.

Pradhan, S., Saha, G.K. & Khan, J.A. (2001). Ecology of the red panda *Ailurus fulgens* in the Singhalila National Park, Darjeeling, India. *Biol. Conserv.* **98**: 11-18.

Prakash, I. (1959). Food of some Indian desert mammals. *J. Biol. Sci.* **2**: 100-109.

Prakash, I. (1975). The population ecology of the rodents of the Rajasthan Desert, India. Pp. 75-116 in: Prakash, I. & Ghosh, P.K. eds. (1975). *Rodents in Desert Environments.* Dr. W. Junk b.v. Publishers, The Hague.

Prange, S. & Gehrt, S.D. (2004). Changes in mesopredator-community structure in response to urbanization. *Can. J. Zool.* **82**: 1804-1817.

Prange, S. & Gehrt, S.D. (2007). Response of skunks to a simulated increase in coyote activity. *J. Mammal.* **88**: 1040-1049.

Prange, S., Gehrt, S.D. & Wiggers, E.P. (2004). Demographic factors contributing to high raccoon densities in urban landscapes. *J. Wildl. Management* **67**: 324.

Prange, S., Jordan, T., Hunter, C. & Gehrt, S.D. (2006). New radiocollars for the detection of proximity among individuals. *Wildl. Soc. Bull.* **34**: 1333-1344.

Prater, S.H. (1980). *The Book of Indian Animals.* 4th edition. Bombay Natural History Society, Oxford University Press, Bombay.

Presley, S.J. (2000). *Eira barbara. Mammal. Species* **636**: 1-6.

Preston, S.J., Portig, A.A., Montgomery, W.I., McDonald, R.A. & Fairley, J.S. (2006). Status and diet of the otter *Lutra lutra* in Northern Ireland. *Proc. Royal Irish Acad. Sect. B Biol. Environm.* **106B**: 57-63.

Prestrud, P. (1992a.) Food habits and observations of the hunting behaviour of Arctic foxes, *Alopex lagopus*, in Svalbard. *Can. Field-Nat.* **106**: 225-236.

Prestrud, P. (1992b). Physical characteristics of Arctic fox (*Alopex lagopus*) dens in Svalbard. *Arctic* **45**: 154-158.

Prestrud, P. (1992c). *Arctic Foxes in Svalbard: Population Ecology and Rabies.* PhD dissertation, Norwegian Polar Institute, Oslo, Norway.

Prevosti, F.J., Soibelzon, L.H., Prieto, A., San Roman, M. & Morello, F. (2003). The southernmost bear: *Pararctotherium* (Carnivora, Ursidae, Tremarctinae) in the latest Pleistocene of southern Patagonia, Chile. *J. Vert. Paleo.* **23**: 709-712.

Prigioni, C., Balestieri, A., Remonti, L., Gargaro, A. & Priore, G. (2006). Diet of the Eurasian otter (*Lutra lutra*) in relation to freshwater habitats and alien fish species in southern Italy. *Ethology, Ecology & Evolution* **18**: 306-320.

Pringle, J.A. & Pringle, V.L. (1979). Observations on the lynx *Felis caracal* in the Bedford District. *South Afr. J. Zool.* **14**: 1-4.

Procter, J. (1963). A contribution to the natural history of the spotted-necked otter (*Lutra maculicollis* Lichtenstein) in Tanganyika. *East Afr. Wildl. J.* **1**: 93-102.

Proctor, M.F., McLellan, B.N., Strobeck, C. & Barclay, R.M.R. (2004). Gender-specific dispersal distances of grizzly bears estimated by genetic analysis. *Can. J. Zool.* **82**: 1108-1118.

Proctor, M.F., McLellan, B.N., Strobeck, C. & Barclay, R.M.R. (2005). Genetic analysis reveals demographic fragmentation of grizzly bears yielding vulnerably small populations. *Proc. Royal Soc. London (Ser. B Biol. Sci.)* **272**: 2409-2416.

Progulske, D.R. (1955). Game animals utilized as food by the bobcat in the southeastern Appalachians. *J. Wildl. Management* **19**: 249-253.

Proulx, G. (2006). Winter habitat use by American marten, *Martes americana*, in western Alberta boreal forests. *Can. Field-Nat.* **120**: 100-105.

Pruss, S.D. (1994). *An Observational Natal Den Study of Wild Swift Fox* Vulpes velox *on the Canadian Prairie.* MSc thesis, Department of Environmental Design, University of Calgary, Calgary.

Pugh, M. (2008). WSPA. Civet Farming Campaign: Raising a stink. URL: **http://www.wspa-international.org/campaigns/civets/civet01.html**

Pulliainen, E. & Ollinmaki, P. (1996). A long-term study of the winter food niche of the pine marten *Martes martes* in northern boreal Finland. *Acta Theriol.* **41**: 337-352.

Pulliainen, E., Lindgren, E. & Tunkkari, P.S. (1995). Influence of food availabiltiy and reproductive status on the diet and body condition of the European lynx in Finland. *Acta Theriol.* **40**: 181-196.

Purves, M.G., Kruuk, H. & Nel, J.A.J. (1994). Crabs *Potamonautes perlatus* in the diet of otter *Aonyx capensis* and water mongoose *Atilax paludinosus* in a fresh-water habitat in South Africa. *Zeitschrift fur Säugetierkunde* **59**: 332-341.

Pusey, A.E. & Packer, C. (1987). The evolution of sex-biased dispersal in lions. *Behaviour* **101**: 275-310.

Putman, R.J. (2000). Diet of pine martens *Martes martes* L. in west Scotland. *J. Nat. Hist.* **34**: 793-797.

Pybus, M.J. (1988). Rabies and rabies control in striped skunks (*Mephitis mephitis*) in three prairie regions of western North America. *J. Wildl. Diseases* **24**: 434-449.

Quadros, J. & Monteiro-Filho, E.L.A. (2001). Diet of the neotropical otter, *Lontra longicaudis*, in an Atlantic Forest Area, Santa Catarina State, southern Brazil. *Stud. Neotrop. Fauna Environm.* **36(1)**: 15-21.

Quigley, H.B. & Crawshaw, P.G. (1992). *The World of the Jaguar.* Taplinger Publishing Co., New York.

Quillen, P. (1981). Hand-rearing the little spotted cat or oncilla. *Int. Zoo Yb.* **21**: 240-242.

Quinn, J. & Whisson, D. (2005). The effects of anthropogenic food on the spatial behaviour of small Indian mongooses (*Herpestes javanicus*) in a subtropical rainforest. *J. Zool., London* **267**: 339-350.

Quinn, N.W.S. & Parker, G. (1987). Lynx. Pp. 683-694 in: Nowak, M., Barker, J.A., Obbard, M.E. & Malloch, B. (1987). *Wild Furbearer Management and Conservation in North America.* Ontario Trappers Association, Ontario.

Quinn, N.W.S. & Thompson, J.E. (1985). Age and sex of trapped lynx, *Felis canadensis*, related to period of capture and trapping technique. *Can. Field-Nat.* **99**: 267-269.

Quinn, N.W.S. & Thompson, J.E. (1987). Dynamics of an exploited Canada lynx population in Ontario. *J. Wildl. Management* **51**: 297-305.

Qumsiyeh, M.B. (1996). *Mammals of the Holy Land.* Texas Tech University Press, Lubbock, Texas.

Rabb, G.B. (1959). Reproductive and vocal behavior in captive pumas. *J. Mammal.* **40**: 616-617.

Rabeantoandro, Z.S. (1997). Contribution à l'étude du *Mungotictis decemlineata* (Grandidier 1867) de la Forêt de Kirindy, Morondava. Unpublished Mémoire de DEA-Science Biologique Appliquée, Université d'Antananarivo.

Rabinowitz, A.R. (1986a). *Jaguar: Struggle and Triumph in the Jungles of Belize.* Arbor House, New York.

Rabinowitz, A.R. (1986b). Jaguar predation on domestic livestock in Belize. *Wildl. Soc. Bull.* **14**: 170-174.

Rabinowitz, A.R. (1988). The clouded leopard in Taiwan. *Oryx* **22**: 46-47.

Rabinowitz, A.R. (1989). The density and behavior of large cats in a dry tropical forest mosaic in Huai Kha Khaeng Wildlife Sanctuary, Thailand. *Nat. Hist. Bull. Siam Soc.* **37**: 235-251.

Rabinowitz, A.R. (1990). Notes on the behavior and movements of leopard cats, *Felis bengalensis*, in a dry tropical forest mosaic in Thailand. *Biotropica* **22**: 397-403.

Rabinowitz, A.R. (1991). Behaviour and movements of sympatric civet species in Huai Kha Khaeng Wildlife Sanctuary, Thailand. *J. Zool.* **223**: 299-305.

Rabinowitz, A.R. (1993). Estimating the Indochinese tiger *Panthera tigris corbetti* population in Thailand. *Biol. Conserv.* **65**: 213-217.

Rabinowitz, A.R. & Khaing, S.T. (1998). Status of selected mammal species in North Myanmar. *Oryx* **32**: 201-208.

Rabinowitz, A.R. & Nottingham, B.G. (1986). Ecology and behaviour of the jaguar (*Panthera onca*) in Belize, Central America. *J. Zool., London* **210**: 149-159.

Rabinowitz, A.R., Andau, P. & Chai, P.P.K. (1987). The clouded leopard in Malaysian Borneo. *Oryx* **21**: 107-111.

Rabor, D.S. (1986). *Guide to Philippine Flora and Fauna.* Ministry of Natural Resources and University of the Philippines, Quezon City, Philippines.

Radinsky, L. (1973). Are stink badgers skunks? Implications of neuroanatomy for mustelid phylogeny. *J. Mammal.* **54**: 585-593.

Radinsky, L. (1975). Viverrid neuroanatomy: phylogenetic and behavioral implications. *J. Mammal.* **56**: 130-150.

Radinsky, L. (1983). Patterns in the evolution of ungulate jaw shape. *Amer. Zool.* **25**: 303-314.

Rahajanirina, L.P. (2003). *Contribution à l'Étude Biologique, Écologique et Éthologique de* Cryptoprocta ferox *(Bennett 1883) Dans la Région du Lac Tsimaloto, du Parc National d'Ankarafantsika, Madagascar.* Mémoire de DEA-Biologie Animale, Université d'Antananarivo.

Rahm, U. (1961). Esquisses mammalogiques de la basse Côte-d'Ivoire. *Bull. IFAN* **23**: 1229-1265.

Rahmani, A.R. (1989). *The Great Indian Bustard.* Final Report. Bombay Natural History Society, Bombay.

Rai, N.D. & Kumar, A. (1993). A pilot study on the conservation of the Malabar civet (*Viverra civettina*). *Small Carniv. Conserv.* **9**: 3-7.

Raine, R.M. (1983). Winter habitat use and responses to snow cover of fisher (*Martes pennanti*) and marten (*Martes americana*) in southwestern Manitoba. *Can. J. Zool.* **61**: 25-34.

Raine, R.M. (1987). Winter food habits and foraging behaviour of fishers (*Martes pennanti*) and martens (*Martes americana*) in southeastern Manitoba. *Can. J. Zool.* **65**: 745-747.

Rajamani, N., Mudappa, D. & Van Rompaey, H. (2002). Distribution and status of the brown palm civet in the Western Ghats, south India. *Small Carniv. Conserv.* **27**: 6-11.

Rajaratnam, R. (2000). *Ecology of the Leopard Cat (*Prionailurus bengalensis*) in Tabin Wildlife Reserve, Sabah, Malaysia.* PhD dissertation, Universiti Kebangsaan Malaysia, Bangi, Malaysia.

Rajaratnam, R., Sunquist, M., Rajaratnam, L. & Ambu, L. (2007). Diet and habitat selection of the leopard cat (*Prionailurus bengalensis borneoensis*) in an agricultural landscape in Sabah, Malaysian Borneo. *J. Trop. Ecol.* **23**: 209-217.

Rajpurohit, K.S. & Krausman, P.R. (2000). Human–sloth-bear conflicts in Madhya Pradesh, India. *Wildl. Soc. Bull.* **28**: 393-399.

Ralls, K. (1971). Mammalian scent marking. *Science* **171**: 443-449.

Ralls, K. & Harvey, P.H. (1985). Geographic variation in size and sexual dimorphism of North American weasels. *Biol. J. Linn. Soc.* **25**: 119-167.

Ralls, K., Cypher, B. & Spiegel, L.K. (2007). Social monogamy in kit foxes: formation, association, duration and dissolution of mated pairs. *J. Mammal.* **88**: 1439-1446.

Ralls, K., Pilgrim, K.L., White, P.J., Paxinos, E.E., Schwartz, M.K. & Fleischer, R.C. (2001). Kinship, social relationships and den sharing in kit foxes. *J. Mammal.* **82**: 858-866.

Ramachandran, K.K. (1990). Recent evidence of the brown palm civet, *Paradoxurus jerdoni* from Silent Valley National Park, India. *Mustel. Viverr. Conserv.* **3**: 15.

Ramakantha, V. (1994). Natural distribution and ecology of mustelids and viverrids in Manipur, north-eastern India. *Small Carniv. Conserv.* **11**: 16-18.

Ramirez-Pulido, J., Gonzalez-Ruiz, N. & Genoways, H.H. (2005). Carnivores from the Mexican State of Puebla: distribution, taxonomy and conservation. *Mastozool. Neotrop.* **12**: 37-52.

Ramsay, M.A. & Dunbrack, R.L. (1986). Physiological constraints on life history phenomena: The example of small bear cubs at birth. *Amer. Nat.* **127**: 735-743.

Ramsay, M.A. & Stirling, I. (1990). Fidelity of female polar bears to winter-den sites. *J. Mammal.* **71**: 233-236.

Rand, A.L. (1935). On the habits of some Madagascar mammals. *J. Mammal.* **16**: 89-104.

Randall, R.M. (1977). *Aspects of the Ecology of the Civet* Civettictis civetta *(Schreber, 1778).* PhD thesis, University of Pretoria, Pretoria, RSA, 250 p.

Randall, R.M. (1979). Perineal gland marking by free-ranging African civet, *Civettictis civetta. J. Mammal.* **60**: 622-627.

Rasa, O.A.E. (1973a). Marking behaviour and its social significance in the African dwarf mongoose (*Helogale undulata rufula*). *Zeitschr. Tierpsychol.* **32**: 293-318.

Rasa, O.A.E. (1973b). Prey capture, feeding techniques and their ontogeny in the African dwarf mongoose, *Helogale undulata rufula. Zeitschr. Tierpsychol.* **32**: 449-488.

Rasa, O.A.E. (1973c). Intra-familial sexual repression in dwarf mongoose *Helogale parvula. Naturwissenschaften* **60**: 303-304.

Rasa, O.A.E. (1976). Invalid care in dwarf mongoose (*Helogale undulata rufula*). *Zeitschr. Tierpsychol.* **42**: 337-342.

Rasa, O.A.E. (1977a). The ethology and sociology of the dwarf mongoose, *Helogale undulata rufula. Zeitschr. Tierpsychol.* **43**: 337-406.

Rasa, O.A.E. (1977b). Differences in group member response to intruding conspecifics and frightening or potentially dangerous stimuli in dwarf mongooses (*Helogale undulata rufula*). *Zeitschrift fur Säugetierkunde* **42**: 108-112.

Rasa, O.A.E. (1979). Effects of crowding on the social relationships and behavior of the dwarf mongoose (*Helogale undulata rufula*). *Zeitschr. Tierpsychol.* **49**: 317-329.

Rasa, O.A.E. (1983a). A case of invalid care in wild dwarf mongooses. *Zeitschr. Tierpsychol.* **62**: 235-240.

Rasa, O.A.E. (1983b). Dwarf mongoose and hornbill mutualism in the Taru Desert, Kenya. *Behav. Ecol. Sociobiol.* **12**: 181-190.

Rasa, O.A.E. (1984). A motivational analysis of object play in juvenile dwarf mongooses (*Helogale undulata rufula*). *Anim. Behav.* **32**: 579-589.

Rasa, O.A.E. (1985). *Mongoose Watch: a Family Observed.* J. Murray, London.

Rasa, O.A.E. (1986a). Coordinated vigilance in dwarf mongoose family groups: the 'Watchman's Song" hypothesis and the costs of guarding. *Ethology* **71**: 340-344.

Rasa, O.A.E. (1986b). Ecological factors and their relationship to group size, mortality and behaviour in the dwarf mongoose *Helogale undulata. Cimbebasia* **8**: 15-21.

Rasa, O.A.E. (1987a). Vigilance behaviour in dwarf mongooses: selfish or altruistic? *South Afr. J. Sci.* **83**: 587-590.

Rasa, O.A.E. (1987b). The dwarf mongoose: a study of behavior and social structure in relation to ecology in a small, social carnivore. *Advances Study Behav.* **17**: 121-163.

Rasa, O.A.E. (1989a). The costs and effectiveness of vigilance behaviour in the dwarf mongoose: implications for fitness and optimal group size. *Ethology, Ecology & Evolution* **1**: 265-282.

Rasa, O.A.E. (1989b). Helping in dwarf mongoose societies: an alternative reproductive strategy. Pp. 61-73 in: Rasa, O.A.E. & Vogel, C. eds. (1989). *The Sociobiology of Sexual and Reproductive Strategies.* Croom Helm, Beckenham, UK.

Rasa, O.A.E. (1994). Altruistic infant care or infanticide: the dwarf mongooses' dilemma. Pp. 301-320 in: Parmigiani, S. & vom Saal, F.S. eds. (1994). *Infanticide and Parental Care.* Harwood Academic Publishers, London.

Rasa, O.A.E., Wenhold, B.A., Howard, P., Marais, A. & Pallett, J. (1992). Reproduction in the yellow mongoose revisited. *South Afr. J. Zool.* **27**: 192-195.

Rasamison, A.A. (1997). *Contribution à l'Étude Biologique, Écologique et Éthologique de* Cryptoprocta ferox *(Bennett, 1833) Dans la Forêt de Kirindy à Madagascar.* Mémoire de DEA, Faculté des Sciences, Université d'Antananarivo.

Rashid, M.A. (1991). Asiatic lion population up. *Cat News* **13**: 12.

Rasoloarison, R.M., Rasolonandrasana, B.P.N., Ganzhorn, J.U. & Goodman, S.M. (1995). Predation on vertebrates in the Kirindy Forest, western Madagascar. *Ecotropica* **1**: 59-65.

Rasolonandrasana, B.P.N. (1994). *Contribution à l'Étude de l'Alimentation de* Cryptoprocta ferox *Bennett (1833) Dans son Milieu Naturel.* Mémoire de DEA, Service de Paléontologie, Université d'Antananarivo.

Rasooli, P., Kiabi, B.H. & Abdoli, A. (2007). On the status and biology of the European otter, *Lutra lutra* (Carnivora: Mustelidae), in Iran. *Zool. Middle East* **41**: 25-29.

Ratajszczak, R. & Cox, R. (1991). Back-striped weasel in Vietnam. *Small Carniv. Conserv.* **4**: 17.

Rathbun, G.B. (2004). The shadow hunter. *Afr. Geogr.* **12**: 18-19.

Rathbun, G.B. & Rathbun, C.D. (2006). Social monogamy in the noki or dassie-rat (*Petromus typicus*) in Namibia. *Mammal. Biol.* **71**: 203-213.

Rathbun, G.B., Cowley, T. & Zapke, O. (2005). Black mongoose (*Galerella nigrata*) home range and social behaviour affected by abundant food at an antelope carcass. *Afr. Zool.* **40**: 154-157.

Ratnam, L., Lim, B.L. & Hussein, N.A. (1995). Mammals of the Sungai Singgor area in Temengor Forest Reserve, Hulu Perak, Malaysia. *Malay. Nat. J.* **48**: 409-423.

Ratnayeke, S., Bixler, A. & Gittleman, J.L. (1994). Home range movements of solitary, reproductive female coatis *Nasua narica*, in south-eastern Arizona. *J. Zool., London* **233**: 322-326.

Ratnayeke, S., Tuskan, G.A. & Pelton, M.R. (2002). Genetic relatedness and female spatial organization in a solitary carnivore, the raccoon, *Procyon lotor. Mol. Ecol.* **11**: 1115-1124.

Ratnayeke, S., Van Manen, F.T. & Padmalal, U.K.G.K. (2007). Home ranges and habitat use of sloth bears *Melursus ursinus inornatus* in Wasgomuwa National Park, Sri Lanka. *Wildl. Biol.* **13**: 272-284.

Ratnayeke, S., Van Manen, F.T., Pieris, R. & Pragash, V.S.J. (2007). Landscape characteristics of sloth bear range in Sri Lanka. *Ursus* **18**: 189-202.

Ratter, J.A., Riveiro, J.F. & Bridgewater, S. (1997). The Brazilian cerrado vegetation and threats to its biodiversity. *Ann. Bot. London* **80**: 223-230.

Rau, J.R., Beltrán, J.F. & Delibes, M. (1985). Can the increase of fox density explain the decrease in lynx numbers at Doñana? *Rev. Écol. (Terre Vie)* **40**: 145-150.

Rau, J.R., Martinez, D.R., Low, J.R. & Tilleria, M.S. (1995). Predation by gray foxes *Pseudalopex griseus* on cursorial, scansorial, and arboreal small mammals in a protected wildlife area of southern Chile. *Rev. Chil. Hist. Nat.* **68**: 333-340.

Rautenbach, I.L. (1982). The mammals of the Transvaal. *Ecoplan Monogr.* **1**: 111-211.

Ray, J.C. (1995). The life in sympatry of *Xenogale naso* and *Atilax paludinosus* in a central African forest. *Small Carniv. Conserv.* **12**: 1-4.

Ray, J.C. (1997). Comparative ecology of two African forest mongooses, *Herpestes naso* and *Atilax paludinosus. Afr. J. Ecol.* **35**: 237-253.

Ray, J.C. (1998). Temporal variation of predation on rodents and shrews by small African forest carnivores. *J. Zool., London* **244**: 363-370.

Ray, J.C. (In press). *Civettictis civetta.* In: Kingdon, J.S. & Hoffmann, M. eds. (In press). *The Mammals of Africa.* Vol. 5. Carnivores, Pangolins, Rhinos and Equids. Academic Press, Amsterdam.

Ray, J.C. & Sunquist, M.E. (2001). Trophic relations in a community of African rainforest carnivores. *Oecologia* **127**: 395-408.

Razafimahatratra, R.E. (1988). Evolution chromosomique des carnivores Malgaches. Pp. 110-115 in: Rakotovao, L., Barre, V. & Sayer, J. eds. (1988). *L'Equilibre des Écosystèmes Forestiers a Madagascar: Actes d'un Séminaire Internationale.* Union Internationale pour la Conservation de la Nature et de ses Ressources, Gland, Switzerland.

Razafimanantsoa, L. (2003). *Mungotictis decemlineata*, narrow-striped Mongoose. Pp. 1357-1360 in: Goodman, S.M. & Benstead, J.P. eds. (2003). *The Natural History of Madagascar*. The University of Chicago Press, Chicago, Illinois.

Read, J.A. (1981). *Geographic Variation in Bobcat* (Felis rufus) *in the Southcentral United States*. MSc thesis, Texas A&M University, College Station, Texas.

Recuenco, S., Eidson, M., Kulldorff, M., Johnson, G. & Cherry, B. (2007). Spatial and temporal patterns of enzootic raccoon rabies adjusted for multiple covariates. *Inter. J. Health Geographics* **6**: 14.

Redford, K.H. & Eisenberg, J.F. (1992). *Mammals of the Neotropics: the Southern Cone*. Vol. 2. The University of Chicago Press, Chicago, Illinois.

Redford, K.H. & Stearman, A.M.C. (1993). Notas sobre la biología de tres procyonidos simpátricos bolivianos (Mammalia, Procyonidae). *Ecol. Bolivia* **21**: 35-44.

Redford, K.H., MacLean, S.A. & Trager, J.C. (1989). The kinkajou (*Potos flavus*) as a myrmecophage. *Mammalia* **53**: 132-134.

Reed, A.W. & Kennedy, M.L. (2000). Conservation status of the eastern spotted skunk *Spilogale putorius* in the Appalachian Mountains of Tennessee. *Amer. Midl. Nat.* **144**: 133-138.

Reese, K.M. (1993). Patented shampoo said to remove skunk odor. *Chem. Engin. News* **12/06**: 82.

Regan, T.W. & Maehr, D.S. (1990). Melanistic bobcats in Florida. *Florida Field Nat.* **18**: 84-87.

Regehr, E.V., Lunn, N.J., Amstrup, S.C. & Stirling, I. (2007). Effects of earlier sea ice breakup on survival and population size of polar bears in western Hudson Bay. *J. Wildl. Management* **71**: 2673-2683.

Reid, D.G. & Gong, J. (1999). Giant panda conservation action plan. Pp. 241-254 in: Servheen, C., Herrero, S. & Peyton, B. eds. (1999). *Bears. Status Survey and Conservation Action Plan*. IUCN/SSC Bear and Polar Bear Specialist Groups, IUCN, Gland & Cambridge.

Reid, D.G., Code, T.E., Reid, A.C.H. & Herrero, S.M. (1994). Spacing, movements, and habitat selection of the river otter in boreal Alberta. *Can. J. Zool.* **72**: 1314-1324.

Reid, D.G., Hu, J. & Huang, Y. (1991). Ecology of the red panda *Ailurus fulgens* in the Wolong Reserve, China. *J. Zool., London* **225**: 347-364.

Reid, D.G., Jiang, M., Teng, Q., Qin, Z. & Hu, J. (1991). Ecology of the Asiatic black bear (*Ursus thibetanus*) in Sichuan, China. *Mammalia* **55**: 221-237.

Reid, F.A. (1997). *A Field Guide to the Mammals of Central America and Southeast Mexico*. Oxford University Press, New York.

Reiger, I. (1979). Scent rubbing in carnivores. *Carnivore* **11**: 17-25.

Reiger, I. & Walzthony, D. (1979). Markieren katzen beim wangenrieben? [Is felid cheek rubbing a scent marking behavior?] *Zeitschrift für Säugetierkunde* **44**: 319-320.

Reimchen, T.E. (1998a). Diurnal and nocturnal behavior of black bears, *Ursus americanus*, on bear trails. *Can. Field-Nat.* **112**: 698-699.

Reimchen, T.E. (1998b). Nocturnal foraging behaviour of black bears, *Ursus americanus*, on Moresby Island, British Columbia. *Can. Field-Nat.* **112**: 446-450.

Remonti, L., Balestrieri, A. & Prigioni, C. (2006). Range of the Eurasian badger (*Meles meles*) in an agricultural area of northern Italy. *Ethology, Ecology & Evolution* **18**: 61-67.

Rensberger, J.M. (1999). Enamel microstructural specialization in the canine of the spotted hyena (*Crocuta crocuta*). *Scanning Microscopy* **13**: 343-361.

Rensberger, J.M. & Stefen, C. (2006). Functional differentiation of the microstructure in the upper carnassial enamel of the spotted hyena. *Palaeontographica (Abt. A)* **278**: 1-6.

Rensberger, J.M. & Wang, X. (2005). Microstructural reinforcement in the canine enamel of the hyaenid *Crocuta crocuta*, the felid *Puma concolor* and the late Miocene canid *Borophagus secundus*. *J. Mammal. Evol.* **12**: 379-403.

Rettig, T. & Divers, J. (1978). Reproduction of captive carnivores. Viverridae. Pp. 692-701 in: Fowler, M.E. ed. (1978). *Zoo and Wild Animal Medicine*. Saunders, Philadelphia, London & Toronto.

Reuther, C., Ehlers, M., Schuhmann, M., Kalz, B. & Fickel, J. (2003). New findings on otters in Guinea-Bissau. *IUCN Otter Special. Group Bull.* **20**: 19-27.

Revilla, E. & Palomares, F. (2002). Spatial organization, group living and ecological correlates in low-density populations of Eurasian badgers, *Meles meles*. *J. Anim. Ecol.* **71**: 497-512.

Revilla, E., Palomares, F. & Fernandez, N. (2001). Characteristics, location and selection of diurnal resting dens by Eurasian badgers (*Meles meles*) in a low density area. *J. Zool., London* **255**: 291-299.

Reynolds, J.E. & Rommel, S.A. (1999). *Biology of Marine Mammals*. Smithsonian Institution Press, Washington, D.C.

Rhim, S.J. & Lee, W.S. (2007). Influence of forest fragmentation on the winter abundance of mammals in Mt. Chirisan National Park, South Korea. *J. Wildl. Management* **71**: 1404-1408.

Richard, E., Giraudo, A. & Abdala, C. (1999). Confirmación de la presencia del aguará guazú (*Chrysocyon brachyurus*, Mammalia: Canidae) en la provincia de Santiago del Estero, Argentina. *Acta Zool. Lilloana* **45**: 155-156.

Richardson, P.R.K. (1985). The social behaviour and ecology of the aardwolf *Proteles cristatus* (Sparrman, 1783) in relation to its food resources. Unpublished PhD thesis, University of Oxford.

Richardson, P.R.K. (1987a). Aardwolf mating system: overt cuckholdry in an apparently monogamous mammal. *South Afr. J. Sci.* **83**: 405-410.

Richardson, P.R.K. (1987b). Aardwolf: the most specialized myrmecophagous mammal? *South Afr. J. Sci.* **83**: 643-646.

Richardson, P.R.K. (1987c). Food consumption and seasonal variation in the diet of the aardwolf *Proteles cristatus* in southern Africa. *Zeitschrift für Säugetierkunde* **52**: 307-325.

Richardson, P.R.K. (1990). The lick of the aardwolf. *Nat. Hist.* **4/90**: 78-85.

Richardson, P.R.K. (1991). Territorial significance of scent marking during the non-mating season in the aardwolf *Proteles cristatus* (Carnivore: Protelidae). *Ethology* **87**: 9-27.

Richardson, P.R.K. (1993). The function of scent marking territories: a resurrection of the intimidation hypothesis. *Trans. Royal Soc. South Afr.* **48**: 195-206.

Richardson, P.R.K. & Bearder, S.K. (1984). The aardwolf. Pp. 158-159 in: Macdonald, D.W. ed. (1984). *The Encyclopaedia of Mammals*. Vol. 1. George Allen & Unwin, London.

Richardson, P.R.K. & Levitan, C.D. (1994). Tolerance of aardwolves to defense secretions of *Trinervitermes trinervoides*. *J. Mammal.* **75**: 84-91.

Richens, V.B. & Hugie, R.D. (1974). Distribution, taxonomic status and characteristics of coyotes in Maine. *J. Wildl. Management* **38**: 447-454.

Rieger, I. (1978). Social behaviour of the striped hyaena at Zürich Zoo. *Carnivore* **1**: 49-60.

Rieger, I. (1979a). A review of the biology of striped hyaenas, *Hyaena hyaena* (Linné, 1758). *Säugetierkunde Mitt.* **27**: 81-95.

Rieger, I. (1979b). Report on rearing of striped hyenas *Hyaena hyaena*. *Vierteljahrsschr. Naturforsch. Gesellsch., Zürich, Jahrg.* **124**: 169-184.

Rieger, I. (1979c). Breeding the striped hyaena *Hyaena hyaena* in captivity. *Int. Zoo Yb.* **19**: 193-198.

Rieger, I. (1979d). Scent rubbing in carnivores. *Carnivore* **11**: 17-25.

Rieger, I. (1981). *Hyaena hyaena*. *Mammal. Species* **150**: 1-5.

Rieger, I. (1984). Oestrous timing in ounces, *Uncia uncia*, Schreber (1775). *Int. Ped. Book Snow Leopards* **4**: 99-103.

Rieger, I. & Peters, G. (1981). Einige Beobachtungen zum Paarungs- und Lautgebungsverhalten von Irbissen (*Uncia uncia*) im Zoologischen Garten. *Zeitschrift für Säugetierkunde* **46**: 35-48.

Rieger, I. & Walzthony, D. (1979). Markieren Katzen beim Wangenrieben? [Is felid cheek rubbing a scent marking behavior?] *Zeitschrift für Säugetierkunde* **44**: 319-320.

Riffel, M. (1991). An update on the Javan ferret-badger *Melogale orientalis* (Horsfield 1821). *Small Carniv. Conserv.* **5**: 2-3.

Riley, G.A. & McBride, R.T. (1972). *A Survey of the Red Wolf (*Canis rufus). Scientific Wildlife Report **162**. US Fish and Wildlife Service, Washington.

Riley, S.P.D., Hadidian, J. & Manski, D.A. (1988). Population density, survival, and rabies in raccoons in an urban national park. *Can. J. Zool.* **76(6)**: 1153–1164.

Ritland, K., Newton, C. & Marshall, H.D. (2001). Inheritance and population structure of the white-phased "Kermode" black bear. *Curr. Biol.* **11**: 1468-1472.

Robbins, C.T., Fortin, J.K., Rode, K.D., Farley, S.D., Shipley, L.A. & Felicetti, L.A. (2007). Optimizing protein intake as a foraging strategy to maximize mass gain in an omnivore. *Oikos* **116**: 1675-1682.

Robbins, R.L. (2000). Vocal communication in free-ranging African wild dogs *Lycaon pictus*. *Behaviour* **137**: 1271-1298.

Roberton, S. & Muir, S. (2005). International Conservation Breeding Program established for Owston's civet. *Small Carniv. Conserv.* **32**: 14.

Roberts, A. (1926). Some new South African mammals and some changes in nomenclature. *Ann. Transvaal Mus.* **11**: 245-263.

Roberts, A. (1951). *The Mammals of South Africa*. Central News Agency, Cape Town.

Roberts, M.S. & Gittleman, J.L. (1984). *Ailurus fulgens*. *Mammal. Species* **222**: 1-8.

Roberts, P.D., Somers, M.J., White, M.R. & Nel, J.A.J. (2007). Diet of the South African large-spotted genet *Genetta tigrina* (Carnivora, Viverridae) in a coastal dune forest. *Acta Theriol.* **52**: 45-53.

Roberts, T.J. (1977). *The Mammals of Pakistan*. Ernest Benn Limited, London.

Robertshaw, J.D. & Harden, R.H. (1985). Ecology of the dingo in north-eastern New South Wales. II. Diet. *Austr. Wildl. Res.* **12**: 39-50.

Robinson, I.H. & Delibes, M. (1988). The distribution of faeces by the Spanish lynx (*Felis pardina*). *J. Zool., London* **216**: 557-582.

Robitaille, J.F. & Raymond, M. (1995). Spacing patterns of ermine, *Mustela erminea* L., in a Quebec agrosystem. *Can. J. Zool.* **73**: 1827-1834.

Rodden, M.D., Rodrigues, F. & Bestelmeyer, S. (2004). Maned wolf *Chrysocyon brachyurus*. Pp. 38-43 in: Sillero-Zubiri, C., Hoffmann, M. & Macdonald, D.W. eds. (2004). *Canids: Foxes, Wolves, Jackals and Dogs. Status Survey and Conservation Action Plan*. IUCN/SSC Canid Specialist Group, Gland & Cambridge.

Rodden, M.D., Sorenson, L.G., Sherr, A. & Kleiman, D.G. (1996). Use of behavioral measures to assess reproductive function in maned wolves *Chrysocyon brachyurus*. *Zoo Biology* **15**: 565-585.

Rode, K.D. & Robbins, C.T. (2000). Why bears consume mixed diets during fruit abundance. *Can. J. Zool.* **78**: 1640-1645.

Rode, K.D., Farley, S.D. & Robbins, C.T. (2006). Sexual dimorphism, reproductive strategy and human activities determine resource use by brown bears. *Ecology* **87**: 2636-2646.

Rode, K.D., Robbins, C.T. & Shipley, L.A. (2001). Constraints on herbivory by grizzly bears. *Oecologia* **128**: 62-71.

Rodgers, W.A. (1974). The lion (*Panthera leo*, Linn.) population of the eastern Selous Game Reserve. *East Afr. Wildl. J.* **12**: 313-317.

Rodgers, W.A., Panwar, H.S. & Mathur, V.B. (2000). *Wildlife Protected Area Network in India: a Review (Executive Summary)*. Wildlife Institute of India, Dehradun, India.

Rodríguez, A. & Delibes, M. (1992). Current range and status of the Iberian lynx *Felis pardina* Temminck, 1824 in Spain. *Biol. Conserv.* **61**: 189-196.

Rodríguez, A., Martín, R. & Delibes, M. (1996). Space use and activity in a Mediterranean population of badgers *Meles meles*. *Acta Theriol.* **41**: 59-72.

Rodriguez, J.V. (1998). *Listas Preliminares de Mamíferos Colombianos con Algún Riesgo a la Extinción*. Informe final presentado al Instituto de Investigación de Recursos Biológicos Alexander von Humboldt, Bogotá.

Rodríguez-Bolaños, A., Cadena, A. & Sánches, P. (2000). Trophic characteristics in social groups of the mountain coati, *Nasuella olivacea* (Carnivora: Procyonidae). *Small Carniv. Conserv.* **23**: 1-6.

Rodríguez-Clark, K.M. & Sánchez-Mercado, A. (2006). Population management of threatened taxa in captivity within their natural ranges: lessons from Andean bears (*Tremarctos ornatus*) in Venezuela. *Biol. Conserv.* **129**: 132-148.

Rodriguez-Estrella, R., Moreno, A.R. & Tam, K.G. (2000). Spring diet of the endemic ring-tailed cat (*Bassariscus astutus insulicola*) population on an island in the Gulf of California, Mexico. *J. Arid Environm.* **44**: 241-246.

Roeder, J.J. (1978). Marking behaviour in genets (*G. genetta* L); seasonal variations and relations to social status in males. *Behaviour* **67**: 521-542.

Roeder, J.J. (1980). Marking behaviour and olfactory recognition in genets (*G. genetta* L., Carnivora: Viverridae). *Behaviour* **72**: 20-210.

Roeder, J.J. & Thierry, B. (1994). Possibility of long-term memory for conspecific scent marks in young genets (*Genetta genetta* L.). *Mammalia* **58**: 105-110.
Roeder, J.J., Kelche, C. & Vogel, E. (1989). Flank rubbing in genets (*Genetta genetta* L.): histological correlates. *Zeitschrift für Säugetierkunde* **54**: 324-328.
Roemer, G.W. (1999). *The Ecology and Conservation of the Island Fox* Urocyon littoralis. PhD thesis, University of California, Los Angeles, California.
Roemer, G.W. & Wayne, R.K. (2003). Conservation in conflict: the tale of two endangered species. *Conserv. Biol.* **17**: 1251-1260.
Roemer, G.W., Coonan, T.J., Garcelon, D.K., Bascompte, J. & Laughrin, L. (2001). Feral pigs facilitate hyperpredation by golden eagles and indirectly cause the decline of the island fox. *Anim. Conserv.* **4**: 307-318.
Roemer, G.W., Coonan, T.J., Munson, L. & Wayne, R.K. (2004). Island fox *Urocyon littoralis*. Pp. 97-105 in: Sillero-Zubiri, C., Hoffmann, M. & Macdonald, D.W. eds. (2004). *Canids: Foxes, Wolves, Jackals and Dogs. Status Survey and Conservation Action Plan.* IUCN/SSC Canid Specialist Group, Gland & Cambridge.
Roemer, G.W., Donlan, C.J. & Courchamp, F. (2002). Golden eagles, feral pigs and insular carnivores: how exotic species turn native predators into prey. *Proc. Natl. Acad. Sci. USA* **99**: 791-796.
Roemer, G.W., Garcelon, D.K., Coonan, T.J. & Schwemm, C. (1994). The use of capture-recapture methods for estimating, monitoring and conserving island fox populations. Pp. 387-400 in: Halvorsen, W.L. & Maender, G.J. eds. (1994). *The Fourth California Islands Symposium: Update on the Status of Resources.* Santa Barbara Museum of Natural History, Santa Barbara, California.
Rogers, C.M. & Caro, M.J. (1998). Song sparrows, top carnivores and nest predation: a test of the mesopredator release hypothesis. *Oecologia* **116**: 227-233.
Rogers, L.L. (1980). Inheritance of coat color and changes in pelage coloration in black bears in northeastern Minnesota. *J. Mammal.* **61**: 324-327.
Rogers, L.L. (1987). Effects of food supply and kinship on social behavior, movements, and population growth of black bears in northeastern Minnesota. *Wildl. Monogr.* **97**: 1-72.
Rogers, P.M. (1978). Predator-prey relationships between rabbit and lynx in southern Spain. *Terre Vie* **32**: 83-87.
Rohland, N., Pollack, J.L., Nagel, D., Beauval, C., Airvaux, J., Paabo, S. & Hofreiter, M. (2005). The population history of extant and extinct hyenas. *Mol. Biol. Evol.* **22**: 2435-2443.
Rohwer, S.A. & Kilgore, D.L. (1973). Interbreeding in arid-land foxes, *Vulpes velox* and *V. macrotis*. *Syst. Zool.* **22**: 157-166.
Roldan, A.I. & Simonetti, J.A. (2001). Plant-mammal interactions in tropical Bolivian forests with different hunting pressures. *Conserv. Biol.* **15**: 617-623.
Rolle, R.E. & Ward, W.D. (1985). Bobcat habitat use in southeastern Oklahoma. *J. Wildl. Management* **49**: 913-920.
Rollings, C.T. (1945). Habits, foods and parasites of the bobcat in Minnesota. *J. Wildl. Management* **9**: 131-145.
Romanowski, J. & Lesinski, G. (1991). A note on the diet of stone marten in southeastern Romania. *Acta Theriol.* **36**: 201-204.
Romer, A.S. & Parsons, T.S. (1986). *The Vertebrate Body.* 6th edition. Saunders College Publishing, Philadelphia, Pennsylvania.
Romero, T. & Aureli, F. (2007). Spatial association and social behaviour in zoo-living female ring-tailed coatis (*Nasua nasua*). *Behaviour* **144**: 179-193.
Romo, M.C. (1995). Food habits of the Andean fox *Pseudalopex culpaeus* and notes on the mountain cat *Felis colocolo* and puma *Felis concolor* in the Río Abiseo National Park, Perú. *Mammalia* **59**: 335-343.
Rondinini, C. & Boitani, L. (2002). Habitat use by beech martens in a fragmented landscape. *Ecography* **25**: 257-264.
Rondinini, C., Ercoli, V. & Boitani, L. (2006). Habitat use and preference by polecats (*Mustela putorius* L.) in a Mediterranean agricultural landscape. *J. Zool., London* **269**: 213-219.
Rood, J.P. (1974). Banded mongoose males guard young. *Nature (London)* **248**: 176-177.
Rood, J.P. (1975). Population dynamics and food habitats of the banded mongoose. *East Afr. Wildl. J.* **13**: 89-111.
Rood, J.P. (1978). Dwarf mongoose helpers at the den. *Zeitschr. Tierpsychol.* **48**: 277-287.
Rood, J.P. (1980). Mating relationships and breeding suppression in the dwarf mongoose. *Anim. Behav.* **28**: 143-150.
Rood, J.P. (1983a). The social system of the dwarf mongoose. Pp. 454-488 in: Eisenberg, J.F. & Kleiman, D.G. eds. (1983). *Advances in the Study of Mammalian Behavior.* American Society of Mammalogists, Lawrence, Switzerland.
Rood, J.P. (1983b). Banded mongoose rescues pack member from eagle. *Anim. Behav.* **31**: 1261-1262.
Rood, J.P. (1986). Ecology and social evolution in the mongooses. Pp. 131-152 in: Rubenstein, D.I. and Wrangham, R.W. eds. (1986). *Ecological Aspects of Social Evolution.* University Press, Princeton, New Jersey.
Rood, J.P. (1987). Dispersal and intergroup transfer in the dwarf mongoose. Pp. 85-103 in: Chepko-Sade, B.D. & Halpin, Z.T. eds. (1987). *Mammalian Dispersal Patterns.* Chicago University Press, Chicago, Illinois.
Rood, J.P. (1989). Male associations in a solitary mongoose. *Anim. Behav.* **38**: 725-728.
Rood, J.P. (1990). Group size, survival, reproduction and routes to breeding in dwarf mongooses. *Anim. Behav.* **39**: 566-572.
Roper, T.J. (1994). The European badger *Meles meles*: food specialist or generalist? *J. Zool., London* **234**: 437-452.
Roper, T.J. & Lups, P. (1995). Diet of badgers (*Meles meles*) in central Switzerland: an analysis of stomach contents. *Zeitschrift für Säugetierkunde* **60**: 9-19.
Roper, T.J., Ostler, J.R., Schmid, T.K. & Christian, S.F. (2001). Sett use in European badgers *Meles meles*. *Behaviour* **138(2)**: 137-187.
Rosalino, L.M. & Santos-Reis, M. (2002). Feeding habits of the common genet *Genetta genetta* (Carnivora: Viverridae) in a semi-natural landscape of central Portugal. *Mammalia* **66**: 195-205.
Rosalino, L.M., Loureiro, F., Santos-Reis, M. & Macdonald, D.W. (2002). First data on the social and spatial structure of an Eurasian badger (*Meles meles* L., 1758) population in a cork oak woodland (SW Portugal). *Rev. Biol.* **20**: 147-154.
Rosas, F.C.W., Zuanon, J.A.S. & Carter, S.K. (1999). Feeding ecology of the giant otter, *Pteronura brasiliensis*. *Biotropica* **31**: 502-506.
Rosas-Rosas, O.C., Valdez, R., Bender, L.C. & Daniel, D. (2003). Food habits of pumas in northwestern Sonora, Mexico. *Wildl. Soc. Bull.* **31**: 528-535.
Rosatte, R.C. (1984). Seasonal occurrence and habitat preference of rabid skunks in southern Alberta. *Can. Vet. J.* **25**: 142-144.
Rosatte, R.C. (1988). Rabies in Canada: history, epidemiology and control. *Can. Vet. J.* **29**: 362-365.
Rosatte, R.C. & Gunson, J.R. (1984a). Dispersal and home range of striped skunks, *Mephitis mephitis*, in an area of population reduction in southern Alberta. *Can. Field-Nat.* **98**: 315-319.
Rosatte, R.C. & Gunson, J.R. (1984b). Presence of neutralizing antibodies to rabies virus in striped skunks from areas free of skunk rabies in Alberta. *J. Wildl. Diseases* **20**: 171-176.
Rosatte, R.C., Power, M.J. & MacInnes, C.D. (1991). Ecology of urban skunks, raccoons and foxes in metropolitan Toronto. Pp. 31-38 in: Adams, L.W. & Leedy, D.L. eds. (1991). *Wildlife Conservation in Metropolitan Environments.* National Institute for Urban Wildlife, Columbia, Maryland.
Rosatte, R.C., Power, M.J., MacInnes, C.D. & Campbell, J.B. (1992). Trap-vaccinate-release and oral vaccination for rabies control in urban skunks, raccoons, and foxes. *J. Wildl. Diseases* **28**: 562-571.
Rosatte, R.C., Pybus, M.J. & Gunson, J.R. (1986). Population reduction as a factor in the control of skunk rabies in Alberta. *J. Wildl. Diseases* **22**: 459-467.
Rosellini, S., Barja, I. & Pineiro, A. (2007). Distribution and feeding habits of the pine marten (*Martes martes*) at Os Montes do Invernadeiro Natural Park (Galicia, NW Spain). *Galemys* **19**: 99-114.
Rosevear, D.R. (1974). *The Carnivores of West Africa.* Trustees of the British Museum (Natural History), London.
Rosing-Asvid, A. (2006). The influence of climate variability on polar bear (*Ursus maritimus*) and ringed seal (*Pusa hispida*) population dynamics. *Can. J. Zool.* **84**: 357-364.
Ross, P.I. & Jalkotzy, M.G. (1996). Cougar predation on moose in southwestern Alberta. *Aleces* **32**: 1-8.
Ross-Gillespie, A. & Griffin, A.S. (2007). Meerkats. *Curr. Biol.* **17**: R442-R443.
Rounds, R.C. (1987). Distribution and analysis of colourmorphs of the black bear (*Ursus americanus*). *J. Biogeogr.* **14**: 521-538.
Rowe, T. (1996). Coevolution of the mammalian middle ear and neocortex. *Science* **273**: 651-654.
Rowe-Rowe, D.T. (1971). The development and behaviour of a rusty-spotted genet, *Genetta rubiginosa* Pucheran. *Lammergeyer* **13**: 29-44.
Rowe-Rowe, D.T. (1972). The African weasel, *Poecilogale albinucha* (Gray): observations on behaviour and general biology. *Lammergeyer* **15**: 39-58.
Rowe-Rowe, D.T. (1977a). Food ecology of otters in Natal, South Africa. *Oikos* **28**: 210-219.
Rowe-Rowe, D.T. (1977b). Prey capture and feeding behaviour of South African otters. *Lammergeyer* **23**: 13-21.
Rowe-Rowe, D.T. (1978a). The small carnivores of Natal. *Lammergeyer* **25**: 1-48.
Rowe-Rowe, D.T. (1978b). Comparative prey capture and food studies of South African mustelines. *Mammalia* **42**: 175-196.
Rowe-Rowe, D.T. (1978c). Reproduction and post-natal development of South African mustelines (Carnivores: Mustelidae). *Zool. Afr.* **13**: 103-114.
Rowe-Rowe, D.T. (1982). Home range and movements of black-backed jackals in an African montane region. *South Afr. J. Wildl. Res.* **12**: 79-84.
Rowe-Rowe, D.T. (1983). Black-backed jackal diet in relation to food availability in the Natal Drakensberg. *South Afr. J. Wildl. Res.* **13**: 18-23.
Rowe-Rowe, D.T. (1992a). Survey of South African otters in a freshwater habitat, using sign. *South Afr. J. Wildl. Res.* **22**: 49-55.
Rowe-Rowe, D.T. (1992b). *The Carnivores of Natal.* Natal Parks Board, Pietermaritzburg, South Africa.
Rowe-Rowe, D.T. (1995). Distribution and status of African otters. *Habitat* **11**: 8-10.
Rowe-Rowe, D.T. & Somers, M.J. (1998). Diet, foraging behaviour and coexistence of African otters and the water mongoose. *Symp. Zool. Soc. London* **71**: 216-227.
Rowlatt, U. (1990). Comparative anatomy of the heart of mammals. *Zool. J. Linn. Soc.* **98**: 73-100.
Roy, S. (2002a). An ecological basis for control of the mongoose *Herpestes javanicus* in Mauritius: is eradication possible? Pp. 266-273 in: Veitch, C.R. & Clout, M.N. ed. (2002). *Turning the Tide: the Eradication of Invasive Species.* IUCN SSC Invasive Species Specialist Group. IUCN, Gland & Cambridge.
Roy, S. (2002b). The small Indian mongoose: probably one of the most successful small carnivores in the world? *Small Carniv. Conserv.* **26**: 21-22.
Roychoudhury, A.K. (1987). White tigers and their conservation. Pp. 380-388 in: Tilson, R.L. & Seal, U.S. eds. (1987). *Tigers of the World: the Biology, Biopolitics, Management and Conservation of an Endangered Species.* Noyes Publications, Park Ridge, New Jersey.
Rozhnov, V.V. (1994). Notes on the behavior and ecology of the binturong (*Arctictis binturong*) in Vietnam. *Small Carniv. Conserv.* **10**: 4-5.
Rozhnov, V.V., Kuznetzov, G.V. & Anh, P.T. (1992). New distributional information on Owston's palm civet. *Small Carniv. Conserv.* **6**: 7.
Rucker, R.A., Kennedy, M.L., Heidt, G.A. & Harvey, M.J. (1989). Population density, movements and habitat use of bobcats in Arkansas. *Southwest. Nat.* **34**: 101-108.
Rudnai, J. (1973a). Reproductive biology of lions (*Panthera leo massaica*, Neumann) in the Nairobi National Park. *East Afr. Wildl. J.* **11**: 241-253.
Rudnai, J. (1973b). *The Social Life of the Lion.* Medical & Technical, Lancaster, UK.
Rudnai, J. (1974). The pattern of lion predation in Nairobi Park. *East Afr. Wildl. J.* **12**: 213-225.

Ruediger, B., Claar, J., Mighton, S., Naney, B., Rinaldi, T., Wahl, F., Warren, N., Wenger, D., Williamson, A., Lewis, L., Holt, B., Patton, G., Trick, J., Vandehey, A. & Gniadek, S. (2000). *Canada Lynx Conservation Assessment and Strategy.* Report to the US Department of Agriculture & US Department of Interior.

Ruff, S. & Wilson, D.E. (2000). *Bats.* Animal Ways. Benchmark Books, White Plains, New York.

Ruggiero, L.F., Aubrey, K.B., Buskirk, S.W., Koehler, G.M., Crebs, C.J., McKelvey, K.S. & Squires, J.R. (1999). *Ecology and Conservation of Canada Lynx in the United States.* University of Oklahoma Press & USDA.

Ruggiero, L.F., Pearson, D.E. & Henry, S.E. (1998). Characteristics of American marten den sites in Wyoming. *J. Wildl. Management* **62**: 663-673.

Ruggiero, R.G. (1991). Prey selection of the lion (*Panthera leo* L.) in the Manovo-Gounda-St. Floris National Park, Central African Republic. *Mammalia* **55**: 23-33.

Ruiz-Garcia, M. (2003). Molecular population genetic analysis of the spectacled bear (*Tremarctos ornatus*) in the northern Andean area. *Hereditas* **138**: 81-93.

Ruiz-Miranda, C., Wells, S., Golden, R. & Seidensticker, J. (1998). Vocalizations and other behavioral responses of male cheetah (*Acinonyx jubatus*) during experimental separation and reunion trials. *Zoo Biology* **17**: 1-16.

Russell, A.F., Brotherton, P.N.M., McIlrath, G.M., Sharpe, L.L. & Clutton-Brock, T.H. (2003). Breeding success in cooperative meerkats: effects of helper number and maternal state. *Behav. Ecol.* **14**: 486-492.

Russell, A.F., Carlson, A.A., McIlrath, G.M., Jordan, N.R. & Clutton-Brock, T. (2004). Adaptive size modification by dominant female meerkats. *Evolution* **58**: 1600-1607.

Russell, A.F., Clutton-Brock, T.H., Brotherton, P.N.M., Sharpe, L.L., McIlrath, G.M., Dalerum, F.D., Cameron, E.Z. & Barnard, J.A. (2002). Factors affecting pup growth and survival in co-operatively breeding meerkats *Suricata suricatta*. *J. Anim. Ecol.* **71**: 700-709.

Russell, A.F., Sharpe, L.L., Brotherton, P.N.M. & Clutton-Brock, T.H. (2003). Cost minimization by helpers in cooperative vertebrates. *Proc. Natl. Acad. Sci. USA* **100**: 3333-3338.

Russell, A.F., Young, A.J., Spong, G., Jordan, N.R. & Clutton-Brock, T.H. (2007). Helpers increase the reproductive potential of offspring in cooperative meerkats. *Proc. Royal Soc. London (Ser. B Biol. Sci.)* **274**: 513-520.

Russell, A.J.M. & Storch, I. (2004). Summer food of sympatric red fox and pine marten in the German Alps. *Eur. J. Wildl. Res.* **50**: 53-58.

Ruth, T.K., Logan, K.A., Sweanor, L.L., Hornocker, M.G. & Temple, L.J. (1998). Evaluating cougar translocation in New Mexico. *J. Wildl. Management* **62**: 1264-1275.

Ryan, J.M., Creighton, G.K. & Emmons, L.H. (1993). Activity patterns of two species of *Nesomys* (Muridae: Nesomyinae) in a Madagascar rainforest. *J. Trop. Ecol.* **9**: 101-107.

Ryon, J. & Brown, R.E. (1990). Urine marking in female wolves (*Canis lupus*): an indicator of dominance status and reproductive state. Pp. 346-351 in: Macdonald, D.W., Müller-Swarze, D. & Natynczuk, S.E. eds. (1990). *Chemical Signals in Vertebrates.* V. Oxford University Press, Oxford.

Saarma, U., Ho, S.Y.W., Pybus, O.G., Kaljuste, M., Tumanov, I.L., Kojola, I., Vorobiev, A.A., Markov, N.I., Saveljev, A.P., Valdmann, H., Lyapunova, E.A., Abramov, A.V., Mannil, P., Korsten, M., Vulla, E., Pazetnov, S.V., Pazetnov, V.S., Putchkovskiy, S.V. & Rokov, A.M. (2007). Mitogenetic structure of brown bears (*Ursus arctos* L.) in northeastern Europe and a new time frame for the formation of European brown bear lineages. *Mol. Ecol.* **16**: 401-413.

Sacchi, O. & Meriggi, A. (1995). Habitat requirements of the stone marten (*Martes foina*) on the tyrrhenian slopes of the northern Apennines. *Hystrix* **7(1-2)**: 99-104.

Sacco, T. & Van Valkenburgh, B. (2004). Ecomorphological indicators of feeding behaviour in the bears (Carnivora: Ursidae). *J. Zool., London* **263**: 41-54.

Sadleir, R.M.F.S. (1966). Notes on reproduction in the larger Felidae. *Int. Zoo Yb.* **6**: 184-187.

Saeki, M. (2001). *Ecology and Conservation of the Raccoon Dog (*Nyctereutes procyonoides*) in Japan.* DPhil dissertation, Wildlife Conservation Research Unit, University of Oxford, Oxford.

Saint Girons, M.C. (1962). Notes sur les dates de reproduction en captivite du fennec, *Fennecus zerda* Zimmerman, 1780. *Zietschrift für Säugertierkunde* **27**: 181-184.

Saksaki, H. (1991). The present status of mustelids and viverrids in Japan. *Mustel. Viverr. Conserv.* **4**: 14-15.

Sale, J.B. & Taylor, M.E. (1970). A new four-toed mongoose from Kenya, *Bdeogale crassicauda nigrescens* ssp. *nov. J. East Afr. Nat. Hist. Soc. & Natl. Mus.* **28**: 11-16.

Saleh, M.A. & Basuony, M.I. (1998). A contribution to the mammalogy of the Sinaï peninsula. *Mammalia* **62**: 557-575.

Saleh, M.A., Helmy, I. & Giegengack, R. (2001). The cheetah *Acinonyx jubatus* (Schreber, 1776) in Egypt. *Mammalia* **65(2)**: 177-194.

Salesa, M., Antón, M., Peigné, S. & Morales, J. (2006). Evidence of a false thumb in a fossil carnivore clarifies the evolution of pandas. *Proc. Natl. Acad. Sci. USA* **103**: 379-382.

Salles, L.O. (1992). Felid phylogenetics: extant taxa and skull morphology (Felidae, Aeluroidea). *Amer. Mus. Novit.* **3047**: 1-67.

Salvatori, V., Vaglio-Laurin, G., Meserve, P.L., Boitani, L. & Campanella, A. (1999). Spatial organization, activity and social interactions of culpeo foxes *Pseudalopex culpaeus* in north-central Chile. *J. Mammal.* **80**: 980-985.

Samelius, G. & Lee, M. (1998). Arctic fox *Alopex lagopus* predation on lesser snow geese *Chen caerulescens* and their eggs. *Can. Field-Nat.* **112**: 700-701.

Samson, C. & Huot, J. (1995). Reproductive biology of female black bears in relation to body mass in early winter. *J. Mammal.* **76**: 68-77.

Samson, C. & Raymond, M. (1998). Movement and habitat preference of radio tracked stoats, *Mustela erminea*, during summer in southern Quebec. *Mammalia* **62**: 165-174.

Samson, F.B. (1979). Multivariate analysis of cranial characteristics among bobcats, with a preliminary discussion on the number of subspecies. Pp. 80-86 in: Blum, L.G. & Escherich, P.C. eds. (1979). *Proceedings of the Bobcat Research Conference.* National Wildlife Federation Science Technical Series **6**.

San, E.D.L., Ferrari, N. & Weber, J.M. (2007). Socio-spatial organization of Eurasian badgers (*Meles meles*) in a low-density population of central Europe. *Can. J. Zool.* **85**: 973-984.

Sanborn, C.C. (1952). Philippine Zoological Expedition 1946-1947: mammals. *Fieldiana Zool.* **33**: 89-158.

Sandegren, F.E., Chu, E.W. & Vandevere, J.E. (1973). Maternal behavior in the California sea otter. *J. Mammal.* **54**: 668-679.

Sanderson, E.W., Redford, K.H., Chetkiewicz, C.B., Medellin, R.A., Rabinowitz, R.A., Robinson, J.G. & Taber, A.B. (2002). Planning to save a species: the jaguar as a model. *Conserv. Biol.* **16**: 1-15.

Sanderson, J.G. (1999). Andean mountain cats (*Oreailurus jacobita*) in northern Chile. *Cat News* **30**: 25-26.

Sanderson, J.G., Sunquist, M.E. & Iriarte, A.W. (2002). Natural history and landscape-use of guignas (*Oncifelis guigna*) on Isla Grande de Chiloé, Chile. *J. Mammal.* **83**: 608-613.

Sankar, K. (1988). Some observations on food habits of jackals *Canis aureus* in Keolaeo National Park, Bharatpur, as shown by scat analysis. *J. Bombay Nat. Hist. Soc.* **85**: 185-186.

Sankhala, K.S. (1977). *Tiger: the Story of the Indian Tiger.* Simon & Schuster, New York.

Santiapillai, C. (1989). The status and conservation of the clouded leopard (*Neofelis nebulosa diardi*) in Sumatra. *Tigerpaper* **16(1)**: 1-7.

Santiapillai, C. & Ashby, K.R. (1988). The clouded leopard in Sumatra. *Oryx* **22**: 44-45.

Santiapillai, C. & Supraham, H. (1985). On the status of the leopard cat (*Felis bengalensis*) in Sumatra. *Tigerpaper* **12**: 8-13.

Santiapillai, C. & Widodo, S.R. (1985). On the status of the tiger (*Panthera tigris sumatae* Pocock, 1829) in Sumatra. *Tigerpaper* **12**: 23-29.

Santiapillai, C. & Widodo, S.R. (1987). Tiger numbers and habitat evaluation in Indonesia. Pp. 85-91 in: Tilson, R.L. & Seal, U.S. eds. (1987). *Tigers of the World: the Biology, Biopolitics, Management and Conservation of an Endangered Species.* Noyes Publications, Park Ridge, New Jersey.

Santiapillai, C., De Silva, M. & Dissanayake, S.R. (2000). The status of mongooses (family: Herpestidae) in Ruhuna National Park, Sri Lanka. *J. Bombay Nat. Hist. Soc.* **97**: 208-214.

Santos, E.F. (1999). *Ecologia Alimentar e Dispersão de Sementes pelo Lobo-guará* (Chrysocyon brachyurus, *Illiger, 1811) em uma Área Rural no Sudeste do Brasil (Carnivora: Canidae).* MSc thesis, UNESP, Rio Claro, Brazil.

Sapozhenkov, Y.F. (1961). On the ecology of *Felis lybica* Forst, in eastern Kara-Kumy. *Zool. Zhurnal* **41**: 1110-1112.

Sargeant, A.B. & Warner, D.W. (1972). Movements and denning habits of a badger. *J. Mammal.* **53**: 207-210.

Sasaki, H. (1991). The present status of mustelids and viverrids in Japan. *Mustel. Viverr. Conserv.* **4**: 14-15.

Sasaki, H. & Ono, Y. (1994). Habitat use and selection of the Siberian weasel *Mustela sibirica coreana* during the non-mating season. *J. Mammal. Soc. Japan* **19**: 21-32.

Sasaki, M., Endo, H., Wiig, O., Derocher, A.E., Tsubota, T., Taru, H., Yamamoto, M., Arishima, K., Hayashi, Y., Kitamura, N. & Yamada, J. (2005). Adaptation of the hindlimbs for climbing in bears. *Ann. Anat.* **187**: 153-160.

Sathyakumar, S. (2001). Status and management of Asiatic black bear and Himalayan brown bear in India. *Ursus* **12**: 21-30.

Sato, J.J., Hosoda, T., Wolsan, M. & Suzuki, H. (2004). Molecular phylogeny of arctoids (Mammalia: Carnivora) with emphasis on phylogenetic and taxonomic positions of the ferret-badgers and skunks. *Zool. Science (Tokyo)* **21**: 111-118.

Sato, J.J., Hosoda, T., Wolsan, M., Tsuchiya, K., Yamamoto, Y. & Suzuki, H. (2003). Phylogenetic relationships and divergence times among mustelids (Mammalia: Carnivora) based on nucleotide sequences of the nuclear interphotoreceptor retinoid binding protein and mitochondrial cytochrome *b* genes. *Zool. Science (Tokyo)* **20**: 243-264.

Sato, J.J., Wolsan, M., Suzuki, H., Hosoda, T., Yamaguchi, Y., Hiyama, K., Kobayashi, M. & Minami, S. (2006). Evidence from nuclear DNA sequences sheds light on the phylogenetic relationships of pinnipedia: single origin with affinity to musteloidea. *Zool. Science (Tokyo)* **23**: 125-146.

Saunders, J.K. (1963). Movements and activities of the lynx in Newfoundland. *J. Wildl. Management* **27**: 390-400.

Saunders, J.K. (1964). Physical characteristics of the Newfoundland lynx. *J. Mammal.* **45**: 36-47.

Saunders, N.J. (1991). *The Cult of the Cat.* Thames & Hudson, London.

Sausman, K. (1997). Sand cat *Felis margarita*: a true desert species. *Int. Zoo Yb.* **35**: 78-81.

Savage, D.E. & Russell, D.E. (1983). *Mammalian Paleofauna of the World.* Addison-Wesley Publishing Company, London.

Scantlebury, M., Russell, A.F., McIlrath, G.M., Speakman, J.R. & Clutton-Brock, T.H. (2002). The energetics of lactation in cooperatively breeding meerkats *Suricata suricatta*. *Proc. Royal Soc. London (Ser. B Biol. Sci.)* **269**: 2147-2153.

Schaffer, N. & Rosenthal, M. (1984). Report on the flat-headed cat reproductive projects initially funded from support from the Institute of Museum Services, Special Conservation Project. Unpublished report to the Lincoln Park Zoo, Chicago, Illinois. 96 pp.

Schaller, G.B. (1967). *The Deer and the Tiger.* University of Chicago Press, Chicago, Illinois.

Schaller, G.B. (1968). Hunting behaviour of the cheetah in the Serengeti National Park, Tanzania. *East Afr. Wildl. J.* **6**: 95-100.

Schaller, G.B. (1972). *The Serengeti Lion: a Study of Predator-Prey Relations.* University of Chicago Press, Chicago, Illinois.

Schaller, G.B. (1998). *Wildlife of the Tibetan Steppe.* University of Chicago Press, Chicago, Illinois.

Schaller, G.B. & Crawshaw, P.G. (1980). Movement patterns of jaguars. *Biotropica* **12(3)**: 161-168.

Schaller, G.B. & Ginsberg, J.R. (2004). Tibetan fox *Vulpes ferrilata*. Pp. 148-151 in: Sillero-Zubiri, C., Hoffmann, M. & Macdonald, D.W. eds. (2004). *Canids: Foxes, Wolves, Jackals and Dogs. Status Survey and Conservation Action Plan.* IUCN/SSC Canid Specialist Group, Gland & Cambridge.

Schaller, G.B. & Vasconcelos, J.M.C. (1978). Jaguar predation on capybara. *Zeitschrift für Säugetierkunde* **43**: 296-301.

Schaller, G.B., Hu, J., Pan, W. & Zhu, J. (1985). *The Giant Pandas of Wolong.* University of Chicago, Chicago, Illinois.

Schaller, G.B., Ren Junrang & Qiu Mingjiang (1988). Status of the snow leopard *Panthera uncia* in Qinghai and Gansu Provinces, China. *Biol. Conserv.* **45**: 179-194.

Schaller, G.B., Teng, Q., Johnson, K.G., Wang, X., Shen, H. & Hu, J. (1989). The feeding ecology of giant pandas and Asiatic black bears in the Tangjiahe Reserve, China. Pp. 212-240 in: Gittleman, J.L. ed. (1989). *Carnivore Behavior, Ecology and Evolution*. Vol. 1. Cornell University Press, Ithaca, New York.

Schaller, G.B., Tserendeleg, J. & Amarsanaa, G. (1994). Observations on snow leopards in Mongolia. Pp. 33-42 in: Fox, J.L. & Du Jizeng eds. (1994). *Proceedings of the Seventh International Snow Leopard Symposium*. International Snow Leopard Trust & Chicago Zoological Society, Seattle, Washington.

Schauenberg, P. (1974). Données nouvelles sur le chat des sables *Felis margarita* Loche, 1858. *Rev. Suisse Zool.* **81**: 949-969.

Schauenberg, P. (1978). Note sur la reproduction du manul *Octocolobus manul* (Pallas, 1776). *Mammalia* **42**: 355-358.

Schauenberg, P. (1979a). Note sur la reproduction du chat du bengale. *Mammalia* **43**: 127-128.

Schauenberg, P. (1979b). La reproduction du chat des marais *Felis chaus* (Guldenstadt, 1776). *Mammalia* **43**: 215-223.

Schauster, E.R., Gese, E.M. & Kitchen, A.M. (2002a). An evaluation of survey methods for monitoring swift fox abundance. *Wildl. Soc. Bull.* **30**: 464-477.

Schauster, E.R., Gese, E.M. & Kitchen, A.M. (2002b). Population ecology of swift foxes *Vulpes velox* in southeastern Colorado. *Can. J. Zool.* **80**: 307-319.

Scheel, D. & Packer, C. (1991). Group hunting behaviour of lions: a search for cooperation. *Anim. Behav.* **41**: 697-709.

Scheffel, W. & Hemmer, H. (1975). Breeding Geoffroy's cat in captivity. *Int. Zoo Yb.* **15**: 152-154.

Schenkel, R. (1966). Play, exploitation and territoriality in the wild lion. *Symp. Zool. Soc. London* **18**: 11-22.

Scheumann, M., Rabesandratana, A. & Zimmermann, E. (2007). Predation, communication and cognition in lemurs. Pp. 100-126 in: Gursky, S.L. & Nekaris, K.A.I. eds. (2007). *Primate Anti-predator Strategies*. Springer Press, New York.

Schlawe, L. (1980). Zur geographischen Verbreitung der Ginsterkatzen, Gattung *Genetta* G. Cuvier, 1816 (Mammalia, Carnivora, Viverridae). *Faun. Abh. (Dresden)* **7**: 147-161.

Schlawe, L. (1981). Material, Fundorte, Text- und Bildquellen als Grundlagen für eine Artenliste zur Revision der Gattung *Genetta* G. Cuvier, 1816. *Zool. Abh. (Dresden)* **37**: 85-182.

Schlegel, H. (1879). Notes XIV. *Paradoxurus musschenbroeckii. Notes Leyden Mus.* **1**: 43.

Schliebe, S., Wiig, Ø., Derocher, A.E. & Lunn, N.J. (2006). *Ursus maritimus* polar bear. In: *2007 IUCN Red List of Threatened Species*. URL: http://www.iucnredlist.org.html

Schlitter, D.A. (1974). Notes on the Liberian mongoose, *Liberiictis kuhni* Hayman 1958. *J. Mammal.* **55**: 438-442.

Schmidly, D.J. (1977). *The Mammals of Trans-Pecos Texas*. Texas A&M University Press, College Station, Texas.

Schmidly, D.J. (1983). *Texas Mammals East of the Balcones Fault Zone*. Texas A&M University Press, College Station, Texas.

Schmidly, D.J. (2002). *Texas Natural History: a Century of Change*. Texas Tech University Press, Lubbock, Texas.

Schmidly, D.J. (2004). *The Mammals of Texas*. Revised edition. University of Texas Press, Austin, Texas.

Schmidly, D.J. & Hendricks, F.S. (1984). Mammals of the San Carlos Mountains of Tamaulipas, Mexico. Pp. 1-234 in: Martin, R.E. & Chapman, B.R. eds. (1984). *Contributions in Mammalogy in Honor of Robert L. Packard*. Special Publications Museum, Texas Tech University, Lubbock, Texas.

Schmidt, G.A., Garcelon, D.K. & Sloan, J. (2002). Fox monitoring and research in support of the San Clemente Loggerhead Shrike Predator Control Program on Naval Auxillary Landing Field, San Clemente Island, California. Institute for Wildlife Studies, Arcata, California. Unpublished report submitted to the US Navy, Natural Resources Management Branch, Southwest Division, Naval Facilities Engineering Command, San Diego, California.

Schmidt, K. (1999). Variation in daily activity of the free-living Eurasian lynx (*Lynx lynx*) in Bialowieza Primeval Forest, Poland. *J. Zool., London* **249**: 417-425.

Schmidt, K., Jedrzejewski, W. & Okarma, H. (1997). Spatial organization and social relations in the Eurasian lynx population in Bialowieza Primeval Forest, Poland. *Acta Theriol.* **42**: 289-312.

Schmidt, K.A. (2003). Nest predation and population declines in Illinois songbirds: a case for mesopredator effects. *Conserv. Biol.* **17**: 1141-1150.

Schmidt-Kittler, N. (1981). Zur Stammesgeschichte der marderverwandten Raubtiergruppen (Musteloidea, Carnivora). *Eclogae Geol. Helv.* **74**: 753-801.

Schoener, T.W. (1974). Resource partitioning in ecological communities. *Science* **185**: 27-39.

Schouteden, H. (1945). De zoogdieren van Belgisch Congo en van Ruanda-Burundi II. Carnivora (2), Ungulata (1). *Annalen van het Museum van belgisch Congo. C. Dierkunde. Reeks II. Deel III. Aflevering* **2**: 169-332.

Schreiber, A., Wirth, R., Riffel, M. & Van Rompaey, H. (1989). *Weasels, Civets, Mongooses and their Relatives. An Action Plan for the Conservation of Mustelids and Viverrids*. IUCN/SSC Mustelid and Viverrid Specialist Group, Gland, Switzerland.

Schultz, W.C. (1966). Breeding and hand-rearing of brown hyaenas at Okahandja Zoopark. *Int. Zoo Yb.* **6**: 173-176.

Schwartz, C.C. & Franzmann, A.W. (1991). Interrelationship of black bears to moose and forest succession in the northern coniferous forest. *Wildl. Monogr.* **113**: 1-58.

Schwartz, C.C., Haroldson, M.A., White, G.C., Harris, R.B., Cherry, S., Keating, K.A., Moody, D. & Servheen, C. (2006). Temporal, spatial and environmental influences on the demographics of grizzly bears in the Greater Yellowstone Ecosystem. *Wildl. Monogr.* **161**: 1-68.

Schwartz, C.C., Keating, K.A., Reynolds, H.V., Barnes, V.G., Sellers, R.A., Swenson, J.E., Miller, S.D., McLellan, B.N., Keay, J., McCann, R., Gibeau, M., Wakkinen, W.F., Mace, R.D., Kasworm, W., Smith, R. & Herrero, S. (2003). Reproductive maturation and senescence in the female brown bear. *Ursus* **14**: 109-119.

Schwartz, C.C., Miller, S.D. & Haroldson, M.A. (2003). Grizzly bear *Ursus arctos*. Pp. 556-586 in: Feldhamer, G.A., Thompson, B.C. & Chapman, J.A. eds. (2003). *Wild Mammals of North America: Biology, Management and Conservation*. 2nd edition. Johns Hopkins University Press, Baltimore, Maryland.

Schwarz, E. (1938). Blue or dilute mutation in Alaskan lynx. *J. Mammal.* **19**: 376.

Schwarz, E. (1947). Colour mutant of the Malay short-tailed Mongoose, *Herpestes brachyurus*. *Proc. Zool. Soc. London* **117**: 79-80.

Schwarzenberger, F., Fredricksson, G., Schaller, K. & Kolter, L. (2004). Fecal steroid analysis for monitoring reproduction in the sun bear (*Helarctos malayanus*). *Theriogenology* **62**: 1677-1692.

Schwenk, K. ed. (2000). *Feeding: Form, Function and Evolution in Tetrapod Vertebrates*. Academic Press, New York.

Scognamillo, D., Maxit, I.E., Sunquist, M. & Polisar, J. (2003). Coexistence of jaguar (*Panthera onca*) and puma (*Puma concolor*) in a mosaic landscape in the Venezuelan llanos. *J. Zool., London* **259**: 269-279.

Scosta-Jamett, G. & Simonetti, J.A. (2004). Habitat use by *Oncifelis guigna* and *Pseudolopex culapeus* in a forest landscape in central Chile. *Biodiversity & Conservation* **13**: 1135-1151.

Scott, J. (1985). *The Leopard's Tale*. Elm Tree Books, London.

Scott, R., Easterbee, N. & Jefferies, D. (1993). A radio-tracking study of wildcats in western Scotland. Pp. 94-97 in: *Seminar on the Biology and Conservation of the Wildcat*. Council of Europe Press, Strasbourg.

Scrocchi, G.J. & Halloy, S.P. (1986). Systematic, ecological, ethological and biogeographical notes on the Andean mountain cat *Felis jacobita* Cornalia (Felidae, Carnivora). *Acta. Zool. Lilloana* **38**: 157-170.

Seaman, G.A. (1952). The mongoose and Caribbean wildlife. *Trans. North Amer. Wildl. Conf.* **17**: 188-197.

Seaman, G.A. & Randall, J.E. (1962). The mongoose as a predator in the Virgin Islands. *J. Mammal.* **43**: 344-345.

Sebastian, A. (2005). Sighting of a Sunda otter civet *Cynogale bennettii* in Sarawak. *Small Carniv. Conserv.* **33**: 24-25.

Seidensticker, J. (1976a). On the ecological separation between tigers and leopards. *Biotropica* **8**: 225-234.

Seidensticker, J. (1976b). Ungulate populations in Chitawan Valley, Nepal. *Biol. Conserv.* **10**: 183-210.

Seidensticker, J. (1977). Notes on early maternal behavior of the leopard. *Mammalia* **41**: 111-113.

Seidensticker, J. (1987). Bearing witness: observations of the extinction of *Panthera tigris balica* and *Panthera tigris sondaica*. Pp. 1-8 in: Tilson, R.L. & Seal, U.S. eds. (1987). *Tigers of the World: the Biology, Biopolitics, Management and Conservation of an Endangered Species*. Noyes Publications, Park Ridge, New Jersey.

Seidensticker, J. & Hai, A. (1983). *The Sundarbans Wildlife Management Plan: Conservation in the Bangladesh Coastal Zone*. IUCN, Gland, Switzerland.

Seidensticker, J. & McDougal, C. (1993). Tiger predatory behaviour, ecology and conservation. *Symp. Zool. Soc. London* **65**: 105-125.

Seidensticker, J., Christie, S. & Jackson, P. eds. (1999). *Riding the Tiger: Tiger Conservation in Human-dominated Landscapes*. Cambridge University Press, Cambridge.

Seidensticker, J., Hornocker, M.G., Wiles, W.V. & Messick, J.P. (1973). *Mountain Lion Social Organization in the Idaho Primitive Area*. Wildlife Monographs **35**. 60 pp.

Seidensticker, J., Sunquist, M.E. & McDougal, C. (1990). Leopards living at the edge of Royal Chitwan National Park, Nepal. Pp. 415-423 in: Daniel, J.C. & Serrao, J.S. eds. (1990). *Conservation in Developing Countries: Problems and Prospects*. Proceedings of the Centenary Seminar of the Bombay Natural History Society. Bombay Natural History Society, Bombay.

Sekiguchi, K., Ogura, G., Sasaki, T., Nagayama, Y., Tsuha, K. & Kawashima, Y. (2002). Food habits of introduced Japanese weasels (*Mustela itatsi*) and impacts on native species of Zamami Island. *Mammal. Sci.* **42**: 153-160.

Selas, V. (1991). Social organization of pine marten. *Fauna, Oslo* **44**: 214-219.

Self, J.T. & Kuntz, R.E. (1967). Host-parasite relations in some Pentastomida. *J. Parasitol.* **53**: 202-206.

Serfass, T.L. (1995). Cooperative foraging by North American river otters, *Lutra canadensis*. *Can. Field-Nat.* **109**: 458-459.

Serfass, T.L. & Rymon, L.M. (1985). Success of river otter introduced in pine creek drainage in northcentral Pennsylvania. *Trans. Northeast Sect. Wildl. Soc.* **41**: 138-149.

Serpell, J. (1991). Domestic cat. Pp. 184-189 in: Seidensticker, J. & Lumpkin, S. eds. (1991). *Great Cats. Majestic Creatures of the Wild*. Merehurst, London.

Serra, R.C. & Sarmento, P. (2006). The Iberian lynx in Portugal: conservation status and perspectives. *Cat News* **45**: 15-16.

Servheen, C. (1989). The status and conservation of the bears of the world. *Int. Conf. Bear Res. Management Monogr.* **2**: 1-32.

Servheen, C., Herrero, S. & Peyton, B. (1999). *Bears. Status Survey and Conservation Action Plan*. IUCN/SSC Bear and Polar Bear Specialist Groups, IUCN, Gland & Cambridge.

Seryodkin, I.V., Kostyria, A.V., Goodrich, J.M., Miquelle, D.G., Smirnov, E.N., Kerley, L.L., Quigley, H.B. & Hornocker, M.G. (2003). Denning ecology of brown bears and Asiatic black bears in the Russian Far East. *Ursus* **14**: 153-161.

Seton, E.T. (1926). *Lives of Game Animals*. Doubleday, Doran & Company, Inc. Garden City, New York.

Setzer, H.W. (1957). A review of Lybian mammals. *J. Egyptian Public Health Assoc.* **32**: 41-82.

Setzer, H.W. (1958). The mustelids of Egypt. *J. Egyptian Public Health Assoc.* **33**: 199-204.

Seymour, K.L. (1989). *Panthera onca. Mammal. Species* **340**: 1-9.

Shannon, J.S. (1989). Social organization and behavioral ontogeny of otters (*Lutra canadensis*) in a coastal habitat in northern California. *IUCN Otter Special. Group Bull.* **4**: 8-13.

Shariff, S.M. (1985). Some observations on otters at Kuala Gula, Perak and National Park Pahang. *J. Wildl. & Parks* **3**: 75-88.

Sharma, I.K. (1979). Habitats, feeding, breeding and reaction to man of the Desert cat *Felis libyca* (Gray) in the Indian Desert. *J. Bombay Nat. Hist. Soc.* **76**: 498-499.

Sharp, N.C.C. (1997). Timed running speed of a cheetah (*Acinonyx jubatus*). *J. Zool., London* **241**: 493-494.

Sharpe, L.L. (2005a). Play does not enhance social cohesion in a cooperative mammal. *Anim. Behav.* **70**: 551-558.

Sharpe, L.L. (2005b). Play fighting does not affect subsequent fighting success in wild meerkats. *Anim. Behav.* **69**: 1023-1029.

Sharpe, L.L. (2005c). Frequency of social play does not affect dispersal partnerships in wild meerkats. *Anim. Behav.* **70**: 559-569.

Sharpe, L.L. (2007). Meerkats at play. *Nat. Hist.* **116**: 28-33.

Sharpe, L.L. & Cherry, M.I. (2003). Social play does not reduce aggression in wild meerkats. *Anim. Behav.* **66**: 989-997.

Sharpe, L.L., Clutton-Brock, T.H., Brotherton, P.N.M., Cameron, E.Z. & Cherry, M.I. (2002). Experimental provisioning increases play in free-ranging meerkats. *Anim. Behav.* **64**: 113-121.

Shaw, J.H. (1975). *Ecology, Behavior and Systematics of the Red Wolf (*Canis rufus*)*. PhD dissertation, Yale University, New Haven, Connecticut.

Sheffield, S.R. & King, C.M. (1994). *Mustela nivalis. Mammal. Species* **454**: 1-10.

Sheffield, S.R. & Thomas, H.H. (1997). *Mustela frenata. Mammal. Species* **570**: 1-9.

Shekar, K.S. (2003). The status of mongooses in central India. *Small Carniv. Conserv.* **29**: 22-23.

Sheng, H. & Xu, H. (1990). Range size and activity pattern of small Indian civet in Zhoushan Islands, Zhejiang Province by radio-telemetry. *J. East China Normal Univ. Mammal. Ecol. Suppl.* 110-112.

Shepard, P. & Sanders, B. (1985). *The Sacred Paw, the Bear in Nature, Myth and Literature.* Donnelly & Sons, Harrisonburg, Virginia.

Shepherd, C.R. & Nijman, V. (2008). The trade in bear parts from Myanmar: an illustration of the ineffectiveness of enforcement of international wildlife trade regulations. *Biodiversity & Conservation* **17**: 35-42.

Shepherdson, D.J., Roper, T.J. & Lups, P. (1990). Diet, food availability and foraging behaviour of badgers (*Meles meles* L.) in southern England. *Zeitschrift für Säugetierkunde* **55**: 81-93.

Sherbina, E.I. (1995). [Corsac fox. Pp. 70-84 in: Kucheruk, V.V. ed. (1995). *Mammals of Turkmenistan*]. Ilim, Ashabad, Turkmenistan. In Russian.

Shetty, J., Shetty, G. & Kanakaraj, S.R. (1990). Vocal activity of the Indian mongoose *Herpestes edwardsii edwardsii* (Geoffroy) in captivity. *J. Bombay Nat. Hist. Soc.* **87**: 47-49.

Shields, G.F., Adams, D., Garner, G., Labelle, M., Pietsch, J., Ramsay, M., Schwartz, C., Titus, K. & Williamson, S. (2000). Phylogeography of mitochondrial DNA variation in brown bears and polar bears. *Mol. Phylogen. Evol.* **15**: 319-326.

Shimek, S.J. & Monk, A. (1977). The daily activity of the sea otter off the Monterey Peninsula, California. *J. Wildl. Management* **41**: 277-283.

Shoemaker, A.H. (1983). 1982 Studbook report on the brown hyena, *Hyaena brunnea*: decline of a pedigree species. *Zoo Biology* **2**: 133-136.

Shortridge, G.C. (1931). *Felis (Microfelis) nigripes thomasi* subsp. nov. *Rec. Albany Mus.* **4**: 1.

Shortridge, G.C. (1934). *The Mammals of South West Africa.* Vol. 1. Heinemann, London.

Shrestha, T.K. (1997). *Mammals of Nepal.* Bimala Shrestha, R.K. Printers, Kathmandu.

Shusei, A., Takayuki, A., Yoshiko, K. & Kiyoko, Y. (2003). Food habit of the Japanese marten (*Martes melampus*) at Kuju Highland in Kyushu, Japan. *Mammal. Sci.* **86**: 19-28.

Sidorov, G.N. & Botvinkin, A.D. (1987). The corsac fox *Vulpes corsac* in Southern Siberia Russian USSR. *Zool. Zhurnal* **66**: 914-927.

Sidorov, G.N. & Polischuk, E.M. (2002). [Corsac fox in Omsk district in XX and beginning of XXI centuries]. *Theriologicheskie issledovaniyk*: 115-124. In Russian.

Sidorovich, V.E., Krasko, D.A. & Dyman, A.A. (2005). Landscape-related differences in diet, food supply and distribution pattern of the pine marten, *Martes martes* in the transitional mixed forest of northern Belarus. *Folia Zool.* **54**: 39-52.

Sidorovich, V.E., Macdonald, D.W., Pikulik, M.M. & Kruuk, H. (2001). Individual feeding specialization in the European mink, *Mustela lutreola* and the American mink, *M. vison* in north-eastern Belarus. *Folia Zool.* **50(1)**: 27-42.

Siegfried, W.R. (1984). An analysis of faecal pellets of the brown hyaena on the Namib Coast. *South Afr. J. Zool.* **19**: 61.

Sielfeld, W.K. (1983). *Mamíferos Marinos de Chile.* Ediciones de la Universidad de Chile, Santiago.

Sillero-Zubiri, C. (1996). Records of honey badger *Mellivora capensis* in Afroalpine habitat, above 4,000m. *Mammalia* **60**: 323-325.

Sillero-Zubiri, C. (2004). Pale fox *Vulpes pallida*. Pp. 199-200 in: Sillero-Zubiri, C., Hoffmann, M. & Macdonald, D.W. eds. (2004). *Canids: Foxes, Wolves, Jackals and Dogs. Status Survey and Conservation Action Plan.* IUCN/SSC Canid Specialist Group, Gland & Cambridge.

Sillero-Zubiri, C. & Bassignani, F. (2001). Observation of large groups of Gambian mongooses (*Mungos gambianus*, Ogilby 1835) in southeastern Senegal. *Hystrix* **12**: 7-9.

Sillero-Zubiri, C. & Gottelli, D. (1992a.) Feeding ecology of spotted hyaena (Mammalia: *Crocuta crocuta*) in a mountain forest habitat. *J. Afr. Zool.* **106**: 169-176.

Sillero-Zubiri, C. & Gottelli, D. (1992b). Population ecology of spotted hyaena in an equatorial mountain forest. *Afr. J. Ecol.* **30**: 292-300.

Sillero-Zubiri, C. & Gottelli, D. (1994). *Canis simensis. Mammal. Species* **485**: 1-6.

Sillero-Zubiri, C. & Gottelli, D. (1995a). Spatial organization in the Ethiopian wolf *Canis simensis*: large packs and small stable home ranges. *J. Zool., London* **237**: 65-81.

Sillero-Zubiri, C. & Gottelli, D. (1995b). Diet and feeding behavior of Ethiopian wolves *Canis simensis*. *J. Mammal.* **76**: 531-541.

Sillero-Zubiri, C. & Macdonald, D.W. (1997). *The Ethiopian Wolf: Status Survey and Conservation Action Plan.* IUCN/SSC Canid Specialist Group, Gland & Cambridge.

Sillero-Zubiri, C. & Macdonald, D.W. (1998). Scent-marking and territorial behaviour of Ethiopian wolves *Canis simensis*. *J. Zool., London* **245**: 351-361.

Sillero-Zubiri, C. & Marino, J. (1997). The status of small carnivore species in Niokolo-Koba National Park, Senegal. *Small Carniv. Conserv.* **17**: 15-19.

Sillero-Zubiri, C. & Marino, J. (2004). Ethiopian wolf *Canis simensis*. Pp. 167-174 in: Sillero-Zubiri, C., Hoffmann, M. & Macdonald, D.W. eds. (2004). *Canids: Foxes, Wolves, Jackals and Dogs. Status Survey and Conservation Action Plan.* IUCN/SSC Canid Specialist Group, Gland & Cambridge.

Sillero-Zubiri, C., Gottelli, D. & Macdonald, D.W. (1996). Male philopatry, extra pack copulations and inbreeding avoidance in Ethiopian wolves *Canis simensis*. *Behav. Ecol. Sociobiol.* **38**: 331-340.

Sillero-Zubiri, C., Johnson, P.J. & Macdonald, D.W. (1998). A hypothesis for breeding synchrony in Ethiopian wolves *Canis simensis*. *J. Mammal.* **79**: 853-858.

Sillero-Zubiri, C., King, A.A. & Macdonald, D.W. (1996). Rabies and mortality in Ethiopian wolves *Canis simensis*. *J. Wildl. Diseases* **32**: 80-86.

Sillero-Zubiri, C., Malcolm, J.R., Williams, S., Marino, J., Tefera, Z., Laurenson, M.K., Gottelli, D., Hood, A., Macdonald, D.W., Wildt, D. & Ellis, S. (2000). *Ethiopian Wolf Conservation Strategy Workshop.* P. 61. IUCN/SSC Canid Specialist Group and Conservation Breeding Specialist Group, Dinsho, Ethiopia.

Sillero-Zubiri, C., Tattersall, F.H. & Macdonald, D.W. (1995a). Habitat selection and daily activity of giant molerats *Tachyoryctes macrocephalus*: significance to the Ethiopian wolf *Canis simensis* in the Afroalpine ecosystem. *Biol. Conserv.* **72**: 77-84.

Sillero-Zubiri, C., Tattersall, F.H. & Macdonald, D.W. (1995b). Bale mountains rodent communities and their relevance to the Ethiopian wolf (*Canis simensis*). *Afr. J. Ecol.* **33**: 301-320.

de Silva, M. & Jayaratne, B.V.R. (1994). Aspects of population ecology of the leopard (*Panthera pardus*) in Ruhuna National Park, Sri Lanka. *J. S. Asian Nat. Hist.* **1**: 3-13.

Silveira, E.K.P. da (1968). Notes on the care and breeding of the maned wolf *Chrysocyon brachyurus* at Brasilia Zoo. *Int. Zoo Yb.* **8**: 21-23.

Silveira, L. (1995). Notes on the distribution and natural history of the Pampas cat, *Felis colocolo*, in Brazil. *Mammalia* **59**: 284-288.

Silveira, L. (1999). *Ecologia e Conservação dos Mamíferos Carnívoros do Parque Nacional das Emas, Goiás.* MSc thesis, Universidade Federal de Goiás, Goiás, Brazil.

Silveira, L., Jácomo, A.T.A., Rodrigues, F.H.G. & Diniz-Filho, J.A.F. (1998). Bush dogs *Speothos venaticus* in Emas National Park, central Brazil. *Mammalia* **62**: 446-449.

Silver, S.C., Ostro, L.E.T., Marsh, L.K., Maffei, L., Noss, A.J., Kelly, M.J., Wallace, R.B., Gomez, H. & Ayala, G. (2004). The use of camera traps for estimating jaguar *Panthera onca* abundance and density using capture/recapture analysis. *Oryx* **38**: 148-154.

Simberloff, D., Dayan, T., Jones, C. & Ogura, G. (2000). Character displacement and release in the small Indian mongoose, *Herpestes javanicus*. *Ecology* **81**: 2086-2099.

Simmons, D.J. (1995). A new location for the white-tailed mongoose, *Ichneumia albicauda* (Cuvier, 1829), Farasan Kabir Island, Red Sea, Saudi Arabia. *Small Carniv. Conserv.* **13**: 3-5.

Simon, N.P.P., Schwab, F.E., LeCoure, M.I. & Phillips, F.R. (1999). Fall and winter diet of martens, *Martes americana*, in central Labrador related to small mammal densities. *Can. Field-Nat.* **113**: 678-680.

Simonetti, J.A. (1986). Human-induced dietary shift in *Dusicyon culpaeus*. *Mammalia* **50**: 406-408.

Simonetti, J.A., Poiani, A. & Raedeke, K. (1984). Food habits of *Dusicyon griseus* in northern Chile. *J. Mammal.* **65**: 515-517.

Simpson, C.D. (1964). Notes on the banded mongoose, *Mungos mungo* (Gmelin). *Arnoldia, Rhodesia* **1**: 1-8.

Simpson, C.D. (1966). The banded mongoose. *Anim. Kingdom* **69**: 52-57.

Simpson, G.G. (1945). The principles of classification and a classification of mammals. *Bull. Amer. Mus. Nat. Hist.* **85**: 1-350.

Singh, H.S. (2005). Status of the leopard *Panthera pardus fusca* in India. *Cat News* **42**: 15-17.

Sitek, H. (1995). Breeding of the Libyan striped weasel *Poecilictis libya* at Poznan Zoo, Poland. *Small Carniv. Conserv.* **13**: 8-9.

Sivasothi, N. & Burhanuddin, H.M.N. (1994). A review of otters (Carnivora: Mustelidae: Lutrinae) in Malaysia and Singapore. *Hydrobiologia* **285**: 1-3.

Skinner, J.D. (1976). Ecology of the brown hyena *Hyaena brunnea* in the Transvaal with a distribution map for southern Africa. *South Afr. J. Sci.* **72**: 262-269.

Skinner, J.D. & Chimimba, C.T. (2005). *The Mammals of the Southern African Subregion.* 3rd edition. Cambridge University Press, Cape Town.

Skinner, J.D. & Ilani, G. (1979). The striped hyaena *Hyaena hyaena* of the Judean and Negev Deserts and a comparison with the brown hyaena *H. brunnea*. *Israel J. Zool.* **28**: 229-232.

Skinner, J.D. & Smithers, R.H.N. (1990). *The Mammals of the Southern African Subregion.* 2nd edition. University of Pretoria Press, Pretoria.

Skinner, J.D. & Van Aarde, R.J. (1981). The distribution and ecology of the brown hyaena *Hyaena brunnea* and spotted hyaena *Crocuta crocuta* in the central Namib Desert. *Madoqua* **12**: 231-239.

Skinner, J.D. & Van Aarde, R.J. (1986). The use of space by the aardwolf *Proteles cristatus*. *J. Zool., London* **209**: 299-301.

Skinner, J.D., Davis, S. & Ilani, G. (1980). Bone collecting by striped hyaenas, *Hyaena hyaena*, in Israel. *Palaeontol. Afr.* **23**: 99-104.

Skinner, J.D., Funston, P.J., Van Aarde, R.J., Dyk, G. & Haupt, M.A. (1992). Diet of spotted hyaenas in some mesic and arid southern African game reserves adjoining farmland. *South Afr. J. Wildl. Res.* **22**: 119-121.

Skinner, J.D., Henschel, J.R. & Van Jaarsveld, A.S. (1986). Bone-collecting habits of spotted hyaenas *Crocuta crocuta* in the Kruger National Park. *South Afr. J. Zool.* **21**: 303-308.

Skinner, J.D., Van Aarde, R.J. & Goss, R.A. (1995). Space and resource use by brown hyenas *Hyaena brunnea* in the Namib Desert. *J. Zool., London* **237**: 123-131.

Slaughter, B.H., Pine, R.H. & Pine, N.E. (1974). Erruption of cheek teeth in Insectivora and Carnivora. *J. Mammal.* **55**: 115-125.

Slauson, K.M., Zielinski, W.J. & Hayes, J.P. (2007). Habitat selection by American martens in coastal California. *J. Wildl. Management* **71**: 458-468.

Sliwa, A. (1994a). Diet and feeding behaviour of the black-footed cat (*Felis nigripes* Burchell, 1824) in the Kimberley Region, South Africa. *Zool. Garten* **64**: 83-96.

Sliwa, A. (1994b). Black-footed cat studies in South Africa. *Cat News* **20**: 15-19.

Sliwa, A. (1994c). Marsh owl (*Asio capensis*) associating with black-footed cat (*Felis nigripes*). *Gabar* **2**: 23.

Sliwa, A. (1995). The black-footed cat - efficient rodent killer. *Farmer's Weekly* **85016**: 16-19.

Sliwa, A. (1997). Black-footed cat field research. *Cat News* **27**: 20-21.

Sliwa, A. (1998). Social organization of the black-footed cat, *Felis nigripes* in the Kimberley Region, South Africa. Page 295 in: *Euro-American Mammals Congress, Santiago de Compostela, Spain, July 19-24 1998.* (Abstract).

Sliwa, A. (2004). Home range size and social organization of black-footed cats (*Felis nigripes*). *Mammal. Biol.* **69**: 96-107.

Sliwa, A. (2006). Seasonal and sex-specific prey composition of black-footed cats *Felis nigripes. Acta Theriol.* **51**: 195-204.

Sliwa, A. & Richardson, P.R.K. (1998). Responses of aardwolves, *Proteles cristatus*, Sparrman 1783, to translocated scent marks. *Anim. Behav.* **56**: 137-146.

Sliwa, A. & Schürer, U. (2000). *International Studbook for the Black-footed Cat (*Felis nigripes*)*. Zoologischer Garten der Stadt Wuppertal, Wuppertal, Germany.

Slough, B.G. & Mowat, G. (1996). Lynx population dynamics in an untrapped refugium. *J. Wildl. Management* **60(4)**: 946-961.

Sludskyi, A.A. & Lazarev, A.A. (1966). [*Corsac Fox: its Ecology and Hunting. Hunting Mammals of Kazakhstan*]. Kaynar, Alma-Ata, USSR. In Russian.

Smale, L., Frank, L.G. & Holekamp, K.E. (1993). Ontogeny of dominance in free-living spotted hyaenas: juvenile rank relations with adults. *Anim. Behav.* **46**: 467-477.

Smale, L., Holekamp, K.E. & White, P.A. (1999). Siblicide revisited in the spotted hyaena: does it conform to obligate or facultative models? *Anim. Behav.* **58**: 545-551.

Smale, L., Nunes, S. & Holekamp, K.E. (1997). Sexually dimorphic dispersal in mammals: patterns, causes and consequences. *Advances Study Behav.* **26**: 181-250.

Smith, A.C. & Schaefer, J.A. (2002). Home-range size and habitat selection by American marten (*Martes americana*) in Labrador. *Can. J. Zool.* **80**: 1602-1609.

Smith, D.S. (1984). *Habitat Use, Home Range and Movements of Bobcats in Western Montana.* MSc thesis, University of Montana, Missoula, Montana.

Smith, D.W., Peterson, R.O. & Houston, D.B. (2003). Yellowstone after wolves. *Bioscience* **53**: 330-340.

Smith, H.T., Meshaka, W.E., Engeman, R.M., Crossett, S.M., Foley, M.E. & Bush, G. (2006). Raccoon predation as a potential limiting factor in the success of the green Iguana in Southern Florida. *J. Kansas Herpetol.* **20**: 7-8.

Smith, J.L.D. (1984). *Dispersal, Communication and Conservation Strategies for the Tiger (*Panthera tigris*) in Royal Chitwan National Park, Nepal.* PhD dissertation, University of Minnesota, St. Paul, Minnesota.

Smith, J.L.D. (1993). The role of dispersal in structuring the Chitwan tiger population. *Behaviour* **124**: 165-195.

Smith, J.L.D. & McDougal, C. (1991). The contribution of variance in lifetime reproduction to effective population size in tigers. *Conserv. Biol.* **5**: 484-490.

Smith, J.L.D., McDougal, C., Ahearn, S.C., Joshi, A. & Conforti, K. (1999). Metapopulation structure of tigers in Nepal. Pp. 176-191 in: Seidensticker, J., Christie, S. & Jackson, P. eds. (1999). *Riding the Tiger: Tiger Conservation in Human-dominated Landscapes.* Cambridge University Press, Cambridge.

Smith, J.L.D., McDougal, C. & Miquelle, D. (1989). Scent marking in free-ranging Tigers, *Panthera tigris. Anim. Behav.* **37**: 1-10.

Smith, J.L.D., McDougal, C. & Sunquist, M.E. (1987). Female land tenure system in tigers. Pp. 97-109 in: Tilson, R.L. & Seal, U.S. eds. (1987). *Tigers of the World: the Biology, Biopolitics, Management and Conservation of an Endangered Species.* Noyes Publications, Park Ridge, New Jersey.

Smith, J.L.D., Tunhikorn, S., Tanhan, S., Simcharoen, S. & Kanchanasaka, B. (1999). Metapopulation structure of tigers in Thailand. Pp. 166-175 in: Seidensticker, J., Christie, S. & Jackson, P. eds. (1999). *Riding the Tiger: Tiger Conservation in Human-dominated Landscapes.* Cambridge University Press, Cambridge.

Smith, K.K. (1992). The evolution of the mammalian pharynx. *Zool. J. Linn. Soc.* **104**: 313-349.

Smith, K.K. (1996). Integration of craniofacial structures during development in mammals. *Amer. Zool.* **36**: 70-79.

Smith, R.M. (1977). Movement patterns and feeding behaviour of leopard in the Rhodes Matopos National Park, Rhodesia. *Arnoldia, Rhodesia* **8**: 1-16.

Smithers, J.D. & Chimimba, C.T. (2005). *The Mammals of the Southern African Subregion.* 3rd edition. Cambridge University Press.

Smithers, R.H.N. (1968). Cat of the pharaohs. *Anim. Kingdom* **71**: 16-23.

Smithers, R.H.N. (1971). *The Mammals of Botswana.* The Trustees of the National Museum of Rhodesia Museum Memoir **4**.

Smithers, R.H.N. (1978). The serval, *Felis serval* Schreber, 1776. *South Afr. J. Wildl. Res.* **8**: 29-37.

Smithers, R.H.N. (1983). *The Mammals of the Southern African Subregion.* University of Pretoria, Pretoria.

Smithers, R.H.N. (1986). *South African Red Data Book - Terrestrial Mammals.* South African National Scientific Programmes Report **125**. Council for Scientific and Industrial Research, Pretoria, South Africa.

Smithers, R.H.N. & Lobão, J.L.P. (1976). Checklist and atlas of the mammals of Moçambique. *Trustees of the National Museums and Monuments, Salisbury, Museum Memoir* **8**: 1-184.

Smithers, R.H.N. & Wilson, V.J. (1979). Check list and atlas of the mammals of Zimbabwe Rhodesia. *Museum Memoirs, National Museums and Monuments of Rhodesia* (Zimbabwe) **9**: 1-147.

Smits van Oyen, M. (1998). Banded together. *BBC Wildlife* **March 1998**: 65-70.

Smuts, G.L. (1979). Diet of lions and spotted hyaenas assessed from stomach contents. *South Afr. J. Wildl. Res.* **9**: 19-25.

Smuts, G.L. (1982). *Lion.* Macmillan, Johannesburg.

Smuts, G.L., Hanks, J. & Whyte, I.J. (1978). Reproduction and social organization of lions from the Kruger National Park. *Carnivores* **1**: 17-28.

Smuts, G.L., Robinson, G.A. & Whyte, I.J. (1980). Comparative growth of wild male and female lions (*Panthera leo*). *J. Zool., London* **190**: 365-373.

Sody, H. (1936). Seventeen new generic, specific and subspecific names for Dutch east Indian mammals. *Overgedrukt uit Natuurk. Tijdschrift* **96**: 42-55.

Sody, H. (1949). Notes on some Primates, Carnivora and the babirusa from the Indo-Malayan and Indo-Australian regions (with descriptions of 10 new species and subspecies). *Treubia* **20**: 121-190.

Soisalo, M.K. & Cavalcanati, S.M.C. (2006). Estimating the density of a jaguar population in the Brazilian Pantanal using camera-traps and capture-recapture sampling in combination with GPS radio-telemetry. *Biol. Conserv.* **129**: 487-496.

Sokolov, V.E. (1982). *Mammal Skin.* University of California Press, Berkeley, California.

Somers, M.J. (2000). Foraging behaviour of Cape clawless otters (*Aonyx capensis*) in a marine habitat. *J. Zool., London* **252**: 473-480.

Somers, M.J. & Nel, J.A.J. (2004). Habitat selection by the Cape clawless otter (*Aonyx capensis*) in rivers in the Western Cape Province, South Africa. *Afr. J. Ecol.* **42**: 298-305.

Somers, M.J. & Purves, M.G. (1996). Trophic overlap between three syntopic semi-aquatic carnivores: Cape clawless otter, spotted-necked otter and water mongoose. *Afr. J. Ecol.* **34**: 158-166.

Sommer, R.S. & Benecke, N. (2005). The recolonization of Europe by brown bears *Ursus arctos* Linnaeus, 1758 after the last glacial maximum. *Mammal Rev.* **35**: 156-164.

Sommer, S., Toto, A. & Seal, U.S. (2002). A population and habitat variability assessment for the highly endangered giant jumping rat (*Hypogeomys antimena*), the largest extant endemic rodent of Madagascar. *Anim. Conserv.* **5**: 263-273.

Sorli, L.E., Martinez, F.D., Lardelli, U. & Brandi, S. (2006). Andean cat in Mendoza, Argentina - furthest south and at lowest elevation ever recorded. *Cat News* **44**: 24.

Soutiere, E.C. (1979). Effects of timber harvesting on marten in Maine. *J. Wildl. Management* **43**: 850-860.

Sovada, M.A. & Carbyn, L.N. eds. (2003). *Ecology and Conservation of Swift Foxes in a Changing World.* Canadian Plains Research Center, University of Regina, Saskatchewan, Canada.

Sovada, M.A., Anthony, R.M. & Batt, B.D.J. (2001). Predation on waterfowl in Arctic tundra and prairie breeding areas: a review. *Wildl. Soc. Bull.* **29**: 6-15.

Sovada, M.A., Roaldson, J.M. & Sargeant, A.B. (1999). Foods of American badgers in west-central Minnesota and southeastern North Dakota during the duck nesting season. *Amer. Midl. Nat.* **142**: 410-414.

Sovada, M.A., Roy, C.C., Bright, J.B. & Gillis, J.R. (1998). Causes and rates of mortality of swift foxes in western Kansas. *J. Wildl. Management* **62**: 1300-1306.

Sovada, M.A., Roy, C.C. & Telesco, D.J. (2001). Seasonal food habits of swift foxes in cropland and rangeland habitats in western Kansas. *Amer. Midl. Nat.* **145**: 101-111.

Sovada, M.A., Slivinski, C.C. & Woodward, R.O. (2003). Home range, habitat use, pup dispersal and litter sizes of swift foxes in western Kansas. Pp. 149-159 in: Sovada, M. & Carbyn, L. eds. (2003). *Ecology and Conservation of Swift Foxes in a Changing World.* Canadian Plains Research Center, University of Regina, Saskatchewan, Canada.

Sovey, K.C., Dollar, L., Kerridge, F., Barber, R.C. & Louis, E.E. (2001). Characterization of seven microsatellite marker loci in the Malagasy civet (*Fossa fossana*). *Mol. Ecol. Notes* **1**: 25-27.

Sowerby, A.D. (1920). Notes on Heude's bears in the Sikawei museum and on the bears of Palaearctic Eastern Asia. *J. Mammal.* **1**: 213-231.

Spanner, A., Stone, G.M. & Schultz, D. (1997). Excretion profiles of some reproductive steroids in the faeces of captive Nepalese red panda (*Ailurus fulgens fulgens*). *Reprod. Fertil. Dev.* **9**: 565-570.

Sparrman, A.P. (1783). *A Voyage to the Cape of Good Hope, Towards the Antarctic Polar Circle and Round the World; but Chiefly to the Country of the Hottentots and Caffres, from the Year 1772 to 1776.* English translation 1785 by George Forester. G.G.J. Robinson & J. Robinson, London.

Spiegel, L.K. ed. (1996). *Studies of the San Joaquin Kit Fox in Undeveloped and Oil-developed Areas.* California Energy Commission, Sacramento, California.

Spong, G. (2002). Space use in lions, *Panthera leo*, in the Selous Game Reserve: social and ecological factors. *Behav. Ecol. Sociobiol.* **52**: 303-307.

Spotorno, A. (1995). Vertebrados. Pp. 299-301 in: Simonetti, J.A., Arroyo, M.T.K., Spotorno, A.E. & Lozada, E. eds. (1995). *Biodiversidad de Chile.* Artegrama Ltda., Santiago.

Srbek-Araujo, A.C. & Chiarello, A.G. (2005). Is camera-trapping an efficient method for surveying mammals in Neotropical forests? A case study in south-eastern Brazil. *J. Trop. Ecol.* **21**: 121-125.

Stahl, P. & Artois, M. (1991). *Status and Conservation of the Wild Cat (*Felis silvestris*) in Europe and Around the Mediterranean Rim.* Council of Europe, Strasbourg.

Stahl, P. & Leger, F. (1992). *Le Chat Sauvage d'Europe (*Felis silvestris, *Schreber, 1777)*. Encyclopédie des Carnivores de France **17**. SFEPM, Norts/Edre, Paris.

Stains, H.J. (1974). Distribution and taxonomy of the Canidae. Pp. 3-26 in: Fox, M.W. ed. (1974). *The Wild Canids: their Systematics, Behavioural Ecology and Evolution.* Von Nostrand Reinhold Company, New York.

Stains, H.J. (1983). Calcanea of members of the Viverridae. *Bull. South. Calif. Acad. Sci.* **82**: 17-38.

Stake, M.M. & Cimprich, D.A. (2003). Using video to monitor predation at black-capped vireo nests. *Condor* **105**: 348-357.

Stander, P.E. (1990). Notes on the foraging habits of cheetah. *South Afr. J. Wildl. Res.* **20**: 130-132.

Stander, P.E. (1991). Demography of lions in the Etosha National Park, Namibia. *Madoqua* **18**: 1-9.

Stander, P.E. (1992a). Cooperative hunting in lions: the role of the individual. *Behav. Ecol. Sociobiol.* **29**: 445-454.

Stander, P.E. (1992b). Foraging dynamics of lions in a semi-arid environment. *Can. J. Zool.* **70**: 8-21.

Stander, P.E. (1997). The ecology of lions and conflict with people in north-west Namibia. Pp. 10-17 in: Van Heerden, J. ed. (1997). *Lions and Leopards as Game Ranch Animals.* The Wildlife Group, South African Veterinary Association, Onderstepoort, South Africa.

Stander, P.E., Haden, P.J., Kaqece & Ghau (1997). The ecology of asociality in Namibian leopards. *J. Zool., London* **242**: 343-364.

Stanford, C.B. (1989). Predation on capped langurs *Presbytis pileata* by cooperatively hunting jackals *Canis aureus. Amer. J. Primatology* **19**: 53-56.

Stefen, C. (1995). Zahnschmelzdifferenzierungen bei raubtieren - Carnivora im vergleich zu vertretern der Creodonta, Arctocyonidae, Mesonychidae, Entelodontidae (Placentalia), Thylacoleonidae, Dasyuridae und Thylacinidae (Marsupialia). Unpublished PhD dissertation, University of Bonn, Germany.

Stefen, C. (1997). Differences in Hunter-Schreger bands of carnivores. Pp. 123-136 in: van Koenigswald, W. & Sander, P.M. eds. (1997). *Tooth Enamel Microstructure.* Balkema Press, Rotterdam.

Steinmetz, R. & Garshelis, D.L. (2008). Distinguishing Asiatic black bears and sun bears by claw marks on climbed trees. *J. Wildl. Management* **72**: 814-821.

Steinmetz, R., Chutipong, W. & Seuaturien, N. (2006). Collaborating to conserve large mammals in Southeast Asia. *Conserv. Biol.* **20**: 1391-1401.

Stenhouse, G.B., Boulanger, J., Lee, J., Graham, K., Duval, J. & Cranston, J. (2005). Grizzly bear associations along the eastern slopes of Alberta. *Ursus* **16**: 31-40.

Stephens, P.A., Russell, A.F., Young, A.J., Sutherland, W.J. & Clutton-Brock, T.H. (2005). Dispersal, eviction and conflict in meerkats (*Suricata suricatta*): an evolutionarily stable strategy model. *Amer. Naturalist* **165**: 120-135.

Sterndale, R.A. (1884). *Natural History of the Mammalia of India and Ceylon.* Thacker, Spink & Co., Calcutta.

Stevens, C.E. & Hume, I.D. (1995). *Comparative Physiology of the Vertebrate Digestive System.* 2nd edition. Cambridge University Press, Cambridge.

Stirling, I. (1988). *Polar Bears.* University of Michigan Press, Ann Arbor, Michigan.

Stirling, I. ed. (1993). *Bears: Majestic Creatures of the Wild.* Rodale Press, Emmaus, Pennsylvania.

Stirling, I. (2002). Polar bears and seals in the eastern Beaufort Sea and Amundsen Gulf: a synthesis of population trends and ecological relationships over three decades. *Arctic* **55** (Suppl.): 59-76.

Stirling, I. & Derocher, A.E. (1990). Factors affecting the evolution and behavioral ecology of the modern bears. *Int. Conf. Bear Res. Management* **8**: 189-204.

Stirling, I. & Øritsland, N.A. (1995). Relationships between estimates of ringed seal (*Phoca hispida*) and polar bear (*Ursus maritimus*) populations in the Canadian Arctic. *Can. J. Fish. Aquatic Sci.* **52**: 2594-2612.

Stirling, I. & Parkinson, C.L. (2006). Possible effects of climate warming on selected populations of polar bears (*Ursus maritimus*) in the Canadian Arctic. *Arctic* **59**: 261-275.

Støen, O.G., Bellemain, E., Sæbø, S. & Swenson, J.E. (2005). Kin-related spatial structure in brown bears *Ursus arctos. Behav. Ecol. Sociobiol.* **59**: 191-197.

Støen, O.G., Zedrosser, A., Sæbø, S. & Swenson, J.E. (2006). Inversely density-dependent natal dispersal in brown bears *Ursus arctos. Oecologia* **148**: 356-364.

Stone, C.P. & Keith, J.O. (1987). Control of feral ungulates and small mammals in Hawaii's national parks: research and management strategies. Pp. 227-287 in: Richards, C.G.J. & Ku, T.T. eds. (1987). *Control of Mammal Pests.* Taylor & Francis, London.

Stone, K. & Cook, J. (2002). Molecular evolution of Holarctic martens (genus *Martes*, Mammalia: Carnivora: Mustelidae). *Mol. Phylogen. Evol.* **24**: 169-179.

Story, H.E. (1945). The external genitalia and perfume gland in *Arctictis binturong. J. Mammal.* **26**: 64-66.

Story, J.D., Galbraith, W.J. & Kitchings, J.T. (1982). Food habits of bobcats in eastern Tennessee. *J. Tennessee Acad. Sci.* **57**: 29-32.

Storz, J.F. & Wozencraft, W.C. (1999). *Melogale moschata. Mammal. Species* **631**: 1-4.

Strahan, R. (1995). *Mammals of Australia.* Smithsonian Institution Press, Washington, D.C.

Strahl, S.D., Silva, J.L. & Goldstein, I.R. (1992). The bush dog *Speothos venaticus* in Venezuela. *Mammalia* **56**: 9-13.

Streicher, U. (2001). The use of xylazine and ketamine in Owston's palm civets *Chrotogale owstoni. Small Carniv. Conserv.* **24**: 18-19.

Stroganov, S.U. (1969). *Carnivorous Mammals of Siberia.* Israel Program for Scientific Translation, Israel.

Stromberg, M.R. & Boyce, M.S. (1986). Systematics and conservation of the swift fox, *Vulpes velox*, in North America. *Biol. Conserv.* **35**: 97-110.

Struhsaker, T.T. & McKey, D. (1975). 2 cusimanse mongooses attack a black cobra. *J. Mammal.* **56**: 721-722.

Stuart, C.T. (1975). Preliminary notes on the mammals of the Namib Desert Park. *Madoqua* **4**: 5-68.

Stuart, C.T. (1976). Diet of the black-backed jackal *Canis mesomelas* in the central Namib Desert, South West Africa. *Zool. Afr.* **11**: 193-205.

Stuart, C.T. (1977). Analysis of *Felis libyca* and *Genetta genetta* scats from the central Namib Desert, South West Africa. *Zool. Afr.* **12**: 239-241.

Stuart, C.T. (1981). Notes on the mammalian carnivores of the Cape Province, South Africa. *Bontebok* **1**: 1-58.

Stuart, C.T. (1982). The distribution of the small-spotted cat (*Felis nigripes*). *The Naturalist* **26**(3): 8-9

Stuart, C.T. (1984). The distribution and status of *Felis caracal* Schreber, 1776. *Säugetierkunde Mitt.* **31**: 197-203.

Stuart, C.T. (1985). The status of two endangered carnivores occurring in the Cape Province, South Africa, *Felis serval* and *Lutra maculicollis. Biol. Conserv.* **32**: 375-382.

Stuart, C.T. (1986). The incidence of surplus killing by *Panthera pardus* and *Felis caracal* in Cape Province, South Africa. *Mammalia* **50**: 556-558.

Stuart, C.T. (1990). The conservation status of mustelids and viverrids in Southern Africa. *Mustel. Viverr. Conserv.* **3**: 16.

Stuart, C.T. (1991). Aspects of the biology of the small grey mongoose *Galerella pulverulenta. Mustel. Viverr. Conserv.* **4**: 1-4.

Stuart, C.T. & Hickman, G.C. (1991). Prey of caracal *Felis caracal* in two areas of Cape Province, South Africa. *J. Afr. Zool.* **105**: 373-381.

Stuart, C.T. & Shaughnessy, P.D. (1984). Content of *Hyaena brunnea* and *Canis mesomelas* scats from southern coastal Namibia. *Mammalia* **48**: 611-612.

Stuart, C.T. & Stuart, M.D. (1997). *Field Guide to the Larger Mammals of Africa.* Struik, Cape Town.

Stuart, C.T. & Stuart, T. (1985). Age determination and development of foetal and juvenile *Felis caracal* Schreber, 1776. *Säugetierkunde Mitt.* **32**: 217-229.

Stuart, C.T. & Stuart, T. (1988). *Field Guide to the Mammals of Southern Africa.* Struik Publishers, Cape Town.

Stuart, C.T. & Stuart, T. (1991). Regional size variation and sexual dimorphism of the leopard. *Cat News* **15**: 9.

Stuart, C.T. & Stuart, T. (1996). *Africa's Vanishing Wildlife.* Southern Book Publishers, Halfway House, South Africa.

Stuart, C.T. & Stuart, T. (1998). A note on the herpestids and viverrids of south-eastern Unguja (Zanzibar) Island. *Small Carniv. Conserv.* **18**: 16-17.

Stuart, C.T. & Stuart, T. (2001). *Field Guide to the Larger Mammals of Africa.* Struik Publishers, Cape Town.

Stuart, C.T. & Stuart, T. (2003). A short note on the analysis of the scats of water mongoose *Atilax paludinosus* and rusty-spotted genet *Genetta maculata* from Kasanka National Park, north-east Zambia. *Small Carniv. Conserv.* **29**: 15.

Stuart, C.T. & Stuart, T. (2004). Cape fox *Vulpes chama.* Pp. 189-193 in: Sillero-Zubiri, C., Hoffmann, M. & Macdonald, D.W. eds. (2004). *Canids: Foxes, Wolves, Jackals and Dogs. Status Survey and Conservation Action Plan.* IUCN/SSC Canid Specialist Group, Gland & Cambridge.

Stuart, C.T. & Stuart, T. (In press a). *Dologale dybowskii.* In: Kingdon, J.S. & Hoffmann, M. eds. (In press). *The Mammals of Africa.* Vol. 5. Carnivores, Pangolins, Rhinos and Equids. Academic Press, Amsterdam.

Stuart, C.T. & Stuart, T. (In press b). *Paracynictis selousi.* In: Kingdon, J.S. & Hoffmann, M. eds. (In press). *The Mammals of Africa.* Vol. 5. Carnivores, Pangolins, Rhinos and Equids. Academic Press, Amsterdam.

Stuart, C.T. & Stuart, T. (In press c). *Rhynchogale melleri.* In: Kingdon, J.S. & Hoffmann, M. eds. (In press). *The Mammals of Africa.* Vol. 5. Carnivores, Pangolins, Rhinos and Equids. Academic Press, Amsterdam.

Stuart, C.T. & Wilson, V.J. (1988). *The Cats of Southern Africa.* Chipangali Wildlife Trust, Bulawayo, Zimbabwe.

Stubblefield, C.H. & Shrestha, M. (2007). Status of Asiatic black bears in protected areas of Nepal and the effects of political turmoil. *Ursus* **18**: 101-108.

Su, S. & Sale, J. (2007). Niche differentiation between common palm civet *Paradoxurus hermaphroditus* and small indian civet *Viverricula indica* in regenerating degraded forest, Myanmar. *Small Carniv. Conserv.* **36**: 30-34.

Suckling, K. & Garcelon, D.K. (2000). *Petition to List Four Island Fox Subspecies as Endangered.* Petition submitted to the US Fish and Wildlife Service, 1 June 2000. Center for Biological Diversity, Tucson, Arizona, and Institute for Wildlife Studies, Arcata, California.

Sullivan, E.G. (1956). Gray fox reproduction, denning, range and weights in Alabama. *J. Mammal.* **37**: 346-351.

Sunde, P. & Kvam, T. (1997). Diet patterns in Eurasian lynx *Lynx lynx*: what causes sexually determined prey size segregation? *Acta Theriol.* **42**: 189-201.

Sunde, P., Kvam, T., Moa, P., Negard, A. & Overskaug, K. (2000). Foraging of lynxes in a managed boreal-alpine environment. *Ecography* **23**: 291-298.

Sunde, P., Kvam, T., Moa, P. & Overskaug, K. (2000). Space use by Eurasian lynxes *Lynx lynx* in central Norway. *Acta Theriol.* **45**: 507-524.

Sunquist, F. (1997). Where cats and herders mix. *Int. Wildl. Mag.* **27**(1): 26-33.

Sunquist, M.E. (1981). *The Social Organization of Tigers* (Panthera tigris) *in Royal Chitawan National Park, Nepal.* Smithsonian Contributions to Zoology **336**. 98 pp.

Sunquist, M.E. (1982). Incidental observations of the spotted linsang (*Prionodon pardicolor*). *J. Bombay Nat. Hist. Soc.* **79**: 185-186.

Sunquist, M.E. (1983). Dispersal of three radiotagged leopards. *J. Mammal.* **64**: 337-341.

Sunquist, M.E. (1992). The ecology of the ocelot: the importance of incorporating life history traits into conservation plans. Pp. 117-128 in: *Felinos de Venezuela: Biología, Ecología y Conservación.* Fundación para el Desarrollo de las Ciencias Físicas, Matemáticas y Naturales, Caracas.

Sunquist, M.E. & Sanderson, J. (1998). Ecology and behavior of the kodkod in a highly fragmented, human dominated landscape. *Cat News* **28**: 17-18.

Sunquist, M.E. & Sunquist, F. (2002). *Wild Cats of the World.* University of Chicago Press, Chicago, Illinois.

Sunquist, M.E., Karanth, K.U. & Sunquist, F.C. (1999). Ecology, behaviour and resilience of the tiger and its conservation needs. Pp. 5-18 in: Seidensticker, J., Christie, S. & Jackson, P. eds. (1999). *Riding the Tiger: Tiger Conservation in Human-dominated Landscapes.* Cambridge University Press, Cambridge.

Sunquist, M.E., Leh, C., Sunquist, F., Hills, D.M. & Rajaratnam, R. (1994). Rediscovery of the Bornean Bay Cat. *Oryx* **28**: 67-70.

Sunquist, M.E., Sunquist, F.C. & Daneke, D.E. (1989). Ecological separation in a Venezuelan llanos carnivore community. Pp. 197-232 in: Redford, K.H. & Eisenberg, J.F. eds. (1989). *Advances in Neotropical Mammalogy.* Sandhill Crane Press, Gainesville, Florida.

Sutcliffe, A.J. (1970). Spotted hyaena: crusher, gnawer, digester and collector of bones. *Nature* **227**: 1110-1113.

Suzan, G. & Ceballos, G. (2005). The role of feral mammals on wildlife infectious disease prevalence in two nature reserves within Mexico City limits. *J. Zoo Wildl. Med.* **36**: 479-484.

Suzuki, T., Yuasa, H. & Machida, Y. (1996). Phylogenetic position of the Japanese river otter *Lutra nippon* inferred from the nucleotide sequence of 224 pb of the mitochondrial cytochrome b gene. *Zool. Science (Tokyo)* **13**(4): 621-626.

Svendsen, G.E. (2003). Weasels and black-footed ferret. Pp. 650-661 in: Feldhamer, G.A., Thompson, B.C. & Chapman, J.A. eds. (2003). *Wild Mammals of North America: Biology, Management and Conservation.* 2nd edition. Johns Hopkins University Press, Baltimore, Maryland.

Swaisgood, R.R., Lindburg, D., White, A.M., Zhang, H. & Zhou, X. (2004). Chemical communication in giant pandas: experimentation and application. Pp. 106-120 in: Lindburg, D. & Baragona, K. eds. (2004). *Giant Pandas. Biology and Conservation.* University of California Press, Berkeley, California.

Swank, W.G. & Teer, J.G. (1989). Status of the jaguar - 1987. *Oryx* **23**(1): 14-21.

Swenson, J.E., Gerstl, N., Dahle, B. & Zedrosser, A. (2000). *Action Plan for the Conservation of the Brown Bear* (Ursus arctos) *in Europe.* Council of Europe, Strasbourg, France.

Swenson, J.E., Jansson, A., Riig, R. & Sandegren, F. (1999). Bears and ants: myrmecophagy by brown bears in central Scandinavia. *Can. J. Zool.* **77**: 551-561.

Szalay, F. (1982). A new appraisal of marsupial phylogeny and classification. Pp. 621-640 in: Archer, M. ed. (1982). *Carnivorous Marsupials.* Royal Zoological Society of New South Wales, Mosman, Australia.

Szykman, M., Engh, A.L., Van Horn, R.C., Funk, S., Scribner, K.T. & Holekamp, K.E. (2001). Association patterns between male and female spotted hyenas reflect male mate choice. *Behav. Ecol. Sociobiol.* **50**: 231-238.

Szykman, M., Van Horn, R.C., Engh, A.L., Boydston, E.E. & Holekamp, K.E. (2007). Courtship and mating in free-living spotted hyenas. *Behaviour* **144**: 815-846.

Taber, A.B., Novaro, A.J., Neris, N. & Colman, F.H. (1997). The food habits of two sympatric large felids in the Paraguayan Chaco. *Biotropica* **29(2)**: 204-213.

Tabor, R. (1991). *Cats. The Rise of the Cat.* BBC Books, London.

Talbot, S.L. & Shields, G.F. (1996). Phylogeography of brown bears (*Ursus arctos*) of Alaska and paraphyly within the Ursidae. *Mol. Phylogen. Evol.* **5**: 477-494.

Tan, B. (1989). Conservation and economic importance of the mustelids and viverrids in China. *Small Carniv. Conserv.* **1**: 5-6.

Tan Bangjie (1984). The status of felids in China. Pp. 33-47 in: *The Plight of the Cats.* Proceedings of the Meeting and Workshop of the IUCN/SSC Cat Specialist Group at Kanha National Park, Madhya Pradesh, India.

Tanaka, H. (2005). Seasonal and daily activity patterns of Japanese badgers (*Meles meles anakuma*) in Western Honshu, Japan. *Mammal Study* **30**: 11-17.

Tanaka, H. (2006). Winter hibernation and body temperature fluctuation in the Japanese badger, *Meles meles anakuma. Zool. Science (Tokyo)* **23**: 991-997.

Tanner, J.B., Dumont, E.R., Sakai, S.T., Lundrigan, B.L. & Holekamp, K.E. (2008). Of arcs and vaults: the biomechanics of bone-cracking in spotted hyenas (*Crocuta crocuta*). *Biol. J. Linn. Soc.* **95**: 246-255.

Tannerfeldt, M. & Angerbjörn, A. (1998). Fluctuating resources and the evolution of litter size in the Arctic fox. *Oikos* **83**: 545-559.

Tannerfeldt, M., Moehrenschlager, A. & Angerbjörn, A. (2003). Den ecology of swift, kit and Arctic foxes: a review. Pp. 167-181 in: Sovada, M. & Carbyn, L. eds. (2003). *Ecology and Conservation of Swift Foxes in a Changing World.* Canadian Plains Research Center, University of Regina, Saskatchewan, Canada.

Tatara, M. (1994). In: Buskirk, S.W., Harestad, A.S., Raphael, M.G. & Powell, R. eds. (1994). *Martens, Sables and Fishers: Biology and Conservation.* Comstock Publishing Press, Ithaca & London.

Tatara, M. & Doi, T. (1994). Comparative analyses on food habits of Japanese marten, Siberian weasel and leopard cat in the Tsushima islands, Japan. *Ecol. Res.* **9**: 99-107.

Tate, G.H.H. (1947). *Mammals of Eastern Asia.* Macmillan Company, New York.

Tate, G.H.H. & Rand, A.L. (1941). A new *Galidia* (Viverridae) from Madagascar. *Amer. Mus. Novit.* **1112**: 1.

Taylor, C.R., Schmidt-Nielsen, K., Dmi'el, R. & Fedak, M. (1971). Effect of hypothermia on heat balance during running in the African hunting dog. *Amer. J. Physiol.* **220**: 823-827.

Taylor, M.E. (1969). Note on the breeding of two genera of viverrids, *Genetta* spp. and *Herpestes sanguineus*, in Kenya. *East Afr. Wildl. J.* **7**: 168-169.

Taylor, M.E. (1970a). Locomotion in some East African viverrids. *J. Mammal.* **51**: 42-51.

Taylor, M.E. (1970b). The distribution of the genets, *Genetta genetta, G. servalina* and *G. tigrina* in East Africa. *J. East Afr. Nat. Hist. Soc.* **28**: 7-9.

Taylor, M.E. (1971). Bone diseases and fractures in East African Viverridae. *Can. J. Zool.* **49**: 1035-1042.

Taylor, M.E. (1972). *Ichneumia albicauda. Mammal. Species* **12**: 1-4.

Taylor, M.E. (1974). The functional anatomy of the forelimb of some African Viverridae (Carnivora). *J. Morph.* **143**: 307-332.

Taylor, M.E. (1975). *Herpestes sanguineus. Mammal. Species* **65**: 1-5.

Taylor, M.E. (1976). The functional anatomy of the hindlimb of some African Viverridae (Carnivora). *J. Morph.* **148**: 227-248.

Taylor, M.E. (1986). The biology of the four-toed mongoose *Bdeogale crassicauda. Cimbebasia (Ser. A)* **8**: 187-193.

Taylor, M.E. (1987). *Bdeogale crassicauda. Mammal. species* **294**: 1-4.

Taylor, M.E. (1988). Foot structure and phylogeny in the Viverridae (Carnivora). *J. Zool., London* **216**: 131-139.

Taylor, M.E. (1989a). New records of two species of rare viverrids from Liberia. *Mammalia* **53**: 122-125.

Taylor, M.E. (1989b). Locomotor adaptations by carnivores. Pp. 382-409 in: Gittleman, J.L. ed. (1989). *Carnivore Behavior, Ecology and Evolution.* Vol. 1. Cornell University Press, Ithaca, New York.

Taylor, M.E. (In press a). *Bdeogale crassicauda.* In: Kingdon, J.S. & Hoffmann, M. eds. (In press). *The Mammals of Africa.* Vol. 5. Carnivores, Pangolins, Rhinos and Equids. Academic Press, Amsterdam.

Taylor, M.E. (In press b). *Herpestes flavescens.* In: Kingdon, J.S. & Hoffmann, M. eds. (In press). *The Mammals of Africa.* Vol. 5. Carnivores, Pangolins, Rhinos and Equids. Academic Press, Amsterdam.

Taylor, M.E. (In press c). *Herpestes ochraceus.* In: Kingdon, J.S. & Hoffmann, M. eds. (In press). *The Mammals of Africa.* Vol. 5. Carnivores, Pangolins, Rhinos and Equids. Academic Press, Amsterdam.

Taylor, M.E. (In press d). *Ichneumia albicauda.* In: Kingdon, J.S. & Hoffmann, M. eds. (In press). *The Mammals of Africa.* Vol. 5. Carnivores, Pangolins, Rhinos and Equids. Academic Press, Amsterdam.

Taylor, M.E. & Dunham, A.E. (In press). *Liberiictis kuhni.* In: Kingdon, J.S. & Hoffmann, M. (In press). *The Mammals of Africa.* Vol. 5. Carnivores, Pangolins, Rhinos and Equids. Academic Press, Amsterdam.

Taylor, M.E. & Goldman, C.A. (1993). The taxonomic status of the African mongooses, *Herpestes sanguineus, H. nigratus, H. pulverulentus* and *H. ochraceus* (Carnivora: Viverridae). *Mammalia* **57**: 375-391.

Taylor, M.K., Akeeagok, S., Andriashek, D., Barbour, W., Born, E.W., Calvert, W., Cluff, H.D., Ferguson, S., Laake, J.L., Rosing-Asvid, A., Stirling, I. & Messier, F. (2001). Delineating Canadian and Greenland polar bear (*Ursus maritimus*) populations by cluster analysis of movements. *Can. J. Zool.* **79**: 690-709.

Taylor P.J. (1993). A systematic and population genetic approach to the rabies problem in the yellow mongoose (Cynictis penicillata). *Onderstepoort J. Vet. Res.* **60**: 379-387.

Taylor, P.J. & Meester, J. (1993). *Cynictis penicillata. Mammal. Species* **432**: 1-7.

Taylor, P.J., Campbell, G.K., van Dyke, D., Watson, J.P., Pallett, J. & Erasmus, B.H. (1990). Genic variation in the yellow mongoose (*Cynictis penicillata*) in Southern Africa. **86**: 256-262.

Taylor, P.J., Campbell, G.K., Meester, J.A.J. & Van Dyck, D. (1991). A study of allozyme evolution in African mongooses (Viverridae: Herpestidae). *Zeitschrift für Säugetierkunde* **56**: 135-145.

Tedford, R.H. & Gustavson, E.P. (1977). The first American record of the extinct panda, *Parailurus. Nature* **265**: 621-623.

Tedford, R.H. & Martin, J. (2001). *Plionarctos*, a tremarctine bear (Ursidae: Carnivora) from Western North America. *J. Vert. Paleo.* **21**: 311-321.

Tehsin, R. (1994). Rusty-spotted cat (*Felis rubiginosa* Geoffroy) sighted near Udaipur. *J. Bombay Nat. Hist. Soc.* **91**: 136.

Tello, J.L. (1986). *The Situation of the Wild Cats (Felidae) in Bolivia.* Report to CITES, Lausanne, Switzerland.

Tembrock, G. (1970). Bioakustische Untersuchungen an Säugetieren des Berliner Tierparkes. *Milu* **3**: 78-96.

Terborgh, J.W., Fitzpatrick, J.W. & Emmons, L.H. (1984). Annotated checklist of bird and mammal species of Cocha Cashu Biological Station, Manu National Park, Peru. *Fieldiana Zool.* **21**: 1-29.

Teska, W.R., Rybak, E.N. & Baker, R.H. (1981). Reproduction and development of the pygmy spotted skunk (*Spilogale pygmaea*). *Amer. Midl. Nat.* **105**: 390-392.

Tewes, M.E. & Schmidly, D.J. (1987). The Neotropical felids: jaguar, ocelot, margay and jaguarundi. Pp. 697-711 in: Nowak, M., Barker, J.A., Obbard, M.E. & Malloch, B. (1987). *Wild Furbearer Management and Conservation in North America.* Ontario Trappers Association, Ontario.

Texera, W.A. (1973). Distribución y diversidad de mamíferos y aves en la provincia de Magallanes. *An. Inst. Pat. Ser. Cienc. Nat. Punta Arenas* **4**: 321-333.

Texera, W.A. (1974). Nuevos antecedentes sobre mamíferos de Magallanes. *An. Inst. Pat. Ser. Cienc. Nat. Punta Arenas* **5**: 189-192.

Thapar, V. (1986). *Tiger: Portrait of a Predator.* William Collins, London.

Thapar, V. (1989). *Tigers: the Secret Life.* Elm Tree Books, London.

Theis, K.R., Greene, K.M., Benson-Amram, S.R. & Holekamp, K.E. (2007). Sources of variation in the long-distance vocalizations of spotted hyenas. *Behaviour* **144**: 557-584.

Theis, K.R., Heckla, A.L., Verge, J.R. & Holekamp, K.E. (2008). The ontogeny of pasting behavior in free-living spotted hyenas (*Crocuta crocuta*). Pp. 179-188 in: Hurst, J. & Beynon, R. eds. (2008). *Chemical Signals in Vertebrates* **11**. Springer, New York.

Thenius, E. (1954). On the origins of the dholes. *Osterreich Zool. Zietshcrift* **5**: 377-388.

Theodat, F.G.S. (1636). *Histoire du Canada: et Voyages que les Freres Mineurs Recollects y ont Faicts pour la Conuersion des Infidelles.* Chez Claude Sonnius, rue S. Jacques a l'Efeu de Basle & au Compas d'or, Paris.

Thevenin, R. (1943). Observations sur la formule dentaire des rhynchogales. *Bull. Mus. Natl. Hist. Nat. Paris* **15**: 380-381.

Thiemann, G.W., Budge, S.M., Iverson, S.J. & Stirling, I. (2007). Unusual fatty acid biomarkers reveal age- and sex- specific foraging in polar bears (*Ursus maritimus*). *Can. J. Zool.* **85**: 505-517.

Thom, M.D., Johnson, D.D.P. & Macdonald, D.W. (2004). The evolution and maintenance of delayed implantation in the mustelidae (Mammalia: Carnivora). *Evolution* **58**: 175-183.

Thomas, O. (1898a). On some new mammals from the neighbourhood of Mount Sahama, Bolivia. *Ann. Mag. Nat. Hist. (Ser. 7)* **1**: 277-283.

Thomas, O. (1898b). Exhibition and description of a specimen of a new skunk, *Spilogale pygmaea*, from Mexico. *Proc. Zool. Soc. London* **1897**: 898-899.

Thomas, O. (1900a). Descriptions of new Neotropical mammals. *Ann. Mag. Nat. Hist. (Ser. 7)* **5**: 217-222.

Thomas, O. (1900b). A new skunk from Peru. *Ann. Mag. Nat. Hist. (Ser. 7)* **5**: 499-500.

Thomas, O. (1902a). On mammals collected at Cruz del Eje, Central Cordova, by Mr. P.O. Simons. *Ann. Mag. Nat. Hist. (Ser. 7)* **9**: 237-245.

Thomas, O. (1902b). On the species of *Mydaus* found in Borneo and the Natuna Islands. *Ann. Mag. Nat. Hist. (Ser. 7)* **9**: 442-444.

Thomas, O. (1905). New Neotropical *Molossus, Conepatus, Nectomys, Proechimys* and *Agouti*, with a note on the genus *Mesomys. Ann. Mag. Nat. Hist. (Ser. 7)* **15**: 584-591.

Thomas, O. (1910). A collection of mammals from eastern Buenos Aires, with descriptions of related new mammals from other localities. *Ann. Mag. Nat. Hist. (Ser. 8)* **5**: 239-247.

Thomas, O. (1919). On small mammals from "Otro Cerro", north-eastern Rioja, collected by Sr. E. Budin. *Ann. Mag. Nat. Hist. (Ser. 9)* **3**: 489-500.

Thomas, O. (1924). New *Callicebus, Conepatus* and *Oecomys* from Peru. *Ann. Mag. Nat. Hist. (Ser. 9)* **14**: 286-288.

Thompson, C.M., Stackhouse, E.L., Roemer, G.W. & Garcelon, D.K. (1998). *Home Range and Density of the Island Fox in China Canyon, San Clemente Island, California.* Report to Department of the Navy, SW Division, Naval Facilities Engineering Command, San Diego, California.

Thompson, G. (1858). *The Palm Land or West Africa, Illustrated.* 2nd. edition. (1969). Dawsons of Pall Mall, London.

Thompson, M.J. & Stewart, W.C. (1994). Cougar(s), *Felis concolor*, with a kill for 27 days. *Can. Field-Nat.* **108**: 497-498.

Thomson, P.C. (1992). The behavioural ecology of dingoes in north-western Australia. *Wildl. Res.* **19**: 519-596.

Thomson, P.C. & Marsack, P.R. (1992). Aerial baiting of dingoes in arid pastoral areas with reference to rabies control. Pp. 125-134 in: O'Brien, P. & Berry, G. eds. (1992). *Wildlife*

Rabies Contingency Planning in Australia. Bureau of Rural Resources Proceedings Number **11**, Australian Government Publishing Service, Canberra.

Thorneycroft, G.V. (1958). African palm civet. *Afr. Wildl.* **12**: 81.

Thornton, A. & McAuliffe, K. (2006). Teaching in wild meerkats. *Science* **313**: 227-229.

Thornton, D.H., Sunquist, M.E. & Main, M.B. (2004). Ecological separation within newly sympatric populations of coyotes and bobcats in south-central Florida. *J. Mammal.* **85**: 973-982.

Thorton, I.W.B. (1978). White tiger genetics - further evidence. *J. Zool., London* **185**: 389-394.

Thorton, I.W.B., Yeung, K.K. & Sankhala, K.S. (1967). The genetics of white tigers in Rewa. *J. Zool., London* **152**: 127-135.

Thulin, C., Simberloff, D., Barun, A., McCracken, G., Pascal, M. & Islam, M. (2006). Genetic divergence in the small Indian mongoose (*Herpestes auropunctatus*), a widely distributed invasive species. *Mol. Ecol.* **15**: 3947-3956.

Thurber, J.M. & Peterson, R.O. (1991). Changes in body size associated with range expansion in the coyote *Canis latrans*. *J. Mamm.* **72**: 750-755.

Tilson, R.L. & Hamilton, W.J. (1984). Social dominance and feeding patterns of spotted hyaenas. *Anim. Behav.* **32**: 715-724.

Tilson, R.L. & Henschel, J.R. (1984). Spotted hyaenas in the central Namib Desert. *South Afr. J. Sci.* **80**: 185.

Tilson, R.L. & Henschel, J.R. (1986). Spatial arrangement of spotted hyaena groups in a desert environment, Namibia. *Afr. J. Ecol.* **24**: 173-180.

Tilson, R.L., von Blottnitz, F. & Henschel, J.R. (1980). Prey selection by spotted hyaena (*Crocuta crocuta*) in the Namib Desert. *Madoqua* **12**: 41-49.

Tilson, R.L., Traylor-Holzer, K. & Qiu Mingjiang (1997). The decline and impending extinction of the South China tiger. *Oryx* **31**: 243-252.

Timm, S.F., Barker, W.D., Johnson, S.A., Sewell, J.H., Sharpe, P.B., Schmidt, G.A. & Garcelon, D.K. (2002). *Island Fox Recovery Efforts on Santa Catalina Island, California, September 2000 – October 2001*. Annual Report. Report prepared for Ecological Restoration Department, Santa Catalina Island Conservancy. Institute for Wildlife Studies, Arcata, California.

Timm, S.F., Stokely, J.M., Gehr, T.B., Peebles, R.L. & Garcelon, D.K. (2000). *Investigation into the Decline of Island Foxes on Santa Catalina Island*. Institute for Wildlife Studies, Arcata, California.

Tinline, R.R. (1988). Persistence of rabies in wildlife. Pp. 301-322 in: Campbell, J.B. & Charlton, K.M. eds. (1988). *Rabies*. Kluwer Academic Publishers, Boston, Massachusetts.

Tischendorf, J.W. & McAlpine, D.F. (1995). A melanistic bobcat from outside Florida. *Florida Field Nat.* **23**: 13-14.

Tizard, R. (2002). Records of little known small carnivores from Thailand, Lao PDR and southern China. *Small Carniv. Conserv.* **26**: 3.

Todd, A.W. & Keith, L.B. (1983). Coyote demography during a snowshoe hare decline in Alberta. *J. Wildl. Management* **47**: 394-404.

Todd, N.B. (1967). The karyotypes and diploid numbers of the African civet (*Civettictis civetta*) and the African palm civet (*Nandinia binotata*), with remarks on satellite chromosomes and taxonomy of the Felidoidea. *Carniv. Genet. Newslett.* **3**: 49-51.

Tolson, N.D., Charlton, K.M., Stewart, R.B., Campbell, J.B. & Wiktor, T.J. (1987). Immuneresponse in skunks to a Vaccinia virus recombinant expressing the rabies virus glycoprotein. *Can. J. Vet. Res.* **51**: 363-366.

Tomich, P.Q. (1969). Movement patterns of the mongoose in Hawaii. *J. Wildl. Management* **33**: 576-584.

Tonkin, B.A. & Kohler, E. (1978). Breeding the African golden cat in captivity. *Int. Zoo Yb.* **18**: 147-150.

Tonkin, B.A. & Kohler, E. (1981). Observations on the Indian Desert cat in captivity. *Int. Zoo Yb.* **21**: 151-154.

Torii, H. (1986). Food habits of the masked palm civet *Paguma larvata* Hamilton-Smith. *J. Mammal. Soc. Japan* **11**: 39-43.

Tortato, M.A. & Oliveira, T.G. (2005). Ecology of the oncilla (*Leopardus tigrinus*) at Serra do Tabuleiro State Park, southern Brazil. *Cat News* **42**: 28-30.

Toweill, D.E. & Anthony, R.G. (1988). Annual diet of bobcats in Oregon's Cascade Range. *Northwest Science* **62**: 99-103.

Toweill, D.E. & Teer, J.G. (1972). Home range and den habits of Texas ringtails (*Bassariscus astutus flavus*). Pp. 1103-1120 in: Chapman, J.A. & Pursley, D. eds. (1972). *Proceedings of the Worldwide Furbearers Conference*. Frostburg, Maryland.

Toweill, D.E. & Teer, J.G. (1977). Food habits of ringtails in the Edwards Plateau region of Texas. *J. Mammal.* **58**: 660-663.

Toweill, D.E., Maser, C., Bryant, L.D. & Johnson, M.L. (1988). Reproductive characteristics of eastern Oregon cougars. *Northwest Science* **62**: 147-150.

Trapp, G.R. & Hallberg, D.L. (1975). Ecology of the gray fox *Urocyon cinereoargenteus*: a review. Pp. 164-178 in: Fox, M.W. ed. (1975). *The Wild Canids*. Van Nostrand Reinhold Company, New York.

Travaini, A., Delibes, M. & Ceballos, O. (1998). Summer foods of the Andean hog-nosed skunk (*Conepatus chinga*) in Patagonia. *J. Zool., London* **246**: 457-460.

Travaini, A., Juste, J., Novaro, A.J. & Capurro, A.F. (2000). Sexual dimorphism and sex identification in the South American culpeo fox, *Pseudalopex culpaeus* (Carnivora: Canidae). *Wildl. Res.* **27**: 669-674.

Travaini, A., Zapata, S.C., Martínez-Peck, R. & Delibes, M. (2000). Percepción y actitud humanas hacia la predación de ganado ovino por el zorro colorado (*Pseudalopex culpaeus*) en Santa Cruz, Patagonia Argentina. *Mastozool. Neotrop.* **7**: 117-129.

Travassos, J.A. (1968). *Fauna Selvagem de Mozambique*. No. 1. Radio Moçambique Mensario. Boletim Mensal de Radio Clube de Moçambique. Lourenço Marques, Mozambique.

Trinkel, M. & Kastberger, G. (2005). Competitive interactions between spotted hyenas and lions in the Etosha National Park, Namibia. *Afr. J. Ecol.* **43**: 220-224.

Trinkel, M., Fleischmann, P.H., Steindorfer, A.F. & Kastberger, G. (2004). Spotted hyenas (*Crocuta crocuta*) follow migratory prey. Seasonal expansion of a clan territory in Etosha, Namibia. *J. Zool., London* **264**: 125-133.

Tripathi, R.S., Jain, A.P., Kashyap, N., Rana, B.D. & Prakash, I. (1992). North Western India. Pp. 357-395 in: Prakash, I. & Ghosh, P.K. eds. (1992). *Rodents in Indian Agriculture*. Vol. 1. Scientific Publishers, Jodhpur, India.

Trolle, M. (2003). Mammal survey in the southeastern Pantanal, Brazil. *Biodiversity & Conservation* **12**: 823-836.

Trolle, M. & Kery, M. (2003). Estimation of ocelot density in the Pantanal using capture-recapture analysis of camera-trapping data. *J. Mammal.* **84**: 607-614.

Troya, V., Cuesta, F. & Pervalo, M. (2004). Food habits of Andean bears in the Oyacahi River Basin, Ecuador. *Ursus* **15**: 57-60.

Tumlinson, R. (1987). *Felis lynx*. *Mammal. Species* **269**: 1-8.

Turnbull-Kemp, P. (1967). *The Leopard*. Howard Timmins, Capetown.

Turner, A. (1997). *The Big Cats and their Fossil Relatives*. Columbia University Press, New York.

Tvrtkovic, N. & Krystufek, B. (1990). Small Indian mongoose *Herpestes auropunctatus* (Hodgson, 1836) on the Adriatic Islands of Yugoslavia. *Bonn Zool. Beitr.* **41**: 3-8.

Tyndale-Biscoe, H. (1973). *Life of Marsupials*. Edward Arnold, Australia.

Tyndale-Biscoe, H. & Renfree, M. (1987). *Reproductive Physiology of Marsupials*. Cambridge University Press, Cambridge.

Ulmer, F.A. (1968). Breeding fishing cats at Philadelphia Zoo. *Int. Zoo Yb.* **8**: 49-55.

Uresk, D.W. & Sharps, J.C. (1986). Denning habitat and diet of the swift fox in western South Dakota. *Great Basin Nat.* **46**: 249-253.

US Fish & Wildlife Service (1990). *Red Wolf Recovery and Species Survival Plan*. US Fish & Wildlife Service, Atlanta, Georgia.

US Fish & Wildlife Service (1998). *Recovery Plan for Upland Species of the San Joaquin Valley, California*. US Fish & Wildlife Service, Portland, Oregon.

Vaisfeld, M.A. & Chestin, I.E. eds. (1993). [*Bears: Brown Bear, Polar Bear, Asian Black Bear. Distribution, Ecology, Use and Protection*]. Nauka, Moscow. In Russian with English summaries.

Valdespino, C. (2000). *The Reproductive System of the Fennec Fox (*Vulpes zerda*)*. PhD dissertation, University of Missouri, St. Louis, Missouri.

Valdespino, C., Asa, C.S. & Bauman, J.E. (2002). Estrous cycles, copulation and pregnancy in the fennec fox *Vulpes zerda*. *J. Mammal.* **83**: 99-109.

Valdiosera, C.E., García, N., Anderung, C., Dalén, L., Crégut-Bonnoure, E., Kahlke, R.D., Stiller, M., Brandstöm, M., Thomas, M.G., Arsuaga, J.L., Götherström, A. & Barnes, I. (2007). Staying out in the cold: glacial refugia and mitochondrial DNA phylogeography in ancient European brown bears. *Mol. Ecol.* **16**: 5140-5148.

Valdiosera, C.E., García-Garitagoitia, J.L., Garcia, N., Doadrio, I., Thomas, M.G., Hänni, C., Arsuaga, J.L., Barnes, I., Hofreiter, M., Orlando, L. & Götherström, A. (2008). Surprising migration and population size dynamics in ancient Iberian brown bears (*Ursus arctos*). *Proc. Natl. Acad. Sci. USA* **105**: 5123-5128.

Valenzuela, D. & Ceballos, G. (2000). Habitat selection, home range and activity of the white-nosed coati (*Nasua narica*) in a Mexican tropical dry forest. *J. Mammal.* **81**: 810-819.

Valenzuela, D. & Macdonald, D.W. (2002). Home-range use by white-nosed coatis (*Nasua narica*): limited water and a test of the resource dispersion hypothesis. *J. Zool., London* **258**: 247-256.

Valverde, J.A. (1957). Mamíferos. Pp. 354-406 in: *Aves del Sahara Español. Estudio Ecológico del Desierto*. Instituto de Estudios Africanos, Consejo Superior de Investigacion Cientificas, Madrid, Spain.

Van Aarde, R.J. & Van Dyk, A. (1986). Inheritance of the king coat colour in cheetahs. *J. Zool., London* **209**: 573-578.

Van Aarde, R.J., Skinner, J.D., Knight, M.H. & Skinner, D.C. (1988). Range use by a striped hyaena (*Hyaena hyaena*) in the Negev Desert. *J. Zool., London* **216**: 575-577.

Van Bemmel, A.C.V. (1952). Contribution to the knowledge of the genera *Muntiacus* and *Arctogalidia* in the Indo-Australian Archipelago (Mammalia, Cervidae & Viverridae). *Beaufortia* **16**: 1-41.

Van Bree, P.J.H. & Boeadi, M.S. (1978). Notes on the Indonesian mountain weasel, *Mustela lutreolina* Robinson and Thomas, 1917. *Zeitschrift für Säugetierkunde* **43**: 166-171.

Van Daele, L.J. (2007). *Population Dynamics and Management of Brown Bears on Kodiak Island, Alaska*. PhD thesis, University of Idaho, Moscow, Idaho.

Van De Graaff, K.M. (1969). *Comparative Osteology of the Skunks of the World*. MSc thesis, University of Utah, Salt Lake City, Utah.

Vanderhaar, J.M. & Hwang, Y.T. (2003). *Mellivora capensis*. *Mammal. Species* **721**: 1-8.

Van Der Zee, D. (1981). Prey of the Cape clawless otter (*Aonyx capensis*) in the Tsitsikama Coastal National Park, South Africa. *J. Zool, London* **194**: 467-483.

Van Der Zee, D. (1982). Density of Cape clawless otters *Aonyx capensis* (Schinz, 1821) in the Tsitsikama Coastal National Park. *South Afr. J. Wildl. Res.* **12**: 8-13.

Van Dyk, A. (1991). *The Cheetahs of DeWildt*. Struik, Cape Town.

Van Dyke, F.G., Brocke, R.H., Shaw, H.G., Ackerman, B.B., Hemker, T.P. & Lindzey, F.G. (1986). Reactions of mountain lions to logging and human activity. *J. Wildl. Management* **50**: 95-102.

Van Gelder, R.G. (1959). A taxonomic revision of the spotted skunks (genus *Spilogale*). *Bull. Amer. Mus. Nat. Hist.* **117**: 229-392.

Van Gelder, R.G. (1977). Mammalian hybrids and generic limits. *Amer. Mus. Novit.* **2635**: 1-25.

Van Gelder, R.G. (1978). A review of canid classification. *Amer. Mus. Novit.* **2646**: 1-10.

Van Heerden, J. (1981). The role of integumental glands in the social and mating behaviour of the hunting dog *Lycaon pictus* Temminck, 1820. *Onderstepoort J. Vet. Res.* **48**: 19-21.

Van Horn, R.C., Engh, A.L., Scribner, K.T., Funk, S.M. & Holekamp, K.E. (2004). Behavioral structuring of relatedness in the spotted hyena (*Crocuta crocuta*) suggests direct fitness benefits of clan-level cooperation. *Mol. Ecol.* **13**: 449-458.

Van Horn, R.C., McElhinny, T.L. & Holekamp, K.E. (2003). Age estimation and dispersal in the spotted hyena (*Crocuta crocuta*). *J. Mammal.* **84**: 1019-1030.

Van Horn, R.C., Wahaj, S.A. & Holekamp, K.E. (2004). Role-reversed nepotistic interactions between sires and offspring in the spotted hyena. *Ethology* **110**: 1-14.

Van Humbeck, J. & Perez, N. (1998). *Estudios del Jagua Yvyguy,* Speothos venaticus, *en el Centro de Investigación de Animales Silvestres de Itaipu, CIASI*. Superintendencia de Medio Ambiente de la Itaipu Binacional, Ciudad del Este, Paraguay.

Van Jaarsveld, A.S. (1993). A comparative investigation of hyaenid and aardwolf life-histories, with notes on spotted hyaena mortality patterns. *Trans. Roy. Soc. S. Afr.* **48**: 219-231.

Van Jaarsveld, A.S., Richardson, P.R.K. & Anderson, M.D. (1995). Post-natal growth and sustained lactational effort in the aardwolf: life-history implications. *Functional Ecol.* **9**: 492-497.

Van Jaarsveld, A.S., Skinner, J.D. & Lindeque, M. (1988). Growth, development and parental investment in the spotted hyaena, *Crocuta crocuta*. *J. Zool., London* **216**: 45-53.
Van Niekerk, C.H., Somers, M.J. & Nel, J.A.J. (1998). Freshwater availability and distribution of Cape clawless otter spraints and resting places along the south-west coast of South Africa. *South Afr. J. Wildl. Res.* **28**: 68-72.
Van Orsdol, K.G. (1982). Ranges and food habits of lions in the Ruwenzori National Park, Uganda. *Symp. Zool. Soc. London* **49**: 325-340.
Van Orsdol, K.G. (1984). Foraging behaviour and hunting success of lions in Queen Elizabeth National Park, Uganda. *Afr. J. Ecol.* **22**: 79-99.
Van Orsdol, K.G., Hanby, J.P. & Bygott, J.D. (1985). Ecological correlates of lion social organization. *J. Zool., London* **206**: 97-112.
Van Rompaey, H. (1978). Longevity of a banded mongoose (*Mungos mungo*, Gmelin) in captivity. *Int. Zoo News* **25**: 32-33.
Van Rompaey, H. (1988). *Osbornictis piscivora*. *Mammal. Species* **309**: 1-4.
Van Rompaey, H. (1991). The Gambian mongoose: a forgotten species. *Mustel. Viverr. Conserv.* **4**: 11-13.
Van Rompaey, H. (1993). The banded linsang, *Prionodon linsang*. *Small Carniv. Conserv.* **9**: 11-15.
Van Rompaey, H. (1995). The spotted linsang, *Prionodon pardicolor*. *Small Carniv. Conserv.* **13**: 10-13.
Van Rompaey, H. (1997). Longevity of the two-spotted palm civet, *Nandinia binotata*, in captivity. *Small Carniv. Conserv.* **17**: 22-23.
Van Rompaey, H. (2000). The short-tailed mongoose, *Herpestes brachyurus*. *Small Carniv. Conserv.* **23**: 17-21.
Van Rompaey, H. & Azlan, M. (2004). Hose's civet, *Diplogale hosei*. *Small Carniv. Conserv.* **30**: 18-19.
Van Rompaey, H. & Colyn, M. (1992). *Crossarchus ansorgei*. *Mammal. Species* **402**: 1-3.
Van Rompaey, H. & Colyn, M. (1998). A new servaline genet (Carnivora, Viverridae) from Zanzibar Island. *South Afr. J. Zool.* **33**: 42-46.
Van Rompaey, H. & Colyn, M. (In press a). *Bdeogale nigripes*. In: Kingdon, J.S. & Hoffmann, M. eds. (In press). *The Mammals of Africa*. Vol. 5. Carnivores, Pangolins, Rhinos and Equids. Academic Press, Amsterdam.
Van Rompaey, H. & Colyn, M. (In press b). *Crossarchus alexandri*. In: Kingdon, J.S. & Hoffmann, M. eds. (In press). *The Mammals of Africa*. Vol. 5. Carnivores, Pangolins, Rhinos and Equids. Academic Press, Amsterdam.
Van Rompaey, H. & Colyn, M. (In press c). *Crossarchus ansorgei*. In: Kingdon, J.S. & Hoffmann, M. eds. (In press). *The Mammals of Africa*. Vol. 5. Carnivores, Pangolins, Rhinos and Equids. Academic Press, Amsterdam.
Van Rompaey, H. & Colyn, M. (In press d). *Nandinia binotata* (Gray). In: Kingdon, J.S. & Hoffmann, M. eds. (In press). *The Mammals of Africa*. Vol. 5. Carnivora, Pholidota, Perissodactyla. Academic Press, Amsterdam.
Van Rompaey, H. & Colyn, M. (In press e). *Genetta cristata*. In: Kingdon, J.S. & Hoffmann, M. eds. (In press). *The Mammals of Africa*. Vol. 5. Carnivores, Pangolins, Rhinos and Equids. Academic Press, Amsterdam.
Van Rompaey, H. & Colyn, M. (In press f). *Genetta piscivora*. In: Kingdon, J.S. & Hoffmann, M. eds. (In press). *The Mammals of Africa*. Vol. 5. Carnivores, Pangolins, Rhinos and Equids. Academic Press, Amsterdam.
Van Rompaey, H. & Colyn, M. (In press g). *Genetta servalina*. In: Kingdon, J.S. & Hoffmann, M. eds. (In press). *The Mammals of Africa*. Vol. 5. Carnivores, Pangolins, Rhinos and Equids. Academic Press, Amsterdam.
Van Rompaey, H. & Colyn, M. (In press h). *Genetta victoriae*. In: Kingdon, J.S. & Hoffmann, M. eds. (In press). *The Mammals of Africa*. Vol. 5. Carnivores, Pangolins, Rhinos and Equids. Academic Press, Amsterdam.
Van Rompaey, H. & Colyn, M. (In press i). *Poiana leightoni*. In: Kingdon, J.S. & Hoffmann, M. eds. (In press). *The Mammals of Africa*. Vol. 5. Carnivores, Pangolins, Rhinos and Equids. Academic Press, Amsterdam.
Van Rompaey, H. & Colyn, M. (In press j). *Poiana richardsoni*. In: Kingdon, J. & Hoffmann, M. eds. (In press). *The Mammals of Africa*. Vol. 5. Carnivores, Pangolins, Rhinos and Equids. Academic Press, Amsterdam.
Van Rompaey, H. & Jayakumar, M.N. (2003). The stripe-necked mongoose, *Herpestes vitticollis*. *Small Carniv. Conserv.* **28**: 14-17.
Van Rompaey, H. & Kingdon, J.S. (In press). *Bdeogale jacksoni*. In: Kingdon, J.S. & Hoffmann, M. eds. (In press). *The Mammals of Africa*. Vol. 5. Carnivores, Pangolins, Rhinos and Equids. Academic Press, Amsterdam.
Van Rompaey, H. & Powell, C.B. (1999). Carnivores of the Niger Delta, Nigeria. *Small Carniv. Conserv.* **21**: 19-22.
Van Rompaey, H. & Sillero-Zubiri, C. (In press). *Mungos gambianus*. In: Kingdon, J.S. & Hoffmann, M. eds. (In press). *The Mammals of Africa*. Vol. 5. Carnivores, Pangolins, Rhinos and Equids. Academic Press, Amsterdam.
Van Staaden, M.J. (1994). *Suricata suricatta*. *Mammal. Species* **483**: 1-8.
Van Valkenburgh, B. (1996). Feeding behavior of free-ranging African carnivores. *J. Mammal.* **77**: 240-254.
Van Vuren, D.H. (2001). Predation on yellow-bellied marmots (*Marmota flaviventris*). *Amer. Midl. Nat.* **145**: 94-100.
Van Why, K.R. & Giuliano, W.M. (2001). Fall food habits and reproductive condition of fishers, *Martes pennanti*, in Vermont. *Can. Field-Nat.* **115**: 52-56.
Van Zyll de Jong, C.G. (1972). A systematic review of the Nearctic and Neotropical river otters (Genus *Lutra*, Mustelidae, Carnivora). *Life Sci. Contr., Royal Ontario Museum* **80**: 1-104.
Van Zyll de Jong, C.G. (1992). A morphometric analysis of cranial variation in holarctic (*Mustela nivalis*). *Zeitschrift für Säugetierkunde* **57**: 77-93.
Vargas, A. & Anderson, S.H. (1998). Ontogeny of black-footed ferret predatory behavior towards prairie dogs. *Can. J. Zool.* **76**: 1696-1704.
Vargas, A., Martinez, F., Bergara, J., Klink, L.D., Rodriguez, J. & Rodriguez, D. (2005). Iberian lynx ex-situ conservation program update. *Cat News* **43**: 21-22.
Vaughan, C., Kotowski, T. & Saénz, L. (1994). Ecology of the Central American cacomistle, *Bassariscus sumichrasti*, in Costa Rica. *Small Carniv. Conserv.* **11**: 4-7.
Vaughan, M.R. (2002). Oak trees, acorns and bears. Pp. 224-240 in: McShea, W.J. & Healy, W.M. eds. (2002). *Oak Forest Ecosystems: Ecology and Management for Wildlife*. Johns Hopkins University Press, Baltimore, Maryland.
Vaughan, T.A., Ryan, J.M. & Czaplewski, N. (2000). *Mammalogy*. Harcourt College Publishers, New York.
Veitch, A.M. & Harrington, F.H. (1996). Brown bears, black bears and humans in Northern Labrador: an historical perspective and outlook to the future. *J. Wildl. Res.* **1**: 245-250.
Venkataraman, A.B. (1998). Male-biased sex ratios and their significance for cooperative breeding in dhole *Cuon alpinus* packs. *Ethology* **104**: 671-684.
Venkataraman, A.B., Arumugam, R. & Sukumar, R. (1995). The foraging ecology of dhole *Cuon alpinus* in Mudumalai Sanctuary, southern India. *J. Zool., London* **237**: 543-561.
Verberne, G. (1976). Chemocommunication among domestic cats, mediated by the olfactory and vomeronasal senses. Part II. The relation between the function of Jacobson's organ (vomeronasal organ) and flehmen behaviour. *Zeitschr. Tierpsychol.* **42**: 113-128.
Verberne, G. & DeBoer, J. (1976). Chemocommunication among domestic cats, mediated by the olfactory and vomernasal senses. Part I. Chemocommunication. *Zeitschr. Tierpsychol.* **42**: 86-109.
Verberne, G. & Leyhausen, P. (1976). Marking behaviour of some Viverridae and Felidae: time-interval analysis of the marking pattern. *Behaviour* **58**: 192-253.
Verheyen, W. (1962). Quelques notes sur la zoogéographie et la crâniologie d'*Osbornictis piscivora* Allen, 1919. *Rev. Zool. Bot. Afr.* **65**: 121-128.
Veron, G. (1994). *Méthodes de Recherche en Biotaxonomie des Mammifères Carnivores. Confrontation des Méthodes de Phylogénie Traditionnelle et Moléculaire Dans la Recherche de la Position Systématique de* Cryptoprocta ferox *(Aeluroidea)*. PhD dissertation, Muséum National d'Histoire Naturelle, Paris.
Veron, G. (1995). La position systématique de *Cryptoprocta ferox* (Carnivora). Analyse cladistique des caractères morphologiques de carnivores Aeluroidea actuels et fossiles. *Mammalia* **59(4)**: 551-582.
Veron, G. (1999). Pads morphology in the Viverridae (Carnivora). *Acta Theriol.* **44**: 363-376.
Veron, G. (2001). The palm civets of Sulawesi. *Small Carniv. Conserv.* **24**: 13-14.
Veron, G. & Catzeflis, F.M. (1993). Phylogenetic relationships of the endemic Malagasy carnivore *Cryptoprocta ferox* (Aeluroidea): DNA/DNA hybridization experiments. *J. Mammal. Evol.* **1**: 169-185.
Veron, G. & Heard, S. (2000). Molecular systematics of the Asiatic Viverridae (Carnivora) inferred from mitochondrial cytochrome b sequence analysis. *J. Zool. Syst. Evol. Res.* **38**: 209-217.
Veron, G., Colyn, M., Dunham, A., Taylor, P. & Gaubert, P. (2004). Molecular systematics and origin of sociality in mongooses (Herpestidae, Carnivora). *Mol. Phylogen. Evol.* **30**: 582-598.
Veron, G., Gaubert, P., Franklin, N., Jennings, A.P. & Grassman, L. (2006). A reassessment of the distribution and taxonomy of the endangered otter civet, *Cynogale bennettii* (Carnivora: Viverridae) of South-east Asia. *Oryx* **40**: 42-49.
Veron, G., Heard, S., Long, B. & Roberton, S. (2004). The molecular systematics and conservation of an endangered carnivore, the Owston's palm civet *Chrotogale owstoni* (Thomas, 1912) (Carnivora, Viverridae, Hemigalinae). *Anim. Conserv.* **7**: 107-112.
Veron, G., Laidlaw, R., Heard, S., Streicher, U. & Roberton, S. (2004). Coat colour variation in the banded palm civet *Hemigalus derbyanus* and in the Owston's civet *Chrotogale owstoni*. *Mammal Rev.* **34**: 307-310.
Veron, G., Patou, M.L., Pothet, G., Simberloff, D. & Jennings, A.P. (2007). Systematic status and biogeography of the Javan and small Indian mongooses (Herpestidae, Carnivora). *Zool. Scr.* **36**: 1-10.
Verts, B.J. (1967). *The Biology of the Striped Skunk*. University of Illinois Press, Urbana, Illinois.
Verts, B.J. & Carraway, L.N. (1998). *Land Mammals of Oregon*. University of California Press, Berkeley, California.
Verts, B.J., Carraway, L.N. & Kinlaw, A. (2001). *Spilogale gracilis*. *Mammal. Species* **674**: 1-10.
Verwoerd, D.J. (1987). Observations on the food and status of the Cape clawless otter *Aonyx capensis* at Betty's Bay, South Africa. *South Afr. J. Zool.* **22**: 33-39.
Vilella, F.J. (1998). Biology of the mongoose (*Herpestes javanicus*) in a rain forest of Puerto Rico. *Biotropica* **30**: 120-125.
Viljoen, S. (1980). Early postnatal development, parental care and interaction in the banded mongoose *Mungos mungo*. *South Afr. J. Zool.* **15**: 119-120.
Villalba, L. & Bernal, N. (1998). [*Distribution and Status of the Andean Mountain Cat in Bolivia*]. Final project report to Cat Action Treasury. In Spanish.
Virgos, E. (2003). Association of the polecat *Mustela putorius* in eastern Spain with montane pine forests. *Oryx* **37**: 484-487.
Virgos, E. & Casanovas, J.G. (1997). Habitat selection of genet *Genetta genetta* in the mountains of central Spain. *Acta Theriol.* **42**: 169-177.
Virgos, E. & Casanovas, J.G. (1999). Badger *Meles meles* sett site selection in low density Mediterranean areas of central Spain. *Acta Theriol.* **44**: 173-182.
Virgos, E., Casanovas, J.G. & Blazquez, T. (1996). Genet (*Genetta genetta* L., 1758) diet shift in mountains of central Spain. *Zeitschrift für Säugetierkunde* **61**: 221-227.
Virgos, E., Llorente, M. & Cortes, Y. (1999). Geographical variation in genet (*Genetta genetta* L.) diet: a literature review. *Mammal Rev.* **29**: 119-128.
Virgos, E., Recio, M.R. & Cortes, Y. (2000). Stone marten (*Martes foina* Erx., 1777) use of different landscape types in the mountains of central Spain. *Zeitschrift für Säugetierkunde* **65**: 375.
Virgos, E., Romero, T. & Mangas, J.G. (2001). Factors determining "gaps" in the distribution of a small carnivore, the common genet (*Genetta genetta*), in central Spain. *Can. J. Zool.* **79**: 1544-1551.
Visser, J. (1976a). Status and conservation of the smaller cats of southern Africa. Pp. 60-66 in: Eaton, R.L. (1976). *The World's Cats*. Vol. 3(1). Carnivore Research Institute, Burke Museum, University of Washington, Seattle, Washington.

Visser, J. (1976b). The black-footed cat. Page 72 in: Eaton, R.L. (1976). *The World's Cats.* Vol. 3(1). Carnivore Research Institute, Burke Museum, University of Washington, Seattle, Washington.

Visser, J. (1977). The black-footed cat. Page 72 in: Eaton, R.L. ed. (1977). *The World Cats 3: Contributions to the Breeding, Biology, Behavior and Husbandry.* Carnivore Research Institute, Univ. Washington, Seattle, Washington.

Voigt, D.R. & Macdonald, D.W. (1984). Variation in the spatial and social behaviour of the red fox *Vulpes vulpes. Acta Zool. Fennica* **171**: 261-265.

Volf, J. (1957). A propos de la reproduction du fennec. *Mammalia* **21**: 454-455.

Volf, J. (1968). Breeding the European wild cat at Prague Zoo. *Int. Zoo Yb.* **8**: 38-42.

Volodina, E.V. (2000). [Vocal repertoire of the cheetah *Acinonyx jubatus* (Carnivora, Felidae) in captivity. Sound structure and their potential for estimating the state of adult animals]. *Zool. Zhurnal* **79**: 833-843. In Russian with English summary.

Vos, A., Pommerening, E., Neubert, L., Kachel, S. & Neubert, A. (2002). Safety studies of the oral rabies vaccine SAD B19 in striped skunk (*Mephitis mephitis*). *J. Wildl. Diseases* **38**: 428-431.

Vosseler, J. (1928). Beobachtungen am Fleckenroller (*Nandinia binotata* Gray). *Zeitschrift für Säugetierkunde* **3**: 80-91.

Vosseler, J. (1929). Beiträg zur Kenntnis der Fossa (*Cryptoprocta ferox* Benn.) und ihrer Fortpflanzung. *Zool. Garten (N.F.)* **2**: 1-9.

Vuillermoz, P. & Sapoznikow, A. (1998). *Hábitos Alimenticios y Selección de Presas de los Carnívoros Medianos en la Reserva de Vida Silvestre „Campos del Tuyú".* Fundación Vida Silvestre Argentina, Boletín Técnico No. **44**, Buenos Aires, Argentina.

Wachter, B., Höner, O.P., East, M.L., Golla, W. & Hofer, H. (2002). Low aggression levels and unbiased sex ratios in a prey-rich environment: no evidence of siblicide in Ngorongoro spotted hyenas (*Crocuta crocuta*). *Behav. Ecol. Sociobiol.* **52**: 348-356.

Wackernagel, H. (1968). A note on breeding the serval cat at Basle Zoo. *Int. Zoo Yb.* **8**: 46-47.

Wade-Smith, J. & Richmond, M.E. (1978a). Induced ovulation, development of the corpus luteum and tubal transport in the striped skunk (*Mephitis mephitis*). *Amer. J. Anat.* **153**: 123-142.

Wade-Smith, J. & Richmond, M.E. (1978b). Reproduction in captive striped skunks (*Mephitis mephitis*). *Amer. Midl. Nat.* **100**: 452-455.

Wade-Smith, J. & Verts, B.J. (1982). *Mephitis mephitis. Mammal. Species* **173**: 1-7.

Wade-Smith, J., Richmond, M.E., Mead, R.A. & Taylor, H. (1980). Hormonal and gestational evidence for delayed implantation in the striped skunk, *Mephitis mephitis. Gen. Comp. Endocrin.* **42**: 509-515.

Wagner, A.P. (2006). *Behavioral Ecology of the Striped Hyaena (*Hyaena hyaena*).* PhD dissertation, Montana State University, Bozeman, Montana.

Wagner, A.P. (In press). *Hyaena hyaena* (Linnaeus). In: Kingdon, J., Happold, D. & Butynski, T. eds. (In press). *The Mammals of Africa.* Elsevier Science, London.

Wagner, A.P., Creel, S., Frank, L.G. & Kalinowski, S.T. (2007). Patterns of relatedness and parentage in an asocial polyandrous striped hyena population. *Mol. Ecol.* **16**: 4356-4369.

Wagner, A.P., Frank, L.G. & Creel, S. (2008). Spatial grouping in behaviourally solitary striped hyaenas (*Hyaena hyaena*). *Anim. Behav.* **75**: 1131-1142.

Wagner, A.P., Frank, L.G., Creel, S. & Coscia, E.M. (2007). Transient genital anomalies in the striped hyena. *Horm. Behav.* **51**: 626-632.

Wahaj, S.A. & Holekamp, K.E. (2006). Functions of sibling aggression in the spotted hyaena (*Crocuta crocuta*). *Anim. Behav.* **71**: 1401-1409.

Wahaj, S.A., Place, N.J., Weldele, M.L., Glickman, S.E. & Holekamp, K.E. (2007). Siblicide in the spotted hyena: analysis with ultrasonic examination of wild and captive individuals. *Behav. Ecol.* **18**: 974-984.

Wahaj, S.A., Van Horn, R.C., Van Horn, T., Dreyer, R., Hilgris, R., Schwarz, J. & Holekamp, K.E. (2004). Kin discrimination in the spotted hyena (*Crocuta crocuta*): nepotism among siblings. *Behav. Ecol. Sociobiol.* **56**: 237-247.

Wainwright, M. (2007). *The Mammals of Costa Rica.* Cornell University Press, Ithaca, New York.

Waits, L.P., Sullivan, J., O'Brien, S.J. & Ward, R.H. (1999). Rapid radiation events in the family Ursidae indicated by likelihood phylogenetic estimation from multiple fragments of mtDNA. *Mol. Phylogen. Evol.* **13**: 82-92.

Waits, L.P., Talbot, S., Ward, R.H. & Shields, G.F. (1998). Mitochondrial DNA phylogeography of the North American brown bear and implications for conservation. *Conserv. Biol.* **12(2)**: 408-417.

Walker, A. (1930). The „hand-stand" and some other habits of the Oregon spotted skunk. *J. Mammal.* **11**: 227-229.

Walker, P.L. & Cant, J.G. (1977). A population survey of kinkajous (*Potos flavus*) in a seasonally dry tropical forest. *J. Mammal.* **58**: 100-102.

Walker, S. (1994). Executive summary of the Asiatic lion PHVA. First draft report. *Zoo Print* **Jan/Feb**: 2-22.

Walker, S. & Novaro, A. (2001). First report on the multinational initiative to determine the status of the Andean mountain cat and priorities for its conservation. Unpublished report to Cat Action Treasury and COCGA.

Wallace, S.C. & Wang, X. (2004). Two new carnivores from an unusual late Tertiary forest biota in eastern North America. *Nature (London)* **432**: 556-559.

Walston, J. & Duckworth, J.W. (2003). The first record of small-toothed palm civet *Arctogalidia trivirgata* from Cambodia, with notes on surveying this species. *Small Carniv. Conserv.* **28**: 12-13.

Walston, J. & Veron, G. (2001). Questionable status of the "Taynguyen civet", *Viverra tainguensis* Sokolov, Rozhnov and Pham Trong Anh, 1997 (Mammalia: Carnivora: Viverridae). *Mammal. Biol.* **66**: 181-184.

Walton, L.R. & Larivière, S. (1994). A striped skunk, *Mephitis mephitis*, repels 2 coyotes, *Canis latrans*, without scenting. *Can. Field-Nat.* **108**: 492-493.

Wan, Q.H., Wu, H. & Fang, S.G. (2005). A new subspecies of giant panda (*Ailurpoda malanoleuca*) from Shaanxi, China. *J. Mammal.* **86**: 397-402.

Wang, H. & Fuller, T. (2001). Notes on the ecology of sympatric small carnivores in southeastern China. *Zeitschrift für Säugetierkunde* **66**: 251-255.

Wang, H. & Fuller, T. (2003a). Ferret badger *Melogale moschata* activity, movements and den site use in southeastern China. *Acta Theriol.* **48**: 73-78.

Wang, H. & Fuller, T. (2003b). Food habits of four sympatric carnivores in southerneastern China. *Mammalia* **67**: 513-519.

Wang, H., Sheng, H., Lu, H. (1976). The analysis on the food habits of the small Indian civet and its use in captivity breeding. *Chinese J. Zool.* **20**: 39-40.

Wang, X. & Qiu, Z. (2004). Late Miocene *Promephitis* (Carnivora, Mephitidae) from China. *J. Vert. Paleo.* **24**: 721-731.

Wang, X., Whistler, D.P. & Takeuchi, G.T. (2005). A new basal skunk *Martinogale* (Carnivora, Mephitinae) from late Miocene Dove Spring formation, California, and origin of new world mephitines. *J. Vert. Paleo.* **25**: 936-949.

Wang Sung (1990). The Chinese desert cat (*Felis bieti*). *Felid* **4(1)**.

Wang Zhenghuan, Wang Xiaoming, Wu Wei, Giraudoux, P., Qiu Jiangmin, Kenichi Takahashi & Craig, P.S. (2003). [Characteristics of the summer Tibetan fox *Vulpes ferrilata* den habitats in Serxu County, western Sichuan province]. *Acta Theriol. Sinica* **23**: 31-38. In Chinese.

Wang Zongyi & Wang Sung (1986). Distribution and recent status of the Felidae in China. Pp. 201-209 in: Miller, S.D. & Everett, D.D. eds. (1986). *Cats of the World: Biology, Conservation and Management.* National Wildlife Federation, Washington, D.C.

Ward, O.G. & Wurster-Hill, D.H. (1990). *Nyctereutes procyonoides. Mammal. Species* **358**: 1-5.

Ward, R.M.P. & Krebs, C.J. (1985). Behavioural responses of lynx to declining snowshoe hare abundance. *Can. J. Zool.* **63**: 2817-2824.

Warrick, G.D. & Cypher, B.L. (1998). Factors affecting the spatial distribution of a kit fox population. *J. Wildl. Management* **62**: 707-717.

Warrillow, J., Culver, M., Hallerman, E. & Vaughan, M. (2001). Subspecific affinity of black bears in the White River National Wildlife Refuge. *J. Heredity* **92**: 226-233.

Waser, P.M. (1980). Small nocturnal carnivores - ecological studies in the Serengeti. *Afr. J. Ecol.* **18**: 167-185.

Waser, P.M. (1981). Sociality or territorial defence? The influence of resource renewal. *Behav. Ecol. Sociobiol.* **8**: 231-237.

Waser, P.M. & Waser, M.S. (1985). *Ichneumia albicauda* and the evolution of viverrid gregariousness. *Zeitschr. Tierpsychol.* **68**: 137-151.

Waser, P.M., Elliott, L.F., Creel, N.M. & Creel, S.R. (1995). Habitat variation and mongoose demography. Pp. 421-448 in: Sinclair, A.R.E. & Arcese, P. eds. (1995). *Serengeti II: Dynamics, Management and Conservation of an Ecosystem.* University Press, Chicago, Illinois.

Waser, P.M., Keane, B., Creel, S.R., Elliott, L.F. & Minchella, D.J. (1994). Possible male coalitions in a solitary mongoose. *Anim. Behav.* **47**: 289-294.

Wassmer, D.A., Guenther, D.D. & Layne, J.N. (1988). Ecology of bobcat in south-central Florida. *Bull. Florida Mus. Nat. Hist.* **33**: 160-228.

Watson, J.P. & Dippenaar, N.J. (1987). The species limits of *Galerella sanguinea* (Ruppell, 1836), *G. Pulverulenta* (Wagner, 1839) and *G. Nigra* (Thomas, 1928) in southern Africa (Carnivora: Viverridae). *Navors. Nas. Mus. Bloemfontein* **5**: 356-413.

Watson, L.H. & Lang, A.J. (2003). Diet of Cape clawless otters in Groenvlei Lake, South Africa. *South Afr. J. Wildl. Res.* **33**: 135-137.

Watts, H.E. (2007). *Socio-ecological Influences on Fitness in the Spotted Hyena.* PhD dissertation, Michigan State University, East Lansing, Michigan.

Watts, H.E. & Holekamp, K.E. (2007). Hyena societies. *Curr. Biol.* **17**: R657-R660.

Wayne, R.K. (1993). Molecular evolution of the dog family. *Trends Genet.* **9**: 218-224.

Wayne, R.K. & Lehman, N. (1992). Mitochondrial DNA analysis of the eastern coyote: origins and hybridization. Pp. 9-22 in: Boer, A.H. ed. (1992). *Ecology and Management of the Eastern Coyote.* Wildlife Research Unit, University of New Brunswick, Fredericton, Canada.

Wayne, R.K., Benveniste, R.E., Janczewski, D.N. & O'Brien, S.J. (1989). Molecular and biochemical evolution of the Carnivora. Pp. 465-494 in: Gittleman, J.L. ed. (1989). *Carnivore Behavior, Ecology and Evolution.* Cornell University Press, Ithaca, New York.

Wayne, R.K., Geffen, E., Girman, D.J., Koeppfli, K.P., Lau, L.M. & Marshall, C.R. (1997). Molecular systematics of the Canidae. *Syst. Biol.* **46**: 622-653.

Wayne, R.K., George, S., Gilbert, D., Collins, P., Kovach, S., Girman, D. & Lehman, N. (1991). A morphologic and genetic study of the island fox *Urocyon littoralis. Evolution* **45**: 1849-1868.

Weber, D. (1989). The diet of polecats (*Mustela putorius* L.) in Switzerland. *Zeitschrift für Säugetierkunde* **54**: 157-171.

Weber, J.M. & Ferrari, N. (2005). Badger *Meles meles* setts in the Swiss Jura Mountains: characteristics and utilization patterns. *Rev. Suisse Zool.* **112**: 677-687.

Weckel, M., Giuliano, W. & Silver, S. (2006). Jaguar (*Panthera onca*) feeding ecology: distribution of predator and prey through time and space. *J. Zool., London* **270**: 25-30.

Wegge, P., Odden, M., Pokharel, C.P. & Storaas, T. (2009). Predator-prey relationships and responses of ungulates and their predators to the establishment of protected areas: a case study of tigers, leopards and their prey in Bardia National Park, Nepal. *Biol. Conserv.* **142**: 189-202.

Wei, F., Feng, Z., Wang, Z. & Hu, J. (1999). Current distribution, status and conservation of wild red pandas *Ailurus fulgens* in China. *Biol. Conserv.* **89**: 285-291.

Wei, F., Feng, Z., Wang, Z. & Hu, J. (2000). Habitat use and separation between the giant panda and the red panda. *J. Mammal.* **81**: 448-455.

Wei, F., Feng, Z., Wang, Z. & Li, M. (1999). Feeding strategy and resource partitioning between giant and red pandas. *Mammalia* **63**: 417-430.

Wei, F., Feng, Z., Wang, Z., Zhou, A. & Hu, J. (1999). Use of the nutrients in bamboo by the red panda (*Ailurus fulgens*). *J. Zool., London* **248**: 535-541.

Wei, F., Lü, X., Li, C., Li, M., Ren, B. & Hu, J. (2005). Influences of mating groups on the reproductive success of the Southern Sichuan red panda (*Ailurus fulgens styani*). *Zoo Biology* **24**: 169-176.

Wei, F., Wang, Z., Feng, Z., Li, M. & Zhou, A. (2000). Seasonal energy utilization in bamboo by the red panda (*Ailurus fulgens*). *Zoo Biology* **19**: 27-33.

Weibel, E.R. & Taylor, C.R. (1981). Design of the mammalian respiratory system. *Respir. Physiol.* **44**: 1-164.

Weibel, E.R., Taylor, C.R. & Bolis, L. (1998). *Principles of Animal Design.* Cambridge University Press, New York.

Weigel, I. (1972). Small felids and clouded leopards. In: Grzimek, B. ed. (1972). *Grzimek's Animal Life Encyclopedia*. Van Nostrand Reinhold Company, New York.

Weinstein, B.M. (1999). What guides early embryonic blood vessel formation? *Developmental Dynamics* **215**: 2-11.

Weir, R.D. & Corbould, F.B. (2007). Factors affecting diurnal activity of fishers in north-central British Columbia. *J. Mammal.* **88**: 1508-1514.

Weisbein, Y. & Mendelssohn, H. (1990). The biology and ecology of the caracal *Felis caracal* in the northern Aravah Valley of Israel. *Cat News* **12**: 20-22.

Welch, C.A., Keay, J., Kendall, K.C. & Robbins, C.T. (1997). Constraints on frugivory by bears. *Ecology* **78(4)**: 1105-1119.

Wells, D.R. (1989). Notes on the distribution and taxonomy of Peninsular Malaysian mongooses (*Herpestes*). *Nat. Hist. Bull. Siam Soc.* **37**: 87-97.

Wells, K., Biun, A. & Gabin, M. (2005). Viverrid and herpestid observations by camera and small mammal cage trapping in the lowland rainforests on Borneo including a record of the Hose's civet, *Diplogale hosei*. *Small Carniv. Conserv.* **32**: 12-14.

Wemmer, C. (1971). Birth, development and behaviour of a fanaloka *Fossa fossa* at the National Zoological Park, Washington, D.C. *Int. Zoo Yb.* **11**: 113-115.

Wemmer, C. (1977). Comparative ethology of the large-spotted genet (*Genetta tigrina*) and some related viverrids. *Smithsonian Contrib. Zool.* **239**: 1-93.

Wemmer, C. & Murtaugh, J. (1981). Copulatory behavior and reproduction in the binturong, *Arctictis binturong*. *J. Mammal.* **62**: 342-352.

Wemmer, C. & Scow, K. (1977). Communication in the Felidae with emphasis on scent marking and contact patterns. Pp. 749-766 in: Sebeok, T.A. ed. (1977). *How Animals Communicate*. Indiana University Press, Bloomington, Indiana.

Wemmer, C. & Watling, D. (1986). Ecology and status of the Sulawesi palm civet *Macrogalidia musschenbroekii* Schlegel. *Biol. Conserv.* **35**: 1-17.

Wemmer, C. & Wozencraft, W.C. (1984). The mongoose family. Pp. 144-145 in: Macdonald, D.W. ed. (1984). *The Encyclopedia of Mammals*. George Allen & Unwin, London.

Wemmer, C., West, J., Watling, D., Collins, L. & Lang, K. (1983). External characters of the Sulawesi palm civet *Macrogalidia musschenbroekii* Schlegel, 1879. *J. Mammal.* **64**: 133-136.

Wenhold, B.A. & Rasa, O.A.E. (1994). Territorial marking in the yellow mongoose (*Cynictis penicillata*): sexual advertisement for subordinates? *Zeitschrift für Säugetierkunde* **59**: 129-138.

Wentzel, J., Stephens, J.C., Johnson, W., Menotti-Raymond, M., Pecon-Slattery, J., Yuhki, N., Carrington, M., Quigley, H.B., Miquelle, D.G., Tilson. R., Manansang, J., Brady, G., Zhi, L., Wenshi, P., Shi-Quang, H., Johnston, L., Sunquist, M., Karanth, U. & O'Brien, S.J. (1999). Subspecies of tigers: molecular assessment using "voucher specimens" of geographically traceable individuals. Pp. 40-49 in: Seidensticker, J., Christie, S. & Jackson, P. eds. (1999). *Riding the Tiger: Tiger Conservation in Human-dominated Landscapes*. Cambridge University Press, Cambridge.

Werdelin, L. (1981). The evolution of lynxes. *Ann. Zool. Fennici* **18**: 37-71.

Werdelin, L. (1983). Morphological patterns in the skulls of cats. *Biol. J. Linn. Soc.* **19**: 375-391.

Werdelin, L. (1989). Constraint and adaptation in the bone-cracking canid *Osteoborus* (Mammalia: Canidae). *Paleobiology* **15**: 387-401.

Werdelin, L. (1990). Taxonomic status of the pardel lynx. *Cat News* **13**: 18.

Werdelin, L. & Nilsonne, A. (1999). The evolution of the scrotum and testicular descent in mammals: a phylogenetic view. *J. Theor. Biol.* **196(1)**: 61-72.

Werdelin, L. & Solounias, N. (1991). The Hyaenidae: taxonomy, systematics and evolution. *Fossils & Strata* **30**: 1-104.

Werneck, F.L. (1948). *Os Malófagos de Mamíferos*. Parte 1. Edicão da Revista Brasileira de Biologia, Rio de Janeiro.

Wesener, T. & Sierwald, P. (2005). New giant pill-millipede species from the littoral forest of Madagascar (Diplopoda, Sphaerotheriida, *Zoosphaerium*). *Zootaxa* **1097**: 1-60.

Wesley-Hunt, G.D. & Flynn, J.J. (2005). Phylogeny of the Carnivora: basal relationships among the carnivoramorphans, and assessment of the position of 'Miacoidea' relative to Carnivora. *J. Syst. Palaeontol.* **3**: 1-28.

West, P.M. & Packer, C. (2002). Sexual selection, temperature and the lion's mane. *Nature* **297**: 1339-1342.

Whateley, A.M. (1980). Comparative body measurements of male and female spotted hyaenas from Natal. *Lammergeyer* **28**: 40-43.

Whateley, A.M. (1981). Density and home range of spotted hyaenas in Umfolozi Game Reserve, Natal. *Lammergeyer* **31**: 15-20.

Whateley, A.M. & Brooks, P.M. (1978). Numbers and movements of spotted hyaenas in Hluhluwe Game Reserve. *Lammergeyer* **26**: 44-52.

Whitaker, J.O. & Hamilton, W.J. (1998). *Mammals of the Eastern United States*. Cornell University Press, Ithaca, New York.

White, D., Kendall, K.C. & Picton, H.D. (1998). Grizzly bear feeding activity at alpine army cutworm moth aggregation sites in northwest Montana. *Can. J. Zool.* **76**: 221-227.

White, P.J. & Ralls, K. (1993). Reproduction and spacing patterns of kit foxes relative to changing pray availability. *J. Wildl. Management* **57**: 861-867.

White, P.J., Ralls, K. & Vanderbilt, C.A. (1995). Overlap in habitat and food use between coyotes and San Joaquin kit foxes. *Southwest. Nat.* **40**: 342-349.

White, T.H.J., Bowman, J.L., Leopold, B.D., Jacobson, H.A., Smith, W.P. & Vilella, F.J. (2000). Influence of Mississippi alluvial valley rivers on black bear movements and dispersal: implications for Louisiana black bear recovery. *Biol. Conserv.* **95**: 323-331.

Whitfield, A.K. & Blaber, S.J.M. (1980). The diet of *Atilax paludinosus* (water mongoose) at St. Lucia, South Africa. *Mammalia* **44**: 315-318.

Whitman, J.S., Ballard, W.B. & Gardner, C.L. (1986). Home range and habitat use by wolverines in southcentral Alaska. *J. Wildl. Management* **50**: 460-463.

Wickens, G.E. (1984). Flora. Pp. 67-75 in: Cloudsley-Thompson, J.L. ed. (1984). *Sahara Desert*. Pergamon Press, Oxford.

Widholzer, F.L., Bergmann, M. & Zotz, C. (1981). Breeding the little spotted cat. *Int. Zoo News* **28(3)**: 17-23.

Wiesel, I. (2006). *Predatory and Foraging Behaviour of Brown Hyenas (*Parahyaena brunnea *Thunberg 1820) at Cape Fur Seal (*Arctocephalus pusillus pusillus *Schreber, 1776) Colonies*. Dissertation, University of Hamburg, Hamburg.

Wiggington, J.D. & Dobson, S.F. (1999). Environmental influences on geographic variation in body size of western bobcats. *Can. J. Zool.* **77**: 802-813.

Wildt, D.E., O'Brien, S.J., Howard, J.G., Caro, T.M., Roelke, M.E., Brown, J.L. & Bush, M. (1987). Similarity in ejaculate-endocrine characteristics in captive versus free-living cheetahs of two subspecies. *Biol. Reprod.* **36**: 351-360.

Wiley, K.S. (1978). Observations of margay behavior. *Carnivore* **1**: 81.

Williams, F.X. (1951). Life-history studies of East African *Achatina* snails. *Bull. Mus. Comp. Zool.* **105**: 295-317.

Williams, J.B., Anderson, M.D. & Richardson, P.R.K. (1997). Seasonal differences in field metabolism, water requirements and foraging behavior of free-living aardwolves. *Ecology* **78**: 2588-2602.

Williamson, D.F. (2002). *In the Black. Status, Management and Trade of the American Black Bear (*Ursus americanus*) in North America*. TRAFFIC North America, World Wildlife Fund, Washington, D.C.

Willis, I. (1895). The fosa (*Cryptoprocta ferox* Benn.). *Antananarivo Ann.* **19**: 378-379.

Wilson, D.E. (1997). *Bats in Question*. Smithsonian Institution Press, Washington, D.C.

Wilson, D.E. & Cole, F.R. (2000). *Common Names of Mammals of the World*. Smithsonian Institution Press, Washington, D.C.

Wilson, D.E. & Reeder, D.M. (1993). *Mammal Species of the World: a Taxonomic and Geographic Reference*. 2nd edition. Smithsonian Institution Press, Washington, D.C

Wilson, D.E. & Reeder, D.M. (2005). *Mammal Species of the World: a Taxonomic and Geographic Reference*. 3rd edition. Johns Hopkins University Press, Baltimore, Maryland.

Wilson, D.E. & Ruff, S. (1999). *The Smithsonian Book of North American Mammals*. Smithsonian Institution Press, Washington, D.C.

Wilson, D.E., Bogan, M.A., Brownell, R.L., Burdin, A.M. & Mamikov, M.K. (1991). Geographic variation in sea otters, *Enhydra lutris*. *J. Mammal.* **72**: 22-36.

Wilson, M.L., Bretsky, P.M., Cooper, G.H., Egbertson, S.H., Van Kruiningen, H.J. & Cartter, M.L. (1997). Emergence of raccoon rabies in Connecticut, 1991-1994: spatial and temporal characteristics of animal infection and human contact. *Amer. J. Trop. Med. Hyg.* **57**: 457-463.

Wilson, P. (1984). Puma predation on guanacos in Torres del Paine National Park, Chile. *Mammalia* **48**: 515-522.

Wilson, P.J., Grewal, S., Lawford, I.D., Heal, J.N.M., Granacki, A.G., Pennock, D., Theberge, J.B., Theberge, M.T., Voigt, D.R., Waddell, W., Chambers, R.E., Paquet, P.C., Goulet, G., Cluff, D. & White, B.N. (2000). DNA profiles of the eastern Canadian wolf and the red wolf provide evidence for a common evolutionary history independent of the gray wolf. *Can. J. Zool.* **78**: 2156-2166.

Wilson, V. (1987). Cats in Ivory Coast. *Cat News* **6**: 33.

Wilson, V.J. (1975). *Mammals of the Wankie National Park, Rhodesia*. Museum Memoir **5**. Trustees of the National Museums and Monuments of Rhodesia, Salisbury.

Wilson, V.J. (1977). The leopard in eastern Zambia. Pp. 29-38 in: Eaton, R.L. (1977). *The World's Cats*. Vol. 3(2). Carnivore Research Institute, Burke Museum, University of Washington, Seattle, Washington.

Wilting, A., Buckley-Beason, V.A., Feldhaaar, H., Gadau, J. & O'Brien, S.J. (2007). Clouded leopard phylogeny revisited: support for species recognition and population division between Borneo and Sumatra. *Front. Zool.* **4**: 15.

Wilting, A., Fischer, F., Bakar, S.A. & Linsenmair, K.E. (2006). Clouded leopards, the secretive top-carnivore of South-East Asian rainforests: their distribution, status and conservation needs in Sabah, Malaysia. *BMC Ecol.* **6**: 16 doi: 10.1186/1472-6785-6-16.

Winegarner, C.E. & Winegarner, M.S. (1982). Reproductive history of a bobcat. *J. Mammal.* **636**: 680-682.

Wingard, J.R. & Zahler, P. (2006). *Silent Steppe: the Illegal Wildlife Trade Crisis in Mongolia*. Mongolia Discussion Papers, East Asia and Pacific Environment and Social Development Department, World Bank, Washington, D.C.

Winkler, W.G. & Adams, D.B. (1972). Utilization of southwestern bat caves by terrestrial carnivores. *Amer. Midl. Nat.* **87**: 191-300.

Winston, R. & Wilson, D.E. eds. (2004). *Human*. Dorling-Kindersley Limited, New York.

Wirth, R. & Van Rompaey, H. (1991). The Nilgiri marten, *Martes gwatkinsii* (Horsfield, 1851). *Small Carniv. Conserv.* **5**: 6.

Wolsan, M. (1999). Oldest mephitine cranium and its implications for the origin of skunks. *Acta Palaeontol. Polonica* **44**: 223-230.

Wong, S.T., Servheen, C. & Ambu, L. (2002). Food habits of Malayan sun bears in lowland tropical forests of Borneo. *Ursus* **13**: 127-136.

Wong, S.T., Servheen, C. & Ambu, L. (2004). Home range, movement and activity patterns, and bedding sites of Malayan sun bears *Helarctos malayanus* in the rainforest of Borneo. *Biol. Conserv.* **119**: 169-181.

Wong, S.T., Servheen, C., Ambu, L. & Norhayati, A. (2005). Impacts of fruit production cycles on Malayan sun bears and bearded pigs in lowland tropical forest of Sabah, Malaysian Borneo. *J. Trop. Ecol.* **21**: 627-639.

Wood, J.E. (1958). Age structure and productivity of a gray fox population. *J. Mammal.* **39**: 74-86.

Wood, W.F. (1990). New components in defensive secretion of the striped skunk, *Mephitis mephitis*. *J. Chem. Ecol.* **16**: 2057-2065.

Wood, W.F., Fisher, C.O. & Graham, G.A. (1993). Volatile components in defensive spray of the hog-nosed skunk, *Conepatus mesoleucus*. *J. Chem. Ecol.* **19**: 837-841.

Wood, W.F., Morgan, C.G. & Miller, A. (1991). Volatile components in defensive spray of the spotted skunk, *Spilogale putorius*. *J. Chem. Ecol.* **17**: 1415-1420.

Wood, W.F., Sollers, B.G., Dragoo, G.A. & Dragoo, J.W. (2002). Volatile components in defensive spray of the hooded skunk, *Mephitis macroura*. *J. Chem. Ecol.* **28**: 1865-1870.

Wooding, S. & Ward, R. (1997). Phylogeography and Pleistocene evolution in the North American black bear. *Mol. Biol. Evol.* **14**: 1096-1105.

Woodroffe, R. & Frank, L.G. (2005). Lethal controls of African lions (*Panthera leo*): local and regional population impacts. *Anim. Conserv.* **8**: 91-98.

Woodroffe, R. & Ginsberg, J.R. (1998). Edge effects and the extinction of populations inside protected areas. *Science* **280**: 2126-2128.

Woodroffe, R., Ginsberg, J.R. & Macdonald, D.W. (1997). *The African Wild Dog: Status Survey and Conservation Action Plan.* IUCN/SSC Canid Specialist Group, Gland & Cambridge.

Woodroffe, R., McNutt, J.W. & Mills, M.G.L. (2004). African wild dog *Lycaon pictus.* Pp. 174-183 in: Sillero-Zubiri, C., Hoffmann, M. & Macdonald, D.W. eds. (2004). *Canids: Foxes, Wolves, Jackals and Dogs. Status Survey and Conservation Action Plan.* IUCN/SSC Canid Specialist Group, Gland & Cambridge.

Woolaver, L., Nichols, R., Rakotombololona, W.F., Volahy, A.T. & Durbin, J. (2006). Population status, distribution and conservation needs of the narrow-striped mongoose *Mungotictis decemlineata* of Madagascar. *Oryx* **40**: 67-75.

Woolf, A. & Hubert, G.F. (1998). Status and management of bobcats in the United States over three decades: 1970s-1990s. *Wildl. Soc. Bull.* **26**: 287-293.

Woolf, A., Nielsen, C.K. & Kieninger, T.G. (2000). Status and distribution of bobcat (*Lynx rufus*) in Illinois. *Trans. Illinois State Acad. Sci.* **93**: 165-173.

Wozencraft, W.C. (1984). *A Phylogenetic Reappraisal of the Viverridae and its Relationship to Other Carnivora.* PhD dissertation, University of Kansas, Lawrence, Kansas.

Wozencraft, W.C. (1986). A new species of striped mongoose from Madagascar. *J. Mammal.* **67**: 561-571.

Wozencraft, W.C. (1987). Emendation of species name. *J. Mammalogy* **68**: 198.

Wozencraft, W.C. (1989). The phylogeny of the recent Carnivora. Pp. 495-535 in: Gittleman, J.L. ed. (1989). *Carnivore Behavior, Ecology and Evolution.* Comstock Publishing Associates, Ithaca, New York.

Wozencraft, W.C. (1990). Alive and well in Tsimanampetsotsa. *Nat. Hist. Mag.* **12/90**: 28-30.

Wozencraft, W.C. (1993). Order Carnivora. Pp. 279-344 in: Wilson, D.E. & Reeder, D.M. eds. (1993). *Mammal Species of the World: a Taxonomic and Geographic Reference.* 2nd edition. Smithsonian Institution Press, Washington, D.C.

Wozencraft, W.C. (2005). Order Carnivora. Pp. 532-628 in: Wilson, D.E. & Reeder, D.M. eds. (2005). *Mammal Species of the World: a Taxonomic and Geographic Reference.* 3rd edition. Johns Hopkins University Press, Baltimore, Maryland.

Wozencraft, W.C. (2008). Order Carnivora. Pp. 388-448 in: Smith, A.T. & Xie, Y. eds. (2008). *The Mammals of China.* Princeton University Press, Princeton, New Jersey & Oxford.

Wright, J.D. & Ernst, J. (2004a). Effects of mid-winter snow depth on stand selection by wolverines, *Gulo gulo luscus,* in the boreal forest. *Can. Field-Nat.* **118**: 56-60.

Wright, J.D. & Ernst, J. (2004b). Wolverine, *Gulo gulo luscus,* resting sites and caching behavior in the boreal forest. *Can. Field-Nat.* **118**: 61-64.

Wright, P.C., Heckscher, S.K. & Dunham, A.E. (1997). Predation on Milne-Edward's sifaka (*Propithecus diadema edwardsi*) by the fossa (*Cryptoprocta ferox*) in the rainforest of southeastern Madagascar. *Folia Primatol.* **68**: 34-43.

Wright, S.J., Carrasco, C., Calderon, O. & Paton, S. (1999). The El Nino southern oscillation, variable fruit production, and famine in a tropical forest. *Ecology* **80**: 1632-1647.

Wright, S.J., Zeballos, H., Dominguez, I., Gallardo, M.M., Moreno, M.C. & Ibanez, R. (2000). Poachers alter mammal abundance, seed dispersal and seed predation in a Neotropical forest. *Conserv. Biol.* **14**: 227-239.

Wu, H.Y. (1999). Is there current competition between sympatric Siberian weasels (*Mustela sibirica*) and ferret badgers (*Melogale moschata*) in a subtropical forest ecosystem of Taiwan? *Zool. Stud.* **38**: 443-451.

Wu Wei, Xiaoming Wang, Wang zhenghuan (2002). [Tibetan fox]. *Chinese Wildl.* **23**: 45-46. In Chinese.

Wurster, D.H. & Benirschke, K. (1967). Chromosome numbers in thirty species of carnivores. *Mammal. Chromosomes Newslett.* **8**: 195-196.

Wurster, D.H. & Benirschke, K. (1968). Comparative cytogenetic studies in the order Carnivora. *Chromosoma* **24**: 336-382.

Wurster-Hill, D.H. & Gray, C.W. (1975). The interrelationships of chromosome banding patterns in procyonids, vivverids, and felids. *Cytogenet. Cell Genet.* **15**: 306-331.

Wyss, A.R. & Flynn, J.J. (1993). A phylogenetic analysis and definition of the Carnivora. Pp. 32-52 in: Szalay, F.S., Novacek, M.J. & McKenna, M.C. eds. (1993). *Mammal Phylogeny: Placentals.* Springer-Verlag, New York.

Ximénez, A. (1975). *Felis geoffroyi.* Mammal. *Species* **54**: 1-4.

Ximénez, A. (1982). Notas sobre félidos neotropicales VIII. Observaciones sobre el contenido estomacal y el comportamiento alimentar de diversas especies de felinos. *Rev. Nordest. Biol.* **5(1)**: 89-91.

Xu, A., Jiang, Z., Li, C., Guo, J., Wu, G. & Cai, P. (2006). Summer food habits of brown bears in Kekexili Nature Reserve, Qinghai-Tibetan Plateau, China. *Ursus* **17**: 132-137.

Xu, H. & Sheng, H. (1994). Reproductive behaviour of the smaller Indian civet (*Viverricula indica*). *Small Carniv. Conserv.* **11**: 13-15.

Xu, J.Y., Chen, L.D., Lu, Y.H. & Fu, B.J. (2007). Sustainability evaluation of the grain for green project: from local people's responses to ecological effectiveness in Wolong Nature Reserve. *Environm. Management* **40**: 113-122.

Xu, L., Jiang, Z., Ma, Y., Jin, A., Wang, Y. & Buskirk, S.W. (1996). Winter food habits of sable (*Martes zibellina*) in Daxinganling Mountains, China. *Acta Theriol. Sinica* **16**: 272-277.

Xu, L., Jiang, Z., Ma, Y., Li, X. & Buskirk, S.W. (1997). Winter home ranges of sables (*Martes zibellina*) in Daxinganling Mountains, China. *Acta Theriol. Sinica* **17**: 113-117.

Yachimori, S. (1997). [*Estimation of Family Relationship and Behavioural Changes among Individuals Constituting a Family of the Wild Raccoon Dogs*]. PhD dissertation, Nihon University, Nihon, Japan. In Japanese.

Yadav, R.N. (1967). Breeding of the smooth-coated Indian otter at Jaipur Zoo. *Int. Zoo Yb.* **7**: 130-131.

Yahnke, C.J. (1995). Metachromism and the insight of Wilfred Osgood: evidence of common ancestry for Darwin's fox and the Sechura fox. *Rev. Chil. Hist. Nat.* **68**: 459-467.

Yahnke, C.J., Johnson, W.E., Geffen, E., Smith, D., Hertel, F., Roy, M.S., Bonacic, C.F., Fuller, T.K., Van, V.B. & Wayne, R.K. (1996). Darwin's fox: a distinct endangered species in a vanishing habitat. *Conserv. Biol.* **10**: 366-375.

Yalden, D.W., Largen, M.J. & Kock, D. (1980). Catalogue of the mammals of Ethiopia. 4. Carnivora. *Monitore Zool. Ital. (New Ser.), Suppl.* **13**: 168-272.

Yalden, D.W., Largen, M.J., Kock, D. & Hillman, J.C. (1996). Catalogue of the mammals of Ethiopia and Eritrea. 7. Revised checklist, zoogeography and conservation. *Tropical Zool.* **9**: 73-164.

Yamada, J.K. & Durrant, B.S. (1988). Vaginal cytology and behavior in the clouded leopard. *Felid* **2**: 1-3.

Yamamoto, I. (1984). Male parental care in the raccoon dog *Nyctereutes procyonoides* during the early rearing period. Pp. 185-195 in: Ito, Y., Brown, J.L. & Kikkawa, J. eds. (1984). *Animal Societies: Theories and Facts.* Japan Scientific Society Press, Tokyo.

Yamamoto, Y., Terao, K., Horiguchi, T., Morita, M. & Yachimori, S. (1994). [Home range and dispersal of the raccoon dog (*Nyctereutes procyonoides viverrinus*) in the Mt. Nyugasa, Nagano Prefecture, Japan]. *Nat. Environm. Sci. Res.* **7**: 53-61. In Japanese.

Yáñez, J. & Jaksic, F.M. (1978). Rol ecológico de los zorros (*Dusicyon*) en Chile central. *An. Mus. Hist. Nat. Valparaiso* **11**: 105-111.

Yáñez, J. & Rau, J. (1980). Dieta estacional de *Dusicyon culpaeus* (Canidae) en Magallanes. *An. Mus. Hist. Nat. Valparaiso* **13**: 189-191.

Yáñez, J.L., Cardenas, J.C., Gezelle, P. & Jaksic, F.M. (1986). Food habits of the southernmost mountain lions (*Felis concolor*) in South America: natural versus livestocked ranges. *J. Mammal.* **67**: 604-606.

Yanosky, A.A. & Mercolli, C. (1992). Habitat preferences and activity in the ring-tailed coati (*Nasua nasua*) at El Bagual Ecological Reserve, Argentina. *Misc. Zool.* **16**: 179-182.

Yanosky, A.A. & Mercolli, C. (1993). Activity pattern of *Procyon cancrivorus* (Carnivora: Procyonidae) in Argentina. *Rev. Biol. Trop.* **41**: 157-159.

Yanosky, A.A. & Mercolli, C. (1994). Notes on the ecology of *Felis geoffroyi* in northeastern Argentina. *Amer. Midl. Nat.* **132**: 202-204.

Yasuma, S. (1981). Feeding behaviour of the Iriomote cat (*Prionailurus iriomotensis* Imaizumi, 1967). *Bull. Tokyo Univ. For.* **70**: 81-140.

Yasuma, S. (1988). Iriomote cat: king of the night. *Anim. Kingdom* **91(6)**: 12-21.

Yasuma, S. (1994). *An Invitation to the Mammals of East Kalimantan.* Pusrehut special publication No. 3. Samarinda, Indonesia.

Yasuma, S. (2004). Observations of a live Hose's civet *Diplogale hosei. Small Carniv. Conserv.* **31**: 3-5.

Yearsley, E.F. & Samuel, D.E. (1982). Use of reclaimed surface mines by foxes in West Virginia. *J. Wildl. Management* **4**: 729-734.

Yensen, E. & Seymour, K.L. (2000). *Oreailurus jacobita. Mammal. Species* **644**: 1-6.

Yensen, E. & Tarifa, T. (2003a). *Galictis vittata. Mammal. Species* **727**: 1-8.

Yensen, E. & Tarifa, T. (2003b). *Galictis cuja. Mammal. Species* **728**: 1-8.

Yoder, A.D. & Flynn, J.J. (2003). Origin of Malagasy Carnivora. Pp. 1253-1256 in: Goodman, S.M. & Benstead, J.P. eds. (2003). *The Natural History of Madagascar.* The University of Chicago Press, Chicago, Illinois.

Yoder, A.D., Burns, M.M., Zehr, S., Delefosse, T., Veron, G., Goodman, S.M. & Flynn, J.J. (2003). Single origin of Malagasy Carnivora from an African ancestor. *Nature (London)* **421**: 734-737.

Yoganand, K., Rice, C.G., Johnsingh, A.J.T. & Seidensticker, J. (2006). Is the sloth bear in India secure? A preliminary report on distribution, threats and conservation requirements. *J. Bombay Nat. Hist. Soc.* **103**: 172-181.

Yoganand, T.R.K. & Kumar, A. (1995). The distribution of small carnivores in the Nilgiri Biosphere, southern India: a preliminary report. *Small Carniv. Conserv.* **13**: 1-2.

Yom-Tov, Y. & Geffen, E. (2006). Geographic variation in body size: the effects of ambient temperature and precipitation. *Oecologia* **148**: 213-218.

Yom-Tov, Y. & Mendelssohn, H. (1988). Changes in the distribution and abundance of vertebrates in Israel during the 20th century. Pp. 515-547 in: Yom-Tov, Y. & Tchernov, E. eds. (1988). *The Zoogeography of Israel.* Dr. W. Junk Publishers, Dordrecht, The Netherlands.

Yonezawa, T., Nikaido, M., Kohno, N., Fukumoto, Y., Okada, N. & Hasegawa, M. (2007). Molecular phylogenetic study on the origin and evolution of Mustelidae. *Gene* **396**: 1-12.

Yonzon, P.B. & Hunter, M.L. (1991a). Cheese, tourists and red pandas in the Nepal Himalayas. *Conserv. Biol.* **5**: 196-202.

Yonzon, P.B. & Hunter, M.L. (1991b). Conservation of the red panda *Ailurus fulgens. Biol. Conserv.* **57**: 1-11.

Yoshioka, M., Kishimoto, M., Nigi, H., Sakanakura, T., Miyamoto, T., Hamasaki, S., Hattori, A., Suzuki, T. & Aida, K. (1990). Seasonal changes in serum levels of testosterone and progesterone on the Japanese raccoon dog *Nyctereutes procyonoides viverrinus.* Proceedings. *Jap. Soc. Comp. Endocrin.* **5**: 17.

Yoshiyuki, M. (1971). On the external and cranial characters of *Aonyx cinerea. J. Mammal Soc. Japan* **5**: 117-119.

Youlatos, D. (2003). Osteological correlates of tail prehensility in carnivorans. *J. Zool., London* **259**: 423-430.

Young, A.J. & Clutton-Brock, T. (2006). Infanticide by subordinates influences reproductive sharing in cooperatively breeding meerkats. *Biology Letters* **2**: 385-387.

Young, A.J., Carlson, A.A. & Clutton-Brock, T. (2005). Trade-offs between extraterritorial prospecting and helping in a cooperative mammal. *Anim. Behav.* **70**: 829-837.

Young, A.J., Carlson, A.A., Monfort, S.L., Russell, A.F., Bennett, N.C. & Clutton-Brock, T.H. (2006). Stress and the suppression of subordinate reproduction in cooperatively breeding meerkats. *Proc. Natl. Acad. Sci. USA* **103**: 12005-12010.

Young, J.Z. & Hobbs, M.J. (1975). *The Life of Mammals.* 2nd edition. Clarendon Press, Oxford.

Young, K.M., Brown, J.L. & Goodrowe, K.L. (2001). Characterization of reproductive cycles and adrenal activity in the black-footed ferret (*Mustela nigripes*) by fecal hormone analysis. *Zoo Biology* **20**: 517-536.

Young, S.P. & Goldman, E.A. (1944). *The Wolves of North America.* American Wildlife Institute, Washington D.C.

Young, S.P. & Goldman, E.A. (1946). *The Puma: Mysterious American Cat.* American Wildlife Institute, Washington, D.C.

Young, S.P. & Jackson, H.H.T. (1951). *The Clever Coyote.* Wildlife Management Institute, Washington D.C.

Youngman, P.M. (1990). *Mustela lutreola. Mammal. Species* **362**: 1-3.

Yu, D.W., Li, H. & Xu, R. (2003). Seroprevalence of SARS coronavirus antibody IgG in wild animals traders in Guangdong. *South China J. Preventive Med.* **29**: 6-7.

Yu, L., Li, Q., Ryder, O.A. & Zhang, Y. (2004). Phylogenetic relationships within mammalian order Carnivora indicated by sequences of two nuclear DNA genes. *Mol. Phylogen. Evol.* **33**: 694-705.

Zabala, J., Zuberogoitia, I., Garin, I. & Aihartza, J. (2003). Landscape features in the habitat selection of European mink (*Mustela lutreola*) in south-western Europe. *J. Zool., London* **260**: 415-421.

Zabala, J., Zuberogoitia, I. & Martinez-Climent, J.A. (2005). Site and landscape features ruling the habitat use and occupancy of the polecat (*Mustela putorius*) in a low density area: a multiscale approach. *Eur. J. Wildl. Res.* **51**: 157-162.

Zabala, J., Zuberogoitia, I. & Martinez-Climent, J.A. (2006). Factors affecting occupancy by the European mink in south-western Europe. *Mammalia* **70**: 193-201.

Zabala, J., Zuberogoitia, I. & Martinez-Climent, J.A. (2007a). Spacing pattern, intersexual competition and niche segregation in American mink. *Ann. Zool. Fennici* **44**: 249-258.

Zabala, J., Zuberogoitia, I. & Martinez-Climent, J.A. (2007b). Winter habitat preferences of feral American mink *Mustela vison* in Biscay, Northern Iberian Peninsula. *Acta Theriol.* **52**: 27-36.

Zager, P. & Beecham, J. (2006). The role of American black bears and brown bears as predators on ungulates in North America. *Ursus* **17**: 95-108.

Zalewski, A. (2000). Factors affecting the duration of activity by pine martens (*Martes martes*) in the Bialowieza National Park, Poland. *J. Zool., London* **251**(4): 439-447.

Zalewski, A. (2001). Seasonal and sexual variation in diel activity rhythms of pine marten *Martes martes* in the Bialowieza National Park (Poland). *Acta Theriol.* **46**(3): 295-304.

Zalewski, A., Jedrzejewski, W. & Jedrzejewska, B. (1995). Pine marten home ranges, numbers and predation on vertebrates in a deciduous forest (Bialowieza National Park, Poland). *Ann. Zool. Fennici* **32**: 131-144.

Zalewski, A., Jedrzejewski, W. & Jedrzejewska, B. (2004). Mobility and home range use by pine martens (*Martes martes*) in a Polish primeval forest. *Ecoscience* **11**: 113-122.

Zapata, S.C., García-Perea, R., Beltrán, J.F., Ferreras, P. & Delibes, M. (1997). Age determination of Iberian lynx (*Lynx pardinus*) using canine radiograph and cementum annuli enumeration. *Zeitschrift für Säugetierkunde* **62**: 119-123.

Zapata, S.C., Travaini, A., Delibes, M. & Martinez-Peck, R. (2005). Annual food habits of the lesser grison (*Galictis cuja*) at the southern limit of its range. *Mammalia* **69**: 85-88.

Zapata, S.C., Travaini, A. & Martinez-Peck, R. (2001). Seasonal feeding habits of the Patagonian hog-nosed skunk *Conepatus humboldtii* in southern Patagonia. *Acta Theriol.* **46**: 97-102.

Zedrosser, A., Bellemain, E., Taberlet, P. & Swenson, J.E. (2007). Genetic estimates of annual reproductive success in male brown bears: the effects of body size, age, internal relatedness and population density. *J. Anim. Ecol.* **76**: 368-375.

Zeveloff, S.I. (2002). *Raccoons: a Natural History.* Smithsonian Institution Press, Washington, D.C.

Zhan, X.J., Li, M., Zhang, Z.J., Goossens, B., Chen, Y.P., Wang, H., Bruford, M.W. & Wei, F. (2006). Molecular censusing doubles giant panda population estimate in a key nature reserve. *Curr. Biol.* **16**: R451-R452.

Zhan, X.J., Zhang, Z.J., Wu, H., Goossens, B., Li, M., Jiang, S.W., Bruford, M.W. & Wei, F.W. (2007). Molecular analysis of dispersal in giant pandas. *Mol. Ecol.* **16**: 3792-3800.

Zhang, H.H. & Ma, J.Z. (2000). Preliminary research on the habitat selection of sable in spring and summer. *Acta Zool. Sinica* **46**: 399-406.

Zhang, Z., Wei, F., Li, M. & Hu, J. (2006). Winter microhabitat separation between giant and red pandas in *Bashania faberi* bamboo forest in Fengtongzhai Nature Reserve. *J. Wildl. Management* **70**: 231-235.

Zhang, Z., Wei, F., Li, M., Zhang, B., Liu, X. & Hu, J. (2004). Microhabitat separation during winter among sympatric giant pandas, red pandas and tufted deer: the effects of diet, body size and energy metabolism. *Can. J. Zool.* **82**: 1451-1458.

Zheng, S. (1985). [Data on the foods of the Tibetan sand fox]. *Acta Theriol. Sinica* **5**: 222. In Chinese.

Zhou, Y., Zhang, L., Kaneko, Y., Newman, C. & Wang, X. (2008). Frugivory and seed dispersal by a small carnivore, the Chinese ferret-badger, *Melogale moschata*, in a fragmented subtropical forest of central China. *For. Ecol. Manage.* **255**: 1595-1603.

Zhu, X., Lindburg, D., Pan, W., Forney, K.A. & Wang, D. (2001). The reproductive strategy of giant pandas (*Ailuropoda melanoleuca*): infant growth and development and mother-infant relationships. *J. Zool., London* **253**: 141-155.

ZICOMA (1999). *Zones d'Importance pour la Conservation des Oiseaux à Madagascar.* Projet ZICOMA, Antananarivo.

Zielinski, W.J., Duncan, N.P., Farmer, E.C., Truex, R.L., Clevenger, A.P. & Barrett, R.H. (1999). Diet of fisher (*Martes pennanti*) at the southernmost extent of their range. *J. Mammal.* **80**: 961-971.

Zielinski, W.J., Truex, R.L., Schlexer, F.V., Campbell, L.A. & Carroll, C. (2005). Historical and contemporary distributions of carnivores in forests of the Sierra Nevada, California, USA. *J. Biogeogr.* **32**: 1385-1407.

Zielinski, W.J., Truex, R.L., Schmidt, G.A., Schlexer, F.V., Schmidt, K.N. & Barrett, R.H. (2004a). Home range characteristics of fishers in California. *J. Mammal.* **85**: 649-657.

Zielinski, W.J., Truex, R.L., Schmidt, G.A., Schlexer, F.V., Schmidt, K.N. & Barrett, R.H. (2004b). Resting habitat selection by fishers in California. *J. Wildl. Management* **68**: 475-492.

Zimmerman, A.L. (1998). *Reestablishment of Swift Fox (*Vulpes velox*) in Northcentral Montana.* MSc thesis, Montana State University, Bozeman, Montana.

Zimmerman, A.L., Irby, L. & Giddings, B. (2003). The status and ecology of swift foxes in north central Montana. Pp. 49-59 in: Sovada, M. & Carbyn, L. eds. (2003). *Ecology and Conservation of Swift Foxes in a Changing World.* Canadian Plains Research Center, University of Regina, Saskatchewan, Canada.

Zimmermann, A., Walpole, M.J. & Leader-Williams, N. (2005). Cattle ranchers' attitudes to conflicts with jaguar *Panthera onca* in the Pantanal of Brazil. *Oryx* **39**: 406-412.

Zimmermann, F., Breitenmoser-Würsten, C. & Breitenmoser, U. (2007). Importance of dispersal for the expansion of a Eurasian lynx *Lynx lynx* population in a fragmented landscape. *Oryx* **41**: 358-368.

Zoellick, B.W., O'Farrell, T.P., McCue, P.M., Harris, C.E. & Kato, T.T. (1987). *Reproduction of the San Joaquin Kit Fox on Naval Petroleum Reserve #1, Elk Hills, California, 1980-1985.* US Department of Energy Topical Report **No. EGG 10282-2144**.

Zuberogoitia, I. & Zabala, J. (2004). Territorial behaviour between male common genets. *Small Carniv. Conserv.* **31**: 13-14.

Zuberogoitia, I., Zabala, J., Garin, I. & Aihartza, J. (2002). Home range size and habitat use of male common genets in the Urdaibai Biosphere Reserve, Northern Spain. *Z. Jagdwiss.* **48**: 107-113.

Zuberogoitia, I., Zabala, J. & Martinez, J.A. (2006). Diurnal activity and observations of the hunting and ranging behaviour of the American mink (*Mustela vison*). *Mammalia* **70**: 310-312.

Zuercher, G.L. & Villalba, R.D. (2002). Records of *Speothos venaticus* Lund, 1842 (Carnivora, Canidae) in eastern Paraguay. *Zeitschrift für Säugetierkunde* **67**: 1-3.

Zuercher, G.L., Swarner, M., Silveira, L. & Carrillo, O. (2004). Bush dog *Speothos venaticus.* Pp. 76-80 in: Sillero-Zubiri, C., Hoffmann, M. & Macdonald, D.W. eds. (2004). *Canids: Foxes, Wolves, Jackals and Dogs. Status Survey and Conservation Action Plan.* IUCN/SSC Canid Specialist Group, Gland & Cambridge.

Zumbaugh, D.M., Choate, J.R. & Fox, L.B. (1985). Winter food habits of the swift fox on the central high plains. *Prairie Nat.* **17**: 41-47.

Zunino, G.E., Vaccaro, O.B., Canevari, M. & Gardner, A.L. (1995). Taxonomy of the genus *Lycalopex* (Carnivora: Canidae) in Argentina. *Proc. Biol. Soc. Washington* **108**: 729-747.

Index

Index